IMPORTANT BIRD AREAS IN EUROPE

Priority sites for conservation

Edited by

Melanie F. Heath and Michael I. Evans

with D. G. Hoccom, A. J. Payne and N. B. Peet

Volume 1: Northern Europe

■

with major sponsorship from

Royal Society for the Protection of Birds
The BirdLife Partner in the United Kingdom and the main sponsor.

landbouw, natuurbeheer en visserij

Ministry of Agriculture, Nature Management and Fisheries, Directorate for Nature Management, through the PIN/ MATRA Funds of the Ministry of Foreign Affairs, The Netherlands.

Vogelbescherming Nederland
The BirdLife Partner in the Netherlands.

BirdLife
INTERNATIONAL

Together for birds and people

Recommended citation

Heath, M. F. and Evans, M. I., eds. (2000) *Important Bird Areas in Europe: Priority sites for conservation.* 2 vols. Cambridge, UK: BirdLife International (BirdLife Conservation Series No. 8).

Where one volume used, indicate title as:
Heath, M. F. and Evans, M. I., eds. (2000) *Important Bird Areas in Europe: Priority sites for conservation.* 1: Northern Europe. Cambridge, UK: BirdLife International (BirdLife Conservation Series No. 8).

For a country chapter, cite as in this example:
Dvorak, M. (2000) Austria. Pp. 67–90 in M. F. Heath and M. I. Evans, eds. *Important Bird Areas in Europe: Priority sites for conservation.* 1: Northern Europe. Cambridge, UK: BirdLife International (BirdLife Conservation Series No. 8).

ISBN   0 946888 34 5   (Volume 1, softback)
       0 946888 35 3   (Volume 2, softback)
       0 946888 36 1   (2 Volume set, softback)
       0 946888 37 X   (2 Volume set, hardback)

British Library-in-Publication Data
A catalogue record for this book is available from the British Library

First published 2000 by BirdLife International

Designed and produced by the Nature Conservation Bureau Limited,
36 Kingfisher Court, Hambridge Road, Newbury, Berkshire RG14 5SJ, United Kingdom

Printed and bound in Great Britain by Butler and Tanner Ltd., Frome and London

Available from: Natural History Book Service, 2–3 Wills Road, Totnes, Devon, TQ9 5XN, United Kingdom
Tel: +44 1803 865913 Fax: +44 1803 865280 email: sales@nhbs.co.uk Internet: www.nhbs.com

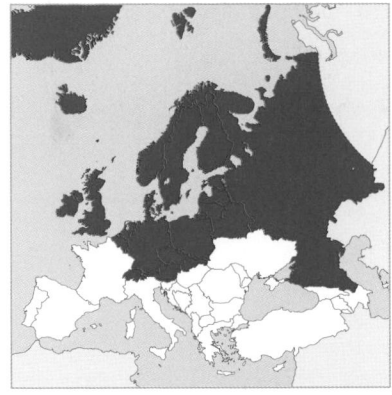

VOLUME 1: NORTHERN EUROPE

AUTHORS OF COUNTRY CHAPTERS

AUSTRIA
Michael Dvorak
BirdLife Austria*

BELARUS
Alexander Kozulin
Bird Conservation Belarus

BELGIUM
Anny Anselin, Jean-Paul Jacob and Willem Van den Bossche
Institute of Nature Conservation; Société d'Etudes Ornithologiques;
Belgische Natuur- en Vogelreservaten/Réserves Naturelles et
Ornithologiques de Belgique (BNVR/RNOB)*

CZECH REPUBLIC
Jan Hora
Czech Society for Ornithology (ČSO)*

DENMARK
Jan F. Rasmussen, Morten Nielsen and Knud N. Flensted
Dansk Ornitologisk Forening (DOF)*

FAROE ISLANDS
Based on data from Grimmett and Jones (1989)
Revised by Føroya Natturugripsavn (FOS)*

GREENLAND
David Boertmann
National Environmental Research Institute, Denmark

ESTONIA
Margus Ots and Andres Kalamees
Estonian Ornithological Society (EOS)*

FINLAND
Mauri Leivo
BirdLife Finland*

FEDERAL REPUBLIC OF GERMANY
Christian Unselt, Claus Mayr and Hans-Günther Bauer
Naturschutzbund Deutschland (NABU)*

ICELAND
Ólafur Einarsson
Icelandic Society for the Protection of Birds (ISPB)*

REPUBLIC OF IRELAND
Jackie Hunt, John Derwin, John Coveney and Stephen Newton
Birdwatch Ireland*

LATVIA
Edmunds Račinskis
Latvijas Ornitologijas Biedrība (LOB)*

LIECHTENSTEIN
Georg Willi
Botanisch-Zoologische Gesellschaft (BZG)*

LITHUANIA
L. Raudonikis, P. Kurlavicius and G. Matiukas
Lithuanian Ornithological Society (LOD)*

LUXEMBOURG
Patric Lorgé
Lëtzeburger Natur-a Vulleschutzliga (LNVL)*

THE NETHERLANDS
Eduard Osieck
Vogelbescherming Nederland (VBN)*

NORWAY
Terje Lislevand, Asbjørn Folvik and Ingar Jostein Øien
Norsk Ornitologisk Forening (NOF)*

SVALBARD AND JAN MAYEN
Terje Lislevand, Asbjørn Folvik and Ingar Jostein Øien
Norsk Ornitologisk Forening (NOF)*

POLAND
Maciej Gromadzki and Maria Wieloch
Polish Society for the Protection of Birds (OTOP)*

RUSSIA
Tanya Sviridova
Russian Bird Conservation Union (RBCU)*

SLOVAKIA
Pavol Kaňuch
Society for the Protection of Birds in Slovakia (SOVS)*

SWEDEN
Lars Lindell, Björn Welander and Steve Dahlfors
Swedish Ornithological Society (SOF)*

SWITZERLAND
Lorenz Heer, Verena Keller, Werner Müller and Hans Schmid
Swiss Association for the Protection of Birds (SVS)*

UNITED KINGDOM, THE CHANNEL ISLANDS AND THE ISLE OF MAN
Ian Fisher, David Gibbons, Guy Thompson and Dave Pritchard
Royal Society for the Protection of Birds (RSPB)*

* Organization is part of the BirdLife International European Partnership
(as of December 1999)

■ CONTENTS

■ FOREWORDS

ONE of the greatest strengths of the Birdlife International Partnership is its ability to focus on priorities for species, sites, habitats and people. There is no better example of putting this focus into practice than BirdLife's Important Bird Area (IBA) programme, now well on its way to identifying and documenting over 20,000 IBAs worldwide.

The beauty of the IBA programme is its simplicity. It identifies important sites for the conservation of the world's birds by applying locally a set of objective criteria to an internationally agreed global standard. This provides the basis for local, national, regional and global action and advocacy. It also generates a conservation agenda from which local and national institutions can strengthen their own capacity and be linked, through IBA programmes across the world, to like-minded institutions.

When the first pan-European inventory of IBAs was launched ten years ago, the designation Important Bird Areas was unknown. Now, IBAs are recognised worldwide and they are rapidly becoming a common and increasingly valuable currency of site conservation. In some places IBAs now have legal status. Both the World Bank and the Global Environment Facility recognise IBAs in their own strategies and action plans, while the European Union has used them as a basis for legal judgements. Communities adjacent to IBAs and dependent on them for their own livelihoods value these sites and play a key role in their conservation. I can think of few concepts in conservation and sustainable development that now have such widespread support and ownership. IBAs unite local people in Burkina Faso, the Philippines, Hungary, Jordan, New York State, Kenya, Spain, Palestine, Panama and many more. They are recognised by inter-governmental bodies and international treaties, such as the Biodiversity and Ramsar Conventions.

This remarkable volume provides detailed information on 3,619 IBAs spread across every country in Europe. It is a unique and powerful source of information that profoundly improves our ability to enable people to conserve birds, biodiversity and the wider environment throughout the region.

Her Majesty Queen Noor of Jordan,
Honorary President of BirdLife International

SINCE its adoption in 1979 the Wild Birds Directive has provided a strong legal basis for the protection of habitats of wild bird species throughout the European Union, especially through the designation of Special Protection Areas (SPAs). The objective is to create a coherent network of protected areas which meets the protection requirements of endangered and migratory bird species and to preserve our common heritage.

The identification and delimitation of sites under this directive is exclusively a scientific exercise. With this in mind, ornithological criteria were elaborated as far back as 1981 when the first inventory of important bird areas of the then European Community was prepared. During the 1980s the European Commission set up a working group, which led to the further identification of Community-wide criteria for the selection of SPAs. This resulted in the preparation of the 1989 inventory of Important Bird Areas (IBAs) in Europe by the forerunner to BirdLife International, the International Council for Bird Preservation (ICBP), with contributions by experts from the Member States.

The 1989 IBA review has proven to be a key scientific reference for the selection of sites to be protected under the Birds Directive. The European Union Court of Justice has concluded that it represents a list of sites of great conservation importance for the conservation of wild birds.

However, more than 10 years have passed since its publication and there have been considerable advances in knowledge on the numbers and distribution of wild birds. The publication of a new inventory of Important Bird Areas is therefore most welcome. I would like to congratulate BirdLife International for the clarity and quality of this work. I am convinced that it will be a standard reference for many years to come.

As most EU Member States have still to actively complete their networks of SPAs it should be a key tool in helping them to fulfil this key requirement of the Birds Directive. Given that it covers all European countries it will also be a valuable reference for those applicants to the European Union as they prepare to take on the nature conservation obligations of membership.

Margot Wallström,
European Commissioner for the Environment

FOLLOWING the publication of the first edition of *Important Bird Areas in Europe* in 1989, the year the iron curtain fell, pan-European cooperation in nature conservation issues has improved enormously. The impressive quantity of new data in this second inventory of *Important Bird Areas of Europe* illustrates just how effectively BirdLife International and its network of national bird conservation societies responded to the new social and political situations. More than 1,000 new IBAs have been designated, mostly in Eastern Europe, and there is valuable new information about existing IBAs. All this was made possible by extensive networks of highly dedicated and scientifically skilled volunteers who undertook field research for this book.

Since 1989, many new NGOs have been established in Europe as a result of BirdLife International programmes. The Dutch Government has supported bird conservation organizations in Central and Eastern Europe—the Russian Federation and the Ukraine in particular—by supporting the collection of field data for this edition of *Important Bird Areas of Europe* and contributed towards its publication. High standards have been applied to submitted data so that the designation Important Bird Area (IBA) is given only to those areas which truly have great ornithological value. In other words, those places which deserve to be protected by existing international conservation frameworks such as Ramsar, the Bonn Convention, the Bern Convention, the EC Birds Directive and the Africa Eurasia Waterbird Agreement.

The work of BirdLife International was of crucial importance in the European Court of Justice case concerning the designation of Special Protection Areas in the Netherlands. Vogelbescherming Nederland, the BirdLife Partner in the Netherlands, had drafted a list of IBAs in the Netherlands, which enabled a quick, efficient designation of a satisfactory number of SPAs, which will be followed by more designations in the future.

The Dutch Government congratulates BirdLife International on the publication of this second edition of *Important Bird Areas of Europe*; without doubt it is a major achievement. We look forward to continuing close cooperation with BirdLife International in conservation projects around the world, particularly with the European Division that is now situated in Wageningen.

G.H. Faber, State Secretary for Agriculture,
Nature Management and Fisheries,
Dutch Government

IT is an honour for me to greet the dear Reader on behalf of the comparatively large family of conservationists in our small country, Hungary.

Biogeographically, Hungary ranks among the richest countries in Europe. Currently, approximately 42,000 animal and 3,000 plant species are known from Hungary, but it is an alarming fact that more than half (62%) of the natural vegetation associations are threatened to some degree and need protection. It was a major step forward in the 1980s and 1990s when it was recognised that it is hopeless to try to protect species without the protection of their habitats. In Hungary, 855 animal and 515 plant species are protected by law. Among them, birds enjoy a particularly favourable status with 278 protected species.

The majority of Important Bird Areas (IBAs) are already protected in Hungary, but in a country that has long been inhabited, urbanised and agriculturally cultivated, isolated protected areas are in a precarious situation and may easily be doomed without the implementation of special protection measures. The total area of Ramsar sites, constituting a major part of IBAs, has increased by 30% during the 1990s and today 19 sites with a total area of 149,000 ha are protected under the Ramsar Convention. The Hungarian BirdLife Partner, the Hungarian Ornithological and Nature Conservation Society, played a key role in the designation of IBAs in Hungary and has established excellent relations with the Hungarian Authority for Nature Conservation, Ministry of the Environment. It is hoped that the future of Hungarian IBAs will be ensured, not only by the declaration of protected status, but also by new measures to support nature-friendly farming.

Many thanks to BirdLife International for their excellent, inspirational and far-reaching programmes, and for creating this remarkable manual. It is an honour that the 106-year-old Hungarian Ornithological Institute and the Hungarian Authority for Nature Conservation could, even if modestly, contribute to this work.

Dr János Tardy PhD, Deputy Secretary of State, Head of the Authority for Nature Conservation, Hungary

■

BEING a mayor of a small town like Třeboň, located at the very heart of Třeboňsko Important Bird Area (IBA) in the unique wetland habitat of Třeboň Basin Biosphere Reserve and Protected Landscape Area, is both a professional task and a public service. It allows intimate daily contact with the surrounding landscape. For example, each time I walk to my office or show guests around my home town or around our ancient fish ponds that give the town its specific character.

Třeboň is the kind of place where one can experience the harmony that still exists between people and nature. It is a town where a glance out of the office window will often provide the magnificent spectacle of migrating flocks of Greylag Geese, or Grey Herons heading towards their nearby colony or even the majestic silhouette of a White-tailed Eagle soaring high in the clouds. I am proud of my town and of all the natural treasures in its vicinity and I am aware of my responsibility for preserving them for future generations. I also appreciate the economic importance of international designations, such as the recognition of Třeboň as an IBA. This attracts thousands of national and international visitors to Třeboň – naturalists, field scientists, participants in ornithological conferences, birdwatchers and nature lovers. All these activities help to make the local economy more viable. In this sense, the IBA status helps me in two ways – to help secure better protection of our birds and habitats and to promote environmentally sound local development.

It is my great pleasure and honour to express my personal feelings on the occasion of the publication of this book. I hope that the updated list of European IBAs will efficiently help to protect birds and nature in the whole of Europe.

Jiri Houdek, Mayor of Třeboň, Czech Republic

■

FOLLOWING the implementation of the Convention on Biological Diversity (CBD) at the end of 1993, over 170 governments have been working to conserve biodiversity and ensure that any use of biological resources is sustainable. Two articles in the CBD set the stage for all others: Article 6 calls for national strategies and action plans; and Article 7 calls for identifying important biodiversity and monitoring its status. Solid science is the foundation upon which both of these critical articles depend, and birds offer a particularly useful group for collecting and presenting information in a way that is useful to politicians, resource managers and the general public. BirdLife International has been working for many years to build a database on birds and their habitats, and now, with the publication of *Important Bird Areas in Europe*, they have produced a valuable source of knowledge that these various interested parties will be able to use to implement the CBD.

BirdLife International, as a member of IUCN, has been a global leader in collecting and presenting essential information on birds and their habitats, and therefore providing solid leadership for implementing the CBD—and other biodiversity-related conventions and agreements—at local, national and regional levels. Their comprehensive approach is particularly useful in enabling countries to coordinate their respective conservation efforts and ensure that transboundary issues are fully addressed. On the basis of this important book, we can confidently expect much more effective conservation action throughout Europe. The challenge now is to extend this innovative and useful approach to the rest of the world and to other taxa. IUCN is pleased to join other partners to help address this challenge.

Jeff McNeely, IUCN Biodiversity Policy Coordination Division

■

SITE-BASED management is a cornerstone of biodiversity conservation, and fundamental to this is readily available knowledge of the location and importance of such sites. BirdLife International's Important Bird Areas programme draws together a wealth of this vital information. The publication in 1989 by ICBP (BirdLife's forerunner) and the International Waterfowl and Wetlands Research Bureau (forerunner of Wetlands International) of Important Bird Areas in Europe was a milestone in providing accessible information on Europe's many and varied places vital for birds. Many of these areas are wetlands. The IBA programme has greatly contributed to identifying the whole network of key sites which are vital for the continued survival of migratory waterbirds, and has provided the foundation for developing an effective bird conservation strategy for Europe.

Wetlands International is pleased to have contributed its knowledge and information on waterbirds to this impressively expanded and updated edition of Important Bird Areas in Europe, both through our volunteer census networks in individual countries and from our population- and flyway-scale information analyses for waterbirds. The new IBA Europe book provides an essential tool for the 21st century in realising the sustainable conservation of waterbirds in Europe and its delivery through the mechanisms of intergovernmental conventions and agreements, notably the Ramsar Convention and Bonn Convention's African-Eurasian Migratory Waterbird Agreement, and in the designation of Special Protection Areas under the EC Birds Directive.

We warmly congratulate BirdLife International on bringing to fruition the huge task of drawing together this wealth of essential information needed for implementing effective bird conservation in Europe. We look forward to continuing to work closely with BirdLife International in progressing this implementation, and in supporting the continuing IBA programme worldwide with our waterbird knowledge and information.

Robin Schaap, International Director, Wetlands International

■ ACKOWLEDGEMENTS

The work of the staff and volunteer networks of the BirdLife International Partnership are at the core of this publication. National Important Bird Areas (IBA) coordinators have worked tirelessly to collate and assess the data in each country through these national networks and have authored individual country chapters. There are hundreds more individuals who have been closely involved in the collation of national data for this project and they are acknowledged in the individual country chapters. For the project team at the BirdLife International Secretariat it has been a great pleasure and honour to collaborate with such a fantastic group of people across Europe. The last five years of working together, often corresponding and exchanging views from a distance, but also the times shared at workshops and meetings, have been of immense importance.

The data, which are the foundations of this inventory, have been collected by many thousands of amateur and professional ornithologists and birdwatchers. They cannot be thanked individually but we owe them a great debt and wish to recognize the important contribution each has made to the identification of Important Bird Areas across Europe.

We are very grateful to the funders of the project and the many BirdLife Partners who have invested substantial resources into the collation of data nationally. We particularly wish to acknowledge the commitment from the Royal Society for the Protection of Birds (RSPB), the BirdLife Partner in the United Kingdom, who have funded the project manager's post and project-coordination activities over the last five years. Mark Avery and David Gibbons (RSPB) arranged this financing and provided advice and words of motivation throughout the course of the project. The Ministry of Agriculture, Nature Management and Fisheries, Directorate for Nature Management, through the PIN/MATRA Funds of the Ministry of Foreign Affairs, The Netherlands, substantially financed this publication. Also Vogelbescherming Nederland, the BirdLife Partner in the Netherlands, have helped in funding overall coordination costs. We thank Mike Rands, Johanna Winkelman and Marco Lambertini for their help in securing these funds.

Many people have provided helpful advice over the course of the project including the BirdLife European Team, which comprised Johanna Winkelman, Neil Burgess, Alistair Gammell, Fritz Hirt, Peter Iankov, Alejandro Sánchez, Joe Sultana, Zoltan Waliczky, David Chandler, Nelly Paleologou and Christel Davidson. We also thank particularly Marco Lambertini and Colin Bibby of the BirdLife Secretariat in Cambridge, for their advice and scientific guidance at all stages of the work and their constructive and helpful comments on draft manuscripts. Our colleague Zoltan Waliczky, the European Conservation Coordinator at the BirdLife Secretariat from 1993–1998, provided substantial help throughout the project including assisting with the development of the IBA database, criteria and thresholds, co-facilitating workshops associated with the project and providing comments on earlier drafts of the manuscript.

Establishing scientifically credible criteria for selecting IBAs was vital to the project. In this regard we thank Lincoln Fishpool and Zoltan Waliczky, who together with MH developed the global categories with input from David Wege and Mike Crosby of the BirdLife International Secretariat. The European criteria, added a further 13 categories to the set of global criteria, the development of which was coordinated by MH in conjunction with the national IBA coordinators in Europe. We also thank Paul Rose, formerly of Wetlands International, for making data available and for generously giving his time to discuss and advise on their application in the context of IBA identification. Mike Brooke and Mark Tasker advised and provided welcome expertise on seabird population estimates. The European Union criteria development was led by Eduard Osieck, together with MH and also David Pritchard, Nelly Paleologou and members of the Birds and Habitats Directive Task Force of BirdLife International. Eduard Osieck is a key figure concerning IBA work in Europe, beginning his involvement in 1981 with the publication of the first work on IBAs, and since then for many years carrying out pioneering work on IBAs in the Netherlands and as Chair of the Birds and Habitats Directive Task Force. He has contributed greatly to this publication and has always being available to offer his expert advice.

Many parts of this publication have been generated from the BirdLife IBA database, an essential tool for storing, managing and analysing the huge quantity of data presented in the country chapters and national and pan-European analysis. We thank Henk van Dijkhuizen for all his work on the original specification of the IBA database, and Mike Crosby and Miriam Langeveld for their work on earlier databases. We recognize the many helpful comments from the BirdLife Partners across Europe during the course of the IBA database development, especially Michael Dvorak, Ian Fisher, Eduard Osieck, Szabolcs Nagy, Tanya Sviridova and Carlota Viada, and also in Asia, particularly Rudyanto (BirdLife Indonesia Programme) and Koyama (Wild Bird Society of Japan, the BirdLife Partner in Japan). Research staff at the BirdLife Secretariat have provided regional input into the development of standardized terms and structure of the database, especially Zoltan Waliczky, Lincoln Fishpool, David Wege, Adrian Long and Mike Crosby. For the programming we are indebted to Peter Bishop of Integra whose skills and patience were fundamental to the success of the computer database we have in use today across more than 35 European countries. We also give special thanks to Andrew Rayner for his skills and always gracious and helpful technical support to the Secretariat and Partners in using and distributing the database.

Very helpful comments were received on drafts of the introductory and analysis chapters and also earlier designs of the site accounts and national overviews from Colin Bibby, Nigel Collar, John Fanshawe, David Gibbons, Marco Lambertini, Adrian Long, Szabolcs Nagy, Eduard Osieck, David Pritchard, Alison Stattersfield, John O'Sullivan, Richard Thomas, Zoltán Waliczky and Johanna Winkelman.

Many colleagues, past and present, at the Secretariat of BirdLife International in Cambridge have given assistance to this project, many of whom have already been mentioned above. We would like to add particular thanks to Mike Rands, Carlos Martín Novella, Laurence Rose, Terry Parker, Chris Spreadbury and Kelly Hague for fundraising, finance and marketing support to the project, and to Mike Rands and Kathleen Rosewarne for negotiations with production companies and designers at earlier stages of the project. Adrian Long oversees the production of the BirdLife Conservation Series and has contributed greatly to this publication through the innovative and constructive input on design and liasing with printers and designers. Margaret Parnwell helped by cataloguing the photographs, and we are very grateful to the photographers who provided them, for the most part, free of charge. Beverly Childs and Anne Collins provided highly valuable secretarial assistance.

Several workshops were held throughout the course of the project and for the generous and excellent logistical help in their organization we would like to thank Dorothy Bashford, Beverley Childs, Anne Collins, Johanna Winkelman and Marianne de Rijk. We also thank the officers working for BirdLife Partners responsible for cross-Partner support for the European Programme for the help they have given in this regard to this project: Johanna Winkelman, Kevin Standring, Norbert Schäffer, Neil Burgess and Fritz Hirt.

Collaboration and support from other organizations was very gratefully received throughout the course of the project. Paul Rose of Wetlands International provided help and data on waterbird populations, Jim Paine and Michael Green of the World Conservation Monitoring Centre (WCMC) provided access to the WCMC Protected Areas Database, Henrik Skov of Ornis Consult advised on marine issues, Dorian Moss from the Institute of Terrestrial Ecology and Mark Roekaerts advised on database systems and Ward Hagermeijer from the European Bird Census Council for advice on atlas data.

For the design, layout, map and graphic production, copy-editing and print management we thank Peter Creed, Rebecca Miles and Tony Vetta of the Nature Conservation Bureau Ltd., whose dedication, professionalism and enthusiasm have added much to the presentation of information in this book.

Finally, this publication builds upon and updates the first pan-European IBA inventory, the authors of which, Richard Grimmett and Tim Jones, are warmly thanked and congratulated for setting such sound foundations upon which the European IBA Programme has evolved to benefit the conservation of IBAs, and from which this new publication has evolved 10 years on.

■ Project Team

Melanie Heath – Project Manager, 1994–1999 Coordinating the production of this publication as part of her job as European Research Manager, including project development, scientific direction and analysis, editing and the development of the European IBA Database.

Michael Evans – Senior Editor, 1997–1999. Responsible for overall editing standards, standardization of terms and nomenclature, and final proof-reading.

Tony Payne – Research Assistant, 1996–1998. Central to the development, functionality and management of the IBA database and the validation of data within it, and technical support to Partners using the database.

David Hoccom – Research Assistant, 1998–1999. Editor of country chapters and producer of national overview graphics.

Nic Peet – Research Assistant, 1999. Editor of country chapters.

Tim Morrissey – Map production for country chapters and pan-European overview.

Regina Pfaff – Editorial support and incorporating editorial changes into the manuscript.

Paulina Phillips – Data-entry and checking.

SUMMARY

WHAT IS THE BIRDLIFE IBA PROGRAMME?

The Important Bird Areas (IBA) Programme of BirdLife International is a worldwide initiative aimed at identifying and protecting a network of critical sites for the conservation of the world's birds. The European IBA Programme is the longest running of a number of regional IBA programmes and for the last decade has addressed site-oriented research and action, encompassing habitat management, monitoring, education, advocacy, and national and international legal protection. This publication presents essential information on all known Important Bird Areas in Europe and builds on and updates the first pan-European IBA inventory, published in 1989.

DATA FOR PRIORITY-SETTING AND DECISION MAKING

Data collection and analysis play a highly influential role in underpinning the conservation and management of IBAs. Useful for conservationists, ornithologists, governmental and non-governmental agencies, policy-makers, researchers, consultants and planners, the data presented here are intended to guide practical management and actions at IBAs and to target political and legal mechanisms to achieve the adequate protection of IBAs.

AN INTERNATIONALLY IMPORTANT NETWORK OF SITES

Through the rigorous application of standard and quantitative ornithological criteria, the international importance of the network of sites identified is assured. The criteria applied justify the importance of each site, and their global standardization facilitates comparisons between sites at local, national, regional and global levels. These criteria are compatible with those used to designate wetlands of international importance under the Ramsar Convention and Special Protection Areas under the EC Birds Directive.

Page 11

THOUSANDS CONTRIBUTE – THE LARGEST NETWORK IN EUROPE

Contributions have been made by a vast network of ornithologists, birdwatchers and conservation experts across Europe. Many hundreds of individuals have been directly involved in the collation of data and many thousands more have laid the foundations for the project, through carrying out field surveys of bird numbers and distributions during the last three decades. In most countries the relevant BirdLife International Partner has coordinated the work nationally, and this has generally involved substantial collaboration with governmental and non-governmental organizations.

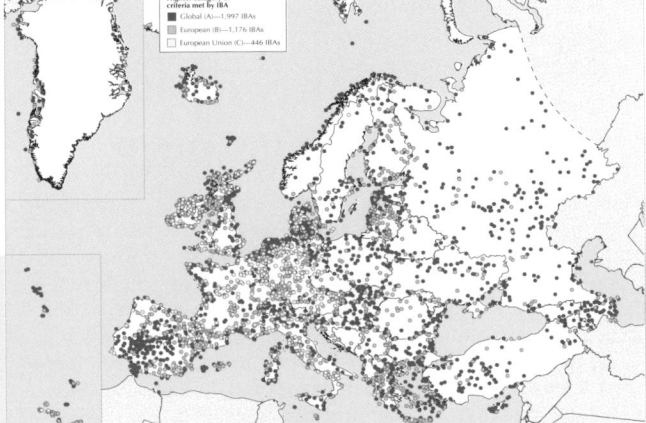

3,619 IBAS COVER 7% OF EUROPE

A comprehensive network of IBAs has been identified across Europe. The effective protection and management of these sites, equivalent to a relatively low percentage of each country's area, is a realistic goal that would make a significant contribution to conserving many bird species in Europe.

OVER 1,000 NEW IBAS IDENTIFIED

A large amount of new data has been gathered as part of this inventory, resulting in improved coverage across the region compared to the previous pan-European IBA inventory in 1989. Since then, no fewer than 1,175 new IBAs have been identified, representing a 48% increase in the number of sites, and a 130% increase in the total surface area covered, with improved coverage particularly in the east of the region.

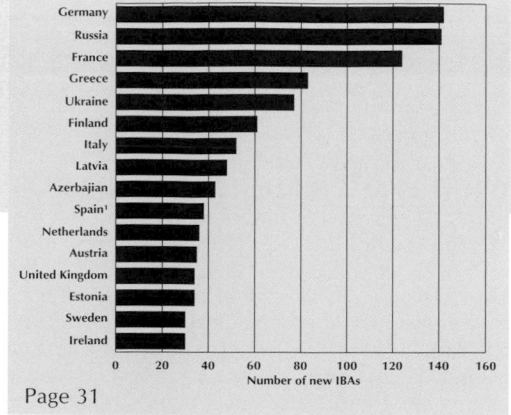

Page 31

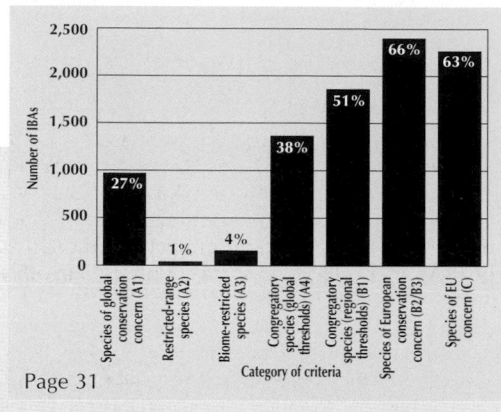

Page 31

SITES IDENTIFIED FOR 378 SPECIES (73% OF EUROPE'S BIRDS)

IBAs are particularly important for species that congregate in large numbers such as wintering and passage waterbirds and breeding seabirds (51% of IBAs in Europe are identified for these species). Many sites have also been identified for species of global conservation concern (27% of IBAs are important for one or more of the 35 such species in Europe), for species of European conservation concern (66% of all IBAs) and for species of concern within the European Union (63% of all IBAs).

ALL MAJOR HABITAT-TYPES COVERED

IBAs encompass all major habitat-types in Europe, with wetlands, forests, grasslands and cultivated/grazed habitats being the most frequent. Each of these habitat-types holds a distinctive but diminishing avifauna which urgently needs recognition and protection against ill-conceived development.

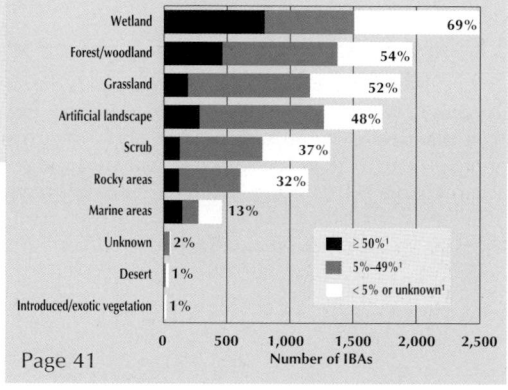

Page 41

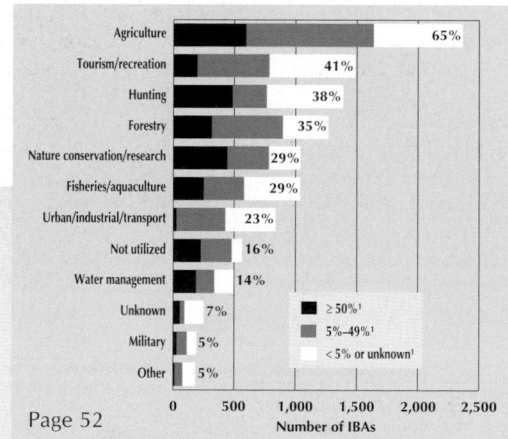

Page 52

IBAS HEAVILY INFLUENCED BY DIVERSE LAND-USE PRACTICES

Land-use practices have been recorded within 95% of IBAs and often cover the entire IBA area, reflecting the high human use of Europe's habitats in general. As a result, the conservation of habitats and birds within IBAs is very much dependent on the land-use practices, policies and programmes affecting these sites and their surroundings. Of particular importance is agriculture, the dominant land-use in Europe, and this is reflected within IBAs, with agricultural activities taking place in 65% of IBAs.

93% OF IBAS CONSIDERED THREATENED

Nearly all IBAs are threatened to some degree by at least one factor, and 42% of IBAs are affected by one or more high-impact threats (actual or potential). Agricultural intensification and/or expansion is the most serious threat affecting IBAs, being cited at more than 1,300 sites and with a high impact at nearly 400 of these. Recreation and tourism, unsustainable exploitation, infrastructure, industrialization and urbanization, drainage, abandonment and reduction of land management, intensification of forestry practices, aquaculture and fisheries, the construction of dams, dykes or barrages and the extraction industry each threaten more (and in many cases significantly more) than 300 IBAs (c.10% of European IBAs).

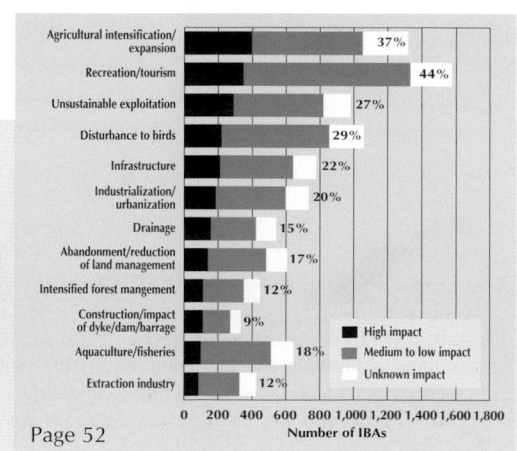

Page 52

IBAS IN THE CONTEXT OF THE WIDER ENVIRONMENT

Increasingly, many environmental problems and potential threats to IBAs are regional or global in scope or origin, and cannot be solely addressed by good protection and management of IBAs themselves. Furthermore, many species breed in a dispersed, non-congregatory fashion, and therefore cannot be conserved successfully by the IBA programme alone. Therefore, it is vital that conservation of the wider environment and the integration of environmental objectives into all policy sectors are also pursued in addition to, and in the context of, IBA conservation.

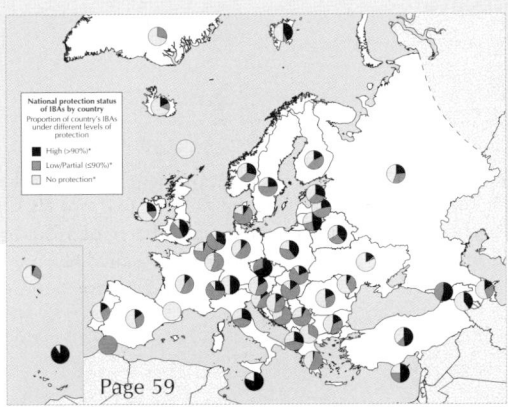

Page 59

40% OF IBAS UNPROTECTED BY NATIONAL LAWS

All European countries have legal and institutional frameworks for the designation and management of protected areas. IBAs should be designated as protected areas under national law where appropriate, but this target has not yet been reached, with 40% of IBAs still unprotected. Additionally, only 21% of European IBAs have more than 90% of their entire area protected at the national level. A higher proportion of IBAs are protected in some countries than others.

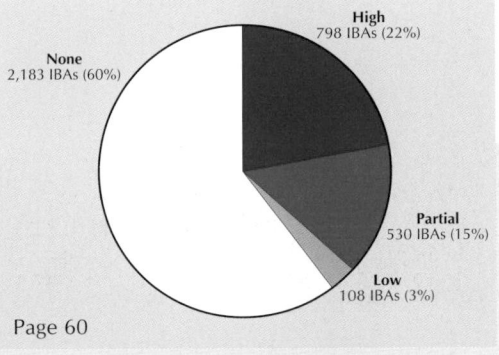

Page 60

60% OF IBAS UNPROTECTED AT THE INTERNATIONAL LEVEL

Substantial international recognition of IBAs has been achieved in the last decade but many IBAs remain inadequately protected or recognized under relevant international agreements, and further designations are required. Only 40% of IBAs have some form of international protection, and in only 22% of IBAs in Europe is more than 90% of the individual IBA area protected at the international level.

- Many IBAs are wetlands of international importance yet only 30% of these have been designated under the Ramsar Convention. Given the compatibility of IBA criteria with Ramsar criteria, it is possible to estimate that a further 1,000 IBAs in Europe should be considered for designation as Ramsar Sites because of the internationally important numbers of waterbirds that they hold.

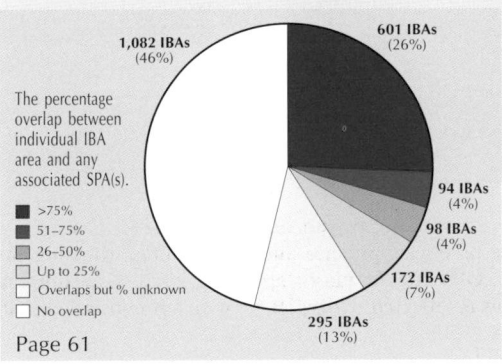

The percentage overlap between individual IBA area and any associated SPA(s).

- ■ >75%
- ■ 51–75%
- ■ 26–50%
- □ Up to 25%
- □ Overlaps but % unknown
- □ No overlap

Page 61

- Many IBAs in the European Union are internationally important for migratory and threatened birds but only 54% have been designated as Special Protection Areas (SPAs) under the EC Birds Directive. A further 1,000 IBAs in the European Union should therefore be designated as SPAs. Additionally, only one quarter of IBAs in the EU have more than 75% of their individual area designated as SPAs.

WHAT ACTIONS NEED TO BE TAKEN?

Immense pressure continues to be placed on the European environment through developments in agriculture, forestry, fisheries, transport, energy, industry, tourism/recreation and urbanization. This publication shows such pressures are severely impacting the most important sites for birds in Europe. Much still needs to be done to conserve IBAs adequately.

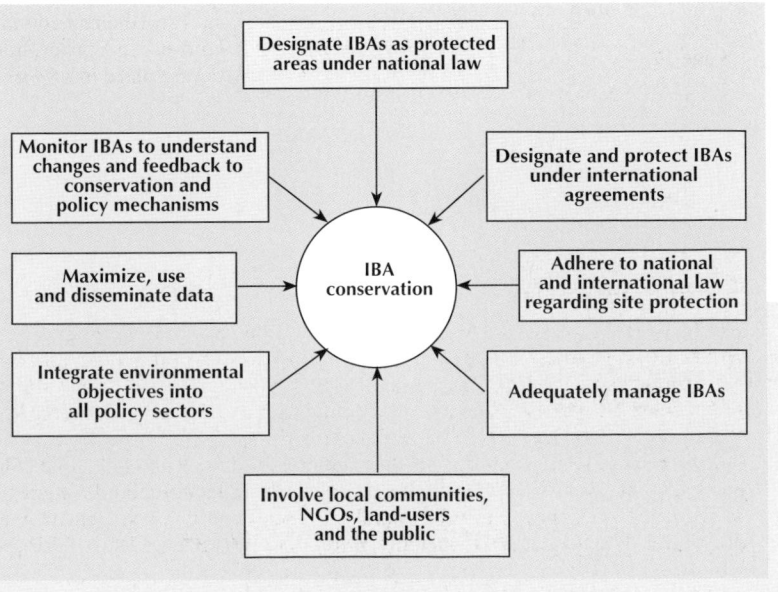

■ INTRODUCTION

EUROPE'S ENVIRONMENT

■ Pressure

The 20th century has seen profound changes in the European environment. Across most of the continent, man's use of the land and sea continues to intensify, driven by technological innovations, market forces, and political and socio-economic changes. Very few areas have escaped the impact of recent developments in agriculture, forestry, fisheries, transport, energy, industry and urbanization, and associated pollution.

In particular, the intensification since 1950 of the two most widespread land-uses in Europe, agriculture and forestry, has led to the 'simplification' of ecosystems across vast areas, giving man greater control over natural variations in the productivity of farmland and forests, but also markedly reducing the biological diversity and complexity of these habitats. Increasingly efficient but indiscriminate harvesting methods are reducing the populations of many marine and freshwater organisms in Europe's rivers and seas, altering food-webs in the process. Under these pressures, less intensive forms of natural-resource use have not been able to compete economically, and have been widely abandoned (Pain and Pienkowski 1997, EEA 1998). Many other semi-natural habitats, such as inland wetlands and dry grasslands, have also been greatly reduced in extent and diversity by man's activities, with the remaining fragments increasingly isolated from each other (Tucker and Evans 1997).

■ Status

These changes in land-use have had a highly detrimental impact on Europe's biodiversity (EEA 1998). About 12% of vertebrate species in Europe are threatened with global extinction (WCMC 1997) and, at least for birds (the only group for which there is adequate data), a much larger proportion of the total (38% of regularly occurring bird species) have an unfavourable conservation status on the continent, most of these species having undergone significant reductions in abundance or range since 1970 (Box 1). Man's activities are implicated as the driving factor in most of these declines. The intensifying use of the environment has also had damaging effects on society within and beyond Europe, e.g. through massive loss of rural livelihoods, over-dependence on subsidies, and the socio-economic impacts of food surpluses and food-safety issues (EEA 1998).

■ Response

Future directions and policies for land-use in Europe are still decided by the orthodox application of economic theory. As yet, mainstream economics do not take into account the full benefits of biodiversity, nor the long-term costs to society of intensification, in terms of biodiversity loss (UNEP 1995). As a result, decisions relevant to future land-use still ignore many of the projected impacts on biodiversity and society, and the phenomenon of biodiversity loss still receives insufficient attention from most sectors of the economy and society.

Although biodiversity is not yet valued in strict economic terms, it is now widely recognized that these negative environmental trends cannot be allowed to continue indefinitely, since the direct and indirect costs to society will be too great (UNEP 1995). The challenge is to find more sustainable ways of using the environment, so-called 'sustainable development'.

At the governmental level, the world community has responded with initiatives such as *Agenda 21* and the Convention on Biological Diversity (Biodiversity Convention), both products of the 'Earth Summit'—the United Nations Conference on Environment and Development—at Rio de Janeiro in 1992. At the European level, the *Pan-European Biological and Landscape Diversity Strategy* has received unanimous endorsement from Europe's environment ministers (McCloskey 1997), and the European Community has responded with *Towards Sustainability*, the fifth environmental action programme of the European Commission (CEC 1993), followed more recently by the *EC Biodiversity Strategy* (CEC 1998).

These international initiatives, whether master-plans, conventions or policy documents, all share similar objectives, that is to promote, within and between nations, the conservation of biodiversity and the sustainable use of natural resources, through the integration of environmental issues and concerns into all sectors of society (including the economy), encouraging closer cooperation between sectors, and advocating a more participatory form of environmental policy-making.

At the local level, one of the ways that individual citizens can participate in policy-making, and help to solve problems in society, is through creating or supporting non-governmental organizations (NGOs). The number and size of NGOs that address environmental problems have increased enormously in recent years, in Europe and elsewhere, indicating the rising level of concern in society world-wide. The combined membership of such NGOs in Europe alone runs into many millions, and gives these bodies authority and democratic basis when seeking to influence governments, businesses and other powerful sectors of society. Indeed, through their research, publicity and action, these groups of like-minded people are a crucial partner to governments in the search for more sustainable forms of development.

THE NEED FOR BIRD CONSERVATION IN EUROPE

Birds are one of the best-researched and most reliable indicators of biodiversity loss in Europe (Tucker and Heath 1994, Tucker and Evans 1997). Nearly 40% of bird species in Europe currently have an unfavourable conservation status (Box 1), mainly as a result of man's intensifying use of the environment and because of other, more direct threats from people, such as disturbance, persecution and excessive hunting (Tucker and Heath 1994). Faced with these rare or declining populations, the conservation of Europe's birds and other biodiversity has become an increasingly important and necessary activity, requiring coordination on an international scale.

In response, BirdLife International, the world-wide partnership of national NGOs devoted to the conservation of birds and their habitats (Box 2), pursues a programme of research, publicity and action in Europe, designed to:

- Prevent the extinction of any bird species.
- Reduce the number of bird species that are globally threatened.
- Maintain and where possible enhance the conservation status of all bird species.
- Conserve sites and habitats important for birds.

Box 1. The status of birds in Europe (Tucker and Heath 1994).

A total of 515 bird species occur regularly in Europe, comprising thousands of millions of individuals which depend on the continent as a breeding, staging or wintering ground. On a world scale, Europe is particularly important for 136 species, supporting the majority of their global population at some stage of their annual cycle.

Nearly 40% of the continent's bird species have an unfavourable conservation status in Europe, based on their rarity or their rate of population decline since 1970. Of these 195 species, 20 are globally threatened with extinction (Collar *et al.* 1994) and a further 15 are also of global conservation concern.

Most bird species in Europe occur widely across the continent, with populations in many different countries. Additionally, the great majority of bird species in Europe are migratory in at least part of their range, crossing many national frontiers, with some species regularly reaching not only southern Africa but also as far as Canada, east Siberia, India and the sub-Antarctic. An international perspective is therefore all-important for most bird-conservation initiatives in Europe.

Box 2. BirdLife International.

BirdLife International consists, in Europe, of 32 Partner organizations with a combined membership of over 2 million people and staff of more than 1,700. In addition, 22 other national organizations in Europe are affiliated to the Partnership, as Representatives or Associates.

BirdLife International, through seeking to conserve all bird species and their habitats on earth, works for the world's biodiversity and for the sustainability of human use of natural resources.

Why birds?

Birds play a special and unique role in connecting humanity to biodiversity and the environment. They occupy almost all habitats on the earth's surface, and are widely dispersed in all countries and regions. They are the best known and documented major taxonomic group of organisms in the world.

Birds are important to society because:

- They are valuable in their own right
- They are sensitive indicators of biological richness and environmental condition
- They are vital for ecological functions in the natural environment
- They have a direct and indirect economic and cultural value to people
- They provide a useful means to improve our scientific knowledge and understanding of the environment
- They are beautiful and inspirational, and a source of happiness and pleasure for many people
- They are very useful for promoting conservation awareness
- Like all species, they have a moral right to a continued existence on Earth.

PRIORITIZATION OF CONSERVATION ACTION

BirdLife International approaches the conservation of birds, in Europe as elsewhere, in three different ways:

1. Conservation of species
2. Conservation of sites
3. Conservation of habitats

Each approach is essential for the effective conservation of a large number of species and, while different, each is complementary and interdependent. Box 3 summarizes the rationale behind each approach.

BirdLife attaches great importance to the identification of priorities, to set targets and guide conservation action on species, sites and habitats. The BirdLife International Partnership has therefore conducted baseline studies across Europe to identify the conservation priorities for species, sites and habitats (Box 3). This publication defines the priority sites for bird conservation in Europe.

THE CONSERVATION OF SITES FOR BIRDS— IMPORTANT BIRD AREAS

Some areas in Europe are particularly important for birds:

- Sites for globally threatened species (Collar *et al.* 1994) and other species of European conservation concern and of European Union concern (Tucker and Heath 1994, CEC 1994).
- Sites for migratory species which congregate in high numbers (Rose and Scott 1997).
- Sites for species unique to a small region (Stattersfield *et al.* 1998).
- Sites that support a species assemblage that is highly representative of a distinct biome.

BirdLife International classifies such sites as Important Bird Areas (IBAs), where a significant part of these species' populations can be found on a regular basis. The protection and management of these high-priority sites, in a network across all relevant countries in the world, could contribute greatly to the effective conservation of these species. One of the main aims of BirdLife International is to build such a global network, through its IBA Programme (Box 4).

Legal mechanisms exist within Europe to protect the ecological integrity of these sites, at a variety of geographical scales. All European countries have legal and institutional frameworks for the designation and management of protected areas, and the perspective beyond national borders (so important for highly mobile organisms such as birds) is provided by a number of international conventions and initiatives that explicitly encourage the designation of international networks of sites that serve a shared conservation purpose (see in Box 2, 'Overview of results' chapter). However, despite this relatively well-developed statutory 'infrastructure', implementation has often been relatively slow, and many IBAs remain without official protection or recognition.

Box 3. Three ways of conserving biodiversity.

1. Conservation of species

This is the protection of species through conservation action, which may take many forms, such as legislation, monitoring, research, prioritization, management of populations, and the acquisition and management of land. Such an approach is often taken for species of economic or cultural importance, and increasingly for species that are threatened with extinction at a local, national or global level.

BirdLife International has identified those species that are threatened with global extinction (Collar *et al.* 1994) or that are otherwise of conservation concern in Europe (Tucker and Heath 1994), and has recently coordinated the production of up-to-date, international action plans for the conservation of the most threatened species in Europe (Heredia *et al.* 1996, CoE in prep.).

2. Conservation of sites

This is the protection of sites to conserve species and habitats and to maintain the integrity of ecosystem processes, by designating areas for the conservation of natural resources, and regulating and managing them according to the needs of the biodiversity which they contain. Apart from the long-term benefits gained by conserving biodiversity, sites also have other important functions for society, including education and research, and have non-material and non-monetary values as well as providing the focus for local or national pride. In moving towards a more sustainable society, all these functions will be increasingly highly valued. The protection and conservation of sites is an integral part of any attempt to achieve sustainability.

The BirdLife International Important Bird Area (IBA) Programme (see Box 4), a world-wide initiative aimed at identifying and protecting a network of critical sites for the world's birds, aims to facilitate the conservation of birds via this approach. This book, which builds upon the first pan-European IBA inventory (Grimmett and Jones 1989), is intended to guide practical on-the-ground conservation management and also to target political and legal mechanisms to achieve adequate protection of Europe's IBAs.

3. Conservation of habitats

A great threat to birds in Europe, and to biodiversity in general, lies in the continuing erosion of the quality and extent of habitats across the entire landscape ('the wider environment'). The loss and degradation is driven by the increasing intensity of human uses of the environment. The conservation of habitat extent and quality across the landscape cannot be achieved solely by the protection of representative areas: a wider approach is needed.

National governments and regional or local authorities can favour and encourage the conservation of the wider environment in the way that they formulate and use their laws, policies, plans, programmes, initiatives, subsidies, taxes, funds, inter-governmental relations and other broad measures. Ideally, these should be fully integrated into land-use policies, regulations and plans, across all sectors of the economy and at all scales. BirdLife International has recently outlined a strategy for conserving birds and their habitats in the wider European environment over the next 20 years (Tucker and Evans 1997).

Box 4. The Important Bird Area Programme of BirdLife International.

- The function of the Important Bird Area (IBA) Programme is to identify, protect and manage a network of sites that are important for the long-term viability of naturally occurring bird populations, across the geographical range of those bird species for which a site-based approach is appropriate.
- The continued ecological integrity of these sites will be decisive in maintaining and conserving such birds. Legal protection, management and monitoring of these crucial sites will all be important targets for action, and many (but not all) bird species may be effectively conserved by these means. Patterns of bird distribution are such that, in most cases, it is possible to select sites that support many species.
- The IBA Programme is global in scale, and it is anticipated that up to 20,000 IBAs will be identified world-wide, using standard, internationally recognized criteria for selection.
- The sites are identified on the basis of the bird numbers and species' complements that they hold, and are selected such that, taken together, they form a network throughout the species' biogeographic distributions.
- This network may be considered as a minimum essential to ensure the survival of these species across their ranges, should there occur a net loss of remaining habitat elsewhere through human, or other, modification. Therefore the consequences of the loss of any one of these sites may be disproportionately large.
- The programme aims to guide the implementation of national conservation strategies, through the promotion and development of national protected-area programmes. It is also intended to assist the conservation activities of international organisations and to promote the implementation of global agreements and regional measures.

There are also, in Europe, many non-statutory protected areas, often smaller, which contribute greatly to biodiversity conservation, such as those owned and/or managed by non-governmental organizations, private bodies, villages, farmers, and urban authorities.

IMPORTANT BIRD AREAS IN EUROPE

The first IBA inventory to cover the whole of Europe was published in 1989 (Grimmett and Jones 1989). *Important Bird Areas in Europe* provided key information on 2,444 high-priority sites in 39 countries or autonomous regions. It represented a major step towards realizing a bird-conservation strategy for Europe, and it accelerated progress in maintaining and enhancing the conservation value of all IBAs. Over the last ten years, BirdLife Partners across 32 countries have increasingly focused their site-conservation activities towards the IBA network, and local volunteers have mobilized at numerous IBAs to help protect, manage or monitor 'their' sites, on the ground. Facilitated since 1990 by a coordinator at the BirdLife International Secretariat and, increasingly, by national IBA coordinators in individual countries, the actions of many individuals have coalesced into a formal IBA programme (Box 4).

As part of this programme, 12 international workshops have been held across Europe, to develop the skills of national IBA coordinators (and their networks of local volunteers and experts) in fund-raising, awareness-raising, monitoring, site management, lobbying, advocacy, dealing with the media, and so on. In addition, the IBA programme has generated hundreds of 'interventions' over the past decade, coordinated actions involving Partners and other NGOs, their members and the general public in concerted lobbying against unsustainable developments at particular sites.

As well as this influence at the grassroots, the inventory has also stimulated advances in statutory or 'top-down' conservation of sites, notably through two judgements of the European Court of Justice, one giving precedent for the legal protection of an IBA (Santoña marshes, Spain, 1993), the other requiring an EU member state to designate a more complete network of Special Protection Areas under the EC Birds Directive, citing the IBA inventory as an example of such a network (case lost by the Netherlands government, 1998). In the same vein, data and data analyses have

been used to influence and have strong input into several international legal frameworks for site conservation, notably the EC Birds Directive (leading to Natura 2000), the Ramsar Convention and HELCOM (further details of these instruments are given in Appendix 1).

■ The new IBA inventory
This book represents an update of the first IBA inventory, ten years on. It presents essential information on all known sites of international importance for the conservation of birds in Europe, targeted at a number of audiences:

- decision-makers and policy-makers
- land-use planners and regulators
- funders
- land managers
- conservationists
- birdwatchers and ornithologists
- environmental consultants
- academic and research bodies.

Since 1989 a considerable amount of new data on birds and sites has become available (Box 5), and as much as possible has been included in this book. Thus 3,619 IBAs are listed and described for Europe, a net increase of 50% since 1989. This book, and the computer database from which it was produced, are two products of five years' work by the BirdLife International Partnership in Europe, together with thousands of other ornithologists and birdwatchers, in 51 countries or autonomous regions.

■ Objectives of the inventory
The principal objectives of this book are:

- to identify and promote awareness of the most important sites in Europe for the conservation of birds
- to help direct conservation activity and available funding towards these sites
- to present the ornithological value of each site in a standardized but also reliable way, using numerical criteria
- to provide a tool for planning and management, at practical and political levels, through the presentation of key information on birds, habitats, land-uses, threats, legal protection, and conservation status
- to develop networks of local experts, fieldworkers and volunteers, and motivate them to monitor and protect IBAs
- to stimulate national and international cooperation and co-ordination in conserving Europe's most important sites for birds

Box 5. Progress in identifying and documenting Important Bird Areas in Europe.

1981: The first ever inventory of IBAs is prepared by the International Council for Bird Preservation (ICBP) (now BirdLife International) for the European Commission (Osieck and Mörzer Bruyns 1981), covering 694 sites in the (then) nine member states of the European Community (EC).

1983–1986: Further IBA inventories are prepared by ICBP for the European Commission, covering new member states of the EC, as well as threatened IBAs in the expanded EC.

1989: The first pan-European IBA inventory is published, covering 2,444 sites in 39 countries or autonomous regions (Grimmett and Jones 1989). In the same year, a separate inventory, commissioned by the European Commission, is produced by ICBP on the IBAs in the (then) 12 member states of the EC (Grimmett and Gammell 1989).

1989–2000: Many new IBAs are identified as a result of field surveys, literature review and expert knowledge, especially in the east and south of Europe. National IBA inventories are published in 16 countries, with substantially revised and enhanced data in many cases (listed in Box 1, 'Data collection' chapter).

2000 – Second pan-European IBA inventory (this book) published, covering 3,619 sites in 51 countries or autonomous regions.

- to establish a more rigorous baseline for measuring Europe's success or failure in conserving its most important sites for birds
- to facilitate the comparison of information at local, national and international scales
- to promote awareness of the value of a site-based approach for the conservation of birds and biodiversity

■ Components of the inventory
This publication is divided into four main sections:

1. Introductory chapters
- Data collection: information on standardized methods and classification schemes.
- Site selection: ascertaining the importance of sites for birds against agreed scientific criteria.
- Data presentation: how to use the book.

2. 'Overview of results' chapter
- Pan-European summary analysis of the data gathered, with conclusions and recommendations.

3. Country chapters: inventory of Important Bird Areas by country
For each country, there is:
- A national overview of the IBAs .
- A detailed site-account for each IBA.

Due to the large number of countries and sites involved, the inventory has been divided into two volumes: each starts with the Introductory chapters and 'Overview of results' chapter (sections 1 and 2, above), followed by a group of country chapters, as follows.

Volume 1: **Northern Europe**—Austria, Belarus, Belgium, Czech Republic, Denmark, Faroe Islands, Greenland, Estonia, Finland, Germany, Iceland, Republic of Ireland, Latvia, Liechtenstein, Lithuania, Luxembourg, Netherlands, Norway, Svalbard and Jan Mayen, Poland, Russia, Slovakia, Sweden, Switzerland, United Kingdom (including Channel Islands and Isle of Man).

Volume 2: **Southern Europe**—Albania, Andorra, Armenia, Azerbaijan, Bosnia and Herzegovina, Bulgaria, Croatia, Cyprus, France, Georgia, Gibraltar, Greece, Hungary, Italy, Former Yugoslav Republic of Macedonia, Malta, Moldova, Portugal, Azores, Madeira, Romania, Slovenia, Spain (including Canary Islands), Turkey, Ukraine, Yugoslavia.

4. Appendices
A series of Appendices give more detailed information, descriptions and analyses, in support of the introductory and overview chapters (the Appendices are provided in both volumes of the publication).

REFERENCES

CEC [COMMISSION OF THE EUROPEAN COMMUNITIES] (1993) *Towards sustainability. The European Community programme of policy and action in relation to the environment and sustainable development.* Luxembourg: Official Journal of the EC (OJ C138, 17 May 1993).

CEC [COMMISSION OF THE EUROPEAN COMMUNITIES] (1994) *Special Protection Areas.* Luxembourg: Official Journal of the EC.

CEC [COMMISSION OF THE EUROPEAN COMMUNITIES] (1998) *The European Community Biodiversity Strategy.* Luxembourg: Official Journal of the EC.

COLLAR, N. J., CROSBY, M. J. AND STATTERSFIELD, A. J. (1994) *Birds to watch 2: the world list of threatened birds.* Cambridge, UK: BirdLife International (Conservation Series No. 4.).

CoE [COUNCIL OF EUROPE] (in prep.) Second tranche of international action plans for high-priority bird species in Europe. Strasbourg, France: CoE.

EEA [EUROPEAN ENVIRONMENTAL AGENCY] (1998) *Europe's environment: the second assessment.* Luxembourg: Office of Official Publications of the European Communities/Oxford, UK: Elsevier.

GRIMMETT R. F. A. AND GAMMELL, A. B. (1989) Inventory of Important Bird Areas in the European Community. (Unpublished report prepared for the Directorate-General for the Environment, Consumer Protection and Nuclear Safety of the European Community, Study contract B6610-54-88.) Cambridge, UK: International Council for Bird Preservation.

GRIMMETT, R. F. A. AND JONES, T. A. (1989) *Important Bird Areas in Europe.* Cambridge, U.K.: International Council for Bird Preservation (Techn. Publ. 9).

HEREDIA, B., ROSE, L. AND PAINTER, M., EDS. (1996) *Globally threatened birds in Europe: action plans.* Strasbourg, France: Council of Europe.

McCLOSKEY, C. (1997) *P.E.B.L.D.S. explained.* Tilburg, Netherlands: IUCN European Programme.

OSIECK, E. R. AND MÖRZER BRUYNS, M. F. (1981) *Important bird areas in the European community.* Cambridge, UK: International Council for Bird Preservation.

PAIN, D. J. AND PIENKOWSKI, M. W., EDS. (1997) *Farming and birds in Europe: the Common Agricultural Policy and its implications for bird conservation.* London: Academic Press.

ROSE, P. M. AND SCOTT, D. A. (1997) *Waterfowl population estimates.* Second edition. Wageningen, Netherlands: Wetlands International (Publication 44).

STATTERSFIELD, A. J., CROSBY, M. J., LONG, A. J. AND WEGE, D. C. (1998) *Endemic bird areas of the world: priorities for bird conservation.* Cambridge, UK: BirdLife International (Conservation Series No. 7).

TUCKER, G. M. AND EVANS, M. I., EDS. (1997) *Habitats for birds in Europe: a conservation strategy for the wider environment.* Cambridge, UK: BirdLife International (Conservation Series No. 6).

TUCKER, G. M. AND HEATH, M. F. (1994) *Birds in Europe: their conservation status.* Cambridge, UK: BirdLife International (Conservation Series No. 3).

UNEP [UNITED NATIONS ENVIRONMENT PROGRAMME] (1995) *Global Biodiversity Assessment.* Nairobi: UNEP.

WCMC [WORLD CONSERVATION MONITORING CENTRE] (1997) Red Data Book of European vertebrates. [Final draft for review at the 17th meeting of the Standing Committee of the Convention on the Conservation of European Wildlife and Natural Habitats, Strasbourg, 1–5 December 1997.] Strasbourg, France: Council of Europe (internal document T-PVS (97) 61 Eng. orig.).

■ DATA COLLECTION

GEOGRAPHICAL DEFINITION OF EUROPE

The geographical area covered by this publication is defined in Figure 1, and is the same as that covered by the previous pan-European Important Bird Area (IBA) inventory 10 years ago (Grimmett and Jones 1989). Thus, Europe here includes the Atlantic archipelagos of the Canary Islands, the Azores and Madeira, as well as western Russia (all administrative regions lying mainly west of the Ural mountains and Ural river), Armenia, Azerbaijan, Georgia, the Faroe Islands, Iceland, Svalbard and Jan Mayen, and the whole of Greenland, Turkey and Cyprus.

In total, 51 countries or autonomous regions are covered in this publication, compared to 39 such entities in the previous pan-European IBA inventory. This difference is due to the large political changes that have taken place during the past decade. No IBAs were identified in Monaco, San Marino or Vatican City (Holy See).

THE BIRDLIFE INTERNATIONAL PARTNERSHIP

A vast network of ornithologists, birdwatchers and conservation experts across Europe have contributed to this inventory (Figure 2). Many hundreds have been involved in the collation of data specifically for this project, and are acknowledged in each country chapter. Indirectly, many thousands more have laid the foundation for the inventory, through carrying out surveys of bird numbers and distributions during the last three decades.

The existence of the BirdLife International Partnership (see Box 2, 'Introduction' chapter) has greatly facilitated the assembly of this huge and diverse network. The 32 Partners of BirdLife International in Europe have endorsed and are implementing the BirdLife IBA Programme, initiated in 1990. Most have an IBA coordinator (or team), responsible for delivering this programme within the country concerned.

In most countries, therefore, it has been the IBA coordinators/teams within Partners who have organized the collation of new and revised IBA information, and who have been responsible for a large network of volunteer contributors to the project (Figure 2). The networks of local IBA experts are usually those who are active in the protection, management and monitoring of IBAs in their area (Figure 2). In a few countries this network has a formal structure (e.g. 'IBA caretaker network') and procedures, e.g. regular reporting to the national coordinator on the status of sites, or distribution of a national IBA newsletter. In most such cases, the IBA coordinator has also been the principal author of the relevant country overview in this publication. In countries without a BirdLife Partner or IBA coordinator, an expert was commissioned to coordinate the collection of data nationally.

In addition, much valuable information has come from beyond the BirdLife Partnership. At local and national levels there has been substantial collaboration with other bodies that collect and hold relevant data, both governmental and non-governmental, and these are duly acknowledged in each country chapter. Special mention should be made of Wetlands International, the leading non-profit

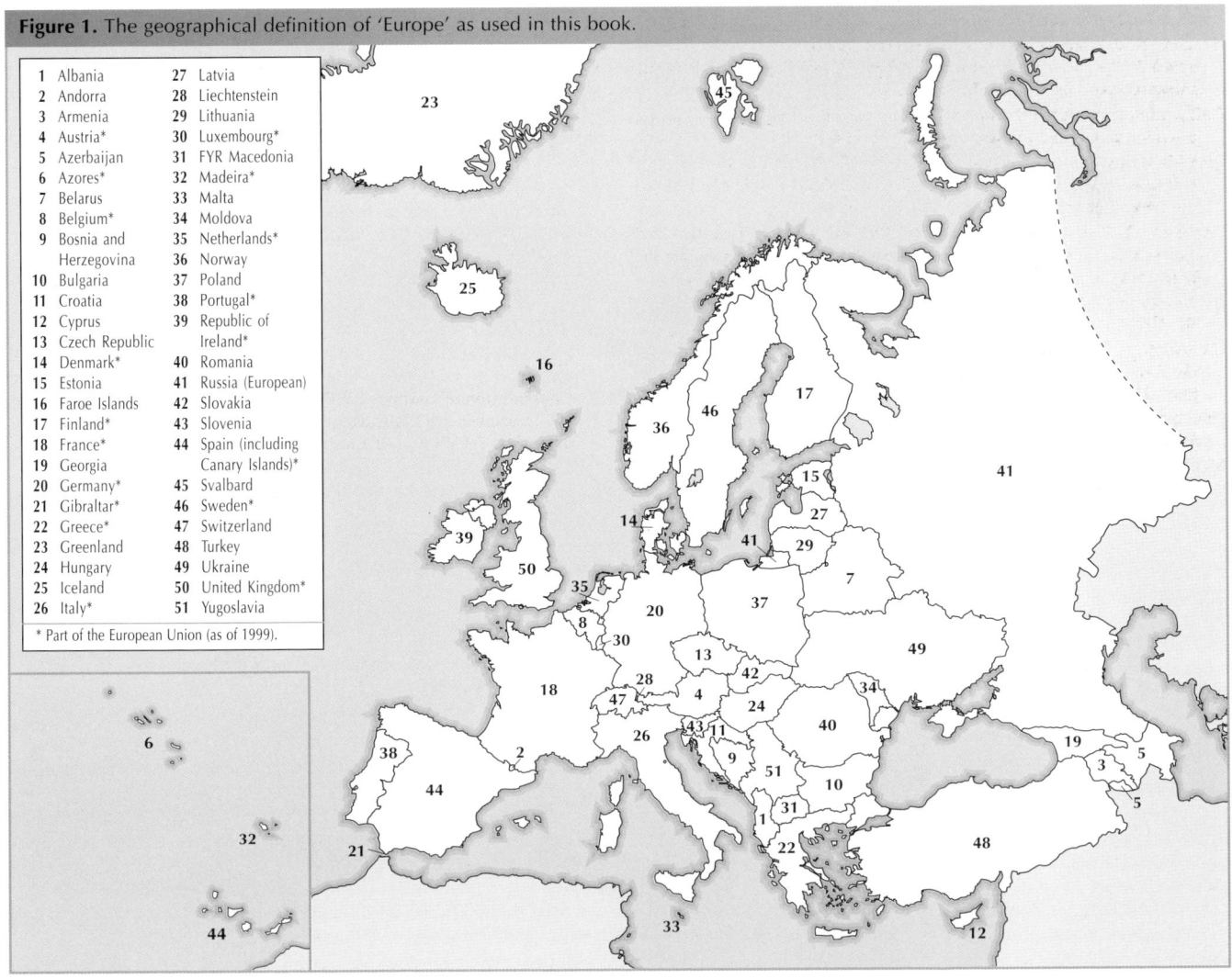

Figure 1. The geographical definition of 'Europe' as used in this book.

1	Albania	27	Latvia
2	Andorra	28	Liechtenstein
3	Armenia	29	Lithuania
4	Austria*	30	Luxembourg*
5	Azerbaijan	31	FYR Macedonia
6	Azores*	32	Madeira*
7	Belarus	33	Malta
8	Belgium*	34	Moldova
9	Bosnia and	35	Netherlands*
	Herzegovina	36	Norway
10	Bulgaria	37	Poland
11	Croatia	38	Portugal*
12	Cyprus	39	Republic of
13	Czech Republic		Ireland*
14	Denmark*	40	Romania
15	Estonia	41	Russia (European)
16	Faroe Islands	42	Slovakia
17	Finland*	43	Slovenia
18	France*	44	Spain (including
19	Georgia		Canary Islands)*
20	Germany*	45	Svalbard
21	Gibraltar*	46	Sweden*
22	Greece*	47	Switzerland
23	Greenland	48	Turkey
24	Hungary	49	Ukraine
25	Iceland	50	United Kingdom*
26	Italy*	51	Yugoslavia

* Part of the European Union (as of 1999).

Figure 2: The Important Bird Area data-collection network.

organization devoted to the conservation of wetlands, which co-produced the first pan-European IBA inventory (Grimmett and Jones 1989) and which has helped in the production of this revised inventory, through the provision of data on population thresholds of waterbirds and, at the national level, on particular wetlands.

SOURCES OF DATA

■ National IBA inventories

The previous pan-European IBA inventory (Grimmett and Jones 1989) stimulated, during the past decade, the production of national IBA inventories for 16 European countries (Box 1). In a high proportion of these publications, the national IBA inventory was a completely revised version, or otherwise contained much new, updated or corrected data. These inventories were a primary source of information for this new pan-European inventory.

■ Other publications

As well as publications focusing on IBAs, a large number of other relevant studies have been published over the last 10 years that have stimulated or facilitated data-collection for IBAs:

- *Birds in Europe: their conservation status* (Tucker and Heath 1994): this BirdLife publication was a comprehensive assessment of the conservation status of all bird species in Europe, based on population sizes and trends, and range trends. Through identifying which species are of European conservation concern, and determining their national population numbers, the results have been central to the identification of IBAs for these species, based on numerical criteria.
- *Birds to Watch 2* (Collar *et al.* 1994): on behalf of IUCN–The World Conservation Union, the universally recognized authority on globally threatened species, BirdLife identified in this publication those species of bird that are of global conservation concern, in Europe and elsewhere. This update of previous such

Box 1: National Important Bird Area inventories that have been produced in Europe since 1989.

All inventories are in the relevant national language; those marked with an asterisk (*) are also available in English. Apart from those indicated below, national IBA inventories are currently also in preparation for Estonia, Finland, Germany, Romania, Russia, Slovenia and Ukraine.

Country	Year	Citation
Austria	1995	Dvorak, M. and Karner, E. *Important Bird Areas in Österreich*. Wien: Bundesministerium für Umwelt (Monographien Bund 71). 454 pp.
Bulgaria	1997	Kostadinova, I. [*Important Bird Areas in Bulgaria.*] Sofia: Bulgarian Society for the Protection of Birds (BSPB Conservation Series, Book 1). 176 pp. (In Bulgarian.)
Czech Republic	1992*	Hora, J. and Kanuch, P. *Vyznamna ptaci uzemi v Evrope* [*Important Bird Areas in Europe—Czechoslovakia*]. Prague: Czechoslovakia Section of the International Council for Bird Preservation. 124 pp.
France	1994	Rocamora, G. *Les Zones Importantes pour la Conservation des Oiseaux en France*. Angoulême, France: Ligue Pour La Protection des Oiseaux/Ministère de l'Environment. 339 pp.
(East) Germany	1991	Naturschutzbund Deutschland (NABU). *Die Europäischen Vogelschutzgebiete (IBA) in den fünf neuen Bundesländern* [*IBAs in the five new Bundesländer of the Federal Republic of Germany*]. Bonn: NABU.
Greece	1994	Hellenic Ornithological Society (HOS). [*IBAs for the birds of Greece*]. Athens: HOS. 271 pp. (In Greek.)
Hungary	1992	Waliczky, Z. *Európai Jelentóségú Madárélóhelyek Magyarországon*. Budapest: Magyar Madártani és Természetvédelmi Egyesület/International Council for Bird Preservation. 118 pp.
	1998	Nagy, S. *Fontos Madárélóhelyek Magyarországon*. Budapest: Magyar Madártani és Természetvédelmi Egyesület. 138 pp.
Ireland	1995	Magee, E. and Coveney, J. *Important Bird Areas (IBAs): threats and protection status*. Monkstown, Ireland: Irish Wildbird Conservancy.
Italy (+ in prep.)	1991	Lambertini, M., Gustin, M., Faralli, U. and Tallone, G. *IBA—Italia. Aree di Importanza Europea per gli Uccelli Selvatici in Italia*. Parma, Italy: Lega Italiana Protezione Uccelli. 263 pp.
Latvia (+ in prep.)	1994*	Viksne, J. *Putniem Nozimigas Vietas Latvija* [*Important Bird Areas in Latvia*]. Riga: Latvijas Ornitologijas Biedriba. 45 pp.
Netherlands	1994*	van den Tempel, R. and Osieck, E. R. [*Areas important for birds in the Netherlands: wetlands and other areas of international or European importance for birds.*] Zeist, Netherlands: Vogelbescherming Nederland (Techn. Rep. 13E). (In Dutch.) 126 pp.
	1996	Eggenhuizen, T. and van den Tempel, R. *Belangrijke Vogelgebieden*. Zeist, Netherlands: Vogelbescherming Nederland. 160 pp.
Poland	1994	Gromadzki, M., Dyrcz, A., Glowacinski, Z. and Wieloch, M. *Ostoje Ptaków W Polsce*. Gdansk: Ogólnopolskie Towarzystwo Ochrony Ptaków. 403 pp.
Slovakia	1992*	Hora, J. and Kanuch, P. [*Important Bird Areas in Europe—Czechoslovakia*.] Prague: Czechoslovakia Section of the International Council for Bird Preservation. 124 pp.
Spain	1992	de Juana, E., ed. *Áreas Importantes para las Aves en España*. Madrid: Sociedad Española de Ornitología (Monografía 3). 183 pp.
	1998	Viada, C. *Áreas Importantes para las Aves en España*. Madrid: Sociedad Española de Ornitología/BirdLife (Monografía 5). 398 pp.
Turkey	1989	Ertan, A., Kiliç A. and Kasparek, M. *Türkiye'nin Önemli Kus Alanlari*. Istanbul: Doğal Hayatı Koruma Derneği. 155 pp.
	1997*	Magnin, G. and Yarar, M. [*Important Bird Areas in Turkey*.] Istanbul: Doğal Hayatı Koruma Derneği. 313 pp.
United Kingdom	1992	Pritchard, D. E., Housden, S. D., Mudge, G. P., Galbraith, C. A. and Pienkowski, M. W., eds. *Important Bird Areas in the UK including the Channel Islands and the Isle of Man*. Sandy, UK: Royal Society for the Protection of Birds. 540 pp.

Box 2. The different types of data collected on Important Bird Areas, and available in the IBA database.

Area accuracy

Reliable	A	accurate to within 10%
Incomplete	B	accurate to within 50%
Poor	C	definitely not accurate to within 50%
Unknown	U	

Land ownership

Private
State
Communal
Religious group
International waters
Mixed
Other
Unknown

Season types	Code	Description
Breeding resident	R	Species breeds in IBA and remains throughout the year.
Breeding visitor	B	Species breeds in IBA but is not present for parts of the year.
Winter visitor	W	Species spends a substantial part of the winter in IBA.
Passage visitor	P	Species stages in IBA during migration.
Non-breeding visitor	N	Species occurs in IBA but does not breed (usually over-summering immature birds or post-breeding moult-gatherings).
Unknown	U	Breeding or seasonal status of species in IBA is unknown or uncertain.

Population abundance

Abundant	Encountered in large numbers in preferred habitat.
Common	Encountered singly or in small numbers in preferred habitat.
Frequent	Often, but not always, met with in preferred habitat.
Uncommon	Encountered sporadically in preferred habitat.
Rare	Rarely seen, often implying less than 10 or so records.
Unknown	Not possible to assess abundance on available information.

Accuracy of Population size/Trend

Reliable	A	accurate to within 10%
Incomplete	B	accurate to within 50%
Poor	C	definitely not accurate to within 50%
Unknown	U	

Estimate of trend (1985–1995)

+2	Large increase
+1	Small increase
0	Stable
-1	Small decrease
-2	Large decrease
F	Fluctuating
N	New breeder
X	Extinct
U	Unknown

Impact of threat

High
Medium
Low
Unknown

Relationship of protected area/IBA

Protected area is contained by IBA
Protected area contains IBA
Protected area overlaps with IBA
Protected area is adjacent to IBA
Relationship unknown

Geographical data

Compiler	Person responsible for the IBA data provided.
Date	Date of completion of data compilation.
IBA codes	Current site-code; national IBA code; previous pan-European inventory (1989) code.
Site names	International name in English; national name in national language.
Country	Country in which IBA is located.
Administrative regions	Administrative region(s) in which IBA is located (at primary and secondary levels).
Area of IBA	Area of IBA in hectares (ha); 100 hectares = 1 km².
Area accuracy	Accuracy to which area of IBA is known.
Central coordinates	Central coordinates of IBA, in degrees and minutes (latitude/longitude; Greenwich).
Altitude	Altitudinal range spanned by IBA (in metres above/below sea level).
Map	Whether a map showing IBA boundaries (in paper or digitized form) is available.
General description	A general description of the IBA, its location and general appearance.
Ownership	An indication of the dominant type of ownership of the land within the IBA (should cover >50% of the IBA area).
Management plan	An indication of whether the IBA is covered (partly or wholly) by any existing management plan(s).

Criteria

Endemic Bird Areas	Name of Endemic Bird Area, if A2 criterion is met; see the following chapter for further explanation.
Biomes	Name of biome(s), if A3 criterion is met; see the following chapter for further explanation.
Criteria	The reasons why the site is considered ornithologically important (summary list of IBA criteria fulfilled at the site). See the following chapter for an explanation of the criteria.

Ornithological data

Species name	See Appendix 2a for a list of scientific and English names of birds used in this book. Taxonomy and nomenclature follow Cramp et al. (1977–1994).
Season	The season in which the species occurs in the IBA.
Year	The year of the latest data on which the population estimate is based.
Population size (minimum and maximum)	An estimate of minimum and maximum population size of the species at the IBA.
Population size accuracy	Accuracy of population-size estimate.
Population abundance	Qualitative estimate of population size. Only completed if minimum and maximum values not available.
Trend	An indication of the population-size trend at the site over the last 10 years.
Trend accuracy	Accuracy of indicated trend.
Criteria	IBA criteria fulfilled by species's population at site (see the following chapter for an explanation of the criteria).

Habitat data

Habitat type	Habitat types covering >5% of the IBA area. Two levels of habitat data can be provided (see Box 3 for classification).
Percentage cover	The percentage of the IBA covered by the habitat type.

Land-use data

Land-use type	Land-uses covering >5% of the IBA area. (See Box 4 for classification.)
Percentage cover	The percentage of the IBA covered by the land-use.

Threat data

Threat type	Key threats impacting on the IBA. (See Box 5 for classification.)
Impact of threat	The seriousness of the threat (the assessment of impact is explained in Appendix 3).

Protection status

Name	The name of the protected area.
Designation	The national or international designation-type (e.g. National Park).
Year	The year of initial designation.
IUCN category	The IUCN protected-area management category (I–VI) (IUCN 1994).
Area	The area, in hectares (ha; 100 ha = 1 km²), of the protected area.
Central coordinates	The central coordinates of the protected area (in degrees/minutes of latitude/longitude; Greenwich).
Relationship to IBA	The spatial relationship between the IBA and the protected area.
Overlap	The extent of overlap in hectares (ha) between the IBA and protected area.

Other data

General ornithological description	A general description of the ornithological importance of the IBA.
Other flora/fauna	Other significant flora and fauna present in the IBA.
Habitats/Land-uses/Threats	Additional text on habitats, land-uses or threats.
Research/conservation projects	Information on research, conservation or management activities at the IBA. Further details on protection, including any proposed protection measures.

publications, together with data in *Birds in Europe*, has allowed more authoritative identification of IBAs for globally threatened species, based on standard, numerical criteria.

- Wetlands International has published new and more accurate information on the sizes and geographical ranges of waterbird populations in Europe (Rose and Scott 1994, 1997)—analysed and mapped in more detail for swans, geese and ducks (Scott and Rose 1996)—and has also stimulated the production of national wetland inventories in Europe, which contain much new information on wetland sites. Together, these data-sources have allowed more reliable and comprehensive identification of IBAs for waterbird species.

- The process of drawing up the most recent international action plans for bird species of global conservation concern in Europe, which was coordinated by BirdLife International, and the subsequent publication of the plans (Heredia *et al.* 1996), have together stimulated many national-scale field surveys of these species. Again, this has led to the discovery of a large number of new IBAs for these key species, and has improved or updated information on known IBAs.

- *United Nations List of Protected Areas* (WCMC/WCPA 1998): this publication has provided much useful information on the location and extent of statutory protected areas in each country, making it much easier to categorize and analyse the legal protection status of IBAs.

■ Field surveys of IBAs

The national monitoring and research programmes of BirdLife Partners have updated and filled gaps in the original 1989 data on IBAs and have improved monitoring of these key sites. In other European countries as well, much new fieldwork has been conducted on IBAs over the last decade, resulting in more detailed and up-to-date information about each site, as well as the identification of many new IBAs. The collation of more detailed information on IBAs has also depended heavily on local IBA experts or caretaker groups (Figure 2). Apart from contributing their own knowledge of the current status of IBAs locally, they have often succeeded in involving many of the other key organizations, individuals and bird-counting networks that study or use IBAs in their area, in the provision of data (often unpublished or otherwise difficult of access).

TYPES OF DATA COLLECTED

For each IBA across Europe, key data have been collected on:

- Location
- Bird species
- Reasons for importance
- Habitats and land-uses
- Threats
- Protection status
- Conservation action

Box 2 presents a fuller explanation of the types of data collected.

For many countries in Europe, especially in the centre and east, this is the first time that such detailed data on sites have been collated. In other countries, such information already existed, at least in part, but was spread across a broad range of sources.

Compared to the previous pan-European IBA inventory (Grimmett and Jones 1989), the data collected for this inventory have been more quantitative, which has allowed a more rigorous analysis. The methods used for compiling and classifying this information have been standardized as much as possible. Standard lists were developed for several of the data-types, to simplify data-collection, and to facilitate any subsequent comparison and analysis of data between sites at local, national, continental and global levels. Thus, for habitats, land-uses and threats, a standard classification was drawn up for each, covering all the possible options that can be encountered at IBAs in Europe, and these are listed in Boxes 3, 4 and 5.

The importance of an individual site for bird conservation was also categorized in a standard way, such that a site may qualify as an IBA on the basis of one or more of 20 ornithological criteria

Box 3. Classification of habitats at Important Bird Areas in Europe. Full definitions are given in Appendix 3. Primary habitats are comparable with other IBAs globally.

Primary	Secondary
Forest/woodland	broadleaved deciduous forest
	native coniferous forest
	mixed forest
	alluvial/very wet forest
	broadleaved evergreen forest
	wooded steppe
	wooded tundra
	treeline ecotone
	wooded desert/semi-desert
Scrub	scrub
	heathland
	sclerophyllous scrub/garrigue/maquis
Grassland	steppe/dry calcareous grassland
	dry siliceous grassland
	alpine/subalpine/boreal grassland
	humid grassland
	mesophile grassland
	tundra
	machair
Desert	desert
	semi-desert
Wetland	tidal river/enclosed tidal water
	mudflat/sandflat
	saltmarsh
	sand-dunes/sand beach
	shingle/stony beach
	coastal lagoon
	standing fresh water
	standing brackish and salt water
	river/stream
	raised bog
	blanket bog
	water-fringe vegetation
	fen/transition mire/spring
Marine areas	open sea
	sea inlet/coastal features
Rocky areas	sea cliff/rocky shore
	rock stacks/islets
	scree/boulders
	inland sand-dunes
	caves
Artificial landscape	highly improved reseeded grassland
	arable land
	perennial crops/orchards/groves
	forestry plantation
	urban parks/gardens
	other urban/industrial areas
	ruderal land
Introduced/exotic vegetation	
Unknown	

Based on: *A classification of Palaearctic habitats* (Devillers and Devillers-Terschuren 1996).

Box 4. Classification of land-uses at Important Bird Areas in Europe. Full definitions are given in Appendix 3.

Agriculture
Fisheries/aquaculture
Forestry
Hunting
Military
Nature conservation/research
Tourism/recreation
Urban/industrial/transport
Water management
Not utilized
Other
Unknown

Box 5. Classification of threats at Important Bird Areas in Europe. Full definitions are given in Appendix 3.

Abandonment/reduction of land management
Afforestation
Agricultural intensification/expansion
Aquaculture/fisheries
Burning of vegetation
Consequences of animal/plant introductions
Construction/impact of dyke/dam/barrage
Deforestation (commercial)
Disturbance to birds
Drainage
Dredging/canalization
Extraction industry
Filling-in of wetlands
Firewood collection
Forest grazing
Groundwater abstraction
Industrialization/urbanization
Infrastructure
Intensified forest management
Natural events
Recreation/tourism
Selective logging/cutting
Shifting agriculture
Unsustainable exploitation
Other
Unknown

(see the following chapter). The ornithological data provided for each site were analysed systematically against these 20 numerical criteria (BirdLife International 1995), to ensure that all sites accepted as IBAs were truly of international importance and that the reasons for qualification were clearly documented. These standard, numerical criteria are fundamental to the IBA concept, and are fully explained in the following chapter.

TOOLS FOR DATA COLLECTION

Two main tools were developed to gather, store and manipulate the data on IBAs:

- Data-form (paper questionnaire)
- Computer database

Important qualities that were required of these tools were compatibility, uniformity and flexibility.

■ Compatibility
The tools were developed as part of the regional IBA programmes of Europe and other continents (particularly Africa), so as to ensure that all user-requirements were fully considered. In addition, elements of the data-collection mechanisms and classifications used by other international organizations, or by directly relevant pan-European initiatives, which were collecting information on sites in Europe—e.g. the Protected Areas Database of the World Conservation Monitoring Centre, the Ramsar Sites Database of the Ramsar Convention Bureau, the Natura 2000 network of the European Commission, and the CORINE Biotopes database of the European Environmental Agency—were taken into account in designing the tools, so as to maximize compatibility (European Commission 1995, WCMC 1996).

■ Uniformity
Both tools have a very similar structure, the IBA Database being a computerized version of the paper data-form, although it must be stressed that the IBA Database forms part of a larger World Bird Database and has many other valuable functions apart from data-collection, explained more fully in Box 6.

Since the tools were designed to collect standardized data, it is possible to compare directly any attribute of an IBA, such as location, ornithological importance or habitats, with that at any other IBA or IBAs, within and between countries or even continents, without encountering methodological problems.

■ Flexibility
The creation of two tools, one paper-based and one computer-based, allowed for the breadth in user-requirements when collecting data. In general, local experts found it most convenient to compile the original IBA data onto paper data-forms (often translated into the local language by the national coordinator), and then sent these in to the national coordinator, who organized the transfer of data onto the IBA computer database. Nearly all national (and sub-national) IBA coordinators used the database in this way. The tools were also designed so as to allow different quantities and detail of data to be collected per site, depending on the level of knowledge, and also for more data to be added at a later date without difficulty.

DATA-COLLECTION PROCEDURE

The general procedure for data-collection is illustrated in Figure 3.

In 1995, 1996 and 1998, international workshops were held involving national IBA coordinators from across the region, in order to share and pass on useful skills and experiences in planning, training and communication. Similarly, many countries held national workshops involving many local coordinators, contributors and experts, to publicize this project and to involve, train and enthuse participants. Most countries translated the data-form into their local language, so as to enable the widest possible dissemination and use of this data-gathering tool. However, the

Box 6. The Important Bird Area Database—a part of the World Bird Database

The IBA Database forms the basis of this book, and contains much additional information that could not be published here due to space constraints. Currently used in more than 35 countries across Europe, the IBA Database is a key part of the larger World Bird Database, which is a tool used by BirdLife International for managing, analysing and reporting on the full spectrum of its data on sites and species, for the purpose of conserving birds and their habitats. The World Bird Database is a distribution network, enabling data to flow between the people who collect the data or update it, those who collate and verify it, and those who make the analyses to turn data into information and targets, in order to influence policy and decision-making—moving from science to conservation action.

Key benefits of the World Bird Database are the ability to:

- Manage and validate a large volume of information on IBAs and globally threatened species
- Analyse trends in data and monitor changes
- Link site (IBA) data with species data, e.g. for international conventions, directives and other initiatives or programmes
- Determine the conservation status of sites or species internationally, regionally and nationally, with background information about the birds
- Produce focused, targeted reports for specific purposes
- Improve the sharing of information and expertise between Partners
- Improve electronic links to non-BirdLife data and information, such as socio-economic and non-bird species data, for use in analyses
- Link to geographic information systems (GIS) for presentation purposes

An overall principle of BirdLife International is to maximize the availability and use of its data for conservation purposes. Information on IBAs in Europe will therefore be made available beyond the BirdLife International Partnership, following the guidelines on use and dissemination of data that are stipulated in the *IBA Data Access Policy* (BirdLife International 1996). This agreement was drawn up by the European Partnership in February 1996 and applies to the IBA Database as it currently stands, plus subsequent updates.

The World Bird Database runs in single-user and multi-user environments and can be made available over the Internet. The development tools are industrial-strength products (Microsoft Visual Basic and Microsoft Access), which offer suitable upgrade paths when new technologies become available. The World Bird Database is simple to use and intuitive in operation, adopting the same look and feel as other widely used Windows products.

Figure 3. The procedure for collecting Important Bird Area data.

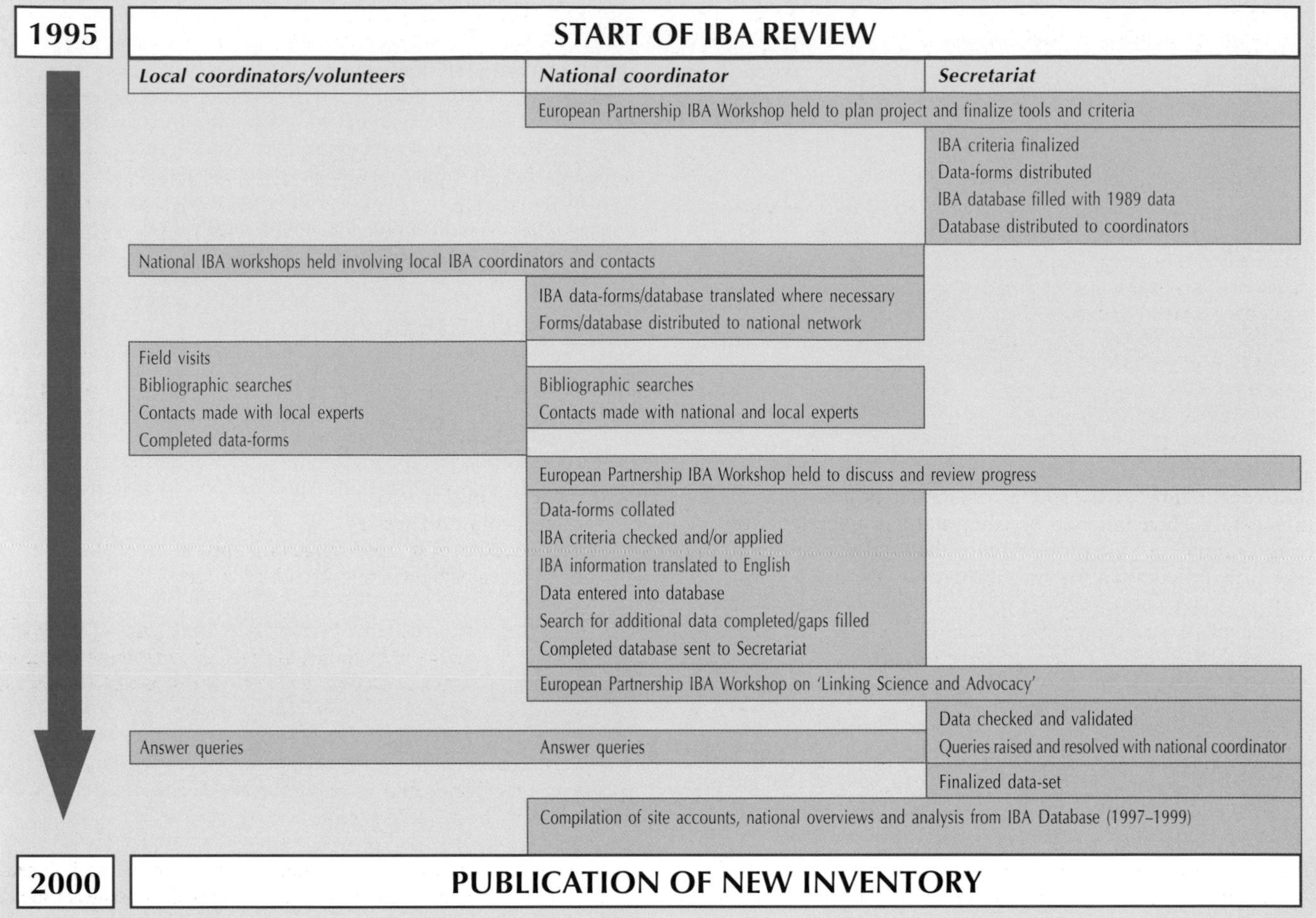

1995	START OF IBA REVIEW		
	Local coordinators/volunteers	*National coordinator*	*Secretariat*
		European Partnership IBA Workshop held to plan project and finalize tools and criteria	
			IBA criteria finalized Data-forms distributed IBA database filled with 1989 data Database distributed to coordinators
	National IBA workshops held involving local IBA coordinators and contacts		
		IBA data-forms/database translated where necessary Forms/database distributed to national network	
	Field visits Bibliographic searches Contacts made with local experts Completed data-forms	Bibliographic searches Contacts made with national and local experts	
		European Partnership IBA Workshop held to discuss and review progress	
		Data-forms collated IBA criteria checked and/or applied IBA information translated to English Data entered into database Search for additional data completed/gaps filled Completed database sent to Secretariat	
		European Partnership IBA Workshop on 'Linking Science and Advocacy'	
			Data checked and validated Queries raised and resolved with national coordinator
	Answer queries	Answer queries	Finalized data-set
		Compilation of site accounts, national overviews and analysis from IBA Database (1997–1999)	
2000	PUBLICATION OF NEW INVENTORY		

exact mechanism for collecting data within a country varied according to the resources available (in terms of time, people-power, expertise, money, and so on) and according to the existing methods for the collection of national bird data. Therefore Figure 3 only shows the general procedure followed.

■ Data checking/validation
Once the national network had submitted a suite of sites as potential IBAs, the data provided were then checked for errors and inconsistencies by national IBA coordinators and the BirdLife Secretariat, before the importance of each site was evaluated against the 20 ornithological criteria mentioned earlier. This evaluation process is explained more fully in the following chapter.

The use of pre-defined selection lists and standardized terms during the data-collection phase helped to reduce the amount of checking needed, and the computer database also allowed the checking and validation of huge quantities of data to be partially automated, at both international and national levels (see Box 6).

REFERENCES

BIRDLIFE INTERNATIONAL (1995) IBA criteria: categories and thresholds. Cambridge, UK: BirdLife International (internal document).

BIRDLIFE INTERNATIONAL (1996) IBA data access policy. Cambridge, UK: BirdLife International (internal document).

COLLAR, N. J., CROSBY, M. J. AND STATTERSFIELD, A. J. (1994) *Birds to watch 2: the world list of threatened birds.* Cambridge, UK: BirdLife International (Conservation Series No. 4.).

CRAMP, S. ET AL. (1977–1994) *The birds of the western Palearctic.* Vols 1–9. Oxford, UK: Oxford University Press.

DEVILLERS, P. AND DEVILLERS-TERSCHUREN (1996) *A classification of Palaearctic habitats.* Strasbourg: Council of Europe (Nature and environment, No. 78).

EUROPEAN COMMISSION (1995) *Natura 2000 Network: Standard Data Form.* March 1995 Version.

GRIMMETT, R. F. A. AND JONES, T. A. (1989) *Important Bird Areas in Europe.* Cambridge, UK: International Council for Bird Preservation (Techn. Publ. 9).

HEREDIA, B., ROSE, L. AND PAINTER, M., EDS. (1996) *Globally threatened birds in Europe: action plans.* Strasbourg, France: Council of Europe.

IUCN (1994) *Guidelines for protected area management categories.* Gland, Switzerland: IUCN—The World Conservation Union.

ROSE, P. M. AND SCOTT, D. A. (1994) *Waterfowl population estimates.* Slimbridge, UK: Wetlands International.

ROSE, P. M. AND SCOTT, D. A. (1997) *Waterfowl population estimates.* Second edition. Wageningen, Netherlands: Wetlands International (Publication 44).

SCOTT, D. A. AND ROSE, P. M. (1996) *Atlas of Anatidae populations in Africa and western Eurasia.* Wageningen, Netherlands: Wetlands International (Publication 41).

TUCKER, G. M. AND HEATH, M. F. (1994) *Birds in Europe: their conservation status.* Cambridge, UK: BirdLife International (BirdLife Conservation Series no. 3).

WCMC/WCPA [WORLD CONSERVATION MONITORING CENTRE/WORLD COMMISSION ON PROTECTED AREAS] (1998) *1997 United Nations List of Protected Areas.* Gland, Switzerland and Cambridge, UK: IUCN.

WCMC [WORLD CONSERVATION MONITORING CENTRE] (1996) *Guide to information management in the Context of the Convention of Biological Diversity.* Nairobi, Kenya: United Nations Environment Programme.

■ IDENTIFYING IMPORTANT BIRD AREAS

WHY APPLY IBA CRITERIA?

The selection of Important Bird Areas (IBAs) is achieved through the application of quantitative ornithological criteria, grounded in up-to-date knowledge of the sizes and trends of bird populations in Europe. The criteria ensure that the sites selected as IBAs have true significance for the international conservation of bird populations, and provide a common currency that all IBAs adhere to, thus creating consistency among, and enabling comparability between, sites at national, continental and global levels. It is crucial to understand why a site is important, and to do this it is necessary to examine its international significance in terms of the presence and abundance of species that occur there in different seasons. The status and nature of these species also need to be taken into account: threat status, breeding/non-breeding status, vulnerability through congregation, and the proportion of the total population of each species that occurs at a site, are all important factors in determining a site's importance.

A main aim of the IBA Programme of BirdLife International is to attain protection for IBAs, and the provision of convincing bird data is an essential part of any argument for statutory protection. Importantly, the application of criteria to significant species, together with future data-gathering and the development of monitoring programmes, permit not only the assessment of changes in species' numbers but also an examination of how these changes impact on the overall importance of the site, thus helping to guide the management and conservation of the area. The more specific, quantitative and comprehensive is the information available on IBAs, with links showing the fulfilment of obligations laid out in various EC directives and international conventions, the stronger

is the case for protection. To this end, the criteria build upon existing international legal instruments such as the EC Birds Directive which obliges the designation of Special Protection Areas in the European Community, and the Ramsar Convention under which contracting parties must designate at least one Ramsar Site.

THE CATEGORIES OF IBA CRITERIA

Twenty IBA criteria have been developed for the selection of IBAs in Europe. These allow the identification of IBAs, based on a site's **international** importance for:

- Threatened bird species
- Congregatory bird species
- Assemblages of restricted-range bird species
- Assemblages of biome-restricted bird species

Criteria have been developed such that, by applying different ('staggered') numerical thresholds, the international importance of a site for a species may be categorized at three distinct geographical levels:

- Global ('A' criteria)
- European ('B' criteria)
- European Union ('C' criteria)

A summary of each of the 20 criteria is given in Table 1. These 20 criteria are based on the criteria used in the first pan-European IBA inventory (Grimmett and Jones 1989), which in turn took

Table 1. Summary of the 20 criteria used in Europe to identify Important Bird Areas.

	Category	Criterion
GLOBAL	A1. Species of global conservation concern	The site regularly holds significant numbers of a globally threatened species, or other species of global conservation concern.
	A2. Restricted-range species	The site is known or thought to hold a significant component of the restricted-range species whose breeding distributions define an Endemic Bird Area (EBA) or Secondary Area (SA).
	A3. Biome-restricted species	The site is known or thought to hold a significant assemblage of the species whose breeding distributions are largely or wholly confined to one biome.
	A4. Congregations	(i) The site is known or thought to hold, on a regular basis, $\geq 1\%$ of a biogeographic population of a congregatory waterbird species.
		(ii) The site is known or thought to hold, on a regular basis, $\geq 1\%$ of the global population of a congregatory seabird or terrestrial species.
		(iii) The site is known or thought to hold, on a regular basis, $\geq 20,000$ waterbirds or $\geq 10,000$ pairs of seabird of one or more species.
		(iv) The site is known or thought to be a 'bottleneck' site where at least 20,000 storks (Ciconiidae), raptors (Accipitriformes and Falconiformes) or cranes (Gruidae) regularly pass during spring or autumn migration.
EUROPEAN	B1. Congregations	(i) The site is known or thought to hold $\geq 1\%$ of a flyway or other distinct population of a waterbird species.
		(ii) The site is known or thought to hold $\geq 1\%$ of a distinct population of a seabird species.
		(iii) The site is known or thought to hold $\geq 1\%$ of a flyway or other distinct population of other congregatory species.
		(iv) The site is a 'bottleneck' site where over 5,000 storks, or over 3,000 raptors or cranes regularly pass on spring or autumn migration.
	B2. Species with an unfavourable conservation status in Europe	The site is one of the 'n' most important in the country for a species with an unfavourable conservation status in Europe (SPEC 2, 3) and for which the site-protection approach is thought to be appropriate.
	B3. Species with a favourable conservation status in Europe	The site is one of the 'n' most important in the country for a species with a favourable conservation status in Europe but concentrated in Europe (SPEC 4) and for which the site-protection approach is thought to be appropriate.
EUROPEAN UNION	C1. Species of global conservation concern	The site regularly holds significant numbers of a globally threatened species, or other species of global conservation concern.
	C2. Concentrations of a species threatened at the European Union level	The site is known to regularly hold at least 1% of a flyway population or of the EU population of a species threatened at the EU level (listed on Annex I and referred to in Article 4.1 of the EC Birds Directive).
	C3. Congregations of migratory species not threatened at the EU level	The site is known to regularly hold at least 1% of a flyway population of a migratory species not considered threatened at the EU level (as referred to in Article 4.2 of the EC Birds Directive) (not listed on Annex I).
	C4. Congregatory – large congregations	The site is known to regularly hold at least 20,000 migratory waterbirds and/or 10,000 pairs of migratory seabirds of one or more species.
	C5. Congregatory – bottleneck sites	The site is a 'bottleneck' site where at least 5,000 storks (Ciconiidae) and/or at least 3,000 raptors (Accipitriformes and Falconiformes) and/or 3,000 cranes (Gruidae) regularly pass on spring or autumn migration.
	C6. Species threatened at the European Union level	The site is one of the five most important in the European region (NUTS region) in question for a species or subspecies considered threatened in the European Union (i.e. listed in Annex I of the EC Birds Directive).
	C7. Other ornithological criteria	The site has been designated as a Special Protection Area (SPA) or selected as a candidate SPA based on ornithological criteria (similar to but not equal to C1–C6) in recognized use for identifying SPAs.

For species lists, see Tables 2–4 and Appendices 2a and 2b.

account of several previous studies of IBA criteria at the level of the European Community (Osieck and Mörzer Bruyns 1981, Grimmett and Gammell 1989). Appendix 4 gives a full comparison between the current criteria and those used in 1989. Adaptation of the 1989 criteria has been driven particularly by the globalization of the IBA programme, with IBAs being identified in the Middle East (Evans 1994), Africa (Fishpool in prep.), Asia and the Americas. This has resulted in:

- The inclusion of criteria to identify sites within areas of high avian endemism, termed Endemic Bird Areas (criterion A2) and listed in Stattersfield et al. (1998), and sites within certain biomes (criterion A3).
- The creation of staggered numerical thresholds (A, B and C levels) to allow meaningful comparison between sites across regions of the world. This is particularly significant in that many countries outside Europe, which are just beginning their IBA programmes, may not have completed an assessment of the threat status of species at the continental or sub-regional level, yet can still proceed in identifying IBAs (of global importance, i.e. using 'A' criteria) at this stage.
- The identification of sites for species of European conservation concern (Box 1), under the B2/B3 criteria.
- The strengthening of links to the EC Birds Directive, through the creation of criteria categories C1–C7 with associated numerical thresholds.

The IBA criteria have been developed by BirdLife International, involving all BirdLife European Partners in several stages of consultation and in workshops held between 1993 and 1996 (BirdLife International 1995, Heath 1995, 1996). The 'Birds and Habitats Directives' Task Force of BirdLife International played a leading role in developing the EU-specific categories and thresholds (C1–C7), to maximize their utility in guiding the selection of Special Protection Areas in EU countries (Osieck 1998).

A total of 515 bird species occur regularly in Europe. IBAs have been identified on the basis of the occurrence of many of these species, provided that they occur in sufficient numbers to meet numerical population thresholds. All 515 bird species are listed in Appendix 2a of this publication, together with the criteria which they can potentially fulfil and the numerical threshold(s) if applicable.

THE APPLICATION OF IBA CRITERIA

For most categories of criteria, application of a criterion involved comparing the data provided for each relevant bird species at the site—usually in the form of an estimate of the number of individuals or pairs of the species using the site—against a numerical threshold for the species concerned (normally representing 1% of the species' population in question, e.g. its global population if applying 'A1' or 'C1' criteria). For only two criteria, A2 and A3, was the application

Box 1. Defining species of European conservation concern (SPECs).

Species of conservation concern on a European scale have been identified by BirdLife International (Tucker and Heath 1994), based on their European Threat Status and the proportion of their world population in Europe.

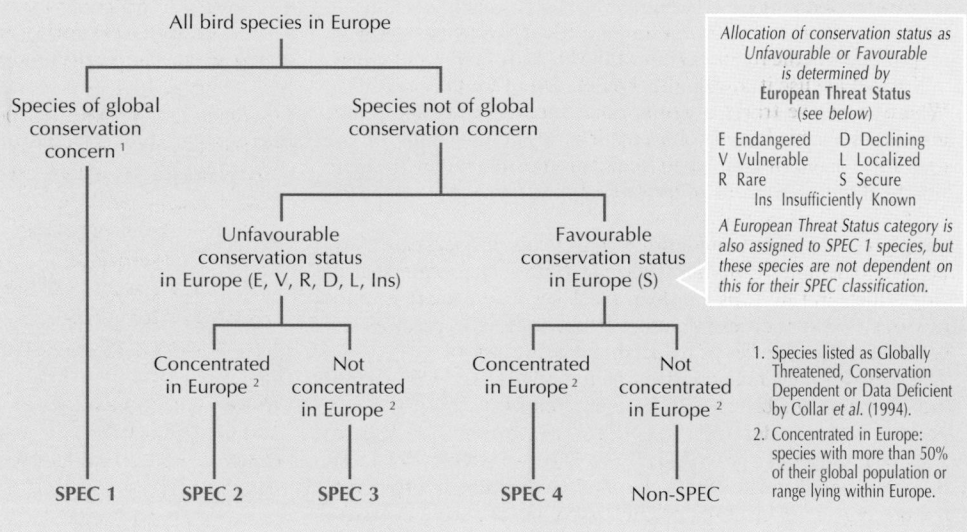

All bird species in Europe

Species of global conservation concern [1]

Species not of global conservation concern

Unfavourable conservation status in Europe (E, V, R, D, L, Ins)

Favourable conservation status in Europe (S)

Concentrated in Europe [2]

Not concentrated in Europe [2]

Concentrated in Europe [2]

Not concentrated in Europe [2]

SPEC 1   SPEC 2   SPEC 3   SPEC 4   Non-SPEC

Allocation of conservation status as Unfavourable or Favourable is determined by **European Threat Status** *(see below)*

E Endangered   D Declining
V Vulnerable   L Localized
R Rare   S Secure
    Ins Insufficiently Known

A European Threat Status category is also assigned to SPEC 1 species, but these species are not dependent on this for their SPEC classification.

1. Species listed as Globally Threatened, Conservation Dependent or Data Deficient by Collar et al. (1994).

2. Concentrated in Europe: species with more than 50% of their global population or range lying within Europe.

European Threat Status: summary of criteria and categories

Criteria: European population size/trend	<250 pairs	<2,500 pairs	<10,000 pairs	>10,000 pairs
Large decline [3]	ENDANGERED	ENDANGERED	ENDANGERED	VULNERABLE
Moderate decline [4]	ENDANGERED	ENDANGERED	VULNERABLE	DECLINING
No decline	ENDANGERED	VULNERABLE	RARE	SECURE

In addition, species that have more than 10,000 pairs in Europe are categorized as **LOCALIZED** if more than 90% of the European population occurs at 10 sites or fewer in Europe. See Tucker and Heath (1994) for full details of criteria.

3. Large decline: applied to a breeding or wintering population which has declined in size or range by at least 20% in at least 66% of the population or by at least 50% in at least 25% of the population between 1970 and 1990, and where the total size of populations that declined is greater than the total size of populations that increased.

4. Moderate decline: applied to a breeding or wintering population which has declined in size or range by at least 20% in 33–65% of the population or by at least 50% in 12–24% of the population between 1970 and 1990, and where the total size of populations that declined is greater than the total size of populations that increased.

Note that:
- Winter population criteria use flyway population levels of less than 1,000, 10,000 and 40,000 individuals as respective equivalents to the figures of 250, 2,500 and 10,000 pairs used above for breeding populations.
- Due to inadequate data for most species, declines in winter populations are only considered for Anatidae, Haematopodidae, Charadriidae and Scolopacidae.

process more qualitative, requiring only that particular assemblages of bird species be present.

Each criterion is associated with a list of relevant species, with each species being accompanied, where necessary, by a numerical population threshold which must be matched or exceeded in order to allow the site to qualify under that criterion. These population thresholds were derived, wherever possible, from internationally recognised sources of bird population data.

In some countries it has not been possible to apply the criteria fully to all relevant species, due to a lack of data on some species. This is known to be the case for a number of bird taxa that are considered threatened at the scale of the European Union, being listed in Annex I of the EC Birds Directive. Therefore, the identification of sites for some of these species, or the data presented on qualifying species at these sites, may be incomplete.

The definitions of the criteria given in this chapter are guidelines for the identification of IBAs. They have been followed as far as possible but, since definitions of this sort cannot cover all possibilities, they are not inflexible rules. The need for scientific objectivity and standardization has had to be balanced by common sense and the practical objectives of the exercise.

DEFINING THE BOUNDARIES OF AN IBA

- A site is defined so that, as far as possible, it:
  i) is different in character or habitat or ornithological importance from the surrounding area;
  ii) exists as an actual or potential protected area, with or without buffer zones, or is an area which can be managed in some way for nature conservation;
  iii) is, alone or with other sites, a self-sufficient area which provides all the requirements of the birds (that it is important for) which use it during the time that they are present.
- Where extensive tracts of continuous habitat occur which are important for birds, only characteristics ii) and iii) apply. This definition is not applicable to migratory bottleneck sites.
- Practical considerations of how best the site may be conserved are the foremost consideration.
- Simple, conspicuous boundaries such as roads or rivers can often be used to delimit site margins, while features such as watersheds, ridge-lines and hilltops can help in places where there are no obvious discontinuities in habitat (transitions of vegetation or substrate). Boundaries of ownership are also relevant.
- There is no fixed maximum or minimum size for IBAs—the biologically sensible should be tempered with the practical. Neither is there a definitive answer on how to treat cases where a number of small sites lie near each other. Whether these are best considered as a series of separate IBAs, or as one larger site containing areas lacking ornithological significance, depends upon the local situation with regard to conservation and management.

DETAILED DEFINITIONS OF OF IBA CRITERIA

A: Important Bird Areas – global importance

Globally threatened species – Category A1

The site regularly holds significant numbers of a globally threatened species, or other species of global conservation concern.

Under this criterion, sites are identified for those species most threatened with extinction at a global level. This includes species classified as 'Critical', 'Endangered' and 'Vulnerable', according to the most recent, universally recognized criteria for global threat status (IUCN 1994), as well as those species classified as 'Conservation Dependent', 'Data Deficient' or 'Near-threatened'. These latter types of species, although not strictly globally threatened, are considered here to be of sufficient global conservation concern to merit the identification of Important Bird Areas at the global level. All of these types of species are listed in Table 2 and in *Birds to Watch 2* (Collar *et al.* 1994).

This category thus allows the identification of IBAs for 35 species in Europe (Table 2). All of these species are also species of European conservation concern (see Box 1). The regular presence of a Critical or Endangered species at a site, irrespective of its abundance at the site, is considered sufficient to propose the site as an IBA. The only such species in Europe are *Pterodroma madeira* and *Numenius tenuirostris*. The remaining 33 species have to be present at a site in 'significant' numbers for a site to qualify under this criterion. The relevant numerical threshold for each species is calculated from the size of the species's global population and also depends on whether the species has a relatively large or small body-size, and whether it has primarily dispersed or colonial nesting habits (see footnote to Table 2).

The words 'regular' and 'significant' in these definitions are intended to exclude instances of vagrancy, marginal occurrence, and ancient or historical records. 'Regularly' includes seasonal presence (and presence at longer intervals, if suitable conditions themselves only occur at extended intervals, e.g. at temporary wetlands).

Table 2. Numerical thresholds for species of global conservation concern in Europe.

Species	Global threat status	Threshold (pairs)
Pterodroma feae Fea's Petrel	VU	5
Pterodroma madeira Zino's Petrel	CR	0
Phalacrocorax pygmeus Pygmy Cormorant	NT	10
Pelecanus crispus Dalmatian Pelican	VU	10
Anser erythropus Lesser White-fronted Goose	VU	5
Branta ruficollis Red-breasted Goose	VU	60 ind
Marmaronetta angustirostris Marbled Teal	VU	5
Aythya nyroca Ferruginous Duck	VU	20
Polysticta stelleri Steller's Eider	VU	30 ind
Oxyura leucocephala White-headed Duck	VU	5
Haliaeetus albicilla White-tailed Eagle	NT	5
Aegypius monachus Cinereous Vulture	NT	5
Circus macrourus Pallid Harrier	NT	10
Aquila clanga Greater Spotted Eagle	VU	2
Aquila heliaca Imperial Eagle	VU	2
Aquila adalberti Spanish Imperial Eagle	VU	2
Falco naumanni Lesser Kestrel	VU	10
Tetrao mlokosiewiczi Caucasian Black Grouse	NT	20
Crex crex Corncrake	VU	20
Tetrax tetrax Little Bustard	NT	60 ind
Otis tarda Great Bustard	VU	30 ind
Glareola nordmanni Black-winged Pratincole	NT	10
Chettusia gregaria Sociable Plover	VU	10
Gallinago media Great Snipe	NT	20
Numenius tenuirostris Slender-billed Curlew	CR	0
Larus audouinii Audouin's Gull	CD	20
Columba trocaz Long-toed Pigeon	CD	10
Columba bollii Dark-tailed Laurel Pigeon	VU	5
Columba junoniae White-tailed Laurel Pigeon	VU	5
Saxicola dacotiae Fuerteventura Chat	NT	5
Acrocephalus paludicola Aquatic Warbler	VU	10
Sitta whiteheadi Corsican Nuthatch	NT	10
Fringilla teydea Blue Chaffinch	CD	10
Loxia scotica Scottish Crossbill	DD	5
Emberiza cineracea Cinereous Bunting	NT	5

All figures are in pairs unless "ind" is given, indicating individuals. To convert between individuals and pairs, a multiplying/dividing factor of 3 was used.

Globally threat status follows Collar *et al.* (1994):
CR Critical
VU Vulnerable
CD Conservation Dependent
DD Data Deficient
NT Near Threatened

Threshold calculations: For Vulnerable, Conservation Dependent, Data Deficient and Near-threatened species the following threshold levels apply at any site:

	European population (pairs)		
Threshold	<1,000	1,000–10,000	>10,000
large sized and/or fairly dispersed species	2	5	10
small sized and/or colonial nesting species	5	10	20

Restricted-range species – Category A2

The site is known or thought to hold a significant component of a group of species whose breeding distributions define an Endemic Bird Area or a Secondary Area.

Under this criterion, the most important sites within Endemic Bird Areas (EBAs) and Secondary Areas are identified.

An EBA is defined as a region to which two or more restricted-range bird species are confined, with 'restricted range' defined as a world distribution of less than 50,000 km² (Stattersfield *et al.* 1998). There are 218 EBAs globally, three of which are in Europe (Table 3): Madeira and the Canary Islands (with nine restricted-range species), the Caucasus (three restricted-range species) and Cyprus (two restricted-range species). Two of these species are also globally threatened, and nearly all are species of European conservation concern (Table 3), thus also qualifying under other criteria.

For many EBAs, which hold a large number of restricted-range species, it is necessary that a network of sites be chosen, using complementarity analysis, to protect adequately all relevant species. The term 'significant component' in the definition of the criterion is intended to avoid the selection of sites solely on the presence of one or more restricted-range species that are common and adaptable within the EBA and which may, therefore, occur at other (many other) chosen sites. Additional sites can, however, be chosen for one or a few species that would otherwise be under-represented or not represented at all.

Also included within this category are species of Secondary Areas. A Secondary Area supports one or more restricted-range species, but does not qualify as an EBA because only a single species is entirely confined to it (Stattersfield *et al.* 1998). There are three Secondary Areas in Europe: 'Corsican mountains' (France) for *Sitta whiteheadi*, 'Caledonian pine forest' (United Kingdom) for *Loxia scotica*, and the Azores (Portugal) for *Serinus canaria* and *Pyrrhula murina*.

Biome-restricted assemblages – Category A3

The site is known or thought to hold a significant component of the group of species whose distributions are largely or wholly confined to one biome.

This category applies to groups of bird species with largely shared distributions (each individual species's distribution being greater than 50,000 km²), which occur mostly or wholly within a particular biome and which are, therefore, of global importance. Many of these assemblages occur in large areas of relatively intact and continuous habitat where delimiting IBAs is particularly difficult.

Biome-restricted species are those species whose entire (global) breeding distribution lies within the defined boundaries of the biome (with a few exceptions where a small part of the distribution may extend to another biome). Seabirds are excluded from these lists because their distributions are thought to be influenced by different factors to those affecting terrestrial species, and their conservation

Table 3. Restricted-range bird species in Europe.

Endemic Bird Area	Global threat status	SPEC category/European threat status
Madeira and the Canary Islands		
Columba trocaz Long-toed Pigeon	CD	1 Vulnerable
Columba bollii Dark-tailed Laurel Pigeon	VU	1 Vulnerable
Columba junoniae White-tailed Laurel Pigeon	VU	1 Vulnerable
Apus unicolor Plain Swift	—	4 Secure
Anthus berthelotii Berthelot's Pipit	—	4 Secure
Saxicola dacotiae Fuerteventura Chat	NT	2 Vulnerable
Regulus teneriffae Tenerife Goldcrest	—	4 Secure
Fringilla teydea Blue Chaffinch	CD	1 Vulnerable
Serinus canaria Canary	—	4 Secure
Caucasus		
Tetrao mlokosiewiczi Caucasian Black Grouse	NT	2 Insufficiently known
Tetraogallus caucasicus Caucasian Snowcock	—	4 Secure
Phylloscopus lorenzii Caucasian Chiffchaff	—	— (Secure)
Cyprus		
Oenanthe cypriaca Cyprus Pied Wheatear	—	2 Rare
Sylvia melanothorax Cyprus Warbler	—	2 Rare
Secondary Area		
Corsican mountains		
Sitta whiteheadi Corsican Nuthatch	NT	2 Vulnerable
Azores		
Serinus canaria Canary	—	4 Secure
Pyrrhula murina Azores Bullfinch		[not assessed]
Caledonian pine forest		
Loxia scotica Scottish Crossbill	DD	1 Insufficiently known

Global threat status follows Collar *et al.* (1994):
VU Vulnerable
CD Conservation Dependent
DD Data Deficient
NT Near Threatened
For key to SPEC category and European threat status, see Box 1.

Table 4. Biome-restricted bird species in Europe.

Arctic/tundra biome
Gavia adamsii White-billed Diver
Cygnus columbianus Bewick's Swan
Anser brachyrhynchus Pink-footed Goose
Anser albifrons White-fronted Goose
Anser erythropus Lesser White-fronted Goose
Branta leucopsis Barnacle Goose
Branta bernicla Brent Goose
Aythya marila Scaup
Somateria spectabilis King Eider
Clangula hyemalis Long-tailed Duck
Melanitta nigra Common Scoter
Buteo lagopus Rough-legged Buzzard
Falco rusticolus Gyrfalcon
Pluvialis squatarola Grey Plover
Calidris canutus Knot
Calidris alba Sanderling
Calidris minuta Little Stint
Calidris temminckii Temminck's Stint
Calidris maritima Purple Sandpiper
Limosa lapponica Bar-tailed Godwit
Tringa erythropus Spotted Redshank
Phalaropus lobatus Red-necked Phalarope
Phalaropus fulicarius Grey Phalarope
Stercorarius pomarinus Pomarine Skua
Stercorarius longicaudus Long-tailed Skua
Larus hyperboreus Glaucous Gull
Pagophila eburnea Ivory Gull
Nyctea scandiaca Snowy Owl
Anthus cervinus Red-throated Pipit
Carduelis hornemanni Arctic Redpoll
Calcarius lapponicus Lapland Bunting
Plectrophenax nivalis Snow Bunting

Boreal biome
Podiceps auritus Slavonian Grebe
Mergus albellus Smew
Lymnocryptes minimus Jack Snipe
Tringa nebularia Greenshank
Surnia ulula Hawk Owl
Strix nebulosa Great Grey Owl
Bombycilla garrulus Waxwing
Phylloscopus borealis Arctic Warbler
Parus cinctus Siberian Tit
Perisoreus infaustus Siberian Jay
Fringilla montifringilla Brambling
Loxia leucoptera Two-barred Crossbill
Loxia pytyopsittacus Parrot Crossbill
Pinicola enucleator Pine Grosbeak
Emberiza rustica Rustic Bunting

Mediterranean biome
Falco eleonorae Eleonora's Falcon
Alectoris graeca Rock Partridge
Caprimulgus ruficollis Red-necked Nightjar
Oenanthe cypriaca Cyprus Pied Wheatear
Oenanthe hispanica Black-eared Wheatear
Oenanthe leucura Black Wheatear
Hippolais olivetorum Olive-tree Warbler
Sylvia sarda Marmora's Warbler
Sylvia conspicillata Spectacled Warbler
Sylvia cantillans Subalpine Warbler
Sylvia melanocephala Sardinian Warbler
Sylvia melanothorax Cyprus Warbler
Sylvia rueppelli Rüppell's Warbler
Sitta krueperi Krüper's Nuthatch
Sitta whiteheadi Corsican Nuthatch
Sitta neumayer Rock Nuthatch
Lanius nubicus Masked Shrike
Sturnus unicolor Spotless Starling
Emberiza cineracea Cinereous Bunting
Emberiza caesia Cretzschmar's Bunting
Emberiza melanocephala Black-headed Bunting

Eurasian high-montane (alpine) biome
Tetrao mlokosiewiczi Caucasian Black Grouse
Tetraogallus caucasicus Caucasian Snowcock
Tetraogallus caspius Caspian Snowcock
Prunella collaris Alpine Accentor
Sitta tephronota Eastern Rock Nuthatch
Tichodroma muraria Wallcreeper
Pyrrhocorax graculus Alpine Chough
Montifringilla nivalis Snowfinch
Serinus citrinella Citril Finch
Carpodacus rubicilla Great Rosefinch

Eurasian steppe biome
Circus macrourus Pallid Harrier
Accipiter brevipes Levant Sparrowhawk
Aquila heliaca Imperial Eagle
Anthropoides virgo Demoiselle Crane
Glareola nordmanni Black-winged Pratincole
Chettusia gregaria Sociable Plover
Larus ichthyaetus Great Black-headed Gull
Melanocephala leucoptera White-winged Lark
Melanocephala yeltoniensis Black Lark

is covered through the application of other criteria categories (see criterion A4).

A biome is defined as a major regional ecological community characterized by distinctive life forms and principal plant species. No global classification of biomes has been found which is suitable for generating bird-species lists for BirdLife's IBA Programme. This has necessitated a regional approach to the identification of biomes and has resulted in inter-regional differences between the biome classifications used but, as far as possible, the overall scale at which biome divisions are recognised—the 'depth' of treatment—is comparable.

Five biomes have been treated under this criterion in Europe: the Arctic/tundra biome (with 32 characteristic bird species in Europe), the boreal biome (15 species), the Mediterranean biome (21 species), the Eurasian high-montane biome (10 species) and the Eurasian steppe biome (nine species). The geographical extent of these biomes in Europe is shown in Box 1 of the 'Overview of results' chapter, and Table 4 lists the bird species characteristic of each biome.

In applying the criterion, there were some important considerations, as follows:

- *Number and area of sites:* The number of sites selected per country under this category took into account both the size of the country and the relative amount of a given biome within it. The size of the site is also relevant; it is preferable to select a few, large sites that reflect the distribution of biome across the country rather than many small ones confined to only a part of it. This ensures that a greater number of species are represented per site and takes account of their geographical distribution. Sites should not, however, be so large that they are not amenable to conservation and, in some cases, small sites with high population densities may be preferable to large ones with lower densities.
- *Coverage of all biome species:* Common sense was used to ensure that sites chosen were rich in biome-restricted species with each in high numbers wherever possible. Some sites, however, were chosen for one or a few species which would otherwise be under-represented, such as those species confined to a relatively small part of the biome.
- *Geographical spread of sites throughout biome:* All of the biomes in Europe (that are treated under this criterion) cross political boundaries, and most have a wide geographical extent. In identifying a network of sites under these criteria, the geographical spread of the biome across political boundaries was taken into account, to try to ensure that the network of IBAs identified covered much of the biological and political extent of the biome.

Globally important congregations – Category A4

The site may qualify on any one of the four criteria listed below:

i)   The site is known or thought to hold, on a regular basis, 1% or more of a biogeographic population of a congregatory waterbird species.

ii) The site is known or thought to hold, on a regular basis, 1% or more of the global population of a congregatory seabird or terrestrial species.

iii) The site is known or thought to hold, on a regular basis, at least 20,000 waterbirds, or at least 10,000 pairs of seabird, of one or more species.

iv) The site is known or thought to be a 'bottleneck site' where at least 20,000 storks (Ciconiidae), raptors (Accipitriformes and Falconiformes) or cranes (Gruidae) pass regularly during spring or autumn migration.

This category was applied to those species that are vulnerable, at the population level, to the destruction or degradation of sites, by virtue of their congregatory behaviour when breeding, wintering or on passage. A total of 160 species were treated when applying these criteria in Europe, and 1% thresholds for all of these species are given in Appendix 2a. A few species of waterbird and raptor that are not considered to be congregatory (in Europe), or which have small, marginal populations in Europe, are not treated under this criteria category.

Criteria A4i and A4iii identify wetlands of international importance (Ramsar Sites), being similar to Ramsar criteria 6 and 5 respectively (see Box 4).

Definition of 'waterbird' and 'seabird'
The term 'waterbird' is used in the same sense as that used for 'waterfowl' under the Ramsar Convention, and covers (in Europe) all bird species in the following families (Rose and Scott 1997): Gaviidae (divers), Podicipedidae (grebes), Pelecanidae (pelecans), Phalacrocoracidae (cormorants), Ardeidae (herons), Ciconiidae (storks), Threskiornithidae (ibises), Phoenicopteridae (flamingos), Anatidae (wildfowl), Gruidae (cranes), Rallidae (rails), Haematopodidae (oystercatchers), Recurvirostridae (stilts, avocets), Burhinidae (stone-curlews), Glareolidae (pratincoles), Charadriidae (plovers), Scolopacidae (sandpipers and allies) and Laridae (gulls and terns). By this definition waterbirds include, for example, cormorants, gulls and terns, which some authors have more traditionally considered as seabirds. The term 'seabird' covers, in Europe, all bird species in the following families: Procellaridae (fulmars, petrels, shearwaters), Hydrobatidae (storm-petrels), Sulidae (gannets), Stercorariidae (skuas) and Alcidae (auks). A list of the criteria categories within which these species are considered is presented in Appendix 2a.

Definition of 'biogeographic population'
'Biogeographic' is used in the sense of a zoogeographic realm, e.g. the Palearctic or Afrotropical realms, which are large geographical regions in which the organisms present tend to be different from those of other realms. Thus such regions are characterized largely through the shared distribution patterns of many species. For European IBAs, the 'biogeographic' region approximates to the western Palearctic, but excludes the Middle East (for which, see Evans 1994). All 'populations' of a given species that are resident or migratory through this region are combined to form the 'biogeographic population'. For most waterbird species, the biogeographic population is taken here to equal the European breeding population. For a few species, part or all of the total passage/wintering population in Europe breeds outside the continent (e.g. in Siberia), therefore the biogeographic populations are calculated by summing the respective national wintering/passage population estimates across Europe. Feral populations of all qualifying species have, as far as possible, been excluded when applying these criteria.

Setting 1% thresholds and applying the criteria
One-percent threshold figures have been defined for all congregatory waterbird species (listed in Appendix 2a), including species for which no thresholds are currently recognised under the Ramsar Convention. Wetlands International has collaborated in generating numeric thresholds from range estimates and from unpublished population data.

There is a logical inconsistency between criterion A4i for waterbirds (1% or more of the **biogeographic** population) and criterion A4ii for seabirds (1% or more of **global** population of seabirds). It was felt, however, that the alternative of using 1% of the global population for waterbirds would, as well as departing from the criteria used under the Ramsar Convention, have insufficient biological justification, since relatively well-defined, discrete flyway populations can be distinguished within Europe for many migratory waterbird species. Taking 1% of global population would over-emphasise waterbirds endemic to Europe, since many widely distributed species may rarely occur at congregations exceeding 1% of the global population, over much of their range. For the same reason, in Europe the biogeographic and global populations are considered the same for regionally endemic waterbird species.

The A4iii and A4iv criteria are applied at the site level only, not to individual species. The most common species under these criteria are recorded in the text of the site-account where possible. The use of the A4iii criterion alone for a site has been discouraged in Europe when bird data for the site exceed 1% threshold levels for one or more individual species (cf. Atkinson-Willes 1976).

The A4iv criterion embraces sites over which flying migrants concentrate, e.g. at narrow sea-crossings, along mountain ranges or through mountain passes. Although it is the airspace here that is important, conservation of the land beneath may be necessary to protect the site and its birds from threats such as shooting and the construction of lethal obstacles such as power-lines and high radio-masts. Also included under A4iv are migratory stop-over sites and nocturnal roosts which may not hold 20,000 or more storks, raptors or cranes at any one time but which, nevertheless, do hold such numbers over a relatively short period due to the rapid turnover of birds on passage.

B: Important Bird Areas – European importance

Regionally important congregations – Category B1

The site may qualify on __any__ __one__ of the four criteria listed below:

i) The site is known or thought to hold 1% or more of a flyway population or other distinct population of a waterbird species.

ii) The site is known or thought to hold 1% or more of a distinct population of a seabird species.

iii) The site is known or thought to hold 1% or more of a flyway population or other distinct population of a congregatory species other than a waterbird or seabird.

iv) The site is a 'bottleneck site' where 5,000 or more storks (Ciconiidae), or 3,000 or more raptors (Accipitriformes and Falconiformes) or cranes (Gruidae), pass regularly on spring or autumn migration.

The aim of this category of criteria is the same as that for the A4 category, that is to identify important sites for species which are vulnerable at sites because of their congregatory nature. However, the B1 category sets lower numerical thresholds, based largely on 1% values of the flyway population or other distinct regional population of congregatory species, and the thresholds for 'bottleneck' sites are also lower.

For species without distinct populations in Europe, as is the case for many of the seabirds, the global and regional thresholds are the same. Appendix 2a lists, for each relevant species, the geographical limits of each flyway population (if any) and the corresponding 1% threshold used, following Rose and Scott (1994, 1997).

Criterion B1i covers wetlands of international importance (Ramsar Sites) identified under Ramsar criterion 6 (see Box 4).

Definition of 'flyway population'

For waterbird species, flyway or other distinct populations in Europe have been identified by Wetlands International (Rose and Scott 1997, Scott and Rose 1996), who refer to these units interchangeably as 'geographic regions', 'biogeographic regions', 'biogeographic populations' or 'geographic limits of every known distinct population of a species or subspecies'. These biogeographic areas vary from species to species, and the resulting 1% thresholds can be applied in different seasons.

Species with an unfavourable conservation status in Europe – Category B2

The site is one of the 'n' most important sites in a country for a species with an unfavourable conservation status in Europe (endangered, vulnerable, rare, declining, localized or insufficiently known in Europe), and for which the site-protection approach is thought to be appropriate.

Under this criterion, sites are identified for those species of European conservation concern (SPECs) of categories 1, 2 and 3 (see Box 1 and Appendix 2a) for which the site-protection approach is thought to be appropriate.

Setting thresholds and applying the criteria

In order to identify a network of IBAs covering a substantial proportion of the European population of each relevant species, throughout its European range, numerical thresholds were defined, as follows.

- For each country holding 1% or more of the minimum European breeding population of a given species, those sites which support 1% or more of the minimum national breeding population should be selected.

Assuming that these thresholds are met for a particular species in a particular country, there is also an upper limit—'n'—to the number of sites allowed to be identified in that country for that species,

ranging from five to 100 depending on the circumstances. The procedure for determining this value is explained further in Box 2.

This criterion addresses the problem of identifying IBAs for species that are widely dispersed across the landscape but which are amenable to conservation through site protection, and is framed so as to limit the maximum number of qualifying sites in countries with large total populations of any species (Box 2). The criterion should, however, be used with caution, for example in countries where absolute populations of a species are low (e.g. 100 pairs or less), since use of the 1% level loses meaning if a site qualifies on the basis of a single pair. Also, for countries which hold less than 1% of the European population of a given species, or for countries which comprise less than 1% of the land area of Europe (i.e. less than c.100,000 km²), sites may still be selected under this criterion if they support similar numbers of the species as sites in other countries which meet this criterion in a standard fashion.

For many widely dispersed SPEC2 and SPEC3 species, the site-protection approach may not be appropriate over large parts of their ranges in Europe. Yet, because they are dispersed, many IBAs identified for other species are likely to hold, overall, a sizeable population of these species. In addition, towards the edge of their range they may occur in well-defined sites, which could be considered important for maintaining the overall range of the species even if the absolute numbers occurring at any one of these 'edge' sites are low.

The B2 criterion is applied to bird data for the season in which the species qualifies as a SPEC. As a result, the great majority of applications of this criterion concern the breeding season (and are computed using breeding-population data), since only a few species in Europe have been identified as SPECs on the basis of their non-breeding populations (see Box 1).

European and national population data

European and national population data are taken from the European Bird Database (1994 version) of BirdLife International/European Bird Census Council. This database was updated in 1998 but as the majority of the IBAs had been proposed by this time, the new figures could not be used for most countries. However, where changes are substantial for a country, these new figures have been taken into account when finalizing the IBA identification.

The proportion of the national population of each SPEC falling within IBAs has been calculated for each country and these figures are presented in the respective national overviews. The figures should be interpreted with care as the national population estimate may not have been updated as recently as the population estimates for each IBA in the country. In addition, the stated count for a species at a site may be the maximum or average over recent years, and summing these may record more birds than are present nationally in any single year. Full documentation of the national population estimates used for each species, the proportions of the European total and calculation ratios cannot be presented in this publication because of space constraints. However, much of the relevant data is published in Tucker and Heath (1994) and Heath and Borggreve (2000).

Species with a favourable conservation status but concentrated in Europe – Category B3

The site is one of the 'n' most important sites in a country for a species with a favourable conservation status in Europe but with its global range concentrated in Europe, and for which the site-protection approach is thought to be appropriate.

This criterion applies to those species of European conservation concern (SPECs) of category 4 (see Box 1)—i.e. those with a favourable conservation status in Europe but with more than 50% of their global range lying within Europe (Appendix 2a)—for which the site-protection approach is thought to be appropriate. In effect, the criterion identifies sites for species with ranges greater than 50,000 km² and which are not restricted to a biome treated under the A3 criterion. The principles and methods used for setting thresholds, calculating the maximum number of sites per species in each country (see Box 2), and applying the criteria, are the same as for the B2 criterion.

Box 2. An example of the application of the B2/B3 criteria.

Identifying IBAs for Common Gull *Larus canus* in Finland

Minimum European breeding population estimate = 420,000 pairs
Minimum national breeding population estimate = 50,000 pairs

1. The country should hold at least 1% of the total European population.
   Finland holds 12% of the European breeding population of Larus
   canus.

2. The proposed site should hold at least 1% of the national population.
   A total of 15 sites in Finland each hold at least 500 pairs of Larus
   canus.

3. Calculate the proportion of the national population relative to the
   European one. This % value corresponds to a guideline figure for
   the maximum number of sites ('n' max) that can be proposed for the
   given species in a country.
   Finland holds 12% of the European breeding population of Larus canus.

The 'n' max figure is determined by the minimum size of the national
population relative to the minimum estimate of the total European
population. The table provides guidelines for calculating the **maximum**
number of sites ('n' max) for any given species. It is emphasized that
these are guidelines for the **maximum** number of sites that can be
proposed and, where it is appropriate to identify a lower number of
sites for a given species in a country, this is entirely acceptable.

Proportion (%) of total European population or range held by the country in question	Maximum number of sites that may be identified in the country in question ('n' max)
1–5	5
10	10
20	16–25
30	26–35
40	36–45
50	46–55
60	56–65
70	66–75
80	76–85
90	86–95
100	96–100

Therefore up to 10 IBAs may be identified for Larus canus *in Finland,
with each having at least 500 pairs of the species. From the 15 sites
that actually hold at least 500 pairs, a maximum of 10 (usually those
with the highest population estimate) were selected as IBAs.*

Note: For countries which hold less than 1% of the total European population of a given species,
it is still possible to propose sites which are thought to hold internationally important numbers of
the species: population levels at these sites were then compared to sites identified in other
countries using the above procedure. Countries with a surface area less than 1% of the total
European territory (see Step 1) were particularly encouraged to use this method (with caution) to
identify potential IBAs for selected species.

C: Important Bird Areas – European Union importance

The 'C' categories of criteria are used for selecting sites in the
European Union which qualify, under the EC Birds Directive, as
Special Protection Areas (SPAs). For details of the EC Birds
Directive, see Appendix 1. These ornithological criteria represent
a consolidation of the criteria which have been used, to date, by
the different member states of the EU. Full details of the
development of the C criteria are presented in Osieck (1998).

Importantly, the C criteria categories are based on those used
in the most recent inventory of IBAs in the European Community
(Grimmett and Gammell 1989), which received legal recognition
as a scientific reference in a ruling by the European Court of Justice

against the government of the Netherlands in 1998 (see Box 3). The
criteria presented here are a logical progression from those of
Grimmett and Gammell (1989), introducing some additional
quantitative thresholds (Appendix 4). The criteria take into account
the conservation requirements of species within the EU territory,
with the geographical spread of sites representing the full extent of
each species' range in the EU (irrespective of the pattern of regional
abundance) as well as sites selected on a basis of relative abundance.
The criteria do not produce a more restricted selection of sites than
those criteria applied in the past.

Seven categories of criteria have been applied (C1–C7), several
of which emulate the higher categories under the global (A) and
European (B) level criteria. It should be noted that Annex I of the
EC Birds Directive lists a number of subspecies that should be

---

Box 3. Legal recognition of the value of the European Important Bird Area inventory by the European Court of Justice.

The 1989 IBA inventory for the European Community (Grimmett and
Gammell 1989) received legal recognition in 1998 in the European
Court of Justice ruling against the government of the Netherlands.
On 19 May 1998 the Court of Justice delivered a significant judgment
against the Netherlands in an infringement case (Case C-3/96
Commission v Netherlands [1998] ECR 1-3031, paragraphs 60–63).
The Court reasoned as follows:

"...while the Member States have a certain margin of discretion in the
choice of SPAs, the classification of those areas is nevertheless subject
to certain ornithological criteria determined by the Directive [...]. It
follows that the Member States' margin of discretion in choosing the
most suitable territories for classification as SPAs does not concern the
appropriateness of classifying as SPAs the territories which appear the
most suitable according to ornithological criteria, but only the
application of those criteria for identifying the most suitable territories
for conservation of the species listed in Annex I to the Directive.
Consequently, Member States are obliged to classify as SPAs all the sites
which, applying ornithological criteria, appear to be the most suitable
for conservation of the species in question. Thus where it appears that a
Member State has classified as SPAs sites the number and total area of
which are manifestly less than the number and total area of the sites
considered to be the most suitable for conservation of the species in
question, it will be possible to find that the Member State has failed to
fulfil its obligation under Article 4(1) of the Directive".

The Court accordingly dismisses the Netherlands Government's
argument that the Commission must establish, territory by territory,
specific infringements of that provision.

[1] "The Court went on to acknowledge the relevance of the *Inventory of
Important Bird Areas in the European Community* [Grimmett and
Gammell 1989] prepared for the competent Directorate-General of the
Commission by the 'Eurogroup for the Conservation of Birds and
Habitats' in conjunction with the International Council for Bird
Preservation [now BirdLife International] and in cooperation with
Commission experts. [Grimmett and Gammell (1989) lists, with one
exception, the same sites as Grimmett and Jones (1989).] That
inventory, although not legally binding on the Member States
concerned, could, by reason of its acknowledged scientific value in
the present case, be used by the Court as a basis of reference for
assessing the extent to which the Kingdom of the Netherlands had
complied with its obligation to classify SPAs. In the circumstances,
IBA89 [Grimmett and Gammell 1989] had proved to be the only
document containing scientific evidence making it possible to assess
whether the defendant State had fulfilled its obligation to classify as
SPAs the most suitable territories in number and area for conservation
of the protected species. The situation would have been different if the
Kingdom of the Netherlands had produced scientific evidence in
particular to show that the obligation in question could be fulfilled by
classifying as SPAs territories whose number and total area were less
than those resulting from IBA89."

"The Commission is continuing Article 171 proceedings against the
Netherlands, to obtain implementation of the judgments." [This means
a subsequent judgment, in which the Court is asked to confirm the
non-implementation of the first judgement and to impose a fine of up
to 220,000 Euro per day in the case of the Netherlands.]

1. Source: Page 78 in *XVIth Report on monitoring the application of Community law*. Brussels: European Commission (COM(1999)301 final, adopted on 09/07/99).

treated independently of their 'mother' species when applying C criteria. These subspecies are listed in Appendix 2b.

Species of global conservation concern – C1

The site regularly holds significant numbers of a globally threatened species, or other species of global conservation concern.

This criterion is identical to the A1 criterion, and the same thresholds apply (see Appendices 2a and 2b).

Concentrations of species threatened at the European Union level – C2

The site is known to regularly hold at least 1% of the flyway or EU population of a species considered to be threatened in the EU.

'Threatened species' refers to species, subspecies and populations listed in Annex I of the EC Birds Directive, for which Special Protection Areas (SPAs) are designated under Article 4.1 of the Directive. The definition of 'flyway population' is the same as that given for the B1 criteria. However, for a small number of species where the European breeding population is significantly larger than the EU breeding population, lower numerical thresholds have been set (see Appendix 2b). This criterion has also been applied for a number of dispersed species on the basis that the site holds more than 1% of the European population of the species.

Migratory non-threatened species – C3

The site is known to regularly hold at least 1% of a flyway population of a migratory species that is not considered to be threatened in the EU.

'Migratory species not considered threatened' refer to species considered under Article 4.2 of the Birds Directive (i.e. regularly occurring migratory species not listed in Annex I). 'Migration' is defined as seasonal long-distance movements from and to breeding areas. The word 'migratory' therefore excludes populations which are largely sedentary or short-distance dispersive (e.g. *Larus argentatus* and *Cepphus grylle* in western Europe). This criterion covers wetlands of international importance (Ramsar Sites) identified under Ramsar criteria category 6, to which reference is made in Article 4.2 of the Birds Directive. Wetlands of international importance uniquely qualifying for waterbirds listed in Annex I of the Birds Directive are covered by IBA criterion C2.

The definition of 'flyway population' is the same as that given for the B1 criteria. Lower numerical thresholds (than those used for B1 criteria) have not been set.

Large congregations – C4

The site is known to regularly hold at least 20,000 migratory waterbirds, or at least 10,000 pairs of migratory seabird, of one or more species.

This criterion is the same as the A4iii criterion and covers all wetlands of international importance identified under Ramsar criteria category 5.

Large congregations – 'bottleneck' sites – C5

The site is a 'bottleneck' site where at least 5,000 storks (Ciconiidae), or at least 3,000 migratory raptors (Accipitriformes and Falconiformes) or cranes (Gruidae), regularly pass on spring or autumn migration.

This criterion is the same as the B1iv criterion. As most of the species concerned are listed in Annex I of the Birds Directive, this criterion refers mainly to sites important in the context of Article 4.1.

Species threatened at the European Union level – C6

The site is one of the five most important in the European region in question for a species or subspecies considered threatened in the European Union.

'Threatened species' refers to species, subspecies and populations listed in Annex I of the EC Birds Directive. 'European region' refers to what are known as NUTS regions (Appendix 5). The Nomenclature of Territorial Units for Statistics (NUTS) was established by Eurostat—the EC Statistical Office—to provide a single uniform breakdown of approximately equal territorial units for the production of regional statistics for the European Union. Although the NUTS has no legal value *per se*, it has been used since 1988 in Community legislation. NUTS regions are equalized on the basis of human population density: regions are larger where population density is lower. The NUTS approach is not ideal for birds, because many species of birds occur preferentially in remote, sparsely populated areas. Different levels of NUTS region have therefore been selected for the purpose of IBA identification, such that the geographical size of the NUTS region used is roughly the same across the European Union (see Appendix 2b).

In general, up to five sites per NUTS region may be identified for a species—however, in exceptional cases, there may be grounds for increasing the number of sites per NUTS region to slightly more than five. In the previous pan-European IBA inventory of 1989, a total of ten sites could be selected per country for those countries which were not, then, part of the EU but which now are (Austria, Finland, German Democratic Republic, Sweden); this option has now been deleted, as NUTS levels have now been defined for these countries or territories as well.

If two or more sites in a given region hold the same number of pairs or individuals of a particular taxon, the relative priority of the sites for selection as IBAs is ranked according to the overall number of threatened (Annex I) species that occurs at each site. The C6 criterion has generally been applied to breeding populations, but may also be applied for non-breeding occurrences if these are not covered well by other criteria in the country concerned. The rationale of the criterion, overall, is to achieve a wide geographical coverage of sites throughout the species' range in the European Union.

Sites meeting C6 should hold appreciable numbers (appreciable at the EU level) of the species or subspecies concerned. This additional condition is necessary to exclude irregular occurrences and sites holding a low number of birds (1% of the regional breeding population or 0.1% of the biogeographical population are suggested as minimum levels), although different countries have adopted different approaches in their definition of 'appreciable'.

Other ornithological criteria – C7

A site which has been designated as a Special Protection Area (SPA), or has been selected as a candidate SPA, based on ornithological criteria (similar to, but not equal to, C1–C6) in recognized use for identifying SPAs.

Application of this criterion is confined to designated SPAs, and to sites which have been selected as SPAs in the framework of a national inventory which has been used by government agencies as such (although not necessarily officially accepted). This criterion should be applied only to a minority of exceptional cases where it would be inadvisable to exclude the sites concerned from the IBA inventory.

HOW DO THE IBA CRITERIA RELATE TO THE IDENTIFICATION OF SPECIAL PROTECTION AREAS UNDER THE EC BIRDS DIRECTIVE?

As the Birds and Habitats Directives are the most important international legal instruments for site protection in the European Union, all sites which qualify under Article 4 of the Birds Directive should be listed as IBAs. Keeping the aim of SPA designation in mind, when selecting IBAs, serves a practical conservation purpose but also helps to keep the process within sensible bounds. All potential Special Protection Areas (SPAs) should meet at least one of the criteria of the IBA criteria category C.

HOW DO THE IBA CRITERIA RELATE TO THE IDENTIFICATION OF RAMSAR SITES UNDER THE RAMSAR CONVENTION?

The Ramsar (or Wetlands) Convention defines a wetland as "an area of marsh, fen, peatland or water, whether natural or artificial, permanent or temporary, with water that is static or flowing, fresh, brackish or salt, including areas of marine water the depth of which at low tide does not exceed 6 m" (Article 1). Article 2.1 of the Convention also states that "the boundaries of each wetland [...] may incorporate riparian and coastal zones adjacent to the wetlands, and islands or bodies of marine water deeper than 6 m at low tide lying within the wetlands, especially where these have importance as waterfowl habitat".

The criteria for identifying wetlands of international importance under the Ramsar Convention, as adopted at the Conference of the Parties on 7 May 1999, fall into eight categories (Box 4). There is a strong relationship between the Ramsar categories for waterbirds and the IBA criteria. Ramsar criterion category 6 was one of the main criteria used in identifying IBAs. It has been used for both non-breeding populations of waterbirds and for breeding concentrations of some congregatory species. Averages (preferably five-year) of seasonal peak numbers have been used to assess whether the 1% threshold is met, although this was not possible for every country due to a lack of five-year data-sets. Ramsar criterion category 5 has also been applied to many IBAs. However, it has not always been applied as an independent criterion, because criterion 6 was given preference where suitable data were available. Many IBAs also comply with Ramsar criteria categories 2, 3 and 4, particularly wetland sites (such as mires, peat-bogs, etc.) that are important for birds other than waterbirds.

Thus, overall, IBA criteria comply with the Ramsar criteria for birds. However, one divergence is that IBA criteria categories A4i,

> **Box 4.** Categories of criteria for site selection under the Ramsar Convention (adopted at the Conference of the Parties, 7 May 1999).
>
> 1. Representative, rare, or unique example of a natural or near-natural wetland type found within the appropriate biogeographic region.
> 2. Supports vulnerable, endangered, or critically endangered species or threatened ecological communities.
> 3. Supports populations of plant and/or animal species important for maintaining the biological diversity of a particular biogeographic region.
> 4. Supports plant and/or animal species at a critical stage in their life cycles, or provides refuge during adverse conditions.
> 5. Regularly supports 20,000 or more waterbirds.
> 6. Regularly supports 1% of the individuals in a population of one species or subspecies of waterbird.
> 7. Supports a significant proportion of indigenous fish subspecies, species or families, life-history stages, species interactions and/or populations that are representative of wetland benefits and/or values and thereby contributes to global biological diversity.
> 8. An important source of food for fishes, spawning ground, nursery and/or migration path on which fish stocks, either within the wetland or elsewhere, depend.

B1i, C2 and C3 may be applied to congregations of waterbirds in grassland and marine habitats (not classifiable as wetland habitat under the Ramsar definition). For example, agricultural grassland IBAs in the Netherlands regularly meet the 1% threshold for *Anser albifrons*, and *Cygnus columbianus* and *Branta leucopsis* also use non-intensive grassland areas for feeding during the winter in the Netherlands. Similarly, many IBAs in Europe contain both coastal wetlands and some marine habitat deeper than 6 m. Thus, even though the 1% thresholds for some waterbirds may be met in these grassland and marine areas (Ramsar criterion 6), the Ramsar wetland definition excludes these sites from consideration under the Convention, therefore their eligibility for designation as Ramsar Sites has to be considered on a case-by-case basis.

REFERENCES

Atkinson-Willes, G. L. (1976) The numerical distribution of ducks, swans and coots as a guide in assessing the importance of wetlands in midwinter. Pp. 199–255 in M. Smart, ed. *Proc. Int. Conf. on the Conservation of Wetlands and Waterfowl, Heiligenhafen.* Slimbridge, UK: International Waterfowl and Wetlands Research Bureau.

BirdLife International (1995) IBA criteria. Categories and thresholds. Cambridge, UK: BirdLife International (unpublished report).

Collar, N. J., Crosby, M. J. and Stattersfield, A. J. (1994) *Birds to watch 2: the world list of threatened birds.* Cambridge, UK: BirdLife International (Conservation Series 4).

Evans, M. I., ed. (1994) *Important Bird Areas in the Middle East.* Cambridge, UK: BirdLife International (BirdLife Conservation Series 2).

Fishpool, L. F. A. (in prep.) *Important Bird Areas in Africa.* Cambridge, UK: BirdLife International.

Grimmett R. F. A. and Gammell, A. B. (1989) Inventory of Important Bird Areas in the European Community. (Unpublished report prepared for the Directorate-General for the Environment, Consumer Protection and Nuclear Safety of the European Community, study contract B6610-54-88.) Cambridge, UK: International Council for Bird Preservation.

Grimmett, R. F. A. and Jones, T. A. (1989) *Important Bird Areas in Europe.* Cambridge, UK: International Council for Bird Preservation (ICBP Technical Publication 9).

Heath, M. F. (1995) Important Bird Areas inventory review project. First workshop, Arnhem 1995. Proceedings. Cambridge, UK: BirdLife International (unpublished report).

Heath, M. F. (1996) Important Bird Areas inventory review project. Second workshop, Finland 1996. Proceedings. Cambridge, UK: BirdLife International (unpublished report).

Heath, M. F. and Borggreve, C. (2000) *BirdLife International/EBCC European Bird Database 1998.* Cambridge, UK: BirdLife International.

IUCN (1994) *IUCN Red List categories.* Gland, Switzerland: IUCN—The World Conservation Union.

Osieck, E.R. (1999) IBA review and the EU Birds Directive. Cambridge, UK: BirdLife International (Internal report; 6th and final draft. 18 April 1998).

Osieck, E. R. and Mörzer Bruyns, M. F. (1981) *Important bird areas in the European Community.* Cambridge, UK: International Council for Bird Preservation.

Rose, P. M. and Scott, D. A. (1994) *Waterfowl population estimates.* UK: International Waterfowl and Wetlands Research Bureau (IWRB Publ. 29).

Rose P. M. and Scott D. A. (1997) *Waterfowl population estimates.* Second edition. Wageningen, Netherlands: Wetlands International (Publication 44).

Scott, D. A. and Rose, P. M. (1996) *Atlas of Anatidae populations in Africa and Western Europe.* Wageningen, Netherlands: Wetlands International (Wetlands International Publ. No. 41).

Stattersfield, A. J., Crosby, M. J., Long, A. J. and Wege, D. C. (1998) *Endemic bird areas of the world: priorities for bird conservation.* Cambridge, UK: BirdLife International (BirdLife Conservation Series no. 7).

Tucker, G. M. and Heath, M. F. (1994) *Birds in Europe: their conservation status.* Cambridge, UK: BirdLife International (BirdLife Conservation Series no. 3).

DATA PRESENTATION

Each chapter contains a national overview of the status of Important Bird Areas (IBAs) and their conservation, followed by a series of site accounts describing the IBAs in the country.

The national overviews have been written in a standard way, summarizing key information on IBAs in the country. The tables, maps and figures in each national overview summarize the data within the site accounts which have, in turn, been derived from the BirdLife International IBA Database. Space for each site account is limited, given the inclusion of 3,619 sites in this publication, and the text has been restricted to key facts. More detailed information is contained within the IBA Database and, for several countries, has also been published in national IBA inventories (see Box 1, 'Data collection' chapter).

NATIONAL OVERVIEW

■ General introduction

This includes basic geographical information about the country, information on the number and distribution of IBAs, the percentage of the country's surface area covered by IBAs, and a comparison of the current IBA inventory with the one presented 10 years previously (Grimmett and Jones 1989) and with any national IBA publications. This section is accompanied by a table listing all IBAs and the reasons for their importance, and a map displaying their location.

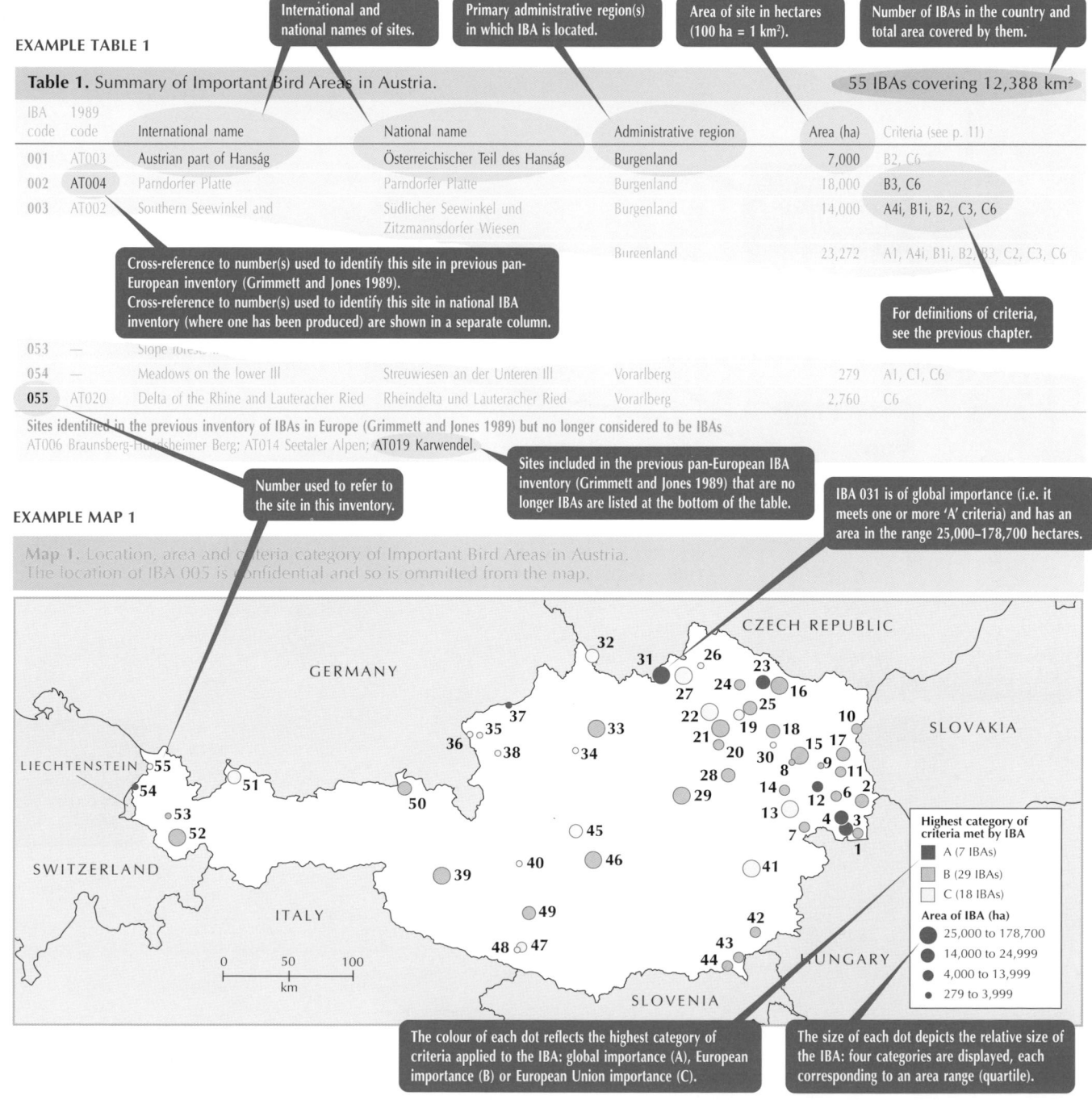

EXAMPLE TABLE 1

International and national names of sites.

Primary administrative region(s) in which IBA is located.

Area of site in hectares (100 ha = 1 km²).

Number of IBAs in the country and total area covered by them.

Table 1. Summary of Important Bird Areas in Austria.

55 IBAs covering 12,388 km²

IBA code	1989 code	International name	National name	Administrative region	Area (ha)	Criteria (see p. 11)
001	AT003	Austrian part of Hanság	Österreichischer Teil des Hanság	Burgenland	7,000	B2, C6
002	AT004	Parndorfer Platte	Parndorfer Platte	Burgenland	18,000	B3, C6
003	AT002	Southern Seewinkel and	Südlicher Seewinkel und Zitzmannsdorfer Wiesen	Burgenland	14,000	A4i, B1i, B2, C3, C6
				Burgenland	23,272	A1, A4i, B1i, B2, B3, C2, C3, C6
053	—	Slope forest ...				
054	—	Meadows on the lower Ill	Streuwiesen an der Unteren Ill	Vorarlberg	279	A1, C1, C6
055	AT020	Delta of the Rhine and Lauteracher Ried	Rheindelta und Lauteracher Ried	Vorarlberg	2,760	C6

Cross-reference to number(s) used to identify this site in previous pan-European inventory (Grimmett and Jones 1989).
Cross-reference to number(s) used to identify this site in national IBA inventory (where one has been produced) are shown in a separate column.

For definitions of criteria, see the previous chapter.

Sites identified in the previous inventory of IBAs in Europe (Grimmett and Jones 1989) but no longer considered to be IBAs
AT006 Braunsberg-Hundsheimer Berg; AT014 Seetaler Alpen; AT019 Karwendel.

Number used to refer to the site in this inventory.

Sites included in the previous pan-European IBA inventory (Grimmett and Jones 1989) that are no longer IBAs are listed at the bottom of the table.

IBA 031 is of global importance (i.e. it meets one or more 'A' criteria) and has an area in the range 25,000–178,700 hectares.

EXAMPLE MAP 1

Map 1. Location, area and criteria category of Important Bird Areas in Austria.
The location of IBA 005 is confidential and so is omitted from the map.

Highest category of criteria met by IBA
- A (7 IBAs)
- B (29 IBAs)
- C (18 IBAs)

Area of IBA (ha)
- 25,000 to 178,700
- 14,000 to 24,999
- 4,000 to 13,999
- 279 to 3,999

The colour of each dot reflects the highest category of criteria applied to the IBA: global importance (A), European importance (B) or European Union importance (C).

The size of each dot depicts the relative size of the IBA: four categories are displayed, each corresponding to an area range (quartile).

■ Ornithological importance

This section summarizes the key facts about birds and IBAs in the country, giving special attention to species meeting IBA criteria and emphasizing those species for which the country is important in an international context, especially species of global or European conservation concern (Collar *et al.* 1994, Tucker and Heath 1994). This section includes up to three tables illustrating the importance of the IBA network for:

- species of global conservation concern
- congregatory species
- species of European conservation concern and species threatened in the European Union (listed on Annex I of the EC Birds Directive).

SPECIES OF GLOBAL CONSERVATION CONCERN

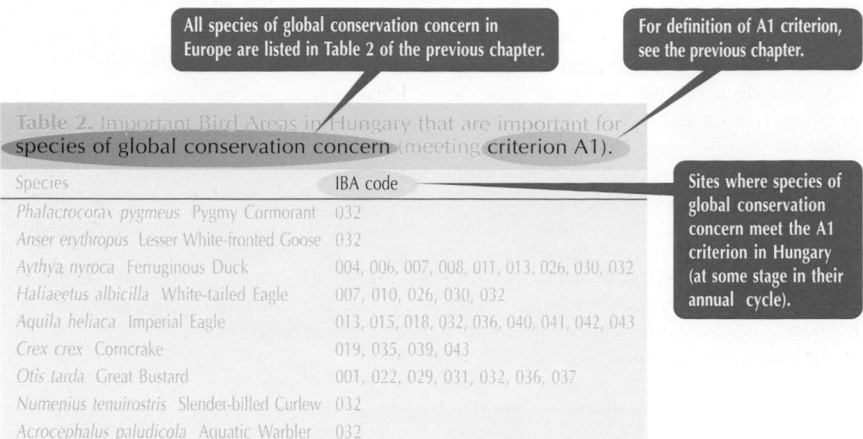

All species of global conservation concern in Europe are listed in Table 2 of the previous chapter.

For definition of A1 criterion, see the previous chapter.

Table 2. Important Bird Areas in Hungary that are important for species of global conservation concern (meeting criterion A1).

Sites where species of global conservation concern meet the A1 criterion in Hungary (at some stage in their annual cycle).

Species	IBA code
Phalacrocorax pygmeus Pygmy Cormorant	032
Anser erythropus Lesser White-fronted Goose	032
Aythya nyroca Ferruginous Duck	004, 006, 007, 008, 011, 013, 026, 030, 032
Haliaeetus albicilla White-tailed Eagle	007, 010, 026, 030, 032
Aquila heliaca Imperial Eagle	013, 015, 018, 032, 036, 040, 041, 042, 043
Crex crex Corncrake	019, 035, 039, 043
Otis tarda Great Bustard	001, 022, 029, 031, 032, 036, 037
Numenius tenuirostris Slender-billed Curlew	032
Acrocephalus paludicola Aquatic Warbler	032

CONGREGATORY SPECIES

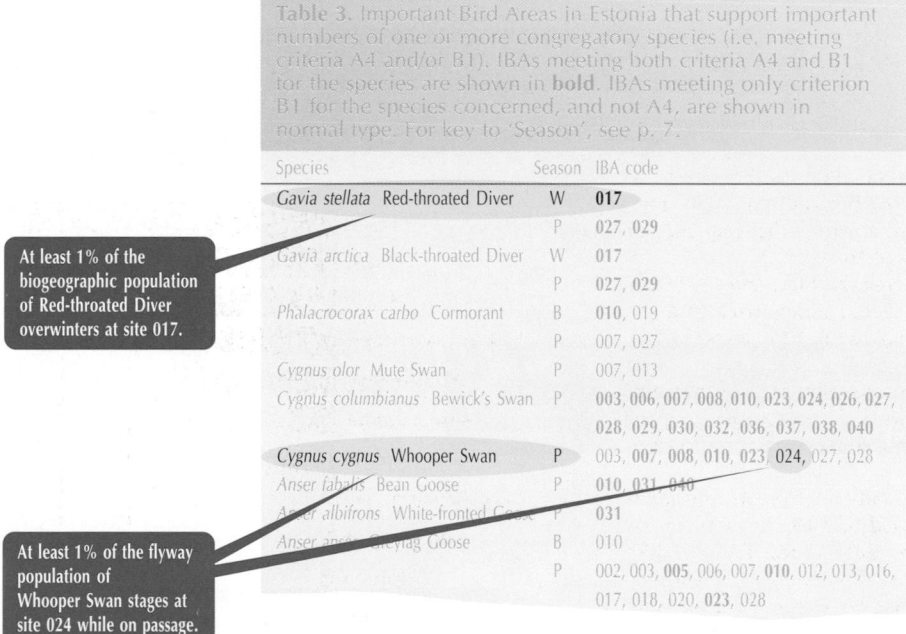

Table 3. Important Bird Areas in Estonia that support important numbers of one or more congregatory species (i.e. meeting criteria A4 and/or B1). IBAs meeting both criteria A4 and B1 for the species are shown in **bold**. IBAs meeting only criterion B1 for the species concerned, and not A4, are shown in normal type. For key to 'Season', see p. 7.

Species	Season	IBA code
Gavia stellata Red-throated Diver	W	**017**
	P	027, 029
Gavia arctica Black-throated Diver	W	**017**
	P	027, 029
Phalacrocorax carbo Cormorant	B	**010**, 019
	P	007, 027
Cygnus olor Mute Swan	P	007, 013
Cygnus columbianus Bewick's Swan	P	**003, 006, 007, 008, 010, 023, 024, 026, 027, 028, 029, 030, 032, 036, 037, 038, 040**
Cygnus cygnus Whooper Swan	P	003, **007, 008, 010, 023, 024**, 027, 028
Anser fabalis Bean Goose	P	010, 031, 040
Anser albifrons White-fronted Goose	P	031
Anser anser Greylag Goose	B	010
	P	002, 003, **005**, 006, 007, **010**, 012, 013, 016, 017, 018, 020, **023**, 028

At least 1% of the biogeographic population of Red-throated Diver overwinters at site 017.

At least 1% of the flyway population of Whooper Swan stages at site 024 while on passage.

SPECIES OF EUROPEAN CONSERVATION CONCERN AND SPECIES THREATENED IN THE EUROPEAN UNION

Red-throated Diver is a species:
- which is of European conservation concern and /or is listed in Annex I of the EC Birds Directive
- for which one or more IBAs have been identified in Finland.

Table 4. Species of European conservation concern and species listed on Annex I of the EC Birds Directive with significant breeding populations at IBAs in Finland (meeting any IBA criteria).

It is estimated that at least 11% of the breeding population of Red-throated Diver in Finland breeds within IBAs.

Species [1]	Minimum national breeding population (pairs) [2]	Proportion (%) of national population breeding at all IBAs in Finland
Gavia stellata Red-throated Diver	900	11
Gavia arctica Black-throated Diver	7,000	5
Podiceps auritus Slavonian Grebe	3,000	5
Botaurus stellaris Bittern	100	84
Perisoreus infaustus Siberian Jay	30,000	11
Loxia pytyopsittacus Parrot Crossbill	10,000	9

1. Only those species of European conservation concern (see Box 1, p. 12) that meet IBA criteria in Finland are listed, together with those species listed on Annex I of the EC Birds Directive that fulfil criterion C6 in IBAs in Finland.
2. Data are taken from the BirdLife/EBCC European Bird Database 1998 (Heath and Borggreve 2000).
3. The percentage of the national population in IBAs exceeds 100%. Usually this is because the national population estimate has not been updated recently whilst the IBA population estimate has been recently updated with new data as a result of comprehensive surveys of IBAs themselves. Also, the individual site count for a species may be the maximum or average over recent years, and summing these may record more birds than are present nationally in any single year.

■ Habitats

This section gives a brief outline of the predominant habitat-types in the country. It examines the most widespread and common habitat-types found within IBAs and discusses the representativeness of IBA coverage from a habitat perspective in a national context.

A bar chart illustrates the occurrence and coverage of different habitat-types within IBAs. For a fuller explanation of the habitat classification used, see Appendix 3.

For some sites, and some countries, the percentage cover of habitat-types has not been estimated; in these cases the bar chart indicates only the frequency of occurrence of habitats at IBAs.

Habitat-types are listed and described in more detail in Appendix 3.

HABITATS AT IBAs

At 35% of IBAs in Slovenia, forest/woodland covers at least 50% of the area of the individual IBA.

At 85% of IBAs in Slovenia, forest/woodland covers at least 5% of the area of the individual IBA.

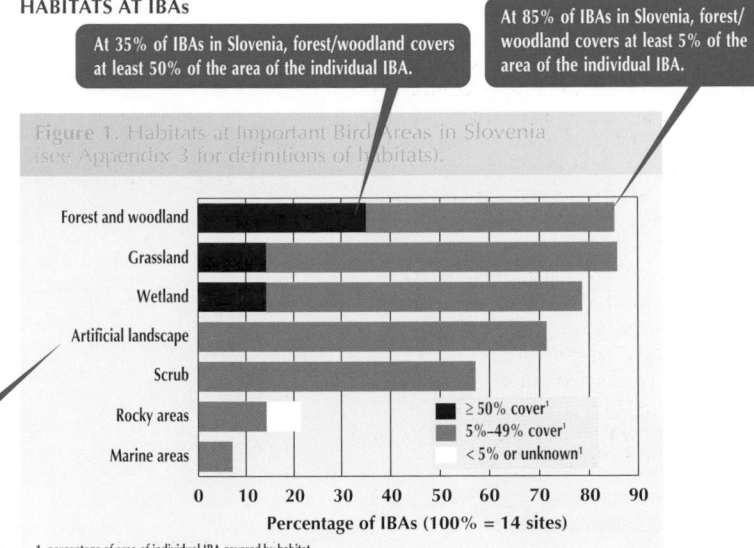

Figure 1. Habitats at Important Bird Areas in Slovenia (see Appendix 3 for definitions of habitats).

Bar chart categories: Forest and woodland, Grassland, Wetland, Artificial landscape, Scrub, Rocky areas, Marine areas.

Legend: ≥ 50% cover[1]; 5%–49% cover[1]; < 5% or unknown[1]

Percentage of IBAs (100% = 14 sites)

1. percentage of area of individual IBA covered by habitat

■ Impacts on IBAs— land-use and threats

The most widespread and common land-uses within IBAs are described and presented in a bar chart. For a fuller explanation of the land-use classification, see Appendix 3.

For some sites, and some countries, the percentage cover of land-use has not been estimated; in these cases the bar chart indicates only the frequency of occurrence of land-uses at IBAs.

Key factors threatening the sites, and their level of impact, are described and summarized in a chart. For a fuller explanation of the classification of threats, see Appendix 3.

For some sites, and some countries, the impact of threats has not been estimated; in these cases, the bar chart indicates only the frequency of occurrence of threats at IBAs.

Any links between land-uses, threats and land-ownership are addressed and the key species or habitats affected are described. Those IBAs considered most threatened are highlighted and any relevant national trends in land-uses and threats are outlined and contrasted with trends at IBAs.

Land-uses are listed and defined in Appendix 3.

LAND-USES AT IBAs

At 20% of IBAs in Russia, at least 50% of the area of the individual IBA is used for forestry.

At 40% of IBAs in Russia, between 5% and 49% of the area of the individual IBA is used for forestry.

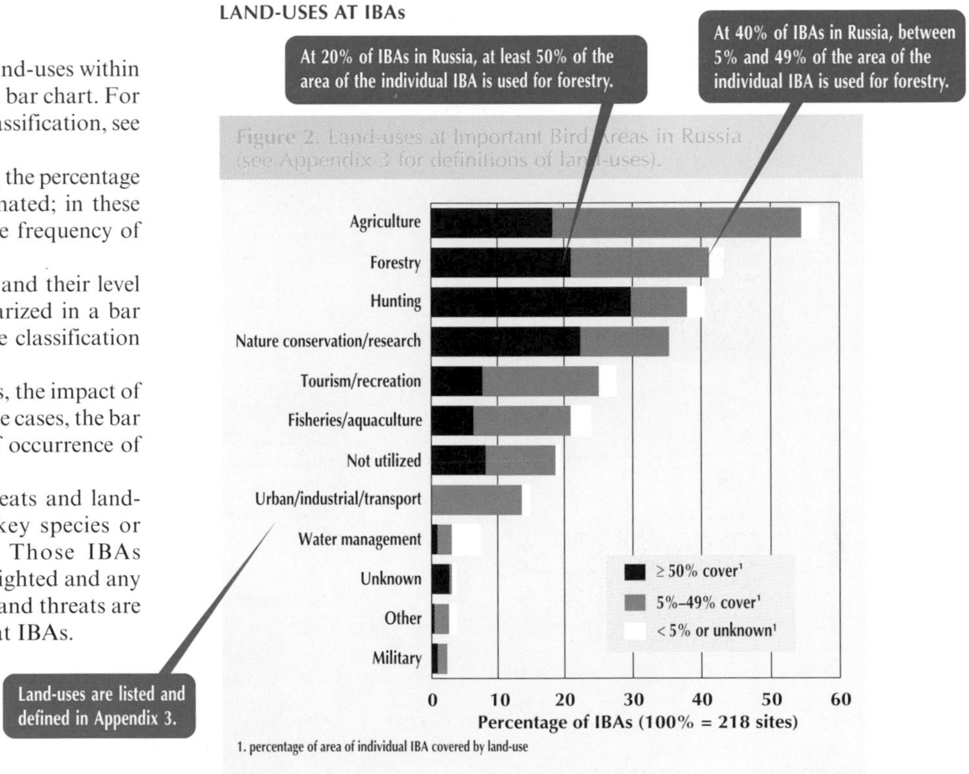

Figure 2. Land-uses at Important Bird Areas in Russia (see Appendix 3 for definitions of land-uses).

Bar chart categories: Agriculture, Forestry, Hunting, Nature conservation/research, Tourism/recreation, Fisheries/aquaculture, Not utilized, Urban/industrial/transport, Water management, Unknown, Other, Military.

Legend: ≥ 50% cover[1]; 5%–49% cover[1]; < 5% or unknown[1]

Percentage of IBAs (100% = 218 sites)

1. percentage of area of individual IBA covered by land-use

THREATS AT IBAs

Ongoing drainage is having (or planned drainage will have) a high impact at about 5% of IBAs in Belarus.

Agricultural intensification/expansion poses a threat at 48% of IBAs in Belarus: at 42% of IBAs in Belarus, the impact is considered to be medium or low, while at 6% of IBAs in Belarus, the degree of impact is not known.

Over 70% of IBAs in Belarus are threatened, to some extent, by drainage.

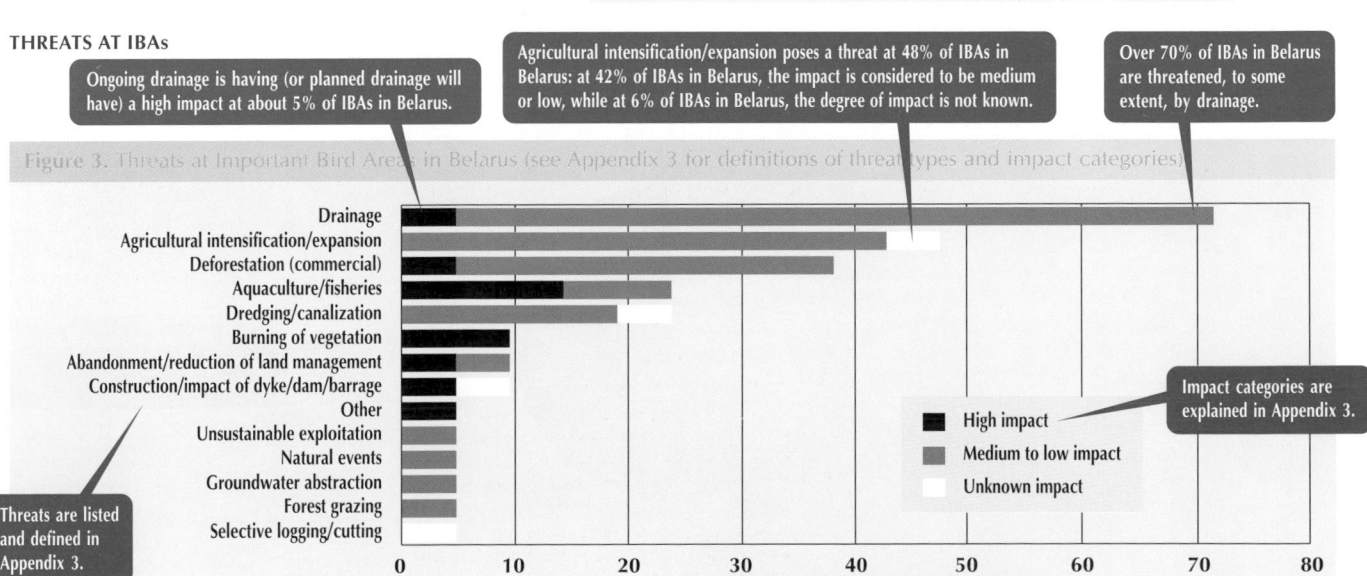

Figure 3. Threats at Important Bird Areas in Belarus (see Appendix 3 for definitions of threat types and impact categories).

Bar chart categories: Drainage, Agricultural intensification/expansion, Deforestation (commercial), Aquaculture/fisheries, Dredging/canalization, Burning of vegetation, Abandonment/reduction of land management, Construction/impact of dyke/dam/barrage, Other, Unsustainable exploitation, Natural events, Groundwater abstraction, Forest grazing, Selective logging/cutting.

Threats are listed and defined in Appendix 3.

Legend: High impact; Medium to low impact; Unknown impact

Impact categories are explained in Appendix 3.

Percentage of IBAs (100% = 21 sites)

PROTECTION STATUS OF IBAs

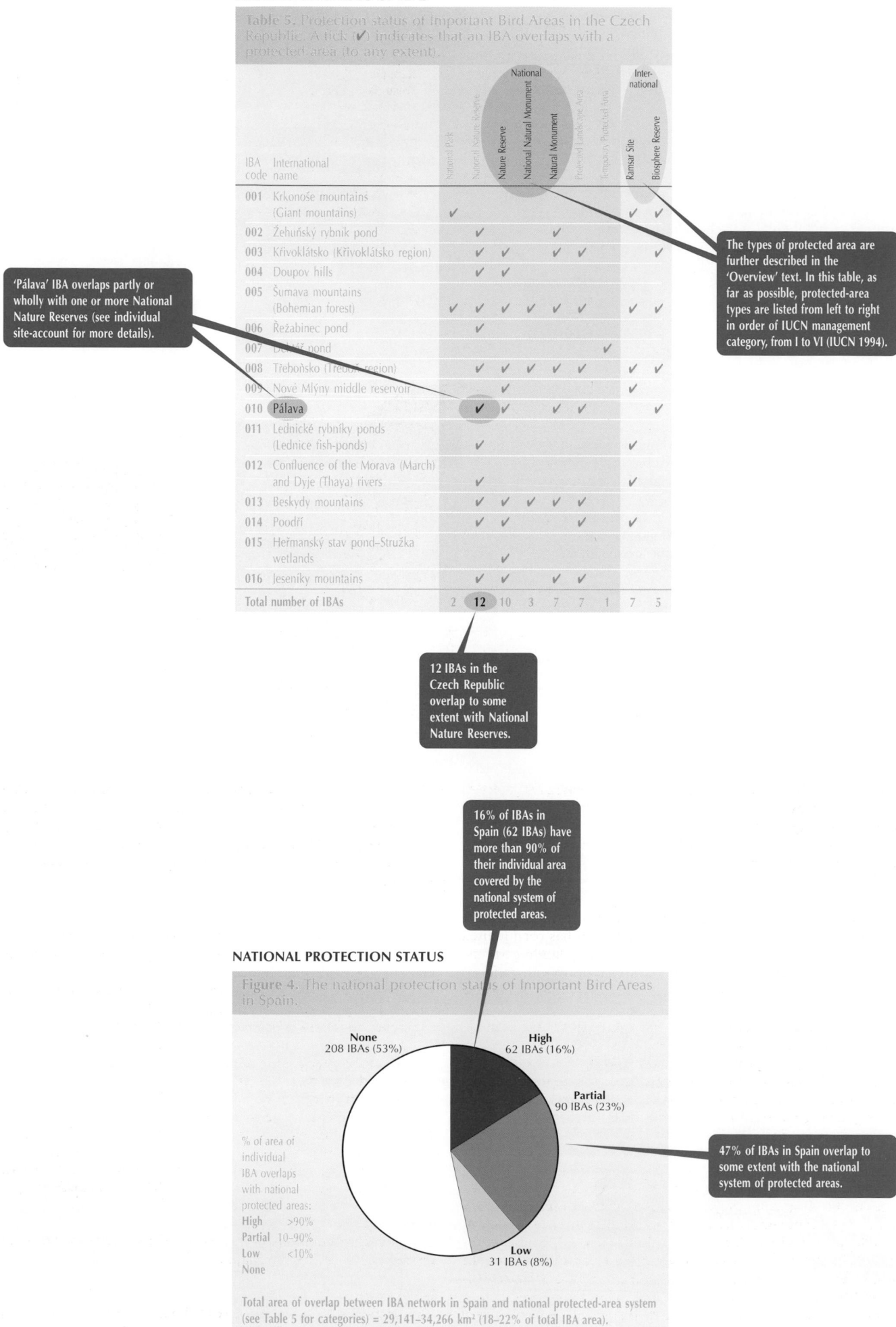

Table 5. Protection status of Important Bird Areas in the Czech Republic. A tick (✔) indicates that an IBA overlaps with a protected area (to any extent).

IBA code	International name	National Park	National Nature Reserve	Nature Reserve	National Natural Monument	Natural Monument	Protected Landscape Area	Temporary Protected Area	Ramsar Site	Biosphere Reserve
001	Krkonoše mountains (Giant mountains)	✔							✔	✔
002	Žehuňský rybník pond		✔		✔					
003	Křivoklátsko (Křivoklátsko region)		✔	✔		✔	✔			✔
004	Doupov hills		✔	✔						
005	Šumava mountains (Bohemian forest)	✔	✔	✔	✔	✔			✔	✔
006	Řežabinec pond		✔							
007	Dehtář pond							✔		
008	Třeboňsko (Třeboň region)		✔	✔	✔	✔	✔		✔	✔
009	Nové Mlýny middle reservoir		✔						✔	
010	Pálava		✔	✔		✔	✔			✔
011	Lednické rybníky ponds (Lednice fish-ponds)		✔						✔	
012	Confluence of the Morava (March) and Dyje (Thaya) rivers		✔						✔	
013	Beskydy mountains		✔	✔	✔	✔	✔			
014	Poodří		✔	✔			✔		✔	
015	Heřmanský stav pond–Stružka wetlands		✔							
016	Jeseníky mountains		✔	✔		✔	✔			
	Total number of IBAs	2	12	10	3	7	7	1	7	5

'Pálava' IBA overlaps partly or wholly with one or more National Nature Reserves (see individual site-account for more details).

The types of protected area are further described in the 'Overview' text. In this table, as far as possible, protected-area types are listed from left to right in order of IUCN management category, from I to VI (IUCN 1994).

12 IBAs in the Czech Republic overlap to some extent with National Nature Reserves.

16% of IBAs in Spain (62 IBAs) have more than 90% of their individual area covered by the national system of protected areas.

NATIONAL PROTECTION STATUS

Figure 4. The national protection status of Important Bird Areas in Spain.

None
208 IBAs (53%)

High
62 IBAs (16%)

Partial
90 IBAs (23%)

Low
31 IBAs (8%)

% of area of individual IBA overlaps with national protected areas:
High   >90%
Partial 10–90%
Low   <10%
None

47% of IBAs in Spain overlap to some extent with the national system of protected areas.

Total area of overlap between IBA network in Spain and national protected-area system (see Table 5 for categories) = 29,141–34,266 km² (18–22% of total IBA area).

INTERNATIONAL LEGISLATION AND INITIATIVES

Box 1. International legislation and initiatives that are relevant to site conservation in Greece (see Appendix 1 for a general description of these agreements).

Global
Biodiversity Convention	✔
Ramsar Convention	✔
Bonn Convention	✔
World Heritage Convention	✔
MAB Programme	✔

Pan-European
Bern Convention	✔

Regional
EC Birds Directive	✔
EC Habitats Directive	✔
Barcelona Convention	✔

✔   Convention ratified/initiative supported
(✔) Convention signed

INTERNATIONAL PROTECTION STATUS

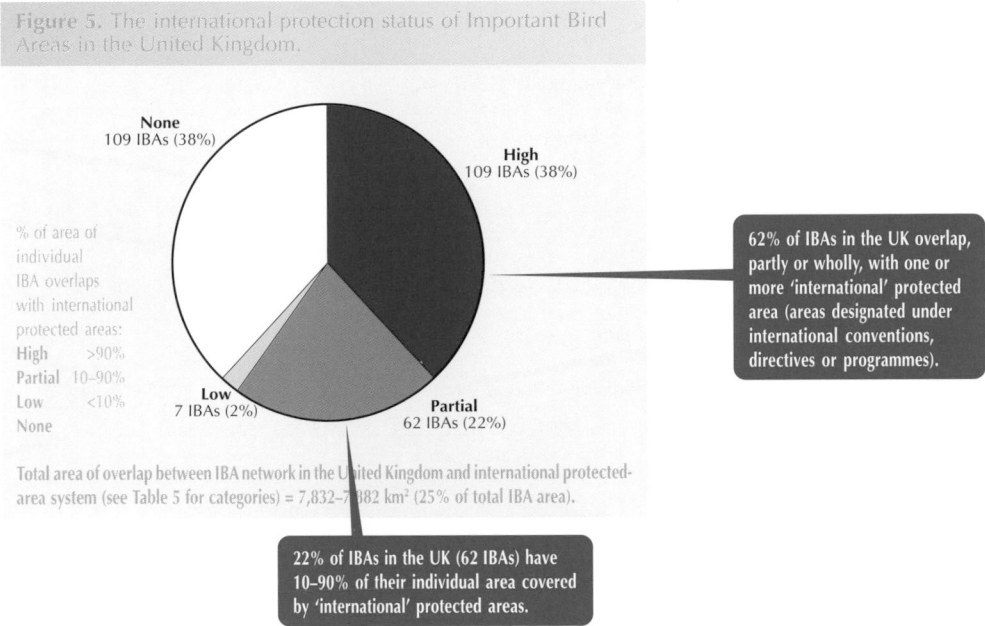

Figure 5. The international protection status of Important Bird Areas in the United Kingdom.

None
109 IBAs (38%)

High
109 IBAs (38%)

% of area of individual IBA overlaps with international protected areas:
High   >90%
Partial 10–90%
Low   <10%
None

Low
7 IBAs (2%)

Partial
62 IBAs (22%)

62% of IBAs in the UK overlap, partly or wholly, with one or more 'international' protected area (areas designated under international conventions, directives or programmes).

Total area of overlap between IBA network in the United Kingdom and international protected-area system (see Table 5 for categories) = 7,832–7,882 km² (25% of total IBA area).

22% of IBAs in the UK (62 IBAs) have 10–90% of their individual area covered by 'international' protected areas.

■ Protection status

This section analyses the extent to which IBAs are legally protected, through their overlap with areas protected by national law and by international agreements.

The overlap (or not) of each IBA with national and international protected areas is recorded in a table.

The main protected-area types in the country are described, together with their legal status, type of management and the authority responsible for implementing protection. In many countries, this list of national designation-types has been limited to those of truly national standing with legally binding status. Therefore most sub-national, local or non-statutory categories of protected area have not been discussed, analysed or otherwise covered, in these countries.

The extent of overlap between individual IBAs and national protected areas is summarized in a pie chart, and the total area of IBAs under national protection is stated. It is possible that the total areas of IBAs under protection is underestimated due to incomplete data on area of overlap between protected areas and IBAs.

Regarding international protection, the main international legislation and initiatives relevant to site-based biodiversity conservation in the country are described.

A box summarizes all of the international legislation and initiatives that can give international recognition or protection to sites in the given country, and indicates whether the country has ratified or signed such conventions or takes part in such initiatives.

The extent of overlap between individual IBAs and internationally designated areas is summarized in a pie chart, and the total area of IBAs under international protection is stated. It is possible that the total area of IBAs under protection is underestimated due to incomplete data on area of overlap between protected areas and IBAs.

■ Conservation

This section summarizes key research, monitoring, site-conservation or site-management initiatives that affect IBAs in the country, drawing together any national trends or conservation issues (e.g. the coverage of IBAs by management plans), as well as any relevant information that is otherwise oft-repeated in the individual site-accounts.

■ Analytical methods

This section provides important information on the preparation of the national inventory and the methodology followed in collecting and analysing the data. It includes information on:

● bird counts, especially the conventions used in counting or estimating numbers of birds at sites at different seasons, and the conventions used in presenting such information, as well as the units used;

● important species in the country that are not adequately covered by the IBA network, either because of their dispersed nature or because of inadequacies in data or observer coverage;

● dates and main sources of the information on IBAs;

● any difficulties encountered in obtaining or categorizing data or in assigning criteria, and how these problems were addressed, as well as any standards or conventions that were followed (if different from, or expanding on, the IBA project guidelines).

■ Glossary

This gives explanations of technical or non-standard terms or abbreviations used in the chapter.

■ Acknowledgements

This section acknowledges all contributors to the IBA review in the country, including financial contributors if appropriate.

■ SITE ACCOUNTS

EXAMPLE SITE ACCOUNT

Primary administrative region(s) in which IBA is located.

Internationally recognized site name.

Central coordinates of the IBA (latitude/ longitude; Greenwich).

Criteria under which the site qualifies as an IBA (see the previous chapter for definitions).

Altitudinal range of IBA, in metres above/below sea level (a minus sign indicates that the site is below sea level).

IBA code: number which identifies this site in this publication.

Danube plain

A1, A4i, B1i, B2   **022**

Admin region Bács-Kiskun, Pest
Coordinates 46°49′N 19°15′E
Altitude 93–103 m **Area** 82,000 ha

Thumbnail map showing location of the IBA.

Habitats are defined in Appendix 3; percentages refer to proportion of IBA area that is covered by primary level habitats. Lack of a percentage indicates either (a) lack of relevant knowledge, or (b) cover is less than 5%.

Land-uses are defined in Appendix 3; percentages refer to proportion of IBA area that is utilized. Lack of a percentage indicates either (a) lack of relevant knowledge, or (b) cover is less than 5%.

■ Site description

A flood-plain lying between natural levees and overlain by loess soils, situated adjacent to the River Danube and main Duna-völgyi canal, between Kiskunlacháza and Szakmár. Human activities include cattle- and sheep-grazing, arable farming, angling and hunting. This area includes two sites that were treated as separate IBAs in the previous international IBA inventory (Grimmett and Jones 1989): 'Kiskunsági szikes-tavak' (former site HU021) and 'Harta-Akasztói puszta' (former site HU042).

Area of the IBA in hectares (100 ha = 1 km²)

40% of the area of the IBA comprises steppe/dry calcareous grassland habitat.

90% of the area of the IBA is affected by agricultural activities.

Habitats Grassland (40%; steppe/dry calcareous grassland), Wetland (5%; standing brackish and salt water; water-fringe vegetation), Artificial landscape (55%; highly improved reseeded grassland; arable land)

Land-use Agriculture (90%), Nature conservation/research (60%), Tourism/recreation (5%), Water management (5%)

Year of population estimate. In cases where the population estimate is derived from a multi-year series, the year given here is the last in the series, and a footnote may give more details of the period covered, if this aspect has not been dealt with already in the 'Analytical methods' section of the national overview.

Minimum and maximum population estimate (see 'Analytical methods' section of national overview for more details on conventions followed).

Season in which species meets criterion/criteria:
• R Breeding resident
• B Breeding visitor
• W Winter visitor
• P Passage visitor
• N Non-breeding visitor
• U Status uncertain.

■ Birds

Species	Season	Year	Pop min	Pop max	Acc	Criteria
[1] *Ardea purpurea* Purple Heron	P	1996	50	50	C	B2
[2] *Anser albifrons* White-fronted Goose	P	1996	2,000	15,000	A	B1i
[2] *Anser anser* Greylag Goose	P	1996	200	5,000	A	A4i, B1i
[1] *Anas acuta* Pintail	P	1996	260	260	A	B1i
[1] *Falco vespertinus* Red-footed Falcon	B	1996	85	85	B	B2
Otis tarda Great Bustard	R	1996	100	290	A	A1, B2
[1] *Limosa limosa* Black-tailed Godwit	B	1996	50	60	B	B2
[3] *Limosa limosa* Black-tailed Godwit	P	1996	150	8,000	A	A4i, B1i
[3] *Numenius arquata* Curlew	B	1996	Common		—	A4i, B1i
[1] *Chlidonias hybridus* Whiskered Tern	B	1996	—	175	A	B2
[1] *Chlidonias niger* Black Tern	B	1996	40	40	B	B2

1. 1992–1996.
2. 1986–1996.
3. Large decrease 1986–1996.

Quality of population data (see 'Data collection' chapter for more details):
• A Reliable
• B Incomplete
• C Poor
• — Unknown

Breeding population data (season code 'R' or 'B') are given in pairs unless stated otherwise in a footnote or in the 'Analytical methods' section of the national overview.

If population figures are unavailable, a qualitative assessment of abundance may be given (see 'Data collection' chapter for further explanation).

Species are listed in taxonomic order. Taxonomy and nomenclature follow *The Birds of the Western Palearctic* (Cramp et al. 1977–1994).

An important area for lowland farmland birds and waterbirds. Species of global conservation concern that do not meet IBA criteria: *Phalacrocorax pygmeus* and *Branta ruficollis* (both on passage), *Aythya nyroca* (6 breeding pairs), and *Haliaeetus albicilla* (2 breeding pairs and 4 wintering birds).

Overlap between IBA and protected area(s), measured as a percentage of the IBA's area, is 'Partial' at the national level and 'Partial' at the international level:
• High   >90% overlap
• Partial 10%–90% overlap
• Low   <10% overlap
• None No overlap

■ Protection status

National Partial **International** Partial
21,200 ha of IBA covered by National Park (Kiskunsági, 53,429 ha). 3,903 ha of IBA covered by Ramsar Site (Kiskunság, 3,903 ha). The IBA also overlaps with the Kiskunság Biosphere Reserve (22,095 ha).

Area of protected area (in hectares; 100 ha = 1 km²).

Official name of protected area.

Area of IBA in hectares (100 ha = 1 km²) that overlaps with protected area. If the entire IBA is covered by the protected area this figure will equal the area of the IBA given in the header.

■ Conservation issues

Threats Abandonment/reduction of land management (A), Agricultural intensification/ expansion (B), Disturbance to birds (C), Drainage (B), Natural events (B), Recreation/tourism (C)

Type of protected area (further described in national overview).

The main threats are changes in habitat composition and quality caused both by the abandonment of grazing and by drought. A *Perdix perdix* recovery project has begun in Apajpuszta, and the National Park Authority is working to increase the breeding success of *Otis tarda*. MME/BirdLife Hungary provides artificial nesting-sites, and a management plan exists for the area. Wildfowl shooting is banned, and the enlargement of the National Park is in process.

Importance score: Calculation of the score is explained in Appendix 3. Lack of a score implies that impact is unknown, and does not imply minimal impact.
• A High impact
• B Medium impact
• C Low impact
• U Unknown impact

Threats are defined in Appendix 3.

■ Header

Each site account has a boxed header which gives key information about the site, including international site name, site code, administrative region(s), central coordinates, altitudinal range, surface area, a thumb-nail map showing the location of the site within the country, and a list of the criteria under which the site qualifies as an IBA.

■ Site description

This section includes a short general description of the site covering relevant information on location and topographical features.

The section includes a table listing the habitats and land-uses at the site, and the percentage cover of each where this is known. Two levels of habitat are listed, e.g. 'Forest/woodland' at the primary level, and 'broadleaved deciduous forest', or 'native coniferous forest' at the secondary level. The percentage cover is given for the primary habitats only. Primary habitats which cover less than 5% of the IBA are usually not listed. If habitat-types are rare or otherwise difficult to classify, they may be listed at the primary level only.

■ Birds

A table presents data on all species meeting IBA criteria at the site. Much more information on these species, and on species not meeting IBA criteria at each site, is contained within the IBA database but, because of space constraints, it has not been possible to publish these extra data.

The table may be supported by additional text summarizing the overall reasons for the site being important, and including non-specific data, for example listing total counts for a group of species such as waterbirds or migrating raptors. If the relevant criteria have been met, reference is also made to the site's occurrence within a biome or an Endemic Bird Area. All species of global conservation concern that occur at the site but which do not meet IBA criteria (sometimes due to lack of data rather than due to insufficient numbers) are also mentioned in the text. Additionally, for some countries, all species that are listed in Annex I of the EC Birds Directive and that breed at the site have also been listed in the text. For some countries, species present at the site in nationally important numbers (e.g. with at least 1% of the national population occurring) are also listed, especially if this factor is relevant to the national application of the EC Birds Directive.

■ Protection status

This section indicates the national and international protection status (High, Partial, Low, None) of the site. This has been calculated as follows:

High   More than 90% of the area of an individual IBA overlaps with national/international protected area(s)

Partial 10–90% of the area of an individual IBA overlaps with national/international protected area(s)

Low   Less than 10% of the area of an individual IBA overlaps with national/international protected area(s)

None No overlap with national/international protected area(s)

This provides an indication of the coverage of each IBA by protected areas (in this publication, 'protected area' usually refers only to statutory areas, with official recognition of their purpose) and is summarized from the more detailed information on the degree of overlap between each individual protected area and the IBA. Where details of overlap are unknown, the 'Partial' category has usually been assigned as a default since it presents the broadest range of overlap. Where this applies, it has been explained in the country overview. It is important to note that the terms 'High', 'Partial' or 'Low' protection do not refer to the strictness of protection prescribed by law, only to the spatial extent of protection, nor do they refer to the success or otherwise of management authorities in implementing protection.

This is followed by details of the protected areas and the extent of their overlap with the IBA. The 'Protection status' portion of the national overview gives more details on each protected-area type, its status in national law, management regime, etc.

■ Conservation issues

This section includes a table summarizing the main threats (actual and potential) impacting on the site and a score of the importance of each (as explained in Appendix 3). Additional text concerning these threats may be given, as may further detail on protection status, including any proposed designations. Key research/monitoring activities and conservation issues may be mentioned, as well as the existence or otherwise of any management plan(s) for the IBA or associated protected areas. This section should be read in conjunction with the 'Conservation' section of the national overview, at the start of the chapter, which summarizes any common conservation issues that would otherwise be repeated across several or many IBAs.

REFERENCES

CRAMP, S. *ET AL.* (1977–1994) *The birds of the western Palearctic*. Vols 1–9. Oxford, UK: Oxford University Press.

GRIMMETT, R. F. A. AND JONES, T. A. (1989) *Important Bird Areas in Europe.* Cambridge, UK: International Council for Bird Preservation (ICBP Techn. Publ. 9).

IUCN (1994) *Guidelines for protected area management categories.* Gland, Switzerland: IUCN—The World Conservation Union.

TUCKER, G. M. AND HEATH, M. F. (1994) *Birds in Europe: their conservation status.* Cambridge, UK: BirdLife International (BirdLife Conservation Series no. 3).

This chapter presents a pan-European analysis of the data given in this publication and details some of the key findings of this first review of Important Bird Areas (IBAs) in Europe.

WHY ARE IBAs IMPORTANT AND HAS A COMPLETE SET OF SITES BEEN FOUND?

■ IBA coverage by country

A comprehensive network of internationally important sites for birds has been identified across Europe. A total of 3,619 Important Bird Areas are distributed among 51 countries or autonomous regions in the continent, covering 931,700 km², which equates to 7% of the continental land area (Figure 1). There has been a tremendous amount of new data gathered as part of this inventory, resulting in improved coverage across the region compared to the previous IBA inventory, 10 years ago (Grimmett and Jones 1989).

The number of IBAs identified in each country depends on many different factors, such as the size of the country, its importance for different species, the extent of particular habitats remaining in the country, the national capacity to gather data and, importantly, the types of criteria applied to identify IBAs. An additional category of criteria ('C' criteria) was applied within the European Union (EU), with lower numeric thresholds, which resulted in a greater number of sites being identified in these countries. Indeed,

2,342 IBAs (65% of the European total) fall within the 15 member states of the EU. A full list of the number and area of IBAs within each country is given in Appendix 6.

The countries with more than 90 IBAs and the countries with over 20,000 km² in IBAs are listed in Figures 2 and 3; it should be noted that the two sets of countries are not the same. Spain has the highest number of IBAs (Figure 2), with 391 in total, covering 160,000 km² or 31% of the land area of the country (Figure 3). Russia has 218 IBAs but these tend to be larger sites (average area 800 km²), including many large protected areas, with the total IBA area being 174,500 km², higher than Spain but equal to just 4% of the land area of European Russia. Overall, the size of IBAs in Europe varies greatly, ranging from 1 hectare to 19,000 km², with a mean area of 259 km².

The percentage of the area of each country covered by IBAs is shown in Figure 4. In the majority of countries, IBAs cover between 5% and 15% of the national land area. The adequate protection and management of the 3,619 IBAs in Europe, equivalent to a relatively low percentage of each country's surface area, is therefore a realistic goal that would make a very significant contribution to conserving those bird species in Europe for which a site-protection approach is appropriate. In several countries, particularly in the east of Europe, in parts of Scandinavia and the Balkans, IBAs cover less than 5% of the national area and it is probable that more sites will be identified in the future to complete the network of IBAs.

Figure 1. The location and criteria category of Important Bird Areas in Europe. There are 3,619 IBAs in Europe, covering 931,700 km², equivalent to 7% of the land area of Europe.

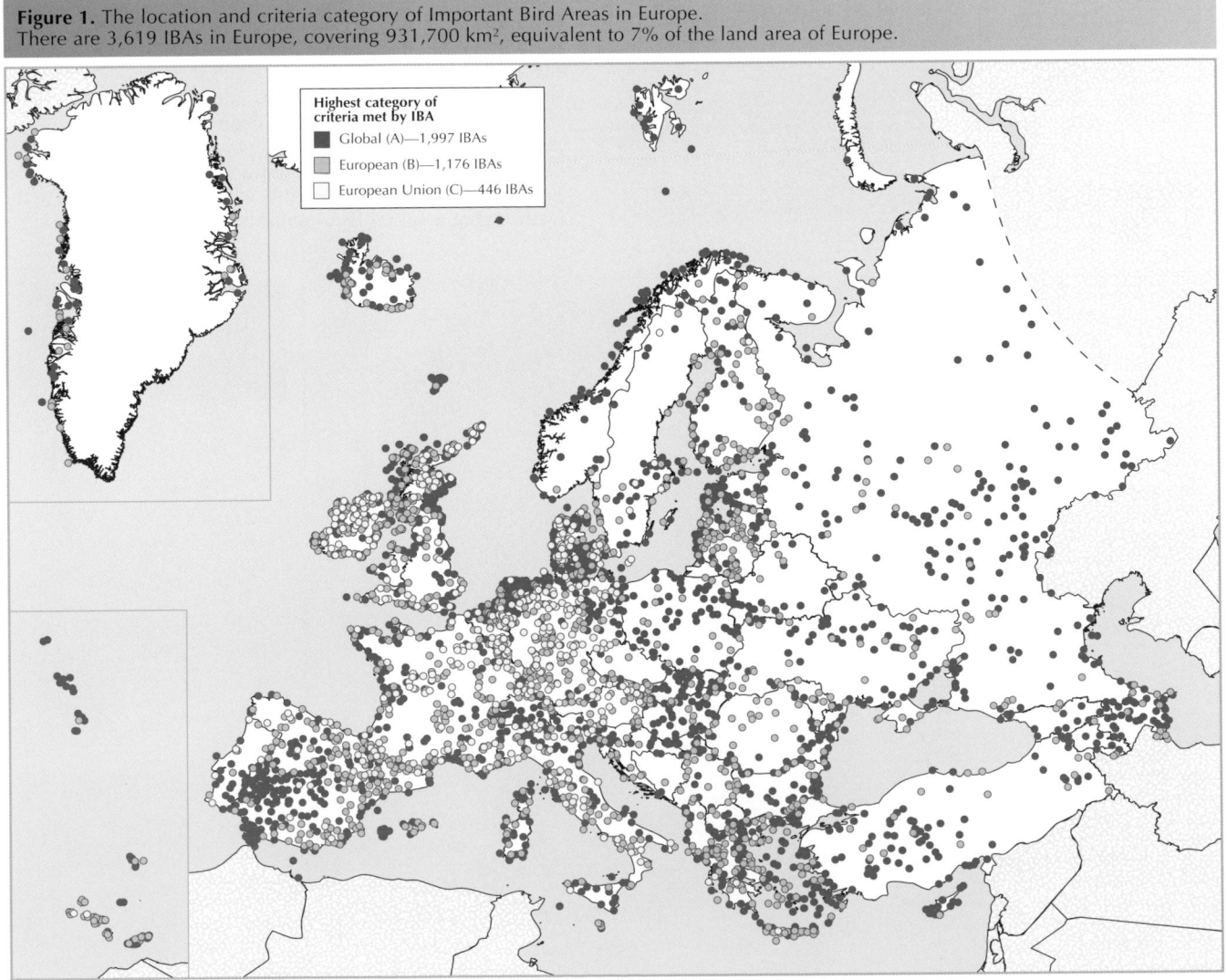

Highest category of criteria met by IBA
- Global (A)—1,997 IBAs
- European (B)—1,176 IBAs
- European Union (C)—446 IBAs

Figure 2. The countries in Europe with more than 90 Important Bird Areas.

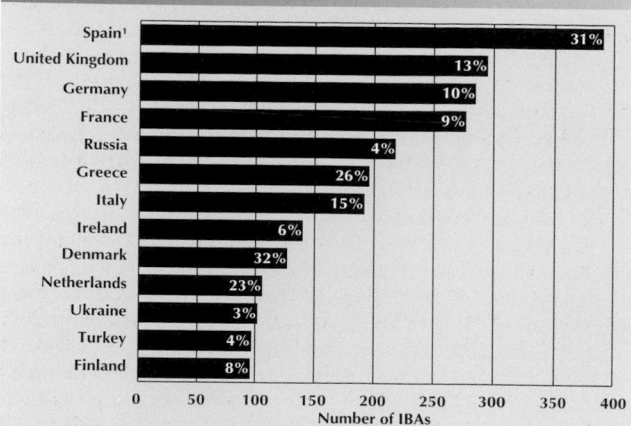

1. Includes data for Canary Islands.

The percentage at the end of each bar indicates the proportion of the country's land area that is equivalent to the total IBA area (for those countries with extensive marine IBAs, e.g. Denmark, this figure exaggerates the actual extent of land covered).

Figure 3. The countries in Europe where the total area of Important Bird Areas exceeds 20,000 km².

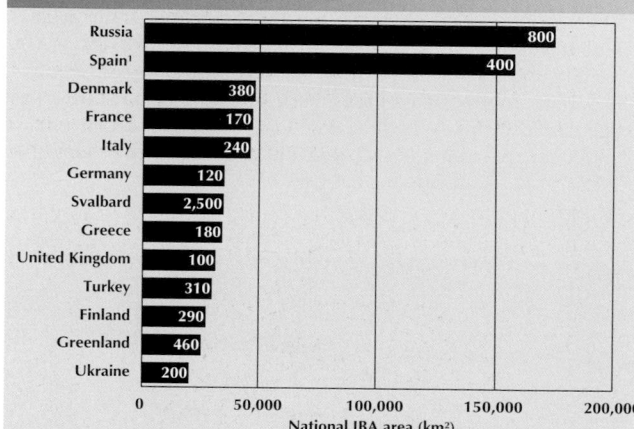

1. Includes data for Canary Islands.

The figure at the end of each bar indicates the mean size (in km²) of IBAs in that country. Across all countries, IBAs range in size from 1 ha to 19,000 km², and their mean size is 259 km².

A total of 1,175 new IBAs have been identified since the previous pan-European IBA inventory was published 10 years ago (Grimmett and Jones 1989), representing a 48% increase in the number of sites, and a 130% increase in the total surface area covered, from 404,600 km² to 931,700 km². Those countries with the greatest change in number of IBAs and area covered since 1989 are shown in Figures 5 and 6. In many countries all over Europe, but particularly in the east, both the number of IBAs and the total area of IBAs have substantially increased. This is particularly evident in Russia where 141 new IBAs have been identified, adding a further 105,000 km² to the total area covered by IBAs. In several smaller countries such as Azerbaijan, Estonia, Georgia, Hungary, Latvia and Ukraine, increases in terms of total number or area of IBAs are also particularly significant. Additionally, many of the original (1989) IBAs have been subdivided into two or more sites, and many others have been amalgamated to form larger ones. With more in-depth knowledge of IBAs, the boundaries of many sites have been refined as well, changing the sites' area.

Overall, 240 sites that were included in the previous (1989) inventory have been excluded from this book. The three main reasons for exclusion were: (1) the availability of improved data on the site showing that it was no longer considered of international importance, although most such sites remain important at the national level; (2) the application of higher population thresholds for some species-based criteria, based on improved knowledge of European population sizes; and (3) the deterioration of the quality of the site, resulting in declines in numbers of birds (however, sites were retained as IBAs if it was considered that the value of the site for birds could be restored).

There are still some countries in Europe where not all IBAs have been identified, and ongoing field and literature studies will identify further sites in the future. Countries where a larger network of IBAs will be identified in the future, either in terms of area and/or number, include:

- Belarus—currently 21 IBAs cover 3% of the country;
- Russia—work is ongoing to identify further IBAs (some regions still have no IBAs whatsoever), e.g. 151 proposed sites were surveyed during 1998–1999 (listed in the national overview of the Russian chapter) and will be described in the forthcoming national inventory for Russia;
- Ukraine—102 IBAs cover 3% of the country; fieldwork during 1998–1999 identified further IBAs which will be included in the forthcoming national IBA publication;

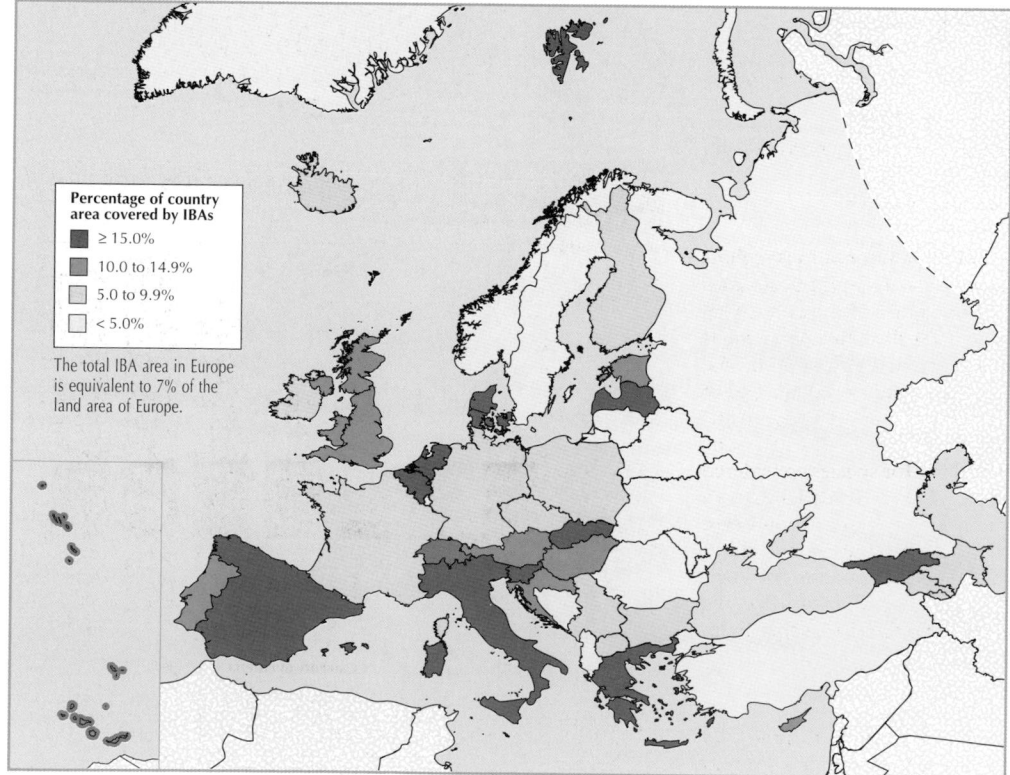

Figure 4. The proportion of the national land area covered by Important Bird Areas in each country in Europe.

Percentage of country area covered by IBAs
- ≥ 15.0%
- 10.0 to 14.9%
- 5.0 to 9.9%
- < 5.0%

The total IBA area in Europe is equivalent to 7% of the land area of Europe.

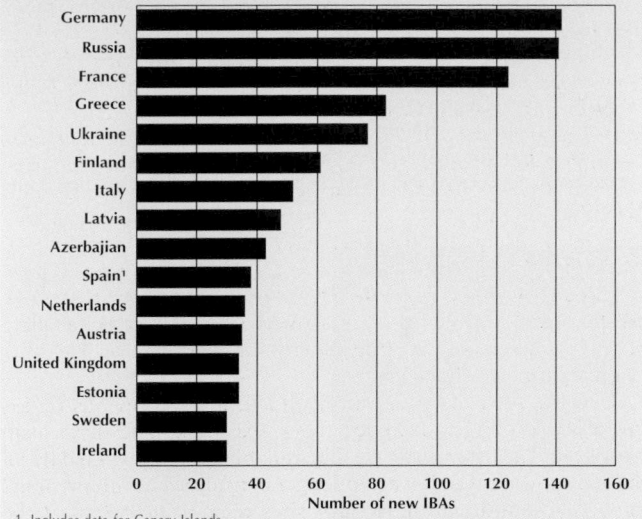

Figure 5. The countries in Europe where the total number of new Important Bird Areas, identified since the previous pan-European IBA inventory (Grimmett and Jones 1989), exceeds 30.

1. Includes data for Canary Islands.

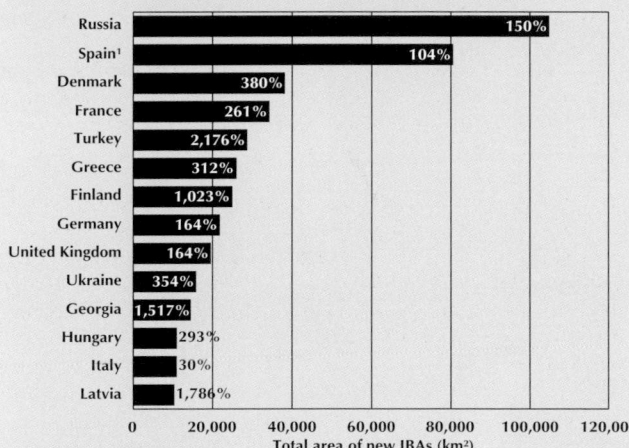

Figure 6. The countries in Europe where the total area of new Important Bird Areas exceeds 10,000 km².

1. Includes data for Canary Islands.

The percentage at the end of each bar indicates the percentage change in the national total IBA area since the previous pan-European IBA inventory (Grimmett and Jones 1989). Such change is mainly attributable to the addition of new IBAs but also involves, in most countries, the enlargement or reduction in size of many original (1989) IBAs as well as the deletion from the current IBA inventory of a small minority of the original sites (rejected as IBAs for various reasons).

- Turkey—97 IBAs cover 4% of the country; many non-wetland IBAs have yet to be identified;
- Sweden—63 IBAs cover 3% of the country.

In addition, for a small number of countries or autonomous regions (Croatia, Macedonia, Faroe Islands, and Bosnia and Herzegovena) fully updated information was not obtained for this publication, thus future revisions will almost certainly result in further changes to the number and area of sites in these countries. With the anticipated accession of several countries to the European Union during the coming decade, the EU-specific criteria for IBAs (category 'C') will be applied, which is likely to result in the identification of additional sites, particularly for species considered threatened in the EU (listed in Annex I of the EC Birds Directive).

A number of IBAs span the borders of two or more countries, often wetlands in river valleys or tracts of forest and alpine habitat in mountainous areas. Details of the these transboundary sites are summarized in Appendix 7. International collaboration for the protection and management of these sites, and the species they hold, is essential.

■ IBA coverage by species and criteria

Through the rigorous application of quantitative ornithological criteria, it is assured that the network of 3,619 identified sites is of international importance. The criteria permit one to distinguish

the importance of sites at three geographical levels: global, European and European Union. Such distinctions are particularly significant when comparing IBAs across regions of the world where, to date, effort has been prioritized on identifying sites of global importance only. A high proportion of Europe's IBAs (55%, 1,997 IBAs) are of global significance (meeting 'A' criteria). A further 1,176 IBAs are important at the European level (and not global) and the remaining 446 IBAs qualify as important at the EU level only (Figure 7). Sites of global importance are distributed across all European countries (Figure 1, Appendix 6).

The reasons for the importance of IBAs, indicated by the criteria that each site fulfils, are shown in Figure 8. A site may be important for many different species and thus may qualify under more than one type of criterion. In general terms, a high percentage of IBAs are important for congregatory species (51% of all IBAs in Europe), species of European conservation concern (66%) and species listed in Annex I of the EC Birds Directive (63%). A lower proportion (27%), though very significant given the small number of species involved, are important for one or more of the 35 species of global conservation concern in Europe. IBAs identified for assemblages of species with small global ranges (A2 criterion), or species restricted to a biome in Europe (A3 criterion), are relatively few but still individually significant at the global level.

Sites are often important for several species, each of which fulfils the same type of criterion, for example, several species of waterbird may congregate at a site in a given season, each in significant numbers that meet the B1i criterion. Overall, over 30,000 applications of criteria have been made to species at the 3,619 IBAs. This is an indication of the strength and substance of the scientific evidence that supports the treatment of each site as worthy of international recognition.

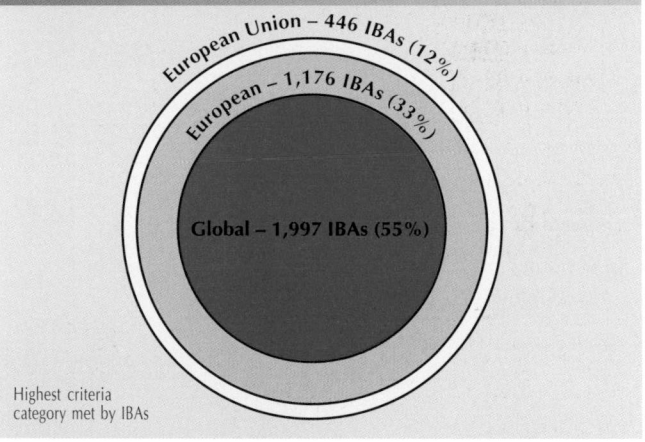

Figure 7. The proportion of Important Bird Areas in Europe that are important at the global, European and EU levels.

Highest criteria category met by IBAs

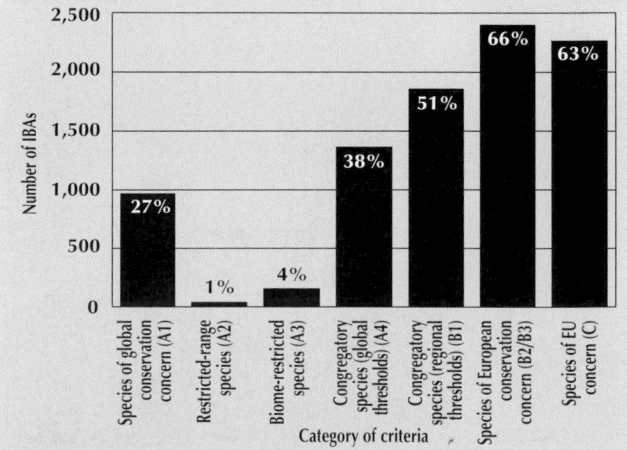

Figure 8. The number of sites meeting different Important Bird Area criteria in Europe.

N.B. A site may be important for more than one bird species (or in more than one way for a particular species) and may thus qualify under more than one criterion. In addition, criteria are nested such that, if higher thresholds are met, criteria are also assigned at lower levels. For example, if a site in the European Union is important because it holds more than 1% of the biogeographic population of a migratory waterbird, then not only is criterion A4i applied, but also B4i and C2/C3.

31

Species of global conservation concern

A network of 938 IBAs (27% of IBAs in Europe) support significant numbers of one or more species of global conservation concern, thus meeting the A1 criterion. Sites have been identified in 41 countries or autonomous regions for these species, and those countries with the highest number of sites identified include Russia (152 sites), Spain (121), Greece (73), Turkey (56) and Italy (51).

The number of sites identified for each species of global conservation concern (under the A1 criterion), and the proportion of the European breeding population within IBAs, are shown in Table 1. (A further 111 IBAs in Europe meet criteria other than A1 (B2, C1, C2, C6) for these species.) Species for which very few sites have been identified include *Pterodroma feae*, *Pterodroma madeira*, *Polysticta stelleri*, *Columba trocaz*, *Saxicola dacotiae*, *Sitta whiteheadi*, *Fringilla teydea* and *Emberiza cineracea*. However, the IBAs for several of these species hold nearly the entire world population of the species concerned. For other species with larger European ranges, more sites have been identified, e.g. *Phalacrocorax pygmeus*, *Haliaeetus albicilla*, *Falco naumanni*, *Crex crex* and *Otis tarda*. For all species, the conservation of IBAs makes a significant contribution to their survival (Table 1) but for those species with highly dispersed distributions, such as *Crex crex*, it is particularly important that conservation of sites is accompanied by conservation of the wider environment (Tucker and Evans 1997).

Dalmatian Pelican *Pelecanus crispus* at Gediz Delta, Turkey (IBA 016). A globally threatened species classified as Vulnerable (Collar *et al.* 1994), its global decline is due to disturbance and degradation of wetlands, hunting and colony destruction by fishermen.
(PHOTO: CÜNEYT OGUZTÜZÜN)

Recent surveys in Belarus and Ukraine have discovered new IBAs for the globally threatened Aquatic Warbler *Acrocephalus paludicola*.
(PHOTO: ALEXANDER KOZULIN)

Lesser Kestrel *Falco naumanni* is a globally threatened species, classified as Vulnerable (Collar *et al.* 1994). It has shown major population declines in large parts of its western Palearctic breeding range.
(PHOTO: CÜNEYT OGUZTÜZÜN)

Table 1. Internationally important sites for species of global conservation concern in Europe (meeting the A1 criterion).

	Number of IBAs qualifying for species				Percentage of the minimum European breeding population occurring at IBAs [2,3]
	Season				
	Breeding	Non-breeding	Status unknown	Total[1]	
Pterodroma feae Fea's Petrel	1	—	—	1	68
Pterodroma madeira Zino's Petrel	1	—	—	1	71
Phalacrocorax pygmeus Pygmy Cormorant	34	90	1	115	100[4]
Pelecanus crispus Dalmatian Pelican	22	50	1	69	100[4]
Anser erythropus Lesser White-fronted Goose	2	33	1	36	2
Branta ruficollis Red-breasted Goose	—	33	—	33	—
Marmaronetta angustirostris Marbled Duck	19	9	1	19	96
Aythya nyroca Ferruginous Duck	62	37	1	92	25
Polysticta stelleri Steller's Eider	—	9	—	9	—
Oxyura leucocephala White-headed Duck	21	41	1	52	100[4]
Haliaeetus albicilla White-tailed Eagle	56	46	1	96	25
Aegypius monachus Cinereous Vulture	30	9	1	40	94
Circus macrourus Pallid Harrier	7	3	—	10	13
Aquila clanga Greater Spotted Eagle	33	17	—	50	13
Aquila heliaca Imperial Eagle	62	8	1	71	48
Aquila adalberti Spanish Imperial Eagle	19	6	—	24	88
Falco naumanni Lesser Kestrel	76	18	2	94	73
Tetrao mlokosiewiczi Caucasian Black Grouse	13	—	—	13	100[4]
Crex crex Corncrake	263	1	—	264	20
Tetrax tetrax Little Bustard	61	17	—	75	15
Otis tarda Great Bustard	74	8	—	78	70
Glareola nordmanni Black-winged Pratincole	10	4	1	15	5
Chettusia gregaria Sociable Plover	—	—	—	—	<1
Gallinago media Great Snipe	45	5	—	50	1
Numenius tenuirostris Slender-billed Curlew	—	31	—	31	—
Larus audouinii Audouin's Gull	43	16	—	58	100[4]
Columba trocaz Long-toed Pigeon	5	—	—	5	41
Columba bollii Dark-tailed Laurel Pigeon	11	—	—	11	38
Columba junoniae White-tailed Laurel Pigeon	11	—	—	11	41
Saxicola dacotiae Fuerteventura Chat	9	—	—	9	8
Acrocephalus paludicola Aquatic Warbler	31	5	—	36	100[4]
Sitta whiteheadi Corsican Nuthatch	4	—	—	4	67
Fringilla teydea Blue Chaffinch	4	—	—	4	9
Loxia scotica Scottish Crossbill	12	3	—	14	2
Emberiza cineracea Cinereous Bunting	4	—	—	4	11

1. The total number of sites identified for a species of global conservation concern does not necessarily equal the sum of breeding, non-breeding and unknown-seasonal-status sites, since a species may meet criteria at an IBA in more than one season.
2. Percentage calculated using the geometric mean of the minimum and maximum population size in IBAs and the geometric mean of the European breeding population.
3. All IBAs where the species breeds (regardless of whether the IBA criteria are met for this species) are included in the total population breeding in IBAs.
4. The percentage of the national population exceeds 100%. Usually this is because the national population estimate has not been updated recently whilst the IBA population estimate has been recently updated with new data as a result of comprehensive surveys of IBAs themselves. Also, the individual site count for a species may be the maximum or average over recent years, and summing these may record more birds than are present nationally in any single year.

Species with restricted global ranges

A total of 47 IBAs in Europe meet the A2 criterion for restricted-range species, i.e. those species with global ranges of less than 50,000 km² (Table 2). Since the entire world ranges of most of these species are confined to 'Endemic Bird Areas' (Stattersfield *et al.* 1998), it is particularly important to conserve the network of IBAs which have been identified for these species. Their restriction to such a small area and number of sites makes them particularly vulnerable to habitat change and other threats. IBAs identified for restricted-range species in Europe are situated within three Endemic Bird Areas (Madeira and the Canary Islands; Cyprus; Caucasus) and three 'Secondary Areas' (Azores; Corsican mountains; Caledonian pine forest) (see 'Identifying IBAs' chapter for definition of Secondary Area). Overall, the network of IBAs for these species is thought to be complete.

The globally threatened Dark-tailed Laurel Pigeon *Columba bollii* is confined to the Canary Islands (La Palma, La Gomera, Tenerife and El Hierro) where its principal habitat is closed-canopy laurel forest. (PHOTO: N. MARTIN)

Table 2. Internationally important sites for restricted-range bird species in Europe (meeting the A2 criterion).

Restricted-range species	Endemic Bird Area	Range states in Europe	Number	IBA codes
Tetrao mlokosiewiczi Caucasian Black Grouse	Caucasus	Armenia, Azerbaijan, Georgia, Russia, Turkey	9	GE001–GE003, GE005–GE008, RU163, RU167
Tetraogallus caucasicus Caucasian Snowcock	Caucasus	Azerbaijan, Georgia, Russia	7	GE001–GE003, GE006, GE007, RU163, RU167
Columba trocaz Long-toed Pigeon	Madeira and the Canary Islands	Madeira	5	ZZ001–ZZ005
Columba bollii Dark-tailed Laurel Pigeon	Madeira and the Canary Islands	Spain (Canary Islands)	4	ES366, ES376, ES379, ES380
Columba junoniae White-tailed Laurel Pigeon	Madeira and the Canary Islands	Spain (Canary Islands)	4	ES366, ES376, ES379, ES380
Apus unicolor Plain Swift	Madeira and the Canary Islands	Madeira, Spain (Canary Islands)	7	ZZ005, ES340, ES346, ES355, ES366, ES376, ES379
Anthus berthelotii Berthelot's Pipit	Madeira and the Canary Islands	Madeira, Spain (Canary Islands)	13	ZZ005, ZZ008, ZZ009, ZZ010, ES338, ES340, ES346, ES354, ES355, ES366, ES370, ES376, ES379
Saxicola dacotiae Fuerteventura Chat	Madeira and the Canary Islands	Spain (Canary Islands)	3	ES338, ES340, ES346
Oenanthe cypriaca Cyprus Pied Wheatear	Cyprus	Cyprus	13	CY002, CY003, CY004, CY005, CY006, CY007, CY008, CY010, CY012, CY013, CY014, CY015, CY016
Sylvia melanothorax Cyprus Warbler	Cyprus	Cyprus	13	CY002, CY003, CY004, CY005, CY006, CY007, CY008, CY010, CY012, CY013, CY014, CY015, CY016
Phylloscopus lorenzii Caucasian Chiffchaff	Caucasus	Armenia, Azerbaijan, Georgia, Russia, Turkey	2	GE007, GE008
Regulus teneriffae Tenerife Goldcrest	Madeira and the Canary Islands	Spain (Canary Islands)	6	ES366, ES369, ES370, ES376, ES379, ES380
Sitta whiteheadi Corsican Nuthatch	Corsican mountains*	France	2	FR269, FR270
Fringilla teydea Blue Chaffinch	Madeira and the Canary Islands	Spain (Canary Islands)	4	ES354, ES355, ES369, ES370
Serinus canaria Canary	Madeira and the Canary Islands; Azores*	Madeira, Spain (Canary Islands); Azores	14	ZZ008, ZZ009, ES354, ES355, ES366, ES369, ES370, ES376, ES379, ES380, QQ001, QQ003, QQ004, QQ013
Pyrrhula murina Azores Bullfinch	Azores*	Azores	1	QQ013

* Secondary Area. It was considered inappropriate to identify IBAs for Scottish Crossbill *Loxia scotica* (Secondary Area: Caledonian pine forest) on the basis of its restricted range. However, several IBAs have been identified for the taxon under other criteria, as it is also a species of European conservation concern and is listed in Annex I of the EC Birds Directive (see UK chapter).

Box 1. Internationally important sites for assemblages of biome-restricted bird species in Europe (meeting the A3 criterion).

A total of 155 Important Bird Areas have been identified on the basis that they support important assemblages of species that are restricted (when breeding in Europe) to a particular biome (thus meeting the A3 criterion). In applying this criterion in Europe, five biomes have been considered:

- Arctic/tundra biome
- Boreal biome
- Mediterranean biome
- Eurasian high-montane (alpine) biome
- Eurasian steppe biome.

Biomes are the world's major (terrestrial) ecological communities, characterized by the occurrence together of similar vegetation, animals and climate. A 'biome' encompasses all flora, fauna, and soils within the geographical region concerned. Biomes are classified by climax vegetation type (e.g. forests, grasslands) and are characterized by the adaptations of their organisms to the particular conditions in which they occur, for example high temperatures, low rainfall, poor soils or periodic flooding. The distributions of biomes therefore strongly match patterns of regional climate (e.g. temperate, tropical). A given biome (e.g. temperate grassland) may be composed of different taxa on different continents. Continent-specific associations of species within a given biome are known as formations and often are known by different local names. For example, the temperate grassland biome is variously called prairie, steppe, pampa, or veld, depending on where it occurs (North America, Eurasia, South America, and South Africa, respectively).

Number of IBAs meeting the A3 criterion

	Arctic/tundra biome	Boreal biome	Mediterranean biome	Eurasian high-montane biome	Eurasian steppe biome	Total
Armenia	–	–	–	1	–	1
Azerbaijan	–	–	–	9	–	9
Bulgaria	–	–	3	1	–	4
Croatia	–	–	1	–	–	1
Cyprus	–	–	3	–	–	3
Finland	5	11	–	–	–	14[1]
France	–	–	4	1	–	5
Georgia	–	–	–	8	–	8
Germany	–	–	–	1	–	1
Greece	–	–	13	5	–	17[1]
Greenland	3	–	–	–	–	3
Italy	–	–	7	12	–	19
Norway	1	1	–	–	–	2
Poland	–	–	–	1	–	1
Russia	5	12	2	3	7	25[1]
Slovakia	–	–	–	1	–	1
Slovenia	–	–	–	1	–	1
Spain	–	–	7	5	–	12
Svalbard	3	–	–	–	–	3
Sweden	4	1	–	–	–	5
Switzerland	–	–	–	14	–	14
Turkey	–	–	–	1	–	1
Ukraine	–	–	–	–	2	2
Yugoslavia	–	–	1	2	–	3
Total number of IBAs	**21**	**25**	**41**	**66**	**9**	**155[1]**

1. The national total is less than the sum of sites qualifying for individual biomes, since some IBAs qualify for two biomes (usually large sites that span the ecotone between biomes).

ARCTIC/TUNDRA BIOME

The Arctic/tundra biome is the northernmost terrestrial biome, restricted to a belt around the Arctic Ocean and adjoined by the boreal biome to the south. In Europe it covers about 680,000 km² (c.7% of the continent). Winters are long and cold and the subsoil is frozen year-round (permafrost), as a result of which there are no trees; mosses dominate the vegetation, with lichens, sedges, grasses, and occasional low bushes and dwarf shrubs. Most bird species characteristic of this biome are highly migratory waterbirds which spend the brief summer raising their young, before departing south, ahead of the onset of winter. Some of these species show extreme adaptation to long-distance migration. Other bird species are mainly raptors and scavengers, and there are few passerines; very few species are resident, possessing adaptations to survive the harsh tundra winter.

(PHOTO: DAVID BOERTMANN)

BOREAL BIOME

The boreal biome, also known in Europe as the taiga, is the largest terrestrial biome on earth. Confined to the northern hemisphere, it extends as a broad and near-continuous band of coniferous forest and open mires across Eurasia and North America, lying immediately south of the Arctic/tundra biome. In Europe this belt and covers at least 1,000,000 km² (10% or more of the continent). The forest is a mosaic of different-aged stands, dominated in Europe by two conifer species, Norway spruce *Picea abies* and Scots pine *Pinus sylvestris*. A few deciduous tree species also occur, especially in disturbed or wet areas. Large, tree-less mires form in poorly drained, glacial depressions, and tundra-like habitats occur above the treeline on higher mountains within this zone (here trated as part of the Arctic/tundra biome). Among birds, insectivores and waterbirds tend to be migratory, leaving after the breeding season since freezing conditions eliminate their food-supply in winter. Small-mammal predators (e.g. owls), seed-eaters (e.g. finches) and omnivores (e.g. ravens) tend to be year-round residents.

(PHOTO: MIKA HONKALINNA)

MEDITERRANEAN BIOME

The Mediterranean biome as considered in this publication—the land in Europe, North Africa and the Levant surrounding the Mediterranean Sea—is the largest of several formations of the Mediterranean biome around the world, covering about 500,000 km² in Europe. In the Mediterranean proper, the vegetation and soils have long been impacted by humans, especially through the frequent use of fire and the grazing of livestock, and dry shrublands with thin, rocky soils are characteristic. Shrubs and trees tend to be evergreen with small, leathery leaves. Where fire and grazing are reduced or absent, shrubland is replaced by regenerating woodland and forest, dominated by evergreen oaks *Quercus* and pines *Pinus*. The flora and fauna are characterized by a high degree of endemism. Among birds, most of the characteristic species are found in shrublands and open, rocky areas rather than in forest habitats.

(PHOTO: MARCO LAMBERTINI)

Biomes

- ☐ Arctic/tundra
- ■ Boreal
- ■ Mediterranean
- ■ Eurasian high-montane
- ■ Eurasian steppe
- • Site for biome-restricted bird species

(PHOTO:
PETER BALWIN/
SCHWEIZER VOGELSCHUTZ)

**ASIAN HIGH-
NTANE (ALPINE) BIOME**

Eurasian high-montane (or alpine)
e is found high on mountains in
sia. The climate is severe, receiving
ture mostly in the form of snow, with high winds, drastic daily temperature changes
sometimes heavy snowfall. Permafrost occurs at the higher altitudes and there are
plants and no trees. Alpine vegetation grows low to the ground above the
mholz (stunted-tree zone), in alpine meadows and alpine stone-fields. Animals
nate, migrate, or live under the snow to survive the harsh winter conditions.
ively few birds in Europe are restricted to this biome during the breeding season,
the majority being passerines, unlike the situation in the Arctic.

EURASIAN STEPPE BIOME

The Eurasian steppes are
temperate grasslands, found
in mid-latitude regions with
relatively cold winter
temperatures. In Eurasia and
elsewhere, such grasslands
occur in the interior of
continents and in rain-
shadows. The climate is semi-
arid and continental, with warm
to hot summers and cold winters.
In Europe, before the onset of
economic development in the 16th
century, the steppes covered perhaps
800,000 km² or more, extending in a belt
300–1,000 km wide from the lower Danube valley east

(PHOTO: PAUL GORIUP)

across the flat lowlands of Ukraine and southern Russia, with temperate broadleaved and
boreal forest lying to the north, and semi-desert to the south around the Caspian Sea.
Vegetation was dominated by perennial grasses and forbs and there were very few trees
except along rivers and streams. However, since the development of the steel plough
nearly all temperate grassland in Europe, indeed Eurasia, has been converted to
agricultural land, and has become densely populated and industrialized. Among birds
restricted to the biome when breeding, open-country species naturally predominate, and
some of the species more dependent on original, unploughed steppe, such as Sociable
Plover *Chettusia gregaria*, are now globally threatened through lack of habitat.

35

Species restricted to biomes

A total of 155 IBAs have been identified on the basis that they support important assemblages of species that are restricted (when breeding in Europe) to a particular biome (thus meeting the A3 criterion). In applying this criterion in Europe, five biomes have been considered:

- Arctic/tundra
- Boreal
- Mediterranean
- Eurasian high-montane
- Eurasian steppe.

The IBAs and their distribution are shown in Box 1.

Congregatory species

Individuals of many bird species traverse political boundaries at some stage in their annual cycle, and many also congregate in large numbers at sites across the continent at some time each year. IBAs are particularly suited to conserving these species, with over 51% of IBAs in Europe (1,858 sites) being important for congregations of birds: 1,364 sites qualify because the site supports globally important congregations of at least one species (meeting the A4 criteria), and an additional 494 sites qualify because the site holds regionally important congregations of at least one species (B1 criteria).

Appendix 6 shows the number of sites identified under each IBA criterion, by country. Countries with at least 60 sites important for

Box 2. Internationally important sites for congregations of non-breeding waterbirds or seabirds in Europe (meeting the A4i/ii/iii and/or B1i/ii criteria).

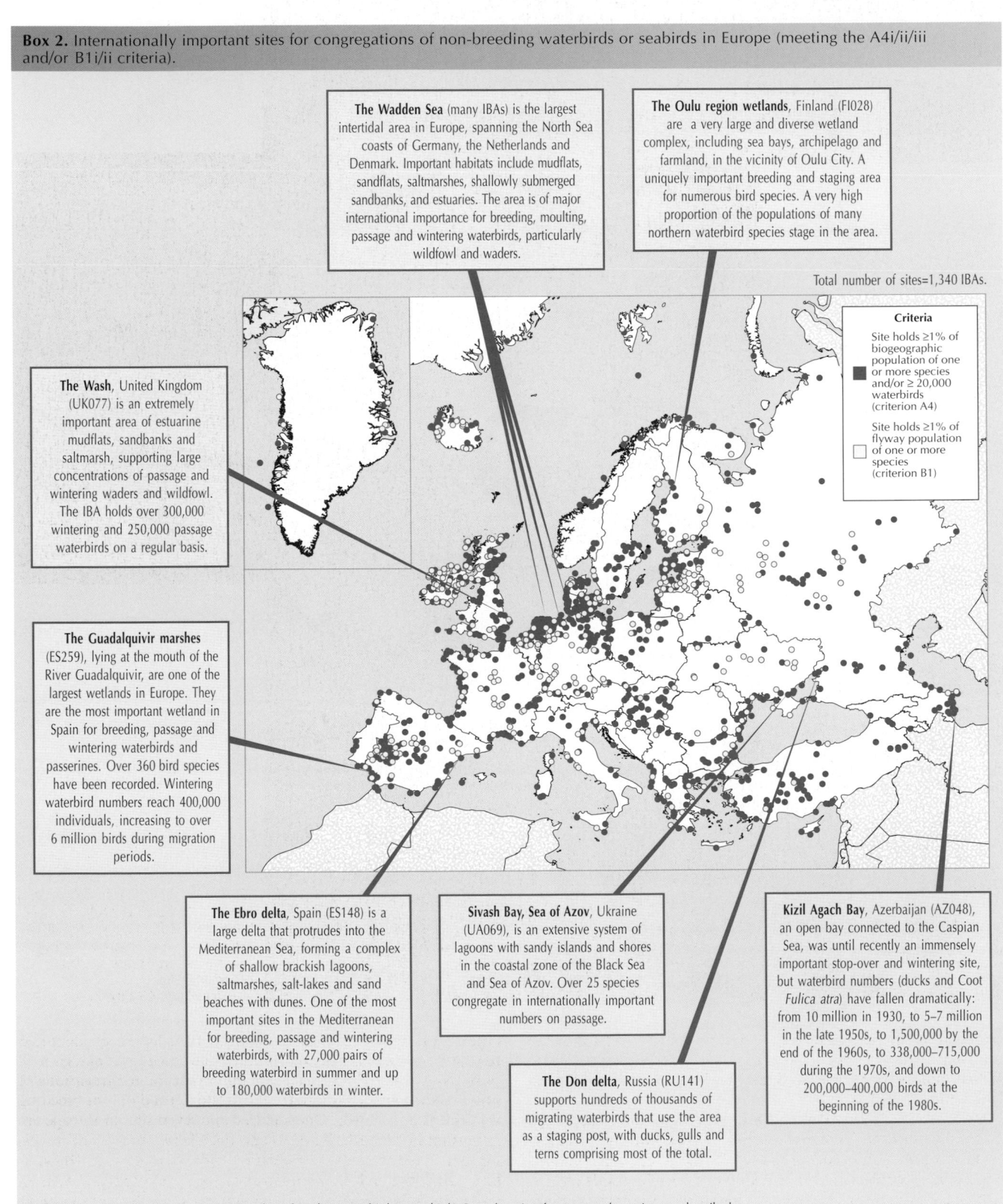

The Wadden Sea (many IBAs) is the largest intertidal area in Europe, spanning the North Sea coasts of Germany, the Netherlands and Denmark. Important habitats include mudflats, sandflats, saltmarshes, shallowly submerged sandbanks, and estuaries. The area is of major international importance for breeding, moulting, passage and wintering waterbirds, particularly wildfowl and waders.

The Oulu region wetlands, Finland (FI028) are a very large and diverse wetland complex, including sea bays, archipelago and farmland, in the vicinity of Oulu City. A uniquely important breeding and staging area for numerous bird species. A very high proportion of the populations of many northern waterbird species stage in the area.

Total number of sites=1,340 IBAs.

Criteria

■ Site holds ≥1% of biogeographic population of one or more species and/or ≥ 20,000 waterbirds (criterion A4)

□ Site holds ≥1% of flyway population of one or more species (criterion B1)

The Wash, United Kingdom (UK077) is an extremely important area of estuarine mudflats, sandbanks and saltmarsh, supporting large concentrations of passage and wintering waders and wildfowl. The IBA holds over 300,000 wintering and 250,000 passage waterbirds on a regular basis.

The Guadalquivir marshes (ES259), lying at the mouth of the River Guadalquivir, are one of the largest wetlands in Europe. They are the most important wetland in Spain for breeding, passage and wintering waterbirds and passerines. Over 360 bird species have been recorded. Wintering waterbird numbers reach 400,000 individuals, increasing to over 6 million birds during migration periods.

The Ebro delta, Spain (ES148) is a large delta that protrudes into the Mediterranean Sea, forming a complex of shallow brackish lagoons, saltmarshes, salt-lakes and sand beaches with dunes. One of the most important sites in the Mediterranean for breeding, passage and wintering waterbirds, with 27,000 pairs of breeding waterbird in summer and up to 180,000 waterbirds in winter.

Sivash Bay, Sea of Azov, Ukraine (UA069), is an extensive system of lagoons with sandy islands and shores in the coastal zone of the Black Sea and Sea of Azov. Over 25 species congregate in internationally important numbers on passage.

The Don delta, Russia (RU141) supports hundreds of thousands of migrating waterbirds that use the area as a staging post, with ducks, gulls and terns comprising most of the total.

Kizil Agach Bay, Azerbaijan (AZ048), an open bay connected to the Caspian Sea, was until recently an immensely important stop-over and wintering site, but waterbird numbers (ducks and Coot *Fulica atra*) have fallen dramatically: from 10 million in 1930, to 5–7 million in the late 1950s, to 1,500,000 by the end of the 1960s, to 338,000–715,000 during the 1970s, and down to 200,000–400,000 birds at the beginning of the 1980s.

1,340 IBAs are important for congregations of non-breeding waterbirds or seabirds. Some key sites from across the region are described.

Oystercatcher *Haematopus ostralegus* congregating at Snettisham, The Wash, in the United Kingdom (IBA 077). (PHOTO: MIKE READ)

Whooper Swan *Cygnus cygnus*, a highly congregatory species, wintering at Shabla lake complex, Bulgaria (IBA 049). (PHOTO: WERNER MÜLLER)

Gannet *Sula bassana* colony at Bass Rock, Forth Islands, in the United Kingdom (IBA 148). Over 90% of the European breeding population of *Sula bassana* breed at IBAs. (PHOTO: C. H. GOMERSALL)

congregatory species (qualifying under the A4 and/or B1 criteria) are Denmark, France, Germany, Greece, Ireland, Italy, Netherlands, Norway, Russia, Spain, Turkey, Ukraine and United Kingdom.

Under these criteria, IBAs can be important for different groups of congregatory species: congregations of waterbirds (criteria A4i and B1i), congregations of seabirds (A4ii and B1ii), congregations of more than 20,000 waterbirds or 10,000 pairs of seabirds (A4iii), 'bottleneck' concentrations of migrating storks, raptors and cranes (A4iv and B1iv) and congregations of other species (B1iii). These criteria may be applied in any season and IBAs have been identified for migrating, wintering, non-breeding and breeding congregations of birds. A total of 1,340 sites are important for congregations of non-breeding waterbirds and seabirds (Box 2) and 811 for breeding waterbirds or seabirds. One hundred and seven sites in Europe are important bottleneck sites through which large numbers of storks, raptors or cranes pass on migration (Box 3): at 45 such IBAs, at least 20,000 storks/raptors/cranes pass through per season (criterion A4iv), while at the remaining 62 sites, the seasonal total exceeds 5,000 storks or 3,000 raptors/cranes (criterion B1iv).

Box 3. Internationally important 'bottleneck' sites for migrating storks, raptors and cranes in Europe (meeting the A4iv/B1iv criteria).

A total of 107 sites in Europe meet the B1iv criterion, with at least 5,000 storks or at least 3,000 raptors or cranes passing through the site. Forty-five out of the 107 sites also meet the A4iv criterion, with at least 20,000 storks, raptors or cranes passing through the site.

The Alps form a major barrier to migrating birds in Europe. In France, 'Haute Chaîne du Jura: défilé de l'écluse, Etournel et Mont Vuache' (FR172) is a major migratory bottleneck, where more than 20,000 raptors pass on a regular basis, including 10,000 Honey Buzzard *Pernis apivorus*, 20,000 Black Kite *Milvus migrans* and 20,000 Buzzard *Buteo buteo*.

Large numbers of raptors, mostly Fennoscandian, pass through Denmark, especially the eastern part, during both spring and autumn migration, with the most significant bottlenecks being at Gilleleje (DK126, spring), Hellebæk (DK124, spring and autumn), Stigsnæs (part of DK095, autumn) and Stevns (DK127, autumn). The most numerous species are Honey Buzzard *Pernis apivorus*, Buzzard *Buteo buteo* and Sparrowhawk *Accipiter nisus*.

The 'North-east Turkey' IBA (TR060) covers three major mountain ranges (Soganli, Kaçkar and Karçal), and includes a major migratory bottleneck, where large numbers of raptors regularly pass in autumn. A count of 380,220 birds of prey was made in 1976, including 138,000 Honey Buzzard *Pernis apivorus*, 5,775 Black Kite *Milvus migrans* and 205,000 Buzzard *Buteo buteo*. Actual numbers may be higher as important new passage points have been discovered in recent years.

Along the Bulgarian Black Sea coast, nine IBAs are bottleneck sites for migratory birds. These sites are the most important concentrations of large soaring birds along the western Black Sea migration route ('Via Pontica'). It is believed that large proportions of the European populations of White Stork *Ciconia ciconia*, White Pelican *Pelecanus onocrotalus*, Honey Buzzard *Pernis apivorus*, Buzzard *Buteo buteo* and Imperial Eagle *Aquila heliaca* migrate along the western Black Sea coast, especially over Cape Emine (BG043) and Atanasovo lake (BG036).

Gibraltar is a well-known migratory bottleneck site for birds of prey, with an estimated 250,000 raptors crossing the Strait per season. If the winds are right most of these birds pass over Gibraltar (GI001), and numbers may in fact be higher. The species involved include Honey Buzzard *Pernis apivorus*, Black Kite *Milvus migrans*, Egyptian Vulture *Neophron percnopterus*, Short-toed Eagle *Circaetus gallicus*, Montagu's Harrier *Circus pygargus* and Booted Eagle *Hieraaetus pennatus*. Large numbers of birds of prey also cross IBAs surrounding the Strait of Gibraltar (ES244, ES245, ES246, ES248, ES250) before moving to Africa, and some stop over at the Guadalquivir marshes (ES259) before crossing to Africa over Ceuta (ES247).

Birds that breed in western Europe cross the Pyrenees at several sites in Spain and France, amongst the most important being the 'Roncesvalles-Irati-Abodi mountain range' (ES085), Cadí mountain range (ES135), 'Haute Soule: Forêt d'Irraty, Organbidexka et Pic des Escaliers' (FR183; more than 20,000 raptors pass regularly, including 18,000 Honey Buzzard *Pernis apivorus*, 13,000 Black Kite *Milvus migrans*, 4,600 Red Kite *M. milvus* and 15,000 Crane *Grus grus*), and 'Etangs de Leucate et Lapalme' (FR214; including 15,000 *Pernis apivorus* and 3,000 *Milvus migrans*).

The Bogaziçi strait (TR005), in western Turkey, runs north–south for c.33 km, and is c.1.5 km wide. Total counts made in the mid-1960s and early 1970s, covering the entire autumn migration period, include 8,318 Black Stork *Ciconia nigra*, 338,353 White Stork *Ciconia ciconia*, 25,751 Honey Buzzard *Pernis apivorus*, 2,707 Black Kite *Milvus migrans*, 32,895 Buzzard *Buteo buteo* and 18,898 Lesser Spotted Eagle *Aquila pomarina*. More recent autumn records include 11,703 *Aquila pomarina* at Çamlica and 11,379 of the same species at Sariyer, both on the same day in September 1990.

IBAs shown on the map: Belgium 044; Bulgaria 034, 036, 040, 041, 043–045, 047, 049; Cyprus 007, 014; Denmark 072, 095, 102, 124–127; Finland 045; France 068, 070, 123, 143–145, 149, 151, 158, 162, 163, 172, 177, 178, 183, 191, 192, 213–215, 217, 218, 222, 225; Georgia 004, 008; Germany 037, 106, 122, 124, 138, 142, 143, 149, 151, 172, 179; Gibraltar 001; Greece 006, 129; Hungary 029; Italy 035, 036, 054, 055, 085, 147, 150, 151, 153; Latvia 015, 021; Lithuania 004; Malta 004; Poland 006, 022; Portugal 031; Russia 050, 141, 163, 167, 212; Spain 078, 085, 095, 116, 135, 244–248, 250, 259; Sweden 042, 057, 061; Switzerland 017; Turkey 002, 005, 060, 073, 078, 081; Ukraine 068, 069; Yugoslavia 012.

Species of European conservation concern

The IBA programme has an important role to play in conserving populations of many species of European conservation concern (SPECs). These species are in particular need of conservation measures as they either have an unfavourable conservation status in Europe (because they are declining in numbers, are present in small numbers or are highly localized) or they are concentrated in Europe (a substantial proportion of their global population occurs in Europe and thus Europe has a special responsibility for their conservation). A total of 2,399 IBAs (66% of all IBAs in Europe) are important for SPECs, meeting B2/B3 criteria, with sites identified for 269 of the 278 species (97%).

The IBA network supports a significant proportion of the European population of many SPECs. Each country chapter gives a summary of the proportions of the national populations of SPECs covered by IBAs. From the data presented in this publication, it is possible to calculate, for individual species, the proportion of the European population found within IBAs across the region. For example, the European breeding population of *Platalea leucorodia* is well covered by the IBA network, with a total of 81 IBAs (distributed throughout the European breeding range) holding significant breeding numbers of the species, which together represent approximately 80% of the breeding population in Europe (Figure 9).

Barrow's Goldeneye *Bucephala islandica* at Lake Mývatn/River Laxá, Iceland (IBA 046), a site which holds 85–90% of the European population of the species.
(PHOTO: JÓHANN ÓLI HILMARSSON)

The breeding distribution of Broad-billed Sandpiper *Limicola falcinellus*, a species of European conservation concern, is poorly known, but it seems likely that at least 10–20% of the European population breeds within IBAs.
(PHOTO: PEKKA KOMI)

Spoonbill *Platalea leucorodia*, a species of European conservation concern, in Atanasovo lake, Bulgaria (IBA 036). The species's breeding sites are well covered by IBAs (see Figure 9).
(PHOTO: SVETISLAV SPOSOV)

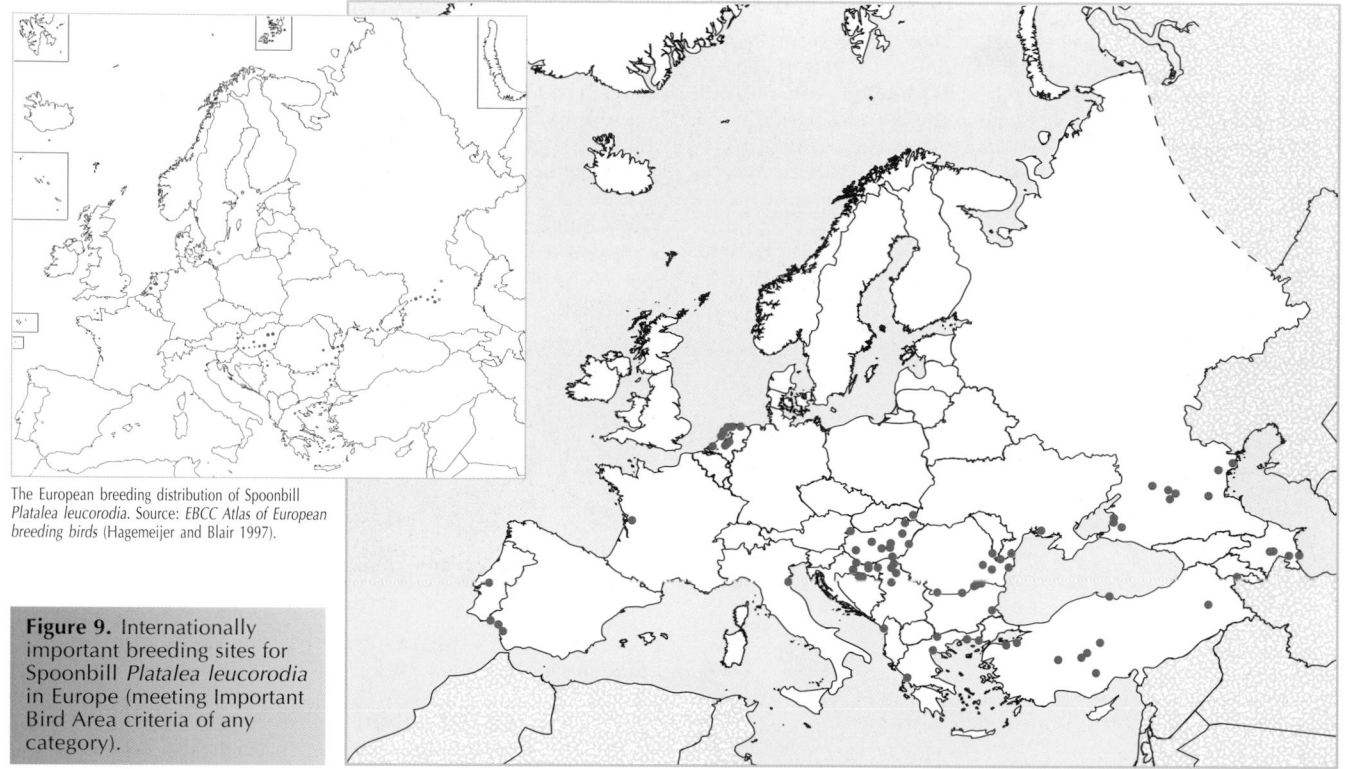

The European breeding distribution of Spoonbill *Platalea leucorodia*. Source: *EBCC Atlas of European breeding birds* (Hagemeijer and Blair 1997).

Figure 9. Internationally important breeding sites for Spoonbill *Platalea leucorodia* in Europe (meeting Important Bird Area criteria of any category).

However, some species of European conservation concern are not well covered by IBAs. Reasons for this may include a lack of data on sites and populations—it is recognized that the network of sites is not yet complete for some SPECs. In addition, many species of European conservation concern breed in a dispersed, non-congregatory fashion, and therefore cannot be conserved successfully by the IBA programme alone. For many SPECs, even though the IBA programme makes a significant contribution to their conservation, it is vital that conservation of the wider environment is also pursued in parallel (Tucker and Evans 1997).

Species meeting criteria in the European Union (level C)
In total, 2,342 IBAs have been identified in the 15 member states of the European Union. Most of the criteria for the importance of IBAs at the EU level parallel the criteria at the European and global levels but some are associated with lower population thresholds. Sites have been identified for species of global conservation concern (criterion C1), migratory and congregatory species (criteria C2, C3,

C4 and C5), species or subspecies considered threatened in the EU (criterion C6) or for other reasons (C7). The numbers of IBAs meeting the different 'C' criteria are shown in Figure 10 and are summarized by country in Appendix 6.

Stone Curlew *Burhinus oedicnemus*, listed in Annex I of the EC Birds Directive and a species of European conservation concern. A total of 94 IBAs across nine countries support significant breeding numbers of this species. (PHOTO: CARLOS SANCHEZ)

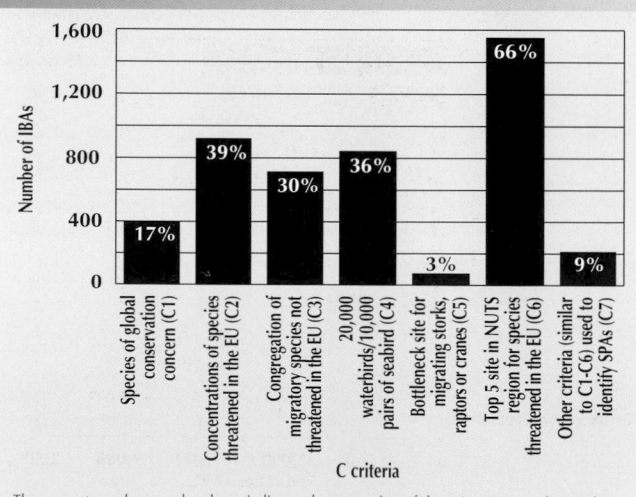

Figure 10. The number of sites meeting the different 'C' criteria in the European Union.

The percentage above each column indicates the proportion of the 2,342 IBAs in the EU that meet the criterion.

N.B. A site may be important for more than one bird species (or in more than one way for a particular species) and may thus qualify under more than one criterion.
For more details of the 'C' criteria, see the 'Identifying IBAs' chapter.

Egyptian Vulture *Neophron percnopterus*, listed in Annex I of the EC Birds Directive and a species of European conservation concern. A total of 89 IBAs across 11 countries support significant numbers of this species.
(PHOTO: JUAN M. SIMON)

While 2,264 IBAs in the EU (97% of the EU total) qualify as IBAs of European Union importance (meeting C criteria), the remaining 78 sites in the EU do not meet C criteria. This is because they qualify for SPECs which are not currently listed in Annex I of the EC Birds Directive, or because they do not meet any criteria for migratory species under Article 4.2 of this Directive, or because they have not been designated as Special Protection Areas (SPAs) under similar national criteria. Since the IBA data provided for some Annex I species are incomplete for some EU countries, it is likely that many of these sites will also meet the C6 criterion in the future, following the availability of more data.

Within the EU, 31 species of global conservation concern occur, all of which are listed in Annex I of the EC Birds Directive. Overall, 396 sites (17% of all IBAs in the EU) are important for these species, with Spain and Greece being particularly important, holding 121 and 73 identified sites respectively (see Appendix 6 for details).

Many sites are important at the EU-level for populations of congregatory species (meeting the C2, C3 and C4 criteria), qualifying for concentrations of species that are threatened in the EU (criterion C2; 918 IBAs) or migratory species that are not threatened in the EU (criterion C3; 712 IBAs). EU countries identifying particularly high numbers of IBAs for congregatory species include France, Germany, Greece, Ireland, Italy, Netherlands, Spain and United Kingdom (Appendix 6). A total of 842 sites in the EU support at least 20,000 waterbirds or 10,000 pairs of seabird (C4 criterion) and 71 sites are important bottlenecks for migrating storks, raptors or cranes (C5 criterion).

In the EU, 1,550 IBAs (66% of the EU total) support important numbers of one or more species or subspecies threatened in the European Union, i.e. listed in Annex I of the EC Birds Directive, thus meeting the C6 criterion. IBAs have been identified for 135 of the 181 species or subspecies listed in this Annex. Countries or autonomous regions with a high proportion (more than 85%) of their IBAs qualifying under criterion C6 include Austria, France, Luxembourg, Portugal, Madeira and Spain (Appendix 6). Others, such as the Netherlands and United Kingdom, have a slightly lower application rate for C6, but many of the sites in these countries have been identified for concentrations of species (under criteria C2, C3 and C4). In some countries, including Germany, Denmark and Finland, the C6 criterion has not been fully applied because of a lack of data on the abundance of Annex I species at sites (see relevant country chapters). In other countries, full networks of sites may not yet have been identified for all species listed in Annex I and thus further applications of C6 are likely to be made in the future.

A total of 210 IBAs (9% of the EU total) meet the C7 criterion, having been designated as Special Protection Areas (SPAs), or selected as candidate SPAs, based on ornithological criteria that are similar to, but not exactly the same as, criteria C1–C6. This criterion has been applied in several countries but efforts have been

made to minimize its use and, where possible, apply other C criteria (more species-based and quantitative) instead.

■ IBA coverage by habitat

All of the main habitat-types in Europe occur at IBAs, with wetland, forest and grassland being the most extensive (Figure 11).
- Wetland IBAs are particularly important for large congregations of birds. Many wetland sites have been identified, with 69% of all IBAs having some wetland habitat. At a large number of sites (at least 22%), wetland is predominant, covering at least 50% of the area of the individual IBA.
- 54% of IBAs in Europe hold forest/woodland, this being the dominant habitat (covering more than 50% of the individual IBA area) at 12% of IBAs.
- Grassland habitats are also frequent within IBAs, being recorded at 52% of all IBAs, although covering more than 50% of the individual IBA area at only 5% of the IBAs in Europe.
- Cultivated or grazed habitats cover most of Europe, and artificial landscapes are thus widespread in IBAs, being recorded at 48% of all sites, and being predominant at 8% of sites.
- Many IBAs contain some scrub or rocky areas but this is usually not the predominant vegetation-type.

Most IBAs are composed of mosaics of habitats on which different bird species depend, therefore several habitat-types are usually recorded within the same IBA.

Figure 11. The number of Important Bird Areas in Europe that contain particular habitats.

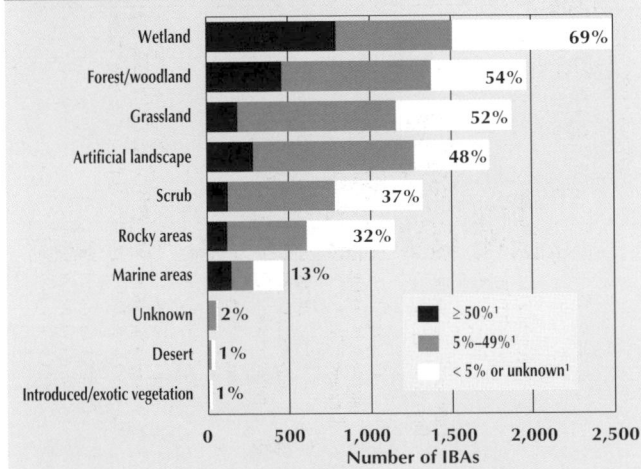

Habitat	%
Wetland	69%
Forest/woodland	54%
Grassland	52%
Artificial landscape	48%
Scrub	37%
Rocky areas	32%
Marine areas	13%
Unknown	2%
Desert	1%
Introduced/exotic vegetation	1%

≥50%[1]
5%–49%[1]
<5% or unknown[1]

Number of IBAs

1. Proportion of individual IBA area covered by habitat

The percentage at the end of each bar indicates the proportion of IBAs in Europe that contain the habitat (no habitat data were recorded at five IBAs). See Appendix 3 for a more detailed description of the habitat classification used.

Liepaja lake in Latvia (IBA 004) is a shallow, nutrient-poor coastal lake with extensive areas of water-fringe vegetation. (PHOTO: EDMUNDS RAČINSKIS)

The flood-plains of the Biebrza river valley in Poland (IBA 025) are one of the most important breeding places in central and western Europe for some threatened or localized species such as Great Snipe *Gallinago media*, Corncrake *Crex crex*, Spotted Crake *Porzana porzana*, Greater Spotted Eagle *Aquila clanga* and White-winged Black Tern *Chlidonias leucopterus*, and are also an important site for migrating waders, ducks, geese and Crane *Grus grus*. (PHOTO: PAWEŁ OLAF SIDŁO)

'Kemihaara mires', in Finland (IBA 017), is a very large complex of aapa mires, riverside forests, herb-rich mires and forested hills and ridges along the upper course of the Kemi river, important for its boreal avifauna, especially breeding waders. (PHOTO: MIKA HONKALINNA)

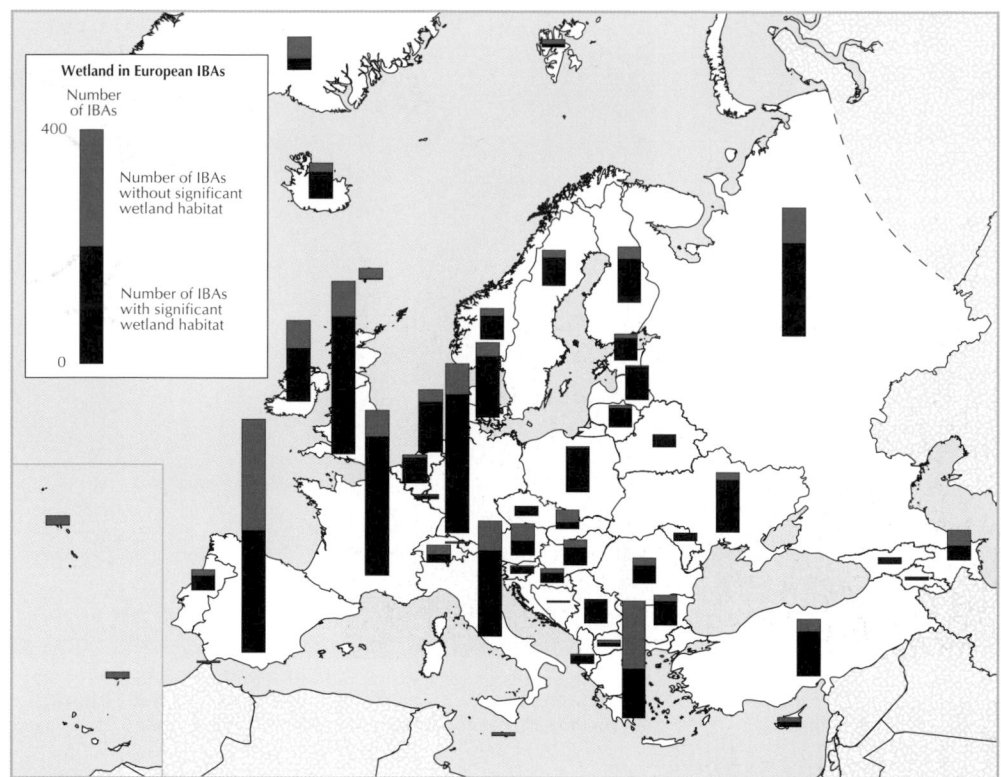

Figure 12. The number of Important Bird Areas in Europe, by country, that contain a significant extent of wetland.

The height of the column is proportional to the total number of IBAs in the country. Overall, at least 2,494 IBAs in Europe contain a significant extent of wetland (i.e. covering at least 5% of the individual IBA area).

Wetland

Sixty-nine percent of all IBAs have at least 5% of their individual area covered by wetland habitats. Figure 12 shows the proportion of IBAs in each country that have a significant extent of wetland habitat. Most countries have a high proportion of wetland IBAs, reflecting the importance of many coastal and inland sites across the region for congregatory waterbirds. There is a broad range of wetland types and their presence in IBAs is shown in Figure 13.

- Of those IBAs with any wetland habitat, 57% include freshwater lakes or ponds (including fish-ponds), many with associated water-fringe vegetation such as reedbeds.
- Rivers and streams occur in 44% of wetland IBAs.
- Concerning mires, 19% of wetland IBAs hold fen or transition mire, 13% hold raised bog and 4% hold blanket bog.
- Many coastal sites include one or more of the following types of wetland habitat: standing brackish/salt water; enclosed tidal water; coastal lagoon; saltmarsh; intertidal mudflat/sandflat; sand-dunes; sand/shingle/stony beach.

Figure 13. The types of wetland present at Important Bird Areas in Europe.

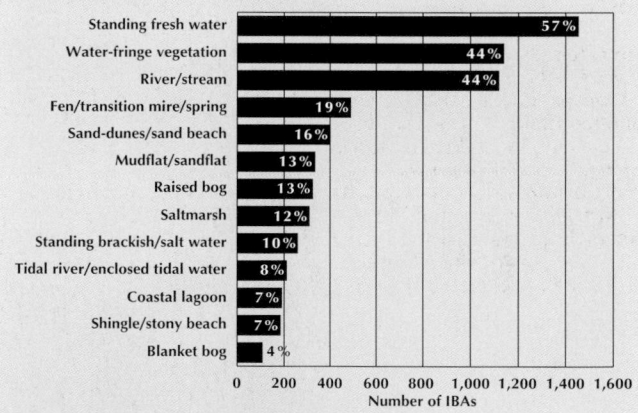

The figure at the end of each bar indicates the percentage of those IBAs containing any wetland (2,563 sites) that actually contain the wetland-type in question. At 2% of the 2,563 wetland IBAs, no types of wetland were distinguished.

Of major international importance for waterbirds all-year-round, the Wadden Sea is the largest intertidal area in Europe, shared between Germany, the Netherlands and Denmark, and comprises many IBAs. Habitats include mudflats, sandflats, saltmarshes, shallow subtidal waters and estuaries. (PHOTO: NATURSCHUTZBUND DEUTSCHLAND)

Broadleaved deciduous forests in central and southern Germany hold rich populations of forest birds such as Red Kite *Milvus milvus*, Grey-headed Woodpecker *Picus canus* and Firecrest *Regulus ignicapillus*. (PHOTO: CHRISTOPH HEINRICH)

Mixed forest occurs at medium altitudes in Yugoslavia, and is an important habitat for breeding raptors at several of the 13 IBAs that are predominantly forested. (PHOTO: BRATISLAV GRUBAČ)

Native coniferous forest and montane meadows at Veľká Fatra, Slovakia (IBA 014), an extensive range of forested mountains in the inner Western Carpathians. (PHOTO: VEĽKÁ FATRA PLA)

Well preserved riverine forests along the River Mura in eastern Slovenia (IBA 013). The area includes the largest alder *Alnus* forest in central Europe, and is dense and uninhabited. (PHOTO: BORUT ŠTUMBERGER)

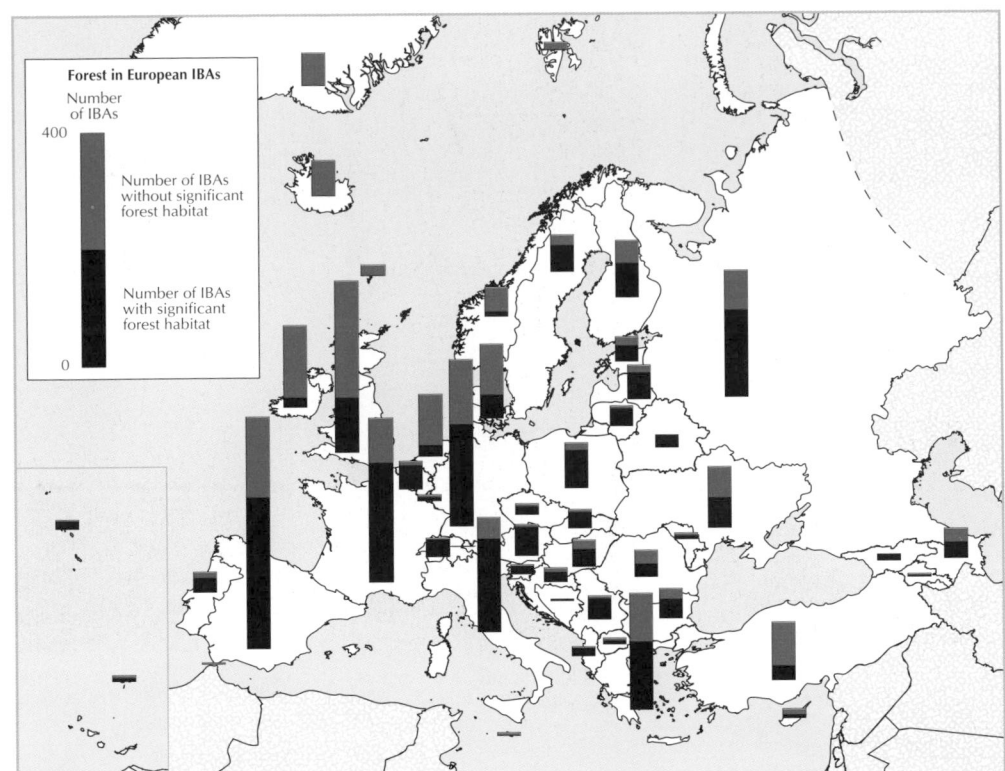

Forest in European IBAs

Number of IBAs

400

Number of IBAs without significant forest habitat

Number of IBAs with significant forest habitat

0

Figure 14. The number of Important Bird Areas in Europe, by country, that contain a significant extent of forest/woodland.

The height of the column is proportional to the total number of IBAs in the country. Overall, at least 1,970 IBAs in Europe contain a significant extent of forest/woodland (i.e. covering at least 5% of the individual IBA area).

Forest and woodland

The total area of forest in Europe has been increasing since the 1920s, due to widespread afforestation of open land and due to forest regeneration following abandonment of agriculture. Forest currently covers about 30% of Europe's land area, but most of this exists as intensively managed plantations, often monocultures of fast-growing conifers or non-native tree species, or as highly fragmented small patches of semi-natural forest. The only large and unbroken tracts of primaeval forest left on the continent are in the north-east of European Russia.

Fifty-four percent of IBAs in Europe hold forest/woodland. Figure 14 shows the proportion of IBAs in each country that have a significant extent of forest/woodland (more than 5% cover of individual IBA). Many countries in the centre, east and south of the continent have a high proportion of IBAs with some forest/woodland cover. The types of forest and woodland found within these IBAs are shown in Figure 15.

- Broadleaved deciduous forest is present in nearly 50% of IBAs with any forest/woodland habitat.
- Native coniferous forest is present in 34% of forest/woodland IBAs.

- Mixed forest (a 50:50 mixture of conifers and broadleaved deciduous trees) is present in 31% of forest/woodland IBAs.
- Alluvial/wet forest is present in 35% of forest/woodland IBAs.
- Broadleaved evergreen forest is present in 14% of forest/woodland IBAs.
- Types of forest/woodland that are less frequent in IBAs include wooded tundra, wooded steppe and treeline ecotone.

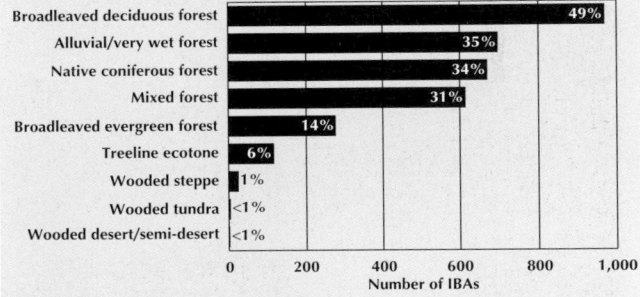

Figure 15. The types of forest/woodland present at Important Bird Areas in Europe.

Broadleaved deciduous forest	49%
Alluvial/very wet forest	35%
Native coniferous forest	34%
Mixed forest	31%
Broadleaved evergreen forest	14%
Treeline ecotone	6%
Wooded steppe	1%
Wooded tundra	<1%
Wooded desert/semi-desert	<1%

The figure at the end of each bar indicates the percentage of those IBAs containing any forest/woodland (1,996 sites) that actually contain the forest-type in question. At 8% of the 1,996 forest/woodland IBAs, no types of forest/woodland were distinguished.

In Spain, the 'dehesas'—open parklands of broadleaved evergreen forest—are important for the conservation of globally threatened or near-threatened species such as Spanish Imperial Eagle *Aquila adalberti* and Cinereous Vulture *Aegypius monachus*. (PHOTO: FERNANDO BARRIO (SEO/BIRDLIFE))

45

Lake Cerknica (IBA 008) is situated on the largest polje (karst field) in Slovenia. A seasonal, nutrient-rich lake which is usually totally dry in summer and late winter, with huge expanses of wet grassland. Important numbers of the globally threatened Corncrake *Crex crex* breed.
(PHOTO: SLAVKO POLAK)

Natural steppe was formerly the dominant habitat in southern Ukraine, but most has been ploughed for cultivation and only small fragments of this habitat remain, as here at Bagerovo (IBA 102).
(PHOTO: PAUL GORIUP)

Mesophile grassland in the Bukovské hills, Slovakia (IBA 027), important for meadow-breeding species such as Corncrake *Crex crex* and Red-backed Shrike *Lanius collurio*.
(PHOTO: Š. PČOLA)

Augstmatthorn, Switzerland (IBA 018), a mountainous area with alpine meadows at higher elevations. In Switzerland, alpine and subalpine grasslands are found at 19 IBAs and are important for species such as Rock Partridge *Alectoris graeca*, Alpine Accentor *Prunella collaris*, Rock Thrush *Monticola saxatilis*, Wallcreeper *Tichodroma muraria*, Alpine Chough *Pyrrhocorax graculus* and Snowfinch *Montifringilla nivalis*.
(PHOTO: LORENZ HEER)

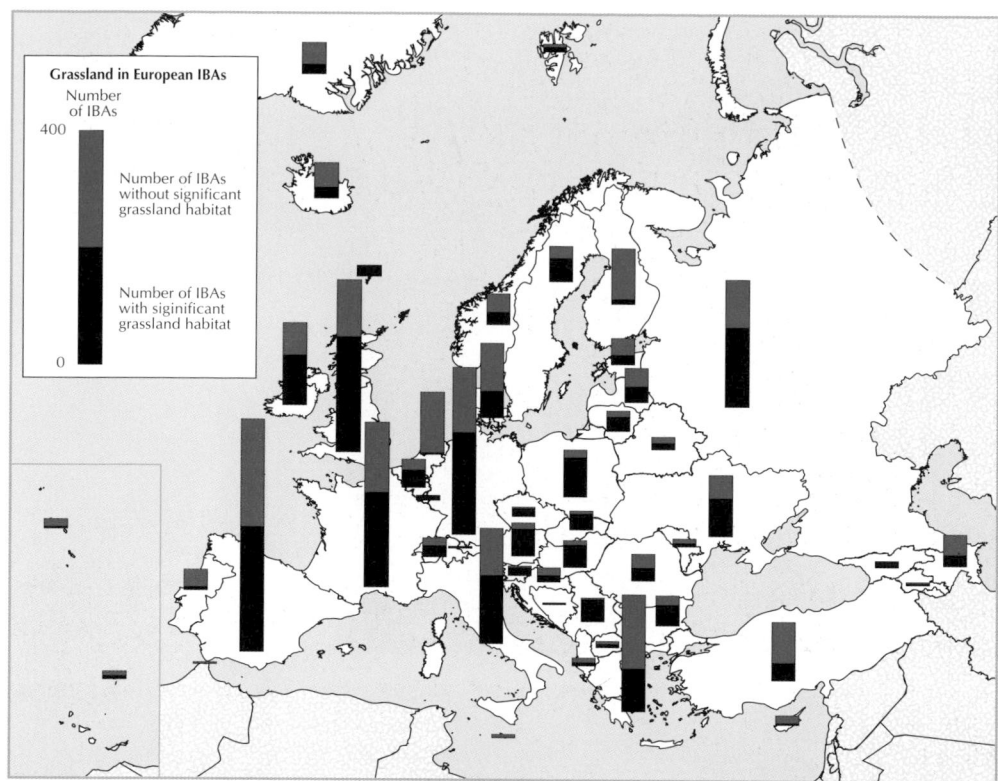

Grassland in European IBAs

Number
of IBAs

400

Number of IBAs
without significant
grassland habitat

Number of IBAs
with siginificant
grassland habitat

0

Figure 16. The number of Important Bird Areas in Europe, by country, that contain a significant extent of grassland.

The height of the column is proportional to the total number of IBAs in the country. Overall, at least 1,877 IBAs in Europe contain a significant extent of grassland (i.e. covering at least 5% of the individual IBA area).

Grassland

Grassland habitats are recorded at 52% of all IBAs. Figure 16 shows the proportion of IBAs in each country that have a significant extent of grassland habitat (at least 5% cover of individual IBA). More than half of IBAs in most countries have significant grassland, and in the countries with alpine habitats (and smaller numbers of IBAs) the proportion is higher. In terms of the number of IBAs with grassland habitat, France, Germany, Ireland, Italy, Russia, Spain and United Kingdom rate highly. The types of grassland found within IBAs are shown in Figure 17.

- Humid grassland is the most frequently recorded type of grassland within IBAs, being recorded at 45% of IBAs with any grassland habitat.
- Steppe or dry calcareous grassland is present at 23% of IBAs with any grassland habitat.
- Mesophile grassland (permanent pasture in the temperate zone) is present at 22% of IBAs with any grassland habitat.
- Alpine, subalpine or boreal grassland is present at 14% of grassland IBAs.
- Tundra and machair are grassland types that are much more rarely recorded at IBAs, occurring at 3% and 1% of grassland IBAs respectively.

Figure 17. The types of grassland present at Important Bird Areas in Europe.

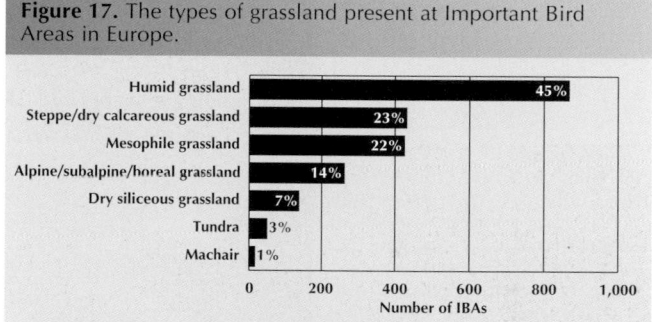

Humid grassland	45%
Steppe/dry calcareous grassland	23%
Mesophile grassland	22%
Alpine/subalpine/boreal grassland	14%
Dry siliceous grassland	7%
Tundra	3%
Machair	1%

Number of IBAs

The figure at the end of each bar indicates the percentage of those IBAs containing any grassland (1,918 sites) that actually contain the grassland-type in question. At 16% of the 1,918 grassland IBAs, no types of grassland were distinguished.

Extensive tundra at Itsako, western Greenland (IBA 018), an important site for moulting and breeding White-fronted Goose *Anser albifrons flavirostris*. (PHOTO: DAVID BOERTMANN)

Extensive tracts of artificial landscape occur in 36% of IBAs in Spain. Rain-fed arable cultivation, which occurs at more than 22% of Spanish IBAs, is of great importance in conserving Great Bustard *Otis tarda*, Little Bustard *Tetrax tetrax* and Lesser Kestrel *Falco naumanni*, three species of global conservation concern. (PHOTO: PAUL GORIUP)

Most perennial crops, orchards and groves in Europe are now managed rather intensively, as large commercial operations, with the notable exception of olive production in the Mediterranean, most groves of which remain family-owned. Olive groves consequently display a higher diversity of structure, making them attractive to many woodland species, together with their oil-rich fruit. (PHOTO: MARCO LAMBERTINI)

Much of the forest cover in Europe is now composed of plantations, as here in Germany. If situated and managed appropriately, such plantations can provide valuable habitat for forest birds and other wildlife. (PHOTO: CHRISTOPH HEINRICH)

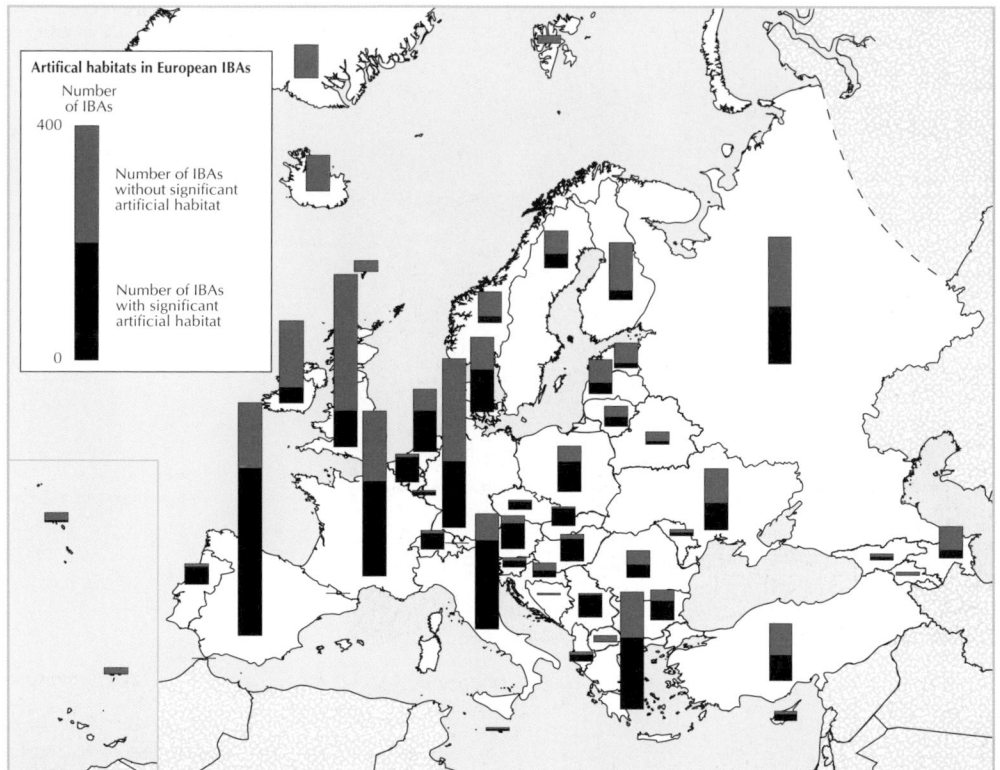

Artifical habitats in European IBAs

Number
of IBAs
400

Number of IBAs
without significant
artificial habitat

Number of IBAs
with significant
artificial habitat

0

Figure 18. The number of Important Bird Areas in Europe, by country, that contain a significant extent of artificial landscape.

The height of the column is proportional to the total number of IBAs in the country. Overall, at least 1,734 IBAs in Europe contain a significant extent of artificial landscape (i.e. covering at least 5% of the individual IBA area).

Artificial landscapes

Artificial landscapes, especially those that are extensively or traditionally managed for agriculture or forestry, support important populations of many bird species. Artificial landscapes have been recorded at IBAs in most countries (Figure 18), with the exception of Greenland, Iceland, Svalbard/Jan Mayen and the Faroe Islands, being recorded in 52% of all IBAs. In Scandinavia and the Baltic countries, the proportion of IBAs with artificial habitats is also very low. In contrast, Belgium, the Netherlands and many central and southern European countries have a high proportion of IBAs containing a significant extent of artificial landscape. The types of artificial landscape found within IBAs are further described in Figure 19.

- Arable land is present in 69% of IBAs with artificial landscapes.
- Perennial crops, orchards and groves are present in 30% of IBAs with artificial landscapes.
- Forestry plantations are present in 26% of IBAs with artificial landscapes.

- Highly improved reseeded grassland is present in 23% of IBAs with artificial landscapes.
- Urban or industrial areas (other than parks/gardens and ruderal land) are present in 21% of IBAs with artificial landscapes.

Figure 19. The types of artificial landscape present at Important Bird Areas in Europe.

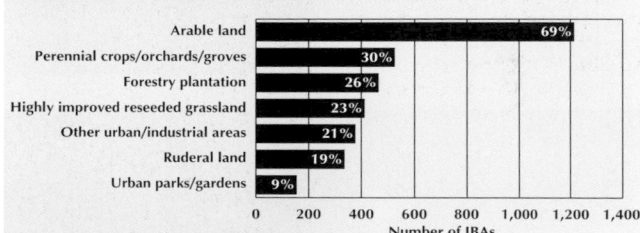

Arable land	69%
Perennial crops/orchards/groves	30%
Forestry plantation	26%
Highly improved reseeded grassland	23%
Other urban/industrial areas	21%
Ruderal land	19%
Urban parks/gardens	9%

The figure at the end of each bar indicates the percentage of those IBAs containing any artificial landscape (1,768 sites) that actually contain the type of artificial landscape in question. At 5% of the 1,768 IBAs, no types of artificial landscape were distinguished.

Improved reseeded grassland at Wexford Wildfowl Reserve, Ireland (IBA 102). This is one of the two most important sites in the world for wintering White-fronted Goose of the Greenland subspecies *Anser albifrons flavirostris*. (PHOTO: ALYN WALSH)

Scrub is a particularly important habitat in the Mediterranean biome, for such species as warblers *Sylvia*, shrikes *Lanius*, nightjars *Caprimulgus* and many other birds. (PHOTO: ALBERTO NARDI/NHPA)

Semi-desert landscape in Azerbaijan. (PHOTO: MICHAEL PATRIKEEV)

Seabird colony on a coastal cliff face in Germania Land, north-eastern Greenland (IBA 053). (PHOTO: DAVID BOERTMANN)

Other habitats

- In Europe, 36% of IBAs have a significant extent of scrub habitat, with 30% of these having sclerophyllous scrub, garrigue or maquis, and 31% heathland.
- Over 30% of IBAs in Europe have a significant extent of rocky areas. Approximately half of these IBAs are coastal, comprising such rocky areas as sea cliffs, rocky shores, rock stacks and islets, with coastal cliffs being particularly important for breeding seabirds. The remaining half of these IBAs are inland areas, with inland cliffs, scree and boulders usually occurring at IBAs in mountainous regions.
- Over 10% of IBAs in Europe are partly or wholly marine. In about two-thirds of these IBAs, 'marine' areas refer to sea inlets and coastal features, whilst the remaining one-third are open sea. See Box 4 for a more detailed discussion of marine IBAs and the difficulties involved in defining and identifying such sites.
- Located mainly in the south-eastern part of the Iberian peninsula and the Canary Islands, as well as in the lowlands of the Caucasus/Caspian region, desert and semi-desert habitats are present in 43 IBAs in Europe.

Box 4. Important marine areas for birds in Europe.

The importance of marine areas for birds

The marine environment is important for birds in Europe. European seas support 62 species of bird that either have an unfavourable conservation status in Europe (Tucker and Heath 1994) or are marine specialists which are highly dependent upon the continuing integrity and quality of marine ecosystems (Tucker and Evans 1997). These 62 species include four species that are globally threatened or near-threatened with extinction. Many of these 62 species congregate at certain times of the year, such as seabirds at breeding colonies or divers *Gavia* and seaduck (Anatidae) at favourable feeding grounds in winter. Yet despite its importance for bird conservation, the marine environment has, until recently, received relatively little attention in terms of the identification of Important Bird Areas. This is due primarily to the difficulty of defining, identifying and delineating priority sites in areas of homogeneous appearance, coupled with the difficulty of stimulating international co-operation to establish integrated protection and management schemes for important sites outside national territorial waters.

This inventory identifies 470 IBAs in Europe that have some marine habitat, including 147 IBAs that have more than 50% marine habitat cover and at least 25 IBAs are solely marine. However, no specific attempt has been made, within the scope of this IBA review, to provide complete listings of marine areas important for birds in Europe.

Previous inventories of marine areas that are internationally important for birds

Two major studies have defined, identified and delineated important areas for birds in European seas: *Important bird areas for seabirds in the North Sea* (Skov *et al.* 1995) and *Important marine areas for wintering birds in the Baltic Sea* (Durinck *et al.* 1994). Further work on the identification of IBAs is in progress, as part of the BirdLife Baltic Sea Programme, the results of which are expected to be published in 2000.

North Sea The study area covered the entire North Sea, the Channel and the Kattegat, bounded by the coastlines of the United Kingdom, Norway, Sweden, Denmark, Germany, the Netherlands, Belgium and France (Skov *et al.* 1995, Skov *et al.* in prep.). It included all territorial and international waters between the western Channel, the Northern Atlantic and the Kattegat. Data were analyzed from coastal and offshore seabird surveys during 1979–1994. The distribution of 30 species provided the basis for identifying important areas for birds. Twenty areas were identified as internationally important for birds in the area, of which the top six sites comprising less than 5 % of the region hold more than 80% of the cumulated sum of proportions for the species in question.

Baltic Sea The study area encompassed the entire Baltic Sea, the Danish Straits and the Kattegat (Durinck *et al.* 1994, Skov *et al.* in prep). Data were presented for 30 species for which 1% or more of their biogeographic population winters in the Baltic Sea. Thirty-nine areas were identified as internationally important for wintering birds in the region, of which the top 10 sites, which cover less than 5% of the region, hold about 90% of the total estimated number of wintering birds.

The conservation of marine areas

The IVth World Congress on National Parks and Protected Areas (IUCN 1993) highlighted the need for increased establishment of marine protected areas in order to conserve biodiversity. Some site-based agreements that are important for the conservation of such areas in Europe are as follows (further details can be found in Appendix 1).

EC Directives: Special Protection Areas (SPAs) and Special Areas for Conservation (SACs) The Habitats Directive calls for the establishment by 2004 of a coherent network of protected areas for biodiversity conservation in the European Union, the Natura 2000 network. The network will be composed of SPAs (designated under national law in fulfillment of the Birds Directive) and SACs (similarly, in fulfillment of the Habitats Directive). These designations apply within the territorial waters of EU Member States. The application of EU law to the offshore Exclusive Economic Zone (EEZ) of member states has recently been clarified by the EU Commission. Although EU law *per se* applies to the territorial sea of coastal member states, it also applies to their EEZ in cases when a member state considers itself competent to apply national law within the same field to the EEZ.

Ministerial Conference on the North Sea This process, devoted to the protection of the North Sea ecosystem, began in 1984 and involves the ministers of North Sea states, Switzerland and the European Commission. The significance of ministerial conferences is that they may consider subjects outside existing conventions and treaties, such as the protection and management of marine IBAs outside territorial waters.

OSPAR Convention (Oslo and Paris Convention) The focus of this convention has been the reduction of land- and sea-based pollution in the north-east Atlantic, but the scope of OSPAR was broadened in July 1998 when ministers, at the meeting of the OSPAR Commission in Sintra (Portugal), adopted a new Annex V to the OSPAR Convention. This opens the way for the Commission to take measures to protect and conserve ecosystems and biological diversity in the north-east Atlantic. One of the agreed tools for doing this is to work towards the establishment of a network of marine protected areas (MPAs). In protecting species and habitats, the OSPAR Commission can recommend to the competent authorities a wide range of measures affecting all relevant sectors, including shipping and fisheries.

Helsinki Convention This convention brings countries bordering the Baltic Sea together with the European Community under the Helsinki Commission (HELCOM). One of HELCOM's most important decisions has been to recommend the establishment of a network of Baltic Sea Protected Areas (BSPAs). Included in this recommendation was provision for the identification of areas important for concentrations of feeding, wintering or staging seabirds (Hägerhäll and Skov 1998).

Barcelona Convention Since 1994–1995 this convention for the protection of the Mediterranean Sea ecosystem has included a greater emphasis on biodiversity conservation. Contracting parties are now required to draw up lists of Mediterranean Specially Protected Areas (MedSPAs) within their territorial waters (previously, this was optional). Such sites should be important for the protection of ecosystems or of special scientific, aesthetic or cultural value. There is also an Annex to the MedSPA Protocol which lists species considered by the contracting parties to be endangered and threatened in the Mediterranean, including seabirds. Parties are required to take appropriate measures to protect these species and their habitats.

Summary and conclusions

- Many bird species that are dependent on the marine environment congregate at certain times of the year. Several hundred marine IBAs have been identified in this publication for such species, and the protection and suitable management of these areas would be a major step towards conserving these marine species in Europe.
- Despite the inclusion of these marine areas within this pan-European inventory, a comprehensive documentation of marine areas important for birds was not achieved. However, work previously undertaken in the North Sea and Baltic Sea (Durinck *et al.* 1994, Skov *et al.* 1995) shows that entirely marine areas important for birds, including congregations of wintering auks, divers and seaducks, can be defined, identified and delineated.
- More than one conservation mechanism is appropriate to the conservation of the marine environment for birds. Most marine birds are distributed in a highly dispersed fashion at some stage of their annual cycle, and given the size, socio-economic importance, and international nature of marine areas that are likely to be important for birds, site-based measures—e.g. the establishment of networks of strictly protected areas suitable for highly congregatory species—need to balanced with the conservation of the wider marine environment, involving the integration of conservation across all relevant sectors, programmes and policies.
- A site-based approach to seabird conservation would be greatly assisted by marine extensions to terrestrial (coastal) protected areas, in order to protect key areas such as off-colony foraging areas and loafing areas at sea.
- A number of different site-based conservation initiatives are in the early stages of implementation, under a variety of international legal agreements.
- Outside territorial waters, international cooperation and coordination will be vital if the marine environment is to be managed to conserve its biodiversity.

LAND-USES AND THREATS AT IBAs

■ Land-uses at IBAs

The great variety and high intensity of land-uses recorded within IBAs reflect the high human use of Europe's habitats in general. Land-use activities have been recorded in 95% of IBAs, and in only 15% of these IBAs is part or all of the individual IBA area classified as 'Not utilized'. As a result, the conservation of habitats and birds within IBAs is very much dependent on the land-use practices, policies and programmes that affect these sites. Figure 20 shows the types of land-use recorded in IBAs:

- Agriculture is the dominant land-use in Europe and this is reflected within IBAs, with agricultural activities taking place in 65% of IBAs and being predominant at 17% of sites (Figure 20). The conservation of most IBAs is therefore much influenced by agricultural practices in the individual IBA and its surroundings, and suitable management is required to conserve species dependent on these habitats.

- Tourism and recreation are the second-most frequently cited land-use, affecting 41% of IBAs. The very high human population densities over much of Europe, the attractiveness as destinations of natural areas such as IBAs, and the relative ease of access to most parts of the continent, explain much of this statistic.

- Hunting takes place at 38% of sites and may be even more wide-spread at IBAs, since this land-use was probably under-recorded.

- At least 54% of IBAs contain forest/woodland or forestry plantation. Much of the area of these forest habitats in Europe is actively managed, with forestry taking place in at least 35% of IBAs.

- Fisheries and/or aquaculture take place in at least 29% of IBAs, especially in marine and coastal areas and, inland, at fish-ponds.

- At least 29% of IBAs are used for nature conservation and research. Generally, this category was recorded only when land was used primarily for this purpose.

- Urban, industrial and transport activities affect at least 23% of IBAs but, in general, affect only a small proportion of the area of each site.

- Water management affects at least 14% of IBAs and includes the drainage, storage and extraction of water, for such purposes as irrigation, flood control and power generation.

Threats facing IBAs are diverse, resulting from lack of effective management and wardening, illegal land-use, regional, industrial or urban development and impact of land-uses from neighbouring areas (e.g. pollution, drainage). The key types of threats affecting IBAs are shown in Figure 23, with the intensification and expansion of agriculture being the most significant, impacting more than 1,300 IBAs. The following sections present further information, with selected examples, on the 12 most common high-impact threats

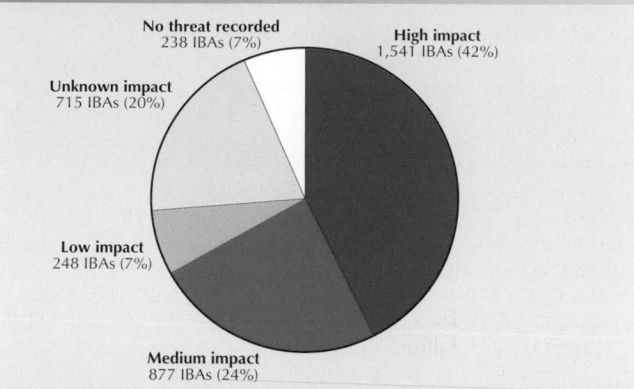

Figure 21. The highest level of threat recorded against individual Important Bird Areas in Europe.

Highest level of impact on individual IBA
The percentage in brackets indicates the proportion of IBAs in Europe that are affected, at this level of impact, by one or more threats. See Appendix 3 for a more detailed description of the system used for estimating the magnitude of impact.

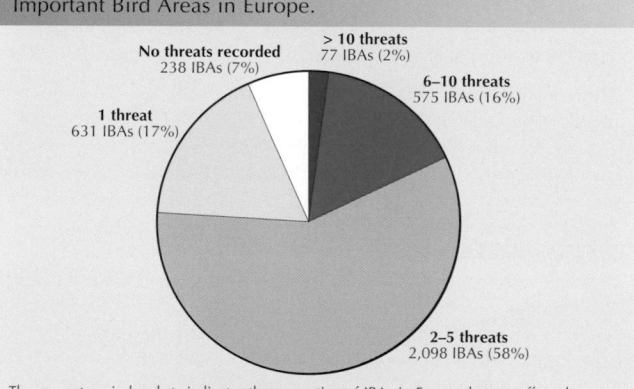

Figure 22. The total number of threats affecting individual Important Bird Areas in Europe.

The percentage in brackets indicates the proportion of IBAs in Europe that are affected.

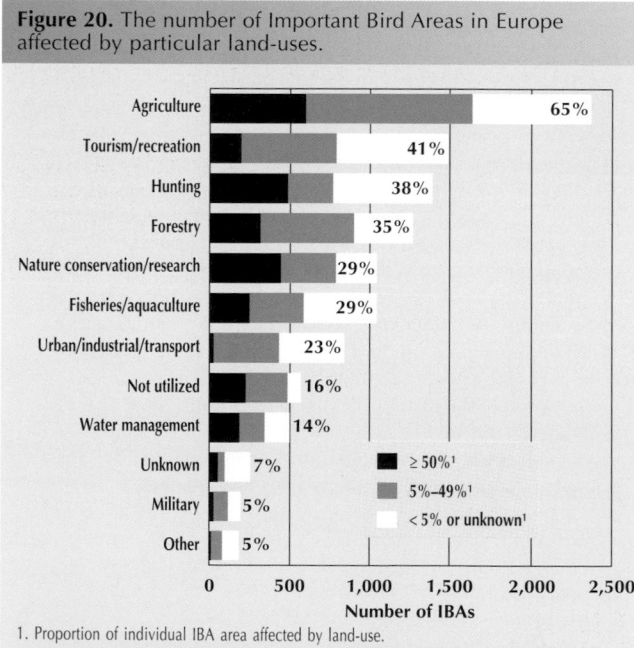

Figure 20. The number of Important Bird Areas in Europe affected by particular land-uses.

1. Proportion of individual IBA area affected by land-use.

The percentage at the end of each bar indicates the proportion of IBAs in Europe that are affected by the land-use (no land-use data were recorded at 155 IBAs). See Appendix 3 for a more detailed description of the land-use classification used.

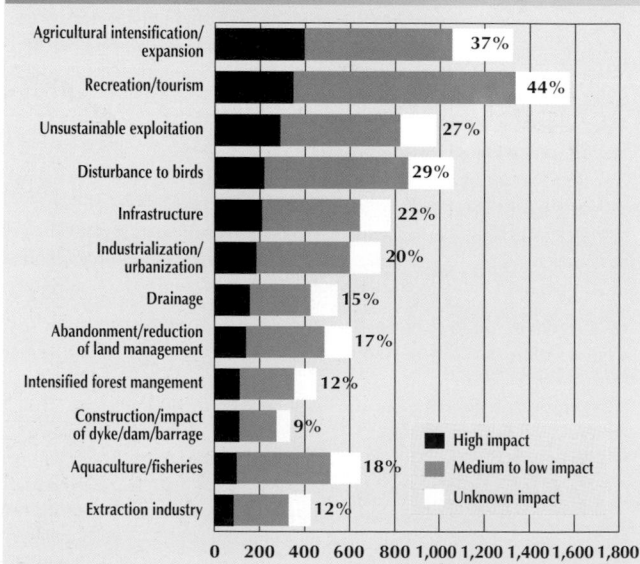

Figure 23. The high-impact threats that are most prevalent at Important Bird Areas in Europe.

Only those threats impacting more than 10% of IBAs in Europe are listed.

The percentage at the end of each bar indicates the proportion of IBAs in Europe that are impacted by the threat. See Appendix 3 for a more detailed description of the threat classification used.

■ Threats at IBAs

At least 93% of IBAs are considered to be threatened to some degree by at least one factor, and 42% of IBAs in Europe are affected by one or more high-impact threats (Figure 21). Most IBAs are threatened by more than one factor (Figure 22), with the majority (58%) being threatened by 2–5 different types of threat.

at IBAs. Other common threats, each impacting more than 250 IBAs, include afforestation (352 IBAs), burning of vegetation (287 IBAs), the consequences of animal or plant introductions (270 IBAs), and commercial deforestation (261 IBAs).

Agricultural intensification and expansion

Agricultural intensification and/or expansion is the most serious threat affecting IBAs across Europe, being cited at more than 1,300 sites and with a high impact at nearly 400 of these. In most countries, with the exception of those with large areas of land at high latitude or altitude, agricultural intensification and expansion threatens more than 20% of the country's IBAs (Figure 24). This threat covers a range of agricultural activities, including:

- the replacement of dry grasslands, rain-fed cereals and steppe with dense, irrigated, fast-growing, heavily fertilized and pesticide-treated crops;
- the lowering of the water-tables of wet grasslands, followed by reseeding, fertilizer applications and high stocking levels; and the conversion to intensive silage crops of mesophile grasslands (hay-meadows and permanent pastures) across the temperate regions of Europe;
- the intensification of arable farmland through high inputs of inorganic fertilizers, crop specialization (at the landscape level), elimination of fallow periods, and increased field-sizes;
- overgrazing of pastures accompanied by excessive soil erosion and compaction; and
- the loss from the farmed landscape of small semi-natural areas and important features, including strips of meadow, hedgerows, copses, small ponds, and tree stands along rivers and lakes.

Some examples of agricultural intensification and/or expansion posing a threat (actual or potential) to IBAs (excerpted from national overviews in this publication)

- In Portugal, agricultural intensification affects 50% of IBAs and is a particular problem for species dependent on non-intensive farming systems (for example Great Bustard *Otis tarda* and Black-bellied Sandgrouse *Pterocles orientalis*), and for farmland species in areas that have already undergone some intensification and are now seeing further measures being taken to increase productivity.
- In Spain, EU livestock headage payments have caused overgrazing problems in steppe areas, increasing erosion and disturbing key breeding birds. Arable production has become more intensive, particularly through the expansion of irrigated

Steppe land in Spain, which supports most of the European population of the globally threatened Great Bustard *Otis tarda*, is increasingly being converted to irrigated cultivation. (PHOTO: GUY DUKE)

crops, resulting in serious loss of steppe habitats and traditional non-irrigated crops, and threatening the most important areas for Great Bustard *Otis tarda*, Little Bustard *Tetrax tetrax* and Lesser Kestrel *Falco naumanni*, including sites 038, 039, 041, 043, 058, 061, 062, 072, 074, 105, 106, 111, 193, 199, 202, 207, 229, 232, 237, 238, 264, 276, 280, 285, 294 and 295.

- In Turkey, agricultural intensification affects 49 out of 97 IBAs. Since the 1950s the land area under cultivation has more than doubled, with the expansion coming partly at the expense of available grazing land. This has led to an increase in grazing pressure in remaining pastures and hence problems of overgrazing and excessive soil erosion. Wetlands have been drained for conversion to arable land and many others have been adversely affected by water-diversion schemes to feed irrigated agriculture. At least 1,300,000 ha of wetland habitat have been drained or otherwise destroyed this century, mainly since 1960. The Konya basin of central Anatolia provides a shocking example of the consequences of large-scale irrigation projects. Two large wetlands with a total area of 30,000 ha have dried up, and three large wetland IBAs totalling 106,000 ha (sites 067–069) have sustained serious damage. A further three wetland IBAs (070–072) now risk long-term damage as a result of pollution from untreated irrigation waste-water.

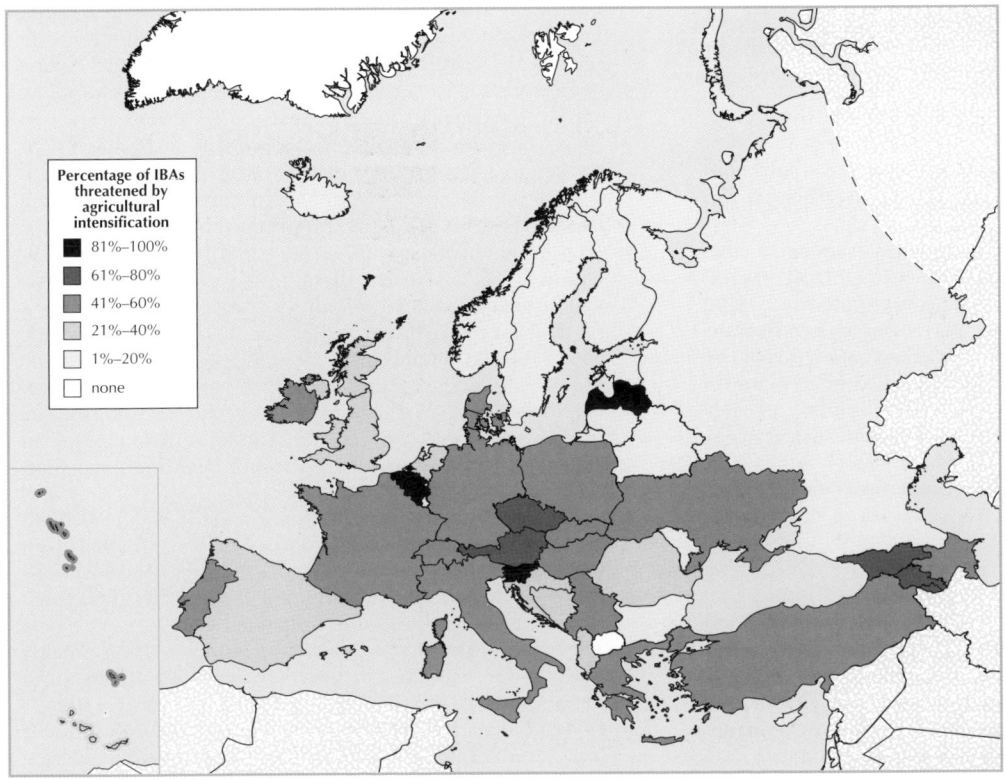

Percentage of IBAs threatened by agricultural intensification

- 81%–100%
- 61%–80%
- 41%–60%
- 21%–40%
- 1%–20%
- none

Figure 24. The percentage of Important Bird Areas, per country, that are threatened by agricultural intensification.

- In Ukraine, the intensification of agriculture in recent decades has caused pollution of soil and fresh water with fertilizers and pesticides. Agricultural intensification is recorded as a high-impact threat at sites 025, 032, 037, 047, 071, 094 and 102.
- In Ireland, agricultural intensification is considered to have a high impact at 11 IBAs, primarily areas where the maintenance of non-intensive farming is crucial for the continued breeding of the globally threatened *Crex crex* (sites 002, 007, 012–014, 041 and 131), sites which have suffered severe overgrazing such as at Owenduff–Nephin Beg (site 046) and water-bodies threatened by nutrient pollution as a result of agricultural run-off (e.g. sites 123 and 138).
- In Denmark 22% of sites are seriously affected by agricultural intensification and expansion, mostly through high inputs of fertilisers and pesticides, which has resulted in uniform landscapes that are poor in the habitat features required by many bird species of European conservation concern. Furthermore, nutrient-laden run-off from intensive agricultural land is believed to be the main factor behind the nutrient pollution of many wetland sites in Denmark.
- In Austria, agricultural intensification and expansion have negatively affected 69% of IBAs, and are regarded as a high-impact threat at 29% of sites, including 003, 007, 014, 015, 019, 024, 025, 028, 030, 038, 041, 042, 043, 045, 054 and 055.
- In Poland, as is the case in many countries in the east of the region, at agricultural IBAs the main threat is posed by an anticipated change in the Polish farming system, away from the current predominance of small, non-intensive farms towards a landscape dominated by large, intensive farms. At least 43% of IBAs in Poland are threatened, to some degree, by the intensification or expansion of agricultural practices.

The development of tourism threatens many coastal areas in the Mediterranean and elsewhere. (PHOTO: MARCO LAMBERTINI)

- In Bulgaria, the growth of recreation and urbanization has been very rapid in recent years, especially along the Black Sea coast. Wetlands near large settlements and industrial zones are particularly vulnerable, with the most affected sites including those bordering the towns of Burgas and Varna: the Mandra–Poda complex (site 034), Burgasko lake (035), Atanasovo lake (036) and Varna–Beloslav lakes complex (047).
- Mountain areas are also particularly affected by recreation and tourism, including activities such as skiing, hiking, climbing, off-road driving and biking. For example, in France skiing or climbing are recorded as a significant threat at Forêts d'altitude du Jura (097), Haute Soule: massif de la Pierre-St-Martin (188) and Bois de Palayson, du Rouet et de Malvoisin (265).

Recreation and tourism

Tourism and/or recreation have been cited as a threat at 1,575 IBAs, with impact considered to be high at 348 IBAs. This threat is particularly serious in Mediterranean wetland, forest, shrubland and rocky habitats, where tourism is probably the main cause of habitat destruction and degradation, as well as of disturbance to birds. The Mediterranean countries are the world's most popular tourist destination. Existing tourist developments are most concentrated along the coasts of Spain, France, Portugal and Italy, but other countries such as Greece and Turkey continue to show explosive growth in this sector. From a 1990 level of 157 million visitors per year to these countries, numbers are predicted to increase to 380 million per year by 2050 if overall economic growth is weak, or up to 760 million if growth is strong (Stanners and Bourdeau 1995). It should be noted that in some cases this threat has also been recorded under 'Disturbance to birds'.

Some examples of recreation/tourism posing a threat (actual or potential) to IBAs (excerpted from national overviews in this publication)
- In Spain, recreation/tourism is the most frequently cited threat to IBAs, often in connection with infrastructural developments. Impacts tend to be concentrated in coastal areas, particularly along the Mediterranean coast and on the Balearic and Canary Islands, where urbanization (driven by tourism) has severely affected or destroyed many habitats that were previously of high importance for birds, especially wetlands. Related infrastructural developments such as major roads and airports are often funded by the EU. Sites where recreation or tourism is regarded a high threat include IBAs 307, 308, 310, 311, 315, 319, 321, 323, 328, 330, 332, 337, 340, 343, 345, 356, 367 and 372.
- Recreation and tourism have a high impact at 33% of Azorean IBAs. Tern *Sterna* colonies along the coast of Flores (001), coast of Faial (003), coast and islets of Graciosa (007) and south-east coast of Terceira (009) are most vulnerable to these threats, which have led to colony desertion and low breeding success. Tourists pose a serious problem at Vila Franca islet (012), where they inadvertently trample and destroy nest-sites of Cory's Shearwater *Calonectris diomedea*.

Unsustainable exploitation

Unsustainable hunting (whether legal or illegal) is considered a threat at more than 950 IBAs, and is particularly significant at nearly 300 sites. As well as shooting, other forms of unsustainable bird exploitation which pose a threat at some IBAs include trapping, the use of lime, and the collection of eggs and young.

Some examples of unsustainable exploitation posing a threat (actual or potential) at IBAs (excerpted from national overviews in this publication)
- Particularly badly affected is Cyprus, where the killing of migratory birds is a serious problem and is listed as a threat at nearly 90% of IBAs. Although the island's hunting (shooting) regulations are fairly comprehensive, law enforcement is inadequate and thousands of birds of many species are illegally shot each year.
- Illegal bird-shooting is a serious problem in Malta, e.g. at Buskett and Wied il-Luq (site 003) which is a major passage site for raptors and nationally important for wintering passerines as well as many trans-Saharan autumn migrants.
- Hunting is a widespread activity in Greece, occurring in almost all IBAs, and is a threat at more than 80% of IBAs, with a high impact at 36% of all sites. Illegal hunting is a particularly severe threat at sites 019, 022, 084, 095, 100, 105, 116, 130, 140, 146 and 172.
- In Spain, hunting is considered a threat at over 40% of IBAs. Additionally, at several globally important wetlands such as the Ebro delta (site 148) and El Hondo wetland (165), lead poisoning of waterbirds, as a result of ingesting spent shot, is a problem.
- In Bulgaria, hunting pressure is particularly high in wetland areas such as the Shabla lakes complex (site 049) and Durankulak lake (050) which both hold large concentrations of wintering waterbirds, including the globally threatened Red-breasted Goose *Branta ruficollis*.
- The predominant threat to IBAs in Georgia is unsustainable exploitation (legal and illegal hunting) which affects seven out of the 11 IBAs (63%), with a high impact at five sites.
- In Azerbaijan, the main threat at IBAs is the unsustainable level of bird exploitation, affecting 63% of IBAs (mainly legal

Freshly killed White Pelican *Pelecanus onocrotalus*. Hunting remains a significant threat at many IBAs, in terms of disturbance as well as mortality. (PHOTO: GERNANT MAGNIN)

and illegal hunting at over 30 IBAs). Waterbirds at Azerbaijan's most important wetlands are severely affected by hunting and poaching, also by the accompanying disturbance which, for some sites, may be a more serious threat than the direct mortality.

Infrastructure

A total of 779 IBAs are threatened by planned or ongoing infrastructural development. This problem looks set to increase, with new transportation infrastructure expected to claim 8,500–12,500 km² in the EU from other land-uses during 1990–2010 (EEA 1999). This will increase the fragmentation and isolation of Europe's remaining patches of semi-natural habitat, and is likely to have a major negative impact on biodiversity.

The total length of motorway in the majority of countries in the EU increased by more than 300% between 1970 and 1994 (EEA 1998). The Trans-European Network planned by the EU will involve around 140 projects for further road construction and improvement in the European Union. Approximately 15,000 km of new road are proposed, as well as rail links, combined transport and waterways. These links are likely to be extended to central and eastern Europe as trade increases and as the EU is enlarged (EEA 1998).

A pilot study (Bina *et al.* 1995) assessed the potential impact of the Trans-European Network on IBAs and statutory protected areas, based on the previous pan-European IBA inventory (Grimmett and Jones 1989). It found that more than 12% of IBAs in the EU are within 10 km of planned road and rail developments, with more than 2% of IBAs in the EU being situated within 2 km of planned road and rail developments.

Some examples of infrastructure posing a threat (actual or potential) to IBAs (excerpted from national overviews in this publication)

- Infrastructure and associated industrialization and urbanization are long-term threats to 50–65% of IBAs in Belgium. Schorren en Polder van de Beneden Schelde (site 011), an important wintering site for waders and other waterbirds, will largely be destroyed by the expansion of Antwerp harbour facilities.

The total length of motorway in the majority of European countries increased by more than 300% between 1970 and 1994 (EEA 1998). (PHOTO: BIRDLIFE INTERNATIONAL)

- In France several very significant IBAs, holding rare species and habitats, remain under threat even though they are designated as Special Protection Areas under the EC Birds Directive. The Crau (site 240), the only large semi-arid plain in France, supporting important populations of typical steppe species, is threatened by state development projects (military activities, motorways).
- In Ireland, individual infrastructure development projects may have a marked impact on specific IBAs, such as road developments within Cork Harbour (site 088) and at Malahide/Swords (113), and planned road development within Dublin Bay (109), while port development threatens the Boyne estuary (119).
- Recent government plans to further develop the road network in Austria could pose a major threat to several IBAs (e.g. sites 006, 012, 045). Plans for other infrastructure development, such as golf courses and recreation parks, and the planned construction of dams on rivers are a constant and recurring threat to several sites (e.g. 013). If implemented, the planned Elbe–Oder–Danube canal could alter dramatically the ecosystem of the March river (010).
- Infrastructure development in Switzerland, particularly increasing road density and other transport networks, is a major threat, affecting 55% of IBAs (13% with a high impact), especially as it facilitates access to remote areas, resulting in more intense disturbance of birds such as Black Grouse *Tetrao tetrix*.
- In Spain, infrastructure development is a high-impact threat at 14% of IBAs and also threatens a further 27% of sites. Most of these threats have arisen since Spain joined the European Union in 1986. Since then, transport and water-related infrastructure (reservoirs, hydroelectric power, irrigation) have been improved but much of the investment has affected natural areas detrimentally. Environmental impact assessments have failed to adequately examine alternative scenarios or projects. Many further water-related developments are planned that will affect IBAs, some of them without real justification and potentially with a highly deleterious impact on sites and their species. Hydroelectric power plants are proliferating on rivers in mountainous areas and few rivers remain unregulated. New wind-energy plants are being constructed in mountainous areas where key bird species migrate, breed or feed.

Disturbance to birds

Disturbance to birds is listed as a threat at over 1,000 IBAs, and is a high-impact threat at 22% of sites. With intensifying use and increasing fragmentation of Europe's habitats by many factors, including infrastructure, urbanization, industrialization, recreation/tourism, agriculture and forestry, the level of human activity in remaining patches of habitat increases, as does disturbance to birds' vital activities such as breeding or foraging.

The impact of disturbance at a particular site is often difficult to quantify, as its effects on the reproductive success of individual species, at the level of national or European population, remain unknown.

Breeding colony of Roseate Tern *Sterna dougallii* being disturbed by fishermen at Alagoa complex on the coast of Flores, Azores (IBA 001). (PHOTO: L. R. MONTEIRO/IMAGDOP)

Industrialization and urbanization

Industrialization and urbanization threaten at least 735 IBAs, and the extent of urban areas in the EU is predicted to increase by 5–8% between 1990 and 2010 (EEA 1999).

Some examples of industrialization and urbanization threatening IBAs (taken from national overviews in this publication)
- More than half of the total forest area in the Czech Republic is affected by industrial air-pollution, a proportion higher than that in any other European country. IBAs containing forests that are being badly impacted by acid rain include Šumava mountains (site 005), Jeseníky mountains (016) and Krkonoše mountains (001).
- In Latvia, the possibility of pollution from Butinge oil terminal in Lithuania is thought to pose a major potential threat to two marine/coastal IBAs in Latvia, on the west coast (site 005) and the Irbe strait (014).
- Industrialization, urbanization and infrastructural developments, such as new industrial areas, housing and roads, are a major threat in Germany, affecting over 20% of IBAs.

Industrialization and/or urbanization threaten more than 700 IBAs in Europe. (PHOTO: MARCO LAMBERTINI)

- Industrial, agricultural, infrastructural and tourist development in Italy, often EU-funded, have in the past destroyed large areas of semi-natural habitat, and in some areas this is still occurring. Industrialization/urbanization is recorded as a threat at 67 IBAs and is considered to pose a high-impact threat at 21 sites.

Drainage

For centuries European wetlands have been drained, particularly for agricultural purposes, and very few now remain in a natural condition. The lower degree of industrialization, urbanization and agricultural intensification in central and eastern Europe, and lower population densities in Fennoscandia, mean that in these areas more extensive areas of natural wetland occur, but expected changes in central and eastern European countries, especially the intensification of agricultural practices, pose a severe threat. For example, 70% of wetlands in Lithuania have been drained during the last 30 years (EEA 1999). Overall, 544 IBAs in Europe are threatened by drainage, of which 157 are threatened to a high degree.

Some examples of drainage posing a threat (actual or potential) to IBAs (excerpted from national overviews in this publication)
- Wetland drainage has affected several wetlands of global importance in eastern Europe, including the Danube delta (site 001 in Romania) and the Volga delta (site 179 in Russia).
- In Hungary, drainage is a widespread threat, affecting over 50% of the land area of 19 IBAs and is listed as a high-impact threat at 11 IBAs (002, 003, 006, 007, 020, 025, 027, 028, 035, 037 and 038).
- In Belarus, a national drainage campaign over the last 30 years has resulted in 25,000 km² of mires being drained. The wetlands that remain (including the IBAs) continue to be influenced by the drastically lowered groundwater levels and by the pollution with nutrients and other chemicals that have followed previous drainage. The unique fens of Dikoe (site 010), Sporovo (014) and Zvanets (016) are the most threatened IBAs in Belarus because of the drainage of surrounding areas, together with the cessation of traditional land-uses, in particular manual haymaking.
- Drainage has also been particularly prevalent in the Mediterranean region, where wetland drainage has affected many IBAs such as the Evros delta (site 006 in Greece and 001 Turkey) and the Nestos delta (012) in Greece, both important sites all-year-round for waterbirds, raptors and passerines.
- Wet meadows are the most threatened habitat for birds in Slovenia, 11 IBAs being seriously affected by drainage, dredging and canalization (sites 002, 004–010, 012–014).
- In Italy, large areas of wetland have been drained for land-claim: while there were 7,640 km² of wetland in Italy in 1865, there are now only 1,800 km² (a 75% reduction). This remains a threat at 28 IBAs including River Po wetlands (sites 028 and 068).

Wetland drainage for agriculture in Turkey. (PHOTO: TOBIAS SALATHÉ)

Abandonment and reduction of land management

One of the indirect effects of agricultural intensification is that remaining marginal land becomes less profitable to farm. Many bird species that have adapted to artificial landscapes such as farmland require methods of non-intensive habitat management for their continued survival in such habitats. The abandonment of such practices is considered a threat at 609 IBAs.

Land abandonment is a significant threat to IBAs in many parts of central and eastern Europe (Figure 25), especially in the 12 countries due to join the European Union, where livestock numbers (especially sheep and cattle) decreased by 30–45% between 1989 and 1997 (Peters 1998). Land abandonment is also an important threat in the Mediterranean region, and in Sweden and other Baltic states.

Some examples of abandonment and reduction of land management posing a threat (actual or potential) to IBAs (taken from national overviews in this publication)

- In Sweden, abandonment and reduction of land management is the single most important threat, affecting 31 sites (49%). Undergrazing is a particular problem at many of these IBAs (for example sites 016, 023, 031, 036, 054, 058 and 059).

Grazed areas such as the coastal meadows on Öland Island, Sweden (IBA 054) hold high densities of breeding waders such as Redshank *Tringa totanus*, Dunlin *Calidris alpina* and Avocet *Recurvirostra avosetta*, and are also important stop-over sites for geese, ducks and waders. (PHOTO: BERTIL BREIFE)

- In Latvia, the state's transition to a market economy has been accompanied by a dramatic decrease in agricultural output in many marginal areas, whilst in more productive areas the intensification of agriculture continues. Large expanses of farmland have been set-aside or abandoned. For the first few years, this land is of increased importance for some birds, for instance the globally threatened *Crex crex*, but it soon loses its suitability for such 'open-country' species as the ground vegetation becomes too dense and the land becomes overgrown with bushes and small trees. This process threatens 30% of IBAs in Latvia.

- In Russia, the management of millions of hectares of agricultural land has been neglected or abandoned, and haymaking and grazing have stopped on many meadows and pastures. Land abandonment is recorded as a threat at 27 sites, with a high impact at nine (sites 027, 042, 098, 109, 119, 161, 206, 214 and 217).

- In Estonia, reduction or abandonment of agricultural land-use activity is having a detrimental effect on key bird species at 29 IBAs (67% of IBAs), largely due to overgrowth of coastal meadows by reed *Phragmites* as a result of undergrazing (e.g. Hiiumaa islands, site 004) and due to the overgrowth of flood-plains by scrub where haymaking has been abandoned (e.g. Soomaa mire complex, site 032).

- In Poland, as in most of the transition countries of central Europe, the main threat to birds at fish-pond IBAs is the likelihood that fishery management will become uneconomic (in the short term) and will be abandoned, leading to the disappearance of these man-maintained wetlands.

- In Slovakia, the abandonment of agricultural land and changes in management practices (for example, reductions in grazing intensity) over the last decade have affected 21 IBAs (66%), impacting three to a high degree (sites 011, 030 and 032).

- The abandonment of traditional land-uses and management practices in Greece is a threat at over 20% of IBAs. In particular, traditional pasture lands and arable cultivation have been abandoned, resulting in natural regeneration of forest and consequent changes in bird communities. The same pattern can be seen in many Mediterranean countries.

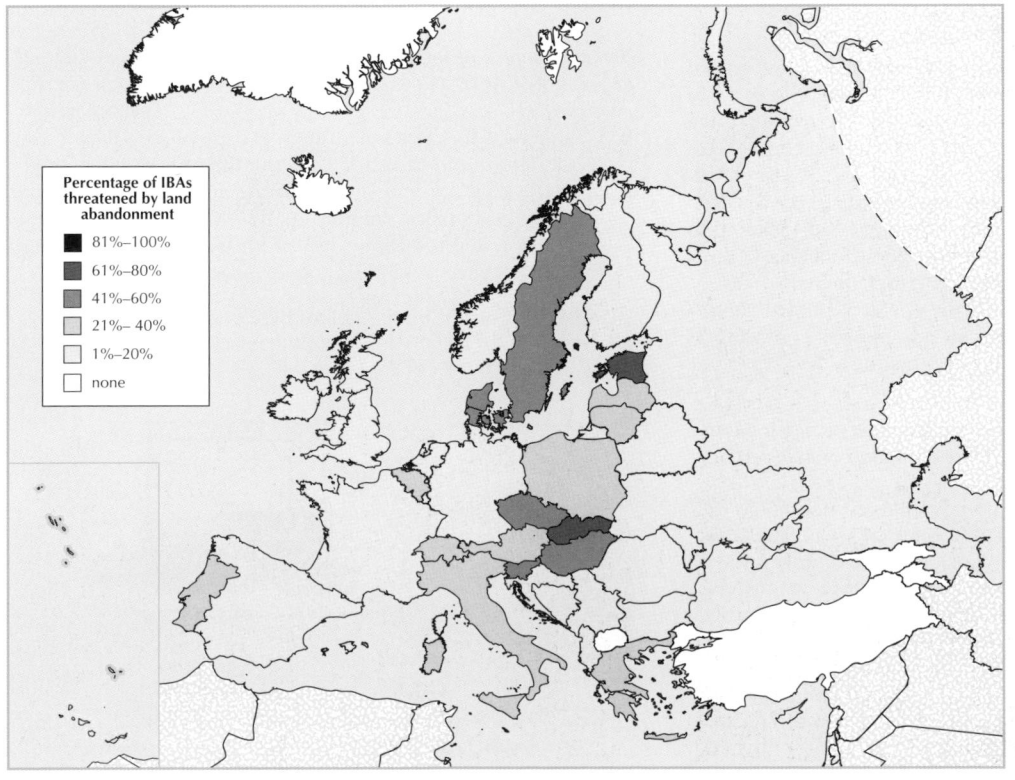

Figure 25. The percentage of Important Bird Areas, per country, that are threatened by land abandonment.

Percentage of IBAs threatened by land abandonment

- 81%–100%
- 61%–80%
- 41%–60%
- 21%–40%
- 1%–20%
- none

Construction/impact of dyke/dam/barrage

A total of 335 IBAs in Europe are threatened by the construction or downstream impact of dykes, dams or barrages.

> *Some examples of the construction/impact of dykes, dams or barrages posing a threat (actual or potential) to IBAs (excerpted from national overviews in this publication)*
> - Srebarna lake (site 033), Shabla lakes complex (049) and Durankulak lake (050) in Bulgaria, all particularly important for wintering geese (including the globally threatened Red-breasted Goose *Branta ruficollis*), are affected by dyke construction which lowers water-levels and destroys habitats such as temporary freshwater bodies and areas of shallow or open water.
> - Two IBAs in Iceland, Thjórsárver (site 059) and Eyjabakkar (061), will be submerged if reservoirs, planned for hydroelectric power-stations, are constructed and filled. The proposals involve the complete submersion of Eyjabakkar and the partial submersion of the Ramsar Site at Thjórsárver. Part of the Sog river (site 021) has already been damaged by reservoirs and other infrastructure for hydroelectric power-stations.
> - Wetlands in Slovenia are seriously affected by drainage, dredging and canalization. Such water management, together with the construction of dykes and dams and attempts to agriculturally improve arable land, all have an influence on groundwater levels and thus indirectly on wetlands. The riverine forests of the River Drava (site 012), River Mura (013) and Krakovo forest (009) are threatened by such activities.
> - The Loire valley (sites 031, 128, 154), containing the last unregulated river in France, is seriously threatened by the possible construction of barrages.

Over 300 IBAs in Europe are threatened by the construction or impact of dykes, dams or barrages. (PHOTO: WWF)

Intensified forest management

A total of 450 IBAs across Europe are threatened by intensified forest management, which can involve the clear-felling of large tracts, re-planting with uniform-aged trees of few species (often non-native), addition of fertilizer in some cases, harvesting of trees long before biological maturity, and extensive use of heavy soil-compacting machinery. Such management is also often accompanied by the construction of new forest roads, leading to increased habitat fragmentation and increased disturbance to birds (through facilitating access to previously remote areas).

In total 924 IBAs are threatened by forestry-related threats encompassing intensified forest management, commercial deforestation, afforestation and selective logging.

> *Some examples of intensified forest management posing a threat (actual or potential) to IBAs (excerpted from national overviews in this publication)*
> - In Finland, the pressure to convert old-growth forest to plantations is very high outside of protected areas. The areas of untouched wilderness in northern and eastern Finland have declined over recent decades as a result of active commercial forestry. This has caused population declines in many species dependent on old-growth forest. Fortunately, the most important IBAs for boreal forest, and its associated birds, are nearly all protected from commercial forestry. However, conversion to plantations is still a threat to 10% of IBAs and selective logging/cutting to a further 9%.

Forestry is widespread in Hungary and forest management is generally intensive. (PHOTO: HONCS)

> - Forestry in Latvia is intensifying and has grown to be the major state export; felling activity has doubled since 1990/1991. Harvesting during the breeding season is causing critical disturbance to sensitive bird species, such as Black Stork *Ciconia nigra* and Lesser Spotted Eagle *Aquila pomarina*, countrywide. Forest structure is changing towards a much lower percentage of older and less disturbed stands. Moreover, a considerable proportion of forest in Latvia has been privatized and thereafter it has become hard if not impossible to influence management towards conservation objectives. Intensified forest management is recorded as a threat in 30 IBAs (51% of IBAs in Latvia).
> - Many lowland forests in Greece are threatened by intensified forest management, in particular through the construction of new forest roads. The latter cause fragmentation and disturbance and greatly facilitate access to previously remote areas. A total of 25 IBAs in Greece are threatened by intensified forest management.
> - The intensification of forestry activities in Ukraine, through increased clear-felling and selective logging, are causing a decrease in the national populations of some raptors. IBAs affected include sites 001, 006, 028, 042 and 046.
> - Intensive forestry practices (logging, construction of forest roads, use of heavy machinery, the introduction of non-native tree species) pose a significant threat to 19 IBAs (59%) in Slovakia.

Aquaculture/fisheries

A total of 648 IBAs in Europe are threatened by fisheries or aquaculture activities.

> *Some examples of aquaculture/fisheries posing a threat (actual or potential) to IBAs (excerpted from national overviews in this publication)*
> - Commercial fisheries are a threat at 15% of the IBAs in the Netherlands, and at nearly 10% the threat is rated as 'high impact'. This specifically refers to shellfish harvesting on intertidal and shallow subtidal mudflats (which causes habitat destruction and food shortage for birds) and to over-fishing on the IJsselmeer and Markermeer (sites 034, 038).

Shellfish are 'mined' from mudflats by suction-dredgers in the Netherlands, as here in the Wadden Sea (IBA 001). (PHOTO: MARTIJN DE JONGE)

- A high proportion of Norwegian IBAs are important for their seabird colonies, and fisheries pose the most serious threat to these birds. In the past, over-exploitation of fish stocks has caused dramatic declines in several seabird populations along the coast of northern Norway, especially Guillemot *Uria aalge* and Puffin *Fratercula arctica*. Sustainable management of the fish stocks is crucial for most of the Norwegian seabird colonies listed in this inventory.

- Clam-dredging is a very localized activity in Greenland, but may occur at the same places as King Eider *Somateria spectabilis* moulting grounds, as at IBA 025 where this activity seems to have contributed to a major decline in numbers of this seaduck at this previously important moulting site.

- In Ireland, intertidal shellfish cultivation is a serious threat at a number of IBAs, including Trawbreaga Bay (site 003), Drumcliff Bay (033) and Dungarvan Harbour (094). Potentially it causes a loss of mudflat habitat and also disturbance to wintering waterbirds.

Extraction industry

A total of 426 IBAs in Europe are threatened by extraction industries, including mining and oil, gas and peat extraction.

Some examples of the extraction industries posing a threat (actual or potential) to IBAs (excerpted from national overviews in this publication)

- Peat mining has remained a constant threat to most peatland IBAs in Latvia. Regeneration can be poor or non-existent.

Peat extraction threatens Cena bog (IBA 030), one of the largest raised bogs in Latvia, important for thousands of geese *Anser* on passage and for breeding and migrating Cranes *Grus grus*. (PHOTO: EDMUNDS RAČINSKIS)

- In the United Kingdom, mineral extraction poses a significant threat to the East Devon Heaths (site 020). These heaths support a range of breeding heathland birds and are reported to be the best lowland heaths for butterflies in England.

- In Belgium, quarrying is destroying valuable habitats at Entre Sambre et Meuse (site 032), Haute Meuse (033), Lesse et Lomme (036) and Sinémurienne (047).

- In Iceland, mining of the bottom sediments of Lake Mývatn, to supply a diatomite factory by the lake, seriously threatens Mývatn–Laxá (site 044), a Ramsar Site. The site holds more than 20,000 waterbirds on a regular basis and several duck species breed at higher densities than anywhere else in Europe.

HOW WELL PROTECTED ARE IBAs?

■ The legal protection status of IBAs

National protection

A total of 2,191 IBAs in Europe (60% of the total) have at least some protection under national law, through their overlap with (mainly statutory) protected areas (Figure 26). However, in only 21% of IBAs in Europe is the extent of overlap classified as 'high', i.e. where more than 90% of the area of the individual IBA is protected. Indeed, in

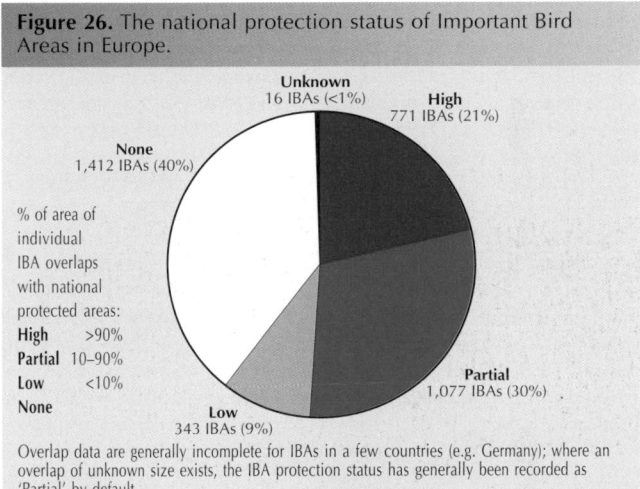

Figure 26. The national protection status of Important Bird Areas in Europe.

% of area of individual IBA overlaps with national protected areas:
High >90%
Partial 10–90%
Low <10%
None

Unknown 16 IBAs (<1%)
High 771 IBAs (21%)
None 1,412 IBAs (40%)
Partial 1,077 IBAs (30%)
Low 343 IBAs (9%)

Overlap data are generally incomplete for IBAs in a few countries (e.g. Germany); where an overlap of unknown size exists, the IBA protection status has generally been recorded as 'Partial' by default.

Figure 27. The national protection status of Important Bird Areas in each European country.

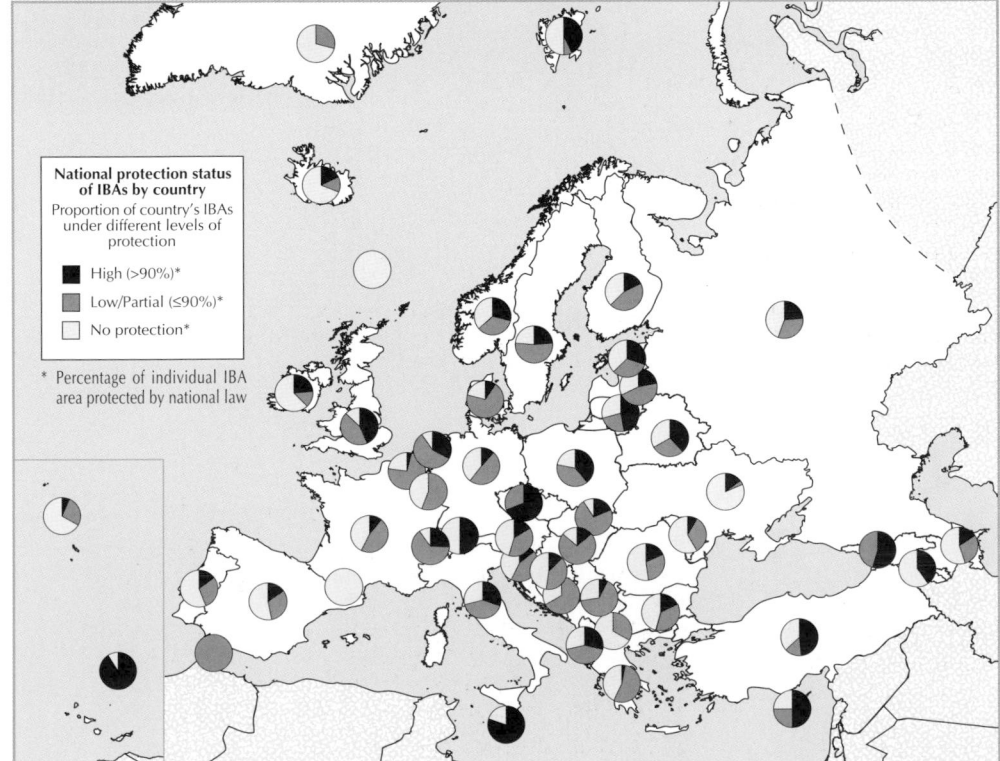

National protection status of IBAs by country
Proportion of country's IBAs under different levels of protection

■ High (>90%)*
▨ Low/Partial (≤90%)*
☐ No protection*

* Percentage of individual IBA area protected by national law

343 IBAs less than 10% of the area of the individual IBA overlaps with protected areas, and in 1,412 IBAs (39% of those in Europe) no form of legal protection is in place at the national level.

A higher proportion of IBAs are protected in some countries than in others (Figure 27). Countries with less than a third of their IBAs having any protection at the national level include Greenland, Faroe Islands, Iceland and Ukraine (see national chapters for more information). Those countries with more than a third of their IBAs receiving a high extent of protection, in terms of individual IBA area covered, include several island-states such as Madeira, Malta and Cyprus, as well as the United Kingdom, Belarus, Poland, Lithuania and Turkey. The Czech Republic stands out particularly in having a high proportion of its IBAs protected and most of these having, individually, a high extent of protection. For some countries the data presented on the extent of national protection of individual IBAs is incomplete.

In many countries, especially those preparing for accession to the EU, changes in the national protected-area legislation are ongoing or imminent, and thus the data presented in this publication may change in future. In addition, despite designation of statutory protected areas at the national level, in many countries the designated type of protection and management may be too weak or otherwise inappropriate for the site in question, and the level of enforcement is often under-resourced or poor.

International protection
Substantial international recognition of IBAs has been achieved in the last decade but many IBAs remain inadequately protected or recognized at the international level, given their relatively small overlap with areas that are listed under international conventions or designated under EC Directives (Figure 28). Only 1,436 IBAs in Europe (40% of the total) have some form of international protection, and in only 22% of all IBAs is the extent of protection classified as 'high', i.e. where more than 90% of the area of the individual IBA is protected. Indeed, at 108 IBAs less than 10% of the area of the individual IBA is protected at the international level, and at 2,183 IBAs (60% of the total) no form of international protection is in place.

A higher proportion of IBAs receive international protection in some countries than in others (Figure 29). Appendix 8 shows the number of IBAs in each country that are wholly or partly covered by the main international site-protection designations. Some forms of international legislation are only applicable in certain countries, for instance the EC Birds Directive is only relevant to the 15 member states of the European Union (see Appendix 1 for details). Due mainly to the application of this Directive, the proportion of

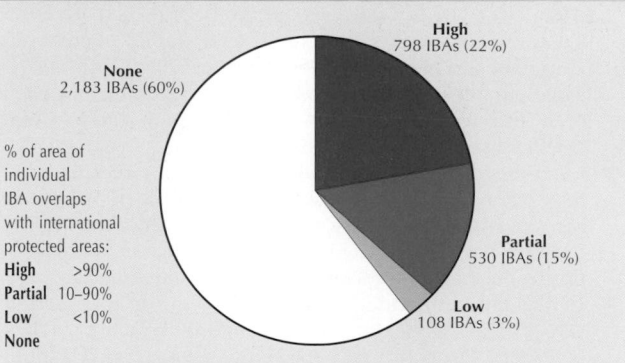

Figure 28. The international protection status of Important Bird Areas in Europe.

% of area of individual IBA overlaps with international protected areas:
High >90%
Partial 10–90%
Low <10%
None

Overlap data are generally incomplete for IBAs in a few countries (e.g. Germany); where an overlap of unknown size exists, the IBA protection status has generally been recorded as 'Partial' by default.

internationally protected IBAs is generally much lower in non-EU than EU countries. Countries outside of the EU with more than one third of their IBAs designated internationally at least in part are Estonia, Czech Republic, Slovakia and Hungary, largely reflecting the designation of Ramsar Sites.

For further details of the key international site-protection mechanisms, see Appendix 1. Currently, there are 23 natural or joint natural/cultural World Heritage Sites in Europe, 17 of which overlap with IBAs, and there are 126 Biosphere Reserves in Europe, 117 of which overlap with IBAs. Ramsar Sites and Special Protection Areas are assessed in more detail as follows (Appendix 8).

Assessment of Ramsar designations
As of 29 September 1999, 636 Ramsar Sites have been designated in Europe, 594 of which overlap partly or wholly with 556 IBAs (see Appendix 1 for details of the Ramsar Convention). A total of 1,700 IBAs in Europe are important at the European level for congregations of waterbirds because they support at least 1% of a biogeographic population of one or more species (criterion A4i), or at least 1% of the flyway population of one or more species (criterion B1i) or at least 20,000 waterbirds overall (criterion A4iii). These three criteria match criteria 5 and 6 of the Ramsar Convention for the identification of wetlands of international importance (Ramsar Sites). However, criteria A4i, A4iii and B1i can also be applied to congregations of waterbirds in certain grassland and

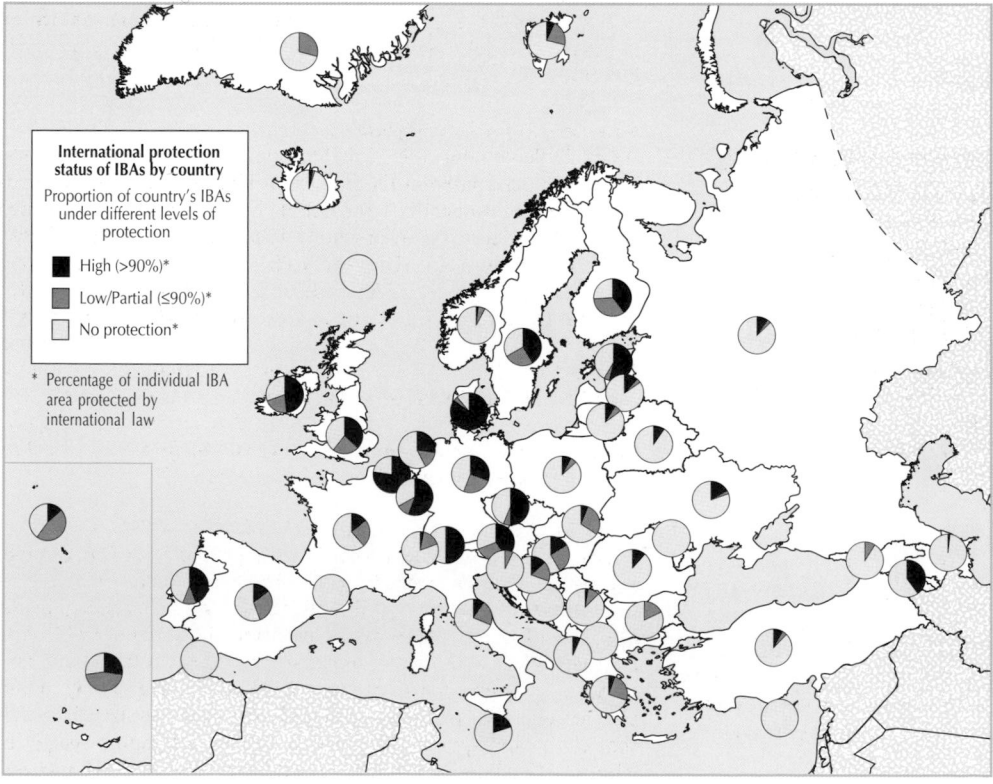

Figure 29. The international protection status of Important Bird Areas in each European country.

International protection status of IBAs by country

Proportion of country's IBAs under different levels of protection

■ High (>90%)*

▨ Low/Partial (≤90%)*

☐ No protection*

* Percentage of individual IBA area protected by international law

Figure 30. The coverage of Important Bird Areas in Europe by Ramsar Sites and by Special Protection Areas: a comparison of the situation in 1989 and 1999.

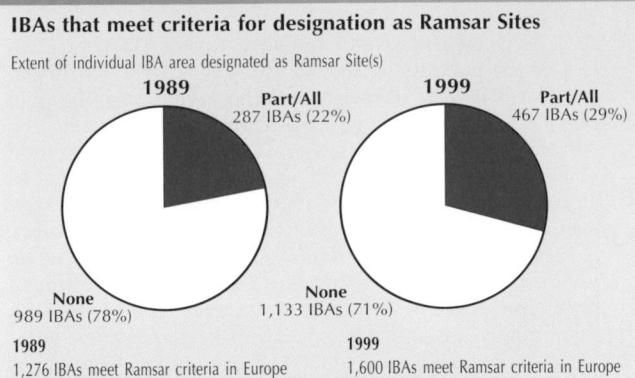

IBAs that meet criteria for designation as Ramsar Sites

Extent of individual IBA area designated as Ramsar Site(s)

1989
Part/All
287 IBAs (22%)

1999
Part/All
467 IBAs (29%)

None
989 IBAs (78%)

None
1,133 IBAs (71%)

1989
1,276 IBAs meet Ramsar criteria in Europe
287 Ramsar Sites in Europe
24 contracting parties in Europe

1999
1,600 IBAs meet Ramsar criteria in Europe
636 Ramsar Sites in Europe
39 contracting parties in Europe

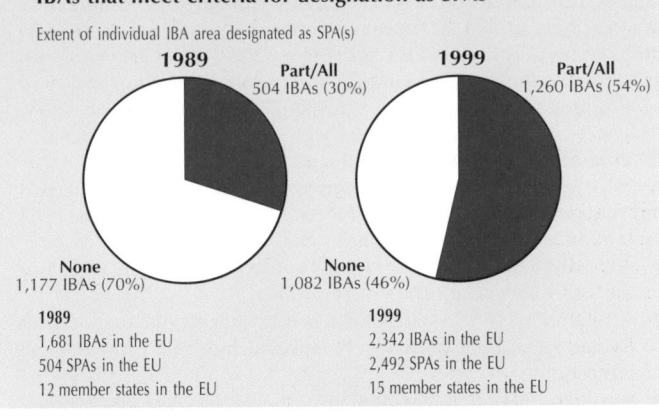

IBAs that meet criteria for designation as SPAs

Extent of individual IBA area designated as SPA(s)

1989
Part/All
504 IBAs (30%)

1999
Part/All
1,260 IBAs (54%)

None
1,177 IBAs (70%)

None
1,082 IBAs (46%)

1989
1,681 IBAs in the EU
504 SPAs in the EU
12 member states in the EU

1999
2,342 IBAs in the EU
2,492 SPAs in the EU
15 member states in the EU

Figure 31. The extent of overlap between individual Important Bird Areas and Ramsar Sites in Europe.

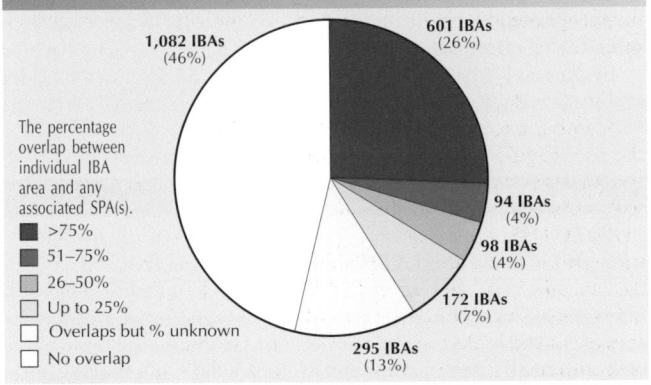

88 IBAs (16%)
290 IBAs (52%)
84 IBAs (15%)
50 IBAs (9%)
44 IBAs (8%)

The percentage overlap between individual IBA area and any associated Ramsar Site(s).
>75% ■
51–75% ■
26–50% ■
Up to 25% □
Overlaps but % unknown □

Figure 33. The extent of overlap between individual Important Bird Areas and Special Protection Areas in the European Union.

1,082 IBAs (46%)
601 IBAs (26%)
94 IBAs (4%)
98 IBAs (4%)
172 IBAs (7%)
295 IBAs (13%)

The percentage overlap between individual IBA area and any associated SPA(s).
>75% ■
51–75% ■
26–50% ■
Up to 25% □
Overlaps but % unknown □
No overlap □

marine habitats that do not qualify as wetland habitat under the Ramsar Convention (see Appendix 1). Approximately 100 of the 1,700 sites are totally marine or grassland. The eligibility of such sites for inclusion in the Ramsar List of wetlands has, therefore, to be considered on a case-by-case basis. Overall it is estimated that 1,600 IBAs in Europe should be considered as potential Ramsar Sites based on concentrations of waterbirds; 467 (29%) of them are actually covered, partly or wholly, by Ramsar Sites (Figure 30).

Many wetland IBAs that are important for non-waterbirds (such as mires) also comply with Ramsar criteria 2, 3 and 4, and thus

Figure 32. The coverage of Important Bird Areas by Special Protection Areas in the European Union.

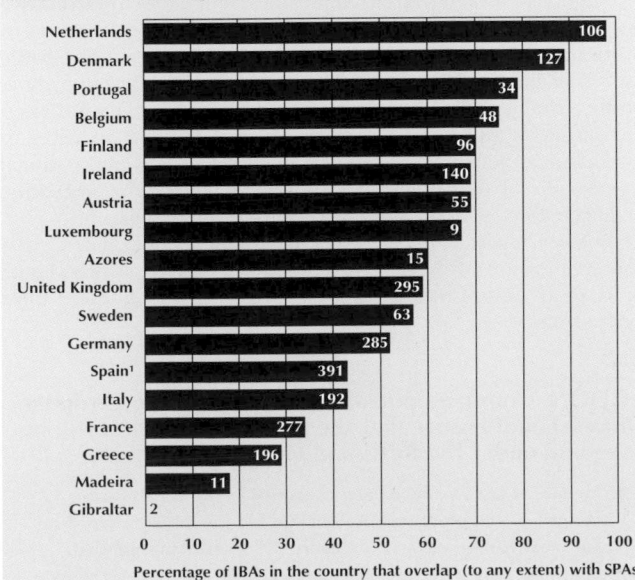

Netherlands	106
Denmark	127
Portugal	34
Belgium	48
Finland	96
Ireland	140
Austria	55
Luxembourg	9
Azores	15
United Kingdom	295
Sweden	63
Germany	285
Spain¹	391
Italy	192
France	277
Greece	196
Madeira	11
Gibraltar	2

0 10 20 30 40 50 60 70 80 90 100

Percentage of IBAs in the country that overlap (to any extent) with SPAs

The figure at the end of each bar equals the total number of IBAs in the country concerned.
1. Includes data for Canary Islands.

represent potential Ramsar Sites too. An assessment of this additional number of potential sites has not been made for this publication. However, 90 IBAs that do not qualify as IBAs for congregations of waterbirds are designated as Ramsar Sites; they may have been designated for terrestrial species dependent on wetlands such as raptors, or they may fulfil other non-ornithological Ramsar Site criteria.

It is also important to know the extent to which individual IBAs are covered by Ramsar Sites (Figure 31). In general, there is a high degree of overlap: in 52% of IBAs which overlap with Ramsar Sites, the Ramsar designation covers more than 75% of the area of the individual IBA.

Assessment of SPA designations
As of 23 September 1999, 2,492 Special Protection Areas (SPAs) have been designated in the European Union under the EC Birds Directive (see Appendix 1 for details of the Directive), of which 1,375 SPAs overlap partly or wholly with 1,260 IBAs—54% of IBAs in the EU (Figure 30). However, 1,082 IBAs (46%) in the EU are not covered at all by SPAs and thus should be considered for designation. Some countries have proceeded further than others in the designation of IBAs as SPAs, with the Netherlands, Denmark, Portugal and Belgium being the only countries that have designated over 75% of their IBAs (partly or wholly) as SPAs (Figure 32). The extent of coverage of individual IBAs is also important to note—in just 26% of IBAs in the European Union do SPAs cover more than 75% of the area of the individual IBA (Figure 33).

Changes in protection status of IBAs between 1989 and 1999
According to available information, the proportion of IBAs under statutory national protection has increased in most countries since 1989, although it is difficult to assess this properly in the absence of comprehensive or detailed data from 1989. Any comparison also needs to compensate for the fact that many new IBAs have been identified since 1989, and a (relatively small) number of 1989 sites have lost their IBA status. Analysis indicates that the proportion of all European IBAs designated (partly or wholly) as Ramsar Sites has increased from 22% in 1989 (Langeveld

and Grimmett 1990), to 29% in 1999 (Figure 30). Although there has been a substantial increase in Ramsar designations (Frazier 1996, 1999), 71% of potential sites (identified in this publication) remain unprotected by this Convention. Similarly, regarding SPA designations, 54% of IBAs are partly or wholly covered by SPAs in 1999, compared to 30% in 1989 (Figure 30). However, given that 46% of IBAs in the EU are unprotected by SPAs and considered to be of international importance, further designations are necessary.

■ **Threats and protection status**

A large number of IBAs that are protected at national and international levels remain threatened. Analysis of threat and protection status data shows that:

- A total of 12,600 records of threat were recorded against 3,381 of the 3,619 IBAs in Europe.
- A total of 1,114 IBAs are threatened by at least one high-impact threat, yet are partly or wholly covered by some form of legal protection.
- A total of 904 IBAs of global importance (meeting one or more 'A' criteria) are threatened by one or more high-impact threats. Of these, 644 are protected (partly or wholly) at either national or international levels, while 408 of them are protected at the international level.
- Of the 1,260 IBAs in the European Union at least partly covered by Special Protection Areas (SPAs), 559 IBAs (44%) are threatened by at least one high-impact threat. Thus the

designation of an IBA as an SPA has not prevented harmful development, or the risk of it in the near future, at these sites.

Development activities in SPAs

At SPAs, member states are required to "avoid [...] deterioration [...] of the habitats of species for which areas have been designated, in so far as such disturbance could be significant in relation to the objectives of this Directive" (as amended by Art. 6(2) of the Habitats Directive 92/43/EEC). The preparation of management plans, although not legally required, would be an appropriate way to achieve the above objective but very few member states have made significant progress in this respect. Contrary to the original provision of the Birds Directive Article 6 of the Habitats Directive contains a derogation of the general protection regime. Any plan or project likely to have a significant effect on the site, shall only be agreed upon "after having ascertained that it will not adversely affect the integrity of the site concerned. If, in spite of a negative assessment of the implications for the site and in the absence of alternative solutions, a plan or project must nevertheless be carried out for imperative reasons of overriding public interest all compensatory measures shall be taken necessary to ensure that the overall coherence of Natura 2000 is protected."

- Of the 557 IBAs that are at least partly covered by Ramsar Sites, 271 IBAs (49%) are also threatened by at least one high-impact threat.

WHAT SHOULD BE DONE NEXT?

KEY RECOMMENDATIONS FOR ACTION

Immense pressure continues to be placed on the European environment through developments in agriculture, forestry, fisheries, transport, energy, industry and urbanization, and, as this publication shows, such pressures are severely impacting the most important sites for birds in Europe. Much still needs to be done to adequately conserve Important Bird Areas.

ACTION: Designate IBAs as protected areas under national law

- 40% of IBAs in Europe are unprotected by national legislation.
- 39% of IBAs in Europe that have some protection by national law are still highly threatened.

Most sites in this inventory should be protected by national law and, where appropriate, managed to conserve their ornithological and biological value. The required level of protection and management will vary from site to site, and the options immediately available will be dictated largely by the protected-area legislation already in force in each country. The appropriate level of protection will vary from protected landscapes, where the management objective is to maintain the landscape character whilst sustaining traditional or non-intensive land-uses and ecological diversity, to strictly protected nature reserves where human presence is minimized. In countries with inadequate nature-conservation legislation, improved legislation is essential. Cooperation between governments and non-governmental organizations can be an effective way to achieve these objectives.

There is also a need to implement existing laws better, including improved commitment to adequate staff and resources, as well as policies and funding that prevent destruction, damage and neglect, and that encourage positive action and management of important biodiversity areas.

ACTION: Protect IBAs under relevant international agreements

- 60% of IBAs in Europe are not protected under any international convention, directive or programme (of these, 49% have some national protection).
- At least 1,100 wetland IBAs in Europe meet Ramsar criteria but are not designated as Ramsar Sites.
- 46% of IBAs in the European Union have no part of their area designated as SPAs.

- All 31 European national reports to the most recent Conference of the Parties to the Convention on Biological Diversity mention measures of in-situ conservation, including protected areas, but only eight reports refer to IBAs.

The populations of most bird species in Europe are shared between many countries, and individuals of most species for which IBAs are identified traverse political boundaries at some stage in their annual cycle. Actions to conserve birds and other biodiversity gain in effectiveness if they are framed in an international context.

The international agreements most relevant to the conservation of IBAs are outlined in Box 2. Apart from the EC Directives, official recognition or listing of an IBA under these international agreements does not normally lead immediately to greater legal powers of protection, but does confer a higher profile and status. Site-based aspects of such agreements are key mechanisms for bringing about positive change, through increased political and public awareness, commitment and support. They provide for the creation of international networks of sites on the ground, and international frameworks of people and institutions to facilitate conservation understanding, awareness and cooperation between nations.

Further details about each agreement and its relevance to IBA conservation are outlined in Appendix 1. All possible efforts should be taken to ensure that IBAs are properly protected under these agreements.

ACTION: Countries pursuing accession to the European Union should ensure that the protection of IBAs will be adequate under the Birds and Habitats Directives

- To date, 433 IBAs have been identified in the 12 accession countries, and more will be identified in the future when the European Union criteria (category 'C' criteria) are applied.
- Only 103 (24%) of these IBAs are partly or wholly covered by any form of international protection, while 305 (70%) are covered by national protection.

Box 2. International agreements relevant to site conservation in Europe (see Appendix 1 for more details).

Convention/initiative	Year of adoption	Year in force	Region covered	Participation in Europe (no. of countries)[1] Ratified or applicable	Signed	Not yet participating	Site-conservation mechanism	No. of sites designated in Europe	Total area in Europe (km²)	As of:
WITH AN ACTIVE SITE-CONSERVATION MECHANISM										
Ramsar Convention	1971	1975	Worldwide	39	—	6[2]	Ramsar Site	636	112,186	29 Sep 99
Man and Biosphere Programme	1970	n/a	Worldwide	35[3]	—	—	Biosphere Reserve	126	808,370	4 Jan 99
World Heritage Convention	1972	1975	Worldwide	39	—	6[2]	World Heritage Site	23[4]	51,711	2 Dec 98
Bern Convention [5]	1979	1982	Member states of Council of Europe (39 states) and invited non-member states in Europe and N and W Africa	33[6]	3	9	Biogenetic Reserves[5]	340	>30,000	21 Dec 98
EC Birds Directive	1979	1981	European Union	15	—	—	Special Protection Area (SPA) — Natura 2000	2,492	169,823	23 Sep 99
EC Habitats Directive	1992	1994	European Union	15	—	—	Special Area for Conservation (SAC) — Natura 2000	9,942[7]	341,344	23 Sep 99
Barcelona Convention	1976	1978	All states riparian to the Mediterranean Sea	11[6]	—	—	Mediterranean Specially Protected Area (MedSPA)	>52	>5,907	12 Oct 99
[New] Helsinki Convention	1992	—	All states in catchment of the Baltic Sea	12[6]	1	—	Baltic Sea Protected Area (BSPA)	65[9]	—	early 1998
CURRENTLY WITHOUT AN ACTIVE SITE-CONSERVATION MECHANISM										
Convention on Biological Diversity	1992	1994	Worldwide	40[6]	3	2				15 Jan 99
Convention on the Conservation of Migratory Species of Wild Animals (Bonn Convention)	1976	1983	Worldwide	27[6]	—	18				1 Sep 99
African-Eurasian Migratory Waterbirds Agreement (under Bonn Convention)	1995	1999	Africa, Europe and west Asia (c.120 sites)	9	6[6]	30				1 Nov 99
OSPAR Convention	1992	1998	All states in catchment of north-east Atlantic Ocean	15[6]	—	—				2 Dec 98
Black Sea Environmental Programme	1992	1994	All states riparian to the Black Sea	6	—	—				26 Apr 97
Pan-European Biological and Landscape Diversity Strategy [8]	1995	n/a	Europe	45	—	—				n/a

1. Totals exclude autonomous or dependant territories (Azores, Canary Islands, Faroe Islands, Greenland, Gibraltar, Madeira, Svalbard/Jan Mayen) as well as Monaco, Vatican City (Holy See) and San Marino.
2. European Union has not ratified/signed as an entity.
3. Total number of active National Man and Biosphere (MAB) Committees.
4. Total is for 'natural' or 'natural/cultural' sites only.
5. The EMERALD Network [new pan-European site-conservation mechanism] is in process of being conceptualized.
6. Figure does not include the European Union, which has also ratified/signed as an entity.
7. Proposed Sites of Community Interest
8. The Pan-European Ecological Network [new integrative framework for all existing site-conservation mechanisms in Europe] is in process of being conceptualized.
9. Number of proposed BSPAs (none have been designated as such, although some are protected at the national level).

In June 1993 the heads of state and governments of the European Union countries agreed that those countries of central and eastern Europe which so desired would be able to join the EU once they met the agreed political and economic conditions. Accession negotiations were opened on 31 March 1998 with the first six countries recommended by the Commission: Czech Republic, Estonia, Hungary, Poland, Slovenia and Cyprus. The second group of accession countries comprises Bulgaria, Latvia, Lithuania, Malta, Romania and Slovakia.

Before EU membership can be attained, each country needs to adopt the 'acquis communautaire' (the accumulated laws and obligations of EU membership), including the extensive 'environmental acquis'. Adoption of the acquis entails the alignment of the national legislation of candidate countries with EU law, and comprises three distinct activities:

- transposition (adoption or change of national laws, rules and procedures so that the requirements of the relevant EU law are fully incorporated into the national legal order);
- implementation or practical application (providing the institutions and budgets necessary to carry out the laws and regulations); and
- enforcement of EU legislation (providing the necessary controls and penalties to ensure that the law is being complied with fully and properly).

Thus the 'approximation' of national nature-conservation legislation to the Birds and Habitats Directives of the EU, including the identification and designation of Special Protection Areas for inclusion in the EU-wide ecological network of

protected areas (entitled 'Natura 2000'), is a key nature-conservation objective of the accession process. It should therefore be ensured that the conservation of IBAs is adequately addressed by this process.

ACTION: Prevent breaches of obligations under national and international law

Using the legal opportunities provided by national laws and the EC Birds and Habitats Directives, it is possible to object to activities that may be harmful to IBAs and to steer development towards sustainability. By registering formal complaints at the European Commission, concerned citizens or organizations can complain against decisions by EU member states which are considered to breach the legal obligations of the Directives. BirdLife Partners have successfully opposed harmful developments at many IBAs, and have highlighted the deficient protective strategies taken by some governments.

ACTION: Plan and carry out adequate management at all IBAs, including habitat or species restoration if necessary, and involve local communities, NGOs and the public in IBA conservation

- 17% of IBAs in Europe (619 sites) have management plans that cover part or all of their area.

Much of the landscape of Europe has been moulded by human influence over thousands of years, and some management is required at most IBAs to maintain, enhance or restore their value for birds. Such management should take into account all biodiversity, as well as social, economic, political and other relevant factors, including the interests of all stakeholders. The nature of this management may best be decided, implemented and monitored through the development of a management plan for the site or wider region. Management planning should take fully into account existing and potential human-uses, and should ensure, where human-use is truly in conflict with conservation objectives, that such use is effectively controlled (Welch 1994).

Often, IBAs can only be conserved effectively with the help and participation of local communities and through collaboration with NGOs and the public. When conservation actions involve or affect local communities, the building of support and mutual understanding more often leads to a sustainable outcome. Local communities have an important stewardship role, and in the long term can benefit from the conservation of IBAs, although this may sometimes conflict with the short-term interests of some economic sectors.

Building local and national capacity to protect these areas requires coordination. A growing number of BirdLife Partners have established 'caretaker' groups that, at the local level, carry out practical conservation actions to safeguard IBAs. The results of such activities include management plans that have been accepted by the competent authorities, site-use agreements that have ended disturbances to birds, and practical habitat-management that has been implemented on the ground.

ACTION: Integrate environmental objectives, including biodiversity conservation, into all policy sectors, and conserve the wider environment

> ● 93% of IBAs in Europe are threatened to some extent. Of these, 1,640 IBAs are threatened by agriculture, 1,575 IBAs by recreation/tourism, 1,057 by man-made changes to the hydrological regime, 924 IBAs by forestry and 779 IBAs by infrastructural development.

Increasingly, many environmental problems and potential threats to IBAs are global or regional in scope or origin, and cannot be effectively addressed or solved solely by good protection and management of the IBAs themselves. Many threats facing birds at sites result from generally unsustainable human development activities. Valuable sites for birds, even when protected, cannot be isolated from surrounding communities or society: IBAs not only receive harmful impacts from human society but also offer a wide range of services from aesthetic and recreation functions to the provision of clean water and air buffering against pollution and protection against erosion. Integrated conservation projects which aim to address broader habitat-conservation issues should be promoted as a tool for conserving those IBAs whose continued importance is dependent upon land-use and development policies in the surrounding countryside.

Financial measures are needed to provide incentives to encourage good management and the protection of wildlife, while perverse incentives, which encourage the destruction and degradation of IBAs, need to be removed and financial penalties and other legal sanctions provided. International funding for development programmes (e.g. through the Structural Funds in the EU) needs to be conditional on the outcomes of environmental impact assessments. Funding should aim to achieve economic development while at the same time being environmentally sustainable, with targeted provisions for biodiversity conservation (BirdLife International 1995).

BirdLife has published habitat conservation strategies for the major habitat-types in Europe (Tucker and Evans 1997), outlining directions for tackling these wider policy issues outside IBAs. It is clear that a broad range of legislation and policies have significant impacts on IBAs, particularly policies on agriculture, forestry, land-use planning, privatization, land ownership, environmental impact assessment and hunting. By ensuring that these laws take into account the principles of nature conservation, damage to important sites can be minimized. Strategic environmental assessments and environmental impact assessments need to be applied to major forestry, agriculture, infrastructural

and other programmes and projects in order to avoid detrimental impacts to IBAs and the wider environment.

ACTION: Maximize the use of data on IBAs and disseminate information to promote their conservation

> ● BirdLife IBA database constructed, coherent across countries.

Much data on IBAs is presented in this publication, with the primary purpose of guiding the conservation of these important sites. This information thus needs to be disseminated widely at local, national and international levels, to ensure that decisions affecting Europe's environment adequately take into account the sites, and the site-based issues such as species status, threats, land-use and protection status, that are most important for bird conservation.

The efficient storage and management of data means that it can be analysed, interpreted and communicated effectively to decision makers and those who need it. Therefore, in addition to this publication, the BirdLife International IBA Database (see Box 6, 'Data collection' chapter) has been established, holding additional data on these sites. Public access to this system is possible, subject to the terms agreed in the IBA Data Access Policy agreed by the European Partnership of BirdLife International (BirdLife International 1996). This database will continue to be updated by the BirdLife International Partnership.

The effective conservation of IBAs will also depend heavily on the work and agendas of other national and international governmental and non-governmental organizations. There is therefore great value in mobilizing scientific information within collaborative networks in support of policy development and decision-making at all levels of society. One international mechanism for the public dissemination of biodiversity data, still in the early stages of development, is the Biodiversity Conservation Information System (BCIS). This is to be created by a coalition of 12 organizations which manage biodiversity information at an international scale (BirdLife International, Botanical Gardens Conservation International, Conservation International, International Species Information System, IUCN Commission on Ecosystem Management, IUCN Environmental Law Programme, IUCN Species Survival Commission, IUCN World Commission on Protected Areas, The Nature Conservancy, TRAFFIC International, Wetlands International, World Conservation Monitoring Centre). Their common challenge lies in harmonizing their data and knowledge, and improving public access to it.

ACTION: Monitor IBAs and continue to collect data for defined purposes

> ● Scientific approach to design of site-selection criteria. Continuity with previous IBA criteria and in parallel with criteria of other site-based mechanisms.
> ● Data in this publication and the IBA database are standardized, permitting easy analysis for monitoring and trend assessments.

Data are required not only to set priorities but also to understand the reasons for change in the status of sites and the species dependent on them. This publication and the BirdLife IBA Database (see Box 6, 'Data collection' chapter), together with the previous pan-European IBA inventory published 10 years ago and national IBA publications, set important baselines from which progress in the conservation of IBAs can be monitored. It is important that the status of IBAs continue to be monitored to identify trends and provide early warning. Results can be used to assess priorities for further conservation action and research, to generate policy-relevant arguments for advocacy programmes, and to judge environmental impacts.

Also important is the continuing identification and conservation of IBAs for European migratory birds when outside Europe, predominantly in Africa, the Middle East, and the Indian subcontinent, and Arctic Siberia and Canada. IBA programmes have been established in these regions and approximately 20,000 IBAs are likely to be identified worldwide.

REFERENCES

BINA, O., BRIGGS, B. AND BUNTING, G. (1995) *The impact of the Trans-European Networks on nature conservation: a pilot project.* Sandy, UK: Royal Society for the Protection of Birds.

BIRDLIFE INTERNATIONAL (1995) *The Structural Funds and biodiversity conservation.* Sandy, UK: Royal Society for the Protection of Birds.

BIRDLIFE INTERNATIONAL (1996) IBA criteria: categories and thresholds. Cambridge, UK: BirdLife International (unpublished report).

COLLAR, N. J., CROSBY, M. J. AND STATTERSFIELD, A. J. (1994) *Birds to watch 2: the world list of threatened birds.* Cambridge, UK: BirdLife International (Conservation Series 4).

DURINCK, J., SKOV, H., JENSEN, F. P. AND PIHL, S. (1994) *Important marine areas for wintering birds in the Baltic Sea.* Copenhagen: Ornis Consult (report on European Commission DG XI research contract no. 224/90-09-01).

EEA [EUROPEAN ENVIRONMENTAL AGENCY] (1998) *Europe's environment: the second assessment.* Luxembourg: Office of Official Publications of the European Communities/Oxford, UK: Elsevier.

EEA [EUROPEAN ENVIRONMENT AGENCY] (1999) *Environment in the European Union at the turn of the century.* Luxembourg: Office for Official Publications of the European Communities (Environment Assessment Report No. 2.).

FRAZIER, S. (1996) *An overview of the world's Ramsar Sites.* Slimbridge, UK: Wetlands International (Wetlands International Publ. 39).

FRAZIER, S. (1999) *Ramsar Sites overview: a synopsis of the world's wetlands of international importance.* Wageningen, Netherlands: Wetlands International.

GRIMMETT, R. F. A. AND JONES, T. A. (1989) *Important Bird Areas in Europe.* Cambridge, UK: International Council for Bird Preservation (Techn. Publ. 9).

HAGEMEIJER, W. J. M. AND BLAIR, M., EDS (1997) *The EBCC atlas of European breeding birds: their distribution and abundance.* London: T. & A. D. Poyser.

HÄGERHÄLL, B. AND SKOV, H. (1998) Proposal for marine Baltic Sea Protected Areas (BSPAs). Copenhagen: Ornis Consult (report to HELCOM Environment Committee).

ICBP (1989) Important Bird Areas in the European Community: a shadow list of Special Protection Areas. Cambridge, UK: International Council for Bird Preservation (unpublished report).

IUCN (1993) *Parks for Life: Report of the Ivth World Congress on National Parks and Protected Areas.* Gland, Switzerland: IUCN.

LANGEVELD, M. J. AND GRIMMETT, R. F. A. (1990) Important Bird Areas in Europe: wetlands for the shadow list of Ramsar Sites. Cambridge and Slimbridge, UK: International Council for Bird Preservation/International Waterfowl and Wetlands Research Bureau (unpublished report).

PETERS, R. (1998) *Agricultural situation and prospects in the central and eastern European countries. Summary report* Brussels: European Commission (Directorate General for Agriculture [DG VI]). Working document.

SKOV, H., DURINCK, J., LEOPOLD, M. F. AND TASKER, M. L. (1995) *Important bird areas for seabirds in the North Sea.* Sandy, UK: Royal Society for the Protection of Birds.

SKOV, H., DURINCK, J., LEOPOLD, M. F. AND TASKER, M. L. (in prep.) A quantitative method for evaluating the importance of marine areas for the conservation of birds.

STANNERS, D. AND BOURDEAU, P., EDS (1995) *Europe's environment: the Dobris report.* Copenhagen: European Environmental Agency.

STATTERSFIELD, A. J., CROSBY, M. J., LONG, A. J. AND WEGE, D. C. (1998) *Endemic bird areas of the world: priorities for bird conservation.* Cambridge, UK: BirdLife International (Conservation Series 7).

TUCKER, G. M. AND EVANS, M. I., EDS (1997) *Habitats for birds in Europe: a conservation strategy for the wider environment.* Cambridge, UK: BirdLife International (Conservation Series 6).

TUCKER, G. M. AND HEATH, M. F. (1994) *Birds in Europe: their conservation status.* Cambridge, UK: BirdLife International (BirdLife Conservation Series no. 3).

WELCH, G. (1994) Site management and planning for conservation. Workshop proceedings, Gdansk, Poland 1994. Cambridge, UK: BirdLife International (unpublished report).

■ AUSTRIA

Michael Dvorak

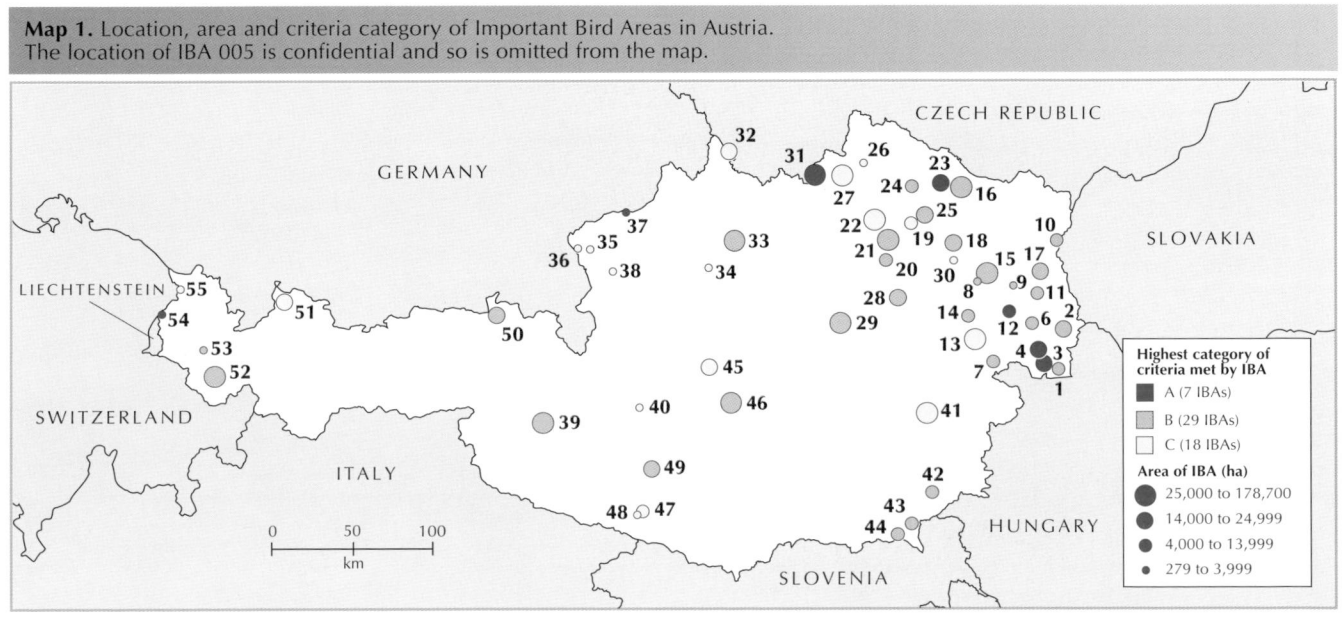

Hohe Tauern National Park (IBA 039). (PHOTO: MICHAEL DVORAK)

GENERAL INTRODUCTION

With an area of 83,849 km², Austria is a comparatively small, landlocked country in central Europe. Almost 70% of its territory is covered by the Alps, the rest consisting of hilly country, a high plateau in the north and lowlands in the east. Climatically, Austria is part of the northern temperate zone and is influenced by both the Atlantic and continental climatic regions.

The present inventory identifies 55 Important Bird Areas (IBAs) with a total area of approximately 12,388 km², comprising about 15% of Austria's surface area (Table 1). However, IBA coverage of individual counties and habitat-types varies widely. In the Alps, most bird species are widely dispersed which makes it very difficult to delimit important areas for species of European conservation concern (SPECs; Tucker and Heath 1994). Therefore eight of the 13 IBAs in the mountains are identical with existing or proposed National Parks and reserves. By way of contrast, river valleys, wetlands and broadleaved forests in the east and north of the country are more easily defined as distinct sites with particular species. More SPECs are found in these parts of the country. These differences are largely responsible for the unequal distribution of Austrian IBAs (Map 1).

Map 1. Location, area and criteria category of Important Bird Areas in Austria. The location of IBA 005 is confidential and so is omitted from the map.

67

Table 1. Summary of Important Bird Areas in Austria.   55 IBAs covering 12,388 km²

IBA code	1989 code	International name	National name	Administrative region	Area (ha)	Criteria (see p. 11)
001	AT003	Austrian part of Hanság	Österreichischer Teil des Hanság	Burgenland	7,000	B2, C6
002	AT004	Parndorfer Platte	Parndorfer Platte	Burgenland	18,000	B3, C6
003	AT002	Southern Seewinkel and Zitzmannsdorfer Wiesen	Südlicher Seewinkel und Zitzmannsdorfer Wiesen	Burgenland	14,000	A4i, B1i, B2, C3, C6
004	AT001	Neusiedler See	Neusiedler See	Burgenland	23,272	A1, A4i, B1i, B2, B3, C1, C2, C3, C6
005	—	Heideboden	Heideboden	Burgenland	5,100	A1, C1
006	—	North-eastern Leithagebirge	Nordöstliches Leithagebirge	Burgenland	8,300	B3, C6
007	—	Surroundings of Mattersburg	Umgebung von Mattersburg	Burgenland	4,000	B2
008	—	Zoological Gardens of Lainz	Lainzer Tiergarten	Wien	2,256	B2, B3, C6
009	—	Lobau	Lobau	Wien	2,090	B2, C6
010	AT005	March/Thaya riverine forest	March/Thaya-Auen	Niederösterreich	12,000	B2, B3, C6
011	AT005	Riverine forests on the Danube east of Vienna	Donauauen östlich von Wien	Niederösterreich	9,500	B2, B3, C6
012	—	Feuchte Ebene–Rauchwarther Platte	Feuchte Ebene–Rauchwarther Platte	Niederösterreich	11,000	A1, C1
013	—	Steinfeld	Steinfeld	Niederösterreich	25,000	C6
014	—	Thermenlinie	Thermenlinie	Niederösterreich, Wien	10,000	B2, C6
015	AT008	Vienna forest	Wienerwald	Niederösterreich, Wien	90,000	B2, B3, C6
016	—	Western Weinviertel	Westliches Weinviertel	Niederösterreich	39,500	B2, C6
017	AT007	Central Marchfeld	Zentrales Marchfeld	Niederösterreich	17,100	B2, C6
018	—	Riverine forests in the Tullnerfeld	Donauauen im Tullnerfeld	Niederösterreich	16,000	B2, C6
019	—	Krems region/lower Krems valley	Raum Krems / Unteres Kremstal	Niederösterreich	5,978	C6
020	—	Lower course of the Pielach	Unterlauf der Pielach	Niederösterreich	4,000	B2, C6
021	AT010	Wachau–Jauerling	Wachau–Jauerling	Niederösterreich	25,000	B2, C6
022	AT010	Southern Waldviertel	Südliches Waldviertel – Ottenschlag	Niederösterreich	41,000	C6
023	AT010	Allentsteig military training area	Truppenübungsplatz Allentsteig	Niederösterreich	16,000	A1, B2, B3, C1, C6
024	AT010	Middle Kamp valley	Mittleres Kamptal	Niederösterreich	5,500	B2, C6
025	AT010	Lower Kamp valley	Unteres Kamptal	Niederösterreich	23,000	B2, C6
026	AT010	Fish-ponds in the Waldviertel	Waldviertler Teiche	Niederösterreich	3,500	C7
027	AT010	Western Waldviertel	Streifenflurenland im westlichen Waldvietel	Niederösterreich	61,000	C6
028	—	Niederösterreichische Randalpen	Niederösterreichische Randalpen	Niederösterreich	16,928	B2, B3, C6
029	AT009	Ötscher–Dürrenstein	Ötscher–Dürrenstein–Gebiet	Niederösterreich, Steiermark	39,000	B2, C6
030	—	Machland–South	Machland–Süd	Niederösterreich	920	C6
031	—	Freiwald	Freiwald	Niederösterreich, Oberösterreich	35,000	A1, C1, C6
032	—	Bohemian forest and Mühl valley	Böhmerwald und Mühltal	Oberösterreich	20,000	C6
033	—	Northern Kalkalpen	Nördliche Kalkalpen	Oberösterreich, Steiermark	75,000	B2, C6
034	—	Lower course of the Traun	Untere Traun	Oberösterreich	2,260	C6
035	—	Ibmer Moor	Ibmer Moor	Oberösterreich	1,000	C6
036	—	Salzach valley	Salzachtal	Oberösterreich, Salzburg	1,840	C6
037	AT011	Storage lakes on the lower Inn	Stauseen am Unteren Inn	Oberösterreich	870	A4iii, C4, C6
038	—	Meadows and lakes in the foreland of the Alps in Salzburg and Upper Austria	Wiesengebiete und Seen im Alpenvorland Salzburgs und Oberösterreichs	Oberösterreich, Salzburg	640	C7
039	AT018	Hohe Tauern National Park	Nationalpark Hohe Tauern	Kärnten, Salzburg, Tirol	178,700	B2, C6
040	AT017	Radstädter Tauern	Radstädter Tauern	Salzburg	3,500	C6
041	—	Styrian Joglland	Steirisches Joglland	Steiermark	45,000	C6
042	—	Unterlammer hill country	Unterlammer Hügelland	Steiermark	6,500	B2
043	AT013	South-east Styrian hill country	Südoststeirisches Hügelland	Steiermark	10,500	B2, C6
044	—	Lower Mur valley	Unteres Murtal	Steiermark	13,600	B2, C6
045	—	Styrian Enns valley	Steirisches Ennstal	Steiermark	24,000	C6
046	AT015, AT016	Niedere Tauern	Niedere Tauern	Steiermark	169,000	B2, C6
047	—	Villacher Alpe–Dobratsch	Villacher Alpe–Dobratsch	Kärnten	7,500	C6
048	—	Lower valley of the Gail	Unteres Gailtal	Kärnten	2,000	C6
049	AT012	Nockberge National Park	Nationalpark Nockberge	Kärnten	18,663	B2, C6
050	—	Kaisergebirge	Kaisergebirge	Tirol	15,000	B2, B3, C6
051	—	Tyrolian Lech valley	Tiroler Lechtal	Tirol	17,700	C7
052	—	Silvretta and Verwall	Silvretta und Verwall	Tirol, Vorarlberg	30,000	B2, B3, C6
053	—	Slope forests in the Klostertal	Steilhangwälder im Klostertal	Vorarlberg	1,500	B2, C6
054	—	Meadows on the lower Ill	Streuwiesen an der Unteren Ill	Vorarlberg	279	A1, C1, C6
055	AT020	Delta of the Rhine and Lauteracher Ried	Rheindelta und Lauteracher Ried	Vorarlberg	2,760	C6

Sites identified in the previous inventory of IBAs in Europe (Grimmett and Jones 1989) but no longer considered to be IBAs
AT006 Braunsberg-Hundsheimer Berg; AT014 Seetaler Alpen; AT019 Karwendel.

Of the 20 sites listed for Austria in the previous pan-European IBA inventory (Grimmett and Jones 1989), three no longer fulfil the revised IBA criteria (Table 1). Of the remaining 17 sites, 14 are included in the current inventory, one has been merged, one (Waldviertel, AT010) has been split into seven separate IBAs and another one (Donau–March–Thayaauen, AT005) into two (Table 1). Thirty-two new IBAs are identified in the current inventory. This can largely be attributed to the greatly increased local knowledge of bird distributions and numbers in Austria, which on the one hand has facilitated a much more comprehensive application of the IBA criteria, and on the other hand has led to the discovery of a number of new sites. In 1994, a new national list of sites was compiled (Dvorak and Karner 1995) and, with some modifications (two sites each were respectively de-listed, merged with other areas, or newly identified), this national overview, in terms of sites identified, is identical to the revised IBA inventory.

ORNITHOLOGICAL IMPORTANCE

A total of 113 species of European conservation concern (SPECs) breed regularly in Austria (Tucker and Heath 1994). Three of them, *Aythya nyroca*, *Crex crex* and *Otis tarda* are classified as globally threatened (Collar *et al.* 1994). Six sites hold important populations of at least one of these species, meeting criterion A1 (Table 2). Lake Neusiedl (004) is one of the most important breeding areas in Europe for *Aythya nyroca*. *Crex crex* occurs regularly in at least 10 IBAs but numbers fluctuate widely at all sites and the A1 criterion is only met at four sites (012, 023, 031, 054). There are five sites in Austria (all IBAs) which still hold small relict populations of *Otis tarda*; the largest of these (005) (where *O. tarda* increased from 20 birds in 1990 to about 100 in 1997, as a result of successful habitat management) is shared with Slovakia (IBA 003) and Hungary (IBA 001) and meets the A1 criterion. The remaining four sites each have 20 birds or less.

A total of 33 IBAs were identified under criteria B2/B3 as important for SPECs (Table 1), with IBAs holding substantial parts of the Austrian population of some of the species listed in Table 4. A total of 49 IBAs meet the C6 criterion for their populations of species listed on Annex I of the EC Birds Directive (Table 1, Table 4). Wetland IBAs Lake Neusiedl (004) and the Seewinkel (003), as well as the riverine forests on the March/Thaya (010) and the Danube east of Vienna (011), hold the highest number of species meeting these criteria. The most important non-wetland site in this respect is the Vienna forest (015). Most SPECs and Annex I species are adequately covered by the present IBA inventory, with either more than 80% of their breeding populations or at least the most important breeding areas in Austria included in IBAs (Table 4). Exceptions are dispersed breeding species such as *Aquila chrysaetos*, *Bonasa bonasia*, *Tetrao tetrix*, and *T. urogallus*.

Table 2. Important Bird Areas in Austria that are important for species of global conservation concern (meeting criterion A1).

Species	IBA code
Aythya nyroca Ferruginous Duck	004
Crex crex Corncrake	012, 023, 031, 054
Otis tarda Great Bustard	005

Table 3. Important Bird Areas in Austria that support important numbers of one or more congregatory species (i.e. meeting criteria A4 and/or B1). IBAs meeting both criteria A4 and B1 for the species are shown in **bold**. IBAs meeting only criterion B1 for the species concerned, and not A4, are shown in normal type. For key to 'Season', see p. 7.

Species	Season	IBA code
Tachybaptus ruficollis Little Grebe	B	**004**
Egretta alba Great White Egret	B	**004**
Anser fabalis Bean Goose	P	**003**
Anser albifrons White-fronted Goose	P	003
Anser anser Greylag Goose	B	004
	P	**003**
Anas strepera Gadwall	P	**003**
Netta rufina Red-crested Pochard	B	004
	P	**003**
Aythya nyroca Ferruginous Duck	R	**004**

Table 4. Species of European conservation concern and species listed on Annex I of the EC Birds Directive with significant breeding populations at IBAs in Austria (meeting any IBA criteria).

Species [1]	Minimum national breeding population (pairs) [2]	Proportion (%) of national population breeding at all IBAs in Austria
Botaurus stellaris Bittern	100	100 [3]
Ixobrychus minutus Little Bittern	100	100 [3]
Nycticorax nycticorax Night Heron	10	100 [3]
Egretta alba Great White Egret	737	87
Ardea purpurea Purple Heron	80	100 [3]
Ciconia nigra Black Stork	115	40
Ciconia ciconia White Stork	308	41
Platalea leucorodia Spoonbill	25	100
Netta rufina Red-crested Pochard	20	100 [3]
Aythya nyroca Ferruginous Duck	100	100 [3]
Pernis apivorus Honey Buzzard	1,500	5
Milvus migrans Black Kite	50	84
Circus aeruginosus Marsh Harrier	200	66
Circus pygargus Montagu's Harrier	10	70
Aquila chrysaetos Golden Eagle	300	12
Falco cherrug Saker	5	20
Falco peregrinus Peregrine	80	21
Bonasa bonasia Hazel Grouse	5,000	1
Tetrao tetrix Black Grouse	10,000	3
Tetrao urogallus Capercaillie	7,000	1
Alectoris graeca Rock Partridge	566	17
Porzana porzana Spotted Crake	20	100 [3]
Porzana parva Little Crake	12,300	100
Crex crex Corncrake	90	100 [3]
Otis tarda Great Bustard	50 individuals	100 [3]
Himantopus himantopus Black-winged Stilt	7	100 [3]
Recurvirostra avosetta Avocet	92	100 [3]
Burhinus oedicnemus Stone Curlew	10	60
Larus melanocephalus Mediterranean Gull	12	8
Sterna hirundo Common Tern	110	100 [3]
Otus scops Scops Owl	35	57
Bubo bubo Eagle Owl	300	33
Glaucidium passerinum Pygmy Owl	1,500	5
Asio flammeus Short-eared Owl	10	100 [3]
Aegolius funereus Tengmalm's Owl	1,000	5
Caprimulgus europaeus Nightjar	250	52
Alcedo atthis Kingfisher	280	53
Coracias garrulus Roller	8	100 [3]
Jynx torquilla Wryneck	2,000	9
Picus canus Grey-headed Woodpecker	2,000	16
Picus viridis Green Woodpecker	5,000	13
Dryocopus martius Black Woodpecker	3,000	4
Dendrocopos medius Middle Spotted Woodpecker	600	86
Dendrocopos leucotos White-backed Woodpecker	300	20
Picoides tridactylus Three-toed Woodpecker	2,000	4
Lullula arborea Woodlark	300	93
Anthus campestris Tawny Pipit	20	55
Luscinia svecica Bluethroat	300	33
Saxicola rubetra Whinchat	5,000	24
Locustella naevia Grasshopper Warbler	1,500	100 [3]
Locustella luscinioides Savi's Warbler	3,000	60
Acrocephalus melanopogon Moustached Warbler	7,000	100 [3]
Acrocephalus palustris Marsh Warbler	10,000	5
Acrocephalus scirpaceus Reed Warbler	30,000	68
Sylvia nisoria Barred Warbler	800	35
Phylloscopus bonelli Bonelli's Warbler	35,000	3
Ficedula parva Red-breasted Flycatcher	1,100	64
Ficedula albicollis Collared Flycatcher	2,000	90
Lanius minor Lesser Grey Shrike	1	100 [3]
Serinus citrinella Citril Finch	5,000	4

1. Only those species of European conservation concern (see Box 1, p. 12) that meet IBA criteria in Austria are listed, together with those species listed on Annex I of the EC Birds Directive that fulfil criterion C6 in IBAs in Austria.
2. Data are taken from the BirdLife/EBCC European Bird Database 1998 (Heath and Borggreve 2000).
3. The percentage of the national population in IBAs exceeds 100%. Usually this is because the national population estimate has not been updated recently whilst the IBA population estimate has been recently updated with new data as a result of comprehensive surveys of IBAs themselves. Also, the individual site count for a species may be the maximum or average over recent years, and summing these may record more birds than are present nationally in any single year.

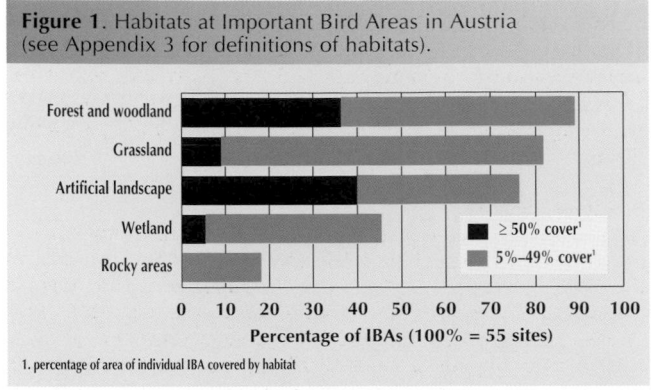

Figure 1. Habitats at Important Bird Areas in Austria (see Appendix 3 for definitions of habitats).

1. percentage of area of individual IBA covered by habitat

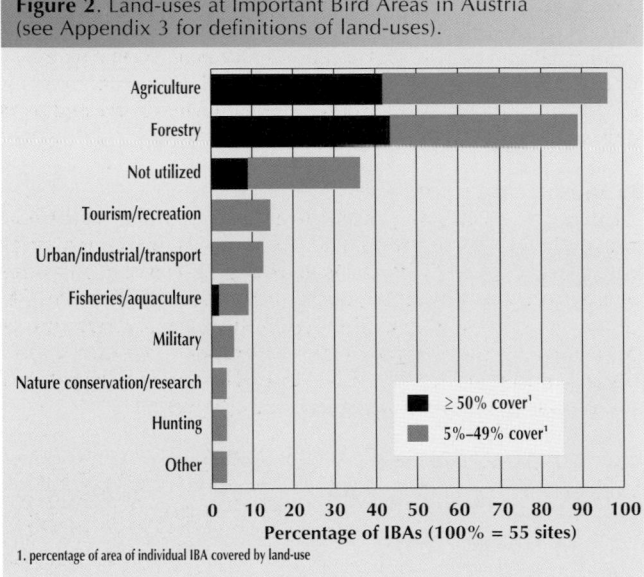

Figure 2. Land-uses at Important Bird Areas in Austria (see Appendix 3 for definitions of land-uses).

1. percentage of area of individual IBA covered by land-use

There are only a few wetlands in Austria which qualify as important for congregatory waterbird species under criteria A4 or B1 (Table 3). The most important site is Lake Neusiedl (004), together with the adjacent Seewinkel (003), mainly as a staging area for geese *Anser*.

HABITATS

Forests dominate the Austrian landscape and cover almost half of the country (Aubrecht 1998). However, most of them are intensively used and a recent inventory classified only 3% of Austrian forests as 'natural', i.e. not used (Aubrecht 1998). Conifer forest occupies approximately 60% of the total forest area, mixed forest about 28% and broadleaved forest only 8%. In hilly country, in particular, many areas originally covered by broadleaved forest have been converted to monoculture spruce *Picea* plantations. A further 36% of the Austrian land area is used for agriculture, mostly arable land in the lowlands and hill areas, and grassland and pastures in the Alps.

The distribution of habitats within IBAs roughly reflects the pattern for Austria as a whole (Figure 1). Twenty IBAs have forests covering more than 50% of their area, and another 29 have at least some forest. Typical species of forest habitats include woodpeckers such as *Dryocopus martius, Dendrocopos medius* and *Picoides tridactylus* and grouse such as *Bonasa bonasia* and *Tetrao urogallus*. Twenty-seven IBAs are dominated by a mixed agricultural landscape and/or large forestry plantations. Among them, 22 are dominated by arable land and/or perennial crops, orchards or vineyards, whilst the remaining five have large proportions of grassland or pasture. In contrast to many other countries, only three Austrian IBAs are dominated by wetland habitats (004, 037, 055).

Alpine grasslands and rocky areas above the treeline (found in 18% of IBAs) cover large areas of the Alps. They are an important habitat for several species, among them a substantial proportion of the European population of *Aquila chrysaetos*.

IMPACTS ON IBAs – LAND-USE AND THREATS

Almost all Austrian IBAs are at least partly used by man either as agricultural land (96%) or for forestry (89%) (Figure 2). There are only four IBAs with the majority of their land area unused by humans. Three of them are situated in the Alps and are dominated by rocky areas, alpine grasslands and subalpine forests on steep slopes (049, 052, 053). Other land-uses generally occupy only very small proportions of Austrian IBAs (Figure 2). Although hunters use large parts of the Austrian land area (including most of the reserves) it is not an exclusive form of land-use.

Accordingly, agricultural intensification and expansion have negatively affected 69% of IBAs, and are regarded as a high-impact threat in 29% (Figure 3). However, the overall negative impact of farming has recently declined as a result of the increasing amount of set-aside land and the implementation of environmentally friendly farming methods in certain areas of high conservation value. Most Austrian forests are utilized for forestry but intensification is only regarded as a high impact threat in 15% of IBAs today (Figure 3).

Recreational activities and tourism are widespread, affecting 60% of IBAs, but rarely have a high negative impact on bird populations (Figure 3). Recent government plans for further development of the road network could become a major threat to

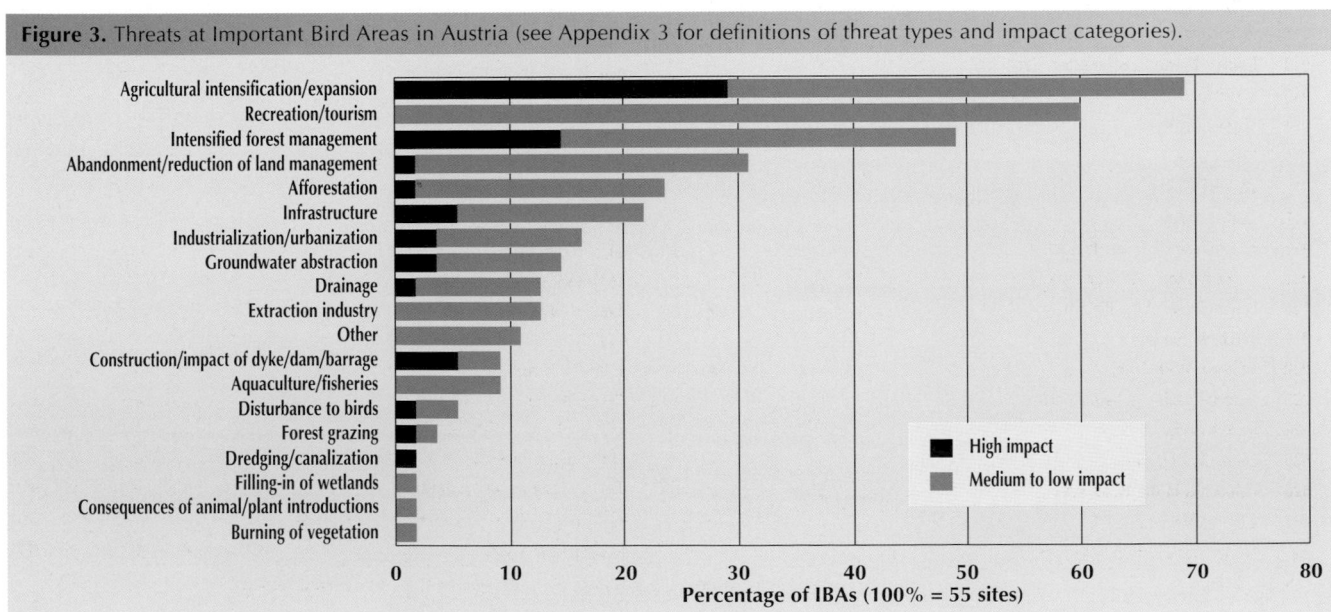

Figure 3. Threats at Important Bird Areas in Austria (see Appendix 3 for definitions of threat types and impact categories).

several IBAs (e.g. 006, 012, 045). Plans for other infrastructure development, such as golf courses and recreation parks, and the planned construction of dams on rivers are a constant and recurring threat to several sites (e.g. 013). If implemented, the planned Elbe–Oder–Danube canal could dramatically alter the ecosystem of the March (010).

PROTECTION STATUS

■ National protection

Austria is a federal state, and nature conservation at the regional and local level is the responsibility of the nine counties. Consequently, there are regional differences in the legal basis for nature conservation. Protected-area systems are similar for the different Austrian counties, comprising the following main categories: National Park, Nature Reserve, Landscape Protection Area, Natural Monument, and Protected Landscape Element; the last three categories have no significance for bird conservation. Fifty-five percent of Austrian IBAs are covered, at least in part, by one of the first two designations, although in only 16% of IBAs is more than 90% of the area protected (Figure 4).

1. National Park

By the end of 1997, there were six legally designated National Parks in Austria; three in the Alps; two in the eastern lowlands; and one on the Bohemian Mass in the north. However, only two of the parks, Lake Neusiedl and the Danube riverine forests, are recognized internationally by IUCN. Kalkalpen National Park will most probably also receive international recognition, but currently Hohe Tauern and Nockberge National Parks are used intensively for tourism, with former land-uses still permitted in most parts. Only a very small part of the total area of these two sites is strictly

protected. A sixth National Park, Thayatal, was established in 1997, and a seventh, Gesäuse in the Styrian Alps, is in an advanced stage of planning. Due to their ornithological importance, five of the six existing National Parks overlap totally or partly with eight IBAs (Table 5), but Thayatal harbours, at least according to current knowledge, no significant numbers of any key bird species and therefore does not feature in this IBA inventory.

2. Nature Reserve

On paper, the strictest category of protected area in Austria, but most of these sites (totalling 328 in 1992) are small (69% are smaller than 100 ha). Almost all of the larger Nature Reserves are found in the Alps and occupy 91% of the total Nature Reserve area (2,818 km², or 3.3% of Austria). In general, the degree of protection given to most sites is very limited and mostly confined to halting further development. Traditional land-uses are permitted (including hunting, fishing and sometimes recreational activities) in most reserves, and almost all lack a buffer zone, which makes them vulnerable to any threats emanating from the surrounding, intensively-used land. Additionally, most reserves lack appropriate management plans and if they exist, they are very rarely implemented. Nature Reserves are only of minor importance for bird conservation in Austria, and cover only small parts of 21 IBAs (Figure 4, Table 5).

■ International protection

Austria is a contracting party to several of the international conventions that are relevant to site-based nature conservation (Box 1), but only the EC Birds Directive and the Ramsar Convention have had any significant impact in Austria to date (Table 5). The proportion of IBAs with some part of their area under international protection (69%) is higher than the proportion with national protection. In total, 40% of Austrian IBAs have international protection for 90% or more of their area (Figure 5).

Table 5. Protection status of Important Bird Areas in Austria.
A tick (✔) indicates that an IBA overlaps with a protected area (to any extent).

IBA code	International name	National Park	Nature Reserve	Ramsar Site	Special Protection Area		IBA code	International name	National Park	Nature Reserve	Ramsar Site	Special Protection Area
001	Austrian part of Hanság	✔					029	Ötscher–Dürrenstein		✔		✔
002	Parndorfer Platte		✔				030	Machland–South				✔
003	Southern Seewinkel and Zitzmannsdorfer Wiesen	✔		✔	✔		031	Freiwald		✔		✔
004	Neusiedler See	✔		✔	✔		032	Bohemian forest and Mühl valley				
005	Heideboden						033	Northern Kalkalpen	✔	✔		✔
006	North-eastern Leithagebirge						034	Lower course of the Traun		✔		✔
007¹	Surroundings of Mattersburg						035	Ibmer Moor		✔		✔
008	Zoological Gardens of Lainz		✔		✔		036	Salzach valley				✔
009	Lobau	✔		✔	✔		037	Storage lakes on the lower Inn		✔	✔	✔
010	March/Thaya riverine forest		✔	✔	✔		038	Meadows and lakes in the foreland of the Alps in Salzburg and Upper Austria		✔		✔
011	Riverine forests on the Danube east of Vienna	✔		✔	✔		039	Hohe Tauern National Park	✔			✔
012	Feuchte Ebene–Rauchwarther Platte		✔		✔		040	Radstädter Tauern		✔		✔
013	Steinfeld						041	Styrian Joglland				✔
014¹	Thermenlinie				✔		042	Unterlammer hill country				
015	Vienna forest				✔		043	South-east Styrian hill country				✔
016	Western Weinviertel				✔		044	Lower Mur valley		✔		
017	Central Marchfeld		✔				045	Styrian Enns valley		✔	✔	✔
018	Riverine forests in the Tullnerfeld				✔		046	Niedere Tauern		✔		✔
019	Krems region/lower Krems valley				✔		047	Villacher Alpe–Dobratsch		✔		
020	Lower course of the Pielach				✔		048	Lower valley of the Gail				
021	Wachau–Jauerling				✔		049	Nockberge National Park	✔			
022	Southern Waldviertel				✔		050	Kaisergebirge		✔		
023	Allentsteig military training area						051	Tyrolian Lech valley				
024	Middle Kamp valley				✔		052	Silvretta and Verwall				✔
025	Lower Kamp valley				✔		053	Slope forests in the Klostertal				✔
026	Fish-ponds in the Waldviertel			✔	✔		054	Meadows on the lower Ill		✔		✔
027	Western Waldviertel				✔		055	Delta of the Rhine and Lauteracher Ried		✔	✔	✔
028	Niederösterreichische Randalpen						**Total number of IBAs**		**8**	**21**	**8**	**38**
	Subtotal of IBAs	5	6	5	19							

1. IBAs 007 and 014 have protected areas of unknown status.

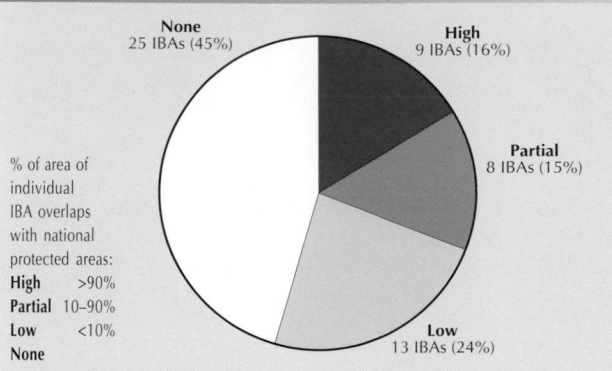

Figure 4. The national protection status of Important Bird Areas in Austria.

% of area of individual IBA overlaps with national protected areas:
High   >90%
Partial 10–90%
Low   <10%
None

Total area of overlap between IBA network in Austria and national protected-area system (see Table 5 for categories) = 2,317–2,871 km² (19–23% of total IBA area).

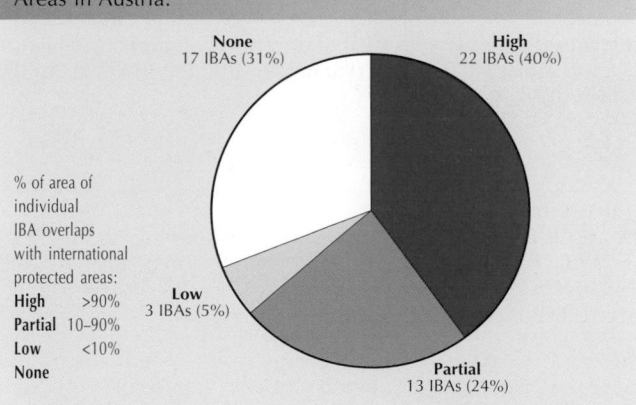

Figure 5. The international protection status of Important Bird Areas in Austria.

% of area of individual IBA overlaps with international protected areas:
High   >90%
Partial 10–90%
Low   <10%
None

Total area of overlap between IBA network in Austria and international protected-area system (see Table 5 for categories) = 6,415–7,258 km² (52–59% of total IBA area).

Box 1. International legislation and initiatives that are relevant to site conservation in Austria (see Appendix 1 for a general description of these agreements).

Global	
Biodiversity Convention	✔
Ramsar Convention	✔
Bonn Convention	
World Heritage Convention	✔
MAB Programme	✔

Pan-European	
Bern Convention	✔

Regional	
EC Birds Directive	✔
EC Habitats Directive	✔

✔ Convention ratified/initiative supported
(✔) Convention signed

Accession to the European Union, has brought some important changes to nature conservation legislation in Austria, and one county has already established the category 'European Reserve', which will comprise all sites in the Natura 2000 network. Progress in designating Special Protection Areas (SPAs) differs greatly between counties and depends largely on the political will and commitment of staff within the federal agencies. Some counties have only designated as SPAs those National Parks and Nature Reserves that already exist, others have also designated most of their IBAs, e.g. Lower Austria, Vorarlberg, and (partly) Burgenland. The national IBA inventory (Dvorak and Karner 1995) was regarded as important in the designation process by most county administrations. Although a final analysis of the extent of designation of IBAs as SPAs has still to be made, as of March 1998 more than 60% of all IBAs were at least partly proposed or designated as SPAs (Figure 5, Table 5).

CONSERVATION ISSUES

- There is no centrally coordinated network of IBA caretakers in Austria, but most areas are covered either by interested local ornithologists, nature conservation NGOs, National Park or Nature Reserve administrations or other interested parties. Most of them are in close contact with BirdLife Austria and there is a free flow of information and communication between these interest groups. There is intensive lobbying by nature conservation NGOs for the inclusion of the remaining IBAs into the Natura 2000 network.
- During the last five years, LIFE or INTERREG projects have been implemented in at least 10 Austrian IBAs (009, 010, 011, 020, 029, 032, 036, 037, 045, 055), most of them focusing on bird conservation amongst other issues.
- Long-term species-protection programs, mostly within the boundaries of IBAs, have been implemented for nationally or locally threatened species in several counties including *Crex crex, Otis tarda, Burhinus oedicnemus, Otus scops, Athene noctua.*

ANALYTICAL METHODS

- Population estimates for single IBAs are largely derived from the National IBA Inventory (Dvorak and Karner 1995) and cover the period 1990–1994. For certain species, especially globally threatened species, more recent data (up to 1998) have been included.
- Information on land-use and threats was extracted from the national IBA inventory (Dvorak and Karner 1995), but was updated in many cases through direct contacts with relevant interest groups.
- Data on the size of the IBAs as well as the extent of habitat-types is based on crude estimates in most cases.
- In many cases there were difficulties assigning coniferous forest to one of the level 2 habitat categories 'forestry plantation' or 'native coniferous forest' because some secondary coniferous forests structurally resemble semi-natural forests more than plantations.

GLOSSARY

INTERREG an EU funding line which supports trans-border infrastructural development (particularly tourism) between members of the European Union and adjoining eastern European countries.
IUCN The World Conservation Union.
LIFE an EU funding line (Regulation 1973/92/EEC) which supports EU environmental legislation including the Birds and Habitats Directives.
Natura 2000 the name given by the European Commission to the 'coherent ecological network' of Special Protection Areas and Special Areas for Conservation that is due to be established within EU member states by June 2004, under the EC Birds and Habitats Directives.
SPA Special Protection Area (designated under Article 4 of the EC Birds Directive).

ACKNOWLEDGEMENTS

The National IBA Inventory for Austria was funded by a grant from the Federal Environment Agency (Austria). Further work on updating information on IBAs in Austria was made possible by a grant from the Ministry of Environment through the Österreichische Gesellschaft für Natur- und Umweltschutz ÖGNU. A large number of contributors provided data for this inventory, and we thank especially the following for their substantial contributions: Gerhard Aubrecht, Hans-Martin Berg, Georg Bieringer, Vinzenz Blum, Johannes Frühauf, Markus Grabherr, Johanna Gressel, Thomas Hochebner, Werner Ilzer, Wolfgang Kantner, Eva Karner, Gerold Kilzer, Rita Kilzer, Karl Lieb, Volker Mauerhofer, Kurt Nadler, Gernot Räuschl, Andreas Ranner, Anton Reiter, Leopold Sachslehner, Peter Sackl, Otto Samwald, Alois Schmalzer, Ernst Schmid, Alexander Schuster, Hannes Seehofer, Leopold Slotta-Bachmayr, Ulrich Straka, Siegfried Wagner, Andreas Wenger, Sabine Werner, Hans Wurm, Lisbeth Zechner, Sabine Zelz, Thomas Zuna-Kratky

■ SITE ACCOUNTS

Austrian part of Hanság
B2, C6 **001**

Admin region Burgenland
Coordinates 47°44′N 16°58′E
° **Altitude** 115–122 m **Area** 7,000 ha

■ Site description
The area is dominated by intensive arable agriculture (including a substantial proportion of set-aside land) with small areas of wet meadows (140 ha) and alluvial forest. Human activities include arable farming, hunting, tourism, and military operations.

Habitats Forest and woodland (10%; alluvial/very wet forest), Grassland (10%; humid grassland), Artificial landscape (80%; arable land; ruderal land)
Land-use Agriculture (90%), Forestry (10%)

■ Birds

Species		Season	Year	Pop min	Pop max	Acc	Criteria
Circus pygargus	Montagu's Harrier	B	1993	1	3	A	C6
[1] *Otis tarda*	Great Bustard	B	1993	15	20	A	B2, C6
Asio flammeus	Short-eared Owl	R	1992	9	10	A	C6
Luscinia svecica	Bluethroat	B	1990	14	20	A	C6

1. Individuals.

An important site for birds associated with arable agriculture and wet meadows. It is one of five Austrian sites for *Otis tarda*. Species of global conservation concern that do not meet IBA criteria: *Crex crex* (3–4 breeding pairs).

■ Protection status
National Low **International** None
140 ha of IBA covered by National Park (Neusiedler See–Seewinkel, 7,650 ha).

■ Conservation issues

Threats Abandonment/reduction of land management (B), Agricultural intensification/expansion (C)

Agricultural intensification has slowed and the area of set-aside has increased (245 ha in 1993). During 1988–1993 intensive research on *Otis tarda* resulted in detailed management recommendations. Since 1994, a regular monitoring program has been conducted by National Park personnel.

Parndorfer Platte
B3, C6 **002**

Admin region Burgenland
Coordinates 47°57′N 16°58′E
Altitude 160–170 m **Area** 18,000 ha

■ Site description
The area is a large, flat, shingle terrace with a thin loess deposit, situated to the north-east of Lake Neusiedl. It is predominantly agricultural with some forestry plantations, interspersed with numerous gravel-pits. Remnants of extensively grazed pastures and the original oak *Quercus* forests exist.

Habitats Forest and woodland (10%), Artificial landscape (90%; arable land; forestry plantation; ruderal land)
Land-use Agriculture (90%), Forestry (10%)

■ Birds

Species		Season	Year	Pop min	Pop max	Acc	Criteria
[1] *Otis tarda*	Great Bustard	B	1994	3	6	A	C6
Acrocephalus palustris	Marsh Warbler	B	1994	149	149	A	B3
Sylvia nisoria	Barred Warbler	B	1994	136	136	A	C6

1. Females.

An important site for birds associated with arable agriculture. It is one of five areas in Austria for *Otis tarda*.

■ Protection status
National Low **International** None
70 ha of IBA covered by Nature Reserve (Zurndorfer Eichenwald, 70 ha).

■ Conservation issues

Threats Afforestation (C), Agricultural intensification/expansion (B), Infrastructure (B), Industrialization/Urbanization (B)

Hunting is permitted across the entire area. The creation of set-aside is being promoted in areas used by *Otis tarda*.

Southern Seewinkel and Zitzmannsdorfer Wiesen
A4i, B1i, B2, C3, C6 **003**

Admin region Burgenland
Coordinates 47°45′N 16°50′E
Altitude 117–124 m **Area** 14,000 ha

■ Site description
The Seewinkel is part of the 'Small Hungarian Plain'. The area is characterized by about 45 small shallow saline lakes with seasonally fluctuating water-levels. These are found within a landscape of wet meadows, hay-meadows, reedbeds (*Phragmites*), dry pastures, arable land, vineyards and small patches of woodland. The Zitzmannsdorfer Wiesen are a large area of continuous wet meadows between the villages of Weiden and Podersdorf.

Habitats Forest and woodland (5%), Grassland (30%; humid grassland; mesophile grassland; steppe/dry calcareous grassland), Wetland (15%; standing brackish and salt water; water-fringe vegetation), Artificial landscape (50%; arable land; forestry plantation; perennial crops/orchards/groves; ruderal land)
Land-use Agriculture (70%), Nature conservation/research (25%), Tourism/recreation (5%)

■ Birds

Species		Season	Year	Pop min	Pop max	Acc	Criteria
Botaurus stellaris	Bittern	B	1997	20	25	A	B2, C6
Ixobrychus minutus	Little Bittern	B	1994	3	5	A	C6
Anser fabalis	Bean Goose	P	1994	20,000	25,000	A	A4i, B1i, C3
Anser albifrons	White-fronted Goose	P	1994	3,000	12,500	A	B1i, C3
Anser anser	Greylag Goose	P	1994	6,500	9,000	A	A4i, B1i, C3
Anas strepera	Gadwall	P	1994	800	1,600	A	A4i, B1i, C3
[1] *Netta rufina*	Red-crested Pochard	P	1996	500	800	A	A4i, B1i, C3
Aythya nyroca	Ferruginous Duck	B	1996	10	15	A	C6
Circus pygargus	Montagu's Harrier	B	1994	2	5	A	C6
[2] *Porzana porzana*	Spotted Crake	B	1994	—	15	A	C6
Himantopus himantopus	Black-winged Stilt	B	1994	11	11	A	C6
Recurvirostra avosetta	Avocet	B	1989	119	119	A	C6
Sterna hirundo	Common Tern	B	1994	50	60	A	C6
Asio flammeus	Short-eared Owl	R	1992	5	7	A	C6
Lanius minor	Lesser Grey Shrike	B	1993	5	5	A	C6

1. Large increase.
2. Calling males.

This is an important area for migrating and breeding wildfowl and waders in wet meadows and saline lakes.

■ Protection status
National Partial **International** High
3,510 ha of IBA covered by National Park (Neusiedler See–Seewinkel, 7,650 ha). 14,000 ha of IBA covered by Ramsar Site (Neusiedlersee, Seewinkel and Hanság, 60,000 ha). 14,000 ha of IBA covered by Special Protection Area (Neusiedlersee–Seewinkel, 41,735 ha).

■ Conservation issues

Threats Abandonment/reduction of land management (B), Afforestation (C), Agricultural intensification/expansion (A), Aquaculture/fisheries (C), Drainage (C), Groundwater abstraction (A), Recreation/tourism (C)

The main threats to the Seewinkel are from groundwater abstraction and intensive agriculture, particularly the use of fertilizers and pesticides. An increasing area of arable land is being put into set-aside and remaining pastures are extensively managed by the National Park. A variety of research and conservation projects have been undertaken.

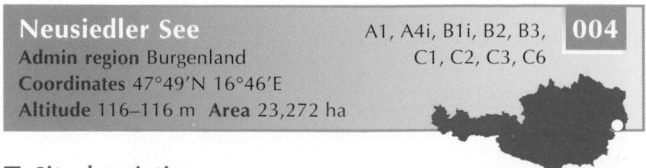

Neusiedler See — 004
Admin region Burgenland
Coordinates 47°49'N 16°46'E
Altitude 116–116 m **Area** 23,272 ha
A1, A4i, B1i, B2, B3, C1, C2, C3, C6

■ Site description
Lake Neusiedl is the most western shallow steppic lake in Europe. Extensive reedbeds (*Phragmites*), up to 5 km wide, fringe the lake. Human activities include annual cutting and burning of the reedbeds ('Other' land-use), recreation, fishing and hunting.

Habitats Wetland (100%; standing fresh water; water-fringe vegetation)
Land-use Fisheries/aquaculture (40%), Nature conservation/research (15%), Not utilized (30%), Other (10%), Tourism/recreation (5%)

■ Birds

Species	Season	Year	Pop min	Pop max	Acc	Criteria
Tachybaptus ruficollis Little Grebe	B	1995	1,000	1,000	A	A4i, B1i, C3
Botaurus stellaris Bittern	B	1994	100	100	A	B2, C6
Ixobrychus minutus Little Bittern	B	1994	100	200	A	C6
¹ *Egretta alba* Great White Egret	B	1996	642	642	A	A4i, B1i, C2, C6
Ardea purpurea Purple Heron	B	1994	87	87	A	C2, C6
Platalea leucorodia Spoonbill	B	1997	25	25	A	C6
Anser anser Greylag Goose	B	1994	300	400	A	B1i, C3
Netta rufina Red-crested Pochard	B	1994	100	200	A	B1i, C3
Aythya nyroca Ferruginous Duck	R	1996	150	200	A	A1, A4i, B1i, C1, C2, C6
Circus aeruginosus Marsh Harrier	B	1994	100	100	A	C6
Porzana porzana Spotted Crake	R	1994	—	30	A	C6
Porzana parva Little Crake	B	1997	12,300	22,000	A	B3, C2, C6
Locustella luscinioides Savi's Warbler	B	1997	1,750	1,750	A	B3
Acrocephalus melanopogon Moustached Warbler	B	1997	8,700	15,600	A	C6
Acrocephalus scirpaceus Reed Warbler	B	1997	20,500	42,000	A	B3

1. Large increase

An important site for breeding herons and birds associated with reedbeds.

■ Protection status
National High **International** High
4,000 ha of IBA covered by National Park (Neusiedler See–Seewinkel, 7,650 ha). 23,272 ha of IBA covered by Ramsar Site (Neusiedlersee, Seewinkel and Hanság, 60,000 ha). 23,272 ha of IBA covered by Special Protection Area (Neusiedlersee–Seewinkel, 41,735 ha).

■ Conservation issues

Threats Agricultural intensification/expansion (B), Burning of vegetation (C), Infrastructure (B), Other (C), Recreation/tourism (C)

The main threats come from the use of the lake for recreation, water pollution from fertilizer inputs and sewage, and infrastructural developments for recreation.

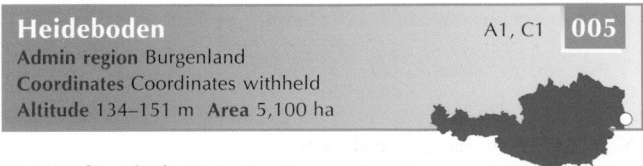

Heideboden — 005
Admin region Burgenland
Coordinates Coordinates withheld
Altitude 134–151 m **Area** 5,100 ha
A1, C1

■ Site description
A flat, almost treeless plain, of predominantly arable land at the border with Slovakia and Hungary. Two small villages are within the boundaries of the area as well as several large gravel-pits.

Habitats Artificial landscape (100%; arable land; ruderal land)
Land-use Agriculture (100%)

■ Birds
An important site for species associated with arable agriculture. The local *Otis tarda* population extends into Hungary and Slovakia.

Species	Season	Year	Pop min	Pop max	Acc	Criteria
¹ *Otis tarda* Great Bustard	R	1996	85	86	A	A1, C1

1. Large increase.

■ Protection status
National None **International** None

■ Conservation issues

Threats Agricultural intensification/expansion (B), Disturbance to birds (C)

The area of set-aside land is increasing. Intensive monitoring of *Otis tarda* is carried out.

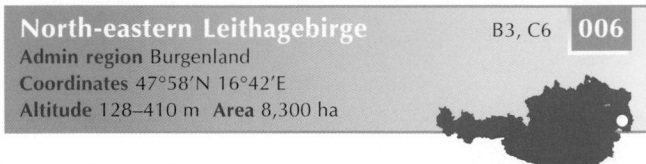

North-eastern Leithagebirge — 006
Admin region Burgenland
Coordinates 47°58'N 16°42'E
Altitude 128–410 m **Area** 8,300 ha
B3, C6

■ Site description
A range of low slate and limestone hills between Purbach and Bruckneudorf. The area is mostly *Quercus-Carpinus* forest with vineyards, arable land and mesophile grassland around the forest edge. Part of the site is a military training area consisting of mesophile grassland and forest. Human activities include forestry and hunting.

Habitats Forest and woodland (80%; broadleaved deciduous forest), Grassland (10%; steppe/dry calcareous grassland; humid grassland; mesophile grassland), Artificial landscape (10%; arable land; perennial crops/orchards/groves)
Land-use Agriculture (5%), Forestry (70%), Military (25%), Not utilized (5%)

■ Birds

Species	Season	Year	Pop min	Pop max	Acc	Criteria
Pernis apivorus Honey Buzzard	B	1994	—	—	B	B3, C6
Caprimulgus europaeus Nightjar	B	1994	10	50	A	C6
Dryocopus martius Black Woodpecker	R	1994	Common	—		C6
Dendrocopos medius Middle Spotted Woodpecker	R	1994	Common	—		B3, C6
Ficedula albicollis Collared Flycatcher	B	1994	—	—		B3, C6

The site is important for forest birds and species found in mixed agricultural landscapes.

■ Protection status
National None **International** None

■ Conservation issues

Threats Abandonment/reduction of land management (C), Agricultural intensification/expansion (B), Infrastructure (C), Intensified forest management (B)

The main threats come from the intensification of forestry, particularly the building of access roads, and the expansion of settlements into grasslands with associated refuse-dumping.

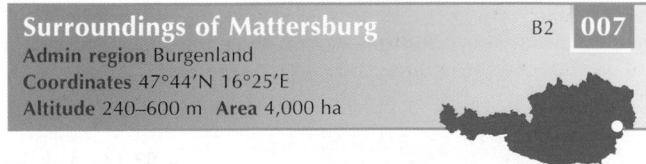

Surroundings of Mattersburg — 007
Admin region Burgenland
Coordinates 47°44'N 16°25'E
Altitude 240–600 m **Area** 4,000 ha
B2

■ Site description
An open, diverse landscape near Mattersburg. The main land-use is low-intensity agriculture and the site consists of arable fields, orchards, grassland and groves dominated by *Castanea sativa*.

Habitats Grassland (30%; mesophile grassland; steppe/dry calcareous grassland), Artificial landscape (65%; arable land; perennial crops/orchards/groves; ruderal land)
Land-use Agriculture (100%)

■ Birds
This site holds important numbers of birds associated with non-intensively managed orchards and open woodland.

Species		Season	Year	Pop min	Pop max	Acc	Criteria
Otus scops	Scops Owl	B	1993	12	19	A	B2

■ Protection status
National Low **International** None
80 ha of IBA covered by protected area (Rohrbacher Kogel, 80 ha).

■ Conservation issues

Threats Abandonment/reduction of land management (A), Agricultural intensification/expansion (A), Industrialization/urbanization (C), Other (B)

Threats include the abandonment of orchards, *Castanea* groves and hay-meadows, and the removal of old trees, nesting sites for *Otus scops*. *Castanea* stands are also threatened by a virus ('Other' threats). A two-year conservation project (1994–1995) has been completed, resulting in detailed management proposals.

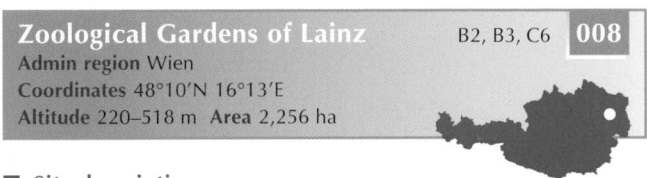

Zoological Gardens of Lainz
B2, B3, C6   **008**
Admin region Wien
Coordinates 48°10'N 16°13'E
Altitude 220–518 m **Area** 2,256 ha

■ Site description
This site is part of the much larger Vienna forest. It is dominated by *Quercus, Carpinus, Fagus, Fraxinus* and *Acer*. Human activities include tourism and recreation, forestry and hunting.

Habitats Forest and woodland (90%; broadleaved deciduous forest), Grassland (10%; mesophile grassland)
Land-use Agriculture (5%), Forestry (90%), Tourism/recreation (5%)

■ Birds

Species		Season	Year	Pop min	Pop max	Acc	Criteria
Picus canus	Grey-headed Woodpecker	R	1994	25	25	A	B2, C6
Picus viridis	Green Woodpecker	R	1994	35	40	A	B2
Dendrocopos medius	Middle Spotted Woodpecker	R	1994	200	300	A	B3, C6
Ficedula parva	Red-breasted Flycatcher	B	1994	100	100	A	C6
Ficedula albicollis	Collared Flycatcher	B	1994	800	800	A	B3, C6

The area contains important populations of species found in old broadleaved forests.

■ Protection status
National High **International** High
2,256 ha of IBA covered by Nature Reserve (Lainzer Tiergarten, 2,260 ha). 2,256 ha of IBA covered by Special Protection Area (Lainzer Tiergarten, 2,256 ha).

■ Conservation issues

Threats Consequences of animal/plant introductions (C), Forest grazing (A), Intensified forest management (B), Recreation/tourism (C)

The main threat to the forest is from high densities of wild boar *Sus scrofa*, fallow deer *Dama dama*, red deer *Cervus elaphus* and mouflon *Ovis musimon* which prevent forest and understorey regeneration. Parts of the forest are also subject to intensive forest management.

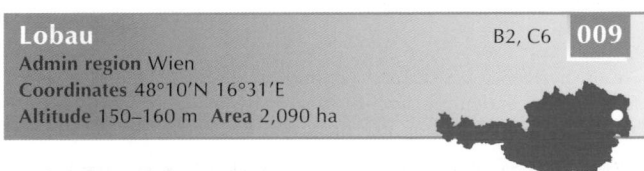

Lobau
B2, C6   **009**
Admin region Wien
Coordinates 48°10'N 16°31'E
Altitude 150–160 m **Area** 2,090 ha

■ Site description
The Lobau is the western part of a large area of riverine forest associated with the Danube. It is divided by the Donau–Oder–Kanal into the Obere (Upper) and Untere (Lower) Lobau. The Obere Lobau is a mixture of agriculture and intensive forestry, but the Untere Lobau contains areas of near-natural forest. Both areas are used for recreational activities, angling and hunting.

Habitats Forest and woodland (80%; alluvial/very wet forest), Grassland (10%; mesophile grassland), Wetland (5%; standing fresh water), Artificial landscape (5%; arable land)
Land-use Agriculture (15%), Fisheries/aquaculture (5%), Forestry (80%)

■ Birds

Species		Season	Year	Pop min	Pop max	Acc	Criteria
Ixobrychus minutus	Little Bittern	B	1994	5	10	A	C6
Milvus migrans	Black Kite	B	1982	2	2	A	C6
Jynx torquilla	Wryneck	B	1982	15	25	A	B2

The site is important for breeding riverine forest species.

■ Protection status
National High **International** High
2,000 ha of IBA covered by National Park (Donau–Auen, 10,000 ha). 1,039 ha of IBA covered by Ramsar Site (Untere Lobau, 1,039 ha). 2,090 ha of IBA covered by Special Protection Area (Donau–Auen (Wiener Anteil), 2,300 ha).

■ Conservation issues

Threats Aquaculture/fisheries (B), Groundwater abstraction (A), Intensified forest management (B), Recreation/tourism (C)

There are no restrictions on forestry, hunting or angling. Incorporation of the IBA into the Donau–Auen National Park (1996) will lead to improved conservation measures.

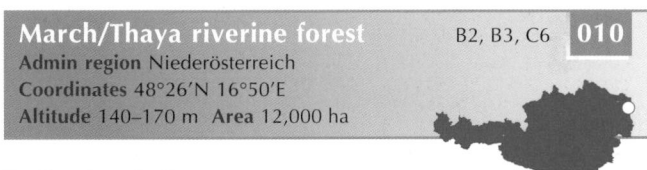

March/Thaya riverine forest
B2, B3, C6   **010**
Admin region Niederösterreich
Coordinates 48°26'N 16°50'E
Altitude 140–170 m **Area** 12,000 ha

■ Site description
This site lies on the border with Slovakia and is the largest lowland river system in Austria. Annual floods inundate large parts of the lowland area. The majority of the IBA consists of alluvial/very wet forest, dominated by *Fraxinus* and *Quercus*, oxbows and wetlands. Wet meadows occupy about 10 km². Human activities include forestry, hunting and angling.

Habitats Forest and woodland (80%; alluvial/very wet forest), Grassland (10%; humid grassland), Wetland (5%; river/stream), Artificial landscape (5%; arable land)
Land-use Agriculture (15%), Forestry (80%), Not utilized (5%)

■ Birds

Species		Season	Year	Pop min	Pop max	Acc	Criteria
Nycticorax nycticorax	Night Heron	B	1989	3	4	A	C6
Ciconia nigra	Black Stork	B	1994	6	8	A	B2, C6
Ciconia ciconia	White Stork	B	1996	95	95	A	C6
Milvus migrans	Black Kite	B	1994	15	18	A	C6
Circus aeruginosus	Marsh Harrier	B	1994	11	15	A	C6
Falco cherrug	Saker	B	1994	1	2	A	B2
Crex crex	Corncrake	B	1996	19	19	A	C6
Alcedo atthis	Kingfisher	B	1994	20	25	A	B2, C6
Locustella luscinioides	Savi's Warbler	B	1994	—	—	—	B3

The site is important for breeding woodland and wetland species. Species of global conservation concern that does not meet IBA criteria: *Haliaeetus albicilla* (8 wintering birds).

■ Protection status
National Partial **International** High
1,687 ha of IBA covered by Nature Reserves (Rabensburger Thaya–Auen, 385 ha; Angerner und Dürnkruter Marchschlingen, 81 ha; Salzsteppe Baumgarten a.d. March, 11 ha; Untere Marchauen, 1,166 ha; Kleiner Breitensee, 44 ha). 12,000 ha of IBA covered by Ramsar Site (Donau–March–Auen, 38,500 ha). 12,000 ha of IBA covered by Special Protection Area (March–Thaya–Auen, 13,009 ha).

■ Conservation issues

Threats Agricultural intensification/expansion (B), Groundwater abstraction (B), Infrastructure (B), Industrialization/urbanization (C), Intensified forest management (C)

The planed Donau–Oder–Kanal could have a dramatic impact on the ecosystem. Plans for a new bridge and road are a serious threat to the northern part of the IBA. Hunting, particularly of wildfowl, occurs.

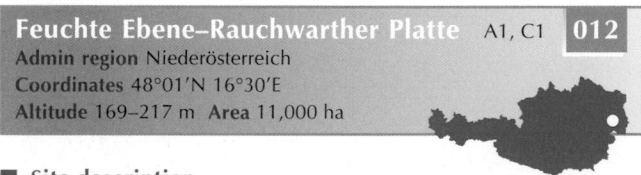

Riverine forests on the Danube east of Vienna
B2, B3, C6 **011**

Admin region Niederösterreich
Coordinates 48°08′N 16°43′E
Altitude 140–150 m **Area** 9,500 ha

■ Site description
The IBA is the only remaining large riverine forest on a free flowing stretch of the Danube in Austria. Close to the river *Salix* and *Populus* dominate, whilst in other areas the forest is dominated by *Fraxinus*, *Quercus* and *Ulmus*. Artificial *Populus* plantations have replaced the natural forest in many places. The forest is interspersed with oxbow lakes, fringed by reedbeds (*Phragmites*). Human activities include forestry, recreation and angling.

Habitats Forest and woodland (80%; alluvial/very wet forest), Grassland (5%; mesophile grassland), Wetland (15%; river/stream; standing fresh water; water-fringe vegetation)
Land-use Agriculture (5%), Forestry (80%), Not utilized (15%)

■ Birds

Species		Season	Year	Pop min	Pop max	Acc	Criteria
Pernis apivorus	Honey Buzzard	B	1989	18	19	A	B3, C6
Milvus migrans	Black Kite	B	1989	18	19	A	C6
Alcedo atthis	Kingfisher	B	1989	41	41	A	B2, C6
Dendrocopos medius	Middle Spotted Woodpecker	R	1989	Common		—	B3

The site is important for forest species, particularly breeding raptors and woodpeckers.

■ Protection status
National High **International** High
7,065 ha of IBA covered by National Park (Donau–Auen, 7,065 ha). 9,500 ha of IBA covered by Special Protection Area (Donau–Auen östlich von Wien, 11,741 ha). 9,500 ha of IBA covered by Ramsar Site (Donau–March–Auen, 38,500 ha).

■ Conservation issues

Threats Construction/impact of dyke/dam/barrage (B), Intensified forest management (C), Recreation/tourism (B)

Intensification of forestry is continuing outside the National Park. Recreational use causes widespread disturbance. Plans are underway to restore oxbow lakes and to halt forestry in some parts of the National Park.

Feuchte Ebene–Rauchwarther Platte
A1, C1 **012**

Admin region Niederösterreich
Coordinates 48°01′N 16°30′E
Altitude 169–217 m **Area** 11,000 ha

■ Site description
The site consists of two parts. The Feuchte Ebene is a semi-open plain, previously with large areas of non-intensive pasture, now largely converted to arable cultivation. There are still substantial areas of humid grassland and small pockets of dry grassland, fens and alluvial forest. The Rauchwarther Platte is an undulating plateau, largely used for arable agriculture. The north of the IBA contains a large *Quercus* forest.

Habitats Forest and woodland (10%; broadleaved deciduous forest; alluvial/very wet forest), Grassland (5%; humid grassland; mesophile grassland), Wetland (5%; water-fringe vegetation), Artificial landscape (80%; arable land; urban parks/gardens; ruderal land)
Land-use Agriculture (90%), Forestry (10%)

■ Birds

Species		Season	Year	Pop min	Pop max	Acc	Criteria
Crex crex	Corncrake	B	1997	16	31	—	A1, C1

An important site for species breeding in humid grasslands and arable land. Species of global conservation concern that do not meet IBA criteria: *Otis tarda* (0–2 pairs).

■ Protection status
National Low **International** Partial
11 ha of IBA covered by Nature Reserve (Pischelsdorfer Wiesen, 11 ha). 6,500 ha of IBA covered by Special Protection Area (Feuchte Ebene–Leithaauen, 10,518 ha).

■ Conservation issues

Threats Agricultural intensification/expansion (B), Drainage (C), Filling-in of wetlands (C), Groundwater abstraction (C), Infrastructure (C), Recreation/tourism (B)

The major threats are from intensive agriculture, drainage and a planned recreation park. Since 1995, BirdLife Austria has been working with local farmers running a conservation project for *Crex crex*.

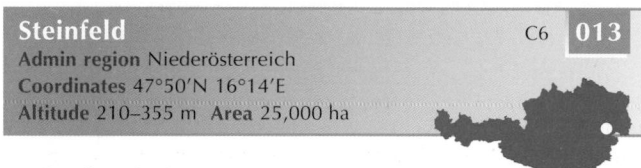

Steinfeld
C6 **013**

Admin region Niederösterreich
Coordinates 47°50′N 16°14′E
Altitude 210–355 m **Area** 25,000 ha

■ Site description
The Steinfeld is an extensive plain south of Vienna. Until recently it was the largest area of primary dry grassland in central Europe. Today, 20 km² of grassland remain, mainly within a military area. The remainder of the IBA is arable land and *Pinus nigra* plantations. There are also several large gravel-pits and two small airfields.

Habitats Grassland (15%; steppe/dry calcareous grassland), Artificial landscape (85%; arable land; forestry plantation; other urban/industrial areas)
Land-use Agriculture (55%), Forestry (20%), Military (10%), Urban/industrial/transport (15%)

■ Birds

Species		Season	Year	Pop min	Pop max	Acc	Criteria
Burhinus oedicnemus	Stone Curlew	B	1994	5	7	A	C6
Caprimulgus europaeus	Nightjar	B	1996	50	50	B	C6
Anthus campestris	Tawny Pipit	B	1994	10	10	A	C6

The area is important for breeding species associated with grassland and arable agriculture. The IBA contains Austria's most important population of *Burhinus oedicnemus* and the largest population of *Caprimulgus europaeus*.

■ Protection status
National None **International** None

■ Conservation issues

Threats Afforestation (B), Agricultural intensification/expansion (B), Extraction industry (B), Industrialization/urbanization (A), Infrastructure (A)

The main threats are from the conversion of grasslands to arable land and gravel-pits, road building and urbanization in ecologically sensitive areas and recreational use and refuse dumps in former gravel-pits. An action plan for of *Burhinus oedicnemus* exist.

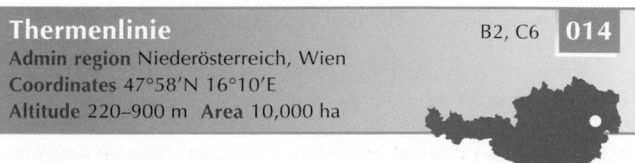

Thermenlinie
B2, C6 **014**

Admin region Niederösterreich, Wien
Coordinates 47°58′N 16°10′E
Altitude 220–900 m **Area** 10,000 ha

■ Site description

Habitats Forest and woodland (10%; broadleaved deciduous forest), Grassland (5%; steppe/dry calcareous grassland), Artificial landscape (85%; arable land; perennial crops/orchards/groves; other urban/industrial areas)
Land-use Agriculture (80%), Forestry (10%), Urban/industrial/transport (5%)

The Thermenlinie lies on the eastern edge of the Alps and is a region of limestone and dolomitic limestone. Land-use is predominantly vineyards interspersed with arable fields, dry calcareous grassland and many small patches of woodland. Human activities include quarrying and recreation.

■ Birds

Species	Season	Year	Pop min	Pop max	Acc	Criteria
Bubo bubo Eagle Owl	R	1994	20	25	A	B2, C6
Lullula arborea Woodlark	B	1994	70	70	A	C6

This site is important for breeding species associated with a mixed agricultural landscape.

■ Protection status

National Low **International** High
84 ha of IBA covered by protected areas (Glaslautererriegel–Heferlberg, 16 ha; Eichkogel, 68 ha). 10,000 ha of IBA covered by Special Protection Area (Wienerwald–Thermenregion, 95,688 ha).

■ Conservation issues

Threats Abandonment/reduction of land management (B), Afforestation (B), Agricultural intensification/expansion (A), Industrialization/urbanization (C), Recreation/tourism (C)

The main threats to the area come from the expansion of human settlements into grassland, recreational activities and agricultural intensification. Most of the smaller grasslands are threatened by the abandonment of their traditional use as pastures.

Vienna forest   B2, B3, C6   015

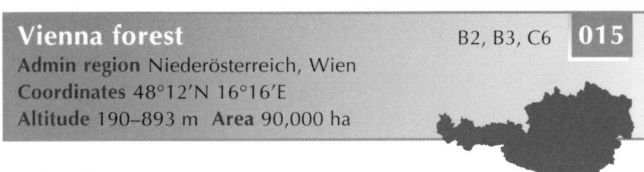

Admin region Niederösterreich, Wien
Coordinates 48°12′N 16°16′E
Altitude 190–893 m **Area** 90,000 ha

■ Site description

The Vienna forest covers the north-eastern foothills of the Alps. The northern and western parts have rolling hills and valleys, whilst the southern part is limestone with steep cliffs and quarries. Approximately 25% of the forest is coniferous, the remainder being dominated by *Carpinus*, *Fagus* and *Quercus*. Forestry and tourism are the main human activities.

Habitats Forest and woodland (90%; broadleaved deciduous forest; native coniferous forest; mixed forest), Grassland (5%; mesophile grassland), Artificial landscape (5%; highly improved reseeded grassland; arable land; other urban/industrial areas)
Land-use Agriculture (10%), Forestry (90%)

■ Birds

Species	Season	Year	Pop min	Pop max	Acc	Criteria
Ciconia nigra Black Stork	B	1994	10	15	A	B2, C6
[1] *Crex crex* Corncrake	B	1994	11	12	A	C6
Picus canus Grey-headed Woodpecker	R	1994	140	180	A	B2, C6
Picus viridis Green Woodpecker	R	1994	250	350	A	B2
Dryocopus martius Black Woodpecker	R	1994	—	—	A	C6
Dendrocopos medius Middle Spotted Woodpecker	R	1994	200	250	A	B3, C6
Ficedula parva Red-breasted Flycatcher	B	1994	500	800	A	C6
Ficedula albicollis Collared Flycatcher	B	1994	800	1,500	A	B3, C6

1. Calling males.

The site holds significant populations of species that occur in broadleaved forests.

■ Protection status

National None **International** High
90,000 ha of IBA covered by Special Protection Area (Wienerwald–Thermenregion, 95,688 ha).

■ Conservation issues

Threats Agricultural intensification/expansion (A), Industrialization/urbanization (A), Intensified forest management (A), Recreation/tourism (B)

The major threat is from intensive forestry with few near-natural areas remaining. Increasing tourism is leading to more house-building and traffic. Non-intensive use of meadows is rare.

Western Weinviertel   B2, C6   016

Admin region Niederösterreich
Coordinates 48°39′N 15°58′E
Altitude 218–400 m **Area** 39,500 ha

■ Site description

A hilly area dominated by arable agriculture near the border with the Czech Republic. Small remnants of wet meadows and dry grasslands remain, each less than 1–2 km² in total. Woodland is confined to small patches.

Habitats Forest and woodland (5%; broadleaved deciduous forest), Artificial landscape (95%; arable land; other urban/industrial areas)
Land-use Agriculture (97%)

■ Birds

Species	Season	Year	Pop min	Pop max	Acc	Criteria
[1] *Otis tarda* Great Bustard	R	1996	22	22	A	B2, C6

1. Individuals.

An important site for breeding farmland birds with an stable *Otis tarda* population.

■ Protection status

National None **International** Partial
28,172 ha of IBA covered by Special Protection Area (Westliches Weinviertel, 28,172 ha).

■ Conservation issues

Threats Abandonment/reduction of land management (B), Agricultural intensification/expansion (B), Afforestation (B), Drainage (C), Infrastructure (C)

Past plans to construct new roads and power-lines have been prevented but remain a threat for the future. The planting of shelterbelts will reduce the available habitat for *Otis tarda*. Since 1996 there has been a species protection programme for *O. tarda*.

Central Marchfeld   B2, C6   017

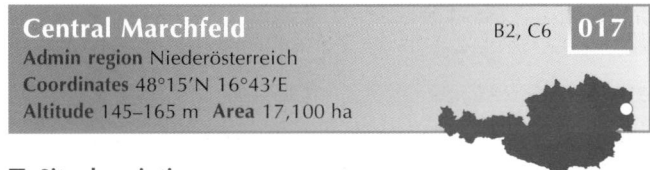

Admin region Niederösterreich
Coordinates 48°15′N 16°43′E
Altitude 145–165 m **Area** 17,100 ha

■ Site description

The Marchfeld is a plain to the north-east of Vienna, dominated by intensive arable agriculture with high levels of irrigation. Small remnants of woodland and dry, sandy grassland remain.

Habitats Forest and woodland (5%; broadleaved deciduous forest), Artificial landscape (95%; arable land; forestry plantation; urban parks/gardens; other urban/industrial areas)
Land-use Agriculture (95%), Forestry (5%)

■ Birds

Species	Season	Year	Pop min	Pop max	Acc	Criteria
[1,2] *Otis tarda* Great Bustard	B	1994	16	16	A	B2, C6
Caprimulgus europaeus Nightjar	B	—	16	18	A	C6

1. Individuals.
2. Large decrease.

The site is one of five in Austria that hold *Otis tarda*.

■ Protection status

National Low **International** None
376 ha of IBA covered by Nature Reserves (Wacholderheide Siebenbrunn, 38 ha; Weikendorfer Remise, 183 ha; Sandberge Oberweiden, 115 ha; Schloßpark Obersiebenbrunn, 40 ha)

■ Conservation issues

Threats Abandonment/reduction of land management (B), Agricultural intensification/expansion (C), Groundwater abstraction (B)

Despite an ongoing protection programme, the *Otis tarda* population is still in decline and threatened by intensive agriculture.

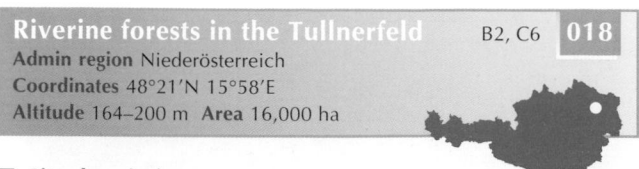

Riverine forests in the Tullnerfeld — B2, C6 — 018

Admin region Niederösterreich
Coordinates 48°21′N 15°58′E
Altitude 164–200 m **Area** 16,000 ha

■ Site description

The area encloses the flood-plain forests of the Danube between Krems and Klosterneuburg. Only small remnants of the original forest communities still exist. Today, most of the area is covered by *Populus* plantations and stands of *Fraxinus* and *Alnus*. Within the forest are numerous oxbow lakes, with reedbeds (*Phragmites*), as well as hay-meadows, arable fields and gravel-pits. Human activities include forestry, agriculture, gravel extraction, recreation, hunting and angling.

Habitats Forest and woodland (70%; broadleaved deciduous forest; alluvial/very wet forest), Grassland (10%; mesophile grassland), Wetland (10%; river/stream; water-fringe vegetation), Artificial landscape (10%; arable land; other urban/industrial areas)
Land-use Agriculture (15%), Forestry (70%), Hunting (15%), Not utilized (10%)

■ Birds

Species	Season	Year	Pop min	Pop max	Acc	Criteria
Ixobrychus minutus Little Bittern	B	1994	5	10	A	C6
Milvus migrans Black Kite	B	1994	5	10	A	C6
Alcedo atthis Kingfisher	B	1990	20	30	B	B2, C6

This site is important for species typical of riverine forests.

■ Protection status

National None **International** High
16,000 ha of IBA covered by Special Protection Area (Tullnerfelder Donau–Auen, 19,483 ha).

■ Conservation issues

Threats Agricultural intensification/expansion (B), Construction/impact of dyke/dam/barrage (A), Extraction industry (C), Intensified forest management (A), Recreation/tourism (C)

Major threats come from intensive forestry and gravel extraction. Two power plants on the Danube negatively affect the water regime of the forest.

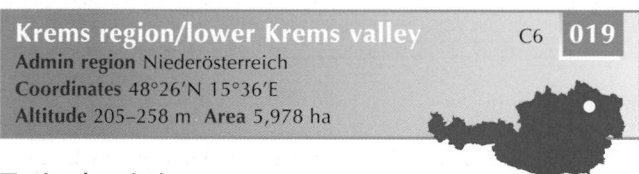

Krems region/lower Krems valley — C6 — 019

Admin region Niederösterreich
Coordinates 48°26′N 15°36′E
Altitude 205–258 m **Area** 5,978 ha

■ Site description

Over 60% of this site is occupied by non-intensive vineyards. These are interspersed with arable land, small patches of woodland, dry grassland, hedgerows and orchards. Broadleaved deciduous forest is found on the steeper slopes. Parts of the river course are still in a near-natural state. The main human activity is viticulture.

Habitats Forest and woodland (35%; broadleaved deciduous forest), Artificial landscape (65%; arable land; perennial crops/orchards/groves; other urban/industrial areas)
Land-use Agriculture (60%), Forestry (35%), Urban/industrial/transport (5%)

■ Birds

Species	Season	Year	Pop min	Pop max	Acc	Criteria
Lullula arborea Woodlark	B	1994	50	50	A	C6

The site holds significant breeding populations of species found in richly structured, open landscapes.

■ Protection status

National None **International** High
5,978 ha of IBA covered by Special Protection Area (Kamp und Kremstal, 42,934 ha).

■ Conservation issues

Threats Abandonment/reduction of land management (B), Afforestation (B), Agricultural intensification/expansion (A), Intensified forest management (C)

Main threats to the area are intensification of viticulture, abandonment of traditional grassland management and the clearance of orchards.

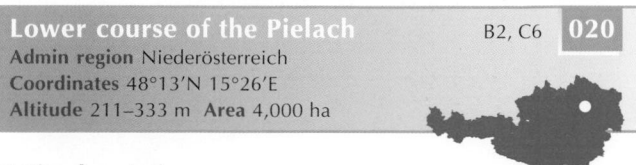

Lower course of the Pielach — B2, C6 — 020

Admin region Niederösterreich
Coordinates 48°13′N 15°26′E
Altitude 211–333 m **Area** 4,000 ha

■ Site description

The course of the Pielach, a tributary of the Danube, is in a near-natural state. Forest dominated by *Alnus*, *Fraxinus*, *Acer* and *Salix* is associated with the river. Adjacent areas are dominated by arable cultivation with two patches of *Quercus* woodland.

Habitats Forest and woodland (30%; broadleaved deciduous forest; alluvial/very wet forest), Wetland (20%; river/stream; standing fresh water), Artificial landscape (50%; arable land; perennial crops/orchards/groves)
Land-use Agriculture (50%), Forestry (30%), Tourism/recreation (10%), Not utilized (10%)

■ Birds

Species	Season	Year	Pop min	Pop max	Acc	Criteria
Alcedo atthis Kingfisher	R	1994	12	14	A	B2, C6

The site is important for breeding riverine species.

■ Protection status

National None **International** High
4,000 ha of IBA covered by Special Protection Area (Nieder-österreichische Alpenvorlandflusse, 16,484 ha).

■ Conservation issues

Threats Agricultural intensification/expansion (B), Dredging/canalization (A), Extraction industry (B), Intensified forest management (A), Recreation/tourism (B)

The riverine forest is threatened with conversion to plantations and the river itself by canalization and shingle mining. The areas of the river that are important for birds are also heavily used for recreation.

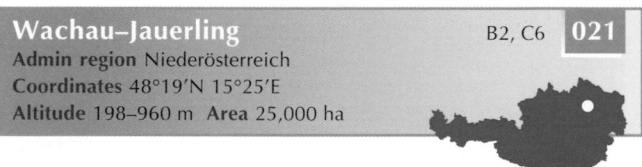

Wachau–Jauerling — B2, C6 — 021

Admin region Niederösterreich
Coordinates 48°19′N 15°25′E
Altitude 198–960 m **Area** 25,000 ha

■ Site description

The Wachau, part of the Danube valley, is characterized by rocky slopes and cliffs. Land-use in the Wachau is mainly vineyards and orchards on the slopes, with arable land on the valley floor. Extensive areas of forest also remain on the slopes but native broadleaved species have been replaced with *Picea*. The Jauerling, a low mountain to the north-west of the Wachau, is covered by non-native *Picea* forests, interspersed with patches of broadleaved forest and grasslands.

Habitats Forest and woodland (40%; broadleaved deciduous forest; native coniferous forest; alluvial/very wet forest), Grassland (5%; humid grassland; mesophile grassland; steppe/dry calcareous grassland), Wetland (5%; river/stream), Artificial landscape (50%; arable land; perennial crops/orchards/groves; forestry plantation; other urban/industrial areas)
Land-use Agriculture (30%), Forestry (70%)

■ Birds

Species	Season	Year	Pop min	Pop max	Acc	Criteria
Ciconia nigra Black Stork	B	1994	1	2	A	B2, C6
Bubo bubo Eagle Owl	R	1991	22	22	A	B2, C6
Ficedula parva Red-breasted Flycatcher	B	1994	20	40	A	C6

The site is important for species characteristic of open woodland, non-intensively managed orchards, rocky slopes and cliffs.

■ Protection status

National None **International** High
25,000 ha of IBA covered by Special Protection Area (Wachau–Jauerling, 45,802 ha).

■ Conservation issues

Threats Abandonment/reduction of land management (C), Afforestation (A), Agricultural intensification/expansion (B), Industrialization/urbanization (C), Intensified forest management (A), Recreation/tourism (C)

The floor of the Wachau is threatened by agricultural intensification, infrastructural development and housing development. Afforestation threatens the remaining grasslands and native broadleaved forest is being converted to *Picea* monocultures.

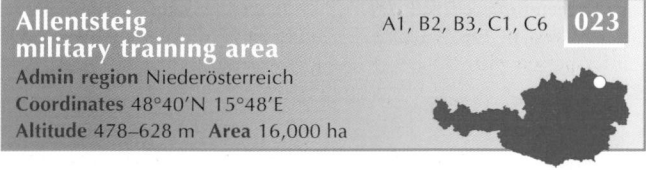

Southern Waldviertel C6 **022**
Admin region Niederösterreich
Coordinates 48°25'N 15°17'E
Altitude 356–923 m **Area** 41,000 ha

■ Site description

This area forms part of the plateau of the Bohemian Mass. The majority of the site is covered by intensively-managed *Picea* plantations with some areas of broadleaved and mixed forest. There are also substantial areas of arable agriculture and mesophile grassland. Wetlands and wet meadows have been reduced to small remnants.

Habitats Forest and woodland (10%; broadleaved deciduous forest), Grassland (20%; mesophile grassland), Artificial landscape (70%; arable land; forestry plantation)
Land-use Agriculture (30%), Forestry (70%)

■ Birds

Species	Season	Year	Pop min	Pop max	Acc	Criteria
Crex crex Corncrake	B	1992	11	37	—	C6
Glaucidium passerinum Pygmy Owl	R	1994	—	—	—	C6
[1] *Aegolius funereus* Tengmalm's Owl	R	1993	13	13	A	C6

1. Calling males.

The area is important for breeding forest and farmland species. The numbers of *Crex crex* fluctuate widely from year to year.

■ Protection status
National None **International** Partial
8,200 ha of IBA covered by Special Protection Area (Waldviertler Teich, Heide und Moorlandschaften, 54,486 ha).

■ Conservation issues

Threats Afforestation (B), Agricultural intensification/expansion (B), Intensified forest management (A)

Conversion of native forests into plantations, forestry operations and agricultural intensification are the main threats. The remaining wet meadows are threatened by afforestation.

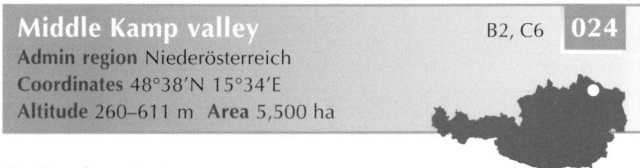

Allentsteig military training area A1, B2, B3, C1, C6 **023**
Admin region Niederösterreich
Coordinates 48°40'N 15°48'E
Altitude 478–628 m **Area** 16,000 ha

■ Site description
The site is a military training area and is closed to the general public. About 70 km² of land were removed from agricultural production in 1941 and this area is now fallow land. The remainder of the area is composed of intensively managed spruce *Picea* forest, arable land, hay-meadows, and a few fish-ponds. Apart from military training, human activities include hunting, fisheries, agriculture and forestry.

Habitats Forest and woodland (10%; mixed forest), Grassland (10%; mesophile grassland), Artificial landscape (80%; arable land; forestry plantation; ruderal land)
Land-use Agriculture (20%), Forestry (35%), Military (30%), Not utilized (45%)

■ Birds
This site is important for species of open and semi-open landscapes. It holds the largest population of *Crex crex* in Austria.

Species	Season	Year	Pop min	Pop max	Acc	Criteria
Crex crex Corncrake	B	1995	11	71	A	A1, C1, C6
Jynx torquilla Wryneck	B	1994	50	60	A	B2
Saxicola rubetra Whinchat	B	1994	1,000	1,500	A	B3
Locustella naevia Grasshopper Warbler	B	1994	1,500	2,500	A	B3
Sylvia nisoria Barred Warbler	B	1994	80	150	A	C6

■ Protection status
National None **International** None

■ Conservation issues

Threats Abandonment/reduction of land management (B), Agricultural intensification/expansion (C), Other (C)

Threats to the site include the intensification of agriculture and the potential impact of military training ('Other' threats).

Middle Kamp valley B2, C6 **024**
Admin region Niederösterreich
Coordinates 48°38'N 15°34'E
Altitude 260–611 m **Area** 5,500 ha

■ Site description
The IBA encompasses part of the Kamp valley and the adjoining plateau. The river course is still unregulated. The slopes are covered by mixed and broadleaved deciduous forest, whilst areas with easier access have largely been replaced by conifer plantations. More open areas are dominated by arable agriculture, within a mosaic of hedgerows, hay-meadows, dry grassland, small wetlands and orchards.

Habitats Forest and woodland (50%; broadleaved deciduous forest; mixed forest), Grassland (5%; steppe/dry calcareous grassland; mesophile grassland), Wetland (5%; river/stream), Artificial landscape (40%; arable land; perennial crops/orchards/groves; forestry plantation)
Land-use Agriculture (40%), Forestry (60%)

■ Birds

Species	Season	Year	Pop min	Pop max	Acc	Criteria
Ciconia nigra Black Stork	B	1994	2	3	A	B2, C6
Bubo bubo Eagle Owl	R	1994	4	5	A	B2, C6
Alcedo atthis Kingfisher	B	1994	7	8	A	C6

The site is important for woodland species.

■ Protection status
National None **International** High
5,500 ha of IBA covered by Special Protection Area (Kamp und Kremstal, 42,934 ha).

■ Conservation issues

Threats Abandonment/reduction of land management (C), Agricultural intensification/expansion (A), Intensified forest management (A), Recreation/tourism (B)

With the exception of areas where forestry is not allowed (in order to protect soil and water resources) intensification of forestry and plantations are a major threat. In arable and grassland areas, intensification and the abandonment of traditional management practices are threats. Planned tourism developments, such as golf courses, provide an additional threat.

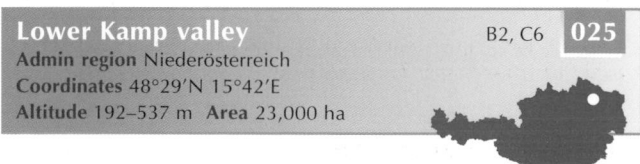

Lower Kamp valley B2, C6 **025**
Admin region Niederösterreich
Coordinates 48°29'N 15°42'E
Altitude 192–537 m **Area** 23,000 ha

■ Site description
This area is contiguous with the Middle Kamp valley but is more developed and populated. Vineyards are the dominant land-use within a matrix of small arable fields, orchards, patches of woodland, dry grasslands and stone walls. Forest on the surrounding plateau and hills is dominated by *Quercus* and *Pinus*, which grow in sparse stands on poor soils.

Habitats Forest and woodland (20%; alluvial/very wet forest; broadleaved deciduous forest; native coniferous forest; mixed forest), Grassland (5%; steppe/dry calcareous grassland), Wetland (5%; river/stream), Artificial landscape (70%; arable land; forestry plantation; perennial crops/orchards/groves; other urban/industrial areas)
Land-use Agriculture (60%), Forestry (30%), Not utilized (10%)

■ **Birds**

Species		Season	Year	Pop min	Pop max	Acc	Criteria
Bubo bubo	Eagle Owl	R	1994	3	4	A	B2, C6

An important area for species typical of mixed agricultural, grassland and wooded habitats, particularly *Lullula arborea* and *Emberiza cia*.

■ **Protection status**
National None **International** High
23,000 ha of IBA covered by Special Protection Area (Kamp und Kremstal, 42,934 ha).

■ **Conservation issues**

Threats Abandonment/reduction of land management (C), Afforestation (B), Agricultural intensification/expansion (A), Recreation/tourism (B)

Field amalgamation is a major threat as it destroys the fine-scale habitat matrix. Remaining grasslands are threatened by afforestation. Several small power-plants and mills on the river have altered the fluvial processes. The valley is used intensively by tourists.

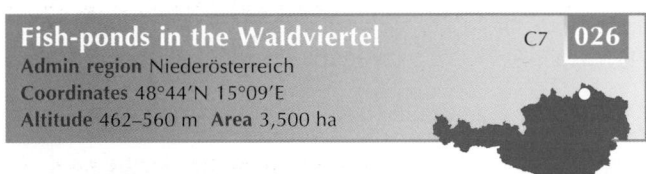

Fish-ponds in the Waldviertel　　　C7　026
Admin region Niederösterreich
Coordinates 48°44′N 15°09′E
Altitude 462–560 m **Area** 3,500 ha

■ **Site description**
There are about 1,400 fish-ponds with a total surface of about 1,700 ha. The IBA consists of six discrete areas isolated from each other. Larger ponds often have extensive stands of reed *Phragmites* and other aquatic vegetation. Wet grassland, hay-meadows and *Picea* forests surround the ponds. The main human activity is fish-farming with some agriculture.

Habitats Forest and woodland (10%; mixed forest), Grassland (20%; mesophile grassland), Wetland (20%; standing fresh water; water-fringe vegetation), Artificial landscape (50%; arable land; forestry plantation)
Land-use Agriculture (50%), Fisheries/aquaculture (20%), Forestry (30%)

■ **Birds**
The site is important for breeding species associated with reedbeds and open water. Species of global conservation concern that do not meet IBA criteria: *Crex crex* (5–10 breeding pairs).

■ **Protection status**
National Low **International** High
160 ha of IBA covered by Nature Reserves (Bruneiteich, 44 ha; Gebhartsteich, 86 ha; Gemeindeau, 30 ha). 3,500 ha of IBA covered by Special Protection Area (Waldviertler Teich, Heide–und Moorlandschaften, 54,486 ha).

■ **Conservation issues**

Threats Agricultural intensification/expansion (B), Aquaculture/fisheries (B)

There is a conflict between intensive fish-farming and piscivorous birds. Reedbeds are occasionally destroyed to increase the area of open water.

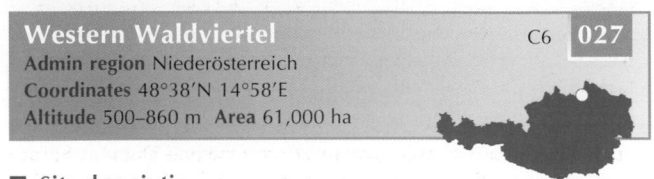

Western Waldviertel　　　C6　027
Admin region Niederösterreich
Coordinates 48°38′N 14°58′E
Altitude 500–860 m **Area** 61,000 ha

■ **Site description**
This area lies on the Bohemian Mass, a large plateau in northern

Austria. The landscape is hilly with stands of conifer and mixed forest, rivers, and a few fish-ponds. A fine-scale habitat mosaic of arable fields, grassland, hedges and small woodlands exists. Agriculture is still of comparatively low intensity.

Habitats Forest and woodland (10%; broadleaved deciduous forest; mixed forest), Grassland (20%; mesophile grassland), Artificial landscape (70%; arable land; forestry plantation)
Land-use Agriculture (80%), Forestry (20%)

■ **Birds**

Species		Season	Year	Pop min	Pop max	Acc	Criteria
Bonasa bonasia	Hazel Grouse	R	1994	—	—	—	C6
Glaucidium passerinum	Pygmy Owl	R	1994	—	—	—	C6
Lullula arborea	Woodlark	B	1994	50	50	B	C6

The site is important for species found in areas of mixed, low-intensity agriculture. Species of global conservation concern that do not meet IBA criteria: *Crex crex* (4 breeding pairs).

■ **Protection status**
National None **International** Partial
6,100 ha of IBA covered by Special Protection Area (Waldviertler Teich, Heide und Moorlandschaften, 54,486 ha).

■ **Conservation issues**

Threats Abandonment/reduction of land management (C), Afforestation (C), Agricultural intensification/expansion (B)

Agricultural intensification, particularly field enlargement, is a potential threat.

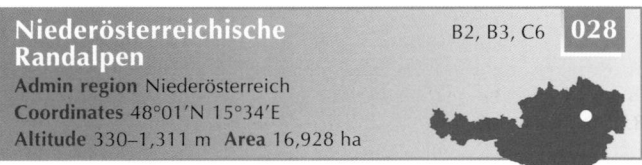

Niederösterreichische Randalpen　　　B2, B3, C6　028
Admin region Niederösterreich
Coordinates 48°01′N 15°34′E
Altitude 330–1,311 m **Area** 16,928 ha

■ **Site description**
This site has two distinct zones. The lower zone has less than 50% forest cover. Agricultural areas are dominated by hay-meadows and pastures, interspersed with old orchards, hedgerows and small woodlands. About one third of the original forest has been converted to *Picea* plantations. The upper zone is 80% forested and dominated by *Fagus* with the proportion of conifers depending upon the altitude. Locally these forests have been replaced by *Picea* plantations.

Habitats Forest and woodland (40%; broadleaved deciduous forest; mixed forest), Grassland (30%; humid grassland; mesophile grassland), Artificial landscape (30%; perennial crops/orchards/groves; forestry plantation)
Land-use Agriculture (35%), Forestry (65%)

■ **Birds**

Species		Season	Year	Pop min	Pop max	Acc	Criteria
Jynx torquilla	Wryneck	B	1994	50	100	A	B2
Picus canus	Grey-headed Woodpecker	R	1994	20	40	A	B2, C6
Picus viridis	Green Woodpecker	R	1994	50	80	A	B2
Ficedula parva	Red-breasted Flycatcher	B	1994	50	100	A	C6
Ficedula albicollis	Collared Flycatcher	B	1994	100	200	A	B3, C6

An important site for forest species, particularly woodpeckers, and species of semi-open habitats.

■ **Protection status**
National None **International** None

■ **Conservation issues**

Threats Agricultural intensification/expansion (A), Intensified forest management (B), Recreation/tourism (C)

The main threats are from the abandonment of traditional orchard management and the intensification of grassland management.

In addition, broadleaved forest is being replaced by conifer plantations.

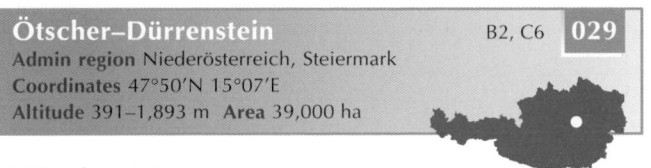

Ötscher–Dürrenstein — B2, C6 — 029
Admin region Niederösterreich, Steiermark
Coordinates 47°50'N 15°07'E
Altitude 391–1,893 m **Area** 39,000 ha

■ Site description
This area of the Alps is characterized by a karst landscape with steep limestone cliffs and deep river gorges. Mixed forests (montane zone) and conifer forests (subalpine zone) dominate. Steep slopes have prevented widespread intensive forestry but in many places original forest has been replaced by monocultures of *Picea*. Above the treeline are small areas of alpine meadows. The valleys contain a few important raised bogs. The area is used for forestry and tourism.

> **Habitats** Forest and woodland (90%; native coniferous forest; mixed forest; treeline ecotone), Grassland (5%; mesophile grassland), Rocky areas (5%)
> **Land-use** Agriculture (5%), Forestry (80%), Not utilized (15%)

■ Birds

Species	Season	Year	Pop min	Pop max	Acc	Criteria
Aquila chrysaetos Golden Eagle	R	1994	3	3	A	C6
Falco peregrinus Peregrine	B	1994	3	3	A	B2, C6
Tetrao urogallus Capercaillie	R	1994	20	25	A	C6
Picus canus Grey-headed Woodpecker	R	1994	30	50	A	B2, C6
Dendrocopos leucotos White-backed Woodpecker	R	1994	Frequent	—		C6

The site is important for species found in montane and subalpine forest, rocky areas and cliffs

■ Protection status
National Low **International** High
855 ha of IBA covered by Nature Reserves (Leckermoos, 34 ha; Lechnergraben, 245 ha, Rothwald I, 277 ha; Rothwald II, 299 ha). 39,000 ha of IBA covered by Special Protection Area (Ötscher–Dürrenstein, 80,235 ha).

■ Conservation issues

> **Threats** Intensified forest management (B), Recreation/tourism (C)

Intensive forestry is the main threat to the IBA. Recreation, particularly winter sports and canoeing, causes habitat loss and disturbance. Hunting is widespread and may affect grouse (Tetraonidae) populations.

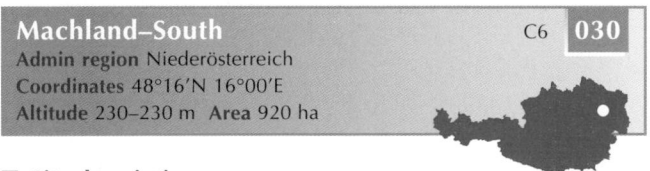

Machland–South — C6 — 030
Admin region Niederösterreich
Coordinates 48°16'N 16°00'E
Altitude 230–230 m **Area** 920 ha

■ Site description
A large area of hay-meadows and arable land, that floods periodically, on the south bank of the Danube. Small stands of riverine forest and a large oxbow lake are included in the IBA.

> **Habitats** Forest and woodland (5%; alluvial/very wet forest), Grassland (45%; mesophile grassland), Artificial landscape (50%; arable land)
> **Land-use** Agriculture (95%), Forestry (5%)

■ Birds

Species	Season	Year	Pop min	Pop max	Acc	Criteria
[1] *Crex crex* Corncrake	B	1995	—	14	A	C6
Alcedo atthis Kingfisher	B	1994	5	10	C	C6
Luscinia svecica Bluethroat	B	1995	20	20	A	C6

1. Calling males.

The area holds one of the last remaining lowland populations of *Crex crex* in Austria. Breeding success is currently very poor.

■ Protection status
National None **International** High
920 ha of IBA covered by Special Protection Area (Machland Sud, 2,076 ha).

■ Conservation issues

> **Threats** Agricultural intensification/expansion (A)

The meadows are threatened by conversion to arable land and intensification. They are currently cut 2–4 times annually and meadow bird species are threatened by early mowing, suffering low breeding success.

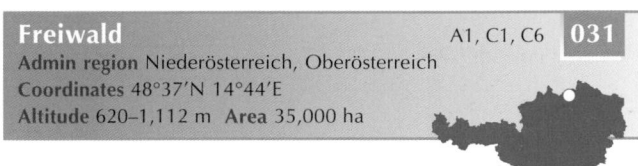

Freiwald — A1, C1, C6 — 031
Admin region Niederösterreich, Oberösterreich
Coordinates 48°37'N 14°44'E
Altitude 620–1,112 m **Area** 35,000 ha

■ Site description
A predominantly forested area on the eastern Bohemian Mass. Large areas of native forest have been replaced with spruce *Picea* plantations but substantial areas of native mixed *Fagus* and *Abies* forest, *Picea* forest and broadleaved forest remain. The majority of the remaining area is mesophile grassland. The site has a number of raised bogs.

> **Habitats** Forest and woodland (35%; broadleaved deciduous forest; native coniferous forest; mixed forest), Grassland (20%; mesophile grassland), Wetland (5%; raised bog), Artificial landscape (40%; arable land; forestry plantation)
> **Land-use** Agriculture (30%), Forestry (65%)

■ Birds

Species	Season	Year	Pop min	Pop max	Acc	Criteria
Ciconia nigra Black Stork	B	1994	2	3	A	C6
[1] *Crex crex* Corncrake	B	1998	20	29	A	A1, C1, C6
[1] *Lullula arborea* Woodlark	B	1995	15	15	A	C6

1. Calling males.

The area is important for breeding forest species and *Crex crex*.

■ Protection status
National Low **International** Partial
189 ha of IBA covered by Nature Reserves (Karlstifter Moore, 64 ha; Bruckangerlau, 3 ha; Tanner Moor, 122 ha). 12,250 ha of IBA covered by Special Protection Area (Waldviertler Teich, Heide und Moorlandschaften, 54,486 ha).

■ Conservation issues

> **Threats** Afforestation (C), Agricultural intensification/expansion (B), Intensified forest management (A), Recreation/tourism (C)

The major threat to the site is from intensive forestry, especially the use of *Picea* plantations and forest-road construction. In more open areas, threats come from the intensification of grassland utilization and arable agriculture.

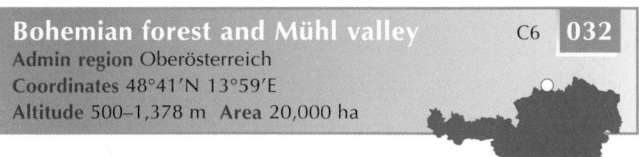

Bohemian forest and Mühl valley — C6 — 032
Admin region Oberösterreich
Coordinates 48°41'N 13°59'E
Altitude 500–1,378 m **Area** 20,000 ha

■ Site description

> **Habitats** Forest and woodland (60%; broadleaved deciduous forest; native coniferous forest; mixed forest), Grassland (5%; humid grassland; mesophile grassland), Artificial landscape (35%; arable land; forestry plantation)
> **Land-use** Agriculture (10%), Forestry (90%)

The Bohemian forest covers the highest peaks of the granitic Bohemian Mass and divides the river systems of the Elbe and Danube. Spruce *Picea* forests dominate, with some mixed and deciduous forest. The main land-use in the Mühl valley is arable agriculture although some wet meadows, dry grasslands and raised bogs remain. The area is used for winter sports.

■ Birds

Species	Season	Year	Pop min	Pop max	Acc	Criteria
[1] *Crex crex* Corncrake	B	1994	5	5	A	C6
Glaucidium passerinum Pygmy Owl	R	1994	15	30	A	C6

1. Calling males.

The IBA is important for species characteristic of both forest and mixed agriculture and grassland.

■ Protection status
National None **International** None

■ Conservation issues

Threats Agricultural intensification/expansion (B), Intensified forest management (B), Other (B), Recreation/tourism (C)

Forestry operations threaten the forests, although a natural age structure and an increased proportion of broadleaved trees are generally promoted. Acid rain ('Other' threats) threatens the forest, particularly at higher altitudes. Winter sports are a source of disturbance. In the Mühl valley, agricultural intensification is the major threat.

Northern Kalkalpen   B2, C6   033
Admin region Oberösterreich, Steiermark
Coordinates 48°12'N 14°08'E
Altitude 385–2,515 m **Area** 75,000 ha

■ Site description
This site comprises four mountain ranges. The Reichramiger Hintergebirge is dominated by near-natural conifer, mixed, and broadleaved forest. The Sengsengebirge also has areas of mixed and conifer forest and extensive areas of treeline ecotone habitat. On the Haller Mauern, forest cover is less extensive. The Totes Gebirge is a largely unvegetated, high-altitude karst plateau, bordered by alpine pastures and montane and subalpine forest.

Habitats Forest and woodland (60%; broadleaved deciduous forest; native coniferous forest; mixed forest; treeline ecotone), Grassland (20%; alpine/subalpine/boreal grassland; mesophile grassland), Rocky areas (20%)
Land-use Agriculture (20%), Forestry (60%), Not utilized (20%)

■ Birds

Species	Season	Year	Pop min	Pop max	Acc	Criteria
Ciconia nigra Black Stork	B	1994	3	5	—	B2, C6
Aquila chrysaetos Golden Eagle	R	1994	5	6	A	B2, C6
Falco peregrinus Peregrine	B	1994	—	—	—	B2, C6

The IBA is important for species of montane and subalpine forests, rocky areas and cliffs.

■ Protection status
National Partial **International** Partial
12,845 ha covered by Nature Reserves (Loser–Bräuning–Zinken, 1,750 ha; Grundlsee mit Teilen des Toten Gebirges, 9,700 ha; Teile des Toten Gebirges, 1,395 ha). 16,509 ha of IBA covered by National Park (Kalkalpen, 16,509 ha). 21,442 ha of IBA covered by Special Protection Area (Kalkalpen, 21,442 ha). 23,346 ha of IBA covered by Special Protection Areas (Totes Gebirge Ost and West, 23,346 ha).

■ Conservation issues

Threats Abandonment/reduction of land management (B), Intensified forest management (B), Recreation/tourism (C)

Intensive forestry is the major threat to the areas outside the National Park. Non-intensively managed alpine pastures are threatened by land abandonment. In the planning stage of the National Park several projects were carried out on the bird communities at different altitudes and in different habitats

Lower course of the Traun   C6   034
Admin region Oberösterreich
Coordinates 48°03'N 13°58'E
Altitude 290–440 m **Area** 2,260 ha

■ Site description
The site consists of the lower and middle courses of the River Traun, a tributary of the Danube, and neighbouring areas of gravel-pits and fish-ponds. Substantial areas of riverine forest remain along the middle course of the river. Surrounding arable land is increasingly being put into set-aside. The area is very popular for recreation, primarily watersports and angling.

Habitats Forest and woodland (40%; broadleaved deciduous forest; alluvial/very wet forest), Wetland (20%; standing fresh water; river/stream; water-fringe vegetation), Artificial landscape (40%; arable land; forestry plantation; urban parks/gardens; other urban/industrial areas; ruderal land)
Land-use Agriculture (30%), Fisheries/aquaculture (10%), Forestry (50%), Urban/industrial/transport (10%)

■ Birds

Species	Season	Year	Pop min	Pop max	Acc	Criteria
Pernis apivorus Honey Buzzard	B	1994	2	2	A	C6
Luscinia svecica Bluethroat	B	1994	11	11	A	C6

An important site for breeding species associated with a mix of wetland and forest. The gravel pits hold a large breeding population of *Riparia riparia* (800–1,700 pairs).

■ Protection status
National Low **International** High
75 ha of IBA covered by Nature Reserve (Fischlhamerau, 75 ha). 2,100 ha of IBA covered by Special Protection Area (Unteres Trauntal, 2,100 ha).

■ Conservation issues

Threats Construction/impact of dyke/dam/barrage (A), Extraction industry (B), Groundwater abstraction (C), Industrialization/urbanization (B), Recreation/tourism (B)

Forested areas are threatened by conversion to arable land, forestry plantations and gravel-pits. A new power plant is under construction within the IBA. The erection of high-tension power-lines has been detrimental to large migrant birds. There is a high degree of disturbance from recreational use of the area.

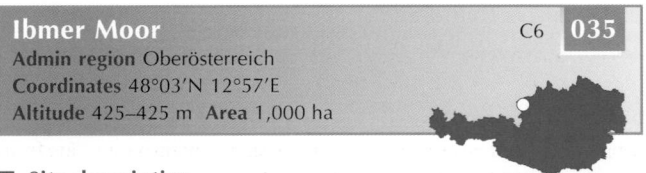

Ibmer Moor   C6   035
Admin region Oberösterreich
Coordinates 48°03'N 12°57'E
Altitude 425–425 m **Area** 1,000 ha

■ Site description
An area of raised bog, partly forested with native broadleaved and conifer forest. Outside the protected core area are wet hay-meadows and pastures, together with two lakes, one of which is used for recreation.

Habitats Forest and woodland (10%; broadleaved deciduous forest; native coniferous forest), Grassland (60%; humid grassland; mesophile grassland), Wetland (15%; raised bog; standing fresh water; water-fringe vegetation), Artificial landscape (15%; arable land; forestry plantation)
Land-use Agriculture (60%), Forestry (15%), Tourism/recreation (5%), Other (5%)

■ Birds

Species	Season	Year	Pop min	Pop max	Acc	Criteria
[1] *Luscinia svecica* Bluethroat	B	1995	8	8	A	C6

1. Calling males.

An important site for species breeding in raised bog and humid grassland such as *Numenius arquata* (13–14 pairs) and *Vanellus vanellus* (35–40 pairs).

■ Protection status
National Partial **International** Low

135 ha of IBA covered by Nature Reserves (Pfeiferanger, 76 ha; Frankinger Moos, 14 ha; Seeleithensee, 14 ha; Heratinger, See 31 ha). 76 ha of IBA covered by Special Protection Area (Pfeifer–Anger, 76 ha).

■ Conservation issues

Threats Abandonment/reduction of land management (C), Drainage (C), Recreation/tourism (B)

Land drainage is small-scale and limited to the margins of the site. An increasing number of farmers are taking up payments for late mowing. Some disturbance occurs as a result of recreational activities.

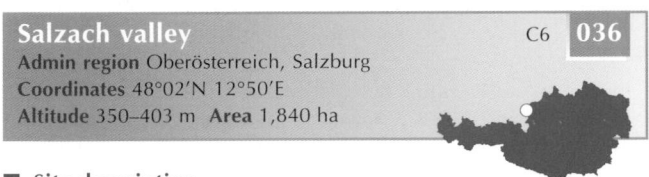

Salzach valley — C6 036

Admin region Oberösterreich, Salzburg
Coordinates 48°02'N 12°50'E
Altitude 350–403 m **Area** 1,840 ha

■ Site description

The site covers the lower course of the River Salzach, a section still free of power plants. Extensive areas of riverine forest remain close to Salzburg, whilst the lower section of the valley is a steep-sided gorge. In the north of the site, an area of agricultural land includes a high proportion of wet meadows.

Habitats Forest and woodland (60%; broadleaved deciduous forest; alluvial/very wet forest), Grassland (5%; humid grassland), Wetland (10%; river/stream), Artificial landscape (25%; arable land; forestry plantation; other urban/industrial areas)
Land-use Agriculture (20%), Forestry (60%), Hunting (20%), Tourism/recreation (5%), Urban/industrial/transport (10%)

■ Birds

Species	Season	Year	Pop min	Pop max	Acc	Criteria
Crex crex Corncrake	B	1993	2	4	A	C6
Alcedo atthis Kingfisher	B	1994	4	6	A	C6

The site is important for species associated with riverine forest and humid grassland.

■ Protection status

National None **International** Partial
500 ha of IBA covered by Special Protection Area (Ettenau, 500 ha). 1,120 ha of IBA covered by Special Protection Area (Salzachauen, 1,120 ha).

■ Conservation issues

Threats Agricultural intensification/expansion (B), Construction/impact of dyke/dam/barrage (B), Extraction industry (B), Intensified forest management (A), Recreation/tourism (B)

Management of riverine forest is increasingly intensive and areas are being converted to plantations. Near Salzburg, riverine forest is being destroyed by gravel extraction and subsequent waste-dumping. Increasing tourism is creating high levels of disturbance. Several power plants are planned which would destroy the riverine ecosystem.

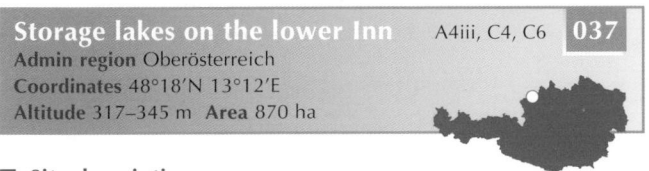

Storage lakes on the lower Inn — A4iii, C4, C6 037

Admin region Oberösterreich
Coordinates 48°18'N 13°12'E
Altitude 317–345 m **Area** 870 ha

■ Site description

The four storage lakes were built between 1938–1961 along the River Inn. High rates of sedimentation have allowed rapid colonization of water-fringe vegetation, especially reedbeds (*Phragmites*), and alluvial woodland, dominated by willow *Salix*. When water-levels are low, large areas of mudflats are exposed.

Habitats Forest and woodland (15%; alluvial/very wet forest), Wetland (85%; river/stream; water-fringe vegetation)
Land-use Forestry (10%), Not utilized (70%), Tourism/recreation (20%)

■ Birds

Species	Season	Year	Pop min	Pop max	Acc	Criteria
Nycticorax nycticorax Night Heron	B	1990	10	12	A	C6
Circus aeruginosus Marsh Harrier	B	1990	9	9	A	C6
Larus melanocephalus Mediterranean Gull	R	1994	1	2	A	C6
Sterna hirundo Common Tern	B	1990	7	7	A	C6
Luscinia svecica Bluethroat	B	1990	15	20	A	C6

An important site for breeding waterbirds and passage waders. The site holds 20,000 or more waterbirds, on a regular basis.

■ Protection status

National High **International** High
870 ha of IBA covered by Nature Reserve (Unterer Inn, 870 ha). 870 ha of IBA covered by Ramsar Site (Stauseen am Unteren Inn, 870 ha). 870 ha of IBA covered by Special Protection Area (Unterer Inn, 870 ha).

■ Conservation issues

Threats Disturbance to birds (A), Recreation/tourism (B)

The main threats are disturbance from angling and hunting, and from recreational activities.

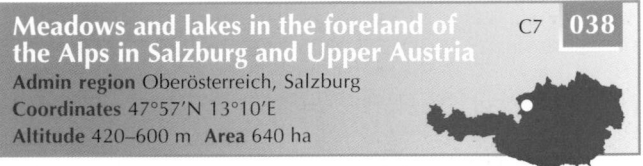

Meadows and lakes in the foreland of the Alps in Salzburg and Upper Austria — C7 038

Admin region Oberösterreich, Salzburg
Coordinates 47°57'N 13°10'E
Altitude 420–600 m **Area** 640 ha

■ Site description

This area contains nine sites with wet meadows adjacent to five lakes. The size of individual sites ranges from 25–270 ha. Originally situated in the inundation zone of the lakes, most of the meadows have been affected by drainage in the past. The area is used for forestry, agriculture and recreation.

Habitats Grassland (90%; humid grassland), Wetland (10%; standing fresh water; water-fringe vegetation)
Land-use Agriculture (90%), Not utilized (10%)

■ Birds

Species	Season	Year	Pop min	Pop max	Acc	Criteria
Numenius arquata Curlew	B	1993	13	19	A	C7

A good area for breeding species in humid grassland, particularly *Vanellus vanellus* (70–81 pairs), *Numenius arquata* (13–19 pairs) and *Gallinago gallinago* (20–25) pairs.

■ Protection status

National High **International** Partial
640 ha of the IBA covered by seven Nature Reserves, total area 1,102 ha. 105 ha of IBA covered by Special Protection Area (Oichtenriede, 105 ha). 298 ha of IBA covered by Special Protection Area (Wallersee–Wenger Moor, 298 ha).

■ Conservation issues

Threats Afforestation (C), Agricultural intensification/expansion (A), Drainage (A), Recreation/tourism (B)

The area is subject to high levels of disturbance from recreational use. Afforestation, drainage and agricultural intensification are additional threats to the site.

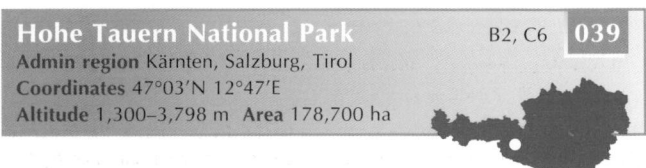

Hohe Tauern National Park — B2, C6 039

Admin region Kärnten, Salzburg, Tirol
Coordinates 47°03'N 12°47'E
Altitude 1,300–3,798 m **Area** 178,700 ha

■ Site description

The Hohen Tauern include the highest mountains in Austria. Between 1,300–1,700 m *Picea* forests, with some *Pinus* and *Abies*, dominates.

Above 1,700 m, *Pinus cembra* and *Larix* occur, but the forests are greatly altered and reduced in size by human use and the creation of pastures. The treeline has been lowered by human activity and extensive areas of treeline dwarf-shrub communities exist. Above the treeline are artificial pastures, alpine grasslands and extensive glaciers.

Habitats Forest and woodland (15%; native coniferous forest; mixed forest; treeline ecotone), Grassland (35%; alpine/subalpine/boreal grassland; mesophile grassland), Rocky areas (35%)
Land-use Agriculture (20%), Forestry (15%), Not utilized (65%)

■ **Birds**

Species	Season	Year	Pop min	Pop max	Acc	Criteria
Aquila chrysaetos Golden Eagle	R	1994	6	6	A	B2, C6
Lagopus mutus Ptarmigan	R	1990	Uncommon		—	C6
Tetrao tetrix Black Grouse	R	1990	Frequent		—	C6
Alectoris graeca Rock Partridge	R	1994	80	90	A	B2, C6
Picoides tridactylus Three-toed Woodpecker	R	1990	Frequent		—	B2, C6

An important site for alpine grassland and subalpine forest species.

■ **Protection status**
National High **International** Partial
37,263 ha of IBA covered by National Park (Hohe Tauern (Kärnten), 37,263 ha) 80,514 ha of IBA covered by National Park (Hohe Tauern (Salzburg), 80,514 ha). 60,996 ha of IBA covered by National Park (Hohe Tauern (Tirol, 60,996 ha). 80,514 ha of IBA covered by Special Protection Area (Hohe Tauern, 80,514 ha). 61,000 ha of IBA covered by Special Protection Area (Hohe Tauern, Tirol, 61,000 ha).

■ **Conservation issues**

Threats Abandonment/reduction of land management (B), Intensified forest management (C), Recreation/tourism (B)

Forestry, grazing, hunting and angling are allowed without restriction outside the core area of the National Park (1,120 km²). Tourism is promoted inside the park although it is free of the infrastructure for winter sports. Strict reserves, without human use, encompass 69 km².

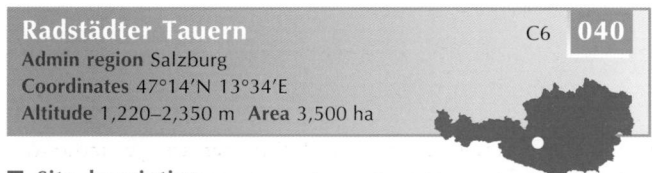

Radstädter Tauern   C6   **040**
Admin region Salzburg
Coordinates 47°14'N 13°34'E
Altitude 1,220–2,350 m **Area** 3,500 ha

■ **Site description**
The main habitats of the area are subalpine conifer forests, alpine pastures and rocky areas above the treeline. In addition, there is an area of raised bog near the town of Obertauern. Utilization of forest and pastures is non-intensive.

Habitats Forest and woodland (15%; native coniferous forest; treeline ecotone), Grassland (60%; alpine/subalpine/boreal grassland; mesophile grassland), Wetland (5%; raised bog), Rocky areas (20%; inland cliff)
Land-use Agriculture (30%), Forestry (15%), Not utilized (35%), Tourism/recreation (15%), Urban/industrial/transport (5%)

■ **Birds**

Species	Season	Year	Pop min	Pop max	Acc	Criteria
Luscinia svecica Bluethroat	B	1994	10	21	A	C6

An important area for alpine grassland and subalpine forest species.

■ **Protection status**
National Low **International** Low
100 ha of IBA covered by Nature Reserve (Hundsfeldmoor, 100 ha). 100 ha of IBA covered by Special Protection Area (Hundsfeldmoor, 100 ha).

■ **Conservation issues**

Threats Groundwater abstraction (C), Infrastructure (B), Recreation/tourism (B)

Obertauern is a centre of winter tourism and there is a large amount of associated infrastructure and disturbance. Snow machines require large quantities of water and this threatens the raised bog area. Plans to use springs to supply water for tourism would seriously affect the water regime of the area.

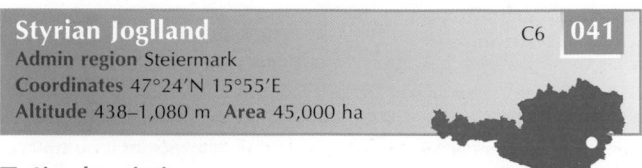

Styrian Joglland   C6   **041**
Admin region Steiermark
Coordinates 47°24'N 15°55'E
Altitude 438–1,080 m **Area** 45,000 ha

■ **Site description**
The landscape is a mix of forested areas and a fine-scale habitat mosaic of small agricultural fields, grassland, pastures, orchards and small villages. The forests consist mainly of *Picea* and *Pinus*, with small stands of *Fagus*.

Habitats Forest and woodland (40%; broadleaved deciduous forest; native coniferous forest; mixed forest), Grassland (10%; mesophile grassland), Artificial landscape (50%; arable land; perennial crops/orchards/groves; forestry plantation; other urban/industrial areas)
Land-use Agriculture (60%), Forestry (40%)

■ **Birds**

Species	Season	Year	Pop min	Pop max	Acc	Criteria
Ciconia nigra Black Stork	B	1994	3	4	A	C6
¹ **Crex crex** Corncrake	B	1995	1	15	A	C6

1. Calling males.

An important area for species characteristic of low-intensity mixed agriculture and woodland.

■ **Protection status**
National None **International** Partial
30,000 ha of IBA covered by Special Protection Area (Teile des Steirischen Jogllandes, 45,524.

■ **Conservation issues**

Threats Agricultural intensification/expansion (A), Intensified forest management (C)

Early mowing dates threaten the *Crex crex* population.

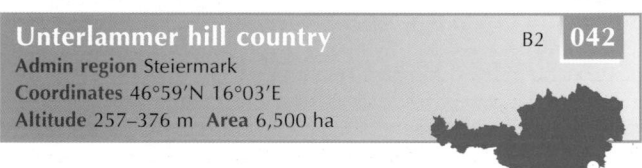

Unterlammer hill country   B2   **042**
Admin region Steiermark
Coordinates 46°59'N 16°03'E
Altitude 257–376 m **Area** 6,500 ha

■ **Site description**
Situated in the south-east of Styria near the border to Hungary, this site is characterized by a mosaic of forests, meadows, orchards, vineyards, and arable fields. Most of the farms are small and agriculture is mainly non-intensive.

Habitats Forest and woodland (50%; broadleaved deciduous forest), Grassland (20%; mesophile grassland), Artificial landscape (30%; arable land; perennial crops/orchards/groves; other urban/industrial areas)
Land-use Agriculture (50%), Forestry (50%)

■ **Birds**

Species	Season	Year	Pop min	Pop max	Acc	Criteria
Picus viridis Green Woodpecker	R	1994	30	60	C	B2

An important area for species characteristic of non-intensive mixed agriculture.

■ **Protection status**
National None **International** None

■ **Conservation issues**

Threats Agricultural intensification/expansion (A), Industrialization/urbanization (C)

Recent moves towards agricultural intensification have led to meadows being converted to arable land and the clearance of orchards.

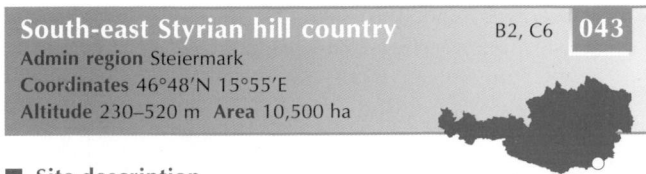

South-east Styrian hill country · B2, C6 · 043

Admin region Steiermark
Coordinates 46°48′N 15°55′E
Altitude 230–520 m **Area** 10,500 ha

■ Site description
An area of hills and river valleys. The hills are covered with broadleaved deciduous forest dominated by *Fagus*, *Carpinus*, and *Quercus*. The valley floors are dominated by arable agriculture with meadows on the steeper slopes and in wet depressions. Vineyards and orchards are also found on the slopes and areas of forest along the rivers.

Habitats Forest and woodland (40%; broadleaved deciduous forest), Grassland (10%; mesophile grassland), Artificial landscape (50%; arable land; forestry plantation; perennial crops/orchards/groves; other urban/industrial areas)
Land-use Agriculture (60%), Forestry (40%)

■ Birds

Species	Season	Year	Pop min	Pop max	Acc	Criteria
Coracias garrulus Roller	B	1994	13	13	A	C6
Picus viridis Green Woodpecker	R	1994	40	60	A	B2

The area is important for populations of species characteristic of low-intensity mixed agriculture.

■ Protection status
National None **International** Partial
Approximately 1,600 ha of IBA covered by Special Protection Area (Teile des Südoststeirischen Hügellandes, 5,462 ha)

■ Conservation issues

Threats Agricultural intensification/expansion (A)

The major threat to the area is continued agricultural intensification, particularly the conversion of grassland and orchards to arable land.

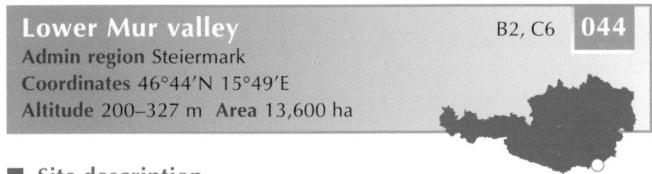

Lower Mur valley · B2, C6 · 044

Admin region Steiermark
Coordinates 46°44′N 15°49′E
Altitude 200–327 m **Area** 13,600 ha

■ Site description
The River Mur forms the border between Austria and Slovenia. The river flow is completely regulated. Riverine forest still exists but parts are no longer flooded. The agricultural land compromises a mosaic of arable fields, patches of forest and woodland, and small fish-ponds. Mixed forests dominate the valley sides, although in many places they have been replaced by *Picea* plantations.

Habitats Forest and woodland (30%; broadleaved deciduous forest; mixed forest; alluvial/very wet forest), Wetland (5%; river/stream), Artificial landscape (65%; arable land; perennial crops/orchards/groves; forestry plantation; other urban/industrial areas)
Land-use Agriculture (45%), Forestry (50%)

■ Birds

Species	Season	Year	Pop min	Pop max	Acc	Criteria
Ciconia nigra Black Stork	B	1994	4	5	A	B2, C6
Caprimulgus europaeus Nightjar	B	1994	3	4	A	C6
Alcedo atthis Kingfisher	B	1994	14	20	A	B2, C6

The site is important for a number of breeding riverine forest and river species.

■ Protection status
National Low **International** None
Part of the IBA is covered by two Nature Reserves, total area less than 10 ha.

■ Conservation issues

Threats Agricultural intensification/expansion (B), Aquaculture/fisheries (C), Extraction industry (C), Groundwater abstraction (B), Intensified forest management (B)

Threats to the site are from gravel extraction, the creation of forestry plantations, the extraction of groundwater, and agricultural intensification.

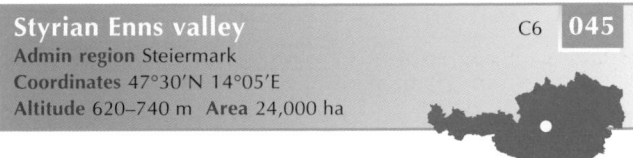

Styrian Enns valley · C6 · 045

Admin region Steiermark
Coordinates 47°30′N 14°05′E
Altitude 620–740 m **Area** 24,000 ha

■ Site description
This area is one of the largest inner-alpine valleys in Austria. Following regulation of the river, only small areas of riverine forest, fen and raised bog remain. Large areas of pasture and intensively-managed grassland exist with small patches of non-intensively managed wet meadows. In places, cliffs enclose the valley. The main human activities are agriculture and recreation.

Habitats Forest and woodland (5%; alluvial/very wet forest), Grassland (50%; humid grassland; mesophile grassland), Wetland (15%; standing fresh water; river/stream; raised bog), Artificial landscape (30%; arable land; forestry plantation; other urban/industrial areas)
Land-use Agriculture (80%), Forestry (10%)

■ Birds

Species	Season	Year	Pop min	Pop max	Acc	Criteria
Falco peregrinus Peregrine	B	1994	3	5	A	C6
[1] *Crex crex* Corncrake	B	1989	10	15	A	C6
Bubo bubo Eagle Owl	R	1985	4	5	A	C6

1. Calling males.

An important area for species breeding in wet meadows and raised bog.

■ Protection status
National Low **International** Low
142 ha of IBA covered by seven Nature Reserves. 62 ha of IBA covered by Ramsar Site (Pürgschachen Moor, 62 ha). 1,569 ha of IBA covered by Special Protection Area (Pürgschachener Moor, 1,569 ha). 407 ha of IBA covered by Special Protection Area (Wörschacher Moor, 407 ha).

■ Conservation issues

Threats Afforestation (B), Agricultural intensification/expansion (A), Infrastructure (A), Recreation/tourism (B)

A road-building project threatens the most valuable sites in the valley. Other threats include drainage, high fertilizer use, groundwater abstraction, building development, and recreational use.

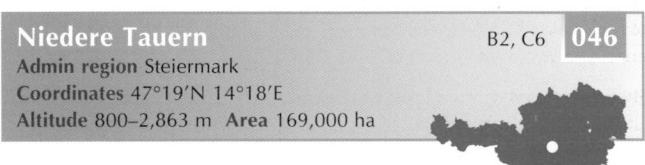

Niedere Tauern · B2, C6 · 046

Admin region Steiermark
Coordinates 47°19′N 14°18′E
Altitude 800–2,863 m **Area** 169,000 ha

■ Site description
A mountainous area of broad glacial valleys. Below 1,900 m most areas are covered by intensively managed forest, with more natural conifer forest limited to steep slopes. The treeline ecotone is dominated by *Alnus*, *Rhododendron*, *Vaccinium* and, locally, *Pinus*. The highest areas are occupied by alpine pastures, alpine grassland, cliffs and rocky slopes.

Habitats Forest and woodland (60%; native coniferous forest; treeline ecotone), Grassland (25%; alpine/subalpine/boreal grassland; mesophile grassland), Rocky areas (15%)
Land-use Agriculture (25%), Forestry (60%), Not utilized (25%)

■ Birds

Species	Season	Year	Pop min	Pop max	Acc	Criteria
Aquila chrysaetos Golden Eagle	R	1994	15	20	B	B2, C6
Falco peregrinus Peregrine	B	1994	2	4	A	C6
Picoides tridactylus Three-toed Woodpecker	R	1994	6	6	A	B2, C6

An important site for species of alpine grassland, montane and subalpine forest.

■ Protection status

National Partial **International** Partial
1,400 ha of IBA covered by Nature Reserve (Bodensee–Sattenbachtal, 1,400 ha). 1,200 ha of IBA covered by Nature Reserve (Klafferkessel, 1,200 ha). 6,245 ha of IBA covered by Nature Reserve (Krakau–Schoeder, 6,245 ha). 1,337 ha of IBA covered by Nature Reserve (Riesachtal, 1,337 ha). 137,742 ha of IBA covered by Special Protection Area (Niedere Tauern, 137,742 ha).

■ Conservation issues

> **Threats** Intensified forest management (B), Recreation/tourism (B)

Alpine pastures and forests are threatened by more intensive management practices, especially forest roads and afforestation with *Picea*. Tourist developments are an additional threat.

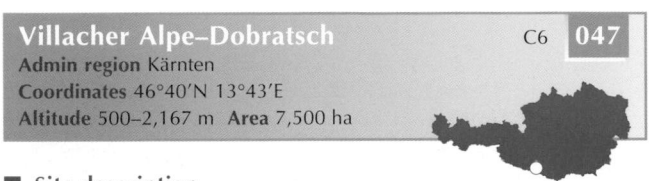

Villacher Alpe–Dobratsch · C6 · 047
Admin region Kärnten
Coordinates 46°40′N 13°43′E
Altitude 500–2,167 m **Area** 7,500 ha

■ Site description

A mountainous area underlain by limestone. Conifer forest occupies most of the site with a small area of mixed forest and a small area of alpine pasture on the treeline. The area is used for winter sports, forestry and hunting.

> **Habitats** Forest and woodland (75%; native coniferous forest; mixed forest), Grassland (5%; alpine/subalpine/boreal grassland), Artificial landscape (5%; arable land), Rocky areas (15%)
> **Land-use** Agriculture (10%), Forestry (75%), Not utilized (15%)

■ Birds

Species	Season	Year	Pop min	Pop max	Acc	Criteria
Bubo bubo Eagle Owl	R	1994	3	3	A	C6
Caprimulgus europaeus Nightjar	B	1994	20	—	B	C6

An important area for montane forest species and cliff-breeding birds.

■ Protection status

National Partial **International** None
1,902 ha of IBA covered by Nature Reserve (Villacher Alpe (Dobratsch), 1,902 ha).

■ Conservation issues

> **Threats** Intensified forest management (C), Recreation/tourism (B)

The major threat is disturbance from winter sports.

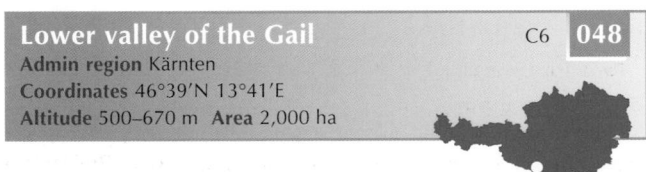

Lower valley of the Gail · C6 · 048
Admin region Kärnten
Coordinates 46°39′N 13°41′E
Altitude 500–670 m **Area** 2,000 ha

■ Site description

In the west of the site there are small areas of fen and adjacent mixed *Picea* and *Fagus* forest. The eastern section comprises stony ground covered by open, mixed *Pinus* and *Fagus* forest, and the river, which has a number of artificial islands. The southern section comprises two more fens. Open areas are mainly used for pasture and some arable agriculture. The major human activity is forestry. Hunting also occurs.

> **Habitats** Forest and woodland (70%; mixed forest; native coniferous forest), Grassland (15%; mesophile grassland), Wetland (5%; river/stream; fen/transition mire/spring), Artificial landscape (10%; arable land; perennial crops/orchards/groves)
> **Land-use** Agriculture (30%), Forestry (70%)

■ Birds

Species	Season	Year	Pop min	Pop max	Acc	Criteria
Caprimulgus europaeus Nightjar	B	1994	20	—	B	C6

An important area for birds of open mixed forest, especially *Caprimulgus europaeus* and *Emberiza cia*.

■ Protection status

National None **International** None

■ Conservation issues

> **Threats** Agricultural intensification/expansion (B), Infrastructure (A)

A road currently under construction will bisect the IBA and seriously affect the integrity of the whole site.

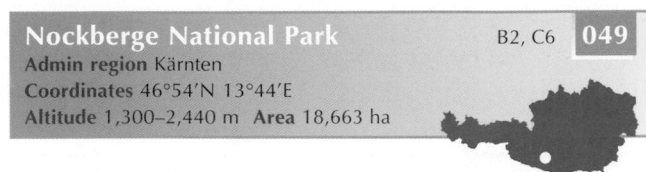

Nockberge National Park · B2, C6 · 049
Admin region Kärnten
Coordinates 46°54′N 13°44′E
Altitude 1,300–2,440 m **Area** 18,663 ha

■ Site description

A mountainous IBA with a mixture of forest and, above 1,900 m, alpine pasture. Below 1,700 m *Picea* forest dominates and is replaced between 1,700–1,900 m by mixed stands of *Larix*, *Picea* and *Pinus*. In most places the forests are intensively managed, with many open areas as a result of historical grazing. Above the treeline, large areas of subalpine and alpine pasture occur.

> **Habitats** Forest and woodland (70%; native coniferous forest; treeline ecotone), Grassland (25%; alpine/subalpine/boreal grassland; mesophile grassland), Rocky areas (5%)
> **Land-use** Agriculture (20%), Forestry (70%), Not utilized (10%)

■ Birds

Species	Season	Year	Pop min	Pop max	Acc	Criteria
Alectoris graeca Rock Partridge	R	1991	Frequent		—	B2, C6

An important area for breeding and resident species characteristic of subalpine forest and alpine pasture.

■ Protection status

National High **International** None
18,663 ha of IBA covered by National Park (Nockberge, 18,663 ha)

■ Conservation issues

> **Threats** Abandonment/reduction of land management (B), Infrastructure (B), Intensified forest management (C), Recreation/tourism (C)

Continued intensive forestry is a threat to the site. Alpine pastures are increasingly being abandoned. Pressure from tourism is high with easy access from a road bisecting the area. Hunting and forestry are not restricted in the National Park.

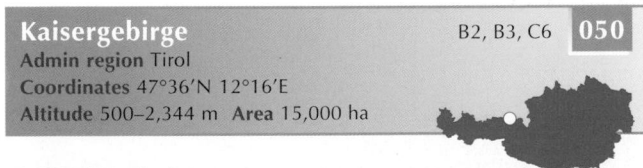

Kaisergebirge · B2, B3, C6 · 050
Admin region Tirol
Coordinates 47°36′N 12°16′E
Altitude 500–2,344 m **Area** 15,000 ha

■ Site description

Most of this site is in the montane and subalpine zones. It is predominantly forested with substantial areas of broadleaved deciduous forest, dominated by *Fagus* on the southern slopes. The majority of the forest is not utilized for forestry, except on the lower slopes.

> **Habitats** Forest and woodland (70%; broadleaved deciduous forest; native coniferous forest; mixed forest; treeline ecotone), Grassland (10%; alpine/subalpine/boreal grassland), Wetland (5%; standing fresh water; raised bog), Rocky areas (10%), Artificial landscape (5%; arable land; perennial crops/orchards/groves)
> **Land-use** Agriculture (15%), Forestry (30%), Not utilized (55%)

■ Birds

An important area for breeding and resident species characteristic of montane and subalpine forest.

Species	Season	Year	Pop min	Pop max	Acc	Criteria
Aquila chrysaetos Golden Eagle	R	1994	3	5	A	B2, C6
Dendrocopos leucotos White-backed Woodpecker	R	1994	5	10	A	C6
Serinus citrinella Citril Finch	B	1994	120	150	A	B3

■ **Protection status**
National Partial **International** None
10,200 ha of IBA covered by Nature Reserve (Kaisergebirge, 10,200 ha).

■ **Conservation issues**

Threats Intensified forest management (C), Recreation/tourism (C)

Some parts of the IBA are affected by intensive forestry and summer tourism. Hunting is very important in the area.

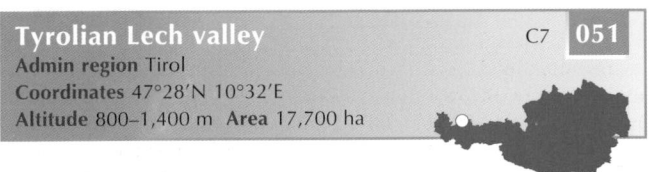

Tyrolian Lech valley — C7 · 051
Admin region Tirol
Coordinates 47°28′N 10°32′E
Altitude 800–1,400 m **Area** 17,700 ha

■ **Site description**
The upper course of the River Lech is largely unregulated and its course has large areas of sand and shingle with surrounding riverine forest of *Salix* and *Alnus*, and extensive areas of *Pinus* on drier sites. The lower slopes of the valley are covered by intensively utilized conifer and mixed forests. The valley floor contains non-intensively managed grasslands, orchards and several settlements.

Habitats Forest and woodland (60%; alluvial/very wet forest; native coniferous forest; mixed forest), Grassland (20%; mesophile grassland), Wetland (10%; river/stream), Artificial landscape (10%; arable land; perennial crops/orchards/groves; other urban/industrial areas)
Land-use Agriculture (25%), Forestry (60%), Urban/industrial/transport (5%)

■ **Birds**
The site is important for breeding upland forest species and breeding species associated with rivers, particularly with extensive shingle areas.

■ **Protection status**
National None **International** None

■ **Conservation issues**

Threats Construction/impact of dyke/dam/barrage (A), Extraction industry (B), Infrastructure (B), Recreation/tourism (C), Other (C)

The most immediate threat to the valley are measures to regulate the river and planned power plants along tributaries. Shingle is extracted from several areas of the river. Further threats come from the expansion of the infrastructure, refuse tipping on shingle beds ('Other' threat) and recreational activities.

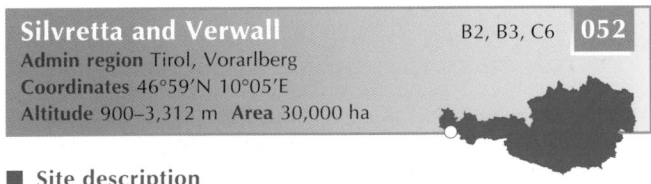

Silvretta and Verwall — B2, B3, C6 · 052
Admin region Tirol, Vorarlberg
Coordinates 46°59′N 10°05′E
Altitude 900–3,312 m **Area** 30,000 ha

■ **Site description**
A mountainous region of subalpine forest, alpine pasture and rocky areas. The forested areas are mainly coniferous. Human utilization of the area is restricted to a small part of the IBA, used for cattle-grazing, forestry, winter sports and power plants.

Habitats Forest and woodland (40%; mixed forest; native coniferous forest; treeline ecotone), Grassland (30%; alpine/subalpine/boreal grassland; mesophile grassland), Rocky areas (30%)
Land-use Agriculture (20%), Forestry (20%), Not utilized (60%)

■ **Birds**
This is an important site for resident and breeding species associated with subalpine forest, alpine pastures, and grasslands and rocky areas above the treeline.

Species	Season	Year	Pop min	Pop max	Acc	Criteria
Aquila chrysaetos Golden Eagle	R	1994	3	4	A	B2, C6
Luscinia svecica Bluethroat	B	1994	7	8	A	C6
Serinus citrinella Citril Finch	B	1994	50	70	A	B3

■ **Protection status**
National None **International** Partial
12,082 ha of IBA covered by Special Protection Area (Verwall, 12,082 ha).

■ **Conservation issues**

Threats Intensified forest management (C), Recreation/tourism (C)

As summer and winter tourism expand the negative impacts are likely to increase.

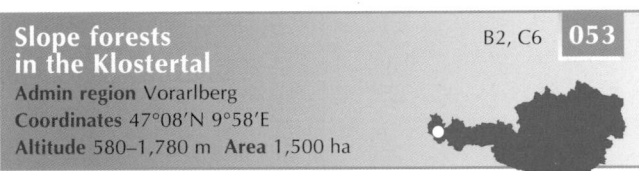

Slope forests in the Klostertal — B2, C6 · 053
Admin region Vorarlberg
Coordinates 47°08′N 9°58′E
Altitude 580–1,780 m **Area** 1,500 ha

■ **Site description**
This alpine valley has a mild, humid climate as a result of the föhn wind from the Rhine valley. Twenty-five kilometres of the valley is covered by near-natural montane and subalpine forest. This consists mainly of species-rich, old-growth stands of broadleaved deciduous forest and mixed forest, interspersed with pioneer communities along ravines and avalanche tracks, and dwarf pines *Pinus* on rocky slopes. Forestry activities are limited to a few sites.

Habitats Forest and woodland (90%; broadleaved deciduous forest; mixed forest; native coniferous forest), Grassland (5%; mesophile grassland), Rocky areas (5%)
Land-use Agriculture (5%), Forestry (40%), Not utilized (55%)

■ **Birds**

Species	Season	Year	Pop min	Pop max	Acc	Criteria
Picus canus Grey-headed Woodpecker	R	1995	30	30	A	B2, C6
Dendrocopos leucotos White-backed Woodpecker	R	1995	11	11	A	C6

An important site for forest species.

■ **Protection status**
National None **International** High
1,500 ha of IBA covered by Special Protection Area (Bergwälder Klostertal, 1,500 ha).

■ **Conservation issues**

Threats Forest grazing (B), Other (B)

Threats include forest dieback as a result of acid rain ('Other' threats, above), exacerbated by traffic pollution from the valley floor, and high levels of grazing by deer preventing regeneration. Problems of access are likely to limit an expansion of forestry.

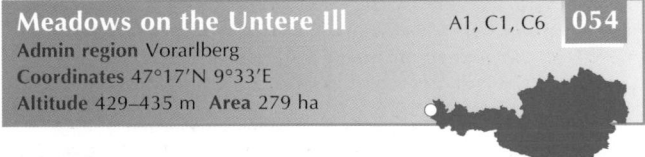

Meadows on the Untere Ill — A1, C1, C6 · 054
Admin region Vorarlberg
Coordinates 47°17′N 9°33′E
Altitude 429–435 m **Area** 279 ha

■ **Site description**
A complex of non-intensively managed wet meadows, hay-meadows and arable fields with small areas of reed *Phragmites* and riverine forest.

Habitats Grassland (70%; humid grassland; mesophile grassland), Artificial landscape (30%; arable land; forestry plantation)
Land-use Agriculture (90%), Forestry (10%)

■ Birds

Species	Season	Year	Pop min	Pop max	Acc	Criteria
Crex crex Corncrake	B	1996	10	31	A	A1, C1, C6

An important site for breeding species associated with non-intensively used wet meadows.

■ Protection status

National High **International** High

63 ha of IBA covered by Nature Reserve (Bangser Ried, 63 ha). 279 ha of IBA covered by Nature Reserve (Matschels, 386 ha). 279 ha of IBA covered by Special Protection Area (Bangser Ried und Matschels, 447 ha).

■ Conservation issues

Threats Agricultural intensification/expansion (A), Drainage (B)

The wet meadows are threatened by nutrient inputs from surrounding arable agriculture and drainage through the canalization of rivers which causes a reduction in water-levels.

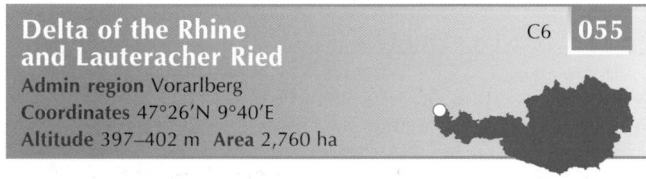

Delta of the Rhine and Lauteracher Ried C6 **055**
Admin region Vorarlberg
Coordinates 47°26'N 9°40'E
Altitude 397–402 m **Area** 2,760 ha

■ Site description

This site encompasses the mouth of the Rhine as it flows into Lake Constance, together with an area of wet grassland, the Lauteracher Ried. Many parts of this grassland have been drained and are now intensively managed. There are some reedbeds (*Phragmites*) along the lakeside. Some intensively managed riverine forest remains. The largest part of the site consists of a large, shallow-water bay.

Habitats Forest and woodland (5%; alluvial/very wet forest), Grassland (30%; humid grassland; mesophile grassland), Wetland (60%; standing fresh water; water-fringe vegetation), Artificial landscape (5%; arable land; forestry plantation)
Land-use Agriculture (35%), Fisheries/aquaculture (60%), Forestry (5%)

■ Birds

Species	Season	Year	Pop min	Pop max	Acc	Criteria
Ixobrychus minutus Little Bittern	B	1994	3	12	A	C6

An important site for species breeding in wet meadows, and passage and wintering waterbirds.

■ Protection status

National Partial **International** High

1,972 ha of IBA covered by Nature Reserve (Rheindelta 1,972 ha), 1,960 ha of IBA covered by Ramsar Site (Rheindelta Bodensee, 1,960 ha). 580 ha of IBA covered by Special Protection Area (Lauteracher Ried, 580 ha). 2,040 ha of IBA covered by Special Protection Area (Rheindelta, 2,040 ha).

■ Conservation issues

Threats Agricultural intensification/expansion (A), Aquaculture/fisheries (B), Disturbance to birds (B), Drainage (B), Intensified forest management (C), Recreation/tourism (B)

Drainage schemes and subsequent agricultural intensification, as well as the high level of human disturbance, are the main threats to the IBA.

REFERENCES

ARNOLD, C. (1980) Die Vogelwelt der Salzburger Voralpenseen Wallersee und Trumer Seen und ihrer Einzugsgebiete. *Stud. Forsch. Salzburg* 1: 49–66.

ARNOLD, C. (1986) Studie zur vogelkundlichen Situation des Salzburger Voralpenseengebiet. *Stud. Forsch. Salzburg* 2: 297–334.

AUBRECHT, G. (1988) Die Vogelwelt des Mühlviertels wenig beachtet international bedeutend. Pp. 187–194 in *Das Mühlviertel Natur Kultur Leben. Beiträge*. Amt der oberösterreichischen Landesregierung, Abteilung Kultur, Linz. 484 pp.

AUBRECHT, G. (1992) Die Bedeutung verschiedener Traunabschnitte in Oberösterreich für überwinternde Wasservögel eine langfristige Populationsanalyse. *Kataloge des Oö. Landesmus. Neue Folge* 54: 53–67.

AUBRECHT, P. (1998) *Corine Landcover Österreich. Vom Satellitenbild zum digitalen Bodenbedeckungsdatensatz*. Wien, Austria: Monographien Band 93, Umweltbundesamt. 61 pp.

BAUER, K. (1955) Zur Ornis der Parndorfer Heide (Burgenland). *Vogelring* 24: 1–16.

BAUER, K., FREUNDL, H. AND LUGITSCH, R. (1955) Weitere Beiträge zur Kenntnis der Vogelwelt des Neusiedlersee Gebietes. *Wiss. Arb. Burgenland* 7: 1–123.

BERG, H. M. AND ZELZ, S. (1993) Situation und Verbreitung der Zwergohreule (Aves: *Otus scops*) im Bezirk Mattersburg/Burgenland. Ergebnisse einer im Jahr 1993 durchgeführten Kartierung. Unveröffentlicher Bericht an die Naturschutzabteilung der Burgenländischen Landesregierung.

BERG, H. M. AND ZUNA KRATKY, T. (1992) Die Brutvögel des Wienerwaldes. Eine kommentierte Artenliste (Stand August 1991). *Vogelkundl. Nachr. Ostösterreich* 3(1): 1–11.

BERG, H. M., LAUERMANN, H. AND SACKL, P. (1995) Ornithologische Kartierung. Pp. 155–222 in *Biotoperhebung Truppenübungsplatz Allentsteig. Dokumentation des Zustandes und Diskussion über Entwicklungsmöglichkeiten der naturräumlichen Ausstattung eines militärischen Sperrgebietes*. Wien, Austria: Bundesministerium für Landesverteidigung, Sektion III, Abteilung Umweltschutz. 284 pp.

BERG, H. M., ZELZ, S. AND ZUNA KRATKY, T. (1992) Zwei bedeutende Vorkommen der Heidelerche (*Lullula arborea*) in Niederösterreich. *Vogelkundl. Nachr. Ostösterreich* 3(4): 1–6.

CZIKELI, H. (1983) Avifaunistische Angaben aus dem Bezirk Liezen im Vergleich zu Höpflinger 1958, "Die Vögel des steirischen Ennstales und seiner Bergwelt". *Mitt. Abt. Zool. Landesmus. Joanneum* 31: 1–32.

DICK, G., DVORAK, M., GRÜLL, A., KOHLER, B. AND RAUER, G. (1994) *Vogelparadies mit Zukunft?* Ramsar Bericht 3 - Neusiedler See - Seewinkel. Wien, Umweltbundesamt. 356 pp.

DVORAK, M. (1988) Verbreitung und Bestand des Wiedehopfs (Upupa epops) im Neusiedler See Gebiet. *Biol. Forschungsinst. Burgenland–Bericht* 66: 33–37.

DVORAK, M. (1988) Zur Verbreitung einiger gefährdeter Singvogelarten im Neusiedlersee Gebiet. *Biol. Forschungsinst. Burgenland–Bericht* 66: 39–55.

DVORAK, M. AND NEMETH, E. (1992) Die Brutvögel der Zitzmannsdorfer Wiesen. *Biol. Forschungsinst. Burgenland–Bericht* 78: 47–64.

DVORAK, M. AND ZUNA KRATKY, T. (1993) Zur aktuellen Situation ausgewählter Kulturlandvögel im Neusiedlersee Gebiet. *Vogelkundl. Nachr. Ostösterreich* 4(4): 125–138.

DVORAK, M., GRÜLL, A. AND KOHLER, B. (1986) Verbreitung und Bestand gefährdeter oder ökologisch wichtiger Brutvögel im Neusiedlerseegebiet 1984. *Biol. Forschungsinst. Burgenland–Bericht* 59: 1–25.

DVORAK, M., GRÜLL, A. AND KOHLER, B. (1987) Verbreitung und Bestand gefährdeter oder ökologisch wichtiger Vogelarten im Neusiedlerseegebiet 1985. *Biol. Forschungsinst. Burgenland–Bericht* 60: 1–23.

DVORAK, M., NEMETH, E., TEBBICH, S., RÖSSLER, M. AND BUSSE, K. (1997) Verbreitung, Bestand und Habitatwahl schilfbewohnender Vogelarten in der Naturzone des Nationalparks Neusiedler See–Seewinkel. *Biol. Forschungsinst. Burgenland–Bericht* 86: 1–69.

DVORAK, M., RANNER, A. AND BERG, H. M. (1993) *Atlas der Brutvögel Österreichs. Ergebnisse der Brutvogelkartierung 1981–1985 der Österreichischen Gesellschaft für Vogelkunde*. Wien, Austria: Österreichische Gesellschaft für Vogelkunde und Umweltbundesamt und Österreichische Gesellschaft für Vogelkunde. 527 pp.

EICHELMANN, U. (1990) *Brutvorkommen von Steilwand, Kies und Röhrichtbrütern im geplanten Nationalpark Donau Auen sowie deren Abhängigkeit von der Hochwasserdynamik*. Wien, Austria: Nationalparkplanung Donauauen. 100 pp. und Anhang.

EICHLER, T. (1991) Zusammenfassung der Wasservogelzählungen in Niederösterreich im Winter 1990/91. *Vogelkundl. Nachr. Ostösterreich* 2(4): 26–30.

ERLACH, O. AND LEGO, E. (1975) Die Vogelarten des Gebietes um Sandl. *Jb. Oö. Mus Ver.* 120: 351–380.

ERLINGER, G. (1965) Die Vogelwelt des Stauseegebietes Braunau Hagenau. *Jb. Oö. Mus. Ver.* 110: 422–445.

ERLINGER, G. (1984) Der Verlandungsprozeß in der Hagenauer Bucht Einfluß auf die Tier und Pflanzenwelt Teil 1. *ÖKO L* 6(3): 15–18.

ERLINGER, G. (1985) Der Verlandungsprozeß in der Hagenauer Bucht Einfluß auf die Tier und Pflanzenwelt Teil 2. *ÖKO L* 7(2): 6–15.

FARASIN, K., SCHRAMAYR, G., KALTENBACH, A., TIEDEMANN, F., PROKOP, P., GRÜNWEIS, F. M. AND HAUSER, M. (1989) *Biotoperhebung Truppenübungsplatz Großmittel*. Wien, Austria: Umweltbundesamt (Monographien Band 10). 139 pp

FESTETICS, A. (1971) Das Niedermoor "Hanság" Vorschlag zu einem burgenländischen Adler und Trappenreservat. *Natur und Land* 57: 125–135.

FESTETICS, A. AND LEISLER, B. (1968) Ökologische Probleme der Vögel des Neusiedlersee Gebietes, besonders des World Wildlife Fund Reservates Seewinkel (I.Teil: Biogeographie des Gebietes. II.Teil: Schwimmvögel.). *Wiss. Arb. Burgenland* 40: 83–130.

FESTETICS, A. AND LEISLER, B. (1970) Ökologische Probleme der Vögel des Neusiedlerseegebietes, besonders des World Wildlife Fund-Reservates Seewinkel. *Wiss. Arb. Burgenland* 44: 301–386.

FIRBAS, W. (1962) Die Vogelwelt des Machlandes. *Naturkundl. Jb. Stadt Linz* 1962: 329–377.

FREY, H. (1992) Bestandsentwicklung und Jungenproduktion des Uhus (*Bubo bubo*) in Niederösterreich zwischen 1969 und 1991. *Egretta* 35: 9–19.

GAMAUF, A. AND HERB, B. (1990) *Greifvogelstudie im Bereich des geplanten Nationalparkes Donau Auen*. Wien, Austria: Nationalparkplanung Donau Auen. 131 pp.

GRABHER, M. AND BLUM, V. (1990) Teil A Naturschutzgebiet Rheindelta Pp. 1–65 in *Ramsar Bericht 1 Rheindelta/Marchauen*. Wien, Austria: Umweltbundesamt (Monographien Band 18). 198 pp.

GRAMMER, R. A. (1994) Qualitative und quanitative Bestandserfassung der Avizönose der oberen montanen bis alpinen Stufe in den Nördlichen Kalkalpen (Totes Gebirge im Gemeindegebiet von Wörschach und Weißenbach). Diplomarbeit Universität Graz. 91 pp.

GRESSEL, J. (1991) Das Blaukehlchen (Luscinia svecica) und seine Verbreitung im Land Salzburg. *Salzburger Vogelkundl. Ber.* 3(1): 10–15.

GRIMMETT, R. F. A. AND JONES T. A. (1989) *Important Bird Areas in Europe*. Cambridge, UK: International Council for Bird Preservation (Tech. Publ. 9).

HAFNER, F. (1994) *Das Steinhuhn in Kärnten*. Klagenfurt, Austria: Naturwissenschaftlicher Verein für Kärnten. 135 pp.

HEATH, M. F. AND BORGGREVE, C. (2000) *BirdLife International/EBCC European Bird Database 1998*. Cambridge, UK: BirdLife International.

HERB, B. (1995) Ornithologische Bedeutung der Brachflächen. Pp. 223–250 in *Biotoperhebung Truppenübungsplatz Allentsteig. Dokumentation des Zustandes und Diskussion über Entwicklungsmöglichkeiten der naturräumlichen Ausstattung eines militärischen Sperrgebietes*. Wien, Austria: Bundesministerium für Landesverteidigung, Sektion III, Abteilung Umweltschutz. 284 pp.

HOCHEBNER, T. (1993) Siedlungsdichte und Lebensraum einer randalpinen Population des Mittelspechts (*Picoides medius*) im niederösterreichischen Alpenvorland. *Egretta* 36: 25–37.

HOCHRATHNER, P. (1991) Die Brutvogelfauna im Sengsengebirge. Kernzone des Nationalpark Planungsgebietes. Obere Subalpin bis Alpinstufe im Kalkalpen. Stand 1991. Endbericht 1991 im Auftrag des Vereins Nationalpark Kalkalpen. *Vogelkundl. Nachr. aus Oberösterreich* 2(2): 3–46.

ILLE, R. (1992) Zur Biologie und Ökologie des Steinkauzes (*Athene noctua*) im Marchfeld: Aktuelle Situation und mögliche Schutzmaßnahmen. *Egretta* 35: 49–57.

ILZER, W. (1993) Qualitative und Quantitative Vogelbestandesaufnahmen im Auwaldgebiet des Unteren Murtales (Grundlagen der ökologischen Bewertung der Auwälder der Steiermark) Diss., Universität Graz.

KILZER, R. (1996) Ornitho-ökologische Bewertung der sonnseitigen Bergwälder im Klostertal. *Vorarlberger Natuschau* 1: 233–264.

KOLLAR, H. P. (1989) Zur Bestandsentwicklung der Großtrappe (*Otis tarda* L.) im Marchfeld. *Egretta* 32: 73–75.

KOLLAR, H. P. AND SEITER, M. (1989) Biotopstrukturen und Vogelfauna in den Donau Auen östlich von Wien. Leopoldsdorf, Austria: Gutachten im Auftrag der österreichischen Donaukraft AG. 43 pp und Tabellen.

KOLLAR, H. P. AND SEITER, M. (1990) Die Vogelwelt einer forstlich biologischen Versuchsfläche in den Donau Auen östlich von Wien, Teil 1: Kommentierte Artenliste. *Wiss. Mitt. Niederösterr. Landesmus.* 7: 301–338.

KRAUS, E. (1984) Die Bedeutung der Teichlandschaft im nördlichen Waldviertel für die Wasservogelwelt Österreichs. *Wiss. Mitt. Niederösterr. Landesmus.* 3: 99–135.

LANDMANN, A. AND BÖHM, C. (1991) Das Flußsystem des Tiroler Lech—Ornithologische Wertigkeit und Bedeutung für den Vogelschutz. *Vogelschutz in Österreich* 5: 21–30.

LANDMANN, A. AND BÖHM, C. (1993) *Verbreitungsmuster und Häufigkeitsverteilung von Wirbeltieren im Tiroler Lechtal*, Band 1 und 2. Innsbruck, Austria: Im Auftrag der Tiroler Landesregierung. 150 + 122 pp.

LANDMANN, A. AND BÖHM, CH. (1990) Das Flußsystem des Tiroler Lech—Ornithologische Wertigkeit und Bedeutung für den Vogelschutz. *Vogelschutz in Österreich* 5: 21–30.

LUKSCHANDERL, L. (1971) Zur Verbreitung und Ökologie der Großtrappe (*Otis tarda* L.) in Österreich. *J. Orn.* 112: 70–93.

LÜTKENS, R. AND EDER, F. (1977) Über das Schicksal von Randpopulationen der Großtrappe (*Otis tarda* L.) in Niederösterreich. *J. Orn.* 118: 93–105.

MARSCHALL, A. F. AND PELZELN, A. (1882) Ornis Vindobonensis. Die Vogelwelt Wiens und seiner Umgebungen. Mit einem Anhang: Die Vögel des Neusiedler See's. Verlag Georg Paul Faesy, Wien. 192 pp.

MERWALD, F. (1964) Die Vogelwelt des Ibmer Moores. *Jb. Oö. Mus. Ver.* 109: 433–453.

MORITZ, U. AND WINDING, N. (1994) Die Vogelfauna der Salzburger Salzachauen. *Salzburger Vogelkundl. Ber.* 6: 2–62.

OHNMACHT, A. M. (1994) *Ramsar Bericht 2, Stauseen am Unteren Inn*. Wien, Austria: Umweltbundesamt (Monographien 47). 117 pp.

RAUER, G. AND KOHLER, B. (1990) Schutzgebietspflege durch Beweidung. *Wiss. Arb. Burgenland Sonderband* 82: 221–278.

RÖSSLER, M. AND ZUNA KRATKY, T. (1992) Die vogelkundliche Bedeutung der Absetzbecken der Zuckerfabrik Hohenau/March. *Vogelschutz in Österreich* 7: 2–12.

RUDOLF VON ÖSTERREICH AND BREHM, A. (1879) Ornithologische Beobachtungen in den Auwäldern der Donau bei Wien. *J. Orn.* 27: 97–129.

SACHSLEHNER, L. M. (1992) Zur Siedlungsdichte der Fliegenschnäpper (Muscicapinae s. str.) auf stadtnahen Wienerwaldflächen Wiens mit Aspekten des Waldsterbens und der Durchforstung. *Egretta* 35: 121–153.

SACKL, P., SABATHY, E. AND SAMWALD, O. (1993) Zur historischen Verbreitung und aktuellen Situation des Steinkauzes (*Athene noctua*) in der Steiermark, Österreich (Aves). *Mitt. Abt. Zool. Landesmus. Joanneum* 47: 27–38.

SAMWALD, O. AND SAMWALD, F. (1989) Die Blauracke (*Coracias g. garrulus*) in der Steiermark Bestandsentwicklung, Phänologie, Brutbiologie, Gefährdung. *Egretta* 32: 37–57.

SAMWALD, O. AND SAMWALD, F. (1992) Brutverbreitung und Bestandsentwicklung der Zwergohreule (*Otus scops*) in der Steiermark. *Egretta* 35: 37–48.

SAMWALD, O. AND SAMWALD, F. (1993) Die historische Brutverbreitung und aktuelle Situation des Schwarzstirnwürgers (*Lanius minor*) in der Steiermark. *Egretta* 36: 1–8.

SCHMALZER, A. (1988) Birkhühner im Mühlviertel Aufstieg und Untergang. Pp. 199–204 in *Das Mühlviertel Natur Kultur Leben. Beiträge*. Linz, Austria: Amt der oberösterreichischen Landesregierung, Abteilung Kultur. 484 pp.

SCHMALZER, A. (1988) Wiesenvögel im Mühlviertel wie lange noch? Pp. 195–198 in *Das Mühlviertel Natur Kultur Leben. Beiträge*. Linz, Austria: Amt der oberösterreichischen Landesregierung, Abteilung Kultur. 484 pp.

SCHUSTER, A. (1990): Die Brutvogelfauna der Traunauen bei Wels und ihre Veränderung im Lauf von 85 Jahren. *Jb. Oö. Mus. Ver.* 135: 263–304.

SCHUSTER, S., BLUM, V., JACOBY, H., KNÖTZSCH, G., LEUZINGER, H., SCHNEIDER, M., SEITZ, E. AND WILLI, P. (1983) *Die Vögel des Bodenseegebietes*. Konstanz, Germany: Ornithologische Arbeitsgemeinschaft Bodensee. 379 pp.

SEITZ, A. (1942) *Die Brutvögel des "Seewinkels" (der "Burgenländischen Salzsteppe") am Ostufer des Neusiedlersees, Gau Niederdonau*. Niederdonau/Natur und Kultur 12. Heft. Verlag Karl Kühne, Wien Leipzig. 52 pp.

SLOTTA BACHMAYR, L. (1992) Die Situation des Großen Brachvogels (*Numenius arquata*) im Salzburger Flachgau und in angrenzenden Gebieten. *Egretta* 35: 173–183.

SLOTTA BACHMAYR, L. (1993) Ergebnisse der Wiesenvogelerhebungen 1993 im Bundesland Salzburg. *Salzburger Vogelkundl. Ber.* 5: 41–50.

SLOTTA-BACHMYR, L. AND LIEB, K. (1996) Die Vogelwelt des Ibmer Moores (IBA). Vergleich der historischen und aktuellen Zusammensetzung der Avifauna unter besonderer Berücksichtigung wiesenbrütender Vogelarten und Bemerkungen zu Amphibien und Reptilien. *Vogelkundl. Nachr. OÖ., Naturschutz aktuell* 4(2): 3–43.

STEINER, E. (1994) Waldviertel. Pp. 183–243 in M. Dvorak, I. Winkler, C. Grabmayer and E. Steiner *Stillgewässer Österreichs als Brutgebiete für Wasservögel*. Wien, Austria: Umweltbundesamt (Monographien 44). 341 pp.

STRAKA, U. (1993) Zum Vorkommen von Greifvögeln in Ackerbaugebieten Ostösterreichs. Beobachtungen im Marchfeld und im südlichen Weinviertel in den Jahren 1984 bis 1993. *Vogelkundl. Nachr. Ostösterreich* 4: 139–145.

TUCKER, G. M. AND HEATH, M. F. (1994) *Birds in Europe: their conservation status*. Cambridge, UK: BirdLife International (BirdLife Conservation Series no. 3).

WARNCKE, K. (1962) Beitrag zur Avifauna der March und unteren Donauauen. *Anz. Orn. Ges. Bayern* 6: 234–268.

WILLI, G. (1996) Vorkommen von Wiesenvögeln im Gebiet Bangs-Matschels. *Vorarlberger Naturschau* 2: 101–118.

WILLI, P. (1985) Langfristige Bestandstaxierungen im Rheindelta. *Egretta* 28: 1–62.

WINDING, N. AND STEINER, H. M. (1983) Donaukraftwerk Hainburg/Deutsch Altenburg Untersuchung der Standortfrage (Zoologischer Teil). 4. Vögel. Pp. 274 303 in M. Welan and K. Wedl *Der Streit um Hainburg in Verwaltungs und Gerichtsakten*. Laxenburg: Akademie für Umwelt und Energie (Niederösterreich Reihe, Band 5).

WINDING, N., WERNER, S., STADLER, S. AND SLOTTA-BACHMAYR, L. (1993) Die Struktur von Vogelgemeinschaften am alpinen Höhengradienten: Quantitative Brutvogel-Bestandsaufnahmen in den Hohen Tauern (Österreichische Zentralalpen). *Wiss. Mitt. aus dem Nationalpark Hohe Tauern* 1: 106–124.

ZIMMERMANN, R. (1943) Beiträge zur Kenntnis der Vogelwelt des Neusiedler Seegebietes. *Ann. Naturhist. Mus. Wien* 54: 1–272.

ZWICKER, E. (1983) *Untersuchung der Vogelwelt der Lobau in Hinblick auf eine ökologische Bewertung des Gebietes*. Wien, Austria: Gutachten im Auftrag der Magistratsabteilung 22. 41 pp.

ZWICKER, E. AND HERB, B. (1989) *Untersuchungen zum Naturraumpotential der Parndorfer Platte und eines Abschnittes der Leithaniederung. Vögel*. Eisenstadt, Austria: Gutachten im Auftrag der Burgenländischen Landesregierung. 59 pp.

BELARUS

Alexander Kozulin

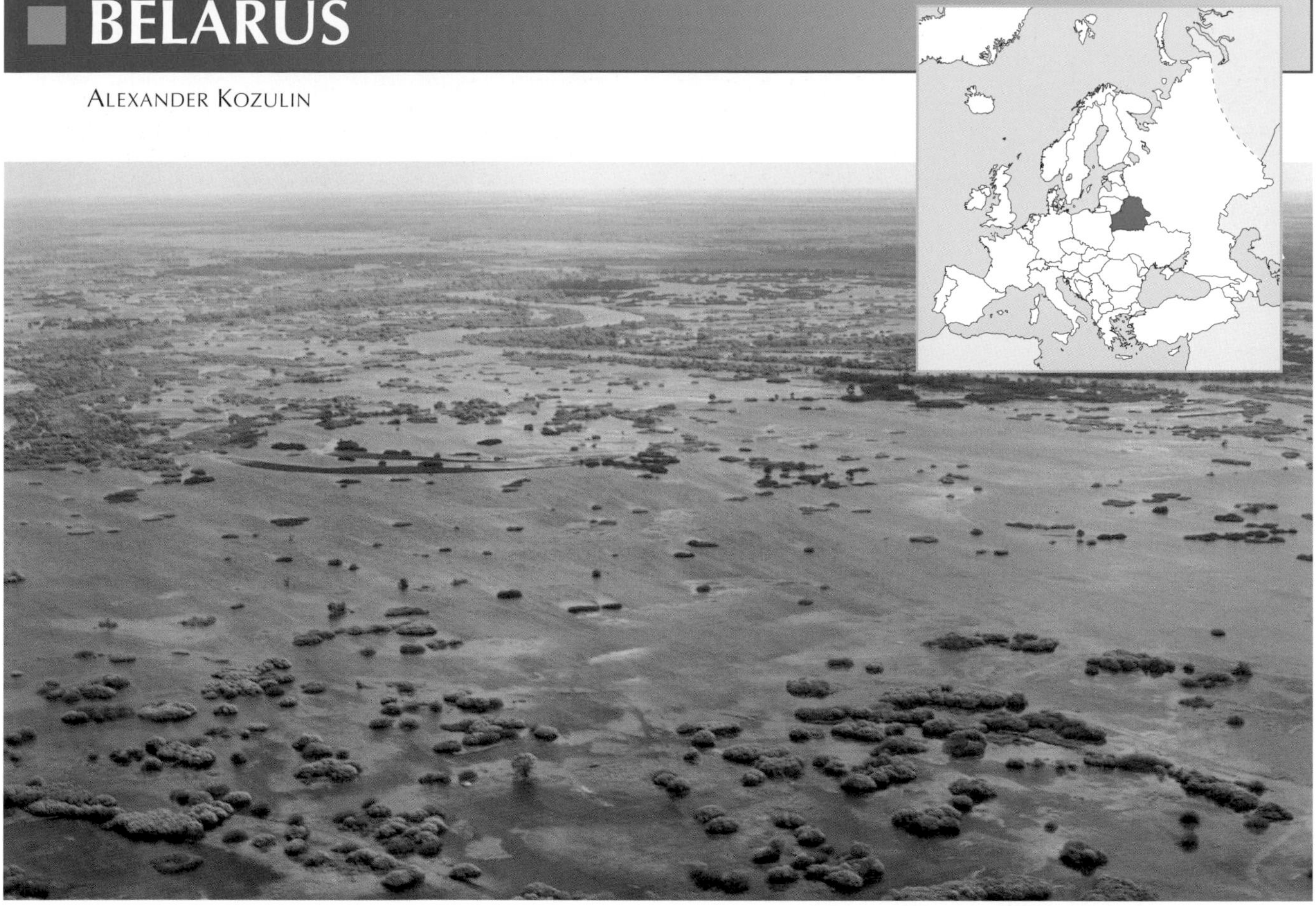

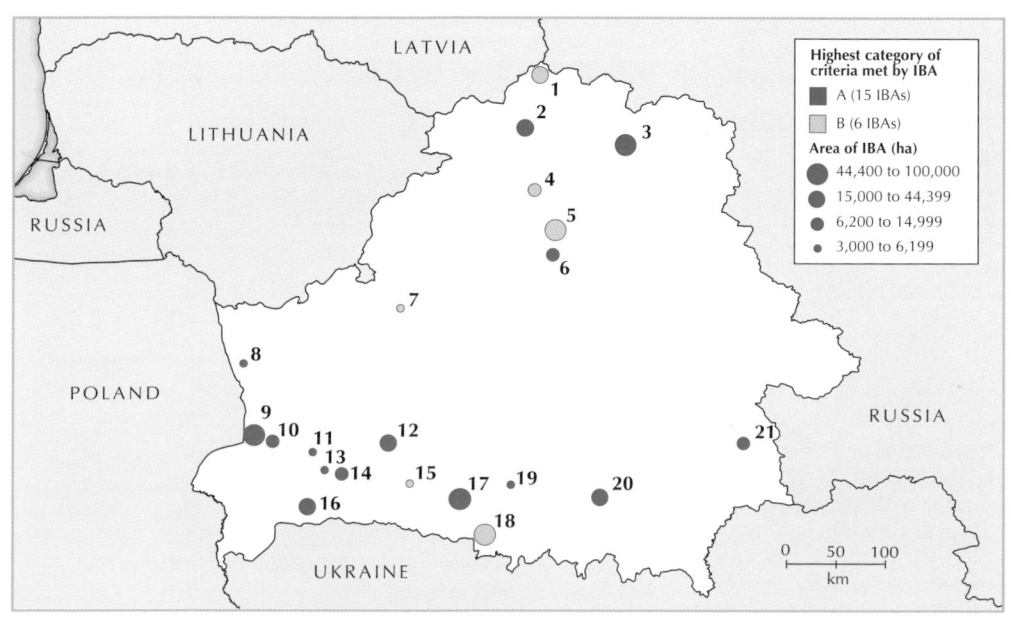

River Pripyat flood-plain (IBA 017). (Photo: Alexander Kozulin)

GENERAL INTRODUCTION

Belarus, covering 207,600 km², is bounded by Poland in the west, by Lithuania, Latvia and Russia in the north and east, and by Ukraine in the south. Belarus lies in the temperate forest zone, beyond the steppe zone which dominates areas of Russia and Ukraine to the south and east. The northern part of Belarus (Poozer'e) is characterized by large tracts of coniferous forest and many lakes, raised bogs and rivers. The central part (the Belarus range) is represented by mostly open, hilly landscapes. The southern part of the country (Polesia) is low-lying, with basin mires and broadleaved forests crossed by lowland rivers with mire-rich flood-plains.

A total of 21 Important Bird Areas (IBAs) have been identified in Belarus, covering 6,175 km² or 3% of the area of the country (Table 1). Most of the IBAs lie in the northern and southern parts of Belarus (Map 1), and are dominated by large tracts of fen and raised bog, as well as by waterlogged river flood-plains. Few IBAs have been identified in eastern Belarus because of the lack of recent surveys in this region. The previous international IBA inventory (Grimmett and Jones 1989) identified seven IBAs in Belarus (as part of the former USSR), three of which are included in the current total of 21 (see Table 1). The other four original sites (listed at the end of Table 1) were not confirmed as IBAs during this review because, based on available data, they do not meet any of the current criteria.

LATVIA
LITHUANIA
RUSSIA
POLAND
RUSSIA
UKRAINE
1
2
3
4
5
6
7
8
9
10
11
13
14
12
15
17
19
20
21
16
18
Highest category of criteria met by IBA
A (15 IBAs)
B (6 IBAs)
Area of IBA (ha)
44,400 to 100,000
15,000 to 44,399
6,200 to 14,999
3,000 to 6,199
0 50 100
km

Map 1. Location, area and criteria category of Important Bird Areas in Belarus.

Table 1. Summary of Important Bird Areas in Belarus. 21 IBAs covering 6,175 km²

IBA code	1989 code	International name	National name	Administrative region	Area (ha)	Criteria (see p. 11)
001	—	Osveya	Osveya	Vitebsk	22,600	B2, B3
002	—	Elnya raised bog	Elnya raised bog	Vitebsk	23,200	A4i, B1i, B2
003	SU112	Kozyany	Kozyany	Vitebsk	44,400	A1, B2, B3
004	—	Golubickaya Pushcha	Golubickaya Pushcha	Vitebsk	6,734	B2
005	SU027	Berezinsky Reserve	Berezinsky Reserve	Vitebsk, Minsk	81,023	B2, B3
006	—	Beresina	Beresina	Minsk	6,200	A1, B2, B3
007	—	West Beresina	West Beresina	Grodno	4,500	B2
008	—	Swisloch	Swisloch	Grodno	3,100	A1, B2
009	SU029	Belovezhskaya Pushcha	Belovezhskaya Pushcha	Brest, Grodno	87,000	A1
010	—	Dikoe	Dikoe	Brest	7,400	A1, B2, B3
011	—	Selets	Selets	Brest	6,000	A1, B2, B3
012	—	Vygonoshchanskoe	Vygonoshchanskoe	Brest	43,000	A1, B2, B3
013	—	Yaselda	Yaselda–Berioza	Brest	3,000	A1, B2
014	—	Sporovo	Sporovo	Brest	8,200	A1, B2
015	—	Polesia fish-farm	Polesie fish-farm	Brest	3,000	B2, B3
016	—	Zvanets	Zvanets	Brest	15,000	A1, B2, B3
017	—	Mid-Pripyat	Mid-Pripyat	Brest, Gomel	100,000	A1, A4i, A4iii, B1i, B2, B3
018	—	Olmany	Olmany	Brest	94,000	B2, B3
019	—	Beloe fish-farm	Beloe fish-farm	Gomel	5,700	A1, B2, B3
020	—	Lower Pripyat	Lower Pripyat	Gomel	40,000	A1, A4i, A4iii, B1i, B2, B3
021	—	Flood-plain of Sozh river	Flood-plain of Sozh river	Gomel	13,400	A1, B2

Sites identified in the previous inventory of IBAs in Europe (Grimmett and Jones 1989) but no longer considered to be IBAs
SU028 Telekhany, Ivatsevichi, and Lyakhovichi, Brest; SU030 Pripyat; Zhitkovichi, Letchitsy and Petrikov, Gomel; SU110* Osveyskoye Ozero (Lake Osveyskoye), Verkhnedvinsk, "Belorussia Oblast"; SU111 Karachevskoye Boloto (Karachevskoye Marsh), Vitebsk and Gorodok.
* Mistakenly treated as part of RSFSR in the previous inventory of IBAs in Europe (Grimmett and Jones 1989).

ORNITHOLOGICAL IMPORTANCE

There are 119 species of European conservation concern (SPECs) which breed regularly in Belarus (Tucker and Heath 1994, Nikiforov et al. 1997). Of these, Aythya nyroca, Aquila clanga, Crex crex and Acrocephalus paludicola are globally threatened, Haliaeetus albicilla and Gallinago media are globally near-threatened, and a further 69 species have an unfavourable conservation status in Europe (Tucker and Heath 1994, Nikiforov et al. 1997).

Table 1 lists the criteria which each site meets in order to qualify as an IBA. Thirteen sites qualify as IBAs because they hold significant numbers of globally threatened or near-threatened species (criterion A1; see Table 2). Acrocephalus paludicola breeds at seven of the sites (Table 2). Indeed, Belarus supports the majority of the world population of this species, according to current knowledge. Crex crex also breeds at seven of the sites, the most important being Mid- and Lower Pripyat (sites 017 and 020) and the flood-plain of the Sozh river (021). Gallinago media breeds at three sites, and Aythya nyroca breeds at two. Breeding Haliaeetus albicilla and Aquila clanga each meet the A1 criterion at one site in Belarus.

All of the IBAs are important breeding sites for waterbirds, and together they cover all of the most significant such sites in Belarus, comprising river flood-plains, fens, raised bogs and highly productive water-bodies (both natural and man-made). Table 3 shows that three of the IBAs support 1% or more of the biogeographic population of one or more waterbird species (criterion A4i), either when breeding (Lower Pripyat, site 020) or when staging during migration (Mid-Pripyat, 017; Elnya raised bog, 002). Six of the 21 sites do not qualify as globally Important Bird Areas (i.e. under any A criteria) but are of European importance (under B2/B3 criteria) for SPECs (001, 004, 005, 007, 015, 018).

Waterbirds migrate over Belarus mainly on a broad front, stopping and congregating at river flood-plains and raised bogs to rest and forage. Most such visible migration activity of waterbirds is confined to Polesia (southern Belarus), with the main axis of movement being along the River Pripyat flood-plain. Through meeting criterion A4i, Mid-Pripyat (site 017) has global importance as a staging area for Anser fabalis, Anser albifrons and Anas penelope, as does Elnya raised bog (002) for Grus grus in the north of the

country. Despite the rapid eastern extension of the wintering range of several species during the past 20 years in Europe, there are no sites with large concentrations of wintering waterbirds in Belarus.

IBAs were identified for the following bird species most often (number of sites in brackets): Crex crex (seven), Acrocephalus

Table 2. Important Bird Areas in Belarus that are important for species of global conservation concern (meeting criterion A1).

Species	IBA code
Aythya nyroca Ferruginous Duck	017, 019
Haliaeetus albicilla White-tailed Eagle	011
Aquila clanga Greater Spotted Eagle	003
[1] Crex crex Corncrake	006, 012, 014, 016, 017, 020, 021
[1] Gallinago media Great Snipe	012, 017, 021
Acrocephalus paludicola Aquatic Warbler	008, 010, 012, 013, 014, 016, 017

1. Also Crex crex and Gallinago media are likely to meet criterion A1 at site 009.

Table 3. Important Bird Areas in Belarus that support important numbers of one or more congregatory species (i.e. meeting criteria A4 and/or B1). IBAs meeting both criteria A4 and B1 for the species are shown in **bold**. IBAs meeting only criterion B1 for the species concerned, and not A4, are shown in normal type. For key to 'Season', see p. 7.

Species	Season	IBA code
Ciconia nigra Black Stork	B	**017**
Anser fabalis Bean Goose	P	**017**
Anser albifrons White-fronted Goose	P	**017**
Anser erythropus Lesser White-fronted Goose	P	017
Anas penelope Wigeon	P	**017**
Anas strepera Gadwall	B	017
Anas platyrhynchos Mallard	B	017, 020
Anas querquedula Garganey	B	017
Grus grus Crane	N	**002**
Tringa totanus Redshank	B	017
Sterna albifrons Little Tern	B	**020**
Chlidonias niger Black Tern	B	017
Chlidonias leucopterus White-winged Black Tern	B	017

Table 4. Species of European conservation concern with significant breeding populations at Important Bird Areas in Belarus (meeting any IBA criteria).

Species [1]	Minimum national breeding population (pairs) [2]	Proportion (%) of national population breeding at all IBAs in Belarus
Botaurus stellaris Bittern	950	68
Ciconia nigra Black Stork	950	16
Ciconia ciconia White Stork	10,500	6
Anas strepera Gadwall	1,000	71
Anas querquedula Garganey	35,000	29
Aythya ferina Pochard	6,000	51
Aythya nyroca Ferruginous Duck	50	100[3]
Pernis apivorus Honey Buzzard	1,000	3
Milvus migrans Black Kite	250	5
Haliaeetus albicilla White-tailed Eagle	50	20
Circaetus gallicus Short-toed Eagle	450	4
Circus cyaneus Hen Harrier	250	6
Circus pygargus Montagu's Harrier	600	17
Aquila clanga Greater Spotted Eagle	20	10
Pandion haliaetus Osprey	120	9
Tetrao tetrix Black Grouse	15,000	6
Porzana porzana Spotted Crake	25,000	5
Porzana parva Little Crake	2,000	15
Crex crex Corncrake	25,000	9
Grus grus Crane	800	25
Gallinago media Great Snipe	2,000	9
Limosa limosa Black-tailed Godwit	6,000	8
Tringa totanus Redshank	40,000	3
Larus minutus Little Gull	1,000	5
Sterna albifrons Little Tern	900	39
Chlidonias niger Black Tern	6,000	18
Bubo bubo Eagle Owl	250	11
Strix aluco Tawny Owl	8,500	6
Asio flammeus Short-eared Owl	500	17
Alcedo atthis Kingfisher	3,000	2
Coracias garrulus Roller	600	7
Picus viridis Green Woodpecker	3,000	4
Riparia riparia Sand Martin	200,000	20
Anthus pratensis Meadow Pipit	180,000	2
Luscinia luscinia Thrush Nightingale	160,000	2
Locustella naevia Grasshopper Warbler	12,000	1
Acrocephalus paludicola Aquatic Warbler	7,000	95
Acrocephalus schoenobaenus Sedge Warbler	600,000	1
Lanius collurio Red-backed Shrike	50,000	1

1. Only those species of European conservation concern (see Box 1, p. 12) that meet IBA criteria in Belarus are listed.
2. Data are taken from the BirdLife/EBCC European Bird Database 1998 (Heath and Borggreve 2000).
3. The percentage of the national population in IBAs exceeds 100%. Usually this is because the national population estimate has not been updated recently whilst the IBA population estimate has been recently updated with new data as a result of comprehensive surveys of IBAs themselves. Also, the individual site count for a species may be the maximum or average over recent years, and summing these may record more birds than are present nationally in any single year.

Figure 1. Habitats at Important Bird Areas in Belarus (see Appendix 3 for definitions of habitats).

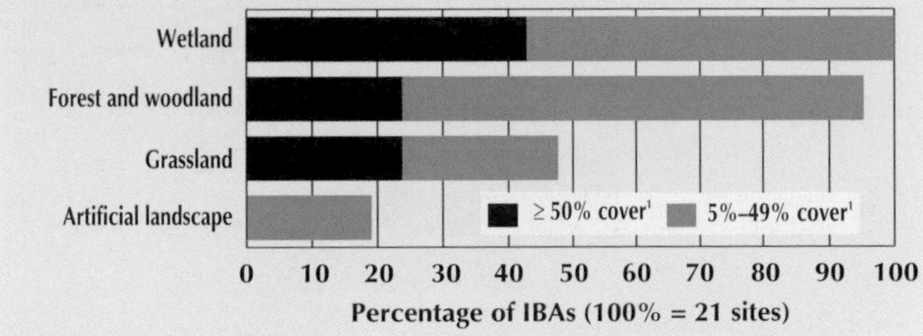

1. percentage of area of individual IBA covered by habitat

HABITATS

Belarus is situated in the transition zone between forest and forest–steppe vegetation in Europe, and thus a wide variety of different vegetation-types occur. The dominant broad habitat-types are grasslands (31,164 km²), pine *Pinus* forests (34,327 km²), mires (20,894 km²), lakes (2,000 km²) and rivers (75,000 km). The following particular habitats are the most important for bird conservation in Belarus: flood-plain meadows (1,697 km²), raised bogs (4,339 km²), open fens (7,476 km²), broadleaved *Betula/Alnus* alluvial forests (973 km²), highly water-logged lowland river flood-plains (4,000 km²) and fish-farm ponds (173 km²).

Figure 1 shows that nine of the 21 IBAs (43%) are predominantly wetlands, five IBAs (24%) are predominantly flood-plain meadows (grassland), and five are predominantly forested. The majority of wetland IBAs cover tracts of open fen and raised bogs, flood-plain water-bodies, rivers and fish-farm ponds. Flood-plain meadows are composed of humid grasslands, steppes and dry calcareous grasslands, while forests comprise alluvial/wet forest and native coniferous forest.

According to these prevailing habitats, IBAs in Belarus can be characterized as follows:

- Large tracts of fen (five IBAs) or raised bog (four IBAs) with surrounding wet forests or drained lands.
- Flood-plains of large and medium-sized rivers with meadows and forests predominating (five IBAs).
- Large, complex mosaics of mire, forest, river and lake flood-plain (three IBAs).
- Fish-farm ponds (three IBAs).
- Large tract of forest (one IBA).

Breeding birds that are especially associated with these key habitats are: *Acrocephalus paludicola* in mesotrophic fens; *Anas querquedula*, *Crex crex* and *Limosa limosa* in flood-plain grasslands; *Botaurus stellaris*, *Aythya ferina* and *Haliaeetus albicilla* in highly productive, standing fresh water (natural and man-made); *Circaetus gallicus*, *Pandion haliaetus* and *Grus grus* in raised bogs; *Ciconia nigra* and *Bubo bubo* in alluvial and very wet forests; *Sterna albifrons* in sand-dunes.

IMPACTS ON IBAs – LAND-USE AND THREATS

Figure 2 summarizes land-use at IBAs in Belarus. In terms of significant land-uses at sites (those uses that cover 5% or more of an IBA), 12 sites (57%) are used to a significant extent for agriculture, 11 (52%) for forestry, nine (43%) for nature conservation and research, seven (33%) for hunting, and 10% for tourism/recreation, while 10 (48%) are 'not utilized' to a significant extent. Regarding the predominant land-uses at sites (those uses that cover 50% or more of an IBA), seven (33%) of the sites are used mainly for nature conservation, 19% mainly for forestry, 10% mainly for agriculture, 14% mainly for fisheries, and 5% mainly for military ranges, while five (24%) are mainly 'not utilized'.

All IBAs are state-owned, but changes in the ownership of protected areas are expected in the near future.

Figure 3 summarizes the threats to IBAs. Some of the threats (e.g. burning of vegetation) have a high impact on particular sites, but only 'reductions in fish-farming activity' have had a high impact on more than 10% of the total number of IBAs. The great majority of negative impacts on IBAs are of low to medium

paludicola (seven), *Botaurus stellaris* (six), *Aythya ferina* (six), *Grus grus* (six), *Ciconia nigra* (five), *Circus pygargus* (five) and *Chlidonias niger* (five). Table 4 lists SPECs which meet any IBA criteria together with the proportion of their national populations covered by IBAs. The table shows that the IBAs in Belarus support more than 30% of the national breeding populations of several wetland species (*Botaurus stellaris*, *Anas strepera*, *Aythya ferina*, *Sterna albifrons*, *Acrocephalus paludicola*), demonstrating an important aspect of this national network. Similarly, more than 10% of the national populations of such species as *Ciconia nigra*, *Anas querquedula*, *Haliaeetus albicilla*, *Circus pygargus* and *Aquila clanga* breed at IBAs. Other bird species in Table 4, for which the IBAs support less then 10% of the national population, have a more dispersed distribution in Belarus when breeding.

Mid-Pripyat (site 017) is probably the most important IBA in the country, qualifying on the basis of its global importance for 13 species (criteria A1, A4i) as well as its regional importance for 17 species (criteria B1i, B2, B3).

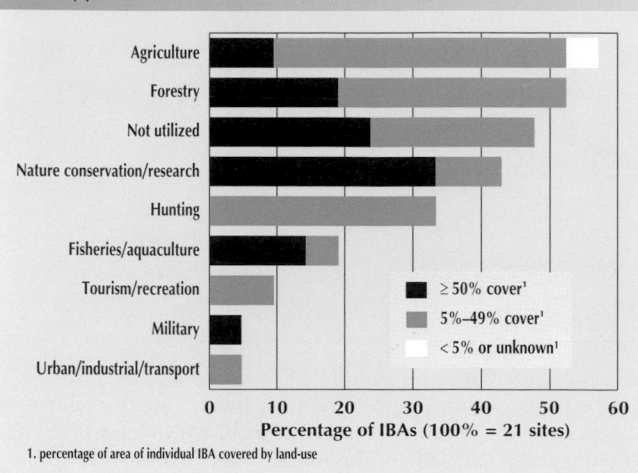

Figure 2. Land-uses at Important Bird Areas in Belarus (see Appendix 3 for definitions of land-uses).

Percentage of IBAs (100% = 21 sites)

1. percentage of area of individual IBA covered by land-use

Table 5. Protection status of Important Bird Areas in Belarus. A tick (✔) indicates that an IBA overlaps with a protected area (to any extent).

IBA code	International name	National			International	
		Zapovednik	National Park	Zakaznik	World Heritage Site	Biosphere Reserve
001	Osveya			✔		
002	Elnya raised bog			✔		
003	Kozyany			✔		
004	Golubickaya Pushcha			✔		
005	Berezinsky Reserve	✔				✔
006	Beresina					
007	West Beresina			✔		
008	Swisloch					
009	Belovezhskaya Pushcha		✔		✔	✔
010	Dikoe			✔		
011	Selets			✔		
012	Vygonoshchanskoe			✔		
013	Yaselda					
014	Sporovo			✔		
015	Polesia fish-farm					
016	Zvanets			✔		
017	Mid-Pripyat			✔		
018	Olmany					
019	Beloe fish-farm					
020	Lower Pripyat	✔				
021	Flood-plain of Sozh river					
Total number of IBAs		**2**	**1**	**11**	**1**	**2**

intensity when looked at individually, and are caused mainly by the drainage of areas surrounding IBAs, together with attendant or consequent threats such as agricultural expansion/intensification, the lowering of the water-table, and the dredging/canalization of rivers. Drainage is actually the most important threat to the majority of habitats and birds throughout the country (not just in IBAs), as a result of a wide-scale national drainage campaign over the last 30 years, during which (for example) c.2.5 million ha of mires were drained. At present no new wide-scale drainage activities are planned, but the wetlands that remain (including the IBAs) continue to be influenced by the drastically lowered groundwater levels and by the pollution with nutrients and other chemicals that have followed previous drainage. Commercial logging also affects many IBAs (38% of the total), while the construction of dams, the abandonment of land management, selective logging, illegal hunting and natural events affect a smaller number of IBAs.

The unique fens of Dikoe (site 010), Sporovo (014) and Zvanets (016) are the most threatened IBAs in Belarus because of the impact of the drainage of the surrounding areas, together with the cessation of traditional land-uses, in particular manual haymaking.

Box 1. International legislation and initiatives that are relevant to site conservation in Belarus (see Appendix 1 for a general description of these agreements).

Global
Biodiversity Convention ✔
Ramsar Convention
Bonn Convention
World Heritage Convention ✔
MAB Programme ✔

Pan-European
Bern Convention

✔ Convention ratified/initiative supported
(✔) Convention signed

PROTECTION STATUS

Table 5 summarizes the protection status of IBAs in Belarus. Of the total IBA area (6,175 km²), about 2,650 km² (28–29%) are not protected under national or international law (Table 5, Figure 4).

■ National protection
Regarding the overlap of individual IBAs with nationally protected areas, eight IBAs are each covered by more than 90%, six IBAs are

covered by 10–90%, and the remaining seven are not legally protected at all (Figure 4). There are three main types of national protected area in Belarus (Table 5).

1. Zapovednik (Strict Nature Reserve)
These provide the highest level of protection. The protection regime is maintained over the whole area, and land-use is permitted only in special zones.

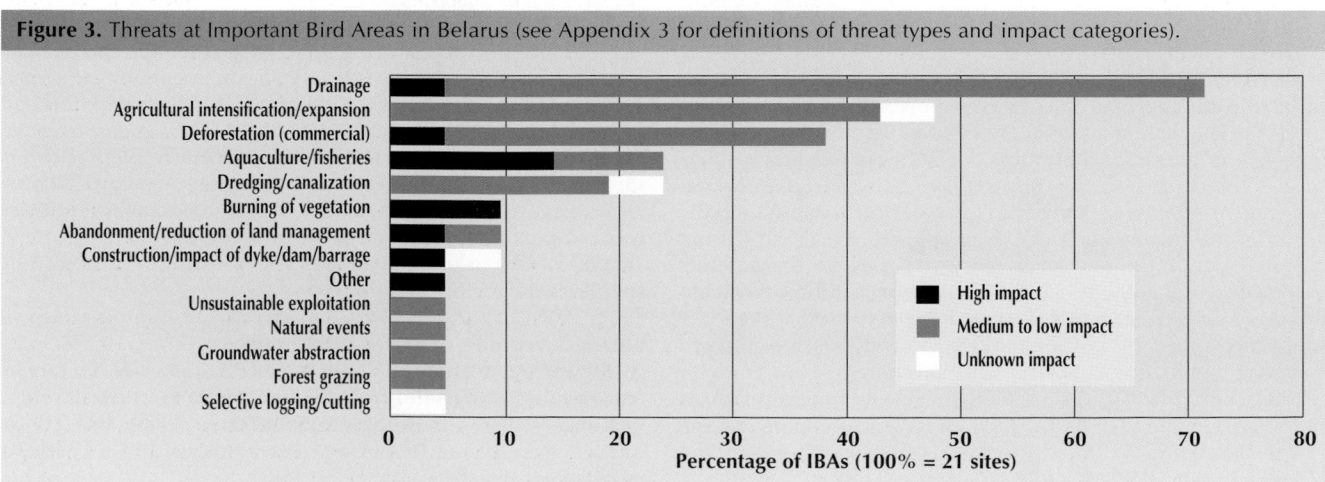

Figure 3. Threats at Important Bird Areas in Belarus (see Appendix 3 for definitions of threat types and impact categories).

■ High impact
■ Medium to low impact
□ Unknown impact

Percentage of IBAs (100% = 21 sites)

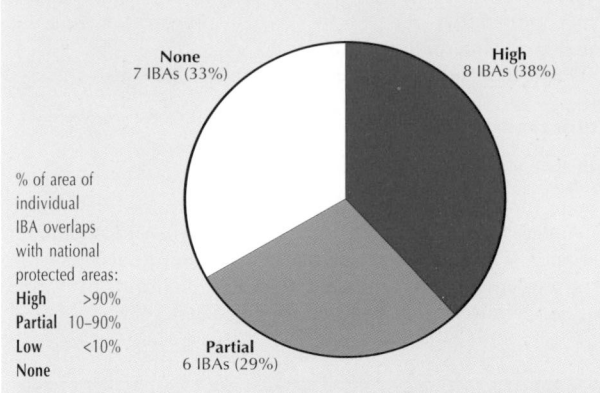

Figure 4. The national protection status of Important Bird Areas in Belarus.

% of area of individual IBA overlaps with national protected areas:
High >90%
Partial 10–90%
Low <10%
None

None 7 IBAs (33%)
High 8 IBAs (38%)
Partial 6 IBAs (29%)

Total area of overlap between IBA network in Belarus and national protected-area system (see Table 5 for categories) = 3,476–3,523 km² (56–57% of total IBA area).

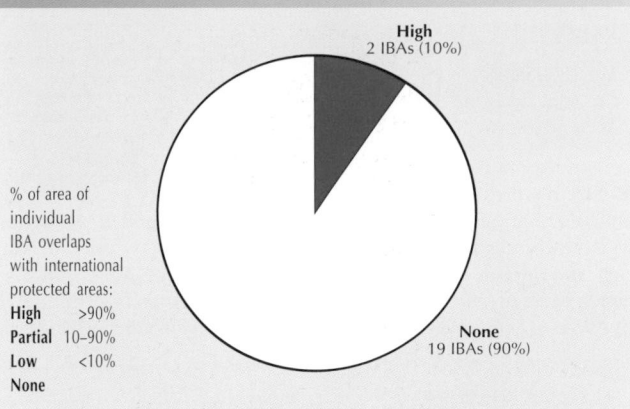

Figure 5. The international protection status of Important Bird Areas in Belarus.

% of area of individual IBA overlaps with international protected areas:
High >90%
Partial 10–90%
Low <10%
None

High 2 IBAs (10%)
None 19 IBAs (90%)

Total area of overlap between IBA network in Belarus and international protected-area system (see Table 5 for categories) = 1,680 km² (27% of total IBA area).

2. National Park

These have lower protection status than Zapovedniks and allow a higher degree of economic activity within the area, including tourism.

3. Zakaznik

These areas are usually used by collective farms (kolkhoz) for restricted economic (mostly agricultural) activities.

■ International protection

Belarus is a contracting party to the World Heritage Convention, takes part in the UNESCO Man and Biosphere Programme and will sign the Ramsar Convention in the near future (Box 1). Only two IBAs have international protected status (Table 5, Figure 5): Berezinsky Reserve (site 005) is a Biosphere Reserve, and Belovezhskaya Pushcha (site 009) is a Biosphere Reserve and a World Heritage Site. At least three of the IBAs qualify as potential Ramsar Sites under IBA criteria A4i and A4iii (002, 017 and 020; see Table 1).

CONSERVATION

- Over the past few years, active fieldwork has been carried out at the most important sites for biodiversity conservation in Belarus, in order to conduct inventories and to prepare for the creation of new protected areas. Preliminary inventories of potential IBAs and potential Ramsar Sites have been carried out. Breeding bird counts have been used as scientific justification for proposed protected areas. The subsequent creation of new Zakazniks, to cover some of the most important unprotected IBAs (sites 013, 017, 018), is almost complete thanks to financial and logistical support to the National Academy of Science from the Ministry of Natural Resources and Environmental Protection, the Michael Otto Foundation for Environmental Protection, the Wildlife Habitat Charitable Trust, Wetlands International, and the MacArthur Foundation.
- One of the main deficiencies of nature conservation in Belarus is the lack of management plans and management structures for the most significant and valuable protected areas (Zakazniks). Only strictly protected areas (Zapovedniks and National Parks) have a form of management plan and a management structure.

ANALYTICAL METHODS

- Published and unpublished material was compiled from the Institute of Zoology, Belarus State University, Vitebsk State University, Belovezhskaya Pushcha National Park, Berezinsky Biosphere Reserve and some other organizations, as well as from personal communication with field ornithologists.

- The bird data (species composition and numbers) in this inventory were obtained by field ornithologists during monitoring work, with counts deriving mainly from the period 1986–1996. Most waterbird counts are of good quality (verification code A or B) and are based on absolute counts of some species at raised bogs and water-bodies, with some helicopter-based counts of wildfowl along river flood-plains, as well as direct counts of migrating birds. Data for passerines are based on transect counts.
- According to preliminary estimates, about 60% of potential IBAs have now been described. However, the majority of highly waterlogged, lowland river flood-plains, and some large tracts of forest and mire (fens and bogs), have still not been investigated.
- A lack of data on the distribution and numbers of *Aquila pomarina*, *Porzana porzana*, *Gallinago media* and *Caprimulgus europaeus* meant that several IBAs, which potentially qualified for these species, could not be designated. In addition, IBAs could not be designated under the B2/B3 criteria for certain breeding SPECs (Tucker and Heath 1994) which are dispersed at low density over the landscape in large territories (*Picus canus*, *Jynx torquilla*, *Dendrocopos medius*, *Picoides tridactylus*, *Saxicola rubetra* and *Muscicapa striata*), since to meet the threshold of '1% or more of national population' such an IBA would have to be rather large, with a minimum area of c.3,000 ha.
- Information on land-uses and threats was based on available data from fieldwork and the literature.

ACKNOWLEDGEMENTS

This IBA inventory was completed as a result of field surveys conducted under the following projects: 'Belarus Forest Biodiversity Protection Project' (Global Environment Facility grant 05/28621-BY), 'Survey of Aquatic Warbler Habitats in Belarus' (grant from the Michael Otto Foundation for Environmental Protection) and 'Evaluation of the Pripyat River Floodplain Significance for Waterbirds' (grant from the Wildlife Habitat Charitable Trust and from Wetlands International).

The main data on the composition and numerical abundance of bird species at potential IBAs were provided by the following ornithologists: V. Biryukov, V. Gritchik, M. Flade, V. Ivanovski, A. Kozulin, M. Nikiforov and A. Tishechkin. The Institute of Zoology (National Academy of Science) and the Ministry of Natural Resources and Environmental Protection also cooperated during the data-gathering phase.

In addition, we would like to extend our thanks to the following ornithologists for their help in data collection at different stages of our field investigations: I. Byshnev, V. Dombrovsky, D. Juravlev, V. Korenchuk, E. Monghin, O. Pareiko, P. Pinchuk, I. Samusenko, N. Tcherkas, S. Shokalo, A. Vinchevski, V. Yurko and V. Yakovitch. We also thank L. Kozulina, T. Pavluschick and B. Roshchin for their help in translation and working with the database.

■ SITE ACCOUNTS

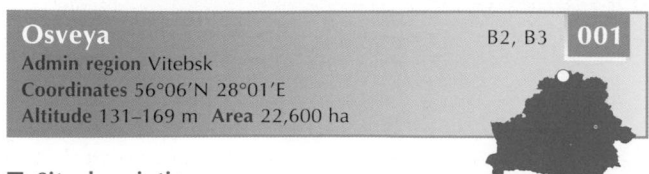

Osveya
B2, B3 001

Admin region Vitebsk
Coordinates 56°06'N 28°01'E
Altitude 131–169 m Area 22,600 ha

■ Site description
One of the largest areas of lakes in Belarus, surrounded by natural wet and coniferous forests and raised bogs. The lakes are nutrient-rich and aquatic vegetation is dominated by reed *Phragmites*, of which there are floating overgrown islets. The forest is dominated by *Picea*, *Alnus* and *Betula*, and bogs are mainly wooded with *Pinus*.

Habitats Forest and woodland (50%; mixed forest), Wetland (50%; standing fresh water; raised bog; water-fringe vegetation)

Land-use Forestry (50%), Hunting (30%), Nature conservation/research (20%)

■ Birds

Species	Season	Year	Pop min	Pop max	Acc	Criteria
Botaurus stellaris Bittern	B	1988	40	60	B	B2
Aythya ferina Pochard	B	1988	400	600	A	B3
Tetrao tetrix Black Grouse	R	1988	80	150	B	B2

Numbers of some breeding waterbirds are very large, and others are also notable, e.g. *Grus grus* (10–15 pairs). Breeding species of global conservation concern that do not meet IBA criteria: *Haliaeetus albicilla* (1–2 pairs).

■ Protection status
National High **International** None
22,600 ha of IBA covered by Zakaznik (Asveisky, 22,600 ha).

■ Conservation issues

Threats Deforestation (commercial) (B), Other (A)

Nutrient enrichment of the lakes is the main threat ('Other' threat, above), caused by decreasing water-levels (due to peat extraction on the lake flood-plain) and by agricultural effluents. Further study of the situation by experts is required. The area is protected as a State Hunting Reserve and is managed by a special hunting service.

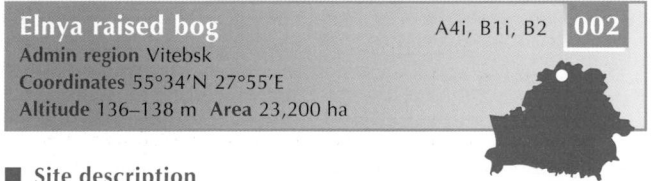

Elnya raised bog
A4i, B1i, B2 002

Admin region Vitebsk
Coordinates 55°34'N 27°55'E
Altitude 136–138 m Area 23,200 ha

■ Site description
The largest raised bog in Belarus to remain in a natural and intact state. Open bog (some areas wooded with *Pinus*) and small nutrient-poor lakes dominate the landscape.

Habitats Forest and woodland (17%; alluvial/very wet forest), Wetland (83%; standing fresh water; raised bog; fen/transition mire/spring)

Land-use Nature conservation/research (80%), Not utilized (20%)

■ Birds

Species	Season	Year	Pop min	Pop max	Acc	Criteria
Circaetus gallicus Short-toed Eagle	B	1990	2	3	A	B2
Tetrao tetrix Black Grouse	R	1990	150	200	B	B2
Grus grus Crane	B	1990	60	60	B	B2
Grus grus Crane	N	1990	2,000	3,000	B	A4i, B1i
Asio flammeus Short-eared Owl	R	1990	40	50	A	B2

Of any IBA in Belarus, this site holds the largest numbers of breeding species typical of bog landscapes, such as *Gavia arctica*, *Lagopus lagopus*, *Pluvialis apricaria*, *Numenius phaeopus*, *Lymnocryptes minimus* and *Tringa nebularia*. Breeding species of global conservation concern that do not meet IBA criteria: *Gallinago media* (min. 20 pairs).

■ Protection status
National High **International** None
23,200 ha of IBA covered by Zakaznik (Elnya, 23,200 ha).

■ Conservation issues

Threats Agricultural intensification/expansion (B), Drainage (B)

The main threat comes from the lowering of water-levels due to the drainage of the surrounding area. Overall the site is relatively well studied. The area is protected as a State Nature Reserve. It is necessary to enlarge the protected area, to enhance its protection status, and to develop a management plan for the site.

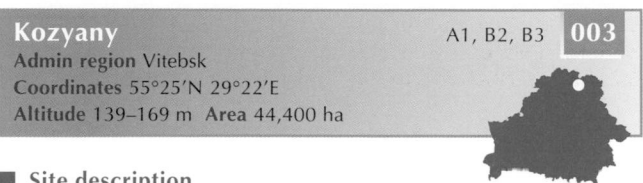

Kozyany
A1, B2, B3 003

Admin region Vitebsk
Coordinates 55°25'N 29°22'E
Altitude 139–169 m Area 44,400 ha

■ Site description
A complex of coniferous forests, raised bogs, transitional mires, small rivers and lakes. Obol, a raised bog with numerous associated lakes, forms the core of the reserve; it was listed as site SU112 (USSR) in the previous international IBA inventory (Grimmett and Jones 1989). Land-uses include forestry and hunting of ungulates, but at low intensity.

Habitats Forest and woodland (65%; native coniferous forest), Wetland (25%; standing fresh water; raised bog), Artificial landscape (10%; arable land)

Land-use Forestry (70%), Hunting (30%)

■ Birds

Species	Season	Year	Pop min	Pop max	Acc	Criteria
Pernis apivorus Honey Buzzard	B	1995	12	15	A	B3
Milvus migrans Black Kite	B	1995	5	5	A	B2
Circaetus gallicus Short-toed Eagle	B	1995	5	5	A	B2
Circus cyaneus Hen Harrier	B	1995	10	10	A	B2
Circus pygargus Montagu's Harrier	B	1995	15	20	B	B3
Aquila clanga Greater Spotted Eagle	B	1995	2	2	A	A1, B2
Pandion haliaetus Osprey	B	1995	5	6	A	B2
Tetrao tetrix Black Grouse	R	1992	300	450	B	B2

The area supports a high diversity and high densities of raptors. Breeding species of global conservation concern that do not meet IBA criteria: *Haliaeetus albicilla* (1 pair). Significant proportion (≥1%) of national population breeding at site: *Aquila chrysaetos* (2 pairs). There are also notable numbers of breeding *Ciconia ciconia* (50–70 pairs).

■ Protection status
National High **International** None
44,400 ha of IBA covered by Zakaznik (Kozyansky, 44,400 ha).

■ Conservation issues

Threats Deforestation (commercial) (B), Drainage (C)

Logging is a threat. The whole site is protected as a State Hunting Reserve, with conservation and management carried out by a special hunting service.

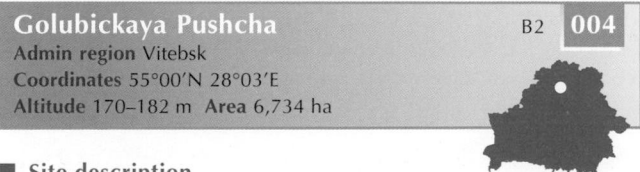

Golubickaya Pushcha
B2 004

Admin region Vitebsk
Coordinates 55°00'N 28°03'E
Altitude 170–182 m Area 6,734 ha

■ Site description

Habitats Forest and woodland (19%; native coniferous forest), Wetland (81%; standing fresh water; raised bog)

Land-use Forestry (50%), Nature conservation/research (50%)

An area of raised bog typical of Vitebsk region. The landscape is mostly open but parts are wooded with *Pinus* and there are small lakes.

■ Birds

Species	Season	Year	Pop min	Pop max	Acc	Criteria
Ciconia nigra Black Stork	B	1993	5	10	A	B2
Pandion haliaetus Osprey	B	1993	6	8	A	B2

The site supports the highest density of breeding *Pandion haliaetus* in Belarus. Breeding species of global conservation concern that do not meet IBA criteria: *Haliaeetus albicilla* (max. 1 pair), *Crex crex* (min. 10 pairs). Significant proportion (≥1%) of national population breeding at site: *Botaurus stellaris* (10–20 pairs). There are also notable numbers of breeding *Circus pygargus* (min. 5 pairs), *Aquila pomarina* (10–20 pairs), *Tetrao tetrix* (70–100 pairs), *Grus grus* (5–15 pairs) and *Bubo bubo* (1–3 pairs).

■ Protection status

National High **International** None
6,734 ha of IBA covered by Zakaznik (Golubitskaya Pushcha, 6,734 ha).

■ Conservation issues

Threats Deforestation (commercial) (B), Drainage (C)

The main threats are deforestation and the drop in water-levels due to drainage of the surrounding area. The area is protected as a Local Nature Reserve. The site is relatively well studied.

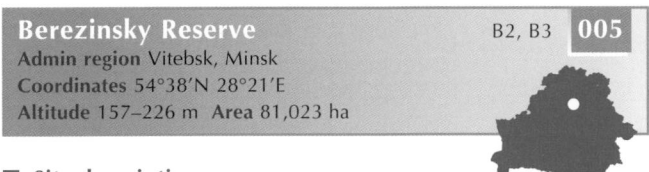

Berezinsky Reserve — B2, B3 — 005

Admin region Vitebsk, Minsk
Coordinates 54°38'N 28°21'E
Altitude 157–226 m **Area** 81,023 ha

■ Site description

A vast tract of predominantly coniferous forests with wet flood-plain habitats. *Pinus* forest, fens, raised bogs and wet meadows predominate. The site was listed as site SU027 (USSR) in the previous international IBA inventory (Grimmett and Jones 1989).

Habitats Forest and woodland (49%; native coniferous forest, alluvial/very wet forest), Grassland (5%; humid grassland), Wetland (46%; raised bog; fen/transition mire/spring)
Land-use Forestry (10%), Nature conservation/research (80%), Tourism/recreation (10%)

■ Birds

Species	Season	Year	Pop min	Pop max	Acc	Criteria
Ciconia nigra Black Stork	B	1990	12	16	A	B2
Pernis apivorus Honey Buzzard	B	1990	8	12	B	B3
Circus pygargus Montagu's Harrier	B	1990	6	12	B	B3
Tetrao tetrix Black Grouse	R	1990	200	300	B	B2
Grus grus Crane	B	1990	30	35	A	B2
Chlidonias niger Black Tern	B	1990	—	150	A	B2
Coracias garrulus Roller	B	1990	5	20	B	B2

The area is rich in forest bird species, and a total of 171 species have been recorded. Breeding species of global conservation concern that do not meet IBA criteria: *Crex crex* (common). Significant proportion (≥1%) of national population breeding at site: *Botaurus stellaris* (10–15 pairs).

■ Protection status

National High **International** High
81,023 ha of IBA covered by Zapovednik (Berezinsky, 81,023 ha). 81,023 ha of IBA covered by Biosphere Reserve (Berezinsky, 81,023 ha).

■ Conservation issues

Threats Agricultural intensification/expansion (C)

A threat with relatively low impact is aerial pollution of the forest ecosystem by heavy metal and sulphur compounds, carried from industrial areas by westerly winds, and which damage tree health and growth. The site was designated as a Zapovednik in 1925.

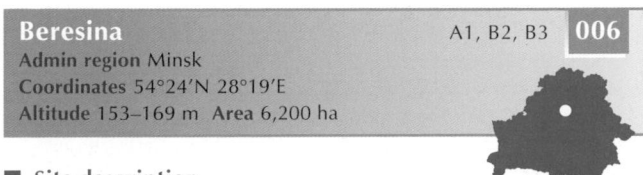

Beresina — A1, B2, B3 — 006

Admin region Minsk
Coordinates 54°24'N 28°19'E
Altitude 153–169 m **Area** 6,200 ha

■ Site description

A lowland, middle-river flood-plain with a natural (seasonal) flooding regime. Wet meadows, fens, alluvial forests and riparian thickets predominate. Land-uses include haymaking, cattle-grazing, hunting and fishing.

Habitats Forest and woodland (15%; alluvial/very wet forest), Grassland (60%; humid grassland), Wetland (25%; standing fresh water; fen/transition mire/spring)
Land-use Agriculture (50%), Not utilized (50%)

■ Birds

Species	Season	Year	Pop min	Pop max	Acc	Criteria
Anas querquedula Garganey	B	1990	400	600	B	B2
Porzana porzana Spotted Crake	B	1986	250	400	B	B3
Crex crex Corncrake	B	1986	200	300	B	A1
Chlidonias niger Black Tern	B	1990	50	200	B	B2
Alcedo atthis Kingfisher	B	1990	15	25	B	B2
Acrocephalus schoenobaenus Sedge Warbler	B	1986	1,000	1,500	B	B3

An important breeding site for several waterbird species.

■ Protection status

National None **International** None

■ Conservation issues

Threats Agricultural intensification/expansion (C), Drainage (C)

Drainage, water abstraction and agricultural intensification pose threats.

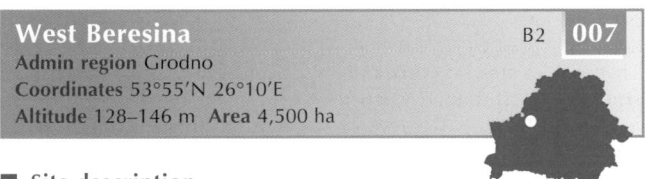

West Beresina — B2 — 007

Admin region Grodno
Coordinates 53°55'N 26°10'E
Altitude 128–146 m **Area** 4,500 ha

■ Site description

The flood-plain of the middle reaches of the West Beresina river (a lowland tributary of the Neman river), still in a predominantly natural and intact state. Alluvial *Quercus* forests, *Salix* thickets and wet meadows dominate the landscape. Land-uses include haymaking and cattle-grazing.

Habitats Forest and woodland (80%; broadleaved deciduous forest), Grassland (15%; humid grassland), Wetland (5%; river/stream)
Land-use Agriculture (20%), Forestry (80%)

■ Birds

Species	Season	Year	Pop min	Pop max	Acc	Criteria
Alcedo atthis Kingfisher	B	1988	20	35	A	B2

The river holds the highest density of *Alcedo atthis* in Belarus. Breeding species of global conservation concern that do not meet IBA criteria: *Crex crex* (min. 20 pairs).

■ Protection status

National Partial **International** None
500 ha of IBA covered by Zakaznik (Naliboksky, 85,400 ha).

■ Conservation issues

Threats Agricultural intensification/expansion (C), Deforestation (commercial) (B), Drainage (B), Dredging/canalization (U)

The main threat is from drainage, and from canalization of the upper river-bed, which together have resulted in lower water-levels on the river. A small part of the flood-plain is included in the State National Nature Reserve (Zakaznik).

Swisloch — A1, B2 — 008

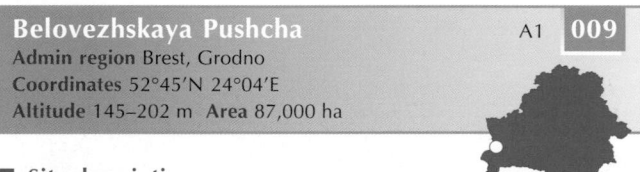

Admin region Grodno
Coordinates 53°24′N 23°55′E
Altitude 108–110 m **Area** 3,100 ha

■ Site description
A riverine flood-plain, most of which is still in a natural state, with wet meadows and fens dominated by sedge *Carex*.

Habitats Forest and woodland (10%; alluvial/very wet forest), Grassland (70%; humid grassland), Wetland (20%; fen/transition mire/spring)
Land-use Agriculture (60%), Not utilized (40%)

■ Birds

Species	Season	Year	Pop min	Pop max	Acc	Criteria
Acrocephalus paludicola Aquatic Warbler	B	1996	30	100	B	A1, B2

An important area of breeding habitat for *Acrocephalus paludicola*, which also supports a rich assemblage of species of flood-plain mires in Europe. Breeding species of global conservation concern that do not meet IBA criteria: *Crex crex* (common), *Gallinago media* (uncommon).

■ Protection status
National None **International** None

■ Conservation issues

Threats Agricultural intensification/expansion (B), Drainage (A)

The main threat is drainage of the flood-plain. The first investigations of the area were carried out in 1996. The development of a local reserve is planned.

Belovezhskaya Pushcha — A1 — 009

Admin region Brest, Grodno
Coordinates 52°45′N 24°04′E
Altitude 145–202 m **Area** 87,000 ha

■ Site description
A low-lying region in the southern taiga subzone, covering parts of the catchments of the Narev and Lesnaya rivers near the border with Poland. The area includes vast tracts of primary forest, as well as fens, raised bogs, meadows and two man-made ponds. The site was listed as site SU029 (USSR) in the previous international IBA inventory (Grimmett and Jones 1989).

Habitats Forest and woodland (92%; broadleaved deciduous forest; native coniferous forest; alluvial/very wet forest), Grassland (1%; humid grassland), Wetland (7%; standing fresh water; river/stream; raised bog; fen/transition mire/spring)
Land-use Forestry (10%), Nature conservation/research (80%), Tourism/recreation (10%)

■ Birds
Species of global conservation concern include *Gallinago media* and *Crex crex* (both breeding), and *Aquila clanga* has been recorded. The large extent of potential breeding habitat for these species suggests that one or more of them will meet the A1 criterion, given further surveys. The avifauna is rich (169 breeding species), and includes the largest number of breeding *Aquila pomarina* at any single site in Belarus.

■ Protection status
National High **International** High
87,000 ha of IBA covered by National Park (Belovezhskaya Pushcha, 87,607 ha). 87,000 ha of IBA covered by Biosphere Reserve (Belovezhskaya Pushcha, 177,100 ha). 87,000 ha of IBA covered by World Heritage Site (Belovezhskaya Pushcha, 87,607 ha).

■ Conservation issues

Threats Forest grazing (B), Groundwater abstraction (B)

The main threats come from the high densities of ungulates in the area, and from the lowering of groundwater levels. The area has been protected in one form or another since the last century.

Dikoe — A1, B2, B3 — 010

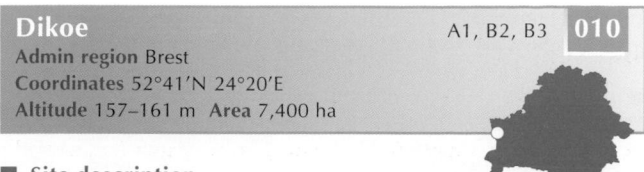

Admin region Brest
Coordinates 52°41′N 24°20′E
Altitude 157–161 m **Area** 7,400 ha

■ Site description
An extensive and intact poor fen, with numerous 'islands' of wet woodland. The vegetation is dominated by mixed stands of sedge *Carex*, grass *Calamagrostis*, mosses (e.g. *Hypnum*) and bare peat. The only exploitative land-use is cranberry *Vaccinium* gathering.

Habitats Forest and woodland (14%; alluvial/very wet forest), Wetland (86%; fen/transition mire/spring)
Land-use Nature conservation/research (100%)

■ Birds

Species	Season	Year	Pop min	Pop max	Acc	Criteria
Anthus pratensis Meadow Pipit	B	1996	3,000	4,000	B	B3
Acrocephalus paludicola Aquatic Warbler	B	1996	1,700	1,800	A	A1, B2

One of the largest remaining areas in the world of suitable breeding habitat for *Acrocephalus paludicola*. Breeding species of global conservation concern that do not meet IBA criteria: *Gallinago media* (10–20 pairs).

■ Protection status
National High **International** None
7,400 ha of IBA covered by Zakaznik (Dikoe, 7,400 ha).

■ Conservation issues

Threats Drainage (B), Dredging/canalization (B)

The main threat comes from changes in the water regime caused by the drainage of surrounding areas by collective farms, following the previous Soviet government policy to enlarge the land area under arable farming. The area has been protected since 1968, and there are plans to make the Zakaznik a part of Belovezhskaya Pushcha National Park (009). Studies of species diversity and census-work have been carried out with financial support from the Michael Otto Foundation for Environmental Protection.

Selets — A1, B2, B3 — 011

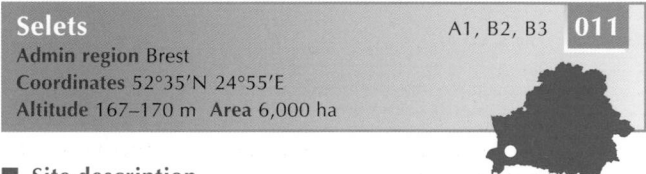

Admin region Brest
Coordinates 52°35′N 24°55′E
Altitude 167–170 m **Area** 6,000 ha

■ Site description
An extensive complex of small and large, man-made fish-ponds with surrounding mixed and wet forests.

Habitats Forest and woodland (25%; mixed forest), Wetland (66%; standing fresh water; water-fringe vegetation), Artificial landscape (9%; arable land)
Land-use Agriculture (5%), Fisheries/aquaculture (70%), Forestry (25%)

■ Birds

Species	Season	Year	Pop min	Pop max	Acc	Criteria
Botaurus stellaris Bittern	B	1990	30	50	B	B2
Aythya ferina Pochard	B	1990	200	300	B	B3
Haliaeetus albicilla White-tailed Eagle	B	1996	4	6	A	A1, B2
Bubo bubo Eagle Owl	R	1995	3	6	A	B2

Waterbirds occur at high densities, especially fish-eating species. There are notable numbers of breeding *Circus pygargus* (3–5 pairs) and *Limosa limosa* (100–150 pairs), and of *Pandion haliaetus* on passage (5–15 birds).

■ Protection status
National Partial **International** None
3,000 ha of IBA covered by Zakaznik (Buslovka, 7,936 ha).

■ Conservation issues

Threats Aquaculture/fisheries (A), Deforestation (commercial) (C)

The main threat comes from the reduction in fish production due to the current economic crisis, resulting in a decreased area of water and reduced food supply for fish-eating birds. Only the forested areas of the site are protected.

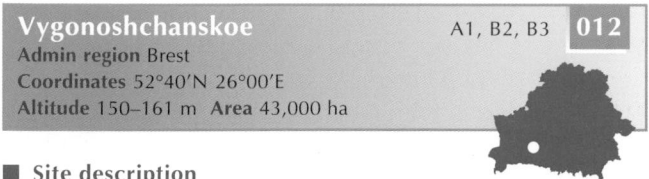

Vygonoshchanskoe
A1, B2, B3 **012**
Admin region Brest
Coordinates 52°40′N 26°00′E
Altitude 150–161 m **Area** 43,000 ha

■ Site description

A large tract of natural wet forests of *Alnus* and *Betula*, fens, raised bogs with *Pinus* trees, and shallow, nutrient-rich lakes. The main land-use is hunting.

Habitats Forest and woodland (35%; alluvial/very wet forest), Grassland (10%; humid grassland), Wetland (55%; standing fresh water; raised bog; fen/transition mire/spring)
Land-use Agriculture (5%), Forestry (30%), Hunting (20%), Nature conservation/research (45%)

■ Birds

Species		Season	Year	Pop min	Pop max	Acc	Criteria
Botaurus stellaris	Bittern	B	1989	40	50	A	B2
Aythya ferina	Pochard	B	1989	200	250	B	B3
Haliaeetus albicilla	White-tailed Eagle	B	1989	2	3	A	B2
Crex crex	Corncrake	B	1996	50	—	B	A1
Grus grus	Crane	B	1989	20	25	B	B2
Gallinago media	Great Snipe	B	1995	20	—	B	A1
Strix aluco	Tawny Owl	R	1989	30	—	—	B3
Acrocephalus paludicola	Aquatic Warbler	B	1996	30	100	B	A1, B2

A variety of rare and threatened species inhabit the area at low densities. There are notable numbers of breeding *Pernis apivorus* (5–8 pairs), *Tetrao urogallus* (15–25 pairs) and *Strix nebulosa* (6–10 pairs).

■ Protection status
National High **International** None
43,000 ha of IBA covered by Zakaznik (Vygonoshchanskoe, 43,000 ha).

■ Conservation issues

Threats Burning of vegetation (A), Deforestation (commercial) (C), Drainage (B)

The main threats are fires (occurring in very dry years), increasing nutrient enrichment of the lake, drainage, and exploitation of peat. The probable reason for the nutrient enrichment and subsequent overgrowth of the lake by vegetation, as well as for the encroachment of scrub onto mires in the site, is the lowering of the water-table due to the drainage of surrounding mires. The area is protected as a State Hunting Reserve (hunting Zakaznik) and is managed by a special hunting service.

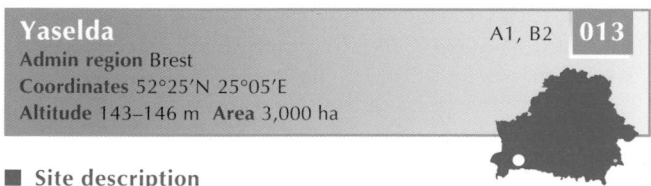

Yaselda
A1, B2 **013**
Admin region Brest
Coordinates 52°25′N 25°05′E
Altitude 143–146 m **Area** 3,000 ha

■ Site description

A predominantly intact, riverine poor fen. The vegetation is dominated by various species of sedge *Carex*, with some wet woodland. Part of the area is used for haymaking.

Habitats Forest and woodland (10%; alluvial/very wet forest), Wetland (90%; fen/transition mire/spring)
Land-use Agriculture (20%), Not utilized (80%)

■ Birds

The density of *Acrocephalus paludicola* at this site is the highest known in Europe. Breeding species of global conservation concern that do not meet IBA criteria: *Crex crex* (frequent).

Species		Season	Year	Pop min	Pop max	Acc	Criteria
Acrocephalus paludicola	Aquatic Warbler	B	1996	940	1,550	B	A1, B2

■ Protection status
National None **International** None

■ Conservation issues

Threats Agricultural intensification/expansion (C), Drainage (B)

The main threat is nutrient pollution by agricultural and industrial waste-water inflows which result from drainage and land 'reclamation'. This is potentially reversible, at least in part. It is planned to create a protected area by joining this site to Sporovsky Zakaznik (see Sporovo, 014). Studies of species diversity and census-work have been carried out with financial support from the Michael Otto Foundation for Environmental Protection.

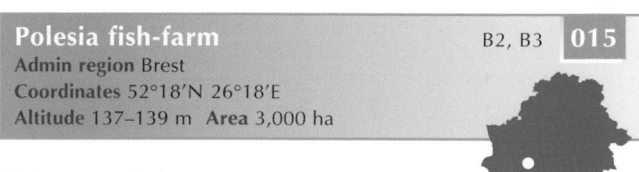

Sporovo
A1, B2 **014**
Admin region Brest
Coordinates 52°23′N 25°20′E
Altitude 142–144 m **Area** 8,200 ha

■ Site description

A seasonally flooded riverine fen. Vegetation is dominated by wet meadows, sedge communities and *Salix* thickets. The area is used for haymaking and cattle-grazing.

Habitats Forest and woodland (13%; alluvial/very wet forest), Grassland (53%; humid grassland), Wetland (30%; standing fresh water; fen/transition mire/spring), Artificial landscape (4%; other urban/industrial areas)
Land-use Agriculture (20%), Not utilized (80%)

■ Birds

Species		Season	Year	Pop min	Pop max	Acc	Criteria
Crex crex	Corncrake	B	1996	30	50	C	A1
Acrocephalus paludicola	Aquatic Warbler	B	1996	420	570	A	A1, B2

An extensive area of suitable breeding habitat for *Acrocephalus paludicola*. Significant proportion (≥1%) of national population breeding at site: *Botaurus stellaris* (10–15 pairs). The site has a high species richness overall.

■ Protection status
National Partial **International** None
2,000 ha of IBA covered by Zakaznik (Sporovsky, 11,300 ha).

■ Conservation issues

Threats Abandonment/reduction of land management (A), Drainage (B), Dredging/canalization (B), Natural events (B)

The main threats come from the changes in water regime over most of the site following drainage for agricultural improvement, and from shrub encroachment. Funding is being sought for the development of a management plan and a protected area. Studies of species diversity and census-work have been carried out with financial support from the Michael Otto Foundation for Environmental Protection.

Polesia fish-farm
B2, B3 **015**
Admin region Brest
Coordinates 52°18′N 26°18′E
Altitude 137–139 m **Area** 3,000 ha

■ Site description

One of the largest complexes of fish-ponds, together with a reservoir, in the Pripyat (Polesia) region. The fish-ponds are stocked with carp *Cyprinus carpio* and are highly productive, with a high cover of water-fringe vegetation.

Habitats Wetland (95%; standing fresh water; water-fringe vegetation), Artificial landscape (5%; other urban/industrial areas)
Land-use Fisheries/aquaculture (95%), Hunting (5%)

■ Birds

Species	Season	Year	Pop min	Pop max	Acc	Criteria
Botaurus stellaris Bittern	B	1995	40	50	A	B2
Aythya ferina Pochard	B	1995	150	200	A	B3

The site holds large concentrations of breeding, moulting and post-breeding waterbirds, especially fish-eating species. Breeding species of global conservation concern that do not meet IBA criteria: *Haliaeetus albicilla* (1 pair). Significant proportion (≥1%) of national population breeding at site: *Aythya ferina* (150–200 pairs). Important non-breeding visitors include *Ciconia nigra* (50–70 birds).

■ Protection status
National None **International** None

■ Conservation issues

Threats Aquaculture/fisheries (A)

The main threat comes from the reduction in fish production due to the current economic crisis, resulting in a decreased area of water and reduced food supply for fish-eating birds. The species composition and numbers of birds are relatively well studied. Although unprotected, the fish-farm is closed to the public and there is no disturbance of nesting birds during the breeding period.

Zvanets A1, B2, B3 016
Admin region Brest
Coordinates 52°05′N 24°50′E
Altitude 145–146 m **Area** 15,000 ha

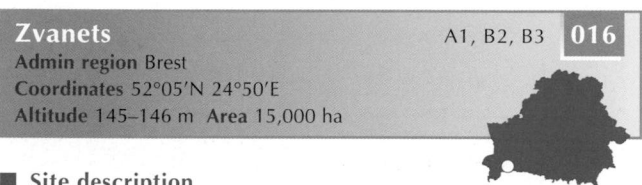

■ Site description
The largest intact fen in Europe, with numerous sand islands. The vegetation is dominated by various sedges *Carex* and reed *Phragmites*. Part of the area is used for haymaking.

Habitats Forest and woodland (13%; alluvial/very wet forest), Grassland (9%; steppe/dry calcareous grassland), Wetland (78%; fen/transition mire/spring)
Land-use Agriculture (20%), Nature conservation/research (50%), Not utilized (30%)

■ Birds

Species	Season	Year	Pop min	Pop max	Acc	Criteria
Circus cyaneus Hen Harrier	B	1996	5	10	C	B2
Circus pygargus Montagu's Harrier	B	1996	10	20	C	B3
Porzana porzana Spotted Crake	B	1996	200	1,000	C	B3
Crex crex Corncrake	B	1996	50	100	C	A1
Grus grus Crane	B	1996	20	30	B	B2
Asio flammeus Short-eared Owl	B	1996	10	20	C	B2
Locustella naevia Grasshopper Warbler	B	1996	100	200	C	B3
Acrocephalus paludicola Aquatic Warbler	B	1996	3,000	4,000	A	A1, B2
Acrocephalus schoenobaenus Sedge Warbler	B	1996	4,000	8,000	B	B3

The most extensive area of suitable breeding habitat in Belarus for *Acrocephalus paludicola*, *Asio flammeus* and *Circus pygargus*. Breeding species of global conservation concern that do not meet IBA criteria: *Gallinago media* (min. 5 pairs). Significant proportion (≥1%) of national population breeding at site: *Botaurus stellaris* (10–20 pairs). There are also good numbers and a wide diversity of other important mire-breeding species such as *Circus cyaneus* (5–10 pairs) and *Grus grus* (20–30 pairs).

■ Protection status
National Partial **International** None
10,460 ha of IBA covered by Zakaznik (Zvanets, 10,460 ha).

■ Conservation issues

Threats Construction/impact of dyke/dam/barrage (B), Drainage (B), Dredging/canalization (B)

The main threat is the ongoing change in dominant vegetation from sedge to reed, probably caused by the increasing water-levels which have followed the construction of embankments around the fen, although this requires further study. Studies of species diversity and census-work have been carried out with financial support from the Michael Otto Foundation for Environmental Protection.

Mid-Pripyat A1, A4i, A4iii, B1i, B2, B3 017
Admin region Brest, Gomel
Coordinates 52°09′N 27°00′E
Altitude 120–150 m **Area** 100,000 ha

■ Site description
A seasonally flooded lowland river valley, comprising the largest tract of natural alluvial landscape to remain in Europe. Alluvial forests of *Quercus*, wet meadows and fens are predominant. Land-uses include haymaking, cattle-grazing, angling and hunting.

Habitats Forest and woodland (38%; alluvial/very wet forest), Grassland (42%; steppe/dry calcareous grassland; humid grassland), Wetland (20%; standing fresh water; fen/transition mire/spring)
Land-use Agriculture (20%), Fisheries/aquaculture (10%), Forestry (5%), Hunting (5%), Not utilized (60%)

■ Birds

Species	Season	Year	Pop min	Pop max	Acc	Criteria
Botaurus stellaris Bittern	B	1989	300	—	B	B2
Ciconia nigra Black Stork	B	1995	50	70	B	A4i, B1i
Ciconia ciconia White Stork	B	1995	300	500	B	B2
Anser fabalis Bean Goose	P	1995	2,000	10,000	A	A4i, B1i
Anser albifrons White-fronted Goose	P	1995	10,000	30,000	B	A4i, B1i
[1] *Anser erythropus* Lesser White-fronted Goose	P	1995	50	250	C	B1i
Anas penelope Wigeon	P	1995	10,000	20,000	B	A4i, B1i
Anas strepera Gadwall	B	1995	600	800	B	A4i, B1i
Anas platyrhynchos Mallard	B	1995	10,000	15,000	B	B1i
Anas querquedula Garganey	B	1995	6,000	10,000	B	A4i, B1i, B2
[1] *Aythya ferina* Pochard	B	1995	1,500	2,000	B	B3
[1] *Aythya nyroca* Ferruginous Duck	B	1995	50	150	C	A1
Circus pygargus Montagu's Harrier	B	1995	50	—	—	B3
Porzana porzana Spotted Crake	B	1996	700	—	—	B3
Porzana parva Little Crake	B	1996	300	—	—	B3
Crex crex Corncrake	B	1995	500	2,000	C	A1, B2
Gallinago media Great Snipe	B	1995	50	—	—	A1
Limosa limosa Black-tailed Godwit	B	1986	500	1,000	C	B2
Tringa totanus Redshank	B	1986	1,000	—	B	A4i, B1i, B2
Larus minutus Little Gull	B	1996	50	100	B	B2
[1] *Sterna albifrons* Little Tern	B	1986	150	250	B	B2
Chlidonias niger Black Tern	B	1995	500	1,000	B	A4i, B1i
Chlidonias leucopterus White-winged Black Tern	B	1995	3,000	7,000	B	A4i, B1i
Bubo bubo Eagle Owl	B	1990	10	20	B	B2
Strix aluco Tawny Owl	R	1990	300	—	B	B3
Asio flammeus Short-eared Owl	R	1996	30	60	B	B2
Coracias garrulus Roller	B	1986	30	—	B	B2
Picus viridis Green Woodpecker	B	1995	100	—	—	B2
Riparia riparia Sand Martin	B	1986	20,000	30,000	B	B2
Acrocephalus paludicola Aquatic Warbler	B	1996	500	1,200	B	A1, B2

1. Only present in some years.

The largest area of habitat in Belarus for breeding waterbirds, and for migrating wildfowl and waders in spring. The site regularly supports 20,000 or more waterbirds for each of three sets of species: breeding waterbirds, breeding gulls and terns, and migrating waterbirds.

■ Protection status
National Partial **International** None
6,733 ha of IBA covered by Zakaznik (Nizovie Jaseldy, 6,733 ha). 1,000 ha of IBA covered by Zakaznik (Nizovie Sluchi, 7,200 ha). 3,440 ha of IBA covered by Zakaznik (Prostyr, 3,440 ha). 288 ha of IBA covered by Zakaznik (Ustie Lani, 288 ha).

■ Conservation issues

Threats Agricultural intensification/expansion (B), Aquaculture/fisheries (C), Construction/impact of dyke/dam/barrage (A), Drainage (B), Unsustainable exploitation (C)

The main threats come from the construction of embankments along both sides of the flood-plain (in order to reduce spring flooding of land), the agricultural improvement of farmland, and the drainage of unprotected parts of the site. About 20% of the flood-plain area is currently protected, and a further Zakaznik is proposed within the site (Yastrebel, 4,000 ha). Investigations aimed at increasing the proportion of the site under protection will be carried out with the financial support from the Michael Otto Foundation for Environmental Protection; it is planned to protect the whole site as a single Zakaznik. Some of the most important fish-spawning areas in Belarus are situated at this site.

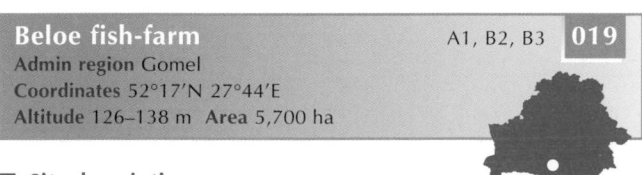

Olmany   B2, B3 018
Admin region Brest
Coordinates 51°50′N 27°15′E
Altitude 128–144 m **Area** 94,000 ha

■ Site description

The largest tract of mire in Polesia. The landscape is dominated by transition mires, fens and raised bogs, in which there are wooded 'islands' of conifer and *Quercus*. Land-uses include forestry, cattle-grazing and hunting.

Habitats Forest and woodland (40%; native coniferous forest; mixed forest), Wetland (44%; raised bog; fen/transition mire/spring), Artificial landscape (16%; other urban/industrial areas)
Land-use Agriculture, Forestry (15%), Hunting (5%), Military (80%)

■ Birds

Species	Season	Year	Pop min	Pop max	Acc	Criteria
Ciconia nigra Black Stork	B	1995	30	50	B	B2
Circaetus gallicus Short-toed Eagle	B	1995	8	15	B	B2
Circus pygargus Montagu's Harrier	B	1995	10	20	B	B3
Grus grus Crane	B	1995	30	40	B	B2
Strix aluco Tawny Owl	R	1995	Common	—	B3

The largest area of breeding habitat for *Circaetus gallicus* in Polesia. Breeding species of global conservation concern that do not meet IBA criteria: *Crex crex* (50–100 pairs).

■ Protection status

National None **International** None

■ Conservation issues

Threats Abandonment/reduction of land management (U), Agricultural intensification/expansion (U), Burning of vegetation (A), Deforestation (commercial) (A), Drainage (B), Selective logging/cutting (U)

The main threats are forest-fire, overgrazing of accessible forest islands, drainage of surrounding areas, and timber-felling. The site is a proposed State Landscape Reserve (Zakaznik), following support from the MacArthur Foundation and the Ministry of Natural Resources. Most of the site is included in the Polessky Military Aviation Range.

Beloe fish-farm   A1, B2, B3 019
Admin region Gomel
Coordinates 52°17′N 27°44′E
Altitude 126–138 m **Area** 5,700 ha

■ Site description

An extensive complex of large and small fish-ponds surrounded by *Quercus* forests.

Habitats Forest and woodland (60%; broadleaved deciduous forest), Wetland (40%; standing fresh water; water-fringe vegetation)
Land-use Fisheries/aquaculture (50%), Forestry (20%), Not utilized (30%)

■ Birds

Species	Season	Year	Pop min	Pop max	Acc	Criteria
Botaurus stellaris Bittern	B	1989	40	60	A	B2
Aythya ferina Pochard	B	1989	500	600	A	B3
Aythya nyroca Ferruginous Duck	B	1991	—	22	A	A1

Waterbirds occur at high densities, especially fish-eating species. Breeding species of global conservation concern that do not meet IBA criteria: *Haliaeetus albicilla* (1 pair), *Crex crex* (min. 10 pairs). Important non-breeding visitors include *Ciconia nigra* (40–50 birds).

■ Protection status

National None **International** None

■ Conservation issues

Threats Aquaculture/fisheries (A), Deforestation (commercial) (C)

The main threat comes from the reduction in fish production due to the current economic crisis, resulting in a decreased area of water and reduced food supply for fish-eating bird species.

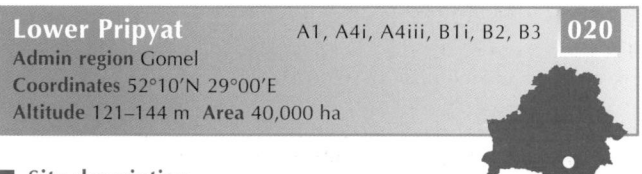

Lower Pripyat   A1, A4i, A4iii, B1i, B2, B3 020
Admin region Gomel
Coordinates 52°10′N 29°00′E
Altitude 121–144 m **Area** 40,000 ha

■ Site description

A large river flood-plain with moderate but long-lasting spring floods. Wet meadows, dry grasslands and alluvial *Quercus* forests predominate in one of the most extensive alluvial landscapes to be protected in Europe.

Habitats Forest and woodland (23%; alluvial/very wet forest), Grassland (72%; steppe/dry calcareous grassland; humid grassland), Wetland (5%; standing fresh water)
Land-use Agriculture (30%), Hunting (5%), Nature conservation/research (50%), Not utilized (10%), Urban/industrial/transport (5%)

■ Birds

Species	Season	Year	Pop min	Pop max	Acc	Criteria
Ciconia nigra Black Stork	B	1993	30	40	B	B2
Ciconia ciconia White Stork	B	1990	100	150	B	B2
Anas platyrhynchos Mallard	B	1993	3,000	7,000	A	B1i
Anas querquedula Garganey	B	1993	3,000	5,000	B	B2
Crex crex Corncrake	B	1986	1,100	—	B	A1, B2
Sterna albifrons Little Tern	B	1994	200	300	B	A4i, B1i, B2
Chlidonias niger Black Tern	B	1995	200	—	C	B2
Strix aluco Tawny Owl	R	1995	100	—	—	B3
Riparia riparia Sand Martin	B	1986	20,000	30,000	B	B2
Luscinia luscinia Thrush Nightingale	B	1995	3,000	5,000	B	B3
Acrocephalus schoenobaenus Sedge Warbler	B	1995	3,000	10,000	B	B3
Lanius collurio Red-backed Shrike	B	1993	500	—	—	B2

One of the largest concentrations in Belarus of breeding waterbirds, and one of the most significant staging areas for geese, ducks and waders on spring migration. The site regularly supports 20,000 or more waterbirds. Significant proportion (≥1%) of national population breeding at site: *Botaurus stellaris* (min. 100 pairs), *Aythya ferina* (70–150 pairs).

■ Protection status

National Partial **International** None
6,500 ha of IBA covered by Zapovednik (Polesski Radio-Ecological, 211,500 ha).

■ Conservation issues

Threats Agricultural intensification/expansion (B), Drainage (B), Dredging/canalization (B)

The main threat is drainage of the unprotected flood-plain area. About 30% of the flood-plain area of the site occurs within the zone of high radioactive fallout from Chernobyl, and research is being carried out only in this area. Some of the most important fish-spawning areas in Belarus are situated at this site.

Flood-plain of Sozh river A1, B2 021

Admin region Gomel
Coordinates 52°40′N 31°05′E
Altitude 130–132 m **Area** 13,400 ha

Species		Season	Year	Pop min	Pop max	Acc	Criteria
Anas querquedula	Garganey	B	1987	400	600	B	B2
Crex crex	Corncrake	B	1987	300	500	B	A1
Gallinago media	Great Snipe	B	1996	60	120	B	A1, B2
Chlidonias niger	Black Tern	B	1987	150	500	B	B2
Alcedo atthis	Kingfisher	B	1996	20	30	B	B2

■ Site description
An extensive river flood-plain, briefly flooded in spring, mainly comprising *Salix* thickets, wet meadows and dry grasslands. Land-uses include haymaking, cattle-grazing, hunting and fishing.

Habitats Forest and woodland (25%; alluvial/very wet forest), Grassland (75%; steppe/dry calcareous grassland; humid grassland), Wetland (25%; standing fresh water)
Land-use Agriculture (20%), Not utilized (80%)

■ Birds
An important wetland for breeding waterbirds and for migrating geese and ducks in spring.

■ Protection status
National None **International** None

■ Conservation issues
Threats Agricultural intensification/expansion (C), Aquaculture/fisheries (C), Drainage (B)

The main threat comes from drainage of the flood-plain. Few field investigations have been carried out.

REFERENCES

BIRYUKOV, V., KOZLOV, V. AND KUZMENKO, V. (1993) [Role of Elnya raised bog (Vitebsk region, Belorussia) as natural reservation of waterfowl and wetland birds.] *The Ring* 15(1–2): 348–350. (In Russian.)

BYRYOUKOV, V. N. (1990) [Breeding records of Slavonian Grebe in Belarus lake-land.] [*Protected Animals of Belarus*] 1: 25. (In Russian.)

BYSHNEV, I. I., STAVROVSKY, D. D., PIKULIK, M. M. AND TISHECHKIN, A. K. (1996) *Atlas of the ground vertebral animals.* Minsk : Nauka and Technika. (In Russian and English.)

CHERKAS, N. D. (1996) *Data on nesting of White-tailed Sea Eagles Haliaeetus albicilla in Polessie (Byelorussia).* Berlin, London and Paris: World Working Group on Birds of Prey (WWGBP).

DEMYANCHIK, V. T. (1990) [Distribution and estimated of Great Grey Owl in Western Belarus.] [*Protected Animals of Belarus*] 1: 9–18. (In Russian.)

DOLBIK, M. S. AND DOROFEEV, A. M. (1978) [*Rare and endangered birds of Belarus*]. Minsk. (In Russian.)

FEDYUSHIN, A. V. AND DOLBIK, M. S. (1967) [*Birds of Belarus*]. Minsk. (In Russian.)

FLADE, M., KOZULIN, A. AND TISHECHKIN, A., EDS. (1997) Distribution of Aquatic Warbler in Europe. Unpublished.

GRICHIK, V. V. AND TISHECHKIN, A. K. (1993) [New data on rare and poor-known bird species in upper Shchara River (Brest region).] [*Protected Animals of Belarus*] 3: 7–9. (In Russian.)

GRICHIK, V., IVANOVSKY, V. AND VOROBIOV, V. (1997) [Common Crane in Belarus]. Unpublished.

GRIMMETT, R. F. A. AND JONES, T. A., EDS. (1989) *Important bird areas in Europe.* Cambridge, UK: International Council for Bird Preservation (Techn. Publ. 3).

HEATH, M. F. AND BORGGREVE, C. (2000) *BirdLife International/EBCC European Bird Database 1998.* Cambridge, UK: BirdLife International.

IVANOVSKY, V. V. (1982) Ecology of the Golden Eagle (*Aquila chrysaetus*) in Northern Byelorussia. *XVIII Congressus Internationalis Ornithologicus. Abstracts of syposia and poster presentations*: 2111. Moscow.

IVANOVSKY, V. V. (1985) [Rare raptorial birds of Belarus lake-land and the ways of their conservation.] Moscow: Institute of Nature Conservation. (doctoral thesis). (In Russian.)

IVANOVSKY, V. V. (1990) [Status of White-tailed Eagle in Belarus.] [*Protected Animals of Belarus*] 2: 25–28. (In Russian.)

KOZULIN, A. V. (1990) [Isolated breeding colony of Smew in Pripyat Polessie.] [*Protected Animals of Belarus*] 2: 28–29. (In Russian.)

KOZULIN, A. V. (1997) Habitat area changes, population estimates and recent trends of waterfowl in Belarus. Unpublished.

KOZULIN, A. V., FLADE, M. AND TISHECHKIN, A. K., EDS. (1997) [Distribution and numbers of Aquatic Warbler in Belarus.] Unpublished. (In Russian.)

KOZULIN, A. V. AND GRICHIK, V. V. (1996) Isolated breeding population of Smew *Mergus albellus* in southern Belarus. *Vogelwelt* 117: 87–88.

KOZULIN, A. V. AND PAVLUSHCHIK, T. E. (1996) The influence of habitat variables and interspecific relations on waterbirds communities of lowland glacial lakes. Unpublished.

KOZULIN, A. AND FLADE, M. (1997) Habitat and status of Aquatic Warbler in Belarus. Unpublished.

KOZULIN, A., NIKIFOROV, M. AND PAREIKO, O. A. (1987) Migration of geese in Belarus. *Bulletin of Goose Study Group.*

NAUMCHICK, A. V. (1987) [Gulls and terns of Belarus – distribution, biology and economic significance.] Moscow: Institute of Nature Conservation (doctoral thesis). (In Russian.)

NIKIFOROV, M. E., KOZULIN, A. V., GRITCHIK, V. V. AND TISHECHKIN, A. K. (1997) [*Birds of Belarus in the edge of XXI century.*] Minsk: Korolev. (In Russian.)

NIKIFOROV, M. E., KOZULIN, A. V. AND YAMINSKY, B. V. (1991) [New data on breeding of Ringed Plover, Oystercatcher and Terek Sandpiper in Belarus]. *Ornithology (Moscow)* 5: 128–129. (In Russian.)

NIKIFOROV, M., SKURATOVICH, A. AND TISHECHKIN, A. (1996) Polessky Military Range – the most significant wetland reserve of Europe. Third International Technical–Practical Conference 'Productive Reuse of Former Military Sites: Environmental and Economic Aspects of Demilitarization', Minsk, September 23–27 1996 (unpublished).

TISHECHKIN, A. K. (1996) *The Osprey Pandion haliaetus in Berezinsky Biosphere Reserve, Belarus.* World Working Group on Birds of Prey.

TISHECHKIN, A. K. AND IVANOVSKY, V. V. (1992) Status and breeding performance of the Osprey *Pandion haliaetus* in northern Byelorussia. *Ornis Fennica* 69: 149–154.

TISHECHKIN, A. K. AND KOZULIN, A. V. (1993) [Data on some bird species in Stviga River basin.] [*Protected Animals of Belarus*] 3: 9–11. (In Russian.)

TUCKER, G. M. AND HEATH, M. F. (1994) *Birds in Europe: their conservation status.* Cambridge, UK: BirdLife International (BirdLife Conservation Series no. 3).

BELGIUM

ANNY ANSELIN, JEAN-PAUL JACOB AND WILLEM VAN DEN BOSSCHE

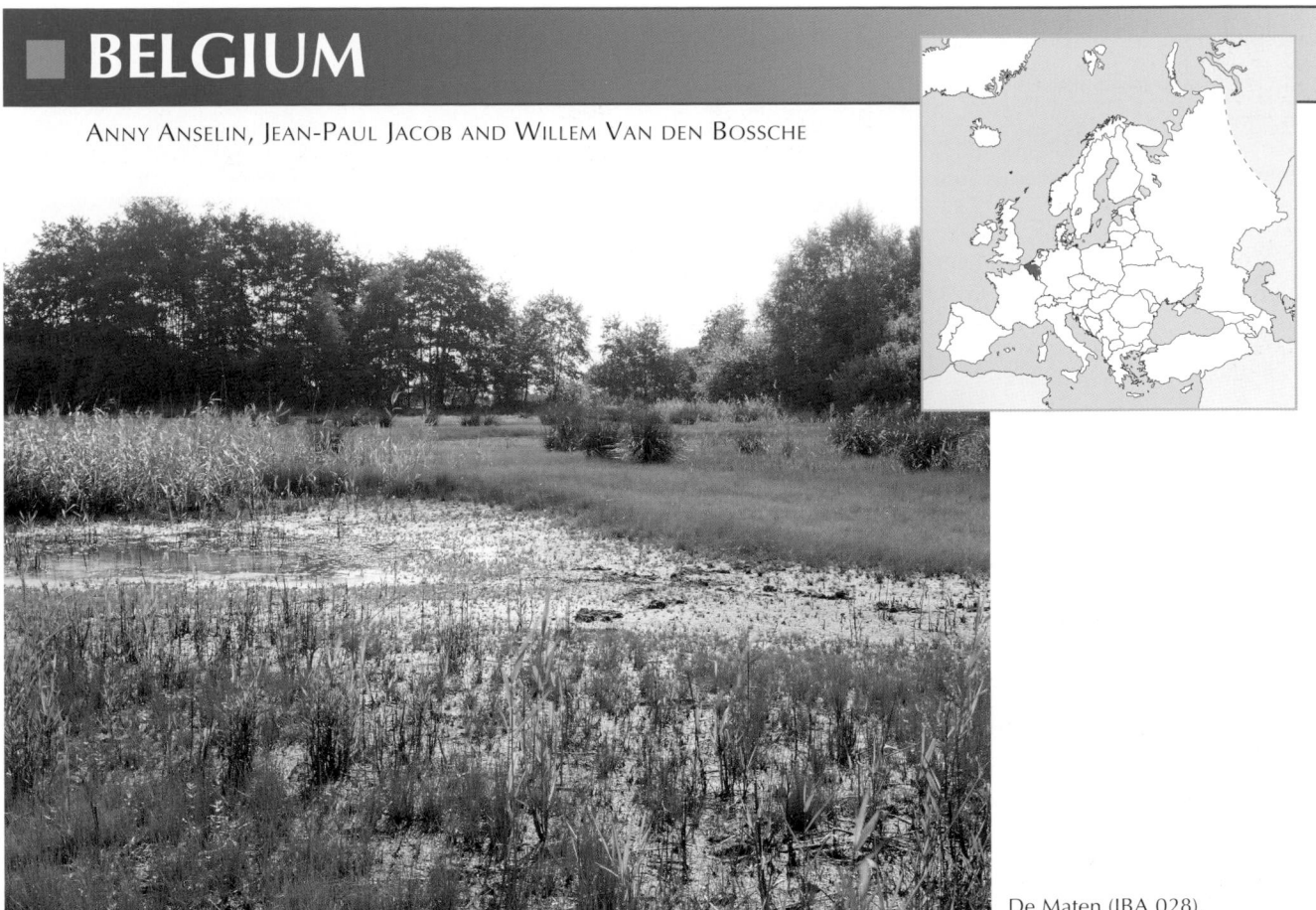

De Maten (IBA 028).
(PHOTO: LUC NAGELS/BNVR/RNOB)

GENERAL INTRODUCTION

Belgium has a surface area of 30,521 km^2 and an average population density of 324 people per km^2. Urban zones occupy a considerable part of the country, in particular in the northern half. Intensive agriculture is prominent throughout the north, whilst in the south larger areas are covered by forests. Belgium can be divided into three regions according to altitude, from west to east: a lowland area (0–50 m) extending from the coast to the central plateau; the medium-altitude zone (50–200 m) extending to the riverine lowlands of Sambre and Meuse; and the upland zone to the east (highest point 694 m).

Belgium has 48 Important Bird Areas (IBAs) covering 6,483 km^2, which is more than 20% of the land area of the country (Table 1,

Map 1). Of these, 28 IBAs are in the Flemish Region (Vlaams Gewest), 19 are in the Walloon Region and one in the Belgian coastal zone, which is federal territory.

The first pan-European IBA inventory (Grimmett and Jones 1989) identified 41 IBAs for Belgium, compared to 48 in this current inventory. The changes can be explained by the division of two sites into four and the identification of five new sites (Table 1). The division concerns Vlaamse Banken en Westkust (site BE001 in the previous inventory) which has been split into two IBAs: Trapegeer-Stroombank (001) and Westkust (002); and the Dyle valley (formerly site BE023) which falls within both the Flemish and Walloon Regions, and is treated separately as sites De Dijlevallei (016) and Vallée de la Dyle (031). The total IBA area has decreased but the division guarantees better protection. The new sites are four

IBA code	1989 code	International/National name	Administrative region	Area (ha)	Criteria (see p. 11)
Table 1. Summary of Important Bird Areas in Belgium.				48 IBAs covering 6,483 km^2	
001	BE001	Trappegeer-Stroombank	Belgian Federal Government	17,000	A4i, B1i, C3
002	BE001	Westkust	Vlaams Gewest	1,415	C7
003	BE002	IJzervallei–De Blankaart	Vlaams Gewest	5,100	A4i, B1i, B2, C2, C3, C6
004	—	Voorhaven Zeebrugge and Baai van Heist	Vlaams Gewest	230	A4i, B1i, C2
005	BE003	Polderkomplex	Vlaams Gewest	9,349	A4i, A4iii, B1i, B2, C2, C3, C4, C6
006	BE004	Zwin	Vlaams Gewest	1,820	B1i, B3, C3, C6
007	BE005	Krekengebied	Vlaams Gewest	780	A4i, B1i, B2, B3, C2, C3, C6
008	—	Bourgoyen-Ossemeersen	Vlaams Gewest	213	B1i, C3
009	—	Gentse Kanaalzone	Vlaams Gewest	700	B1i, C3
010	BE006	Durme en Middenloop van de Schelde	Vlaams Gewest	7,923	A4i, B1i, C3, C6
011	BE007	Schorren en Polders van de Beneden-Schelde	Vlaams Gewest	7,570	A4i, B1i, B3, C2, C3, C6
012	BE008	Kuifeend and Blokkersdijk	Vlaams Gewest	194	A4i, B1i, B3, C2, C3, C6
013	BE010	Kalmthoutse Heide	Vlaams Gewest	2,200	C6
014	BE009	De Maatjes, Wuustwezel Heide en Groot Schietveld	Vlaams Gewest	4,100	C7
015	—	Mechels Rivierengebied, Antwerpen	Vlaams Gewest	2,263	B1i, C3

103

IBA code	1989 code	International/National name	Administrative region	Area (ha)	Criteria (see p. 11)
		Table 1 ... continued. Summary of Important Bird Areas in Belgium.		48 IBAs covering 6,483 km²	
016	BE023	De Dijlevallei	Vlaams Gewest	1,250	C6
017	BE012	Zegge	Vlaams Gewest	91	B1i, C3
018	BE011	Gebieden ten noorden van Turnhout en Ravels	Vlaams Gewest	7,075	B2, C6
019	BE013	Ronde Put	Vlaams Gewest	5,400	C6
020	BE014	Demervallei	Vlaams Gewest	7,010	C6
021	BE015	Vallei van de Zwarte Beek	Vlaams Gewest	8,864	C6
022	BE016	Gebieden gelegen te Peer en Hechtel-Eksel	Vlaams Gewest	10,015	C6
023	BE018	Hamonterheide, Hageven, Buitenheide, Mariahof en Stamprooierbroek	Vlaams Gewest	13,125	C6
024	—	Grensmaas	Vlaams Gewest	2,653	B1i, C3
025	BE017	Gebieden gelegen te Houthalen-Helchteren en Meeuwen-Gruitrode	Vlaams Gewest	2,798	C6
026	BE019	Vijverkomplex van Midden Limburg	Vlaams Gewest	2,560	C6
027	BE020	Bokrijk	Vlaams Gewest	800	C6
028	BE021	De Maten	Vlaams Gewest	600	C6
029	BE022	Mechelse Heide en de Vallei van de Ziepbeek	Vlaams Gewest	2,350	C6
030	BE024	Bassin de la Haine	Région Wallonne	13,715	C6
031	BE023	Vallée de la Dyle	Région Wallonne	1,334	C7
032	BE025	Entre-Sambre-et-Meuse	Région Wallonne	83,866	A1, C1, C2, C6
033	BE026	Haute Meuse	Région Wallonne	7,700	C6
034	BE027	Croix-Scaille	Région Wallonne	36,610	C6
035	BE029	Daverdisse	Région Wallonne	14,914	B3, C6
036	BE028	Lesse et Lomme	Région Wallonne	22,426	B3, C6
037	BE030	Marche en Famenne	Région Wallonne	5,100	C6
038	BE031	Saint-Hubert	Région Wallonne	16,700	C6
039	BE032	Ochamp-Freux	Région Wallonne	10,900	C7
040	BE033	Malchamps	Région Wallonne	41,638	C6
041	BE035	Vallée de la Lienne	Région Wallonne	8,500	C6
042	BE037	Tailles	Région Wallonne	8,494	C6
043	BE036	Wanne-Logbiermé	Région Wallonne	5,700	C6
044	BE034	Hautes Fagnes/Eifel	Région Wallonne	80,304	A4i, B1i, B1iv, C2, C5, C6
045	BE038	Deux Ourthes	Région Wallonne	34,678	C6
046	BE039	Haute Sûre/Ardenne méridionale	Région Wallonne	89,443	B3, C6
047	BE040	Sinémurienne	Région Wallonne	32,541	C6
048	BE041	Côte Bajocienne	Région Wallonne	8,287	C6

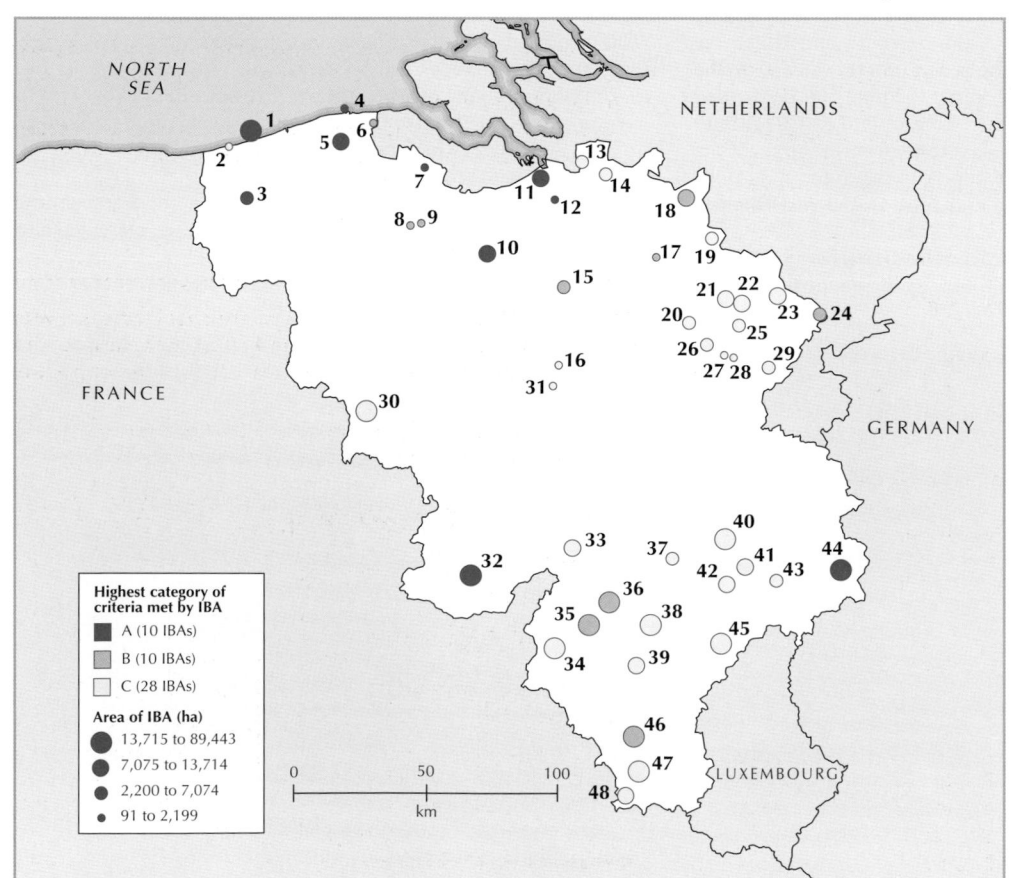

Map 1. Location, area and criteria category of Important Bird Areas in Belgium.

proposed Ramsar Sites and a new proposed Special Protection Area (SPA). Entre-Sambre-et-Meuse (032) and Malchamps (040) significantly increased in surface area. Durme/Middenloop Schelde (010) also increased in surface area to compensate for losses of habitat at Schorren and Polder van de Beneden-Schelde (011) due to harbour development works. Demervallei (020) is larger than mentioned in Grimmett and Jones (1989).

ORNITHOLOGICAL IMPORTANCE

There are 94 species of European conservation concern (SPECs) which regularly breed in Belgium, of which 46 have an unfavourable conservation status in Europe (Tucker and Heath 1994). Entre Sambre et Meuse (032) qualifies under the A1 criterion for its important population of *Crex crex*, a species of global conservation concern (Table 2).

In particular, several of the wetland IBAs in the lowlands are important for wintering waterfowl and geese populations. A total of eight IBAs (001, 004, 005, 007, 010, 011, 012, 044) support more than 1% of the biogeographic population of at least one species (thus meeting criteria A4 and B1), and a further six IBAs (003, 006, 008, 015, 017, 024) support more than 1% of the flyway population of at least one species (criterion B1) (Table 3). Sites with the highest concentrations of wintering and migrating waterfowl are the IJzerbroeken–De Blankaart (003), Poldercomplex (005) (which holds more than 60% of the biogeographic population of wintering *Anser brachyrhynchus*), Durme en Middenloop van de Schelde (010), and Schorren en Polders van de Beneden Schelde (011). A total of 300,000 waterbirds winter yearly in Flanders and an additional 33,000–55,000 waterbirds winter in Wallonia. Particularly important are the wintering numbers of *Anser brachyrhynchus, A. albifrons, Cygnus columbianus, Melanitta nigra, Anas strepera, A. crecca, A. penelope, A. clypeata* and *Aythya ferina*. Additional migratory species meeting the B1 criterion are *Anser fabalis, Anas acuta, Pluvialis apricaria* and *Recurvirostra avosetta*.

Table 2. Important Bird Areas in Belgium that are important for species of global conservation concern (meeting criterion A1).

Species	IBA code
Crex crex Corncrake	032

Table 3. Important Bird Areas in Belgium that support important numbers of one or more congregatory species (i.e. meeting criteria A4 and/or B1). IBAs meeting both criteria A4 and B1 for the species are shown in **bold**. IBAs meeting only criterion B1 for the species concerned, and not A4, are shown in normal type. For key to 'Season', see p. 7.

Species	Season	IBA code
Podiceps cristatus Great Crested Grebe	W	001
Cygnus columbianus Bewick's Swan	W	007
Anser fabalis Bean Goose	W	005
	P	**011**
Anser brachyrhynchus Pink-footed Goose	W	**005**, 006
Anser albifrons White-fronted Goose	W	**005**, 006, **007**
Anser anser Greylag Goose	P	**011**
Anas penelope Wigeon	W	003, **005**, 011
Anas strepera Gadwall	W	010, 011, **012**
	P	017
Anas crecca Teal	W	003, **010**
	P	**011**
Anas acuta Pintail	W	003, 010
Anas clypeata Shoveler	W	003, **005**, 008, 012
	P	**011**, 017
Aythya ferina Pochard	W	015, 024
Grus grus Crane	P	**044**
Recurvirostra avosetta Avocet	B	011
	P	**011**
Pluvialis apricaria Golden Plover	P	005
Larus minutus Little Gull	P	**001**
Sterna sandvicensis Sandwich Tern	B	004
Sterna albifrons Little Tern	B	**004**

Table 4. Species of European conservation concern and species listed on Annex I of the EC Birds Directive with significant breeding populations at IBAs in Belgium (meeting any IBA criteria).

Species [1]	Minimum national breeding population (pairs) [2]	Proportion (%) of national population breeding at all IBAs in Belgium
Botaurus stellaris Bittern	2	100 [3]
Ixobrychus minutus Little Bittern	2	50
Ciconia nigra Black Stork	7	100 [3]
Pernis apivorus Honey Buzzard	300	48
Milvus migrans Black Kite	4	25
Milvus milvus Red Kite	30	87
Circus aeruginosus Marsh Harrier	60	90
Bonasa bonasia Hazel Grouse	80	26
Tetrao tetrix Black Grouse	50	58
Crex crex Corncrake	17	100 [3]
Recurvirostra avosetta Avocet	410	61
Limosa limosa Black-tailed Godwit	865	15
Tringa totanus Redshank	145	45
Larus melanocephalus Mediterranean Gull	123	72
Sterna sandvicensis Sandwich Tern	607	69
Sterna hirundo Common Tern	1,864	86
Sterna albifrons Little Tern	250	100 [3]
Bubo bubo Eagle Owl	20	25
Aegolius funereus Tengmalm's Owl	50	28
Caprimulgus europaeus Nightjar	180	32
Alcedo atthis Kingfisher	250	40
Picus canus Grey-headed Woodpecker	8	100 [3]
Dryocopus martius Black Woodpecker	800	18
Dendrocopos medius Middle Spotted Woodpecker	400	100 [3]
Lullula arborea Woodlark	450	24
Luscinia svecica Bluethroat	1,850	32
Lanius collurio Red-backed Shrike	550	100 [3]

1. Only those species of European conservation concern (see Box 1, p. 12) that meet IBA criteria in Belgium are listed, together with those species listed on Annex I of the EC Birds Directive that fulfil criterion C6 in IBAs in Belgium.
2. Data are taken from the BirdLife/EBCC European Bird Database 1998 (Heath and Borggreve 2000).
3. The percentage of the national population in IBAs exceeds 100%. Usually this is because the national population estimate has not been updated recently whilst the IBA population estimate has been recently updated with new data as a result of comprehensive surveys of IBAs themselves. Also, the individual site count for a species may be the maximum or average over recent years, and summing these may record more birds than are present nationally in any single year.

In addition Voorhaven van Zeebrugge and Baai van Heist (004) holds internationally important breeding numbers of *Sterna albifrons* in the tern colony.

Several species of European conservation concern and species listed on Annex I of the EC Birds Directive have significant populations at IBAs (Table 4).

HABITATS

All terrestrial IBAs contain at least some artificial landscape, with nearly 50% of these having more than half of their surface area covered by this habitat-type. Major artificial landscapes are

Figure 1. Habitats at Important Bird Areas in Belgium (see Appendix 3 for definitions of habitats).

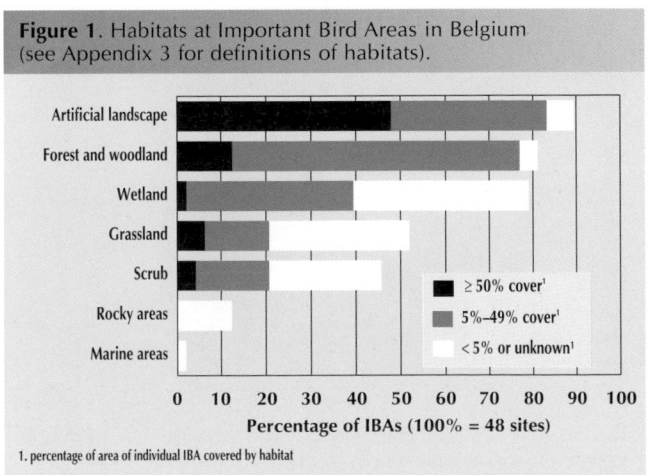

Artificial landscape
Forest and woodland
Wetland
Grassland
Scrub
Rocky areas
Marine areas

≥ 50% cover[1]
5%–49% cover[1]
< 5% or unknown[1]

0 10 20 30 40 50 60 70 80 90 100
Percentage of IBAs (100% = 48 sites)

1. percentage of area of individual IBA covered by habitat

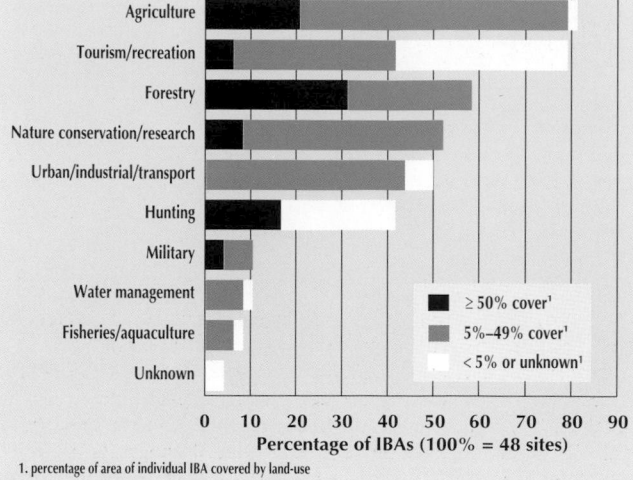

Figure 2. Land-uses at Important Bird Areas in Belgium (see Appendix 3 for definitions of land-uses).

1. percentage of area of individual IBA covered by land-use

intensively used agricultural land and, in Wallonia, large forestry plantations. Over 80% of IBAs have woodland habitat; those with more than 50% of the site area being natural woodland are all situated in Wallonia and are Entre Sambre et Meuse (032), Haute Meuse (033), Daverdisse (035), Saint-Hubert (038), Wanne-Logbiermé (043) and Sinémurienne (047) (Figure 1).

Although nearly 80% of all IBAs have some wetland habitats, these are small, with the exception of Durme en Middenloop van de Schelde (010) which is 80% wetland habitat and Zwin (006) which is 40%. Grassland is present in 50% of IBAs, but only two IBAs have more than 50 % humid grassland: 85 % of IJzervallei–De Blankaart (003) and 60 % of Poldercomplex (005) are humid grassland.

Scrub habitat consists mainly of heathland and dune-scrub vegetation, and is the predominant habitat-type in two IBAs: Houthalen-Helchteren (025) for heathland and Westkust (002) for dune-scrub vegetation. Trapegeer-stroombank (001) is a marine area with sandbanks and shallow water.

IMPACTS ON IBAs – LAND-USE AND THREATS

Over 80% of IBAs are used in some way for agriculture, and in about one quarter of sites it is the dominant land-use, especially for IJzervallei–De Blankaart (003), Poldercomplex (005), Krekengebied (007) and Deux-Ourthes (045), where more than 80% of the surface area of each IBA is used for agriculture.

Nearly 60 % of sites are used for forestry and in 15 IBAs this is the dominant land-use, with forestry activities impacting on more than half of the area of the IBA. All such sites are in Wallonia and include Croix-Scaille (034), Daverdisse (035), Saint-Hubert (038) and Wanne-Logbiermé (043).

Nature conservation is a major land-use in just under 10% of IBAs. In contrast, in nearly 20% of IBAs hunting is the main land-use, especially in Wallonia. Although in only two sites do military activities occur in more than 50% of the area, military areas have

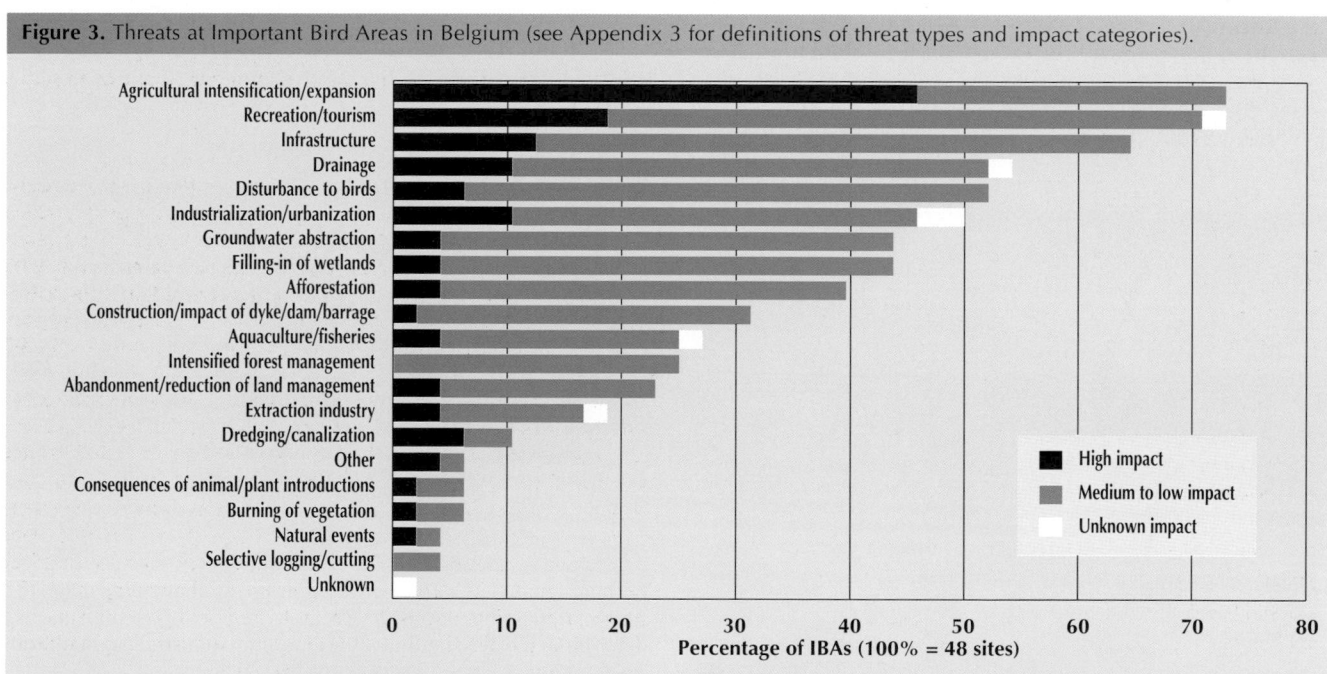

Figure 3. Threats at Important Bird Areas in Belgium (see Appendix 3 for definitions of threat types and impact categories).

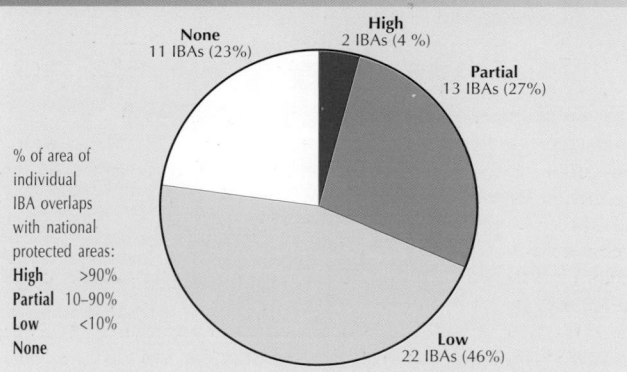

Figure 4. The national protection status of Important Bird Areas in Belgium.

% of area of individual IBA overlaps with national protected areas:
High >90%
Partial 10–90%
Low <10%
None

Total area of overlap between IBA network in Belgium and national protected-area system (see Table 5 for categories) = 757–815 km² (12–13% of total IBA area).

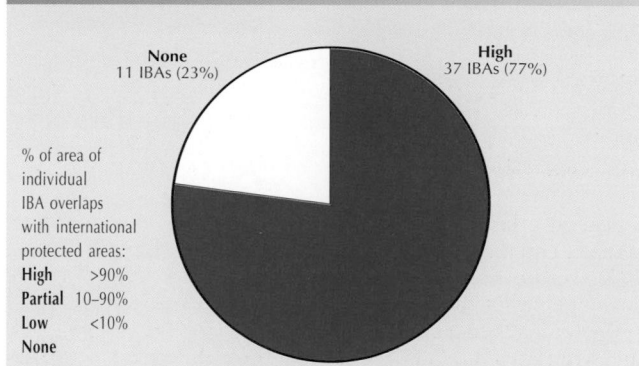

Figure 5. The international protection status of Important Bird Areas in Belgium.

% of area of individual IBA overlaps with international protected areas:
High >90%
Partial 10–90%
Low <10%
None

Total area of overlap between IBA network in Belgium and international protected-area system (see Table 5 for categories) = 5,849 km² (90% of total IBA area).

Table 5. Protection status of Important Bird Areas in Belgium. A tick (✔) indicates that an IBA overlaps with a protected area (to any extent).

IBA International code name	State Nature Reserve	Private Nature Reserve	Nature Park	Ramsar Site	Special Protection Area
	National			International	
001 Trappegeer-Stroombank				✔	
002 Westkust	✔	✔			✔
003 IJzervallei–De Blankaart		✔		✔	✔
004 Voorhaven Zeebrugge and Baai van Heist	✔				
005 Polderkomplex		✔			✔
006 Zwin		✔		✔	✔
007 Krekengebied		✔			✔
008 Bourgoyen-Ossemeersen		✔			
009 Gentse Kanaalzone					
010 Durme en Middenloop van de Schelde	✔	✔			✔
011 Schorren en Polder van de Beneden-Schelde		✔			✔
012 Kuifeend and Blokkersdijk		✔			✔
013 Kalmthoutse Heide	✔			✔	✔
014 De Maatjes, Wuustwezel Heide en Groot Schietveld		✔			✔
015 Mechels Rivierengebied, Antwerpen		✔			
016 De Dijlevallei		✔			✔
017 Zegge		✔			✔
018 Gebieden ten noorden van Turnhout en Ravels		✔			✔
019 Ronde Put		✔			✔
020 Demervallei		✔			✔
021 Vallei van de Zwarte Beek		✔			✔
022 Gebieden gelegen te Peer en Hechtel-Eksel					✔
023 Hamonterheide, Hageven, Buitenheide, Mariahof en Stamprooierbroek		✔			✔
024 Grensmaas		✔			
025 Gebieden gelegen te Houthalen-Helchteren en Meeuwen-Gruitrode					✔
026 Vijverkomplex van Midden Limburg	✔	✔			✔
027 Bokrijk		✔			✔
028 De Maten		✔			✔
029 Mechelse Heide en de Vallei van de Ziepbeek	✔				✔
030 Bassin de la Haine		✔		✔	✔
031 Vallée de la Dyle				✔	✔
032 Entre-Sambre-et-Meuse					✔
033 Haute Meuse		✔			
034 Croix-Scaille		✔			✔
035 Daverdisse		✔			✔
036 Lesse et Lomme		✔			✔
037 Marche en Famenne					
038 Saint-Hubert		✔			
039 Ochamp-Freux					
040 Malchamps		✔			✔
041 Vallée de la Lienne					
042 Tailles		✔			✔
043 Wanne-Logbiermé		✔			
044 Hautes Fagnes/Eifel		✔	✔		✔
045 Deux Ourthes					✔
046 Haute Sûre/Ardenne méridionale		✔			✔
047 Sinémurienne		✔			✔
048 Côte Bajocienne					✔
Total number of IBAs	**6**	**34**	**1**	**6**	**36**

Box 1. International legislation and initiatives that are relevant to site conservation in Belgium (see Appendix 1 for a general description of these agreements).

Global	
Biodiversity Convention	✔
Ramsar Convention	✔
Bonn Convention	✔
World Heritage Convention	✔
MAB Programme	✔

Pan-European	
Bern Convention	✔

Regional	
EC Birds Directive	✔
EC Habitats Directive	✔

✔ Convention ratified/initiative supported
(✔) Convention signed

arable and reseeded landscape, and hedge clearance. The latter two activities are becoming an increasing threat in Wallonia.

Infrastructure, industrialization and urbanization are long-term threats to 50–65 % of IBAs. Schorren en polders van de Beneden Schelde (011) will be largely destroyed by the expansion of harbour facilities. Quarry activities destroy valuable habitats at Entre Sambre et Meuse (032), Haute Meuse (033), Lesse et Lomme (036) and Sinémurienne (047). Recreation and tourism are increasing, affecting over 70% of IBAs, and considered a particularly significant threat to parts of Westkust (002), Kalmthoutse Heide (013) and Haute Fagnes (044). In Belgium most habitats are fragmented, thus the filling-in of wetlands, afforestation and groundwater abstraction have a high impact on these sites.

PROTECTION STATUS

Table 5 summarizes the national and international protection status of Belgian IBAs.

■ National protection

The legislation for the protection of sites is different for Brussels, Wallonia and Flanders. The principal categories of protected areas are: State Nature Reserves, Private Nature Reserves (NGO), Nature Parks (Wallonia only), Forest Reserves, 'Zones humides d'interet biologique' (wetlands of biological importance (Wallonia only)) and Protected Landscape (data on the last three designation-types have not been compiled for this chapter—see 'Analytical methods' section).

Six IBAs are fully or partly protected as State Nature Reserves and 34 as Private Nature Reserves (Table 5); these designations may cover parts of the same IBA. Overall 77% are partially covered by some form of national protected area, but in only 11 IBAs does this cover exceed 10% of the IBA area (Figure 4). Indeed less than 15% of the total surface area of IBAs in Belgium is effectively protected. Protection of a site is generally guaranteed once it has been designated as a green area on the physical planning map. The physical planning map is drawn up by regional governments and determines the designation of the area as an industrial, agricultural, green, military, recreational or residential zone.

■ International protection

Belgium is party to several international initiatives (Box 1). It has also signed the Benelux agreement on nature and landscape conservation. Thirty-six IBAs are designated as Special Protection Areas (SPAs) under the EC Birds Directive and six as Ramsar Sites (five of which are also SPAs). Seven IBAs are proposed SPAs but have not yet been designated (015, 033, 037, 038, 039, 041, 043).

Although 77% of IBAs have some form of international protection (Figure 5) the actual protection of the areas is far from adequate. The main problems are the lack of specific protection measures, in particular habitat protection, and the absence of complete management strategies for the sites. In most SPAs only certain habitats are legally protected within the boundaries of the area, and often these habitats represent only a small percentage of the total IBA area (with the exception of deciduous woodland), and are insufficiently protected. All but 12 IBAs are SPAs and thus are part of the Natura 2000 network of the EU. In Flanders, more than 50% of the area of the IBAs is proposed as a Site of Community Importance, whilst in Wallonia this is less than 5%.

in general a high conservation value, especially for heathland habitats. Houthalen-Helchteren (025), Vallei van de Zwarte Beek (021), Haute Fagne-Eifel (044), Marche en Famenne (037), Sinémurienne (047) are the most important heathland sites.

Figure 3 summarizes the key threats and impacts on IBAs. Intensive agricultural methods are the main threat to bird species in the majority of IBAs, with a high impact in nearly 50% of sites. Throughout Belgium this includes the intensive use of manure, increased fragmentation, drainage, transformation of grassland to

Grasslands in river valleys (potential *Crex crex* habitat), as well as historical polder grasslands (key wintering sites for important geese populations), are still insufficiently protected. Harbour development threatens several areas and although compulsory land compensation is foreseen by the EC Birds Directive, it is becoming increasingly difficult to find such zones of an equal ornithological value.

CONSERVATION ISSUES

- Rare and vulnerable breeding birds are monitored throughout Belgium. A monitoring project for common birds is running in Wallonia and Brussels, while several local projects take place in Flanders. Scientific research and monitoring of wintering and migrating waterfowl populations (including geese) is carried out in the whole country.
- Several IBAs are included within the framework of the 'Ecologisch Impulsgebied', an integrated conservation and development project. This initiative, launched by the Flemish Region, aims to harmoniously combine nature conservation and other land-uses. Several zones within SPAs are subject to management agreements with local farmers, while others are being bought by the Flemish Region and managed as nature reserves. The future of many geese and wader populations on farmed landscapes depend on the success of such initiatives. This affects IBAs 003, 016, 018, 020, 021 and 026.
- For a site to be recognized as a nature reserve by the government, a management plan has to be drawn up. Management plans exist only for small parts of the IBAs protected as reserves. For some of these IBAs overall management plans are currently being developed.
- In Wallonia several local forest management plans are being implemented.
- Agri-environmental agreements take place within the framework of landscape conservation and restoration.
- Subsidies from regional governments, and LIFE funds from the European Union, are increasingly important for the acquisition and management of nature reserves.
- Regional governments are supporting monitoring projects for species and sites.

ANALYTICAL METHODS

- Counts of passage birds are in most cases given as maxima for the period 1990–1996.

- Waterfowl counts are good quality, the range is given for the 1990–1996 period. For geese, the figures for wintering data are not confined to the limits of the IBA, but to the whole east coast polder area.
- Most data on breeding birds are from the period 1993–1996/1997. Data from terns and plovers in the Voorhaven Zeebrugge and Baai van Heist (004) are maxima for the period 1990–1999.
- All key species are covered by the IBA inventory.
- Assigning percentage cover and categories for land-use, habitats and threats in the Walloon region was difficult due to lack of detailed regional information. The figures given are estimates. For the Flemish region, data reflect the 1996 situation and changes may have occurred in the meantime.
- Complete information on all protected sites within IBAs was difficult to obtain, due to lack of an available appropriate database system at the time of data compilation. Therefore data for some national protected-area designations is incomplete.
- Areas of IBAs were calculated using GIS (Geographic Information System) techniques; consequently almost all IBAs areas are different from the figures given for the previous pan-European IBA inventory (Grimmett and Jones 1989).

GLOSSARY

BNVR/RNOB Belgische Natuur- en Vogelreservaten/Réserves Naturelles et Ornithologiques de Belgie, the BirdLife Partner in Belgium.
LIFE an EU funding line (Regulation 1973/92/EEC) which supports EU environmental legislation, including the Birds and Habitats Directives.
MUUM management unit on North Sea mathematical models.
Natura 2000 the name given by the European Commission to the 'coherent ecological network' of Special Protection Areas (SPAs) and Special Areas for Conservation (SACs) that is due to be established within the European Union member states by June 2004, under the Birds and Habitats Directives.
polder a flat area of land, often below sea-level, with an artificially regulated water-regime, having been claimed from the sea or from a lake or river.
SPA Special Protection Area (designated under Article 4 of the EC Birds Directive).

ACKNOWLEDGEMENTS

We would like to thank BNVR/RNOB and all participants in the Centrale Ornithologique Aves, the Bijzondere Broedvogel Project Vlaanderen and the waterfowl counts, who provided a great part of the ornithological data used for this review. We thank Jan Seys and Jeroen Van Waeyenberge (Instituut voor Natuurbehoud) for providing unpublished data on breeding colonies of terns in Zeebrugge.

■ SITE ACCOUNTS

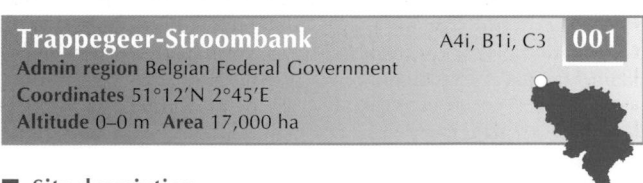

Trappegeer-Stroombank A4i, B1i, C3 **001**
Admin region Belgian Federal Government
Coordinates 51°12′N 2°45′E
Altitude 0–0 m **Area** 17,000 ha

■ Site description
A marine area off the west Belgian coast, with sandbanks that are slightly covered by sea water at all times, and mud- and sandflats that are fully exposed at low tide.

Habitats Marine areas (sea inlet/coastal features), Wetland (mudflat/sandflat)
Land-use Unknown

■ Birds

Species	Season	Year	Pop min	Pop max	Acc	Criteria
Podiceps cristatus Great Crested Grebe	W	—	1,000	—	—	B1i, C3
Larus minutus Little Gull	P	—	—	—	—	A4i, B1i, C3

Other species include passage *Phalacrocorax carbo*, *Sterna sandvicensis*, *S. hirundo*, *S. paradisaea*, *Gavia stellata* (winter >150 birds), *G. arctica*, *Sula bassana*, *Somateria mollissima*, *Uria aalge*, *Alca torda* and *Aythya marila*, and wintering *Melanitta nigra* (1,500–2,000 birds).

■ Protection status
National None **International** High
IBA covered by Vlaamse Banken (Federal) Ramsar Site.

■ Conservation issues

Threats Aquaculture/fisheries

Fishing activities and the illegal setting of fixed nets near the French border should be controlled. Seabirds are regularly counted, studies on benthic communities are taking place and remote-sensing aircraft monitor pollution from ship discharges. The area is a proposed Special Area for Conservation.

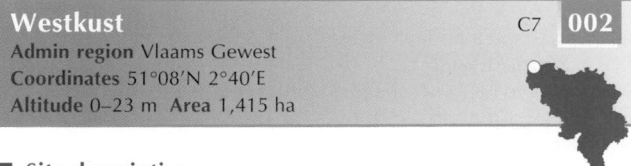

Westkust C7 **002**
Admin region Vlaams Gewest
Coordinates 51°08′N 2°40′E
Altitude 0–23 m **Area** 1,415 ha

■ Site description
The site includes all important dune areas along the western part of the Belgian coast and encompasses the saltmarshes and mudflats of

the River IJzer estuary. Habitats range from sand-beaches, shifting dunes, fixed dunes with herbaceous vegetation, wet and dry depressions with *Lycium barbarum, Salix repens* and wooded areas. The site consists of several large zones separated from each other by urbanized areas.

Habitats Forest and woodland (30%; mixed forest), Scrub (70%; scrub), Wetland (40%; sand-dunes/sand beach)

Land-use Nature conservation/research (90%), Tourism/recreation (10%), Water management (30%)

■ Birds

This is an important staging site for migrating passerines. The site supports nationally important numbers of migrating and wintering waders. *Galerida cristata* breeds at the site (20 pairs, which is 20–25% of the Flemish population).

■ Protection status

National High **International** High

340 ha of IBA covered by State Nature Reserve (De Westhoek, 340 ha). 80 ha of IBA covered by State Nature Reserve (Houtsaegerduinen, 80 ha). 1 ha of IBA covered by Nature Reserve (Doornpanne, 1 ha). 20 ha of IBA covered by Nature Reserve (IJzermonding, 20 ha). 1 ha of IBA covered by Nature Reserve (Ysermonde, 1 ha). 1,415 ha of IBA covered by Special Protection Area (Westkust, 1,415 ha).

■ Conservation issues

Threats Consequences of animal/plant introductions (B), Disturbance to birds (B), Groundwater abstraction (A), Natural events (B), Recreation/tourism (B)

The succession of vegetation within certain dune areas may result in the loss of some habitat-types ('natural event' threat). The entire IBA is designated as a reserve or green area on the physical planning map, and has been protected since 1995 by the 'Dune Decree'. A proposed Site of Community Importance covers 1,400 ha of this site (Duingebieden inclusief IJzermonding en Zwin, 2,891 ha). For most of the zones, a management plan exists or is currently being prepared. A nature development project to restore dune areas is underway in the IJzermonding Reserve. Detailed information on all breeding bird species is collected in the framework of a four-year census project, linked to the study of the effects of nature management measures. Migratory birds are regularly counted.

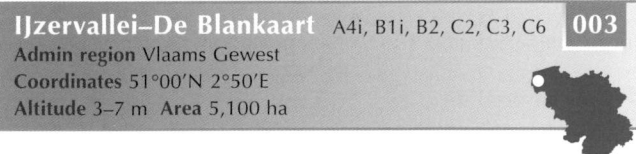

IJzervallei–De Blankaart A4i, B1i, B2, C2, C3, C6 003
Admin region Vlaams Gewest
Coordinates 51°00′N 2°50′E
Altitude 3–7 m **Area** 5,100 ha

■ Site description

A large area of flat and annually (in winter) inundated hay-meadows and grasslands along the IJzer and Handzame rivers. The site includes the Blankaart, a shallow freshwater lake with extensive reedbeds and *Salix* marshes.

Habitats Forest and woodland, Grassland (85%; humid grassland), Wetland (5%; standing fresh water; water-fringe vegetation), Artificial landscape (10%; highly improved reseeded grassland; arable land)

Land-use Agriculture (90%), Hunting (50%), Nature conservation/research (10%), Tourism/recreation (10%), Water management (5%)

■ Birds

Species	Season	Year	Pop min	Pop max	Acc	Criteria
Cygnus columbianus Bewick's Swan	W	—	50	80	A	B2
Anas penelope Wigeon	W	—	25,000	55,000	A	A4i, B1i, C3
Anas crecca Teal	W	—	1,000	5,000	A	B1i, C3
Anas acuta Pintail	W	—	100	900	A	B1i, C3
Anas clypeata Shoveler	W	—	400	850	A	B1i, C3
Circus aeruginosus Marsh Harrier	B	1996	6	8	A	C6
[1] *Chlidonias niger* Black Tern	P	—	—	50	—	C2

1. Daily maximum.

This is an internationally important area for migrating and wintering waders and waterfowl, especially wintering *Anas penelope*. The site is also nationally important for breeding meadow birds.

■ Protection status

National Low **International** High

113 ha of IBA covered by Nature Reserve (Blankaart, 113 ha). 2,160 ha of IBA covered by Ramsar Site (Blankaart, 2,160 ha). 5,100 ha of IBA covered by Special Protection Area (IJzervallei including Blankaart, 5,100 ha).

■ Conservation issues

Threats Agricultural intensification/expansion (A), Construction/impact of dyke/dam/barrage (B), Drainage (A), Dredging/canalization (B), Recreation/tourism (C)

The area is included in the 'Ecologisch Impulsgebied', an integrated conservation and development project. Small zones are managed as nature reserves by BNVR/RNOB and the Flemish Region. A management plan exists for the Blankaart area and several smaller zones. 170 ha (4%) is designated as a green area on the physical planning map of Flanders. Wintering waterbirds have been monitored for the past 15 years and breeding birds intensively for the last five.

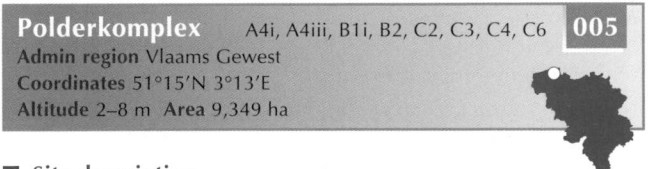

Voorhaven Zeebrugge and Baai van Heist A4i, B1i, C2 004
Admin region Vlaams Gewest
Coordinates 51°21′N 3°11′E
Altitude 0–0 m **Area** 230 ha

■ Site description

An industrial area in Zeebrugge harbour.

Habitats Wetland (sand-dunes/sand beach), Artificial landscape

Land-use Urban/industrial/transport

■ Birds

Species	Season	Year	Pop min	Pop max	Acc	Criteria
Sterna sandvicensis Sandwich Tern	B	—	—	420	—	B1i, C2
Sterna hirundo Common Tern	B	—	1,500	1,800	—	C2
Sterna albifrons Little Tern	B	—	—	1,950	—	A4i, B1i, C2

This is an important tern colony, with the only breeding site for *Sterna albifrons* and *S. sandvicensis* in the country. The area also holds 114 breeding pairs of *Charadrius alexandrinus*.

■ Protection status

National Partial **International** None

45 ha of IBA covered by State Nature Reserve (Baai van Heist, 45 ha).

■ Conservation issues

Threats Industrialization/urbanization

As a result of the development of harbour activities, the available breeding area for terns and plovers has dramatically decreased, while colonization of the (protected) beach area is partly successful but limited by space. The suitable habitats in the most important breeding area of the Voorhaven will be lost in the near future as a result of harbour activities. The area is a proposed Ramsar Site.

Polderkomplex A4i, A4iii, B1i, B2, C2, C3, C4, C6 005
Admin region Vlaams Gewest
Coordinates 51°15′N 3°13′E
Altitude 2–8 m **Area** 9,349 ha

■ Site description

The area includes the most interesting parts of the coastal polders to the north of Brugge which consist of grasslands, extensively used ditches, canals and reedbeds. It also includes a small part of the coastal dunes near Blankenberge.

Habitats Grassland (60%), Artificial landscape (40%; arable land; perennial crops/orchards/groves)

Land-use Agriculture (90%), Nature conservation/research (5%), Tourism/recreation (5%)

■ Birds

Species	Season	Year	Pop min	Pop max	Acc	Criteria
Botaurus stellaris Bittern	P	—	—	15	B	C2
Anser fabalis Bean Goose	W	1989	3,000	3,000	—	B1i, C3
[1] *Anser brachyrhynchus* Pink-footed Goose	W	—	20,000	36,000	A	A4i, B1i, C3
[1] *Anser albifrons* White-fronted Goose	W	—	15,000	30,000	A	A4i, B1i, C3
Anas penelope Wigeon	W	—	10,000	40,000	A	A4i, B1i, C3
Anas clypeata Shoveler	W	—	300	500	A	B1i, C3
Circus aeruginosus Marsh Harrier	B	1996	—	10	A	C6
Pluvialis apricaria Golden Plover	P	—	10,000	15,000	B	B1i, C2
Limosa limosa Black-tailed Godwit	B	1995	100	120	A	B2
Luscinia svecica Bluethroat	B	1993	60	80	A	C6

1. Population estimate refers to east coast polder area.

This is an internationally important wintering site for *Anser brachyrhynchus*, *A. albifrons* and *Anas penelope*. The area is also important for breeding meadow birds.

■ Protection status
National Low **International** High
12 ha of IBA covered by Nature Reserve (De Fonteintjes, 12 ha). 60 ha of IBA covered by Nature Reserve (Uitkerkse Polder, 60 ha). 9,349 ha of IBA covered by Special Protection Area (Poldercomplex Hoeke, Damme, Meetkerke, Uitkerke, 9,530 ha).

■ Conservation issues

Threats Agricultural intensification/expansion (A), Drainage (A), Industrialization/urbanization (B), Infrastructure (B), Recreation/tourism (B)

Because of its ornithological importance the site is well monitored by BNVR/RNOB and the Institute of Nature Conservation. Seventeen percent of the area has been designated as a green area on the physical planning map. Securing the populations of waders and geese on this site will depend on the success of management agreements with farmers, buying of land and an overall management scheme. 25 ha of IBA covered by proposed Site of Community Importance (Dune areas including IJzermonding and Zwin, 2,891 ha). 350 ha of IBA covered by proposed Site of Community Importance (Zilte poldergraslanden, 884 ha).

Zwin — B1i, B3, C3, C6 — 006
Admin region Vlaams Gewest
Coordinates 51°20′N 3°21′E
Altitude 0–7 m **Area** 1,820 ha

■ Site description
An area of saltmarshes and mudflats (a remnant of a former estuary) with a dune system and polders with halophile creeks and grasslands, several reedbeds and canals fringes with reed. The dune and saltmarsh area extends across the border into the Netherlands.

Habitats Forest and woodland, Wetland (10%; mudflat/sandflat; saltmarsh; sand-dunes/sand beach), Artificial landscape (80%; arable land; perennial crops/orchards/groves; forestry plantation)
Land-use Agriculture (70%), Nature conservation/research (15%), Tourism/recreation (5%)

■ Birds

Species	Season	Year	Pop min	Pop max	Acc	Criteria
Anser brachyrhynchus Pink-footed Goose	W	—	—	500	A	B1i, C3
[1] *Anser albifrons* White-fronted Goose	W	—	—	10,000	A	B1i, C3
Circus aeruginosus Marsh Harrier	B	1995	—	4	A	C6
Recurvirostra avosetta Avocet	B	—	—	41	—	B3, C6
Larus melanocephalus Mediterranean Gull	B	1996	—	28	A	C6
Sterna hirundo Common Tern	B	1995	—	62	A	C6

1. Maximum for 1990-1996 period.

The site supports internationally important numbers of wintering geese. Significant numbers of gulls, terns and meadow birds also breed and the dunes are an important staging site for migrating passerines.

■ Protection status
National Low **International** High
125 ha of IBA covered by Nature Reserve (Het Zwin, 125 ha). 1,820 ha of IBA covered by Special Protection Area (Het Zwin, 1,820 ha). 530 ha of IBA covered by Ramsar Site (Zwin, 530 ha).

■ Conservation issues

Threats Agricultural intensification/expansion (A), Drainage (A), Dredging/canalization (A), Natural events (A), Recreation/tourism (B)

Breeding and wintering birds are monitored throughout the site, with the most important areas censused annually. 500 ha of IBA covered by proposed Site of Community Importance (IJzermonding and Zwin, 2,891 ha). 45 ha of IBA covered by proposed Site of Community Importance (Zilte poldergraslanden, 884 ha).

Krekengebied — A4i, B1i, B2, B3, C2, C3, C6 — 007
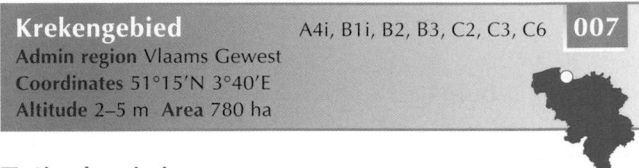
Admin region Vlaams Gewest
Coordinates 51°15′N 3°40′E
Altitude 2–5 m **Area** 780 ha

■ Site description
A complex of old freshwater and brackish sea inlets ('kreken') in a polder landscape. The area encompasses a diverse set of habitats, including remnant saltmarshes, acidic marshes and wet woodlands.

Habitats Wetland (5%), Artificial landscape (90%; arable land; perennial crops/orchards/groves)
Land-use Agriculture (95%), Nature conservation/research (5%), Tourism/recreation (5%)

■ Birds

Species	Season	Year	Pop min	Pop max	Acc	Criteria
[1] *Cygnus columbianus* Bewick's Swan	W	1994	100	384	A	B1i, B2, C2
[2] *Anser albifrons* White-fronted Goose	W	—	1,100	18,000	A	A4i, B1i, C3
Circus aeruginosus Marsh Harrier	B	1996	13	18	A	C6
Recurvirostra avosetta Avocet	B	1995	—	4	A	B3

1. Minimum and maximum for 1993–1996 period
2. Minimum and maximum for 1992–1996 period

This is an internationally important wintering site for *Cygnus columbianus*. The area is is also a nationally important breeding site for *Luscinia svecica* (25 pairs) and reedbed species.

■ Protection status
National Low **International** High
14 ha of IBA covered by Nature Reserve (Grote Geul, 14 ha). 19 ha of IBA covered by Nature Reserve (Meetjeslandse kreken, 19 ha). 780 ha of IBA covered by Special Protection Area (Krekengebied, 780 ha).

■ Conservation issues

Threats Agricultural intensification/expansion (A), Disturbance to birds (B), Drainage (A), Infrastructure (C), Recreation/tourism (C)

One of the main threats is the loss of grassland around the creeks, as a result of fields being ploughed close to reedbeds, thus limiting the size of the water-bodies. Water quality is also deteriorating due to agricultural pollution, and the lowering of the water-table in the area is also a threat. The area is well studied by a local ornithological working group (Vogelwerkgroep Noord-Oost-Vlaanderen). Approximately 350 ha are designated as a green area on the physical planning map.

Bourgoyen-Ossemeersen — B1i, C3 — 008
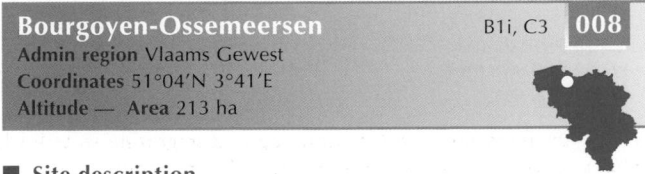
Admin region Vlaams Gewest
Coordinates 51°04′N 3°41′E
Altitude — **Area** 213 ha

■ Site description
A large part of the area consists of humid grasslands inundated during the winter period.

Habitats Grassland (humid grassland)
Land-use Unknown

■ Birds

Species	Season	Year	Pop min	Pop max	Acc	Criteria
Anas clypeata Shoveler	W	—	—	—	—	B1i, C3

The site is important for wintering *Anas clypeata*.

■ Protection status
National Partial **International** None
IBA partly covered by Nature Reserve.

■ Conservation issues
The area is now well protected and there are no immediate threats. It is proposed as a Ramsar Site.

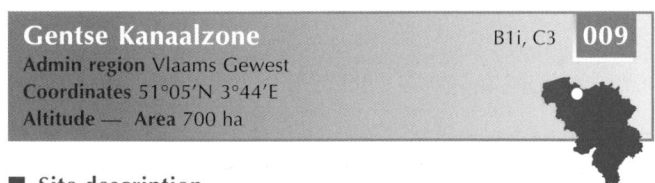

Gentse Kanaalzone
B1i, C3 **009**
Admin region Vlaams Gewest
Coordinates 51°05'N 3°44'E
Altitude — **Area** 700 ha

■ Site description
A large canal passing through an industrial zone, leading from the inland port of Gent towards the Westerschelde, and including several large docks.

Habitats Wetland, Artificial landscape (other urban/industrial areas)
Land-use Urban/industrial/transport

■ Birds
This is a very important site for wintering ducks, particularly for diving ducks, but no data are available for individual species.

■ Protection status
National None **International** None

■ Conservation issues

Threats Unknown

The area is a proposed Ramsar Site.

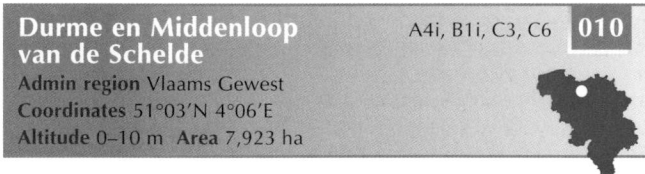

Durme en Middenloop van de Schelde
A4i, B1i, C3, C6 **010**
Admin region Vlaams Gewest
Coordinates 51°03'N 4°06'E
Altitude 0–10 m **Area** 7,923 ha

■ Site description
The area includes long sections of the Schelde and Durme rivers, with very rare freshwater tidal river marshes as well as mudflats, marshes, reedbeds, oxbows and wet meadows.

Habitats Forest and woodland (5%; mixed forest), Wetland (80%; tidal river/enclosed tidal water; standing fresh water), Artificial landscape (20%)
Land-use Agriculture (20%), Nature conservation/research (80%), Tourism/recreation (15%)

■ Birds

Species	Season	Year	Pop min	Pop max	Acc	Criteria
[1] *Anas strepera* Gadwall	W	—	600	1,000	A	B1i, C3
[1] *Anas crecca* Teal	W	—	14,000	15,000	A	A4i, B1i, C3
[1] *Anas acuta* Pintail	W	—	600	1,000	A	B1i, C3
Luscinia svecica Bluethroat	B	1993	100	120	B	C6

1. 1994–1996 period.

This is an important site for wintering and migrating waterfowl. The area is also nationally important for migrating *Botaurus stellaris*, *Ixobrychus minutus* and *Porzana porzana*, and breeding *Alcedo atthis*.

■ Protection status
National Partial **International** High
The IBA is covered by several Nature Reserves; Brede Schoren, 4 ha; 'As State, Daknamse kreken', 12 ha; De Cramp, 8 ha; De Notelaer, 28 ha; Grauwe Plaat, 1 ha; Groot Schoor van Grembergen, 8 ha; Het Molsbroek, 75 ha; Kalkense Meersen, 34 ha; Kijkverdriet, 5 ha; Konkelschoor, 2 ha; Rietsnijderij, 3 ha; Schor aan de Durmemonding, 6 ha; Schorren bij Zele, 12 ha; Schorren van Branst, 20 ha; Sint-Amandsschoor, 6 ha; Sint-Onolfsschor, 5 ha; Vlassenbroekse schorren, 17 ha. 17 ha of IBA covered by State Nature Reserve (Stort bij Weert, 17 ha). 23 ha of IBA covered by State Nature Reserve (Schorren van de Durme, 23 ha). 7,923 ha of IBA covered by Special Protection Area (Durme en de middenloop van de Schelde, 7,923 ha).

■ Conservation issues

Threats Agricultural intensification/expansion (B), Construction/impact of dyke/dam/barrage (A), Infrastructure (B)

The area is included within a project which is preparing an ecological model of the River Schelde estuary, and thus receives detailed study. About 1,560 ha is designated as a green area on the physical planning map. The whole estuarine area is currently subject to designation as a State Nature Reserve, which will highly improve its conservation. 3,800 ha of IBA covered by proposed Site of Community Importance (Schelde-en Durme-estuarium van NL grens tot Gent, 4,139 ha).

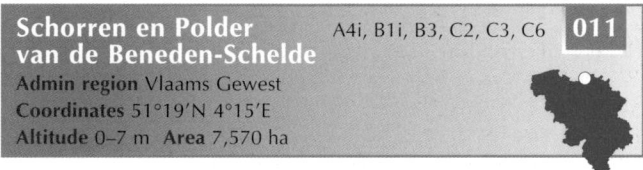

Schorren en Polder van de Beneden-Schelde
A4i, B1i, B3, C2, C3, C6 **011**
Admin region Vlaams Gewest
Coordinates 51°19'N 4°15'E
Altitude 0–7 m **Area** 7,570 ha

■ Site description
A brackish part of the River Schelde on Flemish territory near the border of the Netherlands, encompassing mud and sandflats and brackish marshes. The neighbouring polders are included and comprise grazing-meadows, agricultural land, several large reedbeds, sandy and muddy industrial wasteland, and several deep-water docks connected with the River Schelde.

Habitats Wetland (10%; tidal river/enclosed tidal water; mudflat/sandflat), Artificial landscape (90%; arable land; other urban/industrial areas; ruderal land)
Land-use Agriculture (50%), Nature conservation/research (10%), Urban/industrial/transport (40%)

■ Birds

Species	Season	Year	Pop min	Pop max	Acc	Criteria
Anser fabalis Bean Goose	P	—	4,000	4,000	—	A4i, B1i, C3
[1] *Anser anser* Greylag Goose	P	—	2,200	4,210	A	A4i, B1i, C3
Anas penelope Wigeon	W	—	3,000	15,000	A	B1i, C3
Anas strepera Gadwall	W	—	250	500	A	B1i, C3
Anas crecca Teal	P	—	3,200	—	—	B1i, C3
Anas clypeata Shoveler	P	—	—	1,700	—	B1i, C3
Circus aeruginosus Marsh Harrier	B	1996	—	21	A	C6
Recurvirostra avosetta Avocet	B	—	—	350	—	B1i, B3, C2
Recurvirostra avosetta Avocet	P	—	—	800	—	B1i, C2
Larus melanocephalus Mediterranean Gull	B	1996	—	15	A	C6
Sterna hirundo Common Tern	B	1996	50	60	A	C6
Luscinia svecica Bluethroat	B	1993	70	100	A	C6

1. Minimum and maximum 1990–1995.

This is an internationally important staging and wintering site for waders and waterfowl, especially for *Anser anser* and *Anas crecca*. The area is also nationally important for breeding meadow birds and waders.

■ Protection status
National Low **International** High
45 ha of IBA covered by Nature Reserve (Galgenschoor, 45 ha). 215 ha of IBA covered by Nature Reserve (Groot Buitenschoor, 215 ha). 7,570 ha of IBA covered by Special Protection Area (Schorren en polders van de Beneden-Schelde, 7,570 ha).

■ Conservation issues

Threats Agricultural intensification/expansion (B), Disturbance to birds (A), Industrialization/urbanization (A), Infrastructure (A)

Breeding birds and wintering waterbirds are regularly surveyed. A recent report on the state of nature in part of the IBA is being produced within the framework of future infrastructure development. According to the physical planning scheme of the Flemish Government this site will be destroyed by infrastructure works for the harbour of Antwerp; only very small parts of the IBA will remain free of industrial plants. 400 ha of IBA covered by proposed Site of Community Importance (Schelde and Durme-estuary from Dutch border to Gent, 139 ha).

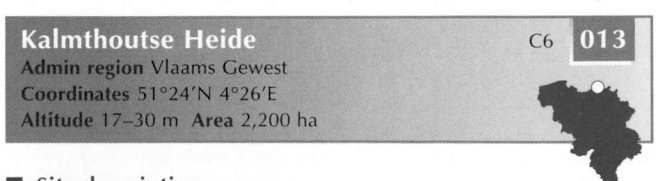

Kuifeend and Blokkersdijk
A4i, B1i, B3,C2, C3, C6 **012**

Admin region Vlaams Gewest
Coordinates 51°16'N 4°21'E
Altitude 0–7 m **Area** 194 ha

■ Site description
This IBA comprises two sites, separated by the River Schelde; Kuifeend, an area of freshwater pools and reedbeds, and Blokkersdijk, a shallow freshwater lake surrounded by reed- and willow-marshes.

Habitats Forest and woodland (5%), Wetland (30%; standing fresh water; water-fringe vegetation), Artificial landscape (40%; arable land; other urban/industrial areas; ruderal land)
Land-use Agriculture (40%), Nature conservation/research (20%), Tourism/recreation (10%), Urban/industrial/transport (20%)

■ Birds

Species	Season	Year	Pop min	Pop max	Acc	Criteria
Anas strepera Gadwall	W	—	1,000	1,500	A	A4i, B1i, C3
Anas clypeata Shoveler	W	—	1,000	1,500	A	B1i, C3
Recurvirostra avosetta Avocet	B	1996	10	20	B	B3, C6
Larus melanocephalus Mediterranean Gull	B	1996	—	90	A	C2, C6

This is an internationally important wintering site for *Anas crecca* and *A. clypeata*. The area is also important for breeding reedbed species and staging and wintering ducks and grebes.

■ Protection status
National Partial **International** High
56 ha of IBA covered by Nature Reserve (Kuifeend, 56 ha). 100 ha of IBA covered by Nature Reserve (Blokkersdijk, 100 ha). 194 ha of IBA covered by Special Protection Area (De Kuifeend en Blokkersdijk, 194 ha).

■ Conservation issues

Threats Filling-in of wetlands (A), Industrialization/urbanization (A), Infrastructure (A)

Breeding and wintering birds have been monitored for almost 20 years by Natuurreservaten Antwerpen-Noord.

Kalmthoutse Heide
C6 **013**

Admin region Vlaams Gewest
Coordinates 51°24'N 4°26'E
Altitude 17–30 m **Area** 2,200 ha

■ Site description
An important and diverse area of dry and wet heathlands, fens and inland sand-dunes of the Antwerpse Kempen.

Habitats Forest and woodland (15%; broadleaved deciduous forest), Scrub (40%; heathland), Wetland (5%; fen/transition mire/spring), Artificial landscape (30%; forestry plantation)
Land-use Forestry (20%), Nature conservation/research (60%), Tourism/recreation (60%), Water management (20%)

■ Birds

Species	Season	Year	Pop min	Pop max	Acc	Criteria
Caprimulgus europaeus Nightjar	B	—	5	10	—	C6

This IBA is also a nationally important staging site for migrating waders and breeding heathland species, including *Lullula arborea*.

■ Protection status
National Partial **International** High
812 ha of IBA covered by State Nature Reserve (Kalmthout, 812 ha). 2,035 ha of IBA covered by Special Protection Area (Kalmthoutse Heide, 2,200 ha). 2,200 ha of IBA covered by Ramsar Site (Kalmthoutse Heide, 2,200 ha).

■ Conservation issues

Threats Burning of vegetation (A), Disturbance to birds (A), Drainage (B), Groundwater abstraction (A), Recreation/tourism (A)

One of the main threats is accidental fire damage during dry periods. There is intensive research on heathland habitats related to management and a detailed management plan exists. The whole site is designated as a green area on the physical planning map. 2,000 ha of IBA covered by proposed Site of Community Importance (Kalmthoutse Heide, 2,018 ha).

De Maatjes, Wuustwezel Heide en Groot Schietveld
C7 **014**

Admin region Vlaams Gewest
Coordinates 51°23'N 4°34'E
Altitude 15–30 m **Area** 4,100 ha

■ Site description
The site includes arable land, grasslands and marshes (De Maatjes), and heaths and mire habitats in military camps (Groot en Klein Schietveld).

Habitats Forest and woodland (5%), Scrub (25%; heathland), Grassland (5%; humid grassland), Wetland (20%; standing fresh water), Artificial landscape (40%; arable land; forestry plantation; ruderal land)
Land-use Agriculture (40%), Forestry (10%), Military (40%), Nature conservation/research (10%)

■ Birds
An important breeding area for meadow and heathland species, e.g. *Limosa limosa* (10–20 pairs). It is also a nationally important staging site for migrating passerines, waders, gulls and raptors. The meadows are an important feeding site for the up to 350 *Larus melanocephalus* and up to 600 *Numenius phaeopus*.

■ Protection status
National Low **International** High
10 ha of IBA covered by Nature Reserve (De Maatjes, 10 ha). 4,100 ha of IBA covered by Special Protection Area (De Maatjes, Wuustwezelheide en Groot Schietveld, 4,100 ha).

■ Conservation issues

Threats Agricultural intensification/expansion (A), Groundwater abstraction (B), Infrastructure (C)

About 10% of the site is designated as a green area on the physical planning map. 1,770 ha of IBA covered by proposed Site of Community Importance (Klein- en Groot Schietveld, 2,042 ha).

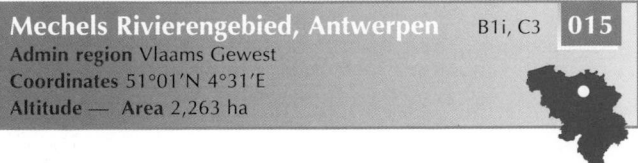

Mechels Rivierengebied, Antwerpen
B1i, C3 **015**

Admin region Vlaams Gewest
Coordinates 51°01'N 4°31'E
Altitude — **Area** 2,263 ha

■ Site description
An area of flat grasslands, small swamps, channels and large artificial lakes along the Dijle, Zenne and Rupel rivers. Human activities include

arable and stock-farming and recreation. There is a high density of human habitation.

Habitats Grassland, Wetland (standing fresh water), Artificial landscape (other urban/industrial areas)
Land-use Agriculture, Recreation/tourism

■ Birds

Species	Season	Year	Pop min	Pop max	Acc	Criteria
Aythya ferina Pochard	W	—	3,950	—	—	B1i, C3

This is an important site for wintering *Aythya ferina*. The area also holds breeding populations of several species listed on Annex I of the EC Birds Directive.

■ Protection status
National Partial **International** None
IBA partly covered by Nature Reserve.

■ Conservation issues

Threats Tourism/recreation, Industrialization/urbanization

Problems include pollution of the rivers, and industrial, recreational and residential development. The site is a proposed Special Protection Area.

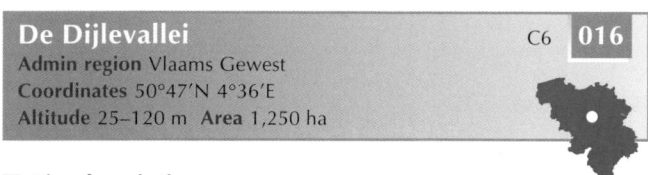

De Dijlevallei
C6 **016**
Admin region Vlaams Gewest
Coordinates 50°47′N 4°36′E
Altitude 25–120 m **Area** 1,250 ha

■ Site description
The Flemish part of the Dijle river valley, located south of Leuven, with ponds, marshes, grasslands and woodlands.

Habitats Forest and woodland (50%; broadleaved deciduous forest; mixed forest), Grassland (10%), Wetland (10%; standing fresh water; water-fringe vegetation), Artificial landscape (20%; arable land; forestry plantation; urban parks/gardens)

■ Birds

Species	Season	Year	Pop min	Pop max	Acc	Criteria
Luscinia svecica Bluethroat	B	—	5	10	—	C6

The area supports staging and wintering waterfowl and is a breeding and staging site for reedbed species.

■ Protection status
National Low **International** High
70 ha of IBA covered by Nature Reserve (Doode Bemde, 70 ha). 1,250 ha of IBA covered by Special Protection Area (De Dijlevallei, 1,250 ha).

■ Conservation issues

Threats Agricultural intensification/expansion (B), Infrastructure (A), Recreation/tourism (B)

The area is included in the 'Ecologisch Impulsgebied', an integrated conservation and development project. Intensive research on the influence of hydrology upon land management is currently carried out. 549 ha of IBA covered by proposed Site of Community Importance (Valleien van de Dijle, Laan en IJsse with forests and swamps, 2,938 ha).

Zegge
B1i, C3 **017**
Admin region Vlaams Gewest
Coordinates 51°11′N 4°56′E
Altitude 14–14 m **Area** 91 ha

■ Site description
A remnant of the once extensive Kleine Nete river valley, with pools and low moorland, overgrown grasslands and alder swamps.

Habitats Forest and woodland (25%; broadleaved deciduous forest; alluvial/very wet forest), Grassland (50%; humid grassland), Wetland (25%; standing fresh water; water-fringe vegetation; fen/transition mire/spring)
Land-use Nature conservation/research (100%)

■ Birds

Species	Season	Year	Pop min	Pop max	Acc	Criteria
Anas strepera Gadwall	P	—	300	700	—	B1i, C3
Anas clypeata Shoveler	P	—	1,170	—	—	B1i, C3

This site is important for passage waterbirds and staging and breeding reedbed species.

■ Protection status
National High **International** High
91 ha of IBA covered by Nature Reserve (De Zegge, 91 ha). 91 ha of IBA covered by Special Protection Area (De Zegge, 91 ha).

■ Conservation issues

Threats Agricultural intensification/expansion (A), Drainage

As the site is small, most threats impacting on it originate from outside the IBA. The site is managed as a nature reserve by the Koninklijke Maatschappij voor Dierkunde Antwerpen, and measures are being taken to address the problems of drainage and water pollution. 91 ha of IBA covered by proposed Site of Community Importance (Kleine Nete en vallei met moerasgebieden en heiden, 2,635 ha).

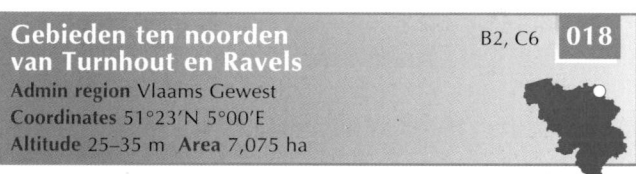

Gebieden ten noorden van Turnhout en Ravels
B2, C6 **018**
Admin region Vlaams Gewest
Coordinates 51°23′N 5°00′E
Altitude 25–35 m **Area** 7,075 ha

■ Site description
An area of grasslands, agricultural land, deciduous and coniferous woodland, and heaths with oligotrophic fens. There is also an ancient park with neglected orchards and ponds.

Habitats Forest and woodland (5%), Scrub (10%; heathland), Grassland (5%; humid grassland), Artificial landscape (60%; arable land; perennial crops/orchards/groves; forestry plantation; ruderal land)
Land-use Agriculture (50%), Forestry (40%), Nature conservation/research (5%), Tourism/recreation (5%)

■ Birds

Species	Season	Year	Pop min	Pop max	Acc	Criteria
Limosa limosa Black-tailed Godwit	B	—	—	68	—	B2
Caprimulgus europaeus Nightjar	B	1996	3	8	B	C6

This is an important area for breeding and migrating meadow birds.

■ Protection status
National Low **International** High
170 ha of IBA covered by Nature Reserve (De Liereman, 170 ha). 12 ha of IBA covered by Nature Reserve (Ravels, 12 ha). 60 ha of IBA covered by Nature Reserve (Turnhouts vennengebied, 60 ha). 7,075 ha of IBA covered by Special Protection Area (Arendonk, Merksplas, Oud-Turnhout, Ravels en Turnhout, 7,075 ha).

■ Conservation issues

Threats Agricultural intensification/expansion (B), Recreation/tourism (B)

The area is included in the 'Ecologisch Impulsgebied', an integrated conservation and development project. Small zones are managed as nature reserves by BNVR/RNOB and the Flemish Region. 2,624 ha of IBA covered by proposed Site of Community Importance (Vennen, heiden en moerassen rond Turnhout, 4,377 ha). 700 ha of IBA covered by proposed Site of Community Importance (Liereman en Korhaan, 854 ha).

Ronde Put

C6 019

Admin region Vlaams Gewest
Coordinates 51°17'N 5°11'E
Altitude 25–35 m **Area** 5,400 ha

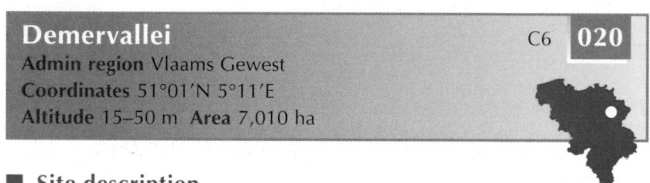

■ Site description

An area of the Turnhoutse Kempen covered with deciduous and coniferous woodlands, small heathlands, and marshes and ponds.

Habitats Forest and woodland (10%; broadleaved deciduous forest), Scrub (5%; heathland), Artificial landscape (85%; arable land; forestry plantation)
Land-use Agriculture (40%), Forestry (40%), Nature conservation/research (10%), Tourism/recreation (10%)

■ Birds

Species	Season	Year	Pop min	Pop max	Acc	Criteria
Pernis apivorus Honey Buzzard	B	—	—	5	—	C6

This IBA is also a staging site for migrating passerines and raptors.

■ Protection status

National Low **International** High
10 ha of IBA covered by Nature Reserve (De Maatjes, 10 ha). 40 ha of IBA covered by Nature Reserve (De Ronde Put, 40 ha). 5,400 ha of IBA covered by Special Protection Area (De Ronde Put, 5,400 ha).

■ Conservation issues

Threats Agricultural intensification/expansion (A), Disturbance to birds (B), Drainage (B), Infrastructure (B), Recreation/tourism (A)

200 ha of IBA covered by proposed Site of Community Importance (Kleine Nete en vallei met moerasgebieden en heiden, 2,635 ha).

Demervallei

C6 020

Admin region Vlaams Gewest
Coordinates 51°01'N 5°11'E
Altitude 15–50 m **Area** 7,010 ha

■ Site description

The area is situated in the Demer river valley, west and east of the town of Diest. It comprises a rich variety of former river arms, peat ponds, marshes, reedbeds, sedge-fields, humid grasslands and alluvial forests, including heathland relicts on the sandy hills bordering the valley.

Habitats Forest and woodland (10%; broadleaved deciduous forest; alluvial/very wet forest), Grassland (15%; humid grassland), Wetland (20%; standing fresh water; water-fringe vegetation), Artificial landscape (60%; arable land; perennial crops/orchards/groves; forestry plantation; urban parks/gardens)
Land-use Agriculture (40%), Forestry (30%), Nature conservation/research (20%), Tourism/recreation (5%), Urban/industrial/transport (10%)

■ Birds

Species	Season	Year	Pop min	Pop max	Acc	Criteria
Luscinia svecica Bluethroat	B	1995	65	80	A	C6

A breeding and staging area for meadow birds, waders and waterfowl.

■ Protection status

National Low **International** High
57 ha of IBA covered by Nature Reserve (Demerbroeken, 57 ha). 62 ha of IBA covered by Nature Reserve (Langdonken, 62 ha). 7,010 ha of IBA covered by Special Protection Area (De Demervallei, 7,010 ha).

■ Conservation issues

Threats Agricultural intensification/expansion (A), Disturbance to birds (B), Infrastructure (A), Recreation/tourism (A)

The area is included in the 'Ecologisch Impulsgebied', an integrated conservation and development project. 1,216 ha of IBA covered by proposed Site of Community Importance (Demervallei ten oosten van Aarschot, 1,432 ha).

Vallei van de Zwarte Beek

C6 021

Admin region Vlaams Gewest
Coordinates 51°07'N 5°20'E
Altitude 32–70 m **Area** 8,864 ha

■ Site description

An extensive heathland on the Kempen plateau, with oligotrophic fens and sand-dunes, and the Zwarte Beek wil valley, a well-preserved, semi-natural landscape with bogs, moorland, marsh, woodland and extensive arable land.

Habitats Forest and woodland (20%; mixed forest), Scrub (30%; heathland), Grassland (10%; humid grassland; mesophile grassland), Artificial landscape (40%; arable land, forestry plantation)
Land-use Agriculture (20%), Military (70%), Nature conservation/research (10%), Tourism/recreation (5%)

■ Birds

Species	Season	Year	Pop min	Pop max	Acc	Criteria
Caprimulgus europaeus Nightjar	B	1993	30	40	A	C6

This is a breeding area for meadow birds and woodland passerines.

■ Protection status

National Partial **International** High
827 ha of IBA covered by Nature Reserve (Vallei van de Zwarte Beek, 827 ha). 8,864 ha of IBA covered by Special Protection Area (Militair domein en de vallei van de Zwarte Beek, 8,864 ha).

■ Conservation issues

Threats Consequences of animal/plant introductions (A), Infrastructure (B), Other (A)

The area suffers from planting with exotic tree species. Additionally, one of the most significant threats to the extensive heathland and inland dunes is the future use of the military area ('Other' threat), as an increasing number of military areas are being sold and developed. The area is included in the 'Ecologisch Impulsgebied', an integrated conservation and development project. Intensive research on the influence of hydrology on land management is currently being carried out. Almost 1,000 ha is managed as a nature reserve by BNVR/RNOB. 8,100 ha of IBA covered by proposed Site of Community Importance (Vallei-en brongebied van Zwarte Beek, Boliserbeek, 8,689 ha).

Gebieden gelegen te Peer en Hechtel-Eksel

C6 022

Admin region Vlaams Gewest
Coordinates 51°07'N 5°25'E
Altitude 48–75 m **Area** 10,015 ha

■ Site description

Extensive grassland with a few extensively cultivated areas, bisected by valleys with old hay-meadows and wet woodlands. Of particular importance are the Abeek, Dommel and Bolliserbeek valleys.

Habitats Forest and woodland (5%; mixed forest; alluvial/very wet forest), Wetland (5%; river/stream), Artificial landscape (80%; arable land; perennial crops/orchards/groves; urban parks/gardens; other urban/industrial areas; ruderal land)
Land-use Agriculture (80%), Nature conservation/research (5%), Tourism/recreation (5%), Urban/industrial/transport (10%)

■ Birds

Species	Season	Year	Pop min	Pop max	Acc	Criteria
Caprimulgus europaeus Nightjar	B	1996	5	15	B	C6

Alcedo atthis also breeds at this site.

■ Protection status

National None **International** High
10,015 ha of IBA covered by Special Protection Area (Bocholt, Hechtel-Eksel, Gruitrode, Neerpelt en Peer, 10,015 ha).

Conservation issues

Threats Abandonment/reduction of land management (A), Agricultural intensification/expansion (A), Dredging/canalization (A), Infrastructure (B)

Several small areas have been managed for *Emberiza hortulana*. The species formerly bred in the area and, up to 10 years ago, was the only site in Flanders where the species still occurred. However, this conservation action probably came too late as only 1–2 singing males are observed annually in the area, and it is doubtful that a viable population will be established. The physical planning map of the Flemish Region designates 17% of the IBA as a green area.

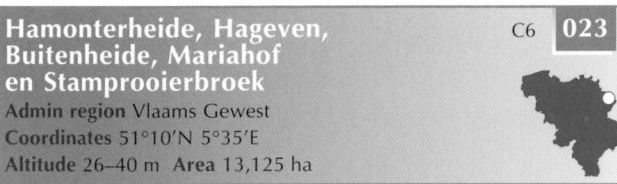

Hamonterheide, Hageven, Buitenheide, Mariahof en Stamprooierbroek — C6 023

Admin region Vlaams Gewest
Coordinates 51°10′N 5°35′E
Altitude 26–40 m **Area** 13,125 ha

Site description
A large site with heathland, marshes, fish-ponds, extensive grassland, deciduous woodland and agriculture land.

Habitats Forest and woodland (35%; broadleaved deciduous forest; alluvial/very wet forest), Scrub (5%; heathland), Artificial landscape (60%; highly improved reseeded grassland; arable land; urban parks/gardens)
Land-use Agriculture (50%), Forestry (40%), Nature conservation/research (10%), Tourism/recreation (5%)

Birds

Species	Season	Year	Pop min	Pop max	Acc	Criteria
Botaurus stellaris Bittern	B	1996	—	4	A	C6
Lullula arborea Woodlark	B	1993	10	15	B	C6

A breeding and staging area for reedbed species and meadow birds.

Protection status
National Low **International** High
170 ha of IBA covered by Nature Reserve (Hageven, 170 ha). 400 ha of IBA covered by Nature Reserve (Stamprooierbroek-Urlobroek, 400 ha). 13,125 ha of IBA covered by Special Protection Area (Hamonterheide, Hageven, Buitenheide, Stamprooierbr, 13,125 ha).

Conservation issues

Threats Agricultural intensification/expansion (A), Drainage (B)

2,897 ha of IBA covered by proposed Site of Community Importance (Abeek met aanliggende moerasgebieden, 3,265 ha). 1,620 ha of IBA covered by proposed Site of Community Importance (Hageven en Dommelvallei, 1,910 ha). 1,839 ha of IBA covered by proposed Site of Community Importance (Itterbeek met Brand, Jagersborg en Schotsheide, 2,254 ha).

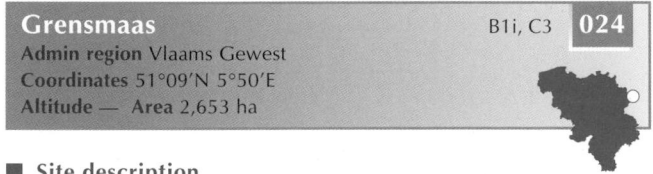

Grensmaas — B1i, C3 024

Admin region Vlaams Gewest
Coordinates 51°09′N 5°50′E
Altitude — **Area** 2,653 ha

Site description
A section of the River Meuse on the Netherlands border, encompassing a free flowing stream in a broad gravel bed with islands and gravel banks, and including nearby flooded gravel pits.

Habitats Wetland (standing fresh water; river/stream)
Land-use Urban/industrial/transport

Birds

Species	Season	Year	Pop min	Pop max	Acc	Criteria
Aythya ferina Pochard	W	—	—	—	—	B1i, C3

This is an important site for wintering *Aythya ferina*.

Protection status
National Partial **International** None
IBA partly covered by Nature Reserve.

Conservation issues

Threats Extraction industry

The area is threatened by the expansion of gravel mining, and silt and waste deposition. The area is a proposed Ramsar Site.

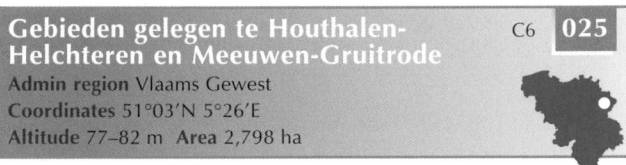

Gebieden gelegen te Houthalen-Helchteren en Meeuwen-Gruitrode — C6 025

Admin region Vlaams Gewest
Coordinates 51°03′N 5°26′E
Altitude 77–82 m **Area** 2,798 ha

Site description
An extensive area of dry and wet heathland on the Kempen plateau, encompassing ponds, marshes, inland dunes, and conifer plantations.

Habitats Forest and woodland (5%; broadleaved deciduous forest), Scrub (70%; heathland), Wetland (5%; fen/transition mire/spring), Artificial landscape (25%; arable land; forestry plantation)
Land-use Agriculture (20%), Military (80%)

Birds

Species	Season	Year	Pop min	Pop max	Acc	Criteria
Tetrao tetrix Black Grouse	B	1996	—	3	A	C6
Lullula arborea Woodlark	B	1993	10	15	A	C6

A breeding and staging site for woodland and heathland species.

Protection status
National None **International** High
2,789 ha of IBA covered by Special Protection Area (Houthalen, Helchteren, Meeuwen, Gruitrode en Peer, 2,789 ha).

Conservation issues

Threats Agricultural intensification/expansion (B), Infrastructure (B), Other (A), Recreation/tourism (B)

One of the most significant threats to the extensive heathland and inland dunes is the future use of the military area ('Other' threat), as an increasing number of military areas are being sold and developed. 2,802 ha of IBA covered by proposed Site of Community Importance (Heide- en vengebieden tussen Houthalen en Gruitrode, 3,882 ha).

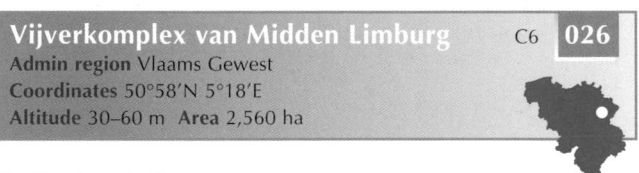

Vijverkomplex van Midden Limburg — C6 026

Admin region Vlaams Gewest
Coordinates 50°58′N 5°18′E
Altitude 30–60 m **Area** 2,560 ha

Site description
An important wetland area including many ponds and marshes and wet woodlands, and covering parts of the Echelbeek, Slangbeek, Roosterbeek and Laambeek.

Habitats Forest and woodland (20%; mixed forest; alluvial/very wet forest), Wetland (25%; standing fresh water), Artificial landscape (40%; arable land; forestry plantation; urban parks/gardens)
Land-use Agriculture (20%), Fisheries/Aquaculture (25%), Forestry (20%), Tourism/recreation (20%), Urban/industrial/transport (15%)

Birds

Species	Season	Year	Pop min	Pop max	Acc	Criteria
Alcedo atthis Kingfisher	B	1994	10	15	A	C6

The IBA is also a breeding and staging site for reedbed species, including *Botaurus stellaris*.

Protection status
National Partial **International** High

90 ha of IBA covered by Nature Reserve (Kolberg, 90 ha). 100 ha of IBA covered by Nature Reserve (Ter Donk, 100 ha). 150 ha of IBA covered by Nature Reserve (Terlamen, 150 ha). 101 ha of IBA covered by State Nature Reserve (De Platwijers, 101 ha). 2,560 ha of IBA covered by Special Protection Area (Vijverkomplex van Midden Limburg, 2,560 ha).

■ Conservation issues

Threats Agricultural intensification/expansion (A), Aquaculture/fisheries (A), Filling-in of wetlands (A), Infrastructure (A), Recreation/tourism (A)

The site is severely impacted by the construction of buildings, camping activities, the filling-in of wetlands and the destruction of trees, reedbeds and all other vegetation bordering the fish-ponds. The area is included in the 'Ecologisch Impulsgebied', an integrated conservation and development project. 800 ha of IBA covered by proposed Site of Community Importance (Valleien van de Laarbeek, Zonderikbeek, Slangbeek, 2,811 ha).

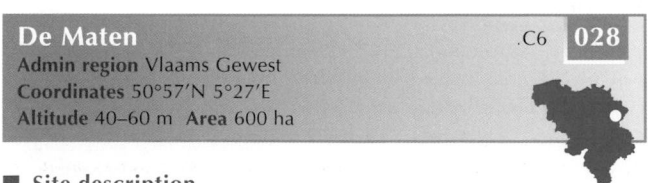

Bokrijk C6 027
Admin region Vlaams Gewest
Coordinates 50°57'N 5°24'E
Altitude 35–55 m **Area** 800 ha

■ Site description
An area of several ponds and fens fed by numerous brooks, with heathland and deciduous, mixed and coniferous woodland and grasslands.

Habitats Forest and woodland (15%; broadleaved deciduous forest; alluvial/very wet forest), Wetland (30%; standing fresh water), Artificial landscape (55%; arable land; perennial crops/orchards/groves; forestry plantation)
Land-use Agriculture (15%), Fisheries/aquaculture (30%), Forestry (40%), Nature conservation/research (25%), Tourism/recreation (25%)

■ Birds

Species	Season	Year	Pop min	Pop max	Acc	Criteria
Botaurus stellaris Bittern	B	—	2	2	—	C6

The area is a breeding and staging site for reedbed species.

■ Protection status
National Partial **International** High
28 ha of IBA covered by Nature Reserve (De Borggravevijver s, 28 ha). 85 ha of IBA covered by Nature Reserve (Het Wik, 85 ha). 800 ha of IBA covered by Special Protection Area (Bokrijk, 800 ha).

■ Conservation issues

Threats Aquaculture/fisheries (A), Recreation/tourism (C)

800 ha of IBA covered by proposed Site of Community Importance (Valleien van de Laarbeek, Zonderikbeek, Slangbeek, 2,811 ha).

De Maten .C6 028
Admin region Vlaams Gewest
Coordinates 50°57'N 5°27'E
Altitude 40–60 m **Area** 600 ha

■ Site description
An extremely diverse area in the Striemerbeek valley, with heathland, marshes, oligotrophic and mesotrophic ponds, wet woodlands and inland dunes.

Habitats Forest and woodland (20%; broadleaved deciduous forest; alluvial/very wet forest), Scrub (25%; heathland), Grassland (5%), Wetland (30%; standing fresh water; water-fringe vegetation; fen/transition mire/spring), Artificial landscape (20%; arable land)
Land-use Agriculture (30%), Fisheries/aquaculture (15%), Nature conservation/research (30%), Tourism/recreation (10%), Urban/industrial/transport (10%)

■ Birds
The IBA is a breeding site for reedbed species.

Species	Season	Year	Pop min	Pop max	Acc	Criteria
Botaurus stellaris Bittern	B	—	2	2	A	C6
Lullula arborea Woodlark	B	1993	5	10	B	C6

■ Protection status
National Partial **International** High
213 ha of IBA covered by Nature Reserve (De Maten, 213 ha). 600 ha of IBA covered by Special Protection Area (De Maten, 600 ha).

■ Conservation issues

Threats Infrastructure (B), Recreation/tourism (B)

561 ha of IBA covered by proposed Site of Community Importance (De Maten, 561 ha).

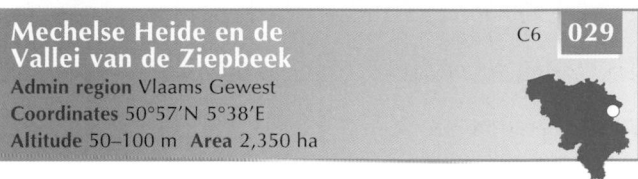

Mechelse Heide en de Vallei van de Ziepbeek C6 029
Admin region Vlaams Gewest
Coordinates 50°57'N 5°38'E
Altitude 50–100 m **Area** 2,350 ha

■ Site description
The site includes the Ziepobeek and the Asbeek valleys, which hold very important areas of wet and dry heath and fen, coniferous and deciduous woodland, and a small bog.

Habitats Forest and woodland (20%; broadleaved deciduous forest), Scrub (20%; heathland), Wetland (5%; river/stream; fen/transition mire/spring), Artificial landscape (60%; forestry plantation; ruderal land)
Land-use Agriculture (20%), Forestry (40%), Nature conservation/research (40%), Tourism/recreation (5%), Urban/industrial/transport (10%)

■ Birds

Species	Season	Year	Pop min	Pop max	Acc	Criteria
Lullula arborea Woodlark	B	1993	20	30	B	C6

A breeding area for heathland and woodland species.

■ Protection status
National Partial **International** High
545 ha of IBA covered by State Nature Reserve (Melchelse Heide, 545 ha). 161 ha of IBA covered by State Nature Reserve (Vallei van de Ziepbeek, 161 ha). 2,350 ha of IBA covered by Special Protection Area (Melchelse Heide en Vallei van de Ziepbeek, 2,350 ha).

■ Conservation issues

Threats Disturbance to birds (B), Extraction industry (A), Infrastructure (B), Recreation/tourism (A)

2,106 ha of IBA covered by proposed Site of Community Importance (Melchelse heide en vallei van de Ziepbeek, 2,371 ha).

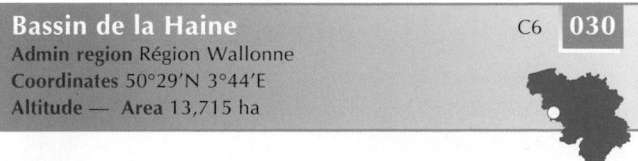

Bassin de la Haine C6 030
Admin region Région Wallonne
Coordinates 50°29'N 3°44'E
Altitude — **Area** 13,715 ha

■ Site description
A complex of ponds, marshes and grasslands in the Haine river basin.

Habitats Forest and woodland (25%; broadleaved deciduous forest; alluvial/very wet forest), Scrub (heathland), Grassland (humid grassland; mesophile grassland), Wetland (10%; standing fresh water; river/stream; water-fringe vegetation; fen/transition mire/spring), Artificial landscape (60%; highly improved reseeded grassland; perennial crops/orchards/groves; forestry plantation; urban parks/gardens; other urban/industrial areas; ruderal land)
Land-use Agriculture (25%), Fisheries/aquaculture (1%), Forestry (50%), Hunting, Nature conservation/research (5%), Tourism/recreation, Urban/industrial/transport (15%), Water management

■ Birds
Passage species include *Pandion haliaetus, Pluvialis apricaria,*

Tringa glareola, Sterna hirundo and *Lullula arborea* (summer and passage).

Species	Season	Year	Pop min	Pop max	Acc	Criteria
Ixobrychus minutus Little Bittern	B	—	1	2	B	C6
Alcedo atthis Kingfisher	B	—	10	20	B	C6
Luscinia svecica Bluethroat	B	—	80	120	B	C6

■ Protection status
National Low **International** High
254 ha of IBA covered by Nature Reserve (Nature Reserves of the Bassin de la Haine, 254 ha). 13,715 ha of IBA covered by Special Protection Area (Bassin de la Haine, 13,715 ha). 550 ha of IBA covered by Ramsar Site (Harchies, 550 ha).

■ Conservation issues
Threats Afforestation (C), Agricultural intensification/expansion (A), Aquaculture/fisheries (C), Construction/impact of dyke/dam/barrage (C), Disturbance to birds (B), Drainage (B), Dredging/canalization (C), Extraction industry (C), Filling-in of wetlands (B), Groundwater abstraction (B), Industrialization/urbanization (B), Infrastructure (B), Intensified forest management (C), Recreation/tourism (B)

Vallée de la Dyle C7 031
Admin region Région Wallonne
Coordinates 50°43'N 4°36'E
Altitude — **Area** 1,334 ha

■ Site description
The Walloon part of the Dijle river valley north of Wavre and including part of the Lasne tributary. The area encompasses ponds, marshes, grasslands and woodlands.

Habitats Forest and woodland (20%; broadleaved deciduous forest), Scrub (heathland), Grassland (humid grassland; mesophile grassland), Wetland (standing fresh water; river/stream; water-fringe vegetation; fen/transition mire/spring), Artificial landscape (70%; highly improved reseeded grassland; perennial crops/orchards/groves; forestry plantation; urban parks/gardens; other urban/industrial areas; ruderal land)
Land-use Agriculture (20%), Fisheries/aquaculture, Forestry (40%), Hunting (50%), Nature conservation/research (5%), Tourism/recreation, Urban/industrial/transport (20%)

■ Protection status
National None **International** High
1,334 ha of IBA covered by Special Protection Area (Vallée de la Dyle, 1,334 ha).

■ Conservation issues
Threats Abandonment/reduction of land management (C), Afforestation (C), Agricultural intensification/expansion (B), Aquaculture/fisheries (C), Construction/impact of dyke/dam/barrage (C), Disturbance to birds (B), Filling-in of wetlands (B), Groundwater abstraction (B), Industrialization/urbanization (A), Infrastructure (B), Intensified forest management (C), Recreation/tourism (B)

Entre-Sambre-et-Meuse A1, C1, C2, C6 032
Admin region Région Wallonne
Coordinates 50°05'N 4°28'E
Altitude — **Area** 83,866 ha

■ Site description
An exceptionally varied zone including parts of the Fagen, Calestienne and Ardennes with semi-natural humid grasslands, dry calcareous grasslands and deciduous woodlands.

Habitats Forest and woodland (50%; broadleaved deciduous forest; alluvial/very wet forest), Scrub (scrub; heathland; sclerophyllous scrub/garrigue/maquis), Grassland (steppe/dry calcareous grassland; dry siliceous grassland; humid grassland; mesophile grassland), Wetland (standing fresh water; river/stream; water-fringe vegetation; fen/transition mire/spring), Rocky areas (scree/boulders; caves), Artificial landscape (45%; highly improved reseeded grassland; perennial crops/orchards/groves; forestry plantation; urban parks/gardens; other urban/industrial areas; ruderal land)

Land-use Agriculture (30%), Fisheries/aquaculture (1%), Forestry (60%), Hunting (90%), Nature conservation/research (1%), Tourism/recreation, Urban/industrial/transport (5%), Water management (1%)

■ Birds

Species	Season	Year	Pop min	Pop max	Acc	Criteria
Pernis apivorus Honey Buzzard	B	—	20	30	B	C6
Crex crex Corncrake	B	—	3	50	—	A1, C1, C2, C6
Bubo bubo Eagle Owl	R	—	3	6	—	C6
Alcedo atthis Kingfisher	B	—	10	20	—	C6
Dryocopus martius Black Woodpecker	R	—	10	20	—	C6
Dendrocopos medius Middle Spotted Woodpecker	R	—	45	55	—	C6
Lanius collurio Red-backed Shrike	B	—	—	100	—	C6

Species listed on Annex I of the EC Birds Directive occurring on passage or in winter include *Phalacrocorax carbo, Egretta alba, Ciconia ciconia, Falco peregrinus, Falco columbarius, Pandion haliaetus, Pluvialis apricaria, Sterna hirundo* and *Chlidonias niger*.

■ Protection status
National None **International** High
83,866 ha of IBA covered by Special Protection Area (Entre-Sambre-et-Meuse, 83,866 ha).

■ Conservation issues
Threats Abandonment/reduction of land management (C), Afforestation (B), Agricultural intensification/expansion (A), Construction/impact of dyke/dam/barrage (C), Disturbance to birds (B), Drainage (B), Extraction industry (C), Filling-in of wetlands (B), Groundwater abstraction (B), Industrialization/urbanization (B), Infrastructure (B), Intensified forest management (C), Recreation/tourism (A)

Haute Meuse C6 033
Admin region Région Wallonne
Coordinates 50°15'N 4°55'E
Altitude — **Area** 7,700 ha

■ Site description
A section of the River Meuse and its tributaries, including hill-slopes with woodlands, dry grasslands and calcareous rocks.

Habitats Forest and woodland (50%; broadleaved deciduous forest; alluvial/very wet forest), Scrub (scrub), Grassland (steppe/dry calcareous grassland; humid grassland; mesophile grassland), Wetland (standing fresh water; river/stream; water-fringe vegetation; fen/transition mire/spring), Rocky areas (inland cliff; caves), Artificial landscape (35%; highly improved reseeded grassland; perennial crops/orchards/groves; forestry plantation; urban parks/gardens; other urban/industrial areas; ruderal land)
Land-use Agriculture (20%), Fisheries/aquaculture (1%), Forestry (60%), Hunting, Nature conservation/research (1%), Tourism/recreation, Urban/industrial/transport (10%), Water management (1%)

■ Birds

Species	Season	Year	Pop min	Pop max	Acc	Criteria
Bubo bubo Eagle Owl	R	—	2	5	B	C6
Alcedo atthis Kingfisher	B	—	10	20	B	C6

Species listed on Annex I of the EC Birds Directive occurring on passage or in winter include *Phalacrocorax carbo, Pandion haliaetus, Sterna hirundo* and *Chlidonias niger*.

■ Protection status
National Low **International** None
219 ha of IBA covered by Nature Reserve (Nature Reserves of Haute Meuse, 219 ha).

■ Conservation issues
Threats Abandonment/reduction of land management (C), Afforestation (C), Agricultural intensification/expansion (B), Aquaculture/fisheries (C), Consequences of animal/plant introductions (C), Construction/impact of dyke/dam/barrage (B), Disturbance to birds (A), Drainage (C), Extraction industry (A), Filling-in of wetlands (C), Groundwater abstraction (C), Industrialization/urbanization (A), Infrastructure (B), Recreation/tourism (A)

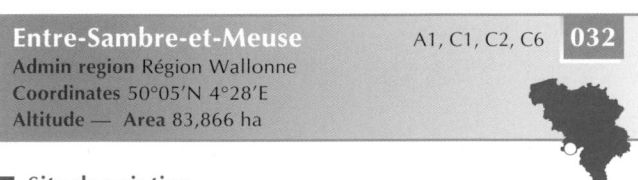

Croix-Scaille   C6 034

Admin region Région Wallonne
Coordinates 49°56'N 4°58'E
Altitude — **Area** 36,610 ha

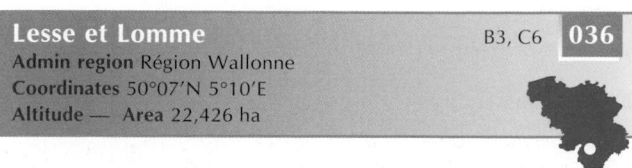

■ Site description
The site comprises the Belgian part of the Croix-Scaille upland plateau and a stretch of the Semois river, with important deciduous woodlands and well-preserved rivers, and remnant bogs and heaths on the upland plateau.

Habitats Forest and woodland (40%; broadleaved deciduous forest; alluvial/very wet forest), Scrub (heathland), Grassland (humid grassland; mesophile grassland), Wetland (standing fresh water; river/stream; raised bog; water-fringe vegetation; fen/transition mire/spring), Artificial landscape (65%; highly improved reseeded grassland; perennial crops/orchards/groves; forestry plantation; urban parks/gardens; other urban/industrial areas; ruderal land)
Land-use Agriculture (15%), Fisheries/aquaculture (1%), Forestry (80%), Hunting, Nature conservation/research (1%), Tourism/recreation, Urban/industrial/transport (5%)

■ Birds

Species	Season	Year	Pop min	Pop max	Acc	Criteria
Ciconia nigra Black Stork	B	—	2	3	A	C6

Species listed on Annex I of the EC Birds Directive occurring on passage or in winter include *Milvus migrans, M. milvus, Circus cyaneus, Pandion haliaetus* and *Lullula arborea*.

■ Protection status
National Low **International** High
211 ha of IBA covered by Nature Reserve (Nature Reserves of the Croix Scaille, 211 ha). 36,610 ha of IBA covered by Special Protection Area (Croix-Scaille, 36,610 ha).

■ Conservation issues

Threats Afforestation (B), Agricultural intensification/expansion (A), Aquaculture/fisheries (C), Construction/impact of dyke/dam/barrage (C), Disturbance to birds (C), Drainage (B), Filling-in of wetlands (C), Groundwater abstraction (C), Industrialization/urbanization (C), Infrastructure (C), Intensified forest management (C), Recreation/tourism (C)

Daverdisse   B3, C6 035

Admin region Région Wallonne
Coordinates 50°02'N 5°06'E
Altitude — **Area** 14,914 ha

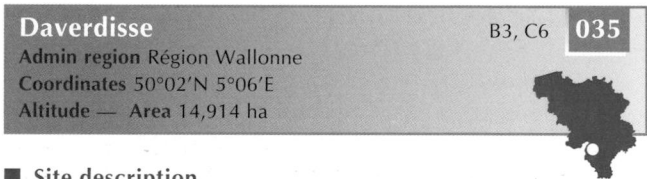

■ Site description
A large plateau of old deciduous woodland in the northern Ardennes.

Habitats Forest and woodland (80%; broadleaved deciduous forest; alluvial/very wet forest), Grassland (humid grassland; mesophile grassland), Wetland (standing fresh water; river/stream; water-fringe vegetation; fen/transition mire/spring), Artificial landscape (20%; highly improved reseeded grassland; perennial crops/orchards/groves; forestry plantation; urban parks/gardens; other urban/industrial areas)
Land-use Agriculture (10%), Fisheries/aquaculture (1%), Forestry (90%), Hunting, Nature conservation/research (1%), Tourism/recreation, Urban/industrial/transport (1%)

■ Birds

Species	Season	Year	Pop min	Pop max	Acc	Criteria
Dendrocopos medius Middle Spotted Woodpecker	R	—	40	80	B	B3, C6

■ Protection status
National Low **International** High
3 ha of IBA covered by Nature Reserve (Nature Reserves in Deverdisse, 3 ha). 14,914 ha of IBA covered by Special Protection Area (Daverdisse, 14,914 ha).

■ Conservation issues

Threats Afforestation (C), Agricultural intensification/expansion (B), Construction/impact of dyke/dam/barrage (B), Disturbance to birds (C), Drainage (C), Filling-in of wetlands (C),

Groundwater abstraction (C), Industrialization/urbanization (C), Intensified forest management (C), Recreation/tourism (C)

Lesse et Lomme   B3, C6 036

Admin region Région Wallonne
Coordinates 50°07'N 5°10'E
Altitude — **Area** 22,426 ha

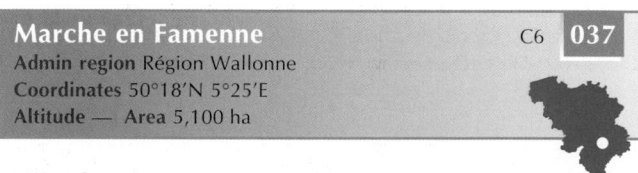

■ Site description
The area includes the most ornithologically interesting parts of the Calestienne and Famenne, along the River Meuse. A large variety of habitats are present including calcareous dry grasslands and woodlands.

Habitats Forest and woodland (40%; broadleaved deciduous forest; alluvial/very wet forest), Scrub (scrub), Grassland (humid grassland; mesophile grassland), Wetland (standing fresh water; river/stream; water-fringe vegetation; fen/transition mire/spring), Rocky areas (scree/boulders; caves), Artificial landscape (45%; highly improved reseeded grassland; perennial crops/orchards/groves; forestry plantation; urban parks/gardens; other urban/industrial areas; ruderal land)
Land-use Agriculture (45%), Fisheries/aquaculture (1%), Forestry (40%), Hunting (90%), Nature conservation/research (1%), Tourism/recreation, Urban/industrial/transport (10%)

■ Birds

Species	Season	Year	Pop min	Pop max	Acc	Criteria
Pernis apivorus Honey Buzzard	B	—	15	20	B	C6
Bonasa bonasia Hazel Grouse	R	—	5	20	B	C6
Crex crex Corncrake	B	—	—	10	B	C6
Dryocopus martius Black Woodpecker	R	—	20	25	A	C6
Dendrocopos medius Middle Spotted Woodpecker	R	—	40	50	A	B3, C6
Lanius collurio Red-backed Shrike	B	—	60	90	B	C6

Species listed on Annex I of the EC Birds Directive occurring on passage or in winter include *Milvus migrans, Circus cyaneus, Falco peregrinus, F. columbarius, Pandion haliaetus* and *Pluvialis apricaria*.

■ Protection status
National Low **International** High
1,419 ha of IBA covered by Nature Reserve (Nature Reserves of lesse et Lomme, 1,419 ha). 22,426 ha of IBA covered by Special Protection Area (Lesse et Lomme, 22,426 ha).

■ Conservation issues

Threats Afforestation (C), Agricultural intensification/expansion (A), Disturbance to birds (C), Drainage (A), Extraction industry (B), Filling-in of wetlands (C), Groundwater abstraction (C), Industrialization/urbanization (B), Infrastructure (B), Recreation/tourism (B)

Marche en Famenne   C6 037

Admin region Région Wallonne
Coordinates 50°18'N 5°25'E
Altitude — **Area** 5,100 ha

■ Site description
A typical area of the Famennian depression, covered by woodlands and pastures, and including the very important Marche en Famenne military camp, which remains free of agricultural disturbance, as well as a stretch of the River Ourthe.

Habitats Forest and woodland (40%; broadleaved deciduous forest; alluvial/very wet forest), Scrub (scrub), Grassland (1%; humid grassland; mesophile grassland), Wetland (standing fresh water; river/stream; water-fringe vegetation; fen/transition mire/spring), Artificial landscape (30%; highly improved reseeded grassland; perennial crops/orchards/groves; forestry plantation; urban parks/gardens; other urban/industrial areas; ruderal land)
Land-use Agriculture (40%), Forestry (60%), Hunting (50%), Military (40%), Nature conservation/research (1%), Tourism/recreation (60%), Urban/industrial/transport (1%)

■ Birds
Species listed on Annex I of the EC Birds Directive occurring on passage or wintering include *Milvus migrans, M. milvus, Circus cyaneus, C. aeruginosus, Falco peregrinus* and *F. columbarius*.

Species		Season	Year	Pop min	Pop max	Acc	Criteria
Crex crex	Corncrake	B	—	—	3	B	C6
Lanius collurio	Red-backed Shrike	B	—	100	130	A	C6

■ Protection status
National None **International** None

■ Conservation issues

Threats Abandonment/reduction of land management (A), Afforestation (B), Agricultural intensification/expansion (B), Disturbance to birds (B), Drainage (C), Dredging/canalization (A), Filling-in of wetlands (B), Groundwater abstraction (C), Industrialization/urbanization (B), Infrastructure (B), Intensified forest management (C), Recreation/tourism (B)

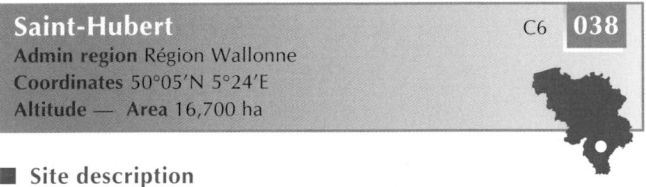

Saint-Hubert — C6 038
Admin region Région Wallonne
Coordinates 50°05′N 5°24′E
Altitude — **Area** 16,700 ha

■ Site description
A large area of old deciduous woodland in the central high Ardennes with well-preserved rivers and streams, remnant peat-bogs and heaths.

Habitats Forest and woodland (50%; broadleaved deciduous forest; alluvial/very wet forest), Grassland (humid grassland; mesophile grassland), Wetland (standing fresh water; river/stream; raised bog; water-fringe vegetation; fen/transition mire/spring), Artificial landscape (50%; highly improved reseeded grassland; perennial crops/orchards/groves; forestry plantation; urban parks/gardens; other urban/industrial areas)
Land-use Agriculture (10%), Fisheries/aquaculture (1%), Forestry (90%), Hunting, Nature conservation/research (1%), Tourism/recreation, Urban/industrial/transport (1%)

■ Birds

Species		Season	Year	Pop min	Pop max	Acc	Criteria
Ciconia nigra	Black Stork	B	—	3	5	B	C6
Aegolius funereus	Tengmalm's Owl	R	—	—	10	B	C6
Dryocopus martius	Black Woodpecker	R	—	10	20	B	C6

Species listed on Annex I of the EC Birds Directive occurring on passage or wintering include *Milvus milvus*, *M. migrans* and *Circus cyaneus*.

■ Protection status
National Low **International** None
23 ha of IBA covered by Nature Reserve (Nature Reserves de St-Hubert, 23 ha).

■ Conservation issues

Threats Afforestation (C), Agricultural intensification/expansion (C), Aquaculture/fisheries (C), Construction/impact of dyke/dam/barrage (C), Disturbance to birds (C), Drainage (C), Filling-in of wetlands (C), Groundwater abstraction (C), Industrialization/urbanization (C), Infrastructure (C), Intensified forest management (C), Recreation/tourism (C)

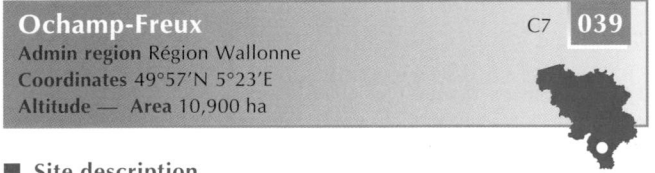

Ochamp-Freux — C7 039
Admin region Région Wallonne
Coordinates 49°57′N 5°23′E
Altitude — **Area** 10,900 ha

■ Site description
A woodland area in the high Ardennes, including many ponds and humid grasslands.

Habitats Forest and woodland (20%; broadleaved deciduous forest), Grassland (humid grassland; mesophile grassland), Wetland (standing fresh water; river/stream; raised bog; water-fringe vegetation; fen/transition mire/spring), Artificial landscape (80%; highly improved reseeded grassland; forestry plantation; urban parks/gardens; other urban/industrial areas)
Land-use Agriculture (30%), Fisheries/aquaculture (1%), Forestry (70%), Hunting (100%), Nature conservation/research (1%), Tourism/recreation, Urban/industrial/transport (1%)

■ Birds
Species listed on Annex I of the EC Birds Directive breeding at the site include *Ciconia nigra*, *Alcedo atthis* and *Lanius collurio*. Species listed on Annex I occurring on passage or wintering include *Milvus migrans*, *M. milvus*, *Circus cyaneus*, *C. aeruginosus*, *Falco columbarius*, *Pandion haliaetus* and *Pluvialis apricaria*.

■ Protection status
National None **International** None

■ Conservation issues

Threats Afforestation (B), Agricultural intensification/expansion (A), Aquaculture/fisheries (C), Construction/impact of dyke/dam/barrage (C), Disturbance to birds (C), Drainage (B), Filling-in of wetlands (B), Groundwater abstraction (B), Industrialization/urbanization (C), Infrastructure (C), Intensified forest management (C), Other (C), Recreation/tourism (C)

Malchamps — C6 040
Admin region Région Wallonne
Coordinates 50°24′N 5°39′E
Altitude — **Area** 41,638 ha

■ Site description
The western ridge of the Fagnes plateau south of Spa, covered by bogs, fens, remnant dry heaths and peaty heaths. The area includes important woodland.

Habitats Forest and woodland (10%; broadleaved deciduous forest), Scrub (heathland), Grassland (dry siliceous grassland; alpine/subalpine/boreal grassland; humid grassland; mesophile grassland), Wetland (standing fresh water; river/stream; raised bog; water-fringe vegetation; fen/transition mire/spring), Artificial landscape (80%; highly improved reseeded grassland; perennial crops/orchards/groves; forestry plantation; urban parks/gardens; other urban/industrial areas; ruderal land)
Land-use Agriculture (20%), Forestry (70%), Hunting, Nature conservation/research (5%), Tourism/recreation, Urban/industrial/transport (5%), Water management (1%)

■ Birds

Species		Season	Year	Pop min	Pop max	Acc	Criteria
Tetrao tetrix	Black Grouse	R	—	1	5	B	C6
Aegolius funereus	Tengmalm's Owl	R	—	1	10	B	C6

Species listed on Annex I of the EC Birds Directive occurring on passage or wintering include *Ciconia nigra*, *Circus cyaneus*, *Circus aeruginosus*, *Falco columbarius*, *Asio flammeus* and *Lullula arborea*.

■ Protection status
National Low **International** High
15 ha of IBA covered by Nature Reserve (Nature Reserves de Malchamps, 15 ha). 41,638 ha of IBA covered by Special Protection Area (Malchamps, 41,638 ha).

■ Conservation issues

Threats Abandonment/reduction of land management (C), Afforestation (C), Agricultural intensification/expansion (A), Disturbance to birds (C), Drainage (B), Extraction industry (C), Filling-in of wetlands (C), Groundwater abstraction (C), Industrialization/urbanization (B), Infrastructure (B), Intensified forest management (C), Recreation/tourism (A)

Vallée de la Lienne — C6 041
Admin region Région Wallonne
Coordinates 50°20′N 5°47′E
Altitude — **Area** 8,500 ha

■ Site description
An example of the traditional grasslands landscape of the high Ardennes valley, and surrounding woodland.

Habitats Forest and woodland (20%; broadleaved deciduous forest; broadleaved evergreen forest), Scrub (scrub; sclerophyllous scrub/garrigue/maquis), Grassland (dry siliceous grassland; humid grassland; mesophile grassland), Wetland (standing fresh water; river/stream; raised bog; water-fringe vegetation; fen/transition mire/spring), Artificial landscape (70%; highly improved reseeded grassland; perennial crops/orchards/groves; forestry plantation; urban parks/gardens; other urban/industrial areas)

Land-use Agriculture (20%), Forestry (70%), Hunting, Nature conservation/research (1%), Tourism/recreation, Urban/industrial/transport (5%)

■ Birds

Species	Season	Year	Pop min	Pop max	Acc	Criteria
Aegolius funereus Tengmalm's Owl	R	—	1	10	B	C6

Species listed on Annex I of the EC Birds Directive occurring on passage or wintering include *Milvus migrans, M. milvus, Circus cyaneus, C. aeruginosus, Falco columbarius* and *Lullula arborea*.

■ Protection status
National None **International** None

■ Conservation issues

Threats Abandonment/reduction of land management (C), Afforestation (B), Agricultural intensification/expansion (B), Disturbance to birds (C), Drainage (B), Filling-in of wetlands (B), Groundwater abstraction (B), Industrialization/urbanization (C), Intensified forest management (C), Recreation/tourism (B)

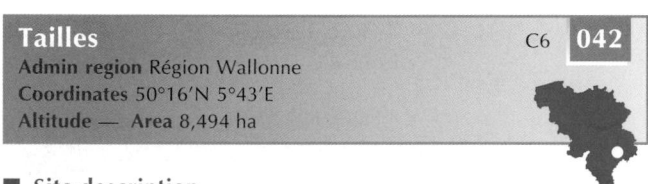

Tailles C6 | 042
Admin region Région Wallonne
Coordinates 50°16'N 5°43'E
Altitude — **Area** 8,494 ha

■ Site description
An area of mires and heaths in a woodland and grassland landscape in the Ardennes.

Habitats Forest and woodland (20%; broadleaved deciduous forest), Scrub, Grassland (dry siliceous grassland; alpine/subalpine/boreal grassland; humid grassland; mesophile grassland), Wetland (standing fresh water; river/stream; raised bog; water-fringe vegetation; fen/transition mire/spring), Artificial landscape (70%; highly improved reseeded grassland; perennial crops/orchards/groves; forestry plantation; urban parks/gardens; other urban/industrial areas; ruderal land)
Land-use Agriculture (20%), Forestry (60%), Hunting (70%), Nature conservation/research (10%), Tourism/recreation, Urban/industrial/transport (5%)

■ Birds

Species	Season	Year	Pop min	Pop max	Acc	Criteria
[1] *Bonasa bonasia* Hazel Grouse	R	—	Rare		—	C6
Aegolius funereus Tengmalm's Owl	R	—	1	15	B	C6
1. Population size unknown.						

Species listed on Annex I of the EC Birds Directive occurring on passage or wintering include *Milvus migrans, M. milvus, Circus cyaneus, C. aeruginosus* and *Falco columbarius*.

■ Protection status
National Low **International** High
468 ha of IBA covered by Nature Reserve (Nature Reserves at Plateau des Tailles, 468 ha). 8,494 ha of IBA covered by Special Protection Area (Plateau des Tailles, 8,494 ha).

■ Conservation issues

Threats Abandonment/reduction of land management (C), Afforestation (A), Agricultural intensification/expansion (B), Burning of vegetation (C), Disturbance to birds (C), Drainage (B), Filling-in of wetlands (B), Groundwater abstraction (B), Industrialization/urbanization (C), Infrastructure (C), Intensified forest management (C), Recreation/tourism (B)

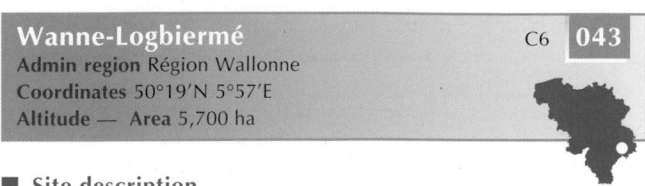

Wanne-Logbiermé C6 | 043
Admin region Région Wallonne
Coordinates 50°19'N 5°57'E
Altitude — **Area** 5,700 ha

■ Site description
A high plateau covered mainly by spruce plantations with remnant acid fens and *Fagus* woodland.

Habitats Forest and woodland (10%; broadleaved deciduous forest), Grassland (humid grassland; mesophile grassland), Wetland (standing fresh water; river/stream; water-fringe vegetation; fen/transition mire/spring), Artificial landscape (90%; highly improved reseeded grassland; forestry plantation; urban parks/gardens; other urban/industrial areas)
Land-use Agriculture (5%), Forestry (90%), Hunting, Nature conservation/research (1%), Tourism/recreation, Urban/industrial/transport (1%)

■ Birds

Species	Season	Year	Pop min	Pop max	Acc	Criteria
Aegolius funereus Tengmalm's Owl	R	—	1	20	B	C6

Species listed on Annex I of the EC Birds Directive occurring on passage or wintering include *Milvus milvus, M. migrans, Circus cyaneus, C. aeruginosus* and *Lullula arborea*.

■ Protection status
National Low **International** None
1 ha of IBA covered by Nature Reserve (Natures Reserves in Wanne-Longbiermé, 1 ha).

■ Conservation issues

Threats Afforestation (A), Agricultural intensification/expansion (C), Aquaculture/fisheries (C), Drainage (C), Filling-in of wetlands (C), Industrialization/urbanization (C), Intensified forest management (B), Recreation/tourism (C)

Hautes Fagnes/Eifel A4i, B1i, B1iv, C2, C5, C6 | 044
Admin region Région Wallonne
Coordinates 50°24'N 6°15'E
Altitude — **Area** 80,304 ha

■ Site description
The site includes the high plateau of the eastern Ardennes, covered by peatbogs, fens and woodland.

Habitats Forest and woodland (20%; broadleaved deciduous forest; alluvial/very wet forest), Scrub (2%; scrub; heathland), Grassland (5%; dry siliceous grassland; alpine/subalpine/boreal grassland; humid grassland; mesophile grassland), Wetland (standing fresh water; river/stream; raised bog; water-fringe vegetation; fen/transition mire/spring), Artificial landscape (60%; highly improved reseeded grassland; perennial crops/orchards/groves; forestry plantation; urban parks/gardens; other urban/industrial areas)
Land-use Agriculture (20%), Forestry (60%), Hunting (90%), Military (4%), Nature conservation/research (10%), Tourism/recreation (90%), Urban/industrial/transport (5%), Water management (5%)

■ Birds

Species	Season	Year	Pop min	Pop max	Acc	Criteria
Pernis apivorus Honey Buzzard	B	—	15	30	B	C6
Milvus milvus Red Kite	B	—	20	30	B	C6
Tetrao tetrix Black Grouse	R	—	25	35	A	C6
Crex crex Corncrake	B	—	—	2	B	C6
Grus grus Crane	P	—	—	5,000	—	A4i,B1i,B1iv,C2,C5
Picus canus Grey-headed Woodpecker	R	—	6	15	B	C6
Dryocopus martius Black Woodpecker	R	—	10	20	B	C6
Lullula arborea Woodlark	B	—	10	20	B	C6
Lanius collurio Red-backed Shrike	B	—	—	100	B	C6

Species listed on Annex I of the EC Birds Directive occurring on passage or wintering include *Circus aeruginosus, Falco columbarius, Pandion haliaetus* and *Grus grus*.

■ Protection status
National Partial **International** High
4,448 ha of IBA covered by Nature Reserve (Nature Reserves in Hautes Fagnes Eiffel, 4,448 ha). 67,800 ha of IBA covered by Natural Park. 80,304 ha of IBA covered by Special Protection Area (Hautes Fagnes/Eifel, 80,304 ha).

■ Conservation issues

Threats Abandonment/reduction of land management (B), Afforestation (C), Agricultural intensification/expansion (A), Burning of vegetation (C), Construction/impact of dyke/dam/barrage (C), Disturbance to birds (B), Drainage (B), Filling-in of wetlands (C),

Groundwater abstraction (C), Industrialization/urbanization (C), Infrastructure (C), Recreation/tourism (A)

Deux Ourthes   C6   045
Admin region Région Wallonne
Coordinates 50°05′N 5°46′E
Altitude — **Area** 34,678 ha

■ Site description
An undisturbed part of the Ourthe valley with wooded slopes.

Habitats Forest and woodland (20%; broadleaved deciduous forest; alluvial/very wet forest), Scrub (scrub; heathland), Grassland (1%; humid grassland; mesophile grassland), Wetland (1%; standing fresh water; river/stream; raised bog; water-fringe vegetation; fen/transition mire/spring), Rocky areas (scree/boulders; caves), Artificial landscape (70%; highly improved reseeded grassland; perennial crops/orchards/groves; forestry plantation; urban parks/gardens; other urban/industrial areas; ruderal land)
Land-use Agriculture (80%), Fisheries/aquaculture (1%), Forestry (15%), Hunting, Nature conservation/research (1%), Tourism/recreation, Urban/industrial/transport (5%), Water management (1%)

■ Birds

Species	Season	Year	Pop min	Pop max	Acc	Criteria
Ciconia nigra Black Stork	B	—	1	3	B	C6
¹ *Bonasa bonasia* Hazel Grouse	R	—	Rare	—		C6

1. Population size unknown.

Species listed on Annex I of the EC Birds Directive occurring on passage or wintering include *Milvus migrans, Circus cyaneus, C. aeruginosus, Pandion haliaetus* and *Lullula arborea*.

■ Protection status
National None   **International** High
34,678 ha of IBA covered by Special Protection Area (Deux Ourthes, 34,678 ha).

■ Conservation issues
Threats Abandonment/reduction of land management (C), Afforestation (C), Agricultural intensification/expansion (A), Aquaculture/fisheries (C), Construction/impact of dyke/dam/barrage (C), Disturbance to birds (C), Drainage (B), Filling-in of wetlands (B), Groundwater abstraction (C), Industrialization/urbanization (B), Infrastructure (C), Recreation/tourism (C)

Haute Sûre/Ardenne méridionale   B3, C6   046
Admin region Région Wallonne
Coordinates 49°44′N 5°28′E
Altitude — **Area** 89,443 ha

■ Site description
An important area of woodland at the southern limit of the Ardennes and the upper basin of the Sûre river, with many old humid grasslands.

Habitats Forest and woodland (40%; broadleaved deciduous forest; alluvial/very wet forest), Scrub (scrub; heathland), Grassland (1%; humid grassland; mesophile grassland), Wetland (1%; standing fresh water; river/stream; raised bog; water-fringe vegetation; fen/transition mire/spring), Rocky areas (caves), Artificial landscape (50%; highly improved reseeded grassland; perennial crops/orchards/groves; forestry plantation; urban parks/gardens; other urban/industrial areas; ruderal land)
Land-use Agriculture (40%), Fisheries/aquaculture (1%), Forestry (50%), Hunting, Nature conservation/research (1%), Not utilized (1%), Tourism/recreation, Urban/industrial/transport (5%), Water management (1%)

■ Birds

Species	Season	Year	Pop min	Pop max	Acc	Criteria
Ciconia nigra Black Stork	B	—	5	8	B	C6
Pernis apivorus Honey Buzzard	B	—	20	40	B	C6
¹ *Bonasa bonasia* Hazel Grouse	R	—	Rare	—		C6
Alcedo atthis Kingfisher	R	—	10	20	B	C6

Species ... continued	Season	Year	Pop min	Pop max	Acc	Criteria
Dendrocopos medius Middle Spotted Woodpecker	R	—	120	150	A	B3, C6

1. Population size unknown.

Species listed on Annex I of the EC Birds Directive occurring on passage or wintering include *Circus cyaneus, C. aeruginosus, Falco columbarius, Pandion haliaetus* and *Lullula arborea*.

■ Protection status
National Low   **International** High
440 ha of IBA covered by Nature Reserve (Nature Reserves Ardennes méridional et Haute Sûre, 440 ha). 89,443 ha of IBA covered by Special Protection Area (Haute Sure/Ardenne meridionale, 89,443 ha).

■ Conservation issues
Threats Abandonment/reduction of land management (C), Afforestation (C), Agricultural intensification/expansion (A), Aquaculture/fisheries (C), Construction/impact of dyke/dam/barrage (C), Disturbance to birds (C), Drainage (B), Extraction industry (C), Filling-in of wetlands (B), Groundwater abstraction (C), Industrialization/urbanization (B), Infrastructure (C), Recreation/tourism (C)

Sinémurienne   C6   047
Admin region Région Wallonne
Coordinates 49°38′N 5°32′E
Altitude — **Area** 32,541 ha

■ Site description
The area includes forests on sandstone in the Sinémuriennen region, and the marshes of the upper Semois river.

Habitats Forest and woodland (50%; broadleaved deciduous forest; alluvial/very wet forest), Scrub (1%; scrub; heathland), Grassland (1%; steppe/dry calcareous grassland; dry siliceous grassland; humid grassland; mesophile grassland), Wetland (1%; standing fresh water; river/stream; raised bog; water-fringe vegetation; fen/transition mire/spring), Artificial landscape (40%; highly improved reseeded grassland; perennial crops/orchards/groves; forestry plantation; urban parks/gardens; other urban/industrial areas; ruderal land)
Land-use Agriculture (40%), Fisheries/aquaculture (1%), Forestry (50%), Hunting, Military (8%), Nature conservation/research (2%), Not utilized (1%), Tourism/recreation, Urban/industrial/transport (5%)

■ Birds

Species	Season	Year	Pop min	Pop max	Acc	Criteria
Pernis apivorus Honey Buzzard	B	—	20	30	B	C6
Milvus migrans Black Kite	B	—	1	4	B	C6
Milvus milvus Red Kite	B	—	5	10	B	C6
Bonasa bonasia Hazel Grouse	R	—	—	10	B	C6
Crex crex Corncrake	B	—	—	2	B	C6
Caprimulgus europaeus Nightjar	B	—	12	15	A	C6
Picus canus Grey-headed Woodpecker	R	—	—	3	B	C6
Dendrocopos medius Middle Spotted Woodpecker	R	—	130	170	A	C6
Lullula arborea Woodlark	B	—	25	33	B	C6

Species listed on Annex I of the EC Birds Directive occurring on passage or wintering include *Circus cyaneus, C. aeruginosus, Falco columbarius* and *Pandion haliaetus.*

■ Protection status
National Low   **International** High
239 ha of IBA covered by Nature Reserve (Nature Reserves in Sinémurienne, 239 ha). 32,541 ha of IBA covered by Special Protection Area (Sinémurienne, 32,541 ha).

■ Conservation issues
Threats Afforestation (C), Agricultural intensification/expansion (A), Aquaculture/fisheries (C), Construction/impact of dyke/dam/barrage (C), Disturbance to birds (C), Drainage (B), Extraction industry (C), Filling-in of wetlands (B), Groundwater abstraction (B), Industrialization/urbanization (B), Infrastructure (C), Recreation/tourism (B), Selective logging/cutting (B)

Côte Bajocienne   C6   048

Admin region Région Wallonne
Coordinates 49°33'N 5°30'E
Altitude — **Area** 8,287 ha

■ Site description
The site comprises the Bajoncienne limestone ridge, covered mainly by woodlands, dry grasslands, copses and marshes.

Habitats Forest and woodland (20%; broadleaved deciduous forest; alluvial/very wet forest), Scrub (1%; scrub), Grassland (1%; steppe/dry calcareous grassland; dry siliceous grassland; humid grassland; mesophile grassland), Wetland (1%; standing fresh water; river/stream; water-fringe vegetation; fen/transition mire/spring), Rocky areas (caves), Artificial landscape (80%; highly improved reseeded grassland; perennial crops/orchards/groves; forestry plantation; urban parks/gardens; other urban/industrial areas; ruderal land)
Land-use Agriculture (65%), Fisheries/aquaculture (1%), Forestry (25%), Hunting, Nature conservation/research (1%), Not utilized (1%), Tourism/recreation, Urban/industrial/transport (10%), Water management (1%)

■ Birds

Species		Season	Year	Pop min	Pop max	Acc	Criteria
Lanius collurio	Red-backed Shrike	B	—	100	120	B	C6

Species listed on Annex I of the EC Birds Directive occurring on passage or wintering include *Circus cyaneus, C. aeruginosus* and *Pandion haliaetus.*

■ Protection status
National None **International** High
8,287 ha of IBA covered by Special Protection Area (Cote Bajocienne, 8,287 ha).

■ Conservation issues
Threats Afforestation (C), Agricultural intensification/expansion (A), Construction/impact of dyke/dam/barrage (C), Disturbance to birds (C), Drainage (C), Filling-in of wetlands (B), Groundwater abstraction (C), Industrialization/urbanization (A), Infrastructure (A), Recreation/tourism (B), Selective logging/cutting (B)

REFERENCES

ANSELIN, A., PAELINCKX, D., DEVOS, K., VAN HOVE, M. AND KUIJKEN, E. (1998) *Voorstel tot aanpassingen van de perimeter van de Vogelrichtlijngebieden in Vlaanderen en tot uitbreiding van het aantal habitats binnen de niet-integraal beschermde gebieden.* Adviesnota niet advries Instituut voor Natuurbehoud, A98/107.

BIGARÉ, H. (1992a) *Vogelrichtlijngebieden in West-Vlaanderen.* Brussels: Natuurreservaten, Knelpuntdossier Deel.

BIGARÉ, H. (1992b) *Vogelrichtlijngebieden in Oost-Vlaanderen en Brabant.* Brussels: Natuurreservaten, Knelpuntdossier Deel.

BIGARÉ, H. (1992c) *Vogelrichtlijngebieden in Antwerpen.* Brussels: Natuurreservaten, Knelpuntdossier Deel.

BIGARÉ, H. (1992d) *Vogelrichtlijngebieden in Limburg.* Brussels: Natuurreservaten, Knelpuntdossier Deel.

DE BLUST, G. AND SLOOTMAEKERS, M. (1997) *De Kalmthoutse Heide.* Leuven, Belgium: Davidsfonds.

DE RIDDER, F. AND GABRIELS, J. (1994) Wijzigingen in het broedvogelbestand in de vogelrichtlijngebieden van de provincie Limburg. Changes in the breeding bird populations in special protection areas of the province of Limburg. *Oriolus* 60(4): 93–101.

DE SCHEEMAEKER, F. AND LUST, P. (1996) Broedvogels in Noord-West-Vlaanderen in 1995. Breeding birds in North-West-Flanders in 1995. *Mergus* 10(4): 266–332.

DEVOS, K. AND ANSELIN, C. (1996) *Kolonievogels en zeldzame broedvogels in Vlaanderen in 1994.* Brussels: Instituut voor Natuurbehoud (Rapport IN 96/20).

DEVOS, K., MEIRE, P. AND KUIJKEN, E. (1996) *Vlaamse bijdrage tot internationale monitoring van watervogels.* Brussels: Instituut voor Natuurbehoud (Rapport IN 96/1).

GABRIELS, J., STEVENS, J. AND VAN SANDEN, J. (1994) *Broedvogelatlas van Limburg.* Hasselt, Belgium: Likona.

GRIMMETT, R. F. A. AND JONES, T. A. (1989) *Important Bird Areas in Europe.* Cambridge, UK: International Council for Bird Preservation (Techn. Publ. 9).

HEATH, M. F. AND BORGGREVE, C. (2000) *BirdLife International/EBCC European Bird Database 1998.* Cambridge, UK: BirdLife International.

JACOB, J.-P. (1993) Etat de l'Environnement wallon. Les oiseaux: tendances observées et interprétation. Pp. 152-161 in *Ministère de la Région Wallonne, Namur: Etat de l'environnement Wallon 1993.*

KUIJKEN, E. (1999). *Toestand van de natuur in Vlaanderen, cijfers voor het beleid.* Brussels: Mededelingen van het Instituut voor Natuurbehoud 6.

KUIJKEN, E. (Ed.) (1998). *Ramsar National Report Belgium.* Brussels: Rapport Instituut voor Natuurbehoud.

TUCKER, G. M. AND HEATH, M. F. (1994) *Birds in Europe: their conservation status.* Cambridge, UK: BirdLife International (BirdLife Conservation Series no. 3).

ULENAERS, P. (1995) *Ecologische situatieschets van het vijvergebied Midden-Limburg. Ecological situation of the vijvergebied Midden-Limburg.* Brussels: Instituut voor Natuurbehoud (Rapport IN 95/2).

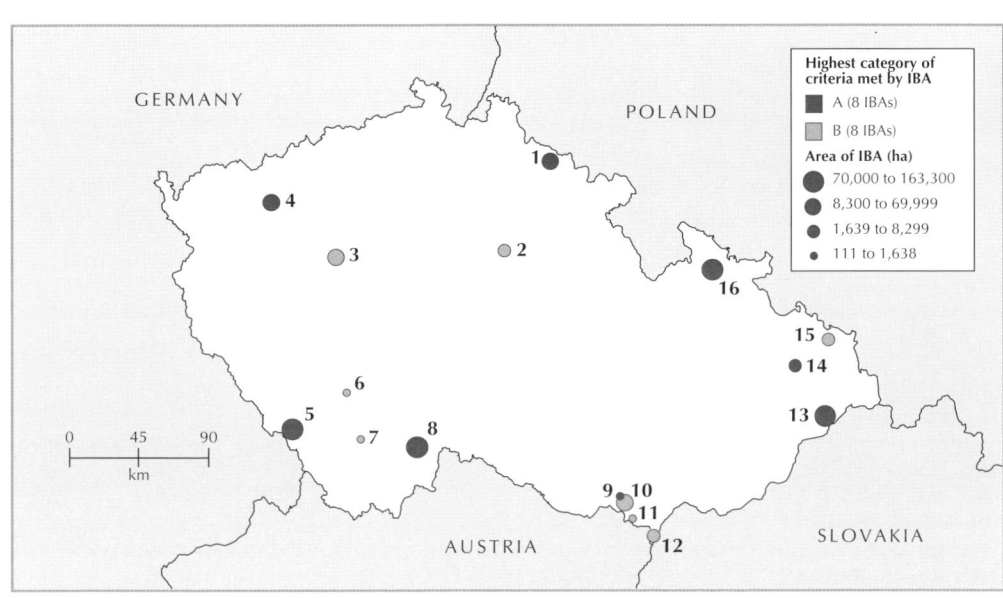

Třeboňsko Rožmberk Ponds (IBA 008). (PHOTO: DR JAN ŠEVČÍK)

GENERAL INTRODUCTION

The Czech Republic, covering 78,864 km² and supporting a population of 10 million, was established on 1 January 1993 following the splitting of the former Czech and Slovak Federal Republic into two independent countries.

Altitude ranges from 149 m above sea level at the confluence of the Morava and Dyje rivers (site 012) to 1,602 m in the Krkonoše mountains (001). The majority of the country's borders are mountainous, while hilly landscapes dominate the interior. The most important lowlands, from an ornithological perspective, are situated along the rivers Elbe, Oder, lower and middle March and Thaya. In spite of the country's small area, geographical, geological and climatic conditions mean that landscape and biological diversity are relatively high.

The Czech Republic has 16 Important Bird Areas (IBAs) covering 6,279 km², or 8% of the land area (Table 1, Map 1). Thirteen IBAs were identified in the previous European IBA inventory (Grimmett and Jones 1989), and 18 were included in the national IBA inventory (Hora and Kaňuch 1992). The five IBAs identified between 1989 and 1992 were Břehyňský rybník pond (CR-07), Skařiny (CR-11), Poodří (CR-16), Beskydy mountains (CR-17) and Jeseníky mountains (CR-18). The application of the current IBA criteria resulted in the disqualification of five of the IBAs included in the 1992 inventory, and the addition of three new IBAs (Table 1).

Map 1. Location, area and criteria category of Important Bird Areas in the Czech Republic.

GERMANY

POLAND

Highest category of criteria met by IBA

■ A (8 IBAs)

■ B (8 IBAs)

Area of IBA (ha)

● 70,000 to 163,300

● 8,300 to 69,999

● 1,639 to 8,299

• 111 to 1,638

1

4

3

2

16

15

14

6

5

13

7

8

9 10

11

12

AUSTRIA

SLOVAKIA

0   45   90
km

123

Table 1. Summary of Important Bird Areas in the Czech Republic. 16 IBAs covering 6,279 km²

IBA code	National code	1989 code	International name	National name	Administrative region	Area (ha)	Criteria (see p. 11)
001	CR-01	CZ001, CZ001-1, CZ001-2	Krkonoše mountains (Giant mountains)	Krkonoše	Trutnov and Semily	54,800	A1, B2, B3
002	CR-08	CZ007	Žehuňský rybník pond	Žehuňský rybník	Nymburk	1,639	B2
003	—	—	Křivoklátsko (Křivoklátsko region)	Křivoklátsko	Rakovník, Beroun, Kladno, Rokycany, Plzeň-sever	62,792	B2, B3
004	—	—	Doupov hills	Doupovské hory	Karlovy Vary, Chomutov and Louny	60,000	A1, B2, B3
005	CR-02	CZ002, CZ002-1, CZ002-2	Šumava mountains (Bohemian forest)	Šumava	Český Krumlov, Prachatice, Klatovy	163,000	A1, B2, B3
006	CR-05	CZ005	Řežabinec pond	Řežabinec	Písek	111	B1i, B2
007	CR-04	CZ004	Dehtář pond	Dehtář	České Budějovice	250	B1i
008	CR-03	CZ003, CZ003-1, CZ003-2, CZ003-3	Třeboňsko (Třeboň region)	Třeboňsko	Jindřichův Hradec, České Budějovice, Tábor	70,000	A1, A4i, B1i, B2, B3
009	CR-14	CZ012	Nové Mlýny middle reservoir	Střední nádrž VDNM	Břeclav	1,080	A1, A4i, A4iii, B1i, B2
010	CR-09	CZ008	Pálava	Pálava	Břeclav	8,300	B2, B3
011	CR-12	CZ010	Lednické rybníky ponds (Lednice fish-ponds)	Lednické rybníky	Břeclav	653	B1i, B2, B3
012	CR-10	CZ009	Confluence of the Morava (March) and Dyje (Thaya) rivers	Soutok	Břeclav	5,000	B2, B3
013	CR-17	—	Beskydy mountains	Beskydy	Nový Jičín, Frýdek-Místek, Vsetín	116,000	A1, B2, B3
014	CR-16	—	Poodří	Poodří	Nový Jičín, Ostrava, Frýdek-Místek	8,150	A4iii, B2, B3
015	—	—	Heřmanský stav pond–Stružka wetlands	Heřmanský stav–Stružka	Ostrava, Karviná	3,000	B2
016	CR-18	—	Jeseníky mountains	Jeseníky	Bruntál, Jeseník, Šumperk	73,078	A1, B2, B3

Sites identified in the previous inventory of IBAs in Europe (Grimmett and Jones 1989) but no longer considered to be IBAs
CZ006 Novozámecký rybník pond; CZ011 Pohořelické rybníky ponds; CZ013 Znojmo area
Sites identified in the inventory of IBAs in the Czech Republic (Hora and Kaňuch 1992) but no longer considered to be IBAs
CR-07 Břehyňský rybník pond; CR-11 Skařiny

ORNITHOLOGICAL IMPORTANCE

Table 1 presents the criteria on which each IBA is qualifying. Seven IBAs support important populations of globally threatened and near-threatened species, and therefore meet the A1 criterion (Table 2). Five sites are identified as being of international importance for wintering and migrating wildfowl, including *Anser fabalis*, *Anser albifrons*, *Anser anser* and *Anas strepera* (Table 3). An additional site (014) holds important congregations of breeding and passage waterbirds (Table 1). Fifteen of the 16 IBAs qualify under the B2/B3 criteria (Table 4), having been identified as nationally important for species of European conservation concern (SPECs; Tucker and Heath 1994).

Of the 390 bird species recorded in the Czech Republic between 1800 and 1994, 186 regularly breed, 133 regularly winter and 184 occur regularly on passage (Hudec *et al.* 1995). One hundred and eleven SPECs regularly occur: three are globally threatened (*Aythya nyroca*, *Crex crex* and *Otis tarda*), 56 have an unfavourable conservation status in Europe, while 52 have a favourable conservation status (Tucker and Heath 1994).

Table 2. Important Bird Areas in the Czech Republic that are important for species of global conservation concern (meeting criterion A1).

Species	IBA code
Haliaeetus albicilla White-tailed Eagle	008, 009
Crex crex Corncrake	001, 004, 005, 013, 016

Table 3. Important Bird Areas in the Czech Republic that support important numbers of one or more congregatory species (i.e. meeting criteria A4 and/or B1). IBAs meeting both criteria A4 and B1 for the species are shown in **bold**. IBAs meeting only criterion B1 for the species concerned, and not A4, are shown in normal type. For key to 'Season' see p. 7.

Species	Season	IBA code
Anser fabalis Bean Goose	W	**009**
Anser albifrons White-fronted Goose	W	**009**
Anser anser Greylag Goose	P	006, 007, **008**, **009**, 011
Anas strepera Gadwall	B	**008**
	P	**008**

Table 4. Species of European conservation concern with significant breeding populations at Important Bird Areas in the Czech Republic (meeting any IBA criteria).

Species [1]	Minimum national breeding population (pairs) [2]	Proportion (%) of national population breeding at all IBAs in the Czech Republic
Nycticorax nycticorax Night Heron	300	90
Ciconia nigra Black Stork	200	33
Ciconia ciconia White Stork	594	11
Anas strepera Gadwall	1,500	72
Netta rufina Red-crested Pochard	160	38
Aythya ferina Pochard	10,000	9
Pernis apivorus Honey Buzzard	600	9
Haliaeetus albicilla White-tailed Eagle	7	71
Crex crex Corncrake	200	100[3]
Columba oenas Stock Dove	3,000	24
Bubo bubo Eagle Owl	600	12
Alcedo atthis Kingfisher	300	22
Jynx torquilla Wryneck	2,500	22
Picus canus Grey-headed Woodpecker	3,000	7
Picus viridis Green Woodpecker	9,000	4
Dendrocopos medius Middle Spotted Woodpecker	3,000	9
Picoides tridactylus Three-toed Woodpecker	300	83
Turdus torquatus Ring Ouzel	1,500	77
Sylvia nisoria Barred Warbler	1,500	43
Ficedula albicollis Collared Flycatcher	25,000	26
Lanius collurio Red-backed Shrike	25,000	13

Estimates of the total numbers of the following SPECs, present in IBAs in the Czech Republic, are not currently available: *Falco tinnunculus*, *Columba palumbus*, *Streptopelia turtur*, *Strix aluco*, *Alauda arvensis*, *Riparia riparia*, *Hirundo rustica*, *Phoenicurus phoenicurus*, *Locustella naevia*, *Locustella fluviatilis* and *Regulus ignicapillus*.

1. Only those species of European conservation concern (see Box 1, p. 12) that meet IBA criteria in the Czech Republic are listed.
2. Data are taken from the BirdLife/EBCC European Bird Database 1998 (Heath and Borggreve 2000).
3. The percentage of the national population in IBAs exceeds 100%. Usually this is because the national population estimate has not been updated recently whilst the IBA population estimate has been recently updated with new data as a result of comprehensive surveys of IBAs themselves. Also, the individual site count for a species may be the maximum or average over recent years, and summing these may record more birds than are present nationally in any single year.

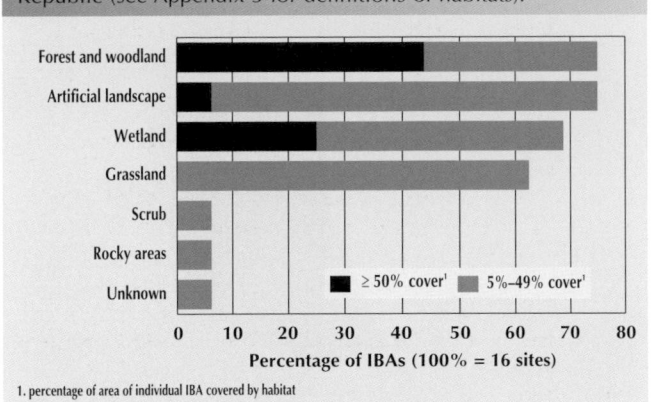

Figure 1. Habitats at Important Bird Areas in the Czech Republic (see Appendix 3 for definitions of habitats).

1. percentage of area of individual IBA covered by habitat

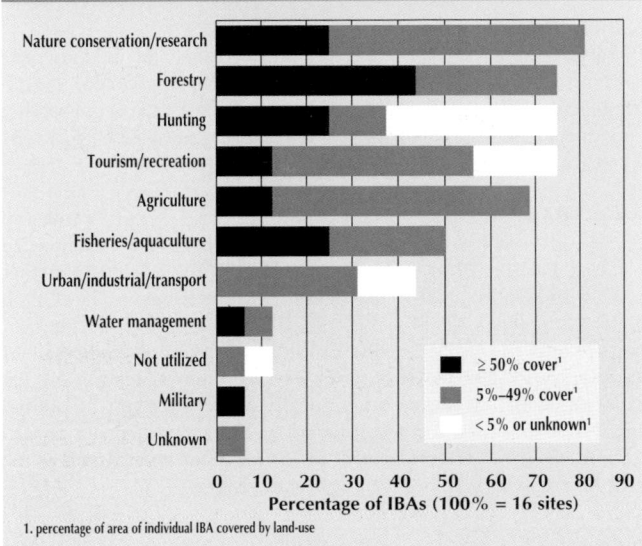

Figure 2. Land-uses at Important Bird Areas in the Czech Republic (see Appendix 3 for definitions of land-uses).

1. percentage of area of individual IBA covered by land-use

The following SPECs are not adequately covered by the IBA network: *Otis tarda*, *Burhinus oedicnemus* and *Grus grus*. Numbers of *O. tarda*, *B. oedicnemus* and *Aythya nyroca* are precariously low in the Czech Republic, and *G. grus* is a new breeder since the 1980s.

HABITATS

In the Czech Republic as a whole, 33% of the land area is covered by forest and 54% by agricultural land. Arable land accounts for c.74% of the latter, although in recent years this proportion has fallen following an increase in the area of fallow land. Only 11% of agricultural land is under permanent grass (meadows and pastures).

Forests cover over 50% of the land area of seven (44%) Czech IBAs (Figure 1), and predominate in mountainous or hilly regions (001, 003, 005, 013, 016). The replacement of native, species-rich forest by coniferous plantations has led to a pronounced change in forest composition, with the majority of forested land now covered by *Picea* monocultures. Native forests consist mainly of deciduous broadleaved species (mostly *Fagus* and *Quercus*), with coniferous species (mostly *Abies*) accounting for one third of the total. Secondary forests, on the other hand, are dominated by coniferous species (in particular *Picea* and *Pinus*) which can account for almost 80% of all trees present (see also Analytical Methods). The proportion of deciduous species in Czech forests as a whole has declined to 20%.

Wetland habitats are present at the majority of Czech IBAs, and four sites (25%) have wetlands covering more than 50% of their area. Fish-ponds are a typical feature of the landscape (002, 006, 007, 008, 011, 014, 015) with c.21,000 ponds covering a total area of c.49,000 ha in the country, and together with water reservoirs (009) provide important feeding opportunities for wintering and passage waterbirds.

Additional habitats of ornithological importance within the Czech Republic include remnant flood-plain forest, peatbog and small areas of alpine meadow, steppe-grassland and forest-steppe.

IMPACTS ON IBAs – LAND-USE AND THREATS

Figure 2 shows the most common forms of land-use in IBAs in the Czech Republic. Nature conservation and research activity is widespread in the core zones of National Parks and Protected Landscape Areas, and in smaller protected areas such as National Nature Reserves. Forestry is the dominant land-use in mountainous regions, and both hunting and recreational activities take place in the majority (75%) of IBAs.

Fisheries are present at 8 IBAs (50%), and form the major land-use at four of these (006, 007, 009, 011). Intensive carp *Cyprinus* rearing has a negative impact on both habitat quality and feeding opportunities for waterbirds (Figure 3).

Eleven of the 16 IBAs (69%) support some form of agricultural activity. Intensive agricultural practices and industrial development have adversely affected the Czech landscape in recent decades. The overall impact of farming has lessened due to increases both in the amount of land under non-intensive management and in the total

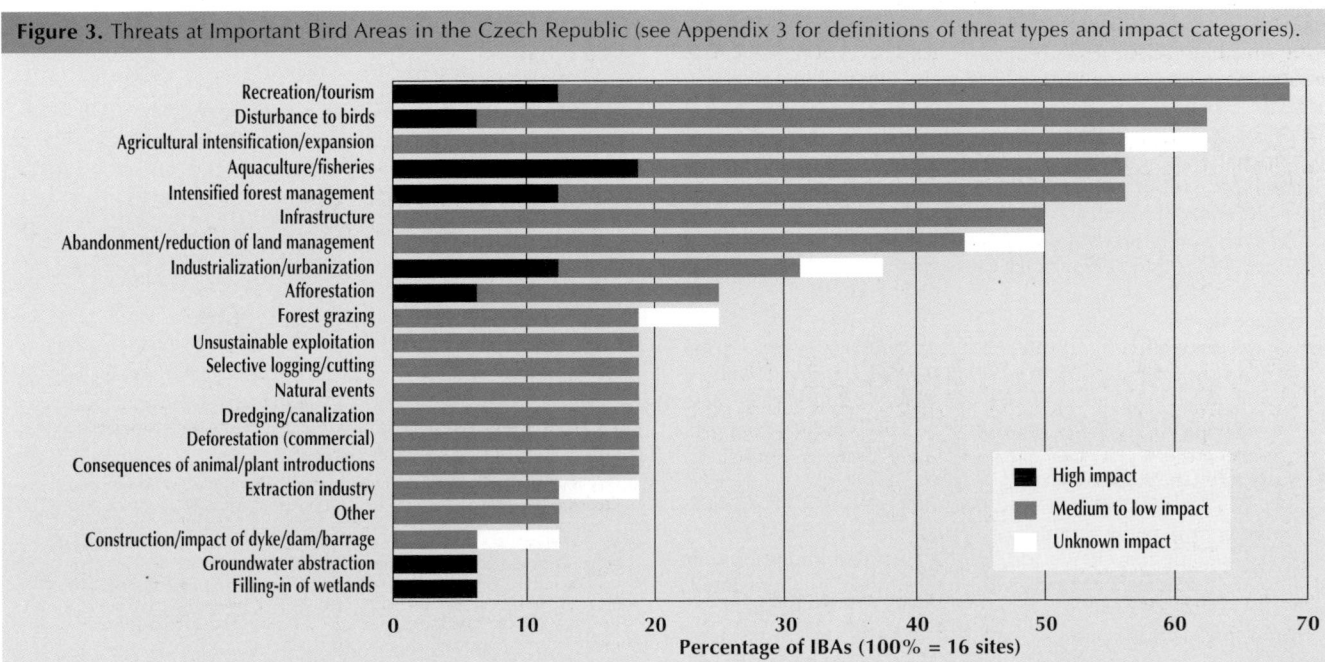

Figure 3. Threats at Important Bird Areas in the Czech Republic (see Appendix 3 for definitions of threat types and impact categories).

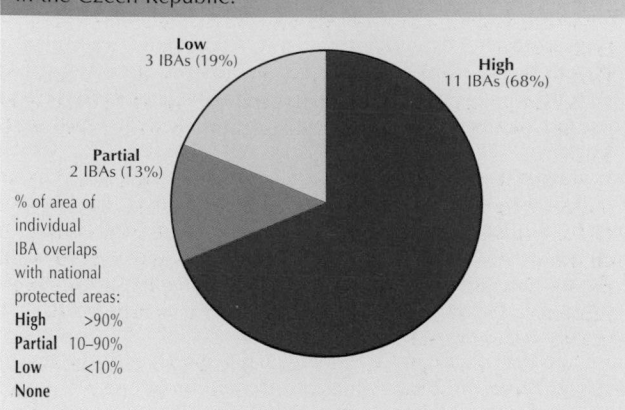

Figure 4. The national protection status of Important Bird Areas in the Czech Republic.

Low
3 IBAs (19%)

High
11 IBAs (68%)

Partial
2 IBAs (13%)

% of area of
individual
IBA overlaps
with national
protected areas:

High >90%
Partial 10–90%
Low <10%
None

Total area of overlap between IBA network in the Czech Republic and national protected-area system (see Table 5 for categories) = 4,912–5,597 km² (78–89% of total IBA area).

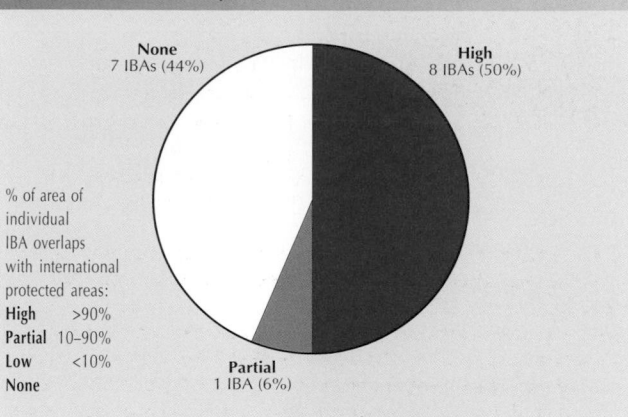

Figure 5. The international protection status of Important Bird Areas in the Czech Republic.

None
7 IBAs (44%)

High
8 IBAs (50%)

% of area of
individual
IBA overlaps
with international
protected areas:

High >90%
Partial 10–90%
Low <10%
None

Partial
1 IBA (6%)

Total area of overlap between IBA network in the Czech Republic and international protected-area system (see Table 5 for categories) = 3,671 km² (58% of total IBA area).

area of abandoned land. However, more than half of the total forest area in the Czech Republic is affected by industrial emissions to the atmosphere, a higher proportion than that in any other European country (EC–UN/ECE 1998). Four IBAs (25%) support forests where acid rain is having a negative impact (threat classified under 'industrialization/urbanization' in Figure 3).

The impact of hunting is especially significant at wetland IBAs (mainly fish-ponds and reservoirs) during the autumn wildfowl migration. Wildfowl shooting is banned at three IBAs (002, 006, 011) and, since 1998, has been considerably reduced in extent at two others (007, 009).

Future threats to IBAs include the development of the transport network, especially highway construction, an increase in large-scale, unregulated tourism and recreational activities, and the planned construction of the Danube–Oder–Elbe channel.

PROTECTION STATUS

Table 5 and Figures 4 and 5 summarize the national and international protection status of all IBAs in the Czech Republic.

■ National protection

There are six relevant categories of nationally protected areas in the Czech Republic:

1. National Park

Large areas of natural or minimally disrupted ecosystems that are important on a national and/or international scale. These areas have enormous scientific and educational value. Any management work undertaken has to further the conservation and improvement of natural habitats.

2. National Nature Reserve

Small areas of enormous natural value that contain nationally or internationally important and/or unique ecosystems. Management work is only undertaken if it helps to conserve or improve natural habitats, and follows detailed conditions.

3. Nature Reserve

Small areas of high natural value that represent ecosystems typical of and important to particular geographical regions. Detailed conditions for conservation management are set down when these are designated.

4. National Natural Monument

Small geological or geomorphological features of ecological, scientific or aesthetic value at the national or international level. This category can also include man-made formations. Detailed conditions for conservation management are set down when these are designated.

5. Natural Monument

As for National Natural Monuments, but of regional importance.

6. Protected Landscape Area

Large geographic areas that have a characteristic relief and may hold remnant primary forest, meadows and/or historical ruins. Management follows zones of protection, with the aims of conserving and improving natural habitats and promoting ecosystem processes. Recreation is permitted, but its impact is controlled.

All 16 IBAs in the Czech Republic are, at least in part, protected under national legislation (Figure 4). Eight IBAs overlap with National Parks or Protected Landscape Areas (Table 5), and a further seven with National Nature Reserves or Nature Reserves. The Czech National Council Act No. 114/1992 Gazette on the Protection of Nature and Landscapes also provides for the establishment of Temporary Protected Areas (007). These confer protection on, for example, sites that support temporally occurring plant or animal species, or sites used for scientific study. Such areas are designated for a predetermined time period, or for recurring events such as the breeding season or period of autumn migration.

Table 5. Protection status of Important Bird Areas in the Czech Republic. A tick (✔) indicates that an IBA overlaps with a protected area (to any extent).

IBA code	International name	National Park	National Nature Reserve	Nature Reserve	National Natural Monument	Natural Monument	Protected Landscape Area	Temporary Protected Area	Ramsar Site	Biosphere Reserve
001	Krkonoše mountains (Giant mountains)	✔							✔	✔
002	Žehuňský rybník pond		✔		✔					
003	Křivoklátsko (Křivoklátsko region)		✔	✔		✔	✔			✔
004	Doupov hills		✔	✔						
005	Šumava mountains (Bohemian forest)	✔	✔	✔	✔	✔	✔		✔	✔
006	Řežabinec pond		✔							
007	Dehtář pond							✔		
008	Třeboňsko (Třeboň region)		✔	✔	✔	✔	✔		✔	✔
009	Nové Mlýny middle reservoir			✔					✔	
010	Pálava		✔	✔		✔	✔			✔
011	Lednické rybníky ponds (Lednice fish-ponds)		✔						✔	
012	Confluence of the Morava (March) and Dyje (Thaya) rivers		✔						✔	
013	Beskydy mountains		✔	✔	✔	✔	✔			
014	Poodří		✔	✔			✔		✔	
015	Heřmanský stav pond–Stružka wetlands			✔						
016	Jeseníky mountains		✔	✔		✔	✔			
	Total number of IBAs	2	12	10	3	7	7	1	7	5

Box 1. International legislation and initiatives that are relevant to site conservation in the Czech Republic (see Appendix 1 for a general description of these agreements).

Global	
Biodiversity Convention	✔
Ramsar Convention	✔
Bonn Convention	✔
World Heritage Convention	✔
MAB Programme	✔
Pan-European	
Bern Convention	✔

✔ Convention ratified/initiative supported
(✔) Convention signed

The system of protected areas in the Czech Republic includes three National Parks, 24 Protected Landscape Areas and 1,820 small protected areas (117 National Nature Reserves, 602 Nature Reserves, 100 National Nature Monuments and 1,001 Nature Monuments; correct as at 1 January 1998). New legislation based on a holistic or integrated approach has been designed to deal with unprotected agricultural and forest lands, using the national approach of the Territorial System of Ecological Stability (TSES).

■ International protection

Box 1 shows which international conventions the Czech Republic has ratified. Ten Ramsar Sites have been designated, six of which overlap with five IBAs (001, 005, 008, 011, 014), with another Ramsar Site overlapping with two IBAs (009, 012) (Table 5). Five IBAs overlap with UNESCO Biosphere Reserves (001, 003, 005, 008, 010). Seven sites are not protected at the international level (Figure 5).

The Czech National Council Act on Protection of Nature and Landscapes, which came into force in June 1992 is in some parts fully comparable with relevant EC legislation (Birds Directive, Habitats Directive, agri-environment regulations).

CONSERVATION

- A network of patron groups covers all IBAs in the Czech Republic, working to the following objectives: to monitor changes in bird communities and habitats; to monitor economic, recreational and other activities and their influence on birds and habitats; to monitor threats to IBAs and to inform the relevant authorities about them; to propose and enforce conservation measures and evaluate their results; to prepare management plan proposals; to take part in negotiations concerning IBAs and to inform local people about the importance of IBAs. Research into *Crex crex* currently takes place in all IBAs where the species occurs.
- The State Nature Conservancy authorities run various monitoring and conservation programmes in all IBAs with National Park or Protected Landscape Area status.
- Management plans have been written for 10 of the 16 IBAs.

ANALYTICAL METHODS

- Bird data (both numbers of breeding pairs and counts of passage birds) were obtained during annual monitoring of IBAs from 1992–1996, unless otherwise stated in the species table footnotes.
- Waterfowl counts are accurate and are based mainly on counts taken regularly throughout the year. Data for globally threatened and near-threatened species are also accurate and

are based on annual counts. Population estimates for the majority of non-passerines (SPECs 2 and 3) are relatively precise, while estimates for some passerines are less accurate due to a lack of data.

- Due to the fact that more than 10 sites hold at least 20 pairs of *Crex crex*, the globally threatened species criterion (A1) threshold for this species was increased from 20 to 40 pairs for the Czech Republic.
- A lack of precise data meant that it was not possible to calculate the relative proportions of individual forest-types present in large IBAs. In addition, many secondary *Pinus* forests exhibit natural characteristics rather than characteristics associated with monocultures. For these reasons 'forestry plantations' and secondary forest were classified as 'native coniferous forest' in the site-account analyses.
- Likewise, a lack of precise data on the composition of grasslands at IBA 014 led to 'highly improved reseeded grassland' being included in the overall total for 'grassland' rather than 'artificial landscape'. This situation has arisen as a result of agricultural transformation, with the relative proportions of arable land, improved reseeded grassland and other agricultural habitats subject to many changes.
- Threats and land-use estimates are based on data from 1995–1996.
- The threat 'forest grazing' always refers to large game animals, predominantly deer.
- New primary administrative regions have yet to be established following the splitting of the former Czech and Slovak Federal Republic into two independent countries. Secondary districts have therefore been used for the purposes of this review.

GLOSSARY

CSO Czech Society for Ornithology (BirdLife International Partner in the Czech Republic).
FACE Foundation Forests Absorbing Carbon Dioxide Emissions Foundation.
GEF Global Environment Facility.

ACKNOWLEDGEMENTS

The CSO IBA Working Group of about 100 members provided data for this inventory of Czech IBAs. Questionnaires were completed by representatives of particular Patron Groups, namely by Jiří Flousek, Petr Bürger, Jiří Bureš, Bohuslav Kloubec, Jiří Pykal, Karel Pecl, Lubor Urbánek, Josef Chytil, Karel Pavelka, Jan Pavelka, Peter Baláž, Milan Tichai, František Pojer, Vít Tejrovský and Zdeněk Polášek. Jan Plesník provided valuable input to the 'General Introduction'. CSO also cooperated with the following organizations: Administrations of the National Parks Krkonoše and Šumava; Administrations of the Protected Landscape Areas Třeboňsko, Pálava, Poodří, Beskydy, Jeseníky and Křivoklátsko; the Agency of Nature Conservation and Landscape Protection of the Czech Republic, Prague, and its regional branches; museums in České Budějovice, Písek, Mikulov and Vsetín; and the Czech Agricultural University, Prague. Funds have been generously provided by the Royal Society for the Protection of Birds (BirdLife International Partner in the United Kingdom), Vogelbescherming Nederland (BirdLife International Partner in the Netherlands), the Czech Ministry for the Environment and the Czech Society for Ornithology (BirdLife International Partner in the Czech Republic).

■ SITE ACCOUNTS

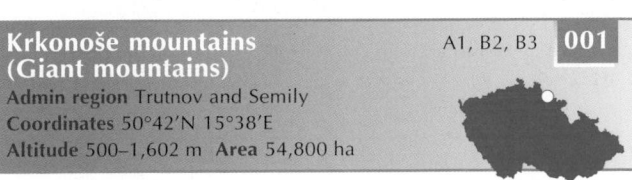

Krkonoše mountains (Giant mountains) · A1, B2, B3 · 001

Admin region Trutnov and Semily
Coordinates 50°42′N 15°38′E
Altitude 500–1,602 m **Area** 54,800 ha

■ Site description

A mountainous region located along the Czech–Polish border, covered mainly by *Fagus* and *Picea/Fagus* forests (500–900 m) and *Picea* forests (900–1,250 m). At higher elevations (1,250–1,450 m) there are *Pinus*

mugo stands, glacial corries, peatbogs and subalpine meadows, with alpine habitats occurring above 1,450 m. Forestry is the most important economic activity. This area includes two areas that were treated as subsites in the previous international IBA inventory (Grimmett and Jones 1989): 'Pančavská and Labská louka peatbogs' (former site CZ001-1) and 'Úpská rašelina peatbog' (former site CZ001-2).

Habitats Forest and woodland (73%; broadleaved deciduous forest; native coniferous forest; mixed forest; treeline ecotone), Grassland (7%; alpine/subalpine/boreal grassland; tundra), Wetland (raised bog), Artificial landscape (20%; highly improved reseeded grassland; arable land; other urban/industrial areas)

Land-use Agriculture (18%), Forestry (70%), Hunting (80%), Nature conservation/research (15%), Tourism/recreation (85%)

■ Birds

Species	Season	Year	Pop min	Pop max	Acc	Criteria
Ciconia nigra Black Stork	B	1994	12	16	B	B2
Pernis apivorus Honey Buzzard	B	1994	5	10	B	B3
Falco tinnunculus Kestrel	R	1994	90	—	—	B2
Crex crex Corncrake	B	1997	100	—	B	A1
Columba oenas Stock Dove	B	1994	80	—	B	B3
Bubo bubo Eagle Owl	R	1994	9	11	A	B2
[1] *Phoenicurus phoenicurus* Redstart	B	1994	300	—	—	B2
Turdus torquatus Ring Ouzel	B	1994	200	—	B	B3
Lanius collurio Red-backed Shrike	B	1994	250	—	—	B2

All data 1991–1994.
1. Large decrease 1991–1994.

The forest bird communities are the most important component of the avifauna. The IBA also supports populations of two species with limited distributions in the Czech Republic: *Anthus spinoletta* and *Prunella collaris*. A total of 153 breeding species were recorded during a 1991–1994 regional survey.

■ Protection status
National High **International** High
54,800 ha of IBA covered by National Park (Krkonoše National Park, 54,800 ha, including transition zone of 18,450 ha). 54,800 ha of IBA covered by Biosphere Reserve (Krkonoše Biosphere Reserve, 54,800 ha). 230 ha of IBA covered by Ramsar Site (Krkonošská rašeliniště (Krkonoše Mountains Mires), 230 ha).

■ Conservation issues

Threats Abandonment/reduction of land management (C), Industrialization/urbanization (A), Infrastructure (B), Recreation/tourism (A)

Air pollution is a serious threat to forest, and has had a negative effect on forest bird populations. The cumulative impact of 6–8 million visitors a year and the abandonment of agricultural land are additional problems. A management plan exists for the National Park and its transition zone (1994–2003), and a Biosphere Reserve action plan is in preparation. Conservation initiatives include forest restoration funded by the Dutch FACE Foundation, and a GEF Biodiversity Project. A breeding birds atlas (1991–1994) is being compiled.

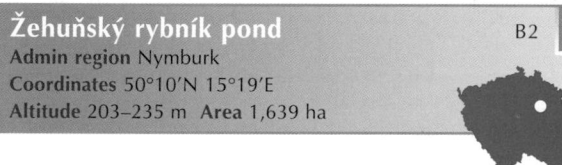

Žehuňský rybník pond B2 002
Admin region Nymburk
Coordinates 50°10′N 15°19′E
Altitude 203–235 m **Area** 1,639 ha

■ Site description
Žehuňský rybník pond itself is shallow with several islets, and supports extensive areas of fringing vegetation (*Phragmites*, *Typha*). Meadows subject to periodic flooding exist around much of its periphery. The Žehuňská obora Game Preserve supports mainly *Quercus*/*Carpinus* forest, and southerly hillsides are covered with vegetation characteristic of very dry conditions. The pond is utilized for carp *Cyprinus* farming with some conservation restrictions.

Habitats Forest and woodland (60%; broadleaved deciduous forest), Scrub (1%; scrub), Grassland (10%; dry siliceous grassland; humid grassland), Wetland (20%; standing fresh water; river/stream; water-fringe vegetation), Artificial landscape (10%; arable land; forestry plantation; urban parks/gardens; other urban/industrial areas)
Land-use Agriculture (20%), Fisheries/aquaculture (15%), Forestry (60%), Hunting (55%), Nature conservation/research (90%), Tourism/recreation (5%), Urban/industrial/transport

■ Birds

Species	Season	Year	Pop min	Pop max	Acc	Criteria
Anas strepera Gadwall	B	1995	3	18	A	B2
Alcedo atthis Kingfisher	R	1995	2	4	A	B2

All data 1990–1995.

The site is important for both breeding and passage waterbirds and raptors. Species of global conservation concern that do not meet IBA criteria: *Haliaeetus albicilla* (2–4 wintering birds; 1 pair occurred regularly during the 1995 breeding season). A total of 243 bird species, over 130 of them breeding, have been recorded in the area.

■ Protection status
National Partial **International** None
1,440 ha of IBA covered by National Nature Reserve (Žehuňský rybník pond and Žehuňská obora Game Preserve, 1,440 ha). 5 ha of IBA covered by Natural Monument (name unknown, 5 ha).

■ Conservation issues

Threats Agricultural intensification/expansion (B), Aquaculture/fisheries (A), Consequences of animal/plant introductions (B), Deforestation (commercial) (C), Disturbance to birds (C), Forest grazing (B), Intensified forest management (B), Natural events (C), Other (C), Recreation/tourism (C), Selective logging/cutting (C)

Threats include pollution from the Cidlina river ('Other' threat, above) and disturbance caused by recreational activities such as wind-surfing. The IBA patron group monitors changes in bird communities and habitats, including 'Action *Acrocephalus*' since 1990.

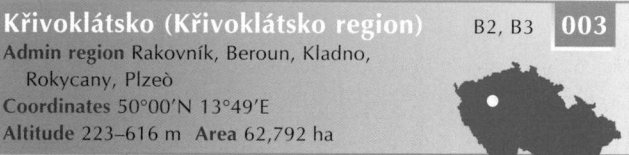

Křivoklátsko (Křivoklátsko region) B2, B3 003
Admin region Rakovník, Beroun, Kladno, Rokycany, Plzeò
Coordinates 50°00′N 13°49′E
Altitude 223–616 m **Area** 62,792 ha

■ Site description
A large area of varied topography situated c.30 km west of Prague. Its axis is the Berounka river, with its deeply carved valleys and canyons. Coniferous tree species dominate the forests, along with *Fagus* and *Quercus*. Valuable non-forest habitats include dry grasslands, ecotonal shrub and herb communities, and communities of exposed rocks and screes. In the Biosphere Reserve core zone, human activities are limited to the monitoring of ecosystem change.

Habitats Forest and woodland (64%; broadleaved deciduous forest; native coniferous forest; mixed forest), Scrub (2%; scrub), Grassland (4%; dry siliceous grassland; humid grassland; mesophile grassland), Wetland (2%; standing fresh water; river/stream; fen/transition mire/spring), Rocky areas (1%; scree/boulders; inland cliff), Artificial landscape (30%; highly improved reseeded grassland; arable land; perennial crops/orchards/groves; urban parks/gardens; other urban/industrial areas)
Land-use Agriculture (30%), Fisheries/aquaculture (1%), Forestry (60%), Hunting, Nature conservation/research (15%), Tourism/recreation (10%), Urban/industrial/transport (5%)

■ Birds

Species	Season	Year	Pop min	Pop max	Acc	Criteria
Ciconia nigra Black Stork	B	1996	6	12	A	B2
Pernis apivorus Honey Buzzard	B	1996	10	15	B	B3
Falco tinnunculus Kestrel	R	1996	100	200	B	B2
Columba oenas Stock Dove	B	1996	150	220	A	B3
Columba palumbus Woodpigeon	B	1996	1,300	2,600	B	B3
Streptopelia turtur Turtle Dove	B	1996	800	1,600	B	B2
[1] *Bubo bubo* Eagle Owl	R	1996	15	30	A	B2
Strix aluco Tawny Owl	R	1996	60	120	B	B3
Alcedo atthis Kingfisher	R	1996	15	25	A	B2
Jynx torquilla Wryneck	B	1996	60	120	B	B2
Picus canus Grey-headed Woodpecker	R	1996	80	150	B	B2
Picus viridis Green Woodpecker	R	1996	200	400	B	B2
Dendrocopos medius Middle Spotted Woodpecker	R	1996	80	150	B	B3
Alauda arvensis Skylark	B	1996	8,000	—	—	B2
Hirundo rustica Swallow	B	1996	8,000	—	C	B2
Phoenicurus phoenicurus Redstart	B	1996	500	1,000	C	B2
Locustella naevia Grasshopper Warbler	B	1996	900	1,800	B	B3
Locustella fluviatilis River Warbler	B	1996	200	400	B	B3
Sylvia nisoria Barred Warbler	B	1996	40	100	B	B3
Ficedula albicollis Collared Flycatcher	B	1996	4,000	8,000	B	B3
Lanius collurio Red-backed Shrike	B	1996	500	1,000	B	B2

All data 1991–1996.
1. Large increase 1992–1996.

The IBA is particularly important for species of broadleaved forest, especially raptors. More than 120 breeding species have been recorded over the last decade.

■ Protection status
National High **International** High
62,792 ha of IBA covered by Protected Landscape Area (Křivoklátsko Protected Landscape Area, 62,792 ha). Included within the PLA are 4 National Nature Reserves (covering 775 ha), 15 Nature Reserves and 5 Natural Monuments. 62,792 ha of IBA covered by Biosphere Reserve (Křivoklátsko Biosphere Reserve, 62,792 ha).

■ Conservation issues

Threats Agricultural intensification/expansion (B), Aquaculture/fisheries (C), Disturbance to birds (C), Dredging/canalization (C), Industrialization/urbanization (C), Infrastructure (C), Intensified forest management (B), Recreation/tourism (C), Selective logging/cutting (B)

Conservation initiatives include mapping the distribution of selected species, and research into *Ciconia nigra* and *Milvus milvus*. The Institute of Botany at the Czech Academy of Science is carrying out a detailed floral inventory and classification of ecosystem types. A management plan exists for the area.

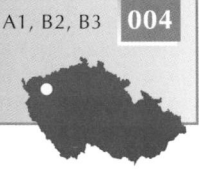

Doupov hills   A1, B2, B3   004
Admin region Karlovy Vary, Chomutov, Louny
Coordinates 50°15′N 13°10′E
Altitude 280–928 m **Area** 60,000 ha

■ Site description
The IBA comprises hills of volcanic origin, situated south and east of the Ohře river. A crater with a diameter of c.30 km forms a central depression, with fish-ponds and water reservoirs located on the periphery of the IBA. *Fagus* forests support a species-rich herb layer, and scree forests also occur. A mosaic of grassland, shrub and broadleaved coppice communities has developed on abandoned agricultural land. Whilst military training is a major land-use, the IBA remains relatively unaffected by human activity.

Habitats Forest and woodland (30%; broadleaved deciduous forest; native coniferous forest; mixed forest), Scrub (15%; scrub), Grassland (20%; humid grassland; mesophile grassland), Wetland (5%; standing fresh water; river/stream; water-fringe vegetation), Rocky areas (5%; scree/boulders; inland cliff), Artificial landscape (25%; highly improved reseeded grassland; arable land; ruderal land)
Land-use Agriculture (5%), Fisheries/aquaculture (2%), Forestry (30%), Military (55%), Nature conservation/research (5%), Tourism/recreation (5%)

■ Birds

Species	Season	Year	Pop min	Pop max	Acc	Criteria
Ciconia nigra Black Stork	B	1995	12	14	A	B2
Pernis apivorus Honey Buzzard	B	1995	15	20	A	B3
Crex crex Corncrake	B	1995	40	50	B	A1
Columba oenas Stock Dove	B	1995	300	500	A	B3
Bubo bubo Eagle Owl	R	1995	25	30	A	B2
Alcedo atthis Kingfisher	R	1995	5	8	A	B2
Jynx torquilla Wryneck	B	1995	80	100	A	B2
Sylvia nisoria Barred Warbler	B	1995	150	200	A	B3
Lanius collurio Red-backed Shrike	B	1995	300	400	A	B2

The IBA supports large numbers of forest and grassland species. The first complete data on avifauna were obtained during a 1987–1989 study, and 220 bird species have now been recorded.

■ Protection status
National Low **International** None
206 ha of IBA covered by National Nature Reserve (Úhošt National Nature Reserve, 206 ha). Included within the IBA are 2 Nature Reserves (covering 50 ha).

■ Conservation issues

Threats Abandonment/reduction of land management (U), Afforestation (C), Agricultural intensification/expansion (C), Aquaculture/fisheries (C), Deforestation (commercial) (B), Disturbance to birds (C), Intensified forest management (B)

A Protected Landscape Area covering c.80% of the IBA has been proposed, and new nature reserves are being identified. Monitoring of bird communities is undertaken.

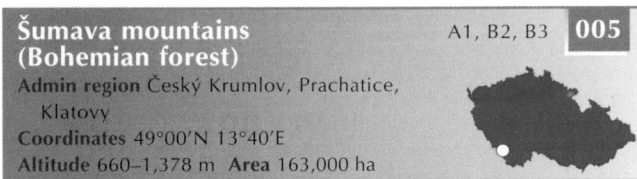

Šumava mountains (Bohemian forest)   A1, B2, B3   005
Admin region Český Krumlov, Prachatice, Klatovy
Coordinates 49°00′N 13°40′E
Altitude 660–1,378 m **Area** 163,000 ha

■ Site description
An extensive mountain range (120 km in length) situated on the border with Bavaria and Austria. Although secondary *Picea* forest is the dominant type, primeval *Picea* forest does occur above 1,200 m, with mixed *Picea/Abies/Fagus* forest at lower altitudes. The Šumava is relatively sparsely inhabited following post-war depopulation, and this has allowed a mosaic of grasslands at various stages of succession to develop. This area includes two areas that were treated as subsites in the previous international IBA inventory (Grimmett and Jones 1989): 'Mount Boubín' (former site CZ002-1) and 'Vltavský luh (River Vltava flood-plain)' (former site CZ002-2).

Habitats Forest and woodland (60%; broadleaved deciduous forest; native coniferous forest; mixed forest; alluvial/very wet forest), Grassland (10%; humid grassland; mesophile grassland), Wetland (15%; standing fresh water; river/stream; raised bog; fen/transition mire/spring), Rocky areas (scree/boulders; inland cliff), Artificial landscape (20%; highly improved reseeded grassland; arable land; perennial crops/orchards/groves; other urban/industrial areas; ruderal land)
Land-use Agriculture (15%), Fisheries/aquaculture (3%), Forestry (50%), Hunting, Military (1%), Nature conservation/research (10%), Not utilized, Tourism/recreation, Urban/industrial/transport, Water management

■ Birds

Species	Season	Year	Pop min	Pop max	Acc	Criteria
Pernis apivorus Honey Buzzard	B	1996	10	20	C	B3
Crex crex Corncrake	B	1996	100	200	A	A1
Bubo bubo Eagle Owl	R	1996	10	—	C	B2
Alcedo atthis Kingfisher	R	1996	5	—	C	B2
Picoides tridactylus Three-toed Woodpecker	R	1996	200	—	—	B2
[1] *Turdus torquatus* Ring Ouzel	B	1996	450	—	—	B3
Regulus ignicapillus Firecrest	B	1996	Abundant	—	—	B3
Lanius collurio Red-backed Shrike	B	1996	Abundant	—	—	B2

1. 30–40% of national population.

The IBA is important for bird species of montane forests and valley grasslands. A total of 145 breeding species were recorded during the period 1985–1995.

■ Protection status
National High **International** High
69,030 ha of IBA covered by National Park (Šumava National Park, 69,030 ha). 94,480 ha of IBA covered by Protected Landscape Area (Šumava Protected Landscape Area, 94,480 ha). Included within the PLA are 33 protected areas (National Nature Reserves, National Natural Monuments, Nature Reserves and Natural Monuments) covering a total area of 7,493 ha. 163,000 ha of IBA covered by Biosphere Reserve (Šumava Biosphere Reserve, 167,000 ha). 6,371 ha of IBA covered by Ramsar Site (Šumava Peatlands, 6,371 ha).

■ Conservation issues

Threats Agricultural intensification/expansion (C), Deforestation (commercial) (C), Disturbance to birds (C), Industrialization/urbanization (U), Infrastructure (C), Intensified forest management (C), Natural events (C), Recreation/tourism (C)

Deforestation is a threat due to the effects of wind and acid rain, and population explosions of insect pests occur in monospecific plantations made more susceptible by the effects of air pollution. Recreational use is likely to increase, and resettlement of the region is expected. Conservation initiatives include studies of *Crex crex*, *Carpodacus erythrinus* and owls, and the reintroduction of *Strix uralensis*. A management plan exists for the area.

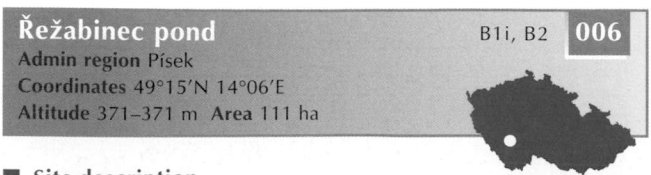

Řežabinec pond

B1i, B2 | **006**

Admin region Písek
Coordinates 49°15′N 14°06′E
Altitude 371–371 m **Area** 111 ha

■ Site description

Located 8 km south-west of Písek, the fish-pond supports a rich littoral community (*Phragmites* and *Carex*), and is surrounded by agricultural land. Small pools on the eastern shore are gradually infilling and becoming overgrown with *Salix*, *Populus* and *Betula*, which are being removed in accordance with the management plan. The reserve is important for research and educational purposes, whilst the main economic activity is carp *Cyprinus* farming.

Habitats Grassland (1%; humid grassland), Wetland (99%; mudflat/sandflat; standing fresh water; water-fringe vegetation; fen/transition mire/spring)
Land-use Agriculture (2%), Fisheries/aquaculture (90%), Nature conservation/research (100%)

■ Birds

Species		Season	Year	Pop min	Pop max	Acc	Criteria
Anser anser	Greylag Goose	P	1995	1,300	2,100	A	B1i
Anas strepera	Gadwall	B	1995	10	20	A	B2

All data 1991–1995.

The IBA is important for both breeding and passage waterbirds.

■ Protection status

National High **International** None
111 ha of IBA covered by National Nature Reserve (Řežabinec pond – Řežabinecké tůně pools, 111 ha).

■ Conservation issues

Threats Aquaculture/fisheries (A)

A serious threat is posed by excessive nutrient enrichment of the pond, caused by fish-farming, agricultural activities and a *Larus ridibundus* colony. The reedbeds have halved in area over the last three decades, and this unfavourable phenomenon is being studied. Since 1977 ornithological training camps for young people have been organized around the 'Action *Acrocephalus*' project. A management plan exists for the site.

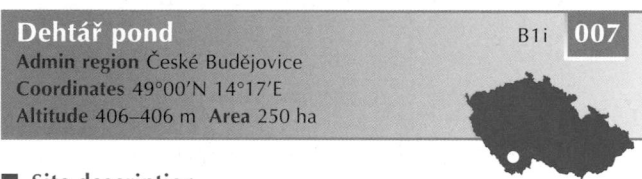

Dehtář pond

B1i | **007**

Admin region České Budějovice
Coordinates 49°00′N 14°17′E
Altitude 406–406 m **Area** 250 ha

■ Site description

A large fish-pond in the midst of extensive agricultural lands, situated 15 km west of České Budějovice. The pond supports an extensive carp *Cyprinus* fishery, and is used for recreational purposes (swimming, boating, wind-surfing) during the summer. Ducks and geese are hunted occasionally during the autumn.

Habitats Wetland (100%; standing fresh water)
Land-use Fisheries/aquaculture (100%), Hunting, Tourism/recreation (50%)

■ Birds

Species		Season	Year	Pop min	Pop max	Acc	Criteria
Anser anser	Greylag Goose	P	1996	50	2,000	A	B1i

The IBA is important for both breeding and passage waterbirds, and wintering raptors. Species of global conservation concern that do not meet IBA criteria: *Haliaeetus albicilla* (2–4 wintering birds).

■ Protection status

National Partial **International** None
120 ha of IBA covered by Temporary Protected Area (Dehtář pond Temporary Protected Area, 120 ha).

■ Conservation issues

Threats Aquaculture/fisheries (B), Disturbance to birds (A), Recreation/tourism (A)

The western half of the fish-pond was recently declared a Temporary Protected Area for the period 15 July–30 November. Swimming, boating and wind-surfing are banned, as is the release of captive-bred ducks. Wildfowl hunting is allowed to take place twice a year.

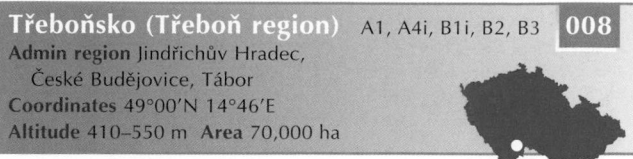

Třeboňsko (Třeboň region)

A1, A4i, B1i, B2, B3 | **008**

Admin region Jindřichův Hradec,
České Budějovice, Tábor
Coordinates 49°00′N 14°46′E
Altitude 410–550 m **Area** 70,000 ha

■ Site description

A flat basin bordered by hills, drained by the Lužnice river, and containing a unique system of c.500 fish-ponds connected by a network of drains, canals and artificial streams. Many of the ponds support littoral vegetation, and there are remnants of wet meadows and *Alnus* riverine forest bordering the shores and watercourses. The region is an important source of gravel, sand and peat, and is highly suitable for recreation and tourism. This area includes three areas that were treated as subsites in the previous international IBA inventory (Grimmett and Jones 1989): 'Ruda peatbog and Horusický rybník pond' (former site CZ003-1), 'Velký and Malý Tisý ponds' (former site CZ003-2) and 'River Stará řeka and Novořecké močály marshes (former site CZ003-3).

Habitats Forest and woodland (45%; broadleaved deciduous forest; native coniferous forest; mixed forest; alluvial/very wet forest), Grassland (5%; humid grassland; mesophile grassland), Wetland (24%; standing fresh water; river/stream; water-fringe vegetation; fen/transition mire/spring), Artificial landscape (37%; highly improved reseeded grassland; arable land; perennial crops/orchards/groves; urban parks/gardens; other urban/industrial areas)
Land-use Agriculture (28%), Fisheries/aquaculture (11%), Forestry (43%), Hunting, Nature conservation/research (20%), Tourism/recreation (5%), Urban/industrial/transport (14%), Water management (1%)

■ Birds

Species		Season	Year	Pop min	Pop max	Acc	Criteria
Nycticorax nycticorax	Night Heron	B	1996	20	40	A	B2
Ciconia nigra	Black Stork	B	1996	10	15	B	B2
Ciconia ciconia	White Stork	B	1996	13	—	A	B2
Anser anser	Greylag Goose	P	1996	3,000	5,000	B	A4i, B1i
Anas strepera	Gadwall	B	1996	950	—	A	A4i, B1i, B2
Anas strepera	Gadwall	P	1996	2,000	3,000	B	A4i, B1i
Netta rufina	Red-crested Pochard	B	1996	20	40	A	B2
Aythya ferina	Pochard	B	1996	790	—	A	B3
Pernis apivorus	Honey Buzzard	B	1996	5	10	B	B3
Haliaeetus albicilla	White-tailed Eagle	R	1996	5	8	A	A1
Haliaeetus albicilla	White-tailed Eagle	W	1996	20	30	A	A1
Bubo bubo	Eagle Owl	R	1996	5	10	B	B2
Strix aluco	Tawny Owl	R	1996	100	200	B	B3
Alcedo atthis	Kingfisher	R	1996	10	30	B	B2
Picus canus	Grey-headed Woodpecker	R	1996	40	80	B	B2
Picus viridis	Green Woodpecker	R	1996	80	150	B	B2
Dendrocopos medius Middle Spotted Woodpecker		R	1996	30	60	B	B3
Riparia riparia	Sand Martin	B	1996	500	1,500	B	B2

The Třeboň region is one of the most important areas for waterbirds in central Europe, with 10,000–20,000 individuals visiting the fish-ponds on autumn migration. More than 150 species nest within the IBA, including a variety of raptors, woodpeckers and forest passerines. Breeding species of global conservation concern that do not meet IBA criteria: *Crex crex* (7–15 pairs).

■ Protection status

National High **International** High
70,000 ha of IBA covered by Protected Landscape Area (Třeboňsko Protected Landscape Area, 70,000 ha). Included within the PLA are 5 National Nature Reserves, 1 National Natural Monument, 19 Nature Reserves and 3 Natural Monuments (covering a total area of 4,023 ha). 70,000 ha of IBA covered by Biosphere Reserve (Třeboňsko Biosphere Reserve, 70,000 ha). 1,080 ha of IBA covered by Ramsar Site (Třeboňsko Peatlands, 1,080 ha). 10,165 ha of IBA covered by Ramsar Site (Třeboňsko Fish-Ponds, 10,165 ha).

■ Conservation issues

Fishery practices, including manuring and manipulation of water-levels, present a particular threat. Hunting, intensive pig-breeding and the generally unfavourable state of farmland pose additional problems. Conservation and research initiatives include the provision of artificial nest-sites for *Ciconia ciconia* and *Sterna hirundo*, the restoration of important sand-dune habitats, investigations into water quality, and zoological/botanical inventories. A management plan exists for the area.

Threats Abandonment/reduction of land management (C), Agricultural intensification/ expansion (B), Aquaculture/fisheries (B), Disturbance to birds (C), Dredging/canalization (C), Extraction industry (C), Infrastructure (C), Intensified forest management (C), Recreation/ tourism (C), Unsustainable exploitation (C)

Nové Mlýny middle reservoir   A1, A4i, A4iii, B1i, B2   009

Admin region Břeclav
Coordinates 48°52′N 16°37′E
Altitude 169–170 m **Area** 1,080 ha

■ Site description
The IBA covers the middle reservoir in the Nové Mlýny complex, which is located at the confluence of the rivers Dyje (Thaya), Svratka and Jihlava. The reservoir contains small islets covered by ruderal communities, and its average depth is c.2 m.

Habitats Wetland (97%; standing fresh water), Artificial landscape (3%; ruderal land)
Land-use Fisheries/aquaculture (97%), Hunting, Nature conservation/research (100%), Water management (100%)

■ Birds

Species	Season	Year	Pop min	Pop max	Acc	Criteria
[1] *Anser fabalis* Bean Goose	W	1996	20,000	80,000	A	A4i, B1i
[1] *Anser albifrons* White-fronted Goose	W	1996	5,000	25,000	A	A4i, B1i
[1] *Anser anser* Greylag Goose	P	1996	1,000	5,000	A	A4i, B1i
[2] *Netta rufina* Red-crested Pochard	B	1996	20	30	A	B2
[1] *Haliaeetus albicilla* White-tailed Eagle	W	1996	15	30	A	A1

1. Large increase 1991–1996.
2. 1991–1996.

The IBA also holds important numbers of breeding waterbirds, and is the only regular breeding site of *Larus melanocephalus* (3–5 pairs) in the country. The reservoir is the most important site nationally for wintering *Phalacrocorax carbo*, *Anser fabalis*, *A. albifrons*, *Mergus albellus* and *Haliaeetus albicilla*. Several thousand wildfowl and hundreds of waders stop-over here on passage.

■ Protection status
National High **International** High
1,017 ha of IBA covered by Nature Reserve (Věstonická nádrž/ Věstonice Reservoir, 1,017 ha). 1,080 ha of IBA covered by Ramsar Site (Wetlands of the Lower Dyje River, 11,500 ha).

■ Conservation issues

Threats Disturbance to birds (B), Other (B), Recreation/tourism (B), Unsustainable exploitation (B)

Threats include recreational activities (angling and canoeing), pressure from which is expected to increase, and hunting (considerably reduced since 1998). 'Other' threats are posed by water-level fluctuations, and the effects of nutrient enrichment and pollution. A management plan adopted in 1996 addresses some of these problems. 1996 also saw construction work begin on a biocorridor connecting riverine habitats above and below the reservoirs. The Agency for Nature Conservation and Landscape Protection and the IBA patron group undertake research and monitoring work, including regular waterbird counts.

Pálava   B2, B3   010

Admin region Břeclav
Coordinates 48°50′N 16°40′E
Altitude 165–550 m **Area** 8,300 ha

■ Site description
An area of limestone outcrops (the Pavlovské hills) that dominate an otherwise undulating lowland landscape. Habitat types present include calcareous rocky slopes, steppe-grassland, dry *Quercus* and *Quercus/ Carpinus* forest, *Quercus*, *Fraxinus*, *Populus* and *Ulmus* flood-plain forest, flooded meadows and two ponds that support reedbeds (*Phragmites*). The region is a popular destination for tourists, and there are many old quarries.

Habitats Forest and woodland (32%; broadleaved deciduous forest; alluvial/very wet forest; wooded steppe), Scrub (4%; scrub), Grassland (5%; steppe/dry calcareous grassland; humid grassland), Wetland (2%; saltmarsh; standing fresh water; water-fringe vegetation), Rocky areas (inland cliff; caves), Artificial landscape (57%; arable land; perennial crops/orchards/groves; other urban/industrial areas)
Land-use Agriculture (55%), Fisheries/aquaculture (2%), Forestry (30%), Hunting (25%), Nature conservation/research (40%), Not utilized (1%), Tourism/recreation (10%), Urban/industrial/transport (4%)

■ Birds

Species	Season	Year	Pop min	Pop max	Acc	Criteria
Ciconia ciconia White Stork	B	1996	10	11	A	B2
Pernis apivorus Honey Buzzard	B	1996	5	8	A	B3
Jynx torquilla Wryneck	B	1996	200	350	A	B2
Dendrocopos medius Middle Spotted Woodpecker	R	1996	70	150	A	B3
Sylvia nisoria Barred Warbler	B	1996	400	800	A	B3
Ficedula albicollis Collared Flycatcher	B	1996	1,000	2,000	A	B3
Lanius collurio Red-backed Shrike	B	1996	1,250	1,500	A	B2

The IBA is important for species of forest and scrub grassland, certain of which (*Buteo buteo*, *Accipiter gentilis* and *Pernis apivorus*) occur at very high densities. It also supports the largest population of *Upupa epops* in the country.

■ Protection status
National High **International** High
8,300 ha of IBA covered by Protected Landscape Area (Pálava Protected Landscape Area, 8,300 ha). Included within the PLA are 4 National Nature Reserves, 6 Nature Reserves and 5 Natural Monuments (covering a total of 794 ha), and 2 Game Preserves (covering a total of 2,100 ha). 8,300 ha of IBA covered by Biosphere Reserve (Pálava Biosphere Reserve, 8,300 ha).

■ Conservation issues

Threats Agricultural intensification/expansion (B), Forest grazing (U), Intensified forest management (C), Recreation/tourism (B)

Overstocking of game preserves has caused immense damage to forest vegetation and soil cover, although a decrease in numbers of game animals has recently been achieved. Projects include regular monitoring of flora and fauna, flagship GEF biodiversity initiatives, and the restoration of the Křivé jezero oxbow lake National Nature Reserve. A management plan exists for the area.

Lednické rybníky ponds (Lednice fish-ponds)   B1i, B2, B3   011

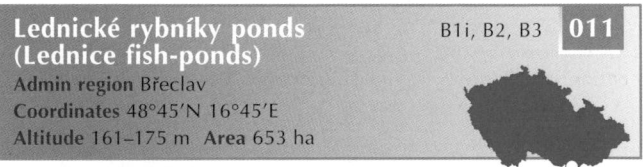

Admin region Břeclav
Coordinates 48°45′N 16°45′E
Altitude 161–175 m **Area** 653 ha

■ Site description
A system of five shallow, highly productive fish-ponds that support varying amounts of reedbed (*Phragmites*). Three contain small islets, some of which hold *Quercus* and *Fraxinus* trees. All five are situated in a park-like landscape, and are managed for fish-farming purposes. The saltmarsh at the western end of Nesyt Pond (Slanisko National Nature Reserve) holds unique salt-tolerant vegetation, and plant communities of open mud are of significance due to their scarcity within central Europe.

Habitats Wetland (90%; saltmarsh; standing fresh water; water-fringe vegetation), Artificial landscape (10%; urban parks/gardens)
Land-use Fisheries/aquaculture (80%), Nature conservation/research (100%), Tourism/recreation

■ Birds
The IBA is important for both breeding and passage waterbirds. The Nesyt Pond reedbeds hold the largest breeding population of *Panurus*

biarmicus in the Czech Republic (up to 100 pairs), and the islets of Zámecký rybník pond support the largest breeding colony nationally of *Nycticorax nycticorax*. The parkland adjacent to the ponds supports a variety of breeding woodpeckers and passerines.

Species	Season	Year	Pop min	Pop max	Acc	Criteria
Nycticorax nycticorax Night Heron	B	1996	250	270	A	B2
Anser anser Greylag Goose	P	1996	2,000	6,000	A	B1i
Netta rufina Red-crested Pochard	B	1996	20	30	A	B2
Jynx torquilla Wryneck	B	1996	40	60	A	B2
Dendrocopos medius Middle Spotted Woodpecker	R	1996	15	25	A	B3
Sylvia nisoria Barred Warbler	B	1996	20	30	A	B3

■ Protection status
National High **International** High
653 ha of IBA covered by National Nature Reserve (Lednické rybníky Ponds (Lednice Fish-Ponds), 653 ha). 640 ha of IBA covered by Ramsar Site (Lednické rybníky (Lednice Fish-Ponds), 665 ha).

■ Conservation issues

Threats Agricultural intensification/expansion (B), Aquaculture/fisheries (A), Recreation/tourism (C)

The intensity of fish-farming practices has been lowered in accordance with a management plan adopted in 1995. Nevertheless these practices have, in conjunction with agricultural activities, caused nutrient pollution of the ponds. Monitoring of waterbirds takes place throughout the year, whilst reedbed passerines are monitored during autumn migration.

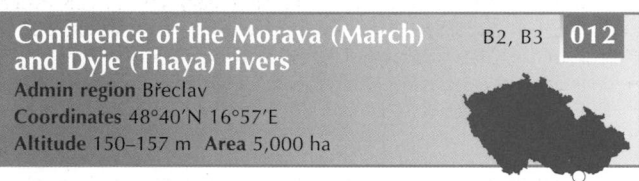

Confluence of the Morava (March) and Dyje (Thaya) rivers — B2, B3 012
Admin region Břeclav
Coordinates 48°40′N 16°57′E
Altitude 150–157 m **Area** 5,000 ha

■ Site description
Situated south of Lanžhot, the IBA comprises a complex of riverine habitats, including *Salix* and *Populus* forest, clear-cuts, numerous channels and streams, temporary and permanent pools and oxbow lakes. Meadows with solitary oaks *Quercus* are a typical feature, with *Quercus*, *Fraxinus* and *Ulmus* at higher elevations. The area is a game preserve for red deer *Cervus elaphus* and fallow deer *Dama dama*.

Habitats Forest and woodland (80%; alluvial/very wet forest), Grassland (15%; humid grassland), Wetland (5%; river/stream; fen/transition mire/spring)
Land-use Agriculture (5%), Forestry (80%), Hunting (90%), Nature conservation/research (2%)

■ Birds

Species	Season	Year	Pop min	Pop max	Acc	Criteria
Ciconia ciconia White Stork	B	1996	20	30	A	B2
Jynx torquilla Wryneck	B	1996	150	250	A	B2
Dendrocopos medius Middle Spotted Woodpecker	R	1996	70	150	A	B3
Ficedula albicollis Collared Flycatcher	B	1996	1,500	3,000	B	B3

The IBA supports a variety of species that breed in the riverine forests and meadows. Species of global conservation concern that do not meet IBA criteria: *Haliaeetus albicilla* (2–4 wintering birds) and *Crex crex* (10–20 breeding birds; numbers are increasing following spring flooding of the meadows).

■ Protection status
National Low **International** High
5,000 ha of IBA covered by Ramsar Site (Wetlands of the Lower Dyje River, 11,500 ha). Included within the IBA are 2 National Nature Reserves (covering 34 ha).

■ Conservation issues

Threats Abandonment/reduction of land management (B), Afforestation (C), Agricultural intensification/expansion (U), Consequences of animal/plant introductions (C), Construction/impact of dyke/dam/barrage (U), Groundwater abstraction (A), Intensified forest management (B), Natural events (C)

The privatization of flood-plain meadows and their subsequent conversion to arable land, and the construction of the Danube–Oder–Elbe channel may pose future threats to the IBA. A GEF biodiversity project and forestry activities are simulating the effects of spring flooding in order to increase groundwater levels. Forestry activities are controlled through a 10-year management plan, and various long-term monitoring programmes are in place.

Beskydy mountains — A1, B2, B3 013
Admin region Nový Jičín, Frýdek-Místek, Vsetín
Coordinates 49°26′N 18°22′E
Altitude 350–1,324 m **Area** 116,000 ha

■ Site description
Situated along the Slovakian border in the Western Carpathians, the IBA includes three mountain ranges: the Moravskoslezské Beskydy mountains (400–1,324 m), the Vsetínské vrchy hills (350–1,024 m) and part of the Javorníky mountains (350–1,071 m). Uniform secondary *Picea* stands dominate, although remnants of both Carpathian *Abies/Fagus* primeval forest and mountain *Picea* forest have been preserved. Farmland covers c.25% of the area, and includes abandoned meadows and pastures.

Habitats Forest and woodland (71%; broadleaved deciduous forest; native coniferous forest; mixed forest), Grassland (16%; humid grassland; mesophile grassland), Wetland (1%; standing fresh water; river/stream; fen/transition mire/spring), Artificial landscape (12%; arable land; perennial crops/orchards/groves; urban parks/gardens; other urban/industrial areas)
Land-use Agriculture (22%), Forestry (71%), Hunting, Nature conservation/research (4%), Tourism/recreation, Urban/industrial/transport (6%), Water management

■ Birds

Species	Season	Year	Pop min	Pop max	Acc	Criteria
Ciconia nigra Black Stork	B	1995	15	25	A	B2
Crex crex Corncrake	B	1995	90	120	A	A1
Columba oenas Stock Dove	B	1995	100	150	A	B3
Alcedo atthis Kingfisher	R	1995	8	25	A	B2
Jynx torquilla Wryneck	B	1995	25	40	A	B2
Picus canus Grey-headed Woodpecker	R	1995	40	80	A	B2
Picus viridis Green Woodpecker	R	1995	60	100	A	B2
Picoides tridactylus Three-toed Woodpecker	R	1995	50	100	B	B2
Phoenicurus phoenicurus Redstart	B	1995	300	500	A	B2
Turdus torquatus Ring Ouzel	B	1995	500	800	A	B3
Sylvia nisoria Barred Warbler	B	1995	20	30	A	B3
Regulus ignicapillus Firecrest	B	1995	1,500	3,000	B	B3
Lanius collurio Red-backed Shrike	B	1995	500	700	A	B2

All data 1992–1995.

The IBA is important for forest birds, and includes the only native population of *Strix uralensis* in the country. An increase in the numbers of *Crex crex* in meadows and grassland has been recorded in recent years.

■ Protection status
National High **International** None
116,000 ha of IBA covered by Protected Landscape Area (Beskydy Protected Landscape Area, 116,000 ha). Included within the PLA are 7 National Nature Reserves (covering 691 ha), 1 National Natural Monument (covering 66 ha), 9 Nature Reserves (covering 253 ha) and 15 Natural Monuments (covering 44 ha).

■ Conservation issues

Threats Abandonment/reduction of land management (B), Afforestation (C), Forest grazing (C), Industrialization/urbanization (C), Infrastructure (C), Intensified forest management (A), Recreation/tourism (C), Selective logging/cutting (B)

Threats include afforestation, intensive forestry practices, grazing pressure, industrial emissions, recreational activities, and the loss of meadow and pasture communities following land abandonment. Conservation and research initiatives include the provision of nest-boxes for *Jynx torquilla*, the reintroduction of *Tetrao urogallus*, mapping of bird distributions and botanical/zoological inventories.

Poodří A4iii, B2, B3 014

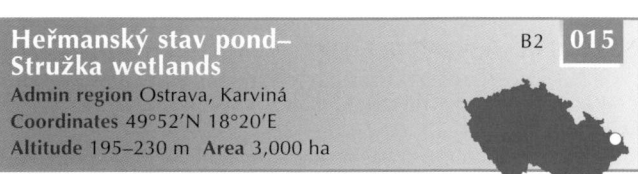

Admin region Nový Jičín, Ostrava, Frýdek-Místek
Coordinates 49°42'N 18°03'E
Altitude 214–289 m **Area** 8,150 ha

■ Site description
The IBA covers the Odra river flood-plain between Mankovice and Ostrava. Habitats include *Quercus* and *Ulmus* riverine forest, alluvial meadows and oxbow lakes. Tributaries, drainage canals and millraces cut the landscape, and five fish-pond systems support reedbeds (*Phragmites* and *Typha*). *Quercus*/*Carpinus* or *Tilia*/*Acer* forest and arable land occur on the river terraces, with human settlements localized on the periphery. The fish-ponds are semi-intensively managed for fish-farming, and ducks are hunted during autumn.

Habitats Forest and woodland (10%; broadleaved deciduous forest; alluvial/very wet forest), Grassland (30%; humid grassland), Wetland (15%; standing fresh water; river/stream; water-fringe vegetation), Artificial landscape (45%; highly improved reseeded grassland; arable land; perennial crops/orchards/groves; urban parks/gardens; other urban/industrial areas)
Land-use Agriculture (65%), Fisheries/aquaculture (8%), Forestry (11%), Hunting (5%), Nature conservation/research (20%), Urban/industrial/transport

■ Birds

Species		Season	Year	Pop min	Pop max	Acc	Criteria
Ciconia ciconia	White Stork	B	1996	10	12	A	B2
Anas strepera	Gadwall	B	1996	100	200	A	B2
Aythya ferina	Pochard	B	1996	150	170	A	B3
Alcedo atthis	Kingfisher	R	1996	10	25	B	B2
Locustella fluviatilis	River Warbler	B	1996	120	140	B	B3

The site holds 22,000–25,000 waterbirds on a regular basis during spring passage and the breeding season, and supports a large *Larus ridibundus* breeding colony. Breeding species of global conservation concern that do not meet IBA criteria: *Crex crex* (2–12 pairs).

■ Protection status
National High **International** Partial
8,150 ha of IBA covered by Protected Landscape Area (Poodří Protected Landscape Area, 8,500 ha). Included within the PLA are 1 National Nature Reserve and 2 Nature Reserves (covering 290 ha in total). 1,500 ha of IBA covered by Ramsar Site (Poodří, 1,500 ha).

■ Conservation issues

Threats Abandonment/reduction of land management (B), Agricultural intensification/expansion (C), Aquaculture/fisheries (B), Disturbance to birds (C), Infrastructure (B), Unsustainable exploitation (C)

The establishment of a market zone and the construction of the Dunaj–Odra canal in the vicinity of the IBA represent serious future threats. Hunting is also a problem. An IBA patron group has been set up with responsibility for coordinating bird monitoring, and the provision of nest-boxes for *Bucephala clangula*.

Heřmanský stav pond– Stružka wetlands B2 015

Admin region Ostrava, Karviná
Coordinates 49°52'N 18°20'E
Altitude 195–230 m **Area** 3,000 ha

■ Site description
The IBA is situated near to the industrial agglomeration of Ostrava, and contains a system of four large fish-ponds (totalling 480 ha) and extensive areas of reedbed (*Phragmites*) (totalling 100 ha). A network of canals and streams empty into the Odra river and its tributary, the Olše river. Oxbow lakes, sandpits and remnants of flood-plain forest adjoin the latter.

Habitats Forest and woodland (15%; broadleaved deciduous forest; mixed forest; alluvial/very wet forest), Grassland (5%; humid grassland), Wetland (30%; standing fresh water; river/stream; water-fringe vegetation), Artificial landscape (45%; arable land; perennial crops/orchards/groves; other urban/industrial areas; ruderal land), Unknown (5%)

Land-use Agriculture (20%), Fisheries/aquaculture (10%), Forestry (5%), Nature conservation/research (10%), Not utilized (20%), Tourism/recreation (5%), Unknown (5%), Urban/industrial/transport (10%), Water management (15%)

■ Birds

Species		Season	Year	Pop min	Pop max	Acc	Criteria
Ciconia ciconia	White Stork	B	1996	5	10	B	B2
[1] *Anas strepera*	Gadwall	B	1995	15	25	B	B2
[2] *Alcedo atthis*	Kingfisher	R	1996	10	—	C	B2

1. 1978–1995.
2. 1978–1996.

Nationally important populations of *Botaurus stellaris*, *Ixobrychus minutus*, *Porzana porzana*, *Tringa totanus*, *Limosa limosa*, *Luscinia svecica cyanecula* and *Panurus biarmicus* breed here. The fish-ponds are also important for up to 5,000 wintering and migrating wildfowl. Species of global conservation concern that do not meet IBA criteria: *Haliaeetus albicilla* (2 wintering birds).

■ Protection status
National Low **International** None
30 ha of IBA covered by Nature Reserve (Skučák Fish-Pond, 30 ha).

■ Conservation issues

Threats Abandonment/reduction of land management (C), Afforestation (A), Agricultural intensification/expansion (C), Aquaculture/fisheries (B), Disturbance to birds (B), Dredging/canalization (B), Extraction industry (B), Filling-in of wetlands (A), Industrialization/urbanization (B), Infrastructure (C)

Threats include the filling of wetlands with colliery waste, recultivation and afforestation initiatives, and intensive fish-farming practices. An IBA patron group has been established with the aim of increasing public and media awareness of wetlands. Monitoring of breeding and migrating waterbirds is carried out.

Jeseníky mountains A1, B2, B3 016

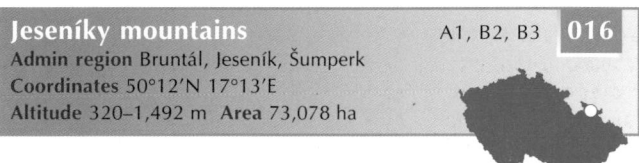

Admin region Bruntál, Jeseník, Šumperk
Coordinates 50°12'N 17°13'E
Altitude 320–1,492 m **Area** 73,078 ha

■ Site description
A mountainous, forested region, with peaks above 1,400 m. Secondary *Picea* stands dominate, with fragments of primary *Abies*/*Fagus* forest preserved at some sites. Alpine meadows exist above the treeline (1,300 m), along with peatbogs and springs. *Alnus* growth covers stream banks, and meadows and pastures, many of them abandoned, dominate the farmland. Forestry is the most important human activity.

Habitats Forest and woodland (81%; broadleaved deciduous forest; native coniferous forest; mixed forest; treeline ecotone), Scrub (1%; scrub), Grassland (1%; alpine/subalpine/boreal grassland; humid grassland; mesophile grassland), Wetland (1%; standing fresh water; river/stream; raised bog; fen/transition mire/spring), Rocky areas (inland cliff), Artificial landscape (19%; highly improved reseeded grassland; arable land; perennial crops/orchards/groves; urban parks/gardens; other urban/industrial areas)
Land-use Agriculture (2%), Forestry (81%), Hunting (82%), Nature conservation/research (7%), Tourism/recreation (30%), Urban/industrial/transport (18%), Water management (1%)

■ Birds

Species		Season	Year	Pop min	Pop max	Acc	Criteria
[1] *Ciconia nigra*	Black Stork	B	1996	5	10	A	B2
[2] *Crex crex*	Corncrake	B	1996	50	60	B	A1
Columba oenas	Stock Dove	B	1996	10	30	B	B3
Turdus torquatus	Ring Ouzel	B	1996	10	20	B	B3

1. 1985–1996.
2. 1990–1996.

The IBA is important for species that breed in the *Picea* forests and alpine meadows, and supports populations of two species with limited distributions in the Czech Republic: *Anthus spinoletta* and *Prunella collaris*.

■ **Protection status**

National High **International** None

73,078 ha of IBA covered by Protected Landscape Area (Jeseníky Protected Landscape Area, 73,078 ha). Included within the PLA are 4 National Nature Reserves (covering 3,763 ha), 11 Nature Reserves (covering 737 ha) and 4 Natural Monuments (covering 4 ha).

■ **Conservation issues**

Threats include acid rain, recreational infrastructure development and disturbance, predation by domestic cats *Felis catus* in the vicinity of chalets and hotels, overgrazing by red deer *Cervus elaphus*, and the construction of hydroelectric plants, antiflood dams and reservoirs. Research projects cover *Ciconia nigra*, *Milvus migrans* and birds of alpine meadows, and a management plan is in place.

Threats Abandonment/reduction of land management (C), Consequences of animal/plant introductions (C), Construction/impact of dyke/dam/barrage (B), Disturbance to birds (C), Extraction industry (U), Forest grazing (C), Industrialization/urbanization (A), Infrastructure (C), Intensified forest management (A), Recreation/tourism (B)

REFERENCES

BEJČEK, V., ŠŤASTNÝ, K. AND HUDEC, K. (1995) [*The Atlas of wintering birds in the Czech Republic 1982–1985.*] Jinočany: H & H and Czech Ministry of Environment. (In Czech, with English summary.)

BUFKA, L. AND KLOUBEC, B. (1997) [Birds in secondary grasslands of military training areas and a former border zone in the Šumava Mts.] *Sylvia* 33: 148–160. (In Czech, with English summary.)

BÜRGER, P., PYKAL, J. AND HORA, J. (1998) [Distribution, numbers and ringing results of Corncrake (*Crex crex*) in the Czech Republic in the period 1993–1997.] *Sylvia* 34: 73–84. (In Czech, with English summary.)

BUŠEK, O., TEJROVSKÝ, V. AND ZAVADIL, V. (1990) [Vertebrata of the Doupov Hills (Aves, Mammalia).] *Sborn. Západočes. muz.*, Plzeň, Přír. 76: 1–52 + xiii. (In Czech, with German summary.)

ČAPEK, M. (1991) Bird species composition of mountain ecosystems damaged by air pollution. *Folia zool.* 40(2): 167–177.

ČAPEK, M. AND KLOUBEC, B. (1990) The avifauna of the Nové Mlýny Waterworks in the period 1981–1985. *Acta Sc. Nat. Brno* 24(6): 1–51.

CHYTIL, J. (1993) [Ramsar site candidate "Wetlands of lower Dyje river" and its importance for the protection of birds.] *Zprávy MOS* 51: 35–49. (In Czech, with English summary.)

EC–UN/ECE (1998) *Forest condition in Europe.* 1998 Executive Report. EC Brussels and UN/ECE Geneva. 37 pp.

FLOUSEK, J. (1988) Bird and mammal communities of the subarctic peatbog in the Krkonoše Mts (Czechoslovakia). *Acta Soc. Zool. Bohemoslov.* 52: 7–21.

FLOUSEK, J. (1989) Impact of industrial emissions on bird populations breeding in mountain spruce forests in Central Europe. *Ann. Zool. Fenn.* 26: 255–263.

FLOUSEK, J. (1992) Breeding bird distribution and air pollution in the Krkonoše Mountains (Czech Republic) in 1983–1992. Pp. 233–238 in E. J. M. Hagemeijer and T. J. Verstrael, eds. *Birds numbers 1992. Distribution, monitoring and ecological aspects. Proc. 12th Int. Conf. IBCC, Noordwijkerhout, the Netherlands.* Voorburg: Statistics, Netherlands.

FLOUSEK, J. AND GRAMSZ, B. (1994) [Atlas of breeding bird distribution in the Krkonoše Mts, Czech Republic, Poland, in 1991–1994 (preliminary report).] Pp. 149–154 in *Geoekologiczne problemy Karkonoszy.* Poland: Jelenia Góra. (In Czech.)

GRIMMETT, R. F. A. AND JONES, T. A. (1989) *Important Bird Areas in Europe.* Cambridge, U.K.: International Council for Bird Preservation (Techn. Publ. 9).

HEATH, M. F. AND BORGGREVE, C. (2000) *BirdLife International/EBCC European Bird Database 1998.* Cambridge, UK: BirdLife International.

HETEŠA, J. AND MARVAN, P., EDS. (1984) [Biology of a newly impounded water reservoir.] *Studie ČSAV* 3: 1–175. (In Czech, with English summary.)

HONZA, M., LITERÁK, I. AND PETRO, R. (1993) Postbreeding occurence of the Reed Bunting (*Emberiza schoeniclus*) in the upper reaches of the Odra River and its migration to the Paduan Lowland. *Ornis Hungarica* 4: 49–55.

HORA, J. AND KAŇUCH, P., EDS. (1992) *Important Bird Areas in Europe. Czechoslovakia.* Prague: Czechoslovak ICBP Section.

HORA, J., BÜRGER, P. AND PYKAL, J. (1997) [Birds of the upper Vltava river floodplain (Šumava Mts., South Bohemia): results of the grid mapping in breeding seasons 1993 and 1994.] *Sylvia* 33: 113–140. (In Czech, with English summary.)

HORA, J., KAŇUCH, P., ET AL., EDS. (1992) [*Proceedings Important Bird Areas in the Czech and Slovak Republics, Třeboň, 24–25 March 1992.*] Prague: International Council for Bird Preservation (Czechoslovak Section). (In Czech, with English summary.)

HORA, J., PLESNÍK, P. AND JANDOVÁ, J., EDS. (1995) [*Proceedings Important Bird Areas in the Czech Republic, Kostelec nad Černými lesy, 7–8 April 1995.*] Prague: Czech Society for Ornithology. (In Czech, with English summary.)

HUDEC, K. AND PELLANTOVÁ, J. (1985) Assessment of the avian community in part of the foot zone of Pavlovské vrchy Hills (Southern Moravia) comprised in a landscape improvement scheme. *Ekológia (ČSSR)* 3(4): 345–363.

HUDEC, K., CHYTIL, J., ŠŤASTNÝ, K. AND BEJČEK, V. (1995) [The birds of the Czech Republic.] *Sylvia* 31: 97–149. (In Czech, with English summary.)

HUDEC, K., HUSÁK, Š., JANDA, J., PELLANTOVÁ, J., ET AL. (1993) *Survey of aquatic and wetland biotopes of the Czech Republic.* Třeboň: Czech Ramsar Committee (Summary Report).

IUCN (1996) [*Importance of fishponds for the Central European landscape. Sustainable use of fishponds in the Třeboňsko Protected Landscape Area and Biosphere Reserve.*] Prague: IUCN Czech Coordination Unit, and Gland, Switzerland and Cambridge, UK: World Conservation Union. (In Czech, with English, German and Russian summaries.)

JANDA, J. (1989) [Contribution to the structure of bird populations in some important habitats of Böhmerwald (Šumava), South Bohemia.] *Staphia* 20: 101–118. (In German, with Czech and English summaries.)

JANDA, J. AND PYKAL, J. (1987) [Structure of avifauna of selected habitats in Šumava Mountains.] Pp. 97–115 in *Proc. Conf. South Bohemian Avifauna and its Changes, České Budějovice, 22–23 February 1986.* (In Czech, with German summary.)

JANDA, J., PYKAL, J. AND VOZÁBAL, L. (1988) [Ornithofauna of Šumava peat-bogs.] *Zprávy MOS* 46: 97–114. (In Czech, with English summary.)

JELÍNEK, M. (1996) [Results of ringing programme "Acrocephalus" in the National Nature Reserve Žehuňský Pond in 1993–1995.] *Zprávy ČSO* 42: 34–35. (In Czech, with English summary.)

JELÍNEK, M. AND URBÁNEK, L. (1993) [Results of Action "Acrocephalus" in the State Nature Reserve Žehuňský Pond.] *Zprávy ČSO* 36: 17–19. (In Czech, with English summary.)

JENÍK, J. AND PRICE, M. F., EDS. (1994) *Biosphere Reserves on the crossroads of Central Europe.* Prague: Czech Nat. MAB Comm.

KLAUS, S. (1991) Effects of forestry on grouse populations: case studies from the Thuringian and Bohemian forests, Central Europe. *Ornis Scand.* 22: 218–223.

KLAUS, S. (1996) Hazel Grouse in Bohemian Forest: results of a 24-year-long study. *Silva Gabreta* 1: 209–219.

KLOUBEC, B. (1995) [Bird species composition of reed stands in Southern Bohemia.] *Sylvia* 31: 38–52. (In Czech, with English summary.)

KLOUBEC, B. AND BUFKA, L. (1997) [Breeding bird communities in fir–spruce–beech virgin forests in the Šumava Mts.(South Bohemia).] *Sylvia* 33: 161–188. (In Czech, with English summary.)

LITERÁK I., HONZA, M. AND KONDĚLKA, D. (1994) Postbreeding migration of the Sedge Warbler *Acrocephalus schoenobaenus* in the Czech Republic. *Ornis Fennica* 71: 151–155.

LITERÁK, I., HONZA, M. AND PAVELKA, K. (1994) Postbreeding migration of the Reed Warbler *Acrocephalus scirpaceus* in the Northeastern Part of the Czech Republic. *Die Vogelwarte* 38(2): 100–105.

LITERÁK, I., HONZA, M. AND PAVELKA, K. (1995) Postbreeding Migration of the Reed Warbler *Acrocephalus scirpaceus* in the Northeastern Part of the Czech Republic. *Die Vogelwarte* 38: 100–105.

LITERÁK, I., HONZA, M. AND STOLARCZYK, J. (1993) [Postbreeding occurrence of Penduline Tit (*Remiz pendulinus*) in reedbeds of the Upper River Odra.] *Egretta* 36(2): 57–66. (In German with an English summary.)

MACHÁČEK, P. (1988) [Influence of water works in South Moravia on waterfowl synusia on the Lednické rybníky ponds.] Brno: ÚSEB ČSAV (CSc. thesis). 194 pp. (In Czech.)

MLČOCH, S., HOŠEK, J. AND PELC, F., EDS. (1998) *Nature conservation and landscape protection state programme of the Czech Republic.* Prague: Ministry of the Environment of the Czech Republic.

MUSIL, P. (1998) [Changes in numbers of breeding populations of water birds on fishponds in the Třeboň basin in the years 1981–1997.] *Sylvia* 34: 13–26. (In Czech, with English summary.)

PAVELKA, J. (1983) [The knowledge of the distribution of the White-backed Woodpecker, *Dendrocopos leucotos* (Bechst.) and Three-toed Woodpecker, *Picoides tridactylus* (L.) in the district of Vsetín.] *Sylvia* 22: 61–68. (In Czech, with English summary.)

PAVELKA, J. (1987) [The bird communities in fir-beech primeval forest Razula in out breeding time.] *Čas. Slez. Muz.*, Opava (A) 36: 159–168. (In Czech, with English and Russian summaries.)

PAVELKA, J. (1988) [The autumn and winter bird communities in the Carpathian fir-beech primeval forest.] *Čas. Slez. Muz.*, Opava (A) 37: 147–159. (In Czech, with English and Russian summaries.)

PAVELKA, J. AND PAVELKA, K. (1990) The bird communities in *Abieto-Fagetum* virgin forests (western Carpathians). Pp. 291–293 in K. Šťastný and V. Bejček, eds. *Bird census and atlas studies. Proc. XIth Int. Conf. on Bird Census and Atlas Work, Prague 1989.*

PAVELKA, K. (1990) Breeding bird communities in three types of primeval forest (western Carpathians). Pp. 287–290 in K. Šťastný and V. Bejček, eds. *Bird Census and Atlas Studies. Proc. XIth Int. Conf. on Bird Census and Atlas Work, Prague 1989.*

PECL, K. (1987) [Ornithological research of the Řežabinec State Nature Reserve in 1976–1984.] Pp. 152–179 in *Proc. Conf. South Bohemian Avifauna and its Changes, České Budějovice, 22–23 February 1986.* (In Czech, with German summary.)

PECL, K. (1994) [Waterfowl occurrence at Řežabinec National Nature Reserve in 1984–1991.] *Sylvia* 30(2): 86–90. (In Czech, with English summary.)

PLESNÍK, J. (1998) Nature conservation in the Czech Republic: basic information on the present status. Report for the 18th Meeting of the Standing Committee of the Convention on the Conservation of European Wildlife and Natural Habitats, Strasbourg 30 November–4 December 1998. Prague: Ministry of the Environment of the Czech Republic. Unpublished report.

PLESNÍK, J. AND ROUDNÁ, M., EDS. (1998) *National biodiversity conservation strategy and action plan in the Czech Republic: status of biological resources and implementation of the Convention on Biological Diversity in the Czech Republic.* Prague: Ministry of the Environment of the Czech Republic.

PYKAL, J. AND JANDA, J. (1994) [Relation between waterfowl numbers on South Bohemian fishponds and fishpond management.] *Sylvia* 30: 3–11. (In Czech, with English summary.)

PYKAL, J., BÜRGER, P. AND HORA, J. (1997) [Bird communities of non-forested landscape in the border area of Nové Údolí–Haidmühle. *Sylvia* 33: 141–147. (In Czech, with English summary.)

PYKAL, J., BÜRGER, P., HORA, J. AND JANDA, J. (1991) [Birds of peatbogs in the Šumava Mountains: a comparison periods 1979–1982 and 1989–1990.] *Sylvia* 28: 65–75 (In Czech, with English summary.)

ŠMAHA, J. (1983) [Avifauna of some biocenoses on the steep slopes in the Křivoklát surroundings.] *Bohemia centralis* 12: 157–181. (In Czech, with German summary.)

ŠMAHA, J. (1988) [Some examples of the dependence of anthropogenic changes in fauna on biotope characters in the Křivoklátsko Biosphere Reserve.] *Bohemia centralis* 17: 245–248. (In Czech, with German summary.)

ŠMAHA, J. (1989) [Diversity of birds and its causality in the Křivoklátsko Biosphere Reserve .] *Bohemia centralis* 18: 275–291. (In Czech, with German summary.)

ŠMAHA, J. (1990) [Report on the status of the orders Columbiformes to Piciformes in the Křivoklátsko Biosphere Reserve.] Pp. 23–32 in J. Sitko and P. Trpák, eds. *Proc. Orn. Conf., Přerov 1989.* Praha: SÚPPOP Praha, OVM J.A. Komenského Přerov, MOS Přerov. (In Czech.)

ŠŤASTNÝ, K. AND BEJČEK, V. (1993) [Breeding bird populations sizes in the Czech Republic.] *Sylvia* 29: 72–81. (In Czech, with English summary.)

ŠŤASTNÝ, K., BEJČEK, V. AND HUDEC, K. (1996) [*The Atlas of breeding birds in the Czech Republic 1985–1989.*] Jinočany: H & H. (In Czech, with English summary.)

ŠŤASTNÝ, K., RANDÍK, A. AND HUDEC K. (1987) [*The Atlas of breeding birds in Czechoslovakia 1973–1977.*] Prague: Academia. (In Czech, with English summary.)

TUCKER, G. M. AND HEATH, M. F. (1994) *Birds in Europe: their conservation status.* Cambridge, U.K.: BirdLife International (BirdLife Conservation Series 3).

ZASADIL, P. (1994) [Bird communities of fishpond dikes in the Třeboň region: a comparison of periods 1970/71 and 1992.] *Sylvia* 30: 32–40. (In Czech, with English summary.)

■ DENMARK

JAN F. RASMUSSEN, MORTEN NIELSEN AND KNUD N. FLENSTED

Magisterkog (IBA 060), an important IBA for staging Barnacle Goose *Branta leucopsis*. (PHOTO: THOMAS W. JOHANSEN)

GENERAL INTRODUCTION

In addition to Denmark itself, Danish Sovereign territory is composed of Greenland and the Faroe Islands. There are separate chapters covering the Important Bird Areas (IBAs) of the Faroe Islands (see p. 179) and Greenland (see p. 187) and this overview is therefore confined to Denmark *per se* ('mainland').

Denmark *per se* covers 43,093 km², and consists of the Jylland peninsula (23,873 km²) connected narrowly with the European mainland, and extensive archipelagic waters with 406 named islands. The largest islands are Sjælland (7,031 km²), Vendsyssel-Thy (4,685 km²), Fyn (2,985 km²), Lolland (1,243 km²) and the outlying Baltic island, Bornholm (588 km²). The total Danish exclusive economic zone (fishing territory), in which several large and significant IBAs are situated, covers approximately 106,000 km².

Denmark is low-lying and mostly gently undulating; altitude ranges from -7.5 m below sea-level to 171 m above sea-level, with

an average of 31 m. The coasts are characterized by a very high degree of indentation resulting in a coastline of 7,950 km in length, with an abundance of fjords, bays, straits, and peninsulas. The seas surrounding Denmark are characterized by large areas of very shallow water.

While the population of Denmark is only 5.3 million people, the small size of the country means that the corresponding average population density of 123 individuals per km² is high. However, the major part of the population live in towns and cities and rural population densities are under 100 people per km².

The 1989 inventory identified 118 IBAs (Grimmett and Jones 1989) with a total extent of more than 10,505 km². The present inventory describes 127 IBAs with a total area of 48,701 km² (Table 1, Map 1); this area includes the Danish parts of a few large transboundary IBAs located partly within the sea territories of Norway, Sweden and Germany. The main reason for the changes since 1989 are the inclusion of large areas of sea now known to be

Table 1. Summary of Important Bird Areas in Denmark. 127 IBAs covering 48,701 km²

IBA code	1989 code	International name	National name	Administrative region	Area (ha)	Criteria (see p. 11)
001	DK001	Ulvedybet and Nibe Bredning	Ulvedybet and Nibe Bredning	Nordjylland	18,530	A4i, A4iii, B1i, B2, B3, C2, C3, C4, C6
002	DK002	Coast between Dokkedal and Lyngså	Ålborg Bugt (northern part)	Nordjylland	1,700	A4i, A4iii, B1i, C2, C3, C4
003	DK003	Madum Sø	Madum Sø	Nordjylland	260	C7
004	DK004	Rold Skov	Rold Skov	Nordjylland	7,420	C6
005	DK005	Råbjerg Mile and surrounding heathlands	Råbjerg Mile and surrounding heathlands	Nordjylland	4,480	C6
006	DK006	Jerup Hede, Råbjerg Mose and Tolshave Mose	Jerup Hede, Råbjerg Mose and Tolshave Mose	Nordjylland	2,320	C7
007	DK007	Lille Vildmose	Lille Vildmose	Nordjylland	7,380	A4i, B1i, C2, C3
008	DK008	Coast from Aggersund to Bygholm Vejle	Kysten fra Aggersund til Bygholm Vejle	Nordjylland	1,660	B2, C7
009	DK009	Nordre Rønner	Nordre Rønner	Nordjylland	2,923	B3, C7
010	DK010	South Læsø	South Læsø	Nordjylland	10,000	A4i, A4iii, B1i, B2, B3, C2, C3, C4, C6
011	DK011	Hirsholmene	Hirsholmene	Nordjylland	220	A4i, B1i, B1ii, B2, B3, C6

Table 1 ... continued. Summary of Important Bird Areas in Denmark. 127 IBAs covering 48,701 km²

IBA code	1989 code	International name	National name	Administrative region	Area (ha)	Criteria (see p. 11)
012	DK012	Løgstør Bredning	Løgstør Bredning	Nordjylland	32,570	C7
013	DK013	Eastern part of Vejlerne	Vejlerne, østlige del	Viborg	4,870	A4i, A4iii, B1i, B2, B3, C2, C3, C4, C6
014	DK014	Lovns Bredning	Lovns Bredning	Viborg	7,590	A4i, B1i, C3
015	DK015	Parts of Randers and Mariager Fjords	Dele af Randers og Mariager Fjorde	Århus	7,500	A4i, A4iii, B1i, B3, C2, C3, C4, C6
016	DK016	Tjele Langsø	Tjele Langsø	Viborg	1,340	C7
017	DK017	Ålvand Klithede and Førby Sø	Ålvand Klithede and Førby Sø	Viborg	1,430	C6
018	DK018	Vangså Hede	Vangså Hede	Viborg	1,410	C7
019	DK019	Lønnerup Fjord	Lønnerup Fjord	Viborg	460	A4i, B1i, C2
020	DK020	Western part of Vejlerne, Arup Holm and Hovsør Røn	Vestlige Vejler, Arup Holm and Hovsør Røn	Viborg	3,850	A4i, B1i, B2, C2, C6
021	DK021	Ovesø	Ovesø	Viborg	750	C7
022	DK022	Hanstholm Reservatet	Hanstholm Reservatet	Viborg	5,110	B1i, C2, C3, C6
023	DK023	Agger Tange and Krik Vig	Agger Tange and Krik Vig	Viborg	5,490	B1i, C3
024	DK024	Hjarbæk Fjord	Hjarbæk Fjord	Viborg	4,260	A4i, B1i, C2, C3
025	DK025	Mågerodde and Karbyodde	Mågerodde and Karbyodde	Viborg	510	C7
026	DK026	Dråby Vig and Buksør Odde	Dråby Vig og Buksør Odde	Viborg	1,680	B1i, C2
027	DK027	Glomstrup Vig, Agerø, Munkholm and Katholm Odde, Lindholm, and Rotholme	Glomstrup Vig, Agerø, Munkholm and Katholm Odde, Lindholm, and Rotholme	Viborg	6,990	B1i, C2, C4
028	DK028	Nissum Bredning	Nissum Bredning	Viborg	13,570	C7
029	DK029	Flyndersø and Skallesø	Flyndersø og Skallesø	Ringkøbing, Viborg	830	C2
030	DK030	Norsminde (Kysing) Fjord	Norsminde (Kysing) Fjord	Århus	370	B1i, C3
031	DK031	Stavnsfjord and adjacent waters	Stavnsfjord and adjacent waters	Århus	15,450	A4i, B1i, B3, C3
032	DK032	Ørkenen and Totten (Anholt island)	Ørkenen og Totten, Anholt	Århus	2,000	B3, C7
033	DK033	Salten Langsø	Salten Langsø	Århus	970	C7
034	DK034	Forest areas south of Silkeborg	Forest areas south of Silkeborg	Århus	5,070	C7
035	DK035	Mossø	Mossø	Århus	2,020	C7
036	DK036	Horsens Fjord, Svanegrunden and Endelave islands	Horsens Fjord, Svanegrunden and Endelave islands	Vejle	42,880	A4i, B1i, B2, C2, C3
037	DK037	Borris Hede	Borris Hede	Ringkøbing	4,760	C6
038	DK038	Nissum Fjord	Nissum Fjord	Ringkøbing	10,890	A4i, B1i, B2, C2, C3, C6
039	DK039	Harboøre Tange, Plet Enge and Gjeller Sø	Harboøre Tange, Plet Enge and Gjeller Sø	Ringkøbing	7,280	A4i, A4iii, B1i, B3, C3, C4
040	DK040	Venø and Venø Sund	Venø and Venø Sund	Viborg	2,920	C7
041	DK041	Stadil Fjord and Veststadil Fjord	Stadil Fjord and Veststadil Fjord	Ringkøbing	6,910	A4i, B1i, B2, C2, C3, C6
042	DK042	Heath areas in Sønder Feldborg Plantage	Heath areas in Sønder Feldborg Plantage	Viborg	120	C7
043	DK043	Ringkøbing Fjord	Ringkøbing Fjord	Ringkøbing	27,720	A4i, A4iii, B1i, B2, B3, C2, C3, C4, C6
044	DK044	Uldum Kær	Uldum Kær	Vejle	1,050	C7
045	DK045	Forest areas along the northern part of Vejle Fjord	Forest areas along the northern part of Vejle Fjord	Vejle	2,690	C7
046	DK046	Randbøl Hede	Randbøl Hede	Ribe, Vejle	1,010	C7
047	DK047	Lillebælt	Lillebælt	Fyn, Sønderjylland	35,060	A4iii, B1i, C3, C4, C6
048	DK048	Heath areas near Store Råbjerg	Heath areas near Store Råbjerg	Ribe	630	C7
049	—	Ho Bugt meadows	Ho Bugt meadows	Ribe	2,700	A4i, A4iii, B1i, C2, C4
050	DK050	Kallesmærsk Hede, Grærup Langsø and surrounding areas	Kallesmærsk Hede, Grærup Langsø and surrounding areas	Ribe	6,570	C7
051	—	Ribe Holme and meadows at Kongeåen	Ribe Holme and meadows at Kongeåen	Ribe	6,660	A4i, A4iii, B1i, B3, C2, C4
052	—	Mandø	Mandø	Ribe	850	A4i, A4iii, B1i, B2, C2, C3, C4
053	—	Fanø	Fanø	Ribe	4,370	A4i, A4iii, B1i, B2, C2, C3, C4, C6
054	DK051	Vejen Mose	Vejen Mose	Ribe	460	C7
055	—	Skallingen and Langli	Skallingen and Langli	Ribe	2,240	A4i, A4iii, B1i, B2, C2, C4, C6
056	DK052	Fiilsø	Fiilsø	Ribe	4,270	A4i, A4iii, B1i, B2, B3, C2, C3, C4, C6
057	DK049	Vadehavet (Wadden Sea)	Vadehavet (Wadden Sea)	Ribe, Sønderjylland	115,850	A4i, A4iii, B1i, B2, B3, C2, C3, C4, C6
058	DK053	Hostrup Sø, Assenholm Mose and Felsted Vestermark	Hostrup Sø, Assenholm Mose and Felsted Vestermark	Sønderjylland	1,330	C6
059	DK054	Pamhule Skov	Pamhule Skov	Sønderjylland	1,100	C7
060	—	Tøndermarsken, Magisterkog and Rudbøl Sø	Tøndermarsken, Magisterkog og Rudbøl Sø	Sønderjylland	6,520	A4i, A4iii, B1i, B2, B3, C2, C3, C4, C6
061	DK055	Kongens Mose and Draved Skov	Kongens Mose and Draved Skov	Sønderjylland	790	C6
062	DK056	Tinglev Mose and Sø	Tinglev Mose and Sø	Sønderjylland	930	C7
063	DK057	Sønder Ådal	Sønder Ådal	Sønderjylland	2,690	C7
064	DK058	Flensborg Fjord and Nybøl Nor	Flensborg Fjord and Nybøl Nor	Sønderjylland	3,350	A4iii, C4
065	—	Rømø	Rømø	Sønderjylland	7,010	A4i, A4iii, B1i, B2, C2, C3, C4

Table 1 ... continued. Summary of Important Bird Areas in Denmark.　　　　　127 IBAs covering 48,701 km²

IBA code	1989 code	International name	National name	Administrative region	Area (ha)	Criteria (see p. 11)
066	DK059	Lindet Skov, Hønning Plantage, Lovrup Skov and Skrøp	Lindet Skov, Hønning Plantage, Lovrup Skov and Skrøp	Sønderjylland	2,340	C7
067	—	Ballum og Husum Enge, Kamper strandenge	Ballum og Husum Enge, Kamper strandenge	Sønderjylland	4,280	A4i, A4iii, B1i, C2, C3, C4
068	DK060	Forests near Gråsten	Forests near Gråsten	Sønderjylland	870	C7
069	DK061	Kogsbøl and Skast Mose	Kogsbøl and Skast Mose	Sønderjylland	560	C7
070	DK062	Frøslev Plantage and Frøslev Mose	Frøslev Plantage og Frøslev Mose	Sønderjylland	1,700	C6
071	DK063	Sydfynske Ø-hav	Sydfynske Ø-hav	Fyn	38,440	A4i, A4iii, B1i, B2, B3, C2, C3, C6
072	DK064	Marstal Bugt and the coast of south-west Langeland	Marstal Bugt and the coast of south-west Langeland	Fyn	4,980	B1iv, C5
073	DK065	Vresen and sea area between Fyn and Langeland	Vresen og havområde mellem Fyn og Langeland	Fyn	3,470	A4iii, B1i, C3, C4
074	DK066	Forests near Brahetrolleborg	Forests near Brahetrolleborg	Fyn	2,570	C7
075	DK067	Odense Fjord	Odense Fjord	Fyn	5,060	A4i, B1i, B2, C2, C3, C6
076	DK068	Nærå coast and Æbelø area	Nærå Coast and Æbelø area	Fyn	13,060	A4i, B1i, C3
077	DK069	Romsø and Hindsholm peninsula	Romsø og Hindsholmhalvøen	Fyn	3,490	A4iii, C4
078	DK070	Arreskov Sø	Arreskov Sø	Fyn	660	C6
079	DK071	Ertholmene east of Bornholm	Ertholmene east of Bornholm	Bornholm	1,257	C7
080	DK072	Almindingen	Almindingen	Bornholm	6,090	C6
081	DK073	Karrebæk, Dybsø and Avnø Fjords (coasts and islands)	Kyster langs og øer i Karrebæk, Dybsø and Avnø Fjorde	Storstrøm	4,480	A4i, A4iii, B1i, B3, C2, C3, C4
082	DK074	Bøtø Nor	Bøtø Nor	Storstrøm	1,710	A4i, B1i, C2, C3
083	DK074	Hyllekrog-Rødsand and Fehmarn Belt	Hyllekrog-Rødsand og Fehmarn Bælt	Storstrøm	100,000	A4i, A4iii, B1i, B1ii, C2, C3, C4
084	DK075	Ulvsund, Grønsund, Farø Fjord and Fanefjord	Ulvsund, Grønsund, Farø Fjord and Fanefjord	Storstrøm	8,160	A4i, A4iii, B1i, C2, C3
085	DK076	Islands in Smålandshavet, north of Lolland	Øer i Smålandshavet north of Lolland	Storstrøm	4,390	A4i, B1i, C3
086	DK077	Guldborgsund	Guldborgsund	Storstrøm	2,820	B1i, C3
087	DK078	Maribo lakes	Maribo lakes	Storstrøm	3,810	A4i, A4iii, B1i, B2, C2, C3, C4, C6
088	DK079	Nakskov Fjord and Indre Fjord	Nakskov Fjord and Indre Fjord	Storstrøm	8,550	A4i, B1i, C2, C3
089	DK080	Præstø Fjord, Ulvshale, Nyord, and Jungshoved Nor	Præstø Fjord, Ulvshale, Nyord, and Jungshoved Nor	Storstrøm	24,640	A4i, A4iii, B1i, B3, C3, C4
090	DK081	Klinteskoven	Klinteskoven	Storstrøm	1,010	C7
091	DK082	Holmegårds Mose and Porsemose	Holmegårds Mose and Porsemose	Storstrøm	1,900	C2
092	DK083	Forests near Vemmetofte	Forests near Vemmetofte	Storstrøm	1,860	C7
093	DK084	Tystrup – Bavelse Søerne	Tystrup – Bavelse Søerne	Vestsjælland	1,960	B1i, C2, C3
094	DK085	Sejrø Bay and Nekselø	Sejrø Bugt og Nekselø	Vestsjælland	40,250	A4i, A4iii, B1i, C3, C4
095	DK086	Skælskør Nor, Skælskør Fjord and Borreby Mose	Skælskør Nor, Skælskør Fjord and Borreby Mose	Vestsjælland	1,950	A4i, B1i, B1iv, C3, C5
096	DK087	Islands and coast between Skælskør Fjord and Glænø	Øer og kyster mellem Skælskør Fjord og Glænø	Vestsjælland	3,220	A4i, A4iii, B1i, B2, B3, C3, C4, C6
097	DK088	Hovvig	Hovvig	Vestsjælland	240	A4i, B1i, C3
098	DK089	Sprogø and Halsskov Rev	Sprogø og Halsskov Rev	Vestsjælland	4,920	A4i, B1i, C3
099	DK090	Saltbæk Vig	Saltbæk Vig	Vestsjælland	3,630	B1i, B3, C3
100	DK091	Tissø, Lille Åmose, and Hallenslev Mose	Tissø, Lille Åmose, and Hallenslev Mose	Vestsjælland	2,890	A4i, B1i, B2, C2, C3, C6
101	DK092	Bregentved and Gisselfeldt lakes	Bregentved and Gisselfeldt lakes	Vestsjælland	600	C7
102	DK093	Korshage, Hundested and surrounding sea area	Korshage og Hundested samt omgivende havområde	Vestsjælland	4,000	A4i, A4iii, B1i, B1iv, C3, C4, C5
103	DK094	Wetland north of Gammel Havdrup	Wetland north of Gammel Havdrup	Roskilde	100	C7
104	DK095	Ramsø Mose	Ramsø Mose	Roskilde	220	C7
105	DK096	Roskilde Fjord, Selsø and Kattinge Søerne	Roskilde Fjord, Selsø and Kattinge Søerne	Frederiksborg	13,180	A4i, A4iii, B1i, B2, B3, C2, C3, C4, C6
106	DK097	Arresø	Arresø	Frederiksborg	4,610	A4i, B1i, C3
107	DK098	Jægerspris Nordskov	Jægerspris Nordskov	Frederiksborg	1,520	C7
108	DK099	Grib Skov	Grib Skov	Frederiksborg	6,130	C6
109	DK100	Furesø and Farum Sø	Furesø and Farum Sø	Frederiksborg	1,290	B1i, C3
110	DK101	Saltholm	Saltholm	København	7,240	A4i, B1i, B3, C2, C3
111	DK102	Vestamager and adjacent sea area	Vestamager and adjacent sea area	København	6,210	A4i, A4iii, B1i, C3
112	DK105	Hjelm	Hjelm	Århus	70	B2, C7
113	DK111	Møllesø and Gjorslev	Møllesø and Gjorslev	Storstrøm	50	B1i, C3
114	DK114	Sjørring Sø	Sjørring Sø	Viborg	400	B1i, C2, C3
115	DK116	Skjern Å	Skjern Å	Ringkøbing	3,850	A4i, B1i, B2, C2
116	—	Bolle and Try meadows	Bolle og Try Enge	Nordjylland	1,500	A4i, B1i, B2, C2
117	—	Store Vildmose, Ryå and Stavad Enge	Store Vildmose, Ryå og Stavad Enge	Nordjylland	6,000	A4i, B1i, B2, C2, C6
118	—	Smålandsfarvandet	Smålandsfarvandet		162,500	A4i, A4iii, B1i, C2, C3, C4
119	—	Northern Kattegat	Nordlige Kattegat		870,000	A4i, A4ii, A4iii, B1i, B1ii, B2, B3, C2, C3, C4

Table 1 ... continued. Summary of Important Bird Areas in Denmark.   127 IBAs covering 48,701 km²

IBA code	1989 code	International name	National name	Administrative region	Area (ha)	Criteria (see p. 11)
120	—	Rønne Banke	Rønne Banke		100,000	A4i, A4iii, B1i, B1ii, C3
121	—	Skagerrak—Southwest Norwegian trench	Skagerrak—Southwest Norwegian trench		1,600,000	A4i, A4ii, A4iii, B1i, B1ii, C3
122	—	Kiel Bay and adjacent waters	Kiel Bugt og tilgrænsende farvande		120,000	A4i, A4iii, B1i, C3, C4
123	—	Eastern German Bight	Østlige Tyskebugt		1,150,000	A4i, B1i, C2, C3
124	—	Hellebæk	Hellebæk	Frederiksborg	800	B1iv, C5
125	—	Skagen	Skagen	Nordjylland	1,800	B1iv, C5
126	—	Gilleleje area	Gilleje området	Frederiksborg	1,250	B1iv, C5
127	—	Stevns	Stevns	Storstrøm	1,000	A4iv, B1iv, C5

Sites identified in the previous inventory of IBAs in Europe (Grimmett and Jones 1989) but no longer considered to be IBAs
DK103 Vilsund and Stokkær Odde; DK104 Klejtrup Sø; DK106 Alssund and Augustenborg Fjord; DK107 Kalundborg Inderfjord; DK108 Sea area between Reersø and Røsnæs; DK109 Skarresø; DK110 Damhussøen; DK112 Rønninge Søgård; DK113 Lykkesholm; DK115 Karup Å; DK117 Gudenå, Norreå, and Skals Å; DK118 Ryå near Store Vildmose.

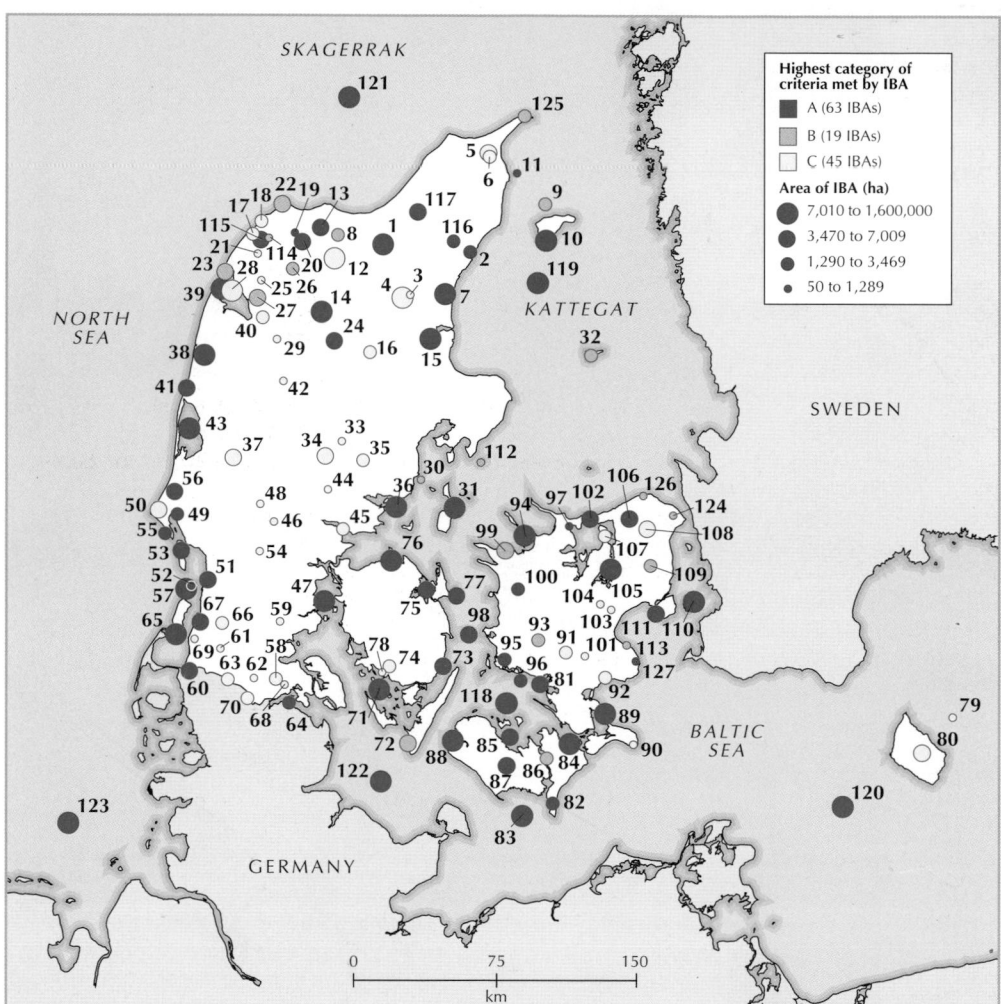

Map 1. Location, area and criteria category of Important Bird Areas in Denmark.

of high importance for wintering seabirds and waterfowl. Boundaries of several areas have changed, most notably those of Northern Kattegat (site 119) and Smålandsfarvandet (site 118) which have been extended to include sea areas formerly included within several smaller IBAs. Twelve sites included in Grimmett and Jones (1989) have not been confirmed as IBAs (Table 1), as they no longer meet the IBA criteria (Table 1).

The Danish IBAs are fairly evenly distributed over the country, though the majority of sites are coastal or marine (Map 1).

ORNITHOLOGICAL IMPORTANCE

Two species of global conservation concern breed in Denmark, *Crex crex* and *Haliaeetus albicilla,* but neither species occur at densities sufficient to meet the A1 criterion at any locality.

The most important Danish IBAs are designated because of large concentrations of divers, grebes, swans, geese, ducks, waders and auks occurring on passage or in winter. A total of 62 sites qualify

because they hold at least 1% of the biogeographic population of one or more such species (A4i/A4ii criteria) and a further 11 sites hold at least 1% of the flyway of one or more species (B1i/B1ii criteria). Especially important areas are Northern Kattegat (119), Smålandsfarvandet (118), Stavnsfjord (031), Hyllekrog-Rødsand and Fehmarn Belt (083) and various transboundary sites. Several coastal and inland wetland sites are also of high importance for both waterfowl and waders: Ulvedybet and Nibe Bredning (001), South Læsø (010), Eastern part of Vejlerne (013), Western part of Vejlerne, Arup Holm and Hovsør Røn (020), Ringkøbing Fjord (043), Fiilsø (056), Maribo lakes (087), Saltholm (110), Meadows area at Ho Bugt (049), Mandø (052) and Skallingen and Langli (055). Several sites listed in this chapter hold very large numbers of seaduck only in harsh winters. These sites remain free of ice longer than other areas and are extremely significant as they provide habitat for these birds at the most critical times. Table 2 details all IBAs important for congregatory species.

Denmark holds important breeding populations of the subspecies *Phlacrocorax carbo sinensis* with eight sites qualifying

Table 2. Important Bird Areas in Denmark that support important numbers of one or more congregatory species (i.e. meeting criteria A4 and/or B1). IBAs meeting both criteria A4 and B1 for the species are shown in **bold**. IBAs meeting only criterion B1 for the species concerned, and not A4, are shown in normal type. For key to 'Season', see p. 7.

Species	Season	IBA code
Gavia stellata Red-throated Diver	W	**083, 118, 119, 123**
Gavia arctica Black-throated Diver	W	**083, 118, 119, 123**
Podiceps cristatus Great Crested Grebe	W	122
Podiceps grisegena Red-necked Grebe	W	083, **119,** 122
	N	**123**
Sula bassana Gannet	W	**121**
Phalacrocorax carbo Cormorant	B	007, **031, 036,** 038, 043, **076, 085, 087, 089, 096,** 097
	N	031, 083
Cygnus olor Mute Swan	W	**084, 089, 096, 105, 118**
	N	**075, 081,** 083, **085, 088, 110**
Cygnus columbianus Bewick's Swan	W	**013, 056**
	P	**019, 105**
	N	**001, 020, 038, 041, 043, 060, 100, 115, 116, 117**
Cygnus cygnus Whooper Swan	W	**001, 013, 015,** 019, **024,** 056, 071, 088 105, **117**
	P	**100**
	N	007, 020, 022, **038, 060,** 075, **081,** 084, **116**
Anser fabalis Bean Goose	N	022
Anser brachyrhynchus Pink-footed Goose	P	**056, 067**
	N	**013, 038, 039, 041, 043, 057**
Anser anser Greylag Goose	P	**056,** 082, **087, 096,** 100
	N	110, 113, 114
Branta leucopsis Barnacle Goose	P	**067**
	N	**057, 060, 082**
Branta bernicla Brent Goose	P	**053, 065, 067**
	N	015, 023, 039, **052, 057, 060, 071**
Tadorna tadorna Shelduck	P	**053**
	N	015, **038, 057, 060**
Anas penelope Wigeon	P	**065, 089**
	N	001, **057**
Anas strepera Gadwall	P	087
Anas crecca Teal	P	065, **067**
	N	038, 043, 099
Anas acuta Pintail	P	**053, 065**
	N	**056, 057, 060**
Anas clypeata Shoveler	P	065, 097
Aythya ferina Pochard	W	086
	N	024, **087**
Aythya fuligula Tufted Duck	W	086, **087, 105, 118,** 122
	N	**071,** 083, 084, 093, **095,** 109, 111
Aythya marila Scaup	W	036, **119**
Somateria mollissima Eider	R	**098**
	W	031, **036,** 047, 073, **094, 102, 119, 122**
	N	**057,** 071

Species	Season	IBA code
Clangula hyemalis Long-tailed Duck	W	**120, 122**
Melanitta nigra Common Scoter	W	**031, 094, 119, 122, 123**
	N	**057**
Melanitta fusca Velvet Scoter	W	**094, 119**
Bucephala clangula Goldeneye	W	**118, 119,** 122
	N	**014, 024,** 071, 089
Mergus serrator Red-breasted Merganser	W	**083, 118**
	N	013, **071, 111**
Mergus merganser Goosander	W	**105, 106, 118**
	N	**014,** 030, **097**
Fulica atra Coot	W	105, **118**
	N	071
Haematopus ostralegus Oystercatcher	P	**053, 065**
	N	**052, 057**
Recurvirostra avosetta Avocet	B	**010,** 01, **043,** 051, **057,** 060
	P	**049, 057, 060**
	N	010
Pluvialis apricaria Golden Plover	P	**002, 013,** 026, **051, 060,** 075, 114
	N	001, 027, **057**
Pluvialis squatarola Grey Plover	P	**053**
	N	**057**
Calidris canutus Knot	P	**053, 060**
	N	**052, 057**
Calidris alba Sanderling	P	053
	N	**057**
Calidris alpina Dunlin	P	**002, 052, 053, 060, 065**
	N	**010,** 038, **057**
Limosa lapponica Bar-tailed Godwit	P	**010, 036, 038, 043, 049, 052, 053, 060, 065**
	N	**055, 057**
Tringa erythropus Spotted Redshank	P	**060**
Tringa totanus Redshank	P	065
	N	057
Stercorarius skua Great Skua	P	**121**
Larus minutus Little Gull	W	**123**
Larus canus Common Gull	W	**123**
Larus argentatus Herring Gull	W	**119, 121**
Larus marinus Great Black-backed Gull	W	**119**
Sterna sandvicensis Sandwich Tern	B	**011, 038, 043, 055**
	P	**123**
Uria aalge Guillemot	N	121
Alca torda Razorbill	W	**119, 121**
Cepphus grylle Black Guillemot	B	011
	W	083, 120
Alle alle Little Auk	W	**121**

under the A4i criterion and a further three under the B1i criterion (Table 2). Some Danish breeding populations of *Recurvirostra avocetta* and *Sterna sandvicensis* are also of international importance, meeting the A4 criteria.

Large numbers of raptors, mostly Fennoscandian, pass through Denmark, especially the eastern part, during both spring and autumn migration. Raptors also pass over other sites in numbers which could meet the B1iv threshold of 3,000 birds. However, criteria have only been applied to the most important Danish bottleneck sites, i.e. those with more than 20,000 raptors (A4iv criterion), the most significant of which are Gilleleje area (IBA 126, spring), Hellebæk (IBA 124, spring and autumn), Stigsnæs (part of IBA 095, autumn) and Stevns (IBA 127, autumn). The most numerous species are *Buteo buteo, Pernis apivorus* and *Accipiter nisus*.

A total of 102 species of European conservation concern (SPECs) breed regularly in Denmark, of which 52 have an unfavourable conservation status in Europe (Tucker and Heath 1994). For several of these species, much larger populations pass through Denmark during migration periods or in winter (e.g. *Branta leucopsis, Somateria mollissima, Calidris alpina* and *Turdus pilaris*).

IBAs qualifying on the basis of breeding populations of SPECs are shown in Table 3, showing that many SPECs and species listed on Annex I of the EC Birds Directive are reasonably well covered by the IBA network. Notable exceptions are dispersed breeding species such as *Pernis apivorus, Circus aeruginosus, Bubo bubo, Caprimulgus europaeus, Alcedo atthis, Dryocopus martius, Lullula arborea, Lanius collurio* and the large winter populations of *Turdus pilaris* and *T. iliacus*. The very high coverage for *Botaurus stellaris* reflects a real increase in the Danish population of this species. The rapidly growing Baltic population of *Branta leucopsis* has recently spread to Denmark, the figure in Table 3 reflects the rapid growth of a still fairly small total population. The percentage figure in Table 3 for *Crex crex* is probably too high as many of the Danish birds occur outside of IBAs. This inaccuracy is probably a reflection of random yearly fluctuations or differing methods of calculating numbers of pairs from numbers of singing males.

Table 3. Species of European conservation concern and species listed on Annex I of the EC Birds Directive with significant breeding populations at IBAs in Denmark (meeting any IBA criteria).

Species [1]	Minimum national breeding population (pairs) [2]	Proportion (%) of national population breeding at all IBAs in Denmark
Botaurus stellaris Bittern	150	100[3]
Branta leucopsis Barnacle Goose	16	100[3]
Haliaeetus albicilla White-tailed Eagle	4	100
Crex crex Corncrake	5	100
Recurvirostra avosetta Avocet	5,000	95
Pluvialis apricaria Golden Plover	6	100[3]
Limosa limosa Black-tailed Godwit	600	100[3]
Tringa totanus Redshank	10,000	16
Tringa glareola Wood Sandpiper	63	97
Larus canus Common Gull	25,000	51
Larus fuscus Lesser Black-backed Gull	4,400	66
Larus marinus Great Black-backed Gull	1,500	62
Sterna sandvicensis Sandwich Tern	4,500	100[3]
Sterna hirundo Common Tern	1,000	100[3]
Sterna paradisaea Arctic Tern	8,000	65
Sterna albifrons Little Tern	400	63
Chlidonias niger Black Tern	100	78
Cepphus grylle Black Guillemot	1,067	65
Aegolius funereus Tengmalm's Owl	1	100[3]
Dryocopus martius Black Woodpecker	200	22
Lanius collurio Red-backed Shrike	1,500	12

1. Only those species of European conservation concern (see Box 1, p. 12) that meet IBA criteria in Denmark are listed, together with those species listed on Annex I of the EC Birds Directive that fulfil criterion C6 in IBAs in Denmark.
2. Data are taken from the BirdLife/EBCC European Bird Database 1998 (Heath and Borggreve 2000).
3. The percentage of the national population in IBAs exceeds 100%. Usually this is because the national population estimate has not been updated recently whilst the IBA population estimate has been recently updated with new data as a result of comprehensive surveys of IBAs themselves. Also, the individual site count for a species may be the maximum or average over recent years, and summing these may record more birds than are present nationally in any single year.

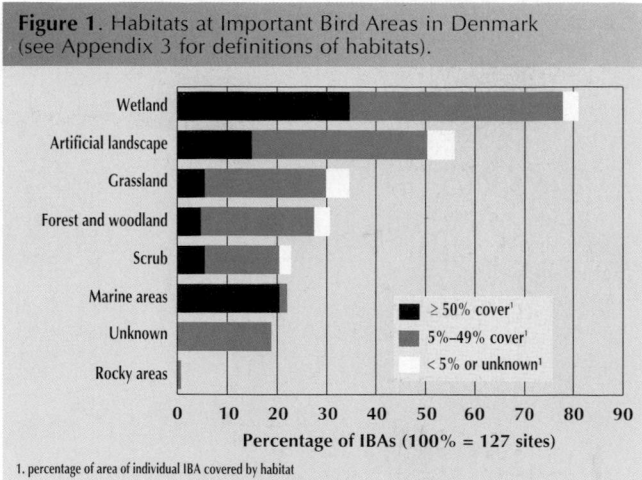

Figure 1. Habitats at Important Bird Areas in Denmark (see Appendix 3 for definitions of habitats).

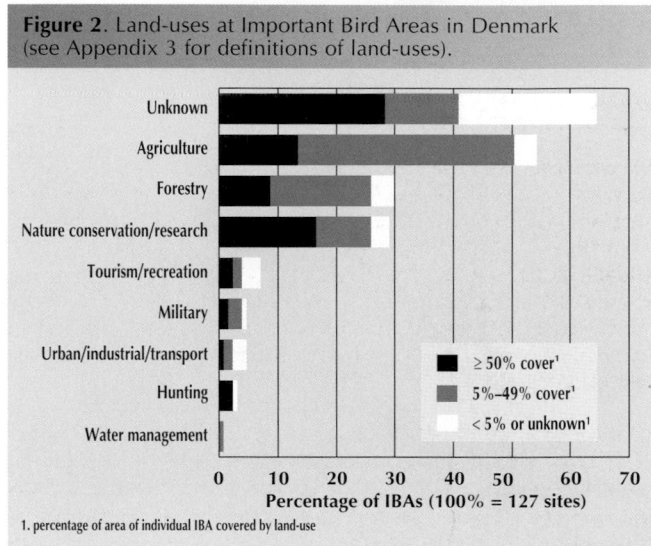

Figure 2. Land-uses at Important Bird Areas in Denmark (see Appendix 3 for definitions of land-uses).

HABITATS

More than 90% of the Danish land surface has been extensively modified by agriculture. Today 12–13% of the land area is regarded as 'forest' but the major part of this is forestry plantation partly of exotic *Pinus* and *Picea* and with large areas of *Fagus*. Only tiny, scattered pockets of natural woodland remain, mainly of *Quercus*, *Carpinus*, *Tilia*, *Fagus*, *Fraxinus* and *Alnus*. Other remaining patches of semi-natural vegetation include sand-dunes, raised bogs, plant communities on steep coastal clay- and chalk-cliffs and coastal reedbeds.

Eighty-one percent of Danish IBAs contain wetland habitats, and in 35% various types of wetland cover more than half the IBA. Artificial landscapes, mostly arable land and forestry plantations, also occur at more than half (56%) of the IBAs, although in most cases these habitats make up only minor proportions of the areas. In contrast, marine areas are included in only 22% of the IBAs, but in 20% of these they account for more than half the total area. Several of the exclusively marine IBAs, notably Northern Kattegat (119) and Smålandsfarvandet (118), are very large and this habitat covers a greater area than the total area of all other habitat-types combined.

Grassland occurs in 35% of IBAs mostly covering a small part of each site. The most important types are humid and mesophile grasslands, but small areas of dry calcareous and dry siliceous grasslands also occur. Scrub is present at 23% of IBAs, mostly covering smaller parts of the sites; in the 5% of sites where this cover exceeds 50% of the IBA, it normally comprises heathland. Thirty percent of Danish IBAs contain forest, but as only tiny patches of natural forest remain in the country, in most cases this habitat accounts for only minor parts of any IBA. The occurrence of forest within IBAs is possibly overestimated as in some cases forestry plantations may have been incorrectly classed as forest.

IMPACTS ON IBAs – LAND-USE AND THREATS

Figure 2 summarizes the most common land-uses within IBAs in Denmark. The data are incomplete; tourism/recreation and hunting should figure more prominently and fisheries/aquaculture also occur at many IBAs. Nevertheless, the data show that the most important land-use in Danish IBAs is agriculture, affecting more than half (52%) of the sites. Other common land-uses are forestry and nature conservation and research, at 29% and 27% of the sites respectively.

Figure 3 shows the threats to Danish IBAs. The majority of IBAs are subjected to at least one threat. As agriculture figures prominently in the land-use data it is hardly surprising that threats related to changes in agricultural practices such as abandonment and reduction of land management and agricultural intensification and expansion are among the most important problems, occurring at 57% and 46% of sites respectively. Abandonment and reduction of land management mainly threatens meadows and saltmarshes, with undergrazing resulting in succession to scrub or reedbeds. Twenty-two percent of sites are seriously affected by agricultural intensification and expansion, mostly through high inputs of fertilisers and pesticides, which has resulted in floristically uniform and poor landscapes. Furthermore the agricultural intensification in Denmark is believed to be the main cause of the nutrient pollution of many wetland sites.

Unsustainable exploitation, mostly excessive hunting, affects 54% of sites, and tourism/recreation has some impact on 43% of IBAs. Though the number of sites affected by these threats is high, the impact is generally low or medium. Intensified forest management is a threat to 18% of IBAs. This threat has probably decreased in recent years as a result of the promotion of more environmentally friendly forestry practices, but also because most possible damage has already been done since very little semi-natural woodland remains in the country.

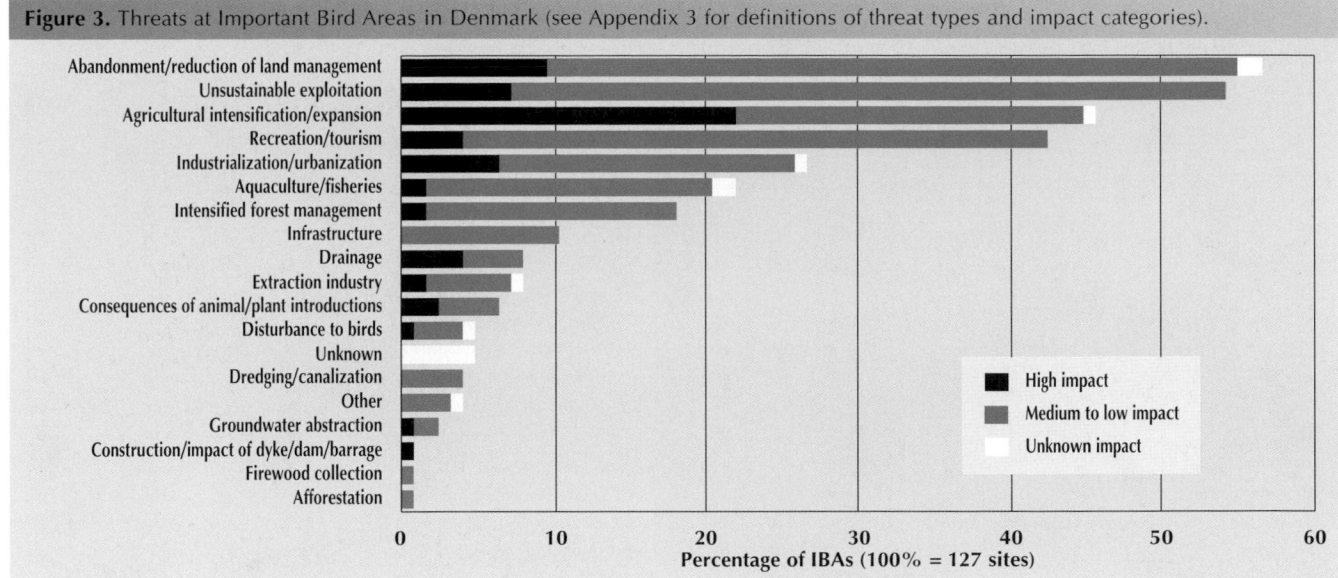

Figure 3. Threats at Important Bird Areas in Denmark (see Appendix 3 for definitions of threat types and impact categories).

PROTECTION STATUS

Denmark has many different categories of protected areas: Nature Conservation Areas and Nature Reserves, Wildlife Reserves (including bird and seal reserves), Scientific Reserves, areas in which the extraction of raw materials is prohibited, areas protected against fishing, Ramsar Sites, European Union Special Protection Areas (SPAs) and EU Special Areas for Conservation (SACs). The legal basis for these areas are the Hunting and Wildlife Management Act, the Protection of Nature Act and the relevant international conventions.

■ National protection

The National Nature and Forest Agency are responsible for the Danish protected areas. Some areas are also protected administratively such as the "Untouched Forest" areas recently set aside in the Danish state-owned forest. These areas are meant

to be untouched in the future, and are not necessarily virgin or even old-growth at present. The category National Nature Area denotes administratively protected state-owned areas.

Furthermore, some habitats are given general protection within Danish law. According to paragraph 3 of the Danish "Protection of Nature Act" it is prohibited to alter the state of natural lakes of more than 100 m². It is likewise prohibited to alter the state of: 1) heaths, bogs, marshes, moors and the like; 2) saltmarshes, swamps and coastal meadows; 3) humid permanent grasslands and uncultivated, dry meadows; when such habitat types total more than 2500 m² either separately, jointly or in combination with lakes of more than 100 m². The protection is not complete as many exemptions are granted, but the law nevertheless has had significant impact on the development of the Danish landscape. Also, in general, it is prohibited to convert forest land to other types of land-use. This, however, does not prevent conversion of mature beech *Fagus* forest to plantations of exotic conifers.

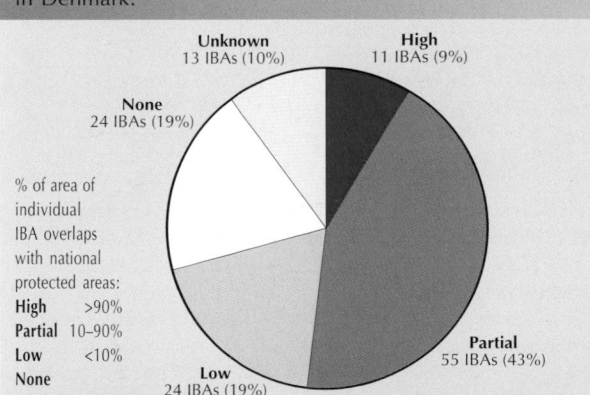

Figure 4. The national protection status of Important Bird Areas in Denmark.

Unknown
13 IBAs (10%)

High
11 IBAs (9%)

None
24 IBAs (19%)

% of area of individual IBA overlaps with national protected areas:
High >90%
Partial 10–90%
Low <10%
None

Partial
55 IBAs (43%)

Low
24 IBAs (19%)

Not possible to calculate total area of overlap between IBA network in Denmark and national protected-area system (see Table 4 for categories) due to incomplete overlap-area data.

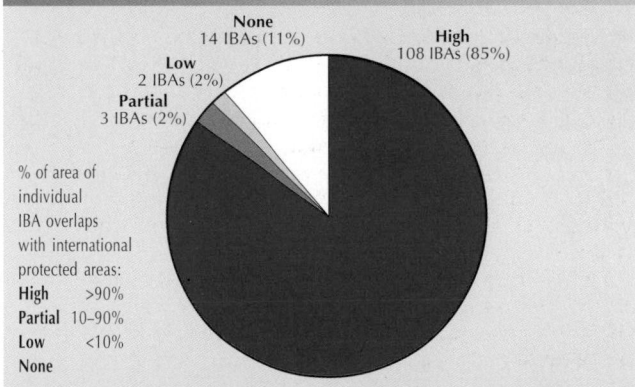

Figure 5. The international protection status of Important Bird Areas in Denmark.

None
14 IBAs (11%)

High
108 IBAs (85%)

Low
2 IBAs (2%)

Partial
3 IBAs (2%)

% of area of individual IBA overlaps with international protected areas:
High >90%
Partial 10–90%
Low <10%
None

Total area of overlap between IBA network in Denmark and international protected-area system (see Table 4 for categories) = 9,667–10,512 km² (20–22% of total IBA area). This figure is low because extensive parts of several large marine IBAs are unprotected.

Table 4. Protection status of Important Bird Areas in Denmark. A tick (✔) indicates that an IBA overlaps with a protected area (to any extent).

IBA International code name	National — Protected Areas	International — Ramsar Site	International — Special Protection Area	IBA International code name	National — Protected Areas	International — Ramsar Site	International — Special Protection Area
001 Ulvedybet and Nibe Bredning	✔	✔	✔	005 Råbjerg Mile and surrounding heathlands	✔		✔
002 Coast between Dokkedal and Lyngså	✔		✔	006 Jerup Hede, Råbjerg Mose and Tolshave Mose			✔
003 Madum Sø	✔		✔	007 Lille Vildmose		✔	✔
004 Rold Skov	✔		✔	008 Coast from Aggersund to Bygholm Vejle	✔	✔	✔
Subtotal of IBAs	4	1	4	Subtotal of IBAs	6	3	8

Table 4 ... continued. Protection status of Important Bird Areas in Denmark.
A tick (✔) indicates that an IBA overlaps with a protected area (to any extent).

IBA International code name	National Protected Areas	International Ramsar Site	International Special Protection Area
009¹ Nordre Rønner		✔	✔
010 South Læsø	✔	✔	✔
011 Hirsholmene	✔	✔	✔
012 Løgstør Bredning	✔	✔	✔
013 Eastern part of Vejlerne	✔	✔	✔
014 Lovns Bredning	✔	✔	✔
015 Parts of Randers and Mariager Fjords	✔	✔	✔
016¹ Tjele Langsø			✔
017 Ålvand Klithede and Førby Sø	✔		✔
018 Vangså Hede	✔		✔
019 Lønnerup Fjord	✔	✔	✔
020 Western part of Vejlerne, Arup Holm and Hovsør Røn	✔	✔	✔
021¹ Ovesø			✔
022 Hanstholm Reservatet	✔		✔
023 Agger Tange and Krik Vig	✔	✔	✔
024 Hjarbæk Fjord	✔		✔
025¹ Mågerodde and Karbyodde			✔
026¹ Dråby Vig and Buksør Odde			✔
027 Glomstrup Vig, Agerø, Munkholm and Katholm Odde, Lindholm, and Rotholme	✔		✔
028 Nissum Bredning			✔
029 Flyndersø and Skallesø	✔		✔
030 Norsminde (Kysing) Fjord	✔		✔
031 Stavnsfjord and adjacent waters	✔	✔	✔
032 Ørkenen and Totten (Anholt island)	✔	✔	✔
033 Salten Langsø	✔		✔
034 Forest areas south of Silkeborg	✔		✔
035 Mossø	✔		✔
036 Horsens Fjord, Svanegrunden and Endelave islands	✔	✔	✔
037 Borris Hede	✔		✔
038 Nissum Fjord	✔	✔	✔
039 Harboøre Tange, Plet Enge and Gjeller Sø	✔	✔	✔
040 Venø and Venø Sund			✔
041 Stadil Fjord and Veststadil Fjord	✔	✔	✔
042¹ Heath areas in Sønder Feldborg Plantage			✔
043 Ringkøbing Fjord	✔	✔	✔
044¹ Uldum Kær			✔
045 Forest areas along the northern part of Vejle Fjord	✔		✔
046 Randbøl Hede	✔		✔
047 Lillebælt		✔	✔
048 Heath areas near Store Råbjerg	✔		✔
049 Ho Bugt meadows	✔		
050 Kallesmærsk Hede, Grærup Langsø and surrounding areas	✔		✔
051 Ribe Holme and meadows at Kongeåen	✔	✔	✔
052 Mandø	✔	✔	✔
053 Fanø	✔	✔	✔
054¹ Vejen Mose			✔
055 Skallingen and Langli	✔		✔
056 Fiilsø	✔	✔	✔
057 Vadehavet (Wadden Sea)	✔	✔	✔
058 Hostrup Sø, Assenholm Mose and Felsted Vestermark			✔
059¹ Pamhule Skov			✔
060 Tøndermarsken, Magisterkog and Rudbøl Sø	✔		✔
061 Kongens Mose and Draved Skov	✔		✔
062 Tinglev Mose and Sø	✔		✔
063¹ Sønder Ådal			✔
064 Flensborg Fjord and Nybøl Nor			✔
065 Rømø	✔	✔	✔
066 Lindet Skov, Hønning Plantage, Lovrup Skov and Skrøp	✔		✔
067 Ballum og Husum Enge, Kamper strandenge	✔		✔
068 Forests near Gråsten	✔		✔
Subtotal of IBAs	**51**	**27**	**67**

IBA International code name	National Protected Areas	International Ramsar Site	International Special Protection Area
069 Kogsbøl and Skast Mose	✔		✔
070 Frøslev Plantage and Frøslev Mose	✔		✔
071 Sydfynske Ø-hav	✔		✔
072 Marstal Bugt and the coast of south-west Langeland	✔		✔
073 Vresen and sea area between Fyn and Langeland	✔		✔
074 Forests near Brahetrolleborg	✔		✔
075 Odense Fjord	✔		✔
076 Nærå coast and Æbelø area		✔	✔
077 Romsø and Hindsholm peninsula	✔		✔
078 Arreskov Sø	✔		✔
079 Ertholmene east of Bornholm	✔	✔	✔
080 Almindingen	✔		✔
081 Karrebæk, Dybsø and Avnø Fjords (coasts and islands)	✔	✔	✔
082 Bøtø Nor	✔		✔
083 Hyllekrog-Rødsand and Fehmarn Belt	✔	✔	✔
084 Ulvsund, Grønsund, Farø Fjord and Fanefjord			✔
085 Islands in Smålandshavet, north of Lolland		✔	✔
086 Guldborgsund	✔		✔
087 Maribo lakes	✔	✔	✔
088 Nakskov Fjord and Indre Fjord	✔	✔	✔
089 Præstø Fjord, Ulvshale, Nyord, and Jungshoved Nor	✔	✔	✔
090 Klinteskoven	✔		✔
091 Holmegårds Mose and Porsemose	✔		✔
092 Forests near Vemmetofte	✔		✔
093 Tystrup – Bavelse Søerne	✔		✔
094 Sejrø Bay and Nekselø	✔	✔	✔
095 Skælskør Nor, Skælskør Fjord and Borreby Mose	✔	✔	✔
096 Islands and coast between Skælskør Fjord and Glænø	✔	✔	✔
097 Hovvig	✔		✔
098 Sprogø and Halsskov Rev	✔		✔
099 Saltbæk Vig	✔	✔	✔
100 Tissø, Lille Åmose, and Hallenslev Mose	✔		✔
101¹ Bregentved and Gisselfeldt lakes			✔
102 Korshage, Hundested and surrounding sea area	✔		✔
103 Wetland north of Gammel Havdrup	✔		✔
104¹ Ramsø Mose			✔
105 Roskilde Fjord, Selsø and Kattinge Søerne	✔		✔
106 Arresø	✔		✔
107 Jægerspris Nordskov	✔		✔
108 Grib Skov	✔		✔
109 Furesø and Farum Sø	✔		✔
110 Saltholm	✔		✔
111 Vestamager and adjacent sea area	✔		✔
112 Hjelm			
113 Møllesø and Gjorslev			
114 Sjørring Sø			
115 Skjern Å			
116 Bolle and Try meadows			
117 Store Vildmose, Ryå and Stavad Enge			
118 Smålandsfarvandet	✔	✔	✔
119 Northern Kattegat	✔	✔	✔
120 Rønne Banke			
121 Skagerrak–Southwest Norwegian trench			
122¹ Kiel Bay and adjacent waters		✔	✔
123 Eastern German Bight			
124 Hellebæk			
125 Skagen			
126 Gilleleje area			
127 Stevns			
Total number of IBAs	**90**	**43**	**113**

1. IBAs 009, 016, 021, 025, 026, 042, 044, 054, 059, 063,101, 105 and 122 have national protected areas of unknown status.

Box 1. International legislation and initiatives that are relevant to site conservation in Denmark (see Appendix 1 for a general description of these agreements).	Global	
	Biodiversity Convention	✔
	Ramsar Convention	✔
	Bonn Convention	✔
	World Heritage Convention	✔
	MAB Programme	✔
	Pan-European	
	Bern Convention	✔
	Regional	
	EC Birds Directive	✔
	EC Habitats Directive	✔
	Helsinki Convention	✔
	✔ Convention ratified/initiative supported	
	(✔) Convention signed	

Comprehensive data on all national protection designations and their relation to IBAs is not readily available and has not been included in this chapter. However, an indication of national protection status is shown in Table 4 and the extent of each IBA that is covered by some form of national protected area has been estimated and included within each site account and presented on Figure 4. These show that 71% of IBAs are afforded some national protection.

■ International protection

Denmark has ratified all relevent agreements relating to site protection (Box 1), under which it has designated 27 Ramsar Sites and 111 Special Protection Areas (these incorporate all of the Ramsar Sites). It has also proposed 194 Special Areas for Conservation under the EC Habitats Directive (with a total area of c.10,000 km²), many of which overlap with, or are identical to, SPAs. No Biosphere Reserves or 'natural' World Heritage Sites have been designated, but joint preparations are underway by Denmark, Germany and Netherlands to seek the designation of the entire Wadden Sea area as both a World Heritage Site and a Biosphere Reserve. Table 4 and Figure 5 show that 89% of IBAs have some form of international protection; 43 IBAs are designated as Ramsar Sites and 113 as Special Protection Areas under the Birds Directive. It should be noted that one protected area may cover more than one IBA.

CONSERVATION

● General monitoring of Danish bird populations is the responsibility of the National Environmental Research Institute. The methods used are bag statistics for huntable species, point counts for passerines, total counts and mid-winter counts for waterfowl. Extensive monitoring activities are also carried out by Dansk Ornitologisk Forening (DOF)—BirdLife Denmark, including bird observatory work and the compilation of migration counts. DOF also monitors the populations of selected species through its 'Rare breeding birds' programme.

● In spring 1998 the Danish parliament passed a resolution that 16,000 ha of mostly drained land should be restored to wetland. The restored areas are mainly intended to act as nutrient catchment areas in order to reduce the run-off of agricultural fertilizer which has already detrimentally affected many IBAs during the last decade. The exact placing and extent of these areas is still being planned.

ANALYTICAL METHODS

● Bird data used in this chapter are generally from within the last ten years, and largely from 1993–1996.

● Counts of non-breeding birds are, where nothing else is stated, daily maximum figures. Notable exceptions from this rule are the large marine localities, where results have been averaged over periods of several years.

● For sites with high numbers of seaduck during harsh winters only, criteria have been applied to peak numbers rather than average numbers in normal years.

● With the changes to boundaries of several areas, as a result of expansion of some to include marine areas, bird data have been divided between terrestrial, coastal and marine sites. As a rule, in marine areas only data on wintering divers, diving ducks, alcids and coots are presented, whilst at coastal sites, only data on swans, geese, dabbling ducks and waders are retained.

● Data on habitats and threats are, in general, considered to be accurately assigned, while the land-use data are somewhat incomplete. Some problems were encountered in assigning categories and especially coverage of habitat-types, land-uses and threats. In these cases data are to be regarded as estimates based on common sense rather than exact figures.

● The data on national protection status are incomplete because of time constraints and priority given to clarifying international protection status.

● Altitudes of sites, when negative, indicate either land below sea-level (most sites down to -8 m) or, if lower than -8 m, the maximum depth of sea-water within the IBA (for marine IBAs).

ACKNOWLEDGEMENTS

We would like to thank Michael Grell and Peer Lindballe for providing data from 'The Birds in Denmark' database and Neil Burgess for reading and providing many helpful comments on earlier versions of this text.

■ SITE ACCOUNTS

Ulvedybet and Nibe Bredning   001

A4i, A4iii, B1i, B2, B3, C2, C3, C4, C6

Admin region Nordjylland
Coordinates 57°02′N 9°35′E
Altitude (-17)–10 m **Area** 18,530 ha

■ Site description

A coastal site including shallow fjord areas, saltmarshes, reedbeds, small freshwater lakes and agricultural land. The Ulvedybet area is a brackish lake that has been dammed-off from the Limfjord.

Habitats Grassland (15%; humid grassland), Wetland (65%; tidal river/enclosed tidal water), Unknown (20%)
Land-use Unknown

■ Birds

Species	Season	Year	Pop min	Pop max	Acc	Criteria
Cygnus columbianus Bewick's Swan	N	1994	4,320	4,320	A	A4i,B1i,B2,C2,C6
Cygnus cygnus Whooper Swan	W	1995	4,086	4,086	B	A4i, B1i, C2
Anas penelope Wigeon	N	1993	—	26,650	A	B1i, C3
Recurvirostra avosetta Avocet	B	1993	156	156	A	B3

Species ... continued	Season	Year	Pop min	Pop max	Acc	Criteria
Pluvialis apricaria Golden Plover	N	1993	—	14,000	—	B1i, C2
Larus canus Common Gull	B	1996	2,210	5,000	—	B2

The site holds more than 20,000 waterfowl and is particularly important for wintering *Cygnus cygnus*. Several species listed on Annex I of the Birds Directive breed at the site including *Platalea leucorodia, Circus aeruginosus, Recurvirostra avosetta, Philomachus pugnax, Sterna sandvicensis, S. hirundo, S. paradisaea* and *S. albifrons*.

■ Protection status

National Partial **International** High
18,530 ha of IBA covered by Ramsar Site (Ulvedybet and Nibe Bredning, 20,304 ha). 18,530 ha of IBA covered by Special Protection Area (Ulvedybet and Nibe Bredning, 18,530 ha).

■ Conservation issues

Threats Aquaculture/fisheries (C), Recreation/tourism (B)

Ulvedybet and a part of Nibe Bredning are non-hunting areas. Ulvedybet and some small islets are wildlife reserves with restricted access.

145

Coast between Dokkedal and Lyngså

A4i, A4iii, B1i, C2, C3, C4 **002**

Admin region Nordjylland
Coordinates 57°05′N 10°22′E
Altitude (-9)–2 m **Area** 1,700 ha

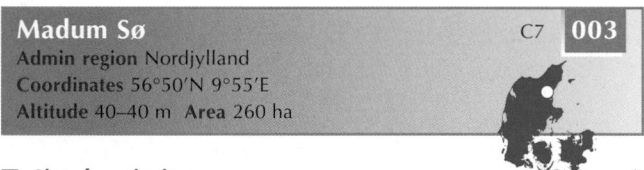

■ Site description
A narrow strip of coastal saltmarsh and some islets. Marine areas surrounding this IBA (and previously included within it following Grimmett and Jones 1989) are included in Northern Kattegat (site 119).

Habitats Wetland (80%; saltmarsh), Unknown (20%)
Land-use Agriculture (30%), Unknown (70%)

■ Birds

Species		Season	Year	Pop min	Pop max	Acc	Criteria
Pluvialis apricaria	Golden Plover	P	1994	—	28,000	—	A4i, B1i, C2
Calidris alpina	Dunlin	P	1994	—	24,000	—	A4i, B1i, C3

This is an important staging area for *Calidris alpina* and *Pluvialis apricaria*. The site holds more than 20,000 waterfowl. Species listed on Annex I of the Birds Directive that breed at the site include *Sterna sandvicensis* and *S. paradisaea*.

■ Protection status
National Partial **International** High
1,700 ha of IBA covered by Special Protection Area (Ålborg Bugt, 31,460 ha).

■ Conservation issues

Threats Aquaculture/fisheries (C), Extraction industry (B), Recreation/tourism (C), Unsustainable exploitation (C)

Madum Sø

C7 **003**

Admin region Nordjylland
Coordinates 56°50′N 9°55′E
Altitude 40–40 m **Area** 260 ha

■ Site description
An oligotrophic (low in nutrients) freshwater lake surrounded by forest. Subaquatic vegetation includes *Isoëtes* and *Lobelia*.

Habitats Forest and woodland (20%; broadleaved deciduous forest), Wetland (80%; standing fresh water)
Land-use Nature conservation/research (100%)

■ Birds
The IBA was designated as a Special Protection Area on the basis of large numbers of moulting *Bucephala clangula*; the high counts (up to 3,000 moulting) have not been confirmed in recent years.

■ Protection status
National High **International** High
260 ha of IBA covered by Special Protection Area (Madum Sø, 260 ha).

■ Conservation issues

Threats Other (B)

Oligotrophic lakes are very rare in Denmark. Nutrient pollution (eutrophication) from a wide range of sources is a threat ('Other' threat).

Rold Skov

C6 **004**

Admin region Nordjylland
Coordinates 56°48′N 9°50′E
Altitude 20–102 m **Area** 7,420 ha

■ Site description
A forested hilly area with scattered glades, wetlands and heathlands. Approximately half the forested area comprises *Picea abies*

plantations, the remainder being mainly broadleaved forest plantations with several smaller areas of mature forest dominated by *Fagus* or *Quercus*.

Habitats Forest and woodland (5%; broadleaved deciduous forest), Wetland (5%; fen/transition mire/spring), Artificial landscape (80%; forestry plantation), Unknown (10%)
Land-use Agriculture (5%), Forestry (80%), Nature conservation/research (10%)

■ Birds

Species		Season	Year	Pop min	Pop max	Acc	Criteria
Dryocopus martius	Black Woodpecker	R	1994	10	13	A	C6

Other species listed on Annex I of the Birds Directive that also breed at the site include *Pernis apivorus*, *Caprimulgus europaeus* and *Lanius collurio*.

■ Protection status
National Low **International** High
7,420 ha of IBA covered by Special Protection Area (Rold Skov, 7,420 ha).

■ Conservation issues

Threats Firewood collection (C), Intensified forest management (B)

The area has suffered damage from intensive forest management and firewood collection. These threats are ongoing but much damage has already been done and most of the remaining valuable areas have some protection.

Råbjerg Mile and surrounding heathlands

C6 **005**

Admin region Nordjylland
Coordinates 57°33′N 10°21′E
Altitude 0–38 m **Area** 4,480 ha

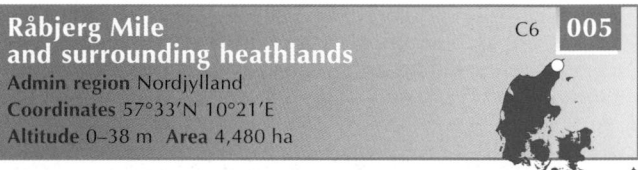

■ Site description
An area of shifting dunes, moorland and wetlands, bordering agricultural areas.

Habitats Scrub (40%; heathland), Wetland (55%; sand-dunes/sand beach; standing fresh water; raised bog), Artificial landscape (5%; forestry plantation)
Land-use Forestry (5%), Nature conservation/research (95%)

■ Birds

Species		Season	Year	Pop min	Pop max	Acc	Criteria
Pluvialis apricaria	Golden Plover	B	1994	—	2	A	C6

Pluvialis apricaria and *Tringa glareola*, listed on Annex I of the EC Birds Directive, breed at the site. The site is also a nationally important staging area for raptors during spring migration.

■ Protection status
National Partial **International** High
4,480 ha of IBA covered by Special Protection Area (Råbjerg Mile, 4,480 ha).

■ Conservation issues

Threats Abandonment/reduction of land management (C), Consequences of animal/plant introductions (B), Recreation/tourism (C)

Heathland areas are invaded by exotic *Pinus mugo*, which is periodically removed by foresters to conserve the heathland.

Jerup Hede, Råbjerg Mose and Tolshave Mose

C7 **006**

Admin region Nordjylland
Coordinates 57°32′N 10°22′E
Altitude 0–13 m **Area** 2,320 ha

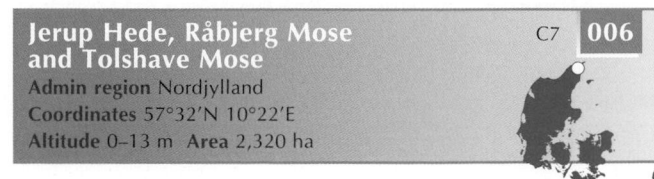

■ Site description
A large moorland and peatbog with some forest plantations and

agricultural areas; the extent of agricultural land is poorly known and may be significantly more than 5–10%.

Habitats Forest and woodland (5%), Scrub (60%; heathland), Wetland (30%; raised bog), Artificial landscape (10%; forestry plantation)
Land-use Agriculture (5%), Unknown (95%)

■ Birds
Several species listed on Annex I of the Birds Directive breed at the site including *Grus grus*, *Tringa glareola*, *Asio flammeus*, *Caprimulgus europaeus* and *Lanius collurio*.

■ Protection status
National None **International** High
2,320 ha of IBA covered by Special Protection Area (Jerup Hede, Råbjerg and Tolshave Mose, 2,320 ha).

■ Conservation issues

Threats Abandonment/reduction of land management (B), Drainage (A)

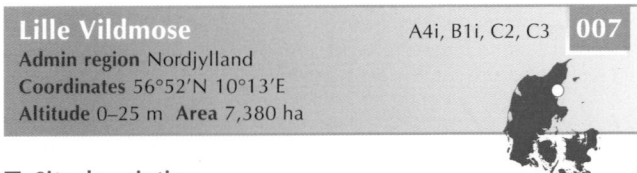

Lille Vildmose — A4i, B1i, C2, C3 — 007
Admin region Nordjylland
Coordinates 56°52'N 10°13'E
Altitude 0–25 m **Area** 7,380 ha

■ Site description
The largest raised bog in Denmark, and one of the best preserved lowland raised bogs in north-west Europe, with small lakes and wooded areas. Høstemark Skov and Tofte Skov hold stands of mature mixed forest dominated by *Fagus* and *Quercus* with *Tilia* and *Alnus*. Areas of natural forest to raised bog ecotone are also preserved in several parts of the IBA. The percentage cover of arable land is uncertain.

Habitats Forest and woodland (20%; broadleaved deciduous forest), Scrub (45%; heathland), Wetland (15%; raised bog), Artificial landscape (20%; arable land)
Land-use Agriculture (20%), Forestry (20%), Nature conservation/research (10%), Unknown (50%)

■ Birds

Species	Season	Year	Pop min	Pop max	Acc	Criteria
Phalacrocorax carbo Cormorant	B	1995	2,901	2,901	A	A4i, B1i, C3
Cygnus cygnus Whooper Swan	N	1995	528	528	—	B1i, C2

Several species listed on Annex I of the EC Birds Directive breed at the site including *Circus aeruginosus*, *Grus grus*, *Philomachus pugnax* and *Lanius collurio*.

■ Protection status
National None **International** High
7,380 ha of IBA covered by Ramsar Site (Vejlerne and Logstor Bredning, 45,280 ha). 1,660 ha of IBA covered by Special Protection Area (Lille Vildmose, 1,660 ha).

■ Conservation issues

Threats Drainage (A), Extraction industry (A), Unsustainable exploitation (C)

Peat extraction presents a major threat.

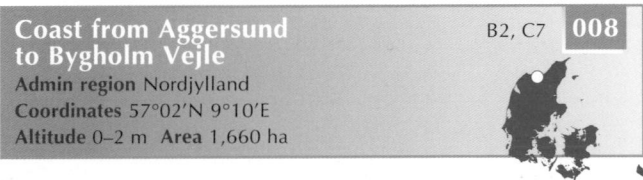

Coast from Aggersund to Bygholm Vejle — B2, C7 — 008
Admin region Nordjylland
Coordinates 57°02'N 9°10'E
Altitude 0–2 m **Area** 1,660 ha

■ Site description
A large area of coastal meadows and adjacent waters with several small islands.

Habitats Wetland (75%; mudflat/sandflat; saltmarsh), Marine areas (20%; sea inlet/coastal features), Unknown (5%)
Land-use Agriculture (40%), Unknown (60%)

■ Birds

Species	Season	Year	Pop min	Pop max	Acc	Criteria
Larus canus Common Gull	B	1995	3,025	3,260	A	B2

The site was also important for large numbers of staging *Cygnus cygnus* and *Tadorna tadorna*, but numbers have declined in recent years. Species listed on Annex I of the EC Birds Directive that breed at the site include *Recurvirostra avosetta* and *Sterna paradisaea*.

■ Protection status
National Partial **International** High
1,660 ha of IBA covered by Special Protection Area (The coast Aggersund to Bygholm Vejle, 1,660 ha). 1,660 ha of IBA covered by Ramsar Site (Vejlerne and Logstor Bredning, 45,280 ha).

■ Conservation issues

Threats Agricultural intensification/expansion (C), Industrialization/urbanization (B), Unsustainable exploitation (B)

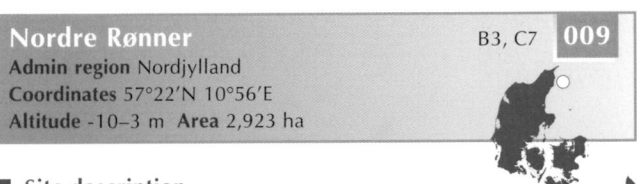

Nordre Rønner — B3, C7 — 009
Admin region Nordjylland
Coordinates 57°22'N 10°56'E
Altitude -10–3 m **Area** 2,923 ha

■ Site description
Stony and sandy islets. Marine areas surrounding this IBA (and previously included within it, following Grimmett and Jones 1989) are now included in site 119.

Habitats Wetland (70%; sand-dunes/sand beach), Unknown (30%)
Land-use Nature conservation/research (100%)

■ Birds

Species	Season	Year	Pop min	Pop max	Acc	Criteria
Larus fuscus Lesser Black-backed Gull	B	1993	187	187	A	B3
Larus marinus Great Black-backed Gull	B	1993	148	148	A	B3

Species listed on Annex I of the EC Birds Directive breeding at the site include *Sterna sandvicensis* and *S. hirundo*.

■ Protection status
National Unknown **International** High
2,923 ha of IBA covered by Ramsar Site (Nordre Rønner, 2,923 ha). 2,920 ha of IBA covered by Special Protection Area (Nordre Rønner, 2,920 ha).

■ Conservation issues

Threats Aquaculture/fisheries (U)

Admittance to the area is prohibited during the breeding season.

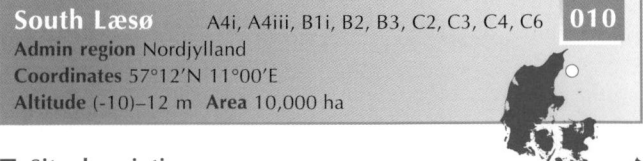

South Læsø — A4i, A4iii, B1i, B2, B3, C2, C3, C4, C6 — 010
Admin region Nordjylland
Coordinates 57°12'N 11°00'E
Altitude (-10)–12 m **Area** 10,000 ha

■ Site description
A coastal site with intertidal mud- and sandflats, shoals, banks, islets and islands, saltmarshes, coastal heathlands and a few cultivated areas. Marine areas surrounding this IBA (and previously included within it, following Grimmett and Jones 1989) are now included in site 119.

Habitats Scrub (25%; heathland), Wetland (60%; mudflat/sandflat; saltmarsh; sand-dunes/sand beach), Artificial landscape (15%; forestry plantation)
Land-use Unknown

■ Birds
The site is a very important staging area for *Calidris alpina*. It also holds several breeding species listed on Annex I of the EC Birds

Directive including *Recurvirostra avosetta*, *Philomachus pugnax*, *Tringa glareola*, *Sterna hirundo*, *S. paradisaea* and *S. albifrons*.

Species	Season	Year	Pop min	Pop max	Acc	Criteria
Recurvirostra avosetta Avocet	B	1996	518	518	A	A4i, B1i, B3, C2
Recurvirostra avosetta Avocet	N	1991	1,000	1,000	—	B1i, C2
Calidris alpina Dunlin	N	1994	40,000	40,000	—	A4i, B1i, C3
Limosa lapponica Bar-tailed Godwit	P	1991	4,000	4,000	—	A4i, B1i, C2
Tringa totanus Redshank	B	1996	331	331	A	B2
Sterna paradisaea Arctic Tern	B	1996	1,062	1,062	A	C6
Sterna albifrons Little Tern	B	1996	22	22	A	B2, C6

■ Protection status
National Low **International** High
10,000 ha of IBA covered by Ramsar Site (Læsø, 67,840 ha). 10,000 ha of IBA covered by Special Protection Area (South Læsø and adjacent sea, 66,380 ha).

■ Conservation issues

Threats Abandonment/reduction of land management (C), Recreation/tourism (C), Unsustainable exploitation (B)

Access is prohibited to some parts of the IBA during the breeding season.

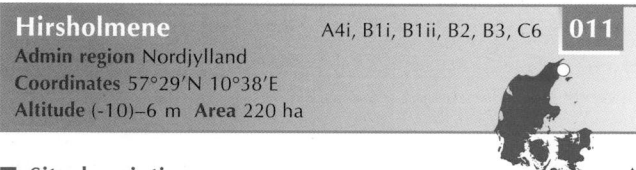

Hirsholmene
A4i, B1i, B1ii, B2, B3, C6 **011**
Admin region Nordjylland
Coordinates 57°29'N 10°38'E
Altitude (-10)–6 m **Area** 220 ha

■ Site description
The IBA comprises stony islets and an area of saltmarsh between Frederikshavn and Strandby. Only the main island of Hirsholm is inhabited. Marine areas surrounding this IBA (and previously included within it, following Grimmett and Jones 1989) are now included in site 119.

Habitats Wetland (100%; saltmarsh; sand-dunes/sand beach)
Land-use Nature conservation/research (100%)

■ Birds

Species	Season	Year	Pop min	Pop max	Acc	Criteria
Larus fuscus Lesser Black-backed Gull	B	1994	775	775	A	B3
Larus marinus Great Black-backed Gull	B	1994	240	240	A	B3
Sterna sandvicensis Sandwich Tern	B	1994	1,356	1,356	A	A4i, B1i, B2, C6
Sterna hirundo Common Tern	B	1994	175	175	A	C6
Cepphus grylle Black Guillemot	B	1994	490	490	A	B1ii

This is an important area for breeding gulls and terns including *Sterna sandvicensis*, *S. hirundo* and *S. paradisaea*, listed on Annex I of the EC Birds Directive.

■ Protection status
National Partial **International** High
220 ha of IBA covered by Ramsar Site (Hirsholmene, 480 ha). 220 ha of IBA covered by Special Protection Area (Hirsholmene, 3,740 ha).

■ Conservation issues

Threats Abandonment/reduction of land management (C), Aquaculture/fisheries (B), Unsustainable exploitation (C)

Løgstør Bredning
C7 **012**
Admin region Nordjylland
Coordinates 56°55'N 9°10'E
Altitude (-22)–43 m **Area** 32,570 ha

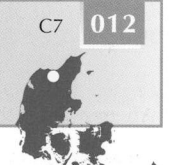

■ Site description
A shallow saline fjord area with shoals and islands, coastal saltmarsh and agricultural land.

Habitats Wetland (100%; tidal river/enclosed tidal water; saltmarsh)
Land-use Unknown (100%)

■ Birds
The site was very important for wintering ducks (in total more than 20,000 individuals, with eight species fulfilling IBA criteria). However, numbers declined sharply during the 1980s, presumably because of deteriorating water quality, and by 1993 insufficient numbers were present to fulfil the criteria. *Recurvirostra avosetta*, listed on Annex I of the EC Birds Directive, breeds at the site.

■ Protection status
National Low **International** High
32,570 ha of IBA covered by Special Protection Area (Løgstør Bredning, 32,570 ha). 32,570 ha of IBA covered by Ramsar Site (Vejlerne and Løgstør Bredning, 45,280 ha).

■ Conservation issues

Threats Aquaculture/fisheries (B), Industrialization/urbanization (A), Recreation/tourism (A), Unsustainable exploitation (B)

If water quality is restored it is probable that birds will return and the site will regain its importance. During the breeding season of birds and seals, access to some areas is prohibited.

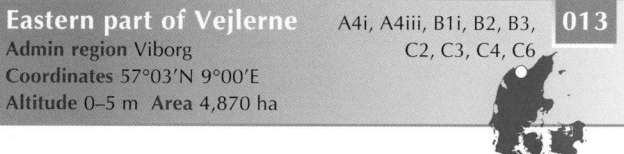

Eastern part of Vejlerne
A4i, A4iii, B1i, B2, B3, C2, C3, C4, C6 **013**
Admin region Viborg
Coordinates 57°03'N 9°00'E
Altitude 0–5 m **Area** 4,870 ha

■ Site description
Partially drained fjords with lakes, reedbeds, meadows and saltmarshes.

Habitats Grassland (30%; humid grassland), Wetland (65%; standing fresh water, saltmarsh, water-fringe vegetation), Unknown (5%)
Land-use Agriculture (30%), Nature conservation/research (100%)

■ Birds

Species	Season	Year	Pop min	Pop max	Acc	Criteria
Botaurus stellaris Bittern	B	1995	92	92	B	B2, C2, C6
Cygnus columbianus Bewick's Swan	W	1994	377	377	A	A4i, B1i, B2, C2
Cygnus cygnus Whooper Swan	W	1994	885	885	A	A4i, B1i, C2
Anser brachyrhynchus Pink-footed Goose	N	1994	2,600	2,600	A	A4i, B1i, C3
Mergus serrator Red-breasted Merganser	N	1994	1,560	1,560	A	B1i, C3
Recurvirostra avosetta Avocet	B	1994	280	280	A	B1i, B3, C2
Pluvialis apricaria Golden Plover	P	1994	18,000	18,000	A	A4i, B1i, C2
Limosa limosa Black-tailed Godwit	B	1994	110	110	A	B2
Chlidonias niger Black Tern	B	1994	28	40	A	C2, C6

The IBA is an important staging area for *Cygnus cygnus*, *C. columbianus* and *Anser fabalis* (nationally important site). Several species listed on Annex I of the EC Birds Directive breed at the site including *Botaurus stellaris*, *Circus aeruginosus*, *Porzana porzana*, *Recurvirostra avosetta*, *Philomachus pugnax*, *Sterna hirundo*, *S. paradisaea* and *Chlidonias niger*.

■ Protection status
National Partial **International** High
4,870 ha of IBA covered by Ramsar Site (Vejlerne and Logstor Bredning, 45,280 ha). 4,870 ha of IBA covered by Special Protection Area (Østlige Vejler, 4,870 ha).

■ Conservation issues

Threats Abandonment/reduction of land management (C), Agricultural intensification/expansion (A), Consequences of animal/plant introductions (A), Industrialization/urbanization (B), Infrastructure (B)

There are plans to inundate some parts of the site with saltwater during winter. Introduced American mink *Mustela vison* prey on breeding birds.

Lovns Bredning
A4i, B1i, C3 **014**
Admin region Viborg
Coordinates 56°40′N 9°10′E
Altitude (-9)–2 m **Area** 7,590 ha

■ Site description
A shallow fjord with coastal saltmarshes and agricultural land (less than 5% of the total IBA area).

Habitats Wetland (100%; tidal river/enclosed tidal water; saltmarsh)
Land-use Agriculture

■ Birds

Species		Season	Year	Pop min	Pop max	Acc	Criteria
Bucephala clangula	Goldeneye	N	1994	3,370	3,370	B	B1i, C3
Mergus merganser	Goosander	N	1993	2,780	2,780	B	A4i, B1i, C3

In 1983 *Anas crecca* and *Mergus serrator* populations also met the IBA criteria and the total number of waterbirds exceeded 20,000 individuals.

■ Protection status
National Low **International** High
7,590 ha of IBA covered by Special Protection Area (Lovns Bredning, 7,590 ha). 7,590 ha of IBA covered by Ramsar Site (Vejlerne and Løgstør Bredning, 45,280 ha).

■ Conservation issues

Threats Abandonment/reduction of land management (C), Aquaculture/fisheries (B), Industrialization/urbanization (A)

Parts of Randers and Mariager Fjords
A4i, A4iii, B1i, B3, C2, C3, C4, C6 **015**
Admin region Århus
Coordinates 56°39′N 10°10′E
Altitude (-9)–5 m **Area** 7,500 ha

■ Site description
Shallow fjords with small islets, saltmarshes and cultivated land including large reclaimed areas near Overgaard. Marine areas surrounding this IBA (and previously included within it, following Grimmett and Jones 1989) are now included in Northern Kattegat (site 119).

Habitats Forest and woodland (15%), Wetland (35%; tidal river/enclosed tidal water), Artificial landscape (50%; arable land)
Land-use Agriculture

■ Birds

Species		Season	Year	Pop min	Pop max	Acc	Criteria
¹*Cygnus cygnus*	Whooper Swan	W	1995	2,000	2,000	B	A4i, B1i, B3, C2, C6
Branta bernicla	Brent Goose	N	1994	3,500	3,500	A	A4i, B1i, C3
Tadorna tadorna	Shelduck	N	1994	5,470	5,670	B	A4i, B1i, C3

1. Partial population estimate.

The site is of high importance for wintering *Cygnus cygnus*. Many bird populations are shared with Northern Kattegat (IBA 119). *Recurvirostra avosetta*, *Sterna hirundo* and *S. paradisaea*, all listed on Annex I of the EC Birds Directive, breed at the site.

■ Protection status
National Low **International** High
7,500 ha of IBA covered by Special Protection Area (Randers and Mariager Fjord and Ålborg Bugt, 39,040 ha). 7,500 ha of IBA covered by Ramsar Site (Randers and Mariager Fjords and adjacent coastal waters, 41,440 ha).

■ Conservation issues

Threats Abandonment/reduction of land management (B), Agricultural intensification/expansion (A), Aquaculture/fisheries (C), Industrialization/urbanization (A), Unsustainable exploitation (B)

Tjele Langsø
C7 **016**
Admin region Viborg
Coordinates 56°32′N 9°40′E
Altitude 20–58 m **Area** 1,340 ha

■ Site description
A freshwater lake with adjacent agricultural land and remnants of semi-natural woodland and grassland.

Habitats Forest and woodland (20%; broadleaved deciduous forest), Grassland (15%; humid grassland), Wetland (45%; standing fresh water), Artificial landscape (20%; arable land)
Land-use Agriculture (35%), Unknown (65%)

■ Birds
The lake is polluted and few birds currently breed. Detailed data are only available from 1983 when the site was considered to be of international importance for staging *Anser fabalis* (1,200 birds).

■ Protection status
National Unknown **International** High
1,340 ha of IBA covered by Special Protection Area (Tjele Langsø, 1,340 ha).

■ Conservation issues

Threats Agricultural intensification/expansion (B), Disturbance to birds (B), Industrialization/urbanization (C), Unsustainable exploitation (B)

The causes of pollution are agricultural intensification and industrialization and urbanization.

Ålvand Klithede and Førby Sø
C6 **017**
Admin region Viborg
Coordinates 56°57′N 8°25′E
Altitude 17–33 m **Area** 1,430 ha

■ Site description
A heathland area with peatbogs, small wetlands and moorland lakes on old dunes.

Habitats Scrub (75%; heathland), Grassland (10%; humid grassland), Wetland (10%; standing fresh water; raised bog)
Land-use Agriculture (5%), Nature conservation/research (100%)

■ Birds

Species		Season	Year	Pop min	Pop max	Acc	Criteria
Tringa glareola	Wood Sandpiper	B	1994	13	15	A	C6

Several other species listed on Annex I of the EC Birds Directive also breed at the site, including *Grus grus* and *Pluvialis apricaria*.

■ Protection status
National Partial **International** High
1,430 ha of IBA covered by Special Protection Area (Ållvand Klithede and Førby Sø, 1,430 ha).

■ Conservation issues

Threats Abandonment/reduction of land management (B), Recreation/tourism (C)

Vangså Hede
C7 **018**
Admin region Viborg
Coordinates 57°01′N 8°28′E
Altitude 0–34 m **Area** 1,410 ha

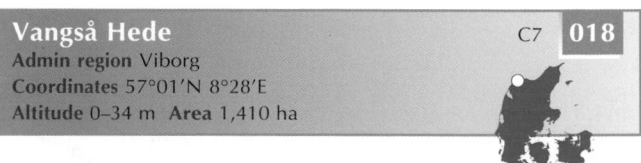

■ Site description
An area of heathland and sand-dunes with small wetlands.

Habitats Scrub (45%; heathland), Wetland (40%; sand-dunes/sand beach; raised bog), Artificial landscape (20%; forestry plantation)
Land-use Unknown

■ **Birds**

Once important for breeding *Tringa glareola*, listed on Annex I of the EC Birds Directive, but the species no longer breeds at the site.

■ **Protection status**

National Partial **International** High

1,410 ha of IBA covered by Special Protection Area (Vangså Hede, 1,410 ha).

■ **Conservation issues**

> **Threats** Abandonment/reduction of land management (B), Recreation/tourism (C)

Heathland areas are being restored.

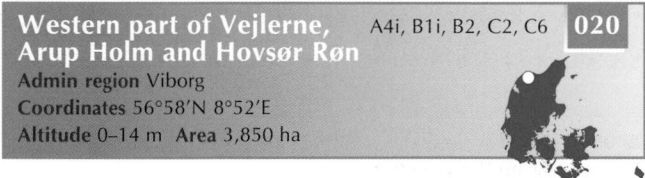

Lønnerup Fjord
A4i, B1i, C2 — 019
Admin region Viborg
Coordinates 57°00′N 8°47′E
Altitude 0–5 m **Area** 460 ha

■ **Site description**

A partly drained fjord area with lakes, lagoons, coastal meadows, saltwater and freshwater marshes, and an associated dyke and dam network.

> **Habitats** Grassland (20%; humid grassland), Wetland (40%; saltmarsh; standing brackish and salt water), Artificial landscape (45%; arable land)
> **Land-use** Agriculture (45%), Nature conservation/research (55%)

■ **Birds**

Species	Season	Year	Pop min	Pop max	Acc	Criteria
Cygnus columbianus Bewick's Swan	P	1994	316	316	A	A4i, B1i, C2
Cygnus cygnus Whooper Swan	W	1994	361	361	A	B1i, C2

Important staging area for *Cygnus cygnus* and *C. columbianus*.

■ **Protection status**

National Partial **International** High

460 ha of IBA covered by Special Protection Area (Lønnerup Fjord, 460 ha). 460 ha of IBA covered by Ramsar Site (Vejlerne and Løgstør Bredning, 45,280 ha).

■ **Conservation issues**

> **Threats** Agricultural intensification/expansion (A), Unsustainable exploitation (C)

Western part of Vejlerne, Arup Holm and Hovsør Røn
A4i, B1i, B2, C2, C6 — 020
Admin region Viborg
Coordinates 56°58′N 8°52′E
Altitude 0–14 m **Area** 3,850 ha

■ **Site description**

A shallow freshwater area, with meadows grazed by cattle, and large expanses of reedbed.

> **Habitats** Grassland (30%; humid grassland), Wetland (65%; standing fresh water; water-fringe vegetation)
> **Land-use** Agriculture (20%), Nature conservation/research (100%)

■ **Birds**

Species	Season	Year	Pop min	Pop max	Acc	Criteria
Botaurus stellaris Bittern	B	1992	24	24	A	B2, C2, C6
Cygnus columbianus Bewick's Swan	N	1994	402	402	A	A4i, B1i, B2, C2
Cygnus cygnus Whooper Swan	N	1994	548	548	A	B1i, C2

This is an important staging area for *Cygnus cygnus* and *C. columbianus*. In total nearly 20,000 waterbirds overwinter or stage at this site. Several species listed on Annex I of the EC Birds Directive breed at the site, including *Circus aeruginosus*, *Porzana porzana*, *Recurvirostra avosetta*, *Philomachus pugnax*, *Sterna hirundo*, *S. paradisaea*, *S. albifrons* and *Chlidonias niger*.

■ **Protection status**

National Partial **International** High

3,850 ha of IBA covered by Ramsar Site (Vejlerne and Løgstør Bredning, 45,280 ha). 3,850 ha of IBA covered by Special Protection Area (Vestlige Vejler; Arup Holme and Hovsør Røn (3,850 ha).

■ **Conservation issues**

> **Threats** Abandonment/reduction of land management (C), Agricultural intensification/expansion (B), Consequences of animal/plant introductions (A)

The entire area is protected and public access is prohibited with the exception of a few trails and roads. Introduced American mink *Mustela vison* prey on breeding birds.

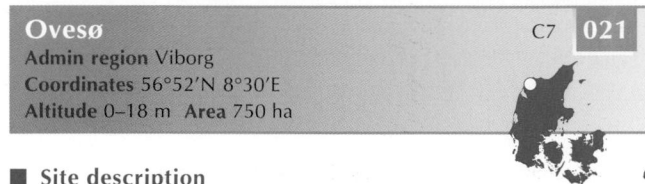

Oveø
C7 — 021
Admin region Viborg
Coordinates 56°52′N 8°30′E
Altitude 0–18 m **Area** 750 ha

■ **Site description**

A freshwater lake with islets surrounded by grazing-meadows, reedbeds and arable land.

> **Habitats** Grassland (20%; humid grassland), Wetland (65%; standing fresh water; water-fringe vegetation), Artificial landscape (15%; arable land)
> **Land-use** Agriculture (35%), Unknown (65%)

■ **Birds**

The site was designated as a Special Protection Area in 1983 when it was internationally important for wintering *Cygnus cygnus*. Latterly data are only available from 1988 when the species was recorded in significantly lower numbers. *Botaurus stellaris*, *Philomachus pugnax* and *Sterna hirundo*, listed on Annex I of the EC Birds Directive, breed in low numbers at the site.

■ **Protection status**

National Unknown **International** High

750 ha of IBA covered by Special Protection Area (Oveø, 750 ha).

■ **Conservation issues**

> **Threats** Agricultural intensification/expansion (A), Recreation/tourism (C), Unsustainable exploitation (B)

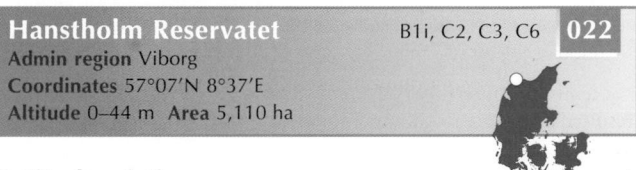

Hanstholm Reservatet
B1i, C2, C3, C6 — 022
Admin region Viborg
Coordinates 57°07′N 8°37′E
Altitude 0–44 m **Area** 5,110 ha

■ **Site description**

An extensive coastal heath with sand hills, moorland and a number of large and small oligotrophic (nutrient-poor) lakes. There are also plantations and scattered habitation.

> **Habitats** Scrub (50%; heathland), Wetland (45%; sand-dunes/sand beach; standing fresh water; raised bog), Artificial landscape (10%; forestry plantation)
> **Land-use** Forestry (10%), Nature conservation/research (100%)

■ **Birds**

Species	Season	Year	Pop min	Pop max	Acc	Criteria
Cygnus cygnus Whooper Swan	N	1993	430	430	—	B1i, C2
Anser fabalis Bean Goose	N	1994	1,050	1,050	—	B1i, C3
Tringa glareola Wood Sandpiper	B	1994	34	44	A	C6

Probably the most important breeding area in Denmark for heathland birds and the most important breeding site nationally for *Circus aeruginosus*, *Grus grus*, *Pluvialis apricaria* and *Tringa glareola*, all listed on Annex I of the EC Birds Directive.

■ **Protection status**

National High **International** High

5,110 ha of IBA covered by Special Protection Area (Hanstholm reservatet, 5,110 ha).

■ Conservation issues

Threats Abandonment/reduction of land management (B), Consequences of animal/plant introductions (B)

This is one of the largest terrestrial protected areas in Denmark. In addition, some areas adjacent to the IBA are protected. Access is prohibited to most of the area throughout the year, and the remainder is closed during the breeding season. The spread of the introduced and invasive pine *Pinus mugo* is causing problems.

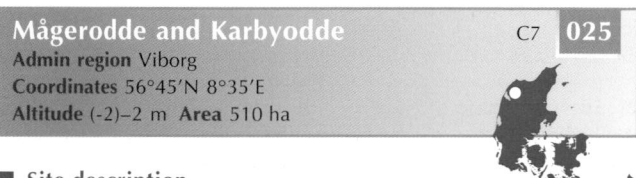

Agger Tange and Krik Vig   B1i, C3   023
Admin region Viborg
Coordinates 56°45'N 8°15'E
Altitude (-5)–2 m **Area** 5,490 ha

■ Site description
Coastal peninsula with an enclosed brackish lagoon, grazing-meadows and shallow fjord area with shoals, banks, intertidal flats and saltmarshes.

Habitats Wetland (100%; tidal river/enclosed tidal water; saltmarsh; sand-dunes/sand beach; coastal lagoon)
Land-use Unknown

■ Birds

Species	Season	Year	Pop min	Pop max	Acc	Criteria
Branta bernicla Brent Goose	N	1994	1,160	1,160	A	B1i, C3

The numbers of most wintering and passage species have declined markedly since 1983 (formerly more than 20,000 waterbirds), when the site was designated as a Special Protection Area. The most recent available breeding bird data are from 1988 when several species, listed on Annex I of the EC Birds Directive, were recorded breeding at the site, including *Recurvirostra avosetta, Philomachus pugnax, Sterna sandvicensis, S. hirundo* and *S. paradisaea*.

■ Protection status
National Partial **International** High
5,490 ha of IBA covered by Special Protection Area (Agger Tange and Krik Vig, 5,490 ha). 5,490 ha of IBA covered by Ramsar Site (Harboøre and Agger Tange, 12,772 ha).

■ Conservation issues

Threats Abandonment/reduction of land management (A), Agricultural intensification/expansion (U), Industrialization/urbanization (U), Unsustainable exploitation (B)

Agricultural intensification, industrialization and urbanization have resulted in the deterioration of water quality, presumably causing bird declines.

Hjarbæk Fjord   A4i, B1i, C2, C3   024
Admin region Viborg
Coordinates 56°33'N 9°20'E
Altitude (-4)–1 m **Area** 4,260 ha

■ Site description
A shallow brackish water arm of the Limfjord, separated from the main fjord by a road embankment and bordered by coastal saltmarshes and agricultural areas.

Habitats Wetland (95%; saltmarsh; standing brackish and salt water), Unknown (5%)
Land-use Agriculture (25%), Unknown (75%)

■ Birds

Species	Season	Year	Pop min	Pop max	Acc	Criteria
Cygnus cygnus Whooper Swan	W	1995	885	885	A	A4i, B1i, C2
Aythya ferina Pochard	N	1988	2,000	4,000	A	B1i, C3
Bucephala clangula Goldeneye	N	1988	5,000	6,000	A	A4i, B1i, C3

The most recent data available for many non-breeding birds date from 1987 and 1988 when more than 20,000 waterbirds occurred at the site. *Philomachus pugnax* and *Recurvirostra avosetta*, listed on Annex I of the EC Birds Directive, bred at the IBA in 1983.

■ Protection status
National Partial **International** High
4,260 ha of IBA covered by Special Protection Area (Hjarbæk Fjord and Simested Å, 4,260 ha).

■ Conservation issues

Threats Abandonment/reduction of land management (C), Agricultural intensification/expansion (A), Aquaculture/fisheries (B), Construction/impact of dyke/dam/barrage (A), Recreation/tourism (C)

Since 1991 the intake of salt and brackish water has been increased in order to restore salinity.

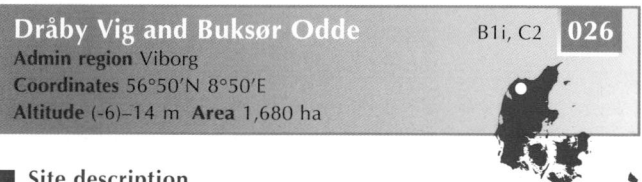

Mågerodde and Karbyodde   C7   025
Admin region Viborg
Coordinates 56°45'N 8°35'E
Altitude (-2)–2 m **Area** 510 ha

■ Site description
A coastal area with saltmarshes and small saline ponds.

Habitats Wetland (100%; tidal river/enclosed tidal water; saltmarsh; standing fresh water)
Land-use Agriculture (45%), Unknown (55%)

■ Birds
More than 20,000 waterbirds occurred and three species listed on Annex I of the EC Birds Directive bred at this site, however, very few non-breeding or breeding birds were recorded in 1994 or 1995.

■ Protection status
National Unknown **International** High
510 ha of IBA covered by Special Protection Area (Mågerodde and Karby Odde, 510 ha).

■ Conservation issues

Threats Abandonment/reduction of land management (C), Disturbance to birds (B), Recreation/tourism (B), Unsustainable exploitation (B)

Dråby Vig and Buksør Odde   B1i, C2   026
Admin region Viborg
Coordinates 56°50'N 8°50'E
Altitude (-6)–14 m **Area** 1,680 ha

■ Site description
A bay with tidal sandflats, saltmarshes and small brackish ponds. Cattle graze on the saltmashes.

Habitats Wetland (100%; tidal river/enclosed tidal water; saltmarsh)
Land-use Agriculture (15%), Unknown (85%)

■ Birds

Species	Season	Year	Pop min	Pop max	Acc	Criteria
Pluvialis apricaria Golden Plover	P	1995	10,000	10,000	B	B1i, C2

This is an important staging area for *Pluvialis apricaria*. *Recurvirostra avosetta* and *Sterna paradisaea*, both listed on Annex I of the EC Birds Directive, bred in 1988, but no recent breeding data are available.

■ Protection status
National Unknown **International** High
1,680 ha of IBA covered by Special Protection Area (Dråby Vig and Buksør Odde, 1,680 ha).

■ Conservation issues

Threats Abandonment/reduction of land management (C), Unsustainable exploitation (B)

Glomstrup Vig, Agerø, Munkholm and Katholm Odde, Lindholm, and Rotholme

B1i, C2, C4 027

Admin region Viborg
Coordinates 56°40'N 8°35'E
Altitude (-9)–18 m **Area** 6,990 ha

■ Site description
A shallow fjord area with shoals, banks and islands, and coastal areas with saltmarsh and agricultural land.

Habitats Wetland (100%; tidal river/enclosed tidal water; saltmarsh)
Land-use Agriculture (15%), Unknown (85%)

■ Birds

Species	Season	Year	Pop min	Pop max	Acc	Criteria
Pluvialis apricaria Golden Plover	N	1994	13,500	13,500	B	B1i, C2

The IBA is an important staging area for *Pluvialis apricaria*. *Recurvirostra avosetta* and *Sterna paradisaea*, listed on Annex I of the EC Birds Directive, breed at the site.

■ Protection status
National Partial **International** High
6,990 ha of IBA covered by Special Protection Area (Glomstrup Vig, Agerø, Munkholm, 6,990 ha).

■ Conservation issues

Threats Abandonment/reduction of land management (B), Agricultural intensification/expansion (C), Aquaculture/fisheries (B), Industrialization/urbanization (C)

Nissum Bredning

C7 028

Admin region Viborg
Coordinates 56°40'N 8°20'E
Altitude (-11)–0 m **Area** 13,570 ha

■ Site description
A shallow fjord area with coastal lagoons and saltmarshes (the latter habitat comprising less than 5% of the area of the IBA) in the western part of Nissum Bredning.

Habitats Wetland (100%; tidal river/enclosed tidal water)
Land-use Unknown

■ Birds
Formerly internationally important for wintering populations of *Bucephala clangula*, *Mergus serrator* and *M. merganser* but these were not recorded in significant numbers in the last midwinter counts in 1991.

■ Protection status
National None **International** High
13,570 ha of IBA covered by Special Protection Area (Nissum Bredning, 13,570 ha).

■ Conservation issues

Threats Agricultural intensification/expansion (A), Industrialization/urbanization (A), Recreation/tourism (C), Unsustainable exploitation (C)

The decrease in bird numbers may be the result of a fall in the birds' food supply of small fish and mussels due to water pollution from agricultural run-off.

Flyndersø and Skallesø

C2 029

Admin region Ringkøbing, Viborg
Coordinates 56°30'N 8°50'E
Altitude 0–0 m **Area** 830 ha

■ Site description
Freshwater lakes in an area of heathland now largely converted to

conifer plantations; some patches of heathland and tiny remnants of natural *Quercus* forest remain.

Habitats Scrub (5%; heathland), Wetland (90%; standing fresh water, river/stream), Artificial landscape (5%; forestry plantation)
Land-use Forestry (5%), Nature conservation/research (100%)

■ Birds

Species	Season	Year	Pop min	Pop max	Acc	Criteria
Cygnus cygnus Whooper Swan	W	1988	145	145	—	C2

Numbers of passage and wintering ducks have declined, probably due to decreasing water quality. *Mergus merganser* and *Anas crecca* were recorded in internationally important numbers (meeting current IBA criterion B1i) in 1983.

■ Protection status
National Partial **International** High
830 ha of IBA covered by Special Protection Area (Flyndersø and Skalle Sø, 830 ha).

■ Conservation issues

Threats Abandonment/reduction of land management (B), Agricultural intensification/expansion (A)

Agricultural intensification has resulted in deteriorating water quality.

Norsminde (Kysing) Fjord

B1i, C3 030

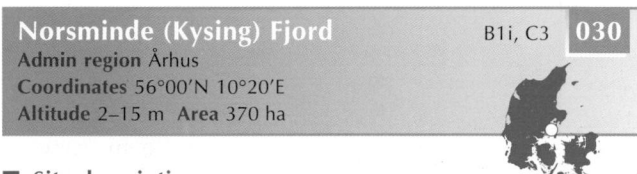

Admin region Århus
Coordinates 56°00'N 10°20'E
Altitude 2–15 m **Area** 370 ha

■ Site description
A shallow, almost enclosed fjord area (connected to the open sea by sluices), surrounded by saltmarshes, meadows and agricultural land.

Habitats Wetland (90%; tidal river/enclosed tidal water; saltmarsh; water-fringe vegetation), Artificial landscape (10%; arable land)
Land-use Agriculture (20%), Nature conservation/research (100%)

■ Birds

Species	Season	Year	Pop min	Pop max	Acc	Criteria
Mergus merganser Goosander	N	1994	32	32	A	B1i, C3

The site is an important staging ground for *Mergus merganser* in cold winters, when regular staging grounds elsewhere are covered in ice. *Circus aeruginosus*, *Recurvirostra avosetta* and *Sterna hirundo*, listed on Annex I of the EC Birds Directive, breed at the site.

■ Protection status
National Partial **International** High
370 ha of IBA covered by Special Protection Area (Norsminde Fjord, 370 ha).

■ Conservation issues

Threats Agricultural intensification/expansion (A), Recreation/tourism (B)

Stavnsfjord and adjacent waters

A4i, B1i, B3, C3 031

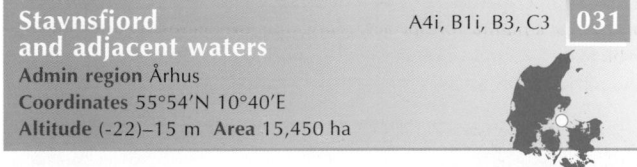

Admin region Århus
Coordinates 55°54'N 10°40'E
Altitude (-22)–15 m **Area** 15,450 ha

■ Site description
The IBA encompasses a group of largely uninhabited islands and surrounding shallow waters. The vegetation on the islands includes saltmarshes, heathland and various grassland types, with some cultivation on a few islands. The sea area surrounding the islands is regarded as a scientific reference area as it is almost unaffected by nutrient pollution.

Habitats Forest and woodland (95%), Wetland (5%)
Land-use Nature conservation/research (100%)

■ **Birds**

Species		Season	Year	Pop min	Pop max	Acc	Criteria
Phalacrocorax carbo	Cormorant	B	1994	2,100	2,100	A	A4i, B1i, C3
Phalacrocorax carbo	Cormorant	N	1994	4,800	4,800	B	B1i, C3
Somateria mollissima	Eider	W	1989	51,000	51,000	—	A4i, B1i, C3
Melanitta nigra	Common Scoter	W	1989	15,500	15,500	—	A4i, B1i, C3
Larus fuscus	Lesser Black-backed Gull	B	1994	390	390	A	B3

The site supports a large colony of *Phalacrocorax carbo* and high numbers of wintering *Somateria mollissima*. *Recurvirostra avosetta*, *Sterna sandvicensis*, *S. paradisaea* and *S. albifrons*, listed on Annex I of the EC Birds Directive, breed at the site.

■ **Protection status**
National High **International** Low
580 ha of IBA covered by Special Protection Area (Stavns Fjord, 15,450 ha). 580 ha of IBA covered by Ramsar Site (Stavns Fjord and adjacent waters, 16,320 ha).

■ **Conservation issues**

Threats Aquaculture/fisheries (C), Disturbance to birds (U), Infrastructure (B), Other (U), Recreation/tourism (B), Unsustainable exploitation (C)

Access to the islands is prohibited. High-speed ferries pose a threat (classified as 'Other' and 'Disturbance to birds').

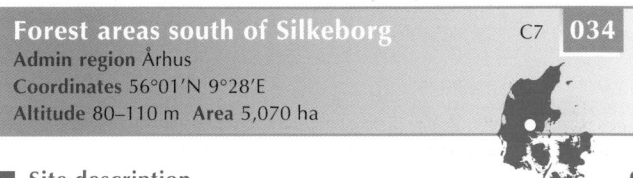

Ørkenen and Totten (Anholt island) B3, C7 | 032
Admin region Århus
Coordinates 56°43′N 11°35′E
Altitude 0–24 m **Area** 2,000 ha

■ **Site description**
A large area of poor sandy soil covered with lichens and scattered dwarf shrubs, with smaller areas of *Pinus mugo* plantations and other conifers. This IBA has been extended to include a larger terrestrial area but the marine areas surrounding this IBA (and previously included within it, following Grimmett and Jones 1989) are now included in the Northern Kattegat IBA (site 119).

Habitats Scrub (100%; heathland), Artificial landscape (5%; forestry plantation)
Land-use Nature conservation/research (100%)

■ **Birds**

Species		Season	Year	Pop min	Pop max	Acc	Criteria
Larus fuscus	Lesser Black-backed Gull	B	1994	1,400	1,400	A	B3

■ **Protection status**
National Low **International** Low
70 ha of IBA covered by Ramsar Site (Anholt Island (waters north of), 12,720 ha). 70 ha of IBA covered by Special Protection Area (Sea area north of Anholt, 11,520 ha).

■ **Conservation issues**

Threats Abandonment/reduction of land management (B), Consequences of animal/plant introductions (B), Recreation/tourism (B)

Pinus mugo, a plantation species, is invading the heathland and causing problems.

Salten Langsø C7 | 033
Admin region Århus
Coordinates 56°06′N 9°35′E
Altitude 20–50 m **Area** 970 ha

■ **Site description**
An eutrophic freshwater lake with reedbeds, surrounded by forest, heathland and agricultural land.

Habitats Forest and woodland (5%), Scrub (5%; heathland), Wetland (70%; standing fresh water; water-fringe vegetation), Artificial landscape (25%; forestry plantation)
Land-use Agriculture (15%), Forestry (25%), Unknown (60%)

■ **Birds**
Numbers of breeding and wintering birds have declined due to deteriorating water quality. Species of global conservation concern that do not meet IBA criteria: *Haliaeetus albicilla* (max. 2, non-breeding). *Pernis apivorus*, *Dryocopus martius* and *Lullula arborea*, listed on Annex I of the EC Birds Directive, breed at the site.

■ **Protection status**
National Partial **International** High
970 ha of IBA covered by Special Protection Area (Salten Langsø, 970 ha).

■ **Conservation issues**

Threats Abandonment/reduction of land management (C), Agricultural intensification/expansion (A), Aquaculture/fisheries (A), Intensified forest management (B), Recreation/tourism (C)

The intensification of agricultural practices has lead to a deterioration in water quality.

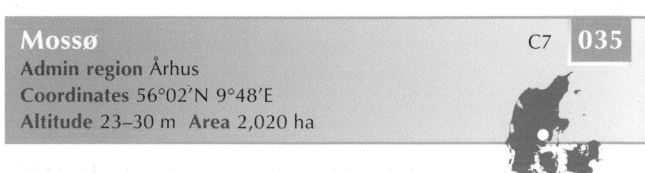

Forest areas south of Silkeborg C7 | 034
Admin region Århus
Coordinates 56°01′N 9°28′E
Altitude 80–110 m **Area** 5,070 ha

■ **Site description**
Large exotic conifer plantations on former heathland with several streams. Some heathland remains and there is one small area (9.5 ha) of natural *Quercus* forest.

Habitats Scrub (10%; heathland), Wetland (15%; standing fresh water; water-fringe vegetation), Artificial landscape (65%; forestry plantation), Unknown (10%)
Land-use Forestry (65%), Nature conservation/research (10%), Unknown (25%)

■ **Birds**
The site holds high numbers of breeding raptors and woodpeckers. Several species listed on Annex I of the EC Birds Directive breed at the site, including *Pernis apivorus*, *Caprimulgus europaeus*, *Alcedo atthis*, *Dryocopus martius*, *Lullula arborea* and *Lanius collurio*.

■ **Protection status**
National Partial **International** High
5,070 ha of IBA covered by Special Protection Area (Forest areas south of Silkeborg, 5,070 ha).

■ **Conservation issues**

Threats Abandonment/reduction of land management (B), Intensified forest management (B)

Mossø C7 | 035
Admin region Århus
Coordinates 56°02′N 9°48′E
Altitude 23–30 m **Area** 2,020 ha

■ **Site description**
A freshwater lake with reedbeds, surrounded by forest and agricultural land.

Habitats Grassland (5%; humid grassland), Wetland (95%; standing fresh water; water-fringe vegetation)
Land-use Agriculture (5%), Unknown (95%)

■ **Birds**
Circus aeruginosus and *Alcedo atthis*, listed on Annex I of the EC Birds Directive, breed at the site. Species of global conservation concern that do not meet IBA criteria: *Haliaeetus albicilla* (max. 2, non-breeding).

■ Protection status
National High **International** High
2,020 ha of IBA covered by Special Protection Area (Mossø, 2,020 ha).

■ Conservation issues

Threats Agricultural intensification/expansion (B), Industrialization/urbanization (B), Recreation/tourism (B)

Horsens Fjord, Svanegrunden and Endelave islands [036]
A4i, B1i, B2, C2, C3
Admin region Vejle
Coordinates 55°51'N 10°10'E
Altitude (-15)–15 m **Area** 42,880 ha

■ Site description
An extensive shallow sea area with three large islands (Alvrø, Hjarnø and Endelave), supporting coastal saltmarshes, lagoons, cultivated land and scattered habitation. Several smaller uninhabited islets as well as intertidal areas are included within the IBA.

Habitats Marine areas (90%; sea inlet/coastal features), Artificial landscape (5%; arable land)
Land-use Agriculture (5%), Unknown (95%)

■ Birds

Species	Season	Year	Pop min	Pop max	Acc	Criteria
[1] *Phalacrocorax carbo* Cormorant	B	1996	4,320	4,320	A	A4i, B1i, C3
Aythya marila Scaup	W	1993	2,469	2,469	—	B1i, B2, C3
[2] *Somateria mollissima* Eider	W	1993	22,150	22,150	—	A4i, B1i, C3
Limosa lapponica Bar-tailed Godwit	P	1993	1,600	1,600	—	A4i, B1i, C2

1. Nearly all population on Vorso island.
2. Numbers higher in cold winters (1983, 80,000).

The site holds a large breeding colony of *Phalacrocorax carbo* and high numbers of wintering *Aythya marila* and *Somateria mollissima*. Breeding data are incomplete since numbers were not available for Alrø, Søby Rev and Svanegrunden islands. Several species listed on Annex I of the EC Birds Directive breed at the site, including *Circus aeruginosus*, *Recurvirostra avosetta*, *Sterna sandvicensis*, *S. paradisaea* and *S. albifrons*.

■ Protection status
National Low **International** High
42,880 ha of IBA covered by Ramsar Site (Horsens Fjord and Endelave, 43,200 ha). 42,880 ha of IBA covered by Special Protection Area (Horsens Fjord and Endelave, 42,880 ha).

■ Conservation issues

Threats Abandonment/reduction of land management (C), Aquaculture/fisheries (C), Recreation/tourism (C), Unsustainable exploitation (B)

Access is prohibited to some areas and in several parts of the IBA hunting is forbidden.

Borris Hede [037]
C6
Admin region Ringkøbing
Coordinates 55°55'N 8°41'E
Altitude 6–27 m **Area** 4,760 ha

■ Site description
A very large heathland with streams, bogs and conifer plantations.

Habitats Scrub (55%; heathland), Wetland (25%; raised bog), Artificial landscape (10%; forestry plantation)
Land-use Forestry (10%), Military (100%), Nature conservation/research (40%)

■ Birds

Species	Season	Year	Pop min	Pop max	Acc	Criteria
Tringa glareola Wood Sandpiper	B	1994	5	7	A	C6

One of the most important areas for heathland birds in Denmark, holding significant numbers of *Tringa glareola* and other scarce heathland species. *Tetrao tetrix* used to breed at the site but went extinct during the 1980s. Several species listed on Annex I of the EC Birds Directive breed at the site, including *Botaurus stellaris*, *Pernis apivorus*, *Circus aeruginosus*, *C. cyaneus*, *Pluvialis apricaria*, *Tringa glareola*, *Asio flammeus*, *Alcedo atthis* and *Lanius collurio*.

■ Protection status
National Partial **International** High
4,760 ha of IBA covered by Special Protection Area (Borris Hede, 4,760 ha).

■ Conservation issues

Threats Abandonment/reduction of land management (C), Other (B)

Airborne nutrient pollution is altering the heathland ('Other' threat).

Nissum Fjord [038]
A4i, B1i, B2, C2, C3, C6
Admin region Ringkøbing
Coordinates 56°21'N 8°14'E
Altitude (-1)–7 m **Area** 10,890 ha

■ Site description
A shallow brackish fjord connected by sluices to the North Sea, with coastal saltmarshes and reedbeds, and heathland vegetation on Fjandø Island.

Habitats Wetland (75%; tidal river/enclosed tidal water; saltmarsh; water-fringe vegetation), Artificial landscape (25%; arable land)
Land-use Agriculture (30%), Unknown (70%)

■ Birds

Species	Season	Year	Pop min	Pop max	Acc	Criteria
Phalacrocorax carbo Cormorant	B	1994	770	770	A	B1i, C3
[1] *Cygnus columbianus* Bewick's Swan	N	1989	320	320	—	A4i, B1i, B2, C2
Cygnus cygnus Whooper Swan	N	1983	1,000	1,000	—	A4i, B1i, C2
Anser brachyrhynchus Pink-footed Goose	N	1983	3,750	3,750	—	A4i, B1i, C3
Tadorna tadorna Shelduck	N	—	4,445	4,445	—	A4i, B1i, C3
Anas crecca Teal	N	1989	4,000	4,000	—	B1i, C3
Calidris alpina Dunlin	N	1983	15,000	15,000	—	B1i, C3
Limosa lapponica Bar-tailed Godwit	P	1983	6,500	6,500	—	A4i, B1i, C2
[2] *Larus canus* Common Gull	B	1995	800	1,200	—	B2
Sterna sandvicensis Sandwich Tern	B	1994	1,050	1,050	A	A4i, B1i, B2, C2, C6

1. Partial population estimate.
2. Total population on Fjando island.

This is an important staging area for *Cygnus cygnus*, *C. columbianus*, *Anser brachyrhynchus* and *Limosa lapponica*; however, numbers of most winter and passage visitors have declined (since the 1980s) to below 20,000 birds in total, due to nutrient pollution. Also a disease affecting the formerly extensive areas of eel-grass *Zostera* has affected foraging, especially for swans *Cygnus* and *Branta bernicla*. Several species listed on Annex I of the EC Birds Directive breed at the site, including *Botaurus stellaris*, *Circus aeruginosus*, *Recurvirostra avosetta*, *Philomachus pugnax*, *Sterna sandvicensis*, *S. hirundo*, *S. paradisaea* and *S. albifrons*.

■ Protection status
National Partial **International** High
10,890 ha of IBA covered by Ramsar Site (Nissum Fjord, 11,600 ha). 10,890 ha of IBA covered by Special Protection Area (Nissum Fjord, 10,890 ha).

■ Conservation issues

Threats Abandonment/reduction of land management (B), Agricultural intensification/expansion (A), Unsustainable exploitation (B)

Several parts of the IBA are afforded protection through entry, hunting and boating restrictions. Reduced grazing of saltmarshes is detrimentally affecting this habitat for birds, and renewed grazing is planned in some state-owned parts of the site.

Harboøre Tange, Plet Enge and Gjeller Sø · A4i, A4iii, B1i, B3, C3, C4 · 039

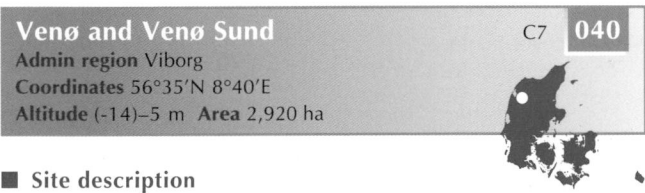

Admin region Ringkøbing
Coordinates 56°40'N 8°15'E
Altitude (-5)–5 m **Area** 7,280 ha

■ Site description
A narrow peninsula with shallow fjord areas containing shoals and banks with an intertidal zone, saltmarsh and some brackish lagoons. There are grazing-meadows on the landward side and cultivated areas with scattered habitation.

Habitats Wetland (90%; tidal river/enclosed tidal water; saltmarsh; sand-dunes/sand beach; water-fringe vegetation), Artificial landscape (5%; arable land)
Land-use Agriculture (15%), Unknown (85%)

■ Birds

Species	Season	Year	Pop min	Pop max	Acc	Criteria
Anser brachyrhynchus Pink-footed Goose	N	1989	3,630	3,630	—	A4i, B1i, C3
Branta bernicla Brent Goose	N	1994	656	656	—	B1i, C3
Recurvirostra avosetta Avocet	B	1988	59	143	B	B3

Several species listed on Annex I of the EC Birds Directive bred at the site in 1988, including *Circus aeruginosus*, *Recurvirostra avosetta*, *Philomachus pugnax*, *Sterna paradisaea*, *S. albifrons* and *Asio flammeus*, but no recent data are available on breeding birds.

■ Protection status
National Partial **International** High
7,280 ha of IBA covered by Ramsar Site (Harboøre and Agger Tange, 12,772 ha). 5,110 ha of IBA covered by Special Protection Area (Hanstholm-reservatet, 5,110 ha).

■ Conservation issues

Threats Aquaculture/fisheries (C), Dredging/canalization (C), Industrialization/urbanization (B), Unsustainable exploitation (A)

Venø and Venø Sund · C7 · 040

Admin region Viborg
Coordinates 56°35'N 8°40'E
Altitude (-14)–5 m **Area** 2,920 ha

■ Site description
A shallow brackish fjord with a small area of saline lagoons, beaches and saltmarsh.

Habitats Forest and woodland (5%), Wetland (95%; tidal river/enclosed tidal water)
Land-use Unknown

■ Birds
Numbers of passage and winter visitors have declined dramatically due to deteriorating water quality: in 1983 several species were present in internationally important numbers including *Bucephala clangula* (meeting IBA criterion A4) and *Mergus serrator* and *Mergus merganser* (meeting IBA criterion B1). *Recurvirostra avosetta*, *Sterna paradisaea* and *S. albifrons*, listed on Annex I of the EC Birds Directive, currently breed at the site.

■ Protection status
National None **International** High
2,920 ha of IBA covered by Special Protection Area (Venø and Venø Sund, 2,920 ha).

■ Conservation issues

Threats Agricultural intensification/expansion (A), Aquaculture/fisheries (C), Industrialization/urbanization (B)

Improvements in water quality will almost certainly restore the site's ornithological importance.

Stadil Fjord and Veststadil Fjord · A4i, B1i, B2, C2, C3, C6 · 041

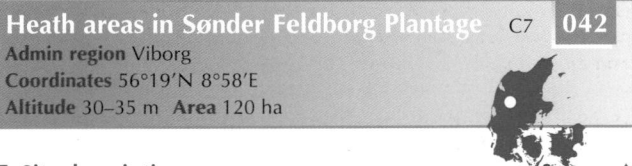

Admin region Ringkøbing
Coordinates 56°11'N 8°09'E
Altitude (-1)–5 m **Area** 6,910 ha

■ Site description
A shallow partially reclaimed fjord area with reedbeds, meadows and agricultural areas.

Habitats Grassland (5%; dry siliceous grassland), Wetland (55%; sand-dunes/sand beach; standing fresh water; standing brackish and salt water), Artificial landscape (45%; arable land)
Land-use Agriculture (45%), Unknown (55%)

■ Birds

Species	Season	Year	Pop min	Pop max	Acc	Criteria
Cygnus columbianus Bewick's Swan	N	1995	1,000	1,000	—	A4i, B1i, B2, C2, C6
Anser brachyrhynchus Pink-footed Goose	N	1995	11,100	11,100	B	A4i, B1i, C3

In 1983, internationally important numbers of six waterbirds visited the site. Currently the site is an important staging area for *Cygnus columbianus* and *Anser brachyrhyncus* and in some years almost 20,000 individuals of these species have been recorded. Several species listed on Annex I of the EC Birds Directive breed at the site, including *Botaurus stellaris*, *Circus aeruginosus* and *Chlidonias niger*. Breeding bird data from Vest Stadil Fjord are unavailable.

■ Protection status
National Partial **International** High
6,910 ha of IBA covered by Ramsar Site (Stadil and Veststadil Fjords, 7,184 ha). 6,910 ha of IBA covered by Special Protection Area (Stadil and West Stadil Fjords, 6,910 ha).

■ Conservation issues

Threats Agricultural intensification/expansion (A), Unsustainable exploitation (A)

In 1994 large parts of the site were purchased by the state for restoration.

Heath areas in Sønder Feldborg Plantage · C7 · 042

Admin region Viborg
Coordinates 56°19'N 8°58'E
Altitude 30–35 m **Area** 120 ha

■ Site description
A small heath surrounded by conifer plantations.

Habitats Scrub (85%; heathland), Wetland (15%; standing fresh water)
Land-use Unknown

■ Birds
Very few birds breed at the site. The site was designated as a Special Protection Area on the basis of important numbers of *Tringa glareola* but the species is no longer present at the site.

■ Protection status
National Unknown **International** High
120 ha of IBA covered by Special Protection Area (Heathlands in Sønder Feldborg Plantage, 120 ha).

■ Conservation issues

Threats Abandonment/reduction of land management (C)

Ringkøbing Fjord · A4i, A4iii, B1i, B2, B3, C2, C3, C4, C6 · 043

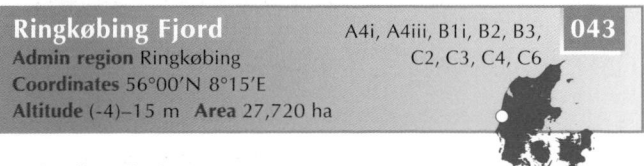

Admin region Ringkøbing
Coordinates 56°00'N 8°15'E
Altitude (-4)–15 m **Area** 27,720 ha

■ Site description
A shallow brackish fjord, encompassing several small islands, and

connected by sluices to the North Sea, with meadows and reedbeds to the south.

Habitats Grassland (5%; humid grassland), Wetland (90%; tidal river/enclosed tidal water; saltmarsh; water-fringe vegetation), Unknown (5%)
Land-use Agriculture (10%), Unknown (90%)

■ Birds

Species		Season	Year	Pop min	Pop max	Acc	Criteria
Phalacrocorax carbo	Cormorant	B	1994	1,000	1,000	A	B1i, C3
Botaurus stellaris	Bittern	B	1994	10	10	A	B2, C6
Cygnus columbianus	Bewick's Swan	N	1994	1,091	1,091	—	A4i,B1i,B2,C2,C6
Anser brachyrhynchus Pink-footed Goose		N	1994	8,000	8,000	—	A4i, B1i, C3
Anas crecca	Teal	N	1994	6,900	6,900	—	B1i, C3
Recurvirostra avosetta	Avocet	B	1994	592	670	A	A4i, B1i, B3, C6
Limosa limosa	Black-tailed Godwit	B	1994	266	272	A	B2
Limosa lapponica	Bar-tailed Godwit	P	—	1,000	1,000	A	A4i, B1i, C2
¹ *Tringa totanus*	Redshank	B	1992	530	530	—	B2
Sterna sandvicensis	Sandwich Tern	B	1996	1,024	1,024	A	A4i,B1i,B2,C6

1. Partial population estimate.

Numbers of many breeding and visiting waterbirds have declined dramatically due to deteriorating water quality. Several species listed on Annex I of the EC Birds Directive breed at the site, including *Botaurus stellaris*, *Circus aeruginosus*, *Porzana porzana*, *Recurvirostra avosetta*, *Philomachus pugnax*, *Sterna sandvicensis*, *S. hirundo*, *S. paradisaea* and *Asio flammeus*.

■ Protection status
National High **International** High
27,520 ha of IBA covered by Ramsar Site (Ringkøbing Fjord, 27,520 ha). 27,720 ha of IBA covered by Special Protection Area (Ringkøbing Fjord, 27,720 ha).

■ Conservation issues

Threats Abandonment/reduction of land management (B), Agricultural intensification/expansion (A), Aquaculture/fisheries (A), Industrialization/urbanization (B), Recreation/tourism (B), Unsustainable exploitation (A)

Nutrient pollution, as a result of agricultural intensification, has affected water quality at the site: by 1979 the area had been polluted to such an extent that algal blooms had formed, which reduced light and resulted in massive reductions in the extent of submerged macrophytes. In recent years water quality has improved and in some areas bottom macrophytes are recolonizing. An ongoing restoration project in the Skjern Å river valley will hopefully further improve water quality, though positive effects on bird populations are expected to take time to become evident.

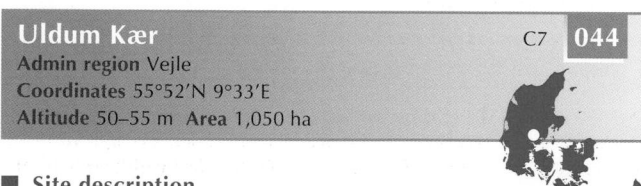

Uldum Kær
C7 044
Admin region Vejle
Coordinates 55°52′N 9°33′E
Altitude 50–55 m **Area** 1,050 ha

■ Site description
The IBA comprises wet meadows, ponds, peatbogs, *Salix* scrub and moist heathland.

Habitats Scrub (10%; scrub), Grassland (70%; humid grassland; mesophile grassland), Wetland (10%; standing fresh water), Artificial landscape (10%; arable land), Unknown (10%)
Land-use Agriculture (30%), Hunting (100%)

■ Birds
Circus aeruginosus, *Crex crex*, *Tringa glareola* and *Alcedo atthis*, listed on Annex I of the EC Birds Directive, were breeding at the site in 1983 but no longer breed.

■ Protection status
National Unknown **International** High
1,050 ha of IBA covered by Special Protection Area (Uldum Kær, 1,050 ha).

■ Conservation issues
Plans are underway to initiate a limited wetland restoration project and to implement measures to reduce hunting.

Threats Abandonment/reduction of land management (A), Agricultural intensification/expansion (C), Infrastructure (C), Unsustainable exploitation (C)

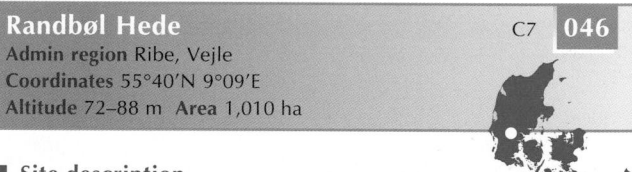

Forest areas along the northern part of Vejle Fjord
C7 045
Admin region Vejle
Coordinates 55°42′N 9°45′E
Altitude 0–60 m **Area** 2,690 ha

■ Site description
Deciduous forests on slopes along the northern part of Vejle fjord.

Habitats Forest and woodland (40%; broadleaved deciduous forest), Wetland (5%), Artificial landscape (60%; arable land; forestry plantation)
Land-use Agriculture (20%), Forestry (60%), Unknown (20%)

■ Birds
Pernis apivorus and *Alcedo atthis*, listed on Annex I of the EC Birds Directive, bred at the site in 1983, and were the basis for the Special Protection Area designation. No recent data are available.

■ Protection status
National Partial **International** High
2,690 ha of IBA covered by Special Protection Area (Forests along the north side of Vejle Fjord, 2,690 ha).

■ Conservation issues

Threats Intensified forest management (C)

Recently some state-owned parts of the IBA have been earmarked for natural forest development, without logging rights.

Randbøl Hede
C7 046
Admin region Ribe, Vejle
Coordinates 55°40′N 9°09′E
Altitude 72–88 m **Area** 1,010 ha

■ Site description
A dry heathland, with large parts dominated by grasses, and with some bogs and small plantations.

Habitats Grassland (10%), Scrub (90%; heathland), Wetland (10%)
Land-use Nature conservation/research (100%)

■ Birds
The site was designated as an SPA in 1983, based on its populations of *Tringa glareola* and *Tetrao tetrix*; both are listed on Annex I of the EC Birds Directive, but are no longer present.

■ Protection status
National Partial **International** High
1,010 ha of IBA covered by Special Protection Area (Randbøl Hede, 1,010 ha).

■ Conservation issues

Threats Abandonment/reduction of land management (A), Agricultural intensification/expansion (C), Consequences of animal/plant introductions (A)

Threats include introductions of *Pinus mugo* and airborne nutrient pollution, largely resulting from intensification of agricultural practices.

Lillebælt
A4iii, B1i, C3, C4, C6 047
Admin region Fyn, Sønderjylland
Coordinates 55°21′N 9°43′E
Altitude (-35)–10 m **Area** 35,060 ha

■ Site description
A narrow strait including islands and peninsulas with coves, lagoons,

saltmarshes, reedbeds, broadleaved forests, cultivated land and some scattered habitation.

> **Habitats** Wetland (5%), Marine areas (80%; sea inlet/coastal features), Artificial landscape (10%; arable land)
> **Land-use** Agriculture (10%), Unknown (90%)

■ Birds

Species	Season	Year	Pop min	Pop max	Acc	Criteria
Somateria mollissima Eider	W	1994	24,200	24,200	—	B1i, C3
Haliaeetus albicilla White-tailed Eagle	R	1996	1	1	A	C6

Up to seven waterbird species are present in significant numbers during cold winters, totalling over 20,000 individuals. Several species listed on Annex I of the EC Birds Directive breed at the site, including *Recurvirostra avosetta*, *Sterna paradisaea* and *S. albifrons*.

■ Protection status
National None **International** High
35,060 ha of IBA covered by Ramsar Site (Lillebælt, 37,330 ha). 35,060 ha of IBA covered by Special Protection Area (Lillebælt, 35,060 ha).

■ Conservation issues

> **Threats** Abandonment/reduction of land management (C), Agricultural intensification/expansion (B), Recreation/tourism (B), Unsustainable exploitation (B)

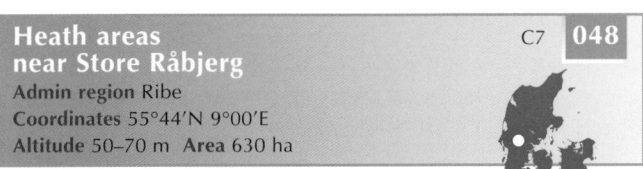

Heath areas near Store Råbjerg — C7 048
Admin region Ribe
Coordinates 55°44'N 9°00'E
Altitude 50–70 m **Area** 630 ha

■ Site description
An area of heathland with bogs, lying between Utoft and Gyttegårds Plantage.

> **Habitats** Scrub (30%; heathland), Wetland (20%; raised bog), Artificial landscape (25%; forestry plantation), Unknown (25%)
> **Land-use** Forestry (50%), Unknown (50%)

■ Birds
The area was designated as a Special Protection Area on the basis of breeding *Tringa glareola* (listed on Annex I of the EC Birds Directive), but it is believed that this species stopped breeding at the site in the 1970s.

■ Protection status
National Partial **International** High
630 ha of IBA covered by Special Protection Area (Heathlands near Store Råbjerg, 630 ha).

■ Conservation issues

> **Threats** Abandonment/reduction of land management (B), Disturbance to birds (A), Recreation/tourism (A)

Ho Bugt meadows — A4i, A4iii, B1i, C2, C4 049
Admin region Ribe
Coordinates 55°36'N 8°19'E
Altitude 0–5 m **Area** 2,700 ha

■ Site description
Saltmarshes around Ho Bugt and freshwater-meadows along the River Varde Å (the largest river system in western Jutland which has not been canalized). The meadows are intensively farmed with high fertilizer input and frequent harvesting.

> **Habitats** Grassland (50%; humid grassland), Wetland (30%; saltmarsh), Unknown (20%)
> **Land-use** Agriculture (100%)

■ Birds

Species	Season	Year	Pop min	Pop max	Acc	Criteria
Recurvirostra avosetta Avocet	P	1994	2,000	2,000	A	A4i, B1i, C2
Limosa lapponica Bar-tailed Godwit	P	1994	1,500	1,500	—	A4i, B1i, C2

More than 20,000 non-breeding waterbirds occur at the site, including *Anas penelope*, *A. acuta* and *Calidris alpina*. Numbers of breeding meadow birds have decreased as a result of the intensification of farming practices. *Circus aeruginosus*, *C. cyaneus*, *C. pygargus*, *Recurvirostra avosetta* and *Luscinia svecica*, listed on Annex I of the EC Birds Directive, breed at the site.

■ Protection status
National High **International** None

■ Conservation issues

> **Threats** Abandonment/reduction of land management (B), Agricultural intensification/expansion (A), Industrialization/urbanization (C), Unsustainable exploitation (B)

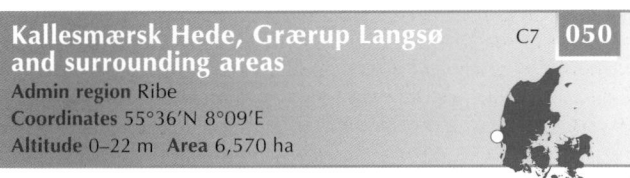

Kallesmærsk Hede, Grærup Langsø and surrounding areas — C7 050
Admin region Ribe
Coordinates 55°36'N 8°09'E
Altitude 0–22 m **Area** 6,570 ha

■ Site description
A large heathland with small conifer plantations, lakes, bogs and dunes.

> **Habitats** Scrub (45%; heathland), Wetland (30%; sand-dunes/sand beach; standing fresh water; raised bog), Artificial landscape (10%; forestry plantation), Unknown (20%)
> **Land-use** Forestry (10%), Military (40%), Unknown (50%)

■ Birds
The site was designated as a Special Protection Area in 1983 on the basis of breeding numbers of *Tringa glareola*. *Tringa glareola*, *Caprimulgus europaeus*, *Lullula arborea* and *Lanius collurio*, listed on Annex I of the EC Birds Directive, currently breed at the site.

■ Protection status
National Low **International** High
6,570 ha of IBA covered by Special Protection Area (Kallesmærsk Hede and Grærup Langsø, 6,570 ha).

■ Conservation issues

> **Threats** Abandonment/reduction of land management (B), Consequences of animal/plant introductions (B), Other (C), Recreation/tourism (C)

Several parts of the IBA have additional national protection. There are plans to raise water-levels at Grærup Langsø lake. The spread of the introduced and invasive *Pinus mugo* threatens the heathland habitat.

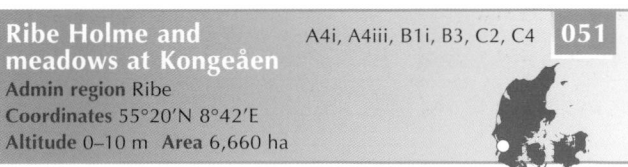

Ribe Holme and meadows at Kongeåen — A4i, A4iii, B1i, B3, C2, C4 051
Admin region Ribe
Coordinates 55°20'N 8°42'E
Altitude 0–10 m **Area** 6,660 ha

■ Site description
Marshland enclosed behind dykes, with several larger streams and canals.

> **Habitats** Grassland (90%; humid grassland), Unknown (10%)
> **Land-use** Agriculture (90%), Unknown (10%)

■ Birds

Species	Season	Year	Pop min	Pop max	Acc	Criteria
Recurvirostra avosetta Avocet	B	1994	300	300	A	B1i, B3, C2
Pluvialis apricaria Golden Plover	P	1994	20,000	20,000	A	A4i, B1i, C2

More than 20,000 waterbirds occur on passage, *Pluvialis apricaria* being the most numerous. Several species listed on Annex I of the EC Birds Directive breed at the site, including *Circus aeruginosus, C. pygargus, Recurvirostra avosetta, Philomachus pugnax, Asio flammeus* and *Luscinia svecica*.

■ Protection status
National Low **International** High
6,600 ha of IBA covered by Special Protection Area (Ribe Holme and meadows by Ribe Å and Kongeåen, 6,600 ha). 6,660 ha of IBA covered by Ramsar Site (Vadehavet (Wadden Sea), 140,830 ha).

■ Conservation issues

Threats Abandonment/reduction of land management (B), Agricultural intensification/expansion (A), Industrialization/urbanization (C), Infrastructure (C), Unsustainable exploitation (A)

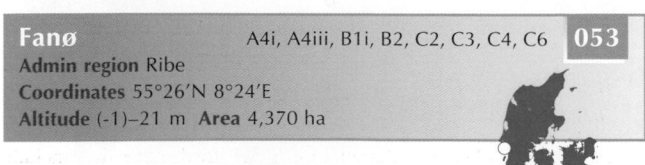

Mandø — A4i, A4iii, B1i, B2, C2, C3, C4 — 052
Admin region Ribe
Coordinates 55°17′N 8°34′E
Altitude 0–10 m **Area** 850 ha

■ Site description
An island in the Wadden Sea with grassland and meadows enclosed by dykes, saltmarshes and mudflats.

Habitats Grassland (45%; humid grassland), Wetland (35%; mudflat/sandflat; saltmarsh), Artificial landscape (20%; arable land; other urban/industrial areas)
Land-use Agriculture (55%), Nature conservation/research (35%), Urban/industrial/transport (10%)

■ Birds

Species	Season	Year	Pop min	Pop max	Acc	Criteria
Branta bernicla Brent Goose	N	1991	12,000	12,000	A	A4i, B1i, C3
Haematopus ostralegus Oystercatcher	N	1991	15,000	15,000	A	A4i, B1i, C3
Calidris canutus Knot	N	1991	20,000	20,000	A	A4i, B1i, C3
Calidris alpina Dunlin	P	1991	75,000	75,000	A	A4i, B1i, C3
Limosa lapponica Bar-tailed Godwit	P	1991	25,000	25,000	A	A4i, B1i, C2
Tringa totanus Redshank	B	1991	136	136	A	B2

This is a very important site for waterbirds, with more than 100,000 individuals using the site. Several species listed on Annex I of the EC Birds Directive breed within the area, including *Circus aeruginosus, Recurvirostra avosetta, Philomachus pugnax, Gelochelidon nilotica, Sterna hirundo* and *S. paradisaea*.

■ Protection status
National Partial **International** High
850 ha of IBA covered by Special Protection Area (Mandø, 850 ha). 850 ha of IBA covered by Ramsar Site (Vadehavet (Wadden Sea), 140,830 ha).

■ Conservation issues

Threats Agricultural intensification/expansion (A), Drainage (A), Recreation/tourism (C), Unsustainable exploitation (B)

Fanø — A4i, A4iii, B1i, B2, C2, C3, C4, C6 — 053
Admin region Ribe
Coordinates 55°26′N 8°24′E
Altitude (-1)–21 m **Area** 4,370 ha

■ Site description
An island in the Wadden Sea surrounded by saltmarshes and mud and sandflats. Terrestrial vegetation mainly comprises various heathland and dune communities and *Pinus* plantations.

Habitats Scrub (35%; heathland), Wetland (50%; mudflat/sandflat; saltmarsh; sand-dunes/sand beach), Artificial landscape (15%; forestry plantation)
Land-use Unknown

■ Birds

Species	Season	Year	Pop min	Pop max	Acc	Criteria
Branta bernicla Brent Goose	P	1994	8,100	8,100	A	A4i, B1i, C3
Tadorna tadorna Shelduck	P	1994	7,600	7,600	A	A4i, B1i, C3
Anas acuta Pintail	P	1994	2,960	2,960	A	B1i, C3
Haematopus ostralegus Oystercatcher	P	1994	16,400	16,400	A	A4i, B1i, C3
Pluvialis squatarola Grey Plover	P	1994	2,872	2,872	A	A4i, B1i, C3
Calidris canutus Knot	P	1994	7,575	7,575	A	B1i, C3
Calidris alba Sanderling	P	1994	2,199	2,199	A	A4i, B1i, C3
Calidris alpina Dunlin	P	1994	88,500	88,500	A	A4i, B1i, C3
Limosa lapponica Bar-tailed Godwit	P	1994	16,700	16,700	A	A4i, B1i, C2
Sterna albifrons Little Tern	B	1994	65	75	A	B2, C6

This is a very important staging area for geese, ducks and waders with total numbers regularly exceeding 20,000 birds. Several species listed on Annex I of the EC Birds Directive breed at the site, including *Botaurus stellaris, Circus aeruginosus, C. pygargus, Recurvirostra avosetta, Sterna paradisaea* and *S. albifrons*.

■ Protection status
National Low **International** High
4,370 ha of IBA covered by Special Protection Area (Fanø, 4,370 ha). 4,370 ha of IBA covered by Ramsar Site (Vadehavet (Wadden Sea), 140,830 ha).

■ Conservation issues

Threats Abandonment/reduction of land management (C), Consequences of animal/plant introductions (C), Recreation/tourism (A), Unsustainable exploitation (C)

The invasion of introduced *Pinus mugo* causes problems.

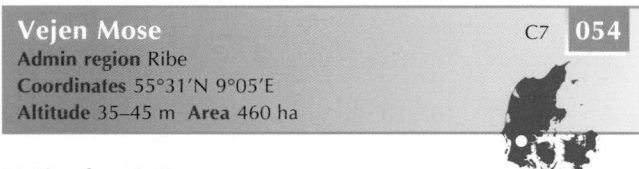

Vejen Mose — C7 — 054
Admin region Ribe
Coordinates 55°31′N 9°05′E
Altitude 35–45 m **Area** 460 ha

■ Site description
A large bog, now damaged by peat extraction and drainage. Part of the area has been invaded by *Betula* and *Salix* and part is grazed by cattle.

Habitats Wetland (100%; standing fresh water; raised bog)
Land-use Agriculture (30%), Unknown (70%)

■ Birds
Fomerly *Tringa glareola, Circus pygargus, Caprimulgus europaeus* and *Crex crex* bred at the site. *Lanius collurio,* also listed on Annex I of the EC Birds Directive, may still breed.

■ Protection status
National Unknown **International** High
460 ha of IBA covered by Special Protection Area (Vejen Mose, 460 ha).

■ Conservation issues

Threats Abandonment/reduction of land management (B), Agricultural intensification/expansion (B)

There are some preliminary plans for a restoration project.

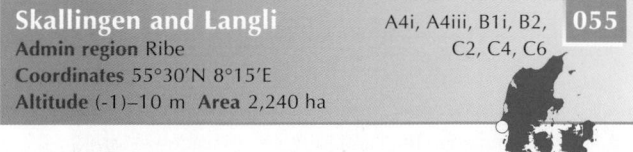

Skallingen and Langli — A4i, A4iii, B1i, B2, C2, C4, C6 — 055
Admin region Ribe
Coordinates 55°30′N 8°15′E
Altitude (-1)–10 m **Area** 2,240 ha

■ Site description
The site encompasses beaches, dunes, moors and extensive saltmarshes, as well as smaller areas of intertidal sand and mudflats.

Habitats Wetland (100%; saltmarsh; sand-dunes/sand beach)
Land-use Unknown

■ Birds

Species	Season	Year	Pop min	Pop max	Acc	Criteria
Limosa lapponica Bar-tailed Godwit	N	1994	1,800	1,800	A	A4i, B1i, C2
Larus canus Common Gull	B	1996	1,168	1,168	A	B2
Sterna sandvicensis Sandwich Tern	B	1996	1,096	1,096	A	A4i, B1i, B2, C6
Sterna albifrons Little Tern	B	1994	20	20	A	B2, C6

Several species listed on Annex I of the EC Birds Directive breed at the site, including *Recurvirostra avosetta*, *Sterna sandvicensis*, *S. hirundo*, *S. paradisaea* and *S. albifrons*. Data on breeding birds are not available for Skallingen.

■ Protection status
National Partial **International** High
2,240 ha of IBA covered by Special Protection Area (Skallingen og Langli, 2,240 ha).

■ Conservation issues

Threats Abandonment/reduction of land management (C), Recreation/tourism (C), Unsustainable exploitation (B)

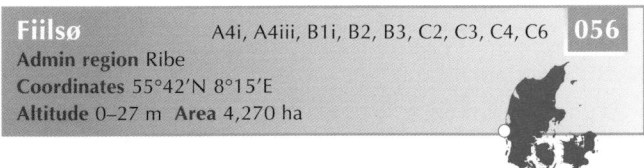

Fiilsø — A4i, A4iii, B1i, B2, B3, C2, C3, C4, C6 — 056
Admin region Ribe
Coordinates 55°42′N 8°15′E
Altitude 0–27 m **Area** 4,270 ha

■ Site description
Mainly open agricultural land on a drained former lake with some small plantations. The site also includes two shallow lakes surrounded by reedbeds with *Alnus* forest and some heathland.

Habitats Scrub (20%; heathland), Wetland (80%; sand-dunes/sand beach; standing fresh water)
Land-use Agriculture (40%), Forestry (5%), Unknown (55%)

■ Birds

Species	Season	Year	Pop min	Pop max	Acc	Criteria
Cygnus columbianus Bewick's Swan	W	1995	479	479	A	A4i, B1i, B2, C2, C6
Cygnus cygnus Whooper Swan	W	1994	471	471	A	B1i, B3, C2
Anser brachyrhynchus Pink-footed Goose	P	1994	30,000	30,000	A	A4i, B1i, C3
Anser anser Greylag Goose	P	1994	22,000	22,000	B	A4i, B1i, C3
Anas acuta Pintail	N	1994	3,000	3,000	B	B1i, C3

An exceptionally important staging area, particularly for *Anser brachyrhynchus* and *A. anser*. *Botaurus stellaris*, *Branta leucopsis*, *Circus aeruginosus* and *Lanius collurio*, listed on Annex I of the EC Birds Directive, breed at the site.

■ Protection status
National Partial **International** High
4,270 ha of IBA covered by Ramsar Site (Fiilsø, 4,320 ha). 1,994 ha of IBA covered by Special Protection Area (Fiilsø, 1,994 ha).

■ Conservation issues

Threats Abandonment/reduction of land management (B), Agricultural intensification/expansion (B), Unsustainable exploitation (C)

In 1994 the first phase of a large restoration project to remove invasive *Salix*, *Pinus mugo* and other trees was implemented; the water-level was raised by 30 cm and further increases are planned.

Vadehavet (Wadden Sea) — A4i, A4iii, B1i, B2, B3, C2, C3, C4, C6 — 057
Admin region Ribe, Sønderjylland
Coordinates 55°16′N 8°32′E
Altitude (-18)–1 m **Area** 115,850 ha

■ Site description
The Wadden Sea is characterized by intertidal mud and sandflats between the mainland and the barrier islands. The flats are traversed by deeper water channels. There are coastal marshes grazed by sheep and cattle and reclaimed coastal marshland behind the dykes with permanent grass and some arable land.

Habitats Wetland (25%; mudflat/sandflat), Marine areas (75%; sea inlet/coastal features)
Land-use Unknown

■ Birds

Species	Season	Year	Pop min	Pop max	Acc	Criteria
Anser brachyrhynchus Pink-footed Goose	N	1994	10,000	10,000	B	A4i, B1i, C3
Branta leucopsis Barnacle Goose	N	1994	7,700	7,700	B	A4i, B1i, C2
Branta bernicla Brent Goose	N	1994	15,000	15,000	B	A4i, B1i, C3
Tadorna tadorna Shelduck	N	1994	31,200	31,200	B	A4i, B1i, C3
Anas penelope Wigeon	N	1994	48,700	48,700	B	A4i, B1i, C3
Anas acuta Pintail	N	1994	4,000	4,000	B	B1i, C3
Somateria mollissima Eider	N	1994	42,600	42,600	B	A4i, B1i, C3
Melanitta nigra Common Scoter	N	1994	35,000	35,000	B	A4i, B1i, C3
Haematopus ostralegus Oystercatcher	N	1994	31,000	31,000	B	A4i, B1i, C3
Recurvirostra avosetta Avocet	B	1991	1,066	1,066	A	A4i, B1i, B3, C2, C6
Recurvirostra avosetta Avocet	P	1994	6,500	6,500	B	A4i, B1i, C2
Pluvialis apricaria Golden Plover	N	1994	43,600	43,600	B	A4i, B1i, C2
Pluvialis squatarola Grey Plover	N	1994	5,500	5,500	B	A4i, B1i, C3
Calidris canutus Knot	N	1994	24,100	24,100	B	A4i, B1i, C3
Calidris alba Sanderling	N	1994	3,000	3,000	B	A4i, B1i, C3
Calidris alpina Dunlin	N	1994	365,000	365,000	B	A4i, B1i, C3
Limosa lapponica Bar-tailed Godwit	N	1994	35,400	35,400	—	A4i, B1i, C2
Tringa totanus Redshank	B	1991	514	514	—	B2
Tringa totanus Redshank	N	1994	1,680	1,680	B	B1i, C3
Sterna albifrons Little Tern	B	1991	43	43	A	B2, C6

An extremely important staging area: at least 20 waterbird species congregate in internationally important numbers in winter or on passage, totalling hundreds of thousands of birds. *Circus aeruginosus*, *C. pygargus*, *Recurvirostra avosetta*, *Philomachus pugnax*, *Sterna hirundo*, *S. paradisaea* and *S. albifrons*, listed on Annex I of the EC Birds Directive, breed at the site, some in large numbers.

■ Protection status
National High **International** High
115,850 ha of IBA covered by Special Protection Area (Vadehavet, 115,850 ha). 115,850 ha of IBA covered by Ramsar Site (Vadehavet (Wadden Sea), 140,830 ha).

■ Conservation issues

Threats Aquaculture/fisheries (B), Dredging/canalization (B), Industrialization/urbanization (B), Recreation/tourism (B), Unsustainable exploitation (B)

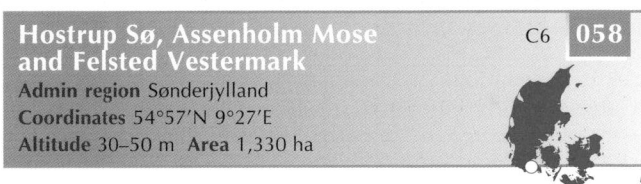

Hostrup Sø, Assenholm Mose and Felsted Vestermark — C6 — 058
Admin region Sønderjylland
Coordinates 54°57′N 9°27′E
Altitude 30–50 m **Area** 1,330 ha

■ Site description
A large lake surrounded by meadows, heathland, bog and forest. Percentage cover of habitat and land-use types are poorly known.

Habitats Scrub (15%; heathland), Grassland (25%; humid grassland), Wetland (30%; standing fresh water), Artificial landscape (30%; arable land; forestry plantation)
Land-use Agriculture (20%), Forestry (15%), Military (30%), Unknown (45%)

■ Birds

Species	Season	Year	Pop min	Pop max	Acc	Criteria
Haliaeetus albicilla White-tailed Eagle	R	1996	1	1	A	C6

Several species listed on Annex I of the EC Birds Directive, including *Botaurus stellaris*, *Circus aeruginosus*, *Haliaeetus albicilla*, *Bubo bubo* and *Lanius collurio*, have been recorded breeding at the site but no recent data are available.

■ Protection status
National None **International** High
1,330 ha of IBA covered by Special Protection Area (Hostrup Sø, 1,330 ha).

■ Conservation issues

Threats Abandonment/reduction of land management (A), Agricultural intensification/expansion (C), Intensified forest management (B), Recreation/tourism (C)

Formerly Hostrup lake was an important botanical locality but nutrient pollution and the abandonment of grazing have resulted in the loss of several rare species.

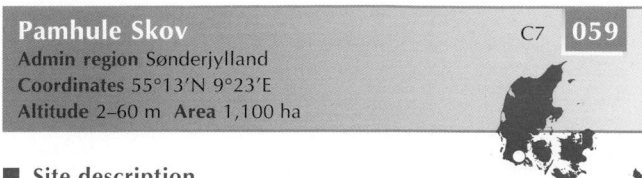

Pamhule Skov
C7 | 059

Admin region Sønderjylland
Coordinates 55°13′N 9°23′E
Altitude 2–60 m **Area** 1,100 ha

■ Site description

An area of good quality *Fagus* forest on fertile soils with meadows and a small lake.

Habitats Forest and woodland (60%; broadleaved deciduous forest), Grassland (5%; humid grassland), Wetland (10%; standing fresh water), Artificial landscape (10%; forestry plantation), Unknown (20%)
Land-use Forestry (70%), Unknown (30%)

■ Birds

The site was designated as a Special Protection Area based on breeding populations of *Pernis apivorus* and *Alcedo atthis*. Recent data are unavailable.

■ Protection status

National Unknown **International** High
1,100 ha of IBA covered by Special Protection Area (Pamhule Skov, 1,100 ha).

■ Conservation issues

Threats Intensified forest management (C)

An ongoing restoration project includes plans to re-establish small wetlands and to improve the forest through non-intensive management, and by prohibiting logging in some areas.

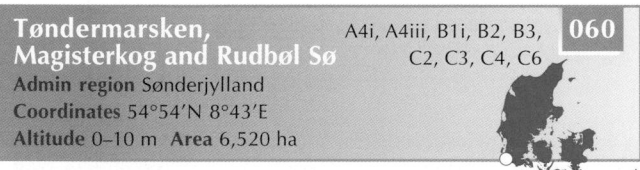

Tøndermarsken, Magisterkog and Rudbøl Sø
A4i, A4iii, B1i, B2, B3, C2, C3, C4, C6 | 060

Admin region Sønderjylland
Coordinates 54°54′N 8°43′E
Altitude 0–10 m **Area** 6,520 ha

■ Site description

A large area of reclaimed land with meadows along the Vidåen river. In the western part a saltwater lagoon is maintained by pumping in seawater. The inner (eastern) parts are mainly agricultural and the outer (western) parts predominantly pasture. There is also some standing freshwater, notably Rudbøl Sø, and reedbeds.

Habitats Wetland (30%; saltmarsh; coastal lagoon), Artificial landscape (70%)
Land-use Agriculture (85%), Nature conservation/research (15%)

■ Birds

Species	Season	Year	Pop min	Pop max	Acc	Criteria
Cygnus columbianus Bewick's Swan	N	1993	332	332	A	A4i, B1i, B2, C2
Cygnus cygnus Whooper Swan	N	1994	941	941	A	A4i, B1i, C2
Branta leucopsis Barnacle Goose	N	1997	30,000	30,000	A	A4i, B1i, C2, C6
Branta bernicla Brent Goose	N	1994	6,800	6,800	A	A4i, B1i, C3
Tadorna tadorna Shelduck	N	1994	6,500	6,500	A	A4i, B1i, C3
Anas acuta Pintail	N	1994	900	900	A	B1i, C3
Recurvirostra avosetta Avocet	B	1994	248	482	A	B1i, B3, C2
Recurvirostra avosetta Avocet	P	1994	1,300	1,300	A	B1i, C2
Pluvialis apricaria Golden Plover	P	1994	25,000	25,000	—	A4i, B1i, C2
Calidris canutus Knot	P	1994	21,300	21,300	A	A4i, B1i, C3
Calidris alpina Dunlin	P	1994	62,000	62,000	A	A4i, B1i, C3
Limosa limosa Black-tailed Godwit	B	1994	110	125	A	B2
Limosa lapponica Bar-tailed Godwit	P	1994	4,600	4,600	A	A4i, B1i, C2
Tringa erythropus Spotted Redshank	P	1994	1,270	1,270	A	A4i, B1i, C3
Chlidonias niger Black Tern	B	1994	36	41	A	C2, C6

This is a very important staging area for several waterbirds, with total numbers exceeding 20,000 individuals. Several species listed on Annex I of the EC Birds Directive breed at the site, including *Botaurus stellaris, Ciconia ciconia, Circus aeruginosus, Circus pygargus, Porzana porzana, Recurvirostra avosetta, Sterna hirundo, S. paradisaea, S. albifrons, Chlidonias niger* (the most important site in Denmark for this species) and *Luscinia svecica*.

■ Protection status

National Partial **International** High
6,520 ha of IBA covered by Special Protection Area (Vidåen, Tøndermarsken and Saltvandsøen, 6,520 ha).

■ Conservation issues

Threats Abandonment/reduction of land management (A), Agricultural intensification/expansion (A), Drainage (A), Unsustainable exploitation (A)

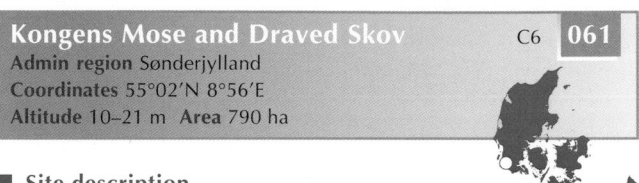

Kongens Mose and Draved Skov
C6 | 061

Admin region Sønderjylland
Coordinates 55°02′N 8°56′E
Altitude 10–21 m **Area** 790 ha

■ Site description

A raised bog and forest, including highly valuable areas of mature (nearly primary) *Fagus, Quercus* and *Tilia* woodland.

Habitats Forest and woodland (45%; broadleaved deciduous forest), Scrub (20%; heathland), Wetland (35%; standing fresh water; raised bog)
Land-use Forestry (40%), Nature conservation/research (70%)

■ Birds

Species	Season	Year	Pop min	Pop max	Acc	Criteria
Tringa glareola Wood Sandpiper	B	1996	3	6	A	C6
Chlidonias niger Black Tern	B	1996	10	10	A	C6

Numbers of breeding birds have declined at this site over the last 20 years and *Tetrao tetrix* has not bred since the 1980s. Nevertheless the site remains an important area for heathland and wetland birds and more recently some species' populations have started to increase as a result of habitat restoration efforts. Several species listed on Annex I of the EC Birds Directive breed at the site, including *Pernis apivorus, Circus aeruginosus, C. pygargus, Tringa glareola, Chlidonias niger, Asio flammeus, Dryocopus martius* and *Lanius collurio*.

■ Protection status

National Partial **International** High
790 ha of IBA covered by Special Protection Area (Kongens Mose and Draved Skov, 790 ha).

■ Conservation issues

Threats Abandonment/reduction of land management (C), Other (C)

A habitat restoration project was initiated in 1992. Airborne nutrient pollution ('Other' threat) is detrimentally affecting wetland areas. Logging is prohibited in all forest areas.

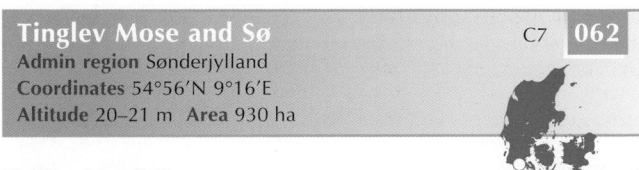

Tinglev Mose and Sø
C7 | 062

Admin region Sønderjylland
Coordinates 54°56′N 9°16′E
Altitude 20–21 m **Area** 930 ha

■ Site description

A partly drained lake with large areas of marshland. The IBA consists of two discrete parts.

Habitats Scrub (10%; scrub), Grassland (65%; humid grassland), Unknown (20%)
Land-use Unknown

■ Birds

The site was designated as a Special Protection Area on the basis of two breeding species listed on Annex I of the EC Birds Directive; *Circus aeruginosus* (no longer breeding) and *C. pygargus* (breeding in some years).

■ **Protection status**
National Partial **International** High
930 ha of IBA covered by Special Protection Area (Tinglev Sø, 930 ha).

■ **Conservation issues**

Threats Abandonment/reduction of land management (B), Drainage (B), Recreation/tourism (B)

Sønder Ådal
C7 063
Admin region Sønderjylland
Coordinates 54°54′N 9°03′E
Altitude 4–11 m **Area** 2,690 ha

■ **Site description**
A small river valley with meadows and marshes. Habitat and land-use data are subjective estimates.

Habitats Grassland (30%; humid grassland), Artificial landscape (70%; arable land; forestry plantation)
Land-use Agriculture (90%), Unknown (10%)

■ **Birds**
The site was designated as a Special Protection Area on the basis of breeding populations of five species listed on Annex I of the EC Birds Directive. With the possible exception of *Botaurus stellaris*, these species no longer breed.

■ **Protection status**
National Unknown **International** High
2,690 ha of IBA covered by Special Protection Area (Sønder Ådal, 2,690 ha).

■ **Conservation issues**

Threats Abandonment/reduction of land management (A), Agricultural intensification/expansion (B)

Flensborg Fjord and Nybøl Nor
A4iii, C4 064
Admin region Sønderjylland
Coordinates 54°50′N 9°35′E
Altitude (-22)–15 m **Area** 3,350 ha

■ **Site description**
The IBA consists of two parts: the marine area of Flensborg Fjord, and Nybøl Nor, a shallow fjord connected by a very narrow strip of open water to Flensborg Fjord.

Habitats Wetland (5%; saltmarsh), Marine areas (100%; sea inlet/coastal features)
Land-use Unknown

■ **Birds**
This is an important site for wintering and passage waterbirds, with numbers exceeding 20,000 individuals in harsh winters. Five species were present in internationally important numbers in 1983 but recent data from January 1991 are much lower: it is possible that this is due to warmer winters in recent years.

■ **Protection status**
National None **International** High
3,350 ha of IBA covered by Special Protection Area (Flensborg Fjord and Nybøl Nor, 3,350 ha).

■ **Conservation issues**

Threats Agricultural intensification/expansion (C), Industrialization/urbanization (A), Recreation/tourism (B)

Rømø
A4i, A4iii, B1i, B2, C2, C3, C4 065
Admin region Sønderjylland
Coordinates 55°03′N 8°32′E
Altitude 0–20 m **Area** 7,010 ha

■ **Site description**
Rømø is an island in the Wadden Sea, surrounded by extensive stretches (1-3 km wide) of flat, very sparsely vegetated sand just above the high tide line. Terrestrial vegetation consists of dunes, heathland, marshes, meadows and small plantations, mainly of *Pinus mugo*.

Habitats Scrub (15%; heathland), Grassland (20%; humid grassland), Wetland (55%; sand-dunes/sand beach), Unknown (10%)
Land-use Unknown

■ **Birds**

Species		Season	Year	Pop min	Pop max	Acc	Criteria
Branta bernicla	Brent Goose	P	1983	6,000	6,000	A	A4i, B1i, C3
Anas penelope	Wigeon	P	1983	28,000	28,000	—	A4i, B1i, C3
Anas crecca	Teal	P	1983	11,000	11,000	—	B1i, C3
Anas acuta	Pintail	P	1983	5,000	5,000	—	B1i, C3
Anas clypeata	Shoveler	P	1983	2,000	2,000	A	B1i, C3
Haematopus ostralegus	Oystercatcher	P	1983	13,800	13,800	A	A4i, B1i, C3
Calidris alpina	Dunlin	P	1983	32,500	32,500	A	A4i, B1i, C3
Limosa lapponica	Bar-tailed Godwit	P	1983	5,400	5,400	A	A4i, B1i, C2
Tringa totanus	Redshank	B	1996	128	128	A	B2
Tringa totanus	Redshank	P	1983	2,200	2,200	A	B1i, C3

Several species listed on Annex I of the EC Birds Directive are believed to breed at the site, including *Circus aeruginosus, C. cyaneus, C. pygargus, Recurvirostra avosetta, Gelochelidon nilotica, Sterna hirundo* and *S. paradisaea*, although there are no recent data available for breeding gulls and terns.

■ **Protection status**
National Partial **International** High
7,010 ha of IBA covered by Special Protection Area (Rømø, 7,010 ha).
7,010 ha of IBA covered by Ramsar Site (Vadehavet (Wadden Sea), 140,830 ha).

■ **Conservation issues**

Threats Abandonment/reduction of land management (A), Recreation/tourism (A), Unsustainable exploitation (C)

Lindet Skov, Hønning Plantage, Lovrup Skov and Skrøp
C7 066
Admin region Sønderjylland
Coordinates 55°09′N 8°54′E
Altitude 30–50 m **Area** 2,340 ha

■ **Site description**
Mainly deciduous woodland and conifer plantations, with smaller areas of heath and bog.

Habitats Forest and woodland (30%; broadleaved deciduous forest), Scrub (10%; heathland), Grassland (10%; humid grassland), Artificial landscape (55%; arable land; forestry plantation)
Land-use Agriculture (20%), Forestry (70%), Nature conservation/research (10%)

■ **Birds**
Pernis apivorus, Tringa glareola, Bubo bubo and *Dryocopus martius*, listed on Annex I of the EC Birds Directive, breed at the site.

■ **Protection status**
National Low **International** High
2,340 ha of IBA covered by Special Protection Area (Lindet Skov, 2,340 ha).

■ **Conservation issues**

Threats Abandonment/reduction of land management (C), Intensified forest management (C)

Ballum og Husum Enge, Kamper strandenge   067
A4i, A4iii, B1i, C2, C3, C4

Admin region Sønderjylland
Coordinates 55°08′N 8°43′E
Altitude 0–5 m **Area** 4,280 ha

■ Site description
Marshland lying behind dykes with several canals and smaller streams. The area is mainly used for cattle-grazing.

Habitats Grassland (85%; humid grassland), Unknown (15%)
Land-use Agriculture (85%), Unknown (15%)

■ Birds

Species	Season	Year	Pop min	Pop max	Acc	Criteria
Anser brachyrhynchus Pink-footed Goose	P	1989	7,200	7,200	A	A4i, B1i, C3
Branta leucopsis Barnacle Goose	P	1989	2,200	2,200	A	A4i, B1i, C2
Branta bernicla Brent Goose	P	1989	5,050	5,050	A	A4i, B1i, C3
Anas crecca Teal	P	1989	4,165	4,165	A	B1i, C3

This is an important staging area for *Anser brachyrhynchus*, *Branta leucopsis* and *B. bernicla*, with total numbers of waterbirds exceeding 20,000 individuals. Most breeding birds declined during 1980–1990; more recent information is not available.

■ Protection status
National High **International** High
4,280 ha of IBA covered by Special Protection Area (Ballum and Husum Enge, Kamper Strandenge, 4,280 ha).

■ Conservation issues
Threats Agricultural intensification/expansion (A), Industrialization/urbanization (C), Unsustainable exploitation (A)

Forests near Gråsten   C7   068
Admin region Sønderjylland
Coordinates 54°56′N 9°32′E
Altitude 10–55 m **Area** 870 ha

■ Site description
A deciduous forest in an undulating landscape, with some conifer plantations and arable land.

Habitats Forest and woodland (50%; broadleaved deciduous forest), Artificial landscape (40%; forestry plantation), Unknown (10%)
Land-use Agriculture (5%), Forestry (85%), Tourism/recreation (10%)

■ Birds
Designated as a Special Protection Area in 1983 based on breeding populations of *Pernis apivorus*, *Circus aeruginosus* and *Alcedo atthis*, listed on Annex I of the EC Birds Directive. No recent data are available.

■ Protection status
National Partial **International** High
870 ha of IBA covered by Special Protection Area (Forest near Gråsten, 870 ha).

■ Conservation issues
Threats Intensified forest management (C)

Logging is prohibited in some areas.

Kogsbøl and Skast Mose   C7   069
Admin region Sønderjylland
Coordinates 55°03′N 8°42′E
Altitude 3–4 m **Area** 560 ha

■ Site description
An area of moist heathland, meadows and *Salix* and *Betula* scrub. The landscape is heavily marked due to former peat extraction.

Habitats Scrub (20%; scrub), Wetland (70%), Artificial landscape (10%; arable land)
Land-use Unknown

■ Birds
Formerly six species listed on Annex I of the EC Birds Directive bred but these were not recorded during the most recent surveys in 1994.

■ Protection status
National Partial **International** High
560 ha of IBA covered by Special Protection Area (Kogsbøl and Skast Mose, 560 ha).

■ Conservation issues
Threats Abandonment/reduction of land management (A), Agricultural intensification/expansion (A), Drainage (C)

Frøslev Plantage and Frøslev Mose   C6   070
Admin region Sønderjylland
Coordinates 54°49′N 9°14′E
Altitude 20–30 m **Area** 1,700 ha

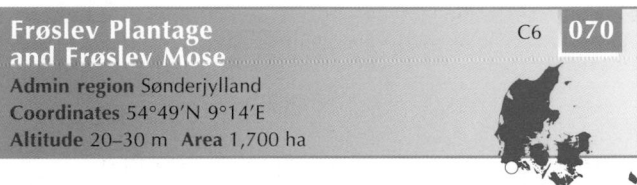

■ Site description
A heathland with areas of bog and a small patch of *Quercus* scrub and forest. The area is contiguous with Jardelunder Moor in Germany.

Habitats Artificial landscape (70%; forestry plantation), Forest and woodland (5%; broadleaved deciduous forest), Grassland (5%; humid grassland), Wetland (20%; raised bog; water-fringe vegetation)
Land-use Forestry (75%), Nature conservation/research (25%)

■ Birds

Species	Season	Year	Pop min	Pop max	Acc	Criteria
Lanius collurio Red-backed Shrike	B	1994	51	55	A	C6

The site holds one of the densest populations of *Lanius collurio* in Denmark. Several additional species listed on Annex I of the EC Birds Directive bred at the site in 1983 but these are no longer present, although it is hoped that *Tringa glareola* and *Chlidonias niger* will recolonize the site following habitat restoration efforts.

■ Protection status
National Partial **International** Partial
410 ha of IBA covered by Special Protection Area (Frøslev Mose, 410 ha).

■ Conservation issues
Threats Abandonment/reduction of land management (B)

A habitat restoration project was initiated in 1987.

Sydfynske Ø-hav   071
A4i, A4iii, B1i, B2, B3, C2, C3, C6

Admin region Fyn
Coordinates 55°00′N 10°20′E
Altitude (-20)–15 m **Area** 38,440 ha

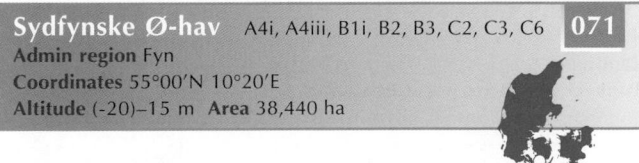

■ Site description
A shallow archipelagic area of sea with shoals and many, generally uninhabited islands, with saltmarsh, reedbeds and small lakes. There is scattered habitation and cultivation on a few islands.

Habitats Wetland (5%; saltmarsh), Marine areas (85%; sea inlet/coastal features), Unknown (10%)
Land-use Agriculture (50%), Hunting (50%), Nature conservation/research (10%)

■ Birds
This is an important staging area for many waterbirds (more than 20,000 waterbirds in total), although recent numbers are lower than

in 1983, with the exception of *Mergus serrator* which has increased. Fluctuations may largely be the result of variability in winter harshness. Several species listed on Annex I of the EC Birds Directive breed at the site, including *Botaurus stellaris, Circus aeruginosus, Recurvirostra avosetta, Sterna sandvicensis, S. paradisaea* and *S. albifrons.*

Species		Season	Year	Pop min	Pop max	Acc	Criteria
Cygnus cygnus	Whooper Swan	W	1996	600	600	A	B1i, B3, C2
Branta bernicla	Brent Goose	N	1994	4,000	4,000	A	A4i, B1i, C3
Aythya fuligula	Tufted Duck	N	1994	13,100	20,000	B	A4i, B1i, C3
Somateria mollissima	Eider	N	1994	15,000	15,000	—	B1i, C3
Bucephala clangula	Goldeneye	N	1994	3,050	3,050	—	B1i, C3
Mergus serrator		N	1994	1,500	4,500	A	A4i, B1i, C3
Red-breasted Merganser							
Fulica atra	Coot	N	1994	15,000	—	—	B1i, C3
Recurvirostra avosetta	Avocet	B	1996	170	180	A	B3
Larus canus	Common Gull	B	1996	1,750	1,750	A	B2
Sterna paradisaea	Arctic Tern	B	1996	350	350	A	C6

■ **Protection status**
National Partial **International** High
38,440 ha of IBA covered by Special Protection Area (Sydfynske Øhav, 38,440 ha).

■ **Conservation issues**

Threats Aquaculture/fisheries (C), Recreation/tourism (B), Unsustainable exploitation (B)

Marstal Bugt and the coast of south-west Langeland   B1iv, C5   **072**
Admin region Fyn
Coordinates 54°47′N 10°40′E
Altitude (-16)–20 m **Area** 4,980 ha

■ **Site description**
A shallow coastal area surrounded by cultivated fields. Some former sea inlets have been dammed and converted to freshwater lakes and meadows. The IBA includes southern Langeland, comprising clay cliffs, broadleaved forest (including non-intensively managed forest dominated by *Corylus* and *Carpinus*), a brackish lagoon, chalk-rich meadows and agricultural land.

Habitats Forest and woodland (broadleaved deciduous forest), Grassland (5%; humid grassland), Wetland (5%; standing fresh water; coastal lagoon; water-fringe vegetation), Marine areas (65%; sea inlet/coastal features), Artificial landscape (arable land)
Land-use Agriculture (25%), Forestry, Nature conservation/research (5%), Unknown (70%)

■ **Birds**
Southern Langeland is an important bottleneck site for raptors during autumn migration. Numbers for the 1993 to 1996 period average 11,055 birds per season (minimum 7,293, maximum 15,896), with large annual fluctuations being the result of variable prevailing winds, and changes in observer coverage. Species of global conservation concern that do not meet IBA criteria: *Haliaeetus albicilla* (max. 5, passage). *Botaurus stellaris* and *Circus aeruginosus,* listed on Annex I of the EC Birds Directive, breed at the site.

■ **Protection status**
National Low **International** High
4,980 ha of IBA covered by Special Protection Area (Marstal Bugt and land areas on Langeland, 4,980 ha).

■ **Conservation issues**

Threats Abandonment/reduction of land management (C), Agricultural intensification/expansion (C), Recreation/tourism (C), Unsustainable exploitation (B)

Two small parts of the IBA are reserves owned by BirdLife Denmark. Two small forest areas are also protected through non-intensive management systems.

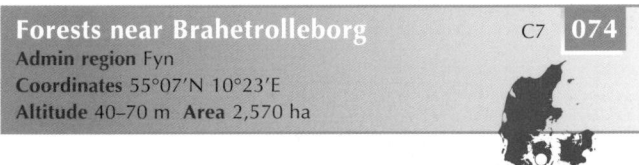

Vresen and sea area between Fyn and Langeland   A4iii, B1i, C3, C4   **073**
Admin region Fyn
Coordinates 55°10′N 10°50′E
Altitude (-10)–2 m **Area** 3,470 ha

■ **Site description**
Vresen is a small islet with a little vegetation, surrounded by shallow sea areas.

Habitats Marine areas (100%; sea inlet/coastal features)
Land-use Unknown (100%)

■ **Birds**

Species		Season	Year	Pop min	Pop max	Acc	Criteria
Somateria mollissima	Eider	W	1993	7,000	7,000	—	B1i, C3

This is an important site for wintering *Somateria mollissima*; although numbers fell in the early 1990s due to siltation of mussel banks caused by the construction of the Great Belt Bridge, numbers in the Great Belt area as a whole seem to have recovered.

■ **Protection status**
National Low **International** High
3,470 ha of IBA covered by Special Protection Area (Vresen and surrounding sea areas, 3,470 ha).

■ **Conservation issues**

Threats Aquaculture/fisheries (C), Dredging/canalization (B), Unsustainable exploitation (B)

Forests near Brahetrolleborg   C7   **074**
Admin region Fyn
Coordinates 55°07′N 10°23′E
Altitude 40–70 m **Area** 2,570 ha

■ **Site description**
Forests (mainly deciduous) around a large eutrophic lake. Formerly the presence of several smaller areas of raised bogs and similar vegetation types were recorded in the area but no recent information is available. Habitat data is incomplete but it is believed that the forest and woodland classification given for this site also includes some coniferous forestry plantations.

Habitats Forest and woodland (75%), Wetland (10%; standing fresh water), Artificial landscape (15%)
Land-use Agriculture (10%), Forestry (75%), Unknown (15%)

■ **Birds**
Pernis apivorus, listed on Annex I of the EC Birds Directive, breeds at the site. Species of global conservation concern that do not meet IBA criteria: *Haliaeetus albicilla* (max. 4, non-breeding).

■ **Protection status**
National Partial **International** High
2,570 ha of IBA covered by Special Protection Area (Brændegårdssøen, Nørresø and surroundings, 2,570 ha).

■ **Conservation issues**

Threats Abandonment/reduction of land management (C), Intensified forest management (B), Unsustainable exploitation (B)

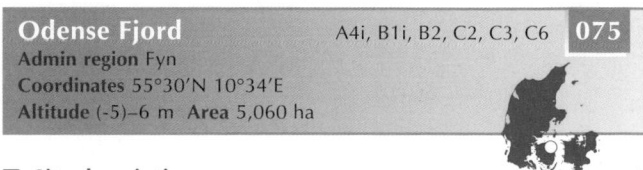

Odense Fjord   A4i, B1i, B2, C2, C3, C6   **075**
Admin region Fyn
Coordinates 55°30′N 10°34′E
Altitude (-5)–6 m **Area** 5,060 ha

■ **Site description**
A shallow fjord with shoals and banks. Islets and coastal areas support

saltmarsh, forest and agricultural land, and smaller areas of plantation and heathland.

Habitats Wetland (10%; saltmarsh), Marine areas (85%; sea inlet/coastal features), Artificial landscape (5%; arable land)
Land-use Agriculture (10%), Unknown (90%)

■ **Birds**

Species	Season	Year	Pop min	Pop max	Acc	Criteria
Cygnus olor Mute Swan	N	1994	3,700	3,700	A	A4i, B1i, C3
Cygnus cygnus Whooper Swan	N	1994	300	300	—	B1i, C2
Aythya marila Scaup	W	1994	2,075	2,075	—	B2
Pluvialis apricaria Golden Plover	P	1996	10,000	10,000	—	B1i, C2
Sterna sandvicensis Sandwich Tern	B	1994	300	300	A	B2, C6

Numbers of wintering *Cygnus olor* and *Branta bernicla* have decreased markedly since 1980 because of reductions in eel-grass *Zostera*, on which both species feed. *Circus aeruginosus*, *Recurvirostra avosetta*, *Sterna sandvicensis* and *S. paradisaea*, listed on Annex I of the EC Birds Directive, breed at the site.

■ **Protection status**
National Partial **International** High
5,060 ha of IBA covered by Special Protection Area (Odense Fjord, 5,060 ha).

■ **Conservation issues**

Threats Abandonment/reduction of land management (C), Agricultural intensification/expansion (A), Aquaculture/fisheries (C), Industrialization/urbanization (B), Recreation/tourism (B), Unsustainable exploitation (C)

Access to 13 of the islands and islets is prohibited during the breeding season.

Nærå coast and Æbelø area
A4i, B1i, C3 **076**
Admin region Fyn
Coordinates 55°36′N 10°13′E
Altitude (-8)–24 m **Area** 13,060 ha

■ **Site description**
A shallow sea area with islands and islets holding saltmarsh, and drained and cultivated areas with scattered habitation. Æbelø also supports smaller areas of woodland including some highly valuable old-growth *Fagus*-dominated forests with other species admixed (*Quercus robur*, *Tilia cordata*, *Tilia platyphyllus* (only site in Denmark), and *Ilex aquifolium*).

Habitats Forest and woodland (5%; broadleaved deciduous forest), Wetland (5%; saltmarsh), Marine areas (75%; sea inlet/coastal features), Artificial landscape (15%; arable land)
Land-use Agriculture (70%), Unknown (30%)

■ **Birds**

Species	Season	Year	Pop min	Pop max	Acc	Criteria
Phalacrocorax carbo Cormorant	B	1994	2,723	2,723	A	A4i, B1i, C3

Circus aeruginosus, *Recurvirostra avosetta*, *Sterna sandvicensis*, *S. paradisaea* and *S. albifrons*, listed on Annex I of the EC Birds Directive, breed at the site. Numbers of wintering birds have for unknown reasons decreased since the site was designated as a Special Protection Area.

■ **Protection status**
National None **International** High
13,060 ha of IBA covered by Ramsar Site (Nærå coast and Æbelø area, 13,800 ha). 13,060 ha of IBA covered by Special Protection Area (Æbelø and the coast near Nærå, 13,060 ha).

■ **Conservation issues**

Threats Abandonment/reduction of land management (A), Agricultural intensification/expansion (B), Recreation/tourism (B), Unsustainable exploitation (B)

Romsø and Hindsholm peninsula
A4iii, C4 **077**
Admin region Fyn
Coordinates 55°30′N 10°50′E
Altitude 0–17 m **Area** 3,490 ha

■ **Site description**
The site encompasses the Hindsholm peninsula, Romsø island and the surrounding sea area. Romsø island is uninhabited and has saltmarsh and mixed deciduous woodland including mature stands of *Fagus*, *Quercus* and *Tilia* together with *Alnus* carr and small patches of agricultural land. The island of Fyn is covered in saltmarsh.

Habitats Wetland (5%), Marine areas (95%; sea inlet/coastal features)
Land-use Unknown (100%)

■ **Birds**
In some years high numbers of seaducks (*Somateria mollissima*, *Melanita fusca* and *M. nigra*) occur at the site.

■ **Protection status**
National Low **International** High
3,490 ha of IBA covered by Special Protection Area (Romsø and the south coast of Hindsholm, 3,490 ha).

■ **Conservation issues**

Threats Recreation/tourism (C)

Replanting on Romsø is permitted, but only with indigenous tree species.

Arreskov Sø
C6 **078**
Admin region Fyn
Coordinates 55°05′N 10°20′E
Altitude 40–70 m **Area** 660 ha

■ **Site description**
Freshwater lake surrounded by forest and agricultural land. Habitat data are incomplete.

Habitats Forest and woodland (15%), Wetland (70%; standing fresh water), Artificial landscape (15%; arable land)
Land-use Agriculture (15%), Forestry (15%), Unknown (70%)

■ **Birds**

Species	Season	Year	Pop min	Pop max	Acc	Criteria
Haliaeetus albicilla White-tailed Eagle	R	1997	1	1	A	C6

Circus aeruginosus and *Haliaeetus albicilla*, listed on Annex I of the EC Birds Directive, breed at the site.

■ **Protection status**
National High **International** High
660 ha of IBA covered by Special Protection Area (Arreskov Sø, 660 ha).

■ **Conservation issues**

Threats Agricultural intensification/expansion (B), Intensified forest management (C), Unsustainable exploitation (C)

Ertholmene east of Bornholm
C7 **079**
Admin region Bornholm
Coordinates 55°19′N 15°11′E
Altitude (-15)–11 m **Area** 1,257 ha

■ **Site description**
A sea area off Bornholm containing rocky islands with cliffs. Two islands are inhabited.

Habitats Marine areas (70%; open sea), Rocky areas (30%; rock stacks/islets)
Land-use Military (100%), Nature conservation/research (100%), Tourism/recreation (100%)

■ Birds
The site is designated as a Special Protection Area because it is the only known Danish site with breeding *Alca torda* (570 pairs) and *Uria aalge* (2,000 pairs), although numbers do not reach C3 thresholds. It is also important for breeding *Somateria mollissima* (3,000 pairs), but numbers are below the C3 threshold.

■ Protection status
National High **International** High
1,257 ha of IBA covered by Ramsar Site (Ertholmene Islands (east of Bornholm), 1,257 ha). 1,257 ha of IBA covered by Special Protection Area (Ertholmene near Bornholm, 1,300 ha).

■ Conservation issues

Threats Aquaculture/fisheries (B), Recreation/tourism (C)

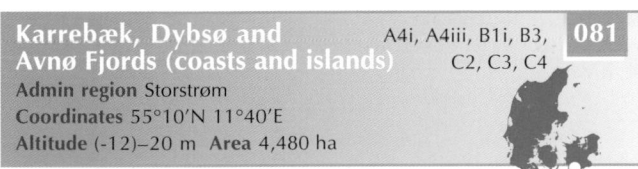

Almindingen
C6 080

Admin region Bornholm
Coordinates 55°08′N 14°58′E
Altitude 40–162 m **Area** 6,090 ha

■ Site description
Large plantations (coniferous and deciduous) on former heathland with glades and many, mostly small, wetlands with bogs and water-fringe vegetation.

Habitats Wetland (10%; standing fresh water), Artificial landscape (85%; forestry plantation)
Land-use Unknown (100%)

■ Birds

Species		Season	Year	Pop min	Pop max	Acc	Criteria
Aegolius funereus	Tengmalm's Owl	B	1995	—	2	A	C6
Dryocopus martius	Black Woodpecker	B	1995	7	10	A	C6

The only known breeding site in Denmark for *Aegolius funereus* (max. 2 pairs). Other species listed on Annex I of the EC Birds Directive that breed at the site include *Pernis apivorus, Milvus milvus, Grus grus, Aegolius funereus, Caprimulgus europaeus, Dryocopus martius* and *Lanius collurio*.

■ Protection status
National Low **International** High
6,090 ha of IBA covered by Special Protection Area (Almindingen, 6,090 ha).

■ Conservation issues

Threats Abandonment/reduction of land management (B), Intensified forest management (C)

Karrebæk, Dybsø and Avnø Fjords (coasts and islands)
A4i, A4iii, B1i, B3, C2, C3, C4 081

Admin region Storstrøm
Coordinates 55°10′N 11°40′E
Altitude (-12)–20 m **Area** 4,480 ha

■ Site description
Islands and peninsulas in shallow fjord areas with cultivated land and scattered habitation as well as grasslands, saltmarshes and reedbeds. Marine areas surrounding this IBA (and previously included within it, following Grimmett and Jones 1989) are now included in Smålandsfarvandet (site 118).

Habitats Forest and woodland (10%), Grassland (10%; dry siliceous grassland; humid grassland), Wetland (25%; saltmarsh; water-fringe vegetation), Artificial landscape (55%; arable land)
Land-use Agriculture (70%), Forestry (10%), Military (5%), Unknown (15%)

■ Birds
This is an important site for migrating waterbirds (regularly more than 20,000 individuals present in total). Non-breeding numbers exclude birds from Avnø Fjord and Karrebæksminde Fjord. Several species

---

listed on Annex I of the EC Birds Directive breed at the site including *Circus aeruginosus, Recurvirostra avosetta, Sterna hirundo, S. paradisaea, S. albifrons* and *Lanius collurio*.

Species		Season	Year	Pop min	Pop max	Acc	Criteria
Cygnus olor	Mute Swan	N	1994	5,699	5,699	A	A4i, B1i, C3
Cygnus cygnus	Whooper Swan	N	1993	850	850	A	A4i, B1i, C2
Recurvirostra avosetta	Avocet	B	1995	70	90	A	B3

■ Protection status
National Low **International** High
4,480 ha of IBA covered by Ramsar Site (Karrebæk, Dybsø and Avnø Fjords, 19,200 ha). 4,480 ha of IBA covered by Special Protection Area (Karrebæk, Dybsø and Avnø Fjords, 18,860 ha).

■ Conservation issues

Threats Abandonment/reduction of land management (B), Agricultural intensification/expansion (B), Intensified forest management (C), Unsustainable exploitation (B)

Several areas have additional national protection. Management includes grazing to maintain open habitats.

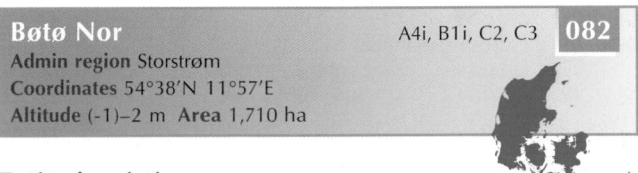

Bøtø Nor
A4i, B1i, C2, C3 082

Admin region Storstrøm
Coordinates 54°38′N 11°57′E
Altitude (-1)–2 m **Area** 1,710 ha

■ Site description
Formerly a fjord but now largely agricultural with the exception of a small lake surrounded by reedbeds (less than 5% of the total area) and meadows. Small plantations, mostly coniferous, are also present.

Habitats Grassland (5%; humid grassland), Artificial landscape (95%; arable land; forestry plantation)
Land-use Agriculture (60%), Forestry (30%), Nature conservation/research (10%)

■ Birds

Species		Season	Year	Pop min	Pop max	Acc	Criteria
Anser anser	Greylag Goose	P	1994	2,000	2,000	A	B1i, C3
Branta leucopsis	Barnacle Goose	N	1994	3,500	3,500	B	A4i, B1i, C2

This is an important staging area for *Anser anser* and *Branta leucopsis*. Several species listed on Annex I of the EC Birds Directive breed at the site, including *Circus aeruginosus, Porzana porzana* and *Lanius collurio*.

■ Protection status
National Low **International** High
1,710 ha of IBA covered by Ramsar Site (Waters between Lolland and Falster including Rødsand, 36,800 ha). 1,710 ha of IBA covered by Special Protection Area (Bøtø Nor, 1,730 ha).

■ Conservation issues

Threats Agricultural intensification/expansion (C), Disturbance to birds (C), Drainage (B), Unsustainable exploitation (C)

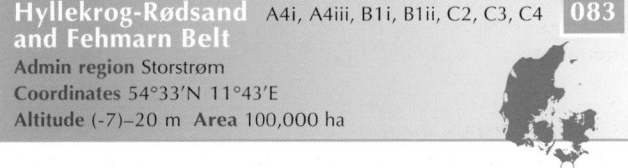

Hyllekrog-Rødsand and Fehmarn Belt
A4i, A4iii, B1i, B1ii, C2, C3, C4 083

Admin region Storstrøm
Coordinates 54°33′N 11°43′E
Altitude (-7)–20 m **Area** 100,000 ha

■ Site description
A sea area with shoals and banks, coastal slopes and uninhabited islands. Some areas are enclosed by dykes. Terrestrial habitats (totalling 5% of the IBA) include broadleaved woodland, saltmarshes, reedbeds, small plantations, agricultural areas, sandflats, dunes and beaches.

Habitats Marine areas (95%; sea inlet/coastal features)
Land-use Unknown (100%)

Birds

Species	Season	Year	Pop min	Pop max	Acc	Criteria
[1,2] *Gavia stellata* Red-throated Diver	W	1993	—	—	—	A4i, B1i, C2
[1,2] *Gavia arctica* Black-throated Diver	W	1993	—	—	—	A4i, B1i, C2
[2] *Podiceps grisegena* Red-necked Grebe	W	1993	200	200	—	B1i, C3
Phalacrocorax carbo Cormorant	N	1989	2,815	2,815	—	B1i, C3
[3,4] *Cygnus olor* Mute Swan	N	1994	13,097	13,097	B	A4i, B1i, C3
Aythya fuligula Tufted Duck	N	1989	22,000	22,000	—	A4i, B1i, C3
[2] *Mergus serrator* Red-breasted Merganser	W	1993	6,500	6,500	—	A4i, B1i, C3
[2] *Cepphus grylle* Black Guillemot	W	1993	700	700	—	B1ii

1. 1,200 *Gavia stellata* and *G. arctica* combined.
2. 1988–1993 average.
3. Partial population estimate.
4. Maximum data for period 1988–1993.

Of high importance for waterbirds (regularly more than 20,000 present in total). Species of global conservation concern that do not meet IBA criteria: *Haliaeetus albicilla* (non-breeding). Several species listed on Annex I of the EC Birds Directive breed at the site, including *Botaurus stellaris, Circus aeruginosus, Recurvirostra avosetta, Sterna sandvicensis, S. hirundo, S. paradisaea* and *S. albifrons*.

Protection status

National Partial **International** Partial
32,970 ha of IBA covered by Special Protection Area (Hyllekrog Rødsand, 32,970 ha). 36,800 ha of IBA covered by Ramsar Site (Waters between Lolland and Falster including Rodsand, 36,800 ha).

Conservation issues

Threats Abandonment/reduction of land management (B), Agricultural intensification/expansion (B), Aquaculture/fisheries (C), Industrialization/urbanization (A), Recreation/tourism (B), Unsustainable exploitation (B)

Ulvsund, Grønsund, Farø Fjord and Fanefjord
A4i, A4iii, B1i, C2, C3 **084**

Admin region Storstrøm
Coordinates 54°55′N 12°00′E
Altitude (-23)–11 m **Area** 8,160 ha

Site description

A shallow sea area with shoals, banks and islands surrounded by saltmarsh and agricultural land.

Habitats Wetland (10%; saltmarsh), Marine areas (90%; sea inlet/coastal features)
Land-use Unknown (100%)

Birds

Species	Season	Year	Pop min	Pop max	Acc	Criteria
Cygnus olor Mute Swan	W	1994	4,200	4,200	B	A4i, B1i, C3
[1] *Cygnus cygnus* Whooper Swan	N	1994	143	143	B	B1i, C2
Aythya fuligula Tufted Duck	N	1994	6,880	6,880	—	B1i, C3

1. Probably much higher numbers occur.

Population data are incomplete but numbers of wintering birds appear to be lower than in 1983 when the site was designated as a Special Protection Area. It is possible that very high numbers only occur in harsh winters, when several more species meet the A4i criterion, and the total number of waterbirds exceeds 20,000 individuals. *Sterna hirundo* and *Sterna paradisaea*, listed on Annex I of the EC Birds Directive, breed at the site.

Protection status

National None **International** High
8,160 ha of IBA covered by Special Protection Area (Ulvsund and Grønsund, 8,160 ha).

Conservation issues

Threats Abandonment/reduction of land management (B), Agricultural intensification/expansion (B), Extraction industry (C), Unsustainable exploitation (B)

Islands in Smålandshavet, north of Lolland
A4i, B1i, C3 **085**

Admin region Storstrøm
Coordinates 54°54′N 11°30′E
Altitude (-8)–10 m **Area** 4,390 ha

Site description

A shallow sea area with several cultivated and inhabited islands and some uninhabited islets with forest, reedbeds and saltmarshes. The majority of forest is plantation, however, tiny but valuable patches of old-growth forest occur. Marine areas surrounding this IBA (and previously included within it following Grimmett and Jones 1989) are included in Smålandsfarvandet (site 118).

Habitats Forest and woodland (5%), Wetland (50%; saltmarsh), Artificial landscape (50%; arable land, forestry plantation)
Land-use Agriculture (60%), Forestry (10%), Unknown (30%)

Birds

Species	Season	Year	Pop min	Pop max	Acc	Criteria
Phalacrocorax carbo Cormorant	B	1994	1,746	1,746	A	A4i, B1i, C3
Cygnus olor Mute Swan	N	1994	9,757	9,757	—	A4i, B1i, C3

Several species listed on Annex I of the EC Birds Directive breed at the site, including *Circus aeruginosus, Recurvirostra avosetta, Philomachus pugnax, Sterna hirundo, S. paradisaea* and *S. albifrons*.

Protection status

National None **International** High
4,390 ha of IBA covered by Ramsar Site (Fejø and Femø Isles (waters south-east of), 32,640 ha). 4,390 ha of IBA covered by Special Protection Area (Smålandshavet north of Lolland, 41,680 ha).

Conservation issues

Threats Abandonment/reduction of land management (C), Agricultural intensification/expansion (B), Unsustainable exploitation (B)

Several smaller areas have additional protection.

Guldborgsund
B1i, C3 **086**

Admin region Storstrøm
Coordinates 54°50′N 11°50′E
Altitude (-8)–6 m **Area** 2,820 ha

Site description

A long, narrow and shallow strait between Lolland and Falster, and a small coastal marsh. Additional habitats (in total less than 10% of the IBA area) include woodlands, arable land, meadows and habitation.

Habitats Wetland (15%; saltmarsh), Marine areas (75%; sea inlet/coastal features), Unknown (10%)
Land-use Agriculture (5%), Forestry (5%), Unknown (90%)

Birds

Species	Season	Year	Pop min	Pop max	Acc	Criteria
[1] *Aythya ferina* Pochard	W	1989	950	950	—	B1i, C3
Aythya fuligula Tufted Duck	W	1989	10,010	10,010	—	B1i, C3

1. Higher numbers in cold winters (1983, 13,000).

Important for wintering waterbirds, with up to four species (*Cygnus olor, Aythya ferina, A. fuligula* and *Mergus merganser*) present in internationally important numbers during harsh winters when the total may exceed 20,000 individuals. More recent data than present in the table are available from 1994, but counts cover only half of the IBA.

Protection status

National Partial **International** High
2,820 ha of IBA covered by Special Protection Area (Guldborgsung, 2,820 ha).

Conservation issues

Threats Recreation/tourism (C), Unsustainable exploitation (C)

Maribo lakes A4i, A4iii, B1i, B2, C2, C3, C4, C6 087
Admin region Storstrøm
Coordinates 54°46'N 11°31'E
Altitude 10–25 m **Area** 3,810 ha

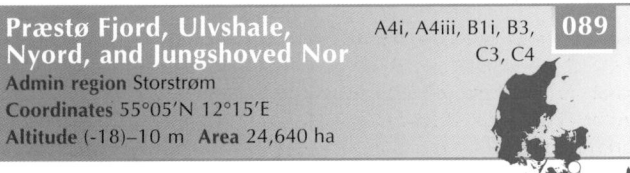

■ Site description
Freshwater lakes with wooded islands and peninsulas. Lake shores have parkland, reedbeds, deciduous forests, meadows, fields and scattered habitations. Artificial landscapes are mainly arable and improved grazing-meadows, and may include some more natural humid grasslands but the extent is unknown. The deciduous forest includes extensive areas of *Alnus* carr, areas of mature *Fagus* and *Quercus* forest, and some conifer plantations.

Habitats Forest and woodland (25%; broadleaved deciduous forest), Wetland (45%; standing fresh water; water-fringe vegetation), Artificial landscape (30%)
Land-use Agriculture (30%), Forestry (25%), Nature conservation/research (100%)

■ Birds

Species	Season	Year	Pop min	Pop max	Acc	Criteria
Phalacrocorax carbo Cormorant	B	1995	2,250	2,250	A	A4i, B1i, C3
Botaurus stellaris Bittern	B	1995	35	35	A	B2, C2, C6
Anser anser Greylag Goose	P	1994	6,700	6,700	A	A4i, B1i, C3
Anas strepera Gadwall	P	1996	328	328	—	B1i, C3
Aythya ferina Pochard	N	1994	15,765	15,765	A	A4i, B1i, C3
Aythya fuligula Tufted Duck	W	1994	23,045	23,045	A	A4i, B1i, C3
Haliaeetus albicilla White-tailed Eagle	B	1997	1	1	A	C6

The most important freshwater area in Denmark for birds and the only Danish freshwater area designated as a Ramsar Site. A very important breeding site for *Botaurus stellaris*. More than 20,000 waterbirds regularly occur on passage. Species of global conservation concern that do not meet IBA criteria: *Haliaeetus albicilla* (1 pair breeding). *Circus aeruginosus* and *Sterna hirundo*, both listed on Annex I of the EC Birds Directive, also breed at the site.

■ Protection status
National Partial **International** High
3,810 ha of IBA covered by Ramsar Site (Maribo lakes, 4,400 ha). 3,810 ha of IBA covered by Special Protection Area (Maribosøerne, 3,810 ha).

■ Conservation issues

Threats Agricultural intensification/expansion (A), Industrialization/urbanization (B), Intensified forest management (B), Recreation/tourism (B), Unsustainable exploitation (C)

Nakskov Fjord and Indre Fjord A4i, B1i, C2, C3 088
Admin region Storstrøm
Coordinates 54°50'N 11°02'E
Altitude (-7)–16 m **Area** 8,550 ha

■ Site description
A fjord area with shoals, banks and islands (a few of which are inhabitated) with saltmarsh, reedbeds and freshwater ponds, and smaller areas of woodland, beaches and dunes.

Habitats Wetland (5%), Marine areas (90%; sea inlet/coastal features), Artificial landscape (5%; arable land)
Land-use Agriculture (10%), Unknown (90%)

■ Birds

Species	Season	Year	Pop min	Pop max	Acc	Criteria
Cygnus olor Mute Swan	N	1994	3,730	3,730	—	A4i, B1i, C3
Cygnus cygnus Whooper Swan	W	1994	330	330	—	B1i, C2

This is an important area for wintering *Cygnus cygnus* and *C. olor*, although numbers are currently lower than in 1983 when more than 20,000 waterbirds were recorded: numbers are believed to be higher in harsh winters. *Circus aeruginosus, Recurvirostra avosetta, Sterna sandvicensis, S. hirundo, S. paradisaea* and *S. albifrons*, listed on Annex I of the EC Birds Directive, bred at the site; several of these species still breed but data are incomplete.

■ Protection status
National Low **International** High
8,550 ha of IBA covered by Special Protection Area (Nakskov Fjord and Indre Fjord, 8,550 ha). 8,550 ha of IBA covered by Ramsar Site (Nakskov Fjord and Inner Fjord, 8,960 ha).

■ Conservation issues

Threats Agricultural intensification/expansion (B), Aquaculture/fisheries (C), Industrialization/urbanization (C), Recreation/tourism (B), Unsustainable exploitation (B)

Indre Fjord, a freshwater lake, is highly polluted by nutrients originating mainly from urban waste, and bottom macrophytes are no longer present. Access to some parts of the site is restricted.

Præstø Fjord, Ulvshale, Nyord, and Jungshoved Nor A4i, A4iii, B1i, B3, C3, C4 089
Admin region Storstrøm
Coordinates 55°05'N 12°15'E
Altitude (-18)–10 m **Area** 24,640 ha

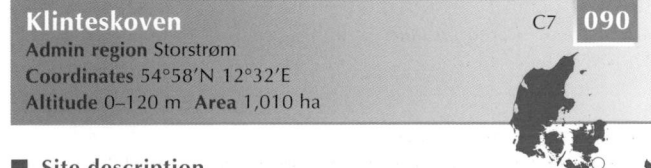

■ Site description
A sea area with shoals, banks and islands. The islands and islets have freshwater and saltmarshes, reedbeds, heathland, grasslands, mature *Quercus, Tilia* and *Carpinus* forests, cultivated land and scattered settlements.

Habitats Wetland (5%; saltmarsh), Marine areas (85%; sea inlet/coastal features), Artificial landscape (10%; arable land; forestry plantation)
Land-use Agriculture (10%), Unknown (90%)

■ Birds

Species	Season	Year	Pop min	Pop max	Acc	Criteria
Phalacrocorax carbo Cormorant	B	1995	2,847	2,847	A	A4i, B1i, C3
Cygnus olor Mute Swan	W	1991	8,675	8,675	C	A4i, B1i, C3
Anas penelope Wigeon	P	1996	36,000	36,000	A	A4i, B1i, C3
Bucephala clangula Goldeneye	N	1991	3,430	3,430	C	B1i, C3
Recurvirostra avosetta Avocet	B	1995	90	110	A	B3

Recent numbers of visiting birds (notably *Aythya fuligula*) are lower than in 1983 when the site was designated a Special Protection Area. In harsh winters, *Bucephala clangula* and *Aythya fuligula* meet A4i criteria. Several species listed on Annex I of the EC Birds Directive breed at the site, including *Botaurus stellaris, Circus aeruginosus, Recurvirostra avosetta, Philomachus pugnax, Sterna sandvicensis, S. hirundo, S. paradisaea, S. albifrons, Dryocopus martius* and *Lullula arborea*.

■ Protection status
National Partial **International** High
24,640 ha of IBA covered by Ramsar Site (Præstø Fjord, Jungshoved Nor, Ulvshale and Nyord, 25,960 ha). 24,640 ha of IBA covered by Special Protection Area (Præstø Fjord, Ulvshale, Nyord, 24,640 ha).

■ Conservation issues

Threats Abandonment/reduction of land management (B), Intensified forest management (C), Recreation/tourism (B), Unsustainable exploitation (B)

Part of Nyord is a reserve owned and managed by BirdLife Denmark.

Klinteskoven C7 090
Admin region Storstrøm
Coordinates 54°58'N 12°32'E
Altitude 0–120 m **Area** 1,010 ha

■ Site description
A deciduous forest dominated by *Fagus* on steep chalk cliffs. The site also includes calcareous grassland, grazing areas with hedges, and some smaller wetlands.

Habitats Forest and woodland (80%; broadleaved deciduous forest), Grassland (15%; steppe/dry calcareous grassland; dry siliceous grassland), Wetland (5%; standing fresh water)
Land-use Unknown

■ **Birds**

The site has a high diversity of birds but numbers of most species are low. *Pernis apivorus*, *Sylvia nisoria* and *Lanius collurio*, listed on Annex I of the EC Birds Directive, breed at the site.

■ **Protection status**

National High **International** High

1,010 ha of IBA covered by Special Protection Area (Klinteskoven, 1,010 ha).

■ **Conservation issues**

Threats Abandonment/reduction of land management (C), Recreation/tourism (C)

One of the most important terrestrial localities in Denmark with probably the highest number of rare and threatened plants and insects recorded at any one site in the country. The site is protected at national level and logging has been prohibited in some forest areas. Restoration projects to expand areas of chalk meadows and dry grasslands on chalk are ongoing. The most valuable areas are state-owned.

Holmegårds Mose and Porsemose   C2   091

Admin region Storstrøm
Coordinates 55°20′N 11°50′E
Altitude 25–50 m **Area** 1,900 ha

■ **Site description**

Bog areas with freshwater ponds, marshes, grazed meadows, cultivated land and woodland (including conifer plantations, areas colonized with *Betula*, *Salix* and *Alnus* and small areas of *Fagus*). Formerly most of the area was one large raised bog; the ponds are the result of the former extraction of peat.

Habitats Forest and woodland (35%), Wetland (55%; standing fresh water; raised bog), Artificial landscape (10%; arable land)
Land-use Agriculture (15%), Forestry (10%), Hunting (100%)

■ **Birds**

Species	Season	Year	Pop min	Pop max	Acc	Criteria
Cygnus cygnus Whooper Swan	W	1994	150	150	A	C2

Significant numbers (but below criteria thresholds) of wintering geese *Anser fabalis* and *A. anser*, and raptors *Pernis apivorus* and *Circus aeruginosus* use the site. *Pernis apivorus* and *Circus aeruginosus*, listed on Annex I of the EC Birds Directive, breed at the site.

■ **Protection status**

National Partial **International** High

1,900 ha of IBA covered by Special Protection Area (Holmegårdsmose and Porsmose, 1,900 ha).

■ **Conservation issues**

Threats Abandonment/reduction of land management (A), Agricultural intensification/expansion (C), Drainage (C), Infrastructure (C), Intensified forest management (C), Unsustainable exploitation (A)

There is high hunting pressure.

Forests near Vemmetofte   C7   092

Admin region Storstrøm
Coordinates 55°15′N 12°12′E
Altitude 0–26 m **Area** 1,860 ha

■ **Site description**

A deciduous forest, with stands of mature *Fagus* and *Quercus*. Conifer plantations and grazing-meadows are also present.

Habitats Forest and woodland (60%), Unknown (40%)
Land-use Agriculture (40%), Forestry (60%)

■ **Birds**

The site was designated as a Special Protection Area on the basis of

breeding *Pernis apivorus*; this possibly still occurs at the site but no recent data area available.

■ **Protection status**

National Partial **International** High

1,860 ha of IBA covered by Special Protection Area (Forests near Vemmetofte, 1,860 ha).

■ **Conservation issues**

Threats Agricultural intensification/expansion (C), Intensified forest management (B)

Tystrup – Bavelse Søerne   B1i, C2, C3   093

Admin region Vestsjælland
Coordinates 55°22′N 11°35′E
Altitude 8–25 m **Area** 1,960 ha

■ **Site description**

Two connected freshwater lakes surrounded by deciduous forest, reedbeds and agricultural land.

Habitats Forest and woodland (10%; broadleaved deciduous forest), Grassland (10%; humid grassland), Wetland (40%; standing fresh water), Artificial landscape (40%; arable land; forestry plantation)
Land-use Unknown

■ **Birds**

Species	Season	Year	Pop min	Pop max	Acc	Criteria
Cygnus cygnus Whooper Swan	N	—	305	305	—	C2
[1] *Aythya fuligula* Tufted Duck	N	1994	2,250	2,550	—	B1i, C3

1. Criteria met in some years only.

Significant numbers of wintering waterbirds (more than 20,000 individuals) and raptors occur in some years. Species of global conservation concern that do not meet IBA criteria: *Haliaeetus albicilla* (max. 5, non-breeding). *Sterna hirundo*, *S. albifrons* and *Alcedo atthis*, listed on Annex I of the EC Birds Directive, breed at the site.

■ **Protection status**

National Partial **International** High

1,960 ha of IBA covered by Special Protection Area (Tystrup-Bavelse lakes, 1,960 ha).

■ **Conservation issues**

Threats Agricultural intensification/expansion (B), Intensified forest management (C), Recreation/tourism (C), Unsustainable exploitation (B)

Sejrø Bay and Nekselø   A4i, A4iii, B1i, C3, C4   094

Admin region Vestsjælland
Coordinates 55°50′N 11°18′E
Altitude (-24)–30 m **Area** 40,250 ha

■ **Site description**

A shallow sea bay and coastal peninsulas with saltmarshes, reedbeds, heathlands, sandy and stony beaches, clay cliffs, unimproved dry grasslands, mixed deciduous forest and small patches of botanically interesting meadow on old shell beds. The site also includes a partly cultivated island with scattered habitation.

Habitats Marine areas (95%; sea inlet/coastal features)
Land-use Agriculture (50%), Nature conservation/research (50%), Tourism/recreation (60%)

■ **Birds**

Species	Season	Year	Pop min	Pop max	Acc	Criteria
Somateria mollissima Eider	W	1989	32,900	32,900	—	A4i, B1i, C3
Melanitta nigra Common Scoter	W	1989	48,920	48,920	—	A4i, B1i, C3
[1] *Melanitta fusca* Velvet Scoter	W	1989	7,450	7,450	—	A4i, B1i, C3

1. Criteria met in some years only.

Of high importance for wintering *Somateria mollissima* and *Melanitta nigra*, but recent quantitative data are unavailable. *Sterna paradisaea*, listed on Annex I of the EC Birds Directive, breeds at the site.

■ **Protection status**
National Low **International** High
40,250 ha of IBA covered by Ramsar Site (Sejerø Bugt, Nekeselø Bugt and Saltbæk Vig, 42,560 ha). 40,250 ha of IBA covered by Special Protection Area (Sejrø Bugt and Nekselø, 40,250 ha).

■ **Conservation issues**

Threats Recreation/tourism (C), Unsustainable exploitation (B)

Skælskør Nor, Skælskør Fjord and Borreby Mose   A4i, B1i, B1iv, C3, C5   **095**
Admin region Vestsjælland
Coordinates 55°15'N 11°20'E
Altitude -10–17 m   **Area** 1,950 ha

■ **Site description**
A coastal area with shallow fjords, brackish lagoons, reedbeds, freshwater-meadows, marshes, agricultural land and woodland. Marine areas surrounding this IBA (and previously included within it, following Grimmett and Jones 1989) are now included in Smålandsfarvandet (site 118).

Habitats Forest and woodland (5%), Grassland (10%; humid grassland), Wetland (15%; saltmarsh), Marine areas (30%; sea inlet/coastal features), Artificial landscape (50%; arable land)
Land-use Agriculture (60%), Forestry (5%), Unknown (35%)

■ **Birds**

Species	Season	Year	Pop min	Pop max	Acc	Criteria
¹*Aythya fuligula* Tufted Duck	N	1989	1,440	1,440	A	A4i, B1i, C3

1. Higher numbers in cold winters (1983, 24,000).

Of high importance for wintering *Aythya fuligula* and as a bottleneck site for passing raptors, especially *Buteo buteo* (15,000 individuals). There are large annual variations in the numbers of migrating raptors due to prevailing winds and observer coverage (min. in 1993 16,647 individuals, max. in 1995 21,833 individuals). Numbers given for diving ducks include marine areas now within site 118. In some years 20,000 ducks occur but numbers have been lower in recent years, probably as a result of mild winters. *Circus aeruginosus, Recurvirostra avosetta, Philomachus pugnax, Sterna hirundo, S. paradisaea* and *S. albifrons*, listed on Annex I of the EC Birds Directive, breed at the site.

■ **Protection status**
National Partial **International** High
2,530 ha of IBA covered by Ramsar Site (Skælskor Nor and Glænø (waters south of), 17,120 ha). 2,530 ha of IBA covered by Special Protection Area (Skælskør Nor, Skælskør Fjord and Gammelsø, 2,530 ha).

■ **Conservation issues**

Threats Agricultural intensification/expansion (B), Industrialization/urbanization (C), Recreation/tourism (B), Unsustainable exploitation (B)

Several parts of the site have additional protection.

Islands and coast between Skælskør Fjord and Glænø   A4i, A4iii, B1i, B2, B3, C3, C4, C6   **096**
Admin region Vestsjælland
Coordinates 55°10'N 11°30'E
Altitude (-39)–10 m   **Area** 3,220 ha

■ **Site description**
Several larger islands with overgrown coastal slopes, dams, marshes, grassland and reedbeds, and some coastal areas with cultivated land and scattered settlements along south-west Zealand. Marine areas surrounding this IBA (previously included within it, following Grimmett and Jones 1989) are now included in Smålandsfarvandet (site 118).

Habitats Forest and woodland (10%), Grassland (5%; humid grassland), Wetland (25%; saltmarsh; standing fresh water), Artificial landscape (60%; arable land)
Land-use Agriculture (70%), Forestry (10%), Unknown (20%)

■ **Birds**

Species	Season	Year	Pop min	Pop max	Acc	Criteria
Phalacrocorax carbo Cormorant	B	1988	3,555	3,555	A	A4i, B1i, C3
Cygnus olor Mute Swan	W	1989	2,440	2,440	—	B1i, C3
Anser anser Greylag Goose	P	1989	11,700	11,700	—	A4i, B1i, C3
Recurvirostra avosetta Avocet	B	1988	178	193	—	B3
Sterna paradisaea Arctic Tern	B	1989	306	306	—	C6
Sterna albifrons Little Tern	B	1988	25	25	—	B2, C6

More than 20,000 waterbirds use the site. Species of global conservation concern that do not meet IBA criteria: *Haliaeetus albicilla* (max. 5, wintering). Several species listed on Annex I of the EC Birds Directive breed at the site, including *Circus aeruginosus, Recurvirostra avosetta, Sterna sandvicensis, S. paradisaea* and *S. albifrons*.

■ **Protection status**
National Low **International** High
3,220 ha of IBA covered by Special Protection Area (Sea area between Skælskør Fjord and Glænø, 15,960 ha). 3,220 ha of IBA covered by Ramsar Site (Skælskor Nor and Glænø (waters south of), 17,120 ha).

■ **Conservation issues**

Threats Aquaculture/fisheries (C), Industrialization/urbanization (C), Intensified forest management (C), Recreation/tourism (C), Unsustainable exploitation (A)

Hovvig   A4i, B1i, C3   **097**
Admin region Vestsjælland
Coordinates 55°55'N 11°40'E
Altitude (-1)–1 m   **Area** 240 ha

■ **Site description**
A dyked lagoon with reedbeds, surrounded by conifer plantations, mixed deciduous scrub, grazed meadows and fields.

Habitats Grassland (40%; humid grassland), Wetland (60%; standing fresh water; standing brackish and salt water)
Land-use Agriculture (30%), Nature conservation/research (70%), Tourism/recreation (5%)

■ **Birds**

Species	Season	Year	Pop min	Pop max	Acc	Criteria
Phalacrocorax carbo Cormorant	B	1994	882	882	A	B1i, C3
Anas clypeata Shoveler	P	1994	600	600	A	B1i, C3
Mergus merganser Goosander	N	—	2,400	2,400	—	A4i, B1i, C3

This small area also holds high densities of staging ducks. *Circus aeruginosus*, listed on Annex I of the EC Birds Directive, breeds at the site.

■ **Protection status**
National Partial **International** High
240 ha of IBA covered by Special Protection Area (Hovvig, 240 ha).

■ **Conservation issues**

Threats Abandonment/reduction of land management (C), Agricultural intensification/expansion (B)

Sprogø and Halsskov Rev   A4i, B1i, C3   **098**
Admin region Vestsjælland
Coordinates 55°20'N 11°00'E
Altitude 0–24 m   **Area** 4,920 ha

■ **Site description**
The small island of Sprogø.

Habitats Wetland (20%; saltmarsh), Artificial landscape (80%; other urban/industrial areas)
Land-use Nature conservation/research (20%), Urban/industrial/transport (80%)

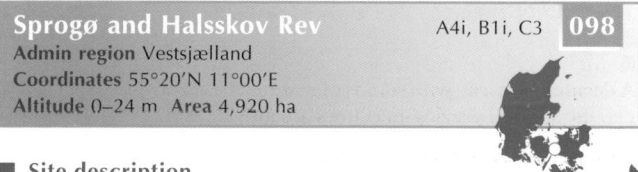

■ Birds

Species		Season	Year	Pop min	Pop max	Acc	Criteria
Somateria mollissima	Eider	R	1989	51,000	51,000	—	A4i, B1i, C3

Numbers of *Somateria mollissima* have now recovered after decreases caused by siltation from the construction of the Great Belt Bridge. *Sterna sandvicensis*, listed on Annex I of the EC Birds Directive, bred at the site in 1983, but almost all breeding gulls and terns have been displaced from the site as a result of the bridge construction work.

■ Protection status
National Partial **International** High
4,920 ha of IBA covered by Special Protection Area (Sprogø and Halskov Rev, 4,920 ha).

■ Conservation issues

Threats Dredging/canalization (B), Infrastructure (B)

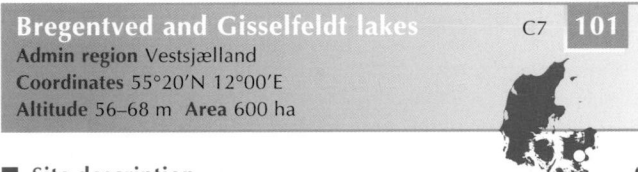

Saltbæk Vig B1i, B3, C3 099
Admin region Vestsjælland
Coordinates 55°45'N 11°10'E
Altitude (-1)–2 m **Area** 3,630 ha

■ Site description
A dyked fjord/lagoon area (a failed land-reclamation project) with saltmarshes, meadows (partly cultivated), reedbeds and plantation areas.

Habitats Wetland (75%; standing brackish and salt water), Artificial landscape (20%; arable land; forestry plantation)
Land-use Agriculture (30%), Unknown (70%)

■ Birds

Species		Season	Year	Pop min	Pop max	Acc	Criteria
Anas crecca	Teal	N	1983	5,500	5,500	—	B1i, C3
Recurvirostra avosetta	Avocet	B	1998	100	500	—	B3

No recent data are available as the area is not well surveyed or monitored. *Circus aeruginosus*, *Recurvirostra avosetta*, *Philomachus pugnax* and *Sterna albifrons*, listed on Annex I of the EC Birds Directive, bred at the site in 1983.

■ Protection status
National Partial **International** High
3,630 ha of IBA covered by Ramsar Site (Sejero Bugt, Nekeselo Bugt and Saltbæk Vig, 42,560 ha). 3,630 ha of IBA covered by Special Protection Area (Saltbæk Vig, 3,630 ha).

■ Conservation issues

Threats Abandonment/reduction of land management (B), Agricultural intensification/expansion (C), Infrastructure (C), Unsustainable exploitation (C)

Entry is prohibited to a large part of the area.

Tissø, Lille Åmose, and Hallenslev Mose A4i, B1i, B2, C2, C3, C6 100
Admin region Vestsjælland
Coordinates 55°35'N 11°20'E
Altitude 2–10 m **Area** 2,890 ha

■ Site description
A large, shallow freshwater lake with associated grazed meadows and reedbeds and a small river valley.

Habitats Wetland (95%; standing fresh water), Artificial landscape (5%; arable land)
Land-use Forestry, Hunting, Tourism/recreation

■ Birds
An important staging area for *Cygnus columbianus*. Lower numbers of swans *Cygnus* recorded in recent years may be due to changes in

---

census timings. *Botaurus stellaris*, *Circus aeruginosus*, *Recurvirostra avosetta* and *Sterna albifrons*, listed on Annex I of the EC Birds Directive, breed at the site. Species of global conservation concern that do not meet IBA criteria: *Haliaeetus albicilla* (non-breeding).

Species		Season	Year	Pop min	Pop max	Acc	Criteria
Cygnus columbianus	Bewick's Swan	N	1996	475	475	A	A4i,B1i,B2,C2,C6
Cygnus cygnus	Whooper Swan	P	1994	1,993	1,993	A	A4i, B1i, C2
Anser anser	Greylag Goose	P	1994	2,024	2,024	A	B1i, C3

■ Protection status
National Low **International** High
2,890 ha of IBA covered by Special Protection Area (Tissø, Lille Åmose and Hallenslev Mose, 2,890 ha).

■ Conservation issues

Threats Abandonment/reduction of land management (B), Groundwater abstraction (C), Industrialization/urbanization (C), Infrastructure (C), Recreation/tourism (C), Unsustainable exploitation (C)

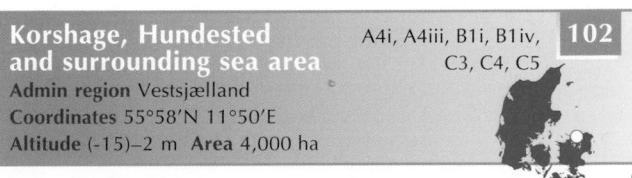

Bregentved and Gisselfeldt lakes C7 101
Admin region Vestsjælland
Coordinates 55°20'N 12°00'E
Altitude 56–68 m **Area** 600 ha

■ Site description
Four freshwater lakes surrounded by reedbeds, forest and agricultural land.

Habitats Forest and woodland (15%; broadleaved deciduous forest), Wetland (40%; standing fresh water), Artificial landscape (40%; arable land)
Land-use Agriculture (40%), Forestry (15%), Unknown (45%)

■ Birds
Aythya fuligula is present in important numbers (reaching B1i threshold) in some years, but no recent data are available. Nielstrup Sø, the smallest of the lakes, holds the majority of breeding birds. *Circus aeruginosus*, listed on Annex I of the EC Birds Directive, breeds at the site.

■ Protection status
National Unknown **International** High
600 ha of IBA covered by Special Protection Area (Lakes near Bregentved and Gisselfeld, 600 ha).

■ Conservation issues

Threats Abandonment/reduction of land management (U), Agricultural intensification/expansion (A), Unsustainable exploitation (C)

Korshage, Hundested and surrounding sea area A4i, A4iii, B1i, B1iv, C3, C4, C5 102
Admin region Vestsjælland
Coordinates 55°58'N 11°50'E
Altitude (-15)–2 m **Area** 4,000 ha

■ Site description
A sea area connecting Isefjorden with Kattegat, and the mouth of a shallow fjord with beaches, sand-dunes, saltmarsh, heathland, clay cliffs, agriculture and urban areas. Terrestrial habitats cover just 2.5% of the IBA.

Habitats Marine areas (100%; sea inlet/coastal features)
Land-use Unknown

■ Birds

Species		Season	Year	Pop min	Pop max	Acc	Criteria
[1] *Somateria mollissima*	Eider	W	1991	2,610	2,610	—	A4i, B1i, C3

1. Higher total numbers of non-breeding birds occur (1983, 34,000).

This site is important for wintering waterbirds (more than 20,000 individuals), especially for *Somateria mollissima*, and other waterbirds in cold winters when the remainder of the Isefjord is frozen over. This is also a significant bottleneck site for migrating raptors, particularly in spring (12,090 in total in spring 1996). High numbers of passerines, especially finches *Fringilla*, occur on passage. Species of global conservation concern that do not meet IBA criteria: *Haliaeetus albicilla* (max. 8, passage). *Dryocopus maritus* and *Lanius collurio*, listed on Annex I of the EC Birds Directive, breed at the site.

■ **Protection status**
National Low **International** High
4,000 ha of IBA covered by Special Protection Area (Sea area between Korshage and Hundested, 4,000 ha).

■ **Conservation issues**

Threats Industrialization/urbanization (C), Infrastructure (C), Recreation/tourism (C), Unsustainable exploitation (C)

Wetland north of Gammel Havdrup   C7   103
Admin region Roskilde
Coordinates 55°34'N 12°09'E
Altitude 28–30 m **Area** 100 ha

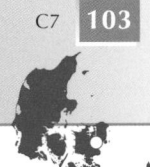

■ **Site description**
A small wetland surrounded by agricultural land.

Habitats Grassland (70%; humid grassland), Wetland (30%; standing fresh water)
Land-use Agriculture (70%), Unknown (30%)

■ **Birds**
Circus aeruginosus and *Chlidonias niger*, listed on Annex I of the EC Birds Directive, formerly bred at the site.

■ **Protection status**
National Partial **International** High
100 ha of IBA covered by Special Protection Area (Snoldelev Mose and Gammel Havdrup Mose, 100 ha).

■ **Conservation issues**

Threats Abandonment/reduction of land management (B), Agricultural intensification/ expansion (A), Disturbance to birds (C), Groundwater abstraction (C), Unsustainable exploitation (C)

Water quality is very poor due to nutrient pollution. The abandonment and reduction of land management is also a threat and restoration efforts are underway, including renewed grazing and *Salix* scrub clearance.

Ramsø Mose   C7   104
Admin region Roskilde
Coordinates 55°35'N 12°03'E
Altitude 15–21 m **Area** 220 ha

■ **Site description**
A small wetland surrounded by agricultural land.

Habitats Wetland (80%; standing fresh water), Artificial landscape (25%; arable land)
Land-use Unknown

■ **Birds**
Circus aeruginosus and *Chlidonias niger*, listed on Annex I of the EC Birds Directive, breed at the site in low numbers.

■ **Protection status**
National Unknown **International** High
220 ha of IBA covered by Special Protection Area (Ramsø Mose, 220 ha).

■ **Conservation issues**
A project to improve water quality and renew grazing is planned.

Threats Abandonment/reduction of land management (A), Agricultural intensification/ expansion (A), Groundwater abstraction (A), Infrastructure (C), Recreation/tourism (C), Unsustainable exploitation (B)

Roskilde Fjord, Selsø and Kattinge Søerne   A4i, A4iii, B1i, B2, B3, C2, C3, C4, C6   105
Admin region Frederiksborg
Coordinates 55°45'N 12°05'E
Altitude (-31)–20 m **Area** 13,180 ha

■ **Site description**
A long shallow fjord with islands and islets. Coastal areas have saltmarshes, agricultural land and forested peninsulas. The *Fagus/ Quercus* forest on Bognæs includes areas of old-growth forest.

Habitats Forest and woodland (5%), Wetland (5%; saltmarsh), Marine areas (80%; sea inlet/coastal features), Artificial landscape (10%; arable land)
Land-use Unknown

■ **Birds**

Species	Season	Year	Pop min	Pop max	Acc	Criteria
Cygnus olor Mute Swan	W	1994	7,155	7,155	—	A4i, B1i, C3
Cygnus columbianus Bewick's Swan	P	1993	300	300	—	A4i, B1i, C2
Cygnus cygnus Whooper Swan	W	1994	306	306	—	B1i, C2
Aythya fuligula Tufted Duck	W	1995	57,000	57,000	—	A4i, B1i, C3
Mergus merganser Goosander	W	1994	3,700	3,700	—	A4i, B1i, C3
Fulica atra Coot	W	1994	19,271	19,271	—	B1i, C3
Recurvirostra avosetta Avocet	B	1994	109	109	A	B3
Larus canus Common Gull	B	1996	1,731	2,277	A	B2
Sterna hirundo Common Tern	B	1994	363	363	A	C6
Sterna paradisaea Arctic Tern	B	1994	301	301	A	C6

This is a very important site for wintering *Cygnus olor*, *Aythya fuligula*, *Mergus merganser* and *Fulica atra*. Winter visitors can exceed 20,000 individuals, but numbers fluctuate widely in relation to winter harshness. *Circus aeruginosus*, *Recurvirostra avosetta*, *Sterna hirundo*, *S. paradisaea* and *S. albifrons*, listed on Annex I of the EC Birds Directive, breed at the site. Species of global conservation concern that do not meet IBA criteria: *Haliaeetus albicilla* (max. 7, wintering).

■ **Protection status**
National Partial **International** High
13,180 ha of IBA covered by Special Protection Area (Roskilde Fjord, Kattinge Vig and Lake, 13,180 ha).

■ **Conservation issues**

Threats Abandonment/reduction of land management (C), Agricultural intensification/ expansion (A), Aquaculture/fisheries (B), Industrialization/urbanization (C), Infrastructure (C), Intensified forest management (A), Recreation/tourism (A), Unsustainable exploitation (C)

It is possible that the site boundaries should be extended to include Isefjord but further data on bird populations are needed.

Arresø   A4i, B1i, C3   106
Admin region Frederiksborg
Coordinates 56°00'N 12°10'E
Altitude (-3)–10 m **Area** 4,610 ha

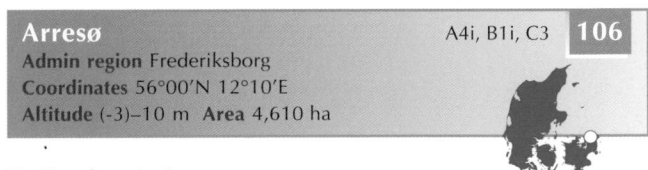

■ **Site description**
A very shallow freshwater lake (the largest in Denmark) surrounded by reedbeds, marsh, cultivated areas and woodland.

Habitats Forest and woodland (5%), Grassland (5%; humid grassland), Wetland (90%; standing fresh water; water-fringe vegetation)
Land-use Agriculture (5%), Forestry (5%), Unknown (90%)

■ **Birds**

Species	Season	Year	Pop min	Pop max	Acc	Criteria
Mergus merganser Goosander	W	1993	5,000	5,000	B	A4i, B1i, C3

Few data are available on bird populations.

■ **Protection status**
National Low **International** High
4,610 ha of IBA covered by Special Protection Area, 4,610 ha.

■ **Conservation issues**

Threats Abandonment/reduction of land management (B), Agricultural intensification/
expansion (A), Industrialization/urbanization (A), Intensified forest management (C),
Recreation/tourism (C)

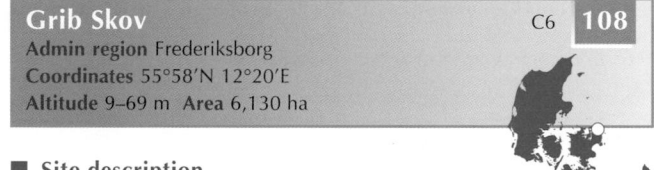

Jægerspris Nordskov — C7 — 107
Admin region Frederiksborg
Coordinates 55°54'N 11°59'E
Altitude 0–20 m **Area** 1,520 ha

■ **Site description**
A heterogeneous forest area with glades, wetlands and saltmarshes.
Until recently these old-growth forests contained three of the oldest
recorded *Quercus* trees (800–2,000 years old) in Europe, but
unfortunately within the last 20 years these have either died or started
to die.

Habitats Forest and woodland (45%; broadleaved deciduous forest), Wetland (5%),
Artificial landscape (50%; forestry plantation)
Land-use Unknown

■ **Birds**
Pernis apivorus, Caprimulgus europaeus, Dryocopus martius and
Lanius collurio, listed on Annex I of the EC Birds Directive, breed at
the site.

■ **Protection status**
National None **International** High
1,520 ha of IBA covered by Special Protection Area (Jægerspris
Nordskov, 1,520 ha).

■ **Conservation issues**

Threats Abandonment/reduction of land management (B), Intensified forest
management (A)

Grib Skov — C6 — 108
Admin region Frederiksborg
Coordinates 55°58'N 12°20'E
Altitude 9–69 m **Area** 6,130 ha

■ **Site description**
A very large forest area with glades, lakes and some small bogs.
Formerly very extensive wetlands occurred within the forest, covering
70% of the site 150 years ago, but most have been drained and only
small areas remain.

Habitats Forest and woodland (25%; broadleaved deciduous forest), Wetland
(10%; standing fresh water), Artificial landscape (60%; forestry plantation),
Unknown (5%)
Land-use Agriculture (5%), Forestry (85%), Unknown (10%)

■ **Birds**

Species	Season	Year	Pop min	Pop max	Acc	Criteria
Dryocopus martius Black Woodpecker	B	1994	13	14	A	C6
Lanius collurio Red-backed Shrike	B	1994	33	36	A	C6

Several species listed on Annex I of the EC Birds Directive breed at
the site, including *Pernis apivorus, Accipiter gentilis, Caprimulgus
europaeus, Dryocopus martius* and *Lanius collurio*.

■ **Protection status**
National Low **International** High
6,130 ha of IBA covered by Special Protection Area (Grib Skov,
6,130 ha).

■ **Conservation issues**

Threats Abandonment/reduction of land management (B), Intensified forest management (C)

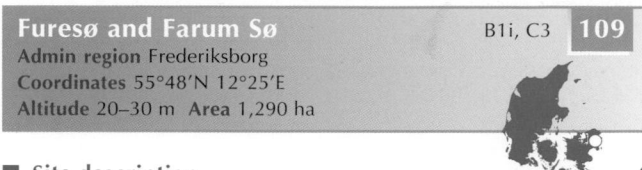

Furesø and Farum Sø — B1i, C3 — 109
Admin region Frederiksborg
Coordinates 55°48'N 12°25'E
Altitude 20–30 m **Area** 1,290 ha

■ **Site description**
A relatively deep eutrophic freshwater lake surrounded by reedbeds
and swampy *Betula* and *Alnus* thickets; close to urban areas.

Habitats Forest and woodland (5%), Grassland (humid grassland), Wetland (75%;
standing fresh water), Unknown (25%)
Land-use Unknown

■ **Birds**

Species	Season	Year	Pop min	Pop max	Acc	Criteria
[1] *Aythya fuligula* Tufted Duck	N	1995	150	150	B	B1i, C3

1. Criteria met in some years only.

Sterna hirundo and *Alcedo atthis*, listed on Annex I of the EC Birds
Directive, breed at the site.

■ **Protection status**
National Partial **International** High
1,290 ha of IBA covered by Special Protection Area (Furesø including
Vaserne and Farum Sø, 1,290 ha).

■ **Conservation issues**

Threats Abandonment/reduction of land management (C), Intensified forest
management (C), Recreation/tourism (C)

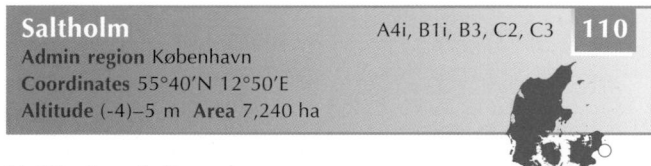

Saltholm — A4i, B1i, B3, C2, C3 — 110
Admin region København
Coordinates 55°40'N 12°50'E
Altitude (-4)–5 m **Area** 7,240 ha

■ **Site description**
A large flat uncultivated island with saltmarshes surrounded by
shallow sea with stony shoals, banks and mudflats; includes the largest
area of saltmarsh in Denmark outside Jylland.

Habitats Grassland (10%; humid grassland), Wetland (20%; saltmarsh), Marine areas
(75%; sea inlet/coastal features)
Land-use Agriculture (25%), Unknown (75%)

■ **Birds**

Species	Season	Year	Pop min	Pop max	Acc	Criteria
Cygnus olor Mute Swan	N	1991	3,818	3,818	—	A4i, B1i, C3
Anser anser Greylag Goose	N	1991	2,616	2,616	—	B1i, C3
Branta leucopsis Barnacle Goose	B	1998	25	25	A	C2
Recurvirostra avosetta Avocet	B	1993	201	201	A	B3
Larus marinus Great Black-backed Gull	B	1995	309	309	—	B3

This is an important wintering site for *Cygnus olor* and breeding ground
for gulls and terns. Several species listed on Annex I of the EC Birds
Directive, breed at the site including *Branta leucopsis, Recurvirostra
avosetta, Philomachus pugnax, Sterna sandvicensis, S. hirundo,
S. paradisaea* and *S. albifrons*.

■ **Protection status**
National Partial **International** High
7,240 ha of IBA covered by Special Protection Area (Saltholm, 7,240 ha).

■ **Conservation issues**

Threats Abandonment/reduction of land management (B), Dredging/canalization (B),
Infrastructure (B), Unsustainable exploitation (B)

Entry is prohibited to most of the site during the breeding season, and to some areas throughout the year.

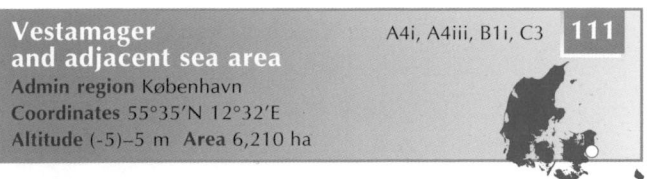

Vestamager and adjacent sea area
A4i, A4iii, B1i, C3 — 111

Admin region København
Coordinates 55°35′N 12°32′E
Altitude (-5)–5 m **Area** 6,210 ha

■ Site description
A shallow sea area and adjacent coast with saltmarshes; also includes a reclaimed area with freshwater lakes and reedbeds. Some wetlands have been restored whilst others have been afforested.

Habitats Scrub (30%; scrub; heathland), Grassland (25%; dry siliceous grassland; humid grassland), Wetland (25%; saltmarsh; standing fresh water; standing brackish and salt water), Artificial landscape (20%; forestry plantation; other urban/industrial areas)
Land-use Forestry (10%), Nature conservation/research (70%), Tourism/recreation (100%), Urban/industrial/transport (30%)

■ Birds

Species	Season	Year	Pop min	Pop max	Acc	Criteria
Aythya fuligula Tufted Duck	N	1991	10,022	10,022	—	B1i, C3
Mergus serrator Red-breasted Merganser	N	—	2,000	2,000	—	A4i, B1i, C3

Numbers of both breeding and visiting birds have declined. In some years total numbers of waterbirds exceed 20,000 individuals. *Recurvirostra avosetta*, *Philomachus pugnax*, *Sterna paradisaea* and *S. albifrons*, listed on Annex I of the EC Birds Directive, breed at the site.

■ Protection status
National Partial **International** High
6,210 ha of IBA covered by Special Protection Area (Western Amager and surrounding sea area, 6,210 ha).

■ Conservation issues

Threats Abandonment/reduction of land management (C), Afforestation (C), Drainage (B), Industrialization/urbanization (B), Infrastructure (B), Recreation/tourism (C), Unsustainable exploitation (C)

Ongoing restoration projects, including raising water-levels in some areas, and the expansion of grazing will probably help reverse the negative trends of some bird species. Some areas are scheduled for urbanization and parts have already been destroyed by road construction.

Hjelm
B2, C7 — 112

Admin region Århus
Coordinates 56°08′N 10°49′E
Altitude 0–45 m **Area** 70 ha

■ Site description
Small grassy and formerly partly cultivated island.

Habitats Forest and woodland (5%), Grassland (35%), Wetland (50%; shingle/stony beach), Artificial landscape (10%; forestry plantation; urban parks/gardens)
Land-use Nature conservation/research (100%)

■ Birds

Species	Season	Year	Pop min	Pop max	Acc	Criteria
Larus canus Common Gull	B	1996	2,000	2,000	A	B2

■ Protection status
National None **International** None

■ Conservation issues

Threats Extraction industry (C), Recreation/tourism (C), Unsustainable exploitation (C)

Mølleso and Gjorslev
B1i, C3 — 113

Admin region Storstrøm
Coordinates 55°25′N 12°20′E
Altitude 5–10 m **Area** 50 ha

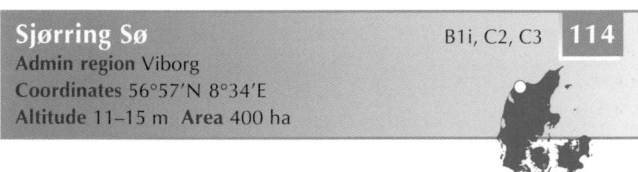

■ Site description
A freshwater lake surrounded by agricultural land and forest.

Habitats Forest and woodland (10%), Wetland (40%; standing fresh water), Artificial landscape (50%; arable land)
Land-use Unknown

■ Birds

Species	Season	Year	Pop min	Pop max	Acc	Criteria
Anser anser Greylag Goose	N	1995	2,250	2,250	A	B1i, C3

Quantitative data on bird numbers other than *Anser anser* are unavailable.

■ Protection status
National None **International** None

■ Conservation issues

Threats Abandonment/reduction of land management (U), Agricultural intensification/expansion (C), Unsustainable exploitation (C)

Sjørring Sø
B1i, C2, C3 — 114

Admin region Viborg
Coordinates 56°57′N 8°34′E
Altitude 11–15 m **Area** 400 ha

■ Site description
Mainly arable land with a few small meadows; a former lake has been drained. Quantitative habitat and land-use data are not available.

Habitats Grassland (10%; humid grassland), Artificial landscape (90%; arable land)
Land-use Agriculture (100%)

■ Birds

Species	Season	Year	Pop min	Pop max	Acc	Criteria
Anser anser Greylag Goose	N	1994	3,500	3,500	A	B1i, C3
Pluvialis apricaria Golden Plover	P	1993	12,000	12,000	—	B1i, C2

Recent data on bird populations are incomplete.

■ Protection status
National None **International** None

■ Conservation issues

Threats Unknown

Skjern Å
A4i, B1i, B2, C2 — 115

Admin region Ringkøbing
Coordinates 56°56′N 8°30′E
Altitude 1–4 m **Area** 3,850 ha

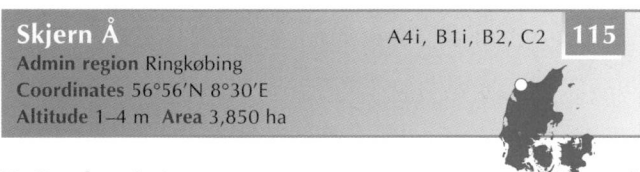

■ Site description
A large river valley with meadows, marshes, moorland and cultivated areas. The Skjern Å river has been canalized and has the highest rate of flow of any in Denmark.

Habitats Grassland (50%; humid grassland; mesophile grassland), Wetland (5%; river/stream), Artificial landscape (45%; arable land)
Land-use Agriculture (90%), Water management (10%)

■ Birds

Species	Season	Year	Pop min	Pop max	Acc	Criteria
Cygnus columbianus Bewick's Swan	N	—	700	700	—	A4i, B1i, B2, C2

This is an important staging area for *Cygnus columbianus*. No quantitative data are available and recent data are incomplete. Species of global conservation concern that do not meet IBA criteria: *Crex crex* (breeding).

■ Protection status
National None **International** None

■ Conservation issues

Threats Agricultural intensification/expansion (A), Drainage (A), Industrialization/urbanization (C), Unsustainable exploitation (A)

An important extensive restoration project is underway which includes 're-meandering' the lower part of the river. It is hoped that the project will help restore the former importance of the site for scarce breeding birds such as *Crex crex*. Several of the side rivers have been severely polluted by ochre as a result of extensive drainage schemes.

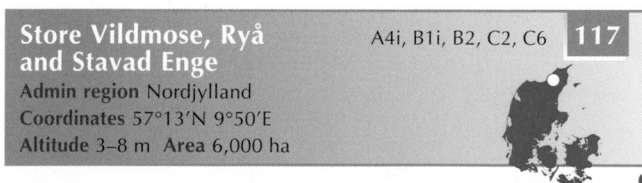

Bolle and Try meadows
A4i, B1i, B2, C2 **116**
Admin region Nordjylland
Coordinates 57°07′N 10°12′E
Altitude 5–13 m **Area** 1,500 ha

■ Site description
Partly drained meadows along a small stream.

Habitats Grassland (humid grassland), Wetland (river/stream; water-fringe vegetation), Artificial landscape (arable land)
Land-use Unknown

■ Birds

Species	Season	Year	Pop min	Pop max	Acc	Criteria
Cygnus columbianus Bewick's Swan	N	1994	2,475	2,475	—	A4i, B1i, B2, C2
Cygnus cygnus Whooper Swan	N	1994	2,090	2,090	—	A4i, B1i, C2

Important staging area for *Cygnus cygnus* and *Cygnus columbianus*. Species of global conservation concern that do not meet IBA criteria: *Crex crex* (max. 1, breeding). *Porzana porzana* also listed on Annex I of the EC Birds Directive, breeds in low numbers.

■ Protection status
National None **International** None

■ Conservation issues

Threats Unknown

Store Vildmose, Ryå and Stavad Enge
A4i, B1i, B2, C2, C6 **117**
Admin region Nordjylland
Coordinates 57°13′N 9°50′E
Altitude 3–8 m **Area** 6,000 ha

■ Site description
Store Vildmose was formerly a large raised bog, but due to drainage and peat extraction is now mostly arable land, although smaller areas of bog remain. The IBA includes the adjacent meadows along the Ryå stream.

Habitats Grassland (humid grassland), Wetland (standing fresh water; raised bog), Artificial landscape (arable land)
Land-use Agriculture, Nature conservation/research

■ Birds

Species	Season	Year	Pop min	Pop max	Acc	Criteria
Cygnus columbianus Bewick's Swan	N	1994	1,179	1,179	—	A4i, B1i, B2, C2
Cygnus cygnus Whooper Swan	W	1994	960	960	—	A4i, B1i, C2
Crex crex Corncrake	B	1998	4	8	—	C6

This is an important staging area for *Cygnus columbianus*. Species of global conservation concern that do not meet IBA criteria: *Crex crex* (max. 4, breeding).

■ Protection status
National None **International** None

■ Conservation issues

Threats Abandonment/reduction of land management (A), Agricultural intensification/expansion (A)

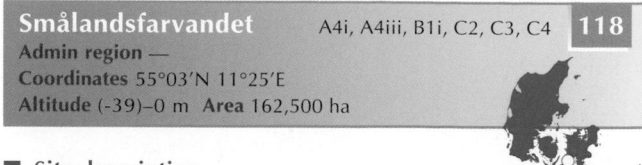

Smålandsfarvandet
A4i, A4iii, B1i, C2, C3, C4 **118**
Admin region —
Coordinates 55°03′N 11°25′E
Altitude (-39)–0 m **Area** 162,500 ha

■ Site description
A large, very shallow bay with stone reefs, numerous islands and several inlets along the coast.

Habitats Marine areas (100%; sea inlet/coastal features)
Land-use Unknown

■ Birds

Species		Season	Year	Pop min	Pop max	Acc	Criteria
[1,2]**Gavia stellata**	Red-throated Diver	W	1993	2,000	3,000	B	A4i, B1i, C2
[1,2]**Gavia arctica**	Black-throated Diver	W	1993	—	—	A	A4i, B1i, C2
[2] **Cygnus olor**	Mute Swan	W	1993	15,445	15,445	A	A4i, B1i, C3
Aythya fuligula	Tufted Duck	W	1993	16,880	16,880	A	A4i, B1i, C3
[2] **Bucephala clangula**	Goldeneye	W	1993	4,575	4,575	A	A4i, B1i, C3
[2] **Mergus serrator**	Red-breasted Merganser	W	1993	3,695	3,695	A	A4i, B1i, C3
[2] **Mergus merganser**	Goosander	W	1993	2,410	2,410	A	A4i, B1i, C3
[2] **Fulica atra**	Coot	W	1993	18,605	18,605	—	B1i, C3

1. 3,280 *Gavia stellata* and *G. arctica* combined.
2. 1988–1993 average.

The area is of high importance for wintering waterbirds, with tens of thousands of birds regularly wintering at the site, including over 8% of the north-west European population of *Cygnus olor*.

■ Protection status
National Partial **International** High
29,216 ha of IBA covered by Ramsar Site (Fejø and Femø Isles (waters south-east of), 32,640 ha). 13,848 ha of IBA covered by Ramsar Site (Karrebæk, Dybsø and Avno Fjords, 19,200 ha). 7,810 ha of IBA covered by Ramsar Site (Nakskov Fjord and Inner Fjord, 8,960 ha). 13,075 ha of IBA covered by Ramsar Site (Skælskør Nor and Glænø (waters south of), 17,120 ha). 2,080 ha of IBA covered by Special Protection Area (Guldborgsung, 2,820 ha). 13,848 ha of IBA covered by Special Protection Area (Karrebæk, Dybsø and Avnø Fjords, 18,860 ha). 7,810 ha of IBA covered by Special Protection Area (Nakskov Fjord and Indrefjord, 8,550 ha). IBA overlaps with Special Protection Area (Sea area between Skælskør Fjord and Glænø, 15,960 ha). IBA overlaps with Special Protection Area (Skælskør Nor, Skælskør Fjord and Gammelsø, 2,530 ha). 29,216 ha of IBA covered by Special Protection Area (Smålandshavet north of Lolland, 41,680 ha).

■ Conservation issues

Threats Extraction industry (C), Industrialization/urbanization (B), Recreation/tourism (C), Unsustainable exploitation (C)

The IBA encompasses the seawater areas of six Special Protection Areas and four Ramsar Sites. Futhermore, the entire area has been proposed as an offshore Baltic Sea Protected Area.

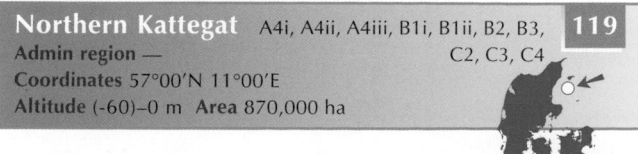

Northern Kattegat
A4i, A4ii, A4iii, B1i, B1ii, B2, B3, C2, C3, C4 **119**
Admin region —
Coordinates 57°00′N 11°00′E
Altitude (-60)–0 m **Area** 870,000 ha

■ Site description
A shallow sea area with a sandy bay, estuaries and a mosaic of hard-bottom banks. The area given here is of the Danish part only; 180,000 ha (17% of the total transboundary area) are within Swedish territory.

Habitats Marine areas (100%; open sea)
Land-use Unknown

■ Birds

Species	Season	Year	Pop min	Pop max	Acc	Criteria
¹ *Gavia stellata* Red-throated Diver	W	1993	1,450	1,450	A	A4i, B1i, C2
¹ *Gavia arctica* Black-throated Diver	W	1993	1,450	1,450	A	A4i, B1i, C2
¹ *Podiceps grisegena* Red-necked Grebe	W	1993	2,350	2,350	A	A4i, B1i, C2
¹ *Aythya marila* Scaup	W	1993	12,000	12,000	A	A4i, B1i, B2, C3
¹ *Somateria mollissima* Eider	W	1993	400,000	400,000	A	A4i, B1i, C3
¹ *Melanitta nigra* Common Scoter	W	1993	495,000	495,000	A	A4i, B1i, C3
¹ *Melanitta fusca* Velvet Scoter	W	1993	82,000	82,000	A	A4i, B1i, B2, C3
¹ *Bucephala clangula* Goldeneye	W	1993	6,425	6,425	A	A4i, B1i, C3
¹ *Larus argentatus* Herring Gull	W	1993	30,000	30,000	A	A4i, B1i
¹ *Larus marinus* Great Black-backed Gull	W	1993	6,350	6,350	A	A4i, B1i, C3
¹ *Alca torda* Razorbill	W	1993	129,000	129,000	A	A4ii, B1ii, B3, C3

1. 1988–1993 average. Figures are for the whole transboundary area (including non-Danish parts).

This is an exceptionally important area for wintering seaduck and pelagic species (divers and auks), with hundreds of thousands of birds wintering at the site. Seaduck are mainly within Danish waters and the pelagic species mainly in the Swedish part. This is the most important wintering area in north-west Europe for *Somateria mollissima* (>13% of the north-west European population), *Melanitta nigra* (>38% of the north-west European population) and *Alca torda* (>10% of the north-west European population).

■ Protection status

National Partial **International** High

12,635 ha of IBA covered by Ramsar Site (Anholt Island (waters north of), 12,720 ha). 480 ha of IBA covered by Ramsar Site (Hirsholmene, 480 ha). 62,880 ha of IBA covered by Ramsar Site (Læsø, 67,840 ha). 2,923 ha of IBA covered by Ramsar Site (Nordre Ronner, 2,923 ha). 35,200 ha of IBA covered by Ramsar Site (Randers and Mariager Fjords and adjacent coastal waters, 41,440 ha). 3,740 ha of IBA covered by Special Protection Area (Hirsholmene, 3,740 ha). 2,920 ha of IBA covered by Special Protection Area (Nordre Rønner, 2,920 ha). 35,200 ha of IBA covered by Special Protection Area (Randers and Mariager Fjord and Ålborg Bugt, 39,040 ha). 11,520 ha of IBA covered by Special Protection Area (Sea area north of Anholt, 11,520 ha). 62,880 ha of IBA covered by Special Protection Area (South Læsø and adjacent sea, 66,380 ha). 21,500 ha of IBA covered by Special Protection Area (Ålborg Bugt, 31,460 ha).

■ Conservation issues

Threats Aquaculture/fisheries (C), Extraction industry (B), Industrialization/urbanization (A), Unsustainable exploitation (C)

The IBA encompasses the seawater areas of six Special Protection Areas and five Ramsar Sites. Furthermore, four offshore Baltic Sea Protected Areas have been proposed, overlapping with, or identical to, existing protected areas.

Rønne Banke

A4i, A4iii, B1i, B1ii, C3 **120**

Admin region —
Coordinates 54°50'N 14°22'E
Altitude (-20)–(-4) m **Area** 100,000 ha

■ Site description

A shallow seawater area, a small part of which falls within German waters.

Habitats Marine areas (100%; open sea)
Land-use Unknown

■ Birds

Species	Season	Year	Pop min	Pop max	Acc	Criteria
¹ *Clangula hyemalis* Long-tailed Duck	W	1993	68,000	68,000	—	A4i, B1i, C3
¹ *Cepphus grylle* Black Guillemot	W	1993	500	500	—	B1ii

1. 1988–1993 average.

■ Protection status

National None **International** None

■ Conservation issues

Threats Aquaculture/fisheries (C), Extraction industry (A), Unsustainable exploitation (C)

Skagerrak – Southwest Norwegian trench

A4i, A4ii, A4iii, B1i, B1ii, C3 **121**

Admin region —
Coordinates 57°40'N 9°00'E
Altitude (-400)–(-20) m **Area** 1,600,000 ha

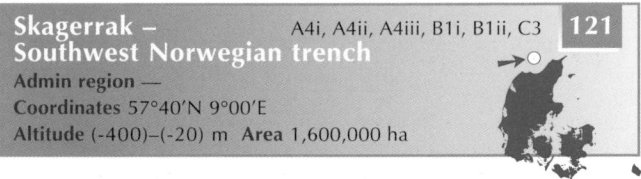

■ Site description

A sea area with complex salinity gradients. 33% of the area is within Danish territory (the area given here), 61% in Norwegian territory and 7% in Swedish. Coordinates are approximate.

Habitats Marine areas (100%; open sea)
Land-use Unknown

■ Birds

Species	Season	Year	Pop min	Pop max	Acc	Criteria
¹ *Sula bassana* Gannet	W	1993	14,000	14,000	—	A4ii, B1ii, C3
¹ *Stercorarius skua* Great Skua	P	1993	3,300	3,300	—	A4ii, B1ii, C3
¹ *Larus argentatus* Herring Gull	W	1993	32,000	32,000	—	A4i, B1i
¹ *Uria aalge* Guillemot	N	1993	46,300	46,300	—	A4ii, B1ii, C3
¹ *Alca torda* Razorbill	W	1993	45,000	45,000	—	A4ii, B1ii, C3
¹ *Alle alle* Little Auk	W	1993	705,000	705,000	—	A4ii, B1ii, C3

1. 1980–1993 average. Figures are for the whole transboundary area (including non-Danish parts).

Of very high importance for pelagic species such as *Sula bassana*, *Stercorarius skua* (nearly 12% of the biogeographic population), *Uria aalge*, *Alca torda* and *Alle alle* (25% of the biogeographic population). Outside of the IBA, in the adjacent area of Jammerbugten, *Melanitta nigra* occurs in high numbers (up to 50,000) in some years.

■ Protection status

National None **International** None

■ Conservation issues

Threats Aquaculture/fisheries (U), Extraction industry (U), Industrialization/urbanization (B)

Currently oil pollution is the most significant threat to the site. Future oil exploitation poses a potential threat.

Kiel Bay and adjacent waters

A4i, A4iii, B1i, C3, C4 **122**

Admin region —
Coordinates 54°35'N 10°30'E
Altitude (-35)–0 m **Area** 120,000 ha

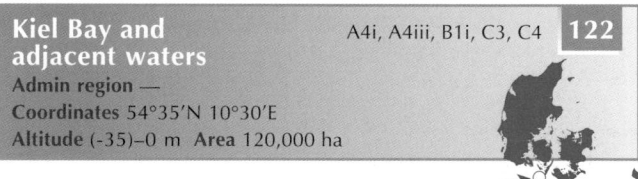

■ Site description

A large bay with many sand- and gravel-banks and estuaries. 193,000 ha (62% of the total transboundary site) is within German territory. Sandbanks and open deeper parts hold communities of shellfish *Macoma* and stone reefs have high densities of mussels *Mytilus*.

Habitats Marine areas (100%; sea inlet/coastal features)
Land-use Unknown

■ Birds

Species	Season	Year	Pop min	Pop max	Acc	Criteria
¹ *Podiceps cristatus* Great Crested Grebe	W	1993	2,070	2,070	A	B1i, C3
¹ *Podiceps grisegena* Red-necked Grebe	W	1993	200	200	A	B1i, C3
¹ *Aythya fuligula* Tufted Duck	W	1993	10,000	10,000	A	B1i, C3
¹ *Somateria mollissima* Eider	W	1993	277,800	277,800	A	A4i, B1i, C3
¹ *Clangula hyemalis* Long-tailed Duck	W	1993	90,000	90,000	A	A4i, B1i, C3
¹ *Melanitta nigra* Common Scoter	W	1993	62,770	62,770	A	A4i, B1i, C3
¹ *Bucephala clangula* Goldeneye	W	1993	4,855	4,855	A	A4i, B1i, C3

1. 1988–1993 average.

The site is of high importance for wintering birds, including c.10% of the north-west European population of *Somateria mollissima*. Most birds are in the German zone.

■ Protection status
National Unknown **International** Partial
Part of IBA covered by Ramsar Site (South Funen Archipelago, 39,200 ha). Part of IBA covered by Special Protection Area (Flensborg Fjord and Nybøl Nor, 3,350 ha). 1,500 ha of IBA covered by Special Protection Area (Marstal Bugt and land areas on Langeland, 4,980 ha). Part of IBA covered by Special Protection Area (Sydfynske Øhav, 38,440 ha).

■ Conservation issues

Threats Extraction industry (C), Unsustainable exploitation (C)

There are several additional protected areas within the German part of the IBA.

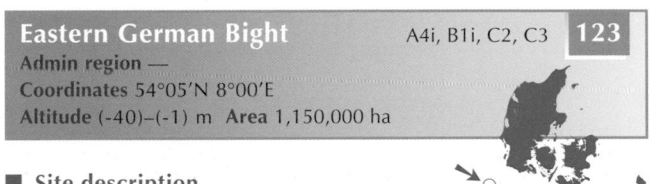

Eastern German Bight   A4i, B1i, C2, C3   123
Admin region —
Coordinates 54°05'N 8°00'E
Altitude (-40)–(-1) m Area 1,150,000 ha

■ Site description
Shallow subtidal area, comprising both Danish and German waters (the area given here refers only to Danish waters). The area is influenced by the freshwater output of the Rivers Elbe and Weser. Food items, and hence birds, are concentrated along the often sharp front between saline and fresh water. The coordinates mark the centre of the international area.

Habitats Marine areas (100%; open sea)
Land-use Unknown

■ Birds

Species	Season	Year	Pop min	Pop max	Acc	Criteria
[1,2]*Gavia stellata* Red-throated Diver	W	1993	—	—	—	A4i, B1i, C2
[1,2]*Gavia arctica* Black-throated Diver	W	1993	—	—	—	A4i, B1i, C2
[2]*Podiceps grisegena* Red-necked Grebe	N	1993	1,850	1,850	—	A4i, B1i, C3
[2]*Melanitta nigra* Common Scoter	W	1993	190,000	190,000	A	A4i, B1i, C3
[2]*Larus minutus* Little Gull	W	1993	2,900	2,900	—	A4i, B1i, C3
[2]*Larus canus* Common Gull	W	1993	37,500	37,500	—	A4i, B1i, C3
[2]*Sterna sandvicensis* Sandwich Tern	P	1993	6,700	6,700	—	A4i, B1i, C2

1. 24,000 *Gavia stellata* and *G. arctica* combined.
2. 1980–1993 average. Figures are for the whole transboundary area (including non-Danish parts).

The site is of high importance for wintering *Gavia stellata* and *Gavia arctica* (totalling over 20% of the biogeographic population) and *Melanitta nigra* (15% of the biogeographic population). 65.6% of the numbers given are within German territory.

■ Protection status
National None **International** None

■ Conservation issues

Threats Aquaculture/fisheries (C), Extraction industry (C), Industrialization/urbanization (B)

Hellebæk   B1iv, C5   124
Admin region Frederiksborg
Coordinates 56°03'N 12°32'E
Altitude 0–36 m Area 800 ha

■ Site description
A mosaic landscape of agricultural areas, broadleaved forest, conifer plantations, a raised bog, several lakes and beaches. Exact delimitation of the area is not possible.

Habitats Forest and woodland (broadleaved deciduous forest), Grassland (mesophile grassland), Wetland (standing fresh water; raised bog), Artificial landscape (highly improved reseeded grassland; forestry plantation)

Land-use Agriculture, Forestry, Military, Nature conservation/research, Tourism/recreation, Urban/industrial/transport

■ Birds
A migration bottleneck during both spring and autumn. Spring totals (raptors and cranes): 7,204 (1995), 19,179 (1996) and 10,109 (1997). Autumn (raptors): 21,802 (1994), 15,522 (1995) and 18,141 (1996). Numbers of migrating raptors are usually higher in autumn as *Buteo buteo* occurs in higher numbers, although most other species occur in lower numbers on autumn migration. Species of global conservation concern that do not meet IBA criteria: *Haliaeetus albicilla* (max. 12, passage).

■ Protection status
National None **International** None

■ Conservation issues
No serious threats are known. Logging is prohibited in several forest pockets.

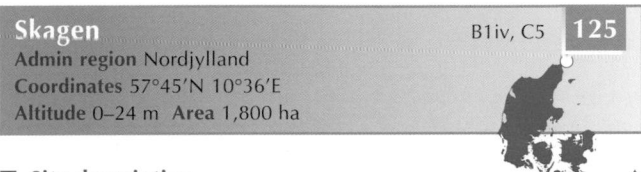

Skagen   B1iv, C5   125
Admin region Nordjylland
Coordinates 57°45'N 10°36'E
Altitude 0–24 m Area 1,800 ha

■ Site description
The nothernmost tip of Jutland, an area of heathland, swamp, dunes and beaches. Exact delimitation of the area is not possible.

Habitats Forest and woodland (broadleaved deciduous forest), Scrub (heathland), Wetland (sand-dunes/sand beach), Artificial landscape (arable land; forestry plantation; urban parks/gardens; other urban/industrial areas)

Land-use Forestry, Nature conservation/research, Tourism/recreation, Urban/industrial/transport

■ Birds
The area is a very important bottleneck for raptors on spring migration. For the 1973–1996 period an average of 7,822 raptors passed through each spring (minimum 3,671 in 1990, maximum 15,252 in 1978). A total of 31 raptor species have been observed for this period, the highest spring diversity in Denmark. Species of global conservation concern that do not meet IBA criteria: *Haliaeetus albicilla* (max. 11, passage).

■ Protection status
National None **International** None

■ Conservation issues

Threats Unknown

Gilleleje area   B1iv, C5   126
Admin region Frederiksborg
Coordinates 56°07'N 12°15'E
Altitude 0–50 m Area 1,250 ha

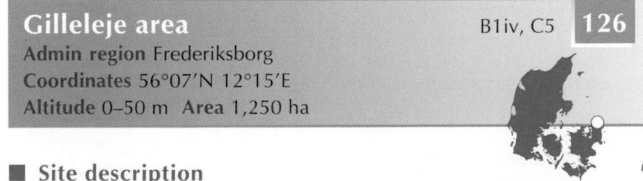

■ Site description
A mainly agricultural area, with forestry plantations, urban areas and beaches. The exact delimitation of the area is not possible.

Habitats Scrub (scrub), Grassland (dry siliceous grassland), Artificial landscape (arable land; forestry plantation; urban parks/gardens)

Land-use Agriculture, Forestry, Nature conservation/research, Tourism/recreation, Urban/industrial/transport

■ Birds
An important bottleneck site for raptors on spring migration. Total raptor numbers for 1993–1996 average 6,365 birds each spring (minimum 4,708 in 1996, maximum 9,515 in 1993) with numbers fluctuating according to prevailing winds. This is also a very important migration corridor for passerines with up to 225,000 passing per day, and up to 800,000 in a season. Species of global conservation

concern that do not meet IBA criteria: *Haliaeetus albicilla* (max. 4, passage).

■ **Protection status**

National None **International** None

■ **Conservation issues**

Threats Unknown

Stevns	A4iv, B1iv, C5	127
Admin region Storstrøm		
Coordinates 55°21'N 12°26'E		
Altitude 0–41 m Area 1,000 ha		

■ **Site description**

A long coastline with low chalk cliffs, agriculture and *Fagus* forest. There is one abandoned and one functional chalk pit in the area. Exact delimitation of the site is not possible.

Habitats Forest and woodland (broadleaved deciduous forest), Scrub (scrub), Grassland (steppe/dry calcareous grassland), Artificial landscape (arable land)

Land-use Unknown

■ **Birds**

An important bottleneck site for migrating raptors, including *Buteo buteo*, in autumn. Numbers for the 1993–1996 period average 17,600 birds per autumn (minimum 12,214 in 1996, maximum 23,854 in 1993). Large annual variations are due to changes in the prevailing winds and also, to some extent, changes in observer coverage. The area receives birds that also migrate through Falsterbo in Sweden (Swedish IBA 061). Species of global conservation concern that do not meet IBA criteria: *Haliaeetus albicilla* (max. 14, passage).

■ **Protection status**

National None **International** None

■ **Conservation issues**

Threats Unknown

REFERENCES

BERTEL, B. (1994) *Fugle over Skagen*. Jyllinge, Denmark. (In Danish.)

DOF [DANSK ORNITOLOGISK FORENING] (1999) The Birds of Denmark: The New Danish Atlas and Birdsite Project 1993–1996. Unpublished data.

DURINCK, J., SKOV, H., JENSEN, F. P. AND PIHL, S. (1994) [*Important areas for wintering birds in the Baltic Sea.*] Copenhagen, Denmark: National Environmental Research Institute & Ornis Consult. (In Danish.)

EMSHOLM, L. (1993) *Oversigt over botaniske lokaliteter. 6. Ringkøbing Amt*. Copenhagen, Denmark: Ministry of the Environment, National Forest and Nature Agency. (In Danish.)

GRAVESEN, P. (1976) *Foreløbig oversigt over botaniske lokaliteter. 1. Sjælland*. Copenhagen, Denmark: Ministry of the Environment, Fredningsstyrelsen. (In Danish.)

GRAVESEN, P. (1979) *Foreløbig oversigt over botaniske lokaliteter. 2. Den fynske øgruppe*. Copenhagen, Denmark: Ministry of the Environment, Fredningsstyrelsen. (In Danish.)

GRAVESEN, P. (1982) *Foreløbig oversigt over botaniske lokaliteter. 3. Lolland, Falster, Møn og Bornholm*. Copenhagen, Denmark: Ministry of the Environment, Fredningsstyrelsen. (In Danish.)

GRAVESEN, P. (1983) *Foreløbig oversigt over botaniske lokaliteter. 4. Sønderjyllands Amt*. Copenhagen, Denmark: Ministry of the Environment, Fredningsstyrelsen. (In Danish.)

GRAVESEN, P. (1986) *Foreløbig oversigt over botaniske lokaliteter. 5. Vejle Amt*. Copenhagen, Denmark: Ministry of the Environment, Fredningsstyrelsen. (In Danish.)

GRIMMETT, R. F. A. AND JONES T. A. (1989) *Important Bird Areas in Europe*. Cambridge, UK: International Council for Bird Preservation (Tech. Publ. 9).

HEATH, M. F. AND BORGGREVE, C. (2000) *BirdLife International/EBCC European Bird Database 1998*. Cambridge, UK: BirdLife International.

JENSEN, F. P. (1996) *Ef-fuglebeskyttelsesområder og Ramsarområder*. Copenhagen, Denmark: Skov- og Naturstyrelsen. (In Danish.)

NIELSEN, M. (1997) *Fuglelokaliteter i Ringkøbing Amt*. Copenhagen, Denmark: Dansk Ornitologisk Forening. (In Danish.)

SKOV, H., DURINCK, J., LEOPOLD, M. F. AND TASKER, M.L. (1995) *Important bird areas for seabirds in the North Sea*. Sandy, UK: Royal Society for the Protection of Birds.

TUCKER, G. M. AND HEATH, M. F. (1994) *Birds in Europe: their conservation status*. Cambridge, UK: BirdLife International (BirdLife Conservation Series no. 3).

WIND, P. (1990) *Oversigt over botaniske lokaliteter. 7. Århus Amt*. Copenhagen, Denmark: Ministry of the Environment, National Forest and Nature Agency. (In Danish.)

WIND, P. (1991) *Oversigt over botaniske lokaliteter. 8. Viborg Amt*. Copenhagen, Denmark: Ministry of the Environment, National Forest and Nature Agency. (In Danish.)

WIND, P. (1992) *Oversigt over botaniske lokaliteter. 9. Nordjyllands Amt*. Copenhagen, Denmark: Ministry of the Environment, National Forest and Nature Agency. (In Danish.)

WIND, P. (1994) *Oversigt over botaniske lokaliteter. 10. Ribe Amt*. Copenhagen, Denmark: Ministry of the Environment, National Forest and Nature Agency. (In Danish.)

Puffin *Fratercula arctica*, an important species at IBAs in the Faroe Islands. (PHOTO: JÓHANN ÓLI HILMARSSON)

GENERAL INTRODUCTION

The Faroe Islands (Føroyar) are a self-governing region of the Kingdom of Denmark. They comprise a group of 18 islands in the north-east Atlantic at about 62°N and 7°W. The total land area is 1,399 km² and the topography is dominated by hills extending to 82 m in height. The human population is 44,817 (in 1998) with an average population density of 32 persons per km².

Nineteen Important Bird Areas (IBAs) are identified, covering an area of 67 km² (Table 1, Map 1).

The data and descriptions presented in this chapter are taken largely from the previous pan-European IBA inventory (Grimmett and Jones 1989).

ORNITHOLOGICAL IMPORTANCE

In all, more than 250 bird species have been recorded in the islands, but most of these are rare or irregular visitors, with less than 50 species breeding regularly (Bloch *et al.* 1996), of which 35 are species

Table 1. Summary of Important Bird Areas in the Faroe Islands.

19 IBAs covering 67 km²

IBA code	1989 code	International/national name	Area (ha)	Criteria (see p. 11)
001	FO001	Mykines and Mykineshólmur	1,028	A4ii, B1ii, B2, B3
002	FO002	Vágar	175	A4ii, B1ii, B2, B3
003	FO003	Streymoy	125	A4ii, B1ii, B2, B3
004	FO004	Eysturoy	60	A4ii, B1ii, B2
005	FO005	Kalsoy	50	A4ii, B1ii, B2
006	FO006	Kunoy	20	A4ii, B1ii, B2
007	FO007	Bordoy	35	A4ii, B1ii, B2
008	FO008	Vidoy	75	A4ii, B1ii, B2
009	FO009	Fugloy	1,118	A4ii, B1ii, B2, B3
010	FO010	Svínoy	100	A4ii, B1ii, B2
011	FO011	Nólsoy	1,028	A4ii, B1ii, B2
012	FO012	Koltur	30	A4ii, B1ii, B2
013	FO013	Hestur	50	A4ii, B1ii, B2
014	FO014	Sandoy	250	A4ii, B1ii, B2, B3
015	FO015	Vøtnini á Sandoy (Lakes of Sandoy)	1,000	B3
016	FO016	Skúvoy	999	A4ii, B1ii, B2, B3
017	FO017	Stóra Dímun	265	A4ii, B1ii, B2
018	FO018	Lítla Dímun	82	A4ii, B1ii, B2
019	FO019	Suduroy	200	A4ii, B1ii, B2, B3

Map 1. Location, area and criteria category of Important Bird Areas in the Faroe Islands.

ATLANTIC OCEAN

Highest category of criteria met by IBA
- A (18 IBAs)
- B (1 IBA)

Area of IBA (ha)
- 1,000 to 1,118
- 175 to 999
- 60 to 174
- 20 to 59

0   15   30
km

Table 2. Important Bird Areas in the Faroe Islands that support important numbers of one or more congregatory species (i.e. meeting criteria A4 and/or B1). IBAs meeting both criteria A4 and B1 for the species are shown in **bold**. IBAs meeting only criterion B1 for the species concerned, and not A4, are shown in normal type. For key to 'Season', see p. 7.

Species	Season	IBA code
Fulmarus glacialis Fulmar	B	**001, 002, 003, 014, 016, 019**
Puffinus puffinus Manx Shearwater	B	**001, 004, 014, 016**
Hydrobates pelagicus Storm Petrel	B	**001, 002, 003, 005, 009, 010, 011, 012, 013, 014, 016, 017, 018, 019**
Uria aalge Guillemot	B	**016**
Cepphus grylle Black Guillemot	B	**001, 002, 003, 004, 005, 006, 007, 008, 009, 010, 011, 012, 013, 014, 016, 017, 019**
Fratercula arctica Puffin	B	**001, 002,** 003, 005, 008, 009, 010, 011, 012, 013, **014,** 016, 017, 018, 019

Table 3. Species of European conservation concern with significant breeding populations at IBAs in the Faroe Islands (meeting criteria B2/B3).

Species [1]	Minimum national breeding population (pairs) [2]	Proportion (%) of national population breeding at all IBAs in the Faroe Islands
Puffinus puffinus Manx Shearwater	25,000	80
Hydrobates pelagicus Storm Petrel	250,000	100 [3]
Sula bassana Gannet	2,000	100
Phalacrocorax aristotelis Shag	1,500	83
Numenius phaeopus Whimbrel	2,500	10
Stercorarius skua Great Skua	450	40
Cepphus grylle Black Guillemot	3,500	97
Fratercula arctica Puffin	550,000	96

1. Only those species of European conservation concern (see Box 1, p. 12) that meet B2/B3 criteria at IBAs in the Faroe Islands are listed.
2. Data are taken from Bloch et al. 1996.
3. The percentage of the national population in IBAs exceeds 100%. This is most likely to be because the national population estimate needs to be reassessed (often as a result of new data on species numbers from comprehensive surveys of IBAs themselves).

of European conservation concern (SPECs; Tucker and Heath 1994).

Inland, species diversity is low (Bloch and Sørensen 1984), and the only species of interest are *Numenius phaeopus*, the c.210 pairs of *Stercorarius skua* (which has a limited global range), and 10–15 pairs of *Gavia stellata*, breeding on some lakes.

Eighteen IBAs have been included largely because of their huge breeding seabird populations which are of major international importance (Table 2). Numbers of *Rissa tridactyla* and *Uria aalge* are also very significant at nearly all IBAs, despite numbers being below the criteria threshold of 1% of the global population. One site (015) is included because it is outstanding for breeding waders. Several of the breeding seabirds are SPECs. Large proportions of the national breeding populations of several SPECs fall within IBAs (Table 3).

The productive waters around the islands provide important foraging areas for seabirds all year-round, and the steep cliffs, grass-covered slopes, and boulder screes facing the sea form ideal nesting sites. The only seabirds that have been censused are *Sula bassana* (Wanless 1987), *Uria aalge* (Dyck and Meltofte 1975; Olsen unpublished) and *Rissa tridactyla* (Olsen unpublished), although

E. Mortensen and B. Olsen have estimated the sizes of the other populations. The most numerous species are *Fulmarus glacialis* (600,000 pairs), *Fratercula arctica* (550,000 pairs), *Hydrobates pelagicus* (250,000 pairs), *Rissa tridactyla* (230,000 pairs) and *Uria aalge* (175,000 pairs).

There has been a dramatic decline in the population of *Uria aalge* since the late 1950s (Dyck and Meltofte 1975; Olsen 1982, 1986, 1992) and the population of *Rissa tridactyla* has also been declining. The *Fulmarus glacialis* population has been increasing since colonization 150 years ago, and the species is now the most numerous bird in the islands.

HABITATS

The base rock of the islands is basalt, which is only partly covered by a thin and stony soil. The main vegetation is grass, with scattered areas of moor, but around the villages there are cultivated hay-fields, gardens with trees, and a few small woods (Figure 1). There are many ponds and a few lakes, some of which are surrounded by peatbogs. The coasts are rugged with steep grass-covered slopes, and the cliffs (especially on the north and west sides) are very steep, with boulder screes.

IMPACTS ON IBAs – LAND-USE AND THREATS

Throughout the islands, sheep are grazed all year-round; some areas (but not the seabird colonies) are also grazed by cattle during the summer.

During the next few years hydrocarbon exploration will be carried out in Faroese waters. This may have consequences for the island's seabird populations.

The brown rat *Rattus norvegicus* is on some of the islands, and has caused great declines and local extinction of *Hydrobates pelagicus*, *Puffinus puffinus* and *Fratercula arctica*. The risk of rats spreading to the currently rat-free islands is high.

Tourism is a relatively new trade in the Faroes and there is no documentation of it having serious negative effects on the birds, although there is some cause for concern. The seabird cliffs are very popular and tourism may become a serious threat if not managed to minimize the effect on the birds.

PROTECTION STATUS

■ National protection

The huge seabird colonies (the majority of the IBAs) are not protected as nature reserves/bird sanctuaries, although they are not currently threatened. Any exploitation must be approved by the island's Nature Conservancy Tribunal, and the shooting of birds closer than three nautical miles from *Uria aalge* colonies and half a nautical mile from *Fratercula arctica* colonies is forbidden.

■ International protection

The Faroes are a self-governing region of the Kingdom of Denmark. Unlike mainland Denmark, the islands are not covered by the Bern Convention, or World Heritage Convention, nor the EC Wild Birds Directive, but the Faroes, as part of Denmark, are covered by the Bonn Convention and the Ramsar Convention although no Ramsar Sites have been designated (Box 1).

Figure 1. Occurrence of habitats at Important Bird Areas in the Faroe Islands (see Appendix 3 for definitions of habitats).

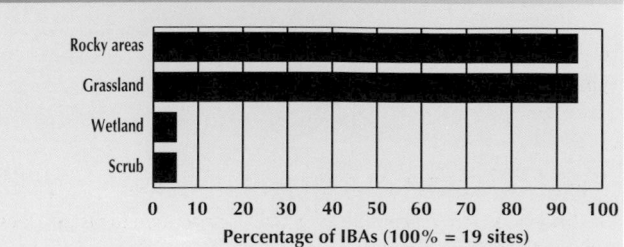

Percentage of IBAs (100% = 19 sites)

Box 1. International legislation and initiatives that are relevant to site conservation in the Faroe Islands (see Appendix 1 for a general description of these agreements).

Global
Biodiversity Convention	
Ramsar Convention	✔
Bonn Convention	✔
World Heritage Convention	
MAB Programme	

Pan-European
Bern Convention	

✔ Convention ratified/initiative supported
(✔) Convention signed

CONSERVATION

- According to the island's game legislation all birds are protected from hunting within the 200 nautical-mile fishing limit, except the following: *Fulmarus glacialis*, *Puffinus puffinus*, *Sula bassana*, *Phalacrocorax aristotelis*, *Stercorarius parasiticus*, *Stercorarius skua*, Laridae, *Uria aalge*, *Alca torda*, *Fratercula arctica*, *Corvus corone* and *Corvus corax*.
- The main quarry species is *Fulmarus glacialis* which can be hunted all year-round. *Phalacrocorax aristotelis*, *Uria aalge*, *Alca torda*, *Fratercula arctica* and young of *Puffinus puffinus* and *Sula bassana* are also hunted, but in restricted periods.
- No important sea areas are included. Ship-based surveys of the marine distribution of seabirds around the Faroes are currently being undertaken and important areas will be identified in the year 2000.

ANALYTICAL METHODS

- The figures given for *Uria aalge* in the text are from 1987 and are individuals seen on the cliffs. Birds out to sea are not included, therefore the figures should probably be increased by at least 50%.
- Numbers of *Rissa tridactyla* and *Uria aalge* are also very significant at nearly all IBAs, despite falling below the criteria threshold of 1% of the global population of the species.

ACKNOWLEDGEMENTS

The site descriptions and overview were compiled from information provided by B. Olsen (all seabird sites) and D. Bloch (Føroya Náttúrugripasavn [Museum of Natural History]) in 1989, with some additional information provided by B. Olsen in 1999.

SITE ACCOUNTS

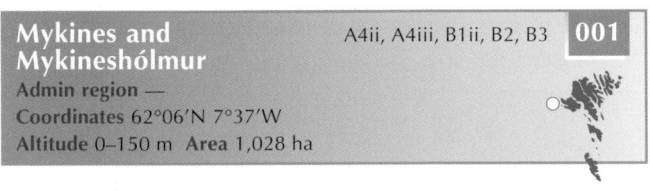

Mykines and Mykineshólmur 001
A4ii, A4iii, B1ii, B2, B3

Admin region —
Coordinates 62°06′N 7°37′W
Altitude 0–150 m **Area** 1,028 ha

Site description
An island and islet with rugged coasts, steep cliffs, and grass-covered slopes. The seabird colonies cover 100 ha of the island. Land-uses include sheep-grazing.

Habitats Grassland, Rocky areas (sea cliff/rocky shore; rock stacks/islets)
Land-use Agriculture

Birds

Species	Season	Year	Pop min	Pop max	Acc	Criteria
Fulmarus glacialis Fulmar	B	1989	—	50,000	—	A4ii, B1ii
Puffinus puffinus Manx Shearwater	B	1989	—	2,500	—	A4ii, B1ii, B2
Hydrobates pelagicus Storm Petrel	B	1989	—	50,000	—	A4ii, B1ii, B2
Sula bassana Gannet	B	1989	—	2,000	—	B2
Phalacrocorax aristotelis Shag	B	1989	—	250	—	B3
Cepphus grylle Black Guillemot	B	1989	—	200	—	A4ii, B1ii
Fratercula arctica Puffin	B	1989	—	125,000	—	A4ii, B1ii, B2

This is an internationally important seabird colony with over 250,000 pairs of breeding seabirds, including *Rissa tridactyla* (23,100 pairs) and *Uria aalge* ((9,500 individuals).

Protection status
National None **International** None

Conservation issues

Threats Unknown

Vágar 002
A4ii, A4iii, B1ii, B2, B3

Admin region –
Coordinates 62°04′N 7°15′W
Altitude 0–150 m **Area** 175 ha

Site description
An island and two islets with rugged coasts and steep grass-covered slopes. Land-uses include sheep-grazing. The site comprises the seabird colonies that are mainly on the north-west, west and south-west coasts.

Habitats Grassland, Rocky areas (sea cliff/rocky shore; rock stacks/islets)
Land-use Agriculture

Birds

Species	Season	Year	Pop min	Pop max	Acc	Criteria
Fulmarus glacialis Fulmar	B	1989	—	100,000	—	A4ii, B1ii

Species ... continued	Season	Year	Pop min	Pop max	Acc	Criteria
Hydrobates pelagicus Storm Petrel	B	1989	—	5,000	—	A4ii, B1ii, B2
Phalacrocorax aristotelis Shag	B	1989	—	500	—	B3
Stercorarius skua Great Skua	B	1989	—	20	—	B3
Cepphus grylle Black Guillemot	B	1989	—	400	—	A4ii, B1ii, B2
Fratercula arctica Puffin	B	1989	—	40,000	—	A4ii, B1ii, B2

This is an internationally important seabird colony with over 50,000 pairs of breeding seabirds, including *Rissa tridactyla* (8,400 pairs) and *Uria aalge* (2,700 individuals).

Protection status
National None **International** None

Conservation issues

Threats Consequences of animal/plant introductions

The brown rat *Rattus norvegicus*, which is present on the island but not the islets, poses a threat to seabird colonies.

Streymoy 003
A4ii, A4iii, B1ii, B2, B3

Admin region —
Coordinates 62°07′N 7°00′W
Altitude 0–200 m **Area** 125 ha

Site description
An island with rugged coasts, steep cliffs, boulder-screes, and grass slopes. Land-uses include sheep-grazing. The site comprises the seabird colonies that are mainly on the north-west coast.

Habitats Grassland, Rocky areas (sea cliff/rocky shore; scree/boulders)
Land-use Agriculture

Birds

Species	Season	Year	Pop min	Pop max	Acc	Criteria
Fulmarus glacialis Fulmar	B	1989	—	75,000	—	A4ii, B1ii
Hydrobates pelagicus Storm Petrel	B	1989	—	2,500	—	A4ii, B1ii, B2
Phalacrocorax aristotelis Shag	B	1989	—	150	—	B3
Stercorarius skua Great Skua	B	1989	—	120	—	B3
Cepphus grylle Black Guillemot	B	1989	—	300	—	A4ii, B1ii, B2
Fratercula arctica Puffin	B	1989	—	20,000	—	B1ii, B2

This is an internationally important seabird colony with c.130,000 pairs of breeding seabirds, including *Rissa tridactyla* (9,000 pairs) and *Uria aalge* (16,300 individuals).

Protection status
National None **International** None

Conservation issues

Threats Consequences of animal/plant introductions

The brown rat *Rattus norvegicus*, which is present on the island, poses a threat to seabird colonies.

Eysturoy
A4ii, A4iii, B1ii, B2 **004**

Admin region —
Coordinates 62°13'N 6°55'W
Altitude 0–200 m **Area** 60 ha

■ Site description

An island with rugged coasts, steep cliffs, boulder-screes and grass slopes. Land-uses include sheep-grazing. The site comprises the seabird colonies that are on the north, north-east, and south-east coasts.

Habitats Grassland, Rocky areas (sea cliff/rocky shore; scree/boulders)
Land-use Agriculture

■ Birds

Species		Season	Year	Pop min	Pop max	Acc	Criteria
Puffinus puffinus	Manx Shearwater	B	1989	—	2,500	—	A4ii, B1ii, B2
Hydrobates pelagicus	Storm Petrel	B	1989	—	500	—	B2
Cepphus grylle	Black Guillemot	B	1989	—	300	—	A4ii, B1ii, B2

This is an internationally important seabird colony with c.50,000 pairs of breeding seabird, including *Rissa tridactyla* (4,600 pairs) and *Uria aalge* (11,100 individuals).

■ Protection status
National None **International** None

■ Conservation issues

Threats Consequences of animal/plant introductions

The brown rat *Rattus norvegicus*, which is present on the island, poses a threat to seabird colonies.

Kalsoy
A4ii, A4iii, B1ii, B2 **005**

Admin region —
Coordinates 62°18'N 6°45'W
Altitude 0–200 m **Area** 50 ha

■ Site description

An island with rugged coasts, steep cliffs, boulder-screes, and grass slopes. Land-uses include sheep-grazing. The site comprises the northern and western coastline of the island.

Habitats Grassland, Rocky areas (sea cliff/rocky shore; scree/boulders)
Land-use Agriculture

■ Birds

Species		Season	Year	Pop min	Pop max	Acc	Criteria
Hydrobates pelagicus	Storm Petrel	B	1989	—	5,000	—	A4ii, B1ii, B2
Cepphus grylle	Black Guillemot	B	1989	—	200	—	A4ii, B1ii
Fratercula arctica	Puffin	B	1989	—	40,000	—	B1ii, B2

This is an internationally important seabird colony with c.70,000 pairs of breeding seabird, including *Rissa tridactyla* (15,600 pairs) and *Uria aalge* (10,700 individuals).

■ Protection status
National None **International** None

■ Conservation issues

Threats Unknown

Kunoy
A4ii, A4iii, B1ii, B2 **006**

Admin region —
Coordinates 62°18'N 6°40'W
Altitude 0–200 m **Area** 20 ha

■ Site description

An island with rugged coasts, steep cliffs, boulder-screes, and grass slopes. Land-uses include sheep-grazing. The site comprises the coastline of the northern tip of the island.

Habitats Grassland, Rocky areas (sea cliff/rocky shore; scree/boulders)
Land-use Agriculture

■ Birds

Species		Season	Year	Pop min	Pop max	Acc	Criteria
Hydrobates pelagicus	Storm Petrel	B	1989	—	250	—	B2
Cepphus grylle	Black Guillemot	B	—	—	200	—	A4ii, B1ii

This is an internationally important seabird colony with over 20,000 pairs of breeding seabird.

■ Protection status
National None **International** None

■ Conservation issues

Threats Consequences of animal/plant introductions

The brown rat *Rattus norvegicus*, which is present on the island, poses a threat to seabird colonies.

Bordoy
A4ii, B1ii, B2 **007**

Admin region —
Coordinates 62°15'N 6°31'W
Altitude 0–200 m **Area** 35 ha

■ Site description

An island with rugged coasts, steep cliffs, boulder-screes, and grass slopes. Land-uses include sheep-grazing. The site comprises the seabird colonies of the northern and south-eastern headlands.

Habitats Grassland, Rocky areas (sea cliff/rocky shore; scree/boulders)
Land-use Agriculture

■ Birds

Species		Season	Year	Pop min	Pop max	Acc	Criteria
Hydrobates pelagicus	Storm Petrel	B	1989	—	250	—	B2
Cepphus grylle	Black Guillemot	B	1989	—	200	—	A4ii, B1ii

This is an internationally important seabird colony.

■ Protection status
National None **International** None

■ Conservation issues

Threats Consequences of animal/plant introductions

The brown rat *Rattus norvegicus*, which is present on the island, poses a threat to seabird colonies.

Vidoy
A4ii, A4iii, B1ii, B2 **008**

Admin region —
Coordinates 62°19'N 6°30'W
Altitude 0–200 m **Area** 75 ha

■ Site description

An island with rugged coast, steep cliffs, boulder-screes, and grass slopes. Land-uses include sheep-grazing. The site comprises the seabird colonies along the northern and eastern sides of the island.

Habitats Grassland, Rocky areas (sea cliff/rocky shore; scree/boulders)
Land-use Agriculture

■ Birds

Species		Season	Year	Pop min	Pop max	Acc	Criteria
Hydrobates pelagicus	Storm Petrel	B	1989	—	500	—	B2
Cepphus grylle	Black Guillemot	B	1989	—	200	—	A4ii, B1ii

Species ... continued	Season	Year	Pop min	Pop max	Acc	Criteria
Fratercula arctica Puffin	B	1989	—	25,000	—	B1ii, B2

This is an internationally important seabird colony with over 50,000 pairs of breeding seabird, including *Rissa tridactyla* (5,300 pairs) and *Uria aalge* (6,700 individuals).

■ **Protection status**
National None **International** None

■ **Conservation issues**

Threats Consequences of animal/plant introductions

The brown rat *Rattus norvegicus,* which is present on the island, poses a threat to seabird colonies.

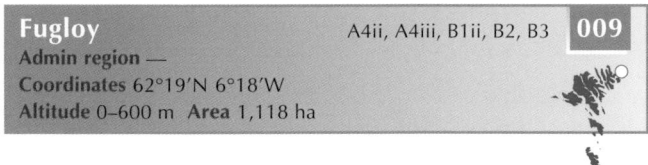

Fugloy A4ii, A4iii, B1ii, B2, B3 **009**
Admin region —
Coordinates 62°19'N 6°18'W
Altitude 0–600 m **Area** 1,118 ha

■ **Site description**
An island with rugged coasts, steep cliffs, boulder-screes, grass slopes, and moorland areas to 600 m. Land-uses include sheep-grazing.

Habitats Grassland, Rocky areas (sea cliff/rocky shore; scree/boulders)
Land-use Agriculture

■ **Birds**

Species	Season	Year	Pop min	Pop max	Acc	Criteria
Hydrobates pelagicus Storm Petrel	B	1989	—	25,000	—	A4ii, B1ii, B2
Numenius phaeopus Whimbrel	B	1989	—	50	—	B3
Cepphus grylle Black Guillemot	B	1989	—	100	—	A4ii, B1ii
Fratercula arctica Puffin	B	1989	—	15,000	—	B1ii

This is an internationally important seabird colony with c.80,000 pairs of breeding seabird, including *Rissa tridactyla* (2,500 pairs) and *Uria aalge* (23,700 individuals).

■ **Protection status**
National None **International** None

■ **Conservation issues**

Threats Unknown

Svínoy A4ii, A4iii, B1ii, B2 **010**
Admin region —
Coordinates 62°15'N 6°25'W
Altitude 0–200 m **Area** 100 ha

■ **Site description**
An island with rugged coasts, steep cliffs, boulder-screes, and grass slopes. Land-uses include sheep-grazing. The site comprises the seabird colonies that surround the island.

Habitats Grassland, Rocky areas (sea cliff/rocky shore; scree/boulders)
Land-use Agriculture

■ **Birds**

Species	Season	Year	Pop min	Pop max	Acc	Criteria
Hydrobates pelagicus Storm Petrel	B	1989	—	25,000	—	A4ii, B1ii, B2
Cepphus grylle Black Guillemot	B	1989	—	100	—	A4ii, B1ii
Fratercula arctica Puffin	B	1989	—	10,000	—	B1ii

Svínoy holds internationally important seabird colonies, with over 30,000 pairs of breeding seabird.

■ **Protection status**
National None **International** None

■ **Conservation issues**

Threats Unknown

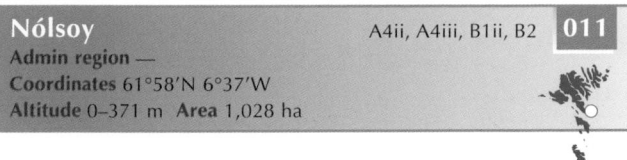

Nólsoy A4ii, A4iii, B1ii, B2 **011**
Admin region —
Coordinates 61°58'N 6°37'W
Altitude 0–371 m **Area** 1,028 ha

■ **Site description**
An island with rugged coasts, steep cliffs, boulder-screes, and grass slopes with important seabird colonies. Inland there are heath and moorland areas. Land-uses include sheep-grazing.

Habitats Scrub (heathland), Grassland, Rocky areas (sea cliff/rocky shore; scree/boulders)
Land-use Agriculture

■ **Birds**

Species	Season	Year	Pop min	Pop max	Acc	Criteria
Hydrobates pelagicus Storm Petrel	B	1989	—	50,000	—	A4ii, B1ii, B2
Cepphus grylle Black Guillemot	B	1989	—	100	—	A4ii, B1ii
Fratercula arctica Puffin	B	1989	—	30,000	—	B1ii, B2

Nólsoy holds internationally important seabird colonies, with c.90,000 pairs of breeding seabird.

■ **Protection status**
National None **International** None

■ **Conservation issues**

Threats Unknown

Koltur A4ii, A4iii, B1ii, B2 **012**
Admin region —
Coordinates 62°00'N 6°58'W
Altitude 0–250 m **Area** 30 ha

■ **Site description**
An island with rugged coasts, steep cliffs, boulder-screes, and grass slopes. Land-uses include sheep-grazing. The site comprises the seabird colonies that almost surround the island.

Habitats Grassland, Rocky areas (sea cliff/rocky shore; scree/boulders)
Land-use Agriculture

■ **Birds**

Species	Season	Year	Pop min	Pop max	Acc	Criteria
Hydrobates pelagicus Storm Petrel	B	1989	—	5,000	—	A4ii, B1ii, B2
Cepphus grylle Black Guillemot	B	1989	—	50	—	A4ii, B1ii
Fratercula arctica Puffin	B	1989	—	20,000	—	B1ii, B2

Koltur holds internationally important seabird colonies, with c.30,000 pairs of breeding seabird.

■ **Protection status**
National None **International** None

■ **Conservation issues**

Threats Unknown

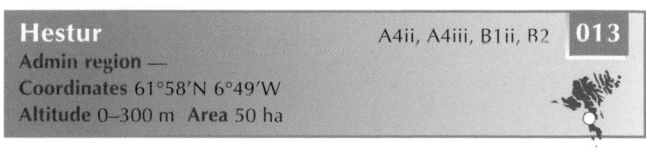

Hestur A4ii, A4iii, B1ii, B2 **013**
Admin region —
Coordinates 61°58'N 6°49'W
Altitude 0–300 m **Area** 50 ha

■ **Site description**
An island with rugged coasts, steep cliffs, boulder-screes, and grass

slopes. Land-uses include sheep-grazing. The site comprises the seabird colonies that almost surround the island.

Habitats Grassland, Rocky areas (sea cliff/rocky shore; scree/boulders)
Land-use Agriculture

■ Birds

Species	Season	Year	Pop min	Pop max	Acc	Criteria
Hydrobates pelagicus	B	1989	—	5,000	—	A4ii, B1ii, B2
Storm Petrel						
Cepphus grylle Black Guillemot	B	1989	—	50	—	A4ii, B1ii
Fratercula arctica Puffin	B	1989	—	25,000	—	B1ii

Hestur holds internationally important seabird colonies, with over 70,000 pairs of breeding seabird, including *Rissa tridactyla* (26,100 pairs) and *Uria aalge* (2,300 individuals).

■ Protection status
National None **International** None

■ Conservation issues

Threats Unknown

Sandoy — A4ii, A4iii, B1ii, B2, B3 — 014
Admin region —
Coordinates 61°51′N 6°48′W
Altitude 0–250 m **Area** 250 ha

■ Site description
An island with rugged coasts, steep cliffs, boulder-screes, and grass slopes. Land-uses include sheep-grazing. The site comprises the seabird colonies that almost surround the island.

Habitats Grassland, Rocky areas (sea cliff/rocky shore; scree/boulders)
Land-use Agriculture

■ Birds

Species	Season	Year	Pop min	Pop max	Acc	Criteria
Fulmarus glacialis Fulmar	B	1989	—	50,000	—	A4ii, B1ii
Puffinus puffinus Manx Shearwater	B	1989	—	5,000	—	A4ii, B1ii, B2
Hydrobates pelagicus	B	1989	—	50,000	—	A4ii, B1ii, B2
Storm Petrel						
Phalacrocorax aristotelis Shag	B	1989	—	150	—	B3
Stercorarius skua Great Skua	B	1989	—	15	—	B3
Cepphus grylle Black Guillemot	B	1989	—	400	—	A4ii, B1ii, B2
Fratercula arctica Puffin	B	1989	—	70,000	—	A4ii, B1ii

The island holds internationally important seabird colonies, with c.170,000 pairs of breeding seabird, including *Rissa tridactyla* (20,500 pairs) and *Uria aalge* (29,500 individuals).

■ Protection status
National None **International** None

■ Conservation issues

Threats Unknown

Vøtnini á Sandoy (Lakes of Sandoy) — B3 — 015
Admin region —
Coordinates 61°49′N 6°49′W
Altitude 0–50 m **Area** 1,000 ha

■ Site description
This site includes the lowland areas around Sandur with moorland and peatbogs, and the lakes Gróthúsvatn, Sandsvatn, Stóravatn and Lítlavatn. There is hay cultivation and sheep-grazing.

Habitats Wetland (standing fresh water; raised bog)
Land-use Agriculture

■ Birds

Species	Season	Year	Pop min	Pop max	Acc	Criteria
Numenius phaeopus Whimbrel	B	1989	100	150	—	B3

This is an important site for breeding waders.

■ Protection status
National None **International** None

■ Conservation issues

Threats Unknown

Skúvoy — A4ii, A4iii, B1ii, B2, B3 — 016
Admin region —
Coordinates 61°46′N 6°49′W
Altitude 0–392 m **Area** 999 ha

■ Site description
An island with rugged coasts, steep cliffs, boulder-screes, and coastal grass slopes. Land-uses include sheep-grazing.

Habitats Grassland, Rocky areas (sea cliff/rocky shore; scree/boulders)
Land-use Agriculture

■ Birds

Species	Season	Year	Pop min	Pop max	Acc	Criteria
Fulmarus glacialis Fulmar	B	1989	—	50,000	—	A4ii, B1ii
Puffinus puffinus Manx Shearwater	B	1989	—	10,000	—	A4ii, B1ii, B2
Hydrobates pelagicus Storm Petrel	B	1989	—	20,000	—	A4ii, B1ii, B2
Numenius phaeopus Whimbrel	B	1989	—	40	—	B3
Stercorarius skua Great Skua	B	1989	—	25	—	B3
[1] *Uria aalge* Guillemot	B	1989	—	135,300	—	A4ii, B1ii
Cepphus grylle Black Guillemot	B	1989	—	150	—	A4ii, B1ii
Fratercula arctica Puffin	B	1989	—	40,000	—	B1ii, B2

1. Individuals.

The site holds internationally important seabird colonies, with c.280,000 pairs of breeding seabird, including *Rissa tridactyla* (22,900 pairs).

■ Protection status
National None **International** None

■ Conservation issues

Threats Unknown

Stóra Dímun — A4ii, A4iii, B1ii, B2 — 017
Admin region —
Coordinates 61°42′N 6°45′W
Altitude 0–395 m **Area** 265 ha

■ Site description
A small island with rugged coasts, steep cliffs, boulder-screes, and grass slopes. Land-uses include sheep-grazing.

Habitats Grassland, Rocky areas (sea cliff/rocky shore; scree/boulders)
Land-use Agriculture

■ Birds

Species	Season	Year	Pop min	Pop max	Acc	Criteria
Hydrobates pelagicus Storm Petrel	B	1989	—	15,000	—	A4ii, B1ii, B2
Cepphus grylle Black Guillemot	B	1989	—	50	—	A4ii, B1ii
Fratercula arctica Puffin	B	1989	—	40,000	—	B1ii, B2

The island holds internationally important seabird colonies, with c.130,000 pairs of breeding seabird, including *Rissa tridactyla* (36,900 pairs) and *Uria aalge* (29,600 individuals).

■ Protection status
National None **International** None

Conservation issues

Threats Unknown

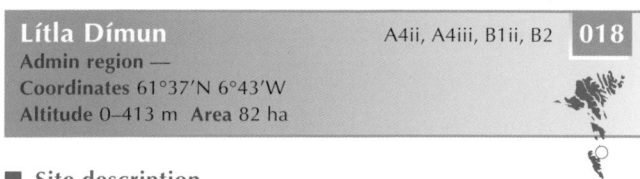

Lítla Dímun   A4ii, A4iii, B1ii, B2   018
Admin region —
Coordinates 61°37′N 6°43′W
Altitude 0–413 m **Area** 82 ha

Site description
A small island with rugged coasts, steep cliffs, boulder-screes, and grass slopes. Land-uses include sheep-grazing.

Habitats Grassland, Rocky areas (sea cliff/rocky shore; scree/boulders)
Land-use Agriculture

Birds

Species	Season	Year	Pop min	Pop max	Acc	Criteria
Hydrobates pelagicus Storm Petrel	B	1989	—	5,000	—	A4ii, B1ii, B2
Fratercula arctica Puffin	B	1989	—	10,000	—	B1ii

The site holds internationally important seabird colonies, with over 30,000 pairs of breeding seabird, including *Rissa tridactyla* (13,100 pairs) and *Uria aalge* (6,200 individuals).

Protection status
National None **International** None

Conservation issues

Threats Unknown

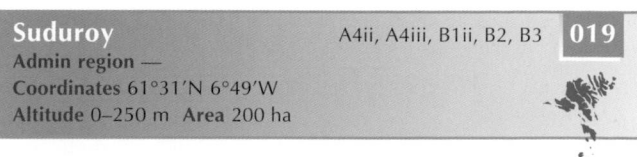

Suduroy   A4ii, A4iii, B1ii, B2, B3   019
Admin region —
Coordinates 61°31′N 6°49′W
Altitude 0–250 m **Area** 200 ha

Site description
An island with rugged coasts, steep cliffs, boulder-screes, and grass slopes. The site comprises the seabird colonies that are mainly along the western side of the island.

Habitats Grassland, Rocky areas (sea cliff/rocky shore; scree/boulders)
Land-use Unknown

Birds

Species	Season	Year	Pop min	Pop max	Acc	Criteria
Fulmarus glacialis Fulmar	B	1989	—	100,000	—	A4ii, B1ii
Hydrobates pelagicus Storm Petrel	B	1989	—	2,500	—	A4ii, B1ii, B2
Phalacrocorax aristotelis Shag	B	1989	—	200	—	B3
Cepphus grylle Black Guillemot	B	1989	—	400	—	A4ii, B1ii, B2
Fratercula arctica Puffin	B	1989	—	20,000	—	B1ii, B2

Suduroy holds internationally important seabird colonies, with nearly 200,000 pairs of breeding seabird, including *Rissa tridactyla* (39,200 pairs) and *Uria aalge* (31,900 individuals).

Protection status
National None **International** None

Conservation issues

Threats Consequences of animal/plant introductions (U)

The brown rat *Rattus norvegicus*, which is present on the island, poses a threat to seabird colonies.

REFERENCES

BLOCH, D. AND SØRENSEN, S. (1984) *Checklist of Faroese birds*. Tórshavn: Føroya Skúlabókagrunnur.

BLOCH, D., JENSEN, J.-K. AND OLSEN, B. (1996) *Liste over fugle der er set på Færøerne*. [*List of the birds seen in the Faroe Islands*.] Tórshavn: Føroya Fuglafrøðifelag and Føroya Skúlabókagrunnur.

DYCK, J. AND MELTOFTE, H. (1975) The Guillemot *Uria aalge* population of the Faroes 1972. *Dansk Orn. Foren. Tidsskr.* 69: 55–64.

GRIMMETT, R. F. A. AND JONES T. A. (1989) *Important Bird Areas in Europe*. Cambridge, UK: International Council for Bird Preservation (Tech. Publ. 9).

JOENSEN, A. H. (1966) *Fuglene på Færøerne*. [*The birds on the Faroe Islands*.] København: Rhodos.

NØRREVANG, A. (1977) *Fuglefangsten på Færøerne*. [*Bird-catching in the Faroe Islands*.] København: Rhodos.

OLSEN, B. (1982) Nogle årsager til nedgangen i den færøske lomviebestand vurderet ud fra mønsteret i tilbagegangen og ringmærkningsresultater. [Some of the reasons for the decline of the Faroese Guillemot population as revealed by the pattern of the decline and by ringing results.] *Viltrapport* 21: 24–30.

OLSEN, B. (1986) *Støðan hjá tí føroyska lomviga- og álkustovninum*. [*Status of the Faroese Guillemot and Razorbill populations*.] Tórshavn: Fisheries Laboratory.

OLSEN, B. (1992) Teljingar av lomviga í Høvdanum á Skúvoynni 1973 til 1991. [Census of guillemots on the Høvdin on Skúvoy.] *Fiskirannsóknir, Tórshavn* 7: 5–15.

OLSEN, B. AND PERMIN, M. (1974) Bestanden av Sule *Sula bassana* på Mykineshólmur 1972. [The population of Gannet *Sula bassana* on Mykineshólmur 1972.] *Dansk Orn. Foren. Tidsskr.* 68: 39–42. (With English summary.)

TUCKER, G. M. AND HEATH, M. F. (1994) *Birds in Europe: their conservation status*. Cambridge, UK: BirdLife International (BirdLife Conservation Series no. 3).

WANLESS, S. (1987) *A survey of the numbers and breeding distribution of the North Atlantic Gannet Sula bassana and an assessment of the changes which have occurred since Operation Seafarer 1969/70*. Peterborough, UK: Nature Conservancy Council (Research and Survey in Nature Conservation no. 4).

■ GREENLAND

David Boertmann

Carey Islands (IBA 005). (PHOTO: David Boertmann)

GENERAL INTRODUCTION

Greenland is a constituent part of the Kingdom of Denmark and has been largely self-governing since 1979, when the foundation for home rule came into force. It is divided into 18 municipalities and one National Park and has an area of c.2,176,000 km², making it the largest island in the world. An extensive ice sheet (the 'Inland Ice') and some smaller local glaciers cover 1,676,000 km² (77%) of the land area. Ice-free areas are restricted to a narrow strip of land, up to 200 km wide, situated between the ice sheet and the surrounding ocean. The terrain is generally mountainous, with flat tundra restricted to valley floors and coastal plains. The coastline is mainly rocky and extensive archipelagos occur, primarily off the western coast.

An Arctic climate prevails across most of Greenland, with average July temperatures remaining below 10°C. Only in some protected fjords in the southernmost part of the island do average July temperatures rise above 10°C, giving rise to subarctic conditions. The waters off south-western Greenland remain ice-free during the winter, forming an extremely important wintering habitat for seabirds. The coast of northern and eastern Greenland is blocked by ice throughout the year, although local polynyas do exist.

Greenland has 55 Important Bird Areas (IBAs), covering c.25,416 km² (5%) of the ice-free land area (Table 1, Map 1). This figure is approximate, as the areas of many sites have not been accurately measured. Large areas of north and south-east Greenland are only sporadically surveyed for their ornithological importance, contributing to the almost total lack of IBAs in these regions (Map 1).

The previous international inventory identified 65 IBAs (Grimmett and Jones 1989), 21 of which do not meet the revised IBA criteria (Table 1). A further ten have been merged together to form three IBAs and 18 new IBAs have been identified.

ORNITHOLOGICAL IMPORTANCE

There are 24 species of European conservation concern (SPECs) breeding regularly in Greenland (Tucker and Heath 1994). No globally threatened species occur; 14 of the 24 SPECs do, however, have an unfavourable conservation status in Europe. Besides a few of those mentioned above, no other SPECs occur regularly on passage, and only one SPEC overwinters regularly. Several subspecies endemic to Greenland have been described: *Anser albifrons flavirostris*, *Anas platyrhynchos conboschas*, *Lagopus mutus* (two of the three subspecies occurring are endemic) and *Calidris alpina arctica*.

Greenland, and in particular west Greenland, is extremely important for breeding seabirds (Table 2). During the summer

Table 1. Summary of Important Bird Areas in Greenland. 55 IBAs covering 25,416 km²

IBA code	1989 code	International name	National name	Administrative region	Area (ha)	Criteria (see p. 11)
001	—	Littleton Island and nearby islets	Pikiulleq and nearby islets	Avanersuaq	300	B1i
002	—	Coastline from Robertson Fjord to Foulke Fjord	Coastline from Robertson fjord to Foulke Fjord	Avanersuaq	40,000	A4ii, A4iii, B1ii
003	GL060	Hakluyt Island	Appaarsuit	Avanersuaq	700	A4iii, B1ii
004	—	Northumberland Island	Kiataq	Avanersuaq	27,000	A4ii, A4iii, B1ii
005	GL059	Carey Islands	Kitsissut	Avanersuaq	1,000	B1ii
006	GL063	Booth Sund area	Booth Sund area	Avanersuaq	8,000	B1i

187

Table 1 ... continued. Summary of Important Bird Areas in Greenland. 55 IBAs covering 25,416 km²

IBA code	1989 code	International name	National name	Administrative region	Area (ha)	Criteria (see p.11)
007	GL064	Dalrymple Rock	Igannaq	Avanersuaq	15	B1i
008	GL058	Saunders Island	Appat	Avanersuaq	300	A4ii, A4iii, B1ii
009	GL065	Qeqertaarsuit (Ederfugleøer)	Qeqertaarsuit (Ederfugleøer)	Avanersuaq	5	B1i
010	GL057	Parker Snow Bay	Parker Snow Bugt	Avanersuaq	100	A4iii, B1ii
011	GL056	Appat Appai	Appat Appai	Avanersuaq	20	A4iii, B1ii
012	—	Coast between Appaliarsulissuaq and Kap Atholl	Coast between Appaliarsulissuaq and Kap Atholl	Avanersuaq	30,000	A4ii, A4iii, B1ii
013	GL045	Kitsissorsuit (Ederfugleøer)	Kitsissorsuit (Ederfugleøer)	Upernavik	250	B1i
014	GL053, GL054	Apparsuit (Kap Shackleton) and Kippaku	Apparsuit (Kap Shackleton) and Kippaku	Upernavik	250	A4ii, A4iii, B1ii
015	GL047	Kingittuarsuk III	Kingittuarsuk III	Upernavik	5	B1i
016	GL039, GL040, GL041, GL048, GL049, GL055	Islands and waters south and west of Upernavik town	Islands and waters south and west of Upernavik town	Upernavik	20,000	A4iii, B1ii, B2
017	—	Umiiarfik	Umiiarfik	Upernavik	15,000	A4i, B1i
018	—	Itsako	Itsako	Uummannaq	8,000	B1i
019	—	Appatsiaat	Appatsiaat	Uummannaq	500	A4iii
020	—	Salleq	Salleq	Uummannaq	100	A4iii
021	—	Innarsuaq	Innarsuaq	Uummannaq	600	A4iii
022	—	Qingartarsuaq	Qingartarsuaq	Uummannaq	400	A4iii
023	GL037	Nordfjord and adjacent valley	Qinnguata Marraa–Kuussuaq	Qeqertarsuaq	18,000	A4i, B1i, B2
024	—	Qeqertaq	Qeqertaq	Qeqertarsuaq	650	A4iii
025	GL033	Aqajarua–Sullorsuaq (Mudderbugten and Kvandalen)	Aqajarua–Sullorsuaq (Mudderbugten and Kvandalen)	Qeqertarsuaq	20,000	A4i, B1i
026	GL032	Appat, Ritenbenk	Appat, Ritenbenk	Ilulissat	100	A4iii
027	—	Northern part of Store Hellefiskebanke	Northern part of Store Hellefiskebanke		500,000	A4i, A4iii, B1i
028	GL034	Assissut (Braendvinsskaerene) near Kronprinsens Ejland	Assissut (Braendvinsskaerene) near Kronprinsens Ejland	Qeqertarsuaq	25	B2
029	GL028	Nunatsiaq (Rotten)	Nunatsiaq (Rotten)	Aasiaat	20	B2
030	GL030	Kitsissunngit (Grønne Ejland)	Kitsissunnguit (Grønne Ejland)	Aasiaat, Qasigiannguit	3,000	A4i, A4iii, B1i
031	GL029	Naternaq (Lersletten)	Naternaq (Lersletten)	Kangaatsiaq, Qasigiannguit	150,000	B1i
032	GL026	Eqalummiut Nunaat–Nassuttuup Nunaa	Eqalummiut Nunaat–Nassuttuup Nunaa		500,000	B1i
033	GL025	Itinneq	Itinneq	Sisimiut	1,500	B1i
034	GL021	Taateraat in Evighedsfjorden	Taateraat in Evighedsfjorden	Maniitsoq	100	A4iii, B1ii, B3
035	GL022	Sermilinnguaq	Sermilinnguaq	Maniitsoq	3,000	A4i, A4iii, B1i, B1ii, B3
036	GL023	Søndre Isortoq	Søndre Isortoq	Maniitsoq	100	A4i, A4iii, B1i, B3
037	—	Fyllas bank off Nuuk	Fyllas bank off Nuuk		160,000	A4i, A4iii, B1i
038	—	Qissuttuut (Ravneøer)	Qissuttuut (Ravneøer)	Nuuk	30	B2
039	—	Islands west and north-west of Simiuttat and south of Qilangarsuit	Islands west and north-west of Simiuttat and south of Qilangarsuit	Nuuk	8,500	B2, B3
040	GL020	Ikkattoq Fjord and islands	Ikkattoq tamatumalu kitaaniittut qeqertat	Nuuk	35,000	B1i, B2
041	GL018	Kitsissut Avalliit (Ydre Kitsissut)	Kitsissut Avalliit (Ydre Kitsissut)	Qaqortoq	8,000	B1ii, B3
042	GL017	Kap Brewster and Volquart Boon's coast	Kap Brewster and Volquart Boon's coast	Scoresbysund	20,000	A4ii, A4iii, B1ii
043	GL016	Liverpool Land coast and mouth of Scoresby Sund	Liverpool Land coast and mouth of Scoresby Sund	Scoresbysund	150,000	A4ii, A4iii, B1ii
044	GL015	Heden	Heden	Scoresbysund	220,000	A4i, B1i, B3
045	GL013	Kjoveland	Kjoveland	Scoresbysund	15,000	B1i
046	GL012	Enhjørningens Dal and Pingel Dal	Enhjørningens Dal and Pingel Dal	Scoresbysund	50,000	B1i
047	GL011	Ørsted Dal and Coloradodal	Ørsted Dal and Coloradodal	Scoresbysund	40,000	B1i, B3
048	GL002	Østersletten and Knudshoved, Hold With Hope	Østersletten and Knudshoved, Hold With Hope	North and North-east Greenland National Park	55,000	B1i
049	GL001, GL004	Stordal–Moskusoksefjord–Badlanddal–Loch Fyne–Myggbukta	Stordal–Moskusoksefjord–Badlanddal–Loch Fyne–Myggbukta	North and North-east Greenland National Park	90,000	A4i, B1i, B2
050	—	Albrecht Sletten (Storsletten), Wollaston Forland	Albrecht Sletten (Storsletten), Wollaston Forland	North and North-east Greenland National Park	30,000	B1i
051	GL005	Hochstetter Forland	Hochstetter Forland	North and North-east Greenland National Park	140,000	A3, A4i, B1i, B3
052	GL007	South coast of Germania Land, and Slaedelandet	South coast of Germania Land, and Slaedelandet	North and North-east Greenland National Park	35,000	A3, B1i, B2
053	—	Eastern part of Germania Land	Eastern part of Germania Land	North and North-east Greenland National Park	100,000	A3, A4i, B1i
054	—	Henrik Krøyer Holme	Henrik Krøyer Holme	North and North-east Greenland National Park	1,000	A4i, B1i, B2
055	GL010	Kilen	Kilen	North and North-east Greenland National Park	35,000	A4i, B1i, B2

Sites identified in the previous inventory of IBAs in Europe (Grimmett and Jones 1989) but no longer considered to be IBAs
GL003 Tobias Dal; GL006 Shannon; GL008 Flade Bugt; GL009 Danmarks Havn and surrounding area, including Skibsso; GL014 Hurry Fjord including Fame Øer and Kap Stewart; GL019 Foxfaldet, Ilorput; GL024 Tasersuaq; GL027 Rifkol; GL031 Sarqaqdalen; GL035 Nipissat, Diskofjord; GL036 Kuannersuit Kuussuat; GL038 Qegertat; GL042 Issortussoq; GL043 Saatoq; GL044 Uigorluk; GL046 Kingittuarsuk II; GL050 Torqussaarsuk; GL051 Torqussaq; GL052 Appalersalik; GL061 Lyon Øer; GL062 Saatut.

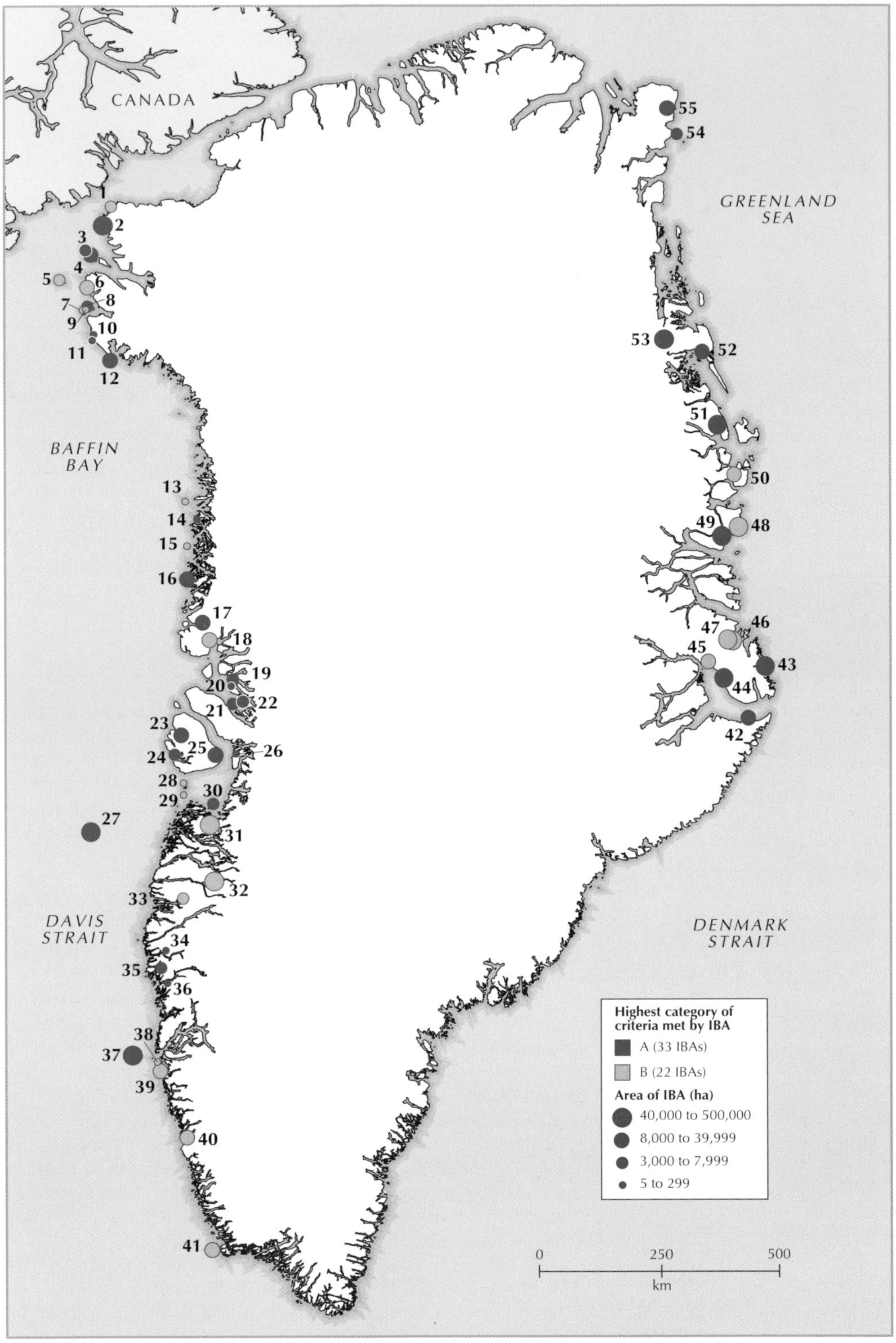

Map 1. Location, area and criteria category of Important Bird Areas in Greenland.

Table 2. Important Bird Areas in Greenland that support important numbers of one or more congregatory species (i.e. meeting criteria A4 and/or B1). IBAs meeting both criteria A4 and B1 for the species are shown in **bold**. IBAs meeting only criterion B1 for the species concerned, and not A4, are shown in normal type. For key to 'Season', see p. 7.

Species	Season	IBA code
Anser brachyrhynchus	N	**044, 049**, 050, **051, 053**
Pink-footed Goose		
Anser albifrons White-fronted Goose	B	032
	P	033
	N	018, 025, 031, 032
Branta leucopsis Barnacle Goose	B	047
	N	044, 045, 046, 047, 048, 049, 051, 052
Branta bernicla Brent Goose	B	055
	N	055
Somateria mollissima Eider	B	001, 006, 007, 009, 013, 015, 049
	P	013
	N	040

Species	Season	IBA code
Somateria spectabilis King Eider	W	**027, 037**
	N	**017, 023, 025**
Mergus serrator	N	040
Red-breasted Merganser		
Larus glaucoides Iceland Gull	B	**035, 036**
Pagophila eburnea Ivory Gull	B	**054, 055**
Sterna paradisaea Arctic Tern	B	**030**
Uria lomvia Brünnich's Guillemot	B	003, 005, **008**, 010, 011, **014**, 016, 034, 035, 041
Cepphus grylle Black Guillemot	B	016
Alle alle Little Auk	B	**002, 004, 012, 042, 043**

Table 3. Species of European conservation concern with significant breeding populations at Important Bird Areas in Greenland (meeting any IBA criteria).

Species [1]	Minimum national breeding population (pairs) [2]	Proportion (%) of national population breeding at all IBAs in Greenland
Gavia stellata Red-throated Diver	5,000	1
Anser brachyrhynchus Pink-footed Goose	5,000	3
Branta leucopsis Barnacle Goose	3,000	5
Branta bernicla Brent Goose	100	70
Haliaeetus albicilla White-tailed Eagle	147	2
Falco rusticolus Gyrfalcon	500	—[3]
Pagophila eburnea Ivory Gull	400	51
Alca torda Razorbill	2,000	52
Cepphus grylle Black Guillemot	25,000	5
Fratercula arctica Puffin	4,000	42
Nyctea scandiaca Snowy Owl	1,000	—[3]

1. Only those species of European conservation concern (see Box 1, p. 12) that meet IBA criteria in Greenland are listed.
2. Data are taken from the BirdLife/EBCC European Bird Database 1998 (Heath and Borggreve 2000).
3. No population data available for Greenland IBAs.

Figure 1. Occurrence of habitats at Important Bird Areas in Greenland (see Appendix 3 for definitions of habitats).

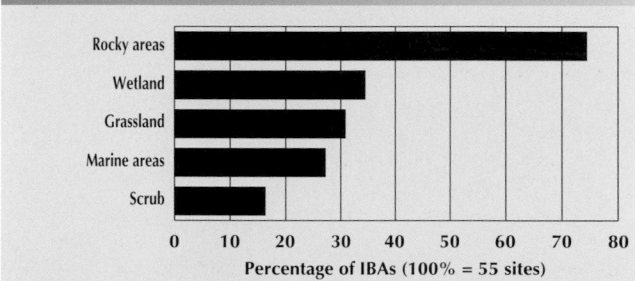

Percentage of IBAs (100% = 55 sites)

Figure 2. Occurrence of land-uses at Important Bird Areas in Greenland (see Appendix 3 for definitions of land-uses).

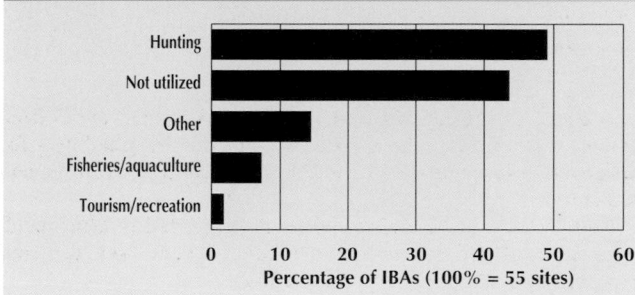

Percentage of IBAs (100% = 55 sites)

season significant numbers of *Fulmarus glacialis*, gulls (Laridae), *Sterna paradisaea* and auks (Alcidae) congregate at coastal colonies. The total number of *Alle alle* breeding in north-west Greenland may comprise up to 80% of the global population (for example, IBAs 002, 004, 012, 042 and 043). Seven such colonies or groups of colonies qualify as IBAs as they hold more than 1% of the global population of those seabird species listed in Table 2, and therefore meet the A4ii criterion.

Also worth noting are the significant numbers of *Pagophila eburnea* that breed in north and east Greenland (Table 3), for example at IBAs 054 and 055, and the fact that the country holds

the vast majority of the European breeding population of *Larus glaucoides* (for example, IBAs 035 and 036).

Discrete Greenland breeding populations of *Anser albifrons flavirostris* and *Branta leucopsis* occur in the west and east of Greenland respectively. *Branta bernicla hrota* breeds partly in the north-east of the country (also on Svalbard), with the north-east Canadian flyway population of this species occurring on passage. *Somateria mollissima* is a common breeder. Important moulting congregations of *Anser brachyrhynchus* and *Somateria spectabilis* occur in east and west Greenland respectively. Wintering concentrations of the latter also form offshore (for example, IBAs 027 and 037). Twenty-seven IBAs have been identified as supporting more than 1% of the flyway population of at least one of these six species (meeting criterion B1i). Numbers are sufficiently high (more than 1% of biogeographic population) at nine of these 27 sites to meet the A4i criterion as well (Table 2).

Greenland supports a small, discrete population of *Haliaeetus albicilla* and large, but unknown, numbers of *Falco rusticolus* and *Nyctea scandiaca* (Table 3). Species such as these are not adequately covered by the IBA inventory due to the dispersed nature of their distributions. IBAs 051, 052 and 053 do however hold significant numbers of up to eight species (including *Falco rusticolus* and *Nyctea scandiaca*) whose European breeding distributions are largely or wholly confined to the Arctic/tundra biome, and therefore meet the A3 criterion.

HABITATS

Seabird colonies are found mainly on rocky coastlines and on small, low-lying offshore islands—this partly explains the high occurrence of rocky habitats (75% of sites) at Greenland IBAs (Figure 1). In north and north-east Greenland sparse precipitation restricts vegetation growth, and barren rock and fell fields are the main habitat-type (for example, IBAs 053 and 055). Elsewhere, dry habitats are characterized by dwarf shrub heaths and in southern areas by *Salix*, *Alnus* and *Betula* scrub. Wetlands are present at 19 IBAs (35%), with marshes and fens widespread in lowlands and bordering rivers and lakes (Figure 1). Lowlands with many ponds and lakes are rare. Saltmarshes occur along low-lying coasts, but are generally restricted in area.

Tundra is the dominant grassland-type at Greenland IBAs, occurring at 16 of the 17 IBAs (Figure 1) that have a grassland component. In north-east Greenland tundra supports large but dispersed breeding populations of geese (for example, *Anser brachyrhynchus* and *Branta leucopsis*), waders (for example, *Charadrius hiaticula*, *Calidris canutus*, *Calidris alba*, *Calidris alpina* and *Arenaria interpres*), *Stercorarius longicaudus* and *Nyctea scandiaca*—numbers of the latter fluctuate with cycles in the lemming *Dicrostonyx* population. Areas of tundra in west Greenland hold a less diverse avifauna, with *Anser albifrons* and a few species of wader (*Calidris maritima* and *Phalaropus lobatus*) breeding.

The most significant habitat to be under-represented by the IBA inventory is open sea; for example, the shallow offshore banks where large flocks of *Somateria spectabilis* winter and stage during the spring migration (IBAs 027 and 037). It is likely that more marine IBAs will be identified in the seas surrounding Greenland, as more data become available.

IMPACTS ON IBAs – LAND-USE AND THREATS

Hunting is the most frequently occurring land-use at Greenland IBAs (49% of sites) (Figure 2). Subsistence and sport hunting of caribou *Rangifer tarandus* and musk oxen *Ovibos moschatus* takes

Figure 3. Occurrence of threats at Important Bird Areas in Greenland (see Appendix 3 for definitions of threat types and impact categories).

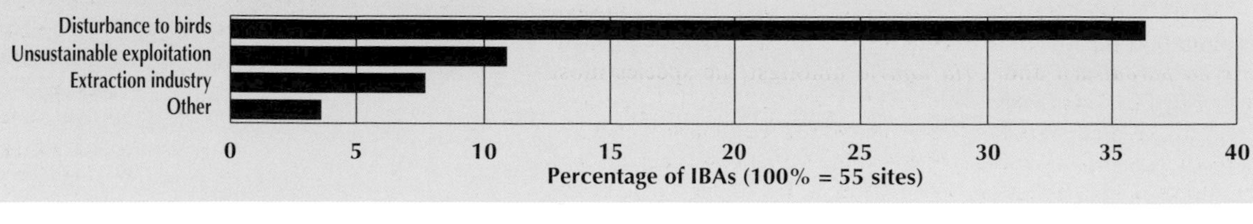

Disturbance to birds	
Unsustainable exploitation	
Extraction industry	
Other	

Percentage of IBAs (100% = 55 sites)

Table 4. Protection status of Important Bird Areas in Greenland.
A tick (✔) indicates that an IBA overlaps with a protected area (to any extent).

IBA code	International name	National Park	Breeding Reserve for Birds	Ramsar Site	Biosphere Reserve
001	Littleton Island and nearby islets				
002	Coastline from Robertson Fjord to Foulke Fjord				
003	Hakluyt Island				
004	Northumberland Island				
005	Carey Islands				
006	Booth Sund area				
007	Dalrymple Rock				
008	Saunders Island				
009	Qeqertaarsuit (Ederfugleøer)				
010	Parker Snow Bay				
011	Appat Appai				
012	Coast between Appaliarsulissuaq and Kap Atholl				
013	Kitsissorsuit (Ederfugleøer)				
014	Apparsuit (Kap Shackleton) and Kippaku		✔		
015	Kingittuarsuk III				
016	Islands and waters south and west of Upernavik town		✔		
017	Umiiarfik				
018	Itsako				
019	Appatsiaat				
020	Salleq		✔		
021	Innarsuaq				
022	Qingartarsuaq				
023	Nordfjord and adjacent valley			✔	
024	Qeqertaq				
025	Aqajarua–Sullorsuaq (Mudderbugten and Kvandalen)			✔	
026	Appat, Ritenbenk		✔		
027	Northern part of Store Hellefiskebanke				
028	Assissut (Braendvinsskaerene) near Kronprinsen Ejland		✔		
Subtotal of IBAs		**0**	**5**	**2**	**0**
029	Nunatsiaq (Rotten)		✔		
030	Kitsissunnguit (Grønne Ejland)		✔	✔	
031	Naternaq (Lersletten)			✔	
032	Eqalummiut Nunaat–Nassuttuup Nunaa			✔	
033	Itinneq				
034	Taateraat in Evighedsfjorden				
035	Sermilinnguaq				
036	Søndre Isortoq				
037	Fyllas bank off Nuuk				
038	Qissuttuut (Ravneøer)				
039	Islands west and north-west of Simiuttat and south of Qilangarsuit				
040	Ikkattoq Fjord and islands			✔	
041	Kitsissut Avalliit (Ydre Kitsissut)		✔	✔	
042	Kap Brewster and Volquart Boon's coast				
043	Liverpool Land coast and mouth of Scoresby Sund				
044	Heden			✔	
045	Kjoveland				
046	Enhjørningens Dal and Pingel Dal				
047	Ørsted Dal and Coloradodal				
048	Østersletten and Knudshoved, Hold With Hope	✔			✔
049	Stordal–Moskusoksefjord–Badlanddal–Loch Fyne–Myggbukta	✔			✔
050	Albrecht Sletten (Storsletten), Wollaston Forland	✔			✔
051	Hochstetter Forland	✔		✔	✔
052	South coast of Germania Land, and Slaedelandet	✔			✔
053	Eastern part of Germania Land	✔			✔
054	Henrik Krøyer Holme	✔			✔
055	Kilen	✔		✔	✔
Total number of IBAs		**8**	**8**	**10**	**8**

place in terrestrial habitats; *Lagopus mutus* is the main bird quarry. Marine areas are extensively used for subsistence and sport hunting. The collection of seabird eggs is a legal activity in Greenland and takes place at eight IBAs (15%) ('Other' land-use—Figure 2).

Agriculture is restricted to those regions in the south experiencing a subarctic climate, where hay is grown and harvested for use as winter forage for sheep. Elsewhere in Greenland land-use, with the exception of hunting, is restricted to settlements and their surrounds (towns, villages, weather stations and military installations). Holiday cottages are, however, becoming increasingly popular, particularly near to the larger towns such as Nuuk and Sisimiut.

Deep-sea shrimp fisheries are the main economic activity in Greenland—these take place in deeper waters and therefore do not impact on IBAs. Gill-nets are set along the coasts, mainly for the fish *Cyclopterus lumpus*, and may harm local breeding populations of *Phalacrocorax carbo* and *Cepphus grylle*. The large-scale drift net fishery previously operational in the eastern Davis Strait, which killed substantial numbers of *Uria lomvia* as by-catch, has now ceased and no longer poses a threat. Clam-dredging is a very localized activity, but may coincide with *Somateria spectabilis* moulting grounds. Just such a conflict looks to have contributed to a major decline in numbers of this seaduck at a previously important moulting site (IBA 025).

Many seabird breeding colonies suffer greatly from human exploitation and disturbance (Figure 3), with *Somateria mollissima*, *Sterna paradisaea* and *Uria lomvia* amongst the species most affected. The *Uria lomvia* colonies close to the town of Upernavik (IBA 016) have declined in size by 80–90% since 1930 as a result of disturbance and the effects of hunting. Large concentrations of moulting *Somateria spectabilis* present in fjords and bays in the

municipalities of Qeqertarsuaq and Upernavik are also at risk from human disturbance. The most important moulting habitats for *Somateria spectabilis* today are those situated away from human settlements.

Mineral resources are not currently exploited in Greenland. Extensive oil exploration takes place offshore however, and exploratory drillings are expected in 2000.

PROTECTION STATUS

Table 4 and Figures 4 and 5 summarize the national and international protection status of all IBAs in Greenland.

■ National protection

Greenland is, in its entirety, government-owned; private land holdings do not exist. Despite this, very few sites that are important for birds are protected (Table 4 and Figure 4). Hunting regulations cover Breeding Reserves for Birds (mainly seabird colonies) where

Box 1. International legislation and initiatives that are relevant to site conservation in Greenland (see Appendix 1 for a general description of these agreements).

Global	
Biodiversity Convention	
Ramsar Convention	✔
Bonn Convention	
World Heritage Convention	
MAB Programme	✔
Pan-European	
Bern Convention	

✔ Convention ratified/initiative supported
(✔) Convention signed

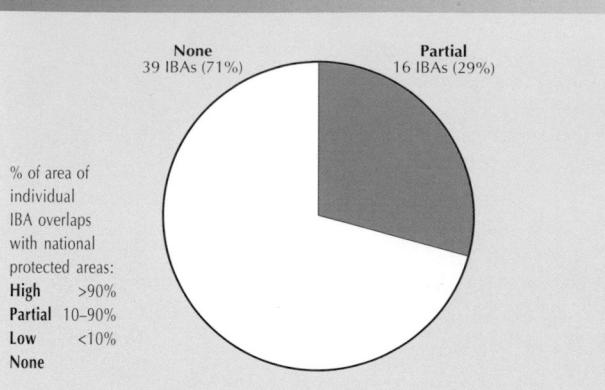

Figure 4. The national protection status of Important Bird Areas in Greenland.

None 39 IBAs (71%) Partial 16 IBAs (29%)

% of area of individual IBA overlaps with national protected areas:
High >90%
Partial 10–90%
Low <10%
None

Not possible to calculate total area of overlap between IBA network in Greenland and national protected-area system (see Table 4 for categories) due to incomplete overlap-area data.

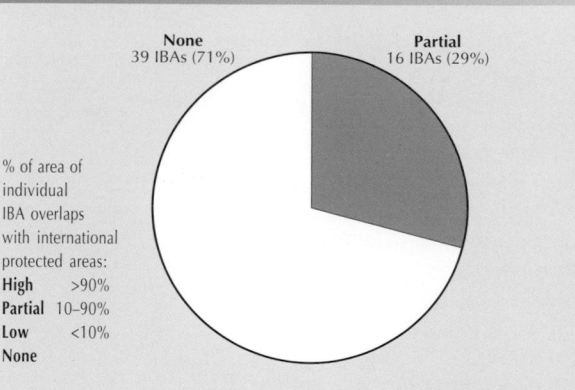

Figure 5. The international protection status of Important Bird Areas in Greenland.

None 39 IBAs (71%) Partial 16 IBAs (29%)

% of area of individual IBA overlaps with international protected areas:
High >90%
Partial 10–90%
Low <10%
None

Not possible to calculate total area of overlap between IBA network in Greenland and international protected-area system (see Table 4 for categories) due to incomplete overlap-area data.

admission is prohibited during the breeding season. Legally protected areas are not otherwise designated specifically for birds. The majority of north and north-east Greenland is, however, included in a National Park that covers 184,750 km² of ice-free land. Eight IBAs are situated within the Park (Table 4). It should be noted that mineral resource exploitation is still possible within the confines of the Park.

■ **International protection**
Box 1 shows which relevant international agreements Greenland has ratified. Eleven Ramsar Sites have been designated, of which 10 overlap with IBAs (Table 4).

CONSERVATION

- The Greenland Institute of Natural Resources has initiated monitoring programmes for breeding *Somateria mollissima* and *Uria lomvia*, as proposed by CAFF.
- A hunting-bag recording system, covering the most important quarry species, was introduced in 1993.
- NERI-AE has undertaken seabird studies in relation to oil exploration activities, with the aim of providing baseline data for environmental impact assessment and contingency planning purposes.

ANALYTICAL METHODS

- Population estimates for colonial seabirds are based mainly on good-quality data from surveys performed during 1992 and 1994, supplemented by data from the literature and personal communications. All such data are stored in a Greenland seabird colony database maintained by NERI-AE.
- Data for geese are generally of good quality and are based on surveys carried out since 1982.

- The numbers of breeding pairs given in the species tables represent one-off counts rather than average numbers recorded over a period of time.
- The numbers of wintering and passage birds given in the species tables are maximum daily counts.
- The following sites were proposed as IBAs but did not meet the current criteria: Spiret in Nassuttooq Fjord; Sarfalik in Nassuttooq Fjord; Akuliarusersuaq in Paakitsoq Fjord; and Tasersuit.
- Data on percentage cover of habitats and land-uses, and level of impact of threats, were not used in the generation of Figures 1 to 3 as the dataset was incomplete. Where such data are present for an IBA, full details are given in the relevant site account.
- Threat data are, in the main, current although it should, however, be noted that a threat identified in the previous international IBA inventory (Grimmett and Jones 1989) may have been included even though it has not been possible to verify the continued presence or absence of the threat in question.
- Data on overlaps between IBAs and protected areas were usually unavailable—a problem compounded further by the fact that the areas of many IBAs are not accurately known.

GLOSSARY

CAFF Conservation of Arctic Flora and Fauna—one of four programs under the Arctic Environmental Protection Strategy (AEPS), adopted by the Arctic nations in Rovaniemi, Finland in 1991.
NERI-AE The Department of the Arctic Environment at the National Environmental Research Institute.
polynya a stretch of open water surrounded by ice, especially in the Arctic seas.
tundra a treeless zone, lying principally north of the Arctic Circle, where winters are long and severe, and summers are short and relatively cool (mean July temperatures not above 10°C). The soil is permanently frozen below the surface layers.

■ SITE ACCOUNTS

Littleton Island and nearby islets B1i 001
Admin region Avanersuaq
Coordinates 78°22′N 72°50′W
Altitude 0–50 m Area 300 ha

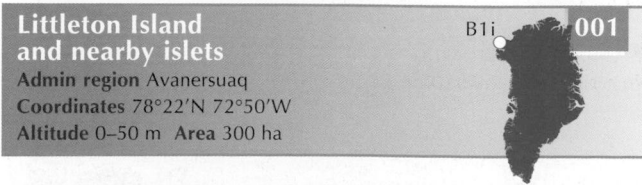

■ **Site description**
A low-lying rocky island with adjacent rocky islets. Egg- and down-collecting takes place ('Other' land-use).

Habitats Rocky areas (100%; sea cliff/rocky shore)
Land-use Hunting, Other

■ **Birds**

Species	Season	Year	Pop min	Pop max	Acc	Criteria
Somateria mollissima Eider	B	1988	1,000	—	B	B1i

Possibly the largest *Somateria mollissima* breeding colony in Greenland.

■ **Protection status**
National None **International** None

■ **Conservation issues**

Threats Unsustainable exploitation (B)

Many thousands of eggs were collected each year until at least 1998.

192

Coastline from Robertson Fjord to Foulke Fjord

A4ii, A4iii, B1ii 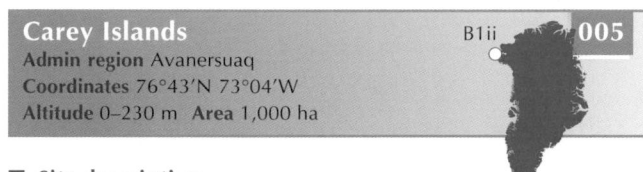 **002**

Admin region Avanersuaq
Coordinates 78°00′N 72°30′W
Altitude 0–700 m **Area** 40,000 ha

■ Site description
A rocky coastline with screes and glaciers, extending from 77°40′N 70°40′W to 78°20′N 72°50′W.

Habitats Rocky areas (100%; sea cliff/rocky shore; scree/boulders)
Land-use Hunting

■ Birds

Species	Season	Year	Pop min	Pop max	Acc	Criteria
[1] *Alle alle* Little Auk	B	1995	—	>1,000,000	C	A4ii, B1ii

1. Many millions of individuals.

Internationally important area for extremely large numbers of *Alle alle*. Colonies extend along c.160 km of coastline and inland along glaciers.

■ Protection status
National None **International** None

■ Conservation issues
With the exception of a local and probably sustainable subsistence catch of *Alle alle*, no serious threats are known at the site.

Hakluyt Island

A4iii, B1ii **003**

Admin region Avanersuaq
Coordinates 77°25′N 72°37′W
Altitude 0–300 m **Area** 700 ha

■ Site description
An island with associated sea cliffs.

Habitats Rocky areas (sea cliff/rocky shore)
Land-use Not utilized (100%)

■ Birds

Species	Season	Year	Pop min	Pop max	Acc	Criteria
[1] *Uria lomvia* Brünnich's Guillemot	B	1987	37,000	37,000	—	B1ii

1. Individuals.

Also holds breeding *Rissa tridactyla* (2,000–5,000 pairs), *Alca torda*, *Cepphus grylle* (200 individuals), *Alle alle* (large numbers) and *Fratercula arctica* (1987 data).

■ Protection status
National None **International** None

■ Conservation issues
No serious threats are known at the site.

Northumberland Island

A4ii, A4iii, B1ii **004**

Admin region Avanersuaq
Coordinates 77°25′N 72°00′W
Altitude 0–500 m **Area** 27,000 ha

■ Site description
Steep rocky cliffs and screes facing the sea.

Habitats Rocky areas (100%; sea cliff/rocky shore; scree/boulders)
Land-use Not utilized (100%)

■ Birds

Species	Season	Year	Pop min	Pop max	Acc	Criteria
[1] *Alle alle* Little Auk	B	1995	—	>1,000,000	C	A4ii, B1ii

1. Many millions of individuals.

Internationally important site for *Alle alle*, which is present in extremely large numbers. Colonies extend along c.50 km of coastline.

■ Protection status
National None **International** None

■ Conservation issues
No serious threats are known at the site.

Carey Islands

B1ii **005**

Admin region Avanersuaq
Coordinates 76°43′N 73°04′W
Altitude 0–230 m **Area** 1,000 ha

■ Site description
Islands with associated sea cliffs.

Habitats Rocky areas (sea cliff/rocky shore)
Land-use Not utilized (100%)

■ Birds

Species	Season	Year	Pop min	Pop max	Acc	Criteria
[1] *Uria lomvia* Brünnich's Guillemot	B	1987	6,700	6,700	—	B1ii

1. Individuals.

Also holds breeding *Larus hyperboreus*, *Alca torda*, *Cepphus grylle* (230 individuals) and *Fratercula arctica* (60 individuals) (1987 data).

■ Protection status
National None **International** None

■ Conservation issues
No serious threats are known at the site.

Booth Sund area

B1i **006**

Admin region Avanersuaq
Coordinates 76°52′N 70°49′W
Altitude 0–50 m **Area** 8,000 ha

■ Site description
A well-vegetated plain located to the south of the Booth Sund inlet, comprising tundra and marsh habitats and several shallow lakes. The shallow inlet contains many small islands.

Habitats Grassland (tundra), Wetland (coastal lagoon; water-fringe vegetation), Marine areas (sea inlet/coastal features), Rocky areas (rock stacks/islets)
Land-use Hunting (100%)

■ Birds

Species	Season	Year	Pop min	Pop max	Acc	Criteria
[1] *Somateria mollissima* Eider	B	1997	866	—	C	B1i

1. Moulting non-breeders also occur.

Also important for breeding *Sterna paradisaea* and moulting *Anser caerulescens*.

■ Protection status
National None **International** None

■ Conservation issues
No serious threats are known at the site.

Dalrymple Rock

B1i 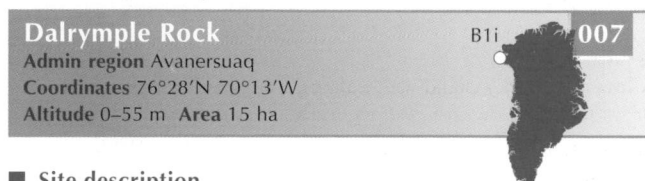 **007**

Admin region Avanersuaq
Coordinates 76°28′N 70°13′W
Altitude 0–55 m **Area** 15 ha

■ Site description
A small rocky island with associated sea cliffs.

Habitats Rocky areas (sea cliff/rocky shore)
Land-use Not utilized (100%)

■ **Birds**

Species		Season	Year	Pop min	Pop max	Acc	Criteria
Somateria mollissima Eider		B	1988	400	400	—	B1i

The site also holds breeding *Fratercula arctica* (50 pairs, 1988).

■ **Protection status**
National None **International** None

■ **Conservation issues**
No serious threats are known at the site.

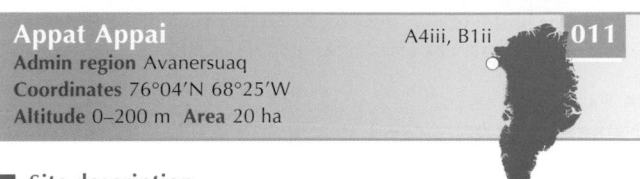

Saunders Island
A4ii, A4iii, B1ii 008
Admin region Avanersuaq
Coordinates 76°34′N 70°03′W
Altitude 0–250 m **Area** 300 ha

■ **Site description**
An island with associated sea cliffs.

Habitats Rocky areas (sea cliff/rocky shore)
Land-use Not utilized (100%)

■ **Birds**

Species		Season	Year	Pop min	Pop max	Acc	Criteria
[1] *Uria lomvia* Brünnich's Guillemot		B	1987	143,000	143,000	—	A4ii, B1ii

1. Individuals.

The site also holds breeding *Fulmarus glacialis* (5,000 individuals) and *Cepphus grylle* (100 individuals) (1987 data).

■ **Protection status**
National None **International** None

■ **Conservation issues**
No serious threats are known at the site.

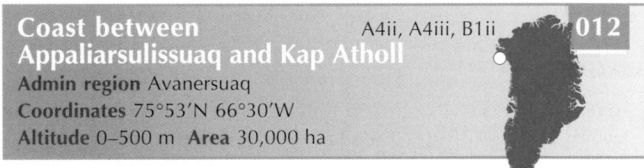

Qeqertaarsuit (Ederfugleøer)
B1i 009
Admin region Avanersuaq
Coordinates 76°30′N 70°04′W
Altitude 0–10 m **Area** 5 ha

■ **Site description**
Small, low-lying islands. Egg-collecting takes place ('Other' land-use).

Land-use Other

■ **Birds**

Species		Season	Year	Pop min	Pop max	Acc	Criteria
Somateria mollissima Eider		B	1988	1,000	1,000	—	B1i

■ **Protection status**
National None **International** None

■ **Conservation issues**
No serious threats are known at the site.

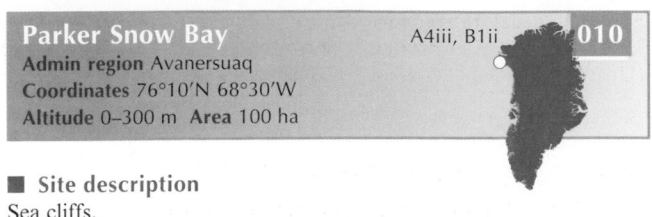

Parker Snow Bay
A4iii, B1ii 010
Admin region Avanersuaq
Coordinates 76°10′N 68°30′W
Altitude 0–300 m **Area** 100 ha

■ **Site description**
Sea cliffs.

Habitats Rocky areas (sea cliff/rocky shore)
Land-use Not utilized (100%)

■ **Birds**

Species		Season	Year	Pop min	Pop max	Acc	Criteria
[1] *Uria lomvia* Brünnich's Guillemot		B	1987	50,000	50,000	—	B1ii

1. Individuals.

The site holds large numbers of breeding seabirds on a regular basis, including *Rissa tridactyla* (2,000 individuals, 1987).

■ **Protection status**
National None **International** None

■ **Conservation issues**
No serious threats are known at the site.

Appat Appai
A4iii, B1ii 011
Admin region Avanersuaq
Coordinates 76°04′N 68°25′W
Altitude 0–200 m **Area** 20 ha

■ **Site description**
Sea cliffs.

Habitats Rocky areas (sea cliff/rocky shore)
Land-use Not utilized (100%)

■ **Birds**

Species		Season	Year	Pop min	Pop max	Acc	Criteria
[1] *Uria lomvia* Brünnich's Guillemot		B	1987	48,000	48,000	—	B1ii

1. Individuals.

The site holds large numbers of breeding seabirds on a regular basis, including *Rissa tridactyla* (5,000 individuals) and *Cepphus grylle* (100 individuals) (1987 data).

■ **Protection status**
National None **International** None

■ **Conservation issues**
No serious threats are known at the site.

Coast between Appaliarsulissuaq and Kap Atholl
A4ii, A4iii, B1ii 012
Admin region Avanersuaq
Coordinates 75°53′N 66°30′W
Altitude 0–500 m **Area** 30,000 ha

■ **Site description**
Steep cliffs and screes facing the sea, as well as several inland cliffs and screes. These habitats occur on the mainland and on several islands.

Habitats Rocky areas (100%; sea cliff/rocky shore; scree/boulders; inland cliff)
Land-use Hunting

■ **Birds**

Species		Season	Year	Pop min	Pop max	Acc	Criteria
[1] *Alle alle* Little Auk		B	1995	—	>1,000,000	C	A4ii, B1ii

1. Many millions of individuals.

Internationally important site for *Alle alle*, which is present in extremely large numbers. Colonies extend along c.200 km of coastline.

■ **Protection status**
National None **International** None

■ **Conservation issues**
With the exception of a local and probably sustainable subsistence catch of *Alle alle*, no serious threats are known at the site.

Kitsissorsuit (Ederfugleøer) B1i 013

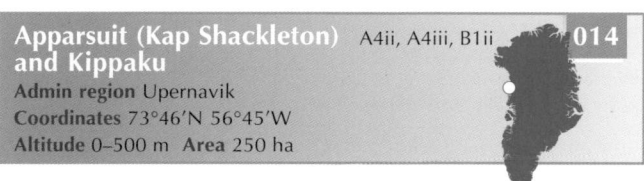

Admin region Upernavik
Coordinates 74°01'N 57°49'W
Altitude 0–80 m **Area** 250 ha

■ Site description
Three rocky islands and associated sea cliffs.

Habitats Grassland (30%; tundra), Wetland (10%; shingle/stony beach), Marine areas (10%; sea inlet/coastal features), Rocky areas (50%; sea cliff/rocky shore)
Land-use Hunting

■ Birds

Species	Season	Year	Pop min	Pop max	Acc	Criteria
Somateria mollissima Eider	B	1994	10	100	B	B1i
[1] *Somateria mollissima* Eider	P	—	—	—	—	B1i

1. Many hundreds occur during spring.

Also holds breeding *Larus glaucoides* (20 pairs), *Alca torda*, *Cepphus grylle* (290 individuals) and *Fratercula arctica* (1994 data).

■ Protection status
National None **International** None

■ Conservation issues

Threats Unsustainable exploitation (C)

This site was once one of the most important *Somateria mollissima* colonies in Greenland—numbers have crashed since the beginning of the 1900s as a result of persecution by humans. If suitable protection measures are introduced then numbers of *Somateria mollissima* will probably begin to increase again.

Apparsuit (Kap Shackleton) and Kippaku A4ii, A4iii, B1ii 014

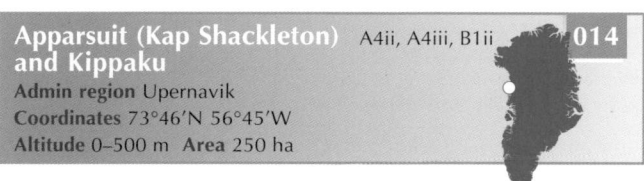

Admin region Upernavik
Coordinates 73°46'N 56°45'W
Altitude 0–500 m **Area** 250 ha

■ Site description
A high rocky island with sea cliffs located mainly on the southern coast. The site also includes Kippaku—a small rocky island (15 ha) with sea cliffs on the northern and north-western sides, which slopes gradually to the south/south-west. The two islands were treated as separate IBAs in the previous international IBA inventory (Grimmett and Jones 1989): Kippaku (former site GL053) and Apparsuit (former site GL054).

Habitats Rocky areas (100%; sea cliff/rocky shore)
Land-use Not utilized (100%)

■ Birds

Species	Season	Year	Pop min	Pop max	Acc	Criteria
[1] *Uria lomvia* Brünnich's Guillemot	B	1994	166,893	166,893	A	A4ii, B1ii

1. Individuals: 153,103 at Apparsuit; 13,790 at Kippaku.

Apparsuit supports the largest seabird colony in west Greenland. The IBA also holds 3,430–4,010 breeding pairs of *Rissa tridactyla* (1994 data).

■ Protection status
National Partial **International** None
IBA overlaps with Breeding Reserve for Birds (Apparsuit).

■ Conservation issues

Threats Disturbance to birds (B)

With the exception of local disturbance caused by hunting, no serious threats are known at the site. These two colonies have not seen the serious declines in *Uria lomvia* numbers recorded elsewhere (e.g. IBA 016), which is probably due to their remoteness from human settlement.

Kingittuarsuk III B1i 015

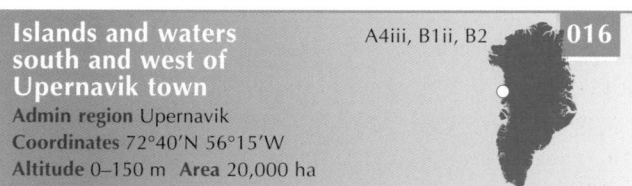

Admin region Upernavik
Coordinates 73°15'N 56°49'W
Altitude 0–70 m **Area** 5 ha

■ Site description
A small rocky island.

Habitats Rocky areas (sea cliff/rocky shore)
Land-use Hunting

■ Birds

Species	Season	Year	Pop min	Pop max	Acc	Criteria
Somateria mollissima Eider	B	1987	200	200	—	B1i

The site also holds small numbers of breeding *Alca torda* and *Fratercula arctica*. *Uria lomvia* no longer breeds at the site.

■ Protection status
National None **International** None

■ Conservation issues

Threats Disturbance to birds (U)

With the exception of local disturbance caused by hunting, no serious threats are known at the site.

Islands and waters south and west of Upernavik town A4iii, B1ii, B2 016

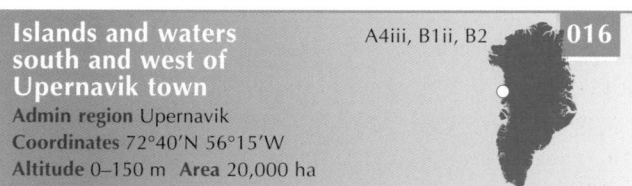

Admin region Upernavik
Coordinates 72°40'N 56°15'W
Altitude 0–150 m **Area** 20,000 ha

■ Site description
The site comprises archipelagoes, small islands and stretches of steep coastline that support several seabird colonies, located between 72°36'N and 72°48'N. This area includes six sites that were treated as separate IBAs in the previous international IBA inventory (Grimmett and Jones 1989): Sanderson's Hope (Upernavik Apparsuit), island of Qaersorssuaq (former site GL039), Appatsiaat, island of Qaersorssuaq (former site GL040), Kingittoq Apparsuit, island of Qaersorssuaq (former site GL041), Avannarleq (Nordø) (former site GL048), Aarrussaq (Hvalø) (former site GL049) and Timmiakulussuit, island of Nutaarmiut (former site GL055).

Habitats Marine areas (open sea), Rocky areas (sea cliff/rocky shore; rock stacks/islets)
Land-use Not utilized (100%)

■ Birds

Species	Season	Year	Pop min	Pop max	Acc	Criteria
[1] *Uria lomvia* Brünnich's Guillemot	B	1994	9,515	9,515	—	B1ii
[1] *Cepphus grylle* Black Guillemot	B	1994	541	541	—	B1ii, B2
[2] *Fratercula arctica* Puffin	B	1994	354	404	—	B2

1. Individuals – 4 colonies.
2. Individuals – 2 colonies.

The site also holds breeding *Fulmarus glacialis* (>5,000 pairs) and *Rissa tridactyla* (3,229 pairs at four colonies) (1994 data). All four *Uria lomvia* colonies are decreasing in size (80–90% reduction in size since 1930)—the largest held 7,000 individuals in 1994.

■ Protection status
National Partial **International** None
IBA overlaps with Breeding Reserve for Birds (Sanderson's Hope (Upernavik Apparsuit), island of Qaersorssuaq).

■ Conservation issues

Threats Disturbance to birds (U), Unsustainable exploitation (U)

The effects of hunting and associated disturbance pose a major threat. Helicopter flights close to *Uria lomvia* colonies also cause disturbance.

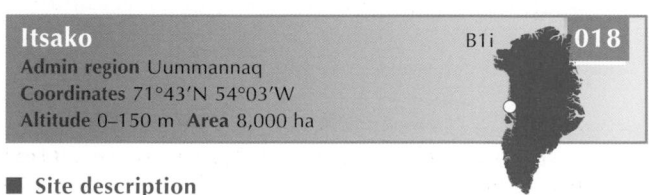

Umiiarfik A4i, B1i 017
Admin region Upernavik
Coordinates 72°00'N 54°40'W
Altitude 0–10 m **Area** 15,000 ha

■ Site description
A long, narrow, shallow fjord.

Habitats Marine areas (100%; sea inlet/coastal features)
Land-use Hunting

■ Birds

Species	Season	Year	Pop min	Pop max	Acc	Criteria
Somateria spectabilis King Eider	N	1994	2,280	—	—	A4i, B1i

Probably the second most important moulting area for *Somateria spectabilis* in Greenland.

■ Protection status
National None **International** None

■ Conservation issues

Threats Disturbance to birds (U)

Disturbance caused to moulting *Somateria spectabilis* may be a problem. The extent to which local residents make use of the IBA is unknown.

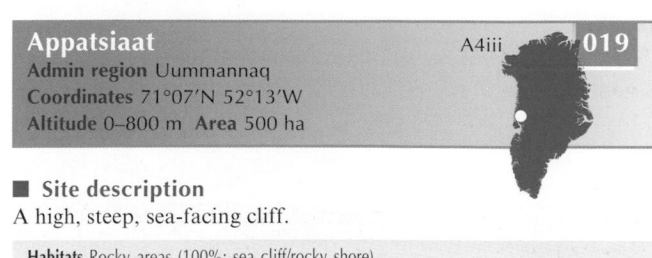

Itsako B1i 018
Admin region Uummannaq
Coordinates 71°43'N 54°03'W
Altitude 0–150 m **Area** 8,000 ha

■ Site description
Extensive tundra with several ponds and large areas of marsh.

Habitats Grassland (50%; tundra), Wetland (50%; mudflat/sandflat; saltmarsh; standing fresh water; river/stream; water-fringe vegetation)
Land-use Hunting

■ Birds

Species	Season	Year	Pop min	Pop max	Acc	Criteria
Anser albifrons White-fronted Goose	N	1992	450	—	—	B1i

Important for moulting and breeding *Anser albifrons flavirostris* and the only site in Greenland where *Cygnus columbianus* regularly occurs.

■ Protection status
National None **International** None

■ Conservation issues
No serious threats are known at the site.

Appatsiaat A4iii 019
Admin region Uummannaq
Coordinates 71°07'N 52°13'W
Altitude 0–800 m **Area** 500 ha

■ Site description
A high, steep, sea-facing cliff.

Habitats Rocky areas (100%; sea cliff/rocky shore)
Land-use Not utilized (100%)

■ Birds
The site holds large numbers of breeding *Fulmarus glacialis* (>15,000 pairs, 1994).

■ Protection status
National None **International** None

■ Conservation issues
No serious threats are known at the site.

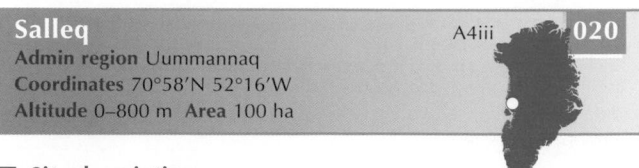

Salleq A4iii 020
Admin region Uummannaq
Coordinates 70°58'N 52°16'W
Altitude 0–800 m **Area** 100 ha

■ Site description
A high, steep, sea-facing cliff.

Habitats Rocky areas (100%; sea cliff/rocky shore)
Land-use Not utilized (100%)

■ Birds
The site holds large numbers of breeding *Fulmarus glacialis* (>10,000 pairs, 1994). *Uria lomvia* formerly bred in very large numbers.

■ Protection status
National Partial **International** None
IBA overlaps with Breeding Reserve for Birds.

■ Conservation issues
No serious threats are known at the site.

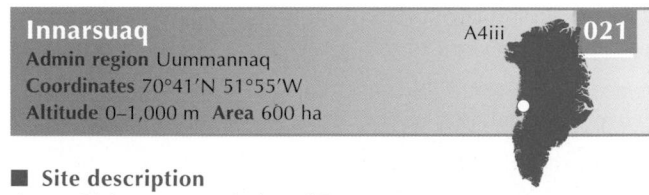

Innarsuaq A4iii 021
Admin region Uummannaq
Coordinates 70°41'N 51°55'W
Altitude 0–1,000 m **Area** 600 ha

■ Site description
A very high, steep, sea-facing cliff.

Habitats Rocky areas (100%; sea cliff/rocky shore)
Land-use Not utilized (100%)

■ Birds
The site holds large numbers of breeding *Fulmarus glacialis* (>10,000 pairs, 1994).

■ Protection status
National None **International** None

■ Conservation issues
No serious threats are known at the site.

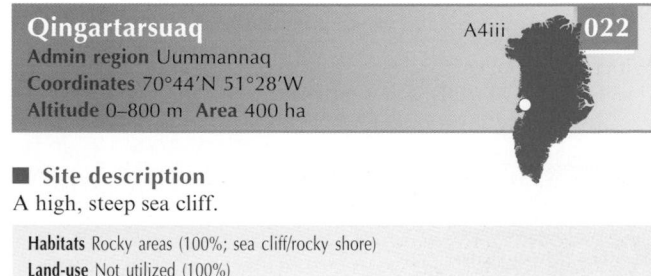

Qingartarsuaq A4iii 022
Admin region Uummannaq
Coordinates 70°44'N 51°28'W
Altitude 0–800 m **Area** 400 ha

■ Site description
A high, steep sea cliff.

Habitats Rocky areas (100%; sea cliff/rocky shore)
Land-use Not utilized (100%)

■ Birds
The site holds large numbers of breeding *Fulmarus glacialis* (>10,000 pairs, 1984).

■ Protection status
National None **International** None

■ Conservation issues
No serious threats are known at the site.

Nordfjord and adjacent valley

A4i, B1i, B2 **023**

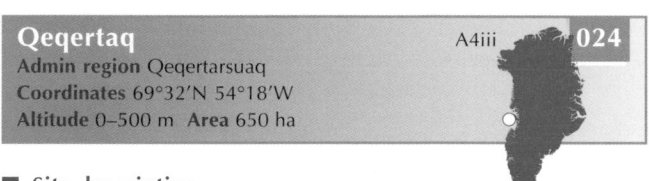

Admin region Qeqertarsuaq
Coordinates 69°55'N 54°16'W
Altitude 0–100 m **Area** 18,000 ha

Site description
A fjord and the adjacent valley, containing lakes and ponds.

Habitats Wetland (standing fresh water; river/stream; water-fringe vegetation), Marine areas (sea inlet/coastal features)
Land-use Fisheries/aquaculture, Hunting

Birds

Species	Season	Year	Pop min	Pop max	Acc	Criteria
[1] *Gavia stellata* Red-throated Diver	B	—	—	—	—	B2
Somateria spectabilis King Eider	N	1995	7,000	7,000	—	A4i, B1i

1. Breeds at high densities.

The fjord is the most important moulting site for *Somateria spectabilis* in Greenland. *Branta bernicla hrota* stop over during autumn migration.

Protection status
National None **International** Partial
IBA overlaps with Ramsar Site (Qinnguata Marraa–Kuussuaq).

Conservation issues

Threats Disturbance to birds (U)

Disturbance caused to moulting *Somateria spectabilis* may intensify if clam-dredging activities increase in scale.

Qeqertaq

A4iii **024**

Admin region Qeqertarsuaq
Coordinates 69°32'N 54°18'W
Altitude 0–500 m **Area** 650 ha

Site description
The site comprises 10 km of steep, south-facing sea cliffs.

Habitats Rocky areas (100%; sea cliff/rocky shore)
Land-use Hunting

Birds
The site holds large numbers of breeding *Fulmarus glacialis* (65,000 individuals, 1992).

Protection status
National None **International** None

Conservation issues

Threats Disturbance to birds (C)

With the exception of local disturbance caused by hunting, no serious threats are known at the site.

Aqajarua–Sullorsuaq (Mudderbugten and Kvandalen)

A4i, B1i **025**

Admin region Qeqertarsuaq
Coordinates 69°42'N 52°15'W
Altitude 0–200 m **Area** 20,000 ha

Site description

Habitats Scrub (5%; heathland), Grassland (20%; tundra), Wetland (25%; mudflat/sandflat; sand-dunes/sand beach; standing fresh water; river/stream; water-fringe vegetation), Marine areas (40%; sea inlet/coastal features), Rocky areas (10%)
Land-use Fisheries/aquaculture (50%), Hunting (100%)

Sullorsuaq is a broad, U-shaped valley with glacial melt-water channels present in its lower reaches. Raised flats of tundra and dwarf-shrub heath vegetation occur, with large areas of freshwater marsh at lower altitudes. Aqajarua is a shallow, soft-bottomed, offshore marine area.

Birds

Species	Season	Year	Pop min	Pop max	Acc	Criteria
Anser albifrons White-fronted Goose	N	1995	1,500	—	—	B1i
Somateria spectabilis King Eider	N	1994	300	500	—	A4i, B1i

Large numbers of moulting *Somateria spectabilis* have been present in the recent past (30,000 individuals in the 1960s).

Protection status
National None **International** Partial
IBA overlaps with Ramsar Site (Aqajarua–Sullorsuaq).

Conservation issues

Threats Disturbance to birds (A)

The importance of Aqajarua as a moulting ground for *Somateria spectabilis* has been greatly reduced, probably due to disturbance from hunting and clam-dredging activities.

Appat, Ritenbenk

A4iii **026**

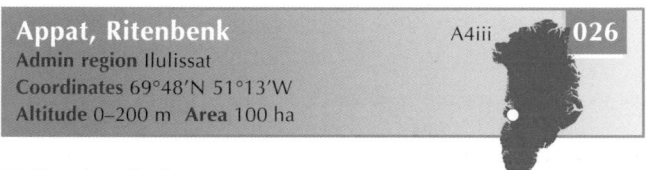

Admin region Ilulissat
Coordinates 69°48'N 51°13'W
Altitude 0–200 m **Area** 100 ha

Site description
Sea cliffs. Egg-collecting takes place ('Other' land-use).

Habitats Rocky areas (100%; sea cliff/rocky shore)
Land-use Other

Birds
The site holds large numbers of breeding seabirds, including *Larus glaucoides* (147 pairs), *Rissa tridactyla* (5,838 pairs), *Uria lomvia* (3,655 individuals), *Alca torda* and *Cepphus grylle* (1994 data). c.35,000 *Rissa tridactyla* were estimated to be present in 1984.

Protection status
National Partial **International** None
IBA overlaps with Breeding Reserve for Birds.

Conservation issues

Threats Disturbance to birds (C)

With the exception of local disturbance caused by hunting, no serious threats are known at the site.

Northern part of Store Hellefiskebanke

A4i, A4iii, B1i **027**

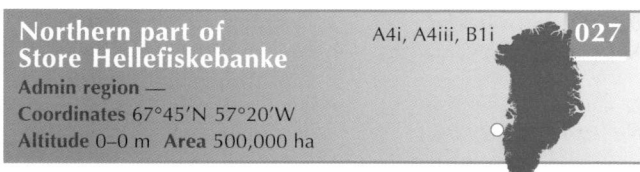

Admin region —
Coordinates 67°45'N 57°20'W
Altitude 0–0 m **Area** 500,000 ha

Site description
A large sea area, falling within the 50 m isobath.

Habitats Marine areas (100%; open sea)
Land-use Fisheries/aquaculture, Hunting

Birds

Species	Season	Year	Pop min	Pop max	Acc	Criteria
[1] *Somateria spectabilis* King Eider	W	1991	110,000	437,000	—	A4i, B1i

1. Estimated.

This site is very important for wintering *Somateria spectabilis*.

Protection status
National None **International** None

■ Conservation issues

Threats Disturbance to birds (U), Other (U)

Oil spills pose a threat ('Other' threat).

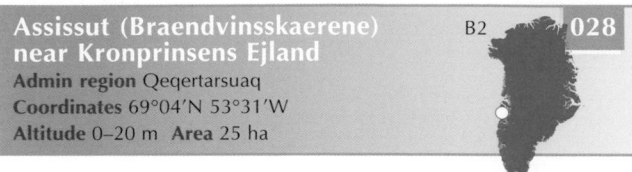

Assissut (Braendvinsskaerene) near Kronprinsens Ejland B2 028
Admin region Qeqertarsuaq
Coordinates 69°04'N 53°31'W
Altitude 0–20 m **Area** 25 ha

■ Site description

Three small islands which are almost devoid of vegetation.

Habitats Rocky areas (rock stacks/islets)
Land-use Not utilized (100%)

■ Birds

Species	Season	Year	Pop min	Pop max	Acc	Criteria
¹ *Fratercula arctica* Puffin	B	1988	800	800	—	B2

1. Individuals.

The site also holds small numbers of breeding *Alca torda*, *Cepphus grylle* and *Alle alle*.

■ Protection status

National Partial **International** None
IBA overlaps with Breeding Reserve for Birds.

■ Conservation issues

No serious threats are known at the site.

Nunatsiaq (Rotten) B2 029
Admin region Aasiaat
Coordinates 68°52'N 53°22'W
Altitude 0–18 m **Area** 20 ha

■ Site description

A small, grass-covered island. Egg-collecting takes place ('Other' land-use).

Habitats Grassland (tundra), Rocky areas (rock stacks/islets)
Land-use Other

■ Birds

Species	Season	Year	Pop min	Pop max	Acc	Criteria
¹ *Fratercula arctica* Puffin	B	1976	1,000	1,000	—	B2

1. Probably individuals.

Possibly the largest *Fratercula arctica* breeding colony in Greenland. The site also holds breeding *Alca torda* (50 individuals) and *Cepphus grylle* (1976 data).

■ Protection status

National Partial **International** None
IBA overlaps with Breeding Reserve for Birds.

■ Conservation issues

Threats Disturbance to birds (U)

Kitsissunnguit (Grønne Ejland) A4i, A4iii, B1i 030
Admin region Aasiaat, Qasigiannguit
Coordinates 68°49'N 51°49'W
Altitude 0–25 m **Area** 3,000 ha

■ Site description

Several small islands covered mainly with tundra and dwarf-shrub heath vegetation, as well as some small lakes and bogs. Egg-collecting takes place ('Other' land-use).

Habitats Scrub (20%; heathland), Grassland (20%; tundra), Marine areas (10%; sea inlet/coastal features), Rocky areas (50%; sea cliff/rocky shore)
Land-use Hunting, Other

■ Birds

Species	Season	Year	Pop min	Pop max	Acc	Criteria
Sterna paradisaea Arctic Tern	B	1996	4,568	10,000	B	A4i, B1i

The archipelago is also important as a staging area for passage waders. *Cepphus grylle* breeds (179 pairs, 1996) and *Rhodostethia rosea* occasionally breeds.

■ Protection status

National Partial **International** Partial
The skerries in the north-western part of the IBA are designated as a Breeding Reserve for Birds. IBA overlaps with Ramsar Site (Kitsissunnguit).

■ Conservation issues

Threats Disturbance to birds (A), Unsustainable exploitation (A)

Egg-collecting is a problem.

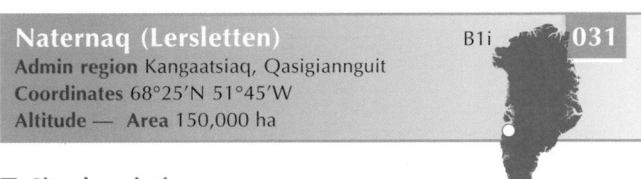

Naternaq (Lersletten) B1i 031
Admin region Kangaatsiaq, Qasigiannguit
Coordinates 68°25'N 51°45'W
Altitude — **Area** 150,000 ha

■ Site description

A plain formed of uplifted marine sediments with vast expanses of grassland and numerous shallow lakes and rivers.

Habitats Grassland (tundra), Wetland (standing fresh water; river/stream; water-fringe vegetation)
Land-use Hunting

■ Birds

Species	Season	Year	Pop min	Pop max	Acc	Criteria
¹ *Anser albifrons* White-fronted Goose	N	1995	2,500	—	—	B1i

1. Also breeds.

This site is very important for both breeding and moulting *Anser albifrons flavirostris*.

■ Protection status

National None **International** Partial
IBA overlaps with Ramsar Site (Naternaq).

■ Conservation issues

No serious threats are known at the site.

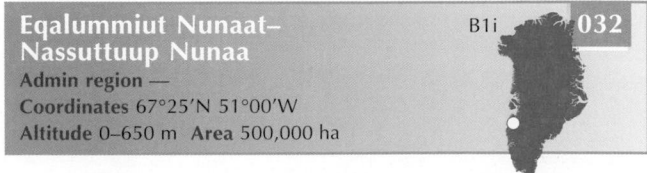

Eqalummiut Nunaat–Nassuttuup Nunaa B1i 032
Admin region —
Coordinates 67°25'N 51°00'W
Altitude 0–650 m **Area** 500,000 ha

■ Site description

A plateau adjacent to the ice-cap, with deeply incised glacial valleys and associated wetlands that are important feeding and staging areas for geese during the spring. Mid-altitude areas, characterized by tundra and Arctic scrub, are important for nesting geese; high-altitude lakes are used as moulting grounds. Hunting is occasional.

Habitats Scrub (heathland), Grassland (tundra), Wetland (standing fresh water; water-fringe vegetation)
Land-use Hunting

■ Birds

Species		Season	Year	Pop min	Pop max	Acc	Criteria
Anser albifrons	White-fronted Goose	B	1979	100	100	—	B1i
Anser albifrons	White-fronted Goose	N	1992	1,150	—	—	B1i

One of the most important sites in Greenland for both breeding and non-breeding *Anser albifrons flavirostris*.

■ Protection status
National None **International** Partial
IBA overlaps Ramsar Site (Eqalummiut Nunaat–Nassuttuup Nunaa).

■ Conservation issues

Threats Extraction industry (U)

Mineral exploration may threaten the site in the future.

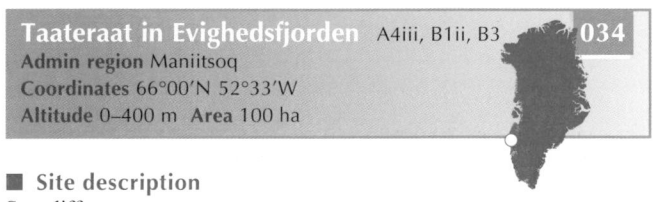

Itinneq   B1i   033
Admin region Sisimiut
Coordinates 67°00′N 52°19′W
Altitude 0–100 m **Area** 1,500 ha

■ Site description
A wide river valley containing many ponds, lakes and fringing marshes.

Habitats Grassland (tundra), Wetland (standing fresh water; river/stream; water-fringe vegetation)
Land-use Hunting

■ Birds

Species		Season	Year	Pop min	Pop max	Acc	Criteria
[1] *Anser albifrons*	White-fronted Goose	P	1997	400	400	—	B1i

1. Spring passage.

Important as a pre-breeding staging area for *Anser albifrons flavirostris*.

■ Protection status
National None **International** None

■ Conservation issues

Threats Disturbance to birds (U)

Illegal hunting may take place during the spring.

Taateraat in Evighedsfjorden A4iii, B1ii, B3   034
Admin region Maniitsoq
Coordinates 66°00′N 52°33′W
Altitude 0–400 m **Area** 100 ha

■ Site description
Sea cliffs.

Habitats Rocky areas (sea cliff/rocky shore)
Land-use Hunting

■ Birds

Species		Season	Year	Pop min	Pop max	Acc	Criteria
[1] *Uria lomvia*	Brünnich's Guillemot	B	1989	8,915	8,915	—	B1ii
[1] *Alca torda*	Razorbill	B	1989	100	100	—	B3

1. Individuals.

The site also holds breeding *Larus glaucoides* (200 individuals), *Rissa tridactyla* (10,000 pairs) and *Uria aalge* (1989 and 1990 data).

■ Protection status
National None **International** None

■ Conservation issues

Threats Disturbance to birds (U)

With the exception of local disturbance caused by hunting, no serious threats are known at the site.

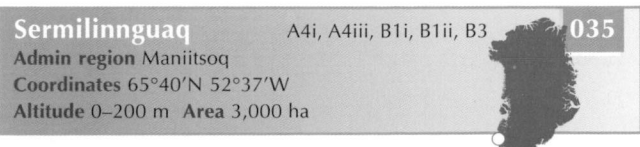

Sermilinnguaq   A4i, A4iii, B1i, B1ii, B3   035
Admin region Maniitsoq
Coordinates 65°40′N 52°37′W
Altitude 0–200 m **Area** 3,000 ha

■ Site description
Sea cliffs bordering a narrow fjord. Egg-collecting takes place ('Other' land-use).

Habitats Marine areas (sea inlet/coastal features), Rocky areas (sea cliff/rocky shore)
Land-use Hunting, Other, Tourism/recreation

■ Birds

Species		Season	Year	Pop min	Pop max	Acc	Criteria
Larus glaucoides	Iceland Gull	B	1992	696	696	B	A4i, B1i
[1] *Uria lomvia*	Brünnich's Guillemot	B	1992	4,540	4,540	B	B1ii
[1] *Alca torda*	Razorbill	B	1992	561	561	B	B3

1. Individuals.

Eight seabird colonies are located within the fjord. These also hold breeding *Rissa tridactyla* (8,618 pairs), *Uria aalge* and *Cepphus grylle* (1992 data).

■ Protection status
National None **International** None

■ Conservation issues

Threats Disturbance to birds (C)

With the exception of local disturbance caused by hunting, no serious threats are known at the site.

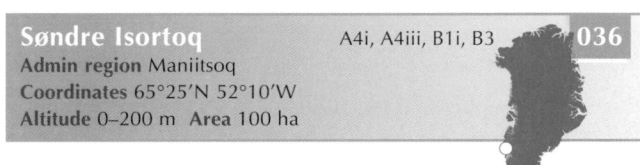

Søndre Isortoq   A4i, A4iii, B1i, B3   036
Admin region Maniitsoq
Coordinates 65°25′N 52°10′W
Altitude 0–200 m **Area** 100 ha

■ Site description
Sea cliffs.

Habitats Rocky areas (sea cliff/rocky shore)
Land-use Hunting

■ Birds

Species		Season	Year	Pop min	Pop max	Acc	Criteria
[1] *Larus glaucoides*	Iceland Gull	B	1990	650	650	—	A4i, B1i
[1] *Alca torda*	Razorbill	B	1990	494	494	—	B3

1. Individuals.

The site holds large numbers of breeding seabirds, including *Rissa tridactyla* (10,610 pairs, 1990) and *Uria lomvia* (2,200 individuals, 1988).

■ Protection status
National None **International** None

■ Conservation issues

Threats Disturbance to birds (U)

With the exception of local disturbance caused by hunting, no serious threats are known at the site.

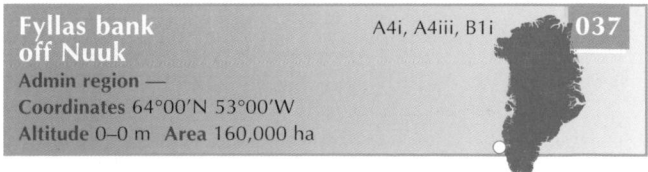

Fyllas bank   A4i, A4iii, B1i   037
off Nuuk
Admin region —
Coordinates 64°00′N 53°00′W
Altitude 0–0 m **Area** 160,000 ha

■ Site description
Large sea area, falling within the 50 m isobath.

Habitats Marine areas (100%; open sea)
Land-use Fisheries/aquaculture, Hunting

■ Birds

Species	Season	Year	Pop min	Pop max	Acc	Criteria
[1] *Somateria spectabilis* King Eider	W	1989	27,000	280,000	—	A4i, B1i

1. Estimated.

This is a very important site for wintering *Somateria spectabilis*.

■ Protection status
National None **International** None

■ Conservation issues

Threats Disturbance to birds (U), Other (U)

Oil spills pose a threat ('Other' threat).

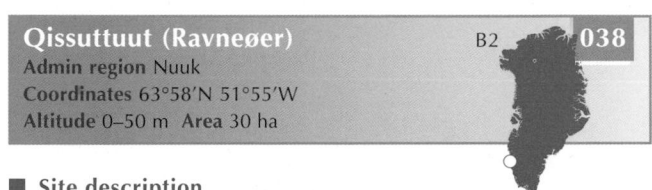

Qissuttuut (Ravneøer)   B2   038
Admin region Nuuk
Coordinates 63°58′N 51°55′W
Altitude 0–50 m **Area** 30 ha

■ Site description
Three small islands located off the outer coast of a larger island.

Habitats Rocky areas (100%; sea cliff/rocky shore)
Land-use Hunting (100%)

■ Birds

Species	Season	Year	Pop min	Pop max	Acc	Criteria
[1] *Fratercula arctica* Puffin	B	1992	390	—	—	B2

1. Individuals.

The site also supports breeding *Alca torda* and moulting *Histrionicus histrionicus*.

■ Protection status
National None **International** None

■ Conservation issues

Threats Disturbance to birds (U)

With the exception of local disturbance caused by hunting, no serious threats are known at the site.

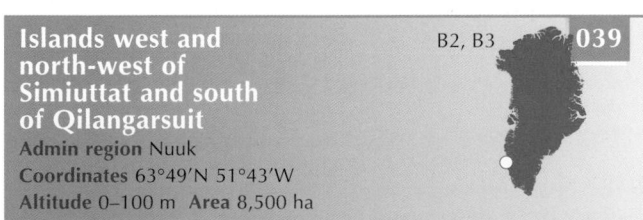

Islands west and north-west of Simiuttat and south of Qilangarsuit   B2, B3   039
Admin region Nuuk
Coordinates 63°49′N 51°43′W
Altitude 0–100 m **Area** 8,500 ha

■ Site description
Several small, low-lying islands situated in shallow waters. Egg-collecting takes place ('Other' land-use).

Habitats Rocky areas (100%; sea cliff/rocky shore; rock stacks/islets)
Land-use Hunting (100%), Other

■ Birds

Species	Season	Year	Pop min	Pop max	Acc	Criteria
[1] *Alca torda* Razorbill	B	1992	221	—	—	B3
[1] *Fratercula arctica* Puffin	B	1992	419	—	—	B2

1. Individuals.

The site holds important numbers of breeding seabirds, including *Uria lomvia* (3,000 individuals), *Cepphus grylle* (134 individuals), and *Sterna paradisaea* (1992 data).

■ Protection status
National None **International** None

■ Conservation issues

Threats Unsustainable exploitation (B)

Hunting and egg-collecting pose a threat.

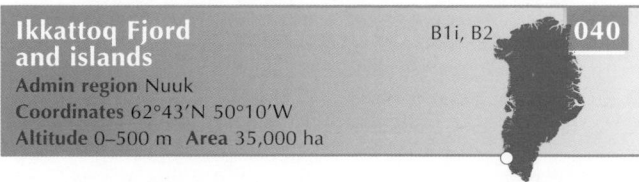

Ikkattoq Fjord and islands   B1i, B2   040
Admin region Nuuk
Coordinates 62°43′N 50°10′W
Altitude 0–500 m **Area** 35,000 ha

■ Site description
A fjord containing several islands, rocky and sandy shorelines, extensive intertidal flats, and areas of shallow water.

Habitats Wetland (mudflat/sandflat), Marine areas (sea inlet/coastal features), Rocky areas (rock stacks/islets)
Land-use Hunting

■ Birds

Species	Season	Year	Pop min	Pop max	Acc	Criteria
Somateria mollissima Eider	N	1989	100	500	—	B1i
Mergus serrator Red-breasted Merganser	N	1989	500	1,000	—	B1i
Haliaeetus albicilla White-tailed Eagle	B	1989	3	4	—	B2

The concentration of moulting *Mergus serrator* is the largest in Greenland.

■ Protection status
National None **International** Partial
IBA overlaps with Ramsar Site (Ikkattoq).

■ Conservation issues

Threats Disturbance to birds (U)

With the exception of local disturbance caused by hunting, no serious threats are known at the site.

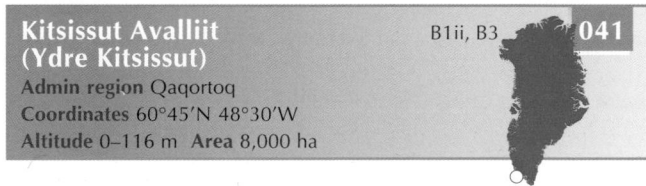

Kitsissut Avalliit (Ydre Kitsissut)   B1ii, B3   041
Admin region Qaqortoq
Coordinates 60°45′N 48°30′W
Altitude 0–116 m **Area** 8,000 ha

■ Site description
A group of small, low-lying, rocky offshore islands with sparse vegetation. Egg-collecting takes place ('Other' land-use).

Habitats Marine areas (open sea), Rocky areas (rock stacks/islets)
Land-use Other

■ Birds

Species	Season	Year	Pop min	Pop max	Acc	Criteria
[1] *Uria lomvia* Brünnich's Guillemot	B	1992	9,300	9,300	—	B1ii
[1] *Alca torda* Razorbill	B	1992	448	448	—	B3

1. Individuals.

Other breeding auks include *Uria aalge*, *Cepphus grylle* and *Fratercula arctica*.

■ Protection status
National Partial **International** Partial
IBA overlaps with Breeding Reserve for Birds. IBA overlaps with Ramsar Site (Kitsissut Avalliit).

■ Conservation issues
Egg-collecting is a problem.

Threats Unsustainable exploitation (U)

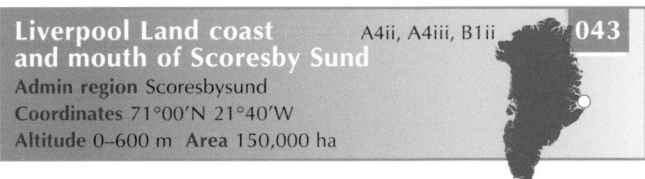

Kap Brewster and Volquart Boon's coast
A4ii, A4iii, B1ii   042

Admin region Scoresbysund
Coordinates 70°10′N 23°22′W
Altitude 0–0 m   **Area** 20,000 ha

■ Site description
Rocky coastline and cliffs located on the south shore of Scoresby Sund (IBA 043), extending from 22°W to 25°W. Subsistence hunting takes place.

Habitats Marine areas (sea inlet/coastal features), Rocky areas (sea cliff/rocky shore; scree/boulders)
Land-use Hunting

■ Birds

Species	Season	Year	Pop min	Pop max	Acc	Criteria
Alle alle Little Auk	B	1989	1,000,000	5,000,000	—	A4ii, B1ii

The area is internationally important for *Alle alle*, which is present in extremely large numbers. Other breeding auks include *Uria lomvia* (15,000 individuals) and possibly *Fratercula arctica*. *Fulmarus glacialis* and *Rissa tridactyla* also breed.

■ Protection status
National None   **International** None

■ Conservation issues

Threats Disturbance to birds (U)

With the exception of local disturbance caused by hunting, no serious threats are known at the site.

Liverpool Land coast and mouth of Scoresby Sund
A4ii, A4iii, B1ii   043

Admin region Scoresbysund
Coordinates 71°00′N 21°40′W
Altitude 0–600 m   **Area** 150,000 ha

■ Site description
A rocky coastline with cliffs and small offshore islands (Raffles Ø and Rathbone Ø), extending from 70°30′N to 71°30′N. Scoresby Sund is the mouth of a wide fjord between Liverpool Land coast and Kap Brewster (IBA 042), which remains ice-free for much of the year due to strong tidal currents (i.e. a polynya). The nutrient-rich waters provide excellent feeding for seabirds. Subsistence hunting takes place.

Habitats Marine areas (open sea; sea inlet/coastal features), Rocky areas (sea cliff/rocky shore; scree/boulders)
Land-use Hunting

■ Birds

Species	Season	Year	Pop min	Pop max	Acc	Criteria
Alle alle Little Auk	B	1989	1,000,000	5,000,000	—	A4ii, B1ii

The area is internationally important for *Alle alle*, which is present in extremely large numbers on all islands and headlands. Other breeding auks include *Uria lomvia* (at least 2,000 individuals on Raffles Ø), *Cepphus grylle*, and possibly *Fratercula arctica*.

■ Protection status
National None   **International** None

■ Conservation issues

Threats Disturbance to birds (U)

With the exception of local disturbance caused by hunting, no serious threats are known at the site.

Heden
A4i, B1i, B3   044

Admin region Scoresbysund
Coordinates 71°00′N 24°07′W
Altitude 0–250 m   **Area** 220,000 ha

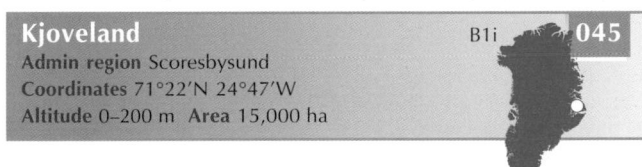

■ Site description
Situated in the western part of Jameson Land, this site comprises flat tundra (mainly dwarf-shrub heath and grassland) and areas of bare ground interspersed with many rivers, lakes and ponds. The primary habitats for geese are areas of marsh and wet grassland adjacent to lakes and streams, and coastal saltmarshes.

Habitats Scrub (heathland), Grassland (humid grassland; tundra), Wetland (saltmarsh; standing fresh water; river/stream; water-fringe vegetation)
Land-use Hunting

■ Birds

Species	Season	Year	Pop min	Pop max	Acc	Criteria
Anser brachyrhynchus Pink-footed Goose	B	1989	50	50	—	B3
[1] *Anser brachyrhynchus* Pink-footed Goose	N	1989	5,300	—	—	A4i, B1i
[2] *Branta leucopsis* Barnacle Goose	N	1989	1,750	—	—	B1i

1. c.5% of Greenland population.
2. c.10% of Greenland population. Also breeds.

This is a very important moulting area for two species of goose.

■ Protection status
National None   **International** Partial
IBA overlaps with Ramsar Site (Heden).

■ Conservation issues

Threats Extraction industry (U)

Oil exploration activity may threaten the site in the future.

Kjoveland
B1i   045

Admin region Scoresbysund
Coordinates 71°22′N 24°47′W
Altitude 0–200 m   **Area** 15,000 ha

■ Site description
An area of tundra and dwarf-shrub heath situated in western Jameson Land, containing lakes, rivers and several marshes. Subsistence hunting takes place.

Habitats Scrub (heathland), Grassland (tundra), Wetland (standing fresh water; river/stream; water-fringe vegetation)
Land-use Hunting

■ Birds

Species	Season	Year	Pop min	Pop max	Acc	Criteria
Branta leucopsis Barnacle Goose	N	1988	621	—	—	B1i

This is an important moulting site for *Branta leucopsis*.

■ Protection status
National None   **International** None

■ Conservation issues
No serious threats are known at the site.

Enhjørningens Dal and Pingel Dal
B1i   046

Admin region Scoresbysund
Coordinates 71°37′N 23°07′W
Altitude 0–200 m   **Area** 50,000 ha

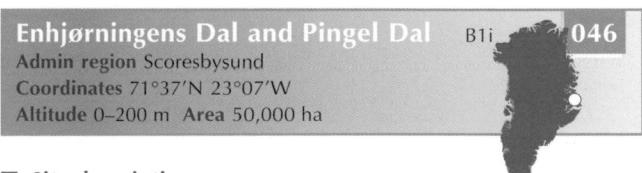

■ Site description
Two river valleys situated in eastern Scoresby Land, with marsh and dwarf-shrub heath vegetation.

Habitats Scrub (heathland), Wetland (river/stream; raised bog)
Land-use Not utilized (100%)

■ **Birds**

Species	Season	Year	Pop min	Pop max	Acc	Criteria
[1] *Branta leucopsis* Barnacle Goose	N	1989	745	—	—	B1i

1. Also breeds.

An important moulting and breeding site for *Branta leucopsis*.

■ **Protection status**
National None **International** None

■ **Conservation issues**

Threats Extraction industry (U)

Oil exploration activity may threaten the site in the future.

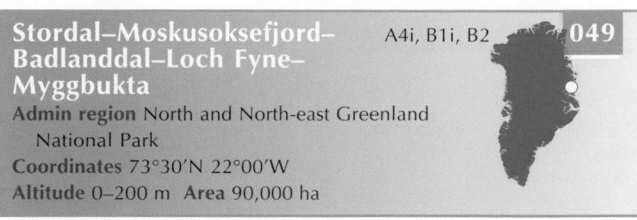

Ørsted Dal and Coloradodal   B1i, B3   **047**
Admin region Scoresbysund
Coordinates 71°40'N 23°22'W
Altitude 0–300 m **Area** 40,000 ha

■ **Site description**
A c.60-km long valley containing marshes, lakes, ponds and gravel plains, bisecting a plateau (700–1,000 m) in Scoresby Land.

Habitats Scrub (heathland), Wetland (standing fresh water; water-fringe vegetation), Rocky areas
Land-use Not utilized (100%)

■ **Birds**

Species	Season	Year	Pop min	Pop max	Acc	Criteria
Anser brachyrhynchus Pink-footed Goose	B	1987	60	60	—	B3
Branta leucopsis Barnacle Goose	B	1987	100	200	—	B1i, B3
Branta leucopsis Barnacle Goose	N	1988	1,864	—	—	B1i

Important as both a breeding and moulting site for two species of goose.

■ **Protection status**
National None **International** None

■ **Conservation issues**

Threats Extraction industry (U)

Oil exploration activity may threaten the site in the future.

Østersletten and Knudshoved,   B1i   **048**
Hold With Hope
Admin region North and North-east Greenland
    National Park
Coordinates 73°34'N 20°45'W
Altitude 0–200 m **Area** 55,000 ha

■ **Site description**
A large, rather dry area of lowland traversed by two rivers. The site includes the mouth of the Tobias Dal valley.

Habitats Grassland (tundra)
Land-use Not utilized (100%)

■ **Birds**

Species	Season	Year	Pop min	Pop max	Acc	Criteria
[1] *Branta leucopsis* Barnacle Goose	N	1988	315	—	—	B1i

1. Possibly breeds.

The site is important for moulting geese.

■ **Protection status**
National Partial **International** Partial

IBA overlaps with National Park (North and North-east Greenland). IBA overlaps with Biosphere Reserve (North and North-east Greenland National Park).

■ **Conservation issues**
No serious threats are known at the site.

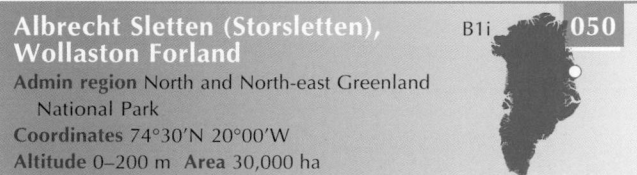

Stordal–Moskusoksefjord–   A4i, B1i, B2   **049**
Badlanddal–Loch Fyne–
Myggbukta
Admin region North and North-east Greenland
    National Park
Coordinates 73°30'N 22°00'W
Altitude 0–200 m **Area** 90,000 ha

■ **Site description**
A series of converging, wide glacial valleys in otherwise mountainous terrain, containing fjords, seasonal stream channels and water-bodies, and tundra vegetation overlying thick glacial deposits. Moskusoksefjord and Loch Fyne are long, narrow sea inlets that continue inland as valleys. The site includes Ternholme—a flat, low-lying island located 2.5 km offshore from Myggbukta. This area includes two sites that were treated as separate IBAs in the previous international IBA inventory (Grimmett and Jones 1989): 'Myggbukta' (former site GL001) and 'Stordal–Moskusoksefjord–Badlanddal–Loch Fyne' (former site GL004).

Habitats Grassland (tundra), Wetland (standing fresh water; river/stream), Marine areas (sea inlet/coastal features), Rocky areas (rock stacks/islets)
Land-use Not utilized (100%)

■ **Birds**

Species	Season	Year	Pop min	Pop max	Acc	Criteria
[1] *Anser brachyrhynchus* Pink-footed Goose	N	1988	—	—	—	A4i, B1i
[2] *Branta leucopsis* Barnacle Goose	N	1988	440	—	—	B1i
[3] *Somateria mollissima* Eider	B	1979	100	100	—	B1i
[4] *Nyctea scandiaca* Snowy Owl	B	1989	—	—	—	B2

1. Occurs in internationally important numbers when moulting; also breeds.
2. Possibly breeds.
3. Breeds on Ternholme.
4. Irregular breeder.

The site is important for breeding waders, ducks and *Stercorarius longicaudus*, and moulting geese.

■ **Protection status**
National Partial **International** Partial
IBA overlaps with National Park (North and North-east Greenland). IBA overlaps with Biosphere Reserve (North and North-east Greenland National Park).

■ **Conservation issues**
No serious threats are known at the site.

Albrecht Sletten (Storsletten),   B1i   **050**
Wollaston Forland
Admin region North and North-east Greenland
    National Park
Coordinates 74°30'N 20°00'W
Altitude 0–200 m **Area** 30,000 ha

■ **Site description**
An extensive area of tundra with several ponds.

Habitats Grassland (tundra), Wetland (standing fresh water; water-fringe vegetation), Rocky areas
Land-use Not utilized (100%)

■ **Birds**

An important site for moulting geese. Also holds breeding *Clangula hyemalis*, waders and *Stercorarius longicaudus*, and possibly *Somateria spectabilis* and *Nyctea scandiaca*.

Species	Season	Year	Pop min	Pop max	Acc	Criteria
Anser brachyrhynchus Pink-footed Goose	N	1989	2,000	—	B	B1i

■ Protection status

National Partial **International** Partial
IBA overlaps with National Park (North and North-east Greenland).
IBA overlaps with Biosphere Reserve (North and North-east Greenland National Park).

■ Conservation issues

No serious threats are known at the site.

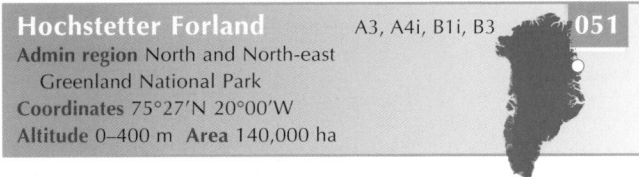

Hochstetter Forland A3, A4i, B1i, B3 **051**
Admin region North and North-east
  Greenland National Park
Coordinates 75°27′N 20°00′W
Altitude 0–400 m **Area** 140,000 ha

■ Site description

An extensive area of coastal tundra with river valleys and wetlands.

Habitats Scrub (heathland), Grassland (tundra), Wetland (river/stream)
Land-use Not utilized (100%)

■ Birds

Species	Season	Year	Pop min	Pop max	Acc	Criteria
Anser brachyrhynchus Pink-footed Goose	B	1989	50	50	—	A3, B3
Anser brachyrhynchus Pink-footed Goose	N	1989	3,000	—	—	A4i, B1i
Branta leucopsis Barnacle Goose	B	1989	50	50	—	A3, B3
Branta leucopsis Barnacle Goose	N	1989	400	—	—	B1i
Somateria spectabilis King Eider	B	—	—	—	—	A3
Clangula hyemalis Long-tailed Duck	B	—	—	—	—	A3
Calidris canutus Knot	B	—	—	—	—	A3
Calidris alba Sanderling	B	—	—	—	—	A3
Phalaropus fulicarius Grey Phalarope	B	—	—	—	—	A3
Stercorarius longicaudus Long-tailed Skua	B	—	—	—	—	A3

Important as a breeding and moulting site for two species of goose. Breeding birds include 8 of the 32 species that are restricted in Europe to the Arctic/tundra biome (when breeding).

■ Protection status

National Partial **International** Partial
IBA overlaps with National Park (North and North-east Greenland).
IBA overlaps with Ramsar Site (Hochstetter Forland). IBA overlaps with Biosphere Reserve (North and North-east Greenland National Park).

■ Conservation issues

No serious threats are known at the site.

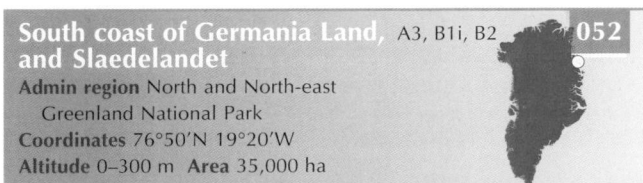

South coast of Germania Land, A3, B1i, B2 **052**
and Slaedelandet
Admin region North and North-east
  Greenland National Park
Coordinates 76°50′N 19°20′W
Altitude 0–300 m **Area** 35,000 ha

■ Site description

Habitats Grassland (tundra), Wetland (sand-dunes/sand beach; standing fresh water;
river/stream; water-fringe vegetation), Rocky areas (sea cliff/rocky shore)
Land-use Not utilized (100%)

A 5–10 km wide expanse of gravel moraines and uplifted former sea floor, separating the large fjord-like Lake Saelsøen from Dove Bay. The area is crossed by several rivers, notably Lakseelven, and there

are numerous small lakes and ponds with narrow fringes of vegetation. Arctic tundra grows on the slopes rising up towards the hinterland. This site includes 'Hvalrosodden–Slamodden, Germania Land' (former site GL007), which was treated as a separate IBA in the previous international IBA inventory (Grimmett and Jones 1989).

■ Birds

Species	Season	Year	Pop min	Pop max	Acc	Criteria
Branta leucopsis Barnacle Goose	B	1989	Common		—	A3
[1] Branta leucopsis Barnacle Goose	N	1989	350	—	B	B1i
Clangula hyemalis Long-tailed Duck	B	1989	Common		—	A3
Falco rusticolus Gyrfalcon	B	1989	Uncommon		—	A3
Calidris canutus Knot	B	1989	Common		—	A3
Calidris alba Sanderling	B	1989	Common		—	A3
Phalaropus fulicarius Grey Phalarope	B	1989	Common		—	A3
Stercorarius longicaudus Long-tailed Skua	B	1989	Common		—	A3
Nyctea scandiaca Snowy Owl	B	1989	Uncommon		—	A3, B2

1. Also breeds.

This site also holds moulting *Anser brachyrhynchus* (1,500 individuals, 1989). Breeding birds include 8 of the 32 species that are restricted in Europe to the Arctic/tundra biome (when breeding).

■ Protection status

National Partial **International** Partial
IBA overlaps with National Park (North and North-east Greenland).
IBA overlaps with Biosphere Reserve (North and North-east Greenland National Park).

■ Conservation issues

No serious threats are known at the site.

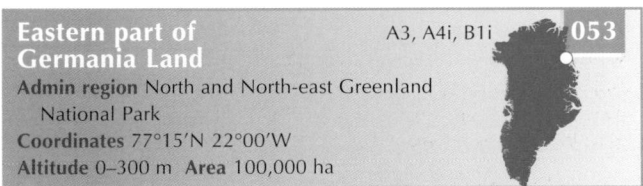

Eastern part of A3, A4i, B1i **053**
Germania Land
Admin region North and North-east Greenland
  National Park
Coordinates 77°15′N 22°00′W
Altitude 0–300 m **Area** 100,000 ha

■ Site description

Rolling tundra lowland with lakes and ponds, situated adjacent to the Inland Ice between 76°45′N and 77°35′N. Large expanses of bare ground (moraine) occur close to the ice sheet.

Habitats Scrub (20%; heathland), Grassland (35%; tundra), Wetland (15%; standing
fresh water; river/stream; water-fringe vegetation), Rocky areas (30%)
Land-use Not utilized (100%)

■ Birds

Species	Season	Year	Pop min	Pop max	Acc	Criteria
Anser brachyrhynchus Pink-footed Goose	N	1988	7,000	—	B	A4i, B1i
Branta leucopsis Barnacle Goose	B	1988	Common		—	A3
Somateria spectabilis King Eider	B	1988	Common		—	A3
Clangula hyemalis Long-tailed Duck	B	1988	Common		—	A3
Calidris alba Sanderling	B	1988	Common		—	A3
Phalaropus fulicarius Grey Phalarope	B	1988	Frequent		—	A3
Stercorarius longicaudus Long-tailed Skua	B	1988	Common		—	A3

This is a significant moulting site for *Anser brachyrhynchus*. Breeding birds include 6 of the 32 species that are restricted in Europe to the Arctic/tundra biome (when breeding).

■ Protection status

National Partial **International** Partial
IBA overlaps with National Park (North and North-east Greenland).
IBA overlaps with Biosphere Reserve (North and North-east Greenland National Park).

■ Conservation issues

No serious threats are known at the site.

Henrik Krøyer Holme

A4i, B1i, B2 · 054

Admin region North and North-east Greenland
National Park
Coordinates 80°45'N 13°45'W
Altitude 0–20 m **Area** 1,000 ha

■ Site description

Three small, low-lying, barren islands located in the north-eastern water polynya.

Habitats Rocky areas (100%; sea cliff/rocky shore)
Land-use Not utilized (100%)

■ Birds

Species	Season	Year	Pop min	Pop max	Acc	Criteria
[1] *Pagophila eburnea* Ivory Gull	B	1993	510	—	—	A4i, B1i, B2

1. Individuals.

Larus sabini, *Sterna paradisaea* and possibly *Rhodostethia rosea* also breed.

■ Protection status

National Partial **International** Partial
IBA overlaps with National Park (North and North-east Greenland). IBA overlaps with Biosphere Reserve (North and North-east Greenland National Park).

■ Conservation issues

No serious threats are known at the site.

Kilen

A4i, B1i, B2 · 055

Admin region North and North-east Greenland
National Park
Coordinates 81°15'N 13°30'W
Altitude 0–300 m **Area** 35,000 ha

■ Site description

A flat, gravel plain comprising polar desert and melt-water rivers, surrounded on three sides by glaciers and on the fourth by the polar sea.

Habitats Wetland (river/stream), Rocky areas
Land-use Not utilized (100%)

■ Birds

Species	Season	Year	Pop min	Pop max	Acc	Criteria
[1] *Branta bernicla* Brent Goose	B	1985	70	70	—	B1i, B2
Branta bernicla Brent Goose	N	1985	625	625	—	B1i
Pagophila eburnea Ivory Gull	B	1985	35	35	—	A4i, B1i, B2

1. Largest known breeding population in Greenland.

This is an important site for breeding geese and gulls (Laridae).

■ Protection status

National Partial **International** Partial
IBA overlaps with National Park (North and North-east Greenland). IBA overlaps with Ramsar Site (Kilen). IBA overlaps with Biosphere Reserve (North and North-east Greenland National Park).

■ Conservation issues

No serious threats are known at the site.

REFERENCES

BAY, C. AND BOERTMANN, D. (1989) *Biologisk-arkæologisk kortlægning af Grønlands østkyst mellem 75°N og 79°30'N. Del 1: Flyrekognoscering mellem Mestersvig (72°12'N) og Nordmarken (78°N)*. Nuuk: Greenland Home Rule, Dpt. Wildl. Mgmt. (Techn. Rep. 4).

BEST, J. R. AND HIGGS, W. J. (1990) Bird population status changes in Thule district, north Greenland. *Dansk Orn. Foren. Tidsskr.* 84: 159–160.

BOERTMANN, D. (1991) Distribution and numbers of moulting non-breeding geese in Northeast Greenland. *Dansk Orn. Foren. Tidsskr.* 85: 77–88.

BOERTMANN, D. (1994) An annotated checklist to the birds of Greenland. *Meddr. Grønland Biosc.* 38: 64 pp.

BOERTMANN, D. AND GLAHDER, C. (1999) *Grønlandske gåsebestande—en oversigt*. Roskilde: National Environmental Research Institute (Techn. Rep. 276).

BOERTMANN, D., FORCHHAMMER, M. AND MELTOFTE, H. (1990) *Biologisk-arkæologisk kortlægning af Grønlands østkyst mellem 75°N og 79°30'N. Del 2: [censuses of birds and mammals in 16 selected areas between 76°N and 78°30'N in the Northeast Greenland Park]*. Nuuk: Greenland Home Rule, Dpt. Wildl. Mgmt. (Techn. Rep. 10).

BOERTMANN, D., MELTOFTE, H. AND FORCHHAMMER, M. (1991) Population densities of birds in central Northeast Greenland. *Dansk Orn. Foren. Tidsskr.* 85: 151–160.

BOERTMANN, D., MOSBECH, A., FALK, K. AND KAMPP, K. (1996) *Seabird colonies in western Greenland*. Copenhagen: NERI (Techn. Rep. 170).

CABOT, D., GOODWILLIE, R. AND VINEY, M. (1988) *Irish expedition to north-east Greenland 1987*. Dublin: Barnacle Books.

DURINCK, J. AND FALK, K. (1996) The distribution and abundance of seabirds off south-western Greenland in autumn and winter 1988–1989. *Polar Research* 15(1): 23–42.

FALK, K. (1998) Review of seabird bycatch in Greenland. Pp. 18–22 in V. Bakken and K. Falk, eds. *Incidental take of seabirds in commercial fisheries in the Arctic countries*. Reykjavik: Circumpolar Seabird Working Group (CAFF Techn. Rep. No.1).

FALK, K. AND KAMPP, K. (1997) *A manual for monitoring thick-billed murre populations in Greenland*. Nuuk: Greenland Institute of Natural Resources (Techn. Rep. 7).

FALK, K., HJORT, C., ANDREASEN, C., CHRISTENSEN, K. D., ELANDER, M., ERICSON, M., KAMPP, K., KRISTENSEN, R. M., MØBJERG, N., MØLLER, S. AND WESLAWSKI J. M. (1997) Seabirds utilizing the northeast water polynya. *J. Marine Systems* 10: 47–65.

FORCHHAMMER, M. (1990) [Ornithological observations in Germania Land and Dove Bugt, Northeast Greenland, 1986–1988.] Nuuk: Greenland Home Rule, Dpt. Wildl. Mgmt. (Techn. Rep. 12). (Danish, with English summary.)

FRICH, A. S. (1997) *Fuglelivet og dets udnyttelse på Grønne Ejland i vestgrønland juni 1996*. Nuuk: Pinngortitaleriffik, Grønlands Naturinstitut (Teknisk Rapport 1).

FRICH, A. S., CHRISTENSEN, K. D. AND FALK, K. (1997) *Ederfugleoptællinger i Kangaatsiaq og Avanersuaq, 1997*. Nuuk: Pinngortitaleriffik, Grønlands Naturinstitut (Teknisk Rapport 10).

KAMPP, K., NETTLESHIP, D. N. AND EVANS, P. G. H. (1994) Thick-billed murres of Greenland: status and prospects. Pp. 133–154 in D. N. Nettleship, J. Burger and M. Gochfeld, eds. *Seabirds on islands, threats, case-studies and action plans*. Cambridge, UK: BirdLife International (Conservation Series No. 1).

GRIMMETT, R. F. A. AND JONES T. A. (1989) *Important Bird Areas in Europe*. Cambridge, UK: International Council for Bird Preservation (Tech. Publ. 9).

HEATH, M. F. AND BORGGREVE, C. (2000) *BirdLife International/EBCC European Bird Database 1998*. Cambridge, UK: BirdLife International.

MANNICHE, A. L. V. (1910) The terrestrial Mammals and Birds of North-East Greenland. *Meddr Grønland* 45(1): 1–200.

MELTOFTE, H. (1975) Ornithological observations in Northeast Greenland between 76°00'N and 78°00'N lat. 1969–71. *Meddr. Grønland* 191(9): 1–72.

MOSBECH, A. AND BOERTMANN, D. (in press) Distribution, abundance and reaction to aerial surveys of post-breeding king eiders (*Somateria spectabilis*) in Western Greenland. *Arctic* 52.

MOSBECH, A. AND JOHNSON, S. (in press) Late winter distribution and abundance of sea-associated birds in south-west Greenland, Davis Strait and southern Baffin Bay. *Polar Research*.

ROSENBERG, N. T., CHRISTENSEN, N. H. AND GENSBØL, B. (1970) Bird observations in Northeast Greenland. *Meddr. Grønland* 191(1): 1–87.

THING, H. (1976) Field notes on birds in Thule District, Greenland 1975. *Dansk. Om. Foren. Tidsskr.* 70: 141–143.

THING, H. AND ETTRUPUNPUBL, H. Rapportering fra Nunavik, 4–11 August 1989. Unpublished field report.

TUCKER, G. M. AND HEATH, M. F. (1994) *Birds in Europe: their conservation status*. Cambridge, UK: BirdLife International (BirdLife Conservation Series no. 3).

■ ESTONIA

Margus Ots and Andres Kalamees

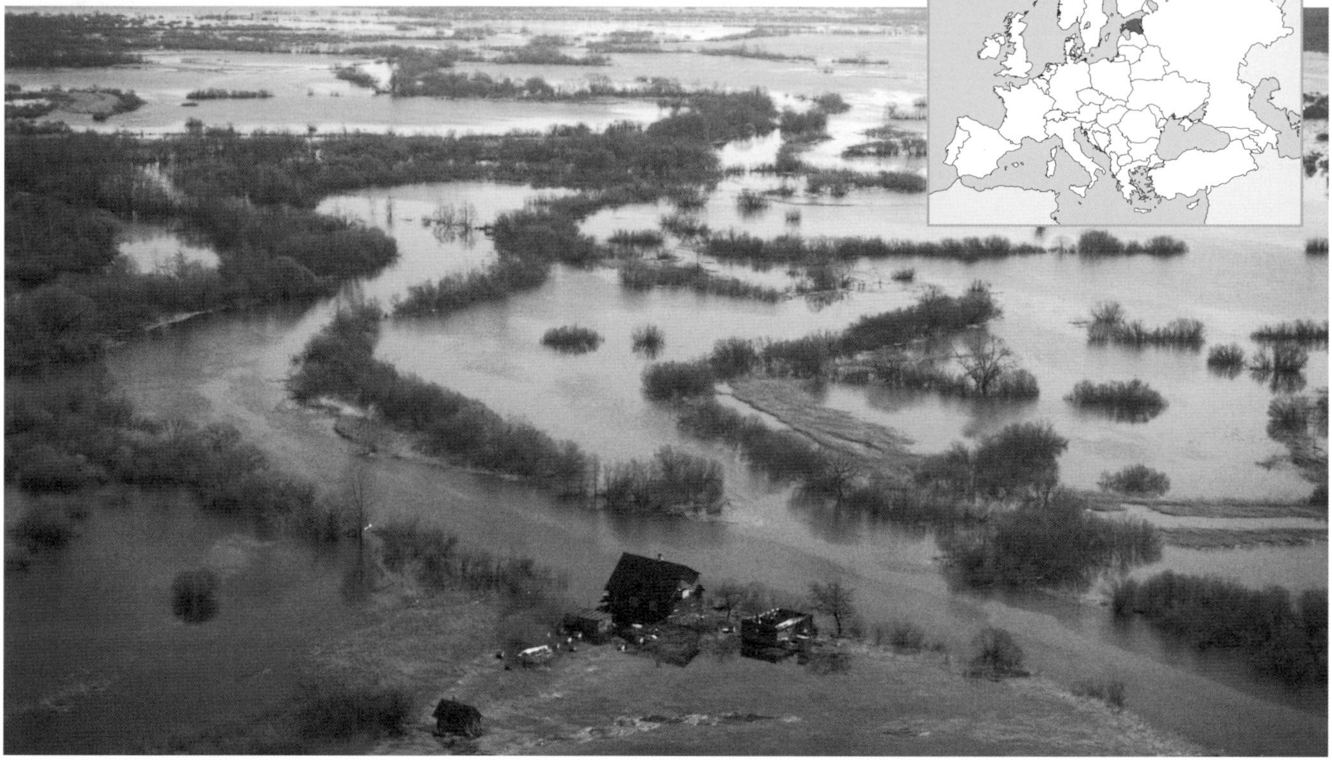

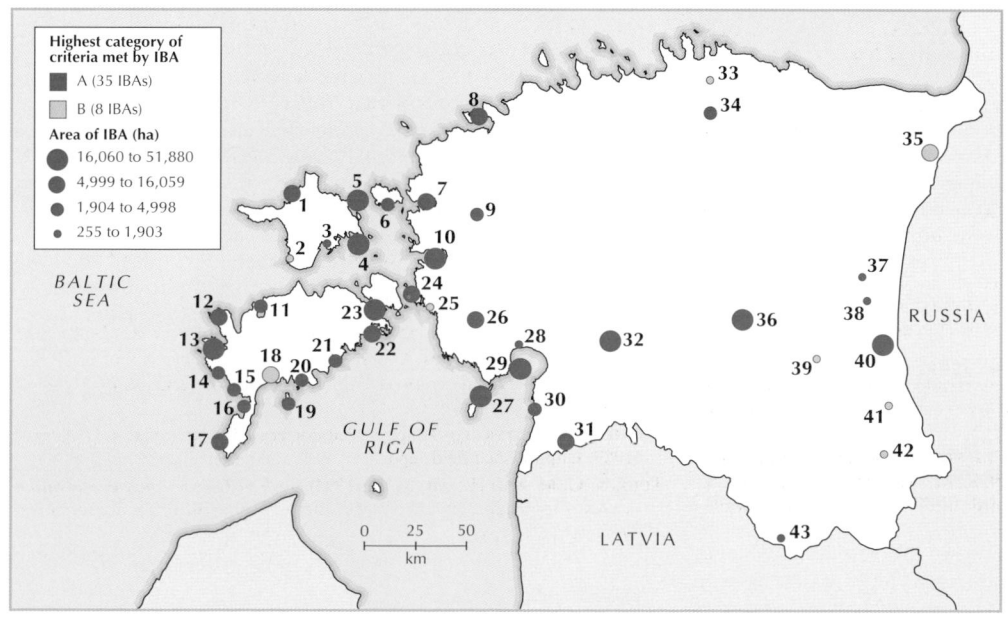

Alam–Pedja wetland complex (IBA 036). (photo: Arne Ader)

GENERAL INTRODUCTION

Estonia has a land area of 45,100 km² and is bounded to the west and north by the Baltic Sea, to the east by Russia and to the south by Latvia. The country is situated on the East European Plain, having a mean elevation of only 50 m and a maximum of 318 m (Suur Munamägi). There are over 1,400 natural and artificial lakes—e.g. Lake Peipsi (3,555 km²) and Narva reservoir (190 km²)—and 420 rivers of over 10 km length. There are more than 1,500 islands in Estonia, of which the largest are Saaremaa (2,673 km²), Hiiumaa (980 km²), Muhu (200 km²) and Vormsi (c.93 km²). The Estonian coastline is approximately 4,000 km long.

Estonia lies in the northern part of the temperate mixed forest zone. About 40% of the country is covered by forest, 34% by agricultural land, 22% by mires (comprising 57% fens, 12% transitional mires and 31% bogs), and 6% by unmanaged areas such as waterways, roads, etc. The dominant tree species are Scots pine *Pinus sylvestris* (41% of forest cover), birch *Betula* (28%), spruce *Picea* (23%), alder *Alnus* (5%) and aspen *Populus tremula* (2%) (Peterson 1994).

Estonia has 43 Important Bird Areas (IBAs) covering 4,756 km², representing c.11% of the land area of the country (Table 1, Map 1). Nine sites were identified in Estonia in the first pan-European inventory of IBAs (Grimmett and Jones 1989). The application of

Map 1. Location, area and criteria category of Important Bird Areas in Estonia.

Highest category of criteria met by IBA
- A (35 IBAs)
- B (8 IBAs)

Area of IBA (ha)
- 16,060 to 51,880
- 4,999 to 16,059
- 1,904 to 4,998
- 255 to 1,903

BALTIC SEA

RUSSIA

GULF OF RIGA

LATVIA

0 25 50 km

Table 1. Summary of Important Bird Areas in Estonia.   43 IBAs covering 4,756 km²

IBA code	National code	1989 code	International name	National name	Administrative region	Area (ha)	Criteria (see p. 11)
001	HI01	—	Kõrgessaare–Mudaste coast	Kõrgessaare-Mudaste rannik	Hiiu	4,999	A4i, B1i
002	HI02	—	Vanamõisa bay	Vanamõisa laht	Hiiu	1,329	B1i
003	HI03	SU008	Käina bay	Käina laht	Hiiu	1,316	A4i, B1i
004	HI04	—	Hiiumaa islets	Hiiumaa laiud	Hiiu	16,060	A4i, B1i
005	HI05	—	Hari Kurk strait	Hari kurk	Hiiu, Lääne	30,290	A4i, B1i
006	LÄ02	—	Hullo and Sviby bays	Hullo ja Sviby lahed	Lääne	2,470	A4i, B1i
007	LÄ01	—	Haapsalu–Noarootsi bays	Haapsalu-Noarootsi lahed	Lääne	15,910	A4i, A4iii, B1i, B2
008	HA01	—	Paldiski bay	Paldiski laht	Harju	14,010	A4i, B1i
009	LÄ04	—	Marimetsa bog	Marimetsa raba	Lääne	4,599	A4i, B1i
010	LÄ03	SU005	Matsalu Bay	Matsalu laht	Lääne	51,880	A1, A4i, A4iii, B1i, B2, B3
011	SA07	—	Küdema bay	Küdema laht	Saare	4,822	A1, A4i, B1i
012	SA06	—	Tagamõisa peninsula	Tagamõisa poolsaar	Saare	11,130	A1, A4i, B1i, B2
013	SA05	SU009	Vilsandi archipelago	Vilsandi saarestik	Saare	18,230	A1, A4i, B1i, B2, B3
014	SA04	—	Karala–Pilguse coast	Karala–Pilguse rannik	Saare	3,114	A4i, B1i
015	SA03	—	Riksu coast	Riksu rannik	Saare	1,904	A4i, B1i
016	SA02	—	Lõu bay	Lõu laht	Saare	4,815	A4i, B1i, B2, B3
017	SA01	—	Sõrve peninsula	Sõrve poolsaar	Saare	14,840	A4i, A4iii, B1i
018	SA08	—	Relict lakes of southern Saaremaa	Lõuna-Saaremaa reliktjärved	Saare	5,735	B1i, B2
019	SA09	—	Abruka island	Abruka saar	Saare	4,707	A4i, B1i
020	SA10	—	Kasti bay	Kasti laht	Saare	3,877	A4i, B1i
021	SA11	—	Siiksaare–Oessaare bays	Siiksaare–Oessaare lahed	Saare	2,917	A4i, B1i
022	SA12	—	Kahtla–Kübassaare coast	Kahtla-Kübassaare rannik	Saare	11,710	A4i, A4iii, B1i, B3
023	SA13	—	Väike Väin strait	Väike väin	Saare	18,480	A4i, A4iii, B1i, B2
024	LÄ05	SU007	Suur Väin strait	Suur väin	Saare, Lääne	16,010	A4i, A4iii, B1i
025	LÄ06	—	Nehatu mire	Nehatu soo	Lääne	681	B1i
026	PÄ01	SU006	Nätsi–Võlla bog	Nätsi-Võlla raba	Pärnu	9,831	A4i, B1i
027	PÄ03	—	Kihnu strait	Kihnu väin	Pärnu	47,910	A4i, A4iii, B1i, B2
028	PÄ02	—	Audru polder	Audru polder	Pärnu	788	A4i, A4iii, B1i
029	PÄ04	—	Pärnu bay	Pärnu laht	Pärnu	17,770	A4i, A4iii, B1i
030	PÄ05	—	Häädemeeste–Võiste coast	Häädemeeste-Võiste rannik	Pärnu	3,630	A4i, B1i
031	PÄ06	SU004	Nigula, Kodaja and Rongu bogs	Nigula, Kodaja ja Rongu rabad	Pärnu	8,850	A1, A4i, B1i, B2
032	VI01	—	Soomaa mire complex	Soomaa soode kompleks	Pärnu, Viljandi	36,890	A1, A4i, B1i, B2
033	LV01	SU001	Laukasoo bog	Laukasoo	Lääne-Viru	1,431	B1i
034	LV02	—	Ohepalu–Udriku mires	Ohepalu–Udriku sood	Harju, Lääne-Viru	2,946	A4i, B1i
035	IV01	—	Puhatu mire	Puhatu soo	Ida-Viru	15,620	B2
036	TA01	—	Alam–Pedja wetland complex	Alam–Pedja märgala	Tartu, Jõgeva, Viljandi	25,850	A1, A4i, B1i, B2
037	TA02	—	Kallaste–Kodavere coast	Kallaste-Kodavere rannik	Tartu	350	A4i, B1i, B2
038	TA03	—	Lahepera lake	Lahepera järv	Tartu	255	A4i, B1i, B2
039	TA04	—	Ropka-Ihaste flood-plain meadow and Aardla lake	Ropka-Ihaste luht ja Aardla järv	Tartu	765	B2, B3
040	TA05	SU003	Mouth of the Emajõgi river and Piirissaar island	Emajõe suudmeala ja Piirissaar	Tartu	31,980	A1, A4i, B1i, B2
041	PÕ01	—	Meelva bog	Meelva raba	Põlva	1,646	B1i
042	PÕ02	—	Meenikunno bog	Meenikunno raba	Põlva	1,820	B1i
043	VA01	—	Flood-plain meadows of Mustjõgi river	Mustjõe luht	Valga, Võru	1,412	A1, B2

Site identified in the previous inventory of IBAs in Europe (Grimmett and Jones 1989) but no longer considered to be an IBA
SU002 Muraka Marsh, Kohtla-Järve

the revised IBA criteria to these sites, as part of this IBA review, led to one of them (Muraka marsh, 1989 code SU002) being disqualified as an IBA. Organized surveys, literature searches and collaboration with other organizations in 1996 resulted in a further 35 IBAs being identified, the majority of which lie in the western part of the country and in the Emajõgi river basin (see Table 1 for a comparison of these 'new' sites with 1989 sites). More than 50 other sites of national ornithological importance have also been recognised in Estonia.

ORNITHOLOGICAL IMPORTANCE

As of 1 January 1998, 339 bird species have been recorded in Estonia, of which 222 are breeders (209 regular, seven irregular and six occasional), with 150 species having been recorded in winter (94 regularly), and 212 species on migration (194 regularly) (Lõhmus *et al.* 1998).

There are 111 species of European conservation concern (SPECs) which breed regularly in Estonia, 62 of which have an unfavourable conservation status in Europe, including four species

of global conservation concern, *Haliaeetus albicilla*, *Aquila clanga*, *Crex crex* and *Gallinago media* (Tucker and Heath 1994, Lõhmus *et al.* 1998). The globally threatened *Polysticta stelleri* winters in the country, and an additional eight species, classed as SPECs based on their winter populations, also winter in Estonia.

Table 1 lists the criteria under which each IBA qualifies. Nine sites support significant numbers of globally threatened and near-threatened species, i.e. they qualify as IBAs under criterion A1 (Table 2), especially for *Crex crex* (20–100 breeding pairs at each site) and *Polysticta stelleri*.

Table 2. Important Bird Areas in Estonia that are important for species of global conservation concern (meeting criterion A1).

Species	IBA code
Polysticta stelleri Steller's Eider	011, 012, 013
Haliaeetus albicilla White-tailed Eagle	040
Aquila clanga Greater Spotted Eagle	036
Crex crex Corncrake	010, 031, 032, 036, 043
Gallinago media Great Snipe	036

The majority of IBAs in Estonia (34 out of 43) qualify under A4i criteria and a further six sites under B1i only, since they support important numbers of congregatory waterbirds (Table 3). These wetlands are situated mainly along the west coast, including Haapsalu bay and the islands of Hiiumaa, Kihnu, Muhu and Saaremaa, and are particularly important for migrating *Gavia stellata*, *G. arctica*, *Cygnus columbianus*, *C. cygnus*, *Anser fabalis*, *A. anser*, *Branta leucopsis*, *Aythya marila*, *Clangula hyemalis*, *Melanitta nigra*, *M. fusca*, *Bucephala clangula*, *Grus grus* and *Charadrius hiaticula*, and also for wintering *Polysticta stelleri*. Matsalu Bay (site 010), a designated Ramsar Site, is probably the most important site in the country, qualifying on the basis of its globally important congregations of waterbirds (14 species).

Eighteen IBAs support important breeding numbers of a total of 21 SPECs, thus qualifying under the B2/B3 criteria (Tables 1 and 4).

Table 3. Important Bird Areas in Estonia that support important numbers of one or more congregatory species (i.e. meeting criteria A4 and/or B1). IBAs meeting both criteria A4 and B1 for the species are shown in **bold**. IBAs meeting only criterion B1 for the species concerned, and not A4, are shown in normal type. For key to 'Season', see p. 7.

Species	Season	IBA code
Gavia stellata Red-throated Diver	W	**017**
	P	**027, 029**
Gavia arctica Black-throated Diver	W	**017**
	P	**027, 029**
Phalacrocorax carbo Cormorant	B	**010**, 019
	P	007, 027
Cygnus olor Mute Swan	P	007, 013
Cygnus columbianus Bewick's Swan	P	003, **006**, **007**, **008**, **010**, 023, **024**, **026**, **027**, **028**, **029**, **030**, 032, **036**, **037**, **038**, **040**
Cygnus cygnus Whooper Swan	P	003, **007**, **008**, **010**, **023**, 024, 027, 028
Anser fabalis Bean Goose	P	**010**, **031**, **040**
Anser albifrons White-fronted Goose	P	**031**
Anser anser Greylag Goose	B	010
	P	002, 003, **005**, 006, 007, **010**, 012, 013, 016, 017, 018, 020, **023**, 028
	N	005
Branta leucopsis Barnacle Goose	P	**001**, **003**, **004**, **006**, **010**, **013**, **014**, **015**, **016**, **019**, **020**, **021**, **022**, **023**, **027**, **028**, **030**
Anas penelope Wigeon	P	010, 023
Anas strepera Gadwall	B	021
	P	007
	N	021
Anas acuta Pintail	P	010
Anas clypeata Shoveler	P	010
	N	010
Aythya ferina Pochard	N	010
Aythya fuligula Tufted Duck	P	010
Aythya marila Scaup	P	**007**, **010**, 013, **024**, **027**, **029**
Somateria mollissima Eider	N	005
Polysticta stelleri Steller's Eider	W	**011**, **012**, **013**
Clangula hyemalis Long-tailed Duck	P	**010**, **017**, **022**, **023**, **024**, **027**, **029**
Melanitta nigra Common Scoter	P	**010**, **024**, **027**, **029**
Melanitta fusca Velvet Scoter	P	**010**, **024**, **027**, **029**
Bucephala clangula Goldeneye	W	011, 012
	P	**010**, **019**, **023**, 027
Mergus albellus Smew	W	016, 017
	P	010, 024, 029, 040
Mergus merganser Goosander	P	013
Fulica atra Coot	P	010
Grus grus Crane	P	002, 003, **007**, **009**, **010**, 013, 018, 022, 025,
	P	032, 033, **034**, 041, 042
Charadrius hiaticula Ringed Plover	P	**010**
Calidris alpina Dunlin	B	010, 023, 027
Tringa totanus Redshank	P	010
Sterna caspia Caspian Tern	B	**010**, **016**
Alca torda Razorbill	W	017
Cepphus grylle Black Guillemot	W	017

Table 4. Species of European conservation concern with significant breeding populations at Important Bird Areas in Estonia (meeting any IBA criteria).

Species [1]	Minimum national breeding population (pairs) [2]	Proportion (%) of national population breeding at all IBAs in Estonia
Botaurus stellaris Bittern	200	27
Branta leucopsis Barnacle Goose	40	100[3]
Anas strepera Gadwall	200	73
Haliaeetus albicilla White-tailed Eagle	35	29
Aquila clanga Greater Spotted Eagle	5	40
Aquila chrysaetos Golden Eagle	30	33
Tetrao tetrix Black Grouse	10,000	6
Porzana porzana Spotted Crake	1,000	24
Crex crex Corncrake	5,000	4
Grus grus Crane	600	30
Gallinago media Great Snipe	50	100[3]
Limosa limosa Black-tailed Godwit	1,000	30
Tringa totanus Redshank	6,000	19
Larus minutus Little Gull	1,000	55
Larus canus Common Gull	10,000	37
Larus marinus Great Black-backed Gull	2,000	59
Sterna caspia Caspian Tern	400	57
Sterna sandvicensis Sandwich Tern	800	35
Sterna albifrons Little Tern	200	28
Chlidonias niger Black Tern	2,000	68
Riparia riparia Sand Martin	20,000	10

1. Only those species of European conservation concern (see Box 1, p. 12) that meet IBA criteria in Estonia are listed.
2. Data are taken from the BirdLife/EBCC European Bird Database 1998 (Heath and Borggreve 2000).
3. The percentage of the national population in IBAs exceeds 100%. Usually this is because the national population estimate has not been updated recently whilst the IBA population estimate has been recently updated with new data as a result of comprehensive surveys of IBAs themselves. Also, the individual site count for a species may be the maximum or average over recent years, and summing these may record more birds than are present nationally in any single year.

HABITATS

The great majority of IBAs (84%) contain some wetland habitat, and at 37% of the sites wetland habitats cover more than half of the individual IBA area (Figure 1). The majority of wetland sites are in areas of raised bog with pools, e.g. sites 009, 025, 031–036 and 040, or occur as complexes with a mosaic of fens, transition mires, bogs, swamp forests, flood-plains, wooded meadows, lakes and rivers. Marine habitats are also common in the IBA network, with nearly 50% of the IBAs being predominantly marine, mainly encompassing shallow sea bays with small islets, including some saltmarsh and reedbeds on the western coast of Estonia, e.g. sites 001, 020 and 030. Forest/woodland and grassland occur within many IBAs but each habitat generally covers less than 50% of the individual IBA's area.

Habitats which are not adequately represented in the national IBA network include broadleaved deciduous forest, old-growth forest, and artificial (agricultural) landscapes (Figure 1), even though these habitat-types support a good number of species of European conservation concern such as woodpeckers (e.g. *Jynx*

Figure 1. Habitats at Important Bird Areas in Estonia (see Appendix 3 for definitions of habitats).

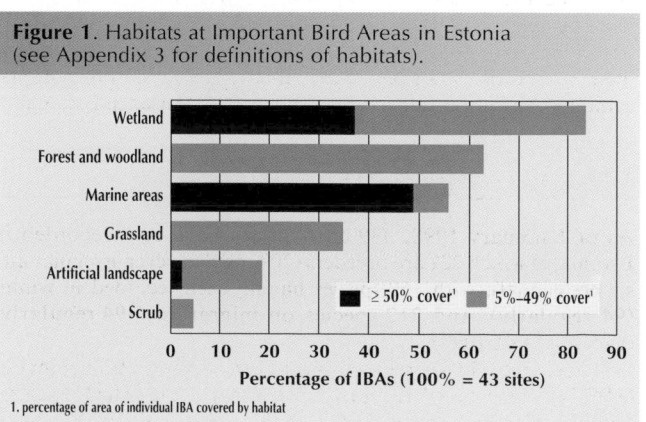

1. percentage of area of individual IBA covered by habitat

207

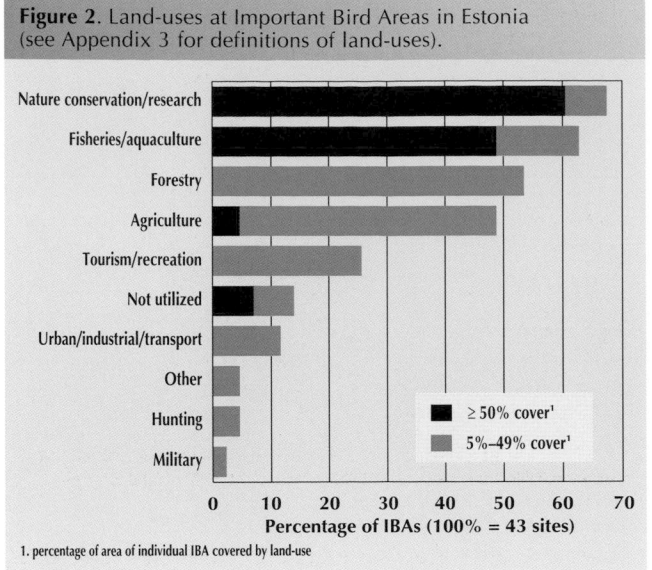

Figure 2. Land-uses at Important Bird Areas in Estonia (see Appendix 3 for definitions of land-uses).

torquilla, Dendrocopos leucotos, Picus viridis), waders (e.g. *Vanellus vanellus, Limosa limosa*), *Coturnix coturnix* and *Alauda arvensis*.

IMPACTS ON IBAs – LAND-USE AND THREATS

Figure 2 shows the most common forms of land-use at IBAs in Estonia. Nature conservation is more frequent and more extensive than any other land-use at IBAs, primarily because many of the IBAs lie within the huge West Estonian Archipelago Biosphere Reserve. Over 60% of IBAs are used as fisheries and this is a major activity at most of them. Forestry activities occur at just over half of the IBAs. Private landowners who own forest within protected areas are allowed to carry out certain forestry operations, according to the existing protection rules or/and management plans. If the IBA is not covered by some type of protected area, forestry is regulated through the private or state forestry management plans which currently, in most cases, do not take into account the status of the area as an IBA. Nearly 50% of IBAs have some agricultural land-use activities; cattle graze some of the coastal meadows, and flood-plains are used for haymaking although the latter is not widespread and is now decreasing rapidly.

Many of the IBAs are on state-owned land. For instance, marine areas, large bogs, mires, swamps and some special, high-priority habitats for important bird species, e.g. nesting eagles (*Aquila/ Haliaeetus*) and *Ciconia nigra*, belong to the state and are protected by the state.

Figure 3 summarizes the key threats to and impacts on IBAs. Recreation/tourism is the most common threat, affecting almost 80% of all IBAs. The impact of this is expected to increase dramatically in the near future, although at most sites the current

impact is low. Abandonment and/or reductions in (agricultural) land-use activity are also having detrimental effects on key bird species at 29 IBAs, largely due to overgrowth of coastal meadows by reed *Phragmites* as a result of undergrazing (e.g. Hiiumaa islands, site 004) and to the overgrowth of flood-plains by scrub where hay-making has been abandoned (e.g. Soomaa mire complex, site 032). Rather paradoxically, some areas are detrimentally affected both by the intensification of agriculture and at the same time by reductions in management activity, e.g. at Audru polder (site 028). Areas such as this require moderate agricultural activity to maintain suitable habitats. Some sites, such as Nehatu mire (site 025), are affected by drainage of land outside the IBA, which in turn lowers water-levels and reduces suitable habitat within the site. The intensification of fishery practices is a threat at 26 IBAs, and at 11 of these the impact is high.

Hunting (classed as 'unsustainable exploitation') impacts more than 65% of IBAs and causes highly significant disturbance and disruption of birds' essential activities. Various types of pollution affect IBAs: intensive shipping in parts of the Baltic Sea results in pollution of wetlands with fuel oil, the ongoing intensification of agriculture is expected to result in nutrient pollution of IBAs in the near future, and intensified fishery activity has increased pollution from discards and also causes disturbance. Deforestation (illegal) affects old-growth forests especially.

PROTECTION STATUS

Table 5 summarizes the national and international protection status of all Estonian IBAs. Overall, five IBAs (sites 028, 029, 038, 039 and 043) receive no protection at all through official legislation at the national or international level (Table 5) and four of them are considered of global importance, either for the large congregations of waterbirds that they support or for the significant presence of a globally threatened species (Table 1).

■ National protection
Nature protection in Estonia is supported mainly by the Act on Protected Natural Objects (adopted in June 1994, improved in February 1998). Protected natural objects include the following: areas, natural and natural-historical monuments and species, fossils and minerals. Protected areas are of the following types: National Park, Nature Protection Area, Protected Landscape or Programme Area. Protected natural objects may be in public or private ownership. All protected areas in Estonia are administered and monitored by the state. The state has the right to pass the control of the protected area to the Governor of the County (e.g. Käina bay, site 003), to the state administration (e.g. Haapsalu–Noarootsi bays, site 007) or to NGOs (e.g. Alam–Pedja wetland complex, site 036). Details of the principal categories of protected area are given below.

1. National Park
A National Park is a protected area of special national importance for the preservation, investigation, and promotion of awareness of

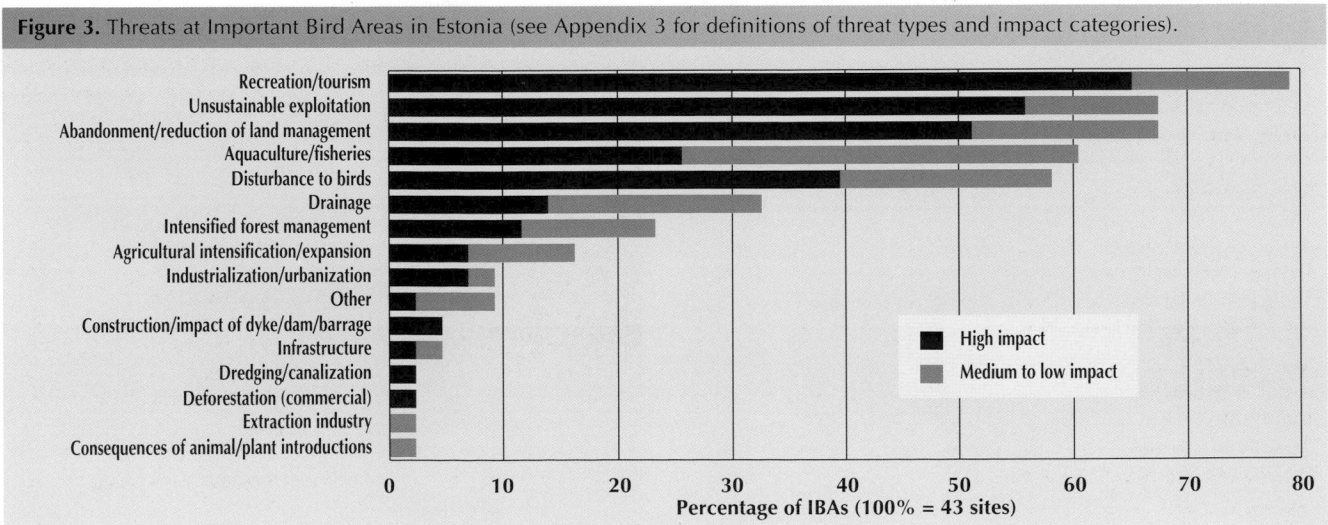

Figure 3. Threats at Important Bird Areas in Estonia (see Appendix 3 for definitions of threat types and impact categories).

Figure 4. The national protection status of Important Bird Areas in Estonia.

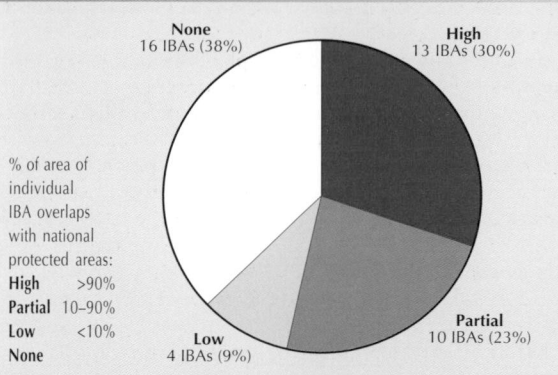

% of area of individual IBA overlaps with national protected areas:
High >90%
Partial 10–90%
Low <10%
None

Total area of overlap between IBA network in Estonia and national protected-area system (see Table 5 for categories) = 2,107–2,141 km² (46–47% of total IBA area).

Figure 5. The international protection status of Important Bird Areas in Estonia.

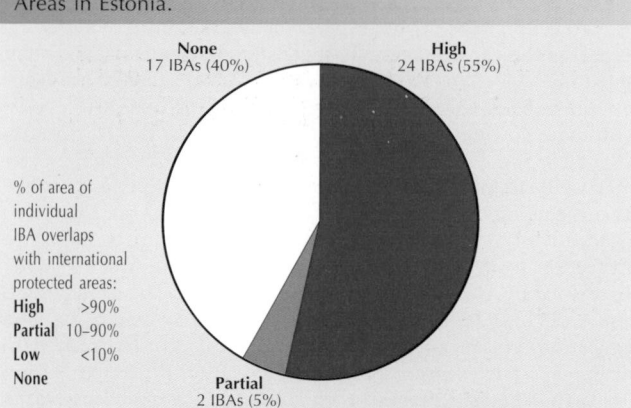

% of area of individual IBA overlaps with international protected areas:
High >90%
Partial 10–90%
Low <10%
None

Total area of overlap between IBA network in Estonia and international protected-area system (see Table 5 for categories) = 3,027–3,067 km² (66–67% of total IBA area).

Table 5. Protection status of Important Bird Areas in Estonia. A tick (✔) indicates that an IBA overlaps with a protected area (to any extent).

IBA code	International name	National Park	Nature Protection Area	Protected Landscape	Ramsar Site	Biosphere Reserve
001	Kõrgessaare–Mudaste coast					✔
002	Vanamõisa bay					✔
003	Käina bay			✔	✔	✔
004	Hiiumaa islets			✔	✔	✔
005	Hari Kurk strait					✔
006	Hullo and Sviby bays			✔		✔
007	Haapsalu–Noarootsi bays		✔			
008	Paldiski bay		✔			
009	Marimetsa bog		✔			
010	Matsalu Bay		✔		✔	
011	Küdema bay					✔
012	Tagamõisa peninsula	✔				✔
013	Vilsandi archipelago	✔			✔	✔
014	Karala–Pilguse coast	✔				✔
015	Riksu coast					✔
016	Lõu bay					✔
017	Sõrve peninsula					✔
018	Relict lakes of southern Saaremaa		✔			✔
019	Abruka island		✔			✔
020	Kasti bay					✔
021	Siiksaare–Oessaare bays					✔
022	Kahtla–Kübassaare coast					✔
023	Väike Väin strait					✔
024	Suur Väin strait			✔	✔	✔
025	Nehatu mire		✔		✔	
026	Nätsi–Võlla bog		✔			
027	Kihnu strait			✔		
028	Audru polder					
029	Pärnu bay					
030	Häädemeeste–Võiste coast			✔		
031	Nigula, Kodaja and Rongu bogs		✔		✔	
032	Soomaa mire complex	✔			✔	
033	Laukasoo bog	✔				
034	Ohepalu–Udriku mires		✔			
035	Puhatu mire		✔			
036	Alam–Pedja wetland complex		✔		✔	
037	Kallaste–Kodavere coast			✔		
038	Lahepera lake					
039	Ropka–Ihaste flood-plain meadow and Aardla lake					
040	Mouth of the Emajõgi river and Piirissaar island			✔	✔	
041	Meelva bog		✔			
042	Meenikunno bog		✔			
043	Flood-plain meadows of Mustjõgi river					
Total number of IBAs		**5**	**14**	**8**	**10**	**20**

the natural and cultural inheritance; it includes ecosystems, examples of biological diversity, landscapes, national culture, and is subject to sustainable nature management. There are four National Parks in Estonia.

2. Nature Protection Area (Nature Reserve)
A Nature Protection Area is an area protected for its nature conservation or scientific value, set aside for the preservation, protection, and investigations of natural processes and endangered or protected plant, animal and fungus species and their habitats, inanimate objects, as well as landscapes and natural monuments. As of 1 June 1998 there were 13 Nature Protection Areas in Estonia.

3. Protected Landscape (Landscape Reserve)/Nature Park
A Protected Landscape or Nature Park is an area of natural or cultural heritage value, which is rare or typical for Estonia, and which is established for nature conservation, cultural or recreational purposes. Parks, arboreta and botanical gardens, which have been taken into protection, are also considered Protected Landscapes. As of 1 June 1998 there were 35 Protected Landscapes and 4 Nature Parks in Estonia.

4. Programme Area
A Programme Area is managed under a local, national or international programme for monitoring, investigation or educational purposes as well as combining conservation and management of natural resources. There are two Programme Areas in Estonia.

All protected areas of the Soviet era in Estonia (more than 200) have to be re-registered under the above-mentioned Act. Since this process is not complete yet, this means that the number of Nature Protection Areas and Protected Landscapes will increase in the future.

Twenty-seven IBAs are afforded some legal protection through their overlap with the national protected-area network, being partly or fully covered by National Parks, Nature Protection Areas or Protected Landscapes (Figure 4, Table 5). It should be stressed that large areas of many of these sites are not legally protected, and that 16 IBAs are afforded no legal protection whatsoever at the national level (Figure 4).

Box 1. International legislation and initiatives that are relevant to site conservation in Estonia (see Appendix 1 for a general description of these agreements).

Global	
Biodiversity Convention	✔
Ramsar Convention	✔
Bonn Convention	
World Heritage Convention	✔
MAB Programme	✔

Pan-European	
Bern Convention	✔

Regional	
Helsinki Convention	✔

✔ Convention ratified/initiative supported
(✔) Convention signed

■ International protection

Estonia is party to the major international conventions relevant to site protection (Box 1), and Figure 5 shows the status of IBAs with respect to these instruments. There are ten designated Ramsar Sites in Estonia, which overlap with ten IBAs (Table 5). Wetlands which are due to be designated as Ramsar Sites by the year 2010 overlap with the following 10 IBAs: 001, 005, 007, 016, 018, 021, 023, 026, 030 and 035.

Twenty IBAs are situated within the West Estonian Biosphere Reserve, which covers some 1.5 million hectares (Table 5). Theoretically this reserve should provide relatively high-level protection to these sites; however, most of them are still highly threatened by at least one factor. Unfortunately the protection of core areas in the Biosphere Reserve is not yet covered by national legislation. This means that IBAs which overlap with core areas do not have any legal protection until the Act on Protected Natural Objects is changed or until core areas are designated as Nature Protection Areas or Protected Landscapes.

CONSERVATION

● Scientific research and monitoring of migratory waterbird populations is carried out at several IBAs, with Matsalu Bay (site 010) being the centre for bird ringing in Estonia.

● Management plans have been written for just three of the 43 IBAs (003, 010, and 036). Since 1997, regular state support has been given towards the implementation of the management plan for Matsalu Bay (010).

● Maps (1:50,000 and 1:10,000) indicating IBA boundaries are available from the Estonian Ornithological Society.

● The borders and status of unprotected IBAs must be reviewed to secure the legal protection of the areas.

ANALYTICAL METHODS

● In 1998 a new, updated list was compiled of Estonian bird species, their status and their national breeding/wintering population sizes (Lõhmus et al. 1998). This data-set was published too late to be incorporated into Table 4, thus whereas most of the numerical data on breeding birds at IBAs are relatively up-to-date (coming from the period 1993–1996), the percentages of the national population breeding within IBAs and meeting criteria, quoted in Table 4, are based on an earlier data-set (see Tucker and Heath 1994) and give a more approximate reflection of the current situation at Estonian IBAs.

● Counts of migratory birds are in most cases given as average figures for the 1990s. For some sites, e.g. Matsalu Bay, the range is given for the 1990–1996 period.

● Most waterbird counts are good quality (verification code A or B) and derive from state monitoring bodies, staff of protected areas and from local bird clubs, with some aerial and ship counts, as well as counts of visible migration. Numbers for wintering

waterbird populations are based on midwinter (January) counts. In some cases (e.g. at mires, raised bogs) absolute counts of bird numbers have also been made. Most bird data are from the period 1987–1996.

● Threats and land-use estimates are based on available information from fieldwork in 1996.

GLOSSARY

EOS Estonian Ornithological Society (BirdLife International Partner in Estonia).

IZB Institute of Zoology and Botany.

ACKNOWLEDGEMENTS

The IBA expert group of the Estonian Ornithological Society (EOS), comprising Andres Kuresoo, Eerik Leibak, Aivar Leito, Vilju Lilleleht, Kaja Peterson and Einar Tammur, provided valuable input into the development of the IBA inventory for Estonia. EOS also cooperated with the following organisations on data-gathering: Institute of Zoology and Botany, Estonian Fund for Nature, Matsalu and Nigula Nature Protection Areas, Vilsandi National Park, Institute of Environmental Protection, Nature Protection Co-operative 'Kotkas' (Eagle), Läänemaa Centre of the West Estonian Archipelago Biosphere Reserve, and the Pärnu, Läänemaa and Saaremaa Bird Clubs. Most of the fieldwork for this IBA review was done by the members of the Estonian Ornithological Society.

Funds for the IBA review were generously provided by the Finnish Ministry of the Environment, BirdLife Suomi–Finland, Royal Society for the Protection of Birds (BirdLife Partner in the UK), BirdLife International Secretariat, Estonian Ministry of the Environment, Estonian Environmental Fund, local environmental funds of Ida-Viru, Narva, Lääne-Viru, Jõgeva, Tartu, Võru and Viljandi Counties, Finnish Twitchers Society ('Bongariliitto'), and the Finnish student organisation OY 'Synapsi'.

Recent (unpublished) data was kindly provided by: A. Ader (IZB), J. Elts (EOS), Estonian Fund for Nature, A. Kalamees (Läänemaa Centre, West Estonian Archipelago Biosphere Reserve/Läänemaa Bird Club), T. Kastepõld (Matsalu Nature Protection Area), M. Kose (Pärnumaa Bird Club 'Buteo'), A. Kullapere (Vilsandi National Park), K. Kullapere (Vilsandi National Park), A. Kuresoo (IZB), A. Kuus (EOS), T. Laur (Pärnumaa Bird Club 'Buteo'), E. Leibak (Estonian Fund for Nature), A. Leito (Nature Conservation Research Centre), A. Leivits (Nigula Nature Protection Area), M. Leivo (Suomen Ympäristökeskus), A. Lepisk (EOS), H. Lipp (Saaremaa Bird Club), A. Lõhmus (Nature Conservation Co-operative 'Kotkas'), H. Luhamaa (EOS), L. Luigujõe (IZB), E. Mägi (Matsalu Nature Protection Area), R. Marja (EOS), M. Martinson (Saaremaa Bird Club), I. Ojaste (Läänemaa Bird Club), I. Ots (EOS), M. Ots (EOS), U. Paal (EOS), H. Pehlak (EOS), P. Raja (Pärnumaa Bird Club 'Buteo'), U. Sellis (Nature Conservation Co-operative 'Kotkas'), E. Tammur (Nature Conservation Co-operative 'Kotkas'), E. Vilbaste (Nigula Nature Protection Area), and V. Volke (Saaremaa Bird Club).

Special thanks to Melanie Heath, Tony Payne, Mike Evans and their colleagues in the BirdLife International Secretariat who did an excellent job on data analysis and helped the IBA coordinator at EOS to prepare the whole national chapter.

■ SITE ACCOUNTS

Kõrgessaare–Mudaste coast   A4i, B1i   001
Admin region Hiiu
Coordinates 59°00′N 22°29′E
Altitude 0–4 m Area 4,999 ha

■ Site description

A complex of shallow (<4 m) bays with small islets and shallow (<1 m) coastal, relict lakes in the north-western part of Hiiumaa island. There are reedbeds and vast coastal meadows. The main economic activities are intensive fishing, and grazing.

Habitats Forest and woodland (6%), Grassland (5%), Wetland (20%; standing brackish and salt water; water-fringe vegetation), Marine areas (67%; sea inlet/coastal features)
Land-use Agriculture (13%), Fisheries/aquaculture (65%), Forestry (5%), Nature conservation/research (100%)

■ Birds

Species	Season	Year	Pop min	Pop max	Acc	Criteria
Branta leucopsis Barnacle Goose	P	1996	2,000	3,000	A	A4i, B1i

The coastal meadows and lakes comprise an important staging site for migrating *Branta leucopsis*, and support a good diversity of breeding waterbirds.

■ Protection status

National None **International** High
4,999 ha of IBA covered by Biosphere Reserve (West Estonian Archipelago, 1,560,000 ha).

■ Conservation issues

The main threats are posed by human disturbance of birds, tourism, unsustainable hunting, fishing, overgrowth of coastal meadows with reed *Phragmites* due to undergrazing, and water pollution by fishery discards and by fuel-oil from boats. About 50% of the IBA is a planned core area of the West Estonian Archipelago Biosphere Reserve, and the IBA is also a potential Ramsar Site. Research involves monitoring of migrating waterbirds.

Threats Abandonment/reduction of land management (A), Aquaculture/fisheries (C), Disturbance to birds (A), Industrialization/urbanization (A), Recreation/tourism (A), Unsustainable exploitation (A)

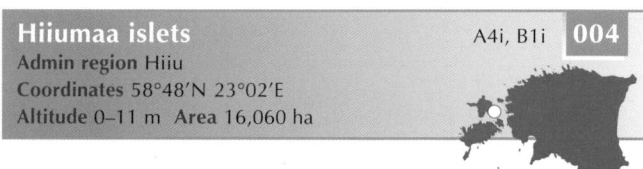

Vanamõisa bay
Admin region Hiiu
Coordinates 58°44′N 22°29′E
Altitude 0–3 m **Area** 1,329 ha
B1i 002

■ Site description
A shallow (<4 m) bay on the south-west coast of Hiiumaa island, with small islets, reedbeds and coastal meadows. The main economic activity is intensive fishing.

Habitats Wetland (20%; water-fringe vegetation), Marine areas (77%; sea inlet/coastal features)
Land-use Fisheries/aquaculture (75%), Nature conservation/research (100%)

■ Birds

Species	Season	Year	Pop min	Pop max	Acc	Criteria
Anser anser Greylag Goose	P	1996	800	800	A	B1i
Grus grus Crane	P	1996	600	1,300	A	B1i

Vanamõisa bay is an important staging site for migrating *Anser anser* and *Grus grus*.

■ Protection status
National None **International** High
1,329 ha of IBA covered by Biosphere Reserve (West Estonian Archipelago, 1,560,000 ha).

■ Conservation issues

Threats Abandonment/reduction of land management (A), Disturbance to birds (A), Recreation/tourism (A), Unsustainable exploitation (A)

Threats include human disturbance of birds, tourism, unsustainable hunting, fishing, and overgrowth of coastal meadows with reed *Phragmites* due to undergrazing. The IBA is a planned core area of the West Estonian Archipelago Biosphere Reserve. Research involves the monitoring of migrating and wintering waterbirds.

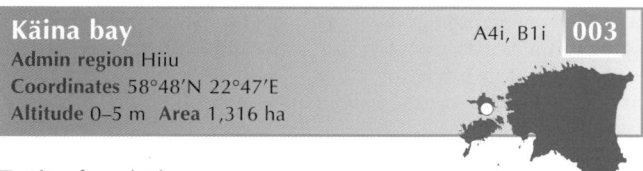

Käina bay
Admin region Hiiu
Coordinates 58°48′N 22°47′E
Altitude 0–5 m **Area** 1,316 ha
A4i, B1i 003

■ Site description
A shallow (<1 m), inland bay (lagoon) fringed by a low coastline of reedbeds, meadows and small islets in the southern part of Hiiumaa island, off the west coast of Estonia. Coastal meadows are used for cattle-grazing. There is a nature trail with three tower-hides.

Habitats Grassland (5%), Wetland (93%; standing brackish and salt water; water-fringe vegetation)
Land-use Agriculture (5%), Nature conservation/research (100%), Tourism/recreation (10%)

■ Birds

Species	Season	Year	Pop min	Pop max	Acc	Criteria
Cygnus columbianus Bewick's Swan	P	1996	200	200	A	A4i, B1i
Cygnus cygnus Whooper Swan	P	1996	300	300	A	B1i
Anser anser Greylag Goose	P	1996	1,000	2,000	A	B1i
Branta leucopsis Barnacle Goose	P	1996	2,000	4,000	A	A4i, B1i
Grus grus Crane	P	1996	1,000	2,000	A	B1i

The bay is an important staging site for migrating wildfowl and *Grus grus*. Nearly 90 bird species have been recorded breeding, including a wide variety of waterbirds.

■ Protection status
National High **International** High
1,316 ha of IBA covered by Protected Landscape (Käina Bay–Kassari, 2,662 ha). 1,316 ha of IBA covered by Ramsar Site (Hiiumaa Islets and Käina Bay, 17,700 ha). 1,316 ha of IBA covered by Biosphere Reserve (West Estonian Archipelago, 1,560,000 ha).

■ Conservation issues

Threats Abandonment/reduction of land management (B), Agricultural intensification/expansion (B), Disturbance to birds (B), Recreation/tourism (A)

Major threats include water pollution from the surrounding area, human disturbance of birds, and overgrowth of coastal meadows with reed *Phragmites* due to undergrazing. There is a management plan for Käina Bay, which is a planned core area of the West Estonian Archipelago Biosphere Reserve. Research involves the monitoring of breeding and migrating waterbirds.

Hiiumaa islets
Admin region Hiiu
Coordinates 58°48′N 23°02′E
Altitude 0–11 m **Area** 16,060 ha
A4i, B1i 004

■ Site description
A complex of shallow (<4 m) bays and small islets on the south-east coast of Hiiumaa island. There are reedbeds, coastal meadows and saltmarshes. The main exploitative land-uses are fishing, tourism and non-intensive agriculture.

Habitats Wetland (7%), Marine areas (85%; sea inlet/coastal features)
Land-use Agriculture (5%), Fisheries/aquaculture (80%), Nature conservation/research (50%), Tourism/recreation (5%)

■ Birds

Species	Season	Year	Pop min	Pop max	Acc	Criteria
Branta leucopsis Barnacle Goose	P	1996	2,000	4,000	A	A4i, B1i

The area is an important staging site for migrating wildfowl, and supports a diverse avifauna, with 190 species recorded (110 of which have been recorded breeding). Significant proportion (≥1%) of national population breeding at site: *Limosa limosa* (min. 10 pairs).

■ Protection status
National Partial **International** High
2,662 ha of IBA covered by Protected Landscape (Hiiumaa Islets, 2,662 ha). 16,060 ha of IBA covered by Ramsar Site (Hiiumaa Islets and Käina Bay, 17,700 ha). 13,398 ha of IBA covered by Biosphere Reserve (West Estonian Archipelago, 1,560,000 ha).

■ Conservation issues

Threats Abandonment/reduction of land management (A), Agricultural intensification/expansion (A), Aquaculture/fisheries (B), Disturbance to birds (A), Recreation/tourism (A), Unsustainable exploitation (A)

Major threats are posed by human disturbance of birds, tourism, unsustainable hunting, fishing, agricultural pollution, and overgrowth of coastal meadows with reed *Phragmites* as a result of undergrazing. The IBA is a planned core area of the West Estonian Archipelago Biosphere Reserve. Research involves monitoring of birds, seals (Phocidae) and plants.

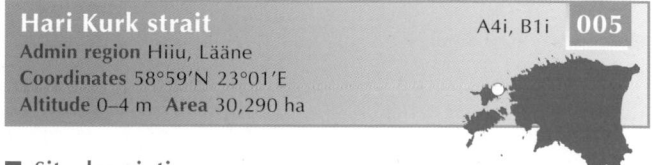

Hari Kurk strait
Admin region Hiiu, Lääne
Coordinates 58°59′N 23°01′E
Altitude 0–4 m **Area** 30,290 ha
A4i, B1i 005

■ Site description
A shallow (<17 m) sea strait between Hiiumaa island and Vormsi island, with small islets, reedbeds and coastal meadows. The main uses of the area are intensive fishing and marine transport.

Habitats Marine areas (95%; sea inlet/coastal features)
Land-use Fisheries/aquaculture (90%), Nature conservation/research (50%)

■ Birds

Species	Season	Year	Pop min	Pop max	Acc	Criteria
Anser anser Greylag Goose	P	1996	2,000	2,500	A	A4i, B1i
[1] *Anser anser* Greylag Goose	N	1996	600	900	A	B1i
[1] *Somateria mollissima* Eider	N	1996	20,000	25,000	A	B1i

1. Moulting (summer).

Hari Kurk strait is an important moulting and staging area for several wildfowl species. Significant proportion (≥1%) of national population breeding at site: *Larus canus* (min. 250 pairs), *Larus marinus* (min. 40 pairs).

■ Protection status
National None **International** High
30,290 ha of IBA covered by Biosphere Reserve (West Estonian Archipelago, 1,560,000 ha).

■ Conservation issues

Threats Abandonment/reduction of land management (B), Aquaculture/ fisheries (B), Disturbance to birds (B), Recreation/tourism (A), Unsustainable exploitation (A)

The main threats are posed by human disturbance of birds, tourism, hunting, fishing, and overgrowth of coastal meadows with reed *Phragmites* due to undergrazing. About 50% of the IBA is a planned core area of the West Estonian Archipelago Biosphere Reserve, and the whole IBA is a potential Ramsar Site. Research involves the monitoring of migrating waterbirds.

Hullo and Sviby bays A4i, B1i 006
Admin region Lääne
Coordinates 58°58′N 23°16′E
Altitude 0–4 m Area 2,470 ha

■ Site description
Hullo and Sviby are shallow (<4 m) bays on the southern coast of Vormsi island, off the west coast of Estonia. There are coastal meadows and small offshore islets.

Habitats Forest and woodland (7%; native coniferous forest), Grassland (8%), Marine areas (80%; sea inlet/coastal features)
Land-use Agriculture (8%), Fisheries/aquaculture (75%), Forestry (7%), Nature conservation/research (100%)

■ Birds

Species	Season	Year	Pop min	Pop max	Acc	Criteria
Cygnus columbianus Bewick's Swan	P	1996	600	600	A	A4i, B1i
Anser anser Greylag Goose	P	1996	300	—	B	B1i
Branta leucopsis Barnacle Goose	P	1996	2,000	2,500	A	A4i, B1i

Hullo and Sviby bays are important staging areas for migratory wildfowl, supporting more than 10,000 ducks and geese at peak counts.

■ Protection status
National High **International** High
2,470 ha of IBA covered by Protected Landscape (Rumpo, 2,600 ha). 2,470 ha of IBA covered by Biosphere Reserve (West Estonian Archipelago, 1,560,000 ha).

■ Conservation issues

Threats Abandonment/reduction of land management (A), Aquaculture/ fisheries (B), Disturbance to birds (B), Recreation/tourism (A), Unsustainable exploitation (B)

Threats include overgrowth of coastal meadows with reed *Phragmites* due to undergrazing, recreation/tourism, unsustainable hunting and intensive fishing. The IBA is a planned core area of the West Estonian Archipelago Biosphere Reserve.

Haapsalu–Noarootsi bays A4i, A4iii, B1i, B2 007
Admin region Lääne
Coordinates 58°59′N 23°35′E
Altitude 0–7 m Area 15,910 ha

■ Site description
A large complex of shallow (<4 m), eutrophic bays and five relict lakes in western Estonia. The lakes are in the northern part of the IBA and have developed from the former sea strait following tectonic land-rise. This complex is fringed by coastal meadows and vast reedbeds, and there are more than 40 offshore islets in the bays. The main human activities are agriculture, fishing, yachting and reed-cutting. About 1,000–2,000 m³ of mud is extracted annually from Haapsalu bay for its curative properties.

Habitats Forest and woodland (12%; mixed forest), Grassland (10%), Wetland (20%; standing brackish and salt water; water-fringe vegetation), Marine areas (43%; sea inlet/ coastal features), Artificial landscape (12%)
Land-use Agriculture (20%), Fisheries/aquaculture (45%), Forestry (12%), Not utilized (10%), Urban/industrial/transport (5%)

■ Birds

Species	Season	Year	Pop min	Pop max	Acc	Criteria
Phalacrocorax carbo Cormorant	P	1996	1,800	2,000	A	B1i
Cygnus olor Mute Swan	P	1996	2,500	3,000	A	B1i
Cygnus columbianus Bewick's Swan	P	1996	600	2,000	A	A4i, B1i
Cygnus cygnus Whooper Swan	P	1996	1,000	3,000	A	A4i, B1i
Anser anser Greylag Goose	P	1996	1,800	—	A	B1i
Anas strepera Gadwall	P	1996	500	500	A	B1i
Aythya marila Scaup	P	1996	15,000	—	B	A4i, B1i
Grus grus Crane	P	1996	2,900	5,750	A	A4i, B1i
Limosa limosa Black-tailed Godwit	B	1995	40	—	B	B2

This wetland complex is an important staging site for migratory waterbirds, especially wildfowl (>40,000 at peak counts) and supports a good diversity of breeding waterbirds. Significant proportion (≥1%) of national population breeding at site: *Tringa totanus* (min. 100 pairs), *Chlidonias niger* (min. 30 pairs).

■ Protection status
National Partial **International** None
Part of IBA covered by Nature Protection Area (Silma, 4,795 ha).

■ Conservation issues

Threats Abandonment/reduction of land management (A), Aquaculture/fisheries (A), Recreation/tourism (A), Unsustainable exploitation (A)

The main threats are posed by intensive fishing, unsustainable hunting, tourism, and overgrowth of coastal meadows with reed *Phragmites* as a result of undergrazing. The area is a proposed Ramsar Site. Research involves monitoring of migrating waterbirds, and geological and ichthyological investigations.

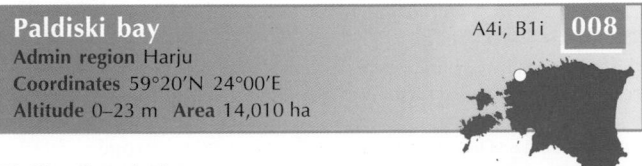

Paldiski bay A4i, B1i 008
Admin region Harju
Coordinates 59°20′N 24°00′E
Altitude 0–23 m Area 14,010 ha

■ Site description
A complex of shallow (<10 m in parts) sea bays and two islands on the north-western coast of Estonia, with coastal reedbeds, meadows and sea-cliffs. The main economic activity is fishing; the islands are used as military practice grounds.

Habitats Forest and woodland (6%), Grassland (7%), Wetland (8%), Marine areas (75%; sea inlet/coastal features)
Land-use Fisheries/aquaculture (70%), Military (25%)

■ Birds

Species	Season	Year	Pop min	Pop max	Acc	Criteria
Cygnus columbianus Bewick's Swan	P	1996	200	300	A	A4i, B1i
Cygnus cygnus Whooper Swan	P	1996	500	700	A	A4i, B1i

Paldiski bay is an important staging area for migrating *Cygnus columbianus* and *Cygnus cygnus*.

■ Protection status
National Partial **International** None
1,450 ha of IBA covered by Protected Landscape (Pakri, 1,450 ha).

■ Conservation issues

Threats Abandonment/reduction of land management (B), Aquaculture/fisheries (C), Recreation/tourism (A), Unsustainable exploitation (A), Other (B)

The main threats are from unsustainable hunting, tourism, overgrowth of coastal meadows with reed *Phragmites* due to undergrazing, and military activities ('Other' threat, above). Research involves monitoring of wintering and breeding waterbirds.

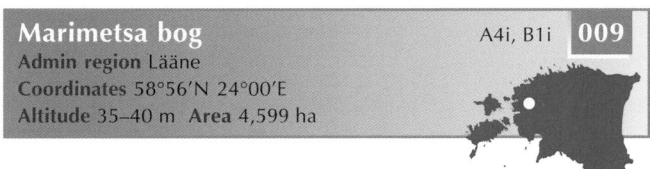

Marimetsa bog
A4i, B1i **009**
Admin region Lääne
Coordinates 58°56′N 24°00′E
Altitude 35–40 m **Area** 4,599 ha

■ Site description
A large raised bog with pools in western Estonia. There is practically no exploitative land-use.

Habitats Forest and woodland (13%; native coniferous forest), Wetland (86%; raised bog)
Land-use Forestry (24%), Nature conservation/research (100%)

■ Birds

Species	Season	Year	Pop min	Pop max	Acc	Criteria
Grus grus Crane	P	1994	1,000	4,000	A	A4i, B1i

The bog is an important roosting place in autumn for migrating *Grus grus*, and a good diversity of mire and forest species breed.

■ Protection status
National High **International** None
4,599 ha of IBA covered by Nature Protection Area (Marimetsa, 4,599 ha).

■ Conservation issues

Threats Intensified forest management (C)

Threats are practically absent. Research involves monitoring of roosting *Grus grus*.

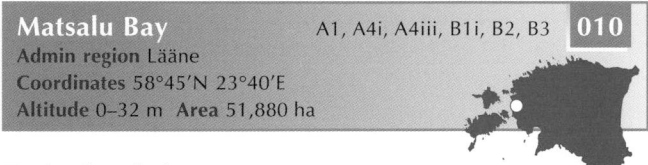

Matsalu Bay
A1, A4i, A4iii, B1i, B2, B3 **010**
Admin region Lääne
Coordinates 58°45′N 23°40′E
Altitude 0–32 m **Area** 51,880 ha

■ Site description
A large wetland complex in western Estonia comprising shallow sea bays with many small islets, the Kasari delta, saltmarshes, extensive reedbeds, and coastal and flood-plain meadows. Fisheries, agriculture and forestry are major human uses of the area.

Habitats Forest and woodland (10%; mixed forest), Grassland (8%; humid grassland), Wetland (10%; water-fringe vegetation), Marine areas (58%; sea inlet/coastal features), Artificial landscape (14%; highly improved reseeded grassland; arable land)
Land-use Agriculture (20%), Fisheries/aquaculture (45%), Forestry (10%), Nature conservation/research (100%)

■ Birds
Matsalu Nature Protection Area is the most important bird area in Estonia, supporting very large numbers of migrating and/or breeding waterbirds, primarily wildfowl and especially seaduck. The site holds more than 20,000 waterbirds on a regular basis. Breeding species of global conservation concern that do not meet IBA criteria: *Haliaeetus albicilla* (3 pairs), *Gallinago media* (3 pairs). Significant proportion (≥1%) of national population breeding at site: *Chlidonias niger* (min. 150 pairs),

Bubo bubo (6 pairs). More than 60,000 divers *Gavia* (*G. stellata*/ *G. arctica*) fly through the area on spring migration (number of staging birds is unknown). The avifauna is very diverse, with 260 species recorded, including 170 breeding species.

Species	Season	Year	Pop min	Pop max	Acc	Criteria
Phalacrocorax carbo Cormorant	B	1996	1,500	1,500	A	A4i, B1i
Botaurus stellaris Bittern	B	1996	20	—	A	B2
Cygnus columbianus Bewick's Swan	P	1996	1,000	16,000	A	A4i, B1i
Cygnus cygnus Whooper Swan	P	1996	1,000	4,000	A	A4i, B1i
Anser fabalis Bean Goose	P	1996	5,000	7,000	A	A4i, B1i
Anser anser Greylag Goose	B	1996	420	—	A	B1i
Anser anser Greylag Goose	P	1996	5,000	10,000	A	A4i, B1i
Branta leucopsis Barnacle Goose	P	1996	1,000	15,000	A	A4i, B1i
Anas acuta Pintail	P	1996	10,000	—	B	B1i
Anas clypeata Shoveler	P	1996	1,000	—	B	B1i
[1] *Anas clypeata* Shoveler	N	1996	2,000	2,000	B	B1i
[1] *Aythya ferina* Pochard	N	1996	9,000	9,000	A	B1i
Aythya fuligula Tufted Duck	P	1996	12,000	—	B	B1i
Aythya marila Scaup	P	1996	10,000	—	A	A4i, B1i
[2] *Clangula hyemalis* Long-tailed Duck	P	1996	250,000	1,600,000	A	A4i, B1i
[2] *Melanitta nigra* Common Scoter	P	1996	200,000	—	A	A4i, B1i
[2] *Melanitta fusca* Velvet Scoter	P	1996	350,000	400,000	A	A4i, B1i
Bucephala clangula Goldeneye	P	1996	10,000	—	A	A4i, B1i
Mergus albellus Smew	P	1996	150	500	A	B1i
Porzana porzana Spotted Crake	B	1996	85	—	C	B3
Crex crex Corncrake	B	1996	30	—	A	A1
Fulica atra Coot	P	1996	10,000	20,000	A	B1i
Grus grus Crane	P	1996	15,000	20,000	A	A4i, B1i
Charadrius hiaticula Ringed Plover	P	1996	3,000	3,000	B	A4i, B1i
Calidris alpina Dunlin	B	1996	90	—	A	B1i
Limosa limosa Black-tailed Godwit	B	1996	150	—	A	B2
Tringa totanus Redshank	B	1996	225	—	A	B2
Tringa totanus Redshank	P	1996	2,000	—	B	B1i
Larus canus Common Gull	B	1996	800	—	A	B1i
Larus marinus Great Black-backed Gull	B	1996	430	—	A	B3
Sterna caspia Caspian Tern	B	1996	140	—	A	A4i, B1i, B2
Sterna albifrons Little Tern	B	1996	45	—	A	B2

1. Moulting (summer).
2. Non-stop migration (number of staging birds is unknown).

■ Protection status
National High **International** High
48,600 ha of IBA covered by Nature Protection Area (Matsalu, 48,600 ha). 48,600 ha of IBA covered by Ramsar Site (Matsalu, 48,600 ha).

■ Conservation issues

Threats Abandonment/reduction of land management (B), Agricultural intensification/ expansion (C), Aquaculture/fisheries (B), Disturbance to birds (C), Recreation/tourism (A), Unsustainable exploitation (C)

The main threats come from tourism, intensive fishing, and the overgrowth of coastal and flood-plain meadows with reed *Phragmites* and scrub as a result of undergrazing or lack of mowing. The wetland is also affected by effluent pollution from surrounding farms. There is a management plan for the Nature Protection Area. Matsalu bay is very important for nature-conservation research, and is the centre for bird-ringing in Estonia.

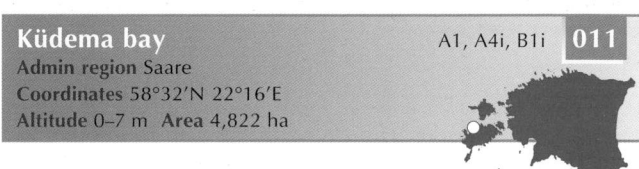

Küdema bay
A1, A4i, B1i **011**
Admin region Saare
Coordinates 58°32′N 22°16′E
Altitude 0–7 m **Area** 4,822 ha

■ Site description
A shallow (<20 m) sea bay on the northern coast of Saaremaa island, with small islets, reedbeds, coastal meadows and saltmarshes. The main economic activities are fishing, forestry and tourism.

Habitats Forest and woodland (10%; mixed forest), Wetland (6%), Marine areas (83%; sea inlet/coastal features)
Land-use Fisheries/aquaculture (80%), Forestry (10%), Nature conservation/ research (100%)

■ Birds
Küdema bay is an important wintering area for two duck species and a notable breeding area for several waterbirds. Significant proportion

(≥1%) of national population breeding at site: *Larus marinus* (min. 105 pairs).

Species		Season	Year	Pop min	Pop max	Acc	Criteria
Polysticta stelleri	Steller's Eider	W	1996	300	400	A	A1, A4i, B1i
Bucephala clangula	Goldeneye	W	1996	3,000	3,000	A	B1i

■ Protection status

National None **International** High
4,822 ha of IBA covered by Biosphere Reserve (West Estonian Archipelago, 1,560,000 ha).

■ Conservation issues

Threats Abandonment/reduction of land management (A), Aquaculture/fisheries (A), Disturbance to birds (A), Recreation/tourism (B), Unsustainable exploitation (C)

Major threats are posed by intensive fishing, overgrowth of coastal meadows with reed *Phragmites* due to undergrazing, and tourism. A planned core area of the West Estonian Archipelago Biosphere Reserve is contained by the IBA. Research involves monitoring of wintering and breeding waterbirds.

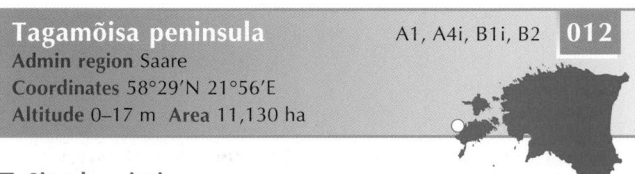

Tagamõisa peninsula   A1, A4i, B1i, B2   **012**
Admin region Saare
Coordinates 58°29'N 21°56'E
Altitude 0–17 m **Area** 11,130 ha

■ Site description

A peninsula on the north-western coast of Saaremaa island, surrounded by a shallow (<20 m) sea with shallow (4 m) bays. There are many small lakes, forest, sand-dunes, coastal meadows and grasslands. The primary land-uses are fishing, and grazing of sheep and cattle.

Habitats Forest and woodland (18%; native coniferous forest), Wetland (10%; standing fresh water), Marine areas (50%; sea inlet/coastal features), Artificial landscape (15%; highly improved reseeded grassland; other urban/industrial areas)
Land-use Agriculture (10%), Fisheries/aquaculture (50%), Forestry (10%), Nature conservation/research (90%), Urban/industrial/transport (5%)

■ Birds

Species		Season	Year	Pop min	Pop max	Acc	Criteria
Anser anser	Greylag Goose	P	1996	900	1,000	B	B1i
Polysticta stelleri	Steller's Eider	W	1996	1,500	3,200	A	A1, A4i, B1i
Bucephala clangula	Goldeneye	W	1996	3,000	3,000	A	B1i
Grus grus	Crane	B	1996	40	60	B	B2

The area is important for several waterbird species, notably *Polysticta stelleri*.

■ Protection status

National Partial **International** High
5,000 ha of IBA covered by National Park (Vilsandi, 16,657 ha). 11,130 ha of IBA covered by Biosphere Reserve (West Estonian Archipelago, 1,560,000 ha).

■ Conservation issues

Threats Abandonment/reduction of land management (C), Aquaculture/fisheries (B), Disturbance to birds (B), Recreation/tourism (A), Other (B)

The main threats are posed by fishing, tourism, and fuel-oil pollution from boats ('Other' threat, above). Research involves monitoring of wintering waterbirds.

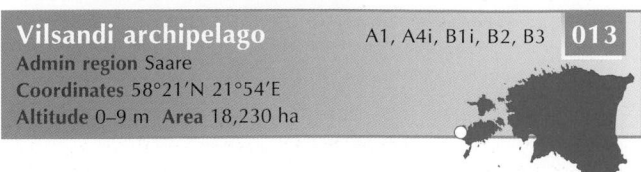

Vilsandi archipelago   A1, A4i, B1i, B2, B3   **013**
Admin region Saare
Coordinates 58°21'N 21°54'E
Altitude 0–9 m **Area** 18,230 ha

■ Site description

A large complex of shallow (<5 m) bays on the western coast of Saaremaa island, with many small islets and some lakes. Vegetation

includes reedbeds, coastal meadows, and forest. The main land-uses are nature-conservation projects and research, and grazing of cattle and sheep.

Habitats Forest and woodland (15%; native coniferous forest), Grassland (5%), Wetland (10%), Marine areas (60%; sea inlet/coastal features), Artificial landscape (5%)
Land-use Nature conservation/research (100%)

■ Birds

Species		Season	Year	Pop min	Pop max	Acc	Criteria
Cygnus olor	Mute Swan	P	1996	2,500	2,500	A	B1i
Anser anser	Greylag Goose	P	1996	600	1,500	A	B1i
Branta leucopsis	Barnacle Goose	B	1996	33	33	A	B3
Branta leucopsis	Barnacle Goose	P	1996	6,000	10,000	A	A4i, B1i
Aythya marila	Scaup	P	1996	3,100	—	B	B1i
Polysticta stelleri	Steller's Eider	W	1996	550	2,500	A	A1, A4i, B1i
Mergus merganser	Goosander	P	1996	1,800	—	A	B1i
Grus grus	Crane	B	1996	30	30	B	B2
Grus grus	Crane	P	1996	900	900	B	B1i
Larus marinus	Great Black-backed Gull	B	1996	200	350	A	B3

Vilsandi archipelago is an important breeding, staging and wintering area for waterbirds, especially wildfowl, and notably *Polysticta stelleri* in winter. Significant proportion (≥1%) of national population breeding at site: *Larus canus* (400 pairs), *Sterna caspia* (3–4 pairs).

■ Protection status

National High **International** High
18,230 ha of IBA covered by National Park (Vilsandi, 23,756 ha). 18,230 ha of IBA covered by Ramsar Site (Vilsandi National Park, 24,100 ha). 18,230 ha of IBA covered by Biosphere Reserve (West Estonian Archipelago, 1,560,000 ha).

■ Conservation issues

Threats Recreation/tourism (A)

Tourism poses a major threat. Research includes large-scale complex monitoring of birds and the environment.

Karala–Pilguse coast   A4i, B1i   **014**
Admin region Saare
Coordinates 58°15'N 21°57'E
Altitude 0–5 m **Area** 3,114 ha

■ Site description

A complex of shallow (<4 m) sea bays and small islets on the west coast of Saaremaa island, with vast coastal meadows, reedbeds, saltmarshes and shallow lakes. The main economic activities are fishing, and grazing of sheep and cattle.

Habitats Forest and woodland (17%; mixed forest), Wetland (30%; standing fresh water; water-fringe vegetation), Marine areas (40%; sea inlet/coastal features), Artificial landscape (13%; highly improved reseeded grassland; arable land)
Land-use Agriculture (20%), Fisheries/aquaculture (40%), Forestry (17%), Nature conservation/research (100%)

■ Birds

Species		Season	Year	Pop min	Pop max	Acc	Criteria
Branta leucopsis	Barnacle Goose	P	1996	10,000	—	A	A4i, B1i

The most important staging area for migrating *Branta leucopsis* in Estonia.

■ Protection status

National Low **International** High
50 ha of IBA covered by National Park (Vilsandi, 16,657 ha). 3,114 ha of IBA covered by Biosphere Reserve (West Estonian Archipelago, 1,560,000 ha).

■ Conservation issues

Threats Abandonment/reduction of land management (A), Agricultural intensification/expansion (A), Aquaculture/fisheries (B), Disturbance to birds (A), Recreation/tourism (A), Unsustainable exploitation (A)

Major threats are posed by unsustainable hunting, tourism, overgrowth of coastal meadows with reed *Phragmites* as a result of undergrazing, and intensive fishing. A core area of the West Estonian Archipelago Biosphere Reserve is planned within the IBA. Naistekivimaa islet (part of the IBA) overlaps with Vilsandi National Park. Research involves monitoring of migrating waterbirds.

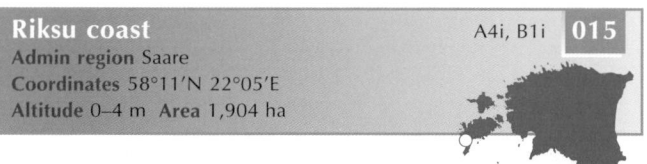

Riksu coast
A4i, B1i 015

Admin region Saare
Coordinates 58°11'N 22°05'E
Altitude 0–4 m **Area** 1,904 ha

■ Site description
A complex of shallow (<4 m) sea bays on the western coast of Saaremaa island, with small offshore islets, vast coastal meadows, saltmarshes and a shallow lake. The main economic activities are fishing and grazing of sheep and cattle.

Habitats Forest and woodland (7%; mixed forest), Grassland (8%), Wetland (17%; standing fresh water; water-fringe vegetation), Marine areas (60%; sea inlet/coastal features)
Land-use Agriculture (10%), Fisheries/aquaculture (60%), Forestry (7%)

■ Birds

Species		Season	Year	Pop min	Pop max	Acc	Criteria
Branta leucopsis	Barnacle Goose	P	1996	3,000	8,000	A	A4i, B1i

Riksu coast is an important staging area for migrating *Branta leucopsis*.

■ Protection status
National None **International** High
1,904 ha of IBA covered by Biosphere Reserve (West Estonian Archipelago, 1,560,000 ha).

■ Conservation issues
Threats Abandonment/reduction of land management (A), Aquaculture/fisheries (B), Disturbance to birds (A), Recreation/tourism (A), Unsustainable exploitation (A)

Threats are posed by unsustainable hunting, tourism, overgrowth of coastal meadows by reed *Phragmites* as a result of undergrazing, and intensive fishing. Research involves monitoring of migrating and wintering waterbirds.

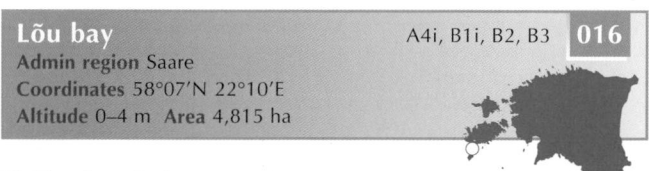

Lõu bay
A4i, B1i, B2, B3 016

Admin region Saare
Coordinates 58°07'N 22°10'E
Altitude 0–4 m **Area** 4,815 ha

■ Site description
A shallow (<8 m) bay with small islets, vast coastal meadows and saltmarshes on the south-western coast of Saaremaa island. The main economic activities are fishing, and grazing of sheep and cattle.

Habitats Grassland (5%), Wetland (5%), Marine areas (90%; sea inlet/coastal features)
Land-use Agriculture (8%), Fisheries/aquaculture (90%)

■ Birds

Species		Season	Year	Pop min	Pop max	Acc	Criteria
Anser anser	Greylag Goose	P	1996	200	—	A	B1i
Branta leucopsis	Barnacle Goose	P	1996	5,000	5,000	A	A4i, B1i
Mergus albellus	Smew	W	1993	250	—	A	B1i
Larus marinus	Great Black-backed Gull	B	1995	200	—	A	B3
Sterna caspia	Caspian Tern	B	1995	70	—	A	A4i, B1i, B2

Lõu bay is an important staging area for geese and a notable breeding area for several waterbirds.

■ Protection status
National None **International** High
4,815 ha of IBA covered by Biosphere Reserve (West Estonian Archipelago, 1,560,000 ha).

■ Conservation issues
Threats Aquaculture/fisheries (B), Disturbance to birds (A), Recreation/tourism (A), Unsustainable exploitation (A)

Major threats are posed by unsustainable hunting, tourism and intensive fishing. The IBA contains a planned core area of the West Estonian Archipelago Biosphere Reserve, and is also a potential Ramsar Site. Research involves monitoring of migrating and wintering waterbirds.

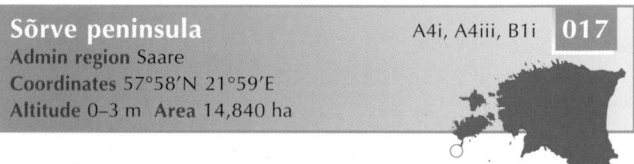

Sõrve peninsula
A4i, A4iii, B1i 017

Admin region Saare
Coordinates 57°58'N 21°59'E
Altitude 0–3 m **Area** 14,840 ha

■ Site description
An area of shallow (<20 m) sea and coast along the southern and western sides of Sõrve peninsula (Saaremaa island), with vast reedbeds, coastal meadows and saltmarshes. The main economic activity is fishing.

Habitats Marine areas (95%; sea inlet/coastal features)
Land-use Fisheries/aquaculture (95%)

■ Birds

Species		Season	Year	Pop min	Pop max	Acc	Criteria
[1] *Gavia stellata*	Red-throated Diver	W	1993	Abundant	—		A4i, B1i
[1] *Gavia arctica*	Black-throated Diver	W	1993	Abundant	—		A4i, B1i
Anser anser	Greylag Goose	P	1996	500	500	A	B1i
Clangula hyemalis	Long-tailed Duck	P	1996	55,000	—	A	A4i, B1i
Mergus albellus	Smew	W	1993	250	250	A	B1i
Alca torda	Razorbill	W	1993	300	300	A	B1i
Cepphus grylle	Black Guillemot	W	1996	300	300	A	B1i

1. >17,000 *G. stellata/G. arctica*.

The area is an important staging area for migrating and wintering waterbirds, especially wintering divers. The site holds 20,000 or more waterbirds on a regular basis.

■ Protection status
National None **International** High
14,840 ha of IBA covered by Biosphere Reserve (West Estonian Archipelago, 1,560,000 ha).

■ Conservation issues
Threats Abandonment/reduction of land management (A), Aquaculture/fisheries (A), Other (B)

Threats are posed by intensive fishing, overgrowth of coastal meadows with reed *Phragmites* as a result of undergrazing, fuel-oil pollution from boats ('Other' threat, above), unsustainable hunting, and tourism. Two planned core areas of the West Estonian Archipelago Biosphere Reserve are contained by the IBA. Research involves monitoring of migrating and wintering waterbirds.

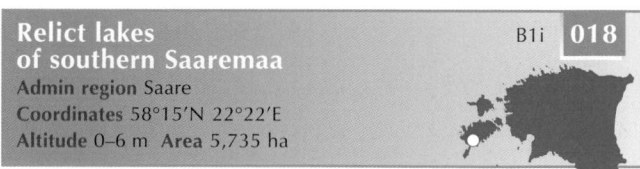

Relict lakes of southern Saaremaa
B1i 018

Admin region Saare
Coordinates 58°15'N 22°22'E
Altitude 0–6 m **Area** 5,735 ha

■ Site description
A complex of shallow (<2 m), relict lakes and vast reedbeds along the southern coast of Saaremaa island. Mud is extracted from Mullutu and Suurlaht lakes for its curative properties. The main economic activities are fishing, reed-cutting ('Other' land-use, below) and hunting.

Habitats Forest and woodland (25%), Wetland (70%; standing brackish and salt water; water-fringe vegetation)
Land-use Agriculture (5%), Fisheries/aquaculture (18%), Forestry (20%), Hunting (20%), Nature conservation/research (100%), Other (35%)

■ Birds

Species	Season	Year	Pop min	Pop max	Acc	Criteria
Botaurus stellaris Bittern	B	1996	15	—	A	B2
Anser anser Greylag Goose	P	1996	500	—	A	B1i
Grus grus Crane	P	1996	1,000	—	A	B1i

The area is an important staging area for migrating *Anser anser* and *Grus grus* and a notable breeding area for several waterbirds. Significant proportion (≥1%) of national population breeding at site: *Grus grus* (10 pairs), *Larus minutus* (50 pairs), *Chlidonias niger* (20 pairs).

■ Protection status
National Low **International** High
285 ha of IBA covered by Nature Protection Area (Linnulaht Lake, 285 ha). 5,735 ha of IBA covered by Biosphere Reserve (West Estonian Archipelago, 1,560,000 ha).

■ Conservation issues

Threats Abandonment/reduction of land management (A), Aquaculture/fisheries (C), Drainage (B), Disturbance to birds (A), Recreation/tourism (A), Unsustainable exploitation (A)

Major threats are posed by unsustainable hunting, tourism, and the overgrowth of coastal meadows with reed *Phragmites* due to undergrazing. The IBA is a planned core area of the West Estonian Archipelago Biosphere Reserve, as well as a potential Ramsar Site. Research involves monitoring of breeding birds and migrating waterbirds.

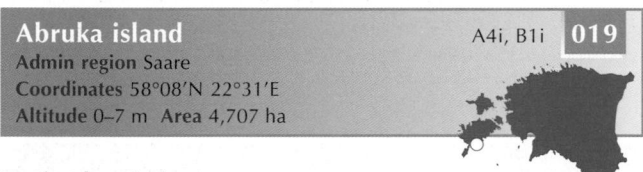

Abruka island
A4i, B1i **019**
Admin region Saare
Coordinates 58°08′N 22°31′E
Altitude 0–7 m **Area** 4,707 ha

■ Site description
An area of shallow (<12 m) sea with small offshore islands and islets along the southern coast of Saaremaa island. The coastline is complex, with vast reedbeds, coastal meadows and saltmarshes. The main human uses of the landscape are fishing, tourism, yachting and sheep-grazing.

Habitats Forest and woodland (10%; broadleaved deciduous forest), Wetland (13%; water-fringe vegetation), Marine areas (75%; sea inlet/coastal features)
Land-use Agriculture (10%), Fisheries/aquaculture (75%), Forestry (10%), Nature conservation/research (100%), Tourism/recreation (30%)

■ Birds

Species	Season	Year	Pop min	Pop max	Acc	Criteria
Phalacrocorax carbo Cormorant	B	1996	800	800	A	B1i
Branta leucopsis Barnacle Goose	P	1996	2,000	3,000	A	A4i, B1i
Bucephala clangula Goldeneye	P	1996	4,500	—	A	A4i, B1i

The area is an important breeding or staging site for several migratory waterbirds. Significant proportion (≥1%) of national population breeding at site: *Larus marinus* (100 pairs), *Sterna caspia* (3 pairs).

■ Protection status
National Low **International** High
103 ha of IBA covered by Nature Protection Area (Abruka, 103 ha). 4,707 ha of IBA covered by Biosphere Reserve (West Estonian Archipelago, 1,560,000 ha).

■ Conservation issues

Threats Abandonment/reduction of land management (A), Aquaculture/fisheries (B), Disturbance to birds (A), Intensified forest management (C), Recreation/tourism (A), Unsustainable exploitation (A)

Major threats are posed by unsustainable hunting, tourism, overgrowth of coastal meadows with reed *Phragmites* due to undergrazing, and intensive fishing. The area is a planned core area of the West Estonian Archipelago Biosphere Reserve. Research involves monitoring of breeding birds and migrating waterbirds.

Kasti bay
A4i, B1i **020**
Admin region Saare
Coordinates 58°14′N 22°37′E
Altitude 0–2 m **Area** 3,877 ha

■ Site description
A complex of shallow (<4 m) bays and small islets on the southern coast of Saaremaa island, with vast reedbeds, coastal meadows and saltmarshes. The main economic activities are fishing, sheep-grazing and forestry.

Habitats Forest and woodland (5%), Grassland (5%), Wetland (25%; saltmarsh, water-fringe vegetation), Marine areas (65%; sea inlet/coastal features)
Land-use Agriculture (15%), Fisheries/aquaculture (60%), Forestry (5%), Nature conservation/research (100%)

■ Birds

Species	Season	Year	Pop min	Pop max	Acc	Criteria
Anser anser Greylag Goose	P	1996	500	—	B	B1i
Branta leucopsis Barnacle Goose	P	1996	3,000	5,000	A	A4i, B1i

Kasti bay is an important staging area for migrating geese and a notable breeding area for several waterbirds. Significant proportion (≥1%) of national population breeding at site: *Sterna albifrons* (min. 10 pairs).

■ Protection status
National None **International** High
3,877 ha of IBA covered by Biosphere Reserve (West Estonian Archipelago, 1,560,000 ha).

■ Conservation issues

Threats Abandonment/reduction of land management (A), Aquaculture/fisheries (B), Disturbance to birds (B), Recreation/tourism (A), Unsustainable exploitation (A)

Major threats are posed by unsustainable hunting, tourism, overgrowth of coastal meadows with reed *Phragmites* due to undergrazing, and intensive fishing. The area is a planned core area of the West Estonian Archipelago Biosphere Reserve. Research involves monitoring of migrating waterbirds.

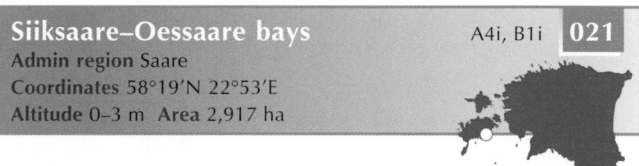

Siiksaare–Oessaare bays
A4i, B1i **021**
Admin region Saare
Coordinates 58°19′N 22°53′E
Altitude 0–3 m **Area** 2,917 ha

■ Site description
A complex of shallow (<2 m) bays and relict lakes on the southern coast of Saaremaa island, with small islets, vast reedbeds, coastal meadows and saltmarshes. The main economic activities are fishing, sheep-grazing and forestry.

Habitats Forest and woodland (15%), Wetland (45%; standing brackish and salt water; water-fringe vegetation), Marine areas (35%; sea inlet/coastal features)
Land-use Agriculture (10%), Fisheries/aquaculture (40%), Forestry (15%), Nature conservation/research (25%), Not utilized (25%)

■ Birds

Species	Season	Year	Pop min	Pop max	Acc	Criteria
Branta leucopsis Barnacle Goose	P	1996	3,000	6,000	A	A4i, B1i
Anas strepera Gadwall	B	1996	120	—	B	B1i
[1] *Anas strepera* Gadwall	N	1996	500	500	B	B1i

1. Moulting (summer).

A diverse selection of migratory waterbirds use the site for staging and/or breeding, with important numbers of several species. Significant proportion (≥1%) of national population breeding at site: *Grus grus* (10 pairs), *Larus canus* (min. 400 pairs), *Larus marinus* (20 pairs).

■ Protection status
National None **International** High
2,917 ha of IBA covered by Biosphere Reserve (West Estonian Archipelago, 1,560,000 ha).

■ Conservation issues

Threats Abandonment/reduction of land management (A), Drainage (B), Recreation/tourism (C), Unsustainable exploitation (A)

The main threats are unsustainable hunting, intensive fishing, overgrowth of coastal meadows with reed *Phragmites* due to undergrazing, and tourism. The IBA is a planned core area of the West Estonian Archipelago Biosphere Reserve, and is also a potential Ramsar Site. Research involves monitoring of migrating waterbirds.

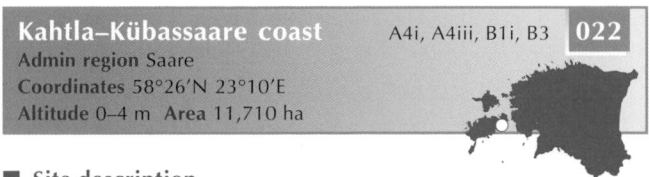

Kahtla–Kübassaare coast   A4i, A4iii, B1i, B3   **022**
Admin region Saare
Coordinates 58°26′N 23°10′E
Altitude 0–4 m   **Area** 11,710 ha

■ Site description

A complex of shallow (<3 m) bays on the south-eastern coast of Saaremaa island, with small islets, vast reedbeds, coastal meadows and saltmarshes. The main economic activities are fishing, grazing of cattle and sheep, and forestry.

Habitats Forest and woodland (7%), Grassland (5%), Wetland (15%; water-fringe vegetation), Marine areas (70%; sea inlet/coastal features)
Land-use Agriculture (10%), Fisheries/aquaculture (70%), Forestry (7%), Nature conservation/research (100%)

■ Birds

Species		Season	Year	Pop min	Pop max	Acc	Criteria
Branta leucopsis	Barnacle Goose	B	1996	45	45	A	B3
Branta leucopsis	Barnacle Goose	P	1996	10,000	10,000	A	A4i, B1i
Clangula hyemalis	Long-tailed Duck	P	1996	50,000	—	A	A4i, B1i
Grus grus	Crane	P	1996	1,500	1,500	A	B1i

A diverse selection of migratory waterbirds use the site for staging and/or breeding, with several species occurring in important numbers. The site holds 20,000 or more waterbirds on a regular basis. Significant proportion (≥1%) of national population breeding at site: *Larus canus* (min. 400 pairs), *Sterna caspia* (5 pairs).

■ Protection status

National None   **International** High
11,710 ha of IBA covered by Biosphere Reserve (West Estonian Archipelago, 1,560,000 ha).

■ Conservation issues

Threats Abandonment/reduction of land management (A), Aquaculture/fisheries (A), Disturbance to birds (A), Recreation/tourism (A), Unsustainable exploitation (A)

The main threats are intensive fishing, unsustainable hunting, tourism, and overgrowth of coastal meadows with reed *Phragmites* as a result of undergrazing. Two planned core areas of the West Estonian Archipelago Biosphere Reserve are contained by the IBA. Research involves monitoring of migrating and breeding waterbirds.

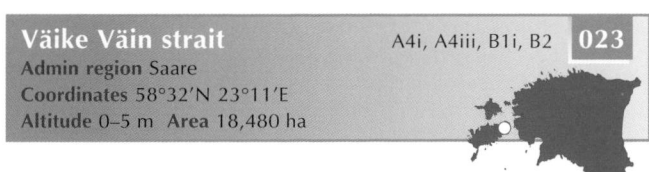

Väike Väin strait   A4i, A4iii, B1i, B2   **023**
Admin region Saare
Coordinates 58°32′N 23°11′E
Altitude 0–5 m   **Area** 18,480 ha

■ Site description

A shallow (<6 m) sea strait between two large islands—Saaremaa and Muhu—in western Estonia. The coast is a complex of shallow (<2 m) bays, meadows and reedbeds. The main human activities are intensive fishing, yachting and tourism, and reed-cutting ('Other' land-use, below).

Habitats Wetland (18%; water-fringe vegetation), Marine areas (75%; sea inlet/coastal features)
Land-use Agriculture (10%), Fisheries/aquaculture (70%), Other (5%), Tourism/recreation (30%)

■ Birds

Väike Väin strait is a very important staging area for migrating wildfowl and an important breeding area for several waders and gull/

tern species. The site holds 20,000 or more waterbirds on a regular basis. Significant proportion (≥1%) of national population breeding at site: *Tringa totanus* (min. 200 pairs), *Larus marinus* (min. 40 pairs).

Species		Season	Year	Pop min	Pop max	Acc	Criteria
Cygnus columbianus	Bewick's Swan	P	1996	500	1,700	A	A4i, B1i
Cygnus cygnus	Whooper Swan	P	1996	500	700	A	A4i, B1i
Anser anser	Greylag Goose	P	1996	3,500	3,500	A	A4i, B1i
Branta leucopsis	Barnacle Goose	P	1996	10,000	10,000	A	A4i, B1i
Anas penelope	Wigeon	P	1995	13,000	—	A	B1i
Clangula hyemalis	Long-tailed Duck	P	1995	150,000	—	A	A4i, B1i
Bucephala clangula	Goldeneye	P	1995	4,500	—	A	A4i, B1i
Calidris alpina	Dunlin	B	1995	75	75	A	B1i
Larus minutus	Little Gull	B	1995	80	80	A	B2
Larus canus	Common Gull	B	1995	700	700	A	B2
Sterna sandvicensis	Sandwich Tern	B	1995	200	200	A	B2

■ Protection status

National None   **International** High
18,480 ha of IBA covered by Biosphere Reserve (West Estonian Archipelago, 1,560,000 ha).

■ Conservation issues

Threats Abandonment/reduction of land management (A), Aquaculture/fisheries (A), Construction/impact of dyke/dam/barrage (A), Disturbance to birds (A), Industrialization/urbanization (A), Infrastructure (A), Recreation/tourism (A), Unsustainable exploitation (A)

Major threats are posed by tourism, nutrient pollution due to fertilizer run-off, fuel-oil pollution from boats, overgrowth of coastal meadows with reed *Phragmites* due to undergrazing, fishing, and unsustainable hunting. The strait is divided into two bays by an embanked road-dam, which has blocked off natural water currents through the strait. Three core areas of the West Estonian Archipelago Biosphere Reserve have been designated in this IBA, which is also a proposed Ramsar Site. Research involves monitoring of migrating waterbirds.

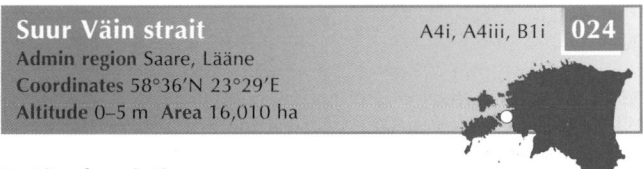

Suur Väin strait   A4i, A4iii, B1i   **024**
Admin region Saare, Lääne
Coordinates 58°36′N 23°29′E
Altitude 0–5 m   **Area** 16,010 ha

■ Site description

A shallow (<19 m) sea strait between Muhu island and the western Estonian mainland, with a complex coast of shallow (<2 m) bays, relict lakes, meadows and reedbeds. The main economic activity is intensive fishing, and there is a busy sea-route between Muhu island and the mainland.

Habitats Marine areas (88%; sea inlet/coastal features)
Land-use Fisheries/aquaculture (85%), Nature conservation/research (21%), Urban/industrial/transport (10%)

■ Birds

Species		Season	Year	Pop min	Pop max	Acc	Criteria
Cygnus columbianus	Bewick's Swan	P	1996	250	250	B	A4i, B1i
Cygnus cygnus	Whooper Swan	P	1996	550	550	B	B1i
Aythya marila	Scaup	P	1990	20,000	20,000	B	A4i, B1i
[1] *Clangula hyemalis*	Long-tailed Duck	P	1996	1,650,000	1,650,000	A	A4i, B1i
[2] *Melanitta nigra*	Common Scoter	P	1990	20,000	20,000	B	A4i, B1i
[3] *Melanitta fusca*	Velvet Scoter	P	1995	9,300	9,300	B	A4i, B1i
Mergus albellus	Smew	P	1996	400	400	B	B1i

1. Non-stop migration.
2. 20,000 staging; 192,000 on non-stop migration.
3. 9,300 staging; 386,000 on non-stop migration.

Suur Väin strait is important for migrating wildfowl and divers *Gavia*, with large numbers staging and huge numbers passing straight through (e.g. 62,600 *Gavia stellata/G. arctica* in spring 1990s; number of staging birds unknown). The site holds 20,000 or more waterbirds on a regular basis.

■ Protection status

National Partial   **International** Partial
3,959 ha of IBA covered by Nature Protection Area (Laelatu–Puhtu–Nehatu, 4,640 ha). 3,959 ha of IBA covered by Ramsar Site (Puhto–

Laleatu–Nehatu, 4,640 ha). 8,000 ha of IBA covered by Biosphere Reserve (West Estonian Archipelago, 1,560,000 ha).

■ Conservation issues

Threats Abandonment/reduction of land management (B), Agricultural intensification/expansion (C), Aquaculture/fisheries (B), Disturbance to birds (B), Industrialization/urbanization (B), Infrastructure (B), Recreation/tourism (A), Unsustainable exploitation (A)

Major threats are posed by tourism, unsustainable hunting, nutrient pollution due to fishery discards and fertilizer run-off, fuel-oil pollution from boats, and overgrowth of coastal meadows with reed *Phragmites* as a result of undergrazing. The IBA is a proposed Ramsar Site. Research includes studies on the migration of Arctic waterbirds, and several botanical studies.

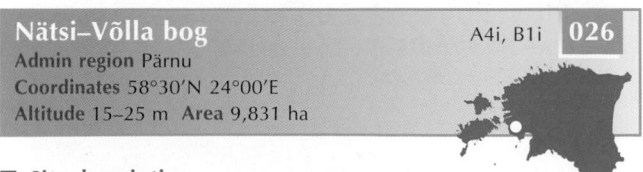

Nehatu mire   B1i 025
Admin region Lääne
Coordinates 58°33′N 23°38′E
Altitude 3–4 m Area 681 ha

■ Site description
A mire with a large number of shallow (<1 m), relict lakes. Habitats include patchy bogs, fens, marshy wooded meadows, and woods. There is practically no exploitative land-use.

Habitats Forest and woodland (40%; alluvial/very wet forest), Wetland (60%; standing fresh water; raised bog; fen/transition mire/spring)
Land-use Not utilized (100%)

■ Birds

Species	Season	Year	Pop min	Pop max	Acc	Criteria
Grus grus Crane	P	1996	200	2,000	A	B1i

Nehatu mire is an important roosting place in autumn for migrating *Grus grus*.

■ Protection status
National High **International** High
681 ha of IBA covered by Nature Protection Area (Laelatu–Puhtu–Nehatu, 4,640 ha). 681 ha of IBA covered by Ramsar Site (Puhto–Laleatu–Nehatu, 4,640 ha).

■ Conservation issues

Threats Drainage (A)

Drainage of the area surrounding the IBA poses a threat. Forest management, improvement of land for agriculture, peat-digging and hunting are all prohibited in the Nature Protection Area. Together with part of site 024 (Suur Väin strait), this site forms the Laelatu–Puhtu–Nehatu wetland complex (Ramsar Site). Research involves counts of roosting and moulting *Grus grus*, and botanical and landscape monitoring are planned.

Nätsi–Võlla bog   A4i, B1i 026
Admin region Pärnu
Coordinates 58°30′N 24°00′E
Altitude 15–25 m Area 9,831 ha

■ Site description
A large raised bog in western Estonia, with many pools.

Habitats Forest and woodland (5%), Wetland (95%; raised bog)
Land-use Forestry (5%), Nature conservation/research (100%), Tourism/recreation (5%)

■ Birds

Species	Season	Year	Pop min	Pop max	Acc	Criteria
Cygnus columbianus Bewick's Swan	P	1996	600	—	A	A4i, B1i

Nätsi–Võlla bog is an important staging area for migrating *Cygnus columbianus*, and supports a diverse assemblage of breeding waders.

Significant proportion (≥1%) of national population breeding at site: *Grus grus* (10–20 pairs), *Limosa limosa* (5–10 pairs).

■ Protection status
National High **International** None
9,831 ha of IBA covered by Nature Protection Area (Nätsi–Võlla, 9,881 ha).

■ Conservation issues

Threats Drainage (A), Recreation/tourism (A)

Major threats are drainage of the surrounding area, and tourism. The IBA is a potential Ramsar Site. Research involves monitoring of birds.

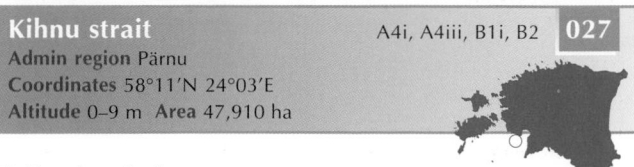

Kihnu strait   A4i, A4iii, B1i, B2 027
Admin region Pärnu
Coordinates 58°11′N 24°03′E
Altitude 0–9 m Area 47,910 ha

■ Site description
A shallow (<12 m) sea strait between Kihnu island and the west Estonian mainland, with a complex of small islets and shallow (<2 m) bays. There is a mosaic of meadows and reedbeds along the coast. Fishing and tourism are intensive in the area.

Habitats Marine areas (95%; sea inlet/coastal features)
Land-use Fisheries/aquaculture (90%), Nature conservation/research (100%), Tourism/recreation (20%)

■ Birds

Species	Season	Year	Pop min	Pop max	Acc	Criteria
[1] Gavia stellata Red-throated Diver	P	1996	Common	—		A4i, B1i
[1] Gavia arctica Black-throated Diver	P	1996	Common	—		A4i, B1i
Phalacrocorax carbo Cormorant	P	1996	3,500	—	A	B1i
Cygnus columbianus Bewick's Swan	P	1996	1,000	3,600	A	A4i, B1i
Cygnus cygnus Whooper Swan	P	1996	300	500	A	B1i
Branta leucopsis Barnacle Goose	P	1996	1,500	3,000	A	A4i, B1i
Aythya marila Scaup	P	1996	30,000	—	A	A4i, B1i
Clangula hyemalis Long-tailed Duck	P	1996	125,000	—	A	A4i, B1i
Melanitta nigra Common Scoter	P	1996	55,000	—	A	A4i, B1i
Melanitta fusca Velvet Scoter	P	1996	80,000	—	A	A4i, B1i
Bucephala clangula Goldeneye	P	1996	5,000	—	B	A4i, B1i
Calidris alpina Dunlin	B	1994	70	100	B	B1i
Limosa limosa Black-tailed Godwit	B	1994	45	—	B	B2
Tringa totanus Redshank	B	1994	340	—	B	B2
Sterna sandvicensis Sandwich Tern	B	1994	80	80	B	B2

1. >2,000 *G. stellata/G. arctica* staging in spring.

Kihnu strait is an important staging area for migrating waterbirds, especially wildfowl, and supports important numbers of breeding waders and gulls/terns (Laridae). The site holds 20,000 or more waterbirds on a regular basis. Significant proportion (≥1%) of national population breeding at site: *Larus canus* (500 pairs), *Sterna caspia* (5 pairs).

■ Protection status
National Low **International** None
21 ha of IBA covered by Protected Landscape (Sangelaid, 21 ha). 201 ha of IBA covered by Protected Landscape (Manilaid and Annilaid, 201 ha). 3 ha of IBA covered by Protected Landscape (Sorgu Island, 3 ha). 21 ha of IBA covered by Protected Landscape (Tõstamaa Islets, 21 ha).

■ Conservation issues

Threats Abandonment/reduction of land management (C), Aquaculture/fisheries (A), Disturbance to birds (A), Recreation/tourism (A), Unsustainable exploitation (A)

The main threats are posed by tourism, fuel-oil pollution from boats, overgrowth of coastal meadows with reed *Phragmites* due to undergrazing, and unsustainable hunting and egg-collection. A small part of the IBA is a potential Ramsar Site (Tõstamaa Islets, 21 ha). A Marine Park (Nature Park) is proposed at Kihnu Väin strait. Research involves studies on the migration and breeding of waterbirds.

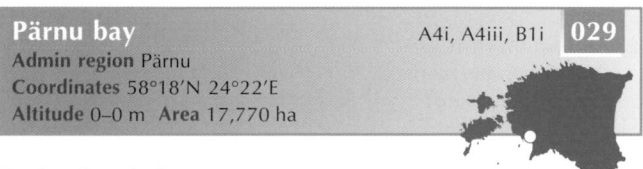

Audru polder
A4i, A4iii, B1i **028**

Admin region Pärnu
Coordinates 58°24'N 24°21'E
Altitude 0–2 m **Area** 788 ha

■ Site description
A polder complex near Pärnu town in western Estonia. The land is used for haymaking and cattle-grazing.

Habitats Artificial landscape (95%; highly improved reseeded grassland)
Land-use Agriculture (95%), Nature conservation/research (100%)

■ Birds

Species	Season	Year	Pop min	Pop max	Acc	Criteria
Cygnus columbianus Bewick's Swan	P	1996	5,000	17,500	A	A4i, B1i
Cygnus cygnus Whooper Swan	P	1996	300	600	A	B1i
Anser anser Greylag Goose	P	1996	400	400	A	B1i
Branta leucopsis Barnacle Goose	P	1996	3,000	6,000	A	A4i, B1i

Audru polder is an important staging area for migrating wildfowl, especially *Cygnus columbianus* for which it is the most important staging site in Europe in spring. The site holds 20,000 or more waterbirds on a regular basis.

■ Protection status
National None **International** None

■ Conservation issues

Threats Abandonment/reduction of land management (A), Agricultural intensification/expansion (A), Disturbance to birds (A), Unsustainable exploitation (A)

The main threats are the intensification of agriculture in some areas and the reduction of land management in other areas, as well as unsustainable hunting. The area requires moderate agricultural activity to maintain habitat suitable for key bird species. Research involves the monitoring of migrating waterbirds.

Pärnu bay
A4i, A4iii, B1i **029**

Admin region Pärnu
Coordinates 58°18'N 24°22'E
Altitude 0–0 m **Area** 17,770 ha

■ Site description
A shallow (<9 m) bay in south-west Estonia. Fishing and ship activity are intense in the area.

Habitats Marine areas (100%; sea inlet/coastal features)
Land-use Fisheries/aquaculture (100%), Urban/industrial/transport (10%)

■ Birds

Species	Season	Year	Pop min	Pop max	Acc	Criteria
[1] *Gavia stellata* Red-throated Diver	P	1996	Common		—	A4i, B1i
[1] *Gavia arctica* Black-throated Diver	P	1996	Common		—	A4i, B1i
Cygnus columbianus Bewick's Swan	P	1996	500	—	A	A4i, B1i
Aythya marila Scaup	P	1996	30,000	—	A	A4i, B1i
Clangula hyemalis Long-tailed Duck	P	1996	50,000	—	A	A4i, B1i
Melanitta nigra Common Scoter	P	1996	30,000	—	A	A4i, B1i
Melanitta fusca Velvet Scoter	P	1996	50,000	—	A	A4i, B1i
Mergus albellus Smew	P	1996	250	—	A	B1i

1. >1,000 *G. stellata/G. arctica* staging in spring.

In spring, Pärnu bay is a very important staging area for migrating divers *Gavia* and wildfowl, especially seaduck. The site holds 20,000 or more waterbirds on a regular basis.

■ Protection status
National None **International** None

■ Conservation issues

Threats Aquaculture/fisheries (A), Other (A)

Major threats are posed by fuel-oil pollution from boats ('Other' threat, above) and intensive fishing. Research involves monitoring of migrating waterbirds.

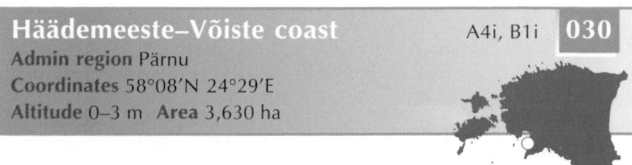

Häädemeeste–Võiste coast
A4i, B1i **030**

Admin region Pärnu
Coordinates 58°08'N 24°29'E
Altitude 0–3 m **Area** 3,630 ha

■ Site description
A complex of shallow sea (<2 m) and small islets, with vast reedbeds and coastal meadows on the south-western coast of Estonia. The main economic activities are fishing (intensive), grazing and hunting.

Habitats Grassland (6%), Wetland (25%; saltmarsh; water-fringe vegetation), Marine areas (65%; sea inlet/coastal features)
Land-use Agriculture (30%), Fisheries/aquaculture (60%), Hunting (20%)

■ Birds

Species	Season	Year	Pop min	Pop max	Acc	Criteria
Cygnus columbianus Bewick's Swan	P	1996	200	600	A	A4i, B1i
Branta leucopsis Barnacle Goose	P	1996	2,000	—	A	A4i, B1i

The area is an important staging site (in spring) for migrating *Cygnus columbianus* and *Branta leucopsis*. The avifauna is diverse, with 185 species recorded, of which 65 have been recorded breeding. Breeding species of global conservation concern that do not meet IBA criteria: *Crex crex* (min. 5 pairs). Significant proportion (≥1%) of national population breeding at site: *Limosa limosa* (min. 10 pairs).

■ Protection status
National Partial **International** None
2,000 ha of IBA covered by Protected Landscape (Rannametsa–Soometsa, 8,085 ha).

■ Conservation issues

Threats Abandonment/reduction of land management (A), Disturbance to birds (A), Recreation/tourism (A), Unsustainable exploitation (A)

The main threats are caused by human disturbance of birds, tourism, unsustainable hunting, fishing, and overgrowth of coastal meadows with reed *Phragmites* due to undergrazing. Häädemeeste coastal meadow is a potential Ramsar Site. Research involves monitoring of birds.

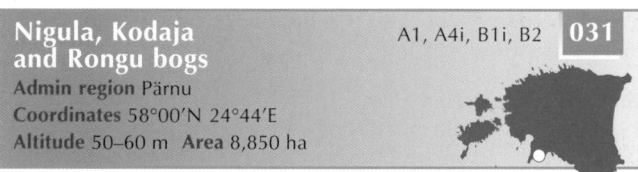

Nigula, Kodaja and Rongu bogs
A1, A4i, B1i, B2 **031**

Admin region Pärnu
Coordinates 58°00'N 24°44'E
Altitude 50–60 m **Area** 8,850 ha

■ Site description
A complex of raised bogs, numerous pools, and broadleaved deciduous and mixed forests in south-west Estonia. The main land-uses are forestry, non-intensive agriculture, nature conservation and research, and tourism.

Habitats Forest and woodland (44%; broadleaved deciduous forest; mixed forest), Wetland (40%; raised bog), Artificial landscape (16%; highly improved reseeded grassland; arable land)
Land-use Agriculture (16%), Forestry (18%), Nature conservation/research (100%), Tourism/recreation (6%)

■ Birds

Species	Season	Year	Pop min	Pop max	Acc	Criteria
Anser fabalis Bean Goose	P	1996	15,000	15,000	B	A4i, B1i
Anser albifrons White-fronted Goose	P	1996	15,000	15,000	B	A4i, B1i
Tetrao tetrix Black Grouse	R	1996	200	—	C	B2
Crex crex Corncrake	B	1996	20	30	A	A1

An important staging area for migratory geese *Anser* (totalling 30,000–40,000 at peak counts) and *Grus grus*, and an important breeding area for several species of mire and forest. Significant proportion (≥1%) of national population breeding at site: *Grus grus* (10 pairs), *Picus canus* (5–10 pairs).

■ Protection status
National Partial **International** Partial

1,590 ha of IBA covered by Nature Protection Area (Kodaja, 1,590 ha). 4,951 ha of IBA covered by Nature Protection Area (Nigula, 4,951 ha). 1,141 ha of IBA covered by Nature Protection Area (Rongu, 1,141 ha). 4,951 ha of IBA covered by Ramsar Site (Nigula, 4,951 ha).

■ Conservation issues

Threats Consequences of animal/plant introductions (C), Drainage (A), Intensified forest management (A), Recreation/tourism (B), Unsustainable exploitation (A)

Major threats are posed by intensification of forestry, drainage, unsustainable hunting, and tourism. Regeneration of deciduous forest is limited due to overbrowsing by introduced red deer *Cervus elaphus*. Research involves monitoring of birds (since 1968) and mire plants.

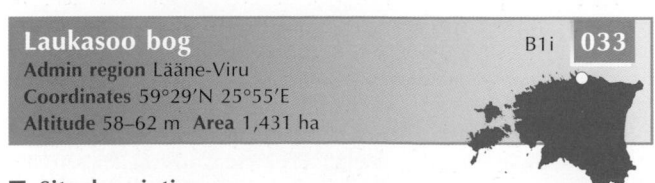

Soomaa mire complex A1, A4i, B1i, B2 032
Admin region Pärnu, Viljandi
Coordinates 58°25'N 25°05'E
Altitude 15–30 m **Area** 36,890 ha

■ Site description

A large complex of raised bogs and extensive forests (including wet alluvial forests) in central Estonia, with fens, transition mires, and unregulated rivers with flood-plain and wooded meadows. The main land-uses are forestry, tourism, small-scale agriculture and berry-picking.

Habitats Forest and woodland (45%; mixed forest; alluvial/very wet forest), Wetland (50%; raised bog; fen/transition mire/spring)
Land-use Forestry (40%), Nature conservation/research (100%), Tourism/recreation (30%)

■ Birds

Species		Season	Year	Pop min	Pop max	Acc	Criteria
Cygnus columbianus	Bewick's Swan	P	1996	500	2,000	A	A4i, B1i
Aquila chrysaetos	Golden Eagle	R	1996	3	4	A	B2
Crex crex	Corncrake	B	1996	50	100	B	A1, B2
Grus grus	Crane	B	1996	20	—	A	B2
Grus grus	Crane	P	1996	1,000	1,000	A	B1i

The mires and forests are important for several breeding species and an important staging area for migrating *Cygnus columbianus* and *Grus grus*.

■ Protection status
National High **International** High
36,890 ha of IBA covered by National Park (Soomaa, 37,121 ha). 36,890 ha of IBA covered by Ramsar Site (Soomaa National Park, 37,121 ha).

■ Conservation issues

Threats Abandonment/reduction of land management (A), Drainage (A), Intensified forest management (A), Recreation/tourism (A), Unsustainable exploitation (A)

Major threats are posed by forestry, drainage, unsustainable hunting, tourism, and the overgrowth of flood-plain meadows by shrubs (haymaking is required to maintain habitat suitable for key bird species). The management plan for Soomaa National Park will be ready in 2000. Research involves monitoring of birds and mire plants.

Laukasoo bog B1i 033
Admin region Lääne-Viru
Coordinates 59°29'N 25°55'E
Altitude 58–62 m **Area** 1,431 ha

■ Site description

A raised bog in northern Estonia, with many pools, coniferous and mixed forest. Nature conservation and research is the only land-use.

Habitats Forest and woodland (35%; native coniferous forest; mixed forest), Wetland (65%; raised bog)
Land-use Nature conservation/research (100%)

■ Birds

Species		Season	Year	Pop min	Pop max	Acc	Criteria
Grus grus	Crane	P	1996	500	800	A	B1i

An important roosting place in autumn for migrating *Grus grus*.

■ Protection status
National High **International** None
1,431 ha of IBA covered by National Park (Lahemaa, 70,926 ha).

■ Conservation issues

Threats Drainage (C)

Drainage of the surrounding area is a significant threat. The IBA lies within the special management zone of the National Park. Research involves monitoring of birds and mire plants.

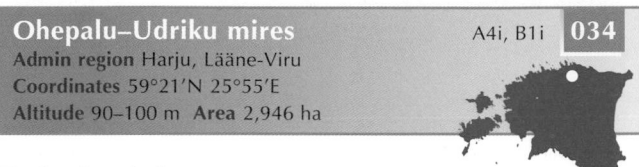

Ohepalu–Udriku mires A4i, B1i 034
Admin region Harju, Lääne-Viru
Coordinates 59°21'N 25°55'E
Altitude 90–100 m **Area** 2,946 ha

■ Site description

A complex of raised bogs, fens, transitional mires, forest and many small lakes in northern Estonia. The main land-use is forestry.

Habitats Forest and woodland (40%), Wetland (57%; standing fresh water; raised bog; fen/transition mire/spring)
Land-use Forestry (25%), Nature conservation/research (30%), Not utilized (35%)

■ Birds

Species		Season	Year	Pop min	Pop max	Acc	Criteria
Grus grus	Crane	P	1996	1,000	2,500	A	A4i, B1i

Ohepalu–Udriku mire complex is an important roosting place for migrating *Grus grus* in autumn.

■ Protection status
National High **International** None
2,946 ha of IBA covered by Nature Protection Area (Ohepalu, 5,058 ha).

■ Conservation issues

Threats Drainage (B), Intensified forest management (B), Recreation/tourism (C)

The main threats are drainage, and intensification of forestry. Udriku mire is designated as a strictly protected area within Ohepalu Nature Protection Area. Research involves monitoring of birds and mire plants.

Puhatu mire B2 035
Admin region Ida-Viru
Coordinates 59°10'N 27°45'E
Altitude 27–45 m **Area** 15,620 ha

■ Site description

A large complex of raised bogs, fens, transition mires, forests, lakes and rivers in north-eastern Estonia. The main land-use is forestry.

Habitats Forest and woodland (25%), Wetland (70%; raised bog; fen/transition mire/spring)
Land-use Forestry (40%), Not utilized (50%)

■ Birds

Species		Season	Year	Pop min	Pop max	Acc	Criteria
Tetrao tetrix	Black Grouse	R	1996	150	150	B	B2

An important breeding area for *Tetrao tetrix* which also supports a notably diverse assemblage of other breeding species of mire and forest. Breeding species of global conservation concern that do not meet IBA criteria: *Haliaeetus albicilla* (one pair), *Crex crex* (1–5 pairs). Significant proportion (≥1%) of national population breeding at site: *Grus grus* (10 pairs).

■ Protection status
National Partial **International** None

12,320 ha of IBA covered by Nature Protection Area (Puhatu, 12,320 ha).

■ Conservation issues

Threats Deforestation (commercial) (A), Drainage (A), Extraction industry (B), Intensified forest management (A), Recreation/tourism (B)

The main threats are drainage, deforestation, intensification of forestry, and tourism. There are plans to mine oil-shale in the northern part of the IBA. The IBA is a potential Ramsar Site. An inventory of the avifauna was completed in 1996.

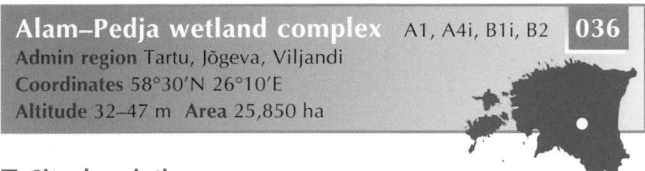

Alam–Pedja wetland complex
A1, A4i, B1i, B2 036

Admin region Tartu, Jõgeva, Viljandi
Coordinates 58°30′N 26°10′E
Altitude 32–47 m **Area** 25,850 ha

■ Site description
A large wetland complex in central Estonia, comprised of raised bogs, fens, transition mires and unregulated rivers with flood-plain meadows, surrounded by extensive alluvial forests. The main land-use is forestry.

Habitats Forest and woodland (35%; broadleaved deciduous forest; mixed forest; alluvial/very wet forest), Grassland (10%; humid grassland), Wetland (55%; raised bog; water-fringe vegetation; fen/transition mire/spring)
Land-use Forestry (25%), Nature conservation/research (100%)

■ Birds

Species	Season	Year	Pop min	Pop max	Acc	Criteria
Cygnus columbianus Bewick's Swan	P	1996	300	600	A	A4i, B1i
Aquila clanga Greater Spotted Eagle	B	1996	2	2	A	A1
Crex crex Corncrake	B	1993	20	—	B	A1
Grus grus Crane	B	1993	20	—	B	B2
Gallinago media Great Snipe	B	1996	50	75	B	A1
Larus minutus Little Gull	B	1993	80	100	B	B2

The most important breeding area for *Gallinago media* in Estonia, which also supports a rich assemblage of breeding species of mire, forest and wetland, notably the globally threatened *Aquila clanga*. Breeding species of global conservation concern that do not meet IBA criteria: *Haliaeetus albicilla* (2 pairs). Significant proportion (≥1%) of national population breeding at site: *Pernis apivorus* (5–7 pairs), *Chlidonias niger* (150–200 pairs), *Caprimulgus europaeus* (min. 20 pairs), *Picus canus* (min. 15 pairs). Numbers of breeding *Tetrao tetrix* (min. 75 pairs) are also notable.

■ Protection status
National High **International** High

25,850 ha of IBA covered by Nature Protection Area (Alam–Pedja, 26,000 ha). 25,850 ha of IBA covered by Ramsar Site (Alam–Pedja Nature Protection Area, 26,000 ha).

■ Conservation issues

Threats Abandonment/reduction of land management (A), Aquaculture/fisheries (C), Drainage (C), Intensified forest management (C), Recreation/tourism (C), Unsustainable exploitation (C)

The main threat lies in the overgrowth of flood-plain meadows with scrub, following abandonment of management. Research involves monitoring of birds.

Kallaste–Kodavere coast
A4i, B1i, B2 037

Admin region Tartu
Coordinates 58°40′N 27°10′E
Altitude 30–40 m **Area** 350 ha

■ Site description
A shallow lake and high sandstone cliffs along the shore of Lake Peipsi.

Habitats Wetland (95%; standing fresh water)
Land-use Fisheries/aquaculture (90%), Tourism/recreation (10%)

■ Birds

Species	Season	Year	Pop min	Pop max	Acc	Criteria
Cygnus columbianus Bewick's Swan	P	1996	1,000	1,000	A	A4i, B1i
Riparia riparia Sand Martin	B	1996	2,000	2,000	A	B2

An important breeding site for *Riparia riparia* (since the beginning of the century) and an important staging area for migrating *Cygnus columbianus*.

■ Protection status
National High **International** None

350 ha of IBA covered by Protected Landscape (Kallaste–Kodavere, area not known).

■ Conservation issues

Threats Aquaculture/fisheries (A), Disturbance to birds (A), Recreation/tourism (A)

Major threats are posed by recreation/tourism and fishing. Research involves monitoring of birds.

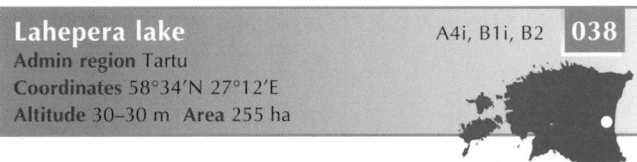

Lahepera lake
A4i, B1i, B2 038

Admin region Tartu
Coordinates 58°34′N 27°12′E
Altitude 30–30 m **Area** 255 ha

■ Site description
A shallow lake with reedbeds on the western shore of Lake Peipsi in eastern Estonia. The main economic activity is fishing.

Habitats Wetland (98%; standing fresh water; water-fringe vegetation)
Land-use Fisheries/aquaculture (90%)

■ Birds

Species	Season	Year	Pop min	Pop max	Acc	Criteria
Cygnus columbianus Bewick's Swan	P	1996	1,000	—	A	A4i, B1i
Chlidonias niger Black Tern	B	1996	250	300	A	B2

An important staging and breeding area for several waterbird species. Significant proportion (≥1%) of national population breeding at site: *Larus minutus* (50–60 pairs).

■ Protection status
National None **International** None

■ Conservation issues

Threats Aquaculture/fisheries (A), Disturbance to birds (A), Recreation/tourism (A), Unsustainable exploitation (A)

Major threats are posed by intensive fishing, unsustainable hunting, and tourism. Research involves monitoring of migrating waterbirds.

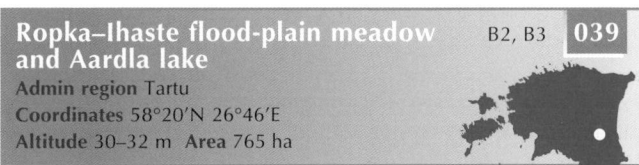

Ropka–Ihaste flood-plain meadow and Aardla lake
B2, B3 039

Admin region Tartu
Coordinates 58°20′N 26°46′E
Altitude 30–32 m **Area** 765 ha

■ Site description
A wetland complex on the flood-plain of the Emajõgi river near the town of Tartu in eastern Estonia, with meadows, lakes, rivers, reedbeds, scrub and reseeded grasslands (polders). The main land-uses are haymaking, sand-mining and recreation.

Habitats Forest and woodland (5%), Scrub (20%), Grassland (20%; humid grassland), Wetland (40%; standing fresh water; river/stream; water-fringe vegetation), Artificial landscape (10%; highly improved reseeded grassland)
Land-use Agriculture (20%), Not utilized (50%), Tourism/recreation (20%), Urban/industrial/transport (10%)

■ Birds
The area is an important breeding site for several waterbird species of flood-plain wetlands. Breeding species of global conservation concern

that do not meet IBA criteria: *Crex crex* (3–5 pairs), *Gallinago media* (5–10 pairs). Significant proportion (≥1%) of national population breeding at site: *Larus minutus* (min. 50 pairs).

Species		Season	Year	Pop min	Pop max	Acc	Criteria
Porzana porzana	Spotted Crake	B	1992	80	—	A	B3
Chlidonias niger	Black Tern	B	1992	250	250	A	B2

■ Protection status
National None **International** None

■ Conservation issues

Threats Abandonment/reduction of land management (A), Agricultural intensification/expansion (C), Aquaculture/fisheries (A), Construction/impact of dyke/dam/barrage (A), Disturbance to birds (A), Drainage (A), Dredging/canalization (A), Industrialization/urbanization (A), Recreation/tourism (A), Unsustainable exploitation (A)

Major threats are posed by nutrient pollution (due to effluents from Tartu town and fertilizer run-off), overgrowth of meadows with scrub due to reduced haymaking, disturbance of birds by angling, recreation/tourism, fuel-oil pollution from boats, unsustainable hunting, drainage and canalization. The area is a proposed Protected Landscape. An inventory of breeding and migrating birds was completed in 1992.

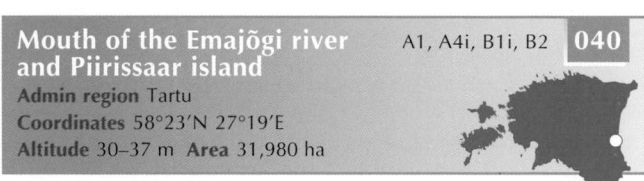

Mouth of the Emajõgi river and Piirissaar island
A1, A4i, B1i, B2 040
Admin region Tartu
Coordinates 58°23'N 27°19'E
Altitude 30–37 m **Area** 31,980 ha

■ Site description
A large wetland complex in eastern Estonia, comprising lakes, rivers, fens, transition mires, bogs, forest and flood-plain meadows. Major land-uses are fishing and forestry.

Habitats Wetland (95%; standing fresh water; raised bog; water-fringe vegetation; fen/transition mire/spring)
Land-use Fisheries/aquaculture (35%), Forestry (10%), Nature conservation/research (80%)

■ Birds

Species		Season	Year	Pop min	Pop max	Acc	Criteria
Botaurus stellaris	Bittern	B	1996	10	—	C	B2
Cygnus columbianus	Bewick's Swan	P	1996	500	800	A	A4i, B1i
Anser fabalis	Bean Goose	P	1996	5,000	—	B	A4i, B1i
Mergus albellus	Smew	P	1996	250	—	B	B1i
Haliaeetus albicilla	White-tailed Eagle	B	1996	4	5	A	A1, B2
Tetrao tetrix	Black Grouse	R	1996	100	—	B	B2
Larus minutus	Little Gull	B	1996	200	—	C	B2
Chlidonias niger	Black Tern	B	1996	500	—	C	B2

The area supports a good diversity of breeding waterbirds, including several species of global conservation concern, and is an important staging area for migratory wildfowl. Breeding species of global conservation concern that do not meet IBA criteria: *Crex crex* (min. 10 pairs), *Gallinago media* (10 pairs). Significant proportion (≥1%) of national population breeding at site: *Porzana porzana* (min. 75 pairs), *Grus grus* (min. 10 pairs).

■ Protection status
National Partial **International** High
21,030 ha of IBA covered by Protected Landscape (Emajõe Suursoo Mire, 21,030 ha). 672 ha of IBA covered by Protected Landscape (Piirissaare, 672 ha). 31,980 ha of IBA covered by Ramsar Site (Emajõe-Suursoo Mire and Piirissaar Island, 32,600 ha).

■ Conservation issues

Threats Abandonment/reduction of land management (A), Aquaculture/fisheries (A), Drainage (C), Intensified forest management (C), Unsustainable exploitation (A)

The main threats come from fishing and unsustainable hunting, and the overgrowth of coastal meadows with reed *Phragmites* as a result of undergrazing and reduced mowing intensity. Research involves monitoring of migrating waterbirds.

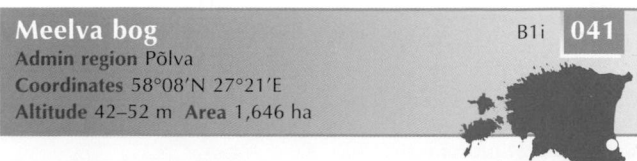

Meelva bog
B1i 041
Admin region Põlva
Coordinates 58°08'N 27°21'E
Altitude 42–52 m **Area** 1,646 ha

■ Site description
A raised bog in eastern Estonia, with small lakes and some forest. The main economic activity is forestry.

Habitats Forest and woodland (10%), Wetland (90%; standing fresh water; raised bog)
Land-use Forestry (10%), Nature conservation/research (100%)

■ Birds

Species		Season	Year	Pop min	Pop max	Acc	Criteria
Grus grus	Crane	P	1996	200	1,000	A	B1i

The site is an important roosting place for migrating *Grus grus* in autumn.

■ Protection status
National Partial **International** None
1,626 ha of IBA covered by Nature Protection Area (Meelva, 2,073 ha).

■ Conservation issues

Threats Drainage (C), Intensified forest management (A)

The main threat is from intensification of forestry. Research involves monitoring of birds and mire plants.

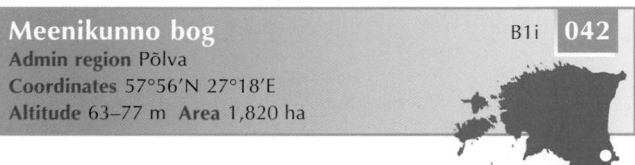

Meenikunno bog
B1i 042
Admin region Põlva
Coordinates 57°56'N 27°18'E
Altitude 63–77 m **Area** 1,820 ha

■ Site description
A raised bog in south-eastern Estonia, with alluvial and mixed forests and small lakes. The main land-uses are forestry and tourism.

Habitats Forest and woodland (40%; mixed forest; alluvial/very wet forest), Wetland (60%; raised bog)
Land-use Forestry (40%), Nature conservation/research (100%), Tourism/recreation (10%)

■ Birds

Species		Season	Year	Pop min	Pop max	Acc	Criteria
Grus grus	Crane	P	1996	400	1,250	A	B1i

Meenikunno bog is an important roosting place for migrating *Grus grus* in autumn.

■ Protection status
National High **International** None
1,757 ha of IBA covered by Mire Reserve (Meenikunno, 1,829 ha).

■ Conservation issues

Threats Disturbance to birds (C), Drainage (B), Intensified forest management (A), Recreation/tourism (A), Unsustainable exploitation (C)

The main threats are posed by tourism, intensification of forestry, and drainage of the surrounding area. Research involves monitoring of birds and mire plants.

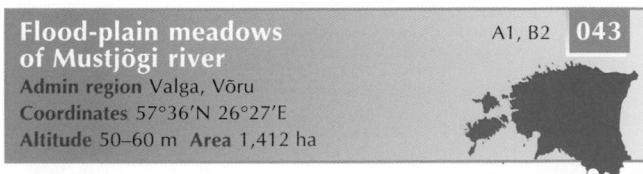

Flood-plain meadows of Mustjõgi river
A1, B2 043
Admin region Valga, Võru
Coordinates 57°36'N 26°27'E
Altitude 50–60 m **Area** 1,412 ha

■ Site description
A large complex of flood-plain meadows and scrub along the Mustjõgi river in south-eastern Estonia. The main land-uses are cattle-grazing and haymaking.

Habitats Scrub (10%; scrub), Grassland (20%; humid grassland), Wetland (70%; river/ stream; water-fringe vegetation)
Land-use Agriculture (90%)

■ Birds

Species	Season	Year	Pop min	Pop max	Acc	Criteria
Crex crex Corncrake	B	1996	50	70	B	A1, B2

An important breeding area for *Crex crex*.

■ Protection status

National None **International** None

■ Conservation issues

Threats Abandonment/reduction of land management (A)

Overgrowth of the meadows by scrub (due to undergrazing) poses a major threat, and regular haymaking is required to maintain suitable habitat.

REFERENCES

ADER, A., KURESOO, A., LUIGUJÕE, L. AND OTS, M. (1993) [Birds of Ropka-Ihaste flood plain meadow in 1992.] Unpublished. (In Estonian.)

ADER, A., KURESOO, A. AND LUIGUJÕE, L. (1996) [On avifauna of coastal lakes of Vilsandi National Park.] Unpublished. (In Estonian.)

DURINCK, J., SKOV, H., JENSEN, F. P. AND PIHL, S. (1994) *Important marine areas for wintering birds in the Baltic Sea*. Copenhagen.

GRIMMETT, R. F. A. AND JONES, T. A. (1989) *Important Bird Areas in Europe*. Cambridge, UK: International Council for Bird Preservation (Techn. Publ. 9). 888 pp.

HEATH, M. F. AND BORGGREVE, C. (2000) *BirdLife International/EBCC European Bird Database 1998*. Cambridge, UK: BirdLife International.

IRDT, A. AND VILBASTE, H. (1974) Bird fauna of the Nigula peat-bog. Pp. 214–229 in *Estonian wetlands and their life*. Estonian Contributions to the International Biological Programme No. 7.

JEESER, M., KOKOVKIN, T. AND VAHTRA, K. (1993) [*Treasures of Hiiumaa*.] Pirrujaak 1, Kärdla. (In Estonian, with English summary.)

JÕGI, A. (1970) [Bird fauna in the environment of Puhtu.] Pp. 205–225 in *Lääne-Eesti rannikualade loodus*. Tallinn. (In Estonian, with English summary.)

KULLAPERE, A., ED. (1983) *Vilsandi-looduskaitseala Eesti NSV läänerannikul*. Tallinn. (In Estonian, with Russian and English summaries.)

KUMARI, A. (1953) [On birdfauna of valleys of Koiva and Mustjõgi rivers.] Pp. 351–364 in *Loodusuurijate Seltsi Juubelikoguteos*. Tallinn. (In Estonian, with Russian summary.)

KUMARI, E., ED. (1985) [Matsalu—a wetland of international importance.] Tallinn. (In Estonian, with English summary).

KURESOO, A. (1996) Väike Väin strait. In: Report of wetland inventory work in Estonia. Estonian Fund for Nature. Unpublished.

KURESOO, A., ADER, A. AND LUIGUJÕE, L. (1994) Concentration areas of non-breeding waterfowl vulnerable to oil pollution in Estonia: progress report. Pp. 59–87 in *Proc. of the International Conference on Oil Terminals, Shipping and Off-shore Activities in the Eastern-Baltic*. Tallinn.

KURESOO, A., ADER, A. AND LUIGUJÕE, L. (1995) Study and conservation of biological values of the Väike Väin strait. Report of the Estonian Fund for Nature, Tartu. Unpublished.

KURESOO, A. AND LUIGUJÕE, L. (1996) Internationally important coastal and marine waterfowl staging areas in Estonia and their conservational status. Pp. 58–64 in *Waterbirds of the Baltic Region. Strategies for Conservation and Utilization*. Maintz.

LÄÄTS, K. (1974) [On the avifauna of Lake Linnulaht.] *Loodusevaatlusi* 1973(1): 106–120. (In Estonian, with Russian and English summaries.)

LEIBAK, E. (1996) Alam-Pedja wetland complex. In: Report of wetland inventory work in Estonia. Estonian Fund for Nature. Unpublished.

LEIBAK, E. (1996) Soomaa wetland complex. In: Report of wetland inventory work in Estonia. Estonian Fund for Nature. Unpublished.

LEITO, A. (1984) [On the bird fauna of Marimetsa bog.] *Loodusevaatlusi* 1981(1): 20–25. (In Estonian, with English summary.)

LEITO, A. (1990) [On the avifauna of Marimetsa Raba bog protection area in 1987.] *Loodusevaatlusi* 1987(1): 112–116. (In Estonian, with English summary.)

LEITO, A. (1996) Käina Bay. In: Report of wetland inventory work in Estonia. Estonian Fund for Nature. Unpublished.

LEITO, A. (1996) The Barnacle Goose in Estonia. *Estonia Maritima* 1: 1–103.

LEITO, A. (1996) The Hiiumaa islets. In: Report of wetland inventory work in Estonia. Estonian Fund for Nature. Unpublished.

LEITO, A. AND LEITO, T. (1991) *Hiiumaa Islets State Landscape Reserve*. Kärdla.

LEITO, A. AND LEITO, T. (1995) *Bird fauna of Hiiumaa*. Pirrujaak 4, Kärdla.

LEIVITS, A. (1990) Long-term dynamics of the breeding bird community in the Nigula mire: a 20-year study in south-western Estonia. Pp. 429–431 in *Bird Censuses and Atlas Studies. Proc. 11th Int. Conf. on Bird Censuses and Atlaswork*.

LEIVITS, A. (1996) [Birds of Puhatu marsh complex.] Unpublished. (In Estonian.)

LEIVITS, A., ADER, A. AND VILBASTE, E. (1996) Nigula bog. In: Report of wetland inventory work in Estonia. Estonian Fund for Nature. Unpublished.

LEIVO, M., RUSANEN, P. AND KONTIOKORPI, J. (1994) Kevään 1993 arktinen muutto Pohjois-Itämerellä. *Linnut* 29(2): 12–19. (In Finnish.)

LEIVO, M., KONTIOKORPI, J. AND RUSANEN, P. (1995) Arktika keväällä 1994. *Linnut* 30(3): 28–31. (In Finnish.)

LEPISK, A. (1987) [Cranes in Meenikunno bog.] *Eesti Loodus* 9: 595–596. (In Estonian.)

LILLELEHT, V. (1976) [On the breeding population of the maritime islets of the Virtsu–Laelatu–Puhtu protection zone in 1953–1975.] *Loodusevaatlusi* 1975(1): 101–121. (In Estonian, with English summary.)

LILLELEHT, V. (1996) Emajõe Suursoo mire and Piirissaar island. In: Report of Wetland Inventory Work in Estonia. Estonian Fund for Nature. Unpublished.

LILLELEHT, V., ED. (1998) [*Red Data Book of Estonia. Threatened fungi, plants and animals*.] 150 pp. (In Estonian, with English summary.)

LILLELEHT, V. AND LEIBAK, E. (1993) [List, status and numbers of Estonian birds.] *Hirundo* 1(12): 3–50. (In Estonian, with English summary.)

LIPP, H. (1977) [On bird fauna of Linnusita and Kirju islets in 1974–1976.] *Loodusevaatlusi* 1976(1): 109–112. (In Estonian, with Russian and English summaries).

LÕHMUS, A., ADER, A., RANDER, R. AND TAMMUR, E. (1994) [On the bird fauna of Laeva-Palupõhja.] *Hirundo* (Suppl. 1994): 3–35. (In Estonian, with English summary.)

LÕHMUS, A. ET AL. (1998) [Status and numbers of Estonian birds.] *Hirundo* 2: 63–83. (In Estonian, with English summary.)

LUIGUJÕE, L., KURESOO, A. AND BEEKMAN, J. H. (1994) Report on study and conservation of the Bewick's Swan in Estonia. Unpublished.

LUIGUJÕE, L. AND KURESOO, A. (1996) Väikeluige *Cygnus columbianus bewickii* rändepeatuspaigad Eestis. Unpublished. (In Estonian.)

MÄGI, E. (1993) [Composition of nesting avifauna in Kasari alluvial meadow.] *Loodusevaatlusi* 1992(1): 41–63. (In Estonian, with English summary.)

MÄGI, E. (1995) [On nesting of Charadriiformes on Moonsund islets in Matsalu Nature Reserve.] *Loodusevaatlusi* 1994: 7–17. (In Estonian, with English summary.)

MÄGI, E., KASTEPÕLD, T. AND PAAKSPUU, T. (1993) [Changes in density and structure of breeding avifauna on Moonsund islands in Matsalu Nature Reserve.] *Loodusevaatlusi* 1991(1): 9–16. (In Estonian, with English summary.)

MÄND, R. (1974) [On the bird fauna of Lake Mullutu–Suurlaht.] *Loodusevaatlusi* 1973(1): 98–105. (In Estonian, with Russian and English summaries.)

MÄND, R. (1981) [On the bird fauna of relict lakes on the southern coast of Saaremaa island.] *Loodusevaatlusi* 1979(1): 132–140. (In Estonian, with Russian and English summaries.)

MANK, A. AND KALLAS, J. (1974) Nesting bird fauna in Käina Bay. Pp. 96–118 in *Estonian wetlands and their life*. Tallinn.

OJASTE, I. AND HAABEL, H. (1996) [About the avifauna at islets of Hullo Bay in summer 1995.] *Läänemaa Linnuklubi Infoleht* 5: 12. (In Estonian.)

OJASTE, I. AND KURESOO, A. (1996) Haapsalu–Noarootsi Bays. In: Report of wetland inventory work in Estonia. Estonian Fund for Nature. Unpublished.

PADARI, A. (1993) [Breeding birds of the Käina Bay.] *Hirundo* 13: 45–48. (In Estonian, with English summary.)

PETERSON, K., ED. (1994) *Nature protection in Estonia*. 48 pp.

POLMA, G. (1993) [Bird census in observation areas in reed-bed of Matsalu in 1986–1988.] *Loodusevaatlusi* 1990(1): 35–39. (In Estonian, with English summary.)

RANDLA, T. (1973) [Birds of Pasilaid islet.] *Loodusevaatlusi* 1972(1): 124–126. (In Estonian, with English summary.)

RANDLA, T. (1975) [On the peculiarity of the bird fauna of the Puhatu wetland.] *Loodusevaatlusi* 1974(1): 116–118. (In Estonian, with Russian and English summaries.)

RENNO, O., ED. (1973) *Matsalu laht ja linnud*. [Matsalu landscape and birds.] Ornitoloogiline kogumik VI. Tallinn: Valgus. (In Estonian, with English summaries.)

ROOTSMÄE, I. AND ROOTSMÄE, L. (1969) [On Puhtu forest birds.] *Loodusuurijate Seltsi Aastaraamat* 60: 121–137. (In Estonian, with English summary.)

RUSANEN, P. (1993) Kevätarktikaa Virossa. *Linnut* 28(3): 7–10. (In Finnish.)

SHERGALIN, J. (1984) [On the breeding population of the islets in the Kurkse Bay.] *Loodusevaatlusi* 1981(1): 31–37. (In Estonian, with Russian and English summaries).

SHERGALIN, J. (1988) [On the breeding populations of the islets in Kurkse Bay from 1982–1986.] *Loodusevaatlusi* 1986(1): 66–70. (In Estonian, with Russian and English summaries.)

TUCKER, G. M. AND HEATH, M. F. (1994) *Birds in Europe: their conservation status*. Cambridge, UK: BirdLife International (BirdLife Conservation Series no. 3). 600 pp.

VALK, U. (1988) [*Estonian peatlands*.] Tallinn. (In Estonian, with English summary.)

VILBASTE, H. (1990) [Number dynamics of the breeding birds in the forests of south-west Estonia.] Pp. 102–117 in O. Renno, ed. [*Communications of the Baltic Commission for the study of bird migration*, vol. 22]. (In Russian, with English summary.)

VILBASTE, H. AND LEIVITS, A. (1990) [Programmes for long-term observations for dynamics of bird populations in the Nigula Nature Reserve.] Pp. 64–83 in O. Renno, ed. [*Communications of the Baltic Commission for the study of bird migration*, vol. 22]. (In Russian, with English summary.)

VISSAK, P. (1996) Nehatu mire. In: Report of wetland inventory work in Estonia. Estonian Fund for Nature. Unpublished.

VISSAK, P. (1996) Puhtu–Laelatu wetland complex. In: Report of wetland inventory work in Estonia. Estonian Fund for Nature. Unpublished.

■ FINLAND

Mauri Leivo

Pygmy Owl *Glaucidium passerinum* in boreal forest.
(PHOTO: MIKA HONKALINNA)

GENERAL INTRODUCTION

Finland, the second most northerly country in the world, lies at the head of the Baltic Sea in the north-eastern corner of Europe. It is bordered by the Gulf of Bothnia in the west and the Gulf of Finland in the south. The mainland of Sweden and Norway border to the north-west and north, whilst Russia lies to the east. Ninety-six sites are identified as Important Bird Areas (IBAs), covering 27,400 km² (8%) of Finland's total land-surface area of 337,000 km². The previous pan-European IBA inventory (Grimmett and Jones 1989) identified 35 sites. Seventy-six new sites have been identified and 11 sites have not been confirmed as IBAs as they do not meet current IBA criteria.

Finland has a long south-north axis, running from 59°30' N to more than 70°00' N. This results in a distinct zonation of climate, vegetation and avifauna. Southern and central Finland are relatively low-lying, rarely exceeding 200 m in altitude. The main part of the human population of 5 million is concentrated in the south and west of this area. The coastal archipelagos of this region have many IBAs, whereas the inland parts of this region are ornithologically less valuable, with the exception of large oligotrophic lakes and many smaller eutrophic lakes which are important for wetland avifauna. The north of the country is more rugged with high plateaus and deep river valleys. The extensive forests and mires of the north and east contain many IBAs.

Table 1. Summary of Important Bird Areas in Finland. 96 IBAs covering 27,400 km²

IBA code	1989 code	International name	National name	Administrative region	Area (ha)	Criteria (see p. 11)
001	FI002	Lätäseno and Jietajoki mires	Lätäsenon–Jietajoen suot	Lapin lääni	43,367	A4i, B1i, B2, B3, C2, C3, C6
002	—	Käsivarsi fjelds	Käsivarren tunturit	Lapin lääni	220,078	A3, B2, B3, C2, C6
003	—	Lemmenjoki–Hammastunturi–Pulju	Lemmenjoki–Hammastunturi–Pulju	Lapin lääni	529,718	A3, A4i, B1i, B2, B3, C2, C3, C6
004	—	Saariselkä and Koilliskaira	Saariselän–Koilliskairan alue	Lapin lääni	309,553	A3, A4i, B1i, B2, B3, C2, C3, C6
005	FI033	Pomokaira–Koitelaiskaira	Pomokaira–Koitelaiskaira	Lapin lääni	141,630	A4i, B1i, B2, B3, C2, C3, C6
006	—	Pallas and Ylläs fjelds	Pallas–Ylläksen tunturialueet	Lapin lääni	89,233	A3, B2, B3, C2, C6
007	—	Värriö–Tuntsa	Värriö–Tuntsa	Lapin lääni	33,670	A3, B2, B3, C2, C6
008	—	Maltio fjelds	Maltion tunturit	Lapin lääni	29,574	B2, B3, C6
009	—	South-eastern Kittilä mires	Kittilän kaakkoisosan suot	Lapin lääni	21,035	B2, C7
010	—	Kevo	Kevo	Lapin lääni	70,075	A3, B2, B3, C2, C6
011	—	Luosto	Luosto	Lapin lääni	7,989	A3
012	—	Riisitunturi	Riisitunturi	Lapin lääni	7,651	B2, C6
013	—	Joutsenaapa–Kaita-aapa	Joutsenaapa–Kaita-aapa	Lapin lääni	10,318	B2, C6
014	—	Lämsänaapa–Sakkala-aapa	Lämsänaapa–Sakkala-aapa	Lapin lääni	4,186	B2, C7
015	—	Pöyrisvuoma mire protection area	Pöyrisvuoma	Lapin lääni	4,270	B2, B3, C7
016	FI001	Sammutinjänkä–Vaijoenjänkä	Sammutinjänkä–Vaijoenjänkä	Lapin lääni	51,750	A3, B2, C7
017	—	Kemihaara (Vuotos) mires and forests	Kemihaaran suot ja metsät (Vuotos)	Lapin lääni	38,294	A3, B2, B3, C2, C6

Table 1 ... continued. Summary of Important Bird Areas in Finland. 96 IBAs covering 27,400 km²

IBA code	1989 code	International name	National name	Administrative region	Area (ha)	Criteria (see p. 11)
018	—	Runkaus–Saariaapa–Tainijärvet	Runkaus–Saariaapa–Tainijärvet	Lapin lääni	13,904	A3, B2, B3, C6
019	—	Karunginjärvi lake	Karunginjärvi	Lapin lääni	660	A4i, B1i, C2
020	—	Veittiaapa–Ristiaapa	Veittiaapa–Ristiaapa	Lapin lääni	3,037	B2, C7
021	FI005	Martimoaapa–Lumiaapa–Penikat	Martimoaapa–Lumiaapa–Penikat	Lapin lääni	12,628	B2, B3, C6
022	—	Kilsiaapa–Ristivuoma	Kilsiaapa–Ristivuoma	Lapin lääni	7,823	B2, C7
023	—	Tornionjoki delta	Tornionjoen suisto	Lapin lääni	526	B1i, C3
024	—	Rumala–Kuvaja–Oudonrimmet	Rumala–Kuvaja–Oudonrimmet	Oulun lääni	4,837	B2, C6
025	—	Elimyssalo	Elimyssalo	Oulun lääni	8,286	A3, B2, C6
026	—	Juortanansalo	Juortanansalo	Oulun lääni	5,454	B2, C6
027	FI006	Krunnit archipelago	Krunnien saaristo	Oulun lääni	4,579	A4i, B1i, B2, B3, C2, C3, C6
028	FI007, FI008, FI009	Oulu region wetlands	Oulun seudun kerääntymisalue	Oulun lääni	81,781	A1, A4i, B1i, B2, B3, C1, C2, C3, C6
029	—	Syöte–Salmitunturi	Syöte–Salmitunturi	Oulun lääni	31,395	B2, B3, C6
030	—	Oulanka–Sukerijärvi	Oulanka–Sukerijärvi	Oulun lääni	29,972	A3, B2, B3, C2, C6
031	—	Närängänvaara–Virmajoki–Romevaara	Närängänvaara–Virmajoki–Romevaara	Oulun lääni	11,211	B2, B3, C6
032	—	Pajupuronsuo–Isosuo–Kivisuo	Pajupuronsuo–Isosuo–Kivisuo	Oulun lääni	5,793	B2, B3, C7
033	FI011	Haapavesi wetlands	Haapaveden lintujärvet	Oulun lääni	2,500	A4i, B1i, B2, C2, C3
034	—	Olvassuo–Oravisuo–Näätäsuo–Sammakkosuo	Olvassuo–Oravisuo–Näätäsuo–Sammakkosuo	Oulun lääni	27,610	B2, B3, C6
035	—	Valtavaara–Pyhävaara	Valtavaara–Pyhävaara	Oulun lääni	810	C7
036	—	Kitka lake	Kitka	Oulun lääni	12,516	B1i, B2, C2, C6
037	—	Litokaira	Litokaira	Oulun lääni	30,405	A3, A4i, B1i, B2, B3, C2, C3, C6
038	—	Ahmasjärvi lake	Ahmasjärvi	Oulun lääni	414	B1i, B2, C3
039	—	Rummelö–Harrbodan	Rummelö–Harrbodan	Oulun lääni	240	A4i, B1i, C2, C3
040	—	Rahja archipelago	Rahjan saaristo	Oulun lääni	11,673	B1i, B2, B3, C3
041	—	Kokkola and Kälviä archipelago	Kokkolan–Kälviän saaristo	Länsi-Suomen lääni	20,340	A4i, B1i, B2, B3, C2, C3, C6
042	FI013, FI014	Sundominlahti Bay and Söderfjärden	Sundominlahti–Söderfjärden	Länsi-Suomen lääni	4,570	A4i, B1i, B2, C2, C3
043	—	Luoto archipelago	Luodon saaristo	Länsi-Suomen lääni	17,240	B2, C6
044	—	Uusikaarlepyy archipelago	Uudenkaarlepyyn saaristo	Länsi-Suomen lääni	7,707	B3, C7
045	FI012	Merenkurkku archipelago	Merenkurkun saaristo	Länsi-Suomen lääni	223,652	A1, A4i, B1i, B1ii, B1iv, B2, B3, C1, C2, C3, C5, C6
046	—	Kristiinankaupunki southern archipelago	Kristiinankaupungin eteläinen saaristo	Länsi-Suomen lääni	7,435	B1i, B2, C3, C6
047	FI015	Lapväärti wetlands	Lapväärtin kosteikot	Länsi-Suomen lääni	1,093	B1i, C3
048	—	Lålby fields	Lålbyn pellot	Länsi-Suomen lääni	200	A4i, B1i, C3
049	—	Alajoki	Alajoki	Länsi-Suomen lääni	438	A4i, B1i, C3
050	—	Värtsilä valley	Värtsilän laakso	Itä-Suomen lääni	745	A1, B2, C1, C6
051	—	Koitajoki area	Koitajoen alue	Itä-Suomen lääni	9,394	B2, B3, C6
052	—	Outokumpu wetlands	Outokummun lintuvedet	Itä-Suomen lääni	1,150	A4i, B1i, B3, C2, C3, C6
053	—	Outokumpu and Kaavi oligotrophic lakes	Outokummun-Kaavin seudun oligotrofiset järvet	Itä-Suomen lääni	14,665	B2, C6
054	—	Viklinrimpi	Viklinrimpi	Itä-Suomen lääni	2,651	B1i, C2
055	FI003	Patvinsuo National Park	Patvinsuon kansallispuisto	Itä-Suomen lääni	10,023	B2, B3, C6
056	—	Pitkäranta	Pitkäranta	Itä-Suomen lääni	490	B2
057	—	Päätyeenlahti Bay	Päätyeenlahti	Itä-Suomen lääni	422	B2, C7
058	—	Ruunaa	Ruunaa	Itä-Suomen lääni	12,061	B2, B3, C6
059	—	Maaninka wetlands	Maaningan lintuvedet	Itä-Suomen lääni	3,370	A4i, B1i, B2, C3
060	—	Talaskangas	Talaskangas	Itä-Suomen lääni	5,826	A3
061	—	Keski–Kallavesi and Kuhanen lake	Keski–Kallavesi ja Kuhanen	Itä-Suomen lääni	5,660	B3, C7
062	—	Linnansaari	Linnansaari	Itä-Suomen lääni	24,006	B3
063	—	Lake Pihlajavesi	Pihlajavesi	Itä-Suomen lääni	48,221	B2, C6
064	—	Kangasala wetlands	Kangasalan lintujärvet	Etelä-Suomen lääni	1,093	A4i, B1i, C3
065	—	Hollola wetlands	Hollolan lintuvedet	Etelä-Suomen lääni	913	B2, C6
066	—	Artjärvi wetlands	Artjärven kirkonkylän kosteikot	Etelä-Suomen lääni	1,506	B1i, C2
067	—	Kukkiajärvi lake	Kukkiajärvi	Etelä-Suomen lääni	6,621	B2, C6
068	—	Koijärvi lake	Koijärvi	Etelä-Suomen lääni	200	B3, C6
069	—	Torronsuo and Lake Talpianjärvi	Torronsuo–Talpianjärvi	Etelä-Suomen lääni	4,923	B1i, B2, B3, C2, C3, C6
070	FI031	Siikalahti Bay and Sammallampi lake	Siikalahti–Sammallampi	Etelä-Suomen lääni	519	B1i, B2, B3, C2, C6
071	—	Kirkkojärvi lake and Lupinlahti Bay	Kirkkojärvi–Lupinlahti	Etelä-Suomen lääni	760	B1i, B2, C2, C6
072	FI030	Itäinen Suomenlahti National Park	Itäisen Suomenlahden kansallispui	Etelä-Suomen lääni	93,253	B1i, B1ii, B2, B3, C2, C3, C6
073	FI029	Kirkon–Vilkkiläntura Bay	Kirkon–Vilkkiläntura	Etelä-Suomen lääni	195	A4i, B1i, C2
074	FI027	Teutjärvi and Suvijärvi lakes	Teutjärvi–Suvijärvi	Etelä-Suomen lääni	1,320	B2, C6
075	—	Pernaja outer archipelago	Pernajan ulkosaaristo	Etelä-Suomen lääni	18,250	B1i, B1ii, B2, B3, C2, C3, C6
076	FI025	Porvoonjoki delta	Porvoonjoen suistoalue	Etelä-Suomen lääni	899	A4i, B1i, B3, C2, C3
077	—	Porvoo outer archipelago	Porvoon ulkosaaristo	Etelä-Suomen lääni	22,570	A4i, B1i, B1ii, B2, C2, C6
078	FI023	Laajalahti Bay, Vanhankaupunginlahti Bay and Viikki	Laajalahti–Vanhankaupunginlahti–Viikki	Etelä-Suomen lääni	1,274	B1i, B3, C3

Table 1 ... continued. Summary of Important Bird Areas in Finland.   96 IBAs covering 27,400 km²

IBA code	1989 code	International name	National name	Administrative region	Area (ha)	Criteria (see p. 11)
079	—	Nuuksio	Nuuksio	Etelä-Suomen lääni	6,700	B2, B3, C6
080	—	Tammisaari and Inkoo western archipelago	Tammisaaren–Inkoon läntinen saaristo	Etelä-Suomen lääni	32,666	A1, A4i, B1i, B2, B3, C1, C2, C6
081	—	Hanko western archipelago	Hangon läntinen saaristo	Etelä-Suomen lääni	11,151	A4i, A4iii, B1i, C3, C4
082	—	Kirkkonummi archipelago	Kirkkonummen saaristo	Etelä-Suomen lääni	11,808	B3, C2
083	FI017, FI018	Pori archipelago and wetlands	Porin lintuvedet ja rannikko	Länsi-Suomen lääni	15,441	A4i, B1i, B2, B3, C2, C3, C6
084	—	Koskeljärvi, Vaaljärvi and Pitkäjärvi lakes	Koskeljärvi–Vaaljärvi–Pitkäjärvi	Länsi-Suomen lääni	2,090	B1i, B3, C3, C6
085	—	Rauma and Luvia archipelagos	Rauman–Luvian saaristot	Länsi-Suomen lääni	27,371	B2, B3, C2
086	—	Puurijärvi–Isosuo wetlands	Puurijärvi–Isosuo ja ympäristön kosteikot	Länsi-Suomen lääni	3,474	A1, B1i, C1, C2
087	—	Köyliönjärvi and Pyhäjärvi lakes	Köyliönjärvi–Pyhäjärvi	Länsi-Suomen lääni	2,759	A1, A4i, B1i, C1, C2, C3
088	—	Oura and Enskeri archipelagos	Ouran–Enskerin saaristot	Länsi-Suomen lääni	9,716	B2, B3, C6
089	—	Korppoo and Nauvo southern archipelago	Korppoon–Nauvon eteläinen saaristo	Länsi-Suomen lääni	73,500	A4i, A4iii, B1i, B1ii, B2, B3, C3, C4
090	—	Paimionlahti Bay	Paimionlahti	Länsi-Suomen lääni	696	A4i, B1i, C3
091	—	Mietoistenlahti Bay	Mietoistenlahti	Länsi-Suomen lääni	2,062	A4i, B1i, C3
092	—	Ruissalo	Ruissalo	Länsi-Suomen lääni	904	B3, C7
093	FI021	Föglö southern archipelago	Föglön eteläinen saaristo	Ahvenanmaan maakunta	17,843	B1ii, B3, C3
094	FI020	Eckerö and Hammarland archipelago	Eckerö–Hammarlandin saaristo	Ahvenanmaan maakunta	16,170	A4i, B1i, B1ii, B2, B3, C2, C3, C6
095	—	Mulklobb	Mulklobb	Ahvenanmaan maakunta	6,642	B1ii, B2, C3
096	—	Lågskär–Nyhamn	Lågskär–Nyhamn	Ahvenanmaan maakunta	2,859	A1, A4i, B1i, B1ii, C1, C3

Sites identified in the previous inventory of IBAs in Europe (Grimmett and Jones 1989) but no longer considered to be IBAs
FI004 Islands of Kainuunkylä, River Tornionjoki; FI010 Letto and Vihaspauha; FI016 Niemijärvi–Itäjärvi; FI019 Halkkoaukko–Oukkulanlahti, Rukanaukko, and Louhisaarenlahti; FI022 Svanvik–Henriksberg, Täcktbukten–Österfjärden and Västerfjärden; FI024 Östersundominlahti; FI026 Pernajanlahti; FI028 Santaniemenselkä–Tyyslahti; FI032 Kesonsuo–Juurikkasuo–Piitsonsuo; FI034 Kiesjärvi, Hautalampi–Jokilampi and Jouhtenuslampi; FI035 Heinä–Suvanto–Suvantojärvi.

Map 1. Location, area and criteria category of Important Bird Areas in Finland.

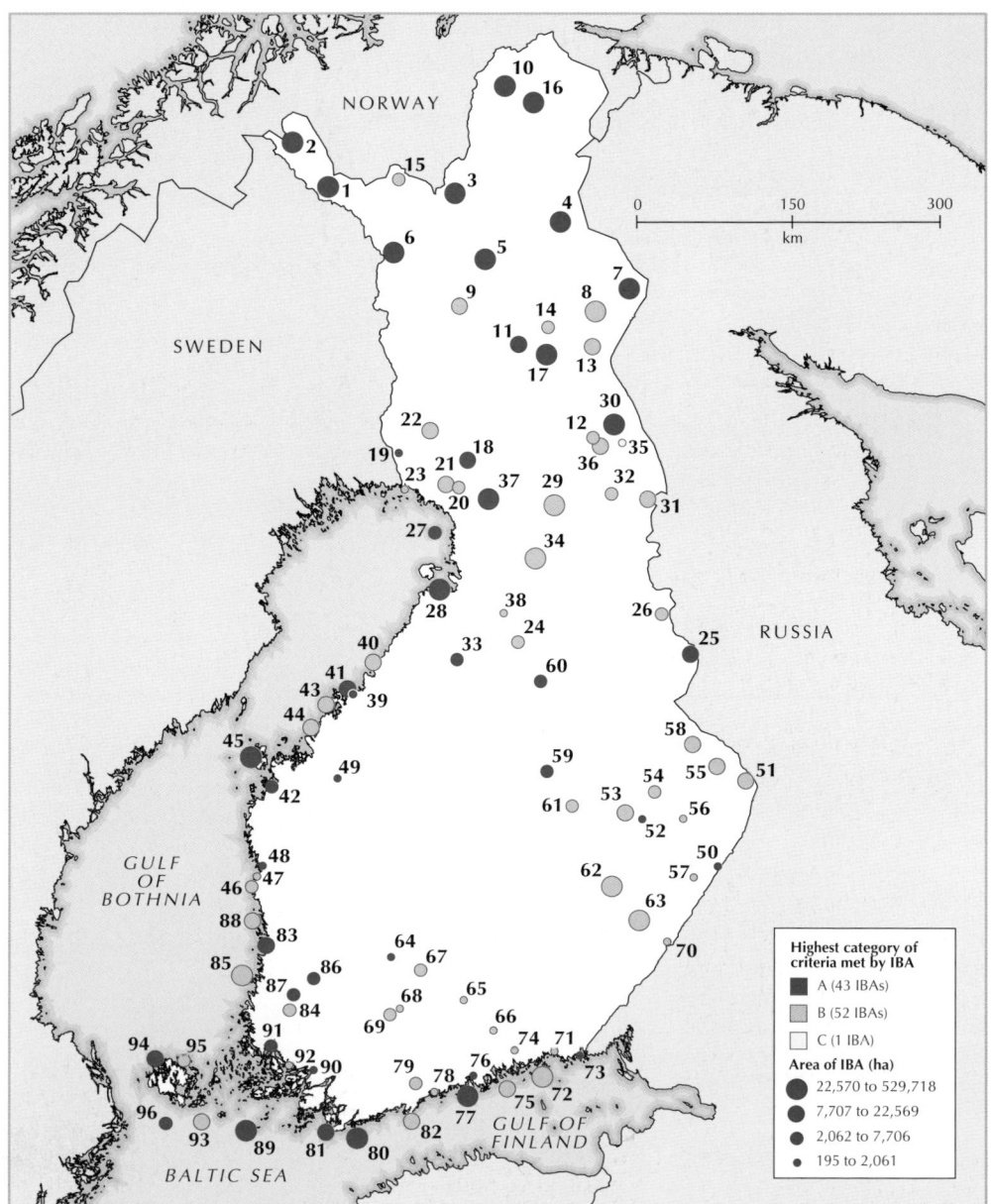

Table 2. Important Bird Areas in Finland that are important for species of global conservation concern (meeting criterion A1).

Species	IBA code
Anser erythropus Lesser White-fronted Goose	028
Polysticta stelleri Steller's Eider	096
Haliaeetus albicilla White-tailed Eagle	Five sites
Crex crex Corncrake	050

Table 3. Important Bird Areas in Finland that support important numbers of one or more congregatory species (i.e. meeting criteria A4 and/or B1). IBAs meeting both criteria A4 and B1 for the species are shown in **bold**. IBAs meeting only criterion B1 for the species concerned, and not A4, are shown in normal type. For key to 'Season', see p. 7.

Species	Season	IBA code
Podiceps grisegena Red-necked Grebe	B	084, 087
Cygnus columbianus Bewick's Swan	P	**073**
Cygnus cygnus Whooper Swan	P	**019**, **033**, 039, **042**, 045, 052, 066, 069, 070, 071, 073, 076, **083**, 086, 087
Anser fabalis Bean Goose	P	**028**, 042, 047, **048**, **049**, 069, 083
Anser anser Greylag Goose	B	028, 047, 083
	P	**028**, 042, 046, 048, 083, 090, **091**
Anas penelope Wigeon	P	**028**
Anas crecca Teal	P	**028**, 083
Anas acuta Pintail	B	028
	P	**028**, 083
Anas clypeata Shoveler	P	039, 083
Aythya fuligula Tufted Duck	P	**028**
Somateria mollissima Eider	B	089
	P	081
Polysticta stelleri Steller's Eider	W	096
Clangula hyemalis Long-tailed Duck	P	045
Melanitta fusca Velvet Scoter	B	045
	P	045
Bucephala clangula Goldeneye	P	**028**, 039, **083**
Mergus albellus Smew	B	036
	P	**028**, **076**
Mergus serrator Red-breasted Merganser	B	**028**, 040, **041**, **045**
	P	**028**, 045
Mergus merganser Goosander	B	**041**, **045**
	P	023, 027, **028**, **045**, **064**, **076**, 078, **083**, **087**, **090**, **091**
Grus grus Crane	B	003, 037, 069
	P	**028**, **042**, 054, 069, 070, 083
Charadrius hiaticula Ringed Plover	B	003
Charadrius morinellus Dotterel	B	003
Pluvialis apricaria Golden Plover	B	003, 004
Calidris minuta Little Stint	P	**028**
Limicola falcinellus Broad-billed Sandpiper	B	**001**, **003**, **004**, **005**, **037**
	P	**028**
Philomachus pugnax Ruff	P	**028**
Lymnocryptes minimus Jack Snipe	B	**003**, **004**, **037**
Numenius phaeopus Whimbrel	B	**004**
Tringa erythropus Spotted Redshank	B	**003**, **005**
	P	**028**, **083**
Tringa totanus Redshank	B	028, 040, 045
	P	**028**
Tringa nebularia Greenshank	B	**003**
	P	**028**
Tringa glareola Wood Sandpiper	B	**003**, **004**, **005**
	P	**028**
Larus minutus Little Gull	B	028, 038, **059**, 083
	P	**028**, **033**, 052
Larus canus Common Gull	B	045
Larus fuscus Lesser Black-backed Gull	B	045, 072
Sterna caspia Caspian Tern	B	027, 041, 045, 075, **077**, **080**, **094**
	P	**028**, 073, 083
Sterna paradisaea Arctic Tern	B	045
Alca torda Razorbill	B	045, 072, 075, 089, 093, 094, 095, 096
Cepphus grylle Black Guillemot	B	045, 072, 075, 077, 089, 094

Table 4. Species of European conservation concern and species listed on Annex I of the EC Birds Directive with significant breeding populations at IBAs in Finland (meeting any IBA criteria).

Species [1]	Minimum national breeding population (pairs) [2]	Proportion (%) of national population breeding at all IBAs in Finland
Gavia stellata Red-throated Diver	900	11
Gavia arctica Black-throated Diver	7,000	5
Podiceps auritus Slavonian Grebe	3,000	5
Botaurus stellaris Bittern	100	84
Cygnus cygnus Whooper Swan	1,400	12
Anser erythropus Lesser White-fronted Goose	10	—
Branta leucopsis Barnacle Goose	80	29
Anas acuta Pintail	20,000	3
Aythya ferina Pochard	12,000	6
Mergus albellus Smew	1,000	23
Circus cyaneus Hen Harrier	2,000	10
Pandion haliaetus Osprey	1,150	5
Falco rusticolus Gyrfalcon	25	16
Tetrao tetrix Black Grouse	100,000	1
Tetrao urogallus Capercaillie	100,000	5
Porzana porzana Spotted Crake	1,000	25
Crex crex Corncrake	500	8
Grus grus Crane	4,000	16
Charadrius morinellus Dotterel	1,500	22
Pluvialis apricaria Golden Plover	40,000	13
Calidris maritima Purple Sandpiper	5	100[3]
Limicola falcinellus Broad-billed Sandpiper	10,000	20
Philomachus pugnax Ruff	20,000	19
Numenius phaeopus Whimbrel	30,000	6
Tringa totanus Redshank	7,000	32
Tringa glareola Wood Sandpiper	200,000	10
Phalaropus lobatus Red-necked Phalarope	10,000	12
Larus minutus Little Gull	8,000	20
Larus canus Common Gull	50,000	35
Larus fuscus Lesser Black-backed Gull	6,000	69
Larus marinus Great Black-backed Gull	2,500	38
Sterna caspia Caspian Tern	700	69
Sterna paradisaea Arctic Tern	50,000	46
Alca torda Razorbill	6,000	84
Cepphus grylle Black Guillemot	12,000	76
Columba oenas Stock Dove	5,000	3
Bubo bubo Eagle Owl	2,500	2
Nyctea scandiaca Snowy Owl	50	20
Asio flammeus Short-eared Owl	2,000	15
Caprimulgus europaeus Nightjar	3,000	1
Picus canus Grey-headed Woodpecker	1,500	2
Picoides tridactylus Three-toed Woodpecker	15,000	11
Riparia riparia Sand Martin	50,000	2
Anthus pratensis Meadow Pipit	700,000	12
Luscinia luscinia Thrush Nightingale	15,000	3
Luscinia svecica Bluethroat	100,000	24
Phoenicurus phoenicurus Redstart	500,000	4
Saxicola rubetra Whinchat	400,000	<1
Turdus viscivorus Mistle Thrush	40,000	3
Acrocephalus schoenobaenus Sedge Warbler	300,000	7
Acrocephalus scirpaceus Reed Warbler	12,000	9
Muscicapa striata Spotted Flycatcher	1,400,000	1
Ficedula hypoleuca Pied Flycatcher	300,000	1
Lanius collurio Red-backed Shrike	50,000	1
Lanius excubitor Great Grey Shrike	4,000	3
Perisoreus infaustus Siberian Jay	30,000	11
Loxia pytyopsittacus Parrot Crossbill	10,000	9

1. Only those species of European conservation concern (see Box 1, p. 12) that meet IBA criteria in Finland are listed, together with those species listed on Annex I of the EC Birds Directive that fulfil criterion C6 in IBAs in Finland.
2. Data are taken from the BirdLife/EBCC European Bird Database 1998 (Heath and Borggreve 2000).
3. The percentage of the national population in IBAs exceeds 100%. Usually this is because the national population estimate has not been updated recently whilst the IBA population estimate has been recently updated with new data as a result of comprehensive surveys of IBAs themselves. Also, the individual site count for a species may be the maximum or average over recent years, and summing these may record more birds than are present nationally in any single year.

ORNITHOLOGICAL IMPORTANCE

More than 420 species of birds have been recorded in Finland with some 240 of them breeding regularly. A total of 115 species of European conservation concern (SPECs) occur in Finland, with 102 breeding regularly, including the globally threatened *Crex crex* and near-threatened *Haliaeetus albicilla* (Tucker and Heath 1994). The globally threatened *Anser erythropus* is now a very rare breeder. Several hundred of the globally threatened *Polysticta stelleri* winter in south-western Finland. Eight IBAs have internationally important populations of these globally threatened or near-threatened species (Table 2).

Forty-eight IBAs hold more than 1% of the biogeographical or flyway populations of the species listed in Table 3 (meeting criteria A4iii or B1iii). Almost all of the most important congregatory areas lie on the coast along the two main migration routes in Finland: the Gulf of Bothnia and the Gulf of Finland. The largest numbers of birds and species occur in the Oulu region wetlands (028), Pori archipelago and wetlands (083), and Merenkurkku archipelago (045). The only important site for wintering congregatory species is Lågskär-Nyhamn (096) which holds up to 400 *Polysticta stelleri*, 6 % of the Baltic Sea wintering population.

Seventy-seven IBAs support important populations of SPECs and species listed on Annex I of the EC Birds Directive, meeting criteria B2, B3 and C6 (Table 4). Finland supports a large proportion of the European breeding population (c.10% or more) of a number of SPECs and Annex I species, for which a number of IBAs have been identified. In particular, these species include breeding ducks and waders associated with boreal and subarctic wetlands, such as *Anas acuta*, *Mergus albellus*, *Tringa glareola* and *Limicola falcinellus*; species associated with boreal forests such as *Tetrao urogallus*, *Picoides tridactylus* and *Perisoreus infaustus*; and coastal breeding waterbirds or seabirds such as *Larus canus*, *Larus fuscus fuscus*, *Sterna caspia* and *Cepphus grylle*.

Fifteen species associated with the Arctic/tundra biome and 15 species associated with the boreal biome breed in Finland. Eleven sites were identified as important for boreal biome species and five sites were identified as Arctic/tundra biome sites (meeting criterion A3). Two sites (003 and 004) meet criterion A3 for both the Arctic/tundra and boreal biomes. Many additional sites in northern and eastern Finland hold populations of several biome-restricted species.

Many boreal forest species such as *Tetrao urogallus*, *Picoides tridactylus* and *Perisoreus infaustus* have dispersed distributions and are therefore inadequately covered by the IBA network. Sites have to be very large to meet numerical criteria for these species and smaller, but nevertheless important, sites for some species are therefore missing from the IBA network as they fail to meet criteria. However criterion C6, which identifies sites for species listed on Annex I of the EC Birds Directive, has not been fully applied (see 'Analytical methods' section). In addition, bird data for the large northern forested IBAs are poor and larger-scale surveys are needed to better understand the ornithological importance of these areas. Bird-data for pastoral habitats such as meadows, grassland and agricultural fields are also lacking. Therefore, species such as *Crex crex*, *Lanius collurio*, *Saxicola rubetra* and *Emberiza hortulana* are likely to be inadequately covered by the IBA network.

HABITATS

Nearly all of Finland lies in the Euro-Siberian boreal vegetation zone. The only exception is the extreme north which is classified as a subarctic region. Forest is the dominant vegetation-type, covering 70% of the country. Peatlands are also widespread, with different types of bogs and mires dominating 10% of the country; there are also more than 60,000 lakes.

Fifty-seven IBAs (59%) contain areas of forest (Figure 1). These are mainly coniferous, being dominated by *Pinus sylvestris* and *Picea abies*. In the southern half of the country, less than 1% of forests are in a natural state and forests are highly fragmented. The majority of natural boreal forests are found in northern Finland. As a result, the north of the country also contains most of the IBAs for forest species such as *Tetrao urogallus*, *Strix nebulosa*, *Picoides tridactylus*, *Perisoreus infaustus*, *Parus cinctus* and *Loxia pytyopsittacus*.

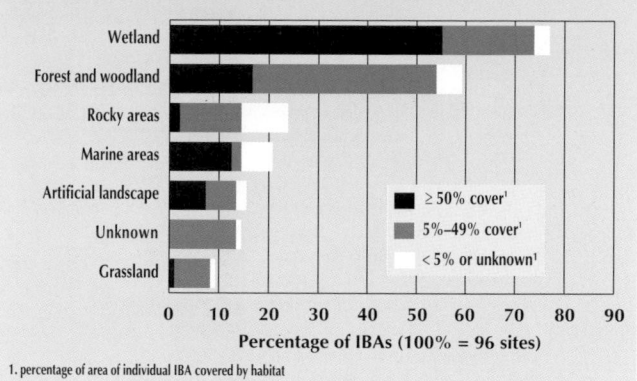

Figure 1. Habitats at Important Bird Areas in Finland (see Appendix 3 for definitions of habitats).

Wetland
Forest and woodland
Rocky areas
Marine areas
Artificial landscape
Unknown
Grassland

■ ≥ 50% cover[1]
▨ 5%–49% cover[1]
□ < 5% or unknown[1]

0 10 20 30 40 50 60 70 80 90
Percentage of IBAs (100% = 96 sites)

1. percentage of area of individual IBA covered by habitat

Seventy-four IBAs (77%) contain wetland habitats (Figure 1). Raised bogs occur mainly in the south and aapa mires in the north. In the most northerly areas palsa mires are also frequent, for example in IBAs 001, 015 and 016. In general, large open aapa mires are ornithologically the most important, holding breeding species such as *Cygnus cygnus*, *Anas acuta*, *Falco peregrinus*, *Grus grus*, *Numenius phaeopus*, *Limicola falcinellus*, *Tringa erythropus* and *T. glareola* (for example IBAs 001, 014, 016, 021 and 037). South-eastern Finland has many large, oligotrophic lakes important for species such as *Gavia arctica*, *Pandion haliaetus* and *Larus fuscus fuscus* (for example IBAs 036, 053, 063 and 067). In agricultural areas, smaller eutrophic lakes are common.

Finland's coastline is complex with numerous peninsulas, bays, some nutrient-rich deltas, and thousands of islands and islets with surrounding marine areas. The western coast has large areas of shallow water important for breeding and migratory species, especially waterbirds, for example IBAs 028, 047 and 083. Sites containing these coastal habitats are important breeding areas for species such as *Haliaeetus albicilla*, *Larus canus*, *L. f. fuscus*, *Sterna caspia* and *Cepphus grylle*.

Agricultural land and grasslands comprise a relatively small amount of the area of IBAs (Figure 1). However, agricultural land and meadows are particularly important for migratory species such as *Anser erythropus*, *A. fabalis*, *Grus grus*, *Pluvialis apricaria* and *Tringa erythropus*, and breeding birds such as *Crex crex*, *Asio flammeus* and *Emberiza hortulana*.

IMPACTS ON IBAs – LAND-USE AND THREATS

Land-use and threats in IBAs are generally poorly-known (Figures 2 and 3). Tourism and recreation is the most widespread known

Figure 2. Land-uses at Important Bird Areas in Finland (see Appendix 3 for definitions of land-uses).

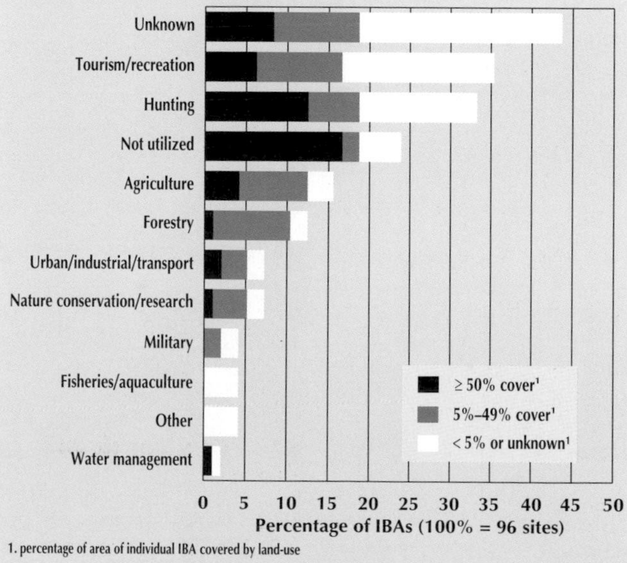

Unknown
Tourism/recreation
Hunting
Not utilized
Agriculture
Forestry
Urban/industrial/transport
Nature conservation/research
Military
Fisheries/aquaculture
Other
Water management

■ ≥ 50% cover[1]
▨ 5%–49% cover[1]
□ < 5% or unknown[1]

0 5 10 15 20 25 30 35 40 45 50
Percentage of IBAs (100% = 96 sites)

1. percentage of area of individual IBA covered by land-use

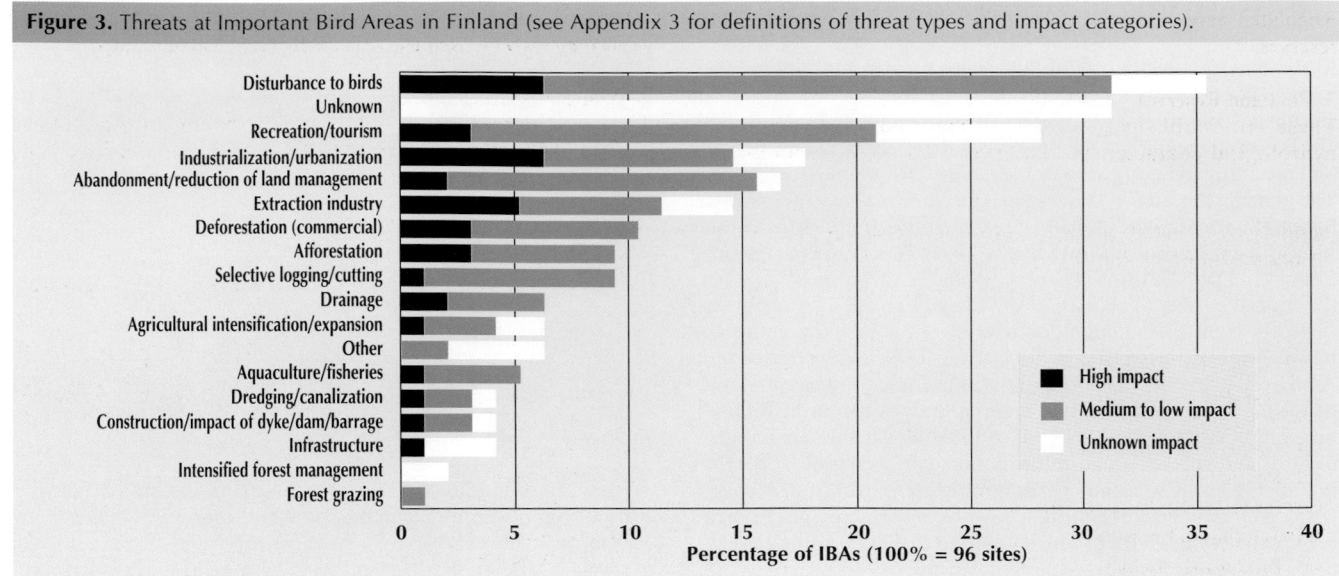

Figure 3. Threats at Important Bird Areas in Finland (see Appendix 3 for definitions of threat types and impact categories).

land-use, occurring in 34 IBAs (35%) and also represents a significant threat in IBAs (Figures 2 and 3). There are normally no restrictions on fishing or boating even in the most important sites for congregatory species. Boating is a particular threat to IBAs in coastal archipelagos. Some areas of archipelagos, as well as large oligotrophic lakes, are also threatened by the construction of holiday cottages. In some IBAs, disturbance caused by recreation and tourism has been classified under disturbance to birds, the two threats being difficult to separate.

Hunting is a common land-use in IBAs, occurring in 33% of them (Figure 2). It is also a major cause of disturbance to birds, the most widespread threat to IBAs (Figure 3). Some scarcer species of wildfowl, such as *Anser fabalis fabalis*, *Melanitta fusca*, *M. nigra* and *Aythya marila*, are subject to high hunting pressure. Hunting is allowed in autumn across the whole country and in spring in the archipelagos of Åland and the Gulf of Finland.

The pressure for deforestation outside protected areas is very high. The areas of untouched wilderness in northern and eastern Finland have declined over recent decades as a result of active commercial forestry. This has caused population declines in many old-forest species (Väisänen *et al.* 1998). Fortunately, the most important IBAs for boreal forest are nearly all protected from commercial forestry. However, deforestation is still a threat to 10% of IBAs and selective logging/cutting to a further 9% (Figure 3).

As well as problems of disturbance, hunting and recreation, some wetland IBAs are threatened by nutrient pollution and the loss of open water to emergent vegetation. This is primarily a result of nutrient run-off from adjacent farmland. The loss of cattle-grazed

pastures in coastal areas and around lakes has resulted in a consequent reduction in the area of open meadows. This has caused a decline in breeding wader species associated with such habitats, such as *Calidris alpina schinzii*.

PROTECTION STATUS

■ National protection

Thirty-seven percent of Finnish IBAs (36 sites) are totally unprotected at the national level (Figure 4). However, all but six of these sites are included in official conservation programmes, and thus should be protected in the near future. Table 5 shows the type of protected areas that overlap with IBAs. The main categories of protected area in Finland are listed below (Asanti *et al.* 1999):

1. National Parks
Areas of outstanding natural beauty which are to be preserved in a pristine condition as far as possible. A National Park can only be established on state-owned land and may be no smaller than 1,000 ha. There is general public access to these areas and they are developed to serve the needs of visitors wanting to enjoy and study nature. Reindeer husbandry as well as fishing and hunting are permitted in some National Parks.

2. Strict Nature Reserves
Areas specifically for conservation, scientific research and education with the general aim of safeguarding sites from development. A Strict Nature Reserve can only be established on state-owned land.

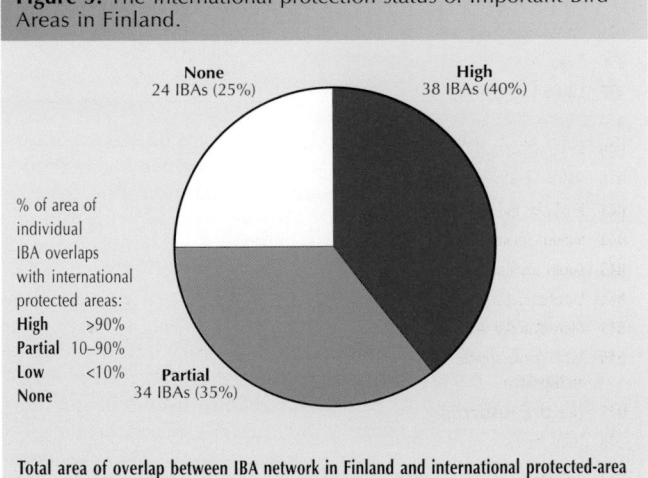

Figure 4. The national protection status of Important Bird Areas in Finland.

None 34 IBAs (35%)
High 18 IBAs (19%)
Partial 29 IBAs (30%)
Low 15 IBAs (16%)

% of area of individual IBA overlaps with national protected areas:
High >90%
Partial 10–90%
Low <10%
None

Total area of overlap between IBA network in Finland and national protected-area system (see Table 5 for categories) = 14,079–17,302 km² (51–63% of total IBA area).

Figure 5. The international protection status of Important Bird Areas in Finland.

None 24 IBAs (25%)
High 38 IBAs (40%)
Partial 34 IBAs (35%)

% of area of individual IBA overlaps with international protected areas:
High >90%
Partial 10–90%
Low <10%
None

Total area of overlap between IBA network in Finland and international protected-area system (see Table 5 for categories) = 13,357–13,365 km² (49% of total IBA area).

Regulated access and reindeer husbandry are allowed in certain reserves.

3. Peatland Reserves
These are established on state-owned land to safeguard the hydrological characteristics and flora and fauna of mires. The

removal of soil, drainage, and the felling of trees is forbidden. The areas may also be used for various recreational activities.

4. Wilderness Areas
These cover large areas of state-owned practically roadless terrain. The use of Wilderness Areas is regulated by the Finnish Forest and

Table 5. Protection status of Important Bird Areas in Finland.
A tick (✓) indicates that an IBA overlaps with a protected area (to any extent).

IBA code	International name	National Park	Strict Nature Reserve	Peatland Reserve	Wilderness Area	Specific Protection Area	Protected Areas on Private Land	Ramsar Site	Biosphere Reserve	Special Protection Area
001	Lätäseno and Jietajoki mires			✓						✓
002	Käsivarsi fjelds				✓					✓
003	Lemmenjoki–Hammastunturi–Pulju	✓			✓					✓
004	Saariselkä and Koilliskaira	✓	✓	✓	✓					✓
005	Pomokaira–Koitelaiskaira			✓				✓		✓
006	Pallas and Ylläs fjelds	✓								
007	Värriö–Tuntsa		✓		✓					
008	Maltio fjelds		✓							
009	South-eastern Kittilä mires			✓						✓
010	Kevo		✓							
011	Luosto									
012	Riisitunturi	✓								
013	Joutsenaapa–Kaita-aapa			✓						✓
014	Lämsänaapa–Sakkala-aapa			✓						✓
015	Pöyrisvuoma mire protection area			✓	✓					✓
016	Sammutinjänkä–Vaijoenjänkä			✓						✓
017	Kemihaara (Vuotos) mires and forests									
018	Runkaus–Saariaapa–Tainijärvet		✓	✓						
019	Karunginjärvi lake									
020	Veittiaapa–Ristiaapa			✓						✓
021	Martimoaapa–Lumiaapa–Penikat			✓				✓		✓
022	Kilsiaapa–Ristivuoma			✓						✓
023	Tornionjoki delta									✓
024	Rumala–Kuvaja–Oudonrimmet			✓						✓
025	Elimyssalo					✓				
026	Juortanansalo					✓				
027	Krunnit archipelago						✓	✓		✓
028	Oulu region wetlands						✓			✓
029	Syöte–Salmitunturi					✓	✓			✓
030	Oulanka–Sukerijärvi	✓	✓							✓
031	Närängänvaara–Virmajoki–Romevaara									✓
032	Pajupuronsuo–Isosuo–Kivisuo			✓						✓
033	Haapavesi wetlands									✓
034	Olvassuo–Oravisuo–Näätäsuo–Sammakkosuo		✓	✓						✓
035	Valtavaara–Pyhävaara					✓				✓
036	Kitka lake									✓
037	Litokaira			✓						✓
038	Ahmasjärvi lake									✓
039	Rummelö–Harrbodan									✓
040	Rahja archipelago									✓
041	Kokkola and Kälviä archipelago									✓
042	Sundominlahti Bay and Söderfjärden									✓
043	Luoto archipelago						✓			✓
044	Uusikaarlepyy archipelago						✓			✓
045	Merenkurkku archipelago						✓	✓		✓
046	Kristiinankaupunki southern archipelago						✓			✓
047	Lapväärti wetlands									✓
048	Lålby fields									
049	Alajoki									
Subtotal of IBAs		**5**	**7**	**16**	**5**	**4**	**7**	**4**	**0**	**36**
050	Värtsilä valley									✓
051	Koitajoki area		✓	✓				✓		✓
052	Outokumpu wetlands									✓
053	Outokumpu and Kaavi oligotrophic lakes									✓
054	Viklinrimpi			✓						
055	Patvinsuo National Park	✓							✓	✓
056	Pitkäranta									
057	Päätyeenlahti Bay							✓		✓
058	Ruunaa						✓			
059	Maaninka wetlands									✓
060	Talaskangas					✓	✓			
061	Keski-Kallavesi and Kuhanen lake									✓
062	Linnansaari	✓								
063	Lake Pihlajavesi									
064	Kangasala wetlands									✓
065	Hollola wetlands									✓
066	Artjärvi wetlands									✓
067	Kukkiajärvi lake									
068	Koijärvi lake						✓			✓
069	Torronsuo and Lake Talpianjärvi	✓								✓
070	Siikalahti Bay and Sammallampi lake									✓
071	Kirkkojärvi lake and Lupinlahti Bay						✓			✓
072	Itäinen Suomenlahti National Park	✓								✓
073	Kirkon–Vilkkiläntura Bay									✓
074	Teutjärvi and Suvijärvi lakes									✓
075	Pernaja outer archipelago						✓	✓		✓
076	Porvoonjoki Delta						✓	✓		✓
077	Porvoo outer archipelago					✓	✓	✓		✓
078	Laajalahti Bay, Vanhankaupunginlahti Bay and Viikki					✓	✓	✓		✓
079	Nuuksio	✓								✓
080	Tammisaari and Inkoo western archipelago	✓								✓
081	Hanko western archipelago					✓	✓			✓
082	Kirkkonummi archipelago					✓	✓			
083	Pori archipelago and wetlands					✓	✓			
084	Koskeljärvi, Vaaljärvi and Pitkäjärvi lakes					✓	✓			
085	Rauma and Luvia archipelagos						✓			
086	Puurijärvi–Isosuo wetlands	✓								✓
087	Köyliönjärvi and Pyhäjärvi lakes									✓
088	Oura and Enskeri archipelagos						✓			
089	Korppoo and Nauvo southern archipelago	✓							✓	✓
090	Paimionlahti Bay						✓			✓
091	Mietoistenlahti Bay						✓	✓		✓
092	Ruissalo						✓			✓
093	Föglö southern archipelago						✓			
094	Eckerö and Hammarland archipelago						✓			
095	Mulklobb									
096	Lågskär–Nyhamn									✓
Total number of IBAs		**13**	**8**	**18**	**5**	**11**	**26**	**11**	**2**	**67**

Box 1. International legislation and initiatives that are relevant to site conservation in Finland (see Appendix 1 for a general description of these agreements).

Global	
Biodiversity Convention	✔
Ramsar Convention	✔
Bonn Convention	✔
World Heritage Convention	✔
MAB Programme	✔
Pan-European	
Bern Convention	✔
Regional	
EC Birds Directive	✔
EC Habitats Directive	✔
Helsinki Convention	✔

✔ Convention ratified/initiative supported
(✔) Convention signed

Park Service on the basis of individual management plans for each area. All Wilderness Areas are situated in northern Lapland.

5. Specific Protected Areas

These are state-owned areas for which the purpose of protection varies. Specific Protected Areas include important areas of eskers and marine ecosystems and sites with a high cultural value.

6. Protected Areas on Private Land

These areas can be established by private individuals, municipalities and organizations. They are established to safeguard important bird colonies, valuable groves, small woodlands and mires. Obtaining protected status for such areas requires the initiative of the land-owner, who in most cases retains some rights to utilize the area.

By the end of 1998, there were 31 National Parks, 19 Strict Nature Reserves, 173 Peatland Reserves, 10 Wilderness Areas, 42 Specific Protection Areas and more than a thousand Protected Areas on Private Land in Finland. They cover a total area of 3,351,500 ha.

■ International protection

Finland supports all international initiatives relevant to site protection for nature conservation (Box 1). Three-quarters of IBAs have some international protection (Figure 5). Sixty-seven out of 96 IBAs overlap with Special Protection Areas and 11 overlap with Ramsar Sites (Table 5). Fifty new Ramsar Sites will potentially soon be designated in Finland and will overlap with 39 IBAs

The Government of Finland has designated 439 sites (2,750,000 ha) as Special Protection Areas under the Birds Directive of the European Union. The majority of these SPAs cover areas of wetlands; some important areas of boreal forest have not been designated. For many species on Annex I of the Birds Directive, the network of Finnish SPAs is not adequate for their conservation. This is particularly true of species occurring in agricultural land and meadows such as *Crex crex*, *Lanius collurio* and *Emberiza hortulana*, and some species associated with boreal forest.

CONSERVATION ISSUES

- The 1923 Nature Conservation Act was revised in 1996. The new act includes several new principles for nature conservation, particularly the special protection of the most threatened species and of key habitats. One of the most significant steps was to harmonize national legislation with EC nature conservation legislation, in particular the Habitats Directive (92/43/EEC) and the Birds Directive (79/409/EEC).
- The Finnish government has a number of well established conservation programmes for the development of national parks and nature reserves, mire conservation, special conservation areas, private conservation areas and wilderness areas. In contrast, wildfowl habitats, old-growth forests and shorelines need urgent measures to conserve remaining habitat. Agricultural habitats have been almost totally absent from conservation programmes, despite their importance for breeding species such as *Crex crex*, *Asio flammeus* and *Emberiza hortulana* and as congregatory areas for many migratory species such as *Anser erythropus*, *A. fabalis* and *Grus grus*. Initiatives are now being taken to address this problem.

ANALYTICAL METHODS

- Almost all the IBA data is from the 1990s, mainly from extensive field work carried out during 1996–1997.
- The reliability of the bird data varies. In general, the most unreliable data comes from very large forest areas in northern Finland, and the most reliable data from the smaller wetlands in the south. The large northern forest areas were surveyed using transect counts. In order to estimate numbers, relatively small areas were sampled and the data used to extrapolate for a much larger area.
- The number of pairs is presented either as a result of a single year survey, the mean number of pairs from a number of years, or as a range of the minimum number of pairs over a number of years.
- In forests, survey methods were mainly dependent upon the size of the area being surveyed. Transect methods were used in larger areas and mapping methods in smaller areas.
- In mire areas, data for breeding waders were obtained using transect and mapping methods.
- In wetlands, counts were mostly made 3–5 times in a breeding season.
- The numbers of congregatory species are normally based on a series of successive counts during the same migration period. However, because only a proportion of all the birds passing through a site during a single migration period are counted, the number of birds passing through a site is usually under-estimated.
- All boundaries were drawn and analyzed using a geographical information system (GIS). These GIS map data are part of a larger conservation-area database, held by the Finnish Environment Institute.
- Criteria B2/B3 population thresholds were lowered for a few species where Finland holds a high proportion of the European population of the species but where no or few sites have at least 1% of the national population. This applied to: *Gavia arctica*, *Circus cyaneus*, *Pandion haliaetus*, *Tetrao tetrix*, *Limicola falcinellus*, *Numenius phaeopus*, *Tringa glareola*, *Larus minutus*, *Bubo bubo*, *Picoides tridactylus*, *Anthus pratensis*, *Phoenicurus phoenicurus*, *Saxicola rubetra*, *Acrocephalus schoenobaenus*, *Muscicapa striata*, *Ficedula hypoleuca*, *Perisoreus infaustus* and *Loxia pytyopsittacus*. Additional sites meeting these lower thresholds may be identified in the future.
- The C6 criterion was not applied to all relevant species, given the timeframe of the project. C6 was applied to all species listed on Annex I of the EC Birds Directive that already qualified under criteria B2 or B3 at a site. For all such applications, the site was considered to be one of the top five sites in the NUTs region (level 3), with the exception of *Circus cyaneus*, *Aquila chrysaetos* and *Tringa glareola* where more than five sites in a NUTs region had B2/B3 assigned and thus these were prioritized for C6 application.

GLOSSARY

aapa mires bogs with a series of nutrient-poor, drier ridges and wet, relatively nutrient-rich depressions.

esker a ridge of glacial deposits (sand and gravel).

flada narrow sea bay.

fjeld relatively low, round-topped mountain, typical of Nordic Lapland.

NUTS Nomenclature des Unités Territoriales Statistiques (the administrative regions of the European Union are called NUTS regions, and are designated by the EC Statistical Office.

oligotrophic lakes nutrient-poor lakes (normally very large) with low primary productivity.

palsa mires subarctic acid bogs with a permafrost layer that form characteristic hummocks as the upper layers of peat melt in the summer.

SAC Special Area for Conservation. Proposed sites to be protected under the EC Habitats Directive, as part of the Natura 2000 network.

SPA Special Protection Area (designated under Article 4 of the EC Birds Directive).

ACKNOWLEDGEMENTS

On behalf of BirdLife Finland, I would like to give special thanks to the Finnish Environment Institute and particularly my colleagues on the IBA team: Timo Asanti, Markku Mikkola-Roos, Patrik Byholm, Aleksi Lehikoinen and Pekka

Rusanen. They have carried out a large part of the Finnish IBA work. Co-members of the IBA specialist group, Antti Below, Pertti Koskimies, Esa Lammi, Janne Lampolahti and Erkki Virolainen, have actively carried the project forward. Matti Helminen, Mika Ohtonen and Heikki Pakkala represented BirdLife Finland in the coordinating committee of the IBA project. Invaluable voluntary assistance has been provided by all the local IBA coordinators of the BirdLife Finland member societies: Jouko Astor, Seppo Grönlund, Esko Gustafsson, Petri Hottola, Juha Huttunen, Tatu Itkonen, Jukka Jantunen, Jukka Jokimäki, Kimmo Kivinummi, Rauno Laine, Janne Lampolahti, Ari Lehtinen, Visa Marttila, Rainer Mäkelä, Harri Okkonen, Vesa Oksanen, Tuukka Pahtamaa, Veijo Peltola, Jorma Pessa, Timo Pylvänäinen, Kai Pynssi, Pentti Rauhala, Jouni Rinta-Keturi, Kalle Ruokolainen, Markku Ryösä, Pekka Räinä, Hannu Tikkanen, Krister Troberg,

Markku Uusitalo, Marko Vauhkonen and Simo Veistola. Hundreds of birdwatchers have spent days and weeks as the prey of clouds of bloodthirsty mosquitoes—only for IBA counts. Grateful thanks to all of them, whose names unfortunately cannot be mentioned here due to space constraints.

Since 1995, the major part of the IBA work in Finland has been funded by the Ministry of Environment. The Finnish Environment Institute has facilitated the IBA work by providing many resources during the project. Financial help for organizing the extensive IBA fieldwork has been provided by regional environment centres, the Finnish Forest and Park Service, the Ministry of Labour, Bongariliitto (Association of Finnish Twitchers), Tringa (Ornithological Society of the Helsinki Region) and many local nature conservation societies. All the local member societies of BirdLife Finland have been supportive during the IBA work.

■ SITE ACCOUNTS

Lätäseno and Jietajoki mires — 001
A4i, B1i, B2, B3, C2, C3, C6
Admin region Lapin lääni
Coordinates 68°38′N 22°21′E
Altitude 500–500 m **Area** 43,367 ha

■ Site description
A large complex of peatlands and wetlands along the Lätäseno and Jietajoki rivers. The area supports well-developed mires characteristic of the palsa mire region of northernmost Lapland. Numerous lakes, ponds, rivers and streams pass through the peatlands, and there are some forests restricted to mineral soils. Since the area is protected, human impact is slight, with some hunting in autumn, and an illegal spring hunting 'season'.

Habitats Forest and woodland (20%), Wetland (80%; raised bog)
Land-use Hunting, Unknown

■ Birds

Species	Season	Year	Pop min	Pop max	Acc	Criteria
Circus cyaneus Hen Harrier	B	1997	10	50	C	B2, C6
Limicola falcinellus Broad-billed Sandpiper	B	1997	200	500	B	A4i, B1i, B2, C3
Tringa glareola Wood Sandpiper	B	1997	500	2,000	C	B2, C6
Phalaropus lobatus Red-necked Phalarope	B	1997	200	500	C	C2
Anthus pratensis Meadow Pipit	B	1997	2,000	5,000	C	B3

An important breeding area for Arctic species, especially waders, e.g. *Limicola falcinellus*, *Calidris alpina* (100–300 pairs), *Tringa glareola*, *T. erythropus* (50–150 pairs) and *Phalaropus lobatus*.

■ Protection status
National High **International** High
43,367 ha of IBA covered by Peatland Reserve (Lätäseno–Hietajoki, 43,367 ha). 43,258 ha of IBA covered by Special Protection Area (Käsivarren erämaa).

■ Conservation issues

Threats Unknown

Part of the area is a candidate SAC.

Käsivarsi fjelds — 002
A3, B2, B3, C2, C6
Admin region Lapin lääni
Coordinates 69°00′N 21°30′E
Altitude 800–1,300 m **Area** 220,078 ha

■ Site description
A very large wilderness of rugged fjelds in north-western Finland. The landscape is open, dominated by rocky mountains isolated by valleys or plateaus, with numerous ponds, small lakes and rivulets. Birch *Betula pubescens* forest covers the lower parts of the fjelds. There are many human settlements along the road bordering the area to the west. Tourism is heavy around Saana in the north for 2–3 months per year, but otherwise the area suffers only minor human impact.

Habitats Grassland (70%; tundra), Wetland (15%; raised bog), Unknown (15%)
Land-use Tourism/recreation, Other

■ Birds

Species	Season	Year	Pop min	Pop max	Acc	Criteria
Gavia stellata Red-throated Diver	B	1996	10	50	C	B2, C2, C6
Anser erythropus Lesser White-fronted Goose	B	1996	0	1	B	A3
Aythya marila Scaup	B	1996	30	50	B	A3
Clangula hyemalis Long-tailed Duck	B	1996	100	100	B	A3
Melanitta nigra Common Scoter	B	1996	50	50	B	A3
Mergus albellus Smew	B	1996	5	20	C	B2, C2
Falco rusticolus Gyrfalcon	R	1996	4	7	A	A3
Charadrius morinellus Dotterel	B	1996	100	300	B	C2
Pluvialis apricaria Golden Plover	B	1996	300	1,000	C	B3, C6
Calidris temminckii Temminck's Stint	B	1996	50	100	B	A3
Calidris maritima Purple Sandpiper	B	1996	10	10	B	A3
Limosa lapponica Bar-tailed Godwit	B	1996	1	5	B	A3
Tringa erythropus Spotted Redshank	B	1996	5	10	B	A3
Tringa totanus Redshank	B	1996	50	200	C	B2
Phalaropus lobatus Red-necked Phalarope	B	1996	200	500	B	A3, C2
Stercorarius longicaudus Long-tailed Skua	B	1996	20	200	B	A3
Nyctea scandiaca Snowy Owl	B	1996	0	10	B	A3, B2, C6
Asio flammeus Short-eared Owl	B	1996	50	200	B	B2, C2, C6
Anthus pratensis Meadow Pipit	B	1996	30,000	—	C	B3
Anthus cervinus Red-throated Pipit	B	1996	50	100	B	A3
Luscinia svecica Bluethroat	B	1996	20,000	20,000	C	C2
Calcarius lapponicus Lapland Bunting	B	1996	500	2,000	C	A3
Plectrophenax nivalis Snow Bunting	B	1996	3,000	8,000	C	A3

An important breeding area for Arctic species. Breeding birds include 15 out of the 32 species in Europe that are restricted to the Arctic/tundra biome (when breeding). Species of global conservation concern that do not meet IBA criteria: *Anser erythropus* (passage).

■ Protection status
National High **International** High
173,264 ha of IBA covered by Wilderness Area (Käsivarsi, 219,989 ha). 219,755 ha of IBA covered by Special Protection Area (Käsivarren erämaa).

■ Conservation issues

Threats Other (U)

Reindeer husbandry ('Other' land-use and threat) has caused some erosion of vegetation. Part of the area is a candidate SAC.

Lemmenjoki–Hammastunturi–Pulju — 003
A3, A4i, B1i, B2, B3, C2, C3, C6
Admin region Lapin lääni
Coordinates 68°35′N 25°30′E
Altitude 400–400 m **Area** 529,718 ha

■ Site description
A very large northern wilderness surrounding the Lemmenjoki and Ivalojoki rivers. In the east of the area the landscape is dominated by

treeless fjeld, separated by large areas of boreal forest, whereas peatlands cover most of the southern and western parts. There are numerous rivers, streams, lakes and ponds. Tourism is common, especially during summer in Lemmenjoki National Park, but in winter human activity is minimal.

Habitats Forest and woodland (50%; broadleaved deciduous forest; native coniferous forest), Grassland (15%; tundra), Wetland (25%; raised bog)
Land-use Tourism/recreation, Other

■ Birds

Species	Season	Year	Pop min	Pop max	Acc	Criteria
Gavia stellata Red-throated Diver	B	1996	10	50	C	B2, C2, C6
Cygnus cygnus Whooper Swan	B	1996	30	70	C	B2, C2, C6
[1] *Mergus albellus* Smew	B	1996	10	50	C	A3, B2, C2
Circus cyaneus Hen Harrier	B	1996	30	100	C	B2, C6
[2] *Buteo lagopus* Rough-legged Buzzard	B	1991	100	300	—	A3
Pandion haliaetus Osprey	B	1996	3	10	C	B2, C6
Tetrao urogallus Capercaillie	R	1991	500	2,000	C	C2
Grus grus Crane	B	1996	30	100	C	B1i, B2, C2, C6
Charadrius hiaticula Ringed Plover	B	1991	300	1,000	C	A4i, B1i, C3
Charadrius morinellus Dotterel	B	1991	100	400	C	A4i, B1i, C2
Pluvialis apricaria Golden Plover	B	1991	1,000	5,000	C	A4i, B1i, B3, C2, C6
[2] *Calidris temminckii* Temminck's Stint	B	1996	1	11	C	A3
Limicola falcinellus Broad-billed Sandpiper	B	1991	500	2,000	C	A4i, B1i, B2, C3
Philomachus pugnax Ruff	B	1991	500	2,000	C	B3, C2, C6
[1] *Lymnocryptes minimus* Jack Snipe	B	1991	200	500	C	A3, A4i, B1i, C3
[2] *Limosa lapponica* Bar-tailed Godwit	B	1996	10	50	C	A3
Numenius phaeopus Whimbrel	B	1991	500	1,500	C	B3
[2] *Tringa erythropus* Spotted Redshank	B	1991	300	1,000	C	A3, A4i, B1i, C3
[1] *Tringa nebularia* Greenshank	B	1991	200	600	C	A3, A4i, B1i, C3
Tringa glareola Wood Sandpiper	B	1991	5,000	15,000	C	A4i, B1i, B2, C2, C6
[2] *Phalaropus lobatus* Red-necked Phalarope	B	1996	50	200	C	A3
[1] *Surnia ulula* Hawk Owl	B	1996	10	100	C	A3, C6
[1] *Strix nebulosa* Great Grey Owl	B	1996	10	50	C	A3, C6
Asio flammeus Short-eared Owl	B	1996	30	100	C	B2, C6
Picoides tridactylus Three-toed Woodpecker	R	1991	300	1,000	C	B2, C2, C6
Anthus pratensis Meadow Pipit	B	1991	20,000	—	C	B3
[1] *Bombycilla garrulus* Waxwing	B	1991	200	500	—	A3
Luscinia svecica Bluethroat	B	1991	1,000	5,000	C	C2
Phoenicurus phoenicurus Redstart	B	1991	5,000	15,000	C	B2
Saxicola rubetra Whinchat	B	1991	500	2,000	C	B3
Acrocephalus schoenobaenus Sedge Warbler	B	1991	1,000	3,000	C	B3
[1] *Phylloscopus borealis* Arctic Warbler	B	1996	10	50	C	A3
Muscicapa striata Spotted Flycatcher	B	1991	1,000	5,000	C	B2
Ficedula hypoleuca Pied Flycatcher	B	1991	300	1,000	C	B3
[1] *Parus cinctus* Siberian Tit	R	1991	2,000	5,000	—	A3
Lanius excubitor Great Grey Shrike	B	1996	30	100	C	B2
[1] *Perisoreus infaustus* Siberian Jay	R	1991	800	2,000	C	A3, B2
[1] *Fringilla montifringilla* Brambling	B	1991	30,000	30,000	—	A3
[1] *Loxia leucoptera* Two-barred Crossbill	B	1996	30	300	C	A3
[1] *Pinicola enucleator* Pine Grosbeak	B	1991	500	1,500	—	A3
[2] *Calcarius lapponicus* Lapland Bunting	B	1991	300	1,000	—	A3
[2] *Plectrophenax nivalis* Snow Bunting	B	1991	500	1,500	—	A3
[1] *Emberiza rustica* Rustic Bunting	B	1991	500	1,500	—	A3

1. Boreal biome.
2. Arctic/tundra biome.

An exceptionally important area for Arctic and boreal avifauna. Breeding birds include seven out of the 32 species in Europe that are restricted to the Arctic/tundra biome (when breeding) and 13 out of the 15 species in Europe that are restricted to the boreal biome (when breeding).

■ Protection status
National High **International** High
182,809 ha of IBA covered by Wilderness Area (Hammastunturi, 182,809 ha). 61,981 ha of IBA covered by Wilderness Area (Pulju, 61,981 ha). 284,928 ha of IBA covered by National Park (Lemmenjoki, 284,928 ha). 490,895 ha of IBA covered by 2 Special Protection Areas (Lemmenjoen kansallispuisto; Pulijun erämaa).

■ Conservation issues

Threats Extraction industry (U), Other (U)

Reindeer husbandry ('Other' land-use and threat) has caused some erosion of vegetation. Mechanized gold washing has changed the natural state of the tributaries of the Lemmenjoki river. Part of the area is a candidate SAC.

Saariselkä and Koilliskaira	A3, A4i, B1i, B2, B3, C2, C3, C6	004
Admin region Lapin lääni		
Coordinates 68°15'N 28°00'E		
Altitude 500–500 m **Area** 309,553 ha		

■ Site description
A huge wilderness of fjelds, boreal forests and peatlands in northeast Lapland. Saariselkä, in the north of the area, is a barren fjeld wilderness with treeless mountain heath. Koilliskaira, to the south, is dominated by coniferous forests and aapa mires. Ponds, rivers and streams bordered by *Picea abies* swamps and herb-rich mires abound. In summer, hundreds or thousands of visitors trek within the area daily.

Habitats Forest and woodland (60%), Wetland (30%; raised bog)
Land-use Tourism/recreation, Other

■ Birds

Species	Season	Year	Pop min	Pop max	Acc	Criteria
Cygnus cygnus Whooper Swan	B	1996	11	50	C	C2
[1] *Mergus albellus* Smew	B	1996	10	30	C	A3, B2, C2
Circus cyaneus Hen Harrier	B	1996	11	50	C	B2, C6
[2] *Buteo lagopus* Rough-legged Buzzard	B	1996	100	300	—	A3
Tetrao tetrix Black Grouse	R	1996	50	200	C	B2, C6
Tetrao urogallus Capercaillie	R	1996	500	2,000	C	C2
Grus grus Crane	B	1996	20	50	C	B2, C6
Charadrius morinellus Dotterel	B	1996	50	200	C	C2
Pluvialis apricaria Golden Plover	B	1996	1,000	5,000	C	B1i, B3, C2, C6
[2] *Calidris temminckii* Temminck's Stint	B	1996	100	300	—	A3
Limicola falcinellus Broad-billed Sandpiper	B	1996	300	1,000	C	A4i, B1i, B2, C3
Philomachus pugnax Ruff	B	1996	300	1,000	C	B3, C6
[1] *Lymnocryptes minimus* Jack Snipe	B	1996	100	300	C	A3, A4i, B1i, C3
[2] *Limosa lapponica* Bar-tailed Godwit	B	1996	11	50	C	A3
Numenius phaeopus Whimbrel	B	1996	500	2,000	C	A4i, B1i, B3, C3
[2] *Tringa erythropus* Spotted Redshank	B	1996	50	200	—	A3
[1] *Tringa nebularia* Greenshank	B	1996	200	500	—	A3
Tringa glareola Wood Sandpiper	B	1996	2,000	5,000	C	A4i, B1i, B2, C2, C6
[2] *Phalaropus lobatus* Red-necked Phalarope	B	1996	51	100	C	A3
[1] *Surnia ulula* Hawk Owl	B	1996	100	500	C	A3, C6
[1] *Strix nebulosa* Great Grey Owl	B	1996	11	50	C	A3, C6
Asio flammeus Short-eared Owl	B	1996	50	200	C	B2, C2, C6
Picoides tridactylus Three-toed Woodpecker	R	1996	500	2,000	C	B2, C2, C6
Anthus pratensis Meadow Pipit	B	1996	10,000	—	C	B3
[2] *Anthus cervinus* Red-throated Pipit	B	1996	30	100	—	A3
[1] *Bombycilla garrulus* Waxwing	B	1996	30	100	—	A3
Phoenicurus phoenicurus Redstart	B	1996	3,000	10,000	C	B2
[1] *Phylloscopus borealis* Arctic Warbler	B	1996	10	30	—	A3
[1] *Muscicapa striata* Spotted Flycatcher	B	1996	1,000	3,000	C	B2
[1] *Parus cinctus* Siberian Tit	R	1996	2,000	5,000	—	A3
[1] *Perisoreus infaustus* Siberian Jay	R	1996	500	2,000	C	A3, B2
[1] *Fringilla montifringilla* Brambling	B	1996	20,000	—	C	A3
[1] *Loxia leucoptera* Two-barred Crossbill	B	1996	50	5,000	C	A3
[1] *Loxia pytyopsittacus* Parrot Crossbill	B	1996	200	1,000	C	A3, B3
[1] *Pinicola enucleator* Pine Grosbeak	B	1996	400	1,200	—	A3
[2] *Plectrophenax nivalis* Snow Bunting	B	1996	100	300	—	A3
[1] *Emberiza rustica* Rustic Bunting	B	1996	500	1,500	—	A3

1. Boreal biome.
2. Arctic/tundra biome.

An exceptionally important area for Arctic and boreal avifauna. Breeding birds include seven out of the 32 species in Europe that are restricted to the Arctic/tundra biome (when breeding) and 14 out of the 15 species in Europe that are restricted to the boreal biome (when breeding).

■ Protection status
National High **International** High

30,029 ha of IBA covered by Wilderness Area (Kemihaara, 30,029 ha). 17,912 ha of IBA covered by Strict Nature Reserve (Sompio, 17,912 ha). 255,000 ha of IBA covered by National Park (Urho Kekkonen, 255,000 ha). 2,208 ha of IBA covered by Peatland Reserve (Uura-aapa, 2,208 ha). 3,296 ha of IBA covered by Peatland Reserve (Vaaranaapa, 3,296 ha). 901 ha of IBA covered by Peatland Reserve (Nalka-aapa, 901 ha). 309,553 ha of IBA covered by Special Protection Area (Urho Kekkosen kansallispuisto–Sompio–Kemihara).

■ **Conservation issues**

Threats Other (U)

Reindeer husbandry ('Other' land-use and threat) has caused some erosion of vegetation. The area is a candidate SAC.

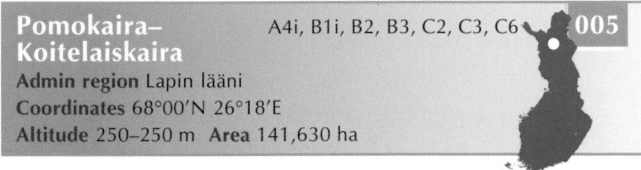

Pomokaira–Koitelaiskaira
A4i, B1i, B2, B3, C2, C3, C6 005
Admin region Lapin lääni
Coordinates 68°00′N 26°18′E
Altitude 250–250 m **Area** 141,630 ha

■ **Site description**
A large complex of boreal habitats south of the Porttipahta and Lokka reservoirs. The mires which dominate the landscape are typically large, wet, and hold a very rich avifauna. Islands of old coniferous forests and pure *Picea abies* forests (mostly over 200 years old) are scattered across the area, which is also traversed by hundreds of kilometres of rivers (the largest being the Kitinen river) and streams bordered by *Salix* bushes, forests, and grassy swamp-forests.

Habitats Forest and woodland (25%), Wetland (75%; raised bog)
Land-use Unknown

■ **Birds**

Species	Season	Year	Pop min	Pop max	Acc	Criteria
Cygnus cygnus Whooper Swan	B	1996	10	50	C	B2, C2, C6
Mergus albellus Smew	B	1996	10	50	C	B2, C2
Circus cyaneus Hen Harrier	B	1994	10	50	C	B2, C6
Grus grus Crane	B	1994	20	50	C	B2, C6
Limicola falcinellus Broad-billed Sandpiper	B	1994	400	1,000	C	A4i, B1i, B2, C3
Philomachus pugnax Ruff	B	1995	400	1,000	C	B3, C6
Numenius phaeopus Whimbrel	B	1994	100	300	C	B3
Tringa erythropus Spotted Redshank	B	1994	100	300	C	A4i, B1i, C3
Tringa glareola Wood Sandpiper	B	1994	2,000	5,000	C	A4i,B1i,B2,C2,C6
Phalaropus lobatus Red-necked Phalarope	B	1996	300	1,000	C	C2
Bubo bubo Eagle Owl	R	1996	5	10	C	B2, C6
Surnia ulula Hawk Owl	B	1994	50	200	C	C6
Strix nebulosa Great Grey Owl	B	1996	5	20	C	C6
Asio flammeus Short-eared Owl	B	1994	20	50	C	B2, C6
Picoides tridactylus Three-toed Woodpecker	R	1994	70	200	C	B2, C6
Anthus pratensis Meadow Pipit	B	1994	5,000	10,000	C	B3
Phoenicurus phoenicurus Redstart	B	1994	2,000	5,000	C	B2
Muscicapa striata Spotted Flycatcher	B	1994	1,000	3,000	C	B2
Ficedula hypoleuca Pied Flycatcher	B	1994	300	600	C	B3
Perisoreus infaustus Siberian Jay	R	1994	500	1,500	C	B2

An exceptionally important area for Arctic and boreal avifauna, especially for waders.

■ **Protection status**
National Partial **International** High
43,665 ha of IBA covered by Peatland Reserve (Pomokaira-Tenniöaapa, 43,665 ha). 34,400 ha of IBA covered by Ramsar Site (Koitelaiskaira, 34,400 ha). 141,532 ha of IBA covered by two Special Protection Areas (Pomokaira; Koitelainen).

■ **Conservation issues**

Threats Extraction industry (U)

The area has valuable ore deposits, which mining companies have staked claim to. These claims threaten the protection of the area. Part of the area is a candidate SAC.

Pallas and Ylläs fjelds
A3, B2, B3, C2, C6 006
Admin region Lapin lääni
Coordinates 68°04′N 24°04′E
Altitude 650–650 m **Area** 89,233 ha

■ **Site description**
A 100-km-long series of fjelds running from the settlement of Hetta in the north to Ylläs in the south. Here the Lapland fjelds meet the Lapland forests and consequently this is the northern or southern limit of distribution for many species of animals and plants. Tourists visit the area year-round; in winter skiing centres lure people to the area, and in summer hundreds or even thousands of people hike daily along the mountain tracks.

Habitats Forest and woodland (65%; native coniferous forest; mixed forest), Grassland (20%; tundra), Wetland (15%; raised bog)
Land-use Other, Tourism/recreation

■ **Birds**

Species	Season	Year	Pop min	Pop max	Acc	Criteria
Mergus albellus Smew	B	1996	1	10	C	A3
Charadrius morinellus Dotterel	B	1986	50	100	C	C2
Pluvialis apricaria Golden Plover	B	1986	500	—	C	B3, C6
Numenius phaeopus Whimbrel	B	1986	100	—	C	B3
Tringa nebularia Greenshank	B	1986	50	—	—	A3
Tringa glareola Wood Sandpiper	B	1986	400	—	C	B2
Surnia ulula Hawk Owl	B	1996	3	10	C	A3
Anthus pratensis Meadow Pipit	B	1986	2,000	—	C	B3
Bombycilla garrulus Waxwing	B	1986	20	50	—	A3
Phoenicurus phoenicurus Redstart	B	1986	2,000	—	C	B2
Muscicapa striata Spotted Flycatcher	B	1986	2,000	—	C	B2
Ficedula hypoleuca Pied Flycatcher	B	1986	500	—	C	B3
Parus cinctus Siberian Tit	R	1986	500	—	—	A3
Perisoreus infaustus Siberian Jay	R	1986	300	—	C	A3, B2
Fringilla montifringilla Brambling	B	1986	10,000	—	—	A3
Loxia leucoptera Two-barred Crossbill	B	1996	50	200	C	A3
Loxia pytyopsittacus Parrot Crossbill	B	1986	100	500	C	A3, B3
Pinicola enucleator Pine Grosbeak	B	1986	200	—	—	A3
Emberiza rustica Rustic Bunting	B	1986	500	500	—	A3

An important area for Arctic and boreal avifauna. Breeding birds include 11 out of the 15 species in Europe that are restricted to the boreal biome (when breeding).

■ **Protection status**
National Partial **International** None
50,912 ha of IBA covered by National Park (Pallas-Ounastunturi, 50,912 ha).

■ **Conservation issues**

Threats Other (U)

Reindeer husbandry ('Other' land-use and threat) has caused some erosion of vegetation. Part of the area is a candidate SAC.

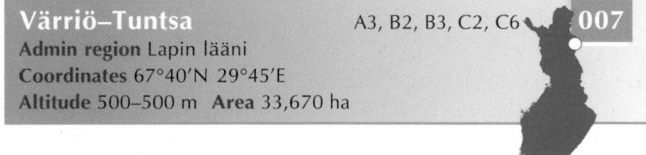

Värriö–Tuntsa
A3, B2, B3, C2, C6 007
Admin region Lapin lääni
Coordinates 67°40′N 29°45′E
Altitude 500–500 m **Area** 33,670 ha

■ **Site description**
A wilderness area comprising two adjacent mountainous conservation units in eastern Lapland: Värriö Strict Nature Reserve, and the Wilderness Area of Tuntsa which reaches the Russian border in the east. The landscape is dominated by low fjelds and high hills, with forested slopes, fertile river valleys and old, natural boreal forests between them. Due to the area's remoteness, human activity is minor.

Habitats Forest and woodland (65%), Grassland (25%; tundra), Wetland (10%; raised bog)
Land-use Tourism/recreation, Nature conservation/research

■ Birds

Species	Season	Year	Pop min	Pop max	Acc	Criteria
Cygnus cygnus Whooper Swan	B	1996	10	20	B	C2
Lymnocryptes minimus Jack Snipe	B	1996	5	10	C	A3
Numenius phaeopus Whimbrel	B	1996	50	100	C	B3
Tringa nebularia Greenshank	B	1996	5	10	—	A3
Surnia ulula Hawk Owl	B	1996	10	20	—	A3
Strix nebulosa Great Grey Owl	B	1996	10	20	C	A3, C6
Bombycilla garrulus Waxwing	B	1996	20	40	—	A3
Phylloscopus borealis Arctic Warbler	B	1996	5	10	—	A3
Parus cinctus Siberian Tit	R	1996	200	400	—	A3
Perisoreus infaustus Siberian Jay	R	1996	200	400	C	A3, B2
Fringilla montifringilla Brambling	B	1996	3,000	6,000	—	A3
Loxia leucoptera Two-barred Crossbill	B	1996	20	100	—	A3
Loxia pytyopsittacus Parrot Crossbill	B	1996	10	50	C	A3, B3
Pinicola enucleator Pine Grosbeak	B	1996	50	100	—	A3
Emberiza rustica Rustic Bunting	B	1996	50	100	—	A3

An important area for boreal avifauna. Breeding birds include 13 out of the 15 species in Europe that are restricted to the boreal biome (when breeding).

■ Protection status

National High **International** None
21,132 ha of IBA covered by Wilderness Area (Tuntsa, 21,132 ha). 12,508 ha of IBA covered by Strict Nature Reserve (Värriö, 12,508 ha).

■ Conservation issues

Threats Unknown

Part of the area is a candidate SAC.

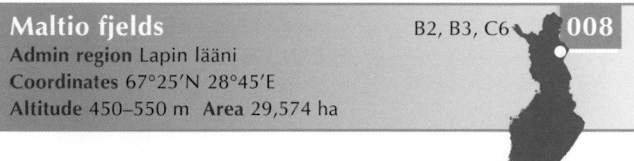

Maltio fjelds

B2, B3, C6   **008**

Admin region Lapin lääni
Coordinates 67°25'N 28°45'E
Altitude 450–550 m **Area** 29,574 ha

■ Site description

A wilderness area comprising three adjacent fjelds in central Lapland. The landscape is very diverse, supporting large aapa mires, natural and very old boreal forests, stony hill-slope forests, numerous streams with small valleys and treeless mountain heath.

Habitats Forest and woodland (75%), Grassland (15%; tundra), Wetland (10%; raised bog)
Land-use Unknown

■ Birds

Species	Season	Year	Pop min	Pop max	Acc	Criteria
Numenius phaeopus Whimbrel	B	1996	100	100	C	B3
Picoides tridactylus Three-toed Woodpecker	R	1996	50	50	C	B2, C6
Phoenicurus phoenicurus Redstart	B	1996	500	500	C	B2
Perisoreus infaustus Siberian Jay	R	1996	50	50	C	B2

An important area for boreal avifauna.

■ Protection status

National Partial **International** None
14,703 ha of IBA covered by Strict Nature Reserve (Maltio, 14,703 ha).

■ Conservation issues

Threats Unknown

The area is a candidate SAC.

South-eastern Kittilä mires

B2, C7   **009**

Admin region Lapin lääni
Coordinates 67°30'N 25°30'E
Altitude 220–220 m **Area** 21,035 ha

■ Site description

A large complex of adjacent mire conservation areas to the south-east of Kittilä settlement. The area supports aapa mires characteristic of the Peräpohjola zone. Old-growth forests with large numbers of both very old (over 200 years) and dead (both standing and fallen) trees are present.

Habitats Forest and woodland (25%), Wetland (75%; raised bog)
Land-use Unknown

■ Birds

Species	Season	Year	Pop min	Pop max	Acc	Criteria
Limicola falcinellus Broad-billed Sandpiper	B	1996	50	100	C	B2

An important area for boreal avifauna.

■ Protection status

National Partial **International** High
1,027 ha of IBA covered by Peatland Reserve (Mustaoja–Nunaravuoma, 1,044 ha). 7,225 ha of IBA covered by Peatland Reserve (Näätävuoma–Sotkavuoma, 7,264 ha). 2,350 ha of IBA covered by Peatland Reserve (Tollovuoma–Vasanvuoma, 2,366 ha). 1,628 ha of IBA covered by Peatland Reserve (Silmäsvuoma, 1,620 ha). 21,035 ha of IBA covered by Special Protection Area (Tollonvuoma–Silmäsvuoma–Nunarvuoma).

■ Conservation issues

Threats Unknown

The area is a candidate SAC.

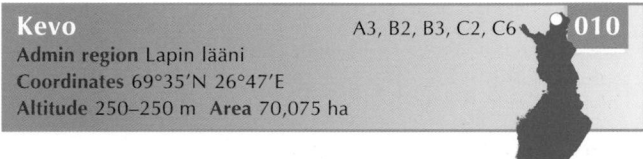

Kevo

A3, B2, B3, C2, C6   **010**

Admin region Lapin lääni
Coordinates 69°35'N 26°47'E
Altitude 250–250 m **Area** 70,075 ha

■ Site description

A very long, impressive, unique ridge valley in northern Lapland surrounded by large areas of subarctic forests. At the heart of the area is the long and shallow Kevojoki river, which runs through the Kevo canyon, considered to be one of the most remarkable geological formations in the country. Vast areas around the ridge valley are dominated by fjeld forests of birch *Betula*. Each summer, large numbers of tourists visit the area, especially the canyon.

Habitats Forest and woodland (80%), Wetland (15%; river/stream; raised bog), Rocky areas (5%)
Land-use Tourism/recreation

■ Birds

Species	Season	Year	Pop min	Pop max	Acc	Criteria
Aythya marila Scaup	B	1997	1	5	C	A3
Melanitta nigra Common Scoter	B	1997	1	5	C	A3
Buteo lagopus Rough-legged Buzzard	B	1997	—	50	C	A3
[1] *Pluvialis apricaria* Golden Plover	B	1996	1,000	3,000	C	B3, C2, C6
Calidris temminckii Temminck's Stint	B	1997	50	200	C	A3
Limosa lapponica Bar-tailed Godwit	B	1996	10	20	C	A3
[2] *Numenius phaeopus* Whimbrel	B	1997	50	200	C	B3
Tringa erythropus Spotted Redshank	B	1997	20	50	C	A3
[2] *Tringa glareola* Wood Sandpiper	B	1997	500	2,000	C	B2
Phalaropus lobatus Red-necked Phalarope	B	1996	10	20	C	A3
Stercorarius longicaudus Long-tailed Skua	B	1997	—	50	C	A3
[2] *Anthus pratensis* Meadow Pipit	B	1997	3,000	8,000	C	B3
Anthus cervinus Red-throated Pipit	B	1997	100	200	C	A3
Carduelis hornemanni Arctic Redpoll	B	1997	20	50	C	A3
Calcarius lapponicus Lapland Bunting	B	1997	300	1,000	C	A3
Plectrophenax nivalis Snow Bunting	B	1997	20	50	C	A3

1. 1985–1996.
2. 1985–1997.

The site supports a diverse Arctic avifauna. Breeding birds include 12 out of the 32 species in Europe that are restricted to the Arctic/tundra biome (when breeding).

■ **Protection status**
National High **International** None
70,075 ha of IBA covered by Strict Nature Reserve (Kevo, 70,175 ha).

■ **Conservation issues**

Threats	Unknown

Part of the area is a candidate SAC.

Luosto — A3 011

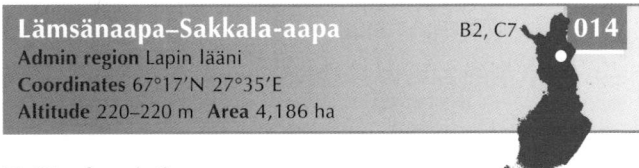

Admin region Lapin lääni
Coordinates 67°08′N 26°52′E
Altitude 450–450 m **Area** 7,989 ha

■ **Site description**
An important area of natural boreal forests, fjelds and peatland in the heart of Lapland. The forests are mostly natural tracts of old *Pinus sylvestris* and *Picea abies* trees. All types of mires found in the Peräpohjola zone are present, including forested, open herb-rich and -poor, twig-abundant and grass-dominated mires.

Habitats	Forest and woodland (70%), Wetland (30%; raised bog)
Land-use	Unknown

■ **Birds**

Species	Season	Year	Pop min	Pop max	Acc	Criteria
Lymnocryptes minimus Jack Snipe	B	1996	5	10	—	A3
Tringa nebularia Greenshank	B	1996	4	5	—	A3
Surnia ulula Hawk Owl	B	1996	6	10	C	A3
Bombycilla garrulus Waxwing	B	1996	1	11	C	A3
Phylloscopus borealis Arctic Warbler	B	1996	—	—	C	A3
Parus cinctus Siberian Tit	R	1996	20	50	—	A3
Perisoreus infaustus Siberian Jay	R	1996	20	50	—	A3
Fringilla montifringilla Brambling	B	1996	500	1,000	—	A3
Loxia leucoptera Two-barred Crossbill	B	1996	50	100	—	A3
Loxia pytyopsittacus Parrot Crossbill	B	1996	1	11	C	A3
Emberiza rustica Rustic Bunting	B	1996	100	200	—	A3

An important area for boreal avifauna. Breeding birds include 11 out of the 15 species in Europe that are restricted to the boreal biome (when breeding).

■ **Protection status**
National None **International** None

■ **Conservation issues**

Threats	Unknown

Part of the area is a candidate SAC.

Riisitunturi — B2, C6 012

Admin region Lapin lääni
Coordinates 66°14′N 28°32′E
Altitude 450–500 m **Area** 7,651 ha

■ **Site description**
A wilderness of natural boreal forests and diverse mire complexes north of Kitka lake. Old coniferous forests on the slopes of Riisitunturi fjeld (which reaches an altitude of 500 m) are characteristic of the area.

Habitats	Forest and woodland (50%), Wetland (50%; raised bog)
Land-use	Unknown

■ **Birds**
An important area for boreal avifauna.

Species	Season	Year	Pop min	Pop max	Acc	Criteria
¹ *Tetrao tetrix* Black Grouse	R	1986	75	75	C	B2, C6
Phoenicurus phoenicurus Redstart	B	1986	650	—	C	B2

Species ... continued		Season	Year	Pop min	Pop max	Acc	Criteria
Muscicapa striata Spotted Flycatcher		B	1986	1,000	—	C	B2
Perisoreus infaustus Siberian Jay		R	1986	55	55	C	B2

1. 1985–1986.

■ **Protection status**
National High **International** None
7,651 ha of IBA covered by National Park (Riisitunturi, 7,651 ha).

■ **Conservation issues**

Threats	Unknown

Part of the area is a candidate SAC.

Joutsenaapa–Kaita-aapa — B2, C6 013

Admin region Lapin lääni
Coordinates 67°05′N 28°38′E
Altitude 220–220 m **Area** 10,318 ha

■ **Site description**
An extensive area of aapa mire in central Lapland, close to the Russian border. The peatland is bisected by numerous rivers and rivulets, which are bordered by *Picea abies* swamps and mire meadows. Areas of coniferous boreal forests are relatively scarce.

Habitats	Forest and woodland (25%), Wetland (75%; raised bog)
Land-use	Unknown

■ **Birds**

Species	Season	Year	Pop min	Pop max	Acc	Criteria
Surnia ulula Hawk Owl	B	1995	10	100	C	C6
Perisoreus infaustus Siberian Jay	R	1995	50	100	C	B2

An important area for boreal avifauna.

■ **Protection status**
National Partial **International** Partial
10,318 ha of IBA covered by Peatland Reserve (Joutenaapa–Kaita-aapa, 10,318 ha). 10,235 ha of IBA covered by Special Protection Area (Joutsenaapa–Kaita-aapa).

■ **Conservation issues**

Threats	Unknown

Part of the area is a candidate SAC.

Lämsänaapa–Sakkala-aapa — B2, C7 014

Admin region Lapin lääni
Coordinates 67°17′N 27°35′E
Altitude 220–220 m **Area** 4,186 ha

■ **Site description**
An extensive area of raised bog along the Luiro river. The area belongs to the aapa mire zone of Peräpohjola and comprises many types of mires. Characteristic are large areas of open-water bogs with high ridges between them. The forests are mainly poor, *Pinus sylvestris*-dominated heath-forests, but flood forests and *Betula* forests also occur along rivers.

Habitats	Forest and woodland (15%), Wetland (85%; raised bog)
Land-use	Unknown

■ **Birds**

Species	Season	Year	Pop min	Pop max	Acc	Criteria
Tringa glareola Wood Sandpiper	B	1995	200	500	B	B2

An important area for boreal avifauna, especially for waders.

■ **Protection status**
National Partial **International** High

4,186 ha of IBA covered by Peatland Reserve (Lämsänaapa–Sakkala-aapa, 4,186 ha). 4,110 ha of IBA covered by Special Protection Area (Lämsänaapa–Sakkala-aapa).

■ **Conservation issues**

Threats Unknown

Part of the area is a candidate SAC.

Pöyrisvuoma mire protection area	B2, B3, C7	015

Admin region Lapin lääni
Coordinates 68°42′N 24°00′E
Altitude 450–450 m **Area** 4,270 ha

■ **Site description**

A large area of palsa mire, numerous lakes and ponds and small forested islands east of Pöyrisjärvi lake in northern Finland. The major Pöyrisjoki river traverses the area. Situated far from settlements and roads, the area experiences virtually no human impact.

Habitats Forest and woodland (15%), Wetland (85%; raised bog)
Land-use Not utilized

■ **Birds**

Species	Season	Year	Pop min	Pop max	Acc	Criteria
Limicola falcinellus	B	1994	50	50	C	B2
Broad-billed Sandpiper						
Tringa glareola Wood Sandpiper	B	1994	500	500	C	B2
Anthus pratensis Meadow Pipit	B	1994	1,000	—	C	B3

An important breeding area for Arctic peatland avifauna.

■ **Protection status**

National High **International** High
4,270 ha of IBA covered by Peatland Reserve (Pöyrisvuoma, 4,270 ha). 4,270 ha of IBA covered by Wilderness Area (Pöyrisjärvi, 127,797 ha). 4,270 ha of IBA covered by Special Protection Area (Pöyrisjärven erämaa).

■ **Conservation issues**

There are no known threats. The area is a candidate SAC.

Sammutinjänkä–Vaijoenjänkä	A3, B2, C7	016

Admin region Lapin lääni
Coordinates 69°25′N 27°30′E
Altitude 150–150 m **Area** 51,750 ha

■ **Site description**

Situated north of Inari lake, a complex of very large peatlands (belonging to the palsa mires typical of Fjeld-Lapland), separated by small areas of ridge forest (*Pinus sylvestris* and *Betula*). Many rivers, streams, lakes and ponds occur in the area, including the Vaijoki river. Due to its remoteness and wetness the area has remained mainly free of human activities.

Habitats Forest and woodland (35%), Wetland (65%; raised bog)
Land-use Not utilized

■ **Birds**

Species	Season	Year	Pop min	Pop max	Acc	Criteria
Anser erythropus	B	1996	—	—	—	A3
Lesser White-fronted Goose						
Aythya marila Scaup	B	1996	1	11	—	A3
Clangula hyemalis Long-tailed Duck	B	1996	1	11	—	A3
Melanitta nigra Common Scoter	B	1996	1	11	—	A3
Mergus albellus Smew	B	1996	6	10	B	B2
Calidris temminckii Temminck's Stint	B	1996	1	11	—	A3
Limosa lapponica Bar-tailed Godwit	B	1996	11	50	—	A3
Phalaropus lobatus	B	1996	11	50	—	A3
Red-necked Phalarope						
Anthus cervinus Red-throated Pipit	B	1996	1	11	—	A3
Calcarius lapponicus Lapland Bunting	B	1996	1	11	—	A3

An important area for Arctic avifauna. Breeding birds include nine out of the 32 species in Europe that are restricted to the Arctic/tundra biome (when breeding).

■ **Protection status**

National High **International** High
51,750 ha of IBA covered by Peatland Reserve (Sammuttijänkä–Vaijoenjänkä, 51,812 ha). 51,693 ha of IBA covered by Special Protection Area (Kaldoaivin erämaa).

■ **Conservation issues**

Threats Unknown

Part of the area is a candidate SAC.

Kemihaara (Vuotos) mires and forests	A3, B2, B3, C2, C6	017

Admin region Lapin lääni
Coordinates 67°05′N 27°42′E
Altitude 150–150 m **Area** 38,294 ha

■ **Site description**

A very large complex of aapa mires, riverside forests, herb-rich mires and forested hills and ridges on the upper course of the Kemi river. The heart of the area is the avifaunally rich Kokonaapa, a large, wet expanse of aapa mires, with numerous lakes and rivers. The site encompasses large areas of semi-natural and natural boreal forest.

Habitats Forest and woodland (55%; native coniferous forest; mixed forest; alluvial/very wet forest), Wetland (45%; raised bog)
Land-use Forestry (60%), Hunting (95%)

■ **Birds**

Species	Season	Year	Pop min	Pop max	Acc	Criteria
Cygnus cygnus Whooper Swan	B	1994	21	21	B	C2
Cygnus cygnus Whooper Swan	P	1994	80	80	C	B3, C6
Mergus albellus Smew	B	1994	64	64	B	A3, B2, C2
Circus cyaneus Hen Harrier	B	1994	32	32	B	B2, C6
Tetrao tetrix Black Grouse	R	1994	474	474	C	B2, C6
Grus grus Crane	B	1994	81	81	B	B2, C6
Limicola falcinellus	B	1996	76	76	B	B2
Broad-billed Sandpiper						
Philomachus pugnax Ruff	B	1994	335	335	B	B3, C6
Lymnocryptes minimus Jack Snipe	B	1994	76	76	—	A3
Tringa nebularia Greenshank	B	1994	70	70	—	A3
Tringa glareola Wood Sandpiper	B	1994	2,278	2,278	B	B2, C6
Surnia ulula Hawk Owl	B	1994	14	14	—	A3
Strix nebulosa Great Grey Owl	B	1994	6	6	—	A3
Picoides tridactylus	R	1994	54	54	C	B2, C6
Three-toed Woodpecker						
Riparia riparia Sand Martin	B	1994	800	800	C	B2
Anthus pratensis Meadow Pipit	B	1994	5,425	5,425	C	B3
Bombycilla garrulus Waxwing	B	1994	20	20	—	A3
Phylloscopus borealis Arctic Warbler	B	1994	7	7	—	A3
Muscicapa striata Spotted Flycatcher	B	1994	2,712	2,712	C	B2
Parus cinctus Siberian Tit	R	1994	746	746	—	A3
Perisoreus infaustus Siberian Jay	R	1994	204	204	C	A3, B2
Fringilla montifringilla Brambling	B	1994	8,000	8,000	—	A3
Loxia leucoptera Two-barred Crossbill	B	1994	1	1	—	A3
Loxia pytyopsittacus Parrot Crossbill	B	1994	41	41	C	A3, B3
Pinicola enucleator Pine Grosbeak	B	1994	7	7	—	A3
Emberiza rustica Rustic Bunting	B	1994	2,577	2,577	—	A3

An important area for boreal avifauna, especially for waders. Breeding birds include 14 out of the 15 species in Europe that are restricted to the boreal biome (when breeding).

■ **Protection status**

National None **International** None

■ **Conservation issues**

Threats Construction/impact of dyke/dam/barrage (A), Deforestation (commercial) (A), Dredging/canalization (A)

A state-owned energy company, Kemijoki Ltd, plans to construct a reservoir above Kokonaapa and its surroundings. Over the last 10 years nature-conservation organizations and conservationists have campaigned against this initiative and for the preservation of the area in its natural state due to its importance for birds, whilst also questioning the long-term profitability of the project. The Finnish government did not propose the area as a Natura 2000 site for political and economical reasons, in spite of its ornithological importance.

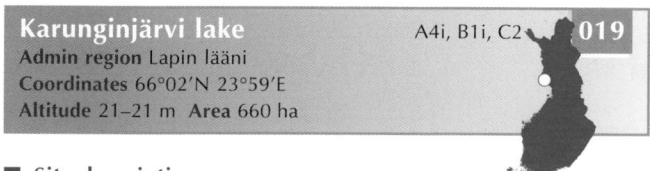

Runkaus–Saariaapa–Tainijärvet
A3, B2, B3, C6 018

Admin region Lapin lääni
Coordinates 66°03'N 25°40'E
Altitude 110–110 m **Area** 13,904 ha

■ Site description
A diverse complex of aapa mires and boreal forests with numerous lakes and ponds, located south of the lower course of the Kemi river. The forests are typically 150 years old and *Pinus-sylvestris*-dominated, with scattered very large aspens *Populus tremula*.

Habitats Forest and woodland (25%; native coniferous forest; alluvial/very wet forest), Wetland (75%; raised bog)
Land-use Forestry (5%), Hunting (50%), Unknown (45%)

■ Birds

Species	Season	Year	Pop min	Pop max	Acc	Criteria
Mergus albellus Smew	B	1995	6	10	B	A3, B2
Circus cyaneus Hen Harrier	B	1995	11	20	C	B2
Grus grus Crane	B	1995	21	50	B	B2, C6
Lymnocryptes minimus Jack Snipe	B	1995	11	20	—	A3
Tringa nebularia Greenshank	B	1995	51	100	—	A3
Tringa glareola Wood Sandpiper	B	1995	501	1,000	C	B2
Surnia ulula Hawk Owl	B	1995	3	5	—	A3
Strix nebulosa Great Grey Owl	B	1995	3	5	C	A3
Bombycilla garrulus Waxwing	B	1995	1	2	—	A3
Parus cinctus Siberian Tit	B	1997	1	2	—	A3
Perisoreus infaustus Siberian Jay	B	1995	3	5	—	A3
Fringilla montifringilla Brambling	B	1995	2,001	5,000	—	A3
Loxia pytyopsittacus Parrot Crossbill	B	1995	21	50	C	A3, B3
Emberiza rustica Rustic Bunting	B	1995	201	500	—	A3

An important area for boreal avifauna. Breeding birds include 11 out of the 15 species in Europe that are restricted to the boreal biome (when breeding).

■ Protection status
National Partial **International** None
7,030 ha of IBA covered by Strict Nature Reserve (Runkaus, 7,030 ha). 1,908 ha of IBA covered by Peatland Reserve (Saariaapa, 1,908 ha).

■ Conservation issues
Threats Deforestation (commercial) (B), Drainage (A)

Part of the area is a candidate SAC.

Karunginjärvi lake
A4i, B1i, C2 019

Admin region Lapin lääni
Coordinates 66°02'N 23°59'E
Altitude 21–21 m **Area** 660 ha

■ Site description
A 1-km-wide, quiet, lake-like section of the Tornio river, near its mouth.

Habitats Wetland (95%; river/stream), Rocky areas (5%; sea cliff/rocky shore)
Land-use Hunting (100%), Unknown (90%)

■ Birds

Species	Season	Year	Pop min	Pop max	Acc	Criteria
Cygnus cygnus Whooper Swan	P	1996	1,150	1,150	A	A4i, B1i, C2

One of the most important staging areas for *Cygnus cygnus* in Finland. The area is less important as a breeding ground, with only a small number of birds breeding on some herb-rich, bushy islands on the river.

■ Protection status
National None **International** None

■ Conservation issues
Threats Disturbance to birds (B)

Veittiaapa–Ristiaapa
B2, C7 020

Admin region Lapin lääni
Coordinates 65°48'N 25°27'E
Altitude 90–90 m **Area** 3,037 ha

■ Site description
A complex of four adjacent aapa mires, four lakes and 15 old coniferous boreal woodlands located just south of the lower course of the Simo river. The mires belong to the Pohjanmaa aapa mires, being characterized by muddy, wet bogs with low, grassy ridges between them.

Habitats Forest and woodland (15%; native coniferous forest; alluvial/very wet forest), Wetland (85%; standing fresh water; raised bog)
Land-use Hunting (100%)

■ Birds

Species	Season	Year	Pop min	Pop max	Acc	Criteria
Limicola falcinellus Broad-billed Sandpiper	B	1988	70	70	B	B2
Tringa glareola Wood Sandpiper	B	1988	240	240	B	B2

An important area for boreal avifauna.

■ Protection status
National High **International** High
2,386 ha of IBA covered by Peatland Reserve (Veittiaapa, 2,386 ha). 3,037 ha of IBA covered by Special Protection Area (Veittiaapa).

■ Conservation issues
Threats Disturbance to birds (C), Drainage (B)

The area is a candidate SAC.

Martimoaapa–Lumiaapa–Penikat
B2, B3, C6 021

Admin region Lapin lääni
Coordinates 65°50'N 25°10'E
Altitude 70–70 m **Area** 12,628 ha

■ Site description
A large complex of six adjacent mires just north of the Simo river. Practically all types of mires of the Kemi-Tornio region are represented. Kivalo, a 10-km-long series of hills, extends through the area, supporting old forests of *Pinus sylvestris* and *Picea abies*.

Habitats Forest and woodland (35%; native coniferous forest; alluvial/very wet forest), Wetland (60%; raised bog)
Land-use Hunting (90%)

■ Birds

Species	Season	Year	Pop min	Pop max	Acc	Criteria
Gavia stellata Red-throated Diver	B	1996	15	15	A	B2, C6
Tetrao tetrix Black Grouse	B	1987	51	100	B	B2, C6
Limicola falcinellus Broad-billed Sandpiper	B	1987	80	80	B	B2
Philomachus pugnax Ruff	B	1987	201	500	B	B3, C6
Tringa glareola Wood Sandpiper	B	1987	800	800	C	B2
Loxia pytyopsittacus Parrot Crossbill	B	1987	21	50	C	B3

An important area for Arctic and boreal avifauna, especially for waders. Species of global conservation concern that do not meet IBA criteria: *Haliaeetus albicilla* (max. 11 individuals, passage and wintering).

■ **Protection status**
National High **International** High
12,628 ha of IBA covered by Peatland Reserve (Martimoaapa–Lumiaapa–Penikat, 12,628 ha). 12,390 ha of IBA covered by Ramsar Site (Martimoaapa–Lumiaapa, 12,390 ha). 12,527 ha of IBA covered by Special Protection Area (Martimoaapa–Lumiaapa–Penikat).

■ **Conservation issues**

Threats Deforestation (commercial) (B), Disturbance to birds (A), Recreation/tourism (C)

Part of the area is a candidate SAC.

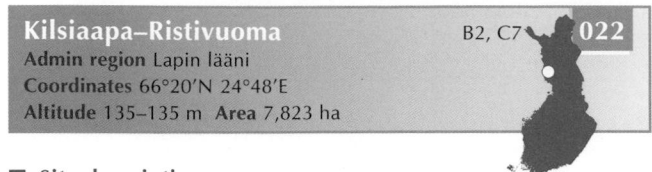

Kilsiaapa–Ristivuoma   B2, C7   022
Admin region Lapin lääni
Coordinates 66°20′N 24°48′E
Altitude 135–135 m **Area** 7,823 ha

■ **Site description**
A complex of five adjacent aapa mires lying between the lower courses of the Kemi and Tornio rivers. Wet bogs are most typical, but various kinds of mire are present ranging from poor fens to herb-rich grass swamps. Numerous stands of old coniferous forests are scattered amongst the mires. Lakes and rivers are scarce.

Habitats Forest and woodland (10%; mixed forest), Wetland (90%; standing fresh water; raised bog)
Land-use Forestry (5%), Hunting (100%)

■ **Birds**

Species	Season	Year	Pop min	Pop max	Acc	Criteria
Limicola falcinellus Broad-billed Sandpiper	B	1990	90	90	B	B2
Tringa glareola Wood Sandpiper	B	1990	501	1,000	B	B2

An important area for boreal avifauna.

■ **Protection status**
National Partial **International** High
7,823 ha of IBA covered by Peatland Reserve (Kilsiaapa–Ristivuoma, 7,823 ha). 7,744 ha of IBA covered by Special Protection Area (Kilsiaapa–Ristivuoma).

■ **Conservation issues**

Threats Deforestation (commercial) (B), Disturbance to birds (C)

Part of the area is a candidate SAC.

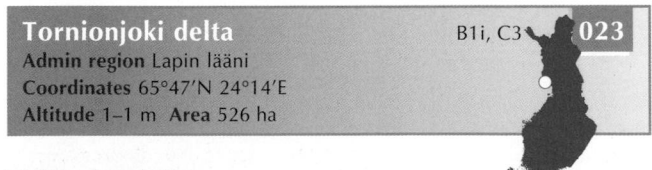

Tornionjoki delta   B1i, C3   023
Admin region Lapin lääni
Coordinates 65°47′N 24°14′E
Altitude 1–1 m **Area** 526 ha

■ **Site description**
The Tornio river delta encompasses forested islands, rocky islets, shoreline vegetation and brackish water.

Habitats Wetland (95%; coastal lagoon), Rocky areas (5%; sea cliff/rocky shore)
Land-use Hunting (100%), Urban/industrial/transport (70%)

■ **Birds**

Species	Season	Year	Pop min	Pop max	Acc	Criteria
Mergus merganser Goosander	P	1992	1,001	2,000	B	B1i, C3

An important staging area in spring for *Mergus merganser*. Additionally, it is perhaps the best area for moulting wildfowl in the Lappi district.

■ **Protection status**
National None **International** Partial
444 ha of IBA covered by Special Protection Area (Pajukari–Uksei–Alkunkarinlahti).

■ **Conservation issues**

Threats Disturbance to birds (B), Extraction industry (B), Industrialization/urbanization (B)

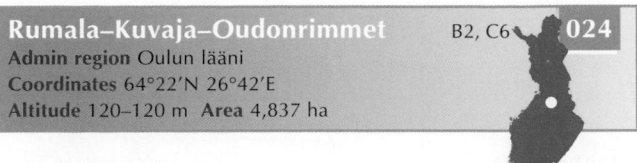

Rumala–Kuvaja–Oudonrimmet   B2, C6   024
Admin region Oulun lääni
Coordinates 64°22′N 26°42′E
Altitude 120–120 m **Area** 4,837 ha

■ **Site description**
A large complex of aapa mires and raised bogs on the western side of Oulujärvi lake. The landscape is dominated by wet, low-ridged mires with numerous pools in the centre and drier sedge mires and forested fens towards the edges.

Habitats Wetland (100%; raised bog)
Land-use Unknown

■ **Birds**

Species	Season	Year	Pop min	Pop max	Acc	Criteria
Gavia stellata Red-throated Diver	B	1997	19	21	A	B2, C6

Probably the most important breeding area of *Gavia stellata* in the country. Also an important breeding site for many other peatland birds.

■ **Protection status**
National Partial **International** High
2,767 ha of IBA covered by Peatland Reserve (Rumala–Kuvaja–Oudonrimmet, 2,767 ha). 4,837 ha of IBA covered by Special Protection Area (Rumala–Kuvaja–Oudonrimmet).

■ **Conservation issues**

Threats Drainage (A)

Part of the area is a candidate SAC.

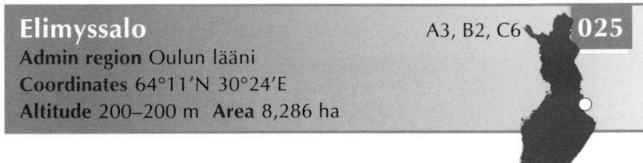

Elimyssalo   A3, B2, C6   025
Admin region Oulun lääni
Coordinates 64°11′N 30°24′E
Altitude 200–200 m **Area** 8,286 ha

■ **Site description**
A large wilderness of boreal forests and mires east of Kuhmo and adjacent to the Russian border. The main features are numerous hills with old coniferous and mixed forest, large mire complexes and riverside forests. A sizeable part of all 'old' forests (more than 150 years) remaining in the Kainuu region exist here, and forests aged over 200 years are not uncommon.

Habitats Forest and woodland (48%), Wetland (52%; standing fresh water; raised bog)
Land-use Unknown

■ **Birds**

Species	Season	Year	Pop min	Pop max	Acc	Criteria
Podiceps auritus Slavonian Grebe	B	1993	1	3	—	A3
Mergus albellus Smew	B	1996	1	5	—	A3
Tetrao tetrix Black Grouse	R	1993	51	100	C	B2, C6
Tringa nebularia Greenshank	B	1993	11	50	—	A3
Surnia ulula Hawk Owl	B	1993	1	5	—	A3
Strix nebulosa Great Grey Owl	B	1993	1	5	—	A3
Picoides tridactylus Three-toed Woodpecker	R	1993	51	100	C	B2, C6
Bombycilla garrulus Waxwing	B	1993	11	50	—	A3
Phylloscopus borealis Arctic Warbler	B	1993	1	5	—	A3
Parus cinctus Siberian Tit	R	1993	11	50	—	A3
Perisoreus infaustus Siberian Jay	R	1993	51	100	C	A3, B2
Fringilla montifringilla Brambling	B	1993	501	1,000	—	A3
Loxia leucoptera Two-barred Crossbill	B	1993	11	50	—	A3
Loxia pytyopsittacus Parrot Crossbill	B	1993	6	10	—	A3
Emberiza rustica Rustic Bunting	B	1993	251	500	—	A3

An important breeding area for boreal avifauna. Breeding birds include 13 out of the 15 species in Europe that are restricted to the boreal biome (when breeding). The only known regular breeding area of *Milvus migrans* (1–5 pairs) in the country.

■ **Protection status**
National Partial **International** None
7,248 ha of IBA covered by Specific Protection Area (Elimyssalo, 7,248 ha).

■ **Conservation issues**

Threats Unknown

The area is a candidate SAC.

Juortanansalo   B2, C6   **026**
Admin region Oulun lääni
Coordinates 64°34′N 29°50′E
Altitude 200–200 m **Area** 5,454 ha

■ **Site description**
A large area of boreal forest and mire east of Oulujärvi lake, and adjacent to the Russian border. Most of the forests are old and coniferous, and in some areas largely untouched by man. The peatlands are dominated by poor, at least partly forested, twig fens, although areas of more fertile mires and swamp bogs are also present. Numerous lakes, ponds and streams are scattered throughout the area.

Habitats Forest and woodland (30%), Wetland (70%; standing fresh water; raised bog)
Land-use Unknown

■ **Birds**

Species	Season	Year	Pop min	Pop max	Acc	Criteria
[1] *Bubo bubo* Eagle Owl	R	1996	4	6	C	B2, C6
Strix nebulosa Great Grey Owl	B	1996	9	13	C	C6
Perisoreus infaustus Siberian Jay	R	1996	68	115	C	B2

1. 1992–1996.

An important breeding area for boreal avifauna.

■ **Protection status**
National Partial **International** None
3,810 ha of IBA covered by Specific Protection Area (Juortanansalo–Lapinsuo, 3,810 ha).

■ **Conservation issues**

Threats Unknown

The area is a candidate SAC.

Krunnit archipelago   A4i, B1i, B2, B3,   **027**
Admin region Oulun lääni   C2, C3, C6
Coordinates 65°23′N 24°55′E
Altitude 0–0 m **Area** 4,579 ha

■ **Site description**
A group of islands in the Bay of Bothnia. The oldest islands are heavily forested, the youngest (more recently formed by continued land uplift) are sandy or swampy with scattered stones. Human impact is minor.

Habitats Marine areas (80%; sea inlet/coastal features), Rocky areas (15%; rock stacks/islets), Forest and woodland (5%)
Land-use Not utilized

■ **Birds**
The most important group of islands for birds in the Bay of Bothnia. The numbers of *Larus fuscus fuscus*, *L. marinus*, *Sterna caspia* (50 pairs, 120 birds in spring and 250 birds in autumn) and *Alca torda* are probably the most significant. The area is also one of the most important staging areas for moulting *Anser anser* (1,200 birds) in the country. Species of global conservation concern that do not meet IBA

criteria: *Polysticta stelleri* (non-breeding), *Haliaeetus albicilla* (max. 3 birds, passage).

Species	Season	Year	Pop min	Pop max	Acc	Criteria
[1] *Mergus merganser* Goosander	P	1997	2,000	2,000	B	B1i, C3
[1,2] *Larus fuscus* Lesser Black-backed Gull	B	1997	170	170	A	B3
[1] *Sterna caspia* Caspian Tern	B	1997	50	60	A	A4i,B1i,B2,C2,C6

1. 1992–1997.
2. *Larus fuscus fuscus*.

■ **Protection status**
National High **International** High
4,434 ha of IBA covered by Protected Area on Private Land (Krunnit, 4,441 ha). 4,319 ha of IBA covered by Ramsar Site (Krunnit, 4,319 ha). 4,443 ha of IBA covered by Special Protection Area (Perämeren saaret).

■ **Conservation issues**

Threats Unknown

Part of the area is a candidate SAC.

Oulu region wetlands   A1, A4i, B1i, B2, B3, **028**
Admin region Oulun lääni   C1, C2, C3, C6
Coordinates 64°55′N 25°10′E
Altitude 0–0 m **Area** 81,781 ha

■ **Site description**
A very large and diverse wetland complex, including sea bays, archipelago and farmland, in the vicinity of Oulu city. The site comprises extensive coastal meadows, early successional young deciduous forests, dry meadows, cattle-grazed farmland, sand beaches, sand-dunes, lagoons and inhabited areas.

Habitats Wetland (70%; coastal lagoon), Artificial landscape (20%), Forest and woodland (5%), Unknown (5%)
Land-use Agriculture (20%), Hunting (80%), Nature conservation/research (20%), Tourism/recreation (10%), Urban/industrial/transport (10%)

■ **Birds**

Species	Season	Year	Pop min	Pop max	Acc	Criteria
[1] *Botaurus stellaris* Bittern	B	1997	8	12	B	B2, C6
[1] *Anser fabalis* Bean Goose	P	1997	20,000	20,000	C	A4i, B1i, C3
[1] *Anser erythropus* Lesser White-fronted Goose	P	1997	50	50	A	A1, C1
[1] *Anser anser* Greylag Goose	B	1997	450	480	C	B1i, C3
[1] *Anser anser* Greylag Goose	P	1997	3,500	3,500	B	A4i, B1i, C3
[1] *Anas penelope* Wigeon	P	1997	50,000	—	C	A4i, B1i, C3
[1] *Anas crecca* Teal	P	1997	50,000	50,000	C	A4i, B1i, C3
[1] *Anas acuta* Pintail	B	1997	300	350	B	B1i, B2, C3
[1] *Anas acuta* Pintail	P	1997	15,000	15,000	C	A4i, B1i, C3
[1] *Aythya fuligula* Tufted Duck	P	1997	50,000	50,000	C	A4i, B1i, C3
[1] *Bucephala clangula* Goldeneye	P	1997	30,000	30,000	C	A4i, B1i, C3
[1] *Mergus albellus* Smew	P	1997	1,000	1,000	C	A4i, B1i, C2
[1] *Mergus serrator* Red-breasted Merganser	B	1997	600	650	C	A4i, B1i, C3
[1] *Mergus serrator* Red-breasted Merganser	P	1997	15,000	15,000	C	A4i, B1i, C3
[1] *Mergus merganser* Goosander	P	1997	20,000	20,000	C	A4i, B1i, C3
[1] *Haliaeetus albicilla* White-tailed Eagle	P	1997	30	30	B	A1, C1
[1] *Circus cyaneus* Hen Harrier	B	1997	10	40	C	B2
[1] *Porzana porzana* Spotted Crake	B	1997	10	30	C	B3, C6
[1] *Grus grus* Crane	B	1997	40	50	C	B2, C6
[1] *Grus grus* Crane	P	1997	3,000	3,000	B	A4i, B1i, C2
[1] *Calidris minuta* Little Stint	P	1997	10,000	10,000	C	A4i, B1i, C3
[1] *Limicola falcinellus* Broad-billed Sandpiper	P	1997	3,000	3,000	B	A4i, B1i, C3
[1] *Philomachus pugnax* Ruff	B	1997	700	750	C	B3, C6
[1] *Philomachus pugnax* Ruff	P	1997	50,000	50,000	C	A4i, B1i, C2
[1] *Tringa erythropus* Spotted Redshank	P	1997	7,000	7,000	B	A4i, B1i, C3
[1] *Tringa totanus* Redshank	B	1997	790	850	C	B1i, B2, C3
[1] *Tringa totanus* Redshank	P	1997	5,000	5,000	C	A4i, B1i, C3
[1] *Tringa nebularia* Greenshank	P	1997	3,000	—	C	A4i, B1i, C3
[1] *Tringa glareola* Wood Sandpiper	B	1997	200	250	C	B2
[1] *Tringa glareola* Wood Sandpiper	P	1997	40,000	40,000	C	A4i, B1i, C2
[1] *Larus minutus* Little Gull	B	1997	400	500	B	A4i, B1i, B2, C3
[1] *Larus minutus* Little Gull	P	1997	3,000	3,000	C	A4i, B1i, C3
[1] *Larus canus* Common Gull	B	1997	1,200	1,300	C	B2

Species ...continued	Season	Year	Pop min	Pop max	Acc	Criteria
[1] *Sterna caspia* Caspian Tern	P	1997	200	—	C	A4i, B1i, C2
[1] *Asio flammeus* Short-eared Owl	B	1997	25	70	C	B2, C6
[1] *Acrocephalus schoenobaenus* Sedge Warbler	B	1997	10,000	—	C	B3

1. 1992–1997.

A uniquely important breeding and staging area for numerous species. A very high proportion of the populations of many northern species stage on the area.

■ Protection status
National Low **International** Partial
764 ha of IBA covered by Private Protection Area (Isomatala–Maasyvä, 764 ha). 128 ha of IBA covered by Protected Area on Private Land (Tauvo, 128 ha). 20,684 ha of IBA covered by six Special Protection Areas (Isomatala–Maasyvänlahti; Liminganlahti; Kempeleenlahden ranta; Akionlahti; Säärenperä ja Karinkannanmata; Siikajoen lintuvedet ja suot).

■ Conservation issues

Threats Abandonment/reduction of land management (C), Afforestation (C), Disturbance to birds (B)

Human impact has detrimentally affected the area, resulting in nutrient pollution of water areas and overgrowth of wetlands and meadows. Conversely, active cultivation of farmland has benefited birds, creating large feeding grounds, especially for geese and cranes. Hunting pressure is very heavy in autumn, when hundreds or thousands of hunters gather here for wildfowling; hunting is prohibited in small parts of the area only. There are several birdwatching towers and wooden trails at Liminganlahti. At Tauvo, on the mouth of the Siikajoki river, a bird observatory has been maintained for many years, where ringing and migration observation are the main activities. Part of the area is a candidate SAC.

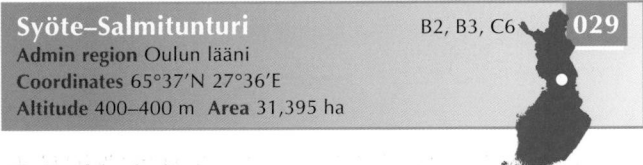

Syöte–Salmitunturi
B2, B3, C6 · 029
Admin region Oulun lääni
Coordinates 65°37′N 27°36′E
Altitude 400–400 m **Area** 31,395 ha

■ Site description
One of the most important areas of boreal forest in the Pohjanmaa region. A 25-km chain of boreal forests lies at the core of the site, with additional forests extending eastwards. The landscape is hilly, with one peak reaching a height of 431 m. The forests are dominated by *Picea*, but deciduous forests cover the lower parts of the hills.

Habitats Forest and woodland (70%), Wetland (30%; raised bog)
Land-use Forestry, Hunting, Tourism/recreation

■ Birds

Species	Season	Year	Pop min	Pop max	Acc	Criteria
[1] *Tetrao tetrix* Black Grouse	R	1997	101	200	C	B2, C6
[2] *Tringa glareola* Wood Sandpiper	B	1997	201	500	C	B2
Picoides tridactylus Three-toed Woodpecker	R	1997	51	100	C	B2, C6
[2] *Phoenicurus phoenicurus* Redstart	B	1997	501	1,000	C	B2
[1] *Muscicapa striata* Spotted Flycatcher	B	1997	2,001	5,000	C	B2
[1] *Perisoreus infaustus* Siberian Jay	R	1997	101	200	C	B2
[1] *Loxia pytyopsittacus* Parrot Crossbill	B	1997	21	50	C	B3

1. 1992–1997.
2. 1994–1997.

An important breeding area for boreal avifauna including *Picoides tridactylus* and also *Tetrao urogallus* (500–1,000 pairs), *Tarsiger cyanurus* (5–15 males), *Perisoreus infaustus* (100–200 pairs), *Parus cinctus* (50–100 pairs) and *Pinicola enucleator* (100–200 pairs).

■ Protection status
National Partial **International** High
5,720 ha of IBA covered by Specific Protection Area (Jaaskamonvaara, 5,755 ha). 46 ha of IBA covered by Protected Area on Private Land (Latvakouva, 46 ha). 31,395 ha of IBA covered by Special Protection Area (Syöte).

■ Conservation issues

Threats Disturbance to birds (B), Recreation/tourism (B)

The area is a candidate SAC.

Oulanka–Sukerijärvi
A3, B2, B3, C2, C6 · 030
Admin region Oulun lääni
Coordinates 66°24′N 29°12′E
Altitude 400–400 m **Area** 29,972 ha

■ Site description
A mosaic of hills, boreal forests and mires lying along the boundary between Oulu and Lappi districts, adjacent to the Russian border. Forested slopes and hills dominate the southern part of the Oulanka National Park, which covers much of the site, whilst the central part holds large areas of old-growth forest, and well-developed aapa mires are typical of the north. Limestone cliffs and numerous rivers and streams increase the diversity of the landscape. Sukerijärvi supports mesotrophic marshy mires interspersed with small islands of *Picea abies* forests.

Habitats Forest and woodland (35%), Wetland (65%; raised bog)
Land-use Tourism/recreation

■ Birds

Species	Season	Year	Pop min	Pop max	Acc	Criteria
Mergus albellus Smew	B	1996	10	20	B	A3, C2
[1] *Tetrao tetrix* Black Grouse	R	1995	50	100	C	B2, C6
[1] *Lymnocryptes minimus* Jack Snipe	B	1995	5	10	—	A3
[1] *Tringa nebularia* Greenshank	B	1995	40	55	—	A3
Tringa glareola Wood Sandpiper	B	1995	500	1,000	C	B2
Bubo bubo Eagle Owl	R	1995	5	7	—	B2, C6
[1] *Surnia ulula* Hawk Owl	B	1995	10	20	—	A3
[1] *Strix nebulosa* Great Grey Owl	B	1995	4	6	—	A3
Picoides tridactylus Three-toed Woodpecker	R	1995	100	200	C	B2, C6
[1] *Bombycilla garrulus* Waxwing	B	1995	20	40	—	A3
[1] *Phoenicurus phoenicurus* Redstart	B	1995	1,000	2,000	C	B2
[1] *Phylloscopus borealis* Arctic Warbler	B	1995	1	2	—	A3
[1] *Ficedula hypoleuca* Pied Flycatcher	B	1995	500	1,000	C	B3
[1] *Parus cinctus* Siberian Tit	R	1995	200	400	—	A3
[1] *Perisoreus infaustus* Siberian Jay	R	1995	100	200	C	A3, B2
[1] *Fringilla montifringilla* Brambling	B	1995	5,000	10,000	—	A3
[1] *Loxia leucoptera* Two-barred Crossbill	B	1995	50	100	—	A3
[1] *Loxia pytyopsittacus* Parrot Crossbill	B	1995	50	100	C	A3, B3
[1] *Pinicola enucleator* Pine Grosbeak	B	1995	10	20	—	A3
[1] *Emberiza rustica* Rustic Bunting	B	1995	1,000	1,500	—	A3

1. 1994–1995.

An important breeding area for boreal avifauna. Breeding birds include 14 out of the 15 species in Europe that are restricted to the boreal biome (when breeding).

■ Protection status
National High **International** High
27,893 ha of IBA covered by National Park (Oulanka, 27,893 ha). 2,079 ha of IBA covered by Strict Nature Reserve (Sukerijärvi, 2,079 ha). 29,867 ha of IBA covered by Special Protection Area (Oulanka).

■ Conservation issues

Threats Unknown

Part of the area is a candidate SAC.

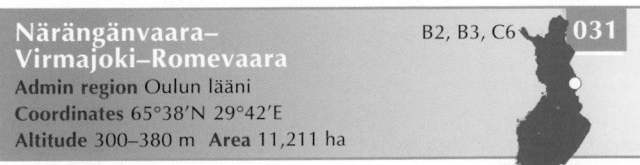

Närängänvaara–Virmajoki–Romevaara
B2, B3, C6 · 031
Admin region Oulun lääni
Coordinates 65°38′N 29°42′E
Altitude 300–380 m **Area** 11,211 ha

■ Site description
Several adjacent areas of boreal forest and mire in southernmost Kuusamo. This is one of the most important areas of old-growth forest in Finland, and its value is increased by its location adjacent to large, intact forest areas in Russia. Standing and fallen dead trees and

400–500 year-old living trees are not uncommon. Aapa mires are also representative, with herb-rich slope swamps and a multitude of natural springs. Barren, natural *Pinus sylvestris* heaths are the most typical feature of the landscape. The IBA has remained largely natural, and current human impact is minor.

Habitats Forest and woodland (60%), Wetland (40%; raised bog)
Land-use Not utilized

■ Birds

Species	Season	Year	Pop min	Pop max	Acc	Criteria
[1] *Tringa glareola* Wood Sandpiper	B	1995	250	350	C	B2
[1] *Picoides tridactylus* Three-toed Woodpecker	R	1995	100	160	C	B2, C6
Phoenicurus phoenicurus Redstart	B	1994	550	800	C	B2
Muscicapa striata Spotted Flycatcher	B	1995	1,200	2,100	C	B2
Loxia pytyopsittacus Parrot Crossbill	B	1995	100	300	C	B3

1. 1993–1995.

An important breeding area for boreal avifauna.

■ Protection status
National None **International** High
11,211 ha of IBA covered by Special Protection Area (Etelä–Kuusamon vanhat metsät).

■ Conservation issues

Threats Unknown

The area is a candidate SAC.

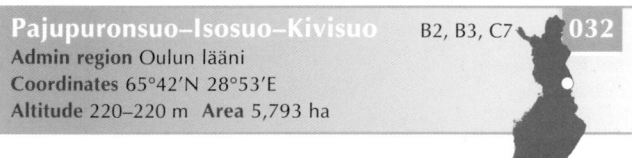

Pajupuronsuo–Isosuo–Kivisuo   B2, B3, C7   032
Admin region Oulun lääni
Coordinates 65°42′N 28°53′E
Altitude 220–220 m **Area** 5,793 ha

■ Site description
A mosaic of aapa mires and old-growth forests, with numerous lakes, ponds and rivers in southern Kuusamo. The forests hold very old trees and large amounts of both standing and fallen dead wood. The area has mostly remained untouched by human activities.

Habitats Forest and woodland (55%), Wetland (45%; raised bog)
Land-use Not utilized

■ Birds

Species	Season	Year	Pop min	Pop max	Acc	Criteria
Perisoreus infaustus Siberian Jay	R	1995	50	100	B	B2
[1] *Loxia pytyopsittacus* Parrot Crossbill	B	1995	40	70	B	B3

1. 1993–1995.

An important breeding area for boreal birds.

■ Protection status
National Partial **International** High
1,356 ha of IBA covered by Peatland Reserve (Isosuo–Kivisuo, 1,356 ha). 5,793 ha of IBA covered by 2 Special Protection Areas (Isosuo–Kivisuo; Etelä–Kuusamon vanhat metsät).

■ Conservation issues

Threats Unknown

The area is a candidate SAC.

Haapavesi wetlands   A4i, B1i, B2, C2, C3   033
Admin region Oulun lääni
Coordinates 64°13′N 25°23′E
Altitude 70–70 m **Area** 2,500 ha

■ Site description
A group of adjacent shallow lakes in the central part of north Pohjanmaa district. The lakes are nutrient-rich, partly resulting from nutrient input from melting snow and rivers. *Equisetum* and *Phragmites* dominate the vegetation, whilst the lakes are bordered by open mires, *Betula* and *Pinus sylvestris* fens, and mixed forests.

Habitats Forest and woodland (5%; broadleaved deciduous forest), Wetland (95%; raised bog)
Land-use Forestry (10%), Hunting (90%)

■ Birds

Species	Season	Year	Pop min	Pop max	Acc	Criteria
[1] *Cygnus cygnus* Whooper Swan	P	1995	800	1,200	A	A4i, B1i, C2
Larus minutus Little Gull	B	1995	79	79	A	B2
Larus minutus Little Gull	P	1995	500	800	B	A4i, B1i, C3

1. 1993–1995.

An important staging area for waterbirds, especially for *Cygnus cygnus* and also *Tringa glareola* (2,500 birds, spring) and *Larus minutus* (500–800 birds, spring).

■ Protection status
National None **International** Partial
1,574 ha of IBA covered by Special Protection Area (Haapaveden lintuvedet ja suot).

■ Conservation issues

Threats Abandonment/reduction of land management (B), Disturbance to birds (B)

Fishing causes some disturbance in spring, and hunting is heavy in autumn when as many as 500–700 hunters gather each day in the area. Overgrowth of the wetland is a threat. Part of the area is a candidate SAC.

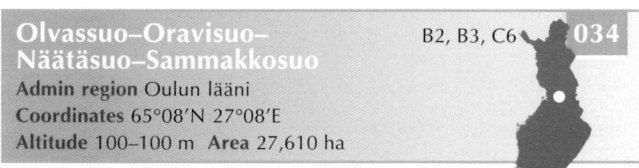

Olvassuo–Oravisuo–Näätäsuo–Sammakkosuo   B2, B3, C6   034
Admin region Oulun lääni
Coordinates 65°08′N 27°08′E
Altitude 100–100 m **Area** 27,610 ha

■ Site description
A large wilderness area between the upper courses of the Iijoki and Kiiminkijoki rivers, with well-developed aapa mires and a multitude of streams and rivulets. Interspersed amongst the peatlands are small islands of mostly primeval boreal forest containing large amounts of dead wood. The area remains predominantly free of human activity.

Habitats Forest and woodland (20%; native coniferous forest), Wetland (80%; raised bog)
Land-use Unknown

■ Birds

Species	Season	Year	Pop min	Pop max	Acc	Criteria
Grus grus Crane	B	1996	11	50	C	B2, C6
Tringa glareola Wood Sandpiper	B	1996	501	1,000	C	B2
Asio flammeus Short-eared Owl	B	1996	11	50	C	B2, C6
Phoenicurus phoenicurus Redstart	B	1996	501	1,000	C	B2
Loxia pytyopsittacus Parrot Crossbill	B	1996	51	100	C	B3

An important breeding area for boreal avifauna, and one of the best breeding sites in Finland for large, shy species such as *Cygnus cygnus*, *Anser fabalis* and *Grus grus*.

■ Protection status
National Partial **International** High
5,980 ha of IBA covered by Strict Nature Reserve (Olvassuo, 5,980 ha). 8,483 ha of IBA covered by Peatland Reserves (Leväsuo–Kärppäsuo, 2,191 ha, Oravisuo–Näätäsuo–Sammakkosuo, 6,327 ha). 27,610 ha of IBA covered by Special Protection Area (Olvassuo).

■ Conservation issues

Threats Unknown

The area is a candidate SAC.

Valtavaara–Pyhävaara   C7   035
Admin region Oulun lääni
Coordinates 66°10'N 29°12'E
Altitude 400–400 m   **Area** 810 ha

■ Site description
Higher elevation *Picea abies* forests in the heart of Kuusamo. Sloping bogs and herb-rich mires are concentrated in the lower parts of the area.

Habitats Forest and woodland (95%)
Land-use Unknown

■ Birds
An important breeding area for boreal avifauna. Also the most traditional site to observe *Tarsiger cyanurus* in Finland.

■ Protection status
National High   **International** High
810 ha of IBA covered by Specific Protection Area (Valtavaara–Pyhäraara, 810 ha). 808 ha of IBA covered by Special Protection Area (Valtavaara–Pyhavaara).

■ Conservation issues

Threats Unknown

The area is a candidate SAC.

Kitka lake   B1i, B2, C2, C6   036
Admin region Oulun lääni
Coordinates 66°09'N 28°42'E
Altitude 220–220 m   **Area** 12,516 ha

■ Site description
A shallow lake, over 9,000 years old, in the heart of Kuusamo. The lake is barren, with sandy and stony shorelines, clear waters and sparse vegetation. The lake holds numerous islands, most of them small, treeless and rocky while the largest are forested and commercially managed. This is one of the only large lakes in Finland where the water-level is not artificially manipulated. Hundreds of summer cottages surround the lake.

Habitats Wetland (90%; standing fresh water), Unknown (10%)
Land-use Unknown

■ Birds

Species	Season	Year	Pop min	Pop max	Acc	Criteria
Gavia arctica Black-throated Diver	B	1996	51	100	B	B2, C6
Mergus albellus Smew	B	1996	51	100	B	B1i, B2, C2

One of the most important breeding areas for *Gavia arctica* and *Mergus albellus* in the country.

■ Protection status
National None   **International** High
12,516 ha of IBA covered by Special Protection Area (Kitka).

■ Conservation issues

Threats Unknown

The area is a candidate SAC.

Litokaira   A3, A4i, B1i, B2, B3, C2, C3, C6   037
Admin region Oulun lääni
Coordinates 65°45'N 26°17'E
Altitude 135–135 m   **Area** 30,405 ha

■ Site description
A large wilderness area lying between the Simo and Siruanjoki rivers with extensive northern aapa mires. The mires are divided by several rivers, lakes and forested 'islands', the latter typically holding very old coniferous trees and large quantities of dead wood. The importance of the site as an old-growth forest reserve is notable, especially as it is surrounded by intensively managed commercial forests.

Habitats Forest and woodland (30%; native coniferous forest; mixed forest), Wetland (70%; standing fresh water; raised bog)
Land-use Unknown

■ Birds

Species	Season	Year	Pop min	Pop max	Acc	Criteria
Gavia stellata Red-throated Diver	B	1996	11	50	B	B2, C2, C6
Mergus albellus Smew	B	1996	6	10	—	A3
Circus cyaneus Hen Harrier	B	1996	11	50	C	B2
Tetrao tetrix Black Grouse	R	1996	101	500	C	B2, C6
Grus grus Crane	B	1996	51	100	C	B1i, B2, C2, C6
Limicola falcinellus Broad-billed Sandpiper	B	1996	101	500	C	A4i, B1i, B2, C3
Lymnocryptes minimus Jack Snipe	B	1996	101	500	C	A3, A4i, B1i, C3
Numenius phaeopus Whimbrel	B	1996	101	500	C	B3
Tringa nebularia Greenshank	B	1996	51	100	—	A3
Tringa glareola Wood Sandpiper	B	1996	501	1,000	C	B2
Surnia ulula Hawk Owl	B	1996	11	50	—	A3
Strix nebulosa Great Grey Owl	B	1996	6	10	—	A3
Asio flammeus Short-eared Owl	B	1996	11	50	C	B2, C6
Picoides tridactylus Three-toed Woodpecker	R	1996	101	500	C	B2, C2, C6
Anthus pratensis Meadow Pipit	B	1996	1,001	5,000	C	B3
Bombycilla garrulus Waxwing	B	1996	11	50	—	A3
Phoenicurus phoenicurus Redstart	B	1996	1,001	5,000	C	B2
Muscicapa striata Spotted Flycatcher	B	1996	1,001	5,000	C	B2
Parus cinctus Siberian Tit	R	1996	51	100	—	A3
Perisoreus infaustus Siberian Jay	R	1996	51	100	C	A3, B2
Fringilla montifringilla Brambling	B	1996	1,001	5,000	—	A3
Loxia leucoptera Two-barred Crossbill	B	1996	101	500	—	A3
Loxia pytyopsittacus Parrot Crossbill	B	1996	11	50	C	A3, B3
Emberiza rustica Rustic Bunting	B	1996	1,001	5,000	—	A3

An important area for boreal avifauna. Breeding birds include 12 out of the 15 species in Europe that are restricted to the boreal biome (when breeding).

■ Protection status
National Partial   **International** High
25,695 ha of IBA covered by Peatland Reserve (Lapiosuo–Iso Äijönsuo, 25,695 ha). 30,405 ha of IBA covered by Special Protection Area (Litokaira).

■ Conservation issues

Threats Unknown

The area is a candidate SAC.

Ahmasjärvi lake   B1i, B2, C3   038
Admin region Oulun lääni
Coordinates 64°38'N 26°25'E
Altitude 70–70 m   **Area** 414 ha

■ Site description
A large eutrophic lake surrounded by farmland, in the vicinity of Oulu lake. The shores are fringed by narrow belts of *Carex* marsh, whilst the shallow waters support stands of *Equisetum*, *Phragmites* and *Scirpus*. Floating vegetation is also abundant. On the shores are numerous settlements whose people fish and hunt on the lake.

Habitats Wetland (100%; standing fresh water)
Land-use Hunting (80%), Unknown

■ Birds

Species	Season	Year	Pop min	Pop max	Acc	Criteria
Larus minutus Little Gull	B	1996	254	254	A	B1i, B2, C3

An important breeding area for *Larus minutus*.

■ Protection status
National None **International** High
414 ha of IBA covered by Special Protection Area (Ahmasjärvi).

■ Conservation issues

Threats Unknown

Rummelö–Harrbodan A4i, B1i, C2, C3 039
Admin region Oulun lääni
Coordinates 63°52'N 23°10'E
Altitude 0–0 m Area 240 ha

■ Site description
A fertile coastal wetland close to the town of Kokkola. Due to continuous geological uplifting of the land, the site holds several habitats at various successional stages, including wet meadows with low vegetation, scrub, young deciduous forests and nutrient-poor *Pinus sylvestris* forests. The area has been managed actively by cutting bushes and cattle-grazing on the tall grass.

Habitats Forest and woodland (10%; broadleaved deciduous forest), Wetland (90%; coastal lagoon)
Land-use Nature conservation/research (5%), Unknown (95%)

■ Birds

Species	Season	Year	Pop min	Pop max	Acc	Criteria
Cygnus cygnus Whooper Swan	P	1992	460	460	B	B1i, C2
Anas clypeata Shoveler	P	1992	101	500	—	B1i, C3
Bucephala clangula Goldeneye	P	1992	5,001	10,000	—	A4i, B1i, C3

An important congregatory area for migrating waterbirds.

■ Protection status
National None **International** High
236 ha of IBA covered by Special Protection Area.

■ Conservation issues

Threats Afforestation (A)

Part of the area is a candidate SAC.

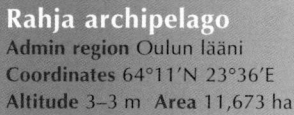

Rahja archipelago B1i, B2, B3, C3 040
Admin region Oulun lääni
Coordinates 64°11'N 23°36'E
Altitude 3–3 m Area 11,673 ha

■ Site description
Lying in the north-east of the Gulf of Bothnia, this is one of the largest and most diverse archipelagos in the Bay of Bothnia. The area holds a remarkable diversity of habitats including the Siipojoki river delta, large forested islands, islands with meadows and beaches, and numerous outer rocky islands and islets. The area has remained largely undeveloped, and much of the shoreline is in a natural state.

Habitats Forest and woodland (30%; native coniferous forest; mixed forest), Marine areas (30%; sea inlet/coastal features), Rocky areas (40%; sea cliff/rocky shore)
Land-use Forestry (10%), Hunting (40%), Tourism/recreation (60%)

■ Birds

Species	Season	Year	Pop min	Pop max	Acc	Criteria
Mergus serrator Red-breasted Merganser	B	1992	101	500	B	B1i, C3
Tringa totanus Redshank	B	1992	101	500	C	B1i, B2, C3
Larus canus Common Gull	B	1992	501	1,000	B	B2
[1] *Larus fuscus* Lesser Black-backed Gull	B	1997	160	170	A	B3
Cepphus grylle Black Guillemot	B	1997	110	110	B	B2

1. *Larus fuscus fuscus.*

An important breeding area for archipelagic avifauna.

■ Protection status
National None **International** Partial
8,555 ha of IBA covered by Special Protection Area (Rahjan saaristo).

■ Conservation issues

Threats Abandonment/reduction of land management (B), Afforestation (B), Disturbance to birds (B), Recreation/tourism (A), Selective logging/cutting (C)

Part of the area is a candidate SAC.

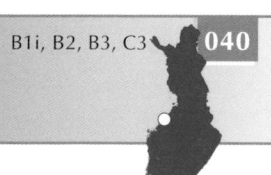

Kokkola and Kälviä archipelago A4i, B1i, B2, B3, C2, C3, C6 041
Admin region Länsi-Suomen lääni
Coordinates 63°56'N 23°04'E
Altitude 0–0 m Area 20,340 ha

■ Site description
A large archipelago in the north-east of the Gulf of Bothnia and some larger, forested islands, offshore of the town of Kokkola. The archipelago comprises numerous high and rocky islands, with large expanses of open water between them.

Habitats Rocky areas (sea cliff/rocky shore; rock stacks/islets), Marine areas (sea inlet/coastal features)
Land-use Tourism/recreation (20%), Unknown (80%)

■ Birds

Species	Season	Year	Pop min	Pop max	Acc	Criteria
[1] *Mergus serrator* Red-breasted Merganser	B	1997	501	1,000	B	A4i, B1i, C3
[2] *Mergus merganser* Goosander	B	1997	101	500	B	A4i, B1i, C3
Larus minutus Little Gull	B	1997	70	80	B	B2
[1] *Larus canus* Common Gull	B	1997	700	900	B	B2
[1,3] *Larus fuscus* Lesser Black-backed Gull	B	1997	400	500	B	B3
[1] *Sterna caspia* Caspian Tern	B	1997	19	19	B	B1i, B2, C2, C6

1. 1994–1997.
2. 1989–1997.
3. *Larus fuscus fuscus.*

An important area for island-breeding birds.

■ Protection status
National None **International** Partial
16,653 ha of IBA covered by Special Protection Area (Kokkolan saaristo).

■ Conservation issues

Threats Disturbance to birds (B), Recreation/tourism (B)

The most serious threats to the area are hunting, boating and other sea traffic, and unregulated recreation. On Tankar island a bird observatory has been maintained for many years where ringing is an important activity. A lighthouse on the island attracts huge numbers of birds, especially passerines, at night. Part of the area is a candidate SAC.

Sundominlahti Bay and Söderfjärden A4i, B1i, B2, C2, C3 042
Admin region Länsi-Suomen lääni
Coordinates 63°00'N 21°35'E
Altitude 0–0 m Area 4,570 ha

■ Site description
A shallow eutrophic sea bay at the mouth of the Laihia river lying south of the town of Vaasa. Most of the bay is open water, although there are wide marshes, and extensive beds of reed *Phragmites*. To the south lies the agricultural area of Söderfjärden, which was previously a sea bay. The IBA also includes an undisturbed area of inner archipelago, where *Grus grus* from the farmland roost.

Habitats Wetland (50%; coastal lagoon; standing fresh water), Artificial landscape (50%; arable land)
Land-use Agriculture (50%), Unknown (50%)

■ Birds

Species	Season	Year	Pop min	Pop max	Acc	Criteria
¹ *Cygnus cygnus* Whooper Swan	P	1996	1,000	1,000	A	A4i, B1i, C2
Anser fabalis Bean Goose	P	1996	1,500	1,500	A	B1i, C3
Anser anser Greylag Goose	P	1996	290	290	A	B1i, C3
¹ *Grus grus* Crane	P	1996	2,800	2,800	A	A4i, B1i, C2
¹ *Larus minutus* Little Gull	B	1996	40	40	A	B2
1. 1989–1996.						

The most important staging area for *Grus grus* in Finland. It is also important for other staging waterbirds.

■ Protection status
National None **International** High
4,328 ha of IBA covered by Special Protection Area (Sundominlahti).

■ Conservation issues

Threats	Afforestation (B), Disturbance to birds (B)

The active use of farmland in Söderfjärden is very important for staging cranes. Some farmers have requested a licence to shoot *Grus grus* since they cause damage to crops. Part of the area is a candidate SAC.

Luoto archipelago
B2, C6  043
Admin region Länsi-Suomen lääni
Coordinates 63°47′N 22°38′E
Altitude 0–0 m **Area** 17,240 ha

■ Site description
A large archipelago in the north-east Gulf of Bothnia supporting sandy beaches, herb-rich meadows, forested islands and less sheltered rocky islands. There are several summer cottages in the area.

Habitats	Marine areas (85%; sea inlet/coastal features), Unknown (15%)
Land-use	Unknown

■ Birds

Species	Season	Year	Pop min	Pop max	Acc	Criteria
Grus grus Crane	B	1996	11	50	C	B2, C6
Bubo bubo Eagle Owl	B	1996	5	5	—	B2, C6

An important area for island-breeding birds.

■ Protection status
National Low **International** High
860 ha of IBA covered by Private Protection Area (Örarn, 807 ha; Eura, 3 ha; Tolumansgrundet, 13 ha; Gäddvik, 6 ha; Flaskskär, 21 ha; Storgrundet, 14 ha; Krokas, 6 ha). 17,310 ha of IBA covered by Special Protection Area (Luodon saaristo).

■ Conservation issues

Threats	Unknown

Part of the area is a candidate SAC.

Uusikaarlepyy archipelago
B3, C7 044
Admin region Länsi-Suomen lääni
Coordinates 63°34′N 22°20′E
Altitude 0–0 m **Area** 7,707 ha

■ Site description
An archipelagic area in the north-east Gulf of Bothnia. The area consists of three sub-areas: Torsö island in the outer archipelago, with a forested interior and sandy, stony or rocky shores; Stubben, a group of largish offshore islands with mainly stony shores; and Storsand island, a natural area of sand-dunes with sparse vegetation.

Habitats	Marine areas (90%; sea inlet/coastal features), Unknown (10%)
Land-use	Unknown

■ Birds

Species	Season	Year	Pop min	Pop max	Acc	Criteria
¹ *Larus fuscus* Lesser Black-backed Gull	B	1996	153	153	A	B3
1. *Larus fuscus fuscus.*						

An important area for island-breeding birds.

■ Protection status
National Low **International** High
599 ha of IBA covered by Private Protection Area (Lotan, 309 ha; Torsö, 290 ha). 7,707 ha of IBA covered by Special Protection Area (Uudenkaarlepyyn saaristo).

■ Conservation issues

Threats	Unknown

Part of the area is a candidate SAC.

Merenkurkku archipelago
A1, A4i, B1i, B1ii, B1iv, B2, B3, C1, C2, C3, C5, C6 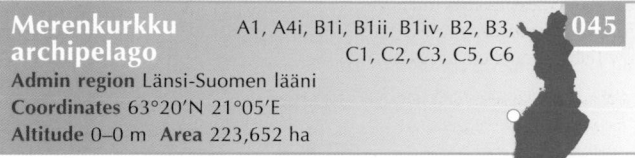 045
Admin region Länsi-Suomen lääni
Coordinates 63°20′N 21°05′E
Altitude 0–0 m **Area** 223,652 ha

■ Site description
A large archipelago encompassing many hundreds (perhaps thousands) of islands at the boundary of the Bothnian Sea and the Bay of Bothnia. The smaller islands are treeless and rocky, the middle-sized ones hold deciduous trees, whilst the largest support mixed and coniferous forests, numerous fladas, lagoons, island lakes, and pools. The site includes extensive areas of open water, which are mainly shallow, stony and biologically productive. Fishing is extensive in many parts of the area and recreational developments are increasing.

Habitats	Forest and woodland (5%), Marine areas (85%; open sea, sea inlet/coastal features), Unknown (10%)
Land-use	Unknown

■ Birds

Species	Season	Year	Pop min	Pop max	Acc	Criteria
Cygnus cygnus Whooper Swan	P	1996	101	500	—	B1i, C2
Clangula hyemalis Long-tailed Duck	P	1996	10,001	100,000	C	A4i, B1i, C3
Melanitta fusca Velvet Scoter	B	1996	3,600	3,600	A	A4i, B1i, C3
Melanitta fusca Velvet Scoter	P	1996	10,001	100,000	C	A4i, B1i, C3
Mergus serrator Red-breasted Merganser	B	1996	1,300	1,300	A	A4i, B1i, C3
Mergus serrator Red-breasted Merganser	P	1996	5,001	10,000	B	A4i, B1i, C3
Mergus merganser Goosander	B	1996	900	900	A	A4i, B1i, C3
Mergus merganser Goosander	P	1996	5,001	10,000	B	A4i, B1i, C3
Pandion haliaetus Osprey	B	1996	15	15	A	B2, C6
Tringa totanus Redshank	B	1996	650	650	A	B1i, B2, C3
Larus canus Common Gull	B	1996	7,000	7,000	A	B1i, B2, C3
¹ *Larus fuscus* Lesser Black-backed Gull	B	1996	920	920	A	B1i, B3, C3
Larus marinus Great Black-backed Gull	B	1996	200	200	A	B3
Sterna caspia Caspian Tern	B	1996	60	60	A	B1i, B2, C2, C6
Sterna paradisaea Arctic Tern	B	1996	14,000	14,000	A	B1i, C2
Alca torda Razorbill	B	1996	1,400	1,400	A	B1ii, B3, C3
Cepphus grylle Black Guillemot	B	1996	6,500	6,500	A	B1ii, B2
Lanius collurio Red-backed Shrike	B	1996	101	500	C	B2, C6
1. *Larus fuscus fuscus.*						

Probably the most important area for island-breeding birds in Finland. The area supports the largest staging populations of many species in the country. An important bottleneck site for migrating *Buteo lagopus* (1,000–5,000 birds per season).

■ Protection status
National Low **International** Partial
14,860 ha of IBA covered by Private Protection Area (Valassaaret, 14,860 ha). 17,700 ha of IBA covered by Ramsar Site (Valassaaret and Björkögrunden, 17,700 ha). 128, 162 ha of IBA covered by Special Protection Area (Merenkurkun saaristo).

■ Conservation issues

Threats Disturbance to birds (U), Extraction industry (U), Industrialization/ urbanization (U)

A bird observatory has been maintained on Valassaaret island for many years; the main activity is observations of migration, especially in spring. Part of the area is a candidate SAC.

Kristiinankaupunki southern archipelago	B1i, B2, C3, C6	046

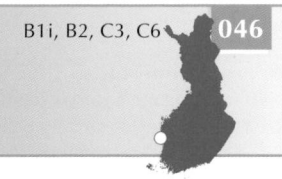

Admin region Länsi-Suomen lääni
Coordinates 62°04'N 21°16'E
Altitude 0–0 m **Area** 7,435 ha

■ Site description
A large archipelago in the south-east of the Gulf of Bothnia. Most of the islands are small, treeless and rocky, whilst the larger ones support forest, treeless heaths, meadows and sand-dunes. Large heaps of wrack *Fucus vesiculosus* line the shores, attracting many birds. There are a few fishermen's cottages in the area.

Habitats Marine areas (80%; sea inlet/coastal features), Rocky areas (20%; sea cliff/ rocky shore; rock stacks/islets)
Land-use Not utilized (95%), Unknown (5%)

■ Birds

Species	Season	Year	Pop min	Pop max	Acc	Criteria
Anser anser Greylag Goose	P	1995	200	200	B	B1i, C3
Larus minutus Little Gull	B	1995	70	70	B	B2
Larus canus Common Gull	B	1995	498	498	A	B2
Sterna caspia Caspian Tern	B	1995	7	7	A	B2, C6

An important area for island-breeding birds and a staging area for waterbirds. Species of global conservation concern that do not meet IBA criteria: *Polysticta stelleri* (1–10 birds, passage), *Haliaeetus albicilla* (max. 5 birds, passage and wintering).

■ Protection status
National Low **International** Partial
151 ha of IBA covered by Private Protection Areas (Kristiinan-kaupungin luodot, 166 ha; Domarkobban, 21 ha). 5,925 ha of IBA covered by Special Protection Area (Kristiinankaupungin saaristo).

■ Conservation issues

Threats Abandonment/reduction of land management (C)

Boating and fishing cause minor disturbance. Overgrowth of the wetland is a threat. Part of the area is a candidate SAC.

Lapväärti wetlands	B1i, C3	047

Admin region Länsi-Suomen lääni
Coordinates 62°10'N 21°22'E
Altitude 0–0 m **Area** 1,093 ha

■ Site description
A complex of shallow and nutrient-rich coastal wetlands surrounding the Lapväärti river delta, including Härkmerifjärden, a shallow, nutrient-rich lake, covered by large beds of reed *Phragmites* and bulrush *Scirpus*. Human activities include fishing and boating.

Habitats Wetland (100%; coastal lagoon; standing fresh water)
Land-use Not utilized (60%), Unknown (40%)

■ Birds

Species	Season	Year	Pop min	Pop max	Acc	Criteria
[1] *Anser fabalis* Bean Goose	P	1995	1,000	3,000	B	B1i, C3
[1] *Anser anser* Greylag Goose	B	1995	80	80	B	B1i, C3
1. 1993–1995.						

An important staging area for waterbirds. Species of global conservation concern that do not meet IBA criteria: *Anser erythropus* (max. 1 bird,

passage), *Haliaeetus albicilla* (max. 2 birds, passage), *Crex crex* (max. 2 pairs, breeding).

■ Protection status
National None **International** Partial
669 ha of IBA covered by Special Protection Area (Lapväärtin kosteikot).

■ Conservation issues

Threats Unknown

Overgrowth of the wetland is a threat. Part of the area is a candidate SAC.

Lålby fields	A4i, B1i, C3	048

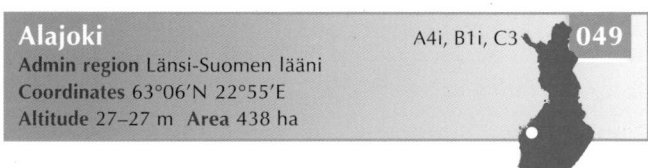

Admin region Länsi-Suomen lääni
Coordinates 62°16'N 21°28'E
Altitude 5–5 m **Area** 200 ha

■ Site description
A small area of farmland close to the Gulf of Bothnia. This open landscape is dominated by potato fields which are essential for staging geese. In years when spring flooding is heavy the area also attracts other staging waterbirds.

Habitats Artificial landscape (100%; arable land)
Land-use Agriculture (100%)

■ Birds

Species	Season	Year	Pop min	Pop max	Acc	Criteria
[1] *Anser fabalis* Bean Goose	P	1996	3,000	5,000	B	A4i, B1i, C3
[1] *Anser anser* Greylag Goose	P	1996	300	500	B	B1i, C3
1. 1993–1996.						

One of the best staging areas for *Anser fabalis fabalis* in Finland. Breeding birds are relatively scarce due to intensive farming practices. Species of global conservation concern that do not meet IBA criteria: *Anser erythropus* (max. 1 bird, passage), *Haliaeetus albicilla* (1–5 birds, passage).

■ Protection status
National None **International** None

■ Conservation issues

Threats Abandonment/reduction of land management (A)

Reductions in potato farming present a threat to the staging geese.

Alajoki	A4i, B1i, C3	049

Admin region Länsi-Suomen lääni
Coordinates 63°06'N 22°55'E
Altitude 27–27 m **Area** 438 ha

■ Site description
Open agricultural fields at the junction of the Lapua and Kauhava rivers. Spring cereals, turnip, rape and potato are the most common crops.

Habitats Wetland (5%; river/stream), Artificial landscape (95%)
Land-use Agriculture (98%), Urban/industrial/transport (2%)

■ Birds

Species	Season	Year	Pop min	Pop max	Acc	Criteria
[1] *Anser fabalis* Bean Goose	P	1996	3,000	5,000	B	A4i, B1i, C3
1. 1990–1996.						

Probably the second-best staging area for *Anser fabalis fabalis* in Finland. The ornithological importance of the area is mainly restricted to periods of spring flooding. Species of global conservation concern that do not meet IBA criteria: *Anser erythropus* (max. 2 birds, passage), *Crex crex* (max. 5 pairs, breeding).

■ Protection status
National None **International** None

■ Conservation issues

Threats Unknown

The importance of the area depends on the continuity of local farming.

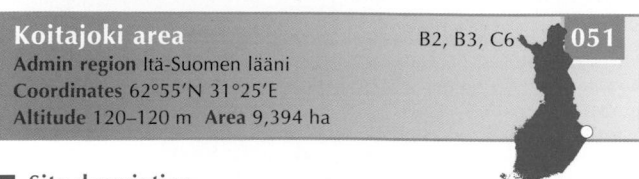

Värtsilä valley · A1, B2, C1, C6 · 050
Admin region Itä-Suomen lääni
Coordinates 62°12′N 30°38′E
Altitude 70–70 m **Area** 745 ha

■ Site description
A diverse, fertile, open valley surrounded by large areas of woodland situated around the settlement of Värtsilä. The area includes two small, shallow, eutrophic lakes, Sääperi and Uudenkylänlampi, surrounded by farmland, mostly cereals, and also by wild meadows. The Jänisjoki river flows across the area, into Lake Ladoga in Russia.

Habitats Forest and woodland (mixed forest), Wetland (40%; standing fresh water), Artificial landscape (55%)
Land-use Agriculture (30%), Hunting (40%), Unknown (25%)

■ Birds

Species	Season	Year	Pop min	Pop max	Acc	Criteria
¹ *Crex crex* Corncrake	B	1996	10	25	A	A1, B2, C1, C6
Larus minutus Little Gull	B	1991	40	40	A	B2

1. 1990–1996.

One of the few known regular breeding sites in Finland for *Emberiza aureola* (3–7 pairs). *Tringa stagnatilis* has bred twice during the 1985–1995 period. Also a nationally important spring staging area for *Anser fabalis* (400–600 birds), *Tringa erythropus* (100–500 birds), *T. nebularia* (100–500 birds) and *Calcarius lapponicus* (1,000–5,000 birds). Species of global conservation concern that do not meet IBA criteria: *Circus macrourus* (max. 3 birds, passage), *Aquila clanga* (max. 1 bird, passage), *Gallinago media* (1–5 birds, passage).

■ Protection status
National None **International** Partial
498 ha of IBA covered by Special Protection Area (Värtsilän laakson luontokokonaisuus).

■ Conservation issues

Threats Abandonment/reduction of land management (C), Afforestation (B), Disturbance to birds (C), Extraction industry (B), Industrialization/urbanization (B)

A few hundred people live in the valley and impact on the area. Disturbance is greatest in autumn when wildfowling starts. There have been attempts to manage the scrub on the shores of Sääperi lake specifically for improving the breeding habitat for *Emberiza aureola*, but without success. Overgrowth of the wetland is a threat. A birdwatching tower is situated on the shore of Sääperi lake. Part of the area is a candidate SAC.

Koitajoki area · B2, B3, C6 · 051
Admin region Itä-Suomen lääni
Coordinates 62°55′N 31°25′E
Altitude 120–120 m **Area** 9,394 ha

■ Site description
A large complex of raised bogs and boreal forests along the Koitajoki river in easternmost Finland. Raised bogs divided by numerous rivers dominate the peatland, with smaller areas of aapa mire, bordered with patches of both natural and previously managed swamp-forests.

Habitats Forest and woodland (30%), Wetland (70%; raised bog)
Land-use Hunting (30%), Tourism/recreation (30%), Unknown (40%)

■ Birds

Species	Season	Year	Pop min	Pop max	Acc	Criteria
¹ *Numenius phaeopus* Whimbrel	B	1997	67	67	C	B3
¹ *Picoides tridactylus* Three-toed Woodpecker	R	1997	55	55	C	B2, C6

1. 1996–1997.

An important breeding area for boreal birds. One of the most significant southernmost breeding areas for *Perisoreus infaustus* (20 pairs) in Finland.

■ Protection status
National Partial **International** High
2,100 ha of IBA covered by Strict Nature Reserve (Koivusuo, 2,100 ha). 1,774 ha of IBA covered by Peatland Reserve (Ruosmesuo–Hanhisuo, 1,774 ha). 9,394 ha of IBA covered by Biosphere Reserve (Northern Karelian, 350,000 ha).

■ Conservation issues

Threats Deforestation (commercial) (B), Industrialization/urbanization (C), Selective logging/cutting (B)

The Koitajoki river flows over the border into Russia; plans have been made to establish a large adjacent conservation area in Russia. Sewage effluent impacts on the area. Several kilometres of board-walks and trails traverse the Koivusuo Strict Nature Reserve, which falls within the IBA. Part of the area is a candidate SAC.

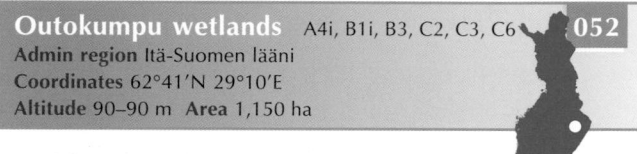

Outokumpu wetlands · A4i, B1i, B3, C2, C3, C6 · 052
Admin region Itä-Suomen lääni
Coordinates 62°41′N 29°10′E
Altitude 90–90 m **Area** 1,150 ha

■ Site description
A complex of shallow, nutrient-rich wetlands south of the town of Outokumpu, surrounded mainly by farmland, but also by young deciduous forests which regularly flood. Areas of formerly quite extensive open, muddy marshes are now overgrown by sedge, grasses and *Salix* bushes. In shallow water, large beds of reed *Phragmites* are abundant.

Habitats Forest and woodland (15%; broadleaved deciduous forest; mixed forest), Wetland (80%; standing fresh water), Unknown (5%)
Land-use Hunting (100%), Nature conservation/research (5%), Tourism/recreation (10%)

■ Birds

Species	Season	Year	Pop min	Pop max	Acc	Criteria
¹ *Cygnus cygnus* Whooper Swan	P	1996	101	500	A	B1i, C2
¹ *Porzana porzana* Spotted Crake	B	1996	15	30	B	B3, C6
¹ *Larus minutus* Little Gull	P	1996	501	1,000	A	A4i, B1i, C3

1. 1990–1996.

Nationally important for breeding *Botaurus stellaris* (7–9 males), *Circus aeruginosus* (5–6 pairs). In 1984, the first evidence of breeding *Tringa stagnatilis* in western Europe was found in the area; it has since bred twice.

■ Protection status
National None **International** Partial
767 ha of IBA covered by Special Protection Area (Sysmäjärvi).

■ Conservation issues

Threats Abandonment/reduction of land management (U), Afforestation (C), Deforestation (commercial) (B), Disturbance to birds (A), Extraction industry (A), Industrialization/urbanization (A), Recreation/tourism (A), Selective logging/cutting (B)

Overgrowth of the wetland is a threat. The area suffers from intense hunting pressure in autumn, and fishing also causes disturbance in some parts, especially to *Cygnus cygnus* and *Anser fabalis*. Excessive nutrient pollution is a serious threat to the whole site; sewage is no longer discharged there, but the inflow of nutrients from surrounding farmland, especially during spring floods, is heavy. Oxygen-generating equipment was installed in Sysmäjärvi lake some years ago to help address this problem. There are several birdwatching towers in the area.

Outokumpu and Kaavi oligotrophic lakes

B2, C6   053

Admin region Itä-Suomen lääni
Coordinates 62°45′N 28°50′E
Altitude 90–90 m **Area** 14,665 ha

■ Site description
A very large complex of lakes on the border of North Carelia and North Savo districts. The site includes extensive areas of open water, small islands with primary forests, undisturbed bays, and cliffs. The lakes are poor in nutrients (oligotrophic), clear-watered with sparse vegetation, and are mostly bordered by forest. Human activities are common all over the lakes, since outside the site boundaries are large areas of summer-only and all-year-round habitation.

> **Habitats** Wetland (80%; standing fresh water), Unknown (20%)
> **Land-use** Not utilized (10%), Tourism/recreation (90%)

■ Birds

Species	Season	Year	Pop min	Pop max	Acc	Criteria
Gavia arctica Black-throated Diver	B	1996	90	110	C	B2, C6

The site holds the most significant *Gavia arctica* population in Finland. It is also a nationally important breeding area for *Falco subbuteo* (15–25 pairs) and *Larus fuscus fuscus* (55–80 pairs).

■ Protection status
National None **International** Partial
3,060 ha of IBA covered by Special Protection Area (Juojärven saaristo).

■ Conservation issues

> **Threats** Disturbance to birds (B), Recreation/tourism

Threats include the construction of summer cottages and recreational boating. Part of the area is a candidate SAC.

Viklinrimpi

B1i, C2   054

Admin region Itä-Suomen lääni
Coordinates 62°56′N 29°28′E
Altitude 120–120 m **Area** 2,651 ha

■ Site description
A series of raised bogs lying north of Höytiäinen lake. The area is dominated by dry, sparsely forested *Sphagnum* peatland with a few larger areas of open mire and small pools. The forest is mainly barren and *Pinus sylvestris*-dominated.

> **Habitats** Forest and woodland (15%; native coniferous forest; alluvial/very wet forest), Wetland (85%; river/stream; raised bog)
> **Land-use** Forestry (15%), Not utilized (85%)

■ Birds

Species	Season	Year	Pop min	Pop max	Acc	Criteria
Grus grus Crane	P	1996	501	1,000	C	B1i, C2

The most important staging area for *Grus grus* in eastern Finland. The site is also important as a breeding area for boreal birds. Species of global conservation concern that do not meet IBA criteria: *Anser erythropus* (max. 1 individual, passage).

■ Protection status
National Partial **International** None
330 ha of IBA covered by Peatland Reserve (Viklinsuo–Rapalahdensuo, 330 ha).

■ Conservation issues

> **Threats** Deforestation (commercial) (B), Disturbance to birds (B), Drainage (B), Extraction industry (A), Industrialization/urbanization (A), Selective logging/cutting (B)

The area has sustained little human impact to date but several potential future impacts threaten the site. Part of the area is a candidate SAC.

Patvinsuo National Park

B2, B3, C6   055

Admin region Itä-Suomen lääni
Coordinates 63°08′N 30°46′E
Altitude 120–120 m **Area** 10,023 ha

■ Site description
A large wilderness area just north of Koitere lake, with mires, more-or-less natural boreal forest and waterways. The mires lie at the junction of the raised bogs of inner Finland and the Pohjanmaa aapa mires. Tourism is evident, especially in summer, with several camping areas, a long network of tracks and board-walks, look-out towers and other facilities. A few roads traverse the area.

> **Habitats** Forest and woodland (35%; native coniferous forest; mixed forest; alluvial/very wet forest), Wetland (65%; standing fresh water; raised bog)
> **Land-use** Not utilized (90%), Tourism/recreation (5%), Urban/industrial/transport (5%)

■ Birds

Species	Season	Year	Pop min	Pop max	Acc	Criteria
Grus grus Crane	B	1996	11	50	A	B2, C6
Numenius phaeopus Whimbrel	B	1996	51	100	A	B3
Loxia pytyopsittacus Parrot Crossbill	B	1996	11	50	C	B3

An important breeding area for boreal birds.

■ Protection status
National High **International** High
10,023 ha of IBA covered by National Park (Patvinsuo, 10,023 ha).
9,683 ha of IBA covered by Ramsar Site (Suomujärvi–Patvinsuo, 9,683 ha).

■ Conservation issues

> **Threats** Disturbance to birds (B), Recreation/tourism (C)

The area is a candidate SAC.

Pitkäranta

B2   056

Admin region Itä-Suomen lääni
Coordinates 62°40′N 30°00′E
Altitude 100–100 m **Area** 490 ha

■ Site description
A small complex of wetland, open mire and riparian vegetation on the lower course of the Pielisjoki river. The area is bordered by an extensive region of ridges with *Pinus sylvestris* heath, and by the Pielisjoki river. Ornithologically, the most important part is the outer zone where peatlands and wetlands meet, with an abundance of small pools, muddy patches and beds of reed *Phragmites*.

> **Habitats** Forest and woodland (10%; native coniferous forest), Wetland (90%; river/stream; raised bog)
> **Land-use** Not utilized (100%)

■ Birds

Species	Season	Year	Pop min	Pop max	Acc	Criteria
Larus minutus Little Gull	B	1996	51	100	B	B2

The area holds both wetland and peatland avifauna, including *Circus aeruginosus* (1 pair), *Circus cyaneus* (1–5 pairs), *Grus grus* (3 pairs), *Lymnocryptes minimus* (5–10 pairs) and *Larus minutus*. Species of global conservation concern that do not meet IBA criteria: *Haliaeetus albicilla* (1–5 individuals, passage).

■ Protection status
National None **International** None

■ Conservation issues

> **Threats** Disturbance to birds (B)

The site is relatively undisturbed, except in autumn when hunting scares birds from the area. A birdwatching tower on the southern edge offers spectacular views across the area.

Päätyeenlahti Bay
B2, C7  057

Admin region Itä-Suomen lääni
Coordinates 62°07'N 30°08'E
Altitude 70–70 m **Area** 422 ha

■ Site description
Päätyeenlahti is a long and shallow bay on Kiteenjärvi lake, with *Equisetum* and *Phragmites* beds and abundant floating vegetation, which covers the bay in August. The shores of the bay are mainly bordered by open, semi-natural and agricultural habitats with settlements and two roads. There are also smaller areas of *Salix* bushes and stands of mixed forest.

Habitats Forest and woodland (25%; broadleaved deciduous forest; native coniferous forest), Wetland (75%; standing fresh water)
Land-use Not utilized (85%), Tourism/recreation (5%), Unknown (10%)

■ Birds

Species	Season	Year	Pop min	Pop max	Acc	Criteria
Larus minutus Little Gull	B	1992	140	140	A	B2

An important breeding area for wetland birds, including one of the largest colonies of *Larus minutus* in Finland.

■ Protection status
National Partial **International** Partial
92 ha of IBA covered by Protected Area on Private Land (Päätyenlahti, 92 ha). 364 ha of IBA covered by Special Protection Area (Päätyeenlahti).

■ Conservation issues

Threats Abandonment/reduction of land management (C), Disturbance to birds (A), Industrialization/urbanization (A), Recreation/tourism (B)

The area has suffered to some extent from fishing and recreational boating, and hunting pressure ('Disturbance to birds' threat) is heavy in autumn. Other threats are the overgrowth of the wetland with vegetation and the impact of sewage effluents discharged into the area. There are two birdwatching towers in the area.

Ruunaa
B2, B3, C6 058

Admin region Itä-Suomen lääni
Coordinates 63°23'N 30°40'E
Altitude 120–120 m **Area** 12,061 ha

■ Site description
A large boreal area located east of Pielinen lake and adjacent to the Russian border. Ruunaa lake lies in the heart of the area and divides the site in two: to the east is a conservation and wilderness area, whilst to the west more recreational activities such as boating and fishing take place. There are many lakes within the site and a spectacular network of rivers and streams. Most of the land is covered by stands of dry *Pinus sylvestris* heath and numerous small bogs.

Habitats Forest and woodland (55%; native coniferous forest; alluvial/very wet forest), Wetland (50%; standing fresh water; river/stream; raised bog)
Land-use Forestry (15%), Not utilized (70%), Tourism/recreation (15%)

■ Birds

Species	Season	Year	Pop min	Pop max	Acc	Criteria
[1] *Grus grus* Crane	B	1996	11	50	C	B2, C6
Picoides tridactylus Three-toed Woodpecker	R	1996	51	100	A	B2, C6
[1] *Turdus viscivorus* Mistle Thrush	B	1996	101	500	C	B3
Loxia pytyopsittacus Parrot Crossbill	B	1996	11	50	C	B3

1. 1980–1996.

An important breeding area for boreal birds including *Tetrao urogallus* (100–500 pairs).

■ Protection status
National Partial **International** None
7,321 ha of IBA covered by Specific Protection Area (Ruunaa, 7,321 ha).

■ Conservation issues

Threats Aquaculture/fisheries (B), Deforestation (commercial) (A), Disturbance to birds (B), Recreation/tourism (B), Selective logging/cutting (A)

Part of the area is a candidate SAC.

Maaninka wetlands
A4i, B1i, B2, C3 059

Admin region Itä-Suomen lääni
Coordinates 63°10'N 27°15'E
Altitude 86–86 m **Area** 3,370 ha

■ Site description
Several adjacent small wetlands around the settlement of Maaninkaj with surrounding agricultural areas and forests. All wetlands are shallow and nutrient-rich due mainly to nutrient run-off from local fields.

Habitats Forest and woodland (5%), Wetland (80%; standing fresh water), Artificial landscape (15%)
Land-use Agriculture (15%), Hunting (90%)

■ Birds

Species	Season	Year	Pop min	Pop max	Acc	Criteria
[1] *Larus minutus* Little Gull	B	1996	100	250	B	A4i, B1i, B2, C3

1. 1980–1996.

Also nationally important for breeding *Botaurus stellaris* (3–5 males), *Circus aeruginosus* (4–7 pairs) and *Porzana porzana* (3–35 males). Staging species include *Grus grus* (150 birds), *Tringa erythropus* (150 birds), *T. glareola* (500 birds) and *Philomachus pugnax* (2,000 birds). Species of global conservation concern that do not meet IBA criteria: *Haliaeetus albicilla* (1–3 individuals, passage), *Crex crex* (1–5 pairs, breeding), *Gallinago media* (max. 3 individuals, passage).

■ Protection status
National None **International** Partial
603 ha of IBA covered by Special Protection Area (Maaningan lintujärvet).

■ Conservation issues

Threats Abandonment/reduction of land management (B), Disturbance to birds (A)

The major human impact on waterbirds at the site is autumn hunting. Overgrowth of the wetland is also a threat. Part of the area is a candidate SAC.

Talaskangas
A3 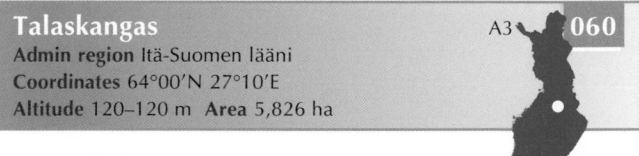 060

Admin region Itä-Suomen lääni
Coordinates 64°00'N 27°10'E
Altitude 120–120 m **Area** 5,826 ha

■ Site description
A large wilderness of old-growth boreal forest and bog on the boundary of the North Savo and Kainuu provinces. A substantial amount of the forest is very old and in a natural state, and includes a considerable number of both standing and fallen dead trees. Some of the younger forests were formerly under management. Small raised bogs with scattered trees (mostly *Pinus sylvestris*) lie between the larger areas of forests. Streams and ponds traverse the area.

Habitats Forest and woodland (40%), Wetland (60%; raised bog)
Land-use Not utilized (80%), Hunting

■ Birds

Species	Season	Year	Pop min	Pop max	Acc	Criteria
[1] *Tringa nebularia* Greenshank	B	1996	22	22	B	A3
[1] *Surnia ulula* Hawk Owl	B	1996	0	9	B	A3
[1] *Strix nebulosa* Great Grey Owl	B	1996	0	5	B	A3
[1] *Bombycilla garrulus* Waxwing	B	1996	6	6	B	A3
[1] *Phylloscopus borealis* Arctic Warbler	B	1996	—	—	B	A3

Species ... continued	Season	Year	Pop min	Pop max	Acc	Criteria
[1] *Perisoreus infaustus* Siberian Jay	B	1996	13	13	B	A3
[1] *Fringilla montifringilla* Brambling	B	1996	750	750	B	A3
[1] *Loxia leucoptera* Two-barred Crossbill	B	1996	1	11	B	A3
[1] *Loxia pytyopsittacus* Parrot Crossbill	B	1996	14	14	B	A3
[1] *Emberiza rustica* Rustic Bunting	B	1996	65	65	B	A3
1. 1989–1996.						

Breeding birds include 10 out of the 15 species in Europe that are restricted to the boreal biome (when breeding).

■ Protection status
National Low **International** Partial
160 ha of IBA covered by Protected Area on Private Land (Talasjärvi, 160 ha). 3,500 ha of IBA covered by Special Protection Area (Talaskangas, 3,500 ha).

■ Conservation issues

Threats Disturbance to birds (U), Intensified forest management (U)

No habitat-changes are anticipated, since a decision has been made by conservation authorities to fully protect the area. The only threat to the avifauna is occasional hunting in autumn. Part of the area is a candidate SAC.

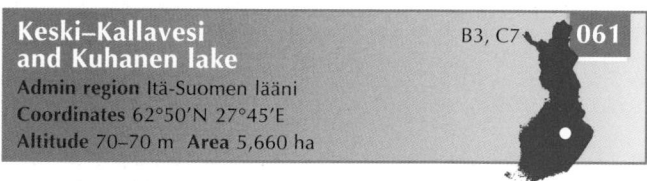

Keski–Kallavesi and Kuhanen lake
B3, C7 **061**
Admin region Itä-Suomen lääni
Coordinates 62°50'N 27°45'E
Altitude 70–70 m **Area** 5,660 ha

■ Site description
The site comprises the majority of the archipelagic part of southern Kallavesi lake in the heart of the province of North Savo, with the addition of the small, eutrophic Kuhanen Bay on the western edge of the lake. The site is mostly open water with some large islands with coniferous forest and numerous small, treeless rocky islets. Kuhanen Bay differs considerably from the rest of the area, being shallow and quite heavily vegetated, and serves as a feeding area for wildfowl, gulls and terns breeding in the archipelago. The lake's shoreline is mainly undeveloped.

Habitats Forest and woodland (15%), Wetland (75%; standing fresh water), Rocky areas (10%)
Land-use Tourism/recreation

■ Birds

Species	Season	Year	Pop min	Pop max	Acc	Criteria
[1] *Larus fuscus* Lesser Black-backed Gull	B	1996	75	75	B	B3
1. 1980–1996.						

An important breeding area of *Larus fuscus fuscus*.

■ Protection status
National None **International** Partial
3,963 ha of IBA covered by Special Protection Area (Keski–Kallaveden saaristo).

■ Conservation issues

Threats Recreation/tourism (U)

Boating and other recreational activities may slightly impact on the avifauna. Part of the area is a candidate SAC.

Linnansaari
B3 **062**
Admin region Itä Suomen lääni
Coordinates 62°05'N 28°30'E
Altitude 70–70 m **Area** 24,006 ha

■ Site description
An extensive, open and barren lakeland area forming part of the very large inland waterway of Saimaa lake. The site mainly comprises open water with small scattered islands, although a few are larger and forested. These forests hold an unusually high proportion of deciduous (mainly *Betula*) trees, as a result of slash-and-burn agriculture which was common in the area until the beginning of this century. The lake is nutrient-poor (oligotrophic) and the shores support only a few beds of sparse reed *Phragmites*.

Habitats Wetland (75%; standing fresh water), Unknown (25%)
Land-use Unknown

■ Birds

Species	Season	Year	Pop min	Pop max	Acc	Criteria
[1] *Loxia pytyopsittacus* Parrot Crossbill	B	1994	36	36	C	B3
1. 1978–1994.						

Also a nationally important breeding area for *Gavia arctica* (10–50 pairs) and *Larus fuscus fuscus* (10–50 pairs). The forests hold breeding populations of the nationally scarce *Dendrocopos leucotos*. Species of global conservation concern that do not meet IBA criteria: *Haliaeetus albicilla* (1–5 individuals, passage).

■ Protection status
National High **International** None
24,006 ha of the IBA covered by National Park (Linnasaari, 24,006 ha).

■ Conservation issues

Threats Recreation/tourism (U)

Boating and landing on small islands is common in summer, which causes disturbance, particularly to *Gavia arctica*, gulls and terns. Part of the area is a candidate SAC.

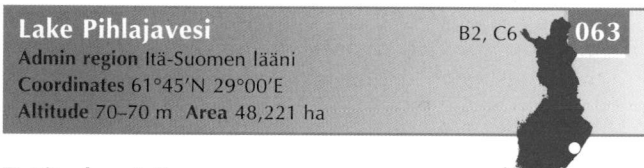

Lake Pihlajavesi
B2, C6 **063**
Admin region Itä-Suomen lääni
Coordinates 61°45'N 29°00'E
Altitude 70–70 m **Area** 48,221 ha

■ Site description
A complex of large areas of open water, numerous islands and long, forested, peninsula-like ridges within the Saimaa catchment area. The area is bordered to the south by Salpausselkä (an impressive glacial ridge formation), to the north-east by Puruvesi lake and to the north-west by Haukivesi lake. Nutrient input to the lake is low and consequently the vegetation on the lake is very sparse. Evidence of the slash-and-burn clearing of forests is visible in some areas, but typically forests are poor, commercially managed *Pinus sylvestris* monocultures. The more remote parts of the site are relatively undisturbed but human activity occurs in nearly all of the site.

Habitats Wetland (60%; standing fresh water), Forest and woodland (30%), Rocky areas (10%)
Land-use Forestry

■ Birds

Species	Season	Year	Pop min	Pop max	Acc	Criteria
Gavia arctica Black-throated Diver	B	1996	40	60	C	B2, C6
Bubo bubo Eagle Owl	R	1996	5	7	C	B2, C6

Also nationally important for breeding *Larus fuscus fuscus* (50–80 pairs). Species of global conservation concern that do not meet IBA criteria: *Crex crex* (1–3 pairs, breeding).

■ Protection status
National None **International** None

■ Conservation issues

Threats Unknown

Part of the area is a candidate SAC.

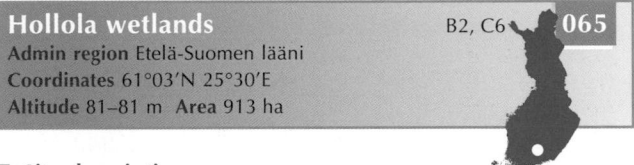

Kangasala wetlands
A4i, B1i, C3 · 064

Admin region Etelä-Suomen lääni
Coordinates 61°27′N 24°04′E
Altitude 70–70 m Area 1,093 ha

■ Site description

A complex of five adjacent wetlands and adjoining agricultural areas in the southern part of the Kangasala municipality. The lakes and bays are shallow and eutrophic, and surrounded mainly by forests. The farmland inside the IBA boundaries floods in spring, and provides valuable feeding grounds for wildfowl and waders. The area is strongly influenced by man and agriculture is intensive.

Habitats Forest and woodland (10%; broadleaved deciduous forest), Wetland (30%; standing fresh water), Artificial landscape (50%; arable land)
Land-use Agriculture (40%), Forestry (5%), Unknown (55%)

■ Birds

Species	Season	Year	Pop min	Pop max	Acc	Criteria
Mergus merganser Goosander	P	1996	1,001	5,000	C	A4i, B1i, C3

An important congregatory area for waterbirds, especially *Mergus merganser*. Species of global conservation concern that do not meet IBA criteria: *Crex crex* (1–5 pairs, breeding).

■ Protection status
National None **International** Partial
305 ha of IBA covered by Special Protection Area (Kirkkojärvi).

■ Conservation issues

Threats Extraction industry (A), Industrialization/urbanization (A), Selective logging/cutting (B)

Part of the area is a candidate SAC.

Hollola wetlands
B2, C6 · 065

Admin region Etelä-Suomen lääni
Coordinates 61°03′N 25°30′E
Altitude 81–81 m Area 913 ha

■ Site description
A large area comprising the shallow bays of Vesijärvi lake and the eutrophic Kutajärvi lake which lie on the southern edge of the Päijänne lake water system. The vegetation is extensive reedbed surrounded by narrow stretches of meadow, and large areas of floating plants.

Habitats Wetland (100%; standing fresh water)
Land-use Hunting (40%), Unknown (60%)

■ Birds

Species	Season	Year	Pop min	Pop max	Acc	Criteria
¹ *Botaurus stellaris* Bittern	B	1996	9	9	A	B2, C6

1. 1990–1996.

An important breeding and congregating area for waterbirds in continental Finland, with breeding species including *Podiceps cristatus* (517 pairs), *P. grisegena* (33 pairs), *Aythya ferina* (73 pairs) and *Larus ridibundus* (650 pairs).

■ Protection status
National None **International** Partial
770 ha of IBA covered by Special Protection Area (Kutajärven alue).

■ Conservation issues

Threats Abandonment/reduction of land management (B), Afforestation (A), Industrialization/urbanization (U)

Large parts of the area have remained undeveloped but there are plans for further housing developments along the shoreline. Overgrowth of the wetland is a threat. The majority of the area is listed under the National Bird Sanctuary Protection Programme, with just the Niemelänlahti area being totally unprotected. Part of the area is a candidate SAC.

Artjärvi wetlands
B1i, C2 · 066

Admin region Etelä-Suomen lääni
Coordinates 60°46′N 26°05′E
Altitude 70–70 m Area 1,506 ha

■ Site description
A complex of habitats, comprising several eutrophic lakes and other wetlands, shore meadows, and flooded fields, around the settlement of Artjärvi. The lakes are shallow and abundant in vegetation and are surrounded mostly by farmland and settlements. The IBA encompasses a large area of cultivated fields which are ornithologically important when flooded in spring.

Habitats Grassland (alpine/subalpine/boreal grassland), Wetland (standing fresh water; raised bog), Artificial landscape (arable land)
Land-use Agriculture, Hunting

■ Birds

Species	Season	Year	Pop min	Pop max	Acc	Criteria
¹ *Cygnus cygnus* Whooper Swan	P	1996	150	300	B	B1i, C2

1. 1990–1996.

One of the most important staging areas for *Cygnus cygnus* in continental Finland. Species of global conservation concern that do not meet IBA criteria: *Crex crex* (max. 4 pairs breeding, 11 birds on passage).

■ Protection status
National None **International** None

■ Conservation issues

Threats Abandonment/reduction of land management (B), Agricultural intensification/expansion (B), Construction/impact of dyke/dam/barrage (B), Dredging/canalization (B)

Human impact is high throughout almost the entire area, which causes some disturbance to the avifauna. However, several activities, such as cattle-grazing and the cultivation of flooded fields, are beneficial to breeding and staging birds. The overgrowth of wetlands in some parts of the site, as a result of insufficient land management, is a threat.

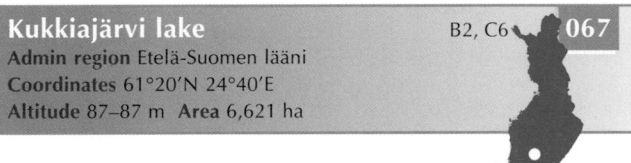

Kukkiajärvi lake
B2, C6 · 067

Admin region Etelä-Suomen lääni
Coordinates 61°20′N 24°40′E
Altitude 87–87 m Area 6,621 ha

■ Site description
A large, mainly nutrient-poor (oligotrophic) lake complex situated west of Päijänne lake, with 230 km of shoreline. The lake is dotted with numerous islands, some of which are large and forested, holding many rare plant species.

Habitats Wetland (95%), Rocky areas (5%; rock stacks/islets)
Land-use Unknown (100%)

■ Birds

Species	Season	Year	Pop min	Pop max	Acc	Criteria
¹ *Gavia arctica* Black-throated Diver	B	1987	48	48	C	B2, C6
¹ *Larus canus* Common Gull	B	1987	618	618	A	B2

1. 1986–1987.

Also one of the best areas in continental Finland for breeding *Larus fuscus fuscus* (83 pairs).

■ Protection status
National None **International** None

■ Conservation issues

Threats Agricultural intensification/expansion (B), Disturbance to birds (A), Extraction industry (A), Industrialization/urbanization (A)

There has been a substantial housing development along most of the lake shoreline over the last few decades, which has detrimentally affected bird populations, particularly *Gavia arctica*. Sewage effluent also impacts on the area. Part of the area is a candidate SAC.

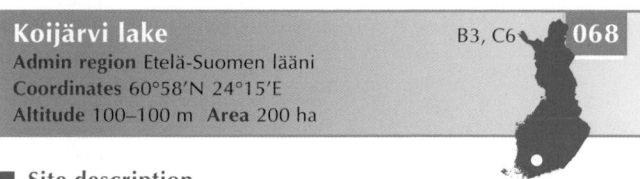

Koijärvi lake — B3, C6 — 068

Admin region Etelä-Suomen lääni
Coordinates 60°58′N 24°15′E
Altitude 100–100 m **Area** 200 ha

■ Site description
A small eutrophic lake surrounded by young deciduous forests in the heart of Häme province. The area of open water is small, with extensive marshes of *Equisetum*, *Carex* and grasses, which were harvested by local people until the 1950s, and now are encroaching on the lake. The major human activity is large-scale hunting in autumn.

Habitats Wetland (100%; standing fresh water, water-fringe vegetation)
Land-use Hunting

■ Birds

Species	Season	Year	Pop min	Pop max	Acc	Criteria
Porzana porzana Spotted Crake	B	1996	11	50	B	B3, C6

One of the best breeding areas for *Porzana porzana* in Finland. Species of global conservation concern that do not meet IBA criteria: *Crex crex* (1–5 pairs, breeding).

■ Protection status
National Partial **International** High
41 ha of IBA covered by Protected Area on Private Land (Koijärvi, 41 ha). 186 ha of IBA covered by Special Protection Area (Koijärvi).

■ Conservation issues

Threats Agricultural intensification/expansion (U)

The major threat to the avifauna is nutrient pollution of the lake by run-off from adjacent agricultural areas. A birdwatching tower is situated within the area. Part of the area is a candidate SAC.

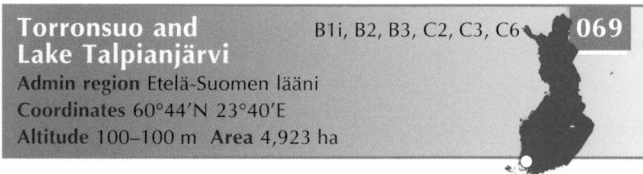

Torronsuo and Lake Talpianjärvi — B1i, B2, B3, C2, C3, C6 — 069

Admin region Etelä-Suomen lääni
Coordinates 60°44′N 23°40′E
Altitude 100–100 m **Area** 4,923 ha

■ Site description
The area encompasses a high diversity of habitats including extensive areas of raised bog (Torronsuo National Park is a near-wilderness area), a large eutrophic lake (Talpianjärvi) which is mostly covered by *Salix*- and *Carex*-dominated marshes due to falling water-levels, and surrounding arable farmlands.

Habitats Wetland (65%; standing fresh water; raised bog), Artificial landscape (35%)
Land-use Agriculture (30%), Not utilized (50%), Unknown (20%)

■ Birds

Species	Season	Year	Pop min	Pop max	Acc	Criteria
¹ *Cygnus cygnus* Whooper Swan	P	1996	101	500	A	B1i, C2
¹ *Anser fabalis* Bean Goose	P	1996	500	2,000	A	B1i, C3
¹ *Porzana porzana* Spotted Crake	B	1996	51	100	B	B3, C2, C6
¹ *Crex crex* Corncrake	B	1996	6	10	B	B2, C6
¹ *Grus grus* Crane	B	1996	51	100	B	B1i, B2, C2, C6
¹ *Grus grus* Crane	P	1996	700	1,500	B	B1i, C2

1. 1990–1996.

The area provides important breeding habitats for both farmland and peatland birds, including *Gavia stellata* (5 pairs) and *Perdix perdix* (35–45 pairs). Most significant are the high numbers of staging *Anser fabalis fabalis* and *Grus grus* (in autumn).

■ Protection status
National Partial **International** Partial

2,600 ha of IBA covered by National Park (Torronsuo, 2,600 ha). 3,385 ha of IBA covered by Special Protection Area (Torronsuo).

■ Conservation issues

Threats Unknown

Human impact is minor, except for farming. Part of the area is a candidate SAC.

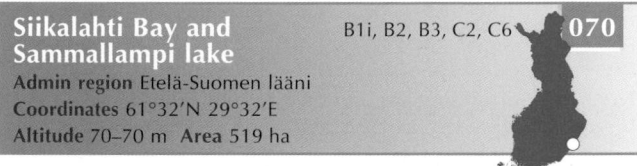

Siikalahti Bay and Sammallampi lake — B1i, B2, B3, C2, C6 — 070

Admin region Etelä-Suomen lääni
Coordinates 61°32′N 29°32′E
Altitude 70–70 m **Area** 519 ha

■ Site description
Siikalahti Bay, one of the most famous wetlands in Finland, is a sheltered, shallow bay of Simpele lake. It is heavily vegetated with *Phragmites*, *Typha* and floating plants like *Nymphaea*, with open water constituting no more than 25% of the lake area. Eutrophication is mostly due to the input of large amounts of nutrient run-off from adjacent farmlands and sewage disposal from nearby settlements. Sammallampi lake, connected to Siikalahti Bay via the Simpele lake water system, is a small eutrophic lake surrounded by farmlands and forests. The vegetation is similar to Siikalahti, but overgrowth does not pose a significant threat in the near future.

Habitats Forest and woodland (15%; broadleaved deciduous forest; mixed forest), Grassland (5%; alpine/subalpine/boreal grassland), Wetland (75%; standing fresh water), Unknown (5%)
Land-use Hunting (15%), Not utilized (50%), Tourism/recreation (15%), Unknown (20%)

■ Birds

Species	Season	Year	Pop min	Pop max	Acc	Criteria
Botaurus stellaris Bittern	B	1996	10	11	A	B2, C6
Cygnus cygnus Whooper Swan	P	1996	101	500	B	B1i, C2
Porzana porzana Spotted Crake	B	1996	45	70	A	B3, C6
Grus grus Crane	P	1996	101	500	B	B1i, C2

Very important for wetland breeding birds. Species of global conservation concern that do not meet IBA criteria: *Anser erythropus* (max. 1, passage), *Crex crex* (1 pair, breeding).

■ Protection status
National None **International** High
512 ha of IBA covered by three Special Protection Areas (Siikalahti, Sammallampi, and Rautalahti).

■ Conservation issues

Threats Abandonment/reduction of land management (A), Disturbance to birds (C)

Although Siikalahti was purchased by the state, its future does not seem promising since overgrowth of vegetation has continued despite some restoration trials. Hunting is forbidden at Siikalahti, but heavy at Sammallampi. The impact on the birds of large-scale nature tourism at Siikalahti is probably minor, as it is concentrated in the vicinity of the tourist centre and a birdwatching tower.

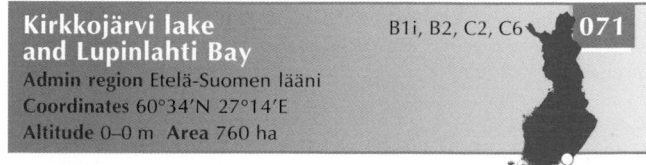

Kirkkojärvi lake and Lupinlahti Bay — B1i, B2, C2, C6 — 071

Admin region Etelä-Suomen lääni
Coordinates 60°34′N 27°14′E
Altitude 0–0 m **Area** 760 ha

■ Site description
Kirkkojärvi lake and Lupinlahti Bay are two wetlands adjacent to the town of Hamina. Kirkkojärvi lake, is almost totally covered by vegetation (reed *Phragmites*, etc.). It was previously heavily polluted by nutrients, and is still prone to silting but is managed by periodically raising the water-level. Lupinlahti Bay is a shallow, 5 km long, narrow

bay of the Gulf of Finland, with reedbeds up to 200 m wide. Some parts of the shoreline are rocky, others have meadows and forests, with several houses and summer cottages.

> **Habitats** Wetland (95%; coastal lagoon; standing fresh water), Unknown (5%)
> **Land-use** Hunting, Military, Tourism/recreation, Unknown, Urban/industrial/transport

■ Birds

Species		Season	Year	Pop min	Pop max	Acc	Criteria
[1] *Botaurus stellaris*	Bittern	B	1997	11	11	A	B2, C6
[1] *Cygnus cygnus*	Whooper Swan	P	1997	250	350	A	B1i, C2

1. 1996–1997.

The area is also a nationally important staging area during spring for *Cygnus columbianus* (100–150 birds). Species of global conservation concern that do not meet IBA criteria: *Haliaeetus albicilla* (1–5 individuals, passage), *Crex crex* (1 pair, breeding).

■ Protection status
National Partial **International** High
54 ha of IBA covered by Protected Area on Private Land (Suviranta, 54 ha). 720 ha of IBA covered by two Special Protection Areas (Kikkojärvi; Pappilansaari–Lupinlahti).

■ Conservation issues

> **Threats** Agricultural intensification/expansion (C), Construction/impact of dyke/dam/barrage (C), Disturbance to birds (A), Dredging/canalization (C), Extraction industry (A), Industrialization/urbanization (A)

Intensive hunting in autumn and professional net fishing almost all-year-round cause disturbance to birds. There is a birdwatching tower at Kirkkojärvi lake. Part of the area is a candidate SAC.

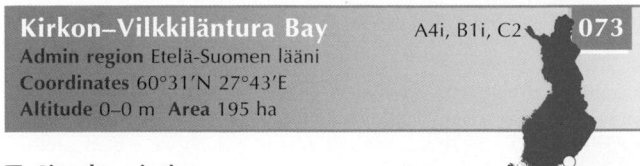

Itäinen Suomenlahti National Park
B1i, B1ii, B2, B3, C2, C3, C6 — 072
Admin region Etelä-Suomen lääni
Coordinates 60°20′N 27°00′E
Altitude 0–0 m **Area** 93,253 ha

■ Site description
A very large area of outer archipelago covering the whole north-east part of the Gulf of Finland. The site comprises extensive areas of open sea scattered with several large and forested islands, and numerous small, rocky islets. There are some remarkable submerged ridges in the area, and, more importantly for the avifauna, extensive spawning areas of the Baltic herring.

> **Habitats** Marine areas, Forest and woodland, Rocky areas
> **Land-use** Tourism/recreation, Hunting

■ Birds

Species		Season	Year	Pop min	Pop max	Acc	Criteria
Larus canus	Common Gull	B	1996	1,000	1,000	A	B2
[1] *Larus fuscus*	Lesser Black-backed Gull	B	1996	1,030	1,030	A	B1i, B3, C3
Sterna caspia	Caspian Tern	B	1996	11	11	A	B2, C6
Sterna paradisaea	Arctic Tern	B	1996	1,200	1,200	A	C2
Alca torda	Razorbill	B	1996	710	710	A	B1ii, B3, C3
Cepphus grylle	Black Guillemot	B	1996	560	560	A	B1ii, B2

1. *Larus fuscus fuscus.*

The area holds the largest population of *Larus fuscus fuscus* in the country, and also is important for other archipelagic species such as *Alca torda* and *Cepphus grylle*. During spring migration hundreds of thousands of Arctic ducks stop over within the IBA.

■ Protection status
National High **International** High
520 ha of IBA covered by National Park (Itäinen Suomenlahti, 520 ha). 93,043 ha of IBA covered by Special Protection Area (Itäisen Suomenlahden saaristo ja vedet).

■ Conservation issues

> **Threats** Disturbance to birds (U)

Human impact is high with all-year-round habitation, persistent recreation, shipping, professional fishing and hunting causing slight to serious disturbance to birds. Spring hunting, once an important dietary supplement for local people, but nowadays just a hobby for young men living in coastal villages, probably causes most disturbance. Part of the area is a candidate SAC.

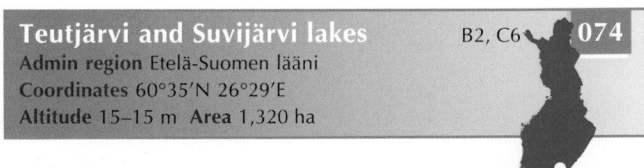

Kirkon–Vilkkiläntura Bay
A4i, B1i, C2 — 073
Admin region Etelä-Suomen lääni
Coordinates 60°31′N 27°43′E
Altitude 0–0 m **Area** 195 ha

■ Site description
A small, shallow bay on the western edge of Virolahti Bay in the Gulf of Finland. Large parts of the area have silted up due to heavy nutrient input from drainage and sewage disposal. Reedbeds (*Phragmites*) dominate the vegetation on the bay, and the shores are bordered both by large marshes of sedges and grasses, and by belts of bushes and deciduous forests.

> **Habitats** Wetland (100%; coastal lagoon)
> **Land-use** Fisheries/aquaculture, Hunting

■ Birds

Species		Season	Year	Pop min	Pop max	Acc	Criteria
Cygnus columbianus	Bewick's Swan	P	1996	51	100	A	A4i, B1i, C2
Cygnus cygnus	Whooper Swan	P	1996	101	500	A	B1i, C2
Sterna caspia	Caspian Tern	P	1996	11	50	A	B1i, C2

The most important staging area in the country for *Cygnus columbianus*. Species of global conservation concern that do not meet IBA criteria: *Haliaeetus albicilla* (1–5 individuals, passage), *Aquila clanga* (2–5 individuals, passage), *Crex crex* (1–5 pairs, breeding), *Gallinago media* (passage).

■ Protection status
National None **International** High
195 ha of IBA covered by Special Protection Area (Kirkon–Vilkkiläntura).

■ Conservation issues

> **Threats** Abandonment/reduction of land management (B), Aquaculture/fisheries (A)

Several human activities threaten the area including hunting in autumn, tourism, fish-farming off Virolahti Bay, continued sewage disposal and overgrowth of the wetland. Birdwatching towers are situated on the shores of the bay. The area is a candidate SAC.

Teutjärvi and Suvijärvi lakes
B2, C6 — 074
Admin region Etelä-Suomen lääni
Coordinates 60°35′N 26°29′E
Altitude 15–15 m **Area** 1,320 ha

■ Site description
The site includes two lakes (Teutjärvi and Suvijärvi) connected by a narrow ditch at the mouth of the Kymi river. Teutjärvi is a large, shallow-shored lake with some reedbeds and surrounded by cultivated farmland. Fishing is regular, and the water-level has been artificially reduced to prevent flooding. Suvijärvi lake has extensive reedbeds.

> **Habitats** Wetland (70%; standing fresh water; river/stream), Artificial landscape (30%; arable land)
> **Land-use** Hunting, Agriculture, Tourism/recreation

■ Birds

Species		Season	Year	Pop min	Pop max	Acc	Criteria
[1] *Crex crex*	Corncrake	B	1996	13	13	A	B2, C6

1. 1992–1996.

Cultivated farmland around the lakes holds fairly good numbers of the globally threatened *Crex crex*. Species of global conservation concern that do not meet IBA criteria: *Haliaeetus albicilla* (passage).

■ Protection status
National None **International** Partial
557 ha of IBA covered by Special Protection Area (Teutjärven ja Suvijärven lintuvedet).

■ Conservation issues

Threats Agricultural intensification/expansion (U)

Part of the area is a candidate SAC.

Pernaja outer archipelago · 075

B1i, B1ii, B2, B3, C2, C3, C6
Admin region Etelä-Suomen lääni
Coordinates 60°13′N 26°20′E
Altitude 0–0 m **Area** 18,250 ha

■ Site description
A fairly large offshore archipelago in the middle of the Gulf of Finland. The mainly small and rocky islands and islets are separated by large expanses of open sea. The larger islands support mixed forest or *Juniperus* stands, sometimes interspersed with small patches of meadow.

Habitats Rocky areas (50%; rock stacks/islets), Marine areas (50%)
Land-use Tourism/recreation, Hunting

■ Birds

Species	Season	Year	Pop min	Pop max	Acc	Criteria
[1] *Sterna caspia* Caspian Tern	B	1997	42	42	A	B1i, B2, C2, C6
[1] *Alca torda* Razorbill	B	1997	320	590	A	B1ii, B3, C3
[1] *Cepphus grylle* Black Guillemot	B	1997	169	267	A	B1ii, B2
1. 1992–1997.						

An important area for island-breeding birds, including the only nationally important breeding cliff for *Uria aalge* (23–28 pairs).

■ Protection status
National Low **International** Partial
731 ha of IBA covered by Protected Area on Private Land (Aspskär, 731 ha). 731 ha of IBA covered by Ramsar Site (Aspskär, 731 ha). 14,277 ha of IBA covered by Special Protection Area (Pernajanlahtien ja Pernajan saariston)

■ Conservation issues

Threats Disturbance to birds (B), Recreation/tourism (A)

Human impact on the area is minor. An ornithological station has been maintained on Aspskär island for several decades. Part of the area is a candidate SAC.

Porvoonjoki delta · 076

A4i, B1i, B3, C2, C3
Admin region Etelä-Suomen lääni
Coordinates 60°21′N 25°40′E
Altitude 0–0 m **Area** 899 ha

■ Site description
A large, richly vegetated delta of the Porvoo river, with few small meadows along the shores. At the heart of the site is a largish, shallow area of open water (Stenbölefjärden) bordered by belts of *Phragmites*.

Habitats Grassland (5%; alpine/subalpine/boreal grassland), Wetland (95%; coastal lagoon)
Land-use Urban/industrial/transport (20%), Tourism/recreation (70%), Not utilized (10%)

■ Birds

Species	Season	Year	Pop min	Pop max	Acc	Criteria
Cygnus cygnus Whooper Swan	P	1996	400	500	A	B1i, C2
Mergus albellus Smew	P	1996	200	250	A	A4i, B1i, C2
Mergus merganser Goosander	P	1996	3,000	3,500	A	A4i, B1i, C3
Acrocephalus scirpaceus Reed Warbler	B	1996	90	130	C	B3

One of the most important breeding and staging areas for waterbirds in the country. Probably the best single congregatory area in spring in Finland for *Mergus merganser* and *M. albellus*. Species of global

conservation concern that do not meet IBA criteria: *Haliaeetus albicilla* (max. 2 individuals, passage), *Crex crex* (max. 3 pairs, breeding).

■ Protection status
National Partial **International** Partial
446 ha of IBA covered by Protected Area on Private Lands (Ruskis, 226 ha, Stensböle, 85 ha, Stenbölefjärden, 273 ha). 235 ha of IBA covered by Ramsar Site (Ruskis, 235 ha). 764 ha of IBA covered by Special Protection Area (Porvoonjoen suisto-Stensböle).

■ Conservation issues

Threats Abandonment/reduction of land management (B), Afforestation (C), Deforestation (commercial) (B), Recreation/tourism (U)

Human impact is considerable in most of the area, with many parts bordered by settlements, while boating and fishing disturbs avifauna in the interior of the site. Overgrowth of the wetland is also a threat. Hunting is permitted throughout the area, except the northernmost part (Ruskis) which remains a sanctuary for staging waterbirds in autumn. A large EU LIFE project has been started in the area. A birdwatching tower is situated at Ruskis, on the mouth of the Porvoo river. Part of the area is a candidate SAC.

Porvoo outer archipelago · 077

A4i, B1i, B1ii, B2, C2, C6
Admin region Etelä-Suomen lääni
Coordinates 60°10′N 25°40′E
Altitude 0–0 m **Area** 22,570 ha

■ Site description
A large offshore archipelago in the middle part of the Gulf of Finland. The area holds many islands with rocky or stony shores. The largest of the islands are forested, with areas of meadows and *Juniperus* stands.

Habitats Forest and woodland, Marine areas, Rocky areas
Land-use Unknown

■ Birds

Species	Season	Year	Pop min	Pop max	Acc	Criteria
[1] *Sterna caspia* Caspian Tern	B	1997	53	53	A	A4i,B1i,B2,C2,C6
[1] *Cepphus grylle* Black Guillemot	B	1997	224	229	A	B1ii, B2
1. 1996–1997.						

An important breeding area for archipelagic avifauna, especially for *Sterna caspia*.

■ Protection status
National Partial **International** Partial
2,134 ha of IBA covered by Protected Area on Private Land (Söderskär, 2,134 ha). 8,338 ha of IBA covered by Specific Protection Area (Långören, 8,338 ha). 10,552 ha of IBA covered by Ramsar Site (Söderskär and Långören, 10,552 ha). 13,061 ha of IBA covered by Special Protection Area (Söderskäin ja Låhgörenin saaristo).

■ Conservation issues

Threats Unknown

A research station has been maintained for decades on Söderskär island, and bird migration has been very actively monitored for more than 20 years on Kummelskär island. Part of the area is a candidate SAC.

Laajalahti Bay, Vanhankaupunginlahti Bay and Viikki · 078

B1i, B3, C3
Admin region Etelä-Suomen lääni
Coordinates 60°12′N 24°56′E
Altitude 0–0 m **Area** 1,274 ha

■ Site description
The site includes two shallow, sea bays, dominated by reed *Phragmites*, and a largish area of adjacent farmland, situated close to Helsinki. The

farmland of Viikki is separated from Vanhankaupunginlahti by a narrow zone of young, wet, deciduous forest and by some older mixed forest.

Habitats Forest and woodland (10%), Wetland (40%; coastal lagoon), Artificial landscape (50%)
Land-use Agriculture (40%), Nature conservation/research (40%), Tourism/recreation (50%)

■ Birds

Species		Season	Year	Pop min	Pop max	Acc	Criteria
[1] *Mergus merganser*	Goosander	P	1996	1,500	2,000	A	B1i, C3
[1] *Acrocephalus scirpaceus*	Reed Warbler	B	1996	110	130	B	B3

1. 1990–1996.

An important breeding and staging area for wetland birds. The site also supports one of the largest national populations of a breeding bird new to Finland, *Panurus biarmicus* (65 pairs).

■ Protection status
National Partial **International** Partial
218 ha of IBA covered by Protected Area on Private Land (Viikki–Vanhankaupunginlahti, 218 ha). 36 ha of IBA covered by Specific Protection Area (Viikki, 36 ha). 141 ha of IBA covered by Specific Protection Area (Laajalahti, 141 ha). 247 ha of IBA covered by Ramsar Site (Viikki, 247 ha). 531 ha of IBA covered by two Special Protection Areas (Laajalahden lintuvesi; Vanhankaupunginlahden lintuvesi).

■ Conservation issues

Threats Extraction industry (B), Industrialization/urbanization (B), Recreation/tourism (B), Selective logging/cutting (C)

The entire area suffers from considerable human impact. All parts of Viikki are cultivated, and recreational activities, especially hiking and birdwatching, are common. Housing development and road construction plans seriously threaten parts of the area. Water quality has improved in recent years as a result of new and effective sewage treatment. Laajalahti and Vanhankaupunginlahti have several bird-watching towers and wooden trails. Part of the area is a candidate SAC.

Nuuksio
B2, B3, C6 **079**
Admin region Etelä-Suomen lääni
Coordinates 60°17′N 24°35′E
Altitude 70–70 m **Area** 6,700 ha

■ Site description
A diverse area west of Helsinki comprising many types of forest, small bogs, numerous lakes, ponds, hills, glacial ridges and rocky ledges. The most typical habitat is nutrient-poor heathland with *Pinus sylvestris*; patches of herb-rich deciduous forest and old, natural mixed forest are scarcer. Overall, the cover and continuity of forest is very good compared to most of southern Finland. Recreational activities are common all-year-round, however, these are mainly restricted to a wide network of natural and wooded tracks; some parts of the area remain relatively unused.

Habitats Forest and woodland (70%), Wetland (30%; standing fresh water, raised bog)
Land-use Forestry (10%), Tourism/recreation (90%)

■ Birds

Species		Season	Year	Pop min	Pop max	Acc	Criteria
Tetrao tetrix	Black Grouse	R	1996	51	100	C	B2, C6
Caprimulgus europaeus	Nightjar	B	1996	20	30	C	B2, C6
Picus canus	Grey-headed Woodpecker	R	1996	15	25	B	B2, C6
Loxia pytyopsittacus	Parrot Crossbill	B	1996	20	40	C	B3

Phylloscopus trochiloides (15–25 pairs), *Glaucidium passerinum* (10–20 pairs), and *Ficedula parva* (10–20 pairs) also breed.

■ Protection status
National Partial **International** None
2,372 ha of IBA covered by National Park (Nuuksio, 2,372 ha). 75 ha of IBA covered by Protected Area on Private Lands (Koivulan lehtopurolaakso 20 ha; Pääskyvuori, 7 ha; Kilpilampi–Lippukallio, 30 ha; Saukonnoro, 3 ha; Haukkalampi-Romvuori; 10 ha, Hynkänlampi, 5 ha).

■ Conservation issues

Threats Intensified forest management, Recreation/tourism

Conservation authorities have restored some key habitats in recent years. New land areas are being purchased with the intention of enlarging the National Park. Part of the area is a candidate SAC.

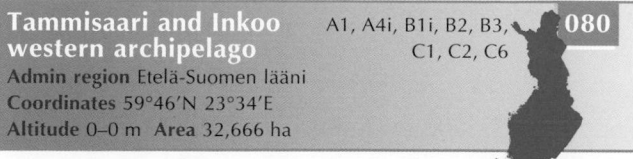

Tammisaari and Inkoo western archipelago
A1, A4i, B1i, B2, B3, C1, C2, C6 **080**
Admin region Etelä-Suomen lääni
Coordinates 59°46′N 23°34′E
Altitude 0–0 m **Area** 32,666 ha

■ Site description
A large archipelago on the eastern side of the Hanko peninsula. Hundreds of islands dominate the landscape, several of which are very large and forested, though most are small and rocky with very sparse vegetation.

Habitats Marine areas (80%), Rocky areas (5%)
Land-use Hunting, Military, Tourism/recreation

■ Birds

Species		Season	Year	Pop min	Pop max	Acc	Criteria
Haliaeetus albicilla	White-tailed Eagle	W	1994	20	30	B	A1, C1
Larus canus	Common Gull	B	1994	800	1,000	B	B2
Larus marinus	Great Black-backed Gull	B	1994	130	160	B	B3
Sterna caspia	Caspian Tern	B	1994	115	115	A	A4i,B1i,B2,C2,C6
Cepphus grylle	Black Guillemot	B	1994	120	120	A	B2

An important area for island-breeding birds with the largest populations of *Sterna caspia* and *Larus marinus* in Finland.

■ Protection status
National Partial **International** Partial
6,173 ha of IBA covered by National Park (Tammisaaren Saaristo, 6,173 ha). 5,360 ha of IBA covered by Protected Area on Private Lands (Hättö, 442 ha; Hummelskär, 14 ha; Strömsö, 334 ha; Gästans, 124 ha; Lill-Skälö, 119 ha; Busö, 134 ha; Nothamn, 3,544 ha; Ahlglo, 786 ha). 25,132 ha of IBA covered by two Special Protection Areas (Tammisaaren ja Hangon saaristo; Inkoon saaristo).

■ Conservation issues

Threats Recreation/tourism (U), Disturbance to birds (U)

Human impact is high in some parts, minor in others. Part of the area is a candidate SAC.

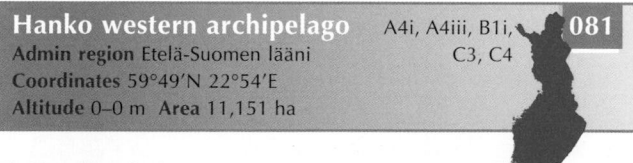

Hanko western archipelago
A4i, A4iii, B1i, C3, C4 **081**
Admin region Etelä-Suomen lääni
Coordinates 59°49′N 22°54′E
Altitude 0–0 m **Area** 11,151 ha

■ Site description
A diverse site situated in the south-west corner of the Hanko peninsula, comprising cliff-lined shores, sand-dunes, wet meadows and an archipelago of mostly small rocky islands. The IBA falls within Salpausselkä, a glacial ridge formation of southern Finland extending several hundred kilometres in length.

Habitats Marine areas (80%), Rocky areas, Unknown (10%)
Land-use Tourism/recreation (50%), Unknown (50%), Urban/industrial/transport (70%)

■ Birds

Species		Season	Year	Pop min	Pop max	Acc	Criteria
[1] *Somateria mollissima*	Eider	P	1996	30,000	30,000	C	A4i, B1i, C3

1. 1985–1996.

One of the most important staging areas for waterbirds in the country, with total numbers exceeding 20,000 individuals. Species of global conservation concern that do not meet IBA criteria: *Polysticta stelleri* (27 birds on passage, irregular and for short periods, 5 individuals in winter), *Haliaeetus albicilla* (4 individuals in winter, 5 on passage), *Gallinago media* (2 individuals, passage).

■ Protection status
National Partial **International** Partial
2,338 ha of IBA covered by Protected Area on Private Land (Tulliniemi, 2,347 ha). 29 ha of IBA covered by Specific Protection Area (Uddskatan, 29 ha). 5,294 ha of IBA covered by Special Protection Area (Tulliniemen linnustonsuojelualue).

■ Conservation issues

Threats Recreation/tourism (B), Selective logging/cutting (B), Infrastructure (U)

An expanding harbour, adjacent to the IBA, is a source of constant disturbance. Pressure from recreation, such as hiking along the shores and boating in the archipelago, also cause disturbance. On the southernmost tip of the Hanko peninsula a bird observatory has been maintained for twenty years, conducting bird ringing and migration observations. Part of the area is a candidate SAC.

Kirkkonummi archipelago   C2   082
Admin region Etelä-Suomen lääni
Coordinates 59°56′N 24°30′E
Altitude 0–0 m **Area** 11,808 ha

■ Site description
A large area of both inner and outer archipelago situated off Porkkala peninsula in the central part of the Gulf of Finland. The archipelago is dominated by large areas of open water. Most of the islands are small, barren and rocky, but a few are larger and forested. Some islands have small areas of low vegetated shore meadows and shallow lagoons. The main human activity is recreational boating but landing is forbidden on many islands. Few islands have cottages or other buildings.

Habitats Marine areas (80%), Rocky areas (20%)
Land-use Hunting (20%), Military (25%), Tourism/recreation (20%)

■ Birds

Species	Season	Year	Pop min	Pop max	Acc	Criteria
Branta leucopsis Barnacle Goose	B	1997	14	14	A	C2
Larus marinus Great Black-backed Gull	B	1997	67	70	A	B3

Nationally important populations of *Larus marinus* (67–70 pairs) and *Larus argentatus* (1,865 pairs) also breed. Species of global conservation concern that do not meet IBA criteria: *Polysticta stelleri* (up to 40 birds on passage, irregular), *Haliaeetus albicilla* (3 individuals, passage).

■ Protection status
National Low **International** None
171 ha of IBA covered by Protected Area on Private Lands (Brändt, 9 ha; Gadd, 15 ha; Sommaröarna, 13 ha; Galjonsgrund, 76 ha; Salmen, 19 ha; Enbusken–Rönnbusken, 41 ha). 506 ha of IBA covered by Specific Protection Area (Porkkalan Saaristo, 372 ha, Kanskogbroken–Bergstadbrotten, 134 ha).

■ Conservation issues

Threats Disturbance to birds (B), Recreation/tourism (B)

There has been a bird observatory on Rönnskär island for many years, carrying out bird ringing and observing migration. The area is a candidate SAC.

Pori archipelago and wetlands   A4i, B1i, B2,   083
Admin region Länsi-Suomen lääni   B3, C2, C3, C6
Coordinates 61°32′N 21°36′E
Altitude 0–0 m **Area** 15,441 ha

■ Site description
A very large and outstanding habitat complex of archipelago, sea bays, river mouths, lagoons and eutrophic lakes at the delta of the Kokemäki river. Large areas of meadow, marsh and deciduous forest on shores

---

considerably increase the diversity of the avifauna. Fishing, boating and hunting are common in some parts of the site.

Habitats Wetland (coastal lagoon), Rocky areas (sea cliff/rocky shore), Marine areas
Land-use Nature conservation/research, Water management, Fisheries/aquaculture, Tourism/recreation, Hunting

■ Birds

Species	Season	Year	Pop min	Pop max	Acc	Criteria
[1] *Botaurus stellaris* Bittern	B	1997	14	14	A	B2, C6
[1] *Cygnus cygnus* Whooper Swan	P	1997	3,000	3,000	B	A4i, B1i, C2
[1] *Anser fabalis* Bean Goose	P	1997	3,500	3,500	B	B1i, C3
[1] *Anser anser* Greylag Goose	B	1997	69	69	B	B1i, C3
[1] *Anser anser* Greylag Goose	P	1997	1,000	1,000	B	B1i, C3
[1] *Anas crecca* Teal	P	1997	4,000	4,000	B	B1i, C3
[1] *Anas acuta* Pintail	P	1997	1,500	1,500	B	B1i, C3
[1] *Anas clypeata* Shoveler	P	1997	500	500	B	B1i, C3
[1] *Aythya ferina* Pochard	B	1997	210	210	B	B3
[1] *Aythya ferina* Pochard	P	1997	2,500	2,500	B	B3
[1] *Bucephala clangula* Goldeneye	P	1997	12,000	12,000	B	A4i, B1i, C3
[1] *Mergus merganser* Goosander	P	1997	3,000	3,000	B	A4i, B1i, C3
[1] *Circus cyaneus* Hen Harrier	B	1997	20	20	B	B2
[1] *Porzana porzana* Spotted Crake	B	1997	25	25	B	B3, C6
[1] *Crex crex* Corncrake	B	1997	2	12	B	B2, C6
[1] *Grus grus* Crane	P	1997	1,200	1,200	B	B1i, C2
[1] *Tringa erythropus* Spotted Redshank	P	1997	1,000	1,000	B	A4i, B1i, C3
[1] *Tringa totanus* Redshank	B	1997	120	120	B	B2
[1] *Tringa totanus* Redshank	P	1997	300	300	B	B2
[1] *Larus minutus* Little Gull	B	1997	228	228	B	B1i, B2, C3
[1] *Larus canus* Common Gull	B	1997	897	897	B	B2
[1] *Sterna caspia* Caspian Tern	P	1997	130	130	A	B1i, C2
[1] *Luscinia luscinia* Thrush Nightingale	B	1997	180	180	B	B3
[1] *Acrocephalus schoenobaenus* Sedge Warbler	B	1997	2,500	2,500	B	B3
[1] *Acrocephalus scirpaceus* Reed Warbler	B	1997	600	600	B	B3

1. 1988–1997.

One of the most important wetlands in the country for breeding and staging waterbirds, including some of the largest breeding populations in Finland of *Podiceps auritus* (29 pairs), *Botaurus stellaris*, *Aythya ferina*, *Circus aeruginosus* (16 pairs), *Fulica atra* (405 pairs), *Calidris alpina schinzii* (25 pairs), *Larus minutus*, *Acrocephalus scirpaceus* and *Panurus biarmicus* (80 pairs). The site is also an important staging area for several species, including nationally important numbers of *Cygnus olor* (1,200 individuals), *Branta canadensis* (1,500 individuals), *Tadorna tadorna* (300 individuals), *Charadrius hiaticula* (1,500 individuals), *Limicola falcinellus* (300 individuals) and *Calidris temminckii* (300 individuals). Species of global conservation concern that do not meet IBA criteria: *Anser erythropus* (max. 8 individuals, passage), *Polysticta stelleri* (max. 30 individuals irregularly occur on passage), *Haliaeetus albicilla* (4 pairs breeding, 12 birds on passage, 6 birds wintering), *Aquila clanga* (max. 2 individuals, passage).

■ Protection status
National Low **International** Partial
141 ha of IBA covered by Protected Area on Private Lands (Herrainpäivä, 16 ha; Enäjärvi, 12 ha; Leveäkari–Riistalanlanti, 13 ha; Halssi, 6 ha; Kokemäensaaret, 117 ha). 8,993 ha of IBA covered by two Special Protection Areas (Kokemäenjoensuisto; Preiviikinlahti).

■ Conservation issues

Threats Construction/impact of dyke/dam/barrage (U), Drainage (B), Dredging/canalization (U), Industrialization/urbanization (U), Recreation/tourism

There are several birdwatching towers within the area. Part of the site is a candidate SAC.

Koskeljärvi, Vaaljärvi   B1i, B3, C3, C6   084
and Pitkäjärvi lakes
Admin region Länsi-Suomen lääni
Coordinates 60°56′N 22°07′E
Altitude 40–40 m **Area** 2,090 ha

■ Site description
Three adjacent, shallow and nutrient-rich lakes with lush vegetation on the upper course of the Lapijoki river. Some parts of the shoreline

are bordered by wide marshes. The water-levels of Koskeljärvi and Pitkäjärvi lakes are regulated, which has increased the lake's value for birds on the former, but on the latter has caused over-eutrophication. Koskeljärvi, the most important ornithologically, is the largest lake in south-western Finland without any settlements on its shores.

Habitats Forest and woodland (10%), Wetland (90%; standing fresh water; raised bog)
Land-use Not utilized (100%)

■ Birds

Species	Season	Year	Pop min	Pop max	Acc	Criteria
[1] *Podiceps grisegena* Red-necked Grebe	B	1997	93	93	A	B1i, C3
[1] *Aythya ferina* Pochard	B	1997	146	146	A	B3
[1] *Porzana porzana* Spotted Crake	B	1997	26	26	A	B3, C6

1. 1991–1997.

An important breeding area for wetland birds, including nationally important numbers of *Circus aeruginosus* (6 pairs). Species of global conservation concern that do not meet IBA criteria: *Haliaeetus albicilla* (max. 6 individuals, passage).

■ Protection status
National Low **International** Partial
18 ha of IBA covered by Protected Area on Private Land (Kirkkolahti, 1 ha). 17 ha of IBA covered by Protected Area on Private Land (Tanska, 17 ha). 1,539 ha covered by Special Protection Area (Koskeljärvi).

■ Conservation issues

Threats Unknown (U)

Part of the area is a candidate SAC.

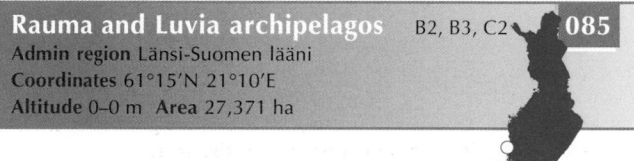

Rauma and Luvia archipelagos   B2, B3, C2   085
Admin region Länsi-Suomen lääni
Coordinates 61°15'N 21°10'E
Altitude 0–0 m **Area** 27,371 ha

■ Site description
A very large archipelago with numerous islands lying offshore of Luvia and Rauma. The central archipelago of Rauma has many very large forested and inhabited islands with smaller islands and islets to its north and south. The other main area is the Luvia archipelago, comprising over 400 islands, most of which are rocky and stony and 0.4–4 ha in size. The larger islands of this archipelago are covered by *Picea*-dominated old forests, belts of *Juniperus* and *Hippophae*, and low heaths.

Habitats Marine areas (93%), Unknown (7%)
Land-use Hunting, Unknown

■ Birds

Species	Season	Year	Pop min	Pop max	Acc	Criteria
[1] *Larus canus* Common Gull	B	1995	1,323	1,323	A	B2
[1] *Larus marinus* Great Black-backed Gull	B	1995	90	90	A	B3
[1] *Sterna paradisaea* Arctic Tern	B	1995	1,430	1,430	B	C2

1. 1988–1995.

An important area for island-breeding birds.

■ Protection status
National Low **International** Partial
121 ha of IBA covered by Protected Area on Private Lands (Omenapuunas, 112 ha; Reksaari, 4 ha; Pihlasenokka, 4 ha; Puuvallinnokka, 4 ha; Kylmäsantakari, 7 ha; Hylkikartta, 3 ha; Marjakari–Pohjoiskallio, 8 ha). 14,041 ha of IBA covered by Special Protection Area (Luvian saaristo).

■ Conservation issues

Threats Afforestation (A), Deforestation (commercial) (A), Disturbance to birds (B), Extraction industry (B), Industrialization/urbanization (B), Recreation/tourism (B)

Condensation water from a nuclear plant impacts on the area. The large, isolated island of Säppi within the IBA has a longstanding bird-ringing station where exceptionally large numbers of waders have been ringed. Part of the area is a candidate SAC.

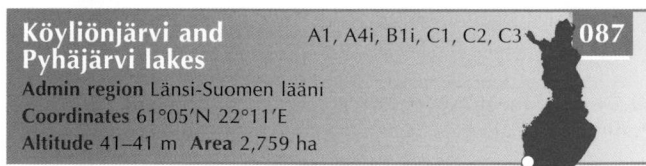

Puurijärvi–Isosuo wetlands   A1, B1i, C1, C2   086
Admin region Länsi-Suomen lääni
Coordinates 61°14'N 22°34'E
Altitude 45–45 m **Area** 3,474 ha

■ Site description
A complex of habitats, comprising the large, shallow and eutrophic Puurijärvi lake, open fields (220 ha) and several adjacent mires along the Kokemäki river. The lake is mainly bordered by forests and in summer becomes almost totally overgrown with vegetation. Isosuo and other mires are large raised bogs with extensive open areas of pools in the centre, and sparse swamp-forests or mixtures of swamps and forests at the edges.

Habitats Wetland (91%; standing fresh water; raised bog), Artificial landscape (7%)
Land-use Agriculture (7%), Not utilized (90%)

■ Birds

Species	Season	Year	Pop min	Pop max	Acc	Criteria
[1] *Cygnus cygnus* Whooper Swan	P	1997	400	400	—	B1i, C2
[1] *Haliaeetus albicilla* White-tailed Eagle	P	1997	10	15	—	A1, C1

1. 1990–1997.

An important staging area for *Haliaeetus albicilla* and *Cygnus cygnus*. *Podiceps grisegena* (20 pairs), *Porzana porzana* (15 pairs) and *Grus grus* (10 pairs) also breed. Species of global conservation concern that do not meet IBA criteria: *Crex crex* (max. 4 pairs, breeding).

■ Protection status
National Partial **International** High
2,538 ha of IBA covered by National Park (Puurijärvi–Isosuo, 2,538 ha). 3,126 ha of IBA covered by Special Protection Area (Puurijärvi–Isosuo).

■ Conservation issues

Threats Recreation/tourism (C)

Puurijärvi lake has a birdwatching tower. Restoration plans include the raising of water-levels.

Köyliönjärvi and Pyhäjärvi lakes   A1, A4i, B1i, C1, C2, C3   087
Admin region Länsi-Suomen lääni
Coordinates 61°05'N 22°11'E
Altitude 41–41 m **Area** 2,759 ha

■ Site description
Two adjacent large lakes lying south-east of Eura. Köyliönjärvi lake is 10 km long, eutrophic and surrounded by farmland and settlements. Several large ridge-like islands with mixed habitats stand in the middle of the lake. Cattle graze some parts of the shoreline keeping meadow vegetation low and deciduous forests open. The IBA also includes some of the most ornithologically important bays of Pyhäjärvi lake, which is otherwise nutrient-poor, (oligotrophic) and unimportant for birds.

Habitats Wetland (80%; standing fresh water), Rocky areas (sea cliff/rocky shore), Artificial landscape, Forest and woodland (broadleaved deciduous forest; mixed forest)
Land-use Agriculture (90%), Fisheries/aquaculture, Forestry (10%), Military (5%), Water management (80%)

■ Birds

Species	Season	Year	Pop min	Pop max	Acc	Criteria
[1] *Podiceps grisegena* Red-necked Grebe	B	1997	101	101	B	B1i, C3
[1] *Cygnus cygnus* Whooper Swan	P	1997	400	400	B	B1i, C2
[1] *Mergus merganser* Goosander	P	1997	3,000	3,000	B	A4i, B1i, C3
[1] *Haliaeetus albicilla* White-tailed Eagle	W	1997	10	15	—	A1, C1

1. 1990–1997.

One of the most important staging areas for *Mergus merganser* (in autumn) in Finland. Species of global conservation concern that do not meet IBA criteria: *Haliaeetus albicilla* (5 individuals, passage), *Crex crex* (1 pair, breeding).

■ Protection status
National None **International** Partial
689 ha of IBA covered by Special Protection Area (Köyliönjärvi).

■ Conservation issues

Threats Abandonment/reduction of land management (B), Agricultural intensification/ expansion (A), Industrialization/urbanization (B), Recreation/tourism (C), Selective logging/cutting (C)

Part of the area is a candidate SAC.

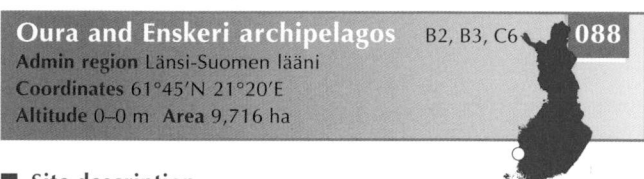

Oura and Enskeri archipelagos B2, B3, C6 088
Admin region Länsi-Suomen lääni
Coordinates 61°45′N 21°20′E
Altitude 0–0 m **Area** 9,716 ha

■ Site description
A large archipelago offshore of Merikarvia. The landscape is dominated by large areas of open sea with several groups of numerous scattered islands. The most important part of this site is the large archipelago of Oura, practically unpopulated by man, and encompassing numerous larger, mainly forested islands, and hundreds of small islets and rocks. Iso-Enskeri and Vähä-Enskeri islands hold a remarkable number of *Pinus* trees in excess of 200 years old.

Habitats Forest and woodland, Marine areas (sea inlet/coastal features), Rocky areas
Land-use Unknown

■ Birds

Species	Season	Year	Pop min	Pop max	Acc	Criteria
[1,2]*Larus fuscus* Lesser Black-backed Gull	B	1996	348	348	A	B3
[1]*Sterna caspia* Caspian Tern	B	1996	8	8	A	B2, C6

1. 1986–1996.
2. *Larus fuscus fuscus*.

The area holds one of the largest populations of *Larus fuscus fuscus* in Finland. Important populations of several other island-breeding species also occur.

■ Protection status
National Low **International** None
340 ha of IBA covered by Protected Area on Private Lands (Mäntyniennennokka, 7 ha; Komopassi–Pitkäniemennokka, 254 ha; Piuskari–Pirttikari, 86 ha).

■ Conservation issues

Threats Disturbance to birds (B), Extraction industry (B), Industrialization/urbanization (B), Recreation/tourism (B)

Part of the area is a candidate SAC.

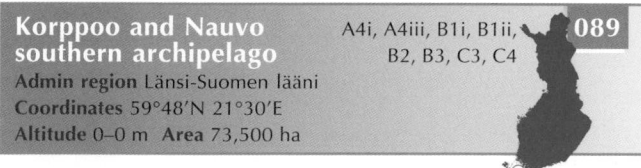

Korppoo and Nauvo southern archipelago A4i, A4iii, B1i, B1ii, B2, B3, C3, C4 089
Admin region Länsi-Suomen lääni
Coordinates 59°48′N 21°30′E
Altitude 0–0 m **Area** 73,500 ha

■ Site description

Habitats Marine areas, Unknown
Land-use Tourism/recreation, Urban/industrial/transport

A very large area of outer archipelago inside the Saaristomeri National Park: the site's boundaries have been drawn to include the most ornithologically important parts of the park. Large areas of open water dominate the landscape, although the numerous islands are also impressive. Most of the islands are small, stony and treeless with steep shores. Jurmo, the largest, is ornithologically the most diverse and important, supporting long stony or sandy ridges and large, open areas of treeless heath. Boating and other human activities are much scarcer than within the inner archipelago.

■ Birds

Species	Season	Year	Pop min	Pop max	Acc	Criteria
[1]*Somateria mollissima* Eider	B	1995	11,500	11,500	A	A4i, B1i, C3
[1]*Larus marinus* Great Black-backed Gull	B	1995	170	190	A	B3
[1]*Alca torda* Razorbill	B	1995	200	220	A	B1ii, C3
[1]*Cepphus grylle* Black Guillemot	B	1995	130	150	A	B1ii, B2

1. 1990–1995.

An exceptionally important breeding area for archipelagic avifauna, with total numbers exceeding 20,000 pairs. Also nationally important as a staging area for waterbirds.

■ Protection status
National High **International** High
73,500 ha of IBA covered by National Park (Saaristomeri, 311,000 ha). 13,601 ha of IBA covered by two Special Protection Areas (Saaristomeri; Jurmo). 73,500 ha of IBA covered by Biosphere Reserve (Saaristomeri, 420,000 ha).

■ Conservation issues
There are no major threats. For many years a bird observatory has been maintained at Jurmo. Part of the area is a candidate SAC.

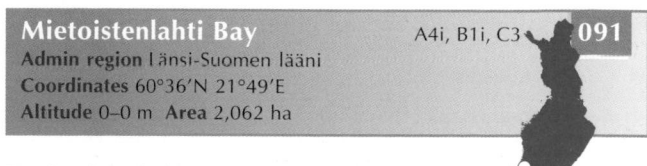

Paimionlahti Bay A4i, B1i, C3 090
Admin region Länsi-Suomen lääni
Coordinates 60°23′N 22°37′E
Altitude 0–0 m **Area** 696 ha

■ Site description
A long, narrow, highly eutrophic bay at the mouth of the Paimio river. The bay is surrounded mainly by forests and scrub, with some farmland and settlements. Along the shores the meadows are grazed, which has increased the ornithological importance of the area.

Habitats Wetland (45%; coastal lagoon; river/stream), Artificial landscape (55%)
Land-use Agriculture, Hunting, Tourism/recreation

■ Birds

Species	Season	Year	Pop min	Pop max	Acc	Criteria
Anser anser Greylag Goose	P	1996	101	500	—	B1i, C3
Mergus merganser Goosander	P	1996	1,001	5,000	B	A4i, B1i, C3

An important staging area for waterbirds.

■ Protection status
National Low **International** High
7 ha of IBA covered by Protected Area on Private Land (Paimionlahti, 7 ha). 696 ha of IBA covered by Special Protection Area (Paimionlahti).

■ Conservation issues

Threats Abandonment/reduction of land management (C), Recreation/tourism (B), Infrastructure

Fishing causes minor disturbance, but continuous recreational boating from a small harbour upriver seriously disturbs birds in the bay, especially staging wildfowl. Abandonment of grazing in some parts of the site have detrimentally affected habitats for birds.

Mietoistenlahti Bay A4i, B1i, C3 091
Admin region Länsi-Suomen lääni
Coordinates 60°36′N 21°49′E
Altitude 0–0 m **Area** 2,062 ha

■ Site description
A long, shallow bay at the mouth of the Laajoki river. The site is dominated by an area of shallow brackish water with extensive beds

of vegetation, especially reed *Phragmites*. Farmland and settlements lie adjacent to the site.

Habitats Wetland (100%; coastal lagoon)
Land-use Fisheries/aquaculture, Tourism/recreation

■ Birds

Species	Season	Year	Pop min	Pop max	Acc	Criteria
Anser anser Greylag Goose	P	1994	1,001	5,000	B	A4i, B1i, C3
Mergus merganser Goosander	P	1994	1,001	5,000	—	A4i, B1i, C3

An internationally important staging area and nationally important breeding area for waterbirds. Species of global conservation concern that do not meet IBA criteria: *Gallinago media* (6–10 birds, passage).

■ Protection status

National Low **International** High
102 ha of IBA covered by Protected Area on Private Land (Topokari, 106 ha). 69 ha of IBA covered by Specific Protection Area (Laajoen suisto, 69 ha). 2,062 ha of IBA covered by Special Protection Area (Mietoistenlahti).

■ Conservation issues

Threats Drainage (B), Aquaculture/fisheries (B), Infrastructure (U)

Professional fishing disturbs the avifauna, especially in spring. for many years by nature conservationists have opposed plans to construct a small harbour within the IBA ('Infrastructure' threat). Cattle-grazing has been used to keep shore meadows open.

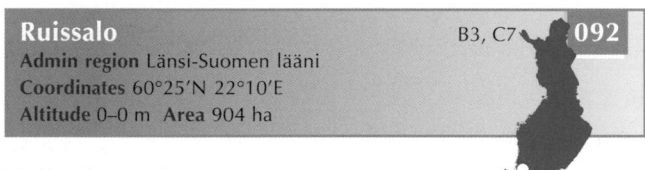

Ruissalo
B3, C7 — 092
Admin region Länsi-Suomen lääni
Coordinates 60°25'N 22°10'E
Altitude 0–0 m **Area** 904 ha

■ Site description

A large, diverse, sparsely populated island closely connected to the city of Turku. Ruissalo is remarkable for both its natural and cultural history. The area supports about half of the natural *Quercus* forest in the country. Between and around the forests are numerous patches of farmland with narrow belts of reedbeds along the shoreline. The site also encompasses some small, barren islands lying off the main island.

Habitats Forest and woodland (68%; broadleaved deciduous forest; native coniferous forest; mixed forest), Grassland (12%; alpine/subalpine/boreal grassland), Artificial landscape (20%; arable land)
Land-use Agriculture (20%), Nature conservation/research (50%), Unknown (30%)

■ Birds

Species	Season	Year	Pop min	Pop max	Acc	Criteria
Columba oenas Stock Dove	B	1992	101	500	B	B3

An important breeding area for forest avifauna, especially for species of deciduous forests, such as *Columba oenas*. The site is also important for *Strix aluco* (10–50 pairs), *Picus canus* (10–50 pairs) and *Dendrocopos minor* (10–50 pairs), although populations of these three species do not meet the IBA criteria at this site.

■ Protection status

National Low **International** Partial
87 ha of IBA covered by Protected Area on Private Land (Ruissalo, 56 ha). 798 ha of IBA covered by Special Protection Area (Ruissalon lehdot).

■ Conservation issues

Threats Disturbance to birds (C), Extraction industry (B), Industrialization/urbanization (B), Recreation/tourism (B)

Cultivation of the land, settlements and traffic, both on the roads and at sea, impact on the island's nature. Part of the area is a candidate SAC.

Föglö southern archipelago
B1ii, B3, C3 — 093
Admin region Ahvenanmaan maakunta
Coordinates 59°52'N 20°35'E
Altitude 0–0 m **Area** 17,843 ha

■ Site description

A large area of outer archipelago to the south-east of Åland. The archipelago is dominated by groups of small, treeless, steep islands separated from each other by extensive areas of open sea.

Habitats Marine areas (100%), Rocky areas
Land-use Not utilized (100%)

■ Birds

Species	Season	Year	Pop min	Pop max	Acc	Criteria
[1] *Alca torda* Razorbill	B	1997	1,000	1,100	A	B1ii, B3, C3

1. 1993–1997.

An important area for many island-breeding species, especially *Alca torda* but also *Somateria mollissima* (1,500 pairs) and *Larus fuscus fuscus*. It is one of the few wintering areas for waterbirds in Finland due to its location on the edge of the Baltic Sea, which normally remains ice-free. Species of global conservation concern that do not meet IBA criteria: *Polysticta stelleri* (1–10 birds, winter), *Haliaeetus albicilla* (5–10 birds, winter).

■ Protection status

National None **International** Partial
2,379 ha of IBA covered by Special Protection Area (Klåvskår).

■ Conservation issues

Threats Infrastructure (A)

There has been very little development on the islands, with the exception of a few summer cottages. The land-owner actively guards the whole area and tries to protect it. The Finnish government has planned to establish a massive shipping channel through the northern part of the area, but this project is currently on hold.

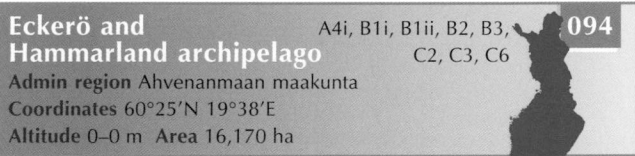

Eckerö and Hammarland archipelago
A4i, B1i, B1ii, B2, B3, C2, C3, C6 — 094
Admin region Ahvenanmaan maakunta
Coordinates 60°25'N 19°38'E
Altitude 0–0 m **Area** 16,170 ha

■ Site description

An area of both outer and middle archipelago with a large number of islands, situated at the western edge of Åland. Most of the islands are bare and almost treeless, but some larger ones hold small patches of forest, swamps, ponds and meadows. Signildskär, one of the largest islands, has the oldest bird observatory in Fennoscandia, founded in 1923. Migration observations have been carried out from the station, but the main activity now is ringing.

Habitats Marine areas (60%), Rocky areas (40%; sea cliff/rocky shore; rock stacks/islets)
Land-use Tourism/recreation (30%), Unknown (10%), Not utilized (60%)

■ Birds

Species	Season	Year	Pop min	Pop max	Acc	Criteria
[1] *Larus marinus* Great Black-backed Gull	B	1997	51	100	B	B3
[1] *Sterna caspia* Caspian Tern	B	1997	101	200	B	A4i,B1i,B2,C2,C6
[1] *Alca torda* Razorbill	B	1997	1,001	2,000	B	B1ii, B3, C3
[1] *Cepphus grylle* Black Guillemot	B	1997	1,001	2,000	B	B1ii, B2

1. 1992–1997.

An important area for island-breeding species, most significantly *Alca torda* and *Cepphus grylle*, but also *Somateria mollissima* (2,000–5,000 pairs), *Arenaria interpres* (50–100 pairs) and *Larus fuscus fuscus* (50–100 pairs).

■ **Protection status**
National None **International** Partial
7,716 ha of IBA covered by Ramsar Site (Signilskär, 11,600 ha).

■ **Conservation issues**

Threats	Aquaculture/fisheries (B), Disturbance to birds (C), Forest grazing (B), Other (B), Recreation/tourism (C)

The archipelago has remained in a fairly natural state. The main threats to birds are oil spills ('Other' threat), nutrient pollution from agriculture and fisheries, increased fish-farming and tourism. The area is a candidate SAC.

Mulklobb B1ii, B2, C3 **095**
Admin region Ahvenanmaan maakunta
Coordinates 60°25′N 20°10′E
Altitude 0–0 m **Area** 6,642 ha

■ **Site description**
A small group of offshore islands in north-east Åland. Most of the islands are bare and rocky, but some of the biggest are sparsely forested. On the eastern side of Mulklobb, most of the auks breed between mounds of rocks. Auks and gulls benefit from the site's proximity to productive marine areas. The area is quite peaceful due to its situation away from ship and boat channels.

Habitats	Marine areas (40%), Rocky areas (60%; sea cliff/rocky shore; rock stacks/islets)
Land-use	Not utilized (100%)

■ **Birds**

Species		Season	Year	Pop min	Pop max	Acc	Criteria
¹ *Alca torda*	Razorbill	B	1997	201	500	B	B1ii, C3
¹ *Cepphus grylle*	Black Guillemot	B	1997	51	100	B	B2

1. 1992–1997.

An important breeding area for auks (*Alca torda* and *Cepphus grylle*).

■ **Protection status**
National None **International** None

■ **Conservation issues**

Threats	Aquaculture/fisheries (B), Disturbance to birds (C), Other (B), Recreation/tourism (C)

The major threat to birds is oil spills from ships and wrecks ('Other' threat). Also, the extension of fish-farming to the outer archipelago may cause harm to birds in the future.

Lågskär–Nyhamn A1, A4i, B1i, B1ii, C1, C3 **096**
Admin region Ahvenanmaan maakunta
Coordinates 59°50′N 19°55′E
Altitude 0–0 m **Area** 2,879 ha

■ **Site description**
An offshore archipelago south of Åland, comprising two large islands (Lågskär and Nyhamn), and numerous much smaller, rocky islets. Between the two main islands is a large area of open water which is excluded from the IBA.

Habitats	Wetland (standing brackish and salt water), Rocky areas (sea cliff/rocky shore; rock stack/islet)
Land-use	Not utilized (100%)

■ **Birds**

Species		Season	Year	Pop min	Pop max	Acc	Criteria
¹ *Polysticta stelleri*	Steller's Eider	W	1996	100	400	B	A1,A4i,B1i,C1,C3
¹ *Alca torda*	Razorbill	B	1996	100	100	B	B1ii, C3

1. 1990–1996.

The area is the only major wintering ground for *Polysticta stelleri* in Finland. Good numbers of *Larus fuscus fuscus*, *Alca torda* and *Cepphus grylle* also breed.

■ **Protection status**
National None **International** Partial
1,737 ha of IBA covered by Ramsar Site (Björkör and Lågskär, 5,760 ha).

■ **Conservation issues**

Threats	Unknown

The area remains relatively sheltered from disturbance, since it lies away from the main shipping channels and is largely free of other human activities. Although not officially nationally protected, the Provincial Government of Åland treats the area as an informal conservation area. One of the most active bird observatories in the country is situated on Lågskär island, its main activities are ringing and migration observation. Part of the area is a candidate SAC.

REFERENCES

ASANTI, T., RUSANEN, P., VIROLAINEN, E. AND BELOW, A., EDS. (in press) *Finnish Wetlands of International Importance: descriptions of Ramsar Convention sites*. Helsinki, Finland.

GRIMMETT, R. F. A. AND JONES, T. A. (1989) *Important Bird Areas in Europe*. Cambridge, UK: International Council for Bird Preservation (Techn. Publ. 9).

HEATH, M. F. AND BORGGREVE, C. (2000) *BirdLife International/EBCC European Bird Database 1998*. Cambridge, UK: BirdLife International.

TUCKER, G. M. AND HEATH, M. F. (1994). *Birds in Europe: their conservation status*. Cambridge, UK: BirdLife International (BirdLife Conservation Series no. 3).

VÄISÄNEN, R., LAMMI, E. AND KOKSIMIES, P. (1998) *Muuttuva pesimälinnusto. [Distribution, numbers and population changes of Finnish breeding birds.]* Keuruu, Finland: Otavan kirjapaino. (In Finnish, with English summary).

FEDERAL REPUBLIC OF
GERMANY

CHRISTIAN UNSELT, CLAUS MAYR AND HANS-GÜNTHER BAUER

Broadleaved deciduous forest, an important habitat at IBAs in Germany. (PHOTO: CHRISTOPH HEINRICH)

Cautionary Note

As a result of the enormous effort needed to coordinate the IBA programme across the federal structure of Germany, data are lacking for a number of sites. The sites presented in this inventory are all valid IBAs because one or more of the criteria are met. However, the data for some of the sites are still incomplete and need to be reviewed again. More importantly, however, for a considerable number of areas (c.60) criteria applications have not yet been finalized (as full data are not yet available), so these sites have had to be omitted from this inventory. Consequently, the list presented here and the accompanying data have to be considered as preliminary. The final version of the complete German IBA inventory is planned for publication in the journal 'Berichte zum Vogelschutz' in the near future.

GENERAL INTRODUCTION

The Federal Republic of Germany occupies parts of north-western and central Europe, covering an area of 357,021 km². The country extends from the Baltic Sea in the north to the Alps in the south, a distance of almost 1,000 km, and comprises 16 federal states, known as Länder. Altitudes range from sea level to 2,962 m. With a population of 82,012,000, at an average density of 230 people km², it is one of the most densely populated countries in Europe.

Germany has 285 Important Bird Areas (IBAs) covering 35,142 km², equivalent to approximately 10% of the country's land area (Table 1, Map 1). The previous European inventory identified 107 IBAs in the former Federal Republic of Germany (Winkel and

Table 1. Summary of Important Bird Areas in the Federal Republic of Germany.　　　　285 IBAs covering 35,142 km²

IBA code	National code	1989 code	International name	National name	Administrative region	Area (ha)	Criteria (see p. 11)
001	SH001	DE001	Heligoland island	Lummenfelsen Helgoland	Schleswig-Holstein	1	C7
002	SH002	DE002	Schleswig-Holstein Wadden Sea National Park	Schleswig-Holsteinisches Wattenmeer	Schleswig-Holstein	278,000	A4i, A4iii, B1i, B2, B3, C2, C3, C4
003	SH003	DE002	Halligen Oland, Langeneß, Nordstrandischmoor, Gröde and Hooge	Halligen Oland, Langeneß, Nordstrandischmoor, Gröde und Hooge	Schleswig-Holstein	1,740	A4i, A4iii, B1i, B2, B3, C2, C3, C4
004	SH004	DE003	Flensburger Innen- and Aussenförde	Flensburger Innen- und Aussenförde	Schleswig-Holstein	—	A4i, A4iii, B1i, B2, C3, C4
005	SH005	DE004	Schlei	Schlei	Schleswig-Holstein	—	A4iii, B1i, B2, B3, C3, C4
006	SH006	DE005	Southern shore of Eckernförder Bucht	Südufer der Eckernförder Bucht	Schleswig-Holstein	—	A4iii, B1i, B2, C3, C4
007	SH007	DE006	Stoller Grund, Gabelsflach and Mittelgrund	Stoller Grund, Gabelsflach und Mittelgrund	Schleswig-Holstein	2,200	A4iii, B1i, C3, C4
008	SH008	DE007	Coastline of Probstei	Küste der Probstei: Laboe Hubertsberg	Schleswig-Holstein	—	A4i, A4iii, B1i, B2, C3, C4
009	SH009	DE008	Selenter See	Selenter See	Schleswig-Holstein	2,141	A4i, A4iii, B1i, C3, C4
010	SH010	DE010	Grosser Plöner See	Grosser Plöner See	Schleswig-Holstein	3,038	A4i, A4iii, B1i, B2, C3, C4
011	SH011	DE011	Warder See	Warder See	Schleswig-Holstein	429	A4i, B1i
012	SH012	DE012	Hohwachter Bucht	Hohwachter Bucht	Schleswig-Holstein	—	A4i, A4iii, B1i, B2, C3, C4
013	SH013	DE013	Grosser and Kleiner Binnensee	Grosser und Kleiner Binnensee	Schleswig-Holstein	630	B1i, C3

Table 1 ... continued. Summary of Important Bird Areas in the Federal Republic of Germany.   285 IBAs covering 35,142 km²

IBA code	National code	1989 code	International name	National name	Administrative region	Area (ha)	Criteria (see p. 11)
014	SH014	DE014	Western bay of the Fehmarnsund	Westbucht des Fehmarnsundes	Schleswig-Holstein	—	A4i, A4iii, B1i, B2, B3, C3, C4
015	SH015	DE015	Strand lakes and fish-ponds in south-western Fehmarn	Strandseen und Fischteiche im Südwesten Fehmarns	Schleswig-Holstein	360	B1i, B3, C3
016	SH016	DE016	Western and northern coast of Fehmarn: Krummsteert–Puttgarden	West- und Nordküste Fehmarns: Krummsteert–Puttgarden	Schleswig-Holstein	—	A4i, A4iii, B1i, B2, C3, C4
017	SH017	DE017	East and south-east coast of Fehmarn: Puttgarden–Burgtiefe	Ost- und Südostküste Fehmarns: Puttgarden–Burgtiefe	Schleswig-Holstein	—	A4i, A4iii, B1i, C3, C4
018	SH018	DE018	Eastern bight of the Fehmarnsund: Burger Binnensee–Grossenbroder Binnenhafen	Ostbucht des Fehmarnsundes: Burger Binnensee–Grossenbroder Binnenhafen	Schleswig-Holstein	—	A4i, A4iii, B1i, B2, C4
019	SH019	DE019	Sagasbank	Sagasbank	Schleswig-Holstein	3,000	A4i, A4iii, B1i, C3, C4
020	SH020	DE020	Eastern coast of Oldenburg: Grossenbroder Kai–Pelzerhaken	Ostküste Oldenburgs: Grossenbroder Kai–Pelzerhaken	Schleswig-Holstein	—	A4i, A4iii, B1i, B2, C3, C4
021	SH021	DE021	Neustädter Bucht: Pelzerhaken–Niendorf	Neustädter Bucht: Pelzerhaken–Niendorf	Schleswig-Holstein	—	A4i, B1i, B2, C3
022	SH022	DE022	Coastline: Niendorf–Travemünde	Brodtener Ufer: Niendorf–Travemünde	Schleswig-Holstein	—	A4i, A4iii, B1i, B2, C3, C4
023	SH023	DE023	Traveförde and Dassower See	Traveförde und Dassower See	Schleswig-Holstein	1,200	A4i, A4iii, B1i, B2, B3, C2, C3, C4
024	SH024	DE025	Lowland of the Rivers Eider, Treene and Sorge	Eider-Treene-Sorge-Niederung	Schleswig-Holstein	60,000	A1, A4i, B1i, B2, B3, C1, C2, C6
025	SH025	DE024	Pinneberg Elbe lowlands	Pinneberger Elbmarschen	Schleswig-Holstein	7,600	A4i, A4iii, B1i, C2, C3, C4
026	SH026	DE026	Aukrug Nature Park	Naturpark Aukrug	Schleswig-Holstein	38,700	C6
027	SH027	DE027	Lauenburgische Seen Nature Park and Schaalsee area	Naturpark Lauenburgische Seen mit Schaalseegebiet	Schleswig-Holstein	50,000	A4i, A4iii, B1i, B2, C3, C4
028	SH028	DE028	Kühren ponds and Lanker See	Kührener Teich und Lanker See	Schleswig-Holstein	470	B1i, B2, C3
029	SH029	DE029	Wesseker See	Wesseker See	Schleswig-Holstein	250	A4i, B1i, C3
030	SH030	DE009	Selent–Plön fish-ponds	Fischteiche Selent–Plön	Schleswig-Holstein	373	A4i, B1i, B2, C6
031	SH031	—	Heidmoor lowlands	Heidmoor-Niederung	Schleswig-Holstein	338	A1, C1
032	SH032	—	Sachsenwald	Sachsenwald	Schleswig-Holstein	7,336	C6
033	SH033	—	Oldenburger Graben	Oldenburger Graben	Schleswig-Holstein	1,745	B3
034	HH001	DE030	Neuwerker and Scharhörner Watt	Neuwerker und Scharhörner Watt	Hamburg	8,193	A4iii
035	HH002	DE031	Duvenstedter Brook	Duvenstedter Brook	Hamburg	780	C6
036	HH003	DE032	Mühlenberger Loch	Mühlenberger Loch	Hamburg	675	A4i, A4iii, B1i, C3, C4
037	MV001	DD003	Westrügen–Hiddensee–Zingst	Westrügen–Hiddensee–Zingst	Mecklenburg-Vorpommern	26,250	A4i, A4iii, A4iv, B1i, B1iv, B2, B3, C2, C3, C4, C5
038	MV002	DD004	Isles of Oie and Kirr	Inseln Oie und Kirr	Mecklenburg-Vorpommern	450	B2, B3, C7
039	MV003	—	Sea area Darß–Hiddensee with Plantagenetgrund	Seegebiet Darß–Hiddensee mit Plantagenetgrund	Mecklenburg-Vorpommern	—	A4i, A4iii, B1i, C3, C4
040	MV004	—	Pomeranian Bay	Pommersche Bucht	Mecklenburg-Vorpommern	295,000	A4i, A4iii, B1i, C2, C3, C4
041	MV005	DD001	Isles of Langenwerder and Walfisch	Inseln Langenwerder und Walfisch	Mecklenburg-Vorpommern	60	A4i, B1i, B2, C3
042	MV006	—	Outer Wismarbucht	Äußere Wismarbucht	Mecklenburg-Vorpommern	30,000	A4i, A4iii, B1i, C3, C4
043	MV007	DD002	Dambecker Seen	Dambecker Seen	Mecklenburg-Vorpommern	204	C7
044	MV008	DD005	Greifswalder Bodden	Greifswalder Bodden	Mecklenburg-Vorpommern	74,850	A4i, A4iii, B1i, B2, C2, C3, C4
045	MV009	DD006	Gothensee and Thurbruch, Isles of Böhmke and Werder	Gothensee und Thurbruch, Inseln Böhmke und Werder	Mecklenburg-Vorpommern	918	C2
046	MV010	—	Usedom lagoon	Kleines Haff und Achterwasser	Mecklenburg-Vorpommern	27,500	A4i, A4iii, B1i, B2, C2, C3, C4
047	MV011	DD007	Kuhlrader Moor and Röggeliner See	Kuhlrader Moor und Röggeliner See	Mecklenburg-Vorpommern	328	C7
048	MV012	DD008	Lewitz ponds	Teichgebiet Lewitz	Mecklenburg-Vorpommern	920	A4i, B1i, C2
049	MV013	DD009	Krakower Obersee	Krakower Obersee	Mecklenburg-Vorpommern	868	B2
050	MV014	DD010	Eastern coast of Lake Müritz, Grosser Schwerin and Steinhorn	Ostufer Müritz, Grosser Schwerin und Steinhorn	Mecklenburg-Vorpommern	5,152	C7
051	MV015	DD011	Serrahn	Serrahn	Mecklenburg-Vorpommern	1,818	C7
052	MV016	DD012	Lake Nonnenhof with Lieps	Nonnenhof mit Lieps	Mecklenburg-Vorpommern	700	C7
053	MV017	DD013	Peenetalmoor and Anklamer Stadtbruch	Peenetalmoor und Anklamer Stadtbruch	Mecklenburg-Vorpommern	3,578	A1, B1i, C1, C3
054	MV018	DD014	Galenbecker See and Putzarer See	Galenbecker See und Putzarer See	Mecklenburg-Vorpommern	1,375	C7
055	MV019	DD015	Koblentzer See and Latzig See	Koblentzer See und Latzig See	Mecklenburg-Vorpommern	497	C7
056	MV020	—	Vorpommern wooded landscape	Vorpommersche Waldlandschaft	Mecklenburg-Vorpommern	18,300	B2, C2
057	MV021	—	Feldberg–Woldegk terminal moraine	Feldberg–Woldegker Endmoräne	Mecklenburg-Vorpommern	33,420	A1, B2, C1, C2
058	NI001	DE033, DE034	Lower Saxony Wadden Sea National Park	Nationalpark Niedersächsisches Wattenmeer	Niedersachsen	250,025	A4i, A4iii, B1i, B2, C2, C3, C4
059	NI002	DE053	Riddagshäuser ponds	Riddagshäuser Teiche	Niedersachsen	226	C7
060	NI003	DE052	Niedersächsischer Drömling	Niedersächsischer Drömling	Niedersachsen	6,200	A1, C1
061	NI004	DE051	Östliches Barnbruch	Östliches Barnbruch	Niedersachsen	1,400	B3, C6
062	NI005	—	Wendesser Moor Nature Reserve	Naturschutzgebiet Wendesser Moor	Niedersachsen	119	C6
063	NI006	DE041	Ems valley from Leer to Emden	Emsmarsch von Leer bis Emden	Niedersachsen	2,173	A4i, A4iii, B1i, B2, B3, C3, C4, C6
064	NI007	—	Terborg	Terborg	Niedersachsen	1,982	A4i, A4iii, B1i, C3, C4
065	NI008	DE043	Lower Weser	Unterweser	Niedersachsen	4,163	A4i, A4iii, B1i, B2, C2, C3, C4, C6
066	NI009	—	Binnendeichsflächen der Wesermündung	Binnendeichsflächen der Wesermündung	Niedersachsen	4,703	B1i, C3

Table 1 ... continued. Summary of Important Bird Areas in the Federal Republic of Germany. 285 IBAs covering 35,142 km²

IBA code	National code	1989 code	International name	National name	Administrative region	Area (ha)	Criteria (see p. 11)
067	NI010	—	Landgraben–Dumme lowlands	Landgraben Dumme-Niederung	Niedersachsen	5,979	C6
068	NI011	—	Rheiderland	Rheiderland	Niedersachsen	14,130	A1, A4i, A4iii, B1i, B2, B3, C1, C2, C3, C4, C6
069	NI012	—	Winsener Elbmarsh	Winsener Elbmarsch	Niedersachsen	844	C7
070	NI013	—	Lucie and Landwehr	Lucie und Landwehr	Niedersachsen	4,067	B3, C6
071	NI014	—	Weser valley near Stolzenau and Landesbergen	Wesertalaue bei Stolzenau und Landesbergen	Niedersachsen	1,218	C7
072	NI015	DE050	Upper Aller lowland	Obere Allerniederung	Niedersachsen	169	C7
073	NI016	—	Seeburger See	Seeburger See	Niedersachsen	139	C7
074	NI017	—	Viehmoor with Leiferder ponds	Viehmoor mit Leiferder Teichen	Niedersachsen	318	C7
075	NI019	—	Heerter See	Heerter See	Niedersachsen	269	C7
076	NI020	—	Dalum Wietmarscher swamp	Dalum-Wietmarscher Moor	Niedersachsen	2,050	C6
077	NI022	—	Aper Tief	Aper Tief	Niedersachsen	1,900	C6
078	NI025	—	Old Picardie	Alte Piccardie	Niedersachsen	1,450	C6
079	NI026	—	Klein- and Großringer Wösten	Klein- und Großringer Wösten	Niedersachsen	1,200	B1i, C3
080	NI029	—	Georgsdorfer swamp	Georgsdorfer Moor	Niedersachsen	2,500	C6
081	NI030	—	Groß Fullener marsh	Groß Fullener Moor	Niedersachsen	1,500	A4i, B1i, B2, C2, C3
082	NI031	—	Leeg-, Melm- and Kuhdammoor	Leeg-, Melm- and Kuhdammoor	Niedersachsen	1,995	C6
083	NI032	—	Esterweger Dose	Esterweger Dose	Niedersachsen	4,970	B3, C6
084	NI033	—	Leda–Jümme lowlands	Leda-Jümme-Niederung	Niedersachsen	5,500	B2, C7
085	NI034	—	Jammertal	Jammertal	Niedersachsen	1,020	C7
086	NI035	—	Wesuwer Brook	Wesuwer Brook	Niedersachsen	600	A4i, B1i, C2, C3
087	NI037	—	Südradde lowland	Südradde Niederung	Niedersachsen	2,720	C6
088	NI038	—	Leine valley near Salzderhelden	Leinetal bei Salzderhelden	Niedersachsen	1,110	A1, B1i, C1, C2, C3, C6
089	NI039	DE040	Valley of the River Ems	Emstal	Niedersachsen	5,317	A1, A4i, A4iii, B1i, C1, C2, C3, C4
090	NI040	—	Jadebusen	Jadebusen	Niedersachsen	8,267	A4iii, B1i, B2, C3, C4
091	NI041	—	Engerhafer Meede	Engerhafer Meede	Niedersachsen	2,000	B1i
092	NI042	—	Alfsee	Alfsee	Niedersachsen	345	A4iii, B1i, C3, C4
093	NI043	—	Butjadingen	Butjadingen	Niedersachsen	10,484	A4i, A4iii, B1i, B2, C3, C4
094	NI044	—	Norden–Esens	Norden-Esens	Niedersachsen	9,948	A4iii, B2, C4
095	NI045	—	Wittmund–Wangerland	Wittmund-Wangerland	Niedersachsen	6,895	A4i, A4iii, B1i, C3, C4
096	NI046	—	Krummhörn–Westermarsch	Krummhörn-Westermarsch	Niedersachsen	11,015	A4i, A4iii, B1i, B3, C2, C3, C4
097	NI047	—	Lower Aller lowlands	Untere Aller-Niederung	Niedersachsen	5,334	A4i, B1i
098	NI048	DE049	Ostenholzer Moor and Meissendorfer ponds	Ostenholzer Moor mit Meissendorfer Teichen	Niedersachsen	3,355	C6
099	NI049	DE048	Steinhuder Meer	Steinhuder Meer	Niedersachsen	5,818	C6
100	NI050	DE047	Diepholzer Moorniederung	Diepholzer Moorniederung	Niedersachsen	13,156	B2, C6
101	NI051	DE046	Dümmer	Dümmer	Niedersachsen	4,370	A4iii, B1i, B2, C2, C3, C4, C6
102	NI052	DE044	Hamme-Niederung	Hamme-Niederung	Niedersachsen	7,100	C6
103	NI053	DE042	Hunte-Niederung near Oldenburg	Hunte-Niederung bei Oldenburg	Niedersachsen	788	C7
104	NI054	DE038	Ostfriesische Meere	Ostfriesische Meere	Niedersachsen	5,400	B2, C6
105	NI055	DE037	Tinner Dose with Staverner Dose	Tinner Dose mit Staverner Dose	Niedersachsen	5,452	C6
106	NI056	DE036	Elbniederung from Schnackenburg to Lauenburg including Amt Neuhaus	Elbniederung von Schnackenburg bis Lauenburg inkl. Amt Neuhaus	Niedersachsen	27,808	A1, A4i, A4iii, B1i, B1iv, B2, B3, C1, C2, C3, C4, C5
107	NI057	DE035	Elbmarsch from Stade to Otterndorf	Elbmarsch von Stade bis Otterndorf	Niedersachsen	18,675	A4i, A4iii, B1i, B2, B3, C2, C3, C4, C6
108	NI058	DE039	Fehntjer Tief	Fehntjer Tief	Niedersachsen	2,942	B2, C6
109	NI059	DE045	Wümme lowlands and St Jürgensland	Wümme-Niederung mit St Jürgensland	Niedersachsen	2,912	B3, C6
110	NI060	—	Wümme meadows near Fischerhude	Wümmewiesen bei Fischerhude	Niedersachsen	1,898	C7
111	NI061	—	Land Wursten	Land Wursten	Niedersachsen	6,647	A4iii, C4
112	NI062	—	Gandersum/Lange Maar	Gandersum/Lange Maar	Niedersachsen	3,500	A4i, A4iii, B1i, B2, C3, C4
113	NI063	—	Lowland of the River Ems near Laten	Emsniederung bei Lathen	Niedersachsen	3,200	A4i, B1i, B2, C2, C3
114	NI064	—	Lüneburg heathlands	Lüneburger Heide	Niedersachsen	23,440	B2
115	BR001	DE045	Borgfelder Wümmewiesen	Borgfelder Wümmewiesen	Bremen	677	A4i, B1i, C2, C3
116	BR002	DE045	Blockland–lower Wümme valley–Westliches Hollerland	Blockland–Untere Wümme–Westliches Hollerland	Bremen	3,503	A4i, B1i, B2, C2, C6
117	BR003	—	Werderland	Werderland	Bremen	1,100	B2, C6
118	BR004	—	Niedervieland, Ochtumniederung	Niedervieland, Ochtumniederung	Bremen	1,365	B3
119	BR005	—	Mittelwesermarsch	Mittelwesermarsch	Bremen	350	C6
120	ST001	DD017	Steckby-Lödderitz forest	Steckby-Lödderitzer Forst	Sachsen-Anhalt	3,850	A4i, B1i, B2, C3
121	ST002	DD017	Zerbst lands	Zerbster Land	Sachsen-Anhalt	5,700	A4i, A4iii, B1i, B2, C3, C4
122	ST003	DD025	Helmestausee Berga–Kelbra	Helmestausee Berga–Kelbra	Sachsen-Anhalt, Thüringen	1,359	B1i, B1iv, C3, C5
123	ST004	DD026	Hakel forest	Hakel	Sachsen-Anhalt	1,300	B2, B3, C7
124	ST005	—	Aland–Elbe lowlands	Aland-Elbe-Niederung	Sachsen-Anhalt	3,250	A4i, A4iii, B1i, B1iv, B3, C2, C3, C4, C5

Table 1 ... continued. Summary of Important Bird Areas in the Federal Republic of Germany. 285 IBAs covering 35,142 km²

IBA code	National code	1989 code	International name	National name	Administrative region	Area (ha)	Criteria (see p. 11)
125	ST006	—	Drömling bird-protection area	Vogelschutzgebiet Drömling	Sachsen-Anhalt	27,821	A4i, B1i, C3
126	ST007	—	Landgraben-Dumme lowlands	Landgraben-Dumme-Niederung	Sachsen-Anhalt	2,110	C6
127	ST008	—	Milde lowlands	Milde-Niederung	Sachsen-Anhalt	1,500	B1i, C3
128	ST009	—	Elbe valley Jerichow	Elbaue Jerichow	Sachsen-Anhalt	4,800	A4i, A4iii, B1i, C2, C3, C4
129	ST010	—	Saale-Elster valley	Saale-Elster-Aue	Sachsen-Anhalt	3,800	A1, B2, C1
130	ST011	—	Wulfen meadows	Wulfener Bruch	Sachsen-Anhalt	1,500	A4i, A4iii, B1i, C3, C4, C6
131	ST012	—	Ploetzkau flood-plain forest	Auewald Ploetzkau	Sachsen-Anhalt	268	B2
132	ST013	—	Fiener Bruch	Fiener Bruch	Sachsen-Anhalt, Brandenburg	9,000	A4i, A4iii, B1i, B2, C3, C4
133	ST014	—	Salziger See	Salziger See	Sachsen-Anhalt	550	B1i, C3
134	ST015	—	North-eastern lower Harz mountains	Nordöstlicher Unterharz	Sachsen-Anhalt	13,400	B3
135	ST016	—	Deciduous forests and heathlands of north-east Haldensleben	Hudewälder und Heideflächen nordöstlich Haldensleben	Sachsen-Anhalt	4,200	B2
136	BB001	—	Spreewald	Spreewald	Brandenburg	35,000	A4i, B1i, B2, B3, C3
137	BB002	—	Havelland between Brandenburg and Potsdam	Havelland zwischen Brandenburg und Potsdam	Brandenburg	7,350	A4i, A4iii, B1i, B2, B3, C3, C4, C6
138	BB003	DD019	Upper Rhinluch–Nauener Luch	Oberes Rhinluch–Nauener Luch	Brandenburg	7,140	A4i, A4iii, A4iv, B1i, B1iv, B3, C3, C4, C5
139	BB004	—	Döberitz heathlands	Döberitzer Heide	Brandenburg	4,717	B3, C2
140	BB005	DD020	Rietzer See	Rietzer See	Brandenburg	1,134	A4iii, B1i, B3, C3, C4
141	BB006	DD035	Peitz and Bärenbrück ponds, and Lasszins meadows	Peitzer Teiche mit dem Teichgebiet Bärenbrück und Lasszinswiesen	Brandenburg	1,556	A4iii, B1i, C3, C4
142	BB007	DD023, DD024	Lower Oder valley	Unteres Odertal	Brandenburg	12,017	A1, A4i, A4iii, B1i, B1iv, B2, B3, C1, C2, C3, C4, C5
143	BB008	DD016	Schorfheide–Chorin	Schorfheide–Chorin	Brandenburg	42,700	A1, A4i, A4iii, B1i, B1iv, B2, B3, C1, C2, C3, C4, C5, C6
144	BB009	—	Deichvorland Oderbruch	Deichvorland Oderbruch	Brandenburg	3,916	A1, B2, B3, C1, C2
145	BB010	DD021	Lower Rhinluch–Lake Dreetz– Havelländisches Luch–Belziger Landschaftswiesen	Unteres Rhinluch–Dreetzer See– Havelländisches Luch–Belziger Landschaftswiesen	Brandenburg	13,989	A1, A4i, A4iii, B1i, B2, C1, C3, C4
146	BB011	—	Uckermärkische Seenlandschaft	Uckermärkische Seenlandschaft	Brandenburg	54,667	A1, B2, B3, C1, C6
147	BB012	—	Stechlin	Stechlin	Brandenburg	7,928	B2, C7
148	BB013	—	Märkische Schweiz	Märkische Schweiz	Brandenburg	17,862	A4i, A4iii, B1i, C3, C4
149	BB014	—	Lower Elbe valley	Unteres Elbtal	Brandenburg	52,825	A1, A4i, A4iii, B1i, B1iv, B2, C1, C2, C3, C4, C5
150	BB015	—	Former military training area east and west of Jüterbog	Truppenübungsplatz Jüterbog West und Jüterbog Ost	Brandenburg	20,200	B2, B3, C2
151	BB016	DD018	Lower Havel–Lake Schollene– Lake Gülpe	Untere Havel–Schollener See– Gülper See	Sachsen-Anhalt, Brandenburg	13,890	A1, A4i, A4iii, B1i, B1iv, B2, B3, C1, C2, C3, C4, C5, C6
152	BE001	—	Die Bänke an der Müggelspree	Die Bänke an der Müggelspree	Berlin	16	C2
153	NW001	—	Niers valley	Niersaue	Nordrhein-Westfalen	1,971	B2
154	NW002	DE059, DE060	Schwalm–Nette–Platte and Grenzwald	Schwalm–Nette–Platte und Grenzwald	Nordrhein-Westfalen	9,968	B2, C7
155	NW003	DE055	Bogs and heathlands of the Westmünsterland	Moore und Heiden des Westmünsterlandes	Nordrhein-Westfalen	3,650	B1i, C3
156	NW004	—	Hellwegbörde	Hellwegbörde	Nordrhein-Westfalen	55,000	A1, B2, B3, C1
157	NW005	DE054	Weser Dam Schlüsselburg	Weserstaustufe Schlüsselburg	Nordrhein-Westfalen	2,980	B1i, B3, C2, C3
158	NW006	DE061	Bastau-Niederung	Bastau-Niederung	Nordrhein-Westfalen	3,260	C7
159	NW007	—	Wahn heathlands	Wahner Heide	Nordrhein-Westfalen	4,112	C7
160	NW008	DE056	Lower Rhine area	Unterer Niederrhein	Nordrhein-Westfalen	48,000	A1, A4i, A4iii, B1i, B2, C1, C2, C3, C4, C6
161	NW009	—	Heubachniederung/Schwarzes Venn/ Borkenberge/Halterner Seen	Heubachniederung/Schwarzes Venn/ Borkenberge/Halterner Seen	Nordrhein-Westfalen	6,000	B1i, B2, C3
162	NW010	DE057	Sewage farms of Münster	Rieselfelder Münster	Nordrhein-Westfalen	435	B1i, C3
163	NW011	—	Recker Moor/Düsterdieker Niederung/ Seester Feld	Recker Moor/Düsterdieker Niederung/ Seester Feld	Nordrhein-Westfalen	2,700	C6
164	NW012	—	Meadows and forests around Burbach	Feuchtwiesen und Wälder um Burbach	Nordrhein-Westfalen	4,280	C6
165	NW013	—	Emsaue (Rietberger Emsniederung- Steinhorster Becken)	Emsaue (Rietberger Emsniederung- Steinhorster Becken)	Nordrhein-Westfalen	1,200	B2
166	NW014	—	Oppenweher Moor	Oppenweher Moor	Nordrhein-Westfalen	490	C7
167	NW015	—	Medebacher Bucht	Medebacher Bucht	Nordrhein-Westfalen	22,000	B2
168	NW016	—	Sennelager training area	Truppenübungsplatz Senne	Nordrhein-Westfalen	12,000	B2
169	NW017	DE058	Möhnesee	Möhnesee	Nordrhein-Westfalen	1,200	C7
170	HE001	—	Kellerwald	Kellerwald	Hessen	31,000	B2, B3
171	HE002	—	Burgwald	Burgwald	Hessen	23,000	C6
172	HE003	—	Vogelsberg	Vogelsberg	Hessen	47,000	A4iv, B2, B3
173	HE004	—	Hessian Rothaar mountains	Hessisches Rothaargebirge	Hessen	32,000	C6

Table 1 ... continued. Summary of Important Bird Areas in the Federal Republic of Germany.   285 IBAs covering 35,142 km²

IBA code	National code	1989 code	International name	National name	Administrative region	Area (ha)	Criteria (see p. 11)
174	HE005	—	Knüll	Knüll	Hessen	35,000	B2
175	HE006	—	High Westerwald around Driedorf	Hoher Westerwald um Driedorf	Hessen	8,500	B2
176	HE007	—	Waldeck upland	Waldeckisches Upland	Hessen	27,000	C6
177	HE008	—	Lahn valley from Marburg to Wetzlar	Lahntal von Marburg bis Wetzlar	Hessen	6,200	B2
178	HE009	—	Eder alluvion	Ederaue	Hessen	4,280	B2
179	HE010	—	Northern Wetterau	Nördliche Wetterau	Hessen	4,300	B1iv, B3, C5
180	HE011	—	Alluvion of the Lower Schwalm near Borken	Untere Schwalm-Aue bei Borken	Hessen	3,300	B2
181	HE012	DE064, DE065	Hessian Rhine alluvion	Hessische Rheinauen	Hessen	9,500	B1i, B2, B3, C3
182	HE013	—	Gladenbach mountain country east of Herborn	Gladenbacher Bergland östlich Herborn	Hessen	9,000	B3
183	HE014	—	Rheingau	Rheingau	Hessen	4,700	C6
184	HE015	—	Dune and aeolian sand area: Dudenhofen, Babenhausen, Seligenstadt	Dünen- und Flugsandgebiet Dudenhofen, Babenhausen, Seligenstadt	Hessen	5,000	B2
185	HE016	—	Lorsch forest and Viernheim heathland	Lorscher Wald und Viernheimer Heide	Hessen	7,000	C6
186	HE017	—	Rothenbach pond	Rothenbachteich	Hessen	25	C7
187	HE018	—	Reichlos pond	Reichloser Teich	Hessen	39	C7
188	HE019	—	Ober-Moos pond	Ober-Mooser-Teich	Hessen	57	C7
189	HE020	—	Rotes Moor	Rotes Moor	Hessen	315	C7
190	HE021	—	Rhäden near Obersuhl and Bosserode	Rhäden bei Obersuhl und Bosserode	Hessen	120	C7
191	HE022	—	Reservoir near Affoldern	Stausee von Affoldern	Hessen	165	C7
192	HE023	—	Alluvion of the middle Horloff	Mittlere Horloffaue	Hessen	184	C7
193	HE024	—	Twiste reservoir	Vorsperre Twistetalsperre	Hessen	24	C7
194	TH001	DE084	Rhön Biosphere Reserve	Biosphaerenreservat Rhoen	Hessen, Bayern, Thüringen	187,606	A1, B2, B3, C1, C2
195	TH002	—	Herbsleben ponds	Herbsleber Teiche	Thüringen	50	C7
196	TH003	—	Plothen ponds	Plothener Teiche	Thüringen	2,350	C7
197	TH004	DD030	Uhlstädt heathlands	Uhlstädter Heide	Thüringen	1,082	C7
198	TH005	DD030	Wurzelbergfarmde	Wurzelbergfarmde	Thüringen	233	C6
199	TH006	DD030	Assberg–Hasenleite	Assberg–Hasenleite	Thüringen	580	C7
200	TH007	DD030	Meura heathlands	Meuraer Heide	Thüringen	375	C7
201	TH008	DD029	Schwarza valley	Schwarzatal	Thüringen	1,800	C7
202	TH009	DD028	Vesser Valley Biosphere Reserve	Biosphärenreservat Vessertal	Thüringen	7,464	C6
203	SN001	DD027	Pressel wooded heath and mire	Presseler Heidewald- und Moorgebiet	Sachsen	5,000	B1i, C3
204	SN002	—	Ponds and Elbe valley near Torgau	Teichgebiet und Elbaue bei Torgau	Sachsen	6,000	A1, A4i, A4iii, B1i, B2, B3, C1, C3, C4
205	SN003	DD033, DD034	Oberlausitz heathland and fish-ponds	Oberlausitzer Heide- und Teichgebiet	Sachsen	39,243	A1, A4i, A4iii, B1i, B2, C1, C3, C4, C6
206	SN004	—	Eschefeld ponds	Eschefelder Teiche	Sachsen	270	C7
207	SN005	—	Westerzgebirge	Westerzgebirge	Sachsen	4,800	C7
208	SN006	DD031	Erzgebirgskamm near Satzung	Erzgebirgskamm bei Satzung	Sachsen	750	C6
209	SN007	—	Grosshartmannsdorfer Grossteich	Grosshartmannsdorfer Grossteich	Sachsen	157	C7
210	SN008	—	Erzgebirgskamm near Deutscheinsiedel	Erzgebirgskamm bei Deutscheinsiedel	Sachsen	1,200	C7
211	SN009	DD032	Sächsische Schweiz National Park	Nationalpark Sächsische Schweiz	Sachsen	9,292	B2, C7
212	SN010	—	Fürstenau	Fürstenau	Sachsen	3,600	C6
213	RP001	DE063	Rheinauen: Eltville–Bingen	Rheinauen: Eltville–Bingen	Hessen, Rheinland-pfalz	475	C7
214	RP002	DE066	Gimbsheim-Eicher Altrhein and Fischsee	Gimbsheim-Eicher Altrhein und Fischsee	Rheinland-pfalz	430	C7
215	RP003	DE067	Hördter Rheinaue	Hördter Rheinaue	Rheinland-pfalz	1,000	C7
216	SL001	—	Saar/Bliesgau/Westrich	Saar/Bliesgau/Westrich	Saarland	24,100	B2
217	BW001	DE069	Wagbach lowlands	Wagbachniederung	Baden-Württemberg	1,050	C6
218	BW003	DE068	Hockenheimer Rheinbogen	Hockenheimer Rheinbogen	Baden-Württemberg	2,500	B1i, C3, C6
219	BW004	DE108	Orchard landscape between Hohenstaufen and Teck in the mid-Albvorland	Streuobstwiesenlandschaft zwischen Hohenstaufen und Teck im mittleren Albvorland	Baden-Württemberg	68,000	B3, C6
220	BW005	DE071	Rhine flats: Kehl–Helmlingen	Rheinniederung Kehl–Helmlingen	Baden-Württemberg	2,120	B1i, B2, C3
221	BW006	DE070	Rhine: Greffern–Murgmündung–Neuburgweier	Rhein: Greffern–Murgmündung–Neuburgweier	Baden-Württemberg	6,623	B1i, C3
222	BW007	DE072	Rhine flats: Nonnenweier–Kehl	Rheinniederung Nonnenweier–Kehl	Baden-Württemberg	3,800	A4i, B1i, B2, C3, C6
223	BW008	DE073	Rhine flats: Sasbach–Wittenweier	Rheinniederung Sasbach–Wittenweier	Baden-Württemberg	4,400	A4i, B1i, B2, B3, C3, C6
224	BW009	DE074	Rhine flats: Neuenburg–Breisach	Rheinniederung Neuenburg–Breisach	Baden-Württemberg	2,000	B1i, C3
225	BW010	DE075	Rhine flats: Haltingen–Neuenburg and foothills	Rheinniederung Haltingen Neuenburg mit Vorbergzone	Baden-Württemberg	1,550	C7
226	BW011	DE076	Öpfinger Donau-Stausee, Rißniederung and Rißtissener Kiesseen	Öpfinger Donau-Stausee, Rißniederung und Rißtissener Kiesseen	Baden-Württemberg	506	B1i, C3
227	BW015	DE081	Lake Constance–Obersee, and the adjacent Seerhein	Obersee: Konstanzer Bucht mit angrenzendem Seerhein	Baden-Württemberg	330	A4i, A4iii, B1i, C3, C4

Table 1 ... continued. Summary of Important Bird Areas in the Federal Republic of Germany.   285 IBAs covering 35,142 km²

IBA code	National code	1989 code	International name	National name	Administrative region	Area (ha)	Criteria (see p. 11)
228	BW016	DE083	Federsee	Federsee	Baden-Württemberg	2,900	C6
229	BW017	—	Northern Black Forest, west of the Murg	Nordschwarzwald westlich der Murg	Baden-Württemberg	60,000	B2, B3, C6
230	BW018	—	Northern Black Forest, east of the Murg	Nordschwarzwald östlich der Murg	Baden-Württemberg	48,000	B3
231	BW019	DE077–DE081	Untersee of Lake Constance	Untersee des Bodensees	Baden-Württemberg	7,300	A4i, A4iii, B1i, C3, C4, C6
232	BW020	—	Silzen meadows and bog, near Stettfeld	Silzenwiesen und Bruch bei Stettfeld	Baden-Württemberg	250	C6
233	BW021	—	Philippsburger Altrhein and Rheinschanzinsel	Philippsburger Altrhein und Rheinschanzinsel	Baden-Württemberg	600	C6
234	BW022	—	Schiltach and Berneck valleys, near Schramberg	Schiltach- und Bernecktal bei Schramberg	Baden-Württemberg	1,800	C6
235	BW023	—	Middle-eastern Black Forest	Mittlerer Ostschwarzwald	Baden-Württemberg	25,000	C6
236	BW024	—	Schwarza and Schlücht valleys	Schwarza- und Schlüchttal	Baden-Württemberg	500	C6
237	BW025	—	Feldberg in the Black Forest	Feldberg im Schwarzwald	Baden-Württemberg	1,300	C7
238	BW026	—	Kocher and adjoining valleys	Kocher mit Seitentäler	Baden-Württemberg	200	C7
239	BW027	—	South-eastern Alb and Upper Danube valley	Südwestalb und Oberes Donautal	Baden-Württemberg	85,000	B2, C6
240	BW028	—	Simonswald–Rohrhardsberg	Simonswald–Rohrhardsberg	Baden-Württemberg	20,000	B2, B3, C6
241	BW029	—	Northern Karlsruhe Hardt	Nördliche Karlsruher Hardt	Baden-Württemberg	4,950	C6
242	BW030	—	Lake Überlingen (Lake Constance)	Überlinger See des Bodensees	Baden-Württemberg	7,500	B1i, C3, C6
243	BW031	—	Jagst and adjoining valleys	Jagst mit Seitentäler	Baden-Württemberg	400	B2, C6
244	BW032	—	Rhine flats: Karlsruhe–Rheinsheim	Rheinniederung Karlsruhe–Rheinsheim	Baden-Württemberg	2,900	B1i, C3, C6
245	BW033	—	Orchards and vineyards between Waldhausen and Geradstetten	Streuobst- und Weinberggebiet zwischen Waldhausen and Geradstetten	Baden-Württemberg	1,400	B3, C6
246	BW034	—	Wutach ravine	Wutachschlucht	Baden-Württemberg	4,650	C6
247	BW035	—	Kaiserstuhl	Kaiserstuhl	Baden-Württemberg	9,500	C6
248	BW036	—	Stromberg	Stromberg	Baden-Württemberg	4,000	B3, C2, C6
249	BW037	—	Rhine flats: Breisach–Sasbach with Limberg	Rheinniederung Breisach–Sasbach mit Limberg	Baden-Württemberg	1,050	C7
250	BW038	—	Orchards and *Quercus* woodlands near Filderstadt and Echterdingen	Streuobstwiesen und Eichenwälder bei Filderstadt und Echterdingen	Baden-Württemberg	2,000	B3, C6
251	BW040	—	Enz valley: Mühlhausen–Roßwag	Enztal Mühlhausen–Roßwag	Baden-Württemberg	215	C6
252	BW041	—	Schönbuch	Schönbuch	Baden-Württemberg	18,000	B3, C6
253	BW042	—	Orchards, heathlands and forests around Wel der Stadt	Streuobstwiesen, Heiden und Wälder um Wel der Stadt	Baden-Württemberg	3,600	B3, C6
254	BY001	DE100	Vogelfreistätte Mittlere Isar-Stauseen	Vogelfreistätte Mittlere Isar-Stauseen	Bayern	570	B1i, C3
255	BY002	DE092	Rötelsee–Weihergebiet including Regen-Aue	Rötelsee–Weihergebiet einschliesslich Regenaue	Bayern	500	B1i, B2, C3
256	BY003	DE099	Isar-Tal: Gottfrieding–Plattling including Isar-Mündungsbereich	Isar-Tal: Gottfrieding–Plattling einschliesslich Isar-Mündungsbereich	Bayern	8,000	C6
257	BY004	DE101	Ismaninger Speichersee and fish-ponds	Ismaninger Speichersee und Fischteiche	Bayern	955	A4i, B1i, C3
258	BY005	DE088	Main-Tal near Volkach: Fahr-Dettelbach	Main-Tal bei Volkach: Fahr Dettelbach	Bayern	1,800	C6
259	BY006	DE093	Bayerischer Wald National Park with Arbergebiet and Hohen Bogen	Nationalpark Bayerischer Wald	Bayern	32,000	B2, C7
260	BY007	DE107	Berchtesgaden National Park	Nationalpark Berchtesgaden	Bayern	20,800	A3, B2, C2, C6
261	BY008	DE091	Altmühl-Tal: Ornbau–Gunzenhausen Altmühlsee and Wiesmet	Altmühltal: Ornbau–Gunzenhausen	Bayern	1,500	B1i, C3
262	BY009	DE102	Ammersee	Ammersee	Bayern	6,520	A4iii, B1i, C3, C4
263	BY010	DE104	Chiemsee and Chiemseemore	Chiemsee	Bayern	9,800	A1, A4i, A4iii, B1i, C1, C3, C4
264	BY011	DE097	Donau-Tal: Regensburg–Vilshofen	Donautal: Regensburg–Vilshofen	Bayern	18,200	B2
265	BY012	—	Rotwand-Gebiet	Rotwand-Gebiet	Bayern	4,445	B2, C6
266	BY013	DE094	Donau-Auen: Neu-Ulm–Lauingen including Faiminger Stausee, Donau-Moos, and Gundelfinger Moos	Donau-Auen: Neu-Ulm–Lauingen einschliesslich Faiminger Stausee, Donau-Moos, und Gundelfinger Moos	Bayern	12,500	A4iii, B1i, B2, B3, C2, C3, C4
267	BY014	DE106	Karwendel and Karwendel-Vorgebirge	Karwendel und Karwendel-Vorgebirge	Bayern	20,000	B2, B3, C6
268	BY015	DE105	Ammergauer Berge	Ammergauer Berge	Bayern	27,600	B2, B3, C6
269	BY016	—	Nürnberger Reichswald	Nürnberger Reichswald	Bayern	35,000	B2, B3
270	BY017	—	Vorderer Steigerwald–Windsheimer Bucht–Gollach-Gau–Steigerwald-Vorland	Vorderer Steigerwald–Windsheimer Bucht–Gollach-Gau–Steigerwald-Vorland	Bayern	95,000	B2, B3
271	BY018	DE096	Lech–Donau–Winkel: Lechstausee Feldheim and Donaustausee Bertoldsheim	Lech–Donau–Winkel: Lechstausee Feldheim und Donaustausee Bertoldsheim	Bayern	239	B1i, C3
272	BY019	DE095	Donau-Auen and Donau-Ried: Höchstädt–Donauwörth	Donau-Auen und Donau-Ried: Höchstädt–Donauwörth	Bayern	9,500	C7
273	BY020	—	Orchards bordering the River Main	Streuobstwiesen am Untermain	Hessen, Bayern	60,000	B2
274	BY021	DE090	Charlottenhofer Weihergebiet	Charlottenhofer Weihergebiet	Bayern	900	C7
275	BY022	DE087	Aisch–Regnitz–Grund	Aisch–Regnitz–Grund	Bayern	68,000	B2, C6
276	BY023	DE103	Starnberger See	Starnberger See	Bayern	6,500	B1i, C3

Table 1 ... continued. Summary of Important Bird Areas in the Federal Republic of Germany. 285 IBAs covering 35,142 km²

IBA code	National code	1989 code	International name	National name	Administrative region	Area (ha)	Criteria (see p. 11)
277	BY024	DE085	Main-Tal: Eltmann–Hassfurt	Main-Tal: Eltmann–Hassfurt	Bayern	560	C7
278	BY025	—	Murnauer Moos and Loisach-Kochel Moore	Murnauer Moos und Loisach-Kochel Moore	Bayern	8,200	A1, C1, C2
279	BY026	DE086	Main-Tal near Schweinfurt	Main-Tal bei Schweinfurt	Bayern	1,100	C7
280	BY027	DE089	Vogelfreistätte Alter and Neuer See	Vogelfreistätte Alter und Neuer See	Bayern	40	C7
281	BY028	—	Northern part of the Steigerwald	Nördlicher Steigerwald	Bayern	13,000	B2, B3
282	BY029	DE098	Lower Inn: Haiming–Neuhaus, including the Neuhaus, Egglfing, Ering and Simbach reservoirs	Unterer Inn: Haiming–Neuhaus einschliesslich Stauseen Neuhaus, Egglfing, Ering, und Simbach	Bayern	5,000	B1i, C3
283	BY030	—	Nassanger near Trieb and surrounding gravel-pits	Nassanger bei Trieb und umgebende Baggerseen	Bayern	200	C7
284	BY031	DE082	Obersee: Schachener Bucht	Obersee: Schachener Bucht	Bayern	200	C7
285	BY032	—	Manteler forest	Manteler Forst	Bayern	2,500	B2

Map 1. Location, area and criteria category of Important Bird Areas in the Federal Republic of Germany.

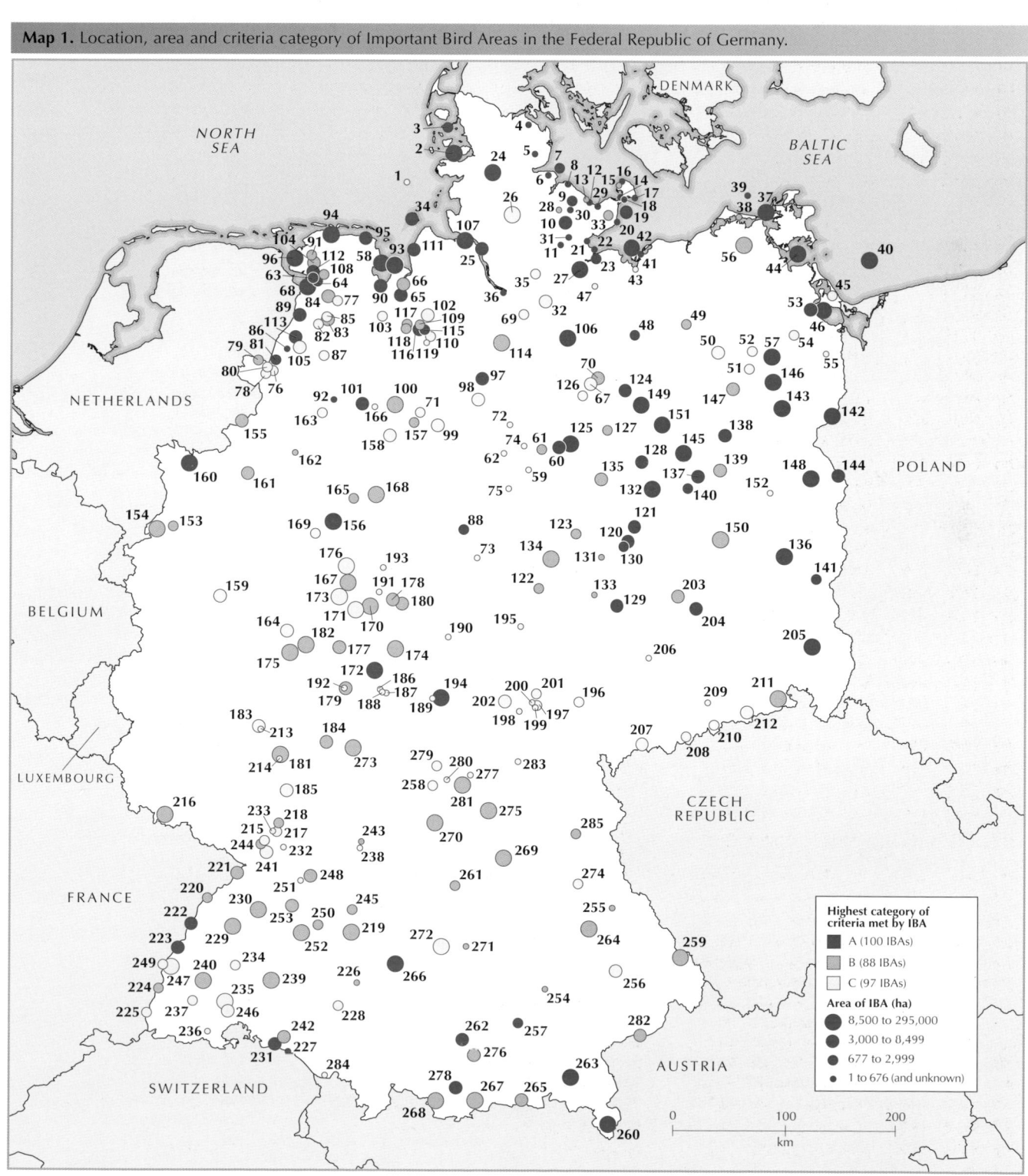

269

Table 2. Important Bird Areas in the Federal Republic of Germany that are important for species of global conservation concern (meeting criterion A1).

Species	IBA code
Haliaeetus albicilla White-tailed Eagle	057, 143, 146, 204, 205
Crex crex Corncrake	024, 031, 060, 068, 088, 089, 106, 129, 142, 143, 144, 149, 151, 156, 160, 194, 263, 278

Species	IBA code
Otis tarda Great Bustard	145
Acrocephalus paludicola Aquatic Warbler	053, 142

Table 3. Important Bird Areas in the Federal Republic of Germany that support important numbers of one or more congregatory species (i.e. meeting criteria A4 and/or B1). IBAs meeting both criteria A4 and B1 for the species are shown in **bold**. IBAs meeting only criterion B1 for the species concerned, and not A4, are shown in normal type. (See 'Cautionary Note' p. 263.) For key to 'Season', see p. 7.

Species	Season	IBA code
Podiceps cristatus Great Crested Grebe	W	006
	P	010, **027**
	N	009, 027
Podiceps grisegena Red-necked Grebe	W	**040**
Podiceps auritus Slavonian Grebe	W	**040**
Phalacrocorax carbo Cormorant	R	037, **044**
	W	160, 161, 181, 223
	P	002, 010, 036, 244
Cygnus columbianus Bewick's Swan	W	**065, 081, 086, 106, 107, 113, 151, 160**
	P	**011**, 024, 025, **044**, 048, **089**, 097, 115, 116, 124, 149
Cygnus cygnus Whooper Swan	W	**023, 106, 124, 151**, 157
	P	**044, 142, 149**
Anser fabalis Bean Goose	W	**023, 027, 081**, 086, **106, 107**, 112, **120, 121**, 124, 125, 127, 128, 130, 132, 157, 160, 181, 204, 218, 221
	P	037, **044**, 053, 063, **068**, 079, 088, **089**, 101, 113, **132**, 133, **136, 137, 138**, 140, 141, **142, 143, 145, 148, 149**, 151, 203, **205**, 220, 224
Anser albifrons White-fronted Goose	W	023, 027, 063, **106, 107**, 112, 160
	P	037, **044**, 053, 064, 066, **068, 089**, 090, 121, 124, 128, **132, 137, 138**, 140, 141, **142, 143**, 145, 148, 149, 151, **205**
Anser anser Greylag Goose	W	**027**, 101, **107**, 160
	P	**011**, 015, 025, **044, 096**, 140, **142, 151**
Branta leucopsis Barnacle Goose	W	**002, 058, 068, 107, 112**
	P	**002**, 025, 063, 064, **096**
Branta bernicla Brent Goose	W	**002, 003, 107**
	P	**002**
Tadorna tadorna Shelduck	W	**002, 058**, 107
	P	**002**
Anas penelope Wigeon	W	**002, 003, 058**
	P	**002, 044**, 095, 142
Anas strepera Gadwall	W	221, 226, 254, 263, 271, 282
	P	**029, 030, 044**, 220, **222, 223, 231**, 255
	N	028, **257**
Anas crecca Teal	W	002, 065, 107
	P	**002**, 036, 058, 122, 142, 231
Anas platyrhynchos Mallard	W	002
Anas acuta Pintail	P	**002**
Anas clypeata Shoveler	R	107
	W	002, 088, 092, 101, 107, 160
	P	002, 029, 036, 115, 122, 124, 138, 142, 151, 162, 231, 261
	N	257
Netta rufina Red-crested Pochard	B	262
	W	276
	P	**231**, 242, **257, 263**
	N	257
Aythya ferina Pochard	W	023, 157, 226, **227**, 263
	P	181, **231**, 242
	N	013, 257, 266
Aythya fuligula Tufted Duck	W	004, 005, **010**, 014, **017, 018**, 020, **022, 023, 227, 262, 263**
	P	**231**, 242
	N	009, 027
Aythya marila Scaup	W	**004, 008**, 012, **014, 018**, 020, **021, 022, 023, 041**
	P	013, **017**, 044
Somateria mollissima Eider	W	**002**, 004, 007, **008**, 012, **016**, 019, **042**
	P	002, 014, 017, 020
Clangula hyemalis Long-tailed Duck	W	**039, 040**

Species	Season	IBA code
Melanitta nigra Common Scoter	W	**002, 019, 040**
	P	**016**
Melanitta fusca Velvet Scoter	W	040
Bucephala clangula Goldeneye	W	006, **016, 022, 037**, 046
	P	**044**
	N	023
Mergus albellus Smew	W	**037, 046**
	P	088
Mergus serrator Red-breasted Merganser	W	040
Mergus merganser Goosander	W	037, **044, 046**
Fulica atra Coot	W	022, 263
Grus grus Crane	P	106, 142
Haematopus ostralegus Oystercatcher	R	002
	W	**002, 058**
	P	002
Recurvirostra avosetta Avocet	B	002
	W	107
	P	002, 058, 096
Charadrius hiaticula Ringed Plover	P	002, 058
Charadrius alexandrinus Kentish Plover	P	002
Pluvialis apricaria Golden Plover	W	107
	P	002, 058, **068**, 091
Pluvialis squatarola Grey Plover	W	002
	P	002, 058
Vanellus vanellus Lapwing	W	160
Calidris canutus Knot	W	002
	P	002, 058
Calidris alba Sanderling	P	002
Calidris ferruginea Curlew Sandpiper	P	002
Calidris alpina Dunlin	W	002
	P	002, 058
Limosa limosa Black-tailed Godwit	P	155
Limosa lapponica Bar-tailed Godwit	W	002, 003
	P	002, 058, 096
Numenius arquata Curlew	W	002, 058, 093
	P	002, 095, 096
Tringa erythropus Spotted Redshank	W	107
	P	002, 058
Tringa totanus Redshank	R	002
	W	002, 058
	P	002
Tringa nebularia Greenshank	P	002, 058
Arenaria interpres Turnstone	W	002
	P	002, 058
Larus minutus Little Gull	P	009, 010, 025, 036
Larus ridibundus Black-headed Gull	P	002
Larus canus Common Gull	P	002, 058
Larus fuscus Lesser Black-backed Gull	P	002
Larus argentatus Herring Gull	R	002
	W	002
	P	002, 058
Gelochelidon nilotica Gull-billed Tern	B	107
Sterna caspia Caspian Tern	P	037
Sterna sandvicensis Sandwich Tern	B	002
	P	002
Sterna hirundo Common Tern	B	002
	P	002
Sterna albifrons Little Tern	B	002
	P	002

Franzen 1987, Grimmett and Jones 1989) and 35 IBAs in the German Democratic Republic (Grimmett and Jones 1989, Rheinwald 1990). Following the reunification of Germany in 1990, Naturschutzbund Deutschland (NABU) produced a new IBA inventory for the five new Länder, with 56 IBAs (Langeveld 1991, Mayr 1991). In the western part of Germany, from 1990 to 1994, six new IBAs were added (Rheinwald 1990, Mayr 1991, Mayr 1993, Waliczky 1994), so that by 1998 Germany had 169 IBAs covering 22,029 km² or 6.2% of the country's surface (Ssymank et al. 1998). In the current inventory the number of IBAs has increased considerably.

ORNITHOLOGICAL IMPORTANCE

Germany has a total of 240 regularly breeding indigenous bird species and 17 species which breed irregularly (15 naturalized species also breed). A total of 122 of the regular breeders are species of European conservation concern (SPECs: Tucker and Heath 1994) with a further four SPECs breeding sporadically. Of these 122 SPECs, four are of global conservation concern (SPEC 1), 16 breed mainly within Europe on a global scale and have an unfavourable conservation status in Europe (SPEC 2), 44 also have an unfavourable conservation status in Europe but breed mainly outside Europe (SPEC 3), and 58 have a favourable conservation status in Europe but breed mainly within Europe (SPEC 4).

Regarding the species of global conservation concern, Aythya nyroca is now very rare in Germany and does not meet IBA criteria at any site. Crex crex has a population of 800–3,500 calling males in Germany (Mammen and Schäffer, in prep.) and several sites hold globally important numbers, thus meeting criterion A1 (Table 2). Otis tarda has an isolated population of less than 60 individuals in Brandenburg, a single site meeting the A1 criterion (Table 2), and small numbers of Acrocephalus paludicola occur in Germany, with two sites meeting the A1 criterion (Table 2).

Germany is of particular importance for migrating and wintering waterbirds. A total of 114 IBAs hold 1% or more of the biogeographic populations (meeting criterion A4i) or flyway populations (meeting criterion B1i) of the 60 waterbird species listed in Table 3. The Wadden Sea is of major international importance for many of these species (sites 002, 034, 058). In spring and autumn, the German part of the Sea holds 1.0–1.5 million Anseriformes and 3–4 million Charadriiformes (Rösner et al. 1995), including Haematopus ostralegus (max. 463,000), Calidris canutus (max. 400,000), C. alpina (max. 628,000), Numenius arquata (max. 97,000) and Limosa lapponica (max. 192,000). A total of 150,000 Tadorna tadorna moult between mid-July and September in the Wadden Sea National Park (002).

Major proportions of the flyway populations of a number of other waterbirds migrate through or winter in Germany, including 90% of the flyway population of Anser albifrons, 79% of Anser fabalis, 65% of Cygnus columbianus, 30–40% of C. cygnus, 57% of Branta leucopsis, and 50% of B. bernicla. Large wintering concentrations of seaduck also occur offshore, with 35% of the flyway population of Melanitta fusca and 38% of the flyway population of M. nigra wintering in the Bay of Pomerania in the Baltic Sea (site 040) and the German Bay and Lister Tief in the North Sea (sites 002 and 058) (Sudfeldt et al. 1997).

Also of great importance for waterbirds are large rivers and lakes, in particular Lake Constance (with up to 250,000 wintering waterbirds). Lake Constance holds up to 50% of the south-west/central European flyway population of Netta rufina (site 231), and high proportions of the flyway populations of Aythya fuligula (30%), A. ferina (28%) and Anas strepera (40%) also occur at IBAs in the area.

Table 1 shows that a large number of sites are important for breeding species with an unfavourable conservation status in Europe (thus meeting B2/B3 criteria) and for species listed on Annex I of the EC Birds Directive (meeting C6 criterion). Table 4 lists these species, and shows that the IBA network in Germany holds a significant proportion of the national breeding population for some species.

IBAs in the meadows, dunes and marshes along the North Sea and Baltic Sea coasts, and on some small islands in the Baltic Sea, together hold important breeding numbers of waders, gulls and

Table 4. Species of European conservation concern and species listed on Annex I of the EC Birds Directive with significant breeding populations at IBAs in the Federal Republic of Germany.

Species [1]	Minimum national breeding population (pairs) [2]	Proportion (%) of national population breeding at all IBAs in Germany
Botaurus stellaris Bittern	400	28
Ixobrychus minutus Little Bittern	100	44
Ciconia nigra Black Stork	250	24
Ciconia ciconia White Stork	3,900	14
Anas strepera Gadwall	2,000	34
Netta rufina Red-crested Pochard	450	30
Aythya ferina Pochard	7,000	6
Milvus migrans Black Kite	2,500	18
Milvus milvus Red Kite	10,000	10
Haliaeetus albicilla White-tailed Eagle	264	26
Circus aeruginosus Marsh Harrier	4,000	19
Circus pygargus Montagu's Harrier	200	47
Aquila pomarina Lesser Spotted Eagle	130	34
Hieraaetus pennatus Booted Eagle	1	100
Pandion haliaetus Osprey	267	25
Falco tinnunculus Kestrel	37,000	1
Falco peregrinus Peregrine	415	27
Bonasa bonasia Hazel Grouse	1,500 individuals	71
Tetrao tetrix Black Grouse	1,600 individuals	20
Tetrao urogallus Capercaillie	2,100 individuals	29
Perdix perdix Partridge	40,000	3
Porzana porzana Spotted Crake	600	65
Crex crex Corncrake	800	93
Grus grus Crane	1,900	25
Otis tarda Great Bustard	80 individuals	61
Recurvirostra avosetta Avocet	6,800	50
Charadrius alexandrinus Kentish Plover	489	56
Pluvialis apricaria Golden Plover	10	100[3]
Limosa limosa Black-tailed Godwit	6,000	51
Tringa totanus Redshank	10,000	32
Larus canus Common Gull	18,000	45
Larus fuscus Lesser Black-backed Gull	11,800	7
Gelochelidon nilotica Gull-billed Tern	51	100[3]
Sterna sandvicensis Sandwich Tern	10,100	71
Sterna hirundo Common Tern	11,000	43
Sterna paradisaea Arctic Tern	5,500	73
Sterna albifrons Little Tern	750	66
Chlidonias niger Black Tern	790	69
Columba oenas Stock Dove	20,000	5
Tyto alba Barn Owl	7,800	3
Bubo bubo Eagle Owl	400	11
Athene noctua Little Owl	4,500	21
Asio flammeus Short-eared Owl	50	82
Caprimulgus europaeus Nightjar	3,000	27
Alcedo atthis Kingfisher	3,500	21
Picus canus Grey-headed Woodpecker	12,000	10
Dendrocopos medius Middle Spotted Woodpecker	9,000	24
Dendrocopos leucotos White-backed Woodpecker	200	69
Picoides tridactylus Three-toed Woodpecker	450	55
Lullula arborea Woodlark	25,000	6
Riparia riparia Sand Martin	50,000	35
Luscinia svecica Bluethroat	1,800	69
Turdus torquatus Ring Ouzel	9,000	10
Locustella luscinioides Savi's Warbler	4,000	14
Acrocephalus paludicola Aquatic Warbler	42	100
Acrocephalus scirpaceus Reed Warbler	150,000	2
Sylvia nisoria Barred Warbler	5,000	27
Ficedula parva Red-breasted Flycatcher	1,500	18
Ficedula albicollis Collared Flycatcher	4,000	25
Lanius collurio Red-backed Shrike	90,000	9
Lanius excubitor Great Grey Shrike	1,400	24
Serinus citrinella Citril Finch	2,500	17

1. Only those species of European conservation concern (see Box 1, p. 12) that meet IBA criteria in the Federal Republic of Germany are listed, together with those species listed on Annex I of the EC Birds Directive that fulfil criterion C6 in IBAs in Germany.
2. Data are taken from the BirdLife/EBCC European Bird Database 1998 (Heath and Borggreve 2000).
3. The percentage of the national population in IBAs exceeds 100%. Usually this is because the national population estimate has not been updated recently whilst the IBA population estimate has been recently updated with new data as a result of comprehensive surveys of IBAs themselves. Also, the individual site count for a species may be the maximum or average over recent years, and summing these may record more birds than are present nationally in any single year.

terns (meeting B2, B3 and C criteria), including *Recurvirostra avosetta*, *Gelochelidon nilotica*, *Sterna sandvicensis*, *S. hirundo*, *S. paradisaea* and *S. albifrons*. Several IBAs were identified in the north German lowlands where the shallow lakes, fish-ponds, river basins and fens hold significant breeding populations of *Haliaeetus albicilla*, *Pandion haliaetus*, *Aquila pomarina* and *Grus grus*.

Large parts of central and southern Germany are covered by extensive temperate broadleaved and mixed forests which hold rich populations of woodland birds. IBAs with this habitat hold important breeding numbers of such species as *Milvus milvus* (sites 123, 170, 172, 194), *Dendrocopos medius*, *Picus canus* and *Regulus ignicapillus*. In particular, Germany holds approximately 19% of the European breeding population of *Picus canus* (sites 172, 174, 194, 269, 281). IBAs in the mixed and coniferous forests of the montane and subalpine zones of central and southern Germany support substantial populations of characteristic species such as *Bonasa bonasia*, *Tetrao urogallus*, *Dendrocopos leucotos*, *Picoides tridactylus* and *Ficedula albicollis*.

A single IBA (site 260) meets the A3 criterion, since it supports five of the 10 species in Europe that are restricted (when breeding) to the Eurasian high-montane biome.

HABITATS

Geographically, the country is divided into seven major regions (Ssymank *et al.* 1998): the North Western German Lowlands (Norddeutsches Tiefland); the North Eastern German Lowlands, the Central European Uplands, Western part (Zentraleuropäisches Mittelgebirge); the Central European Uplands, Eastern part; the Southern German Scarplands (Südwestdeutsches Mittelgebirgs–Stufenland) with the Upper Rhine Valley (Oberrheingraben); the Prealpine Lowland (Süddeutsches Alpenvorland); the German (or Bavarian) Alps (Bayerische Alpen).

Germany's importance for waterbirds is reflected in the high frequency of occurrence of wetland habitats at IBAs (over 80%; Figure 1). These include the vast intertidal mudflats of the Wadden Sea, the marshlands, fens and bogs of the North German Lowlands, and the lakes of the Prealpine Lowland.

A substantial proportion of Europe's remaining temperate broadleaved deciduous forest is found in Germany, dominated by beech *Fagus* and oak *Quercus*. In montane and subalpine zones, there is much mixed and coniferous forest. Overall, forests and woodlands are the joint-second most frequently occurring habitat at IBAs, being found at over 60% (Figure 1).

Grasslands are equally widespread at IBAs, also occurring at over 60%. They comprise a wide variety of different types, ranging from salt meadows, permanent pastures and wet meadows in the northern lowlands to reseeded grasslands, subalpine and alpine pastures and meadows in the south; each with their respective bird communities.

IMPACTS ON IBAs – LAND-USE AND THREATS

Nationally, the most widespread land-use is agriculture, occupying 55% of the country's land area. This is reflected at IBAs, where agriculture is the most frequent land-use, occurring at over 60% (Figure 2). Agricultural intensification is one of the greatest and most widespread threats to IBAs, affecting more than 40% and regarded as having a high impact at 7% (Figure 3).

Forestry occurs over 29% of the country and is a frequent land-use at IBAs, being found in 40% (Figure 2). Intensified forest management and afforestation are significant threats, affecting 16% and 11% of IBAs respectively (Figure 3).

Tourism and recreation are major land-uses at IBAs, occurring in 46% (Figure 2). They are also the most frequent threat, affecting 48% of sites (Figure 3). Around the Wadden Sea, the Baltic Sea coast and around large lakes, such as Lake Constance, tourism developments and activities, such as hotels, golf courses and marinas, are leading to habitat loss and are causing disturbance to birds' essential activities.

Infrastructure developments such as new industrial areas, housing and roads are a major threat, affecting over 20% of IBAs (Figure 3). In parts of the Wadden Sea, with its internationally

important IBAs, exploitation of oil and gas continues and additional problems have arisen with the establishment of wind-energy parks.

IBAs alongside the large Rivers Rhine, Elbe, Saale, Danube and Oder are not only affected by their use as major shipping routes but also by the extension of flood-control schemes, boating, the construction of marinas, the extraction of sand and gravel, and the destruction of riverine forests (sites 025, 106, 129, 137, 142, 149, 160, 181, 218, 239, 264).

A particular threat is posed to sites in the Länder of North Rhine-Westphalia and Brandenburg by existing or planned brown-coal mines, which cause the groundwater level to fall and therefore result in the drying-out of wetlands and forests.

PROTECTION STATUS

Strictly protected areas, including both national designations such as National Parks and Nature Reserves and international designations recognized under German law (some Biosphere Reserves), cover only 3.5% of the country's area. Half of this area is represented by coastal and inland water-bodies.

■ National protection
Sixty percent of the IBAs have at least part of their area under some form of national protection (Figure 4). Overlaps between individual IBAs and protected areas are detailed in Table 5.

At a federal level, nature conservation legislation exists as a framework law, the Bundesnaturschutzgesetz (BNatSchG), which

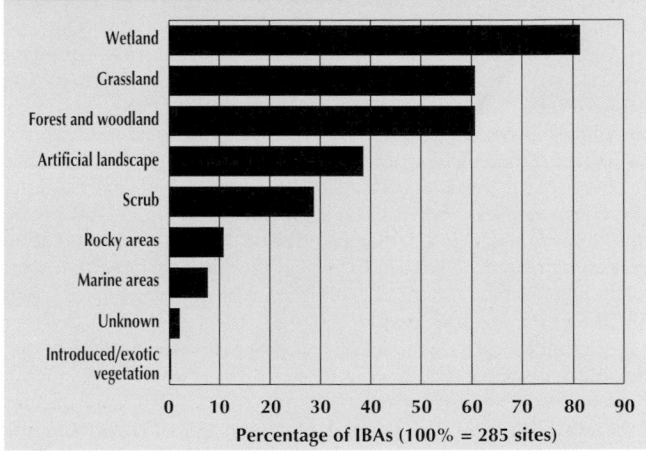

Figure 1. Occurrence of habitats at Important Bird Areas in the Federal Republic of Germany (see Appendix 3 for definitions of habitats).

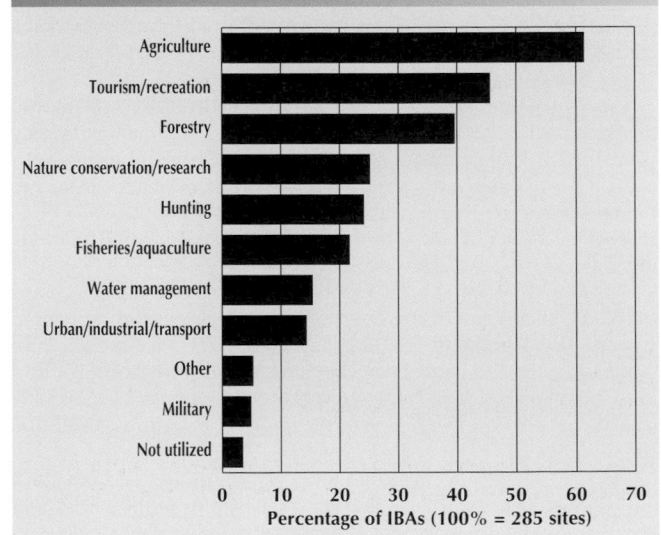

Figure 2. Occurrence of land-uses at Important Bird Areas in the Federal Republic of Germany (see Appendix 3 for definitions of land-uses).

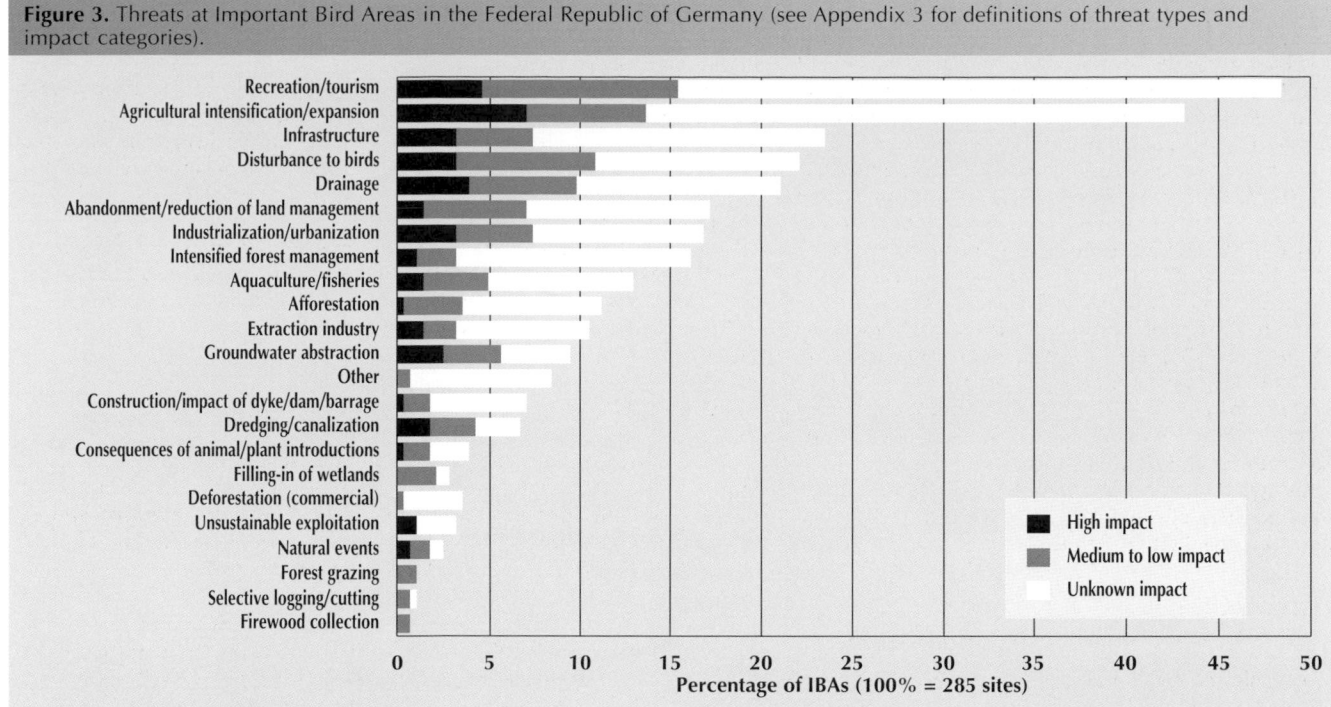

Figure 3. Threats at Important Bird Areas in the Federal Republic of Germany (see Appendix 3 for definitions of threat types and impact categories).

outlines the general categories and criteria for protected areas. Implementation of nature-conservation legislation is primarily the responsibility of individual Länder, as is the designation of protected areas, in cooperation with local authorities. There are slight differences in the definition of nature conservation laws between Länder. Under the framework law, the following categories of protected area are recognized:

1. Nature Reserves (Naturschutzgebiete)
These are sites of ecological value, supporting rare plant and/or animal communities. They are designated by the local authorities and are used to protect threatened ecosystems, usually very small areas (on average less than 50 ha). At many sites hunting, fishing, agriculture and forestry are allowed and are often detrimental. By 1998, about 6,200 sites (with an area of 835,000 ha) had been designated, covering 2.3% of Germany's total land surface.

2. National Parks (Nationalparke)
These are large areas with limited human influence, which in the main are protected like nature reserves. According to the law, National Parks, at least outside their core areas, can also be used for educational purposes. By spring 1999, Germany had designated 14 National Parks ranging in size from 3,000 ha (Jasmund, Mecklenburg-Western Pomerania) to 285,000 ha (Schleswig-Holstein part of the Wadden Sea National Park), equivalent to 2% of the country's area. However, only two National Parks in Germany

(Bayerischer Wald and Berchtesgaden) meet the IUCN definition of a National Park.

3. Biosphere Reserves
The aim, in designating Biosphere Reserves, is to develop areas as Model Regions for Integrated Conservation and Sustainable Development (ICD). Their core areas are protected like nature reserves, but outside the core zones human influence and use is allowed. In Biosphere Reserves there are projects to develop 'soft' tourism, environmentally-friendly farming practices, regional marketing of goods, etc. Biosphere Reserves existed in the former German Democratic Republic and in 1998 this designation was included in the federal conservation framework law (BNatSchG). Germany has 13 Biosphere Reserves, covering 15,811 km² (as of December 1998). This equals about 4.4% of the country's surface area, but several of the Biosphere Reserves are identical with National Parks: e.g. the three Wadden Sea National Parks of Schleswig-Holstein, Hamburg and Lower Saxony, and the Bavarian National Parks Bayerischer Wald and Berchtesgaden. Most, but not all, of these sites are also included in the international UNESCO Man and Biosphere (MAB) Programme.

4. Landscape Protection Areas (Landschaftsschutzgebiete)
These are protected parts of the countryside which are intended to contribute to its beauty and variety. Normally, use and development for agriculture, forestry, fishing and hunting are allowed and cause

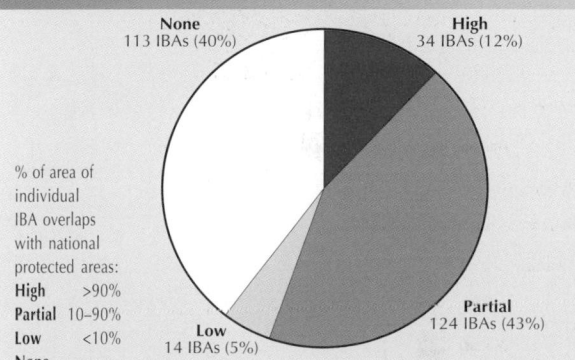

Figure 4. The national protection status of Important Bird Areas in the Federal Republic of Germany.

None
113 IBAs (40%)

High
34 IBAs (12%)

% of area of individual IBA overlaps with national protected areas:
High >90%
Partial 10–90%
Low <10%
None

Low
14 IBAs (5%)

Partial
124 IBAs (43%)

Not possible to calculate total area of overlap between IBA network in Germany and national protected-area system (see Table 5 for categories) due to incomplete overlap-area data.

Figure 5. The international protection status of Important Bird Areas in the Federal Republic of Germany.

None
126 IBAs (44%)

High
87 IBAs (31%)

% of area of individual IBA overlaps with international protected areas:
High >90%
Partial 10–90%
Low <10%
None

Low
17 IBAs (6%)

Partial
55 IBAs (19%)

Not possible to calculate total area of overlap between IBA network in Germany and international protected-area system (see Table 5 for categories) due to incomplete overlap-area data.

Table 5. Protection status of Important Bird Areas in the Federal Republic of Germany. A tick (✔) indicates that an IBA overlaps with a protected area (to any extent).

IBA code	International name	National — Landscape Protected Area	National Park	Nature Park	Nature Reserve	Biosphere Reserve	International — Ramsar Site	Special Protection Area
001	Heligoland island				✔			✔
002	Schleswig-Holstein Wadden Sea National Park	✔			✔	✔	✔	
003	Halligen Oland, Langeneß, Nordstrandischmoor, Gröde and Hooge							
004	Flensburger Innen- and Aussenförde				✔			✔
005	Schlei				✔			✔
006	Southern shore of Eckernförder Bucht							
007	Stoller Grund, Gabelsflach and Mittelgrund							
008	Coastline of Probstei							
009	Selenter See				✔			✔
010	Grosser Plöner See				✔			✔
011	Warder See							
012	Hohwachter Bucht							✔
013	Grosser and Kleiner Binnensee				✔			✔
014	Western bay of the Fehmarnsund							
015	Strand lakes and fish-ponds in south-western Fehmarn							
016	Western and northern coast of Fehmarn: Krummsteert–Puttgarden							
017	East and south-east coast of Fehmarn: Puttgarden–Burgtiefe							
018	Eastern bight of the Fehmarnsund: Burger Binnensee–Grossenbroder Binnenhafen							
019	Sagasbank							
020	Eastern coast of Oldenburg: Grossenbroder Kai–Pelzerhaken				✔			✔
021	Neustädter Bucht: Pelzerhaken–Niendorf							
022	Coastline: Niendorf–Travemünde							✔
023	Traveförde and Dassower See							✔
024	Lowland of the Rivers Eider, Treene and Sorge				✔			✔
025	Pinneberg Elbe lowlands				✔			
026	Aukrug Nature Park							
027	Lauenburgische Seen Nature Park and Schaalsee area							
028	Kühren ponds and Lanker See							
029	Wesseker See				✔			✔
030	Selent–Plön fish-ponds							✔
031	Heidmoor lowlands				✔			
032	Sachsenwald							
033	Oldenburger Graben				✔			
034	Neuwerker and Scharhörner Watt		✔			✔	✔	✔
035	Duvenstedter Brook				✔			✔
036	Mühlenberger Loch						✔	✔
037	Westrügen–Hiddensee–Zingst		✔				✔	✔
038	Isles of Oie and Kirr		✔					✔
039	Sea area Darß–Hiddensee with Plantagenetgrund							✔
040	Pomeranian Bay							
041	Isles of Langenwerder and Walfisch				✔			✔
042	Outer Wismarbucht							✔
043	Dambecker Seen							✔
044	Greifswalder Bodden	✔						✔
045	Gothensee and Thurbruch, Isles of Böhmke and Werder				✔			✔
046	Usedom lagoon							
047	Kuhlrader Moor and Röggeliner See							✔
048	Lewitz ponds	✔						✔
049	Krakower Obersee							✔
050	Eastern coast of Lake Müritz, Grosser Schwerin and Steinorn	✔	✔				✔	✔
	Subtotal of IBAs	**3**	**5**	**0**	**15**	**2**	**6**	**28**
051	Serrahn	✔						
052	Lake Nonnenhof with Lieps							
053	Peenetalmoor and Anklamer Stadtbruch	✔						✔
054	Galenbecker See and Putzarer See				✔		✔	✔
055	Koblentzer See and Latzig See				✔			✔
056	Vorpommern wooded landscape							
057	Feldberg–Woldegk terminal moraine							
058	Lower Saxony Wadden Sea National Park		✔				✔	✔
059	Riddagshäuser ponds				✔			✔
060	Niedersächsischer Drömling	✔						✔
061	Östliches Barnbruch				✔			✔
062	Wendesser Moor Nature Reserve				✔			
063	Ems valley from Leer to Emden							✔
064	Terborg							
065	Lower Weser							✔
066	Binnendeichsflächen der Wesermündung							
067	Landgraben Dumme–lowlands							
068	Rheiderland							
069	Winsener Elbmarsh							✔
070	Lucie and Landwehr							
071	Weser valley near Stolzenau and Landesbergen							✔
072	Upper Aller lowland							✔
073	Seeburger See							✔
074	Viehmoor with Leiferder ponds							✔
075	Heerter Klärteich							✔
076	Dalum Wietmarscher swamp							
077	Aper Tief							
078	Old Picardie							
079	Klein- and Großringer Wösten							
080	Georgsdorfer swamp				✔			
081	Groß Fullener marsh							
082	Leeg-, Melm- and Kuhdammoor				✔			
083	Esterweger Dose							
084	Leda–Jümme lowlands				✔			
085	Jammertal				✔			✔
086	Wesuwer Brook							
087	Südradde lowland							
088	Leine valley near Salzderhelden							✔
089	Valley of the River Ems							
090	Jadebusen	✔					✔	
091	Engerhafer Meede							
092	Alfsee				✔			
093	Butjadingen							
094	Norden–Esens							
095	Wittmund–Wangerland							
096	Krummhörn–Westermarsch							
097	Lower Aller lowlands				✔			✔
098	Ostenholzer Moor and Meissendorfer ponds							✔
099	Steinhuder Meer						✔	✔
100	Diepholzer Moorniederung						✔	✔
101	Dümmer						✔	✔
102	Hamme-Niederung							✔
103	Hunte-Niederung near Oldenburg							✔
104	Ostfriesische Meere							✔
105	Tinner Dose with Staverner Dose				✔			
106	Elbniederung from Schnackenburg to Lauenburg including Amt Neuhaus				✔		✔	✔
107	Elbmarsch from Stade to Otterndorf				✔			✔
	Subtotal of IBAs	**6**	**7**	**0**	**29**	**3**	**13**	**54**

Table 5 ... continued. Protection status of Important Bird Areas in the Federal Republic of Germany. A tick (✔) indicates that an IBA overlaps with a protected area (to any extent).

IBA code	International name	Landscape Protected Area	National Park	Nature Park	Nature Reserve	Biosphere Reserve	Ramsar Site	Special Protection Area
108	Fehntjer Tief							✔
109	Wümme lowlands and St Jürgensland							✔
110	Wümme meadows near Fischerhude							✔
111	Land Wursten							
112	Gandersum/Lange Maar							
113	Lowland of the River Ems near Laten							
114	Lüneburg heathlands				✔			
115	Borgfelder Wümmewiesen				✔			✔
116	Blockland–lower Wümme valley–Westliches Hollerland	✔			✔			✔
117	Werderland	✔			✔			✔
118	Niedervieland, Ochtumniederung	✔			✔			✔
119	Mittelwesermarsch	✔			✔			
120	Steckby-Lödderitz forest				✔	✔		✔
121	Zerbst lands	✔			✔			✔
122	Helmestausee Berga–Kelbra	✔		✔	✔		✔	✔
123	Hakel forest	✔			✔			✔
124	Aland–Elbe lowlands				✔			✔
125	Drömling bird-protection area			✔				✔
126	Landgraben-Dumme lowlands				✔			✔
127	Milde lowlands							✔
128	Elbe valley Jerichow				✔			
129	Saale-Elster valley				✔			
130	Wulfen meadows				✔			
131	Ploetzkau flood-plain forest				✔			
132	Fiener Bruch				✔			
133	Salziger See				✔			
134	North-eastern lower Harz mountains				✔			
135	Deciduous forests and heathlands of north-east Haldensleben				✔			
136	Spreewald	✔			✔	✔		
137	Havelland between Brandenburg and Potsdam				✔			✔
138	Upper Rhinluch–Nauener Luch				✔			
139	Döberitz heathlands				✔			✔
140	Rietzer See				✔			✔
141	Peitz and Bärenbrück ponds, and Lasszins meadows				✔		✔	✔
142	Lower Oder valley	✔	✔				✔	✔
143	Schorfheide–Chorin					✔		✔
144	Deichvorland Oderbruch							✔
145	Lower Rhinluch–Lake Dreetz–Havelländisches Luch–Belziger Landschaftswiesen				✔			✔
146	Uckermärkische Seenlandschaft			✔				✔
147	Stechlin				✔			✔
148	Märkische Schweiz			✔				✔
149	Lower Elbe valley					✔		✔
150	Former military training area east and west of Jüterbog			✔	✔			
151	Lower Havel–Lake Schollene–Lake Gülpe	✔			✔		✔	✔
152	Die Bänke an der Müggelspree	✔						✔
153	Niers valley			✔	✔			
154	Schwalm-Nette–Platte and Grenzwald				✔			✔
155	Bogs and heathlands of the Westmünsterland							✔
156	Hellwegbörde							
157	Weser Dam Schlüsselburg						✔	✔
158	Bastau-Niederung				✔			
159	Wahn heathlands				✔			
160	Lower Rhine area						✔	✔
161	Heubachniederung/Schwarzes Venn/Borkenberge/Halterner Seen				✔			
	Subtotal of IBAs	17	8	6	63	7	19	87

IBA code	International name	Landscape Protected Area	National Park	Nature Park	Nature Reserve	Biosphere Reserve	Ramsar Site	Special Protection Area
162	Sewage farms of Münster				✔		✔	✔
163	Recker Moor/Düsterdieker Niederung/Seester Feld				✔			
164	Meadows and forests around Burbach				✔			
165	Emsaue (Rietberger Emsniederung–Steinhorster Becken)				✔			
166	Oppenweher Moor							
167	Medebacher Bucht				✔			
168	Sennelager training area							
169	Möhnesee							✔
170	Kellerwald			✔				
171	Burgwald							
172	Vogelsberg							
173	Hessian Rothaar mountains							
174	Knüll							
175	High Westerwald around Driedorf							
176	Waldeck upland							
177	Lahn valley from Marburg to Wetzlar	✔						
178	Eder alluvion							
179	Northern Wetterau							
180	Alluvion of the Lower Schwalm near Borken							
181	Hessian Rhine alluvion				✔			✔
182	Gladenbach mountain country east of Herborn							
183	Rheingau							
184	Dune and aeolian sand area: Dudenhofen, Babenhausen, Seligenstadt							
185	Lorsch forest and Viernheim heathland							
186	Rothenbach pond				✔			✔
187	Reichlos pond				✔			✔
188	Ober-Moos pond				✔			✔
189	Rotes Moor	✔			✔	✔		
190	Rhäden near Obersuhl and Bosserode				✔			✔
191	Reservoir near Affoldern	✔			✔			✔
192	Alluvion of the middle Horloff				✔			✔
193	Twiste reservoir				✔			✔
194	Rhön Biosphere Reserve					✔		
195	Herbsleben ponds				✔			✔
196	Plothen ponds	✔		✔	✔			✔
197	Uhlstädt heathlands				✔			✔
198	Wurzelbergfarmde	✔		✔	✔			✔
199	Assberg–Hasenleite	✔		✔	✔			✔
200	Meura heathlands	✔		✔	✔			✔
201	Schwarza valley	✔			✔			✔
202	Vesser Valley Biosphere Reserve				✔	✔	✔	✔
203	Pressel wooded heath and mire				✔			✔
204	Ponds and Elbe valley near Torgau				✔			✔
205	Oberlausitz heathland and fish-ponds						✔	✔
206	Eschefeld ponds				✔			✔
207	Westerzgebirge							✔
208	Erzgebirgskamm near Satzung							✔
209	Grosshartmannsdorfer Grossteich				✔			✔
210	Erzgebirgskamm near Deutscheinsiedel							✔
211	Sächsische Schweiz National Park		✔					✔
212	Fürstenau							✔
213	Rheinauen: Eltville–Bingen				✔		✔	✔
214	Gimbsheim-Eicher Altrhein and Fischsee				✔			✔
215	Hördter Rheinaue				✔			
216	Saar/Bliesgau/Westrich			✔				
217	Wagbach lowlands				✔			✔
	Subtotal of IBAs	25	9	13	93	11	21	118

Table 5 ... continued. Protection status of Important Bird Areas in the Federal Republic of Germany. A tick (✓) indicates that an IBA overlaps with a protected area (to any extent).

IBA code	International name	Landscape Protected Area	National Park	Nature Park	Nature Reserve	Biosphere Reserve	Ramsar Site	Special Protection Area
			National				International	
218	Hockenheimer Rheinbogen	✓			✓			
219	Orchard landscape between Hohenstaufen and Teck in the mid-Albvorland	✓			✓			
220	Rhine flats: Kehl–Helmlingen	✓			✓			
221	Rhine: Greffern–Murgmündung–Neuburgweier	✓			✓			
222	Rhine flats: Nonnenweier–Kehl				✓			✓
223	Rhine flats: Sasbach–Wittenweier	✓			✓			
224	Rhine flats: Neuenburg–Breisach				✓			✓
225	Rhine flats: Haltingen–Neuenburg and foothills	✓			✓			✓
226	Öpfinger Donau-Stausee, Rißniederung and Rißtissener Kiesseen	✓						
227	Lake Constance–Obersee, and the adjacent Seerhein							
228	Federsee	✓			✓			✓
229	Northern Black Forest, west of the Murg	✓			✓			✓
230	Northern Black Forest, east of the Murg	✓			✓			✓
231	Untersee of Lake Constance	✓			✓		✓	✓
232	Silzen meadows and bog, near Stettfeld				✓			
233	Philippsburger Altrhein and Rheinschanzinsel							
234	Schiltach and Berneck valleys, near Schramberg	✓						
235	Middle-eastern Black Forest	✓						
236	Schwarza and Schlücht valleys	✓			✓			
237	Feldberg in the Black Forest				✓			✓
238	Kocher and adjoining valleys	✓			✓			✓
239	South-eastern Alb and Upper Danube valley	✓			✓			✓
240	Simonswald–Rohrhardsberg	✓			✓			✓
241	Northern Karlsruhe Hardt	✓			✓			
242	Lake Überlingen (Lake Constance)	✓			✓			✓
243	Jagst and adjoining valleys	✓			✓			✓
244	Rhine flats: Karlsruhe–Rheinsheim	✓			✓			✓
245	Orchards and vineyards between Waldhausen and Geradstetten	✓			✓			
246	Wutach ravine	✓			✓			✓
247	Kaiserstuhl	✓			✓			✓
248	Stromberg	✓			✓			✓
249	Rhine flats: Breisach–Sasbach with Limberg	✓			✓			✓
250	Orchards and *Quercus* woodlands near Filderstadt and Echterdingen	✓						
251	Enz valley: Mühlhausen–Roßwag	✓			✓			
252	Schönbuch	✓			✓			✓
253	Orchards, heathlands and forests around Weil der Stadt	✓			✓			✓
	Subtotal of IBAs	59	9	13	123	11	22	138
254	Vogelfreistätte Mittlere Isar-Stauseen				✓			✓
255	Rötelsee–Weihergebiet including Regen-Aue				✓			
256	Isar-Tal: Gottfrieding–Plattling including Isar-Mündungsbereich				✓			
257	Ismaninger Speichersee and fish-ponds						✓	
258	Main-Tal near Volkach: Fahr-Dettelbach	✓						
259	Bayerischer Wald National Park with Arbergebiet and Hohen Bogen		✓			✓		✓
260	Berchtesgaden National Park		✓					✓
261	Altmühl-Tal: Ornbau–Gunzenhausen Altmühlsee and Wiesmet				✓			
262	Ammersee						✓	✓
263	Chiemsee and Chiemseemore				✓		✓	✓
264	Donau-Tal: Regensburg–Vilshofen	✓			✓			✓
265	Rotwand-Gebiet	✓			✓			
266	Donau-Auen: Neu-Ulm–Lauingen including Faiminger Stausee, Donau-Moos, and Gundelfinger Moos	✓			✓		✓	
267	Karwendel and Karwendel-Vorgebirge				✓			✓
268	Ammergauer Berge				✓			✓
269	Nürnberger Reichswald				✓			
270	Vorderer Steigerwald–Windsheimer Bucht–Gollach-Gau-Steigerwald-Vorland				✓			
271	Lech–Donau–Winkel: Lechstausee Feldheim and Donaustausee Bertoldsheim	✓			✓		✓	
272	Donau-Auen and Donau-Ried: Höchstädt–Donauwörth	✓			✓			
273	Orchards bordering the River Main							
274	Charlottenhofer Weihergebiet				✓			✓
275	Aisch–Regnitz–Grund							✓
276	Starnberger See	✓			✓		✓	
277	Main-Tal: Eltmann–Hassfurt							
278	Murnauer Moos and Loisach-Kochel-Moore				✓			
279	Main-Tal near Schweinfurt	✓			✓			
280	Vogelfreistätte Alter and Neuer See				✓			
281	Northern part of the Steigerwald				✓			
282	Lower Inn: Haiming–Neuhaus, including the Neuhaus, Egglfing, Ering and Simbach reservoirs				✓		✓	✓
283	Nassanger near Trieb and surrounding gravel-pits							
284	Obersee: Schachener Bucht							
285	Manteler forest			✓				
	Total number of IBAs	63	11	14	144	12	29	149

massive disturbance. Land coverage by Landscape Protection Areas varies between 15% and 40% of the surface area of Länder, with an average of 25%. However, their value for nature conservation is rather limited.

5. Nature Parks (Naturparke)
Nature Parks are large areas with similar objectives to Landscape Protection Areas but, particularly in the western part of Germany, with a strong bias towards outdoor recreation. Indeed, in about 60 of the 84 Nature Parks the primary purpose is recreational activities and tourism. Nature Parks cover about 18.7% of the country's surface.

6. Natural Monuments (Naturdenkmale) and Protected Parts of the Countryside (Geschützte Landschaftsbestandteile)
These are very small sites or single features of scientific, historic or traditional interest, which in only a few cases cover areas larger than 3 ha.

■ International protection
Germany is party to the international conventions and initiatives detailed in Box 1. However, only the Ramsar Convention, MAB Programme, EC Birds Directive, EC Habitats Directive and Helsinki Convention have an influence on site protection in Germany. Fifty-six percent of IBAs in Germany are covered (at least in part) by some form of international conservation designation (Figure 5)—Biosphere Reserves are treated as a national designation (see above). Special Protection Areas (SPAs) and Ramsar Sites do not receive official legal protection unless part or all of their area is protected under a national designation such as Nature Reserve or National Park. The IBAs overlapping

Box 1. International legislation and initiatives that are relevant to site conservation in the Federal Republic of Germany (see Appendix 1 for a general description of these agreements).

Global	
Biodiversity Convention	✔
Ramsar Convention	✔
Bonn Convention	✔
World Heritage Convention	✔
MAB Programme	✔

Pan-European	
Bern Convention	✔

Regional	
EC Birds Directive	✔
EC Habitats Directive	✔
Helsinki Convention	✔

✔ Convention ratified/initiative supported
(✔) Convention signed

with international protected-area designations are illustrated in Table 5.

A total of 149 IBAs overlap with SPAs (Table 5). However, coverage varies across the country. A previous analysis (Mayr 1993) showed that, in the western part of Germany, only 23% of IBAs have been fully, and 28% partly, designated as SPAs. However, in the five new Länder, nearly 90% of the IBAs are designated as SPAs and protected under national law as Nature Reserves, National Parks or Biosphere Reserves. Twenty-nine IBAs overlap with one or more Ramsar Sites (Table 5). Only 40% of the area of the 29 German Ramsar Sites had been designated as SPAs by 1995 (Mayr 1995) but this figure has now increased to 87%, primarily as a result of the designation of Schleswig-Holstein Wadden Sea National Park (site 002) as a Special Protection Area.

CONSERVATION

- Besides legislative protection, the Länder which are responsible for nature conservation try in some cases to minimize human impacts, especially from agriculture, through schemes such as EU LIFE projects or programmes under the EU Common Agricultural Policy, such as the Agri-environment Regulation (2078/92/EEC).

- The German Ministry of Environment grants limited funds for scientific conservation projects ('F+E-Projects') within the framework of the annual 'Environmental Research Plan' (Umwelt-Forschungsplan, UFO-PLAN). These and other projects (E+E-Projects, the financial support for representative sites of national importance, etc.) are designed to form the basis of, or to support conservation decisions and measures taken by, the German Government. At present, the majority of national monitoring programmes are not government-funded.

- In addition to Federal State Agencies, NGOs play a very important role in monitoring species, sites and habitats and are also indispensable in the monitoring and management of protected areas. NABU, BUND, WWF Germany, DDA and other NGOs carry out monitoring and conservation projects at a national level. They are also heavily involved in local and regional conservation projects and in the management of nature reserves and other protected areas, as are many of the more local or regional NGOs in individual Länder, of which NGOs like LBV and BN in Bavaria and regional branches of NABU (or BUND) are the most noteworthy.

- There are a number of national species-protection projects for particular birds, including those on *Ciconia ciconia*, *Pandion haliaetus*, *Falco peregrinus*, *Grus grus*, *Otis tarda*, *Crex crex*, *Bubo bubo*, and others, but these are far outnumbered by regional and local projects dealing with rarer or more localized species such as *Aquila chrysaetos*, *Apus melba* and *Lanius* species.

- Among the different regional and national monitoring programmes, one covers the majority of Red List species, and others deal with 'flagship' species such as *Ciconia ciconia*, *Grus grus*, raptors and owls. There are also monitoring programmes for many, but not all protected areas. In particular, wetland IBAs are regularly monitored through the International Waterfowl counts of ZWFD and Wetlands International. However, a specific monitoring scheme for IBAs (or SPAs) does not exist in Germany.

ANALYTICAL METHODS

- Population estimates are based mainly on data collected during 1996–1997, provided by local experts or by other national or regional bird-monitoring bodies. In several cases, data were updated in 1998 and spring 1999.

- Threats and land-use data are from the same period, although for some sites data are unavailable. The lack of data for the percentage cover of habitats and land-uses at sites means that Figures 1 and 2 indicate simply the frequency of occurrence.

- As a result of a lack of data, the overlap between IBAs and protected areas could not often be assigned to one of three standard categories (<10% overlap by area = 'low'; 10–90% overlap = 'partial'; >90% overlap = 'high'). Where the degree of overlap is unknown, 'partial' has been used as a default option. Exceptions occur where national experts indicated that the degree of overlap fitted one of the three categories. As a result of this problem, analysis of Figures 4 and 5 has been limited to indicating only the number of IBAs with some part of their area under protection. No attempt was made in the analysis to differentiate between low, partial and high levels of protection.

- Site boundaries were delineated on official topographical maps, normally at a scale of 1:25,000 and stored with the original data-sheets at the Institut für Ökologie und Naturschutz (IfÖN). Digitization using a geographical information system (GIS) is planned.

GLOSSARY

Aue river-plain.
bei near.
Berg mountain.
BN Bund Naturschutz in Bayern–Bavarian regional branch of BUND.
Bucht bight; bay.
BUND Bund für Umwelt und Naturschutz Deutschland—Friends of the Earth partner in Germany.
DDA Dachverband Deutscher Avifaunisten—umbrella organization of 44 regional ornithological societies.
DRV Deutscher Rat für Vogelschutz (German Council for Bird Protection)—Associate member of BirdLife International.
IfÖN Institut für Ökologie und Naturschutz (Institute for Ecology and Nature Conservation), a non-governmental institution associated with NABU.
LBV Landesbund für Vogelschutz in Bayern—Associate member of BirdLife International.
LIFE an EU funding line (Regulation 1973/92/EEC) which supports EU environmental legislation including the Birds and Habitats Directives.
Meer mere; shallow, nutrient-rich water-body.
Moor mire; marsh; wet heathland.
NABU Naturschutzbund Deutschland—the BirdLife Partner in Germany.
See lake.
SPA Special Protection Area (designated under Article 4 of the EC Birds Directive).
Teich pond.
ZWFD Zentrale für Wasservogelforschung und Feuchtgebietsschutz in Deutschland (Centre for Waterfowl Research and Wetland Protection in Germany)—a voluntary working group of the DDA.

ACKNOWLEDGEMENTS

Data were collected by numerous voluntary co-workers for NABU's regional branches and various regional ornithological societies. Some of the Länder's bird-protection agencies ('Staatliche Vogelschutzwarten') added useful information. For helpful coordination work at the Länder-level special thanks go to Bernd Koop (Schleswig-Holstein), Dr Matthias Schreiber (Lower Saxony), Michael Gerhard (North Rhine-Westphalia), Mark Harthun (Hesse), Martin Klatt (Baden-Württemberg) and Dr Andreas von Lindeiner (Bavaria). Coordination of data collection, checking and input into the database were executed on behalf of NABU by the Institute for Ecology and Nature Conservation (IfÖN), namely by its director Christian Unselt and his co-workers Annette Mayer, Knut Bartels and Nicolaj Klapkarek. Claudia Lindenberg assisted in controlling data and data-sheets as well as in the compilation of the country chapter.

■ SITE ACCOUNTS

Heligoland island C7 001

Admin region Schleswig-Holstein
Coordinates 54°14′N 8°22′E
Altitude 0–0 m **Area** 1 ha

■ Site description
Sea cliffs on the island of Heligoland.

Habitats Rocky areas (100%; sea cliff/rocky shore)
Land-use Nature conservation/research

■ Birds
The only cliff-nesting seabird colony in Germany.

■ Protection status
National High **International** High
1 ha of IBA covered by Nature Reserve (Lummenfelsen Helgoland, 1 ha). IBA overlaps with Special Protection Area.

■ Conservation issues

Threats Recreation/tourism (U)

There is pressure from tourism with erosion adversely affecting the cliffs.

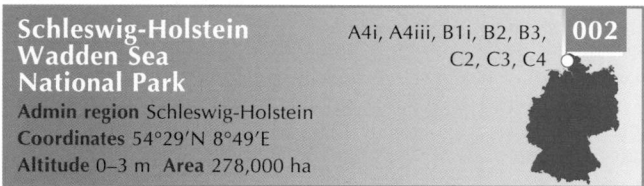

Schleswig-Holstein Wadden Sea National Park
A4i, A4iii, B1i, B2, B3, C2, C3, C4 002

Admin region Schleswig-Holstein
Coordinates 54°29′N 8°49′E
Altitude 0–3 m **Area** 278,000 ha

■ Site description
A large coastal area with estuarine mudflats, sandbanks, saltmarsh, lagoons, wet meadows and freshwater marshes. Intensively used for sheep-grazing, wildfowl hunting, military training and oil, sand and gravel extraction.

Habitats Grassland (humid grassland); Wetland (54%; tidal river/enclosed tidal water; mudflat/sandflat; saltmarsh; sand-dunes/sand beach; coastal lagoon; water-fringe vegetation), Marine areas (46%; open sea; sea inlet/coastal features)
Land-use Agriculture (3%), Fisheries/aquaculture (50%), Hunting, Military, Tourism/recreation, Urban/industrial/transport (50%), Water management (99%)

■ Birds

Species	Season	Year	Pop min	Pop max	Acc	Criteria
Phalacrocorax carbo Cormorant	P	1997	1,605	1,605	—	B1i, C3
Branta leucopsis Barnacle Goose	W	1997	25,667	25,667	—	A4i, B1i, B2, C2
Branta leucopsis Barnacle Goose	P	1997	101,716	101,716	—	A4i, B1i, C2
Branta bernicla Brent Goose	W	1997	3,948	3,948	—	A4i, B1i, C3
Branta bernicla Brent Goose	P	1997	133,216	133,216	—	A4i, B1i, C3
Tadorna tadorna Shelduck	W	1997	74,877	74,877	—	A4i, B1i, C3
Tadorna tadorna Shelduck	P	1997	200,000	200,000	—	A4i, B1i, C3
Anas penelope Wigeon	W	1997	85,597	85,597	—	A4i, B1i, C3
Anas penelope Wigeon	P	1997	137,737	137,737	—	A4i, B1i, C3
Anas crecca Teal	W	1997	4,950	4,950	—	B1i, C3
Anas crecca Teal	P	1997	19,467	19,467	—	A4i, B1i, C3
Anas platyrhynchos Mallard	W	1997	66,138	66,138	—	B1i, C3
Anas acuta Pintail	P	1997	104,000	104,000	—	A4i, B1i, C3
Anas clypeata Shoveler	W	1997	848	848	—	B1i, C3
Anas clypeata Shoveler	P	1997	1,768	1,768	—	B1i, C3
Somateria mollissima Eider	W	1997	150,000	150,000	—	A4i, B1i, C3
Somateria mollissima Eider	P	1997	215,000	215,000	—	A4i, B1i, C3
Melanitta nigra Common Scoter	W	1997	46,000	46,000	—	A4i, B1i, C3
Haematopus ostralegus Oystercatcher	R	1997	6,400	6,400	—	A4i, B1i, C3
Haematopus ostralegus Oystercatcher	W	1997	139,344	139,344	—	A4i, B1i, C3
Haematopus ostralegus Oystercatcher	P	1997	176,686	176,686	—	A4i, B1i, C3
Recurvirostra avosetta Avocet	B	1997	2,380	2,380	—	A4i, B1i, B3, C2
Recurvirostra avosetta Avocet	P	1997	8,464	8,464	—	A4i, B1i, C2
Charadrius hiaticula Ringed Plover	P	1997	9,653	9,653	—	A4i, B1i, C3

Species ... continued	Season	Year	Pop min	Pop max	Acc	Criteria
Charadrius alexandrinus Kentish Plover	B	1997	270	270	—	B2
Charadrius alexandrinus Kentish Plover	P	1997	1,040	1,040	—	A4i, B1i, C3
Pluvialis apricaria Golden Plover	P	1997	69,703	69,703	—	A4i, B1i, C2
Pluvialis squatarola Grey Plover	W	1997	7,022	7,022	—	A4i, B1i, C3
Pluvialis squatarola Grey Plover	P	1997	4,500	4,500	—	A4i, B1i, C3
Calidris canutus Knot	W	1997	25,256	25,256	—	A4i, B1i, C3
Calidris canutus Knot	P	1997	471,208	471,208	—	A4i, B1i, C3
Calidris alba Sanderling	P	1997	27,504	27,504	—	A4i, B1i, C3
Calidris ferruginea Curlew Sandpiper	P	1997	19,425	19,425	—	A4i, B1i, C3
Calidris alpina Dunlin	W	1997	78,040	78,040	—	A4i, B1i, C3
Calidris alpina Dunlin	P	1997	471,208	471,208	—	A4i, B1i, C3
Limosa lapponica Bar-tailed Godwit	W	1997	14,024	14,024	—	A4i, B1i, C2
Limosa lapponica Bar-tailed Godwit	P	1997	146,050	146,050	—	A4i, B1i, C2
Numenius arquata Curlew	W	1997	44,405	44,405	—	A4i, B1i, B2, C3
Numenius arquata Curlew	P	1997	52,445	52,445	—	A4i, B1i, C3
Tringa erythropus Spotted Redshank	P	1997	9,853	9,853	—	A4i, B1i, C3
Tringa totanus Redshank	R	1997	1,600	1,600	—	A4i, B1i, B2, C3
Tringa totanus Redshank	W	1997	4,231	4,231	—	A4i, B1i, C3
Tringa totanus Redshank	P	1997	13,610	13,610	—	A4i, B1i, C3
Tringa nebularia Greenshank	P	1997	7,363	7,363	—	A4i, B1i, C3
Arenaria interpres Turnstone	W	1997	789	789	—	A4i, B1i, C3
Arenaria interpres Turnstone	P	1997	2,932	2,932	—	A4i, B1i, C3
Larus ridibundus Black-headed Gull	P	1997	71,198	71,198	—	A4i, B1i, C3
Larus canus Common Gull	P	1997	38,861	38,861	—	A4i, B1i, C3
Larus fuscus Lesser Black-backed Gull	R	1997	830	830	—	B3
Larus fuscus Lesser Black-backed Gull	P	1997	2,354	2,354	—	B1i, C3
Larus argentatus Herring Gull	R	1997	5,000	5,000	—	B1i
Larus argentatus Herring Gull	W	1997	30,891	30,891	—	A4i, B1i
Larus argentatus Herring Gull	P	1997	56,145	56,145	—	A4i, B1i
Gelochelidon nilotica Gull-billed Tern	B	1997	10	10	—	B2
Sterna sandvicensis Sandwich Tern	B	1997	6,850	6,850	—	A4i, B1i, B2, C2
Sterna sandvicensis Sandwich Tern	P	1997	15,364	15,364	—	A4i, B1i, C2
Sterna hirundo Common Tern	B	1997	2,800	2,800	—	A4i, B1i, C2
Sterna hirundo Common Tern	P	1997	7,482	7,482	—	B1i, C2
Sterna paradisaea Arctic Tern	B	1997	3,800	3,800	—	C2
Sterna albifrons Little Tern	B	1997	230	230	—	B1i, B2, C2
Sterna albifrons Little Tern	P	1997	750	750	—	B1i, C2
Asio flammeus Short-eared Owl	R	1997	3	3	—	B2

Part of the Wadden Sea, of major international importance for breeding, moulting, passage and wintering waterbirds, particularly wildfowl (Anatidae) and waders.

■ Protection status
National Partial **International** High
IBA overlaps with National Park. IBA overlaps with Ramsar Site, Biosphere Reserve and Special Protection Area.

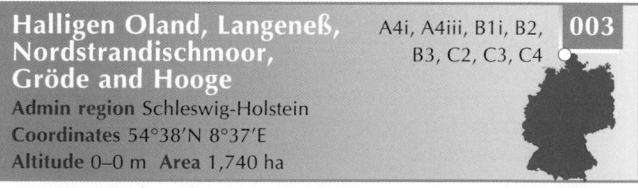

Halligen Oland, Langeneß, Nordstrandischmoor, Gröde and Hooge
A4i, A4iii, B1i, B2, B3, C2, C3, C4 003

Admin region Schleswig-Holstein
Coordinates 54°38′N 8°37′E
Altitude 0–0 m **Area** 1,740 ha

■ Site description
The Halligen comprises a mosaic of saltmarsh communities, varying according to tidal regime and flooding frequency.

Habitats Wetland (saltmarsh)

■ Birds

Species	Season	Year	Pop min	Pop max	Acc	Criteria
Branta bernicla Brent Goose	W	1998	68,000	68,000	—	A4i, B1i, C3
Anas penelope Wigeon	W	1998	13,000	13,000	—	B1i, C3
Recurvirostra avosetta Avocet	B	1998	188	191	—	B3
Limosa lapponica Bar-tailed Godwit	W	1998	12,130	12,130	—	A4i, B1i, C2
Sterna albifrons Little Tern	B	1998	12	15	—	B2

The site holds 20,000 or more waterbirds in winter, on a regular basis.

■ Protection status
National None **International** None

Flensburger Innen- and Aussenförde

A4i, A4iii, B1i, B2, C3, C4 **004**

Admin region Schleswig-Holstein
Coordinates 54°52′N 9°36′E
Altitude 0–0 m **Area** —

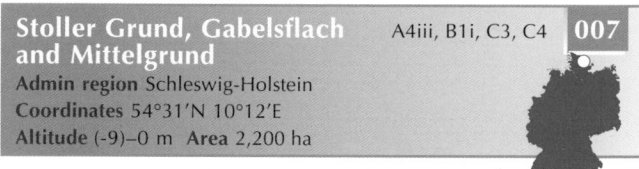

■ Site description
A 62-km section of low-lying coastline situated east of Flensburg. Includes the inshore waters of a sandy bay (up to 1,400 m wide). Tourism, boat traffic and fishing are the main human activities.

Habitats Marine areas (sea inlet/coastal features)
Land-use Fisheries/aquaculture, Tourism/recreation, Urban/industrial/transport

■ Birds

Species	Season	Year	Pop min	Pop max	Acc	Criteria
Aythya fuligula Tufted Duck	W	1997	—	10,000	—	B1i, C3
Aythya marila Scaup	W	1997	—	7,000	—	A4i, B1i, B2, C3
Somateria mollissima Eider	W	1997	—	20,600	—	B1i, C3

The site holds more than 20,000 wintering wildfowl on a regular basis.

■ Protection status
National Partial **International** High
775 ha of IBA covered by Nature Reserve (Geltinger Birk, 775 ha). 363 ha of IBA covered by Nature Reserve (Holnis, 363 ha). IBA overlaps with Special Protection Area.

Schlei

A4iii, B1i, B2, B3, C3, C4 **005**

Admin region Schleswig-Holstein
Coordinates 54°35′N 9°50′E
Altitude 0–0 m **Area** —

■ Site description
The IBA is a 43-km long and 3–4-km wide tidal fjord with fringing saltmarsh and sand-dunes (135 km of coastline in all). Human settlements, industrial plants and harbours are being developed along the shore and tourist boat traffic is increasing.

Habitats Marine areas (sea inlet/coastal features), Wetland (saltmarsh; sand-dunes/sand beach), Artificial landscape (other urban/industrial areas)
Land-use Tourism/recreation, Urban/industrial/transport

■ Birds

Species	Season	Year	Pop min	Pop max	Acc	Criteria
Aythya fuligula Tufted Duck	W	1997	—	15,000	—	B1i, C3
Recurvirostra avosetta Avocet	B	1996	21	—	—	B3
Larus canus Common Gull	R	1996	582	—	—	B2

The site regularly holds more than 20,000 wintering waterbirds.

■ Protection status
National Partial **International** High
250 ha of IBA covered by Nature Reserve (Oehe-Schleimünde, 250 ha). 120 ha of IBA covered by Nature Reserve (Reesholm, 120 ha). IBA overlaps with Special Protection Area.

Southern shore of Eckernförder Bucht

A4iii, B1i, B2, C3, C4 **006**

Admin region Schleswig-Holstein
Coordinates 54°28′N 10°03′E
Altitude 0–0 m **Area** —

■ Site description
A bay with a sandy/stony coastline 26 km long. Tourism is the main human activity.

Habitats Marine areas (sea inlet/coastal features), Wetland (sand-dunes/sand beach; shingle/stony beach)
Land-use Tourism/recreation

■ Birds

Species	Season	Year	Pop min	Pop max	Acc	Criteria
Podiceps cristatus Great Crested Grebe	W	1997	—	2,700	—	B1i, C3
Aythya marila Scaup	W	1997	—	2,000	—	B2
Bucephala clangula Goldeneye	W	1997	—	3,000	—	B1i, C3
Sterna albifrons Little Tern	B	1996	14	—	—	B2

The site holds more than 20,000 wintering waterbirds on a regular basis.

■ Protection status
National None **International** None

Stoller Grund, Gabelsflach and Mittelgrund

A4iii, B1i, C3, C4 **007**

Admin region Schleswig-Holstein
Coordinates 54°31′N 10°12′E
Altitude (-9)–0 m **Area** 2,200 ha

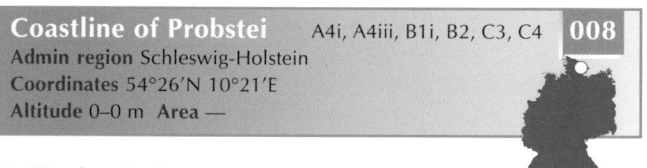

■ Site description
Shallow waters with sand and gravel-banks in the Baltic Sea.

Habitats Marine areas (open sea)
Land-use Urban/industrial/transport

■ Birds

Species	Season	Year	Pop min	Pop max	Acc	Criteria
Somateria mollissima Eider	W	1997	—	13,000	—	B1i, C3

The site holds more than 20,000 wintering seaduck on a regular basis.

■ Protection status
National None **International** None

■ Conservation issues

Threats Extraction industry (U), Other (U)

Boat traffic ('Other' threat) and gravel extraction are destroying the area.

Coastline of Probstei

A4i, A4iii, B1i, B2, C3, C4 **008**

Admin region Schleswig-Holstein
Coordinates 54°26′N 10°21′E
Altitude 0–0 m **Area** —

■ Site description
A sandy/stony coastal zone with 25 km of coastline.

Habitats Marine areas (sea inlet/coastal features), Wetland (sand-dunes/sand beach; shingle/stony beach)
Land-use Tourism/recreation

■ Birds

Species	Season	Year	Pop min	Pop max	Acc	Criteria
Aythya marila Scaup	W	1997	6,000	—	—	A4i, B1i, B2, C3
Somateria mollissima Eider	W	1997	—	35,000	—	A4i, B1i, C3
Sterna albifrons Little Tern	B	1996	30	—	—	B2

The site holds more than 20,000 wintering waterbirds on a regular basis.

■ Protection status
National None **International** None

■ Conservation issues

Threats Other (U), Recreation/tourism (U)

Tourism (bathing, camping, boating and wind-surfing) and pollution ('Other' threat) are the main threats.

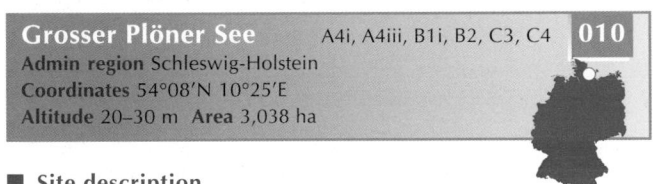

Selenter See   A4i, A4iii, B1i, C3, C4   009

Admin region Schleswig-Holstein
Coordinates 54°18'N 10°27'E
Altitude 0–37 m Area 2,141 ha

■ Site description
A eutrophic lake bordered by semi-natural forest.

Habitats Wetland (standing fresh water)
Land-use Tourism/recreation

■ Birds

Species	Season	Year	Pop min	Pop max	Acc	Criteria
Podiceps cristatus Great Crested Grebe	N	1997	—	2,000	—	B1i, C3
Aythya fuligula Tufted Duck	N	1998	—	10,000	—	B1i, C3
Larus minutus Little Gull	P	1998	—	7,000	—	A4i, B1i, C3

The site holds more than 20,000 non-breeding waterbirds on a regular basis.

■ Protection status
National Partial **International** Partial
IBA overlaps with Nature Reserve. IBA overlaps with Special Protection Area.

■ Conservation issues

Threats Recreation/tourism (U)

Increasing pressure from tourism is causing disturbance.

Grosser Plöner See   A4i, A4iii, B1i, B2, C3, C4   010

Admin region Schleswig-Holstein
Coordinates 54°08'N 10°25'E
Altitude 20–30 m Area 3,038 ha

■ Site description
A eutrophic lake with reedbeds (*Phragmites*).

Habitats Wetland (standing fresh water; water-fringe vegetation)
Land-use Tourism/recreation

■ Birds

Species	Season	Year	Pop min	Pop max	Acc	Criteria
Podiceps cristatus Great Crested Grebe	P	1997	—	1,600	—	B1i, C3
Phalacrocorax carbo Cormorant	P	1997	—	4,000	—	B1i, C3
Aythya fuligula Tufted Duck	W	1997	—	20,000	—	A4i, B1i, C3
Larus minutus Little Gull	P	1998	—	9,200	—	A4i, B1i, C3
Larus canus Common Gull	R	1997	—	600	—	B2

■ Protection status
National Partial **International** Low
IBA overlaps with Nature Reserve. IBA overlaps with Special Protection Area.

■ Conservation issues

Threats Recreation/tourism (U)

Boating, camping, and walking are the main threats.

Warder See   A4i, B1i, C2, C3   011

Admin region Schleswig-Holstein
Coordinates 53°58'N 10°25'E
Altitude 15–25 m Area 429 ha

■ Site description
A lake situated in an agricultural landscape with small copses.

Habitats Wetland (standing fresh water)

■ Birds

Species	Season	Year	Pop min	Pop max	Acc	Criteria
Cygnus columbianus Bewick's Swan	P	1997	—	300	—	A4i, B1i, C2
Anser anser Greylag Goose	P	1997	—	4,000	—	A4i, B1i, C3

■ Protection status
National None **International** None

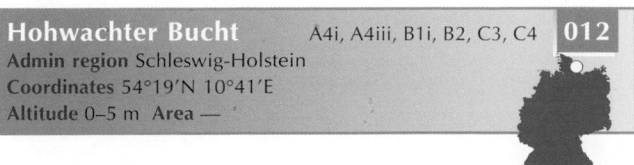

Hohwachter Bucht   A4i, A4iii, B1i, B2, C3, C4   012

Admin region Schleswig-Holstein
Coordinates 54°19'N 10°41'E
Altitude 0–5 m Area —

■ Site description
Hohwachter Bucht is part of Kieler Bucht and has a sandy/stony shoreline 38 km long. Tourism and military training are the main human activities.

Habitats Marine areas (sea inlet/coastal features), Wetland (sand-dunes/sand beach; shingle/stony beach)
Land-use Military, Tourism/recreation

■ Birds

Species	Season	Year	Pop min	Pop max	Acc	Criteria
Aythya marila Scaup	W	1997	—	3,400	—	B1i, B2, C3
Somateria mollissima Eider	W	1997	—	35,000	—	A4i, B1i, C3
Riparia riparia Sand Martin	B	1997	—	—	—	B2

The site holds more than 20,000 wintering seaduck on a regular basis.

■ Protection status
National None **International** Partial
IBA overlaps with Special Protection Area.

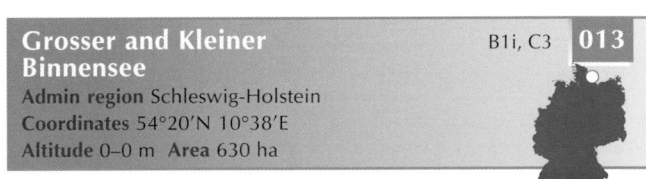

Grosser and Kleiner Binnensee   B1i, C3   013

Admin region Schleswig-Holstein
Coordinates 54°20'N 10°38'E
Altitude 0–0 m Area 630 ha

■ Site description
A shallow eutrophic lake and a brackish lake surrounded by saltmarsh. Wildfowl hunting takes place.

Habitats Wetland (saltmarsh; standing fresh water; standing brackish and salt water)
Land-use Agriculture, Hunting

■ Birds

Species	Season	Year	Pop min	Pop max	Acc	Criteria
Aythya ferina Pochard	N	1997	—	4,500	—	B1i, C3
Aythya marila Scaup	P	1997	—	3,300	—	B1i, C3

■ Protection status
National Partial **International** Partial
IBA overlaps with Nature Reserve. IBA overlaps with Special Protection Area.

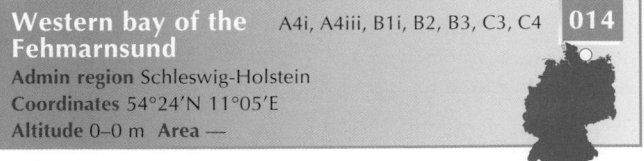

Western bay of the Fehmarnsund   A4i, A4iii, B1i, B2, B3, C3, C4   014

Admin region Schleswig-Holstein
Coordinates 54°24'N 11°05'E
Altitude 0–0 m Area —

■ Site description
A low-lying coastal area, 27 km in length, with sandy/stony shores and brackish lagoons. Tourism is the main human activity.

Habitats Marine areas (sea inlet/coastal features), Wetland (sand-dunes/sand beach; shingle/stony beach; coastal lagoon)
Land-use Tourism/recreation

■ Birds

Species	Season	Year	Pop min	Pop max	Acc	Criteria
Aythya fuligula Tufted Duck	W	1997	—	11,400	—	B1i, C3
Aythya marila Scaup	W	1997	—	8,000	—	A4i, B1i, B2, C3
Somateria mollissima Eider	P	1997	—	13,200	—	B1i, C3
Recurvirostra avosetta Avocet	B	1996	21	—	—	B3
Larus canus Common Gull	B	1996	2,450	—	—	B2

The site holds more than 20,000 wintering and passage waterbirds on a regular basis.

■ Protection status
National None **International** None

Strand lakes and fish-ponds in south-western Fehmarn
B1i, B3, C3 **015**

Admin region Schleswig-Holstein
Coordinates 54°29'N 11°02'E
Altitude 0–0 m **Area** 360 ha

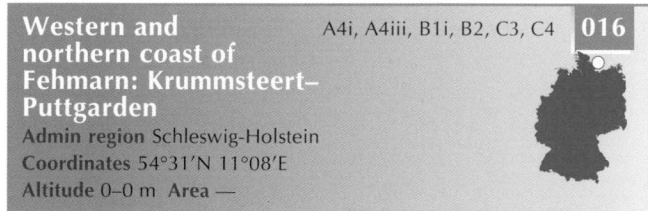

■ Site description
Fish-ponds that were originally coastal lakes.

Habitats Wetland (standing fresh water)
Land-use Hunting

■ Birds

Species	Season	Year	Pop min	Pop max	Acc	Criteria
Anser anser Greylag Goose	P	1997	—	2,000	—	B1i, C3
Recurvirostra avosetta Avocet	B	1996	24	34	—	B3

■ Protection status
National None **International** None

■ Conservation issues
Wildfowl hunting takes place in unprotected areas.

Western and northern coast of Fehmarn: Krummsteert–Puttgarden
A4i, A4iii, B1i, B2, C3, C4 **016**

Admin region Schleswig-Holstein
Coordinates 54°31'N 11°08'E
Altitude 0–0 m **Area** —

■ Site description
A low-lying, flat sandy coastal zone, 27 km in length and up to 15 km in width.

Habitats Marine areas (sea inlet/coastal features)
Land-use Fisheries/aquaculture, Tourism/recreation

■ Birds

Species	Season	Year	Pop min	Pop max	Acc	Criteria
Somateria mollissima Eider	W	1997	—	40,000	—	A4i, B1i, C3
Melanitta nigra Common Scoter	P	1997	—	28,500	—	A4i, B1i, C3
Bucephala clangula Goldeneye	W	1997	—	5,700	—	A4i, B1i, C3
Sterna albifrons Little Tern	B	1997	—	—	—	B2

The site holds more than 20,000 wintering and passage seaduck on a regular basis.

■ Protection status
National None **International** None

East and south-east coast of Fehmarn: Puttgarden–Burgtiefe
A4i, A4iii, B1i, C3, C4 **017**

Admin region Schleswig-Holstein
Coordinates 54°25'N 11°17'E
Altitude 0–0 m **Area** —

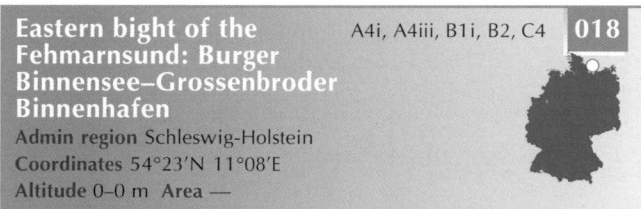

■ Site description
A low-lying, flat sandy coastal zone, 20 km in length and up to 3.5 km in width.

Habitats Marine areas (sea inlet/coastal features)
Land-use Tourism/recreation

■ Birds

Species	Season	Year	Pop min	Pop max	Acc	Criteria
Aythya fuligula Tufted Duck	W	1997	—	31,400	—	A4i, B1i, C3
Aythya marila Scaup	P	1997	—	11,400	—	A4i, B1i, C3
Somateria mollissima Eider	P	1997	—	18,100	—	B1i, C3

The site holds more than 20,000 wintering and passage waterbirds on a regular basis.

■ Protection status
National None **International** None

■ Conservation issues

Threats Recreation/tourism (U)

Eastern bight of the Fehmarnsund: Burger Binnensee–Grossenbroder Binnenhafen
A4i, A4iii, B1i, B2, C4 **018**

Admin region Schleswig-Holstein
Coordinates 54°23'N 11°08'E
Altitude 0–0 m **Area** —

■ Site description
A stretch of sandy coastline with a brackish lagoon.

Habitats Marine areas (sea inlet/coastal features), Wetland (sand-dunes/sand beach; coastal lagoon)
Land-use Tourism/recreation

■ Birds

Species	Season	Year	Pop min	Pop max	Acc	Criteria
Aythya fuligula Tufted Duck	W	1997	—	23,500	—	A4i, B1i, C3
Aythya marila Scaup	W	1997	—	8,100	—	A4i, B1i, B2, C3

The site holds more than 20,000 wintering and passage waterbirds on a regular basis.

■ Protection status
National None **International** None

■ Conservation issues

Threats Recreation/tourism (U)

The area is adversely affected by tourism and boat traffic.

Sagasbank
A4i, A4iii, B1i, C3, C4 **019**

Admin region Schleswig-Holstein
Coordinates 54°18'N 11°12'E
Altitude (-10)–0 m **Area** 3,000 ha

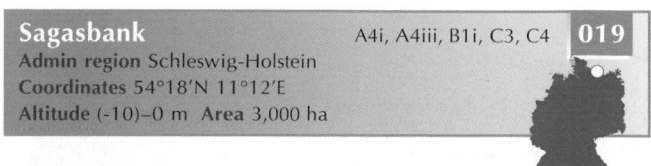

■ Site description
Shallow waters with banks of sand and gravel, in the Baltic Sea.

Habitats Marine areas (open sea)
Land-use Urban/industrial/transport

■ Birds

Species	Season	Year	Pop min	Pop max	Acc	Criteria
Somateria mollissima Eider	W	1997	—	20,000	—	B1i, C3
Melanitta nigra Common Scoter	W	1997	—	25,000	—	A4i, B1i, C3

The site holds more than 20,000 wintering seaduck on a regular basis.

■ Protection status

National None **International** None

■ Conservation issues

Threats Disturbance to birds (U)

Boat traffic creates some disturbance.

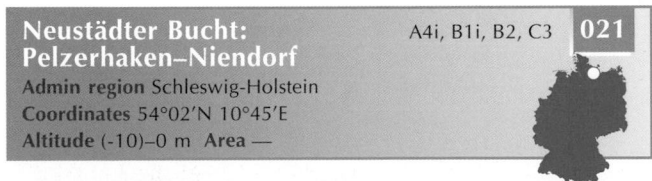

Eastern coast of Oldenburg: Grossenbroder Kai–Pelzerhaken   A4i, A4iii, B1i, B2, C3, C4   020

Admin region Schleswig-Holstein
Coordinates 54°13′N 11°06′E
Altitude (-10)–0 m **Area** —

■ Site description

A stretch of sandy coastline, 38 km in length, with zones of shallow water.

Habitats Marine areas (sea inlet/coastal features), Wetland (sand-dunes/sand beach)
Land-use Tourism/recreation

■ Birds

Species	Season	Year	Pop min	Pop max	Acc	Criteria
Aythya fuligula Tufted Duck	W	1997	—	15,500	—	B1i, C3
Aythya marila Scaup	W	1997	—	12,500	—	A4i, B1i, B2, C3
Somateria mollissima Eider	P	1997	—	16,300	—	B1i, C3
Sterna albifrons Little Tern	B	1996	35	—	—	B2
Riparia riparia Sand Martin	B	1997	—	—	—	B2

The site holds more than 20,000 wintering waterbirds on a regular basis.

■ Protection status

National Partial **International** Partial
IBA overlaps with Nature Reserve. IBA overlaps with Special Protection Area.

■ Conservation issues

Threats Recreation/tourism (U)

Tourist activities adversely affect the site.

Neustädter Bucht: Pelzerhaken–Niendorf   A4i, B1i, B2, C3   021

Admin region Schleswig-Holstein
Coordinates 54°02′N 10°45′E
Altitude (-10)–0 m **Area** —

■ Site description

A shallow sandy bay with zones of deep water, 22 km in length. Habitats include brackish lagoons (162 ha), small reedbeds (*Phragmites*) and marsh.

Habitats Marine areas (sea inlet/coastal features), Wetland (coastal lagoon; water-fringe vegetation)
Land-use Tourism/recreation

■ Birds

Species	Season	Year	Pop min	Pop max	Acc	Criteria
Aythya marila Scaup	W	1997	—	7,000	—	A4i, B1i, B2, C3

■ Protection status

National None **International** None

■ Conservation issues

Intensive tourist activity causes disturbance.

Threats Recreation/tourism (U)

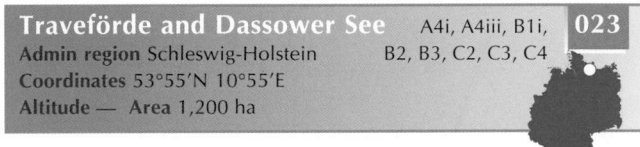

Coastline: Niendorf–Travemünde   A4i, A4iii, B1i, B2, C3, C4   022

Admin region Schleswig-Holstein
Coordinates 53°59′N 10°52′E
Altitude (-10)–0 m **Area** —

■ Site description

A low-lying, flat stretch of sandy coastline, 8 km in length.

Habitats Marine areas (sea inlet/coastal features), Wetland (sand-dunes/sand beach)
Land-use Fisheries/aquaculture, Tourism/recreation

■ Birds

Species	Season	Year	Pop min	Pop max	Acc	Criteria
Aythya fuligula Tufted Duck	W	1997	—	20,800	—	A4i, B1i, C3
Aythya marila Scaup	W	1997	—	8,600	—	A4i, B1i, B2, C3
Bucephala clangula Goldeneye	W	1997	—	6,300	—	A4i, B1i, C3
Fulica atra Coot	W	1997	—	20,000	—	B1i, C3

The site holds more than 20,000 wintering waterbirds on a regular basis.

■ Protection status

National None **International** Partial
IBA overlaps with Special Protection Area.

■ Conservation issues

Threats Aquaculture/fisheries (U), Recreation/tourism (U)

Tourism and fishing adversely affect the site.

Traveförde and Dassower See   A4i, A4iii, B1i, B2, B3, C2, C3, C4   023

Admin region Schleswig-Holstein
Coordinates 53°55′N 10°55′E
Altitude — **Area** 1,200 ha

■ Site description

A low-lying, flat sandy bay. Human activities include industry, intensive tourism and boat traffic.

Habitats Marine areas (sea inlet/coastal features), Wetland (sand-dunes/sand beach)
Land-use Tourism/recreation, Urban/industrial/transport

■ Birds

Species	Season	Year	Pop min	Pop max	Acc	Criteria
Cygnus cygnus Whooper Swan	W	1997	—	1,000	—	A4i, B1i, B3, C2
Anser fabalis Bean Goose	W	1997	5,000	—	—	A4i, B1i, C3
Anser albifrons White-fronted Goose	W	1997	10,000	—	—	B1i, C3
Aythya ferina Pochard	W	1997	—	5,300	—	B1i, C3
Aythya fuligula Tufted Duck	W	1997	—	22,300	—	A4i, B1i, C3
Aythya marila Scaup	W	1997	—	15,300	—	A4i, B1i, B2, C3
Bucephala clangula Goldeneye	N	1997	—	8,600	—	A4i, B1i, C3

The site holds more than 20,000 wintering wildfowl on a regular basis.

■ Protection status

National None **International** Partial
IBA overlaps with Special Protection Area.

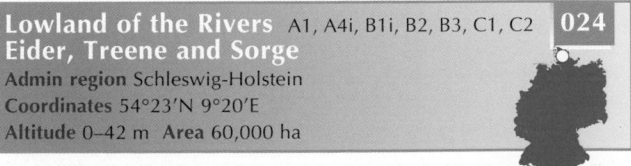

Lowland of the Rivers Eider, Treene and Sorge   A1, A4i, B1i, B2, B3, C1, C2   024

Admin region Schleswig-Holstein
Coordinates 54°23′N 9°20′E
Altitude 0–42 m **Area** 60,000 ha

■ Site description

Flood-plains of the Rivers Eider, Treene and Sorge. Part of the site is below sea-level. The area is dominated by grassland, parts of which are used non-intensively, interspersed with moraines and raised bogs.

Habitats Forest and woodland (broadleaved deciduous forest, Grassland (humid grassland; mesophile grassland), Wetland (river/stream; raised bog; water-fringe vegetation), Artificial landscape (highly improved reseeded grassland; arable land)

Land-use Agriculture (80%), Nature conservation/research (14%)

■ Birds

Species	Season	Year	Pop min	Pop max	Acc	Criteria
Ciconia ciconia White Stork	B	1997	39	39	A	B2
Cygnus columbianus Bewick's Swan	P	1992	1,526	1,526	A	A4i, B1i, C2
¹ *Circus pygargus* Montagu's Harrier	B	1996	6	6	A	B3
Crex crex Corncrake	B	1998	27	30	B	A1, C1
Limosa limosa Black-tailed Godwit	B	1997	195	195	A	B2, C6

1. Large decrease.

■ Protection status

National Low **International** Partial

660 ha of IBA covered by Nature Reserve (Alte-Sorge-Schleife, 660 ha). 620 ha of IBA covered by Nature Reserve (Dellstedter Birkwildmoor, 620 ha). 191 ha of IBA covered by Nature Reserve (Delver Koog, 191 ha). 364 ha of IBA covered by Nature Reserve (Hohner See, 364 ha). 205 ha of IBA covered by Nature Reserve (Tetenhuser Moor, 205 ha). 631 ha of IBA covered by Nature Reserve (Wildes Moor, 631 ha). IBA overlaps with Special Protection Area.

■ Conservation issues

Threats Agricultural intensification/expansion (A), Drainage (A), Unsustainable exploitation (A)

The government of Schleswig-Holstein has started an integrated project to develop the area.

Pinneberg Elbe lowlands — 025
A4i, A4iii, B1i, C2, C3, C4

Admin region Schleswig-Holstein
Coordinates 53°49′N 9°24′E
Altitude 1–4 m **Area** 7,600 ha

■ Site description

Includes a riverine island (Pagensand) and the edges of the tidal River Elbe, along with riverine forest, pasture, reedbeds (*Phragmites*) and arable land. Human activities include intensive agriculture and wildfowl hunting.

Habitats Forest and woodland (alluvial/very wet forest), Scrub (scrub), Grassland (humid grassland), Wetland (tidal river/enclosed tidal water; mudflat/sandflat; sand-dunes/sand beach; standing fresh water; water-fringe vegetation), Artificial landscape (highly improved reseeded grassland; arable land)

Land-use Agriculture, Fisheries/aquaculture, Hunting, Military, Nature conservation/research, Tourism/recreation, Water management

■ Birds

Species	Season	Year	Pop min	Pop max	Acc	Criteria
Cygnus columbianus Bewick's Swan	P	1995	—	220	—	A4i, B1i, C2
Anser anser Greylag Goose	P	1995	—	2,820	—	B1i, C3
Branta leucopsis Barnacle Goose	P	1996	—	3,000	—	A4i, B1i, C2
Larus minutus Little Gull	P	1996	—	1,660	—	A4i, B1i, C3

The site holds more than 20,000 passage waterbirds on a regular basis. Species of global conservation concern that do not meet IBA criteria: *Crex crex* (11 breeding pairs).

■ Protection status

National Partial **International** None

306 ha of IBA covered by Nature Reserve (Eschschallen, 306 ha). 2,056 ha of IBA covered by Nature Reserve (Haseldorfer Binnenelbe mit Elbvorland, 2,056 ha). 540 ha of IBA covered by Nature Reserve (Pagensand, 540 ha).

■ Conservation issues

Threats Agricultural intensification/expansion (U), Construction/impact of dyke/dam/barrage (U), Disturbance to birds (U), Drainage (U), Dredging/canalization (U), Groundwater abstraction (U), Infrastructure (U), Other (U), Recreation/tourism (U)

Threats include water pollution ('Other'), installation of electric power-lines, dredging of the River Elbe and the construction of a major road.

Aukrug Nature Park — C6 026

Admin region Schleswig-Holstein
Coordinates 54°06′N 9°43′E
Altitude 10–70 m **Area** 38,700 ha

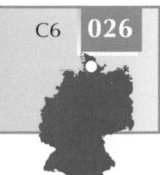

■ Site description

A diverse landscape with patches of forest, bog, meadow, marsh, agricultural land and scattered settlements.

Habitats Forest and woodland, Grassland (humid grassland), Wetland (water-fringe vegetation), Artificial landscape (arable land)

Land-use Agriculture, Forestry, Tourism/recreation

■ Birds

Species	Season	Year	Pop min	Pop max	Acc	Criteria
Ciconia nigra Black Stork	B	1997	2	2	—	C6

■ Protection status

National None **International** None

Lauenburgische Seen Nature Park and Schaalsee area — 027
A4i, A4iii, B1i, B2, C3, C4

Admin region Schleswig-Holstein
Coordinates 53°37′N 10°54′E
Altitude 10–70 m **Area** 50,000 ha

■ Site description

Lakes surrounded by broadleaved forest, interspersed with bog and agricultural land.

Habitats Forest and woodland (broadleaved deciduous forest), Wetland (standing fresh water; fen/transition mire/spring), Artificial landscape (arable land)

Land-use Agriculture, Forestry, Tourism/recreation

■ Birds

Species	Season	Year	Pop min	Pop max	Acc	Criteria
Podiceps cristatus Great Crested Grebe	P	1997	—	4,500	—	A4i, B1i, C3
Podiceps cristatus Great Crested Grebe	N	1997	—	2,600	—	B1i, C3
Anser fabalis Bean Goose	W	1997	—	12,300	—	A4i, B1i, C3
Anser albifrons White-fronted Goose	W	1997	—	7,200	—	B1i, C3
Anser anser Greylag Goose	W	1997	—	7,200	—	A4i, B1i, C3
Aythya fuligula Tufted Duck	N	1997	—	15,000	—	B1i, C3
Grus grus Crane	B	1997	—	40	—	B2

The site holds more than 20,000 wintering wildfowl on a regular basis.

■ Protection status

National None **International** None

Kühren ponds and Lanker See — B1i, B2, C3 028

Admin region Schleswig-Holstein
Coordinates 54°13′N 10°18′E
Altitude 15–25 m **Area** 470 ha

■ Site description

A shallow eutrophic lake with islands (wooded or under pasture), fen and fish-ponds.

Habitats Forest and woodland, Grassland (humid grassland), Wetland (standing fresh water; fen/transition mire/spring)

Land-use Agriculture, Fisheries/aquaculture, Tourism/recreation

■ Birds

Species	Season	Year	Pop min	Pop max	Acc	Criteria
Anas strepera Gadwall	R	1997	—	100	—	B2
Anas strepera Gadwall	N	1997	—	580	—	B1i, C3
Larus canus Common Gull	R	—	—	850	—	B2

■ **Protection status**
National None **International** None

■ **Wesseker See**   A4i, B1i, C3   **029**
Admin region Schleswig-Holstein
Coordinates 54°18′N 10°48′E
Altitude (-1)–0 m **Area** 250 ha

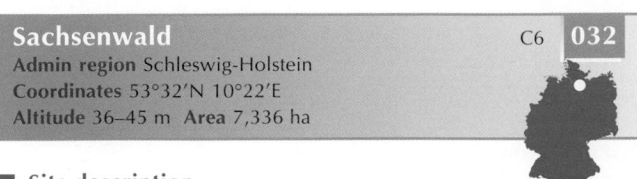

■ **Site description**
A freshwater marsh holding one of the largest reedbeds (*Phragmites*) in Schleswig-Holstein. Human activities include traditional reed-cutting ('Other' land-use).

Habitats Wetland (water-fringe vegetation)
Land-use Agriculture, Hunting, Other

■ **Birds**

Species		Season	Year	Pop min	Pop max	Acc	Criteria
Anas strepera	Gadwall	P	1997	—	1,500	—	A4i, B1i, C3
Anas clypeata	Shoveler	P	1997	—	400	—	B1i, C3

■ **Protection status**
National Partial **International** High
IBA overlaps with Nature Reserve. IBA overlaps with Special Protection Area.

■ **Selent–Plön fish-ponds**   A4i, B1i, B2, C6   **030**
Admin region Schleswig-Holstein
Coordinates 54°14′N 10°27′E
Altitude 20–30 m **Area** 373 ha

■ **Site description**
Fish-ponds with large reedbeds (*Phragmites*) surrounded by an agricultural landscape and small copses.

Habitats Wetland (standing fresh water; water-fringe vegetation)

■ **Birds**

Species		Season	Year	Pop min	Pop max	Acc	Criteria
Botaurus stellaris	Bittern	R	1997	6	6	—	B2, C6
Anas strepera	Gadwall	P	1997	—	2,400	—	A4i, B1i, C3

■ **Protection status**
National None **International** Partial
IBA overlaps with Special Protection Area.

■ **Conservation issues**

Threats Aquaculture/fisheries (U), Unsustainable exploitation (U)

■ **Heidmoor lowlands**   A1, C1   **031**
Admin region Schleswig-Holstein
Coordinates 54°02′N 10°30′E
Altitude 29–30 m **Area** 338 ha

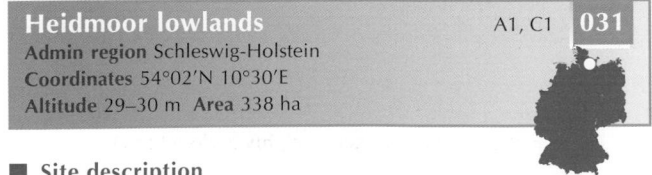

■ **Site description**
A lowland area with slightly improved wet meadows and the remnants of a raised bog.

Habitats Grassland (humid grassland), Wetland (raised bog)

■ **Birds**

Species		Season	Year	Pop min	Pop max	Acc	Criteria
[1] *Crex crex*	Corncrake	B	1998	21	21	—	A1, C1

1. 1997–1998.

■ **Protection status**
National Partial **International** None
70 ha of IBA covered by Nature Reserve (Heidmoor, 70 ha).

■ **Conservation issues**

Threats Agricultural intensification/expansion (U), Natural events (U), Unsustainable exploitation (U)

■ **Sachsenwald**   C6   **032**
Admin region Schleswig-Holstein
Coordinates 53°32′N 10°22′E
Altitude 36–45 m **Area** 7,336 ha

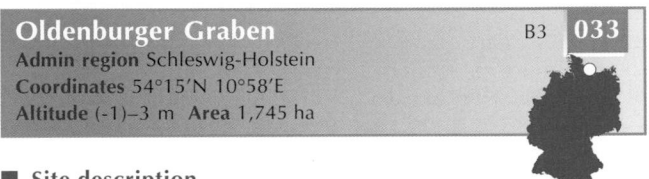

■ **Site description**
The site is the largest wooded area in Schleswig-Holstein.

Habitats Forest and woodland

■ **Birds**

Species		Season	Year	Pop min	Pop max	Acc	Criteria
[1] *Ciconia nigra*	Black Stork	B	1998	1	1	—	C6

1. 1990–1998.

■ **Protection status**
National None **International** None

■ **Conservation issues**

Threats Infrastructure (U), Intensified forest management (U), Unsustainable exploitation (U)

■ **Oldenburger Graben**   B3   **033**
Admin region Schleswig-Holstein
Coordinates 54°15′N 10°58′E
Altitude (-1)–3 m **Area** 1,745 ha

■ **Site description**
The site is on the flood-plain of the Oldenburg drainage line and comprises reed *Phragmites*, open water-bodies, tall perennial herb communities, *Salix* scrub and grassland.

Habitats Scrub (scrub), Grassland, Wetland (standing fresh water; river/stream; water-fringe vegetation)

■ **Birds**

Species		Season	Year	Pop min	Pop max	Acc	Criteria
[1] *Porzana porzana*	Spotted Crake	B	1998	20	20	—	B3

1. 1988–1998.

This is an important site for breeding wetland species.

■ **Protection status**
National Partial **International** None
IBA overlaps with 2 Nature Reserves.

■ **Conservation issues**

Threats Agricultural intensification/expansion (U), Infrastructure (U), Unsustainable exploitation (U)

■ **Neuwerker and Scharhörner Watt**   A4iii, C4   **034**
Admin region Hamburg
Coordinates 53°55′N 8°25′E
Altitude 0–0 m **Area** 8,193 ha

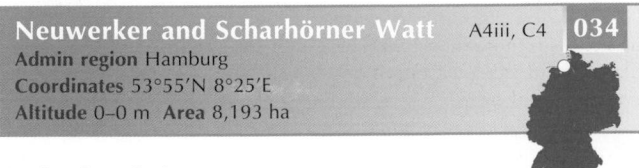

■ **Site description**
Tidal zone of the Wadden Sea, including the islands of Neuwerk and Scharhörn.

■ Birds

Of major international importance for breeding, moulting, passage and wintering waterbirds, particularly wildfowl (Anatidae) and waders.

■ Protection status

National Partial **International** High
IBA overlaps with National Park. IBA overlaps with Biosphere Reserve and Special Protection Area, Ramsar Site.

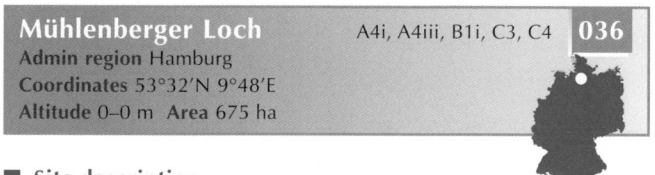

Duvenstedter Brook — C6 — 035
Admin region Hamburg
Coordinates 53°43'N 10°10'E
Altitude 25–30 m **Area** 780 ha

■ Site description

A mosaic of fen and transition mire, interspersed with remnants of raised bog and wet meadows (slightly agriculturally improved).

Habitats Forest and woodland (broadleaved deciduous forest; mixed forest; alluvial/very wet forest), Grassland (humid grassland; mesophile grassland), Wetland (standing fresh water; raised bog; fen/transition mire/spring), Artificial landscape (arable land; forestry plantation)
Land-use Agriculture (10%), Hunting (100%), Nature conservation/research (100%), Tourism/recreation

■ Birds

Species	Season	Year	Pop min	Pop max	Acc	Criteria
Porzana porzana Spotted Crake	B	1998	—	10	A	C6

A total of 90–100 bird species, including *Grus grus*, regularly breed here, and a further 70 are regular visitors. Species of global conservation concern that do not meet IBA criteria: *Crex crex* (breeding).

■ Protection status

National High **International** Partial
780 ha of IBA covered by Nature Reserve (Duvenstedter Brook, 780 ha). IBA overlaps with Special Protection Area.

■ Conservation issues

Threats Disturbance to birds (C), Other (U), Recreation/tourism (C)

Conservation work has been undertaken for *Grus grus*.

Mühlenberger Loch — A4i, A4iii, B1i, C3, C4 — 036
Admin region Hamburg
Coordinates 53°32'N 9°48'E
Altitude 0–0 m **Area** 675 ha

■ Site description

A large area of mudflats with water-levels influenced by tidal changes.

Habitats Wetland (tidal river/enclosed tidal water; mudflat/sandflat)
Land-use Fisheries/aquaculture (10%), Tourism/recreation (100%)

■ Birds

Species	Season	Year	Pop min	Pop max	Acc	Criteria
[1] *Phalacrocorax carbo* Cormorant	P	1996	—	1,260	A	B1i, C3
Anas crecca Teal	P	1996	—	4,583	A	B1i, C3
Anas clypeata Shoveler	P	1996	—	2,000	A	B1i, C3
Larus minutus Little Gull	P	—	—	1,400	—	A4i, B1i, C3

1. Large increase.

The site holds more than 20,000 passage waterbirds on a regular basis. This is one of the most important passage sites for *Anas clypeata* in north-western Europe.

■ Protection status

National None **International** High
675 ha of IBA covered by Ramsar Site (Mühlenberger Loch, 675 ha). IBA overlaps with Special Protection Area.

■ Conservation issues

Threats Disturbance to birds (A), Dredging/canalization (B), Industrialization/urbanization (B), Recreation/tourism (A)

The wetland is subject to infilling for industrial development. There are plans to artificially deepen the Elbe.

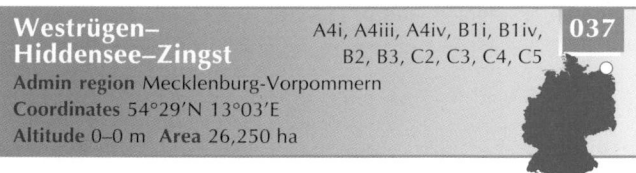

Westrügen–Hiddensee–Zingst — A4i, A4iii, A4iv, B1i, B1iv, B2, B3, C2, C3, C4, C5 — 037
Admin region Mecklenburg-Vorpommern
Coordinates 54°29'N 13°03'E
Altitude 0–0 m **Area** 26,250 ha

■ Site description

An extensive coastal region in the southern Baltic Sea, comprising islands and vast stretches of shallow water (less than 1 m in depth). The shores support reedbeds (*Phragmites*) and saltmarsh, with a hinterland comprising forest, meadows and small-holdings.

Habitats Marine areas (sea inlet/coastal features), Wetland (saltmarsh; water-fringe vegetation)
Land-use Agriculture, Fisheries/aquaculture

■ Birds

Species	Season	Year	Pop min	Pop max	Acc	Criteria
Phalacrocorax carbo Cormorant	R	1996	740	—	—	B1i, C3
[1] *Anser fabalis* Bean Goose	P	1987	5,000	—	—	A4i, B1i, C3
[1] *Anser albifrons* White-fronted Goose	P	1987	20,000	—	—	A4i, B1i, C3
Anas strepera Gadwall	R	1996	14	120	—	B2
[2] *Bucephala clangula* Goldeneye	W	1987	—	8,000	—	A4i, B1i, C3
Mergus albellus Smew	W	1987	—	500	—	A4i, B1i, C2
Mergus merganser Goosander	W	1987	—	2,000	—	B1i, C3
Recurvirostra avosetta Avocet	B	1996	21	140	—	B3
Tringa totanus Redshank	B	1996	15	200	—	B2
[1] *Sterna caspia* Caspian Tern	P	1996	200	200	—	A4i, B1i, C2
Sterna sandvicensis Sandwich Tern	B	1996	3	700	—	B2
Sterna hirundo Common Tern	B	1996	163	900	—	C2
Sterna albifrons Little Tern	B	1996	95	—	—	B2
Riparia riparia Sand Martin	B	1987	2,000	—	—	B2

1. Autumn passage.
2. Also occurs on autumn passage.

The site holds more than 20,000 passage waterbirds on a regular basis, and is also a major migratory bottleneck site, where up to 25,000 *Grus grus* regularly pass during the autumn.

■ Protection status

National Partial **International** High
IBA overlaps with National Park. IBA overlaps with Ramsar Site and Special Protection Area.

■ Conservation issues

Threats Other (U)

Eutrophication is a problem ('Other' threat).

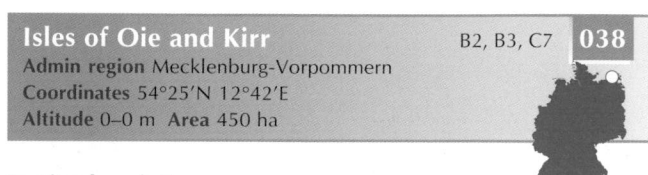

Isles of Oie and Kirr — B2, B3, C7 — 038
Admin region Mecklenburg-Vorpommern
Coordinates 54°25'N 12°42'E
Altitude 0–0 m **Area** 450 ha

■ Site description

Two islands in the Barther Bodden (a highly enclosed bay).

■ Birds

Species	Season	Year	Pop min	Pop max	Acc	Criteria
Recurvirostra avosetta Avocet	B	1996	95	—	—	B3
Sterna sandvicensis Sandwich Tern	B	1996	252	—	—	B2

■ Protection status

National Partial **International** High
IBA overlaps with National Park. IBA overlaps with Special Protection Area.

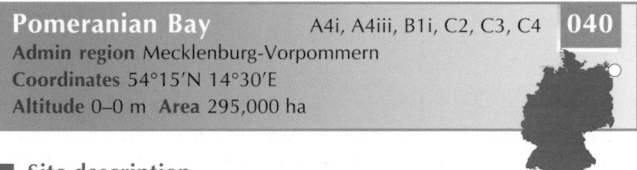

Sea area Darß–Hiddensee with Plantagenetgrund
A4i, A4iii, B1i, C3, C4 039

Admin region Mecklenburg-Vorpommern
Coordinates 54°35′N 12°46′E
Altitude 0–0 m **Area** —

■ Site description
A marine area inside the 20 m bathymetric line. The dominant substrates are sand and gravel and contain a rich benthic fauna.

Habitats Marine areas (open sea)

■ Birds

Species	Season	Year	Pop min	Pop max	Acc	Criteria
[1] *Clangula hyemalis* Long-tailed Duck	W	1997	44,000	95,000	A	A4i, B1i, C3

1. 1994–1997.

This is an important site for wintering seaducks. The site holds 20,000 or more waterbirds in winter, on a regular basis.

■ Protection status
National None **International** Partial
IBA overlaps with Special Protection Area.

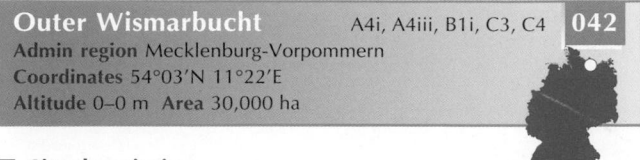

Outer Wismarbucht
A4i, A4iii, B1i, C3, C4 042

Admin region Mecklenburg-Vorpommern
Coordinates 54°03′N 11°22′E
Altitude 0–0 m **Area** 30,000 ha

■ Site description
A marine area inside the 20 m bathymetric line. The dominant substrates are sand and gravel and contain a rich benthic fauna.

Habitats Marine areas (open sea)

■ Birds

Species	Season	Year	Pop min	Pop max	Acc	Criteria
Somateria mollissima Eider	W	1997	35,000	45,000	—	A4i, B1i, C3

This is an important site for wintering seaducks. The site holds 20,000 or more waterbirds in winter, on a regular basis.

■ Protection status
National None **International** High
IBA overlaps with Special Protection Area.

Pomeranian Bay
A4i, A4iii, B1i, C2, C3, C4 040

Admin region Mecklenburg-Vorpommern
Coordinates 54°15′N 14°30′E
Altitude 0–0 m **Area** 295,000 ha

■ Site description
An open, shallow bay with mainly sand and gravel sediments rich in benthic fauna, lying offshore from Vorpommern (Germany) and Poland. The IBA comprises only the German part of the bay.

Habitats Marine areas (open sea; sea inlet/coastal features)

■ Birds

Species	Season	Year	Pop min	Pop max	Acc	Criteria
Podiceps grisegena Red-necked Grebe	W	1993	425	—	—	A4i, B1i, C3
Podiceps auritus Slavonian Grebe	W	1993	570	—	—	A4i, B1i, C2
Clangula hyemalis Long-tailed Duck	W	1993	273,020	—	—	A4i, B1i, C3
Melanitta nigra Common Scoter	W	1993	31,099	—	—	A4i, B1i, C3
Melanitta fusca Velvet Scoter	W	1993	121,451	—	—	B1i, C3
Mergus serrator Red-breasted Merganser	W	1993	1,807	—	—	B1i, C3

The site is a wintering area for approximately 1.25 million seaducks, one of the largest concentrations in Europe.

■ Protection status
National None **International** None

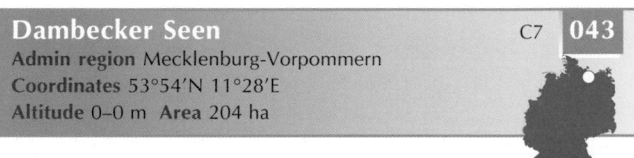

Dambecker Seen
C7 043

Admin region Mecklenburg-Vorpommern
Coordinates 53°54′N 11°28′E
Altitude 0–0 m **Area** 204 ha

■ Site description
Two shallow lakes, the water-levels of which are managed to provide suitable habitat for waterbirds. Fishing takes place on the lakes and the surrounds are used for grazing and arable farming.

Habitats Wetland (standing fresh water)

■ Protection status
National None **International** High
IBA overlaps with Special Protection Area.

■ Conservation issues

Threats Agricultural intensification/expansion (U)

The input of organic matter to the lakes due to intensive agricultural practices is a serious problem.

Isles of Langenwerder and Walfisch
A4i, B1i, B2, C3 041

Admin region Mecklenburg-Vorpommern
Coordinates 54°01′N 11°30′E
Altitude 0–0 m **Area** 60 ha

■ Site description
Two islands in the Wismarbucht, a vast, shallow bay in the Baltic Sea. Sand-dumping has caused the artificial enlargement of Walfisch.

Habitats Wetland (sand-dunes/sand beach)

■ Birds

Species	Season	Year	Pop min	Pop max	Acc	Criteria
[1] *Aythya marila* Scaup	W	1987	4,520	7,700	—	A4i, B1i, B2, C3
Larus canus Common Gull	R	1996	3,700	—	—	B2

1. 1981–1986. January average = 4,520; January max. = 7,700.

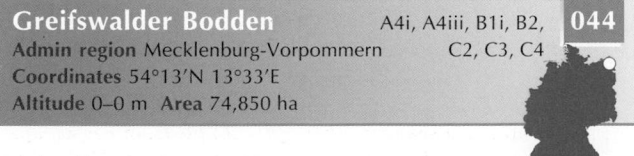

Greifswalder Bodden
A4i, A4iii, B1i, B2, C2, C3, C4 044

Admin region Mecklenburg-Vorpommern
Coordinates 54°13′N 13°33′E
Altitude 0–0 m **Area** 74,850 ha

■ Site description
A bay on the southern shore of the Baltic Sea, comprising large shoals, intertidal zones and saltmarsh. An ice-free zone around a nuclear power-station outfall has increased the bay's importance for wintering waterbirds. The hinterland is used for pasture and haymaking; traditional fishing takes place at sea.

Habitats Grassland (humid grassland), Marine areas (sea inlet/coastal features), Wetland (saltmarsh)

Land-use Agriculture, Fisheries/aquaculture, Urban/industrial/transport

■ Birds

Species	Season	Year	Pop min	Pop max	Acc	Criteria
[1] *Phalacrocorax carbo* Cormorant	R	1996	3,523	—	—	A4i, B1i, C3

Species ... continued	Season	Year	Pop min	Pop max	Acc	Criteria
Cygnus columbianus Bewick's Swan	P	1987	600	—	—	A4i, B1i, C2
[2] *Cygnus cygnus* Whooper Swan	P	1987	—	800	—	A4i, B1i, C2
[2] *Anser fabalis* Bean Goose	P	1987	8,000	—	—	A4i, B1i, C3
[2] *Anser albifrons* White-fronted Goose	P	1987	70,000	—	—	A4i, B1i, C3
[2] *Anser anser* Greylag Goose	P	1996	10,000	—	—	A4i, B1i, C3
[2] *Anas penelope* Wigeon	P	1987	20,000	—	—	A4i, B1i, C3
[2] *Anas strepera* Gadwall	P	1996	3,000	—	—	A4i, B1i, C3
[3] *Aythya marila* Scaup	P	1987	3,000	—	—	B1i, C3
[2] *Bucephala clangula* Goldeneye	P	1987	—	7,000	—	A4i, B1i, C3
Mergus merganser Goosander	W	1996	4,000	8,000	—	A4i, B1i, C3
Sterna albifrons Little Tern	B	1987	40	—	—	B2

1. Also occurs on passage (1,000 individuals).
2. Autumn passage.
3. Spring passage.

The site holds more than 20,000 passage waterbirds on a regular basis.

■ **Protection status**
National Partial **International** High
IBA overlaps with Landscape Protected Area. IBA overlaps with Special Protection Area.

■ **Conservation issues**
A management plan exists for the site.

Gothensee and Thurbruch, Isles of Böhmke and Werder   C2 045
Admin region Mecklenburg-Vorpommern
Coordinates 53°57'N 14°05'E
Altitude 0–0 m   **Area** 918 ha

■ **Site description**
A large, shallow eutrophic lake connected to the sea, with surrounding areas of peatland and reedbed (*Phragmites*). Böhmke and Werder are two small islands in the western part of the lake. Fishing takes place and surrounding meadows are grazed.

Habitats Wetland (coastal lagoon; raised bog; water-fringe vegetation)
Land-use Agriculture, Fisheries/aquaculture, Tourism/recreation

■ **Birds**

Species	Season	Year	Pop min	Pop max	Acc	Criteria
Chlidonias niger Black Tern	B	1987	30	40	—	C2

■ **Protection status**
National Partial **International** High
IBA overlaps with Nature Reserve. IBA overlaps with Special Protection Area.

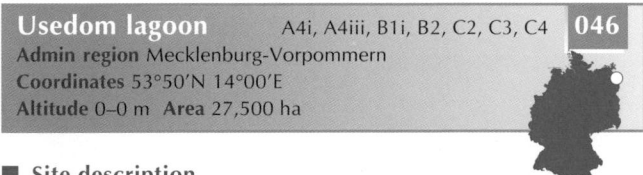

Usedom lagoon   A4i, A4iii, B1i, B2, C2, C3, C4 046
Admin region Mecklenburg-Vorpommern
Coordinates 53°50'N 14°00'E
Altitude 0–0 m   **Area** 27,500 ha

■ **Site description**
The site comprises a shallow bay, largely cut off from the sea apart from at three places. As a result the water is brackish. The water is nutrient-rich from rivers flowing into the lagoon.

Habitats Wetland (coastal lagoon)

■ **Birds**

Species	Season	Year	Pop min	Pop max	Acc	Criteria
Aythya marila Scaup	W	1993	1,770	—	—	B2
Bucephala clangula Goldeneye	W	1993	2,945	—	—	B1i, C3
Mergus albellus Smew	W	1993	2,755	—	—	A4i, B1i, C2
Mergus merganser Goosander	W	1993	4,535	—	—	A4i, B1i, C3

The site regularly holds 20,000 or more waterbirds in winter.

■ **Protection status**
National None **International** None

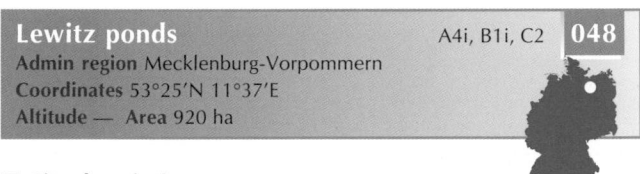

Kuhlrader Moor and Röggeliner See   C7 047
Admin region Mecklenburg-Vorpommern
Coordinates 53°43'N 10°58'E
Altitude —   **Area** 328 ha

■ **Site description**
A lake with an island, adjacent peatbog (Kuhlrader Moor) and scrub (*Alnus*, *Salix* and *Betula*). Fishing takes place on the lake; the area around the peatbog is used for agriculture.

Habitats Scrub (scrub), Wetland (standing fresh water; raised bog)
Land-use Agriculture

■ **Birds**
Species of global conservation concern that do not meet IBA criteria: *Aythya nyroca* (breeding).

■ **Protection status**
National None **International** High
IBA overlaps with Special Protection Area.

Lewitz ponds   A4i, B1i, C2 048
Admin region Mecklenburg-Vorpommern
Coordinates 53°25'N 11°37'E
Altitude —   **Area** 920 ha

■ **Site description**
Part of a large (c.10,000 ha) lowland marsh on the River Elde, including several fish-pond complexes and extensive meadow-land. The ponds are generally 20–100 ha in extent and 1 m in depth. The shores are mainly unvegetated, although there are some areas of reedbed (*Phragmites*) and vegetated islands. The wet meadows hold *Carex* and *Phalaris* and are dissected by a network of ditches.

Habitats Grassland (humid grassland), Wetland (standing fresh water; water-fringe vegetation)
Land-use Fisheries/aquaculture

■ **Birds**

Species	Season	Year	Pop min	Pop max	Acc	Criteria
Cygnus columbianus Bewick's Swan	P	1989	300	800	—	A4i, B1i, C2

Species of global conservation concern that do not meet IBA criteria: *Aythya nyroca* (breeding).

■ **Protection status**
National Partial **International** High
IBA overlaps with Landscape Protected Area. IBA overlaps with Special Protection Area.

■ **Conservation issues**

Threats Aquaculture/fisheries (U)

Intensification of fish-farming has resulted in a reduction in the area of reedbed.

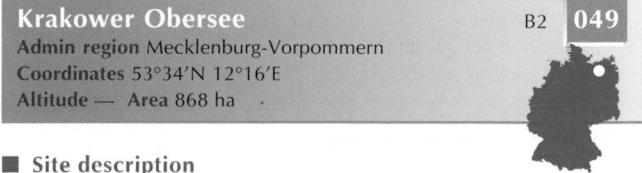

Krakower Obersee   B2 049
Admin region Mecklenburg-Vorpommern
Coordinates 53°34'N 12°16'E
Altitude —   **Area** 868 ha   .

■ **Site description**
A large coastal lake with eight islands (totalling 26 ha) and surrounded by forest, pasture and cultivated land. Parts of the islands are grazed.

Habitats Wetland (coastal lagoon)
Land-use Agriculture

■ Birds

Species	Season	Year	Pop min	Pop max	Acc	Criteria
Alcedo atthis Kingfisher	B	—	120	200	—	B2

■ Protection status
National None **International** Partial
IBA overlaps with Ramsar Site.

Eastern coast of Lake Müritz, Grosser Schwerin and Steinhorn C7 050
Admin region Mecklenburg-Vorpommern
Coordinates 53°24'N 12°44'E
Altitude — **Area** 5,152 ha

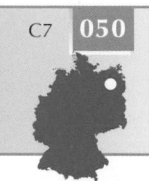

■ Site description
A large freshwater lake with a range of natural, semi-natural and man-made habitats. There are bays and zones of shallow water, and a rich shoreline vegetation (especially reedbeds (*Phragmites*) and submerged plants). Swamps, *Carex* beds, sand-dunes, *Juniperus* heath and *Pinus/Fagus* forest surround the lake. Hunting (not of birds) occurs.

Habitats Forest and woodland (mixed forest), Scrub (heathland), Wetland (sand-dunes/sand beach; standing fresh water; water-fringe vegetation)
Land-use Hunting

■ Protection status
National Partial **International** High
IBA overlaps with Landscape Protected Area and National Park. IBA overlaps with Ramsar Site and Special Protection Area.

■ Conservation issues

Threats Abandonment/reduction of land management (U), Agricultural intensification/expansion (U)

Threats include the effects of intensive agriculture and scrub invasion.

Serrahn C7 051
Admin region Mecklenburg-Vorpommern
Coordinates 53°19'N 13°10'E
Altitude — **Area** 1,818 ha

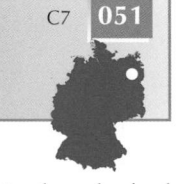

■ Site description
A well-forested moraine landscape with *Pinus* stands and mixed deciduous/coniferous areas. There are scattered lakes with areas of open water, reedbeds (*Phragmites*) and *Alnus* swamps.

Habitats Forest and woodland (mixed forest; alluvial/very wet forest), Wetland (standing fresh water; water-fringe vegetation)
Land-use Forestry

■ Protection status
National Partial **International** High
IBA overlaps with Landscape Protected Area. IBA overlaps with Special Protection Area.

■ Conservation issues

Threats Other (U)

Water regulation may adversely affect the site ('Other' threat).

Lake Nonnenhof with Lieps C7 052
Admin region Mecklenburg-Vorpommern
Coordinates 53°27'N 13°10'E
Altitude — **Area** 700 ha

■ Site description
A shallow lake and peninsula with scrub, forest, reedbed (*Phragmites*), bogs and sand-dunes.

Habitats Forest and woodland, Scrub (scrub), Wetland (sand-dunes/sand beach; standing fresh water; water-fringe vegetation)

■ Protection status
National None **International** None

■ Conservation issues

Threats Abandonment/reduction of land management (U), Agricultural intensification/expansion (U), Industrialization/urbanization (U)

Increasing pollution from waste water and fertilizers, and succession in open meadows are serious problems.

Peenetalmoor and Anklamer Stadtbruch A1, B1i, C1, C3 053
Admin region Mecklenburg-Vorpommern
Coordinates 53°49'N 13°49'E
Altitude — **Area** 3,578 ha

■ Site description
An area of fen-dominated flood-plain interspersed with reedbed (*Phragmites*) and *Salix/Betula* scrub. Human activities include reed-cutting ('Other' land-use), boating and hunting (not of birds).

Habitats Forest and woodland (alluvial/very wet forest), Grassland (humid grassland), Wetland (water-fringe vegetation; fen/transition mire/spring)
Land-use Fisheries/aquaculture, Forestry, Hunting, Other, Tourism/recreation

■ Birds

Species	Season	Year	Pop min	Pop max	Acc	Criteria
Anser fabalis Bean Goose	P	1998	1,000	1,500	A	B1i, C3
Anser albifrons White-fronted Goose	P	1998	5,000	6,000	A	B1i, C3
Acrocephalus paludicola Aquatic Warbler	B	1998	6	10	A	A1, C1

Important as a stop-over site for passage wildfowl as well as for breeding species of wet meadows. Breeding species of global conservation concern that do not meet IBA criteria: *Crex crex* (2–4 pairs).

■ Protection status
National Partial **International** High
IBA overlaps with Landscape Protected Area. IBA overlaps with Special Protection Area.

■ Conservation issues

Threats Other (U)

The area may be threatened by changing land-use, which has resulted in eutrophication and an increased frequency of flooding ('Other' threat).

Galenbecker See and Putzarer See C7 054
Admin region Mecklenburg-Vorpommern
Coordinates 53°37'N 13°40'E
Altitude — **Area** 1,375 ha

■ Site description
Two shallow, eutrophic, freshwater lakes located in the depressions of a drained fen. The Galenbecker See (depth 0.5–1 m) has reedbeds (*Phragmites*), mudbanks and large vegetated areas that are slowly silting up. The Putzarer See (depth 0.25–0.5 m) has reedbeds and extensive vegetated areas. Human activities include fishing (mainly in the Galenbecker See), with grazing and forestry in nearby areas.

Habitats Wetland (mudflat/sandflat; standing fresh water; water-fringe vegetation)

■ Protection status
National Partial **International** High
IBA overlaps with Nature Reserve. IBA overlaps with Ramsar Site and Special Protection Area.

■ Conservation issues

Threats Drainage (U), Other (U)

Eutrophication ('Other' threat) and drainage adversely affect the site.

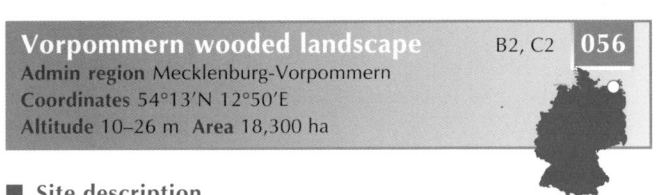

Koblentzer See and Latzig See · C7 · 055
Admin region Mecklenburg-Vorpommern
Coordinates 53°31′N 14°07′E
Altitude — **Area** 497 ha

■ Site description
Two shallow lakes with surrounding reedbeds (*Phragmites*), *Alnus/Fraxinus* forest and meadows. Human activities include fishing, intensive haymaking and grazing.

Habitats Forest and woodland (alluvial/very wet forest), Grassland (humid grassland), Wetland (standing fresh water; water-fringe vegetation)
Land-use Agriculture, Fisheries/aquaculture

■ Protection status
National Partial **International** High
IBA overlaps with Nature Reserve. IBA overlaps with Special Protection Area.

■ Conservation issues
The area of reedbed has diminished over the last ten years.

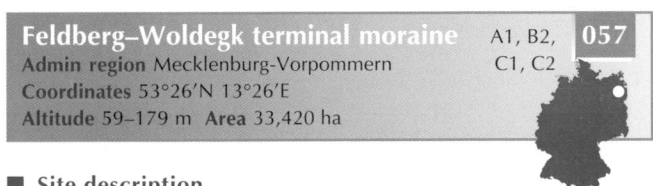

Vorpommern wooded landscape · B2, C2 · 056
Admin region Mecklenburg-Vorpommern
Coordinates 54°13′N 12°50′E
Altitude 10–26 m **Area** 18,300 ha

■ Site description
The site comprises deciduous and mixed forests and agricultural areas.

Habitats Forest and woodland (broadleaved deciduous forest; mixed forest)

■ Birds

Species	Season	Year	Pop min	Pop max	Acc	Criteria
Aquila pomarina Lesser Spotted Eagle	B	1998	16	—	A	B2, C2

Species of global conservation concern that do not meet IBA criteria: *Crex crex* (breeding).

■ Protection status
National None **International** None

Feldberg–Woldegk terminal moraine · A1, B2, C1, C2 · 057
Admin region Mecklenburg-Vorpommern
Coordinates 53°26′N 13°26′E
Altitude 59–179 m **Area** 33,420 ha

■ Site description
A terminal moraine landscape rich in forests and lakes.

Habitats Forest and woodland, Wetland (standing fresh water)

■ Birds

Species	Season	Year	Pop min	Pop max	Acc	Criteria
Ciconia nigra Black Stork	B	1998	3	5	—	B2
Ciconia ciconia White Stork	B	1998	36	—	A	B2
Haliaeetus albicilla White-tailed Eagle	R	1998	6	—	— A	A1, B2, C1
Aquila pomarina Lesser Spotted Eagle	B	1998	16	—	A	B2, C2
Grus grus Crane	B	1998	50	80	A	B2

Species of global conservation concern that do not meet IBA criteria: *Crex crex* (breeding).

■ Protection status
National None **International** None

Lower Saxony Wadden Sea National Park · A4i, A4iii, B1i, B2, C2, C3, C4 · 058
Admin region Niedersachsen
Coordinates 53°33′N 8°10′E
Altitude 0–24 m **Area** 250,025 ha

■ Site description
An area of mudflats, beaches and offshore sand-dune islands on the North Sea coast of Lower Saxony. The site featured in the previous pan-European IBA inventory (Grimmett and Jones 1989) as former site DE034, but also includes former site DE033 (Dollart; 5,000 ha).

Habitats Wetland (mudflat/sandflat; sand-dunes/sand beach), Marine areas (sea inlet/coastal feature)

■ Birds

Species	Season	Year	Pop min	Pop max	Acc	Criteria
Branta leucopsis Barnacle Goose	W	1993	11,390	11,390	A	A4i, B1i, B2, C2
Tadorna tadorna Shelduck	W	1993	19,357	19,357	A	A4i, B1i, C3
Anas penelope Wigeon	W	1993	21,372	21,372	A	A4i, B1i, C3
Anas crecca Teal	P	1990	7,958	7,958	A	B1i, C3
Haematopus ostralegus Oystercatcher	W	1993	144,597	144,597	A	A4i, B1i, C3
Recurvirostra avosetta Avocet	P	1990	20,077	20,077	A	A4i, B1i, C2
Charadrius hiaticula Ringed Plover	P	1991	2,714	2,714	A	A4i, B1i, C3
Pluvialis apricaria Golden Plover	P	1990	18,076	18,076	A	A4i, B1i, C2
Pluvialis squatarola Grey Plover	P	1991	19,068	19,068	A	A4i, B1i, C3
Calidris canutus Knot	P	1990	38,184	38,184	A	A4i, B1i, C3
Calidris alpina Dunlin	P	1991	159,771	159,771	A	A4i, B1i, C3
Limosa lapponica Bar-tailed Godwit	P	1991	25,173	25,173	A	A4i, B1i, C2
Numenius arquata Curlew	W	1993	46,086	46,086	A	A4i, B1i, C3
Tringa erythropus Spotted Redshank	P	1991	3,834	3,834	A	A4i, B1i, C3
Tringa totanus Redshank	W	1993	3,293	3,293	A	A4i, B1i, C3
Tringa nebularia Greenshank	P	1991	2,226	2,226	A	A4i, B1i, C3
Arenaria interpres Turnstone	P	1991	1,493	1,493	A	A4i, B1i, C3
Larus canus Common Gull	P	1993	23,884	23,884	A	A4i, B1i, C3
Larus argentatus Herring Gull	P	1993	26,664	26,664	A	B1i

A site of international importance for breeding, moulting, passage and wintering waterbirds, especially wildfowl (Anatidae) and waders.

■ Protection status
National Partial **International** Partial
IBA overlaps with National Park. IBA overlaps with Ramsar Site and Biosphere Reserve.

■ Conservation issues

Threats Aquaculture/fisheries (U), Other (U), Recreation/tourism (U)

Threats include drilling for oil, and military training ('Other' threat).

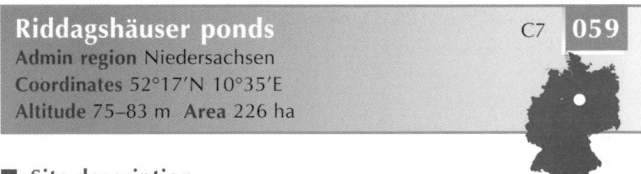

Riddagshäuser ponds · C7 · 059
Admin region Niedersachsen
Coordinates 52°17′N 10°35′E
Altitude 75–83 m **Area** 226 ha

■ Site description
A lowland area containing eutrophic ponds with water vegetation, surrounded by reedbeds (*Phragmites*), heathland and wet forest.

Habitats Forest and woodland (15%; broadleaved deciduous forest; alluvial/very wet forest), Scrub (heathland), Grassland (11%; humid grassland), Wetland (66%; standing fresh water; raised bog), Artificial landscape (8%; arable land)
Land-use Agriculture, Forestry, Tourism/recreation

■ Protection status
National Partial **International** High
IBA overlaps with Nature Reserve. IBA overlaps with Special Protection Area.

■ Conservation issues

Threats Agricultural intensification/expansion (U), Intensified forest management (U), Recreation/tourism (U)

Niedersächsischer Drömling — A1, C1 — 060
Admin region Niedersachsen
Coordinates 52°29′N 10°54′E
Altitude 56–60 m **Area** 6,200 ha

■ Site description
A large alluvial basin comprising lowland mire, periodically flooded grassland (1,600 ha), *Alnus* and *Betula* forest (510 ha), alluvial forest (*Fraxinus–Ulmus–Prunus*) (127 ha), reed *Phragmites* and sedge areas (212 ha), hedgerows (150 ha) and ditches.

Habitats Forest and woodland (broadleaved deciduous forest; alluvial/very wet forest), Grassland (humid grassland), Wetland (water-fringe vegetation; fen/transition mire/spring)
Land-use Agriculture (50%), Forestry (21%)

■ Birds

Species	Season	Year	Pop min	Pop max	Acc	Criteria
Crex crex Corncrake	B	1996	5	20	—	A1, C1

■ Protection status
National Partial **International** High
IBA overlaps with Landscape Protected Area. IBA overlaps with Special Protection Area.

■ Conservation issues
Threats Abandonment/reduction of land management (U), Agricultural intensification/expansion (U), Dredging/canalization (U), Groundwater abstraction (U)

Östliches Barnbruch — B3, C6 — 061
Admin region Niedersachsen
Coordinates 52°27′N 10°42′E
Altitude 53–55 m **Area** 1,400 ha

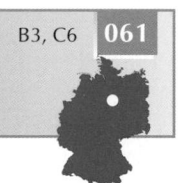

■ Site description

Habitats Forest and woodland (14%; native coniferous forest; alluvial/very wet forest), Grassland (36%; humid grassland), Wetland (10%; standing fresh water; water-fringe vegetation)
Land-use Agriculture, Forestry, Other, Urban/industrial/transport

■ Birds

Species	Season	Year	Pop min	Pop max	Acc	Criteria
Porzana porzana Spotted Crake	B	1996	12	20	—	B3, C6

Species of global conservation concern that do not meet IBA criteria: *Aythya nyroca* (passage), *Crex crex* (2–6 breeding pairs) and *Acrocephalus paludicola* (passage).

■ Protection status
National Low **International** Partial
120 ha of IBA covered by Nature Reserve (Ilkerbruch, 120 ha). IBA overlaps with Special Protection Area (Barnbruchwiessen, 243 ha).

■ Conservation issues
Threats Abandonment/reduction of land management (U), Agricultural intensification/expansion (U), Drainage (U), Infrastructure (U), Other (U)

Wendesser Moor Nature Reserve — C6 — 062
Admin region Niedersachsen
Coordinates 52°22′N 10°14′E
Altitude 65–68 m **Area** 119 ha

■ Site description
A small bog and wetland area in the midst of large fields. The wetland includes patches of open water, reedbeds (*Phragmites*), *Salix* thickets, and a small *Pinus* forest.

Habitats Forest and woodland (5%; broadleaved deciduous forest; native coniferous forest; alluvial/very wet forest), Grassland (85%; humid grassland; mesophile grassland), Wetland (10%; standing fresh water; raised bog; water-fringe vegetation; fen/transition mire/spring)
Land-use Agriculture (70%), Forestry (10%), Hunting (100%), Not utilized (20%)

■ Birds

Species	Season	Year	Pop min	Pop max	Acc	Criteria
Porzana porzana Spotted Crake	B	1998	6	10	A	C6

Species of global conservation concern that do not meet IBA criteria: *Crex crex* (resident).

■ Protection status
National Partial **International** None
63 ha of IBA covered by Nature Reserve (Wendesser Moor, 63 ha).

■ Conservation issues
Threats Abandonment/reduction of land management (C), Afforestation (C), Agricultural intensification/expansion (B), Disturbance to birds (C), Drainage (A), Filling-in of wetlands (C), Groundwater abstraction (A), Industrialization/urbanization (B), Recreation/tourism (C)

Research is being carried out on the biology of rails (Rallidae). There is long-term monitoring of bird migration.

Ems valley from Leer to Emden — A4i, A4iii, B1i, B2, B3, C3, C4, C6 — 063
Admin region Niedersachsen
Coordinates 53°19′N 7°20′E
Altitude 1–6 m **Area** 2,173 ha

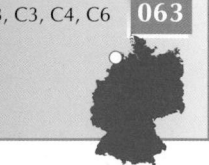

■ Site description
A delta area.

Habitats Wetland

■ Birds

Species	Season	Year	Pop min	Pop max	Acc	Criteria
Anser fabalis Bean Goose	P	1990	—	2,110	—	B1i, C3
Anser albifrons White-fronted Goose	W	1996	—	7,555	—	B1i, C3
Branta leucopsis Barnacle Goose	P	1997	—	14,520	—	A4i, B1i, C2
Recurvirostra avosetta Avocet	B	1997	—	537	—	B3
Limosa limosa Black-tailed Godwit	B	1997	—	234	—	B2, C6
Numenius arquata Curlew	W	1997	—	460	—	B2
Tringa totanus Redshank	R	1996	—	335	—	B2

This is an important area for breeding waders. The site holds 20,000 or more waterbirds on passage, on a regular basis. Species of global conservation concern that do not meet IBA criteria: *Crex crex* (breeding).

■ Protection status
National None **International** Partial
IBA overlaps with Special Protection Area.

■ Conservation issues
Threats Agricultural intensification/expansion (U)

Terborg — A4i, A4iii, B1i, C3, C4 — 064
Admin region Niedersachsen
Coordinates 53°18′N 7°24′E
Altitude 0–6 m **Area** 1,982 ha

■ Site description
Mesophile grassland on the former flood-plain of the River Ems, connected to the 'Rheiderland' IBA (site 068).

Habitats Grassland (85%; humid grassland; mesophile grassland)
Land-use Agriculture (95%), Hunting (90%), Other

■ Birds

Species		Season	Year	Pop min	Pop max	Acc	Criteria
Anser albifrons	White-fronted Goose	P	1998	6,454	—	—	B1i, C3
Branta leucopsis	Barnacle Goose	P	1998	7,670	—	—	A4i, B1i, C2

The site holds 20,000 or more waterbirds on passage, on a regular basis.

■ Protection status

National None **International** None

■ Conservation issues

Threats Agricultural intensification/expansion (B), Consequences of animal/plant introductions (B), Extraction industry (B), Infrastructure (B), Other (B)

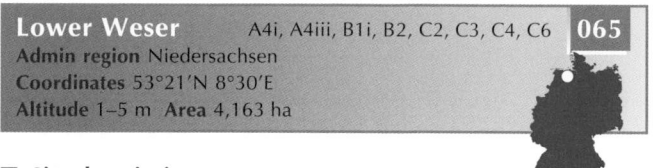

Lower Weser · A4i, A4iii, B1i, B2, C2, C3, C4, C6 · 065
Admin region Niedersachsen
Coordinates 53°21′N 8°30′E
Altitude 1–5 m **Area** 4,163 ha

■ Site description

A non-navigable tidal branch of the River Weser, with mudflats and fringed by grassland and reedbeds (*Phragmites*).

Habitats Wetland (tidal river/enclosed tidal water; mudflat/sandflat; water-fringe vegetation), Grassland

■ Birds

Species		Season	Year	Pop min	Pop max	Acc	Criteria
Cygnus columbianus	Bewick's Swan	W	1992	—	360	—	A4i, B1i, C2
Anas crecca	Teal	W	1992	—	13,525	—	B1i, C3
Limosa limosa	Black-tailed Godwit	B	1996	107	—	—	C6
Asio flammeus	Short-eared Owl	B	1990	6	6	—	B2

The site holds 20,000 or more waterbirds in winter, on a regular basis. Species of global conservation concern that do not meet IBA criteria: *Crex crex* (10 breeding pairs).

■ Protection status

National None **International** Partial
IBA overlaps with Special Protection Area (Rechter Nebenarm der Weser bei Brake).

■ Conservation issues

Threats Drainage (U)

The area is candidate Special Area for Conservation.

Binnendeichsflächen der Wesermündung · B1i, C3 · 066
Admin region Niedersachsen
Coordinates 53°26′N 8°30′E
Altitude 0–4 m **Area** 4,703 ha

■ Site description

Grassland in the former Lower Weser flood-plain.

Habitats Grassland (91%; humid grassland; mesophile grassland)
Land-use Agriculture (90%), Hunting (90%), Other (10%)

■ Birds

Species		Season	Year	Pop min	Pop max	Acc	Criteria
Anser albifrons	White-fronted Goose	P	1997	6,200	6,200	—	B1i, C3

■ Protection status

National None **International** None

■ Conservation issues

Threats Agricultural intensification/expansion (B), Extraction industry (B), Industrialization/urbanization (A), Infrastructure (A)

Landgraben–Dumme lowlands · C6 · 067
Admin region Niedersachsen
Coordinates 52°54′N 11°10′E
Altitude 17–32 m **Area** 5,979 ha

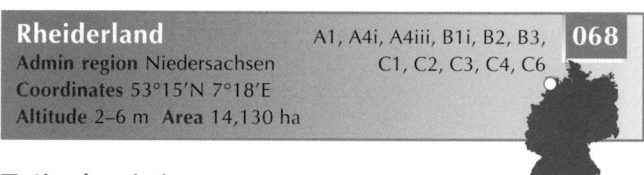

■ Site description

An area of periodically flooded humid and mesophile grassland and alluvial forest around the Rivers Dumme and Landgraben.

Habitats Forest and woodland (60%; alluvial/very wet forest), Grassland (20%; humid grassland; mesophile grassland)

■ Birds

Species		Season	Year	Pop min	Pop max	Acc	Criteria
Grus grus	Crane	B	1996	14	14	—	C6

■ Protection status

National None **International** None

■ Conservation issues

Threats Agricultural intensification/expansion (U), Drainage (U)

The area is a candidate Special Protection Area.

Rheiderland · A1, A4i, A4iii, B1i, B2, B3, C1, C2, C3, C4, C6 · 068
Admin region Niedersachsen
Coordinates 53°15′N 7°18′E
Altitude 2–6 m **Area** 14,130 ha

■ Site description

A large area of marsh and polders, intensively used for agriculture. Water-levels are regulated.

Habitats Wetland (fen/transition mire/spring), Grassland (humid grassland; mesophile grassland)

■ Birds

Species		Season	Year	Pop min	Pop max	Acc	Criteria
Anser fabalis	Bean Goose	P	1990	15,190	—	—	A4i, B1i, C3
Anser albifrons	White-fronted Goose	P	1997	49,000	—	—	A4i, B1i, C3
Branta leucopsis	Barnacle Goose	W	1997	36,000	—	—	A4i, B1i, B2, C2
Crex crex	Corncrake	B	1997	39	39	—	A1, C1
Recurvirostra avosetta	Avocet	B	1998	132	132	—	B3
Pluvialis apricaria	Golden Plover	P	1997	20,000	—	—	A4i, B1i, C2
Limosa limosa	Black-tailed Godwit	B	1996	320	—	—	B2, C6
Numenius arquata	Curlew	W	1997	—	1,700	—	B2
Tringa totanus	Redshank	R	1996	149	—	—	B2

This is an important passage and wintering area for geese and waders. The site holds more than 20,000 waterbirds on passage and in winter, on a regular basis. Species of global conservation concern that do not meet IBA criteria: *Branta ruficollis* (wintering).

■ Protection status

National None **International** None

■ Conservation issues

Threats Agricultural intensification/expansion (U), Drainage (U)

Winsener Elbmarsch · C7 · 069
Admin region Niedersachsen
Coordinates 53°23′N 10°12′E
Altitude 2–7 m **Area** 844 ha

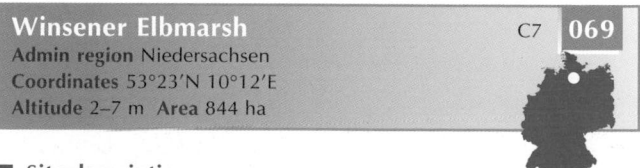

■ Site description

The Seeve area of the site is predominantly mesophile and humid grassland on peat soil, subject to periodic flooding. The Ilmenau area is a tidal-influenced marsh with mudflats, reedbeds (*Phragmites*) and mesophile grassland.

Habitats Grassland (67%; humid grassland; mesophile grassland), Wetland (33%; tidal river/enclosed tidal water; mudflat/sandflat; standing fresh water; fen/transition mire/spring)

■ **Birds**

Species of global conservation concern that do not meet IBA criteria: *Crex crex* (breeding).

■ **Protection status**

National None **International** None

IBA overlaps with Special Protection Area (Winsener Elbmarsch).

■ **Conservation issues**

Threats Drainage (U), Recreation/tourism (U)

Part of the area is a candidate Special Area for Coservation.

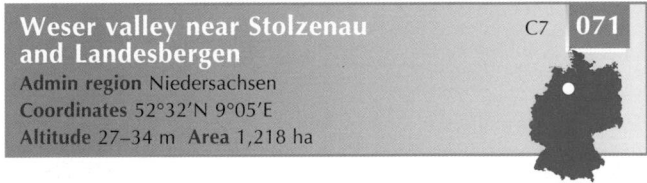

Lucie and Landwehr B3, C6 070
Admin region Niedersachsen
Coordinates 53°03′N 11°14′E
Altitude 150–170 m **Area** 4,067 ha

■ **Site description**

A large area of woodland and grassland with some areas of wetland.

Habitats Forest and woodland (70%; broadleaved deciduous forest; native coniferous forest; mixed forest), Grassland (28%; humid grassland; mesophile grassland)
Land-use Agriculture, Forestry

■ **Birds**

Species	Season	Year	Pop min	Pop max	Acc	Criteria
Grus grus Crane	B	1996	13	13	—	C6
Sylvia nisoria Barred Warbler	B	—	110	110	—	B3

A regionally important area for *Grus grus*.

■ **Protection status**

National None **International** None

■ **Conservation issues**

Threats Afforestation (U), Agricultural intensification/expansion (U)

The area is a candidate Special Protection Area.

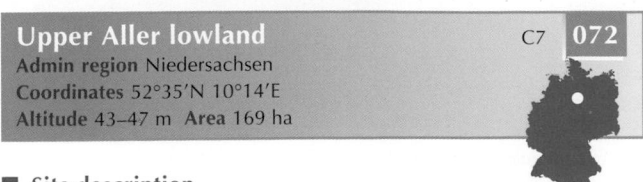

Weser valley near Stolzenau and Landesbergen C7 071
Admin region Niedersachsen
Coordinates 52°32′N 9°05′E
Altitude 27–34 m **Area** 1,218 ha

■ **Site description**

A valley of the River Weser. Scrub and trees line the river. Lakes are present as a result of gravel extraction. The site borders the 'Weser dam Schlüsselburg' IBA (site 157).

Habitats Forest and woodland, Scrub

■ **Protection status**

National None **International** Partial

IBA overlaps with Special Protection Area.

Upper Aller lowland C7 072
Admin region Niedersachsen
Coordinates 52°35′N 10°14′E
Altitude 43–47 m **Area** 169 ha

■ **Site description**

An area of heathland and periodically flooded humid and mesophile grassland. Open sewage farms and oxbow lakes are also present.

Habitats Scrub (62%; heathland), Grassland (35%; humid grassland; mesophile grassland)

■ **Protection status**

National None **International** Partial

IBA overlaps with Special Protection Area (Obere Allerniederung)

■ **Conservation issues**

Threats Agricultural intensification/expansion (U), Drainage (U)

This area is part of a *Ciconia ciconia* protection programme. Part of the area is a candidate Special Area for Conservation.

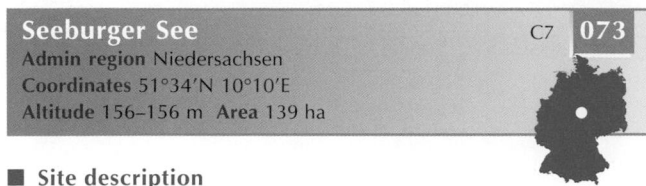

Seeburger See C7 073
Admin region Niedersachsen
Coordinates 51°34′N 10°10′E
Altitude 156–156 m **Area** 139 ha

■ **Site description**

A eutrophic shallow lake with huge reedbeds (*Phragmites*).

Habitats Grassland (9%; humid grassland), Wetland (74%; standing fresh water; water-fringe vegetation; fen/transition mire/spring)

■ **Birds**

This is an important area for passage waterbirds.

■ **Protection status**

National None **International** Partial

IBA overlaps with Special Protection Area (Seeburger See).

■ **Conservation issues**

Threats Aquaculture/fisheries (U), Recreation/tourism (U)

The area is a candidate Special Area for Conservation.

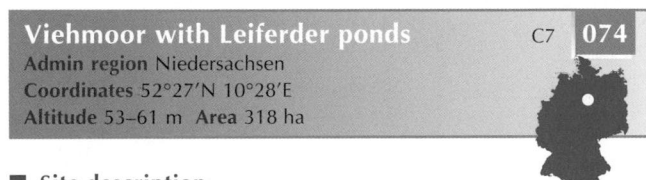

Viehmoor with Leiferder ponds C7 074
Admin region Niedersachsen
Coordinates 52°27′N 10°28′E
Altitude 53–61 m **Area** 318 ha

■ **Site description**

Humid grassland and the 37 ha Leiferder ponds.

Habitats Forest and woodland (6%; broadleaved deciduous forest), Grassland (79%; mesophile grassland), Unknown (11%)

■ **Birds**

This is an important feeding area for *Ciconia ciconia*.

■ **Protection status**

National None **International** Partial

IBA overlaps with Special Protection Area (Viehmoor with Leiferder ponds).

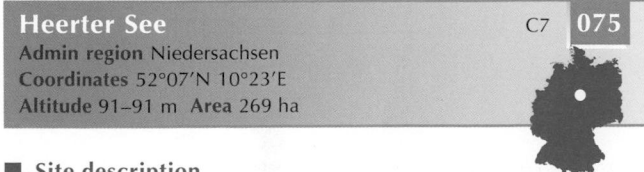

Heerter See C7 075
Admin region Niedersachsen
Coordinates 52°07′N 10°23′E
Altitude 91–91 m **Area** 269 ha

■ **Site description**

The site was formerly a clearing pond for an iron-ore company. The water is brackish.

Habitats Wetland (96%; standing brackish and salt water; water-fringe vegetation)

■ **Birds**

This is an important area for waterbirds and species breeding in reedbeds (*Phragmites*). Species of global conservation concern that do not meet IBA criteria: *Crex crex* (passage).

■ Protection status
National None **International** None
IBA overlaps with Special Protection Area (Heerter Klärteich).

■ Conservation issues

Threats Other (U), Recreation/tourism (U)

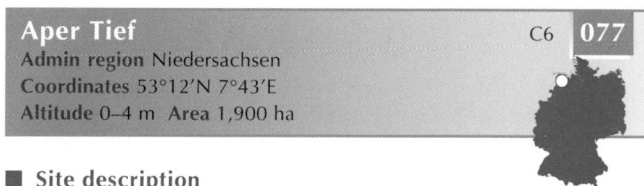

Dalum Wietmarscher swamp   C6   **076**
Admin region Niedersachsen
Coordinates 52°35′N 7°08′E
Altitude — Area 2,050 ha

■ Site description
A nearly natural raised bog with wet forests and grassland.

Habitats Forest and woodland (alluvial/very wet forest), Grassland (humid grassland; mesophile grassland), Wetland (raised bog)
Land-use Agriculture, Nature conservation/research

■ Birds

Species		Season	Year	Pop min	Pop max	Acc	Criteria
Pluvialis apricaria	Golden Plover	R	1997	4	4	—	C6

■ Protection status
National None **International** None

■ Conservation issues

Threats Afforestation (U), Agricultural intensification/expansion (U), Drainage (U), Extraction industry (U)

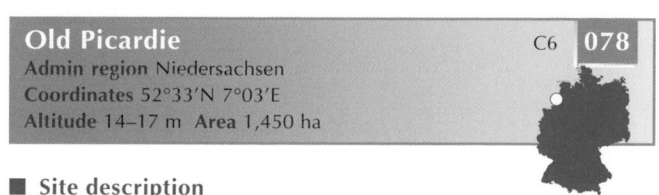

Aper Tief   C6   **077**
Admin region Niedersachsen
Coordinates 53°12′N 7°43′E
Altitude 0–4 m Area 1,900 ha

■ Site description
Humid and mesophile grassland with streams, ditches and temporary standing fresh water.

Habitats Grassland (humid grassland; mesophile grassland), Wetland (river/stream; fen/transition mire/spring), Artificial landscape (arable land)
Land-use Agriculture

■ Birds

Species		Season	Year	Pop min	Pop max	Acc	Criteria
Limosa limosa	Black-tailed Godwit	B	1991	—	95	—	C6

This is an important area for grassland birds.

■ Protection status
National None **International** None

■ Conservation issues

Threats Agricultural intensification/expansion (U), Drainage (U)

Old Picardie   C6   **078**
Admin region Niedersachsen
Coordinates 52°33′N 7°03′E
Altitude 14–17 m Area 1,450 ha

■ Site description
Humid grassland with streams.

Habitats Grassland (humid grassland), Wetland (river/stream)
Land-use Nature conservation/research, Other

■ Birds

Species		Season	Year	Pop min	Pop max	Acc	Criteria
Limosa limosa	Black-tailed Godwit	B	1998	—	116	—	C6

This site is an important area for breeding grassland birds. Species of global conservation concern that do not meet IBA criteria: *Crex crex*.

■ Protection status
National None **International** None

■ Conservation issues

Threats Agricultural intensification/expansion (U)

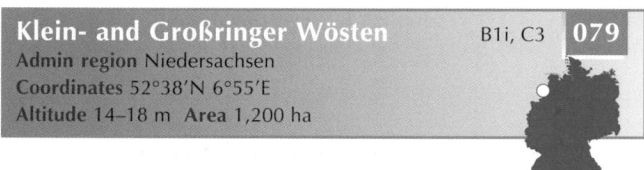

Klein- and Großringer Wösten   B1i, C3   **079**
Admin region Niedersachsen
Coordinates 52°38′N 6°55′E
Altitude 14–18 m Area 1,200 ha

■ Site description
Grassland and shallow ponds in the Holleberger wetland.

Habitats Grassland (humid grassland), Wetland (standing fresh water; river/stream)
Land-use Agriculture

■ Birds

Species		Season	Year	Pop min	Pop max	Acc	Criteria
Anser fabalis	Bean Goose	P	1998	—	950	—	B1i, C3

This site is an important area for breeding grassland birds and passage geese.

■ Protection status
National None **International** None

■ Conservation issues

Threats Agricultural intensification/expansion (U)

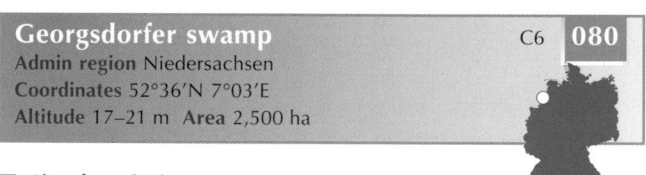

Georgsdorfer swamp   C6   **080**
Admin region Niedersachsen
Coordinates 52°36′N 7°03′E
Altitude 17–21 m Area 2,500 ha

■ Site description
The site is a near-natural area of raised bog with forests and humid grassland.

Habitats Forest and woodland (alluvial/very wet forest), Grassland (humid grassland; mesophile grassland), Wetland (raised bog)
Land-use Agriculture, Forestry, Water management

■ Birds

Species		Season	Year	Pop min	Pop max	Acc	Criteria
Pluvialis apricaria	Golden Plover	R	1997	3	3	—	C6

This is an important area for species breeding in bogs.

■ Protection status
National Low **International** None
IBA overlaps with Nature Reserve (30 ha).

■ Conservation issues

Threats Afforestation (U), Agricultural intensification/expansion (U), Drainage (U), Extraction industry (U), Groundwater abstraction (U)

Groß Fullener marsh · A4i, B1i, B2, C2, C3 · 081

Admin region Niedersachsen
Coordinates 52°40′N 7°08′E
Altitude 14–19 m **Area** 1,500 ha

■ Site description

Arable land with meadows, pastures, flooded gravel-pits and hedges.

Habitats Scrub (scrub), Grassland (mesophile grassland), Wetland (standing fresh water), Artificial landscape (arable land)
Land-use Agriculture

■ Birds

Species	Season	Year	Pop min	Pop max	Acc	Criteria
Cygnus columbianus Bewick's Swan	W	1997	—	441	—	A4i, B1i, B2, C2
Anser fabalis Bean Goose	W	1997	—	10,000	—	A4i, B1i, C3

This is an important area for wintering swans and geese.

■ Protection status

National None **International** None

■ Conservation issues

Threats Agricultural intensification/expansion (U), Drainage (U)

Leeg-, Melm- and Kuhdammoor · C6 · 082

Admin region Niedersachsen
Coordinates 53°00′N 7°33′E
Altitude 5–12 m **Area** 1,995 ha

■ Site description

A raised bog with peat banks bordering on humid grassland.

Habitats Grassland (humid grassland), Wetland (standing fresh water; raised bog)
Land-use Agriculture, Nature conservation/research

■ Birds

Species	Season	Year	Pop min	Pop max	Acc	Criteria
Limosa limosa Black-tailed Godwit	B	1998	83	83	A	C6

The area is important for breeding birds of wet grassland.

■ Protection status

National High **International** None
440 ha of IBA covered by Nature Reserve (Leegmoor, 440 ha).

■ Conservation issues

Threats Agricultural intensification/expansion (U), Drainage (U)

Esterweger Dose · B3, C6 · 083

Admin region Niedersachsen
Coordinates 53°03′N 7°39′E
Altitude 8–12 m **Area** 4,970 ha

■ Site description

Raised bog, partly degenerated and partly used for peat-cutting.

Habitats Grassland, Wetland (river/stream; raised bog; fen/transition mire/spring)
Land-use Nature conservation/research, Other

■ Birds

Species	Season	Year	Pop min	Pop max	Acc	Criteria
Circus pygargus Montagu's Harrier	B	1990	1	5	—	B3, C6
Pluvialis apricaria Golden Plover	R	1997	8	8	—	C6

■ Protection status

National None **International** None

■ Conservation issues

Threats Agricultural intensification/expansion (U), Drainage (U), Extraction industry (U)

Leda–Jümme lowlands · B2, C7 · 084

Admin region Niedersachsen
Coordinates 53°13′N 7°35′E
Altitude 0–5 m **Area** 5,500 ha

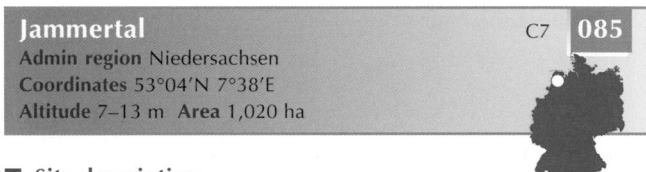

■ Site description

A marsh-meadow area with humid grassland, rivers and flooded areas.

Habitats Grassland (humid grassland; mesophile grassland), Wetland (river/stream)
Land-use Agriculture

■ Birds

Species	Season	Year	Pop min	Pop max	Acc	Criteria
Limosa limosa Black-tailed Godwit	B	1991	—	194	—	B2, C7

This is an important area for birds breeding in grassland.

■ Protection status

National Low **International** None
IBA overlaps with Nature Reserve (10 ha).

■ Conservation issues

Threats Agricultural intensification/expansion (U), Construction/impact of dyke/dam/barrage (U), Infrastructure (U)

Jammertal · C7 · 085

Admin region Niedersachsen
Coordinates 53°04′N 7°38′E
Altitude 7–13 m **Area** 1,020 ha

■ Site description

Raised bog with grassland, wet meadows, standing fresh water, near-natural rivers, and hedges.

Habitats Grassland (humid grassland; mesophile grassland), Wetland (standing fresh water; river/stream; raised bog)
Land-use Agriculture

■ Protection status

National Partial **International** Partial
IBA overlaps with a Nature Reserve. IBA overlaps with Special Protection Area.

■ Conservation issues

Threats Agricultural intensification/expansion (U), Drainage (U)

Wesuwer Brook · A4i, B1i, C2, C3 · 086

Admin region Niedersachsen
Coordinates 52°46′N 7°14′E
Altitude 10–15 m **Area** 600 ha

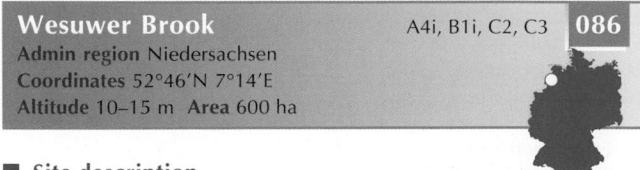

■ Site description

An area of meadows, open water and arable land.

Habitats Grassland (humid grassland; mesophile grassland), Wetland (standing fresh water; river/stream), Artificial landscape (arable land)
Land-use Agriculture

■ Birds

This is an important wintering site for swans and geese.

Species	Season	Year	Pop min	Pop max	Acc	Criteria
[1] *Cygnus columbianus* Bewick's Swan	W	1997	—	264	—	A4i, B1i, C2

Species ... continued	Season	Year	Pop min	Pop max	Acc	Criteria
Anser fabalis Bean Goose	W	1997	—	1,800	—	B1i, C3

1. Large decrease.

■ Protection status
National None **International** None

■ Conservation issues

Threats Agricultural intensification/expansion (U), Infrastructure (U)

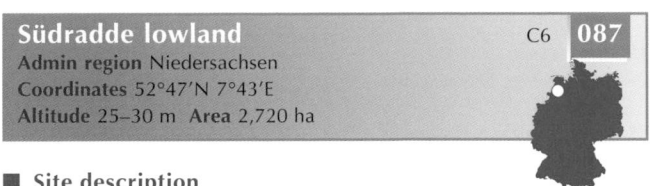

Südradde lowland
C6 · 087
Admin region Niedersachsen
Coordinates 52°47′N 7°43′E
Altitude 25–30 m **Area** 2,720 ha

■ Site description
Humid grassland in the Radde lowland.

Habitats Grassland (humid grassland; mesophile grassland)
Land-use Agriculture, Forestry

■ Birds

Species	Season	Year	Pop min	Pop max	Acc	Criteria
Limosa limosa Black-tailed Godwit	B	1992	88	137	A	C6

Species of global conservation concern that do not meet IBA criteria: *Crex crex* (5 breeding pairs).

■ Protection status
National None **International** None

■ Conservation issues

Threats Agricultural intensification/expansion (A)

The site is a candidate Special Protection Area.

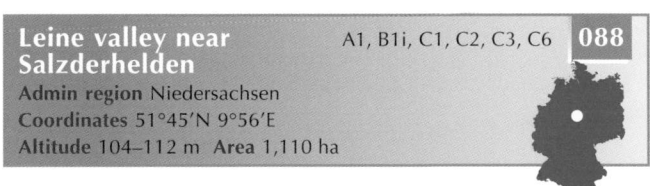

Leine valley near Salzderhelden
A1, B1i, C1, C2, C3, C6 · 088
Admin region Niedersachsen
Coordinates 51°45′N 9°56′E
Altitude 104–112 m **Area** 1,110 ha

■ Site description
The site includes lakes left as a result of mining operations, the largest humid grassland complex in the south of Lower Saxony, and agricultural land.

Habitats Forest and woodland (broadleaved deciduous forest), Grassland (humid grassland; mesophile grassland), Wetland (standing fresh water)
Land-use Agriculture, Fisheries/aquaculture, Hunting, Other, Tourism/recreation, Urban/industrial/transport

■ Birds

Species	Season	Year	Pop min	Pop max	Acc	Criteria
Anser fabalis Bean Goose	P	1996	2,000	—	—	B1i, C3
Anas clypeata Shoveler	W	1996	400	—	—	B1i, C3
Mergus albellus Smew	P	1996	250	250	—	B1i, C2
Porzana porzana Spotted Crake	B	1996	12	—	—	C6
Crex crex Corncrake	B	1996	50	—	—	A1, C1, C2

■ Protection status
National None **International** Partial
IBA overlaps with Special Protection Area (Leinetal bei Salzderhelden).

■ Conservation issues

Threats Agricultural intensification/expansion (B), Aquaculture/fisheries (C), Extraction industry (B), Infrastructure (B), Recreation/tourism (C)

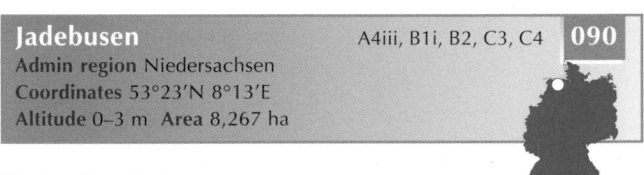

Valley of the River Ems
A1, A4i, A4iii, B1i, C1, C2, C3, C4 · 089
Admin region Niedersachsen
Coordinates 53°02′N 7°17′E
Altitude 1–6 m **Area** 5,317 ha

■ Site description
Mainly farmland with oxbow lakes, riverine forest and dry grassland.

Habitats Forest and woodland (alluvial/very wet forest), Grassland (dry siliceous grassland; standing fresh water), Artificial landscape (arable land)
Land-use Agriculture, Forestry

■ Birds

Species	Season	Year	Pop min	Pop max	Acc	Criteria
Cygnus columbianus Bewick's Swan	P	1998	766	803	—	A4i, B1i, C2
Anser fabalis Bean Goose	P	1998	4,531	4,531	—	A4i, B1i, C3
Anser albifrons White-fronted Goose	P	1998	14,800	14,800	—	A4i, B1i, C3
Crex crex Corncrake	B	1997	46	46	—	A1, C1, C2

The site regularly holds 20,000 or more waterbirds on passage.

■ Protection status
National None **International** None

■ Conservation issues

Threats Abandonment/reduction of land management (A), Afforestation (B), Aquaculture/fisheries (B), Dredging/canalization (A), Recreation/tourism (B)

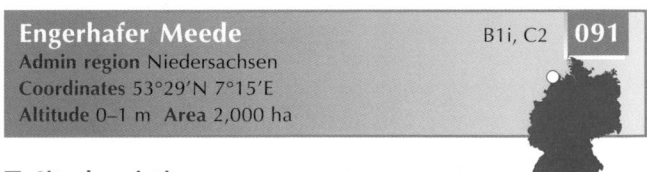

Jadebusen
A4iii, B1i, B2, C3, C4 · 090
Admin region Niedersachsen
Coordinates 53°23′N 8°13′E
Altitude 0–3 m **Area** 8,267 ha

■ Site description
Intensively used arable land with large areas of humid grassland and some open water and reedbeds (*Phragmites*).

Habitats Grassland (36%; humid grassland; mesophile grassland), Artificial landscape (50%; arable land)
Land-use Agriculture (90%), Hunting (90%), Other (69%)

■ Birds

Species	Season	Year	Pop min	Pop max	Acc	Criteria
Anser albifrons White-fronted Goose	P	1997	6,250	—	—	B1i, C3
Numenius arquata Curlew	W	1996	1,926	1,926	—	B2

The site holds 20,000 or more waterbirds on passage, on a regular basis.

■ Protection status
National Partial **International** Partial
IBA overlaps with National Park. IBA overlaps with Ramsar Site.

■ Conservation issues

Threats Agricultural intensification/expansion (B), Industrialization/urbanization (A)

Engerhafer Meede
B1i, C2 · 091
Admin region Niedersachsen
Coordinates 53°29′N 7°15′E
Altitude 0–1 m **Area** 2,000 ha

■ Site description
A large area of wet grassland.

Habitats Grassland (60%; humid grassland; mesophile grassland), Wetland (30%; raised bog), Artificial landscape (5%; arable land)

■ Birds

Species	Season	Year	Pop min	Pop max	Acc	Criteria
Pluvialis apricaria Golden Plover	P	1997	10,000	10,000	—	B1i, C2

■ **Protection status**
National None **International** None

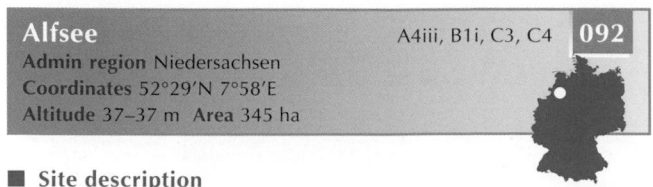

Alfsee A4iii, B1i, C3, C4 **092**
Admin region Niedersachsen
Coordinates 52°29′N 7°58′E
Altitude 37–37 m **Area** 345 ha

■ **Site description**
An artificial lake used for recreation from April to October. The use of boats in winter is not permitted.

Habitats Forest and woodland (5%; broadleaved deciduous forest; mixed forest), Grassland (16%; dry siliceous grassland; humid grassland), Wetland (70%; standing fresh water)
Land-use Tourism/recreation, Water management

■ **Birds**

Species	Season	Year	Pop min	Pop max	Acc	Criteria
¹ *Anas clypeata* Shoveler	W	1997	403	627	—	B1i, C3

1. 1995–1997.

■ **Protection status**
National Partial **International** None
123 ha of IBA covered by Nature Reserve (Alfsee-Reservebecken, 123 ha).

■ **Conservation issues**

Threats Disturbance to birds (U), Recreation/tourism (B)

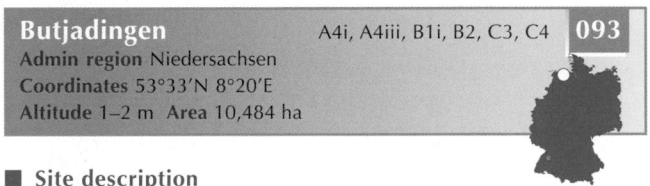

Butjadingen A4i, A4iii, B1i, B2, C3, C4 **093**
Admin region Niedersachsen
Coordinates 53°33′N 8°20′E
Altitude 1–2 m **Area** 10,484 ha

■ **Site description**
An extensive area of grassland on the border with Niedersächsisches Wattenmeer National Park.

Habitats Grassland (80%; humid grassland; mesophile grassland), Artificial landscape (10%; arable land)
Land-use Agriculture

■ **Birds**

Species	Season	Year	Pop min	Pop max	Acc	Criteria
¹ *Numenius arquata* Curlew	W	1997	2,691	8,165	—	A4i, B1i, B2, C3

1. 1996–1997.

The site holds 20,000 or more waterbirds on passage, on a regular basis (including *Anser albifrons* 5,004; *Pluvialis apricaria* 9,292; *Vanellus vanellus* 28,493; *Larus canus* 9,860).

■ **Protection status**
National None **International** None

■ **Conservation issues**

Threats Industrialization/urbanization (U)

Norden–Esens A4iii, B2, C4 **094**
Admin region Niedersachsen
Coordinates 53°40′N 7°26′E
Altitude 0–2 m **Area** 9,948 ha

■ **Site description**
Predominantly intensively used arable land with a widespread system of ditches containing reeds *Phragmites*.

Habitats Grassland (30%; mesophile grassland), Artificial landscape (61%; arable land; forestry plantation)
Land-use Agriculture

■ **Birds**

Species	Season	Year	Pop min	Pop max	Acc	Criteria
Branta leucopsis Barnacle Goose	W	1995	370	370	—	B2
Numenius arquata Curlew	W	1995	2,425	2,425	—	B2

The site holds 20,000 or more waterbirds on passage, on a regular basis, including *Pluvialis apricaria* (8,826), *Vanellus vanellus* (9,363), *Larus ridibundus* (14,514) and *Larus canus* (11,764).

■ **Protection status**
National None **International** None

■ **Conservation issues**

Threats Disturbance to birds (U), Infrastructure (U), Recreation/tourism (C)

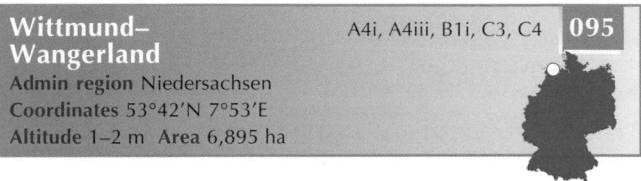

Wittmund–Wangerland A4i, A4iii, B1i, C3, C4 **095**
Admin region Niedersachsen
Coordinates 53°42′N 7°53′E
Altitude 1–2 m **Area** 6,895 ha

■ **Site description**
Predominantly intensively used arable land with a widespread system of ditches containing reeds *Phragmites*.

Habitats Grassland (30%; mesophile grassland), Artificial landscape (65%; arable land)
Land-use Agriculture

■ **Birds**

Species	Season	Year	Pop min	Pop max	Acc	Criteria
¹ *Anas penelope* Wigeon	P	1996	5,060	12,440	—	B1i, C3
Numenius arquata Curlew	P	1995	4,539	4,539	—	A4i, B1i, C3

1. 1995–1996.

The site holds 20,000 or more waterbirds on passage, on a regular basis.

■ **Protection status**
National None **International** None

■ **Conservation issues**

Threats Disturbance to birds (U), Industrialization/urbanization (U)

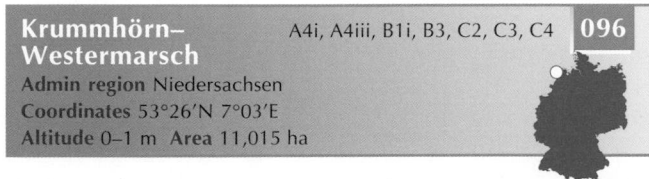

Krummhörn–Westermarsch A4i, A4iii, B1i, B3, C2, C3, C4 **096**
Admin region Niedersachsen
Coordinates 53°26′N 7°03′E
Altitude 0–1 m **Area** 11,015 ha

■ **Site description**
Predominantly intensively used arable land with a widespread system of ditches containing reeds *Phragmites*.

Habitats Wetland (water-fringe vegetation), Artificial landscape (arable land)
Land-use Agriculture

■ **Birds**

Species	Season	Year	Pop min	Pop max	Acc	Criteria
¹ *Anser anser* Greylag Goose	P	1996	—	3,580	—	A4i, B1i, C3
Branta leucopsis Barnacle Goose	P	1997	2,032	14,156	—	A4i, B1i, C2
² *Recurvirostra avosetta* Avocet	B	1998	280	280	—	B3
Recurvirostra avosetta Avocet	P	1996	—	3,450	—	A4i, B1i, C2

Species ... continued	Season	Year	Pop min	Pop max	Acc	Criteria
Limosa lapponica Bar-tailed Godwit	P	1996	1,500	1,500	—	A4i, B1i, C2
[2] *Numenius arquata* Curlew	P	1998	2,300	6,000	—	A4i, B1i, C3

1. 1995–1996.
2. 1995–1998.

The site holds 20,000 or more waterbirds on passage, on a regular basis.

■ **Protection status**
National None **International** None

■ **Conservation issues**

Threats Disturbance to birds (U), Industrialization/urbanization (U)

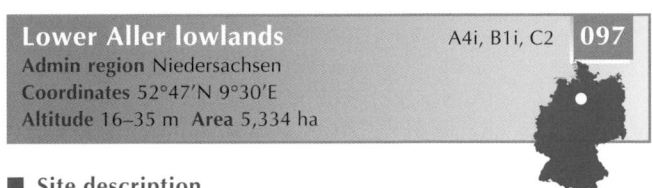

Lower Aller lowlands
A4i, B1i, C2 **097**

Admin region Niedersachsen
Coordinates 52°47′N 9°30′E
Altitude 16–35 m **Area** 5,334 ha

■ **Site description**
The flood-plain of the River Aller including the river, oxbow lakes, wet meadows and regularly flooded grassland.

Habitats Grassland (74%; humid grassland; mesophile grassland), Wetland (20%; standing fresh water; fen/transition mire/spring)
Land-use Agriculture

■ **Birds**

Species	Season	Year	Pop min	Pop max	Acc	Criteria
Cygnus columbianus Bewick's Swan	P	—	400	400	—	A4i, B1i, C2

Species of global conservation concern that do not meet IBA criteria: *Crex crex* (15 breeding pairs).

■ **Protection status**
National None **International** None
IBA overlaps with Nature Reserve (140 ha). IBA overlaps with Special Protection Area.

■ **Conservation issues**

Threats Agricultural intensification/expansion (U), Construction/impact of dyke/dam/barrage (U)

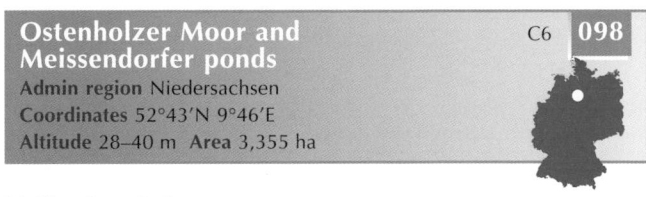

Ostenholzer Moor and Meissendorfer ponds
C6 **098**

Admin region Niedersachsen
Coordinates 52°43′N 9°46′E
Altitude 28–40 m **Area** 3,355 ha

■ **Site description**
A lowland area that contains the River Meise and some large fish-ponds. The site also includes a large bog, patches of woodland, wet meadows and heathland.

Habitats Forest and woodland (23%; mixed forest), Grassland (31%; humid grassland; mesophile grassland), Wetland (44%; standing fresh water; raised bog)
Land-use Agriculture, Forestry, Military, Tourism/recreation

■ **Birds**

Species	Season	Year	Pop min	Pop max	Acc	Criteria
Ciconia nigra Black Stork	B	1995	2	2	—	C6

Species of global conservation concern that do not meet IBA criteria: *Crex crex* (breeding).

■ **Protection status**
National None **International** High
IBA overlaps with Special Protection Area.

■ **Conservation issues**

Threats Agricultural intensification/expansion (U), Recreation/tourism (U)

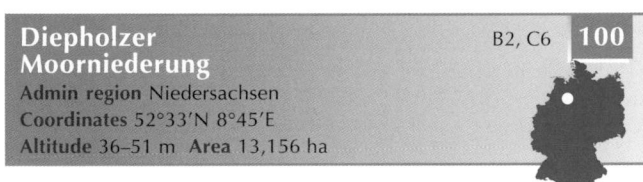

Steinhuder Meer
C6 **099**

Admin region Niedersachsen
Coordinates 52°28′N 9°20′E
Altitude 38–42 m **Area** 5,818 ha

■ **Site description**
A large, eutrophic lake (2,800 ha), surrounded by wet meadows and bogs.

Habitats Grassland (humid grassland), Wetland (standing fresh water; raised bog)
Land-use Agriculture, Tourism/recreation, Urban/industrial/transport

■ **Birds**

Species	Season	Year	Pop min	Pop max	Acc	Criteria
Caprimulgus europaeus Nightjar	B	1996	34	34	—	C6

Species of global conservation concern that do not meet IBA criteria: *Crex crex* (10 breeding pairs).

■ **Protection status**
National None **International** High
IBA overlaps with Ramsar Site and Special Protection Area.

■ **Conservation issues**

Threats Drainage (U), Extraction industry (U), Recreation/tourism (U)

Peat extraction and drainage are adversely affecting the IBA.

Diepholzer Moorniederung
B2, C6 **100**

Admin region Niedersachsen
Coordinates 52°33′N 8°45′E
Altitude 36–51 m **Area** 13,156 ha

■ **Site description**
A lowland area with marshes, wet meadows and bogs.

Habitats Grassland (humid grassland), Wetland (raised bog)
Land-use Agriculture, Other

■ **Birds**

Species	Season	Year	Pop min	Pop max	Acc	Criteria
Pluvialis apricaria Golden Plover	R	1997	8	8	—	C6
Lanius excubitor Great Grey Shrike	R	1997	40	40	—	B2

■ **Protection status**
National None **International** High
IBA overlaps with Ramsar Site and Special Protection Area.

■ **Conservation issues**

Threats Agricultural intensification/expansion (U), Drainage (U), Extraction industry (U)

Dümmer
A4iii, B1i, B2, C2, C3, C4, C6 **101**

Admin region Niedersachsen
Coordinates 52°30′N 8°20′E
Altitude 37–39 m **Area** 4,370 ha

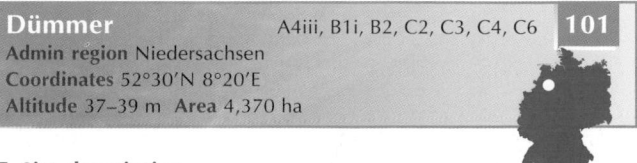

■ **Site description**

Habitats Grassland (humid grassland), Wetland (standing fresh water; fen/transition mire/spring)
Land-use Agriculture

A large, shallow, eutrophic lake (1,300 ha), surrounded by pasture and bog.

■ **Birds**

Species		Season	Year	Pop min	Pop max	Acc	Criteria
Anser fabalis	Bean Goose	P	1990	—	3,500	—	B1i, C3
Anser anser	Greylag Goose	W	1990	—	2,300	—	B1i, C3
Anas clypeata	Shoveler	W	1990	—	480	—	B1i, C3
Porzana porzana	Spotted Crake	B	1995	14	14	—	C6
Limosa limosa	Black-tailed Godwit	B	1995	88	88	—	C6
Chlidonias niger	Black Tern	B	1995	48	48	—	B2, C2

The site regularly holds more than 20,000 wintering wildfowl. Species of global conservation concern that do not meet IBA criteria: *Crex crex* (6 breeding pairs).

■ **Protection status**
National None **International** High
IBA overlaps with Ramsar Site and Special Protection Area.

■ **Conservation issues**

Threats Drainage (U)

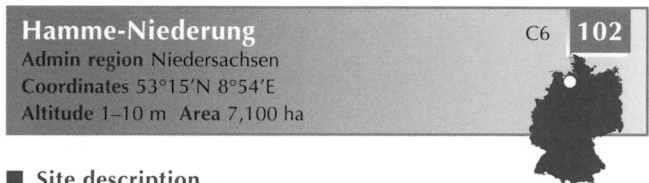

Hamme-Niederung C6 102
Admin region Niedersachsen
Coordinates 53°15'N 8°54'E
Altitude 1–10 m **Area** 7,100 ha

■ **Site description**
A large, intact area of wet meadows situated along the River Hamme, interspersed with oxbow lakes, and ditches. A bog is located in the northern part of the IBA which was formerly subject to spring flooding.

Habitats Grassland (humid grassland), Wetland (standing fresh water; river/stream; raised bog)
Land-use Agriculture

■ **Birds**

Species		Season	Year	Pop min	Pop max	Acc	Criteria
Circus pygargus	Montagu's Harrier	B	1996	3	3	—	C6

Species of global conservation concern that do not meet IBA criteria: *Crex crex* (18 breeding pairs).

■ **Protection status**
National None **International** High
IBA overlaps with Special Protection Area.

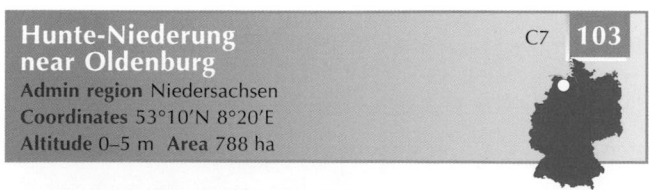

Hunte-Niederung near Oldenburg C7 103
Admin region Niedersachsen
Coordinates 53°10'N 8°20'E
Altitude 0–5 m **Area** 788 ha

■ **Site description**
Wet meadows situated along the River Hunte and traversed by dykes. The area often floods in spring and autumn.

Habitats Grassland (91%; humid grassland; mesophile grassland), Wetland (5%; standing fresh water)
Land-use Agriculture, Water management

■ **Protection status**
National None **International** Partial
IBA overlaps with Special Protection Area (Hunteniederung).

■ **Conservation issues**

Threats Agricultural intensification/expansion (U), Other (U)

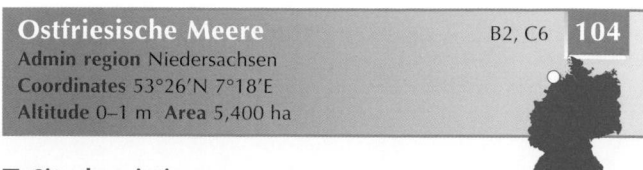

Ostfriesische Meere B2, C6 104
Admin region Niedersachsen
Coordinates 53°26'N 7°18'E
Altitude 0–1 m **Area** 5,400 ha

■ **Site description**
One of the few large areas of bog and lakes remaining in Lower Saxony. The lakes are surrounded by reedbeds (*Phragmites*) and meadows.

Habitats Grassland (humid grassland; mesophile grassland), Wetland (standing fresh water; raised bog; water-fringe vegetation)
Land-use Agriculture

■ **Birds**

Species		Season	Year	Pop min	Pop max	Acc	Criteria
Circus pygargus	Montagu's Harrier	B	1995	3	3	—	C6
Limosa limosa	Black-tailed Godwit	B	1995	184	184	—	B2, C6
Asio flammeus	Short-eared Owl	R	1995	8	8	—	B2

■ **Protection status**
National None **International** Partial
IBA overlaps with Special Protection Area.

■ **Conservation issues**

Threats Agricultural intensification/expansion (U), Drainage (U), Industrialization/urbanization (U)

The area is a candidate Special Area for Conservation.

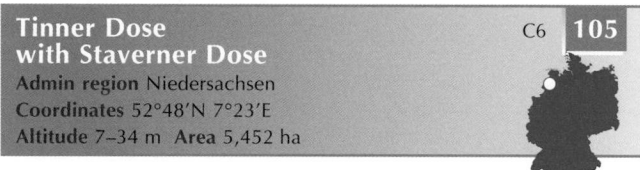

Tinner Dose with Staverner Dose C6 105
Admin region Niedersachsen
Coordinates 52°48'N 7°23'E
Altitude 7–34 m **Area** 5,452 ha

■ **Site description**
The largest intact bog in central Europe; used as a military training area.

Habitats Forest and woodland (5%; mixed forest), Grassland (17%; humid grassland; mesophile grassland), Wetland (77%; raised bog)
Land-use Agriculture, Military

■ **Birds**

Species		Season	Year	Pop min	Pop max	Acc	Criteria
Circus pygargus	Montagu's Harrier	B	1994	3	3	—	C6

■ **Protection status**
National None **International** Partial
IBA overlaps with 2 Nature Reserves (Tinner u. Staverner Dose and Sprakeler Heide).

■ **Conservation issues**

Threats Drainage (U), Infrastructure (U), Other (U)

The area is a candidate Special Area for Conservation.

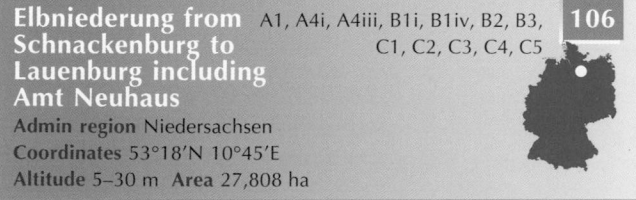

Elbniederung from Schnackenburg to Lauenburg including Amt Neuhaus
A1, A4i, A4iii, B1i, B1iv, B2, B3, C1, C2, C3, C4, C5 106
Admin region Niedersachsen
Coordinates 53°18'N 10°45'E
Altitude 5–30 m **Area** 27,808 ha

■ **Site description**
Flood-plain of the slow-flowing River Elbe with remnant riverine forests, oxbow lakes, wet grassland, flooded meadows and dunes.

Habitats Forest and woodland (broadleaved deciduous forest; mixed forest; alluvial/very wet forest), Grassland (humid grassland; mesophile grassland), Wetland (sand-dunes/ sand beach; standing fresh water; river/stream), Artificial landscape (arable land)
Land-use Agriculture, Forestry, Tourism/recreation

■ Birds

Species	Season	Year	Pop min	Pop max	Acc	Criteria
Cygnus columbianus Bewick's Swan	W	1990	—	2,155	—	A4i, B1i, B2, C2
Cygnus cygnus Whooper Swan	W	1990	—	2,540	—	A4i, B1i, B3, C2
Anser fabalis Bean Goose	W	1990	—	46,380	—	A4i, B1i, C3
Anser albifrons White-fronted Goose	W	1990	—	33,180	—	A4i, B1i, C3
Crex crex Corncrake	B	1996	26	26	—	A1, C1
Grus grus Crane	P	1990	—	4,768	—	B1i, C2
Numenius arquata Curlew	W	1990	—	296	—	B2

The site holds 20,000 or more waterbirds in winter, on a regular basis. The site is a migratory bottleneck, where more than 3,000 *Grus grus* regularly pass. Species of global conservation concern that do not meet IBA criteria: *Anser erythropus* (wintering).

■ Protection status
National Partial **International** Partial
IBA overlaps with several Nature Reserves. IBA overlaps with Special Protection Area (Elbniederung von Schnackenburg bis Lauenburg inkl. Amt Neuhaus, 27,808 ha) and Ramsar Site (Elbniederung von Schnackenburg bis Lauenburg inkl. Amt Neuhaus, 7,560 ha).

■ Conservation issues

Threats Agricultural intensification/expansion (U), Drainage (U)

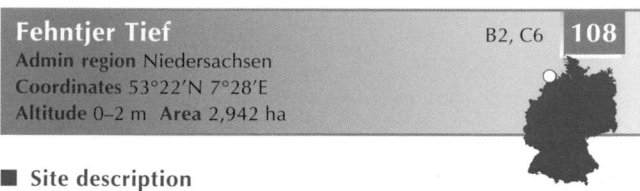

Elbmarsch from Stade to Otterndorf
A4i, A4iii, B1i, B2, B3, C2, C3, C4, C6   **107**
Admin region Niedersachsen
Coordinates 53°51′N 9°10′E
Altitude 0–4 m **Area** 18,675 ha

■ Site description
The tidal lower reaches of the River Elbe.

Habitats Grassland (56%; humid grassland), Wetland (41%; saltmarsh; standing fresh water)
Land-use Agriculture, Water management

■ Birds

Species	Season	Year	Pop min	Pop max	Acc	Criteria
Cygnus columbianus Bewick's Swan	W	1990	—	1,627	—	A4i, B1i, B2, C2
Anser fabalis Bean Goose	W	1990	—	2,023	—	B1i, C3
Anser albifrons White-fronted Goose	W	1990	—	15,192	—	A4i, B1i, C3
Anser anser Greylag Goose	W	1990	—	11,342	—	A4i, B1i, C3
Branta leucopsis Barnacle Goose	W	1990	—	31,600	—	A4i, B1i, B2, C2
Branta bernicla Brent Goose	W	1990	—	3,803	—	A4i, B1i, C3
Tadorna tadorna Shelduck	W	1990	—	3,370	—	B1i, C3
Anas strepera Gadwall	R	1995	110	110	—	B2
Anas crecca Teal	W	1990	—	4,349	—	B1i, C3
Anas clypeata Shoveler	R	1995	245	245	—	B1i, C3
Anas clypeata Shoveler	W	1990	—	1,572	—	B1i, C3
Circus pygargus Montagu's Harrier	B	1995	4	4	—	B3, C6
Porzana porzana Spotted Crake	B	1995	9	9	—	C6
Recurvirostra avosetta Avocet	B	1995	166	166	—	B3
Recurvirostra avosetta Avocet	W	1990	—	2,441	—	A4i, B1i, B2, C2
Pluvialis apricaria Golden Plover	W	1990	—	20,443	—	A4i, B1i, C2
Limosa limosa Black-tailed Godwit	B	1995	725	725	—	B2, C6
Numenius arquata Curlew	W	1990	—	1,984	—	B2
Tringa erythropus Spotted Redshank	W	1990	—	3,890	—	A4i, B1i, C3
Tringa totanus Redshank	R	1995	512	512	—	B2
Gelochelidon nilotica Gull-billed Tern	B	1995	53	53	—	B1i, B2, C2
Asio flammeus Short-eared Owl	R	1995	11	11	—	B2

The site holds 20,000 or more waterbirds in winter, on a regular basis. Species of global conservation concern that do not meet IBA criteria: *Crex crex* (breeding).

■ Protection status
National Partial **International** Partial
IBA overlaps with Nature Reserve. IBA overlaps with Special Protection Area (Niederelbe zwischen Stade und Ottendorf, 10,500 ha).

■ Conservation issues

Threats Agricultural intensification/expansion (U), Construction/impact of dyke/dam/ barrage (U), Disturbance to birds (U)

Fehntjer Tief
B2, C6   **108**
Admin region Niedersachsen
Coordinates 53°22′N 7°28′E
Altitude 0–2 m **Area** 2,942 ha

■ Site description
Intensively used mesophile grassland with bog and wet *Alnus* forest.

Habitats Forest and woodland (alluvial/very wet forest), Grassland (humid grassland; mesophile grassland), Wetland (raised bog)
Land-use Agriculture

■ Birds

Species	Season	Year	Pop min	Pop max	Acc	Criteria
Circus pygargus Montagu's Harrier	B	1996	3	3	—	C6
Limosa limosa Black-tailed Godwit	B	1996	110	110	—	B2, C6

The site is nationally important for breeding *Circus aeruginosus*.

■ Protection status
National None **International** High
IBA overlaps with Special Protection Area.

■ Conservation issues

Threats Drainage (U), Infrastructure (U)

Wümme lowlands and St Jürgensland
B3, C6   **109**
Admin region Niedersachsen
Coordinates 53°10′N 8°50′E
Altitude 1–3 m **Area** 2,912 ha

■ Site description
An area of lowland in the Wümme river valley, comprising mainly wet meadows that are subject to spring flooding.

Habitats Grassland (93%; humid grassland; mesophile grassland)
Land-use Agriculture

■ Birds

Species	Season	Year	Pop min	Pop max	Acc	Criteria
Circus pygargus Montagu's Harrier	B	1996	4	4	—	B3, C6

Species of global conservation concern that do not meet IBA criteria: *Crex crex* (breeding).

■ Protection status
National None **International** High
IBA overlaps with Special Protection Area.

■ Conservation issues

Threats Agricultural intensification/expansion (U), Drainage (U)

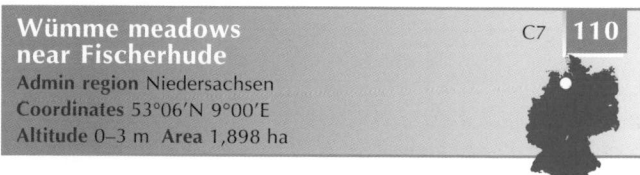

Wümme meadows near Fischerhude
C7   **110**
Admin region Niedersachsen
Coordinates 53°06′N 9°00′E
Altitude 0–3 m **Area** 1,898 ha

■ Site description
An area of humid grassland and bog on the flood-plain of the Rivers Hamme and Wümme.

Habitats Grassland (humid grassland), Wetland (river/stream)
Land-use Agriculture

■ **Birds**
Species of global conservation concern that do not meet IBA criteria: *Crex crex* (resident).

■ **Protection status**
National None **International** Partial
IBA overlaps with Special Protection Area.

■ **Conservation issues**

Threats Agricultural intensification/expansion (U), Dredging/canalization (U), Recreation/tourism (U)

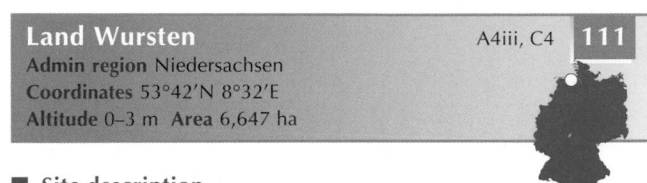

Land Wursten
A4iii, C4 **111**
Admin region Niedersachsen
Coordinates 53°42′N 8°32′E
Altitude 0–3 m **Area** 6,647 ha

■ **Site description**
The site consists of an area of mainly arable land and a small area of grassland on the border of the Niedersächsisches Wattenmeer National Park.

Habitats Grassland (humid grassland; mesophile grassland), Artificial landscape (arable land)
Land-use Agriculture, Urban/industrial/transport

■ **Birds**
The site holds 20,000 waterbirds on passage on a regular basis, including 12,820 *Vanellus vanellus* and 4,235 *Larus canus*.

■ **Protection status**
National None **International** None

■ **Conservation issues**

Threats Agricultural intensification/expansion (U), Disturbance to birds (U), Industrialization/urbanization (U)

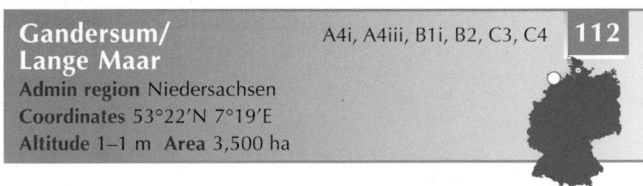

Gandersum/ Lange Maar
A4i, A4iii, B1i, B2, C3, C4 **112**
Admin region Niedersachsen
Coordinates 53°22′N 7°19′E
Altitude 1–1 m **Area** 3,500 ha

■ **Site description**

Habitats Grassland (50%), Wetland (5%; standing fresh water), Artificial landscape (45%; arable land)
Land-use Agriculture, Tourism/recreation

■ **Birds**

Species	Season	Year	Pop min	Pop max	Acc	Criteria
Anser fabalis Bean Goose	W	1995	—	1,500	—	B1i, C3
Anser albifrons White-fronted Goose	W	1998	—	16,890	—	A4i, B1i, C3
Branta leucopsis Barnacle Goose	W	1997	—	6,920	—	A4i, B1i, B2, C2

The site holds 20,000 or more waterbirds in winter, on a regular basis.

■ **Protection status**
National None **International** None

■ **Conservation issues**

Threats Agricultural intensification/expansion (U), Infrastructure (U), Recreation/tourism (U)

Lowland of the River Ems near Laten
A4i, B1i, B2, C2, C3 **113**
Admin region Niedersachsen
Coordinates 52°52′N 7°18′E
Altitude 7–10 m **Area** 3,200 ha

■ **Site description**
Arable land and mesophile grassland on the flood-plain of the River Ems.

Habitats Grassland (40%; mesophile grassland), Artificial landscape (50%; arable land)
Land-use Agriculture (90%), Hunting (95%), Urban/industrial/transport (15%)

■ **Birds**

Species	Season	Year	Pop min	Pop max	Acc	Criteria
[1] *Cygnus columbianus* Bewick's Swan	W	1997	716	716	—	A4i, B1i, B2, C2
Anser fabalis Bean Goose	P	1997	1,200	1,200	—	B1i, C3

1. In cold winters only occurs on passage.

■ **Protection status**
National None **International** None

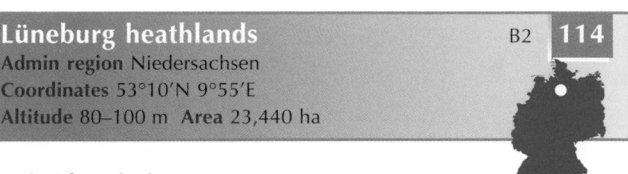

Lüneburg heathlands
B2 **114**
Admin region Niedersachsen
Coordinates 53°10′N 9°55′E
Altitude 80–100 m **Area** 23,440 ha

■ **Site description**

Habitats Forest and woodland (30%), Scrub (50%; heathland), Wetland (10%; river/stream; raised bog)
Land-use Agriculture, Forestry, Tourism/recreation

■ **Birds**

Species	Season	Year	Pop min	Pop max	Acc	Criteria
Caprimulgus europaeus Nightjar	B	—	66	66	—	B2
Lullula arborea Woodlark	B	—	173	173	—	B2

■ **Protection status**
National Partial **International** None
IBA overlaps with Nature Reserve (Lünburger Heide, 23,440 ha).

■ **Conservation issues**

Threats Groundwater abstraction (U), Recreation/tourism (U)

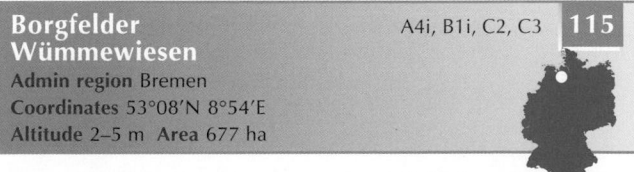

Borgfelder Wümmewiesen
A4i, B1i, C2, C3 **115**
Admin region Bremen
Coordinates 53°08′N 8°54′E
Altitude 2–5 m **Area** 677 ha

■ **Site description**
This area is part of the Wümmeniederung (the Bremer wet-grassland belt) and is one of the few remaining large expanses of wet grassland left in the country.

Habitats Grassland (10%; humid grassland), Wetland (90%; river/stream; raised bog)
Land-use Agriculture (80%), Nature conservation/research (100%), Tourism/recreation (5%), Water management (10%)

■ **Birds**

Species	Season	Year	Pop min	Pop max	Acc	Criteria
Cygnus columbianus Bewick's Swan	P	1995	2	220	A	A4i, B1i, C2
Anas clypeata Shoveler	P	1994	400	400	A	B1i, C3

Species of global conservation concern that do not meet IBA criteria: *Crex crex* (8–9 breeding pairs).

■ Protection status

National Partial **International** Partial
IBA overlaps with Nature Reserve. IBA overlaps with Special Protection Area.

■ Conservation issues

Threats Disturbance to birds (C), Recreation/tourism (C)

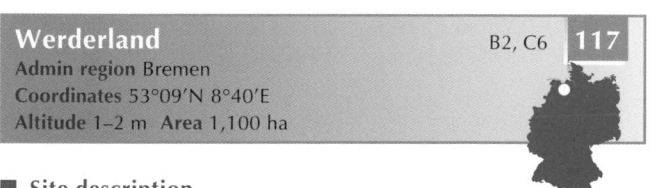

Blockland– lower Wümme valley– Westliches Hollerland
A4i, B1i, B2, C2, C6 **116**

Admin region Bremen
Coordinates 53°08′N 8°50′E
Altitude 0–2 m **Area** 3,503 ha

■ Site description

The site includes the Bremer section of the Wümmemarsch, an extensive grassland traversed by numerous drainage ditches. Habitats include wet forest and areas of scrub and reed *Phragmites*.

Habitats Forest and woodland (5%; alluvial/very wet forest), Grassland (80%; humid grassland), Wetland (15%; tidal river/enclosed tidal water; standing fresh water; river/stream; water-fringe vegetation)
Land-use Agriculture (80%), Hunting (80%), Nature conservation/research (20%), Tourism/recreation (10%), Water management (15%)

■ Birds

Species	Season	Year	Pop min	Pop max	Acc	Criteria
Cygnus columbianus Bewick's Swan	P	1993	392	392	A	A4i, B1i, C2
¹ *Limosa limosa* Black-tailed Godwit	B	1997	160	160	A	B2, C6

1. Large decrease 1994–1997

Species of global conservation concern that do not meet IBA criteria: *Crex crex* (breeding).

■ Protection status

National Partial **International** Partial
IBA overlaps with Landscape Protected Area and Nature Reserve. IBA overlaps with Special Protection Area.

■ Conservation issues

Threats Agricultural intensification/expansion (B), Disturbance to birds (B), Industrialization/urbanization (A), Infrastructure (A), Recreation/tourism (C)

Restrictions on agricultural practice in the Hollerland nature protection area have been highly beneficial for grassland birds.

Werderland
B2, C6 **117**

Admin region Bremen
Coordinates 53°09′N 8°40′E
Altitude 1–2 m **Area** 1,100 ha

■ Site description

The site is part of the Bremer wet-grassland belt (Bremer Wesermarsch) comprising agricultural meadows and pasture traversed by ditches. The Dunger See is the largest water-body in the area.

Habitats Scrub (10%; scrub), Grassland (80%; humid grassland), Wetland (10%; standing fresh water)
Land-use Agriculture (80%), Hunting, Nature conservation/research (30%), Tourism/recreation (30%)

■ Birds

Species	Season	Year	Pop min	Pop max	Acc	Criteria
¹ *Botaurus stellaris* Bittern	B	1996	1	12	A	B2, C6

1. 1991–1996.

This site is also important for breeding species of wet grassland. Species of global conservation concern that do not meet IBA criteria: *Crex crex* (breeding).

■ Protection status

National Partial **International** Partial
IBA overlaps with Landscape Protected Area and Nature Reserve. IBA overlaps with Special Protection Area.

■ Conservation issues

Threats Recreation/tourism (A)

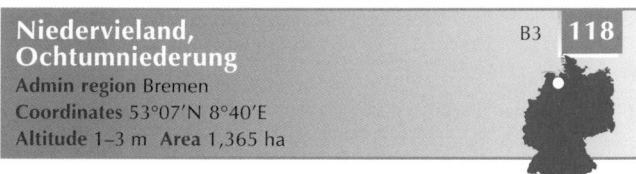

Niedervieland, Ochtumniederung
B3 **118**

Admin region Bremen
Coordinates 53°07′N 8°40′E
Altitude 1–3 m **Area** 1,365 ha

■ Site description

The site is part of the Bremer wet-grassland belt, comprising agricultural meadows and pasture traversed by ditches. Areas of reed *Phragmites* and wet scrub are found between the Senator-Appelt-Straße and Neustädter harbour.

Habitats Forest and woodland (5%; alluvial/very wet forest), Grassland (80%; humid grassland), Wetland (10%; tidal river/enclosed tidal water; water-fringe vegetation), Unknown (5%)
Land-use Agriculture (80%), Hunting, Nature conservation/research (20%), Not utilized (5%), Water management (10%)

■ Birds

Species	Season	Year	Pop min	Pop max	Acc	Criteria
Porzana porzana Spotted Crake	B	1997	20	30	A	B3

This site is also an important habitat for breeding and passage waterbirds and waders. Species of global conservation concern that do not meet IBA criteria: *Crex crex* (breeding).

■ Protection status

National Partial **International** Partial
IBA overlaps with Landscape Protected Area. IBA overlaps with Special Protection Area.

■ Conservation issues

Threats Industrialization/urbanization (B), Infrastructure (B)

The construction of polders and the diversion of the River Ochtum have been the focus of scientific study for the last 10 years. The designation of Ochtumniederung bei Brockhuchting (380 ha) as a Nature Protection Area is planned for the near future.

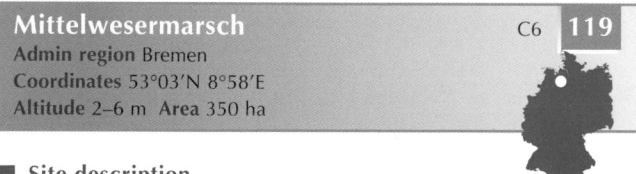

Mittelwesermarsch
C6 **119**

Admin region Bremen
Coordinates 53°03′N 8°58′E
Altitude 2–6 m **Area** 350 ha

■ Site description

The grasslands that surround the dykes of the Mittelwesermarsch and six flooded gravel-pits connected together by the River Weser. The grasslands often flood in spring.

Habitats Forest and woodland (10%; alluvial/very wet forest), Grassland (70%; humid grassland), Wetland (10%; standing fresh water), Unknown (10%)
Land-use Agriculture (70%), Fisheries/aquaculture (5%), Hunting, Nature conservation/research (10%), Water management (10%)

■ Birds

Species	Season	Year	Pop min	Pop max	Acc	Criteria
Cygnus cygnus Whooper Swan	W	1993	36	36	A	C6

This site is important for migrating waterbirds and waders.

■ Protection status

National Partial **International** None
IBA overlaps with Landscape Protected Area and Nature Reserve.

■ Conservation issues

Threats Industrialization/urbanization (A), Infrastructure (A)

Floating breeding platforms are provided for *Sterna hirundo*.

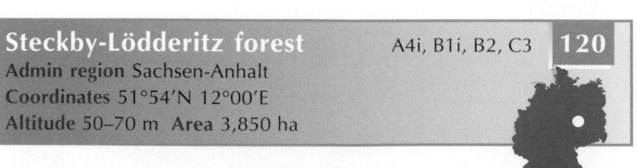

Steckby-Lödderitz forest   A4i, B1i, B2, C3 120
Admin region Sachsen-Anhalt
Coordinates 51°54′N 12°00′E
Altitude 50–70 m **Area** 3,850 ha

■ Site description

Habitats Forest and woodland (broadleaved deciduous forest; mixed forest; alluvial/very wet forest), Scrub (scrub), Grassland (humid grassland; mesophile grassland), Wetland (standing fresh water; river/stream; water-fringe vegetation; fen/transition mire/spring), Artificial landscape (highly improved reseeded grassland; arable land; forestry plantation; ruderal land)
Land-use Agriculture, Forestry, Nature conservation/research, Water management

■ Birds

Species	Season	Year	Pop min	Pop max	Acc	Criteria
[1] *Anser fabalis* Bean Goose	W	1995	—	10,000	A	A4i, B1i, C3
Aquila pomarina Lesser Spotted Eagle	B	1995	—	1	A	B2

1. 1991–1995.

Species of global conservation concern that do not meet IBA criteria: *Crex crex* (5 breeding pairs).

■ Protection status
National Partial **International** High
IBA overlaps with Nature Reserve. 3,850 ha of IBA covered by Biosphere Reserve (Middle Elbe Biosphere Reserve, 43,000 ha). IBA overlaps with Special Protection Area.

■ Conservation issues
A management plan exists for the Biosphere Reserve.

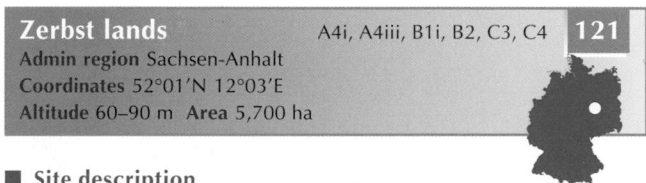

Zerbst lands   A4i, A4iii, B1i, B2, C3, C4 121
Admin region Sachsen-Anhalt
Coordinates 52°01′N 12°03′E
Altitude 60–90 m **Area** 5,700 ha

■ Site description
Predominantly arable land, with a few copses.

Habitats Forest and woodland (mixed forest), Scrub (scrub), Artificial landscape (arable land; forestry plantation; ruderal land), Unknown
Land-use Agriculture, Forestry, Nature conservation/research

■ Birds

Species	Season	Year	Pop min	Pop max	Acc	Criteria
[1] *Anser fabalis* Bean Goose	W	1995	—	20,000	A	A4i, B1i, C3
[1] *Anser albifrons* White-fronted Goose	P	1995	—	10,000	A	B1i, C3
[1,2] *Otis tarda* Great Bustard	R	1995	2	7	A	B2

1. 1991–1995.
2. Individuals

The site holds 20,000 or more waterbirds in winter, on a regular basis.

■ Protection status
National Partial **International** High
100 ha of IBA covered by Nature Reserve (Osterwesten, 100 ha). 5,000 ha of IBA covered by Landscape Protected Area (Zerbster Land, 5,000 ha). IBA overlaps with Special Protection Area.

■ Conservation issues

Threats Agricultural intensification/expansion (U)

There are extensification programmes and management plans for the area.

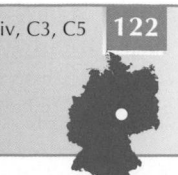

Helmestausee Berga–Kelbra   B1i, B1iv, C3, C5 122
Admin region Sachsen-Anhalt, Thüringen
Coordinates 51°26′N 11°00′E
Altitude 150–165 m **Area** 1,359 ha

■ Site description
A storage lake used for water management since 1967, sometimes dry in winter. It is surrounded by grassland with reeds *Phragmites*, scrub, and alluvial forest flooded by the River Helme.

Habitats Forest and woodland (alluvial/very wet forest), Scrub (5%; scrub), Grassland (9%; humid grassland; mesophile grassland), Wetland (21%; mudflat/sandflat; saltmarsh; standing fresh water; water-fringe vegetation), Artificial landscape (58%; highly improved reseeded grassland; arable land), Unknown (12%)
Land-use Agriculture (67%), Fisheries/aquaculture (13%), Hunting, Nature conservation/research (7%), Tourism/recreation (22%), Water management (30%)

■ Birds

Species	Season	Year	Pop min	Pop max	Acc	Criteria
Anas crecca Teal	P	1994	—	4,000	B	B1i, C3
[1] *Anas clypeata* Shoveler	P	1995	—	750	A	B1i, C3

1. 1991–1995.

The site is a migratory bottleneck, where up to 4,000 *Grus grus* regularly pass. Species of global conservation concern that do not meet IBA criteria: *Crex crex* (5 breeding pairs).

■ Protection status
National Partial **International** High
669 ha of IBA covered by Landscape Protected Area (Helmestausee, 1,717 ha). 669 ha of IBA covered by Nature Park (Kyffhäuser, 11,000 ha). IBA overlaps with Nature Reserve. 1,359 ha of IBA covered by Ramsar Site (Helmestausee Berga-Kelbra, 1,630 ha). IBA overlaps with Special Protection Area.

■ Conservation issues

Threats Agricultural intensification/expansion (A), Aquaculture/fisheries (A), Disturbance to birds (A), Drainage (U), Recreation/tourism (B)

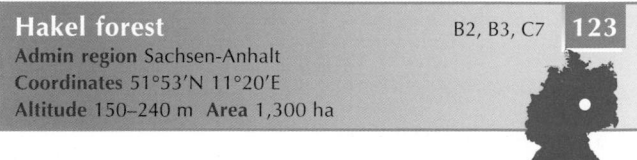

Hakel forest   B2, B3, C7 123
Admin region Sachsen-Anhalt
Coordinates 51°53′N 11°20′E
Altitude 150–240 m **Area** 1,300 ha

■ Site description
An area of mixed forest (predominantly *Tilia* and *Quercus* with some *Carpinus*) situated in the foothills of the Harz mountains and surrounded by arable land.

Habitats Forest and woodland (broadleaved deciduous forest; mixed forest), Scrub (scrub), Artificial landscape (arable land; forestry plantation)
Land-use Agriculture, Forestry, Nature conservation/research

■ Birds

Species	Season	Year	Pop min	Pop max	Acc	Criteria
[1] *Milvus milvus* Red Kite	B	1995	30	120	A	B3
[1] *Aquila pomarina* Lesser Spotted Eagle	B	1995	2	4	A	B2
[1] *Hieraaetus pennatus* Booted Eagle	B	1995	—	1	A	B2

1. 1991–1995.

This is an important site for breeding raptors and woodpeckers.

■ Protection status
National Partial **International** High
IBA overlaps with Landscape Protected Area and Nature Reserve. IBA overlaps with Special Protection Area.

■ Conservation issues

Threats Agricultural intensification/expansion (U), Intensified forest management (U)

Aland–Elbe lowlands

A4i, A4iii, B1i, B1iv, B3, C2, C3, C4, C5   **124**

Admin region Sachsen-Anhalt
Coordinates 53°00′N 11°37′E
Altitude 15–20 m **Area** 3,250 ha

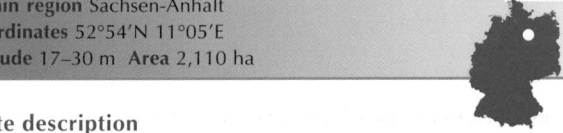

■ Site description
The flood-plain of the Rivers Aland and Elbe with grassland, standing water and alluvial forest.

Habitats Forest and woodland (alluvial/very wet forest), Scrub (scrub), Grassland (humid grassland; mesophile grassland), Wetland (standing fresh water; river/stream; water-fringe vegetation; fen/transition mire/spring), Artificial landscape (highly improved reseeded grassland; arable land; ruderal land)
Land-use Agriculture, Fisheries/aquaculture, Forestry, Nature conservation/research, Urban/industrial/transport, Water management

■ Birds

Species	Season	Year	Pop min	Pop max	Acc	Criteria
[1] *Cygnus columbianus* Bewick's Swan	P	1995	—	600	A	A4i, B1i, C2
[1] *Cygnus cygnus* Whooper Swan	W	1995	—	870	A	A4i, B1i, B3, C2
Anser fabalis Bean Goose	W	1995	—	10,000	A	A4i, B1i, C3
[1] *Anser albifrons* White-fronted Goose	P	1995	—	15,000	A	A4i, B1i, C3
[2] *Anas clypeata* Shoveler	P	1997	—	2,000	A	B1i, C3

1. 1991–1995.
2. 1991–1997.

The site holds 20,000 or more waterbirds on passage, on a regular basis. It is also a migratory bottleneck, where up to 5,000 *Grus grus* regularly pass. Breeding species of global conservation concern that do not meet IBA criteria: *Aythya nyroca* and *Crex crex* (2–6 pairs).

■ Protection status
National High **International** High
1,600 ha of IBA covered by Nature Reserve (Elbaue Beuster-Wahrenberg, 1,600 ha). 1,650 ha of IBA covered by Nature Reserve (Garbe-Aland-Niederung, 1,650 ha). IBA overlaps with Special Protection Area.

■ Conservation issues

Threats Agricultural intensification/expansion (U)

Designation of the area as a Ramsar Site is planned. There are management plans for the extensification of land-use and water management.

Drömling bird-protection area

A4i, B1i, C3   **125**

Admin region Sachsen-Anhalt
Coordinates 52°32′N 11°03′E
Altitude 50–60 m **Area** 27,821 ha

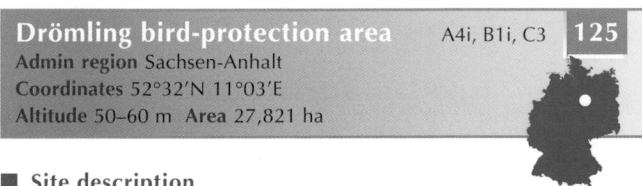

■ Site description
A diverse landscape including grasslands, wet meadows and riverine forest.

Habitats Forest and woodland (broadleaved deciduous forest; mixed forest; alluvial/very wet forest), Scrub (scrub), Grassland (humid grassland; mesophile grassland), Wetland (river/stream; water-fringe vegetation; fen/transition mire/spring), Artificial landscape (highly improved reseeded grassland; arable land; ruderal land)
Land-use Agriculture, Forestry, Nature conservation/research, Not utilized, Water management

■ Birds

Species	Season	Year	Pop min	Pop max	Acc	Criteria
[1] *Anser fabalis* Bean Goose	W	1995	—	15,000	A	A4i, B1i, C3

1. 1991–1995.

Species of global conservation concern that do not meet IBA criteria: *Crex crex* (1–6 breeding pairs).

■ Protection status
National Partial **International** High
5,800 ha of IBA covered by Nature Park (Drömling, 25,706 ha). Part of IBA overlaps with Special Protection Area (5,800 ha).

■ Conservation issues

Threats Agricultural intensification/expansion (U), Drainage (U), Intensified forest management (U)

There are programmes for land-use extensification and water management.

Landgraben-Dumme lowlands

C6   **126**

Admin region Sachsen-Anhalt
Coordinates 52°54′N 11°05′E
Altitude 17–30 m **Area** 2,110 ha

■ Site description
An area of transition mire with wet broadleaved deciduous forest and humid grassland

Habitats Forest and woodland (broadleaved deciduous forest; mixed forest; alluvial/very wet forest), Scrub (scrub), Grassland (humid grassland; mesophile grassland), Wetland (river/stream; water-fringe vegetation; fen/transition mire/spring), Artificial landscape (highly improved reseeded grassland; ruderal land)
Land-use Agriculture, Forestry, Nature conservation/research, Urban/industrial/transport

■ Birds

Species	Season	Year	Pop min	Pop max	Acc	Criteria
[1] *Ciconia nigra* Black Stork	B	1995	—	2	A	C6

1. 1991–1995.

This is an important area for breeding raptors, storks and *Grus grus*.

■ Protection status
National Partial **International** High
IBA overlaps with Nature Park. IBA overlaps with Special Protection Area.

■ Conservation issues

Threats Agricultural intensification/expansion (U), Drainage (U), Intensified forest management (U)

Improved protection and land-use extensification programmes are urgently needed.

Milde lowlands

B1i, C3   **127**

Admin region Sachsen-Anhalt
Coordinates 52°41′N 11°29′E
Altitude 25–30 m **Area** 1,500 ha

■ Site description
A large alluvial grassland with a few woodlands, partly flooded by the River Milde.

Habitats Forest and woodland (alluvial/very wet forest), Scrub (scrub), Grassland (humid grassland; mesophile grassland), Wetland (river/stream; water-fringe vegetation; fen/transition mire/spring), Artificial landscape (highly improved reseeded grassland; arable land; ruderal land)
Land-use Agriculture, Nature conservation/research, Tourism/recreation, Water management

■ Birds

Species	Season	Year	Pop min	Pop max	Acc	Criteria
[1] *Anser fabalis* Bean Goose	W	1995	—	3,000	A	B1i, C3

1. 1991–1995.

An important area for grassland birds. Species of global conservation concern that do not meet IBA criteria: *Crex crex* (breeding).

■ Protection status
National None **International** High
IBA overlaps with Special Protection Area.

■ Conservation issues

Threats Agricultural intensification/expansion (U), Drainage (U), Recreation/tourism (U), Unsustainable exploitation (U)

Improved protection and land-use extensification programmes are urgently needed.

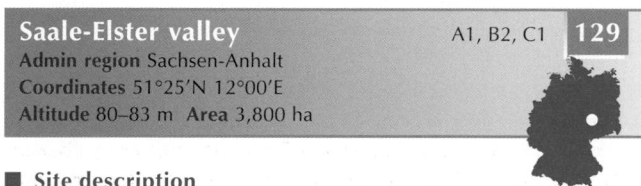

Elbe valley Jerichow
A4i, A4iii, B1i, C2, C3, C4 | 128
Admin region Sachsen-Anhalt
Coordinates 52°30′N 12°00′E
Altitude 29–35 m **Area** 4,800 ha

■ Site description
Extensive meadows in the Elbe valley with reeds *Phragmites*, scrub, flood-plain forest and Lake Schelldorf.

Habitats Forest and woodland (alluvial/very wet forest), Scrub (scrub), Grassland (humid grassland; mesophile grassland), Wetland (standing fresh water; river/stream; water-fringe vegetation; fen/transition mire/spring), Artificial landscape (highly improved reseeded grassland; arable land; ruderal land)
Land-use Agriculture, Fisheries/aquaculture, Nature conservation/research, Water management

■ Birds

Species	Season	Year	Pop min	Pop max	Acc	Criteria
¹ *Anser fabalis* Bean Goose	W	1995	—	21,000	B	A4i, B1i, C3
¹ *Anser albifrons* White-fronted Goose	P	1995	—	10,000	B	B1i, C3
¹ *Chlidonias niger* Black Tern	B	1995	20	70	B	C2

1. 1991–1995.

The site holds 20,000 or more waterbirds in winter, on a regular basis. Species of global conservation concern that do not meet IBA criteria: *Crex crex* (5–15 breeding pairs).

■ Protection status
National Partial **International** None
IBA overlaps with Nature Reserve (Bucher Brack–Bölsdorfer Haken, 1,000 ha).

■ Conservation issues

Threats Agricultural intensification/expansion (U), Recreation/tourism (U)

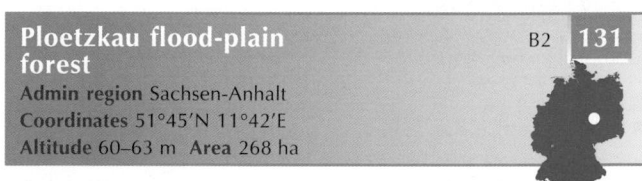

Saale-Elster valley
A1, B2, C1 | 129
Admin region Sachsen-Anhalt
Coordinates 51°25′N 12°00′E
Altitude 80–83 m **Area** 3,800 ha

■ Site description
The flood-plain of the Rivers Saale and Elster, including alluvial forest and wet meadows.

Habitats Forest and woodland (11%; alluvial/very wet forest), Grassland (43%; humid grassland; mesophile grassland), Wetland (10%; standing fresh water; river/stream; fen/transition mire/spring), Artificial landscape (37%; highly improved reseeded grassland; arable land; perennial crops/orchards/groves; other urban/industrial areas)
Land-use Agriculture (63%), Forestry (11%), Hunting, Nature conservation/research (26%), Not utilized (8%), Water management (5%)

■ Birds

Species	Season	Year	Pop min	Pop max	Acc	Criteria
¹ *Milvus migrans* Black Kite	B	1996	46	54	A	B2
¹ *Crex crex* Corncrake	B	1996	15	40	A	A1, C1

1. 1995–1996.

Two hundred and fifty-two species have been recorded. The site holds high densities of raptors. Species of global conservation concern that do not meet IBA criteria: *Aythya nyroca* (resident and passage), *Otis tarda* (passage) and *Acrocephalus paludicola* (passage).

■ Protection status
National Partial **International** None
IBA overlaps with Nature Reserve (820 ha).

■ Conservation issues
Improved protection is urgently needed.

Threats Abandonment/reduction of land management (B), Afforestation (U), Agricultural intensification/expansion (B), Aquaculture/fisheries (C), Construction/impact of dyke/dam/barrage (C), Disturbance to birds (B), Drainage (B), Groundwater abstraction (B), Infrastructure (A)

Wulfen meadows
A4i, A4iii, B1i, C3, C4, C6 | 130
Admin region Sachsen-Anhalt
Coordinates 51°51′N 11°57′E
Altitude 50–60 m **Area** 1,500 ha

■ Site description
Large meadows with arable land in the Landgraben-Taube lowland area. The site also includes the Neolith pond and the Diebziger forest.

Habitats Forest and woodland (broadleaved deciduous forest; mixed forest; alluvial/very wet forest), Scrub (scrub), Grassland (humid grassland; mesophile grassland), Wetland (standing fresh water; river/stream; water-fringe vegetation; fen/transition mire/spring), Artificial landscape (highly improved reseeded grassland; arable land; forestry plantation; ruderal land)
Land-use Agriculture, Fisheries/aquaculture, Forestry, Hunting, Nature conservation/research, Tourism/recreation, Water management

■ Birds

Species	Season	Year	Pop min	Pop max	Acc	Criteria
¹ *Ixobrychus minutus* Little Bittern	B	1992	—	3	A	C6
¹ *Anser fabalis* Bean Goose	W	1992	10,000	30,000	A	A4i, B1i, C3

1. 1991–1995.

The site holds 20,000 or more waterbirds in winter, on a regular basis. Species of global conservation concern that do not meet IBA criteria: *Crex crex* (2–5 breeding pairs).

■ Protection status
National Partial **International** None
IBA overlaps with three Nature Reserves (Neolith pond, 101 ha; Diebzig forest, 374 ha; Wulfen meadows, 430 ha).

■ Conservation issues

Threats Agricultural intensification/expansion (U), Consequences of animal/plant introductions (U), Disturbance to birds (U), Drainage (U), Groundwater abstraction (U)

Part of the site is managed by NABU. A water management plan is needed.

Ploetzkau flood-plain forest
B2 | 131
Admin region Sachsen-Anhalt
Coordinates 51°45′N 11°42′E
Altitude 60–63 m **Area** 268 ha

■ Site description
Alluvial forest along the River Saale with previous river courses and large reedbeds (*Phragmites*).

Habitats Forest and woodland (mixed forest; alluvial/very wet forest), Scrub (scrub), Wetland (standing fresh water; river/stream; water-fringe vegetation; fen/transition mire/spring), Artificial landscape (forestry plantation; ruderal land)
Land-use Forestry, Nature conservation/research, Not utilized, Water management

■ Birds

Species	Season	Year	Pop min	Pop max	Acc	Criteria
¹ *Aquila pomarina* Lesser Spotted Eagle	B	1993	—	1	A	B2

1. 1991–1995.

This is an important site for breeding raptors and herons.

■ Protection status
National Partial **International** None
IBA overlaps with Nature Reserve (268 ha).

■ Conservation issues

Threats Agricultural intensification/expansion (U), Extraction industry (U), Infrastructure (U), Recreation/tourism (U)

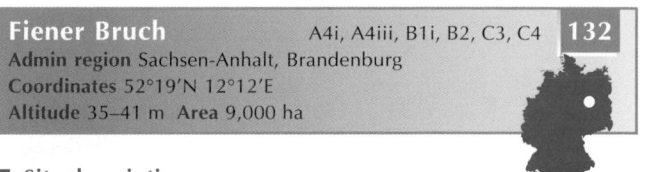

Fiener Bruch — A4i, A4iii, B1i, B2, C3, C4 — 132
Admin region Sachsen-Anhalt, Brandenburg
Coordinates 52°19'N 12°12'E
Altitude 35–41 m **Area** 9,000 ha

■ Site description
A large bog in the lowland area of the Baruther Urstromtal with inland dunes, reedbeds (*Phragmites*), wet forest and a widespread system of ditches.

Habitats Grassland (17%; humid grassland; mesophile grassland), Wetland (90%; fen/transition mire/spring), Artificial landscape (60%; highly improved reseeded grassland; arable land; ruderal land)
Land-use Agriculture (95%), Nature conservation/research (20%), Tourism/recreation (30%)

■ Birds

Species		Season	Year	Pop min	Pop max	Acc	Criteria
Anser fabalis	Bean Goose	W	1997	1,000	—	—	B1i, C3
Anser fabalis	Bean Goose	P	1997	5,000	15,000	—	A4i, B1i, C3
Anser albifrons	White-fronted Goose	P	1997	8,000	15,000	—	A4i, B1i, C3
Asio flammeus	Short-eared Owl	R	1998	2	3	—	B2

One of the three sites in Germany for *Otis tarda*. The site regularly holds 20,000 or more waterbirds on passage. Species of global conservation concern that do not meet IBA criteria: *Crex crex* (5 breeding pairs) and *Otis tarda* (10–11 birds).

■ Protection status
National Low **International** None
143 ha of IBA covered by Nature Reserve (Fiener Bruch, 143 ha).

■ Conservation issues

Threats Agricultural intensification/expansion (U), Drainage (U)

There are land-use extensification, water-management and predator-control programmes. 1,700 ha are covered by an *Otis tarda* protection area.

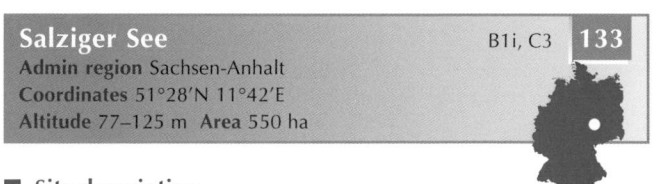

Salziger See — B1i, C3 — 133
Admin region Sachsen-Anhalt
Coordinates 51°28'N 11°42'E
Altitude 77–125 m **Area** 550 ha

■ Site description
The IBA is the site of a former large lake, drained at the beginning of the 20th century. Standing fresh water, reedbeds (*Phragmites*) and wet ruderal areas exist with arable land on higher sites.

Habitats Grassland (humid grassland), Wetland (standing fresh water; water-fringe vegetation), Artificial landscape (arable land; ruderal land)
Land-use Agriculture, Nature conservation/research, Water management

■ Birds

Species		Season	Year	Pop min	Pop max	Acc	Criteria
Anser fabalis	Bean Goose	P	1997	3,000	3,500	—	B1i, C3

The site is important for breeding and roosting waterbirds.

■ Protection status
National Partial **International** None
448 ha of IBA covered by Nature Reserve (Salziger See, 448 ha).

■ Conservation issues

Threats Agricultural intensification/expansion (U)

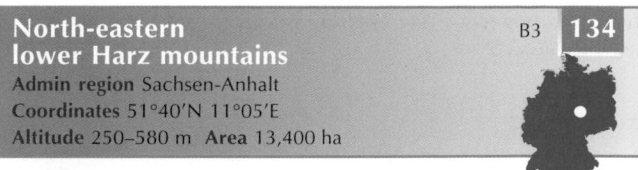

North-eastern lower Harz mountains — B3 — 134
Admin region Sachsen-Anhalt
Coordinates 51°40'N 11°05'E
Altitude 250–580 m **Area** 13,400 ha

■ Site description
The lower part of the mountainous area of Harz, with predominantly semi-natural broadleaved forests.

Habitats Forest and woodland (broadleaved deciduous forest; mixed forest; alluvial/very wet forest), Scrub (scrub; heathland), Wetland (river/stream; water-fringe vegetation; fen/transition mire/spring), Rocky areas (scree/boulders; caves), Artificial landscape (forestry plantation)
Land-use Forestry, Hunting, Nature conservation/research, Not utilized, Tourism/recreation, Water management

■ Birds

Species		Season	Year	Pop min	Pop max	Acc	Criteria
Dendrocopos medius	Middle Spotted Woodpecker	R	1995	120	150	A	B3

This is an important site for hole-nesting species.

■ Protection status
National Partial **International** None
IBA overlaps with Nature Reserves.

■ Conservation issues

Threats Extraction industry (U), Infrastructure (U), Intensified forest management (U)

There are existing grassland-management programmes. There are plans to construct reservoirs in the area.

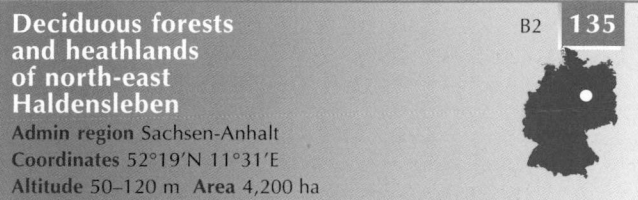

Deciduous forests and heathlands of north-east Haldensleben — B2 — 135
Admin region Sachsen-Anhalt
Coordinates 52°19'N 11°31'E
Altitude 50–120 m **Area** 4,200 ha

■ Site description
A complex of semi-natural deciduous forests, dominated by *Quercus, Tilia* and *Carpinus* with many caves, conifer forests and large open areas. Open areas comprise dry grassland, *Calluna* heaths and bare areas. Water-filled depressions and damp areas enrich the site. It is a military training area.

Habitats Forest and woodland (broadleaved deciduous forest; mixed forest), Scrub (scrub; heathland), Grassland (dry siliceous grassland), Wetland (standing fresh water; fen/transition mire/spring), Artificial landscape (forestry plantation)
Land-use Forestry, Military (100%), Tourism/recreation, Water management

■ Birds

Species		Season	Year	Pop min	Pop max	Acc	Criteria
Caprimulgus europaeus	Nightjar	B	—	40	—	—	B2

The site is important for species characteristic of heathlands. Species of global conservation concern that do not meet IBA criteria: *Crex crex* (passage).

■ Protection status
National Low **International** None
180 ha of IBA covered by Nature Reserve (Colbitzer Lindenwald NSG, 180 ha).

■ Conservation issues

Threats Abandonment/reduction of land management (B), Afforestation (B), Groundwater abstraction (B), Intensified forest management (B)

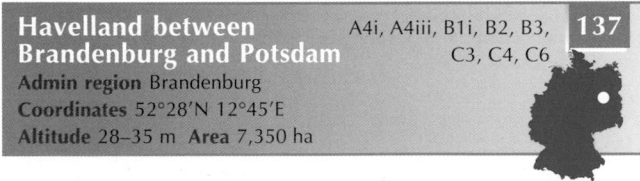

Spreewald A4i, B1i, B2, B3, C3 136
Admin region Brandenburg
Coordinates 51°59′N 13°59′E
Altitude 43–88 m **Area** 35,000 ha

■ Site description
A heterogeneous, sparsely populated lowland landscape with many water-bodies.

Habitats Forest and woodland (25%; broadleaved deciduous forest; mixed forest; alluvial/very wet forest), Scrub (scrub), Grassland (15%; humid grassland), Wetland (8%; standing fresh water; river/stream; raised bog; water-fringe vegetation; fen/transition mire/spring), Rocky areas (inland sand-dunes), Artificial landscape (52%; highly improved reseeded grassland; arable land; perennial crops/orchards/groves; forestry plantation; urban parks/gardens; other urban/industrial areas; ruderal land)
Land-use Agriculture (52%), Fisheries/aquaculture (8%), Forestry (15%), Hunting (100%), Nature conservation/research (20%), Tourism/recreation (90%), Urban/industrial/ transport (5%), Water management (8%)

■ Birds

Species	Season	Year	Pop min	Pop max	Acc	Criteria
Ciconia ciconia White Stork	B	1996	—	80	A	B2
Anser fabalis Bean Goose	P	1997	—	5,000	—	A4i, B1i, C3
¹*Porzana porzana* Spotted Crake	B	1993	76	—	A	B3
Dendrocopos medius Middle Spotted Woodpecker	R	1997	100	170	B	B3

1. Large increase.

Species of global conservation concern that do not meet IBA criteria: *Crex crex* (10 calling males).

■ Protection status
National High **International** Partial
IBA overlaps with Landscape Protected Area and Nature Reserve. IBA overlaps with Biosphere Reserve.

■ Conservation issues

Threats Abandonment/reduction of land management (C), Agricultural intensification/ expansion (A), Construction/impact of dyke/dam/barrage (A), Disturbance to birds (C), Drainage (A), Dredging/canalization (C), Filling-in of wetlands (C), Groundwater abstraction (B), Intensified forest management (A), Recreation/tourism (A), Unsustainable exploitation (A)

There is an EU-funded project to restore and encourage extensive use of the small water-bodies. NABU owns 100 ha of important humid grassland (KV Lübben Spreewald).

Havelland between Brandenburg and Potsdam A4i, A4iii, B1i, B2, B3, C3, C4, C6 137
Admin region Brandenburg
Coordinates 52°28′N 12°45′E
Altitude 28–35 m **Area** 7,350 ha

■ Site description
Part of the flood-plain of the River Havel, comprising swamp and alluvial forests, humid grasslands, bogs, reedbeds (*Phragmites*) and clay pits.

Habitats Forest and woodland (alluvial/very wet forest), Scrub (scrub), Grassland (humid grassland), Wetland (river/stream; raised bog; water-fringe vegetation)
Land-use Agriculture

■ Birds

Species	Season	Year	Pop min	Pop max	Acc	Criteria
Botaurus stellaris Bittern	R	1997	5	10	A	B2, C6
Anser fabalis Bean Goose	P	1997	—	25,000	—	A4i, B1i, C3
Anser albifrons White-fronted Goose	P	1997	—	25,000	—	A4i, B1i, C3
¹*Locustella luscinioides* Savi's Warbler	B	1996	100	130	B	B3

1. Large increase.

The site holds more than 20,000 passage waterbirds, on a regular basis. Species of global conservation concern that do not meet IBA criteria: *Crex crex* (breeding).

■ Protection status
National None **International** High
IBA overlaps with Nature Reserve. IBA overlaps with Special Protection Area.

■ Conservation issues

Threats Agricultural intensification/expansion (U), Dredging/canalization (A)

Threats include the enlargement of the Havel for shipping.

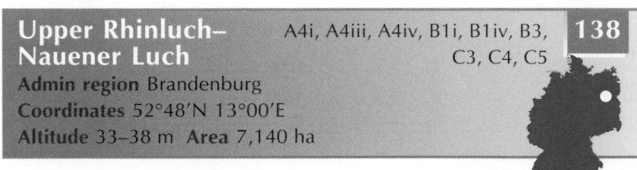

Upper Rhinluch–Nauener Luch A4i, A4iii, A4iv, B1i, B1iv, B3, C3, C4, C5 138
Admin region Brandenburg
Coordinates 52°48′N 13°00′E
Altitude 33–38 m **Area** 7,140 ha

■ Site description
An area of wet grassland and alkaline fen with associated sand islands, the former being extensively grazed by cattle. One sand island in the Nauener Luch holds 28 ha of sewage-sludge ponds.

Habitats Forest and woodland (9%; alluvial/very wet forest), Scrub (5%; scrub), Grassland (67%; humid grassland), Wetland (93%; standing fresh water; water-fringe vegetation; fen/transition mire/spring), Artificial landscape (5%; highly improved reseeded grassland; arable land)
Land-use Agriculture (70%), Fisheries/aquaculture (5%), Forestry, Hunting (95%), Nature conservation/research (15%), Water management (100%)

■ Birds

Species	Season	Year	Pop min	Pop max	Acc	Criteria
Anser fabalis Bean Goose	P	1997	—	12,500	—	A4i, B1i, C3
Anser albifrons White-fronted Goose	P	1997	—	12,500	—	A4i, B1i, C3
Anas clypeata Shoveler	P	1997	—	550	—	B1i, C3
Locustella luscinioides Savi's Warbler	B	1997	—	47	A	B3

The site holds more than 20,000 passage waterbirds, on a regular basis, and is also a major migratory bottleneck site, where up to 32,000 *Grus grus* regularly pass. Species of global conservation concern that do not meet IBA criteria: *Crex crex* (4–6 breeding pairs) and *Otis tarda* (resident).

■ Protection status
National Partial **International** High
IBA overlaps with Nature Reserve.

■ Conservation issues

Threats Agricultural intensification/expansion (B), Construction/impact of dyke/dam/ barrage (B), Disturbance to birds (B), Drainage (A), Groundwater abstraction (A), Infrastructure (B), Recreation/tourism (B)

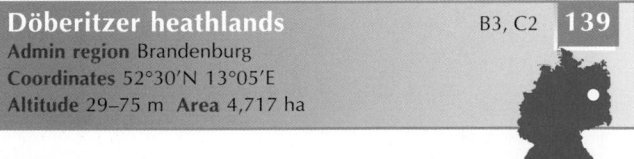

Döberitzer heathlands B3, C2 139
Admin region Brandenburg
Coordinates 52°30′N 13°05′E
Altitude 29–75 m **Area** 4,717 ha

■ Site description
A mosaic of heathland, dry sandy grassland, wetland and ruderal land. Access to some areas is still restricted following years of use as a military training area. Human activities include extensive sheep-grazing.

Habitats Forest and woodland (53%; broadleaved deciduous forest), Scrub (14%; scrub; heathland), Grassland (19%; dry siliceous grassland), Wetland (5%; raised bog), Artificial landscape (7%; ruderal land)
Land-use Agriculture, Nature conservation/research (100%)

■ Birds

Species	Season	Year	Pop min	Pop max	Acc	Criteria
Sylvia nisoria Barred Warbler	B	1997	265	—	—	B3, C2

Species of global conservation concern that do not meet IBA criteria: *Aythya nyroca* (non-breeding) and *Crex crex* (breeding).

■ **Protection status**
National Partial **International** High
4,000 ha of IBA covered by Nature Reserve (Döberitzer Heide and Ferbitzer Bruch, 4,000 ha). IBA overlaps with Special Protection Area.

■ **Conservation issues**

Threats Agricultural intensification/expansion (C), Disturbance to birds (C), Industrialization/urbanization (B), Recreation/tourism (B)

Rietzer See | A4iii, B1i, B3, C3, C4 | 140
Admin region Brandenburg
Coordinates 52°22'N 12°39'E
Altitude 29–30 m **Area** 1,134 ha

■ **Site description**
A shallow, nutrient-rich lake with large areas of reedbed (*Phragmites*), surrounded by meadows and cultivated land.

Habitats Grassland (19%; humid grassland), Wetland (75%; standing fresh water; raised bog; water-fringe vegetation; fen/transition mire/spring)
Land-use Agriculture (60%), Hunting (50%), Nature conservation/research (100%), Tourism/recreation (10%), Water management (50%)

■ **Birds**

Species	Season	Year	Pop min	Pop max	Acc	Criteria
Anser fabalis Bean Goose	P	1997	—	3,000	—	B1i, C3
[1] *Anser albifrons* White-fronted Goose	P	1997	—	12,000	A	B1i, C3
Anser anser Greylag Goose	P	1997	—	2,400	—	B1i, C3
Locustella luscinioides Savi's Warbler	B	1997	70	100	—	B3

1. Large increase.

The site holds more than 20,000 passage waterbirds on a regular basis. Species of global conservation concern that do not meet IBA criteria: *Crex crex* (breeding).

■ **Protection status**
National High **International** High
IBA overlaps with Nature Reserve. IBA overlaps with Special Protection Area.

■ **Conservation issues**

Threats Abandonment/reduction of land management (U)

There is a programme of non-intensive land-use. Unchecked vegetation growth is adversely affecting wader breeding habitats.

Peitz and Bärenbrück ponds, and Lasszins meadows | A4iii, B1i, C3, C4 | 141
Admin region Brandenburg
Coordinates 51°51'N 14°25'E
Altitude 60–60 m **Area** 1,556 ha

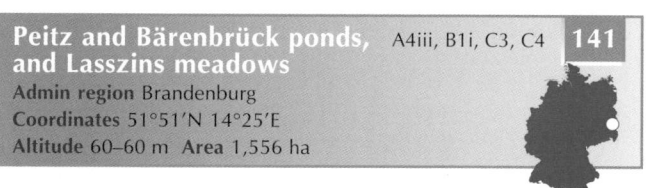

■ **Site description**
The IBA, north of Cottbus, comprises 39 seasonal fish-ponds (depth 0.8–1.2 m). The ponds are fed by the River Spree.

Habitats Grassland (humid grassland), Wetland (standing fresh water)
Land-use Fisheries/aquaculture (80%), Hunting (100%), Tourism/recreation

■ **Birds**

Species	Season	Year	Pop min	Pop max	Acc	Criteria
Anser fabalis Bean Goose	P	1997	1,000	5,000	—	B1i, C3
Anser albifrons White-fronted Goose	P	1997	1,000	5,000	—	B1i, C3

The site holds 20,000 or waterbirds on passage, on a regular basis. Species of global conservation concern that do not meet IBA criteria: *Crex crex* (7–8 breeding pairs).

■ **Protection status**
National Partial **International** High

IBA overlaps with Nature Reserve. IBA overlaps with Ramsar Site and Special Protection Area.

■ **Conservation issues**

Threats Abandonment/reduction of land management (U), Aquaculture/fisheries (U), Disturbance to birds (U), Extraction industry (U), Groundwater abstraction (U), Recreation/tourism (U), Unsustainable exploitation (U)

Phalacrocorax carbo are shot.

Lower Oder valley | A1, A4i, A4iii, B1i, B1iv, B2, B3, C1, C2, C3, C4, C5 | 142
Admin region Brandenburg
Coordinates 53°04'N 14°19'E
Altitude 1–50 m **Area** 12,017 ha

■ **Site description**
A large embanked river and shipping canal (Talaue der Oder), flowing south–north through a moraine landscape. The banks are vegetated with reed *Phragmites* and herbaceous growth; the surrounds are polders subject to flooding during high tides. Human activities include shipping, intensive grassland cultivation and arable production.

Habitats Forest and woodland (alluvial/very wet forest); Grassland (humid grassland), Wetland (river/stream; water-fringe vegetation), Artificial landscape (arable land)
Land-use Agriculture, Fisheries/aquaculture, Hunting, Urban/industrial/transport

■ **Birds**

Species	Season	Year	Pop min	Pop max	Acc	Criteria
Cygnus cygnus Whooper Swan	P	1998	—	1,500	—	A4i, B1i, C2
Anser fabalis Bean Goose	P	1994	—	28,300	—	A4i, B1i, C3
Anser albifrons White-fronted Goose	P	1994	—	40,000	—	A4i, B1i, C3
Anser anser Greylag Goose	P	1997	—	3,800	—	A4i, B1i, C3
Anas penelope Wigeon	P	1997	—	15,300	—	B1i, C3
Anas crecca Teal	P	1997	—	9,000	—	B1i, C3
Anas clypeata Shoveler	P	1997	—	3,200	—	B1i, C3
Aquila pomarina Lesser Spotted Eagle	B	1997	1	2	—	B2
Porzana porzana Spotted Crake	B	1997	20	70	—	B3
Crex crex Corncrake	B	1997	150	200	—	A1, C1, C2
Grus grus Crane	B	1997	20	25	—	B2
Grus grus Crane	P	—	8,500	8,500	—	A4i, B1i, C2
Chlidonias niger Black Tern	B	1996	150	200	—	B2, C2
Locustella luscinioides Savi's Warbler	B	1997	80	130	—	B3
Acrocephalus paludicola Aquatic Warbler	B	1996	36	—	—	A1, B2, C1, C2
Sylvia nisoria Barred Warbler	B	1997	150	—	—	B3, C2

The site holds the highest density of breeding *Crex crex* in Germany, and is one of only two breeding sites for *Acrocephalus paludicola*. The site regularly holds 20,000 or more waterbirds, and the site is a migratory bottleneck, where 8,500 *Grus grus* reglarly pass.

■ **Protection status**
National Partial **International** High
IBA overlaps with Landscape Protected Area and National Park. IBA overlaps with Ramsar Site and Special Protection Area.

■ **Conservation issues**

Threats Agricultural intensification/expansion (U), Infrastructure (U), Recreation/tourism (U)

Threats include sport fishing and tourism development.

Schorfheide–Chorin | A1, A4i, A4iii, B1i, B1iv, B2, B3, C1, C2, C3, C4, C5, C6 | 143
Admin region Brandenburg
Coordinates 53°04'N 13°40'E
Altitude 20–170 m **Area** 42,700 ha

■ **Site description**
The area is a mosaic of moraine lakes, reedbeds (*Phragmites*), fens, peatbogs and forest.

Habitats Forest and woodland, Wetland (standing fresh water; raised bog; water-fringe vegetation; fen/transition mire/spring)
Land-use Agriculture, Fisheries/aquaculture, Forestry, Hunting, Tourism/recreation

Birds

Species	Season	Year	Pop min	Pop max	Acc	Criteria
Botaurus stellaris Bittern	R	1997	5	15	—	B2, C2, C6
Ciconia nigra Black Stork	B	1997	4	6	—	B2
Ciconia ciconia White Stork	B	1997	40	60	—	B2
Anser fabalis Bean Goose	P	1997	15,000	25,000	—	A4i, B1i, C3
Anser albifrons White-fronted Goose	P	1997	15,000	25,000	—	A4i, B1i, C3
Haliaeetus albicilla White-tailed Eagle	R	1997	10	11	—	A1, B2, C1
Aquila pomarina Lesser Spotted Eagle	B	1997	4	6	—	B2
Pandion haliaetus Osprey	B	1997	23	28	—	B2
Crex crex Corncrake	B	1997	10	20	—	A1, C1
Grus grus Crane	B	1997	150	180	—	B2
Chlidonias niger Black Tern	B	1997	40	60	—	B2, C2
Caprimulgus europaeus Nightjar	B	1997	30	60	—	B2
Alcedo atthis Kingfisher	R	1997	40	80	—	B2
Dendrocopos medius Middle Spotted Woodpecker	R	1997	70	100	—	B3
Sylvia nisoria Barred Warbler	B	1997	150	250	—	B3, C2
Ficedula parva Red-breasted Flycatcher	B	1997	100	200	—	C6

The site regularly holds more than 20,000 passage waterbirds, and is a migratory bottleneck site—up to 3,000 *Grus grus* regularly pass. Species of global conservation concern that do not meet IBA criteria: *Otis tarda* (breeding).

Protection status
National None **International** High
IBA overlaps with Biosphere Reserve (Schorfheide–Chorin) and Special Protection Area.

Conservation issues

Threats Recreation/tourism (U), Intensified forest management (U)

Deichvorland Oderbruch   A1, B2, B3, C1, C2   144
Admin region Brandenburg
Coordinates 52°38′N 14°30′E
Altitude 1–16 m Area 3,916 ha

Site description
A mainly agricultural area situated between Frankfurt and Güstebieser Loose, on either side of the River Oder embankment.

Habitats Forest and woodland (alluvial/very wet forest), Grassland (humid grassland), Wetland (water-fringe vegetation), Artificial landscape (arable land)
Land-use Agriculture

Birds

Species	Season	Year	Pop min	Pop max	Acc	Criteria
Crex crex Corncrake	B	1996	20	—	—	A1, C1
Chlidonias niger Black Tern	B	1996	70	—	—	B2, C2
Sylvia nisoria Barred Warbler	B	1997	200	—	—	B3, C2

Protection status
National None **International** High
IBA overlaps with Special Protection Area.

Conservation issues

Threats Agricultural intensification/expansion (U), Dredging/canalization (U)

The main threats are river enlargement and agricultural intensification.

Lower Rhinluch–Lake Dreetz–   A1, A4i, A4iii, B1i,   145
Havelländisches Luch–   B2, C1, C3, C4
Belziger Landschaftswiesen
Admin region Brandenburg
Coordinates 52°31′N 12°35′E
Altitude 24–46 m Area 13,989 ha

Site description
An area of flood-plain meadows and pastures dissected by ditches, with a few deciduous trees and bushes. The IBA has three separate parts: Belziger Landschaftswiesen (Bustard Protection Area), Havelländisches Luch, and Unteres Rhinluch/Dreetzer See.

Habitats Forest and woodland (alluvial/very wet forest), Grassland (humid grassland), Wetland (standing fresh water; river/stream)
Land-use Agriculture, Fisheries/aquaculture, Hunting, Tourism/recreation

Birds

Species	Season	Year	Pop min	Pop max	Acc	Criteria
Anser fabalis Bean Goose	P	1997	—	35,000	—	A4i, B1i, C3
Anser albifrons White-fronted Goose	P	1997	—	35,000	—	A4i, B1i, C3
[1] *Otis tarda* Great Bustard	R	1997	46	—	—	A1, B2, C1

1. Individuals

Approximately 80% of the German *Otis tarda* population occurs in the site. The site holds more than 20,000 passage waterbirds on a regular basis. Species of global conservation concern that do not meet IBA criteria: *Crex crex* (5–16 breeding pairs).

Protection status
National Partial **International** High
IBA overlaps with Nature Reserve. IBA overlaps with Special Protection Area.

Conservation issues

Threats Agricultural intensification/expansion (U)

The land is intensively cultivated resulting in some adverse ecological changes.

Uckermärkische Seenlandschaft   A1, B2, B3,   146
Admin region Brandenburg   C1, C6
Coordinates 53°15′N 13°30′E
Altitude 45–128 m Area 54,667 ha

Site description
An area with a great variety of habitats including forests, lakes, fens and natural rivers.

Habitats Forest and woodland (alluvial/very wet forest), Wetland (standing fresh water; river/stream; fen/transition mire/spring)
Land-use Agriculture, Fisheries/aquaculture, Forestry, Hunting, Tourism/recreation

Birds

Species	Season	Year	Pop min	Pop max	Acc	Criteria
Botaurus stellaris Bittern	R	1997	10	—	—	B2, C6
Ciconia nigra Black Stork	B	1997	4	6	—	B2
Milvus migrans Black Kite	B	1997	11	50	—	B2
Haliaeetus albicilla White-tailed Eagle	R	1997	8	10	—	A1, B2, C1
Aquila pomarina Lesser Spotted Eagle	B	1997	3	5	—	B2
Pandion haliaetus Osprey	B	1997	15	20	—	B2
Grus grus Crane	B	1997	40	—	—	B2
Dendrocopos medius Middle Spotted Woodpecker	R	1997	51	100	—	B3
Lullula arborea Woodlark	B	1997	101	250	—	B2

Species of global conservation concern that do not meet IBA criteria: *Crex crex* (3–5 breeding pairs).

Protection status
National Partial **International** None
IBA overlaps with Nature Reserve. IBA overlaps with Special Protection Area.

Conservation issues

Threats Afforestation (U), Intensified forest management (U)

Protection of more areas within the IBA is planned.

Stechlin   B2, C7   147
Admin region Brandenburg
Coordinates 53°09′N 13°00′E
Altitude 36–86 m Area 7,928 ha

Site description
Forest interspersed with numerous lakes and fen habitats.

Habitats Forest and woodland, Wetland (standing fresh water; fen/transition mire/spring)
Land-use Fisheries/aquaculture, Forestry, Hunting, Tourism/recreation

■ **Birds**

Species	Season	Year	Pop min	Pop max	Acc	Criteria
Milvus migrans Black Kite	B	1997	11	30	—	B2
Pandion haliaetus Osprey	B	1997	12	—	—	B2
Grus grus Crane	B	1997	15	—	—	B2

This is an important site for forest species.

■ **Protection status**
National Partial **International** High
IBA overlaps with Nature Reserve. IBA overlaps with Special Protection Area.

■ **Conservation issues**

Threats Intensified forest management (U), Recreation/tourism (U)

Tourism adversely affects parts of the IBA.

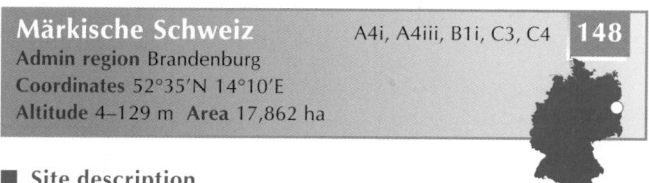

Märkische Schweiz
A4i, A4iii, B1i, C3, C4 — 148
Admin region Brandenburg
Coordinates 52°35′N 14°10′E
Altitude 4–129 m **Area** 17,862 ha

■ **Site description**
A glacial landscape that includes a range of forest-types, lakes, the Altfriedland fish-ponds, and streams.

Habitats Forest and woodland, Wetland (standing fresh water)
Land-use Agriculture, Fisheries/aquaculture, Forestry, Hunting, Tourism/recreation

■ **Birds**

Species	Season	Year	Pop min	Pop max	Acc	Criteria
Anser fabalis Bean Goose	P	1997	—	10,000	—	A4i, B1i, C3
Anser albifrons White-fronted Goose	P	1997	—	10,000	—	A4i, B1i, C3

The site holds more than 20,000 passage waterbirds on a regular basis.

■ **Protection status**
National Partial **International** High
IBA overlaps with Nature Park. IBA overlaps with Special Protection Area.

■ **Conservation issues**

Threats Recreation/tourism (U)

Disturbance due to tourism is a problem in some areas. There are management plans for waders and ducks.

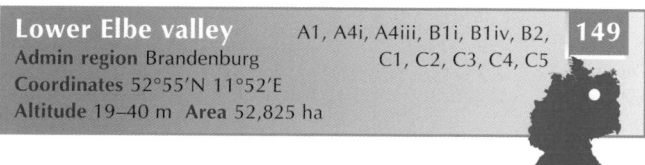

Lower Elbe valley
A1, A4i, A4iii, B1i, B1iv, B2, C1, C2, C3, C4, C5 — 149
Admin region Brandenburg
Coordinates 52°55′N 11°52′E
Altitude 19–40 m **Area** 52,825 ha

■ **Site description**
Humid grasslands (pastures and meadows) along the River Elbe, interspersed with ditches, reedbeds (*Phragmites*) and arable land.

Habitats Forest and woodland (alluvial/very wet forest), Grassland (humid grassland), Wetland (standing fresh water; river/stream; water-fringe vegetation), Artificial landscape (arable land)
Land-use Agriculture, Fisheries/aquaculture, Forestry, Hunting

■ **Birds**

Species	Season	Year	Pop min	Pop max	Acc	Criteria
Ciconia ciconia White Stork	B	1997	120	150	—	B2
Cygnus columbianus Bewick's Swan	P	1997	—	3,000	—	A4i, B1i, C2
Cygnus cygnus Whooper Swan	P	1997	—	1,500	—	A4i, B1i, C2

Species ... continued	Season	Year	Pop min	Pop max	Acc	Criteria
Anser fabalis Bean Goose	P	1997	—	17,500	—	A4i, B1i, C3
Anser albifrons White-fronted Goose	P	1997	—	17,500	—	A4i, B1i, C3
Pandion haliaetus Osprey	B	1997	5	7	—	B2
Crex crex Corncrake	B	1997	5	20	—	A1, C1

The site holds more than 20,000 passage waterbirds on a regular basis, and is also a migratory bottleneck site, where up to 4,000 *Grus grus* regularly pass.

■ **Protection status**
National None **International** High
IBA overlaps with Biosphere Reserve and Special Protection Area.

■ **Conservation issues**

Threats Infrastructure (U), Recreation/tourism (U)

The enlargement of the Elbe is a threat.

Former military training area east and west of Jüterbog
B2, B3, C2 — 150
Admin region Brandenburg
Coordinates 52°02′N 13°10′E
Altitude 50–178 m **Area** 20,200 ha

■ **Site description**
A glacial landscape supporting habitats typical of sandy lowlands. Heathland and scrub, dry siliceous grassland and various forest-types are present along with mires, peatbogs and areas of standing fresh water.

Habitats Forest and woodland (6%; broadleaved deciduous forest; native coniferous forest; mixed forest; alluvial/very wet forest), Scrub (75%; heathland), Grassland (dry siliceous grassland), Artificial landscape (13%; highly improved reseeded grassland; arable land; forestry plantation; ruderal land)
Land-use Forestry (5%), Hunting (60%), Nature conservation/research (50%), Tourism/recreation (10%)

■ **Birds**

Species	Season	Year	Pop min	Pop max	Acc	Criteria
Caprimulgus europaeus Nightjar	B	1997	270	320	—	B2
Lullula arborea Woodlark	B	1997	250	300	—	B2
Sylvia nisoria Barred Warbler	B	1997	100	150	—	B3, C2

■ **Protection status**
National Partial **International** High
IBA overlaps with Nature Park and Nature Reserve.

■ **Conservation issues**

Threats Afforestation (U), Infrastructure (U)

Conservation programmes exist in the IBA.

Lower Havel–Lake Schollene–Lake Gülpe
A1, A4i, A4iii, B1i, B1iv, B2, B3, C1, C2, C3, C4, C5, C6 — 151
Admin region Sachsen-Anhalt, Brandenburg
Coordinates 52°48′N 12°11′E
Altitude 23–30 m **Area** 13,890 ha

■ **Site description**
A large area of flood-plain, subject to irregular flooding by the River Havel, with *Salix* bushes, remnant alluvial forest, levees and the Schollener, Gülper and Pritzerber lakes.

Habitats Forest and woodland (broadleaved deciduous forest; mixed forest; alluvial/very wet forest), Scrub (scrub), Grassland (humid grassland; mesophile grassland), Wetland (standing fresh water; river/stream; raised bog; water-fringe vegetation; fen/transition mire/spring), Artificial landscape (highly improved reseeded grassland; arable land; forestry plantation; ruderal land)
Land-use Agriculture, Forestry, Hunting, Nature conservation/research, Urban/industrial/transport, Water management

■ Birds

Species		Season	Year	Pop min	Pop max	Acc	Criteria
Botaurus stellaris	Bittern	B	1997	6	13	A	B2, C6
Ciconia ciconia	White Stork	B	1997	30	35	A	B2
Cygnus columbianus	Bewick's Swan	W	1997	—	450	A	A4i, B1i, B2, C2
Cygnus cygnus	Whooper Swan	W	1997	—	1,200	A	A4i, B1i, B3, C2
Anser fabalis	Bean Goose	P	1997	—	60,000	A	A4i, B1i, C3
Anser albifrons	White-fronted Goose	P	1997	—	60,000	—	A4i, B1i, C3
Anser anser	Greylag Goose	P	1997	—	10,000	A	A4i, B1i, C3
Anas clypeata	Shoveler	P	1997	—	1,700	—	B1i, C3
Porzana porzana	Spotted Crake	B	1997	10	25	A	B3
Crex crex	Corncrake	B	1997	20	45	A	A1, C1, C2
Grus grus	Crane	B	1997	15	20	A	B2
Chlidonias niger	Black Tern	B	1997	100	140	A	B2, C2
Locustella luscinioides	Savi's Warbler	B	1997	70	110	—	B3

The IBA is important as a stop-over site for passage wildfowl particularly geese (over 100,000 individuals), as well as being a migratory bottleneck, where up to 8,000 *Grus grus* regularly pass. Species of global conservation concern that do not meet IBA criteria: *Aythya nyroca* (non-breeding).

■ Protection status
National Partial **International** High
362 ha of IBA covered by Nature Reserve (Stremel NSG, 362 ha). Part of IBA covered by Nature Reserve (Pritzberber See). 2,850 ha of IBA covered by Landscape Protected Area (Untere Havel, 21,940 ha). IBA overlaps with Ramsar Site. IBA overlaps with Special Protection Area.

■ Conservation issues

Threats Infrastructure (U)

Die Bänke an der Müggelspree C2 152
Admin region Berlin
Coordinates 52°26′N 13°41′E
Altitude 32–32 m **Area** 16 ha

■ Site description
The Bänke is a mesotrophic tributary of the River Müggelspree and is gradually silting up. Reedbeds (*Phragmites*) are present.

Habitats Wetland (100%; standing fresh water; water-fringe vegetation)
Land-use Fisheries/aquaculture (100%), Tourism/recreation (80%), Urban/industrial/transport (40%), Water management (100%)

■ Birds

Species		Season	Year	Pop min	Pop max	Acc	Criteria
[1] *Chlidonias niger*	Black Tern	B	1997	31	37	A	C2

1. Large increase 1985–1991.

■ Protection status
National High **International** High
16 ha of IBA covered by Landscape Protected Area (Müggelspree, 126 ha). IBA overlaps with Special Protection Area.

■ Conservation issues

Threats Aquaculture/fisheries (B), Disturbance to birds (A), Industrialization/urbanization (A), Recreation/tourism (A)

Floating breeding platforms are provided for *Chlidonias niger*.

Niers valley B2 153
Admin region Nordrhein-Westfalen
Coordinates 51°17′N 6°24′E
Altitude 29–38 m **Area** 1,971 ha

■ Site description
A low-lying area associated with the River Niers. A variety of habitats occur including wet grassland (much of which has been drained), *Populus*, *Quercus* and *Fagus* forests in addition to wet forest. The main human activity is agriculture.

Habitats Forest and woodland (25%; broadleaved deciduous forest; alluvial/very wet forest), Grassland (55%; humid grassland), Wetland (15%; standing fresh water; river/stream; fen/transition mire/spring), Artificial landscape (5%; ruderal land)
Land-use Agriculture (80%), Forestry (20%), Water management (5%)

■ Birds

Species		Season	Year	Pop min	Pop max	Acc	Criteria
Athene noctua	Little Owl	R	1996	50	80	—	B2

■ Protection status
National Partial **International** None
IBA overlaps with Nature Park and Nature Reserve.

■ Conservation issues

Threats Agricultural intensification/expansion (A), Construction/impact of dyke/dam/barrage (U), Disturbance to birds (C), Drainage (A), Dredging/canalization (B), Filling-in of wetlands (C), Groundwater abstraction (C), Industrialization/urbanization (C), Infrastructure (U), Intensified forest management (B), Recreation/tourism (C)

Schwalm–Nette–Platte and Grenzwald B2, C7 154
Admin region Nordrhein-Westfalen
Coordinates 51°14′N 6°13′E
Altitude 45–75 m **Area** 9,968 ha

■ Site description
The valleys of the Schwalm and Nette rivers, comprising *Pinus* forest, wet forest, heathland, wet grassland, lakes, sand-dunes and bog.

Habitats Forest and woodland (74%; broadleaved deciduous forest; alluvial/very wet forest), Scrub (5%; heathland), Grassland (9%; humid grassland), Wetland (12%; standing fresh water; river/stream; fen/transition mire/spring)
Land-use Agriculture (5%), Forestry (74%), Hunting (100%), Nature conservation/research (5%), Tourism/recreation (5%)

■ Birds

Species		Season	Year	Pop min	Pop max	Acc	Criteria
Riparia riparia	Sand Martin	B	1995	—	800	—	B2

■ Protection status
National Partial **International** Partial
IBA overlaps with Nature Reserves. IBA overlaps with Special Protection Area.

■ Conservation issues

Threats Abandonment/reduction of land management (B), Agricultural intensification/expansion (A), Disturbance to birds (C), Drainage (C), Dredging/canalization (A), Filling-in of wetlands (C), Groundwater abstraction (C), Industrialization/urbanization (B), Infrastructure (U), Intensified forest management (B), Other (U), Recreation/tourism (C)

Threats include water pollution ('Other' threat), river/stream regulation, and vegetation succession.

Bogs and heathlands of the Westmünsterland B1i, C3 155
Admin region Nordrhein-Westfalen
Coordinates 52°10′N 6°54′E
Altitude 26–47 m **Area** 4,030 ha

■ Site description
Two areas (3,650 ha and 380 ha) of raised bog, wet heathland and humid grassland. The main human activity is agriculture.

Habitats Forest and woodland (10%; broadleaved deciduous forest; alluvial/very wet forest), Scrub (heathland), Grassland (20%; humid grassland), Wetland (70%; raised bog; fen/transition mire/spring)

Land-use Agriculture (20%), Forestry (10%), Hunting (10%), Nature conservation/research (30%), Tourism/recreation (30%)

■ Birds

Species	Season	Year	Pop min	Pop max	Acc	Criteria
Limosa limosa Black-tailed Godwit	P	1988	3,650	— —		B1i, C3

Species of global conservation concern that do not meet IBA criteria: *Crex crex* (breeding).

■ Protection status
National None **International** Partial
IBA overlaps with Special Protection Area.

■ Conservation issues

Threats Abandonment/reduction of land management (B), Agricultural intensification/expansion (A), Disturbance to birds (B), Drainage (B), Extraction industry (B), Groundwater abstraction (A), Infrastructure (B), Recreation/tourism (C)

Management includes the maintenance and restoration of bogs and heathlands and the extensification of agriculture.

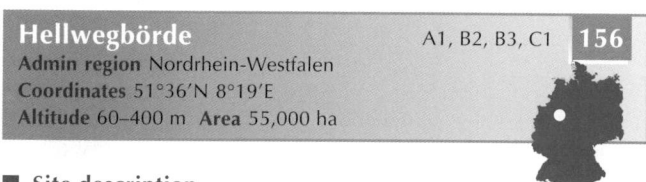

Hellwegbörde
A1, B2, B3, C1 **156**
Admin region Nordrhein-Westfalen
Coordinates 51°36′N 8°19′E
Altitude 60–400 m **Area** 55,000 ha

■ Site description
Arable land with dry valleys and native broadleaved deciduous forest.

Habitats Forest and woodland (10%; broadleaved deciduous forest), Artificial landscape (90%; highly improved reseeded grassland; arable land; perennial crops/orchards/groves; forestry plantation)
Land-use Agriculture (90%), Forestry (10%)

■ Birds

Species	Season	Year	Pop min	Pop max	Acc	Criteria
¹ *Circus pygargus* Montagu's Harrier	B	1996	45	50	A	B3
¹ *Falco tinnunculus* Kestrel	R	1996	70	200	A	B2
¹ *Perdix perdix* Partridge	R	1996	450	550	B	B2
¹ *Crex crex* Corncrake	B	1996	10	20	B	A1, C1
¹ *Tyto alba* Barn Owl	R	1996	30	100	A	B2
¹ *Athene noctua* Little Owl	R	1996	70	90	A	B2

1. 1993–1996.

Species of global conservation concern that do not meet IBA criteria: *Otis tarda* (10 wintering individuals).

■ Protection status
National None **International** None

■ Conservation issues

Threats Afforestation (C), Agricultural intensification/expansion (A), Disturbance to birds (B), Extraction industry (A), Industrialization/urbanization (A), Infrastructure (B), Intensified forest management (C), Recreation/tourism (B)

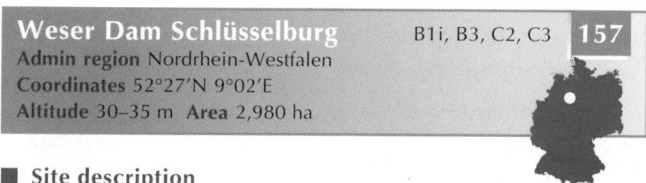

Weser Dam Schlüsselburg
B1i, B3, C2, C3 **157**
Admin region Nordrhein-Westfalen
Coordinates 52°27′N 9°02′E
Altitude 30–35 m **Area** 2,980 ha

■ Site description
A 25-km long section of the embanked River Weser. The valley is dominated by meadows, gravel-pits and arable land.

Habitats Grassland (20%; humid grassland), Wetland (25%; standing fresh water; river/stream), Artificial landscape (55%; highly improved reseeded grassland; arable land; ruderal land)
Land-use Agriculture (70%), Fisheries/aquaculture (15%), Hunting (90%), Military (100%), Nature conservation/research (30%), Tourism/recreation (90%), Urban/industrial/transport (5%), Water management (10%)

■ Birds

Species	Season	Year	Pop min	Pop max	Acc	Criteria
¹ *Cygnus cygnus* Whooper Swan	W	1996	384	—	A	B1i, B3, C2
¹ *Anser fabalis* Bean Goose	W	1996	—	1,000	A	B1i, C3
² *Aythya ferina* Pochard	W	1996	100	4,800	A	B1i, C3

1. Large increase.
2. Large decrease.

The area is also nationally important as an inland wintering site for *Bucephala clangula*.

■ Protection status
National None **International** High
IBA overlaps with Ramsar Site and Special Protection Area.

■ Conservation issues

Threats Agricultural intensification/expansion (A), Aquaculture/fisheries (B), Construction/impact of dyke/dam/barrage (B), Disturbance to birds (A), Dredging/canalization (A), Extraction industry (A), Industrialization/urbanization (B), Recreation/tourism (A)

Disturbance to birds from work on the river course, hunting, and military training are the most important threats to the IBA. There are plans to open up the Weser meadow for recreational use.

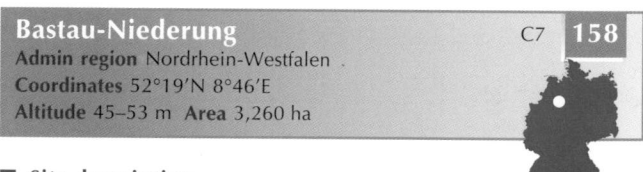

Bastau-Niederung
C7 **158**
Admin region Nordrhein-Westfalen
Coordinates 52°19′N 8°46′E
Altitude 45–53 m **Area** 3,260 ha

■ Site description
Wet grassland and bog in the valley of a tributary of the River Weser.

Habitats Forest and woodland (10%; broadleaved deciduous forest; alluvial/very wet forest), Wetland (6%; fen/transition mire/spring), Artificial landscape (80%; highly improved reseeded grassland)
Land-use Agriculture, Tourism/recreation

■ Protection status
National Partial **International** None
IBA overlaps with Nature Reserves.

■ Conservation issues

Threats Abandonment/reduction of land management (C), Agricultural intensification/expansion (A), Drainage (A), Recreation/tourism (B)

The site is adversely affected by agricultural intensification and drainage. Wet grassland and bog habitats are being re-created.

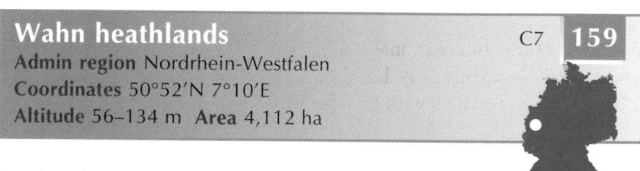

Wahn heathlands
C7 **159**
Admin region Nordrhein-Westfalen
Coordinates 50°52′N 7°10′E
Altitude 56–134 m **Area** 4,112 ha

■ Site description
The site contains a range of habitats including *Pinus*, *Quercus* and wet forest, heathland, small bogs, standing fresh water and streams. There is an airport and the area is used for military purposes.

Habitats Forest and woodland (80%; broadleaved deciduous forest; native coniferous forest; mixed forest; alluvial/very wet forest), Scrub (12%; scrub; heathland), Wetland (6%; standing fresh water; river/stream; fen/transition mire/spring)
Land-use Forestry (50%), Hunting (80%), Military (70%), Nature conservation/research (55%), Tourism/recreation (55%), Urban/industrial/transport (35%), Water management (35%)

■ Birds
One hundred and seventy species have been recorded with 95 species breeding regularly. This is an important site for species associated with mixed woodland, heathland and open habitats, including *Caprimulgus europaeus* (up to 4 breeding pairs), *Dendrocopos medius* (32–35 breeding pairs) and *Lullula arborea* (up to 46 breeding pairs).

■ **Protection status**
National Partial **International** None
IBA overlaps with Nature Reserves.

■ **Conservation issues**

Threats Abandonment/reduction of land management (A), Afforestation (C), Drainage (A), Groundwater abstraction (C), Industrialization/urbanization (A), Infrastructure (A), Recreation/tourism (A)

The main threats are the expansion of the airport and the demise of traditional land-uses.

Lower Rhine area
160
A1, A4i, A4iii, B1i, B2, C1, C2, C3, C4, C6
Admin region Nordrhein-Westfalen
Coordinates 51°46′N 6°24′E
Altitude 9–30 m **Area** 48,000 ha

■ **Site description**
A low-lying area around the River Rhine, predominantly humid grassland. An anthropogenic landscape with hedgerows and pollarded *Salix* trees, and a dyked area in the north of the IBA.

Habitats Grassland (55%; humid grassland), Wetland (15%; standing fresh water; river/stream), Artificial landscape (27%; arable land; urban parks/gardens)
Land-use Agriculture (80%), Hunting, Nature conservation/research (5%), Tourism/recreation (25%), Urban/industrial/transport (20%)

■ **Birds**

Species	Season	Year	Pop min	Pop max	Acc	Criteria
[1] *Phalacrocorax carbo* Cormorant	W	1997	500	4,000	A	B1i, C3
[2] *Cygnus columbianus* Bewick's Swan	W	1997	50	300	A	A4i, B1i, B2, C2
[2] *Anser fabalis* Bean Goose	W	1997	7,000	45,000	A	A4i, B1i, C3
Anser albifrons White-fronted Goose	W	1997	120,000	180,000	A	A4i, B1i, C3
Anser anser Greylag Goose	W	1997	800	2,200	A	B1i, C3
Branta leucopsis Barnacle Goose	W	1997	80	350	A	B2
Anas clypeata Shoveler	W	1997	300	600	A	B1i, C3
Perdix perdix Partridge	R	1997	200	400	A	B2
[2] *Crex crex* Corncrake	B	1997	5	20	A	A1, C1
[2] *Vanellus vanellus* Lapwing	W	1997	30,000	100,000	A	A4i, B1i, C3
[2] *Limosa limosa* Black-tailed Godwit	B	1997	100	270	A	B2, C6
Numenius arquata Curlew	W	1997	100	500	A	B2
Athene noctua Little Owl	R	1997	400	600	A	B2

1. Large increase.
2. Large decrease.

This is an important passage and wintering area for waterbirds, particularly geese. The site regularly holds 20,000 or more waterbirds in winter. Species of global conservation concern that do not meet IBA criteria: *Anser erythropus* (wintering), *Branta ruficollis* (wintering).

■ **Protection status**
National None **International** Partial
IBA overlaps with Ramsar Site and Special Protection Area.

■ **Conservation issues**

Threats Abandonment/reduction of land management (C), Agricultural intensification/expansion (A), Construction/impact of dyke/dam/barrage (B), Disturbance to birds (A), Drainage (A), Dredging/canalization (B), Extraction industry (A), Filling-in of wetlands (C), Groundwater abstraction (A), Industrialization/urbanization (A), Infrastructure (A), Recreation/tourism (B), Selective logging/cutting (C), Unsustainable exploitation (A)

The main threats are the intensification of agriculture and urbanization of the landscape.

Heubachniederung/ Schwarzes Venn/Borkenberge/ Halterner Seen
161
B1i, B2, C3
Admin region Nordrhein-Westfalen
Coordinates 51°48′N 7°08′E
Altitude 39–134 m **Area** 6,000 ha

■ **Site description**
The IBA includes humid grassland, bog, dry and wet heathland,

---

broadleaved deciduous forest, rivers, streams and two reservoirs. Traditional uses of heathland are maintained.

Habitats Forest and woodland (broadleaved deciduous forest; alluvial/very wet forest), Scrub (heathland), Grassland (humid grassland), Wetland (river/stream; raised bog; fen/transition mire/spring), Rocky areas (inland sand-dunes)
Land-use Agriculture, Fisheries/aquaculture, Military, Tourism/recreation

■ **Birds**

Species	Season	Year	Pop min	Pop max	Acc	Criteria
Phalacrocorax carbo Cormorant	W	1998	1,300	—	—	B1i, C3
Caprimulgus europaeus Nightjar	B	1992	60	—	—	B2

Species of global conservation concern that do not meet IBA criteria: *Crex crex* (breeding).

■ **Protection status**
National Partial **International** None
IBA overlaps with Nature Reserves.

■ **Conservation issues**

Threats Agricultural intensification/expansion (A), Aquaculture/fisheries (B), Drainage (B), Dredging/canalization (B), Extraction industry (B), Infrastructure (B), Recreation/tourism (B)

Sewage farms of Münster
162
B1i, C3
Admin region Nordrhein-Westfalen
Coordinates 52°02′N 7°39′E
Altitude 48–51 m **Area** 435 ha

■ **Site description**
An artificial wetland situated near to the town of Münster (the fields were used for disposing of treated sewage). Reeds *Phragmites* are present along with broadleaved forest (*Quercus* and *Betula*).

Habitats Forest and woodland (11%; broadleaved deciduous forest; mixed forest; alluvial/very wet forest), Grassland (20%; humid grassland), Wetland (62%; mudflat/sandflat; standing fresh water; water-fringe vegetation; fen/transition mire/spring), Artificial landscape (7%; other urban/industrial areas; ruderal land)
Land-use Agriculture (20%), Nature conservation/research (100%), Tourism/recreation (30%), Water management (75%)

■ **Birds**

Species	Season	Year	Pop min	Pop max	Acc	Criteria
Anas clypeata Shoveler	P	1992	650	—	A	B1i, C3

■ **Protection status**
National Partial **International** High
IBA overlaps with Nature Reserve. 233 ha of IBA covered by Ramsar Site (Rieselfelder Münster, 233 ha). IBA overlaps with Special Protection Area.

■ **Conservation issues**

Threats Disturbance to birds (B), Infrastructure (B), Recreation/tourism (B)

There is an ongoing LIFE project to ensure effective management of the Special Protection Area.

Recker Moor/Düsterdieker Niederung/Seester Feld
163
C6
Admin region Nordrhein-Westfalen
Coordinates 52°22′N 7°52′E
Altitude 47–72 m **Area** 2,700 ha

■ **Site description**
The IBA contains lakes, humid grassland and a wetland area.

Habitats Forest and woodland (mixed forest; alluvial/very wet forest), Scrub (15%; heathland), Grassland (humid grassland)
Land-use Agriculture, Military, Tourism/recreation

■ Birds

Species	Season	Year	Pop min	Pop max	Acc	Criteria
¹ *Crex crex* Corncrake	B	1998	8	8	A	C6

1. Calling males

■ Protection status

National Partial **International** None
IBA overlaps with Nature Reserves.

■ Conservation issues

Threats Agricultural intensification/expansion (A), Drainage (B), Dredging/canalization (C), Recreation/tourism (B)

The site has been proposed as an Special Protection Area.

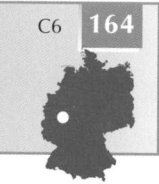

Meadows and forests around Burbach   C6 164

Admin region Nordrhein-Westfalen
Coordinates 50°44'N 8°04'E
Altitude 300–610 m **Area** 4,280 ha

■ Site description

Most of the site is extensively used grassland, with surrounding woodland and forests. Woodland is traditionally used.

Habitats Forest and woodland (65%; broadleaved deciduous forest; mixed forest; alluvial/very wet forest), Scrub (5%; scrub; heathland), Grassland (25%; dry siliceous grassland; humid grassland; mesophile grassland), Artificial landscape (10%; arable land; perennial crops/orchards/groves; forestry plantation; urban parks/gardens; other urban/industrial areas; ruderal land)
Land-use Agriculture (25%), Forestry (65%), Hunting (85%), Urban/industrial/transport (10%)

■ Birds

Species	Season	Year	Pop min	Pop max	Acc	Criteria
Ciconia nigra Black Stork	B	1997	1	1	A	C6

Species of global conservation concern that do not meet IBA criteria: *Crex crex* (breeding).

■ Protection status

National Partial **International** None
IBA overlaps with Nature Reserves.

■ Conservation issues

Threats Abandonment/reduction of land management (C), Afforestation (C), Agricultural intensification/expansion (C), Aquaculture/fisheries (C), Drainage (C), Infrastructure (A), Industrialization/urbanization (B), Recreation/tourism (C)

The main threat is an extension to the airport in the IBA.

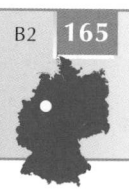

Emsaue (Rietberger Emsniederung–Steinhorster Becken)   B2 165

Admin region Nordrhein-Westfalen
Coordinates 51°48'N 8°30'E
Altitude 79–91 m **Area** 1,200 ha

■ Site description

A low-lying area around the River Ems with wetland, humid grassland and wet forest. There are also old ponds with reed *Phragmites*.

Habitats Forest and woodland (6%), Grassland (20%; humid grassland), Wetland (9%; standing fresh water; river/stream; water-fringe vegetation), Artificial landscape (65%; highly improved reseeded grassland; arable land)
Land-use Agriculture, Other, Water management

■ Birds

Species	Season	Year	Pop min	Pop max	Acc	Criteria
Riparia riparia Sand Martin	B	1992	8,548	—	—	B2

This is an important site for passage and breeding waterbirds, and for wintering swans and geese.

■ Protection status

National Partial **International** None
IBA overlaps with Nature Reserves.

■ Conservation issues

Threats Agricultural intensification/expansion (A), Drainage (B)

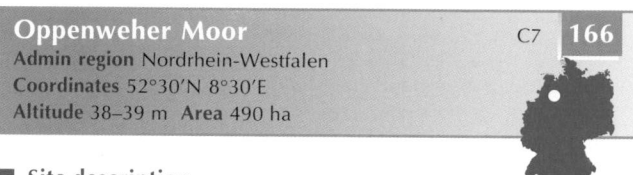

Oppenweher Moor   C7 166

Admin region Nordrhein-Westfalen
Coordinates 52°30'N 8°30'E
Altitude 38–39 m **Area** 490 ha

■ Site description

An area of raised bog adversely affected by intensive agriculture in the past. However, there is a good chance for restoration. The site also includes grassland and heathland habitats.

Habitats Scrub (14%; heathland), Grassland (20%; humid grassland), Wetland (60%; raised bog)
Land-use Agriculture, Other

■ Birds

Criterion C7 has been applied as the site is an officially proposed Special Protection Area and full bird data are not available. The site holds *Circus cyaneus* (20 wintering), *Asio flammeus* (breeding and wintering), and *Gallinago gallinago* (15 breeding pairs).

■ Protection status

National High **International** None
490 ha of IBA covered by Nature Reserve.

■ Conservation issues

Threats Abandonment/reduction of land management (A), Infrastructure (B)

The site is a proposed Special Protection Area.

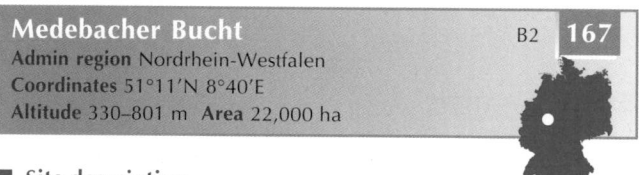

Medebacher Bucht   B2 167

Admin region Nordrhein-Westfalen
Coordinates 51°11'N 8°40'E
Altitude 330–801 m **Area** 22,000 ha

■ Site description

An anthropogenic landscape with mainly extensively-used grasslands, broadleaved deciduous and conifer forests, and rivers and streams.

Habitats Forest and woodland (55%; broadleaved deciduous forest), Scrub (scrub), Grassland (30%), Wetland (river/stream), Artificial landscape (5%; other urban/industrial areas)
Land-use Agriculture (39%), Forestry (55%)

■ Birds

Species	Season	Year	Pop min	Pop max	Acc	Criteria
Ciconia nigra Black Stork	B	1992	3	5	—	B2
Lanius excubitor Great Grey Shrike	R	1992	35	35	—	B2

Species of global conservation concern that do not meet IBA criteria: *Crex crex* (breeding).

■ Protection status

National Partial **International** None
IBA overlaps with Nature Reserves.

■ Conservation issues

Threats Abandonment/reduction of land management (C), Afforestation (A), Agricultural intensification/expansion (A), Drainage (C), Groundwater abstraction (C), Industrialization/urbanization (B), Infrastructure (C), Other (B), Recreation/tourism (B)

Sennelager training area | B2 | 168

Admin region Nordrhein-Westfalen
Coordinates 51°52'N 8°46'E
Altitude 115–255 m **Area** 12,000 ha

■ Site description
A heathland with bogs and inland dunes, dry grassland, rivers and wet woodland. It has been used for military purposes for about 100 years.

Habitats Forest and woodland (57%; broadleaved deciduous forest; native coniferous forest; alluvial/very wet forest), Scrub (17%; heathland), Grassland (15%; dry siliceous grassland; humid grassland), Wetland (6%; standing fresh water; river/stream; raised bog; fen/transition mire/spring), Rocky areas (5%; inland sand-dunes)
Land-use Forestry, Hunting, Military, Water management

■ Birds

Species	Season	Year	Pop min	Pop max	Acc	Criteria
Caprimulgus europaeus Nightjar	B	1992	60	—	—	B2

■ Protection status
National None **International** None

■ Conservation issues

Threats Drainage (B), Other (U)

The main threat is the conclusion of military use of the site and a change to other uses, including urban and infrastructure developments ('Other' threat, above).

Möhnesee | C7 | 169

Admin region Nordrhein-Westfalen
Coordinates 51°29'N 8°08'E
Altitude 213–236 m **Area** 1,200 ha

■ Site description
A dammed water-body with water-fringe vegetation.

Habitats Wetland (standing fresh water; river/stream; water-fringe vegetation)
Land-use Water management

■ Protection status
National None **International** High
IBA overlaps with Special Protection Area.

■ Conservation issues

Threats Disturbance to birds (C)

Kellerwald | B2, B3 | 170

Admin region Hessen
Coordinates 51°03'N 9°00'E
Altitude 238–675 m **Area** 31,000 ha

■ Site description
An upland area, 60% of which is forest, intersected with streams.

Habitats Forest and woodland (broadleaved deciduous forest; mixed forest), Scrub (scrub), Grassland (humid grassland), Wetland (river/stream), Rocky areas (scree/boulders), Artificial landscape (arable land; perennial crops/orchards/groves; ruderal land)
Land-use Agriculture, Forestry, Nature conservation/research, Tourism/recreation

■ Birds

Species	Season	Year	Pop min	Pop max	Acc	Criteria
Ciconia nigra Black Stork	B	1998	3	5	A	B2
Milvus milvus Red Kite	B	1998	100	125	B	B3

This is an important site for breeding raptors, *Ciconia ciconia* and hole-nesting species.

■ Protection status
National Low **International** None
1,100 ha of IBA covered by Nature Reserve.

■ Conservation issues

Threats Abandonment/reduction of land management (U), Afforestation (U), Disturbance to birds (U), Infrastructure (U), Intensified forest management (U), Recreation/tourism (U)

NABU has proposed the establishment of a National Park in the area.

Burgwald | C6 | 171

Admin region Hessen
Coordinates 51°00'N 8°50'E
Altitude 229–443 m **Area** 23,000 ha

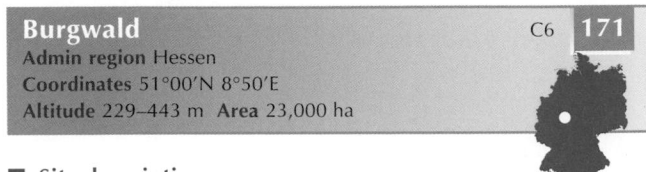

■ Site description
A large area of forest with areas of non-intensive agriculture, streams and a bog.

Habitats Forest and woodland (broadleaved deciduous forest; mixed forest), Scrub (scrub), Grassland (humid grassland), Wetland (raised bog; fen/transition mire/spring), Artificial landscape (arable land)
Land-use Agriculture, Forestry, Nature conservation/research

■ Birds

Species	Season	Year	Pop min	Pop max	Acc	Criteria
Ciconia nigra Black Stork	B	1998	1	3	A	C6

This is an important area for breeding forest species.

■ Protection status
National None **International** None

■ Conservation issues

Threats Abandonment/reduction of land management (U), Intensified forest management (U), Other (U), Recreation/tourism (U)

Vogelsberg | A4iv, B1iv, B2, B3, C5 | 172

Admin region Hessen
Coordinates 50°33'N 9°15'E
Altitude 259–773 m **Area** 47,000 ha

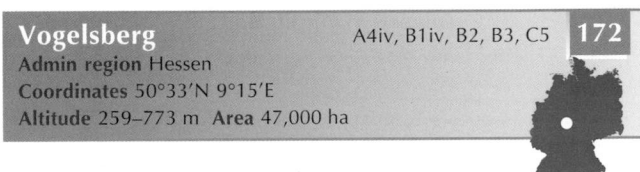

■ Site description
The Vogelsberg has a mix of wooded and open habitats. The woodland is dominated by *Pinus*.

Habitats Forest and woodland (native coniferous forest); Grassland
Land-use Agriculture

■ Birds

Species	Season	Year	Pop min	Pop max	Acc	Criteria
Ciconia nigra Black Stork	B	1998	3	5	A	B2
Milvus milvus Red Kite	B	1998	100	140	B	B3
Picus canus Grey-headed Woodpecker	R	1998	150	—	B	B2
Lanius excubitor Great Grey Shrike	R	1998	30	—	B	B2

The site is a major migratory bottleneck, where more than 20,000 *Grus grus* regularly pass.

■ Protection status
National None **International** None

■ Conservation issues

Threats Groundwater abstraction (U)

Hessian Rothaar mountains
C6 **173**

Admin region Hessen
Coordinates 51°04′N 8°40′E
Altitude 306–674 m **Area** 32,000 ha

■ Site description
The eastern part of the Rothaar mountains with extensive deciduous forests.

Habitats Forest and woodland (broadleaved deciduous forest; mixed forest), Scrub (scrub), Grassland (humid grassland), Wetland (river/stream; fen/transition mire/spring), Rocky areas, Artificial landscape (arable land; perennial crops/orchards/groves; ruderal land)
Land-use Agriculture, Forestry, Nature conservation/research, Tourism/recreation, Urban/industrial/transport

■ Birds

Species		Season	Year	Pop min	Pop max	Acc	Criteria
Ciconia nigra	Black Stork	B	1998	2	4	A	C6

This is an important site for species associated with both open and wooded habitats.

■ Protection status
National None **International** None

■ Conservation issues

Threats Abandonment/reduction of land management (U), Afforestation (U), Disturbance to birds (U), Infrastructure (U), Industrialization/urbanization (U), Other (U), Recreation/tourism (U)

Two major roads are being constructed in the IBA.

Knüll
B2 **174**

Admin region Hessen
Coordinates 50°54′N 9°25′E
Altitude 230–634 m **Area** 35,000 ha

■ Site description
The site has a wide variety of habitats, changing with altitude. These range from dry grassland to *Fagus* forests and moist *Quercus–Carpinus* woods.

Habitats Forest and woodland (broadleaved deciduous forest), Grassland (steppe/dry calcareous grassland), Artificial landscape (arable land)
Land-use Agriculture

■ Birds

Species		Season	Year	Pop min	Pop max	Acc	Criteria
Bubo bubo	Eagle Owl	R	1998	4	5	A	B2
Picus canus	Grey-headed Woodpecker	R	1998	120	140	B	B2
Lanius excubitor	Great Grey Shrike	R	1998	30	—	B	B2

This is an important site for forest and grassland species, particularly *Ciconia nigra* and *Lanius excubitor*.

■ Protection status
National None **International** None

■ Conservation issues

Threats Abandonment/reduction of land management (U), Afforestation (U), Recreation/tourism (U)

There is a conservation management project involving cattle-grazing.

High Westerwald around Driedorf
B2 **175**

Admin region Hessen
Coordinates 50°35′N 8°10′E
Altitude 294–642 m **Area** 8,500 ha

■ Site description
The site has a varied landscape of non-intensively managed

agricultural habitats including humid grassland, rough grazing-pastures, mesophile hay-meadows, *Juniperus* scrub, arable land and many hedgerows.

Habitats Forest and woodland (broadleaved deciduous forest), Scrub (scrub; heathland), Grassland (humid grassland; mesophile grassland), Artificial landscape (arable land; perennial crops/orchards/groves; ruderal land)
Land-use Agriculture, Fisheries/aquaculture, Forestry, Nature conservation/research, Tourism/recreation, Urban/industrial/transport

■ Birds

Species		Season	Year	Pop min	Pop max	Acc	Criteria
Lanius excubitor	Great Grey Shrike	R	1998	30	—	B	B2

This is an important site for species associated with a mosaic of non-intensively managed agricultural habitats.

■ Protection status
National None **International** None

■ Conservation issues

Threats Abandonment/reduction of land management (U), Afforestation (U), Recreation/tourism (U)

Waldeck upland
C6 **176**

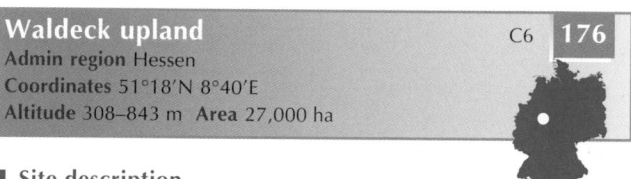

Admin region Hessen
Coordinates 51°18′N 8°40′E
Altitude 308–843 m **Area** 27,000 ha

■ Site description
A mountainous area with non-intensive land-uses, woodland areas and numerous small rivers and streams.

Habitats Forest and woodland (broadleaved deciduous forest; native coniferous forest; mixed forest), Scrub (scrub; heathland), Grassland (humid grassland), Wetland (standing fresh water; river/stream; raised bog; fen/transition mire/spring), Rocky areas, Artificial landscape (arable land; perennial crops/orchards/groves; ruderal land)
Land-use Agriculture, Forestry, Nature conservation/research, Tourism/recreation

■ Birds

Species		Season	Year	Pop min	Pop max	Acc	Criteria
Ciconia nigra	Black Stork	B	1998	1	2	A	C6

This is an important site for woodland birds and *Alcedo atthis*.

■ Protection status
National None **International** None

■ Conservation issues

Threats Abandonment/reduction of land management (U), Afforestation (U), Disturbance to birds (U), Intensified forest management (U), Recreation/tourism (U)

Lahn valley from Marburg to Wetzlar
B2 **177**

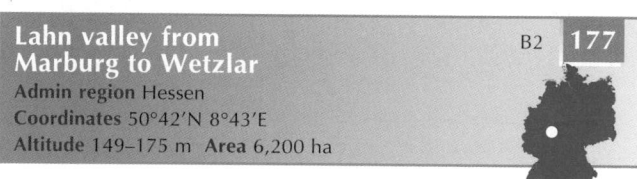

Admin region Hessen
Coordinates 50°42′N 8°43′E
Altitude 149–175 m **Area** 6,200 ha

■ Site description
An alluvial area dominated by grassland in areas that flood and arable agriculture in areas that do not.

Habitats Forest and woodland (broadleaved deciduous forest; alluvial/very wet forest), Scrub (scrub), Grassland (humid grassland; mesophile grassland), Wetland (standing fresh water; river/stream; water-fringe vegetation), Artificial landscape (highly improved reseeded grassland; arable land; perennial crops/orchards/groves; ruderal land)
Land-use Agriculture, Nature conservation/research, Tourism/recreation, Urban/industrial/transport

■ Birds

Species	Season	Year	Pop min	Pop max	Acc	Criteria
Riparia riparia Sand Martin	B	1998	500	—	B	B2

An important area for passage migrants. Species of global conservation concern that do not meet IBA criteria: *Crex crex* (4–9 breeding pairs).

■ Protection status
National Partial **International** None
IBA overlaps with Landscape Protected Area.

■ Conservation issues

Threats Abandonment/reduction of land management (C), Agricultural intensification/expansion (A), Consequences of animal/plant introductions (C), Disturbance to birds (A), Drainage (B), Dredging/canalization (A), Industrialization/urbanization (B), Recreation/tourism (A)

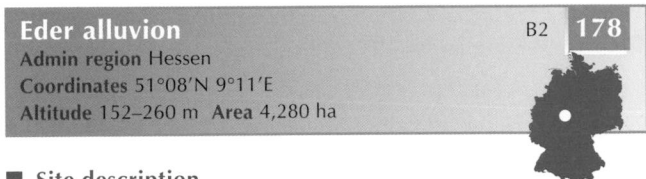

Eder alluvion
B2 178

Admin region Hessen
Coordinates 51°08′N 9°11′E
Altitude 152–260 m **Area** 4,280 ha

■ Site description
An upland river and lake fringed by sedge. Human activities include gravel mining, recreation, tourism and agriculture.

Habitats Forest and woodland (broadleaved deciduous forest), Scrub (scrub), Grassland (humid grassland), Wetland (standing fresh water; river/stream; water-fringe vegetation), Artificial landscape (highly improved reseeded grassland; arable land; perennial crops/orchards/groves; ruderal land)
Land-use Agriculture, Nature conservation/research, Tourism/recreation, Urban/industrial/transport

■ Birds

Species	Season	Year	Pop min	Pop max	Acc	Criteria
Riparia riparia Sand Martin	B	1988	100	2,000	—	B2

This is an important area for passage migrants and waterbirds.

■ Protection status
National None **International** None

■ Conservation issues

Threats Aquaculture/fisheries (U), Disturbance to birds (U), Extraction industry (U), Industrialization/urbanization (U), Recreation/tourism (U)

Northern Wetterau
B1iv, B3, C5 179

Admin region Hessen
Coordinates 50°25′N 8°55′E
Altitude 130–130 m **Area** 4,300 ha

■ Site description
The area consists of streams with surrounding flood-plain meadows and arable land. There are also lakes and ponds.

Habitats Grassland (humid grassland; mesophile grassland), Wetland (standing fresh water; river/stream; water-fringe vegetation; fen/transition mire/spring), Artificial landscape (arable land; ruderal land)
Land-use Agriculture, Nature conservation/research, Tourism/recreation, Urban/industrial/transport

■ Birds

Species	Season	Year	Pop min	Pop max	Acc	Criteria
Porzana porzana Spotted Crake	B	1998	10	40	A	B3

The site is a migratory bottleneck where more than 3,000 *Grus grus* regularly pass.

■ Protection status
National None **International** None

■ Conservation issues

Threats Agricultural intensification/expansion (A), Consequences of animal/plant introductions (C), Disturbance to birds (C), Drainage (B), Groundwater abstraction (A), Industrialization/urbanization (B), Recreation/tourism (C)

Approximately 1,000 ha of the area are under an agricultural extensification programme. There is a programme of pond restoration and creation.

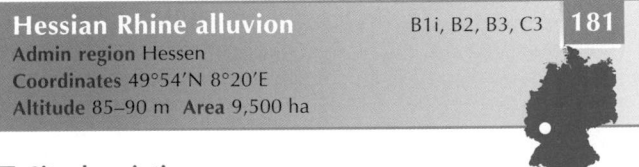

Alluvion of the Lower Schwalm near Borken
B2 180

Admin region Hessen
Coordinates 51°04′N 9°20′E
Altitude 163–222 m **Area** 3,300 ha

■ Site description
The alluvial plain of the River Schwalm with meadows and abandoned sites of open-cast and gravel mining.

Habitats Forest and woodland (broadleaved deciduous forest), Scrub (scrub), Grassland (humid grassland), Wetland (standing fresh water; river/stream), Artificial landscape (highly improved reseeded grassland; arable land; perennial crops/orchards/groves; other urban/industrial areas)
Land-use Agriculture, Forestry, Not utilized, Urban/industrial/transport

■ Birds

Species	Season	Year	Pop min	Pop max	Acc	Criteria
Riparia riparia Sand Martin	B	1998	800	1,000	A	B2

An important area for breeding *Riparia riparia* and passage *Grus grus*.

■ Protection status
National None **International** None

■ Conservation issues

Threats Afforestation (U), Disturbance to birds (U), Extraction industry (U), Groundwater abstraction (U)

Hessian Rhine alluvion
B1i, B2, B3, C3 181

Admin region Hessen
Coordinates 49°54′N 8°20′E
Altitude 85–90 m **Area** 9,500 ha

■ Site description
The site comprises the old course of the River Rhine with oxbow lakes. The flood-plain area is dominated by meadows. The IBA comprises two sites from the previous pan-European IBA inventory (Grimmett and Jones 1989): Kühkopf–Knoblauchsaue (former site DE064) and Lampertheimer Altrhein (former site DE065).

Habitats Grassland (humid grassland), Wetland (standing fresh water)
Land-use Agriculture, Fisheries/aquaculture, Hunting, Tourism/recreation

■ Birds

Species	Season	Year	Pop min	Pop max	Acc	Criteria
Phalacrocorax carbo Cormorant	W	1994	900	2,500	A	B1i, C3
Anser fabalis Bean Goose	W	1995	200	1,200	B	B1i, C3
Aythya ferina Pochard	P	—	4,000	—	—	B1i, C3
Milvus migrans Black Kite	B	1994	40	50	—	B2
Dendrocopos medius Middle Spotted Woodpecker	R	1994	100	—	—	B3
Acrocephalus scirpaceus Reed Warbler	B	1994	800	1,000	—	B3

This is an important area for breeding and wintering waterbirds and is nationally important for breeding *Luscinia svecica*, as well as for species of global conservation concern that do not meet IBA criteria: *Aythya nyroca, Crex crex* (breeding).

■ Protection status
National Partial **International** Partial

IBA overlaps with Nature Reserves (Kühkopf–Knoblauchsaue, 2,369 ha and Lampertheimer Altrhein, 525 ha). IBA overlaps with Special Protection Areas (Kühkopf–Knoblauchsaue, 2,369 ha and Lampertheimer Altrhein, 525 ha).

■ Conservation issues

Threats Agricultural intensification/expansion (U), Aquaculture/fisheries (U), Recreation/tourism (U)

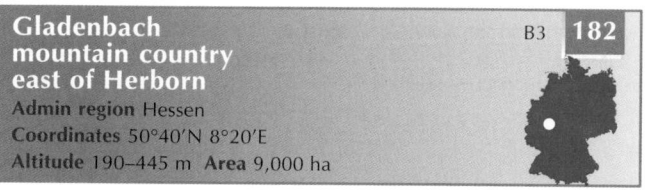

Gladenbach mountain country east of Herborn B3 182
Admin region Hessen
Coordinates 50°40′N 8°20′E
Altitude 190–445 m **Area** 9,000 ha

■ Site description

A mountainous area comprised of *Quercus* woods, a reservoir, *Juniperus* pastures, and grassland.

Habitats Forest and woodland (broadleaved deciduous forest; mixed forest), Scrub (scrub; heathland), Grassland (dry siliceous grassland; humid grassland; mesophile grassland), Wetland (standing fresh water), Artificial landscape (arable land; perennial crops/orchards/groves; forestry plantation; ruderal land)
Land-use Agriculture, Forestry, Nature conservation/research, Tourism/recreation, Urban/industrial/transport, Water management

■ Birds

Species	Season	Year	Pop min	Pop max	Acc	Criteria
Dendrocopos medius Middle Spotted Woodpecker	R	1998	100	200	C	B3

This is an important area for woodland species.

■ Protection status
National None **International** None

■ Conservation issues

Threats Abandonment/reduction of land management (U), Afforestation (U), Filling-in of wetlands (U), Industrialization/urbanization (U), Intensified forest management (U), Recreation/tourism (U)

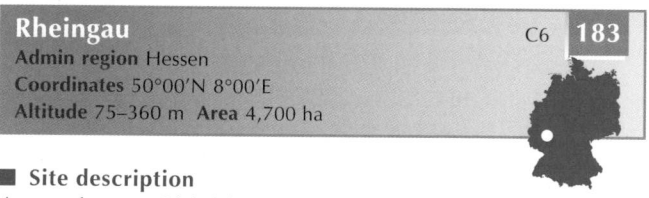

Rheingau C6 183
Admin region Hessen
Coordinates 50°00′N 8°00′E
Altitude 75–360 m **Area** 4,700 ha

■ Site description
An area between Biebrich and Bingen, subdivided by numerous small valleys.

Habitats Forest and woodland, Scrub (scrub), Rocky areas, Artificial landscape (perennial crops/orchards/groves)
Land-use Agriculture, Forestry, Hunting, Tourism/recreation

■ Birds

Species	Season	Year	Pop min	Pop max	Acc	Criteria
Falco peregrinus Peregrine	R	1998	1	1	A	C6

This site is regionally important for *Falco peregrinus* and *Emberiza cia*.

■ Protection status
National None **International** None

■ Conservation issues

Threats Abandonment/reduction of land management (U), Disturbance to birds (U), Recreation/tourism (U)

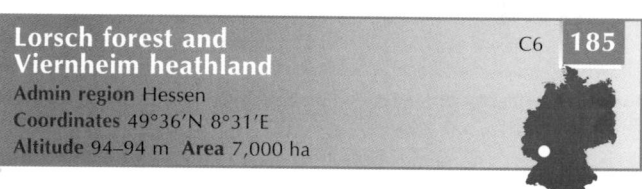

Dune and aeolian sand area: Dudenhofen, Babenhausen, Seligenstadt B2 184
Admin region Hessen
Coordinates 50°00′N 8°55′E
Altitude 122–141 m **Area** 5,000 ha

■ Site description
The site is dominated by *Pinus* forests which occur on sand-dunes and aeolian sand areas.

Habitats Forest and woodland (native coniferous forest), Rocky areas (inland sand-dunes)
Land-use Forestry

■ Birds

Species	Season	Year	Pop min	Pop max	Acc	Criteria
Caprimulgus europaeus Nightjar	B	1998	20	30	A	B2

The site holds species associated with dry coniferous forests including *Falco subbuteo* and *Caprimulgus europaeus*.

■ Protection status
National None **International** None

■ Conservation issues

Threats Intensified forest management (U)

Lorsch forest and Viernheim heathland C6 185
Admin region Hessen
Coordinates 49°36′N 8°31′E
Altitude 94–94 m **Area** 7,000 ha

■ Site description
The site is dominated by *Pinus* forest with small areas of *Fagus* forest. The substrate is sand and there are large areas of dunes and open sand.

Habitats Forest and woodland (broadleaved deciduous forest; native coniferous forest), Rocky areas (inland sand-dunes)
Land-use Forestry, Tourism/recreation

■ Birds

Species	Season	Year	Pop min	Pop max	Acc	Criteria
Caprimulgus europaeus Nightjar	B	1996	10	—	A	C6

This is an important area for woodpeckers with six species occurring.

■ Protection status
National None **International** None

■ Conservation issues

Threats Groundwater abstraction (U), Other (U)

'Other' threats include air pollution and intensive military use of the site.

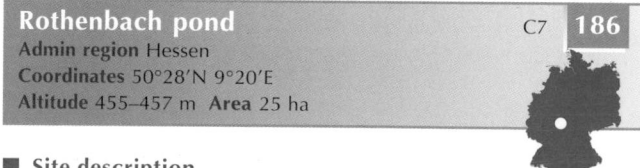

Rothenbach pond C7 186
Admin region Hessen
Coordinates 50°28′N 9°20′E
Altitude 455–457 m **Area** 25 ha

■ Site description
An 18th century fish-pond with near-natural water-fringe vegetation including reedbeds (*Phragmites*), sedge, wet grassland and *Alnus* carr woodland.

Habitats Forest and woodland (60%; broadleaved deciduous forest; alluvial/very wet forest), Wetland (37%; standing fresh water; water-fringe vegetation; fen/transition mire/spring)

Land-use Forestry, Tourism/recreation

■ Birds
This is an important area for breeding and passage waterbirds. Species of global conservation concern that do not meet IBA criteria: *Aythya nyroca* (passage).

■ Protection status
National High **International** High
25 ha of IBA covered by Nature Reserve (Rothenbachteich, 25 ha). IBA overlaps with Special Protection Area.

■ Conservation issues

Threats Intensified forest management (U), Recreation/tourism (U)

Artificial nest platforms have been installed for *Pandion haliaetus*.

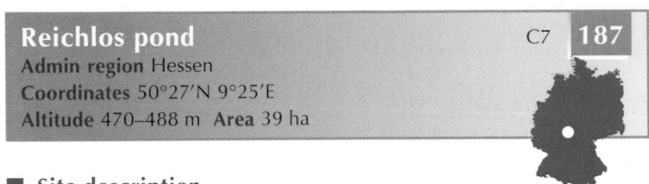

Reichlos pond
C7 187
Admin region Hessen
Coordinates 50°27′N 9°25′E
Altitude 470–488 m **Area** 39 ha

■ Site description
A pond with near-natural surrounding vegetation, including reeds *Phragmites*, sedge, abandoned wet meadows, grassland, and relicts of scrub heath and *Alnus* carr woodland.

Habitats Forest and woodland (23%; alluvial/very wet forest), Scrub (heathland), Grassland (30%; humid grassland), Wetland (40%; standing fresh water; water-fringe vegetation; fen/transition mire/spring), Artificial landscape (7%)
Land-use Fisheries/aquaculture, Forestry

■ Birds
This is an important area for breeding and passage waterbirds.

■ Protection status
National High **International** High
39 ha of IBA covered by Nature Reserve (Reichloser Teich, 39 ha). IBA overlaps with Special Protection Area.

■ Conservation issues

Threats Abandonment/reduction of land management (U), Agricultural intensification/expansion (U), Intensified forest management (U), Recreation/tourism (U)

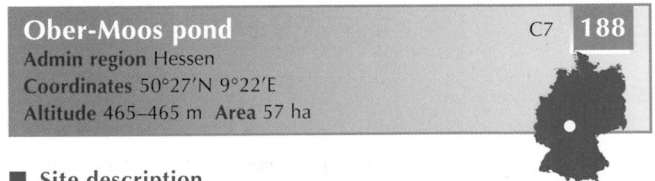

Ober-Moos pond
C7 188
Admin region Hessen
Coordinates 50°27′N 9°22′E
Altitude 465–465 m **Area** 57 ha

■ Site description
A pond with a broad fringe of reed *Phragmites* and sedge, surrounded by wet meadows and grassland.

Habitats Forest and woodland (25%), Grassland (9%; dry siliceous grassland; humid grassland), Wetland (64%; standing fresh water; water-fringe vegetation; fen/transition mire/spring)

■ Birds
This is an important area for breeding and passage waterbirds.

■ Protection status
National High **International** Partial
57 ha of IBA covered by Nature Reserve (Ober-Mooser Teich, 57 ha). IBA overlaps with Special Protection Area.

■ Conservation issues

Threats Agricultural intensification/expansion (A), Consequences of animal/plant introductions (A), Intensified forest management (A), Recreation/tourism (B)

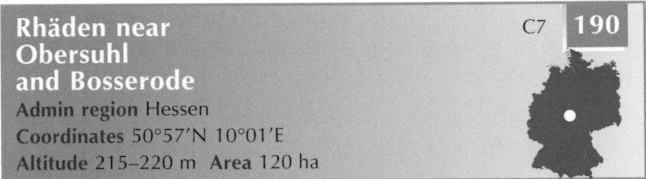

Rotes Moor
C7 189
Admin region Hessen
Coordinates 50°29′N 09°59′E
Altitude 800–800 m **Area** 315 ha

■ Site description
A typical high-montane landscape for the Rhön area consisting of raised and transitional bogs, birch *Betula* swamp-forest, wet meadows, wet *Salix* scrub, *Alnus* swamp-forest and grassland.

Habitats Forest and woodland (50%; broadleaved deciduous forest), Scrub (8%), Grassland (35%; dry siliceous grassland; humid grassland; mesophile grassland), Wetland (6%; standing fresh water; raised bog; fen/transition mire/spring)
Land-use Forestry, Tourism/recreation

■ Protection status
National High **International** High
315 ha of IBA covered by Landscape Protected Area (Hohe Rhön, 45,750 ha). 315 ha of IBA covered by Nature Reserve (Rotes Moor, 315 ha). 315 ha of IBA covered by Biosphere Reserve (Rhön, 130,488 ha). IBA overlaps with Special Protection Area.

■ Conservation issues

Threats Afforestation (B), Consequences of animal/plant introductions (B), Recreation/tourism (A)

There is a wetland restoration project.

Rhäden near Obersuhl and Bosserode
C7 190
Admin region Hessen
Coordinates 50°57′N 10°01′E
Altitude 215–220 m **Area** 120 ha

■ Site description
A wet area with open water-bodies, reed *Phragmites*, sedge, *Salix* scrub, grassland and forests.

Habitats Forest and woodland (35%; broadleaved deciduous forest), Grassland (36%; humid grassland; mesophile grassland), Wetland (26%; standing fresh water; water-fringe vegetation; fen/transition mire/spring)
Land-use Agriculture, Forestry

■ Birds
This is an important site for passage wildfowl, waders and *Grus grus*.

■ Protection status
National Low **International** High
120 ha of IBA covered by Nature Reserve (Rhäden bei Obersuhl und Bosserode, 120 ha). IBA overlaps with Special Protection Area.

■ Conservation issues

Threats Agricultural intensification/expansion (A), Disturbance to birds (A), Intensified forest management (B), Natural events (A)

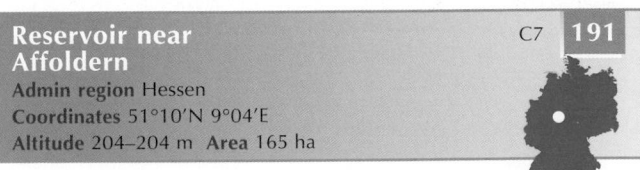

Reservoir near Affoldern
C7 191
Admin region Hessen
Coordinates 51°10′N 9°04′E
Altitude 204–204 m **Area** 165 ha

■ Site description
A reservoir with a planted scrub fringe and a *Fagus* wood in the south. Areas of open water remain ice-free throughout the winter.

Habitats Forest and woodland (7%; broadleaved deciduous forest), Wetland (90%; standing fresh water)
Land-use Fisheries/aquaculture, Tourism/recreation

■ Birds

This is an important area for passage and wintering waterbirds. Species of global conservation concern that do not meet IBA criteria: *Aythya nyroca* (passage).

■ Protection status

National High **International** High

165 ha of IBA covered by Landscape Protected Area (Auenverbund Eder, 4,900 ha). 165 ha of IBA covered by Nature Reserve (Stausee von Affoldern, 165 ha). IBA overlaps with Special Protection Area.

■ Conservation issues

Threats Aquaculture/fisheries (C), Construction/impact of dyke/dam/barrage (U), Recreation/tourism (C)

Nest-boxes have been installed for *Mergus merganser*.

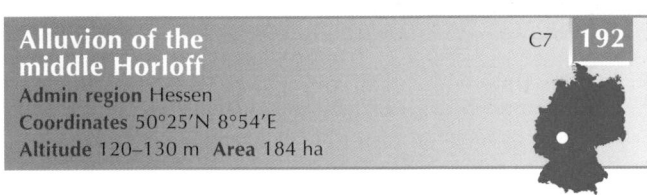

Alluvion of the middle Horloff
C7 192

Admin region Hessen
Coordinates 50°25′N 8°54′E
Altitude 120–130 m **Area** 184 ha

■ Site description

A near-natural flood-plain with reeds *Phragmites*, wet meadows, sedge, *Alnus* forest, and orchards.

Habitats Grassland (65%; humid grassland), Wetland (34%; standing fresh water; water-fringe vegetation)
Land-use Agriculture, Forestry, Tourism/recreation

■ Birds

Species of global conservation concern that do not meet IBA criteria: *Aythya nyroca* (passage), *Crex crex* (breeding).

■ Protection status

National High **International** High

184 ha of IBA covered by Nature Reserve (Mittlere Horloffaue, 184 ha). IBA overlaps with Special Protection Area.

■ Conservation issues

Threats Agricultural intensification/expansion (B), Drainage (A), Intensified forest management (A), Recreation/tourism (U)

There is a programme of shallow-water restoration.

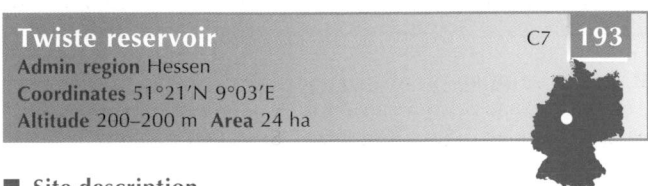

Twiste reservoir
C7 193

Admin region Hessen
Coordinates 51°21′N 9°03′E
Altitude 200–200 m **Area** 24 ha

■ Site description

A reservoir surrounded by highly improved grassland and arable land. The site also includes the Twiste valley.

Habitats Forest and woodland (10%; broadleaved deciduous forest), Grassland (20%; humid grassland; mesophile grassland), Wetland (40%; standing fresh water), Artificial landscape (30%; arable land)
Land-use Agriculture, Forestry

■ Birds

This is an important area for breeding and passage waterbirds.

■ Protection status

National High **International** High

24 ha of IBA covered by Nature Reserve (Vorsperre Twistetalsperre, 25 ha). IBA overlaps with IBA.

■ Conservation issues

Threats Agricultural intensification/expansion (A)

Rhön Biosphere Reserve
A1, B2, B3, C1, C2 194

Admin region Hessen, Bayern, Thüringen
Coordinates 50°30′N 10°05′E
Altitude 280–950 m **Area** 187,606 ha

■ Site description

A diverse subalpine area with semi-natural forests, grassland, large fens, springs, rivers and streams

Habitats Forest and woodland (broadleaved deciduous forest; mixed forest; alluvial/very wet forest), Grassland (steppe/dry calcareous grassland; alpine/subalpine/boreal grassland; humid grassland), Wetland (river/stream; raised bog; fen/transition mire/spring)
Land-use Agriculture, Fisheries/aquaculture, Forestry, Hunting, Tourism/recreation

■ Birds

Species		Season	Year	Pop min	Pop max	Acc	Criteria
Ciconia nigra	Black Stork	B	1994	3	20	—	B2
¹ *Milvus milvus*	Red Kite	R	1994	21	200	—	B3
Falco tinnunculus	Kestrel	R	1994	200	—	—	B2
¹ *Crex crex*	Corncrake	B	1994	21	200	—	A1, C1, C2
¹ *Tyto alba*	Barn Owl	R	1994	21	200	—	B2
¹ *Bubo bubo*	Eagle Owl	R	1994	3	20	—	B2
¹ *Alcedo atthis*	Kingfisher	R	1994	21	200	—	B2
¹ *Picus canus*	Grey-headed Woodpecker	R	1994	21	200	—	B2
¹ *Lanius excubitor*	Great Grey Shrike	R	1994	21	200	—	B2

1. 1980–1994.

This is an important site for woodland, heathland and wetland birds.

■ Protection status

National None **International** Partial

IBA overlaps with Biosphere Reserve.

■ Conservation issues

Threats Agricultural intensification/expansion (U), Infrastructure (U), Recreation/tourism (U)

There are programmes to encourage non-intensive land-use and low-impact tourism.

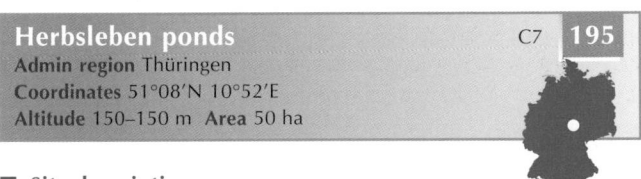

Herbsleben ponds
C7 195

Admin region Thüringen
Coordinates 51°08′N 10°52′E
Altitude 150–150 m **Area** 50 ha

■ Site description

An area of fish-ponds with reeds *Phragmites*, ditches and wet meadows. One of only a small number of wetlands in Thüringen.

Habitats Forest and woodland (alluvial/very wet forest), Scrub (scrub), Grassland (humid grassland; mesophile grassland), Wetland (standing fresh water; water-fringe vegetation), Artificial landscape (arable land)
Land-use Agriculture, Nature conservation/research, Other, Tourism/recreation

■ Birds

This is an important site for breeding wetland and passage waterbirds.

■ Protection status

National Partial **International** High

IBA overlaps with Nature Reserve. IBA overlaps with Special Protection Area.

■ Conservation issues

Threats Recreation/tourism (U)

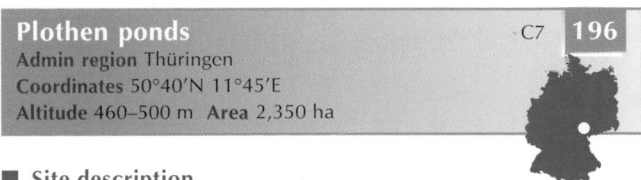

Plothen ponds
C7 196

Admin region Thüringen
Coordinates 50°40′N 11°45′E
Altitude 460–500 m **Area** 2,350 ha

■ Site description

A large area of fish-ponds, established in the 11th–12th century, between the Rivers Saale and Weisse Elster. They have associated water-fringe vegetation, bogs and broadleaved deciduous forest.

Habitats Forest and woodland (broadleaved deciduous forest; native coniferous forest), Scrub (scrub), Grassland (mesophile grassland), Wetland (standing fresh water; water-fringe vegetation), Artificial landscape (highly improved reseeded grassland; arable land), Unknown
Land-use Agriculture, Fisheries/aquaculture, Forestry, Hunting, Nature conservation/research, Tourism/recreation

■ Birds
This is an important site for breeding ducks, raptors and species associated with reedbeds.

■ Protection status
National High **International** High
39 ha of IBA covered by Nature Reserve (Drebaer Teiche NSG, 39 ha). 5 ha of IBA covered by Nature Reserve (Hädrichsteiche NSG, 5 ha). 1,896 ha of IBA covered by Landscape Protected Area (Plothener Teichgebiet, 1,896 ha). 590 ha of IBA covered by Landscape Protected Area (Thüringer Schiefergebirge und Frankenwald LSG, 44,000 ha). 2,350 ha of IBA covered by Nature Park (Thüringer Schiefergebirge/ Obere Saale NP, 85,000 ha). IBA overlaps with Special Protection Area.

■ Conservation issues
Threats Recreation/tourism (U)

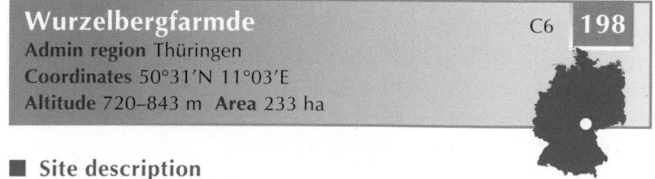

Uhlstädt heathlands
Admin region Thüringen
Coordinates 50°35′N 11°15′E
Altitude 248–450 m **Area** 1,082 ha
C7 197

■ Site description
A forested part of the Saale sandstone plain situated between the Saale valley and the Orla-Senke. The forest is dominated by *Pinus* interspersed with *Fagus* with a *Vaccinium/Pteridium* field layer.

Habitats Forest and woodland (broadleaved deciduous forest; native coniferous forest), Scrub (heathland)
Land-use Forestry, Hunting, Nature conservation/research, Tourism/recreation

■ Birds
One of the last breeding sites of *Tetrao urogallus* in Thüringen.

■ Protection status
National High **International** High
1,082 ha of IBA covered by Nature Reserve (Uhlstädter Heide, 1,082 ha). IBA overlaps with Special Protection Area.

■ Conservation issues
Threats Recreation/tourism (U)

A conservation project for *Tetrao urogallus* is underway.

Wurzelbergfarmde
Admin region Thüringen
Coordinates 50°31′N 11°03′E
Altitude 720–843 m **Area** 233 ha
C6 198

■ Site description
Picea forest with a *Vaccinium* field layer. Mixed forest is present in the area known as 'Hohes Thüringer Schiefergebirge-Frankenwald'.

Habitats Forest and woodland (native coniferous forest; mixed forest)
Land-use Forestry, Hunting, Nature conservation/research, Tourism/recreation

■ Birds

Species		Season	Year	Pop min	Pop max	Acc	Criteria
Tetrao urogallus	Capercaillie	R	1996	2	2	A	C6

This site is regionally important for *Tetrao urogallus*.

■ Protection status
National High **International** High
233 ha of IBA covered by Landscape Protected Area (Thuringer Wald, 189,713 ha). 233 ha of IBA covered by Nature Park (Thüringer Wald/ Westliches Schiefergebirge NP, 200,000 ha). 233 ha of IBA covered by Nature Reserve (Wurzelbergfarmde, 233 ha). IBA overlaps with Special Protection Area.

■ Conservation issues
Threats Intensified forest management (U), Recreation/tourism (U)

A conservation project for *Tetrao urogallus* is underway.

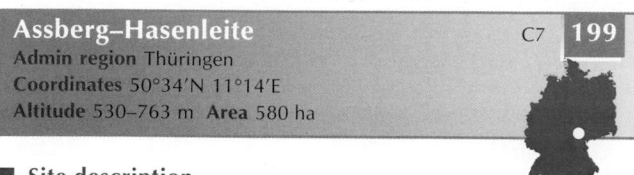

Assberg–Hasenleite
Admin region Thüringen
Coordinates 50°34′N 11°14′E
Altitude 530–763 m **Area** 580 ha
C7 199

■ Site description
An area of coniferous (*Pinus*, *Picea* and *Abies*) and broadleaved deciduous forest in the western Thüringer mountain range.

Habitats Forest and woodland (broadleaved deciduous forest; native coniferous forest), Scrub (heathland)
Land-use Forestry, Hunting, Nature conservation/research, Tourism/recreation

■ Birds
Breeding species include *Tetrao tetrix* and *T. urogallus*.

■ Protection status
National High **International** High
580 ha of IBA covered by Nature Reserve (Assberg-Hasenleite NSG, 580 ha). 580 ha of IBA covered by Landscape Protected Area (Thuringer Wald, 189,713 ha). 580 ha of IBA covered by Nature Park (Thüringer Wald/Westliches Schiefergebirge NP, 200,000 ha). IBA overlaps with Special Protection Area.

■ Conservation issues
Threats Afforestation (U), Intensified forest management (U), Recreation/tourism (U)

A conservation project for *Tetrao urogallus* is underway.

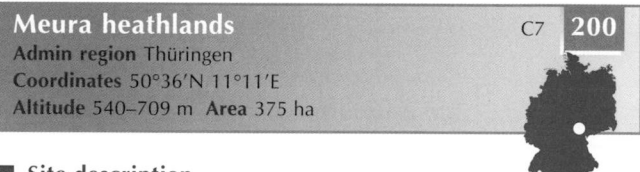

Meura heathlands
Admin region Thüringen
Coordinates 50°36′N 11°11′E
Altitude 540–709 m **Area** 375 ha
C7 200

■ Site description
An area of broadleaved deciduous forest (on poor soils) and conifer plantations in the western Thüringer mountain range.

Habitats Forest and woodland (broadleaved deciduous forest; native coniferous forest), Scrub (heathland)
Land-use Forestry, Hunting, Nature conservation/research, Tourism/recreation

■ Birds
This is an important area for heathland and woodland species and particularly for *Tetrao urogallus*.

■ Protection status
National High **International** High
375 ha of IBA covered by Nature Reserve (Meuraer Heide NSG, 375 ha). 375 ha of IBA covered by Landscape Protected Area (Thuringer Wald, 189,713 ha). 375 ha of IBA covered by Nature Park (Thüringer Wald/Westliches Schiefergebirge NP, 200,000 ha). IBA overlaps with Special Protection Area.

■ Conservation issues
Threats Afforestation (U), Intensified forest management (U), Recreation/tourism (U), Other (U)

Soil acidification is reducing the food supply for species of Tetraonidae ('Other' threat). A *Tetrao urogallus* conservation project is in operation.

Schwarza valley   C7 201

Admin region Thüringen
Coordinates 50°40'N 11°13'E
Altitude 230–550 m Area 1,800 ha

■ Site description
A wooded, steeply-sloping section of the Schwarze river valley in the Thüringer mountains. The *Fagus* and *Picea* forests are floristically diverse; rocky cliffs are also present.

Habitats Forest and woodland (broadleaved deciduous forest; native coniferous forest; mixed forest), Scrub (scrub), Wetland (river/stream; water-fringe vegetation), Rocky areas (inland cliff)
Land-use Forestry, Hunting, Nature conservation/research, Tourism/recreation

■ Birds
This is an important site for woodland species..

■ Protection status
National High **International** High
1,800 ha of IBA covered by Landscape Protected Area (Thüringer Wald, 189,713 ha). 1,800 ha of IBA covered by Nature Reserve (Thüringer Wald/Westliches Schiefergebirge NP, 200,000 ha). IBA overlaps with Special Protection Area.

■ Conservation issues

Threats Intensified forest management (U), Recreation/tourism (U)

Vesser Valley Biosphere Reserve   C6 202

Admin region Thüringen
Coordinates 50°34'N 10°51'E
Altitude 420–980 m Area 7,464 ha

■ Site description
A wooded area on the southern slopes of the Thüringer Wald mountains with the valleys of the River Vesser and its tributaries. Rich forests (*Fagus*, *Pinus*, *Abies*) and riverine vegetation create a mosaic of diverse habitats.

Habitats Forest and woodland (88%; broadleaved deciduous forest; native coniferous forest; mixed forest), Grassland (7%), Artificial landscape (5%)
Land-use Agriculture, Fisheries/aquaculture, Forestry, Hunting, Nature conservation/research, Tourism/recreation, Urban/industrial/transport

■ Birds

Species	Season	Year	Pop min	Pop max	Acc	Criteria
Ciconia nigra Black Stork	B	1996	2	2	A	C6

There are 92 breeding species. The site is important for woodland species, particularly hole-nesting birds.

■ Protection status
National High **International** High
40 ha of IBA covered by Nature Reserve (Beerbergmoor NSG, 40 ha). 21 ha of IBA covered by Nature Reserve (Erbskopf NSG, 21 ha). 20 ha of IBA covered by Nature Reserve (Harzgrund NSG, 20 ha). 420 ha of IBA covered by Nature Reserve (Marktal und Morast NSG, 420 ha). 182 ha of IBA covered by Nature Reserve (Oberlauf der Gabeltaler NSG, 182 ha). 40 ha of IBA covered by Nature Reserve (Schneekopfmoor am Teufelskreis NSG, 48 ha). 55 ha of IBA covered by Nature Reserve (Seiffertsburg NSG, 55 ha). 7,464 ha of IBA covered by Nature Reserve (Vessertal, 10,875 ha). 7,464 ha of IBA covered by Nature Park (Thüringer Wald/Westliches Schiefergebirge NP, 200,000 ha). IBA overlaps with Biosphere Reserve and Special Protection Area.

■ Conservation issues

Threats Afforestation (U), Intensified forest management (U), Recreation/tourism (U)

Pressel wooded heath and mire   B1i, C3 203

Admin region Sachsen
Coordinates 51°34'N 12°45'E
Altitude 110–130 m Area 5,000 ha

■ Site description
A mixture of extensive reedbed (*Phragmites*), *Alnus/Betula* stands, scrub, fen and bog. Agricultural and forestry activities take place within the framework of a management plan, including the replacement of *Pinus* plantations with deciduous forest.

Habitats Forest and woodland (broadleaved deciduous forest; alluvial/very wet forest), Scrub (scrub), Wetland (water-fringe vegetation; fen/transition mire/spring), Artificial landscape (forestry plantation)
Land-use Agriculture, Forestry

■ Birds

Species	Season	Year	Pop min	Pop max	Acc	Criteria
[1] *Anser fabalis* Bean Goose	P	1984	—	2,000	—	B1i, C3

1. Autumn passage.

■ Protection status
National Partial **International** High
IBA overlaps with Nature Reserve. IBA overlaps with Special Protection Area.

■ Conservation issues

Threats Agricultural intensification/expansion (U), Drainage (U)

Ponds and Elbe valley near Torgau   A1, A4i, A4iii, B1i, B2, B3, C1, C3, C4 204

Admin region Sachsen
Coordinates 51°30'N 13°00'E
Altitude 80–105 m Area 6,000 ha

■ Site description
The Elbe valley between Staritz and Dommitzsch. Large areas are used for agriculture and there are also dykes, ponds and woodlands.

Habitats Forest and woodland (native coniferous forest; mixed forest; alluvial/very wet forest), Grassland (humid grassland), Wetland (river/stream; water-fringe vegetation), Artificial landscape (highly improved reseeded grassland; arable land)
Land-use Agriculture, Fisheries/aquaculture, Forestry, Nature conservation/research, Tourism/recreation, Water management

■ Birds

Species	Season	Year	Pop min	Pop max	Acc	Criteria
Ciconia nigra Black Stork	B	1996	2	6	A	B2
Ciconia ciconia White Stork	B	1996	30	35	A	B2
Anser fabalis Bean Goose	W	1996	5,000	30,000	A	A4i, B1i, C3
Aythya ferina Pochard	R	1996	225	278	A	B3
Haliaeetus albicilla White-tailed Eagle	R	1995	4	7	A	A1, B2, C1
Pandion haliaetus Osprey	B	1995	4	10	A	B2

The site holds 20,000 or more waterbirds in winter, on a regular basis. Passage species of global conservation concern that do not meet IBA criteria: *Branta ruficollis* and *Aythya nyroca*.

■ Protection status
National High **International** High
6,000 ha of IBA covered by Nature Reserve (Teichgebiet und Elbaue bei Torgau, 6,000 ha). IBA overlaps with Special Protection Area.

■ Conservation issues

Threats Abandonment/reduction of land management (U), Agricultural intensification/expansion (U), Aquaculture/fisheries (U), Disturbance to birds (U), Dredging/canalization (U), Extraction industry (U), Recreation/tourism (U)

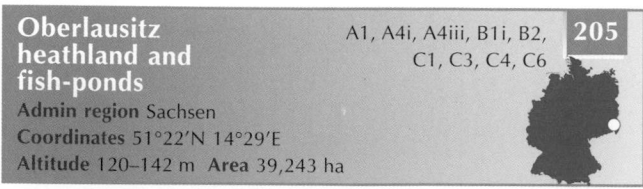

Oberlausitz heathland and fish-ponds

A1, A4i, A4iii, B1i, B2, C1, C3, C4, C6 | **205**

Admin region Sachsen
Coordinates 51°22'N 14°29'E
Altitude 120–142 m **Area** 39,243 ha

■ Site description
An area with numerous fish-ponds and heathland, including two sites that were included in the previous pan-European IBA inventory (Grimmett and Jones 1989): 'Teiche bei Königswartha' and 'Teichgebiet Niederspree', former sites DD033 and DD034 in the then German Democratic Republic.

Habitats Forest and woodland, Scrub (heathland), Wetland (standing fresh water)

■ Birds

Species	Season	Year	Pop min	Pop max	Acc	Criteria
Botaurus stellaris Bittern	R	1996	5	—	—	B2, C6
Anser fabalis Bean Goose	P	1996	—	20,000	A	A4i, B1i, C3
Anser albifrons White-fronted Goose	P	1996	—	30,000	A	A4i, B1i, C3
Haliaeetus albicilla White-tailed Eagle	R	1996	15	—	A	A1, B2, C1
Grus grus Crane	B	1996	—	30	—	B2

The site is important for breeding ducks and raptors. The site holds 20,000 or more waterbirds on passage, on a regular basis. Species of global conservation concern that do not meet IBA criteria: *Aythya nyroca*.

■ Protection status
National None **International** High
IBA overlaps with Biosphere Reserve and Special Protection Area.

■ Conservation issues

Threats Infrastructure (U), Other (U)

A management plan exists for the Biosphere Reserve. Threats include road construction, and waste dumping ('Other' threat).

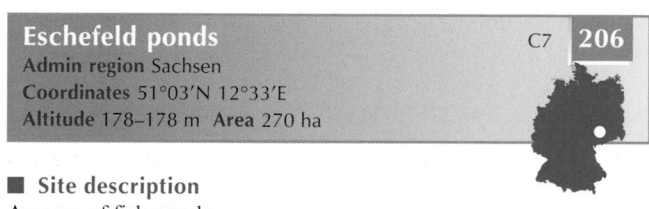

Eschefeld ponds

C7 | **206**

Admin region Sachsen
Coordinates 51°03'N 12°33'E
Altitude 178–178 m **Area** 270 ha

■ Site description
An area of fish-ponds.

Habitats Wetland (standing fresh water)

■ Birds
Species of global conservation concern that do not meet IBA criteria: *Crex crex*.

■ Protection status
National Partial **International** High
IBA overlaps with Nature Reserve. IBA overlaps with Special Protection Area.

■ Conservation issues

Threats Aquaculture/fisheries (U), Recreation/tourism (U)

Westerzgebirge

C7 | **207**

Admin region Sachsen
Coordinates 50°26'N 12°36'E
Altitude 850–1,214 m **Area** 4,800 ha

■ Site description
A high-altitude montane area with *Picea* forests, moors, bogs, wet meadows, pastures and cultivated land.

Habitats Forest and woodland (native coniferous forest), Grassland (humid grassland; mesophile grassland), Wetland (raised bog), Artificial landscape (arable land)
Land-use Agriculture, Forestry, Tourism/recreation

■ Birds
This is an important site for forest species.

■ Protection status
National None **International** High
IBA overlaps with Special Protection Area.

■ Conservation issues

Threats Agricultural intensification/expansion(U), Intensified forest management (U), Recreation/tourism (U)

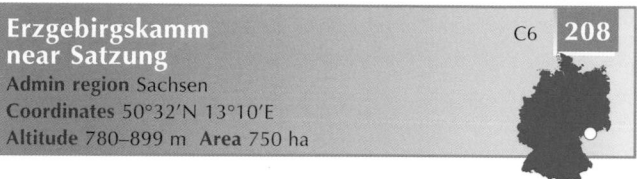

Erzgebirgskamm near Satzung

C6 | **208**

Admin region Sachsen
Coordinates 50°32'N 13°10'E
Altitude 780–899 m **Area** 750 ha

■ Site description
A high-altitude plain in the Erzgebirge with *Picea* forest, bog, wet meadows, pasture and cultivated land.

Habitats Forest and woodland (native coniferous forest), Grassland (humid grassland), Wetland (raised bog)
Land-use Agriculture, Forestry

■ Birds

Species	Season	Year	Pop min	Pop max	Acc	Criteria
Ciconia nigra Black Stork	B	1996	1	—	—	C6

Species of global conservation concern that do not meet IBA criteria: *Crex crex* (breeding).

■ Protection status
National None **International** High
IBA overlaps with Special Protection Area.

■ Conservation issues

Threats Agricultural intensification/expansion (U), Infrastructure (U), Intensified forest management (U)

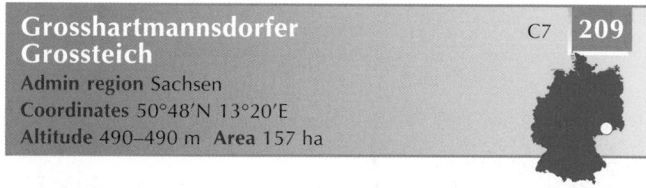

Grosshartmannsdorfer Grossteich

C7 | **209**

Admin region Sachsen
Coordinates 50°48'N 13°20'E
Altitude 490–490 m **Area** 157 ha

■ Site description
A large fish-pond near Grosshartmannsdorf.

Habitats Wetland (standing fresh water)
Land-use Fisheries/aquaculture

■ Birds
This is an important site for passage waterbirds.

■ Protection status
National Partial **International** High
IBA overlaps with Nature Reserve (110 ha). IBA overlaps with Special Protection Area.

■ Conservation issues

Threats Aquaculture/fisheries (U)

Erzgebirgskamm near Deutscheinsiedel

C7 **210**

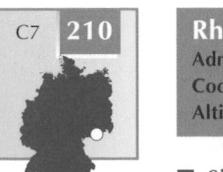

Admin region Sachsen
Coordinates 50°40'N 13°30'E
Altitude 780–842 m **Area** 1,200 ha

■ Site description
A high-altitude mountain area with *Picea* forests and cultivated land.

Habitats Forest and woodland (native coniferous forest), Grassland (humid grassland), Wetland (raised bog; river/stream), Artificial landscape (arable land)
Land-use Agriculture, Forestry

■ Birds
This is an important area for woodland birds.

■ Protection status
National None **International** High
IBA overlaps with Special Protection Area.

■ Conservation issues
Threats Intensified forest management (U), Recreation/tourism (U)

Sächsische Schweiz National Park

B2, C7 **211**

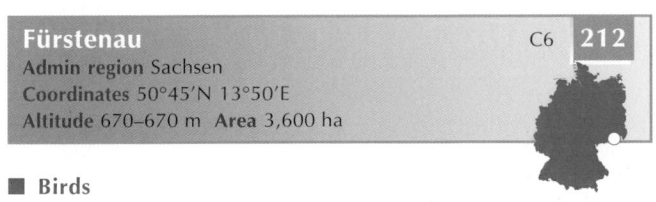

Admin region Sachsen
Coordinates 50°55'N 14°15'E
Altitude 180–556 m **Area** 9,292 ha

■ Site description
A wooded area with narrow canyons, rivers, and limestone cliffs.

Habitats Forest and woodland, Wetland (river/stream), Rocky areas (inland cliff)

■ Birds

Species		Season	Year	Pop min	Pop max	Acc	Criteria
Falco peregrinus	Peregrine	R	1997	6	6	—	B2
Bubo bubo	Eagle Owl	R	1996	3	—	—	B2

The site is nationally important for woodland birds.

■ Protection status
National Partial **International** High
IBA overlaps with National Park (Sächsische Schweiz, 9,292 ha). IBA overlaps with Special Protection Area.

■ Conservation issues
Threats Infrastructure (U), Intensified forest management (U), Recreation/tourism (U)

Fürstenau

C6 **212**

Admin region Sachsen
Coordinates 50°45'N 13°50'E
Altitude 670–670 m **Area** 3,600 ha

■ Birds

Species		Season	Year	Pop min	Pop max	Acc	Criteria
Ciconia nigra	Black Stork	B	1996	1	—	—	C6

Species of global conservation concern that do not meet IBA criteria: *Crex crex* (breeding).

■ Protection status
National None **International** High
IBA overlaps with Special Protection Area.

■ Conservation issues
Threats Infrastructure (U)

Rheinauen: Eltville–Bingen

C7 **213**

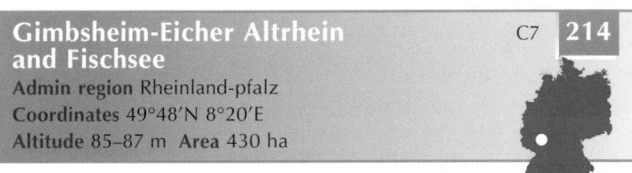

Admin region Hessen, Rheinland-pfalz
Coordinates 49°59'N 8°02'E
Altitude 81–83 m **Area** 475 ha

■ Site description
A wetland with fragments of riverine forest along the River Rhine. Also small islands, wet grassland and water-fringe vegetation.

Habitats Forest and woodland (alluvial/very wet forest), Grassland (humid grassland), Wetland (water-fringe vegetation)
Land-use Hunting, Water management

■ Birds
An important site for wintering waterbirds.

■ Protection status
National High **International** Partial
196 ha of IBA covered by Nature Reserve (Mariannenaue, 196 ha). 475 ha of IBA covered by Nature Reserve (Rheinauen Bingen Erbach, 475 ha). 29 ha of IBA covered by Nature Reserve (Rüdesheimer Aue, 29 ha). IBA overlaps with Ramsar Site (475 ha). IBA overlaps with Special Protection Area (Mariannenaue and Rüdesheimer Aue, 225 ha).

■ Conservation issues
Threats Recreation/tourism (U)

Gimbsheim-Eicher Altrhein and Fischsee

C7 **214**

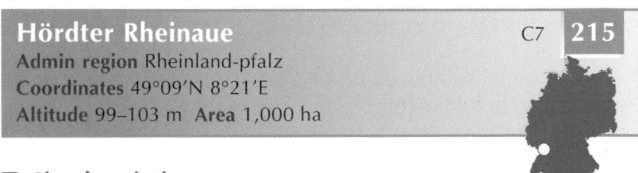

Admin region Rheinland-pfalz
Coordinates 49°48'N 8°20'E
Altitude 85–87 m **Area** 430 ha

■ Site description
A wetland along a previous course of the Rhine with large beds of *Phragmites* and *Typha*, small ponds and wet meadows.

Habitats Wetland (fen/transition mire/spring, water-fringe vegetation)
Land-use Agriculture, Fisheries/aquaculture, Tourism/recreation

■ Protection status
National Partial **International** Partial
IBA overlaps with Nature Reserve. IBA overlaps with Special Protection Area.

■ Conservation issues
Threats Agricultural intensification/expansion (U), Aquaculture/fisheries (U), Recreation/tourism (U)

Hördter Rheinaue

C7 **215**

Admin region Rheinland-pfalz
Coordinates 49°09'N 8°21'E
Altitude 99–103 m **Area** 1,000 ha

■ Site description
An old branch of the Rhine with large reedbeds (*Phragmites*), a gravel-pit and riverine forest.

Habitats Forest and woodland (alluvial/very wet forest), Wetland (standing fresh water; water-fringe vegetation)
Land-use Fisheries/aquaculture, Tourism/recreation

■ Birds
This is an important site for breeding herons, woodland species and wintering wildfowl.

■ Protection status
National Partial **International** None
Part of IBA overlaps with Nature Reserve (812 ha).

■ **Conservation issues**

Threats Intensified forest management (U)

Saar/Bliesgau/Westrich B2 216

Admin region Saarland
Coordinates 49°12′N 7°10′E
Altitude 190–401 m **Area** 24,100 ha

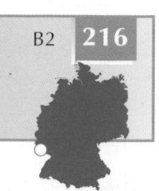

■ **Site description**
The site comprises slightly improved grasslands, arable land, *Fagus*, *Quercus*, *Alnus* and *Salix* forest, small villages and urban areas.

Habitats Forest and woodland (broadleaved deciduous forest; mixed forest; alluvial/very wet forest), Scrub (scrub), Grassland (steppe/dry calcareous grassland; humid grassland; mesophile grassland), Wetland (standing fresh water; river/stream; water-fringe vegetation; fen/transition mire/spring), Artificial landscape (highly improved reseeded grassland; arable land; perennial crops/orchards/groves; forestry plantation; other urban/industrial areas; ruderal land), Introduced/exotic vegetation
Land-use Agriculture (55%), Forestry (20%), Nature conservation/research (5%), Urban/industrial/transport (15%)

■ **Birds**

Species		Season	Year	Pop min	Pop max	Acc	Criteria
Tyto alba	Barn Owl	B	1998	50	—	B	B2

The site is important for grassland species. Species of global conservation concern that do not meet IBA criteria: *Crex crex* (breeding).

■ **Protection status**
National Low **International** None
1,800 ha of IBA covered by Nature Reserve (1,800 ha).

■ **Conservation issues**

Threats Abandonment/reduction of land management (B), Afforestation (C), Agricultural intensification/expansion (C), Disturbance to birds (C), Drainage (C), Filling-in of wetlands (C), Groundwater abstraction (C), Industrialization/urbanization (C), Infrastructure (C), Natural events (C), Recreation/tourism (B)

Threats include agriculture, urbanization, airfield expansion and disturbance from tourism. There is a proposal to create a Biosphere Reserve of 2,300 ha in the IBA.

Wagbach lowlands C6 217

Admin region Baden-Württemberg
Coordinates 49°16′N 8°30′E
Altitude 96–105 m **Area** 1,050 ha

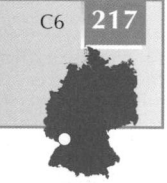

■ **Site description**
A wetland complex in the Rhine valley, comprising flooded gravel-pits, former settling ponds, reedbeds (*Phragmites*) and areas of small-scale cultivation. Additional habitats include mudflats, wet meadows and patches of forest.

Habitats Forest and woodland (10%; alluvial/very wet forest), Scrub (scrub), Grassland (humid grassland; mesophile grassland), Wetland (50%; standing fresh water; water-fringe vegetation; fen/transition mire/spring), Artificial landscape (35%; arable land; perennial crops/orchards/groves; ruderal land)
Land-use Agriculture (25%), Forestry (10%), Hunting (100%), Nature conservation/research (30%), Tourism/recreation (30%), Urban/industrial/transport (5%)

■ **Birds**

Species		Season	Year	Pop min	Pop max	Acc	Criteria
Luscinia svecica	Bluethroat	B	1998	150	200	—	C6

Breeding species include *Ixobrychus minutus*, *Ardea purpurea* and *Aythya ferina*. The site also supports a variety of wintering and passage waterbirds. Passage species of global conservation concern that do not meet IBA criteria: *Anser erythropus*, *Branta ruficollis*, *Aythya nyroca* (2–5 individuals), *Crex crex* and *Acrocephalus paludicola*.

■ **Protection status**
National Partial **International** High
224 ha of IBA covered by Nature Reserve (Wagbachniederung, 224 ha). IBA overlaps with Special Protection Area.

■ **Conservation issues**

Threats Agricultural intensification/expansion (U), Disturbance to birds (U), Recreation/tourism (U)

Water management is planned. The area is a candidate Special Area for Conservation.

Hockenheimer Rheinbogen B1i, C3, C6 218

Admin region Baden-Württemberg
Coordinates 49°20′N 8°30′E
Altitude 93–101 m **Area** 2,500 ha

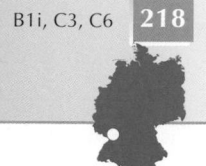

■ **Site description**
Part of the lower Rhine flood-plain which, as a result of embankment construction and river engineering, now only floods irregularly. Habitats include reed *Phragmites*-filled ditches, abandoned gravel- and clay-pits and riverine forests (mainly *Populus* sp. with *Salix* in inundated areas). Used primarily for agriculture, this IBA was known as 'Insultheimer Hof: Ludwig-See und Im Schacher' (former site DE068) in the previous pan-European IBA inventory (Grimmett and Jones 1989).

Habitats Forest and woodland (10%; alluvial/very wet forest), Scrub (scrub), Grassland (15%; humid grassland; mesophile grassland), Wetland (standing fresh water; water-fringe vegetation), Artificial landscape (70%; arable land; perennial crops/orchards/groves; ruderal land)
Land-use Agriculture (80%), Forestry (8%), Hunting (100%), Nature conservation/research (100%), Tourism/recreation (20%), Urban/industrial/transport (10%), Water management (10%)

■ **Birds**

Species		Season	Year	Pop min	Pop max	Acc	Criteria
Anser fabalis	Bean Goose	W	1996	—	2,000	A	B1i, C3
Luscinia svecica	Bluethroat	B	1997	15	30	A	C6

■ **Protection status**
National High **International** None
IBA overlaps with Landscape Protected Area and Nature Reserve.

■ **Conservation issues**

Threats Abandonment/reduction of land management (B), Agricultural intensification/expansion (C), Disturbance to birds (B), Drainage (B), Dredging/canalization (C), Recreation/tourism (B)

The area is a candidate Special Area for Conservation.

Orchard landscape between Hohenstaufen and Teck in the mid-Albvorland B3, C6 219

Admin region Baden-Württemberg
Coordinates 48°39′N 9°37′E
Altitude 284–822 m **Area** 68,000 ha

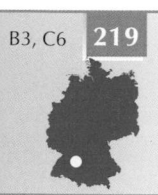

■ **Site description**
A heterogeneous landscape comprising areas of calcareous grassland, heathland with *Juniperus*, and orchards.

Habitats Forest and woodland (broadleaved deciduous forest; alluvial/very wet forest), Scrub (scrub; heathland), Grassland (steppe/dry calcareous grassland; humid grassland), Wetland (standing fresh water; river/stream; raised bog; water-fringe vegetation; fen/transition mire/spring), Rocky areas (rock stacks/islets; scree/boulders; caves), Artificial landscape (highly improved reseeded grassland; arable land; perennial crops/orchards/groves; forestry plantation; urban parks/gardens; other urban/industrial areas; ruderal land)
Land-use Agriculture, Forestry, Nature conservation/research, Urban/industrial/transport, Water management

■ Birds

Species	Season	Year	Pop min	Pop max	Acc	Criteria
Dendrocopos medius Middle Spotted Woodpecker	R	1996	90	90	—	B3
Ficedula albicollis Collared Flycatcher	B	1996	190	190	—	B3, C6

Breeding species include *Pernis apivorus*, *Milvus milvus*, *Falco peregrinus*, *Bubo bubo*, *Athene noctua*, *Picus canus* and *Lanius senator*.

■ Protection status

National Partial **International** None
IBA overlaps with Landscape Protected Area and Nature Reserve.

■ Conservation issues

Threats Abandonment/reduction of land management (U), Afforestation (U), Agricultural intensification/expansion (U), Disturbance to birds (U), Industrialization/ urbanization (U), Infrastructure (U), Recreation/tourism (U), Selective logging/cutting (U)

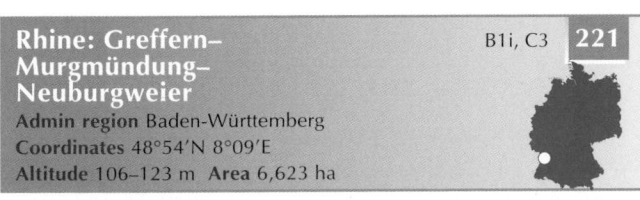

Rhine flats: Kehl–Helmlingen
B1i, B2, C3 **220**
Admin region Baden-Württemberg
Coordinates 48°40′N 7°53′E
Altitude 125–140 m **Area** 2,120 ha

■ Site description

The site comprises part of the former flood-plain of the now embanked River Rhine. Habitats include *Quercus–Ulmus*, *Quercus–Carpinus* and *Populus* forest, relict *Alnus* swamp-forest, springs, fish-ponds, arable land, meadows, and large abandoned gravel-pits.

Habitats Forest and woodland (broadleaved deciduous forest; alluvial/very wet forest), Grassland (humid grassland; mesophile grassland), Wetland (standing fresh water; river/ stream; fen/transition mire/spring), Artificial landscape (arable land)
Land-use Agriculture, Forestry, Tourism/recreation

■ Birds

Species	Season	Year	Pop min	Pop max	Acc	Criteria
¹ **Anser fabalis** Bean Goose	P	1998	220	1,200	—	B1i, C3
¹ **Anas strepera** Gadwall	P	1998	200	760	—	B1i, C3
Riparia riparia Sand Martin	B	1997	650	650	—	B2

1. 1993–1998.

This is an important stop-over site for passage wildfowl. Nationally important numbers of breeding *Larus melanocephalus* are present.

■ Protection status

National Partial **International** None
IBA overlaps with Landscape Protected Area and Nature Reserve.

■ Conservation issues

Threats Agricultural intensification/expansion (U), Construction/impact of dyke/dam/ barrage (U), Deforestation (commercial) (U), Extraction industry (U), Industrialization/ urbanization (U), Recreation/tourism (U)

Rhine: Greffern– Murgmündung– Neuburgweier
B1i, C3 **221**
Admin region Baden-Württemberg
Coordinates 48°54′N 8°09′E
Altitude 106–123 m **Area** 6,623 ha

■ Site description

Situated in the Rhine valley, where the main river is slow-flowing. Additional habitat-types present include oxbow lakes and riverine forest.

Habitats Forest and woodland (alluvial/very wet forest), Wetland (standing fresh water; river/stream)

■ Birds

Species	Season	Year	Pop min	Pop max	Acc	Criteria
Anser fabalis Bean Goose	W	1998	400	1,020	—	B1i, C3
Anas strepera Gadwall	W	1998	190	565	—	B1i, C3

■ Protection status

National Partial **International** None
IBA overlaps with Nature Reserve and Landscape Protected Area.

Rhine flats: Nonnenweier–Kehl
A4i, B1i, B2, C3, C6 **222**
Admin region Baden-Württemberg
Coordinates 48°27′N 7°46′E
Altitude 139–157 m **Area** 3,800 ha

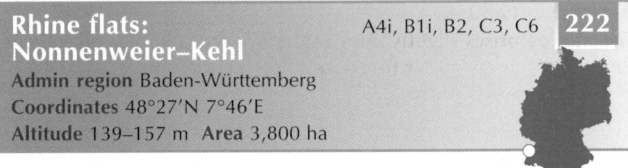

■ Site description

Situated in the valley of the embanked Rhine, the IBA comprises *Quercus–Ulmus* and *Quercus–Carpinus* riverine forest, dry grassland, meadows, large gravel-pits, reedbeds (*Phragmites*), springs, arable land and orchards.

Habitats Forest and woodland (broadleaved deciduous forest; alluvial/very wet forest), Grassland (dry siliceous grassland; humid grassland; mesophile grassland), Wetland (river/stream; water-fringe vegetation; fen/transition mire/spring), Artificial landscape (arable land; perennial crops/orchards/groves)
Land-use Forestry, Tourism/recreation

■ Birds

Species	Season	Year	Pop min	Pop max	Acc	Criteria
¹ **Anas strepera** Gadwall	P	1996	1,000	1,450	—	A4i, B1i, C3
Alcedo atthis Kingfisher	R	1996	32	32	—	B2, C6

1. 1988–1996.

This is an important stop-over site for a range of passage waterbirds. Breeding species include *Anas strepera*, *Alcedo atthis* and *Dendrocopos medius*.

■ Protection status

National Partial **International** Low
IBA overlaps Nature Reserve. IBA overlaps with Special Protection Area.

■ Conservation issues

Threats Abandonment/reduction of land management (U), Consequences of animal/ plant introductions (U), Construction/impact of dyke/dam/barrage (U), Deforestation (commercial) (U), Extraction industry (U), Infrastructure (U), Recreation/tourism (U)

Rhine flats: Sasbach–Wittenweier
A4i, B1i, B2, B3, C3, C6 **223**
Admin region Baden-Württemberg
Coordinates 48°15′N 7°41′E
Altitude 155–180 m **Area** 4,400 ha

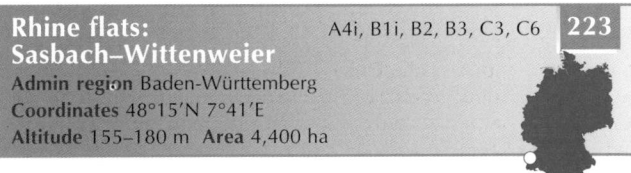

■ Site description

The site comprises part of the former flood-plain of the now embanked River Rhine. Habitat-types include riverine forest, relict *Alnus* swamp-forest, springs, gravel-pits, reedbeds (*Phragmites*), dry grassland, meadows, arable land and orchards. An introduced species of herb (*Solidago*) is spreading within the native vegetation.

Habitats Forest and woodland (broadleaved deciduous forest; alluvial/very wet forest), Grassland (dry siliceous grassland; mesophile grassland), Wetland (river/stream; water- fringe vegetation; fen/transition mire/spring), Artificial landscape (arable land; perennial crops/orchards/groves)
Land-use Forestry, Tourism/recreation

■ Birds

This is an important stop-over site for passage wildfowl, and is nationally important for breeding *Sterna hirundo*.

Species	Season	Year	Pop min	Pop max	Acc	Criteria
[1] *Phalacrocorax carbo* Cormorant	W	1996	600	1,800	—	B1i, C3
[1] *Anas strepera* Gadwall	P	1996	1,000	1,530	—	A4i, B1i, C3
Alcedo atthis Kingfisher	R	1995	27	27	—	B2, C6
[1] *Dendrocopos medius* Middle Spotted Woodpecker	R	1996	110	—	—	B3
Lanius collurio Red-backed Shrike	B	1996	416	416	—	B2, C6

1. 1989–1996.

■ Protection status
National Partial **International** None
IBA overlaps with Landscape Protected Area and Nature Reserve.

■ Conservation issues

Threats Consequences of animal/plant introductions (U), Construction/impact of dyke/dam/barrage (U), Deforestation (commercial) (U), Extraction industry (U), Recreation/tourism (U)

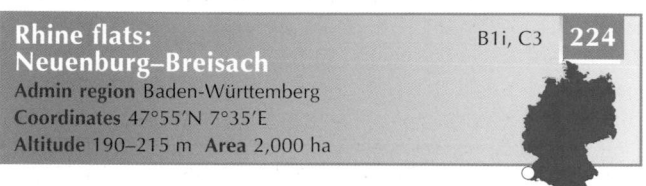

Rhine flats: Neuenburg–Breisach   B1i, C3   224
Admin region Baden-Württemberg
Coordinates 47°55′N 7°35′E
Altitude 190–215 m   **Area** 2,000 ha

■ Site description
An 18-km stretch of the River Rhine containing riverine forest, *Salix* scrub, small rapids, gravel-banks and springs. A further 10 km of the river is embanked. Additional habitat-types include dry former riverine forest, *Pinus* forest, dry grassland and gravel-pits.

Habitats Forest and woodland (broadleaved deciduous forest; alluvial/very wet forest), Scrub (scrub), Grassland (dry siliceous grassland), Wetland (standing fresh water; river/stream; fen/transition mire/spring), Artificial landscape (other urban/industrial areas)
Land-use Forestry, Tourism/recreation, Urban/industrial/transport

■ Birds

Species	Season	Year	Pop min	Pop max	Acc	Criteria
Anser fabalis Bean Goose	P	1998	650	1,250	—	B1i, C3

This is an important site for wintering wildfowl.

■ Protection status
National Partial **International** Low
IBA overlaps Nature Reserve. IBA overlaps with Special Protection Area.

■ Conservation issues

Threats Construction/impact of dyke/dam/barrage (U), Deforestation (commercial) (U), Extraction industry (U), Recreation/tourism (U)

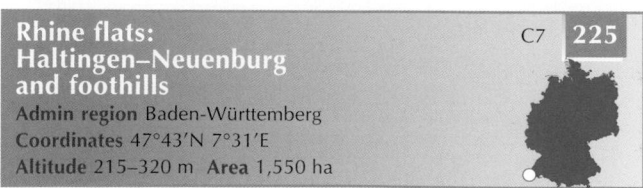

Rhine flats: Haltingen–Neuenburg and foothills   C7   225
Admin region Baden-Württemberg
Coordinates 47°43′N 7°31′E
Altitude 215–320 m   **Area** 1,550 ha

■ Site description
A stretch of the Rhine river valley comprising riverine forest, dry, over-utilized riparian forest, *Salix* scrub, rough meadows, rapids, gravel-banks, springs, gravel-pits, arable land and the slopes of the foothills.

Habitats Forest and woodland (alluvial/very wet forest), Scrub (scrub), Grassland (dry siliceous grassland; mesophile grassland), Wetland (river/stream; fen/transition mire/spring), Artificial landscape (arable land; other urban/industrial areas)
Land-use Tourism/recreation, Urban/industrial/transport

■ Birds
Breeding species include *Pernis apivorus* and *Alcedo atthis*. The site is nationally important for wintering wildfowl.

■ Protection status
National Partial **International** Low
IBA overlaps with Landscape Protected Area and Nature Reserve. IBA overlaps with Special Protection Area.

■ Conservation issues

Threats Extraction industry (U), Infrastructure (U), Recreation/tourism (U)

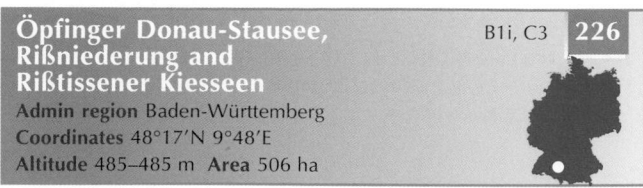

Öpfinger Donau-Stausee, Rißniederung and Rißtissener Kiesseen   B1i, C3   226
Admin region Baden-Württemberg
Coordinates 48°17′N 9°48′E
Altitude 485–485 m   **Area** 506 ha

■ Site description
A reservoir connected to the River Danube, with small reedbeds (*Phragmites*) and patches of forest. The site also includes the lower reaches of the River Riß and the dredged ponds near Rißtissen. A hydroelectric power-station is situated adjacent to the reservoir.

Habitats Forest and woodland, Wetland (standing fresh water; water-fringe vegetation)
Land-use Tourism/recreation, Urban/industrial/transport

■ Birds

Species	Season	Year	Pop min	Pop max	Acc	Criteria
Anas strepera Gadwall	W	1994	—	450	—	B1i, C3
Aythya ferina Pochard	W	1994	—	8,900	—	B1i, C3

The site is important for wintering waterbirds. Breeding birds include *Ciconia ciconia*.

■ Protection status
National Low **International** None
IBA overlaps with Landscape Protected Area.

■ Conservation issues

Threats Disturbance to birds (U), Infrastructure (U), Recreation/tourism (U)

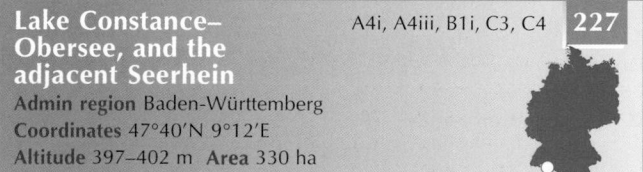

Lake Constance–Obersee, and the adjacent Seerhein   A4i, A4iii, B1i, C3, C4   227
Admin region Baden-Württemberg
Coordinates 47°40′N 9°12′E
Altitude 397–402 m   **Area** 330 ha

■ Site description
The IBA comprises the bay where the Rhine leaves Lake Constance and part of the River Rhine itself, adjoining Swiss IBA 015. The bay remains ice-free during the winter.

Habitats Wetland (standing fresh water; river/stream)
Land-use Tourism/recreation

■ Birds

Species	Season	Year	Pop min	Pop max	Acc	Criteria
Aythya ferina Pochard	W	1994	—	20,000	—	A4i, B1i, C3
Aythya fuligula Tufted Duck	W	1994	—	16,000	—	A4i, B1i, C3

The site holds more than 20,000 wintering wildfowl on a regular basis.

■ Protection status
National None **International** None

■ Conservation issues

Threats Disturbance to birds (U), Recreation/tourism (U)

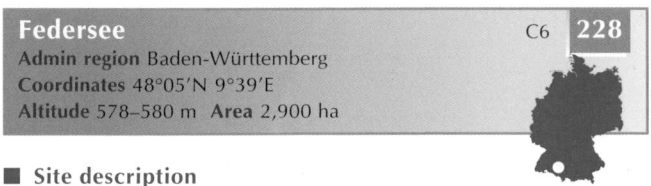

Federsee   C6   **228**
Admin region Baden-Württemberg
Coordinates 48°05′N 9°39′E
Altitude 578–580 m **Area** 2,900 ha

■ Site description
The largest area of mire in Baden-Württemberg, with lakes, forested areas of fen, and raised bogs all present. Increasingly large areas of bog are no longer utilized; smaller areas are still used for agriculture.

Habitats Forest and woodland (5%; alluvial/very wet forest), Wetland (95%; standing fresh water; raised bog; fen/transition mire/spring)
Land-use Agriculture (60%), Forestry (2%)

■ Birds

Species	Season	Year	Pop min	Pop max	Acc	Criteria
Circus aeruginosus Marsh Harrier	B	1997	15	18	A	C6
Porzana porzana Spotted Crake	B	1998	—	8	—	C6
Crex crex Corncrake	B	1997	2	11	—	C6

105 species regularly breed; 267 species have been recorded in total.

■ Protection status
National High **International** High
2,900 ha of IBA covered by Nature Reserve (Federseemoor, 2,900 ha). IBA overlaps with Landscape Protected Area. IBA overlaps with Special Protection Area.

■ Conservation issues

Threats Abandonment/reduction of land management (A), Afforestation (U), Agricultural intensification/expansion (C), Drainage (A), Industrialization/urbanization (U), Infrastructure (U)

There is an ongoing LIFE project relating to the protection of nature in the Federsee area.

Northern Black Forest,   B2, B3, C6   **229**
west of the Murg
Admin region Baden-Württemberg
Coordinates 48°30′N 8°15′E
Altitude 250–1,163 m **Area** 60,000 ha

■ Site description
An upland landscape supporting *Fagus* and *Quercus* forest, native montane coniferous forest and near-natural montane mixed forest (*Fagus–Abies–Picea*). Interspersed with these are areas of heathland, dry grassland, moist meadow, lightly improved meadow and pasture, raised bog, tarns and screes.

Habitats Forest and woodland (broadleaved deciduous forest; native coniferous forest; mixed forest), Scrub (heathland), Grassland (dry siliceous grassland; humid grassland; mesophile grassland), Wetland (standing fresh water; river/stream; raised bog), Rocky areas (scree/boulders)
Land-use Agriculture, Forestry, Tourism/recreation

■ Birds

Species	Season	Year	Pop min	Pop max	Acc	Criteria
Falco peregrinus Peregrine	R	1998	15	20	—	B2, C6
Bonasa bonasia Hazel Grouse	R	1998	10	15	—	C6
Turdus torquatus Ring Ouzel	B	1998	110	165	—	B3
Serinus citrinella Citril Finch	B	1998	160	250	—	B3

An important site for breeding species of upland habitats such as *Falco peregrinus*, *Tetrao urogallus*, *Glaucidium passerinum* and *Aegolius funereus*.

■ Protection status
National Partial **International** Low

IBA overlaps with Landscape Protected Area and Nature Reserve. IBA overlaps with Special Protection Area.

■ Conservation issues

Threats Abandonment/reduction of land management (U), Agricultural intensification/expansion (U), Industrialization/urbanization (U), Infrastructure (U), Intensified forest management (U), Recreation/tourism (U)

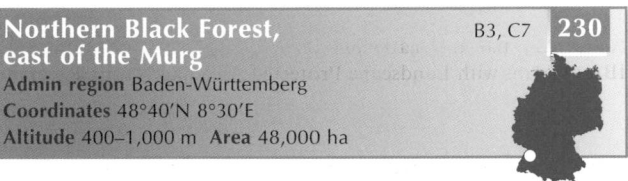

Northern Black Forest,   B3, C7   **230**
east of the Murg
Admin region Baden-Württemberg
Coordinates 48°40′N 8°30′E
Altitude 400–1,000 m **Area** 48,000 ha

■ Site description
An upland landscape supporting *Fagus* and *Quercus* forest, native montane coniferous forest and near-natural montane mixed forest (*Fagus–Abies–Picea*). Interspersed with these are areas of heathland, dry grassland, moist meadow, lightly improved meadow and pasture, raised bog, reed- *Phragmites* and sedge-beds, springs and screes.

Habitats Forest and woodland (broadleaved deciduous forest; native coniferous forest; mixed forest), Scrub (scrub; heathland), Grassland (dry siliceous grassland; humid grassland; mesophile grassland), Wetland (river/stream; raised bog; water-fringe vegetation; fen/transition mire/spring), Rocky areas (scree/boulders)
Land-use Forestry, Tourism/recreation

■ Birds

Species	Season	Year	Pop min	Pop max	Acc	Criteria
[1] *Serinus citrinella* Citril Finch	B	1998	30	60	—	B3
1. 1986–1998.						

An important site for breeding species of upland and forest habitats such as *Tetrao urogallus*, *Glaucidium passerinum* and *Aegolius funereus*.

■ Protection status
National Partial **International** Low
IBA overlaps with Landscape Protected Area and Nature Reserve. IBA overlaps with Special Protection Area.

■ Conservation issues

Threats Abandonment/reduction of land management (U), Afforestation (U), Industrialization/urbanization (U), Infrastructure (U), Intensified forest management (U), Recreation/tourism (U)

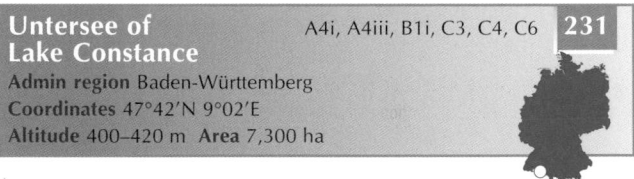

Untersee of   A4i, A4iii, B1i, C3, C4, C6   **231**
Lake Constance
Admin region Baden-Württemberg
Coordinates 47°42′N 9°02′E
Altitude 400–420 m **Area** 7,300 ha

■ Site description
The Untersee is a large shallow lake situated on the course of the River Rhine, adjacent to Swiss IBA 014. Habitat-types include riverine forest, *Alnus* swamp-forest, dry grassland, wet meadows, lightly improved grassland, shallow water zones, reed- *Phragmites* and sedge-beds, mudflats and gravel-banks.

Habitats Forest and woodland (alluvial/very wet forest), Scrub, Grassland (steppe/dry calcareous grassland; humid grassland; mesophile grassland), Wetland (mudflat/sandflat; standing fresh water; water-fringe vegetation)
Land-use Fisheries/aquaculture, Tourism/recreation

■ Birds

Species	Season	Year	Pop min	Pop max	Acc	Criteria
[1] *Anas strepera* Gadwall	P	1998	—	11,667	—	A4i, B1i, C3
[2] *Anas crecca* Teal	P	1998	—	11,000	—	B1i, C3
[3] *Anas clypeata* Shoveler	P	1998	—	3,846	—	B1i, C3

Species ... continued		Season	Year	Pop min	Pop max	Acc	Criteria
[4] *Netta rufina*	Red-crested Pochard	P	1998	—	10,803	—	A4i, B1i, C3
[5] *Aythya ferina*	Pochard	P	1998	—	44,450	—	A4i, B1i, C3
[6] *Aythya fuligula*	Tufted Duck	P	1998	—	53,672	—	A4i, B1i, C3
Porzana porzana	Spotted Crake	B	1998	5	15	—	C6

1. Mean = 6,500 individuals. 1993–1998.
2. Mean = 4,200 individuals. 1993–1998.
3. Mean = 2,100 individuals. 1993–1998.
4. Mean = 5,500 individuals. 1993–1998.
5. Mean = 32,000 individuals. 1993–1998.
6. Mean = 34,000 individuals. 1993–1998.

This is an important stop-over site for passage wildfowl. Species of global conservation concern that do not meet IBA criteria: *Aythya nyroca* (breeding).

■ **Protection status**

National High **International** High
IBA overlaps with Landscape Protected Area and Nature Reserve. IBA overlaps with Ramsar Site and Special Protection Area.

■ **Conservation issues**

Threats Aquaculture/fisheries (U), Industrialization/urbanization (U), Infrastructure (U), Recreation/tourism (U)

Silzen meadows and bog, near Stettfeld — C6 232

Admin region Baden-Württemberg
Coordinates 49°10′N 8°37′E
Altitude 109–111 m **Area** 250 ha

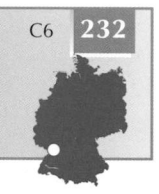

■ **Site description**

An area of *Alnus* swamp-forest, wet grassland, reed *Phragmites* and sedge-beds located in the Kinzig-Murg depression. Other habitat-types present include fallow land with wet hollows, ponds and wet *Salix* scrub.

Habitats Forest and woodland (alluvial/very wet forest), Scrub (scrub), Grassland (humid grassland), Wetland (standing fresh water; river/stream; water-fringe vegetation; fen/transition mire/spring), Artificial landscape (arable land; ruderal land)
Land-use Agriculture

■ **Birds**

Species		Season	Year	Pop min	Pop max	Acc	Criteria
Luscinia svecica	Bluethroat	B	1998	5	6	—	C6

■ **Protection status**

National Partial **International** None
IBA overlaps with Nature Reserve (97 ha).

■ **Conservation issues**

Threats Abandonment/reduction of land management (U), Agricultural intensification/expansion (U), Industrialization/urbanization (U), Infrastructure (U)

Philippsburger Altrhein and Rheinschanzinsel — C6 233

Admin region Baden-Württemberg
Coordinates 49°16′N 8°27′E
Altitude 94–98 m **Area** 600 ha

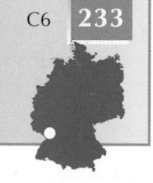

■ **Site description**

A wetland situated in the upper Rhine valley, including riverine forest (mainly *Populus*), drainage ditches, reedbeds (*Phragmites*), gravel-pits and extensive arable lands. The site also includes the Philippsburg nuclear power-station.

Habitats Forest and woodland (alluvial/very wet forest), Wetland (river/stream; water-fringe vegetation), Artificial landscape (arable land; other urban/industrial areas)
Land-use Agriculture, Urban/industrial/transport

■ **Birds**

Species		Season	Year	Pop min	Pop max	Acc	Criteria
Luscinia svecica	Bluethroat	B	1998	10	13	—	C6

■ **Protection status**

National None **International** None

■ **Conservation issues**

Threats Agricultural intensification/expansion (U), Construction/impact of dyke/dam/barrage (U), Drainage (U)

Schiltach and Berneck valleys, near Schramberg — C6 234

Admin region Baden-Württemberg
Coordinates 48°13′N 8°23′E
Altitude 370–820 m **Area** 1,800 ha

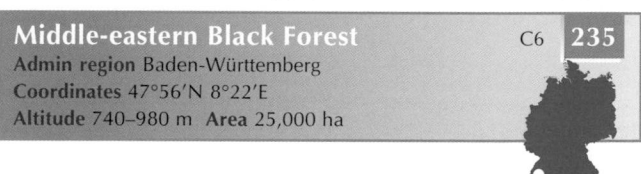

■ **Site description**

The site comprises mixed forests (*Picea*, *Abies*, *Pinus*, *Fagus*, *Fraxinus*, *Acer* and *Quercus*), some on steep slopes, relict *Corylus* copses, granite outcrops, scree and a quarry.

Habitats Forest and woodland (mixed forest), Wetland (river/stream), Rocky areas (scree/boulders; inland cliff), Artificial landscape (other urban/industrial areas)
Land-use Forestry, Tourism/recreation

■ **Birds**

Species		Season	Year	Pop min	Pop max	Acc	Criteria
[1] *Bonasa bonasia*	Hazel Grouse	R	1998	10	—	—	C6

1. 1993–1998.

■ **Protection status**

National Partial **International** None
IBA overlaps with Landscape Protected Area.

■ **Conservation issues**

Threats Infrastructure (U), Intensified forest management (U), Recreation/tourism (U)

Middle-eastern Black Forest — C6 235

Admin region Baden-Württemberg
Coordinates 47°56′N 8°22′E
Altitude 740–980 m **Area** 25,000 ha

■ **Site description**

The site comprises mainly coniferous forest (*Picea*, *Abies*, *Pinus*), with a diverse shrub layer. Riverine forest, hill-slope forest (including *Acer* and *Quercus*), relict coppice, forest moors, streams with tall herb communities, sedge-beds and screes are also present.

Habitats Forest and woodland (native coniferous forest; mixed forest; alluvial/very wet forest), Wetland (river/stream; water-fringe vegetation; fen/transition mire/spring), Rocky areas (scree/boulders; inland cliff)
Land-use Forestry, Tourism/recreation

■ **Birds**

Species		Season	Year	Pop min	Pop max	Acc	Criteria
Falco peregrinus	Peregrine	R	1998	3	4	—	C6

■ **Protection status**

National Partial **International** None
IBA overlaps with Landscape Protected Area.

■ **Conservation issues**

Threats Infrastructure (U), Intensified forest management (U), Recreation/tourism (U)

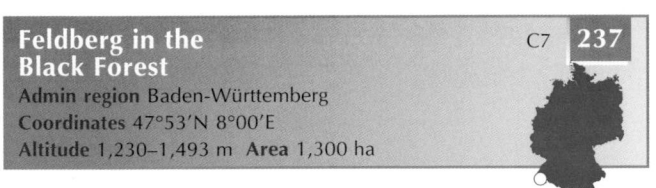

Schwarza and Schlücht valleys — C6 236

Admin region Baden-Württemberg
Coordinates 47°41′N 8°15′E
Altitude 420–830 m **Area** 500 ha

■ Site description
Deciduous and mixed forest (*Abies–Fagus*, *Quercus–Fagus*, *Tilia–Acer*) with riverine and relict *Pinus* forests, cliffs and screes.

Habitats Forest and woodland (broadleaved deciduous forest; native coniferous forest; mixed forest; alluvial/very wet forest), Wetland (river/stream), Rocky areas (scree/boulders; inland cliff)

■ Birds

Species	Season	Year	Pop min	Pop max	Acc	Criteria
Falco peregrinus Peregrine	R	1998	4	—	—	C6

The site holds the largest breeding population of *Phylloscopus bonelli* in the Black Forest.

■ Protection status
National High **International** None
IBA overlaps with Landscape Protected Area and Nature Reserve.

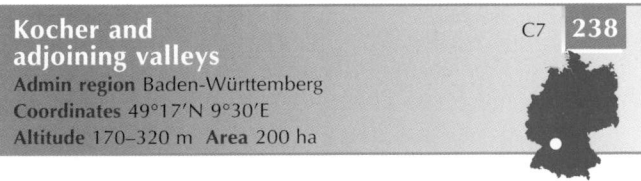

Feldberg in the Black Forest — C7 237

Admin region Baden-Württemberg
Coordinates 47°53′N 8°00′E
Altitude 1,230–1,493 m **Area** 1,300 ha

■ Site description
A treeless plateau of high montane to subalpine grassland, used mainly for rough pasture. The exposed northern slopes support semi-natural montane mixed forest (*Picea*, *Abies*, *Acer*). Additional habitats include small fens and transitional bogs, springs and tarns.

Habitats Forest and woodland (mixed forest), Grassland (alpine/subalpine/boreal grassland), Wetland (fen/transition mire/spring), Rocky areas (inland cliff)
Land-use Agriculture, Tourism/recreation

■ Birds
The site is important for breeding *Picoides tridactylus*, *Anthus pratensis* and *A. spinoletta*.

■ Protection status
National High **International** Partial
IBA overlaps with Nature Reserve. IBA overlaps with Special Protection Area.

■ Conservation issues
Threats Recreation/tourism (U)

Kocher and adjoining valleys — C7 238

Admin region Baden-Württemberg
Coordinates 49°17′N 9°30′E
Altitude 170–320 m **Area** 200 ha

■ Site description
A semi-natural river with adjoining side valleys.

Habitats Wetland (river/stream)
Land-use Fisheries/aquaculture, Tourism/recreation

■ Protection status
National Partial **International** Low
IBA overlaps with Landscape Protected Area and Nature Reserve. IBA overlaps with Special Protection Area.

■ Conservation issues
Threats Aquaculture/fisheries (U), Construction/impact of dyke/dam/barrage (U), Recreation/tourism (U)

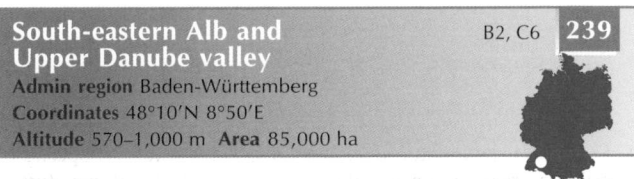

South-eastern Alb and Upper Danube valley — B2, C6 239

Admin region Baden-Württemberg
Coordinates 48°10′N 8°50′E
Altitude 570–1,000 m **Area** 85,000 ha

■ Site description
The heterogeneous landscape of the Swabian Alb is composed mainly of extensive, rough *Juniperus* grassland and large, coherent blocks of mature forest situated on the Alb plateau. The slopes of the Alb are characterized by forest, steppe-heath, cliffs and slag-heaps. The valleys hold riverine forest, stream habitats and tall herb communities.

Habitats Forest and woodland (broadleaved deciduous forest; native coniferous forest; mixed forest), Grassland (steppe/dry calcareous grassland; mesophile grassland), Wetland (river/stream; fen/transition mire/spring), Rocky areas (scree/boulders; inland cliff)
Land-use Agriculture, Forestry, Tourism/recreation

■ Birds

Species	Season	Year	Pop min	Pop max	Acc	Criteria
[1] *Falco peregrinus* Peregrine	R	1998	35	45	—	B2, C6
[1] *Bubo bubo* Eagle Owl	R	1998	5	11	—	B2
Lanius collurio Red-backed Shrike	B	1998	300	350	—	B2, C6

1. 1990–1998.

This is an important site for breeding raptors, *Lullula arborea* and *Lanius excubitor*. Species of global conservation concern that do not meet IBA criteria: *Crex crex* (2–7 breeding pairs).

■ Protection status
National Partial **International** Low
IBA overlaps with Landscape Protected Area and Nature Reserve. IBA overlaps with Special Protection Area.

■ Conservation issues
Threats Abandonment/reduction of land management (U), Afforestation (U), Agricultural intensification/expansion (U), Consequences of animal/plant introductions (U), Industrialization/urbanization (U), Intensified forest management (U), Recreation/ tourism (U)

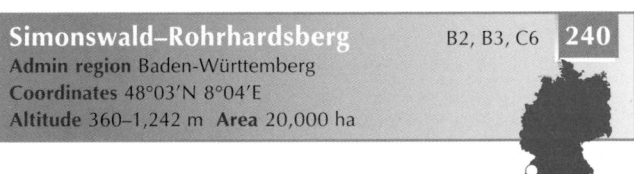

Simonswald–Rohrhardsberg — B2, B3, C6 240

Admin region Baden-Württemberg
Coordinates 48°03′N 8°04′E
Altitude 360–1,242 m **Area** 20,000 ha

■ Site description
The site comprises plateau, slope and valley habitats, including semi-natural deciduous and mixed forest (dry *Quercus* and *Fagus–Abies*), ravine and riverine forest, coppice forest, *Picea* and other coniferous forest, meadows, pasture, arable land, cliffs, screes and mountain streams.

Habitats Forest and woodland (broadleaved deciduous forest; native coniferous forest; mixed forest; alluvial/very wet forest), Grassland (humid grassland), Wetland (river/stream), Rocky areas (scree/boulders; inland cliff), Artificial landscape (arable land)

■ Birds

Species	Season	Year	Pop min	Pop max	Acc	Criteria
[1] *Falco peregrinus* Peregrine	R	1996	—	6	—	B2, C6
[1] *Bonasa bonasia* Hazel Grouse	R	1996	10	15	—	C6
Lanius collurio Red-backed Shrike	B	1996	1,000	1,860	—	B2, C6
[1] *Serinus citrinella* Citril Finch	B	1996	35	45	—	B3

1. 1989–1996.

■ Protection status
National Partial **International** Low

IBA overlaps with Landscape Protected Area and Nature Reserve.
IBA overlaps with Special Protection Area.

■ **Conservation issues**

Land-use Agriculture (U)

Northern Karlsruhe Hardt   C6 241

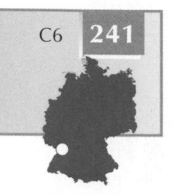

Admin region Baden-Württemberg
Coordinates 49°06′N 8°26′E
Altitude 108–114 m **Area** 4,950 ha

■ **Site description**
Mainly *Pinus* forest with *Fagus*, *Quercus*, *Carpinus* and *Tilia* on sandy
substrates. Also includes large cultivated areas, abandoned gravel-
pits with reeds *Phragmites*, and extensive areas of shallow water.

Habitats Forest and woodland (mixed forest), Wetland (standing fresh water; water-fringe vegetation),
Artificial landscape (arable land; perennial crops/orchards/groves; other urban/industrial areas)
Land-use Agriculture, Forestry

■ **Birds**

Species	Season	Year	Pop min	Pop max	Acc	Criteria
Caprimulgus europaeus Nightjar	B	1998	7	13	—	C6

■ **Protection status**
National Partial **International** None
IBA overlaps with Landscape Protected Area and Nature Reserve.

■ **Conservation issues**

Threats Deforestation (commercial) (U), Industrialization/urbanization (U), Infrastructure (U)

Lake Überlingen (Lake Constance) B1i, C3, C6 242

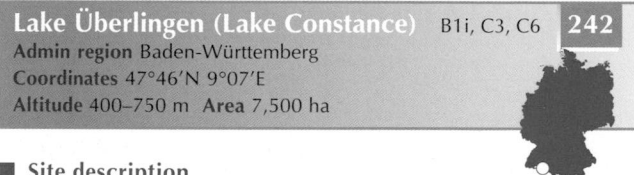

Admin region Baden-Württemberg
Coordinates 47°46′N 9°07′E
Altitude 400–750 m **Area** 7,500 ha

■ **Site description**
Part of Lake Constance with reedbeds (*Phragmites*) and extensive areas
of mud. Inland are tracts of riverine forest (mainly *Salix*), dry forest
(*Pinus* and *Fagus*), ravine and hill-slope mixed forest, lightly improved
hay-meadows, calcareous dry grassland, orchards, springs and cliffs.

Habitats Forest and woodland (broadleaved deciduous forest; native coniferous forest;
mixed forest; alluvial/very wet forest), Grassland (steppe/dry calcareous grassland;
humid grassland; mesophile grassland), Wetland (mudflat/sandflat; standing fresh water;
river/stream; water-fringe vegetation; fen/transition mire/spring), Rocky areas (inland
cliff), Artificial landscape (perennial crops/orchards/groves)
Land-use Agriculture, Tourism/recreation

■ **Birds**

Species	Season	Year	Pop min	Pop max	Acc	Criteria
¹ *Netta rufina* Red-crested Pochard	P	1998	655	655	—	B1i, C3
² *Aythya ferina* Pochard	P	1998	8,361	8,361	—	B1i, C3
² *Aythya fuligula* Tufted Duck	P	1998	11,179	11,179	—	B1i, C3
Falco peregrinus Peregrine	R	1998	3	4	—	C6

1. 1994–1998. Also breeds.
2. 1994–1998.

This is an important stop-over site for passage species of wildfowl.

■ **Protection status**
National High **International** Partial
IBA overlaps with Landscape Protected Area and Nature Reserve.
IBA overlaps with Special Protection Area.

■ **Conservation issues**

Threats Agricultural intensification/expansion (U), Industrialization/urbanization (U),
Recreation/tourism (U)

Jagst and adjoining valleys   B2, C6 243

Admin region Baden-Württemberg
Coordinates 49°20′N 9°30′E
Altitude 145–410 m **Area** 400 ha

■ **Site description**
A deep, narrow cliff-lined river valley that broadens out into a
landscape comprising riverine forest, grassland, arable land, small
ponds, springs and gravel-banks.

Habitats Forest and woodland (broadleaved deciduous forest; alluvial/very wet forest),
Grassland (humid grassland; mesophile grassland), Wetland (standing fresh water;
river/stream; fen/transition mire/spring), Rocky areas (inland cliff), Artificial landscape
(arable land)
Land-use Agriculture, Tourism/recreation

■ **Birds**

Species	Season	Year	Pop min	Pop max	Acc	Criteria
Alcedo atthis Kingfisher	R	1998	25	40	—	B2, C6

■ **Protection status**
National Partial **International** Low
IBA overlaps with Landscape Protected Area and Nature Reserve.
IBA overlaps with Special Protection Area.

■ **Conservation issues**

Threats Recreation/tourism (U)

Rhine flats: Karlsruhe–Rheinsheim   B1i, C3, C6 244

Admin region Baden-Württemberg
Coordinates 49°11′N 8°23′E
Altitude 98–103 m **Area** 2,900 ha

■ **Site description**
An alluvial flood-plain in the meander zone of the upper Rhine.
Former riverbeds are surrounded by broad reed *Phragmites* fringes,
softwood riparian forest and relict hardwood riverine forest. Other
lowland habitat-types include arable land, meadows, groves and
hedges.

Habitats Forest and woodland (alluvial/very wet forest), Grassland (humid grassland;
mesophile grassland), Wetland (standing fresh water; river/stream; water-fringe
vegetation), Artificial landscape (arable land; perennial crops/orchards/groves)
Land-use Agriculture

■ **Birds**

Species	Season	Year	Pop min	Pop max	Acc	Criteria
¹ *Phalacrocorax carbo* Cormorant	P	1998	1,200	1,200	—	B1i, C3
Luscinia svecica Bluethroat	B	1998	15	25	—	C6

1. 1993–1998.

■ **Protection status**
National Partial **International** Partial
IBA overlaps with Landscape Protected Area and Nature Reserve.
IBA overlaps with Special Protection Area.

Orchards and vineyards between Waldhausen and Geradstetten   B3, C6 245

Admin region Baden-Württemberg
Coordinates 48°49′N 9°34′E
Altitude 250–450 m **Area** 1,400 ha

■ **Site description**
Orchards and vineyards interspersed with meadows, pasture, small
ponds, arable land, hedges, groves, gardens and fallow land.

Habitats Grassland (humid grassland; mesophile grassland), Wetland (standing fresh water; water-fringe vegetation), Artificial landscape (arable land; perennial crops/ orchards/groves; urban parks/gardens; other urban/industrial areas; ruderal land)
Land-use Agriculture, Tourism/recreation

■ Birds

Species	Season	Year	Pop min	Pop max	Acc	Criteria
¹*Ficedula albicollis* Collared Flycatcher	B	1998	65	120	—	B3, C6
Lanius collurio Red-backed Shrike	B	1998	210	280	—	C6

1. 1989–1998.

■ Protection status
National Partial **International** None
IBA overlaps with Landscape Protected Area and Nature Reserve.

■ Conservation issues

Threats Abandonment/reduction of land management (U), Agricultural intensification/ expansion (U), Industrialization/urbanization (U), Recreation/tourism (U)

Wutach ravine
C6 **246**
Admin region Baden-Württemberg
Coordinates 47°52′N 8°25′E
Altitude 480–930 m **Area** 4,650 ha

■ Site description
Deep ravines with the Wutach and Gauchach streams. Gravel-banks support *Petasites* communities. Habitat-types include *Alnus* riverine forest, ravine forest (*Fagus*, *Abies-Fagus* and *Pinus-Abies*), *Salix* scrub, dry grassland, lightly agriculturally-improved meadows, cliff communities, fallow land, orchards and gravel-pits.

Habitats Forest and woodland (broadleaved deciduous forest; native coniferous forest; mixed forest; alluvial/very wet forest), Scrub (scrub), Grassland (steppe/dry calcareous grassland; mesophile grassland), Wetland (river/stream), Rocky areas (inland cliff), Artificial landscape (perennial crops/orchards/groves; other urban/industrial areas; ruderal land)
Land-use Agriculture, Tourism/recreation

■ Birds

Species	Season	Year	Pop min	Pop max	Acc	Criteria
Lanius collurio Red-backed Shrike	B	1998	100	130	—	C6

■ Protection status
National High **International** High
IBA overlaps with Landscape Protected Area and Nature Reserve. IBA overlaps with Special Protection Area.

■ Conservation issues

Threats Afforestation (U), Agricultural intensification/expansion (U), Industrialization/ urbanization (U), Recreation/tourism (U)

Kaiserstuhl
C6 **247**
Admin region Baden-Württemberg
Coordinates 48°06′N 7°40′E
Altitude 180–557 m **Area** 9,500 ha

■ Site description
A loess-covered mountain range of volcanic origin. Although vineyards predominate, many traditional landscape elements still occur. Habitat-types include *Fagus* and *Quercus–Carpinus* forest, sub-Mediterranean scrub communities, dry grassland, loess cliffs, orchards, abandoned quarries and arable land.

Habitats Forest and woodland (broadleaved deciduous forest), Scrub (scrub), Grassland (steppe/dry calcareous grassland), Rocky areas (inland cliff), Artificial landscape (arable land; perennial crops/orchards/groves; urban parks/gardens; other urban/industrial areas)
Land-use Agriculture, Tourism/recreation

■ Birds

Species	Season	Year	Pop min	Pop max	Acc	Criteria
Lanius collurio Red-backed Shrike	B	1998	200	300	—	C6

A nationally important site for breeding *Merops apiaster* and *Saxicola torquata*.

■ Protection status
National Partial **International** Low
IBA overlaps with Landscape Protected Area and Nature Reserve. IBA overlaps with Special Protection Area.

■ Conservation issues

Threats Agricultural intensification/expansion (U), Industrialization/urbanization (U), Recreation/tourism (U)

Stromberg
B3, C2, C6 **248**
Admin region Baden-Württemberg
Coordinates 49°00′N 9°00′E
Altitude 210–450 m **Area** 4,000 ha

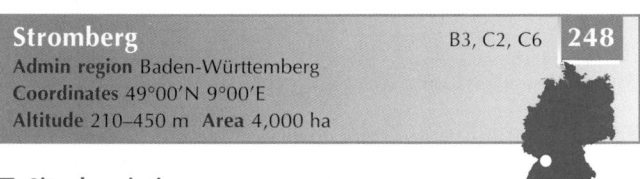

■ Site description
An upland landscape that comprises *Quercus* and *Fagus* forest, orchards and vineyards (partly abandoned; interspersed with fallow land and dry walls), dry grassland and hedges. The valleys support riverine forest and wet meadows.

Habitats Forest and woodland (broadleaved deciduous forest; alluvial/very wet forest), Scrub, Grassland (steppe/dry calcareous grassland; humid grassland; mesophile grassland), Wetland (standing fresh water; river/stream; water-fringe vegetation), Artificial landscape (perennial crops/orchards/groves)
Land-use Agriculture, Forestry, Tourism/recreation

■ Birds

Species	Season	Year	Pop min	Pop max	Acc	Criteria
¹*Dendrocopos medius* Middle Spotted Woodpecker	R	1998	300	500	—	B3, C2
Ficedula albicollis Collared Flycatcher	B	1998	150	200	—	B3, C6

1. 1993–1998.

■ Protection status
National Partial **International** Low
IBA overlaps with Landscape Protected Area and Nature Reserve. IBA overlaps with Special Protection Area.

■ Conservation issues

Threats Agricultural intensification/expansion (U), Intensified forest management (U), Recreation/tourism (U)

Rhine flats: Breisach–Sasbach with Limberg
C7 **249**
Admin region Baden-Württemberg
Coordinates 48°06′N 7°34′E
Altitude 190–270 m **Area** 1,050 ha

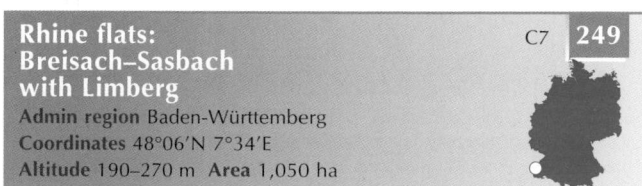

■ Site description
The site comprises part of the former flood-plain of the now embanked River Rhine. Habitat-types include *Quercus–Ulmus*, *Quercus–Carpinus* and *Populus* forest, springs and large gravel-pits.

Habitats Forest and woodland (broadleaved deciduous forest; alluvial/very wet forest), Wetland (standing fresh water; river/stream; fen/transition mire/spring)
Land-use Forestry, Tourism/recreation

■ Birds

A nationally important site for breeding *Alcedo atthis* and for passage and wintering wildfowl.

■ Protection status

National Partial **International** Low
IBA overlaps with Landscape Protected Area and Nature Reserve.
IBA overlaps with Special Protection Area.

■ Conservation issues

Threats Consequences of animal/plant introductions (U), Construction/impact of dyke/dam/barrage (U), Deforestation (commercial) (U), Extraction industry (U), Recreation/tourism (U)

The area is a proposed Ramsar Site.

Orchards and *Quercus* woodlands near Filderstadt and Echterdingen

B3, C6 **250**

Admin region Baden-Württemberg
Coordinates 48°39′N 9°13′E
Altitude 310–495 m **Area** 2,000 ha

■ Site description

A heterogeneous landscape comprising *Quercus–Carpinus*, *Picea* and riverine forest, orchards, meadows, pasture, hedges and small gardens.

Habitats Forest and woodland (broadleaved deciduous forest; alluvial/very wet forest), Scrub, Grassland (mesophile grassland), Wetland (river/stream), Artificial landscape (perennial crops/orchards/groves; urban parks/gardens)
Land-use Agriculture, Forestry

■ Birds

Species	Season	Year	Pop min	Pop max	Acc	Criteria
Ficedula albicollis Collared Flycatcher	B	1997	40	60	—	B3, C6

■ Protection status

National Partial **International** None
IBA overlaps with Landscape Protected Area and Nature Reserve.

■ Conservation issues

Threats Agricultural intensification/expansion (U), Disturbance to birds (U), Industrialization/urbanization (U), Infrastructure (U), Intensified forest management (U)

Enz valley: Mühlhausen–Roßwag

C6 **251**

Admin region Baden-Württemberg
Coordinates 48°57′N 8°54′E
Altitude 200–280 m **Area** 215 ha

■ Site description

The valley of the meandering River Enz, comprising riverine forest, dry *Pinus* forest with areas of heathland and scrub, wet meadows, springs, 20–30 m high limestone cliffs, vineyards and a quarry.

Habitats Forest and woodland (broadleaved deciduous forest; native coniferous forest), Grassland (humid grassland; mesophile grassland), Wetland (river/stream; fen/transition mire/spring), Rocky areas (inland cliff), Artificial landscape (perennial crops/orchards/groves; other urban/industrial areas)
Land-use Agriculture, Fisheries/aquaculture, Forestry, Tourism/recreation

■ Birds

Species	Season	Year	Pop min	Pop max	Acc	Criteria
Crex crex Corncrake	B	1998	1	4	—	C6

A nationally important site for breeding *Falco peregrinus* and *Bubo bubo*.

■ Protection status

National Partial **International** None
IBA overlaps with Landscape Protected Area and Nature Reserve.

■ Conservation issues

Threats Agricultural intensification/expansion (U), Aquaculture/fisheries (U), Intensified forest management (U), Recreation/tourism (U)

Schönbuch

B3, C6 **252**

Admin region Baden-Württemberg
Coordinates 48°34′N 9°03′E
Altitude 335–580 m **Area** 18,000 ha

■ Site description

The site comprises deciduous (*Quercus*, *Fagus* and *Carpinus*) and coniferous forest, orchards, scrub, dry calcareous grassland, meadows, hedges, streams and vineyards.

Habitats Forest and woodland (broadleaved deciduous forest; native coniferous forest), Scrub (scrub), Grassland (steppe/dry calcareous grassland; mesophile grassland), Wetland (river/stream), Artificial landscape (perennial crops/orchards/groves)
Land-use Agriculture, Forestry, Tourism/recreation

■ Birds

Species	Season	Year	Pop min	Pop max	Acc	Criteria
[1] *Ficedula albicollis* Collared Flycatcher	B	1998	80	130	—	B3, C6
Lanius collurio Red-backed Shrike	B	1998	100	—	—	C6

1. 1993–1998.

■ Protection status

National Partial **International** Low
IBA overlaps with Landscape Protected Area and Nature Reserve.
IBA overlaps with Special Protection Area.

■ Conservation issues

Threats Abandonment/reduction of land management (U), Agricultural intensification/expansion (U), Industrialization/urbanization (U), Infrastructure (U), Intensified forest management (U), Recreation/tourism (U)

Orchards, heathlands and forests around Weil der Stadt

B3, C6 **253**

Admin region Baden-Württemberg
Coordinates 48°45′N 08°52′E
Altitude 400–550 m **Area** 3,600 ha

■ Site description

Heterogeneous landscape comprising *Quercus–Carpinus*, *Quercus–Fagus* and *Picea* forest, scrub, calcareous dry grassland with *Juniperus*, meadows, hedges, orchards, vineyards, gardens, arable land and quarries.

Habitats Forest and woodland (broadleaved deciduous forest; mixed forest), Scrub (scrub), Grassland (steppe/dry calcareous grassland; humid grassland; mesophile grassland), Wetland (river/stream; water-fringe vegetation; fen/transition mire/spring), Artificial landscape (arable land; perennial crops/orchards/groves; urban parks/gardens; other urban/industrial areas)
Land-use Agriculture, Forestry, Tourism/recreation, Urban/industrial/transport

■ Birds

Species	Season	Year	Pop min	Pop max	Acc	Criteria
Ficedula albicollis Collared Flycatcher	B	1997	40	60	—	B3, C6

■ Protection status

National Partial **International** Low
IBA overlaps with Landscape Protected Area and Nature Reserve.
IBA overlaps with Special Protection Area.

■ Conservation issues

Threats Abandonment/reduction of land management (U), Agricultural intensification/expansion (U), Deforestation (commercial) (U), Disturbance to birds (U), Industrialization/urbanization (U), Infrastructure (U), Recreation/tourism (U)

Vogelfreistätte Mittlere Isar-Stauseen   B1i, C3   254

Admin region Bayern
Coordinates 48°30'N 12°01'E
Altitude 402–410 m **Area** 570 ha

■ Site description
Reservoirs situated on the River Isar, surrounded by reedbeds (*Phragmites*) and remnant riverine forest. Water-levels are controlled due to the presence of a power-station.

Habitats Forest and woodland (broadleaved deciduous forest), Wetland (standing fresh water; water-fringe vegetation)
Land-use Fisheries/aquaculture, Hunting

■ Birds

Species	Season	Year	Pop min	Pop max	Acc	Criteria
Anas strepera Gadwall	W	1997	—	1,066	—	B1i, C3

■ Protection status
National High **International** High
IBA overlaps with Nature Reserve. IBA overlaps with Special Protection Area.

■ Conservation issues

Threats Construction/impact of dyke/dam/barrage (U), Disturbance to birds (U)

Rötelsee–Weihergebiet including Regen-Aue   B1i, B2, C3   255

Admin region Bayern
Coordinates 49°12'N 12°35'E
Altitude 361–364 m **Area** 500 ha

■ Site description
Part of the Regen valley with many fish-ponds and wet meadows.

Habitats Grassland (humid grassland), Wetland (standing fresh water; river/stream; raised bog; water-fringe vegetation; fen/transition mire/spring), Artificial landscape (arable land)
Land-use Agriculture (65%), Fisheries/aquaculture (5%), Nature conservation/research (30%)

■ Birds

Species	Season	Year	Pop min	Pop max	Acc	Criteria
[1] *Botaurus stellaris* Bittern	B	1994	—	1	A	B2
[2] *Anas strepera* Gadwall	P	1995	210	490	A	B1i, C3

1. 1992–1994.
2. Large increase.

Species of global conservation concern that do not meet IBA criteria: *Crex crex* (1–6 breeding pairs).

■ Protection status
National Partial **International** None
IBA overlaps with Nature Reserve.

■ Conservation issues

Threats Agricultural intensification/expansion (B), Aquaculture/fisheries (C), Disturbance to birds (B), Drainage (C), Filling-in of wetlands (C), Groundwater abstraction (C), Recreation/tourism (B)

Isar-Tal: Gottfrieding–Plattling including Isar-Mündungsbereich   C6   256

Admin region Bayern
Coordinates 48°43'N 12°50'E
Altitude 310–345 m **Area** 8,000 ha

■ Site description
Lower part of the River Isar with many oxbow lakes, and riverine forest.

Habitats Forest and woodland (alluvial/very wet forest), Wetland (river/stream)

Land-use Agriculture, Forestry

■ Birds

Species	Season	Year	Pop min	Pop max	Acc	Criteria
Ixobrychus minutus Little Bittern	B	1986	1	4	—	C6

■ Protection status
National Partial **International** None
IBA overlaps with Nature Reserve.

■ Conservation issues

Threats Afforestation (U), Dredging/canalization (U), Other (U)

The area is a candidate Special Area for Conservation.

Ismaninger Speichersee and fish-ponds   A4i, B1i, C3   257

Admin region Bayern
Coordinates 48°13'N 11°46'E
Altitude 496–497 m **Area** 955 ha

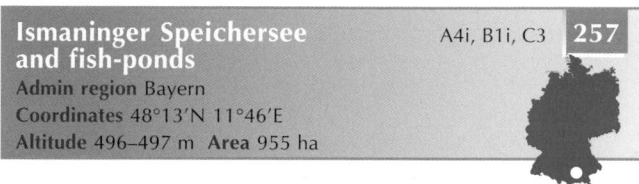

■ Site description
An artificial reservoir and a large number of fish-ponds.

Habitats Wetland (standing fresh water)
Land-use Fisheries/aquaculture (28%), Water management (87%)

■ Birds

Species	Season	Year	Pop min	Pop max	Acc	Criteria
[1] *Anas strepera* Gadwall	N	1996	—	4,877	A	A4i, B1i, C3
[1] *Anas clypeata* Shoveler	N	1994	—	802	A	B1i, C3
Netta rufina Red-crested Pochard	P	1994	—	2,805	A	A4i, B1i, C3
[2] *Netta rufina* Red-crested Pochard	N	1996	—	1,494	A	A4i, B1i, C3
[3] *Aythya ferina* Pochard	N	1996	—	5,170	A	B1i, C3

1. Moulting individuals.
2. Moulting individuals. Large decrease 1994–1996.
3. Moulting individuals. Large decrease.

This is an important area for moulting waterbirds.

■ Protection status
National None **International** Partial
IBA overlaps with Ramsar Site.

■ Conservation issues

Threats Other (U)

A reduction in water and nutrient supply threaten the site.

Main-Tal near Volkach: Fahr-Dettelbach   C6   258

Admin region Bayern
Coordinates 49°52'N 10°10'E
Altitude 185–318 m **Area** 1,800 ha

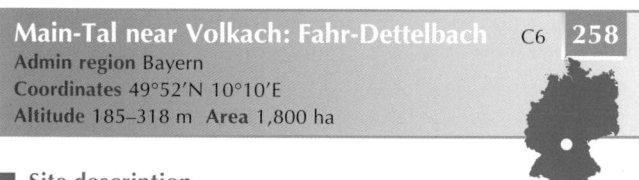

■ Site description
Part of the Main valley with oxbow lakes, wet meadows, dry grassland, wooded slopes and sandy heathland.

Habitats Forest and woodland (broadleaved deciduous forest), Scrub (heathland), Grassland (humid grassland), Wetland (standing fresh water; river/stream)
Land-use Agriculture, Fisheries/aquaculture, Forestry, Military, Tourism/recreation

■ Birds

Species	Season	Year	Pop min	Pop max	Acc	Criteria
Ixobrychus minutus Little Bittern	B	1987	1	3	—	C6

■ Protection status
National Partial **International** None
IBA overlaps with Nature Reserve.

■ Conservation issues

Threats Agricultural intensification/expansion (U), Aquaculture/fisheries (U), Industrialization/urbanization (U), Recreation/tourism (U)

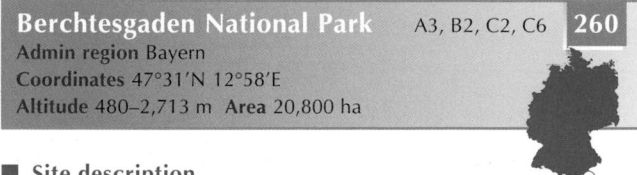

Bayerischer Wald National Park with Arbergebiet and Hohen Bogen   B2, C7   259
Admin region Bayern
Coordinates 48°55′N 13°30′E
Altitude 690–1,450 m   **Area** 32,000 ha

■ Site description
A mountain range with ancient and managed forest, mountain lakes, alpine meadows, peatbogs, cliffs and ridges.

Habitats Forest and woodland (95%; native coniferous forest; mixed forest; alluvial/very wet forest; treeline ecotone), Scrub (25%; river/stream; raised bog), Rocky areas (5%; scree/boulders)
Land-use Forestry (15%), Hunting (75%), Nature conservation/research (50%), Tourism/recreation (100%), Urban/industrial/transport (5%)

■ Birds

Species	Season	Year	Pop min	Pop max	Acc	Criteria
Picoides tridactylus Three-toed Woodpecker	R	1989	70	140	B	B2

This is an important site for species associated with old forest.

■ Protection status
National Partial **International** Partial
13,100 ha of IBA covered by National Park (Bayerischer Wald, 13,100 ha). 13,100 ha of IBA overlaps with Special Protection Area. IBA overlaps with Biosphere Reserve.

■ Conservation issues

Threats Abandonment/reduction of land management (U), Aquaculture/fisheries (C), Deforestation (commercial) (B), Disturbance to birds (U), Drainage (C), Natural events (A), Recreation/tourism (A)

There is increasing development for tourism. A conservation project for *Tetrao urogallus* is in operation. The area is a candidate Special Area for Conservation.

Berchtesgaden National Park   A3, B2, C2, C6   260
Admin region Bayern
Coordinates 47°31′N 12°58′E
Altitude 480–2,713 m   **Area** 20,800 ha

■ Site description
A mountainous region with cliffs, large and small mountain lakes, glaciers and snow-fields.

Habitats Forest and woodland (broadleaved deciduous forest; native coniferous forest; mixed forest; alluvial/very wet forest; treeline ecotone), Scrub (scrub), Grassland (alpine/subalpine/boreal grassland), Wetland (standing fresh water; river/stream; raised bog; water-fringe vegetation), Rocky areas (scree/boulders), Artificial landscape (highly improved reseeded grassland; forestry plantation; ruderal land)
Land-use Agriculture, Fisheries/aquaculture, Forestry, Hunting, Military, Nature conservation/research, Not utilized, Tourism/recreation

■ Birds

Species	Season	Year	Pop min	Pop max	Acc	Criteria
Falco peregrinus Peregrine	B	1996	1	10	—	B2
[1] *Tetrao tetrix* Black Grouse	B	1996	101	1,000	—	B2
Bubo bubo Eagle Owl	B	1996	1	10	—	B2
[1] *Picoides tridactylus* Three-toed Woodpecker	B	1996	101	1,000	—	B2, C2
Prunella collaris Alpine Accentor	R	1996	101	1,000	—	A3
Ficedula parva Red-breasted Flycatcher	B	1996	11	100	—	C6
Tichodroma muraria Wallcreeper	R	—	—	—	—	A3
Pyrrhocorax graculus Alpine Chough	R	—	—	—	—	A3

Species ... continued	Season	Year	Pop min	Pop max	Acc	Criteria
Montifringilla nivalis Snowfinch	B	1996	1	100	—	A3
Serinus citrinella Citril Finch	B	1996	1	100	—	A3

1. Number of pairs unknown.

Breeding birds include five of the 10 species in Europe that are restricted (when breeding) to the Eurasian high-montane biome.

■ Protection status
National High **International** High
IBA overlaps with National Park. IBA overlaps with Special Protection Area.

■ Conservation issues

Threats Abandonment/reduction of land management (U), Agricultural intensification/expansion (C), Disturbance to birds (B), Forest grazing (B), Natural events (C), Recreation/tourism (A), Selective logging/cutting (B)

The area is a candidate Special Area for Conservation.

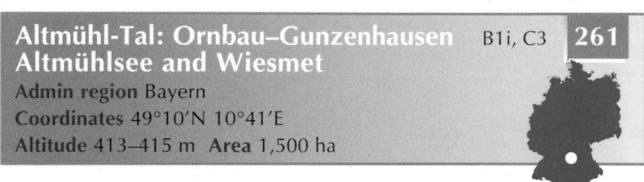

Altmühl-Tal: Ornbau–Gunzenhausen Altmühlsee and Wiesmet   B1i, C3   261
Admin region Bayern
Coordinates 49°10′N 10°41′E
Altitude 413–415 m   **Area** 1,500 ha

■ Site description
A river valley with large meadows and an artificial reservoir.

Habitats Grassland (humid grassland), Wetland (standing fresh water)
Land-use Agriculture, Tourism/recreation, Water management

■ Birds

Species	Season	Year	Pop min	Pop max	Acc	Criteria
Anas clypeata Shoveler	P	1995	125	520	A	B1i, C3

This is an important area for breeding species associated with meadows. Species of global conservation concern that do not meet IBA criteria: *Aythya nyroca* (passage), *Crex crex* (breeding).

■ Protection status
National Partial **International** None
IBA overlaps Nature Reserve.

■ Conservation issues

Threats Drainage (U), Recreation/tourism (U)

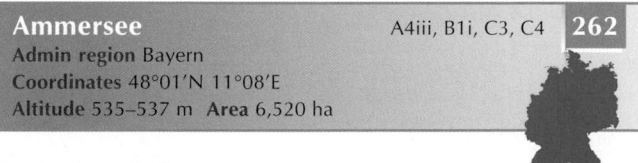

Ammersee   A4iii, B1i, C3, C4   262
Admin region Bayern
Coordinates 48°01′N 11°08′E
Altitude 535–537 m   **Area** 6,520 ha

■ Site description
A lake with reedbeds (*Phragmites*) and wet meadows surrounded by riverine forests.

Habitats Wetland (88%; standing fresh water; river/stream; water-fringe vegetation; fen/transition mire/spring)
Land-use Agriculture (10%), Fisheries/aquaculture (73%), Hunting (100%), Nature conservation/research (100%), Tourism/recreation (73%)

■ Birds

Species	Season	Year	Pop min	Pop max	Acc	Criteria
[1] *Netta rufina* Red-crested Pochard	B	1996	20	310	A	B1i, C3
[2] *Aythya fuligula* Tufted Duck	W	1996	2,387	10,186	A	B1i, C3

1. Large increase 1985–1996.
2. 1985–1996.

The site holds 20,000 or more waterbirds in winter, on a regular basis.

■ Protection status
National None **International** Partial
527 ha of IBA overlaps with Special Protection Area. IBA overlaps with Ramsar Site.

■ Conservation issues

Threats Agricultural intensification/expansion (B), Aquaculture/fisheries (A), Disturbance to birds (A), Drainage (A), Groundwater abstraction (A), Recreation/tourism (A)

The site is heavily used for watersports. The area is a candidate Special Area for Conservation.

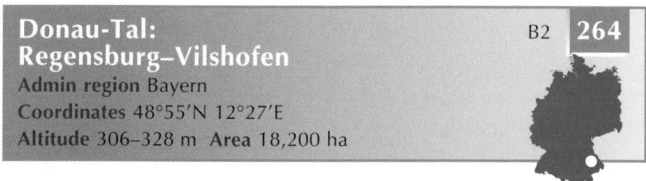

Chiemsee and Chiemseemore	A1, A4i, A4iii,	263
Admin region Bayern	B1i, C1, C3, C4	
Coordinates 47°53′N 12°28′E		
Altitude 520–520 m **Area** 9,800 ha		

■ Site description
A lake with an area of fen and riverine forest. The lake and its surrounds are intensively used for tourism from May to October, as a fishery all year-round, and also for hunting, forestry and agriculture.

Habitats Forest and woodland (5%; alluvial/very wet forest), Wetland (95%; standing fresh water; water-fringe vegetation; fen/transition mire/spring)
Land-use Agriculture (5%), Fisheries/aquaculture (80%), Forestry (5%), Hunting (70%), Nature conservation/research (10%), Tourism/recreation (80%)

■ Birds

Species	Season	Year	Pop min	Pop max	Acc	Criteria
Anas strepera Gadwall	W	1996	60	500	A	B1i, C3
Netta rufina Red-crested Pochard	P	1996	200	2,000	A	A4i, B1i, C3
Aythya ferina Pochard	W	1996	2,000	9,000	A	B1i, C3
Aythya fuligula Tufted Duck	W	1996	5,000	20,000	A	B1i, C3
Crex crex Corncrake	B	1996	10	20	B	A1, C1
Fulica atra Coot	W	1996	7,000	20,000	A	B1i, C3

The site holds 20,000 or more waterbirds in winter on a regular basis.

■ Protection status
National Partial **International** Partial
IBA overlaps with Nature Reserve. IBA overlaps with Special Protection Area. IBA overlaps with Ramsar Site.

■ Conservation issues

Threats Aquaculture/fisheries (A), Disturbance to birds (B), Drainage (C), Firewood collection (C), Forest grazing (C), Recreation/tourism (A)

Donau-Tal: Regensburg–Vilshofen	B2	264
Admin region Bayern		
Coordinates 48°55′N 12°27′E		
Altitude 306–328 m **Area** 18,200 ha		

■ Site description
An intact part of the Danube valley with flooded areas, wet meadows, oxbows and riverine forests.

Habitats Forest and woodland (alluvial/very wet forest), Wetland (standing fresh water; water-fringe vegetation)
Land-use Agriculture, Fisheries/aquaculture, Forestry, Hunting, Tourism/recreation, Urban/industrial/transport

■ Birds

Species	Season	Year	Pop min	Pop max	Acc	Criteria
Anas strepera Gadwall	R	1994	—	133	—	B2

This is an important site for wintering waterbirds. Species of global conservation concern that do not meet IBA criteria: *Aythya nyroca* (wintering), *Crex crex* (breeding), *Acrocephalus paludicola* (passage).

■ Protection status
National Partial **International** Low
IBA overlaps with Landscape Protected Area and Nature Reserve. 612 ha of IBA overlaps with 3 Special Protection Areas.

■ Conservation issues

Threats Abandonment/reduction of land management (U), Agricultural intensification/expansion (U), Construction/impact of dyke/dam/barrage (U), Dredging/canalization (U)

The site is threatened by major alterations to the river, including construction of dykes to facilitate ship navigation and the installation of power-plants. The surrounding land is threatened by agricultural intensification.

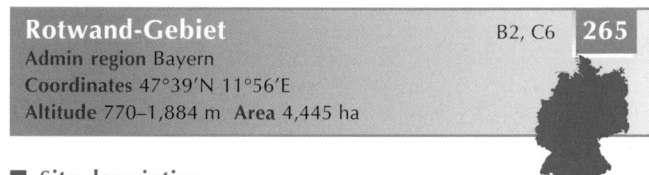

Rotwand-Gebiet	B2, C6	265
Admin region Bayern		
Coordinates 47°39′N 11°56′E		
Altitude 770–1,884 m **Area** 4,445 ha		

■ Site description
The IBA is situated in the north of the Alps, close to the Austrian border. It comprises forest (*Fagus*, *Acer*, *Abies* and *Picea*), alpine meadows and rocky areas. A diverse flora exists due to the varying calcareous/silicate ground conditions.

Habitats Forest and woodland (70%; broadleaved deciduous forest; native coniferous forest; mixed forest; treeline ecotone), Scrub (10%; scrub; heathland), Grassland (20%; dry siliceous grassland; alpine/subalpine/boreal grassland; humid grassland), Wetland (standing fresh water; river/stream; raised bog; water-fringe vegetation; fen/transition mire/spring), Rocky areas (15%; scree/boulders; inland cliff)
Land-use Agriculture (20%), Fisheries/aquaculture (1%), Forestry (70%), Hunting (80%), Nature conservation/research (90%), Tourism/recreation (40%)

■ Birds

Species	Season	Year	Pop min	Pop max	Acc	Criteria
Dendrocopos leucotos White-backed Woodpecker	R	1997	—	20	—	C6
Picoides tridactylus Three-toed Woodpecker	R	1997	—	20	—	B2

■ Protection status
National High **International** None
4,412 ha of IBA covered by Landscape Protected Area (Rotwand, 4,412 ha). IBA overlaps with Nature Reserve.

■ Conservation issues

Threats Abandonment/reduction of land management (C), Afforestation (C), Agricultural intensification/expansion (B), Deforestation (U), Disturbance to birds (B), Drainage (C), Firewood collection (C), Forest grazing (B), Infrastructure (A), Natural events (B), Recreation/tourism (B)

Current problems include infrastructure expansion and disturbance caused by tourism.

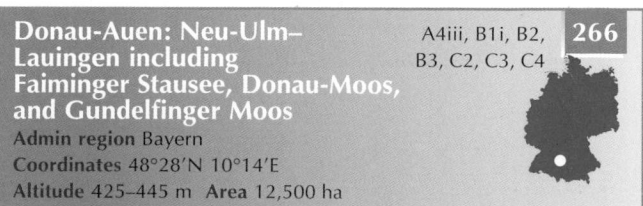

Donau-Auen: Neu-Ulm–Lauingen including Faiminger Stausee, Donau-Moos, and Gundelfinger Moos	A4iii, B1i, B2, B3, C2, C3, C4	266
Admin region Bayern		
Coordinates 48°28′N 10°14′E		
Altitude 425–445 m **Area** 12,500 ha		

■ Site description
Dammed stretches and reservoirs along the Danube surrounded by riverine forest and meadows.

Habitats Forest and woodland (alluvial/very wet forest), Wetland (standing fresh water; raised bog)
Land-use Agriculture, Forestry, Nature conservation/research

Birds

Species	Season	Year	Pop min	Pop max	Acc	Criteria
Aythya ferina Pochard	N	1998	—	6,000	—	B1i, C3
Riparia riparia Sand Martin	B	1998	500	1,000	—	B2
Ficedula albicollis Collared Flycatcher	B	1998	300	—	—	B3, C2

The site holds 20,000 or more non-breeding waterbirds, on a regular basis, including *Anas platyrhynchos* (15,000) and *Aythya fuligula* (6,000). Species of global conservation concern that do not meet IBA criteria: *Aythya nyroca* (passage), *Crex crex* (breeding), *Acrocephalus paludicola* (passage).

Protection status
National Partial **International** Partial
IBA overlaps with Landscape Protected Area and three Nature Reserves. IBA overlaps with Ramsar Site.

Conservation issues

Threats Agricultural intensification/expansion (B), Disturbance to birds (B), Extraction industry (A), Groundwater abstraction (A), Infrastructure (A), Recreation/tourism (A)

The site is threatened by the extraction of water and gravel, intensification of agriculture, tourism, and the construction of a new railway line.

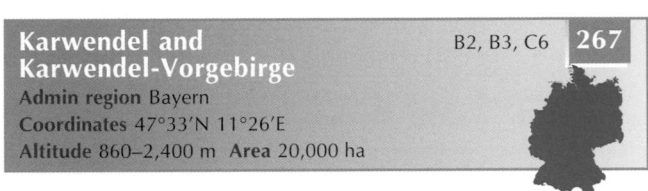

Karwendel and Karwendel-Vorgebirge B2, B3, C6 **267**
Admin region Bayern
Coordinates 47°33'N 11°26'E
Altitude 860–2,400 m **Area** 20,000 ha

Site description
Part of the northern Alps with semi-natural forests dominated by *Fagus, Abies, Picea,* and *Acer,* alpine meadows and rocky areas above the treeline.

Habitats Forest and woodland (mixed forest), Grassland (alpine/subalpine/boreal grassland)
Land-use Agriculture, Forestry, Hunting, Military, Tourism/recreation

Birds

Species	Season	Year	Pop min	Pop max	Acc	Criteria
Falco peregrinus Peregrine	R	1997	3	5	—	B2
Bubo bubo Eagle Owl	R	1986	3	4	—	B2
Dendrocopos leucotos White-backed Woodpecker	R	1986	30	50	—	C6
Picoides tridactylus Three-toed Woodpecker	R	1986	50	150	—	B2
Turdus torquatus Ring Ouzel	B	1986	300	—	—	B3
¹ *Serinus citrinella* Citril Finch	B	1986	100	100	—	B3

1. Large decrease.

Protection status
National Partial **International** Partial
IBA overlaps with Nature Reserve. IBA overlaps with Special Protection Area.

Conservation issues

Threats Disturbance to birds (U), Infrastructure (U), Recreation/tourism (U)

The area is a candidate Special Area for Conservation.

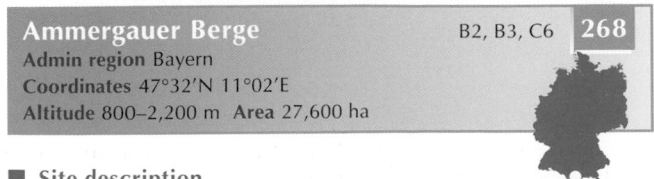

Ammergauer Berge B2, B3, C6 **268**
Admin region Bayern
Coordinates 47°32'N 11°02'E
Altitude 800–2,200 m **Area** 27,600 ha

Site description
A mountainous area dominated by mixed and conifer forests dominated by *Fagus, Abies* and *Picea.*

Habitats Forest and woodland (native coniferous forest; mixed forest), Grassland (alpine/subalpine/boreal grassland)

Land-use Agriculture, Forestry, Hunting, Nature conservation/research, Tourism/recreation

Birds

Species	Season	Year	Pop min	Pop max	Acc	Criteria
Falco peregrinus Peregrine	R	1997	8	10	—	B2
Bubo bubo Eagle Owl	R	1986	3	4	—	B2
Dendrocopos leucotos White-backed Woodpecker	R	1986	80	120	—	C6
Picoides tridactylus Three-toed Woodpecker	R	1986	15	—	—	B2
Turdus torquatus Ring Ouzel	B	1986	400	—	—	B3
Ficedula parva Red-breasted Flycatcher	B	1986	50	80	—	C6
¹ *Serinus citrinella* Citril Finch	B	1986	100	100	—	B3

1. Large decrease.

Protection status
National Partial **International** Partial
IBA overlaps with Nature Reserve. IBA overlaps with Special Protection Area.

Conservation issues

Threats Agricultural intensification/expansion (U), Infrastructure (U), Recreation/tourism (U)

The site is a candidate Special Area for Conservation.

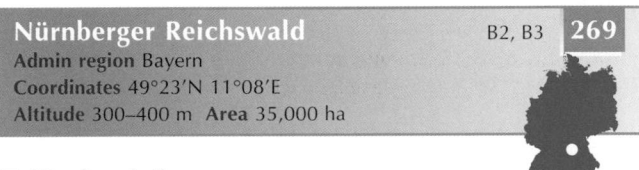

Nürnberger Reichswald B2, B3 **269**
Admin region Bayern
Coordinates 49°23'N 11°08'E
Altitude 300–400 m **Area** 35,000 ha

Site description
A large block of sustainably managed forest near to the city of Nürnberg, interspersed with a variety of different habitat-types.

Habitats Forest and woodland (100%; broadleaved deciduous forest; native coniferous forest; mixed forest; alluvial/very wet forest), Scrub (5%; heathland), Wetland (standing fresh water; raised bog; water-fringe vegetation; fen/transition mire/spring), Rocky areas (inland sand-dunes), Artificial landscape (12%; forestry plantation; ruderal land)
Land-use Forestry

Birds

Species	Season	Year	Pop min	Pop max	Acc	Criteria
Caprimulgus europaeus Nightjar	B	1996	—	100	—	B2
Picus canus Grey-headed Woodpecker	R	1996	—	120	—	B2
Dendrocopos medius Middle Spotted Woodpecker	R	1996	—	160	—	B3

Protection status
National Low **International** None
934 ha of IBA covered by Nature Reserve.

Conservation issues

Threats Disturbance to birds (U), Industrialization/urbanization (U), Infrastructure (U)

The site is a candidate Special Area for Conservation.

Vorderer Steigerwald–Windsheimer Bucht–Gollach-Gau–Steigerwald-Vorland B2, B3 **270**
Admin region Bayern
Coordinates 49°36'N 10°18'E
Altitude 200–450 m **Area** 95,000 ha

Site description
Broadleaved forest dominated by *Quercus.* The IBA also includes arable land on clay soils.

Habitats Forest and woodland (broadleaved deciduous forest; mixed forest), Scrub (scrub), Wetland (standing fresh water; river/stream), Artificial landscape (arable land; perennial crops/orchards/groves; forestry plantation; urban parks/gardens; other urban/industrial areas; ruderal land)
Land-use Agriculture

■ **Birds**

Species	Season	Year	Pop min	Pop max	Acc	Criteria
Circus pygargus Montagu's Harrier	B	1998	—	9	A	B3
Tyto alba Barn Owl	R	1998	60	80	A	B2
Dendrocopos medius Middle Spotted Woodpecker	R	1998	—	100	B	B3
Lanius excubitor Great Grey Shrike	R	1998	15	45	A	B2

A nationally important site for *Circus pygargus*

■ **Protection status**
National Low **International** None
530 ha of IBA covered by eight Nature Reserves.

■ **Conservation issues**

Threats Agricultural intensification/expansion (U), Extraction industry (U), Intensified forest management (U)

Lech–Donau–Winkel: Lechstausee Feldheim and Donaustausee Bertoldsheim — B1i, C3 — 271
Admin region Bayern
Coordinates 48°44′N 10°59′E
Altitude 387–420 m **Area** 239 ha

■ **Site description**
Reservoirs on the Danube (Bertoldsheimer Stau) and River Lech (Feldheimer Stau) with shallow zones covered by reedbeds (*Phragmites*) and surrounded by large riverine forests.

Habitats Forest and woodland (alluvial/very wet forest), Wetland (standing fresh water; water-fringe vegetation), Artificial landscape (forestry plantation)
Land-use Fisheries/aquaculture, Forestry, Tourism/recreation, Water management

■ **Birds**

Species	Season	Year	Pop min	Pop max	Acc	Criteria
Anas strepera Gadwall	W	1995	—	736	—	B1i, C3

■ **Protection status**
National Partial **International** Partial
IBA overlaps with Landscape Protected Area and Nature Reserve. IBA overlaps with Ramsar Site.

■ **Conservation issues**

Threats Aquaculture/fisheries (U), Consequences of animal/plant introductions (U), Disturbance to birds (U), Groundwater abstraction (U), Tourism and recreation (U)

Intensification of forestry and extraction of water are potential threats, whilst fishing and boat traffic create some disturbance.

Donau-Auen and Donau-Ried: Höchstädt–Donauwörth — C7 — 272
Admin region Bayern
Coordinates 48°39′N 10°42′E
Altitude 430–455 m **Area** 9,500 ha

■ **Site description**
A diverse landscape in the Danube valley with oxbow lakes, wet meadows, bogs and riverine forests. The area is used for agriculture, gravel extraction, wildfowl hunting and angling.

Habitats Forest and woodland (alluvial/very wet forest), Wetland (standing fresh water; raised bog), Artificial landscape (arable land)

Land-use Agriculture, Fisheries/aquaculture, Forestry, Hunting, Nature conservation/research

■ **Birds**
Species of global conservation concern that do not meet IBA criteria: *Crex crex* (breeding).

■ **Protection status**
National Partial **International** None
7 ha of IBA covered by Landscape Protected Area (Altwasser bei Donauworth, 7 ha). 11 ha of IBA covered by Landscape Protected Area (Altwasser bei Rettingen, 11 ha). 1,095 ha of IBA covered by Landscape Protected Area (Donauauen zwischen Blindheim und Tapfheim, 1,095 ha). 142 ha of IBA covered by Nature Reserve (Mertinger Hölle, NSG, 142 ha). 46 ha of IBA covered by Nature Reserve (Neugeschüttwörth, Naturwaldreservat, 46 ha).

■ **Conservation issues**

Threats Agricultural intensification/expansion (U), Aquaculture/fisheries (U), Disturbance to birds (U), Extraction industry (U)

Orchards bordering the River Main — B2 — 273
Admin region Hessen, Bayern
Coordinates 50°00′N 9°10′E
Altitude 100–300 m **Area** 60,000 ha

■ **Site description**
Extensive orchards interspersed with small parcels of land under diverse use.

Habitats Scrub (scrub), Grassland (mesophile grassland), Artificial landscape (highly improved reseeded grassland; arable land; perennial crops/orchards/groves; ruderal land)
Land-use Agriculture (90%), Not utilized (5%), Other (5%)

■ **Birds**

Species	Season	Year	Pop min	Pop max	Acc	Criteria
Athene noctua Little Owl	R	1998	300	—	—	B2

The site holds 90% of the Bavarian population of *Athene noctua*.

■ **Protection status**
National None **International** None

■ **Conservation issues**

Threats Abandonment/reduction of land management (B), Infrastructure (B)

Charlottenhofer Weihergebiet — C7 — 274
Admin region Bayern
Coordinates 49°21′N 12°11′E
Altitude 370–380 m **Area** 900 ha

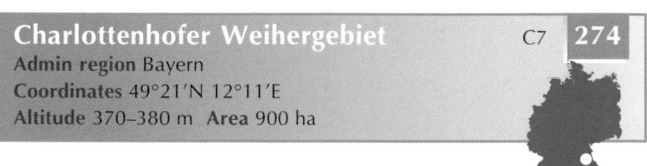

■ **Site description**
A diverse landscape with fish-ponds, marshes and bogs.

Habitats Forest and woodland (broadleaved deciduous forest), Wetland (standing fresh water; raised bog)
Land-use Agriculture, Fisheries/aquaculture, Forestry, Hunting

■ **Protection status**
National Partial **International** Partial
833 ha of IBA covered by Nature Reserve (Charlottenhofer Weihergebiet, 833 ha). IBA overlaps with Special Protection Area.

■ **Conservation issues**

Threats Aquaculture/fisheries (U)

The area is a candidate Special Area for Conservation.

Aisch–Regnitz–Grund
B2, C6 | **275**

Admin region Bayern
Coordinates 49°41′N 10°56′E
Altitude 250–325 m **Area** 68,000 ha

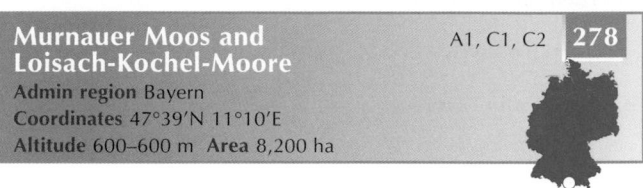

■ Site description
A lowland area with about 2,000 fish-ponds (total area c.2.500 ha), surrounded by agricultural land, many rivers, wet meadows and forests.

Habitats Forest and woodland (broadleaved deciduous forest), Grassland (humid grassland), Wetland (standing fresh water; river/stream)
Land-use Agriculture, Fisheries/aquaculture, Forestry, Tourism/recreation, Water management

■ Birds

Species	Season	Year	Pop min	Pop max	Acc	Criteria
Botaurus stellaris Bittern	R	1998	5	9	—	B2, C6
Ixobrychus minutus Little Bittern	B	1998	10	15	—	C6
Alcedo atthis Kingfisher	R	1998	60	60	—	B2

Species of global conservation concern that do not meet IBA criteria: *Crex crex* (breeding).

■ Protection status
National None **International** Low
128 ha of IBA covered by Special Protection Area.

■ Conservation issues

Threats Agricultural intensification/expansion (U), Aquaculture/fisheries (U), Filling-in of wetlands (U), Groundwater abstraction (U), Infrastructure (U), Recreation/tourism (U)

Starnberger See
B1i, C3 | **276**

Admin region Bayern
Coordinates 47°54′N 11°18′E
Altitude 584–590 m **Area** 6,500 ha

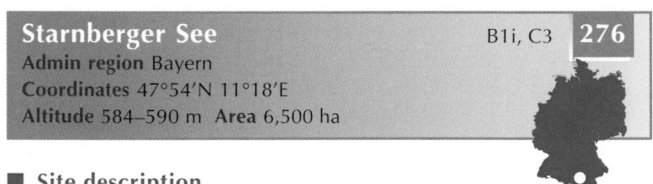

■ Site description
A mesotrophic freshwater lake. The southern part has reedbeds (*Phragmites*) and borders an area of bog. There are also a lot of small lakes (c.1 ha) with reeds.

Habitats Wetland (standing fresh water; raised bog; water-fringe vegetation)
Land-use Other, Tourism/recreation

■ Birds

Species	Season	Year	Pop min	Pop max	Acc	Criteria
Netta rufina Red-crested Pochard	W	1998	—	315	—	B1i, C3

■ Protection status
National Partial **International** Partial
IBA overlaps with Landscape Protected Area and Nature Reserve. IBA overlaps with Ramsar Site.

■ Conservation issues

Threats Disturbance to birds (U), Natural events (U), Recreation/tourism (U)

The area is a candidate Special Area for Conservation.

Main-Tal: Eltmann–Hassfurt
C7 | **277**

Admin region Bayern
Coordinates 50°00′N 10°36′E
Altitude 217–310 m **Area** 560 ha

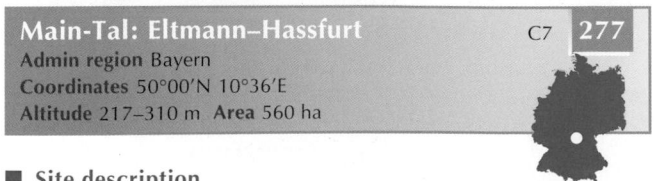

■ Site description
Oxbow lakes, wet meadows, sedge-beds, riverine forest and wooded slopes in the Main valley.

Habitats Forest and woodland (5%; alluvial/very wet forest), Wetland (92%; standing fresh water; river/stream; water-fringe vegetation; fen/transition mire/spring)

Land-use Fisheries/aquaculture (90%), Hunting (100%), Nature conservation/research (10%), Tourism/recreation, Water management (10%)

■ Birds
Species of global conservation concern that do not meet IBA criteria: *Aythya nyroca* (wintering) and *Crex crex* (breeding).

■ Protection status
National None **International** None

■ Conservation issues

Threats Aquaculture/fisheries (A), Disturbance to birds (A), Filling-in of wetlands (C), Industrialization/urbanization (A), Recreation/tourism (B)

Murnauer Moos and Loisach-Kochel-Moore
A1, C1, C2 | **278**

Admin region Bayern
Coordinates 47°39′N 11°10′E
Altitude 600–600 m **Area** 8,200 ha

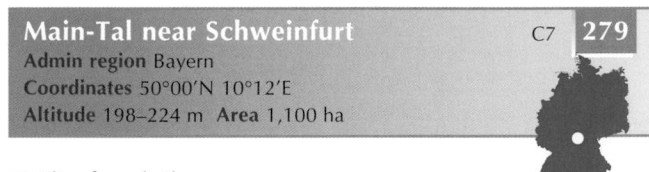

■ Site description
A fen-rich area situated in the southern foothills of the Alps. The main habitat-types are fen, raised bog, reedbeds (*Phragmites*), wet meadows, forest, ponds and small rivers.

Habitats Forest and woodland, Grassland (humid grassland; mesophile grassland), Wetland (standing fresh water; river/stream; raised bog; water-fringe vegetation; fen/transition mire/spring)
Land-use Agriculture, Forestry

■ Birds

Species	Season	Year	Pop min	Pop max	Acc	Criteria
Crex crex Corncrake	B	1998	50	60	—	A1, C1, C2

■ Protection status
National Partial **International** None
2,355 ha of IBA covered by Nature Reserve (Murnauer Moos, 2,355 ha).

■ Conservation issues

Threats Agricultural intensification/expansion (U)

The area is a candidate Special Area for Conservation.

Main-Tal near Schweinfurt
C7 | **279**

Admin region Bayern
Coordinates 50°00′N 10°12′E
Altitude 198–224 m **Area** 1,100 ha

■ Site description
Remnant stretches of the River Main with oxbow lakes, patches of riverine forest, vegetated sand-dunes and wet meadows.

Habitats Forest and woodland (alluvial/very wet forest), Grassland (humid grassland), Wetland (sand-dunes/sand beach; standing fresh water; river/stream)
Land-use Agriculture, Fisheries/aquaculture, Forestry, Tourism/recreation

■ Birds
Species of global conservation concern that do not meet IBA criteria: *Aythya nyroca* (passage).

■ Protection status
National Partial **International** None
IBA overlaps with Landscape Protected Area and Nature Reserve.

■ Conservation issues

Threats Agricultural intensification/expansion (U), Aquaculture/fisheries (U), Disturbance to birds (U), Infrastructure (U), Intensified forest management (U), Recreation/tourism (U)

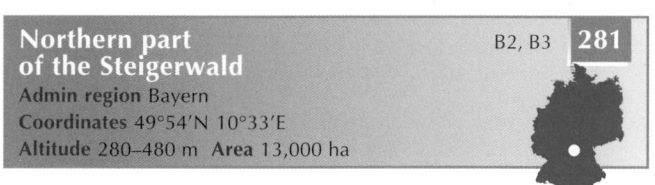

Vogelfreistätte Alter and Neuer See

C7 **280**

Admin region Bayern
Coordinates 49°56'N 10°21'E
Altitude 225–235 m **Area** 40 ha

■ Site description
Two small lakes surrounded by reedbeds (*Phragmites*) and agricultural land.

Habitats Grassland, Wetland (standing fresh water; water-fringe vegetation)
Land-use Agriculture, Hunting

■ Birds
Species of global conservation concern that do not meet IBA criteria:
Aythya nyroca (passage).

■ Protection status
National Partial **International** None
IBA overlaps with Nature Reserve.

■ Conservation issues

Threats Abandonment/reduction of land management (U), Agricultural intensification/expansion (U), Disturbance to birds (U), Recreation/tourism (U)

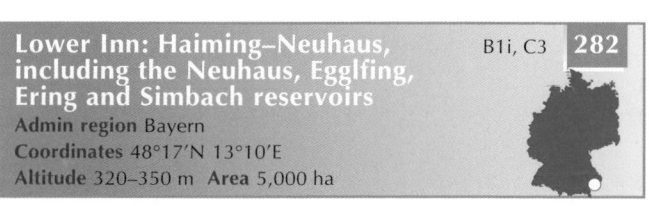

Northern part of the Steigerwald

B2, B3 **281**

Admin region Bayern
Coordinates 49°54'N 10°33'E
Altitude 280–480 m **Area** 13,000 ha

■ Site description
A large block of continuous *Fagus* and *Quercus* forest with *Alnus–Fraxinus* forest present in the valleys.

Habitats Forest and woodland (broadleaved deciduous forest; alluvial/very wet forest), Grassland (mesophile grassland), Wetland (standing fresh water), Artificial landscape (forestry plantation)
Land-use Agriculture (5%), Forestry (95%), Hunting (100%), Tourism/recreation (15%)

■ Birds

Species		Season	Year	Pop min	Pop max	Acc	Criteria
Columba oenas	Stock Dove	B	1998	250	500	A	B3
Picus canus	Grey-headed Woodpecker	R	1998	80	120	B	B2
Dendrocopos medius		R	1998	50	90	B	B3
Middle Spotted Woodpecker							
Ficedula albicollis	Collared Flycatcher	B	1998	100	150	A	B3

■ Protection status
National Low **International** None
250 ha of IBA covered by Nature Reserve.

■ Conservation issues

Threats Aquaculture/fisheries (U), Deforestation (U), Intensified forest management (C), Recreation/tourism (C)

Lower Inn: Haiming–Neuhaus, including the Neuhaus, Egglfing, Ering and Simbach reservoirs

B1i, C3 **282**

Admin region Bayern
Coordinates 48°17'N 13°10'E
Altitude 320–350 m **Area** 5,000 ha

■ Site description
Four reservoirs with many islands, shallow bays, deltas and stretches of riverine forest along the river.

Habitats Forest and woodland (alluvial/very wet forest), Wetland (river/stream)
Land-use Forestry, Not utilized

■ Birds

Species		Season	Year	Pop min	Pop max	Acc	Criteria
Anas strepera	Gadwall	W	1997	—	1,251	—	B1i, C3

■ Protection status
National Partial **International** Partial
IBA overlaps with Nature Reserve. IBA overlaps with Ramsar Site and Special Protection Area.

■ Conservation issues

Threats Abandonment/reduction of land management (B), Aquaculture/fisheries (U)

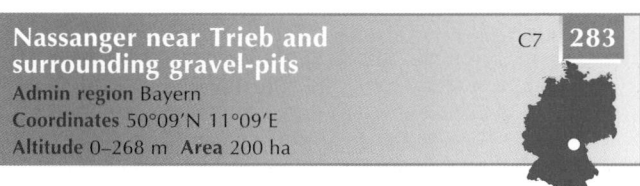

Nassanger near Trieb and surrounding gravel-pits

C7 **283**

Admin region Bayern
Coordinates 50°09'N 11°09'E
Altitude 0–268 m **Area** 200 ha

■ Site description
Fish-ponds and gravel-pits with reedbeds (*Phragmites*), surrounded by arable land and meadows.

Habitats Wetland (standing fresh water; water-fringe vegetation), Artificial landscape (arable land)
Land-use Agriculture, Fisheries/aquaculture

■ Protection status
National None **International** None

■ Conservation issues

Threats Infrastructure (U)

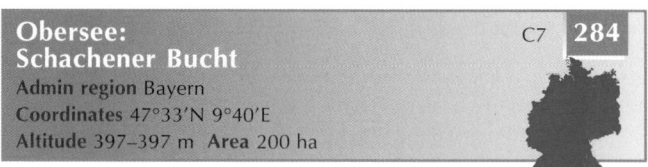

Obersee: Schachener Bucht

C7 **284**

Admin region Bayern
Coordinates 47°33'N 9°40'E
Altitude 397–397 m **Area** 200 ha

■ Site description
A shallow bay on the shore of Lake Constance, near to Lindau. The shoreline is artificial.

Habitats Wetland (standing fresh water), Artificial landscape

■ Birds
There has been a large decrease in ornithological importance over recent years.

■ Protection status
National None **International** None

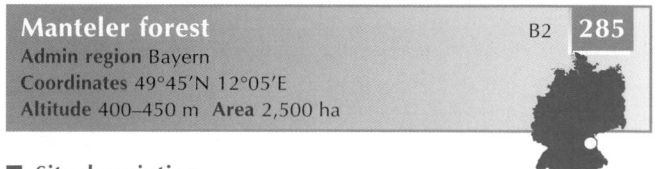

Manteler forest

B2 **285**

Admin region Bayern
Coordinates 49°45'N 12°05'E
Altitude 400–450 m **Area** 2,500 ha

■ Site description
Predominantly *Pinus* forest with a small occurrence of *Picea*.

Habitats Forest and woodland (native coniferous forest)
Land-use Forestry

■ Birds

Species		Season	Year	Pop min	Pop max	Acc	Criteria
Caprimulgus europaeus	Nightjar	B	—	30	—	—	B2

■ **Protection status**
National Low **International** None
109 ha of IBA covered by Nature Reserve.

■ **Conservation issues**

Threats Extraction industry (U)

REFERENCES

AQUATIC WARBLER CONSERVATION TEAM (in press) World population, trends and threat status of the Aquatic Warbler *Acrocephalus paludicola*. *Vogelwelt* 120.

BAUER, H.-G. AND BERTHOLD, P. (1997) *Die Brutvögel Mitteleuropas. Bestand und Gefährdung.* 2nd revised edition. Wiesbaden, Germany: Aula-Verlag.

BAUER, H.-G., BURDORF, K. AND HERKENRATH, P. (1997) "Exoten und Gänsemix": Folgen und Gefahren der Aussetzung, Fremdansiedlung und Gefangenschaftsflucht nichtheimischer und heimischer Vogelarten für die indigene Avifauna—Eine Übersicht mit Handlungsempfehlungen. *Ber. Vogelschutz* 35: 67–90. (In German, with English summary.)

FLADE, M. (1998) Neue Prioritäten im deutschen Vogelschutz: Kleiber oder Wiedehopf? *Der Falke* 45: 348–355.

GREEN, R. E., ROCAMORA, G. AND SCHÄFFER, N. (1997) Populations, ecology and threats to the Corncrake *Crex crex* in Europe. *Vogelwelt* 118: 117–134.

GRIMMETT, R. F. A. AND JONES, T. A. (1989) *Important Bird Areas in Europe.* Cambridge, UK: International Council for Bird Preservation (Techn. Publ. 9).

HEATH, M. F. AND BORGGREVE, C. (2000) *BirdLife International/EBCC European Bird Database 1998.* Cambridge, UK: BirdLife International.

KNIEF, W., SCHWENNESEN, W. AND BERNDT, R. K. (1998) Ergebnisse der Brutbestandserfassung in den Naturschutzgebieten an der schleswig-holsteinischen Ostseeküste 1996. *Seevögel* 19: 17–18.

KÖPPEN, U. AND GRAUMANN, G. (1998) Brutbestände der Küstenvögel in den Schutzgebieten Mecklenburg-Vorpommerns 1993, 1994 und 1996. *Seevögel* 19: 11–16.

LANGEVELD, M. (1991) *Important Bird Areas in the European Community: a shadow list of Special Protection Areas.* Cambridge, UK: International Council for Bird Preservation.

MÄDLOW, W. AND MAYR, C. (1996) [Population trends of some scarce breeding birds in Germany 1990–1994.] *Vogelwelt* 117: 249–260. (In German, with English summary.)

MAYR, C. (1991) Europäische Vogelschutzgebiete (IBA) in Deutschland—Entwicklung seit 1990. *Ber. Dtsch. Sekt. Int. Rat Vogelschutz* 30: 35–53.

MAYR, C. (1993) [Fourteen years EC Wild Birds Directive. Balance of its application in the Federal Republic of Germany.] *Ber. Vogelschutz* 31: 13–22. (In German, with English summary.)

MAYR, C. (1995) [Protection of Ramsar sites under the European Union Birds and Habitats Directives.] *Ber. Vogelschutz* 33: 61–68. (In German, with English summary.)

NAACKE, J. (1989) Zum Beitrag der DDR für die Erfassung der "Gebiete mit bedeutenden Vogelvorkommen in Europa". *Mitteilungen der DDR-Sektion des Internationalen Rates für Vogelschutz* 1: 18–24.

RHEINWALD, G. (1990) [Important Bird Areas (IBA) in the Federal Republic of Germany.] *Ber. Dtsch. Sekt. Int. Rat Vogelschutz* 29: 19–42. (In German.)

RÖSNER, H.-U., BLEW, J., FRIKKE, J., MELTOFTE, H. AND SMIT, C. J. (1995) [Numbers and distribution of waterbirds in the Wadden Sea.] *Natur u. Landschaft* 70: 412–419. (In German, with English summary.)

SCHMIDT, D. (1996) [Breeding numbers and distribution of Ospreys *Pandion haliaetus* in Germany—a short review.] *Vogelwelt* 117: 337–340. (In German, with English summary.)

SSYMANK, A., HAUKE, U., RÜCKRIEM, C., SCHRÖDER, E. AND MESSER, D. (1998) Das europäische Schutzgebietssystem NATURA 2000. BfN-Handbuch zur Umsetzung der Fauna-Flora-Habitat-Richtlinie (92/43/EWG) und der Vogelschutzrichtlinie (79/409/EWG). *Schr. R. Landschaftspfl. Naturschutz* 53.

SUDFELDT, C., NAACKE, J., RUTSCHKE, E. AND MOOIJ, J. (1997) Bestandssituation und -entwicklung ziehender und überwinternder Wasservögel in Deutschland. *Schr. R. Landschaftspfl. Naturschutz* 51: 89–129.

SÜDBECK, P. AND HÄLTERLEIN, B. (1999) Brutvogelbestände an der deutschen Nordseeküste im Jahr 1997–11 Erfassung durch die Arbeitsgemeinschaft "Seevogelschutz". *Seevögel* 20: 9–16.

TUCKER, G. M. AND HEATH, M. F. (1994) *Birds in Europe: their conservation status.* Cambridge, UK: BirdLife International (BirdLife Conservation Series no. 3).

WALICZKY, Z. (1994) *Important Bird Areas in the European Union: an interim list of sites qualifying as Special Protected Areas under the Directive 79/409/EEC.* Cambridge, UK: International Council for Bird Preservation.

WINKEL, W. AND FRANZEN, M. (1987) Erfassung von "Important Bird Areas" der Bundesrepublik Deutschland. *Ber. Dtsch. Sekt. Int. Rat Vogelschutz* 27: 13–58.

WITT, K., BAUER, H.-G., BERTHOLD, P., BOYE, P., HÜPPOP, O. AND KNIEF, W. (1996) [Red Data list of breeding birds of Germany. New version of 1.6.1996.] *Ber. Vogelschutz* 43: 11–35. (In German, with English summary.)

ZWFD (1993) *Die Feuchtgebiete internationaler Bedeutung in der Bundesrepublik Deutschland.* Münster, Germany: ZWFD.

ICELAND

ÓLAFUR EINARSSON

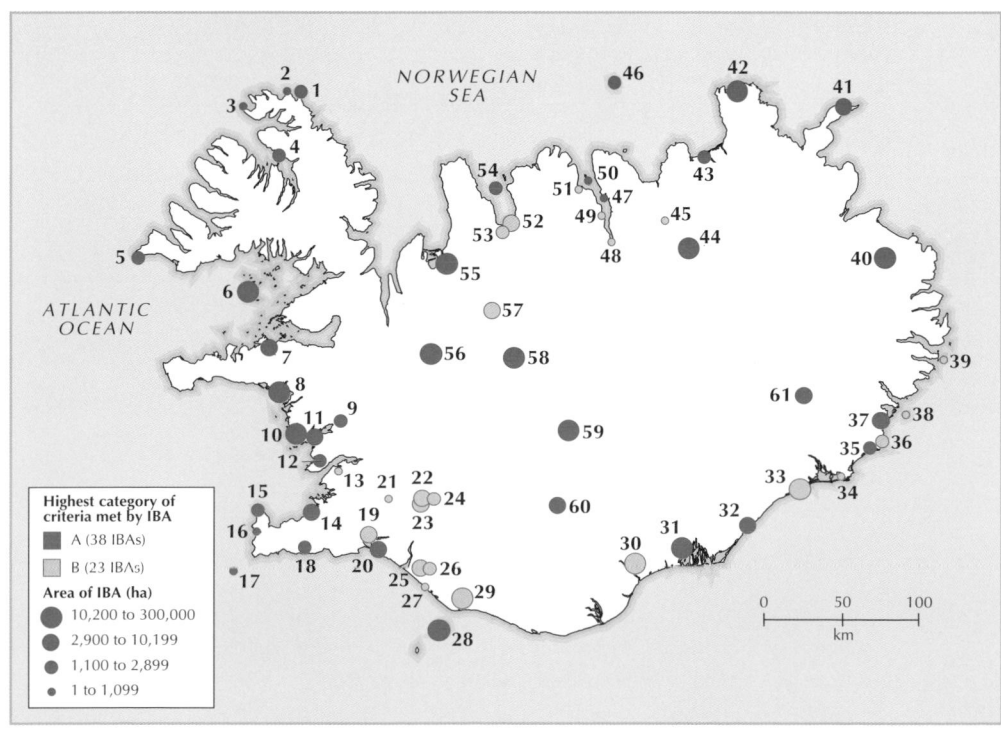

Gyrfalcon *Falco rusticolus*, Iceland's national bird. (PHOTO: JÓHAN ÓLI HILMARSSON)

GENERAL INTRODUCTION

Iceland is the second largest island in Europe, situated in the North Atlantic Ocean and covering a land area of 103,000 km². As a result of its location on the Mid-Atlantic Ridge, an active volcanic zone cuts across the country from the south-west to the north-east. Close to the volcanic zone the bedrock is porous basalt and there are extensive lava plains. Further to the east and west of

this zone the bedrock is made of older Tertiary basalt and former lava plains that have been shaped by glaciers and rivers.

The landscape of Iceland is variable. Many fjords and bays cut into the mainland, and offshore islands are numerous, particularly on the west coast. There are flat, lowland areas, valleys of all kinds, hummocks and hills, mountains, highland plateaus and glaciers. About 70% of the country lies above 300 m altitude.

Map 1. Location, area and criteria category of Important Bird Areas in Iceland.

NORWEGIAN SEA

ATLANTIC OCEAN

Highest category of criteria met by IBA

- A (38 IBAs)
- B (23 IBAs)

Area of IBA (ha)

- 10,200 to 300,000
- 2,900 to 10,199
- 1,100 to 2,899
- 1 to 1,099

0   50   100
km

341

Table 1. Summary of Important Bird Areas in Iceland.

61 IBAs covering 7,345 km²

IBA code	1989 code	International name	National name	Administrative region	Area (ha)	Criteria (see p. 11)
001	IS032	Hornbjarg	Hornbjarg	Norður-Ísafjarðarsýsla	1,100	A4ii, B1ii, B3
002	IS031	Hælavíkurbjarg	Hælavíkurbjarg	Norður-Ísafjarðarsýsla	1,000	A4i, A4ii, A4iii, B1i, B1ii, B3
003	IS030	Ritur	Ritur	Norður-Ísafjarðarsýsla	700	A4i, A4ii, A4iii, B1i, B1ii
004	—	Ædey	Æðey	Norður-Ísafjarðarsýsla	1,100	A4i, B1i, B1ii, B2
005	IS029	Látrabjarg	Látrabjarg	Vestur-Barðastrandasýsla	2,000	A4i, A4ii, A4iii, B1i, B1ii, B2, B3
006	IS028	Breidafjördur	Breiðafjörður	Snæfellsnes og Hnappadalssýsla, Dalasýsla, Austur-Barðastrandasýsla, Vestur-Barðastrandasýsla	300,000	A1, A4i, A4ii, A4iii, B1i, B1ii, B2, B3
007	IS027	Álftafjördur–Hofsstadavogur	Álftafjörður–Hofsstaðavogur	Snæfellsnes og Hnappadalssýsla	3,000	A4i, B1i
008	IS026	Löngufjörur	Löngufjörur	Mýrasýsla, Snæfellsnes og Hnappadalssýsla	17,000	A1, A4i, B1i
009	IS024	Ferjubakkaflói–Nordurá	Ferjubakkaflói–Norðurá	Mýrasýsla	1,500	A4i, B1i
010	IS025	Álftanes–Akrar	Álftanes–Akrar	Mýrasýsla	13,300	A4i, B1i, B2
011	IS023	Borgarfjördur	Borgarfjörður	Borgarfjarðarsýsla, Mýrasýsla	7,000	A4i, B1i
012	IS022	Innstavogsnes–Grunnafjördur	Innstavogsnes–Grunnafjörður	Borgarfjarðarsýsla	1,900	A4i, B1i
013	IS021	Hvalfjardareyri–Laxárvogur	Hvalfjarðareyri–Laxárvogur	Kjósarsýsla	900	B1i
014	IS020	Skerjafjördur	Skerjafjörður	Kjósarsýsla, Reykjavík, Garðabær, Kópavogur, Seltjarnarnesbær	3,300	A4i, B1i
015	IS018	Stafnes–Gardur	Stafnes–Garður	Gullbringusýsla	1,330	A4i, B1i, B3
016	IS017	Ósar	Ósar	Gullbringusýsla	400	A4i, B1i
017	IS016	Eldey	Eldey	Gullbringusýsla	1	A4ii, B1ii, B2
018	IS015	Krísuvíkurberg	Krísuvíkurberg	Gullbringusýsla	1,200	A4ii, A4iii, B1i, B1ii, B3
019	IS014	Ósasvædi Ölfusár	Ósasvæði Ölfusár	Árnessýsla	7,400	B1i, B2
020	IS012	Stokkseyri–Eyrarbakki	Stokkseyri–Eyrarbakki	Árnessýsla	4,300	A4i, B1i
021	IS013	Sog	Sog	Árnessýsla	500	B1i, B2
022	IS011	Apavatn–Laugarvatn	Apavatn–Laugarvatn	Árnessýsla	4,900	B1i, B2
023	—	Brúará	Brúará	Árnessýsla	2,900	B1i, B2
024	IS010	Pollengi–Hrosshagavík	Pollengi–Hrosshagavík	Árnessýsla	1,400	B1i
025	IS009	Vetleifsholtsbugar–Thykkvabæjarvatn	Vetleifsholtsbugar–Þykkvabæjarvatn	Rangárvallasýsla	5,600	B1i
026	IS008	Oddaflód–Lambhagavatn	Oddaflóð–Lambhagavatn	Rangárvallasýsla	1,500	B1i
027	IS007	Skúmsstadavatn	Skúmsstaðavatn	Rangárvallasýsla	800	B1i
028	IS006	Vestmannaeyjar	Vestmannaeyjar	Vestmannaeyjar	27,500	A4i, A4ii, A4iii, B1i, B1ii, B2
029	—	Markarfljótsaurar	Markarfljótsaurar	Rangárvallasýsla	10,500	B3
030	—	Brunasandur	Brunasandur	Vestur-Skaftafellssýsla	14,000	B1ii
031	—	Skeidarársandur	Skeiðarársandur	Austur-Skaftafellssýsla, Vestur-Skaftafellssýsla	33,100	A4ii, B1ii, B3
032	—	Breidamerkursandur	Breiðamerkursandur	Austur-Skaftafellssýsla	6,900	A4ii, B1ii, B2
033	—	Hestgerdislón–Hornafjardarfljót	Hestgerðislón–Hornafjarðarfljót	Austur-Skaftafellssýsla	12,700	B1i
034	IS002	Skardsfjördur	Skarðsfjörður	Austur-Skaftafellssýsla	1,050	B1i
035	IS001	Lónsfjördur	Lónsfjörður	Austur-Skaftafellssýsla	2,700	A4i, B1i, B3
036	—	Hvalnesskridur–Thvottárskridur	Hvalnesskriður–Þvottárskriður	Austur-Skaftafellssýsla	1,800	B1i
037	IS053	Álftafjördur–Hamarsfjördur	Álftafjörður–Hamarsfjörður	Suður-Múlasýsla	3,500	A4i, B1i
038	IS052	Papey	Papey	Suður-Múlasýsla	540	B2
039	IS051	Skrúdur	Skrúður	Suður-Múlasýsla	92	B2
040	IS050	Úthérad	Úthérað	Norður-Múlasýsla	36,200	A4i, B1i, B1ii, B2
041	IS048, IS049	Skoruvík–Skálabjarg	Skoruvík–Skálabjarg	Norður-Þingeyjarsýsla	5,300	A4i, A4ii, A4iii, B1i, B1ii, B3
042	—	Melrakkaslétta	Melrakkaslétta	Norður-Þingeyjarsýsla	24,600	A4i, B1i, B3
043	IS047	Öxarfjördur	Öxarfjörður	Norður-Þingeyjarsýsla	2,500	A4i, A4ii, B1i, B1ii
044	IS046	Mývatn–Laxá	Mývatn–Laxá	Suður-Þingeyjarsýsla	10,200	A4i, A4iii, B1i, B2, B3
045	IS045	Vestmannsvatn	Vestmannsvatn	Suður-Þingeyjarsýsla	600	B1i
046	IS041	Grímsey	Grímsey	Eyjafjarðarsýsla	2,300	A4i, A4ii, A4iii, B1i, B1ii, B3
047	—	Höfdahverfi	Höfðahverfi	Suður-Þingeyjarsýsla	60	A4i, B1i
048	IS043	Hólmarnir	Hólmarnir	Eyjafjarðarsýsla	700	B1i
049	IS038	Hörgárósar	Hörgárósar	Eyjafjarðarsýsla	540	B1i
050	—	Hrísey	Hrísey	Eyjafjarðarsýsla	767	A4i, B1i
051	IS042	Svarfadardalur	Svarfaðardalur	Eyjafjarðarsýsla	540	B1i
052	IS034	Austara Eylendid	Austara Eylendið	Skagafjarðarsýsla	3,300	B1i, B2
053	IS036	Miklavatn–Skógar	Miklavatn–Skógar	Skagafjarðarsýsla	2,100	B1i
054	IS040	Drangey	Drangey	Skagafjarðarsýsla	1,500	A4iii
055	IS037	Hóp–Vatnsdalur	Hóp–Vatnsdalur	Austur-Húnavatnssýsla	12,000	A4i, B1i
056	IS033	Arnarvatnsheidi–Tvídægra	Arnarvatnsheiði–Tvídægra	Mýrasýsla, Vestur-Húnavatnssýsla	60,000	A4i, B1i
057	IS035	Eyjavatn–Fridmundarvötn	Eyjavatn–Friðmundarvötn	Austur-Húnavatnssýsla	7,500	B1i
058	—	Gudlaugstungur–Álfgeirstungur	Guðlaugstungur–Álfgeirstungur	Austur-Húnavatnssýsla	11,500	A4i, B1i
059	IS005	Thjórsárver	Þjórsárver	Rangárvallasýsla, Árnessýsla	37,500	A4i, B1i, B3
060	IS004	Veidivötn	Veiðivötn	Rangárvallasýsla	7,600	A4i, B1i, B2
061	—	Eyjabakkar	Eyjabakkar	Norður-Múlasýsla	6,800	A4i, B1i

Sites identified in the previous inventory of IBAs in Europe (Grimmett and Jones 1989) but no longer considered to be IBAs
IS003 Steinsmýrarflód; IS019 Ástjörn; IS039 Höfdavatn; IS044 Sandur–Sílalækur

A total of 61 Important Bird Areas (IBAs) are identified in Iceland, covering 7,345 km² or c.7% of the land area of the country (Table 1). This compares with 53 sites listed for Iceland in the previous pan-European inventory of IBAs (Grimmett and Jones 1989). Forty-nine of the original 53 sites have been included in the current inventory, although 'Langanes' (former site 049) has been merged with 'Skoruvík' (former site 048) to form 'Skoruvík–Skálabjarg' (current site 041), also the boundaries have been redefined for some other IBAs, and a few now appear under a

different name because of changes in administrative regions. The remaining four original sites do not meet current (revised) IBA criteria; they are listed in Table 1. The IBAs are well distributed across the country, but are more numerous in the south and west than in the east (Map 1). The three largest IBAs are Breidafjördur (site 006; 41% of the total IBA area), Arnarvatnsheidi–Tvídægra (site 056; 8%) and Thjórsárver (site 059; 5%). The average IBA size is c.120 km², but the three smallest ones (sites 017, 039 and 047) cover less than 1 km² each (Table 1).

Table 2. Important Bird Areas in Iceland that support important numbers of one or more congregatory species (i.e. meeting criteria A4 and/or B1). IBAs meeting both criteria A4 and B1 for the species are shown in **bold**. IBAs meeting only criterion B1 for the species concerned, and not A4, are shown in normal type. For key to 'Season', see p. 7.

Species	Season	IBA code
Gavia immer Great Northern Diver	B	**042**, **056**, **060**
Podiceps auritus Slavonian Grebe	R	043
	B	040, **044**, 045, 052
Fulmarus glacialis Fulmar	B	**005**, **028**
Puffinus puffinus Manx Shearwater	B	**028**
Hydrobates pelagicus Storm Petrel	B	**028**
Oceanodroma leucorhoa Leach's Petrel	B	**028**
Sula bassana Gannet	B	**017**, **028**
Phalacrocorax carbo Cormorant	R	**006**
Phalacrocorax aristotelis Shag	R	**006**
Cygnus cygnus Whooper Swan	B	033, **056**
	W	**044**
	P	**007**, **009**, 020, 021, 024, 025, 027, **035**, 037, 055
	N	**010**, **035**, 043, **044**, 053, 057
Anser brachyrhynchus Pink-footed Goose	B	**058**, **059**
	N	**061**
Anser albifrons White-fronted Goose	P	009, 019, 024, 025, 026, 027
Anser anser Greylag Goose	R	023
	B	**006**, **040**, 052
	N	**006**, 037, **040**, 042, **043**, 049, 053, 055
Branta leucopsis Barnacle Goose	P	033, 051, **055**
Branta bernicla Brent Goose	P	**006**, **007**, **010**, **012**, 013, 014
Aythya marila Scaup	B	**044**
	N	053
Somateria mollissima Eider	R	**004**, **006**, 014, 042, **047**, 050
	W	**015**
	N	**008**, **011**, 034, 036
Histrionicus histrionicus Harlequin Duck	B	**044**
	W	**016**
Mergus merganser Goosander	W	021, 022, 044
Calidris canutus Knot	P	**006**, **007**, **008**, **010**, 012, 013, 014, 020, 042
Calidris alba Sanderling	P	**015**
Calidris maritima Purple Sandpiper	W	**010**, **014**, **015**, **020**
Calidris alpina Dunlin	B	019
	P	034
Gallinago gallinago Snipe	B	019
Limosa limosa Black-tailed Godwit	B	052
	P	027, 048
Arenaria interpres Turnstone	W	**015**
	P	**010**, **014**, **015**, 042
Stercorarius parasiticus Arctic Skua	B	030, 040
Stercorarius skua Great Skua	B	**031**, **032**, **043**
Larus hyperboreus Glaucous Gull	R	**006**
Larus marinus Great Black-backed Gull	R	**006**
Rissa tridactyla Kittiwake	B	**002**, **003**, **005**, **006**, 018, **028**, **041**, **046**
Sterna paradisaea Arctic Tern	B	**050**
Uria aalge Guillemot	B	**002**, 003, **005**, 018, **028**, 041, **046**
Uria lomvia Brünnich's Guillemot	B	**002**, **005**
Alca torda Razorbill	B	**001**, **002**, **003**, **005**, 018, **031**, **041**, **046**
Cepphus grylle Black Guillemot	R	**006**
	B	**004**
Fratercula arctica Puffin	B	**006**, **028**, **046**

ORNITHOLOGICAL IMPORTANCE

A total of 88 bird species breed regularly in Iceland, a low figure in comparison with other European countries, but many of these species have particularly large national populations, with thousands of breeding pairs. The breeding avifauna is characterized by many species of wildfowl, seabirds and waders. A total of 42 species of European conservation concern (SPECs) breed regularly in Iceland, of which 25 have an unfavourable conservation status in Europe, including one of global conservation concern, *Haliaeetus albicilla* (Tucker and Heath 1994).

The majority of the IBAs (38 out of 61) are of global importance, qualifying under the 'A' criteria (Table 1, Map 1). IBAs that hold globally important numbers of congregatory waterbirds and seabirds (meeting the A4i/ii criteria) also number 38, while a further 23 IBAs qualify as important on a European scale for such birds, meeting the B1i/ii criteria but not A4i/ii (Table 1).

The most important sites for breeding waterbirds in general are Lake Mývatn (site 044) and Thjórsárver (059), both designated Ramsar Sites (Table 2). At Mývatn many thousands of ducks breed in a unique landscape, while Thjórsárver is the most important breeding site for *Anser brachyrhynchus* in the world. Key areas for breeding seabirds are sites 001, 002, 005, 006 and 028 (Table 2). Huge numbers of *Rissa tridactyla*, *Uria aalge*, *Uria lomvia*, *Alca torda*, *Cepphus grylle* and *Fratercula arctica* breed at these sites, and Vestmannaeyjar (site 028) also holds a globally significant number of breeding *Hydrobates pelagicus* and *Oceanodroma leucorhoa*.

Several sites qualify because they support important numbers of birds outside the breeding season (Table 2). This applies mainly

Table 3. Species of European conservation concern with significant breeding populations at Important Bird Areas in Iceland (meeting any IBA criteria).

Species [1]	Minimum national breeding population (pairs) [2]	Proportion (%) of national population breeding at all IBAs in Iceland
Gavia stellata Red-throated Diver	1,000	23
Puffinus puffinus Manx Shearwater	7,000	100[3]
Hydrobates pelagicus Storm Petrel	50,000	100[3]
Oceanodroma leucorhoa Leach's Petrel	80,000	100
Sula bassana Gannet	25,400	97
Phalacrocorax aristotelis Shag	8,000	75
Anser brachyrhynchus Pink-footed Goose	30,000	22
Histrionicus histrionicus Harlequin Duck	2,000	11
Bucephala islandica Barrow's Goldeneye	800	100[3]
Calidris maritima Purple Sandpiper	10,000	1
Limosa limosa Black-tailed Godwit	7,000	4
Numenius phaeopus Whimbrel	200,000	1
Stercorarius skua Great Skua	5,500	100
Larus marinus Great Black-backed Gull	50,000	24
Alca torda Razorbill	380,000	65
Cepphus grylle Black Guillemot	30,000	3[4]
Fratercula arctica Puffin	2,000,000	61

1. Only those species of European conservation concern (see Box 1, p. 12) that meet IBA criteria in Iceland are listed.
2. Data are taken from the BirdLife/EBCC European Bird Database 1998 (Heath and Borggreve 2000).
3. The percentage of the national population in IBAs exceeds 100%. Usually this is because the national population estimate has not been updated recently whilst the IBA population estimate has been recently updated with new data as a result of comprehensive surveys of IBAs themselves. Also, the individual site count for a species may be the maximum or average over recent years, and summing these may record more birds than are present nationally in any single year.
4. Data are for Flatey (part of IBA 006) and Æday (004) only; actual percentage is much higher (possibly 50% or more).

Figure 1. Habitats at Important Bird Areas in Iceland (see Appendix 3 for definitions of habitats).

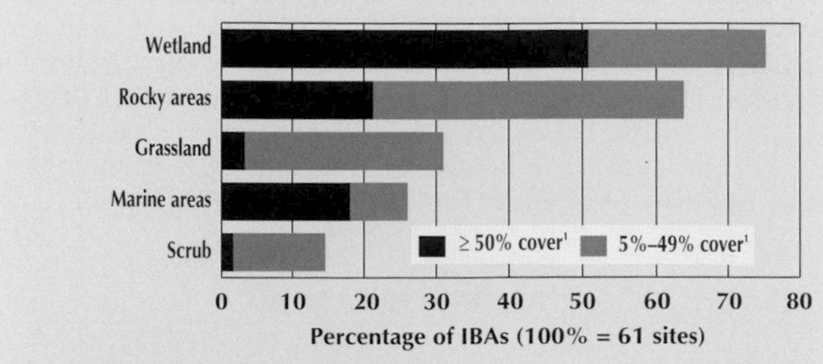

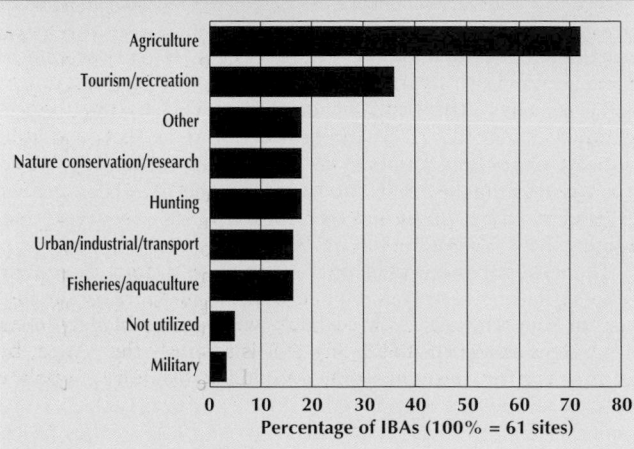

1. percentage of area of individual IBA covered by habitat

Figure 2. Occurrence of land-uses at Important Bird Areas in Iceland (see Appendix 3 for definitions of land-uses).

to birds staging on migration but also to birds moulting after the breeding season. Iceland is an essential 'refueling' station for migratory bird species that breed in the Arctic and winter further south, such as *Branta bernicla* and *Anser albifrons*. Waders such as *Calidris canutus* and *Calidris alba* also pass through in thousands at sites in the south and west of the country (Table 2). Species that congregate at sites to moult in important numbers are *Anser brachyrhynchus* (site 061), *Cygnus cygnus* (sites 035, 010 and 007), *Somateria mollissima* (sites 011, 008 and 036) and *Anser anser* (sites 006, 049, 043 and 040).

Sites with important numbers of wintering waterbirds lie mainly along the south-west and west coast of Iceland (sites 014–016 and 020). Data from west Iceland on wintering waterbirds are not systematic, but IBAs there are thought to support significant numbers of wintering waders and wildfowl. Important wintering haunts for wildfowl are also found inland on ice-free rivers, namely sites 021–023 and 044.

The number of bird species meeting criteria at individual sites ranges from one to 11, with the great majority of sites having less than five qualifying species. The sites with the highest number of

qualifying species are Breidafjördur (11), Vestmannaeyjar (eight), Álftanes–Akrar (seven) and Stafnes–Gardur (five).

Most seabird SPECs that breed in Iceland are well covered by the IBA network, as is *Bucephala islandica* (Table 3). Species that breed in a rather dispersed, non-congregatory fashion, such as *Calidris maritima*, *Limosa limosa* and *Numenius phaeopus*, are inadequately covered by the IBA network in Iceland (Table 3). For similar reasons, several other breeding SPECs are not covered at all by the IBA network: *Falco rusticolus*, *Pluvialis apricaria*, *Tringa totanus*, *Larus fuscus* and *Anthus pratensis*.

HABITATS

Woodland and scrub of birch *Betula* apparently covered most of the Icelandic lowlands at the time of first settlement in c.874 AD. Severe erosion followed settlement, causing dramatic losses of plant cover over large areas of the highlands as well as in some parts of the lowlands, such that the extent of vegetated land was reduced from about 60,000–70,000 km² to about 25,000 km² at present. Birch woodland and scrub, in particular, decreased from 30,000–40,000 km² to 1,250 km² currently (Thorsteinsson 1985). Lowland habitats (below 300 m) are now characterized by heathland (moss and dwarf shrubs), grassland, wetlands and cultivated land. Heathland is predominant in vegetated areas in the low alpine zone (300–600 m). Extensive wetlands are found on the highland plateau; permafrost is present beneath some of them, causing the formation of palsa mires. Above 600 m the vegetation cover is sparse in most areas. Glaciers cover about 12,000 km² at the higher altitudes.

Wetland is the most common habitat at Icelandic IBAs and is found at most of the sites, often covering large tracts (Figure 1). Lakes, pools, different kinds of marshes and mires, rivers and streams characterize the majority of wetland IBAs, for instance at sites 019, 024, 044, 053, 059 and 061. Mudflats, tidal rivers and coastal lagoons are the main wetland-types at a few of the sites, e.g. sites 034, 035 and 049. The habitat-type 'Rocky areas' is also common, being found at more than 60% of the IBAs (Figure 1), most frequently as sea cliffs or as glacial outwash plains of eroded gravel (classed as 'Rocky areas' for this analysis). Less common habitat-types are grassland, found at 31% of the sites, marine habitat at 26%, and scrub at 15%.

IMPACTS ON IBAs – LAND-USE AND THREATS

Agriculture is the main form of land-use, occurring at 72% of IBAs (Figure 2), and its impact on habitats has been widespread. The main type of agriculture at IBAs is livestock-grazing, primarily sheep and horses. Extensive areas of wetland have been drained for agriculture since the late 1940s, dramatically changing the hydrology of remaining wetlands, especially in the southern lowlands where only a few marshes remain intact. Drainage is one of the most common threats to IBAs in Iceland (Figure 3).

Tourism and recreation have increased a lot in Iceland during the 1980s and 1990s, and rank as the second-most frequent land-use and threat at IBAs (Figures 2 and 3). Disturbance of birds by

Figure 3. Occurrence of threats at Important Bird Areas in Iceland (see Appendix 3 for definitions of threat types and impact categories).

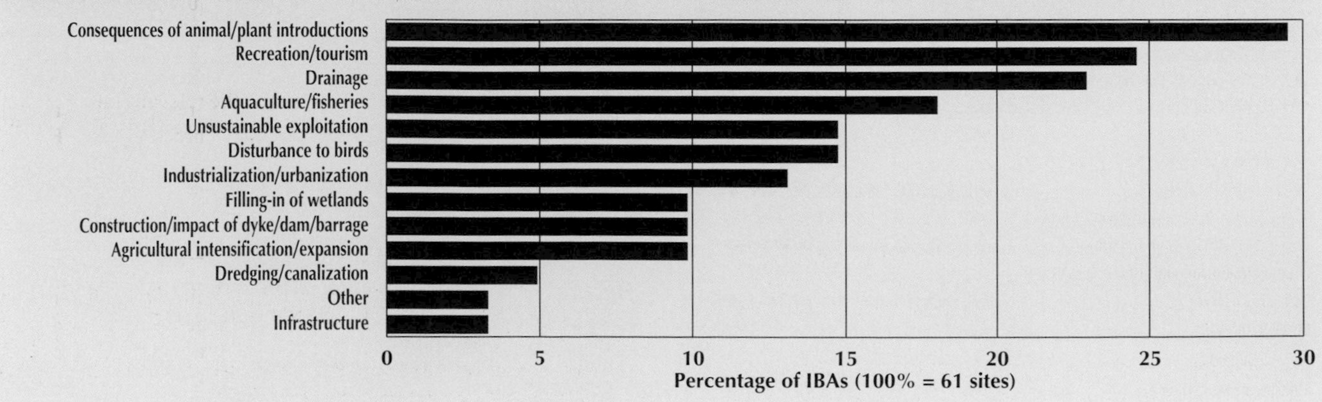

Table 4. Protection status of Important Bird Areas in Iceland. A tick (✔) indicates that an IBA overlaps with a protected area (to any extent).

IBA code	International name	Nature Reserve	Nature Reserve (Landscape)	Scientific Reserve	Conservation Area	Ramsar Site
		National				International
001	Hornbjarg		✔			
002	Hælavíkurbjarg		✔			
003	Ritur		✔			
004	Ædey					
005	Látrabjarg					
006	Breidafjördur	✔	✔		✔	
007	Álftafjördur–Hofsstadavogur				✔	
008	Löngufjörur					
009	Ferjubakkaflói–Nordurá					
010	Álftanes–Akrar					
011	Borgarfjördur					
012	Innstavogsnes–Grunnafjördur	✔				✔
013	Hvalfjardareyri–Laxárvogur					
014	Skerjafjördur	✔				
015	Stafnes–Gardur					
016	Ósar					
017	Eldey			✔		
018	Krísuvíkurberg					
019	Ósasvædi Ölfusár	✔				
020	Stokkseyri–Eyrarbakki					
021	Sog					
022	Apavatn–Laugarvatn					
023	Brúará					
024	Pollengi–Hrosshagavík	✔				
025	Vetleifsholtsbugar–Thykkvabæjarvatn					
026	Oddaflód–Lambhagavatn	✔				
027	Skúmsstadavatn					
028	Vestmannaeyjar			✔		
029	Markarfljótsaurar					
030	Brunasandur					
031	Skeidarársandur		✔			
032	Breidamerkursandur					
033	Hestgerdislón–Hornafjardarfljót					
034	Skardsfjördur					
035	Lónsfjördur					
036	Hvalnesskridur–Thvottárskridur					
037	Álftafjördur–Hamarsfjördur					
038	Papey					
039	Skrúdur	✔				
040	Úthérad					
041	Skoruvík–Skálabjarg					
042	Melrakkaslétta					
043	Öxarfjördur					
044	Mývatn–Laxá				✔	✔
045	Vestmannsvatn	✔				
046	Grímsey					
047	Höfdahverfi					
048	Hólmarnir					
049	Hörgárósar					
050	Hrísey					
051	Svarfadardalur	✔				
052	Austara Eylendid					
053	Miklavatn–Skógar	✔				
054	Drangey					
055	Hóp–Vatnsdalur					
056	Arnarvatnsheidi–Tvídægra					
057	Eyjavatn–Fridmundarvötn					
058	Gudlaugstungur–Álfgeirstungur					
059	Thjórsárver	✔				✔
060	Veidivötn					
061	Eyjabakkar					
	Total number of IBAs	**11**	**5**	**2**	**3**	**3**

Box 1. International legislation and initiatives that are relevant to site conservation in Iceland (see Appendix 1 for a general description of these agreements).

Global

Biodiversity Convention	✔
Ramsar Convention	✔
Bonn Convention	
World Heritage Convention	✔
MAB Programme	✔

Pan-European

Bern Convention	✔

✔ Convention ratified/initiative supported
(✔) Convention signed

human activities is considerable in some areas, particularly in the vicinity of the more populated centres.

Introduced animals and plants pose the most common threat to IBAs in Iceland, affecting nearly 30% of sites (Figure 3). The main problem species are American mink *Mustela vison* and Nootka lupin *Lupinus nootkatensis*. The mink is a highly adaptable, semi-aquatic carnivore which is a serious hazard to nesting waterbirds and seabirds in particular, while the lupin (also North American in origin) is a highly invasive shrub that alters vegetation structure at IBAs and outcompetes native plant species. Various other threats feature at less than 15% of IBAs, including those posed by dam-building. Two IBAs, Thjórsárver (site 059) and Eyjabakkar (061), are under serious threat of submersion if reservoirs, planned for hydroelectric power-stations, are constructed and filled. The proposals involve the complete submersion of Eyjabakkar and the partial submersion of the Ramsar Site at Thjórsárver. Part of the Sog river (site 021) has already been damaged by reservoirs and other infrastructure for hydroelectric power-stations. Mývatn–Laxá (site 044) is another Ramsar Site that is seriously threatened, by the mining of the bottom sediments of Lake Mývatn to supply a diatomite factory by the lake.

PROTECTION STATUS

■ National protection

The Nature Conservancy Agency manages protected areas according to the Nature Conservation Act No. 93 (1996). Five levels of protection are recognized: (1) National Parks; (2) Nature Reserves; (3) Country Parks; (4) Natural Monuments; (5) protection of individual species of plant or animal, their habitats and ecosystems (Náttúruverndarád 1996). Seventy-four areas have been designated under this Act. In addition, three areas are protected by special laws, and the Nature Conservancy Agency is also responsible for the management of two unprotected areas (Náttúruverndarád 1996).

Before 1996 the types of designation were different. Table 4 lists those IBAs in Iceland that have some legal protection at the national and/or international level, through their overlap with the network of statutory protected areas, using pre-1996 protected-area designations.

Only 18% of IBAs overlap to a high degree with national protected areas, and a further 13% overlap to a lesser degree, leaving 69% without any legal protection whatsoever (Figure 4). The protected IBAs are very diverse in size (Table 4), from 1 ha up to 300,000 ha. In total, some 4,056 km^2 of the IBA network is under some form of protection by national law, equivalent to 55% of the total IBA area (Figure 4).

■ International protection

Iceland is a contracting party to most of the relevant international site-conservation agreements (Box 1) and three IBAs are Ramsar Sites (Table 4, Figure 5).

CONSERVATION

- There is a coordinated research and monitoring programme at only one IBA, Mývatn–Laxá, and that has been running for a number of years (Einarsson 1994). The data on bird numbers at other areas is not as complete, and nowhere else in the country are bird numbers monitored as thoroughly.

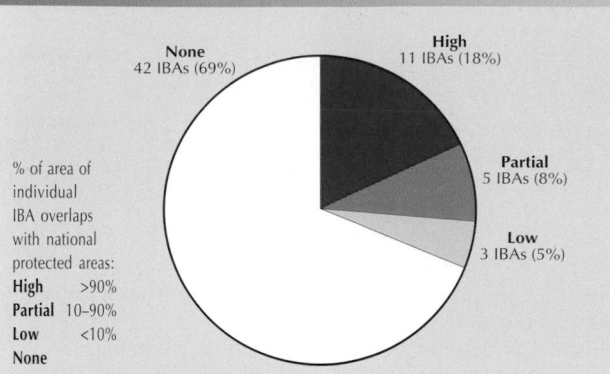

Figure 4. The national protection status of Important Bird Areas in Iceland.

% of area of individual IBA overlaps with national protected areas:
High >90%
Partial 10–90%
Low <10%
None

Total area of overlap between IBA network in Iceland and national protected-area system (see Table 4 for categories) = 3,596 km² (49% of total IBA area).

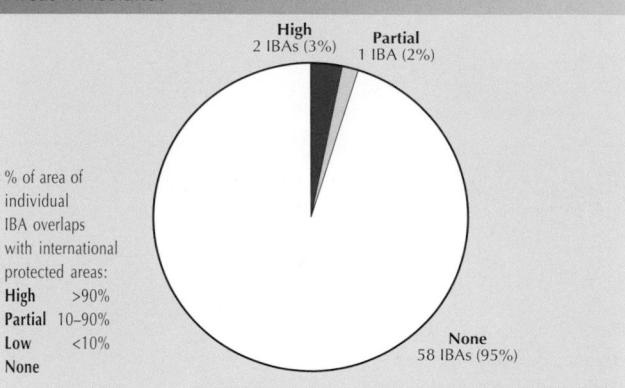

Figure 5. The international protection status of Important Bird Areas in Iceland.

% of area of individual IBA overlaps with international protected areas:
High >90%
Partial 10–90%
Low <10%
None

Total area of overlap between IBA network in Iceland and international protected-area system (see Table 4 for categories) = 492 km² (7% of total IBA area).

- A management plan is in preparation for one IBA, Breidafjördur (site 006) in west Iceland, and will probably be ready in 1999. A management plan for the bird reserve within Ósasvædi Ölfusár (019) will be developed during 1999. No other IBAs have management plans, nor has work begun on them, even for protected IBAs.

- In the 1990s wetland restoration began in Iceland, as an initiative of the Icelandic Society for the Protection of Birds. Most of the work has been done at the bird reserve within Ósasvædi Ölfusár (site 019), but also on a small scale at a few other wetlands (not IBAs). Increasing awareness and discussion of wetland issues in Iceland have also resulted in more publications, for instance in 1998 a book on Icelandic wetlands was published by the University Press of Iceland in collaboration with the Icelandic Society for the Protection of Birds and the Icelandic Biological Society (Ólafsson 1998).

- A publication in Icelandic on IBAs has not been produced, but would be an important step in advocating the conservation of these areas and in focusing attention on the IBA concept.

ANALYTICAL METHODS

- The foundation for the IBA work in 1997 was the previous compilation for Iceland made by Arnthór Gardarsson and Ólafur K. Nielsen and published in Grimmett and Jones (1989). This overview was also partly based on the former overview. For the new IBA database an extensive literature search was carried out and information gathered from birdwatchers and ornithologists in Iceland. For logistic reasons, no field surveys of sites were organized for this compilation.

- Most of the bird data are from the 1980s and 1990s. The quality of the data is highly variable between sites and bird species. There is published information of good quality for some bird species at individual IBAs, e.g. *Sula bassana*, *Phalacrocorax carbo*,

Phalacrocorax aristotelis and some of the wildfowl such as *Branta bernicla* and waders at spring staging sites. The auks have also been counted at the major sea cliffs and the results published. Data for other species are less systematic.

- Information on habitats, land-uses and threats was limited for many of the IBAs. The data presented give only a rough indication for most of the sites, since field visits could not be arranged in relation to the IBA work, and detailed information was not available for most of the sites. Therefore, it is essential in the future to systematically collect data on habitats, land-uses and threats for each of the IBAs. It is clear that changes will be made to the Icelandic IBA database in the near future, as better information comes in. For instance, it is considered appropriate to enlarge the Borgarfjördur IBA (site 011) to include the inner part of the firth because of the latter's importance for waders and *Anser albifrons*.

ACKNOWLEDGEMENTS

Many individuals assisted and contributed to the new inventory of Important Bird Areas in Iceland, and I am most grateful to them: Arnór Th. Sigfússon, Arnthór Gardarsson, Árni Einarsson, Björn G. Arnarson, Björn Hjaltason, Brynjúlfur Brynjólfsson, Einar Ó. Thorleifsson, Gudmundur A. Gudmundsson, Halldór W. Stefánsson, Jóhann Óli Hilmarsson, Kristinn H. Skarphédinsson, Ólafur K. Nielsen, Skarphédinn G. Thórisson, Sverrir Thorstensen, Tómas Gunnarsson, Trausti Baldursson, Thorbergur H. Jónsson, Thorsteinn Thorsteinsson, Thorvaldur Th. Björnsson and Ævar Petersen. Ólafur K. Nielsen and Jóhann Óli Hilmarsson commented on the draft of the overview and site accounts.

A generous grant was provided by the Royal Society for the Protection of Birds (the BirdLife Partner in the United Kingdom) to the Icelandic Society for the Protection of Birds, which allowed the work on the IBA database in Iceland to be initiated. All additional expenses were met by the Icelandic Institute of Natural History.

■ SITE ACCOUNTS

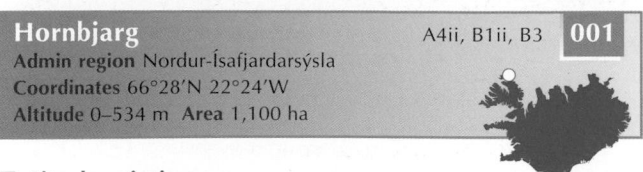

Hornbjarg　　　　　　　　A4ii, B1ii, B3　**001**
Admin region Nordur-Ísafjardarsýsla
Coordinates 66°28′N 22°24′W
Altitude 0–534 m **Area** 1,100 ha

■ Site description
Sea cliffs in the extreme north-west of mainland Iceland, rising to 534 m. The adjacent waters are also important and are included in the IBA. Recreation is the main human activity in the area, and there is no permanent settlement.

Habitats Rocky areas (100%; sea cliff/rocky shore)
Land-use Tourism/recreation

■ Birds

Species	Season	Year	Pop min	Pop max	Acc	Criteria
Alca torda Razorbill	B	—	—	35,000	C	A4ii, B1ii, B3

An important seabird colony with the total number of breeding auks numbering c.400,000 pairs. A total of 70,000 pairs of *Alca torda* nest at this site and at Hælavíkurbjarg (site 031) combined, although it is less common at this site, while less than 10,000 pairs of *Fratercula arctica* nest at the two sites in total (probably closer to 4,000–5,000 pairs). The site also holds more than 1% of the Icelandic population of *Rissa tridactyla*, *Uria aalge* and *Uria lomvia*.

■ Protection status
National High **International** None

1,100 ha of IBA covered by Nature Reserve (Landscape) (Hornstrandir, 58,000 ha).

■ **Conservation issues**
No serious threats are known. Tourism (including hiking) is increasing in the Hornstrandir area, and may pose a threat in the future.

Hælavíkurbjarg A4i, A4ii, A4iii, B1i, B1ii, B3 002
Admin region Nordur-Ísafjardarsýsla
Coordinates 66°28′N 22°36′W
Altitude 0–489 m **Area** 1,000 ha

■ **Site description**
Mainland sea cliffs in the extreme north-west of Iceland. Recreation is the main human activity in the area. There is no permanent settlement in the neighbourhood. Eggs are collected traditionally from auks at certain places along the cliff.

Habitats Rocky areas (100%; sea cliff/rocky shore)
Land-use Tourism/recreation

■ **Birds**

Species	Season	Year	Pop min	Pop max	Acc	Criteria
Rissa tridactyla Kittiwake	B	1985	195,000	195,000	A	A4i, B1i
Uria aalge Guillemot	B	1985	237,000	674,000	A	A4ii, B1ii
Uria lomvia Brünnich's Guillemot	B	1985	214,000	612,000	A	A4ii, B1ii
Alca torda Razorbill	B	—	35,000	—	C	A4ii, B1ii, B3

The site supports a huge number of breeding seabirds. A total of 70,000 pairs of *Alca torda* nest at this site and at Hornbjarg (site 001) combined, although it is more common at this site, while less than 10,000 pairs of *Fratercula arctica* nest at the two sites in total (probably closer to 4,000–5,000 pairs).

■ **Protection status**
National High **International** None
1,000 ha of IBA covered by Nature Reserve (Landscape) (Hornstrandir, 58,000 ha).

■ **Conservation issues**
No serious threats are known. Tourism (including hiking) is increasing in the Hornstrandir area, and may pose a threat in the future.

Ritur A4i, A4ii, A4iii, B1i, B1ii 003
Admin region Nordur-Ísafjardarsýsla
Coordinates 66°22′N 23°12′W
Altitude 0–482 m **Area** 700 ha

■ **Site description**
A sea cliff in the extreme north-west of mainland Iceland. Recreation is the main land-use. There is no permanent settlement in the neighborhood. Eggs are collected traditionally from the auks at certain places on the cliff ('Other' land-use).

Habitats Rocky areas (100%; sea cliff/rocky shore)
Land-use Other

■ **Birds**

Species	Season	Year	Pop min	Pop max	Acc	Criteria
Rissa tridactyla Kittiwake	B	1985	12,200	12,200	A	A4i, B1i
Uria aalge Guillemot	B	1985	9,100	29,600	A	B1ii
Alca torda Razorbill	B	1985	1,190	6,200	A	A4ii, B1ii

Important for its large numbers of breeding seabirds; other abundant species are *Fulmarus glacialis*, *Fratercula arctica* and *Uria lomvia* (12,000 pairs).

■ **Protection status**
National High **International** None
700 ha of IBA covered by Nature Reserve (Landscape) (Hornstrandir, 58,000 ha).

■ **Conservation issues**
No serious threats are known.

Ædey A4i, B1i, B1ii, B2 004
Admin region Nordur-Ísafjardarsýsla
Coordinates 66°06′N 22°40′W
Altitude 0–34 m **Area** 1,100 ha

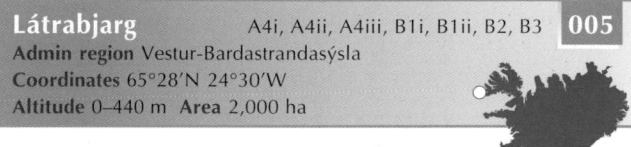

■ **Site description**
An island (200 ha) and adjacent area in the middle of the Ísafjördur firth, by Snæfjallaströnd, north-north-east of Ísafjördur town. Land-uses include grazing and eider husbandry (*Somateria mollissima*) ('Other' land-use).

Habitats Grassland (80%), Rocky areas (20%; sea cliff/rocky shore)
Land-use Agriculture, Other

■ **Birds**

Species	Season	Year	Pop min	Pop max	Acc	Criteria
Somateria mollissima Eider	R	—	—	10,000	—	A4i, B1i
Cepphus grylle Black Guillemot	B	—	500	600	—	B1ii, B2

One of the largest breeding colonies of *Somateria mollissima* in the country, and *Sterna paradisaea* and *Fratercula arctica* are also common breeders.

■ **Protection status**
National None **International** None

■ **Conservation issues**

Threats Consequences of animal/plant introductions (U)

Predation by introduced American mink *Mustela vison* is a threat.

Látrabjarg A4i, A4ii, A4iii, B1i, B1ii, B2, B3 005
Admin region Vestur-Bardastrandasýsla
Coordinates 65°28′N 24°30′W
Altitude 0–440 m **Area** 2,000 ha

■ **Site description**
A sea cliff in the westernmost part of Iceland. Half of the cliff is a sheer precipice, practically without vegetation, but the upper and more eastern parts are less steep and are covered with lush herbaceous vegetation. Rock-falls have formed screes in several places. Eggs are collected traditionally from the auks at certain places on the cliff every spring ('Other' land-use).

Habitats Rocky areas (100%; sea cliff/rocky shore; scree/boulders)
Land-use Other, Tourism/recreation

■ **Birds**

Species	Season	Year	Pop min	Pop max	Acc	Criteria
Fulmarus glacialis Fulmar	B	1985	120,000	—	—	A4ii, B1ii
Rissa tridactyla Kittiwake	B	1985	46,600	46,600	A	A4i, B1i
Uria aalge Guillemot	B	1985	209,000	402,000	B	A4ii, B1ii
Uria lomvia Brünnich's Guillemot	B	1985	80,000	164,000	A	A4ii, B1ii
Alca torda Razorbill	B	—	152,000	329,000	A	A4ii, B1ii, B3
[1] *Fratercula arctica* Puffin	B	—	Abundant		—	B2

1. At least 100,000 pairs are thought to breed (believed to exceed threshold).

The site supports huge numbers of breeding seabirds, including the largest colony of *Alca torda* in the world, and one of the largest colonies of *Fratercula arctica* in Iceland.

■ **Protection status**
National None **International** None

■ **Conservation issues**

Threats Recreation/tourism (U)

Tourism may pose threats.

Breidafjördur A1, A4i, A4ii, A4iii, B1i, B1ii, B2, B3 006

Admin region Snæfellsnes og Hnappadalssýsla, Dalasýsla,
Austur-Bardastrandasýsla, Vestur-Bardastrandasýsla
Coordinates 65°19'N 23°00'W
Altitude 0–41 m **Area** 300,000 ha

■ Site description

A very large area of coastal waters off western Iceland, containing
thousands of islands and islets. The bay is rather shallow and there
are extensive intertidal areas adjoining the heavily indented coastline.
Habitat also includes marshes and grassland on some of the islands.
Land-uses include seaweed-harvesting, exploitation of seals
(Phocidae), eider husbandry (*Somateria mollissima*), traditional
harvesting of eggs of *Rissa tridactyla*, *Sterna paradisaea* and *Larus
marinus*, chicks of *Phalacrocorax aristotelis* and *P. carbo*, and adults
of *Fratercula arctica*, and net-fishing for lumpfish *Cyclopterus lumpus*.

Habitats Wetland (5%; tidal river/enclosed tidal water; saltmarsh; standing fresh water),
Marine areas (80%; sea inlet/coastal features), Rocky areas (15%; sea cliff/rocky shore;
rock stacks/islets)
Land-use Agriculture, Fisheries/aquaculture, Hunting, Nature conservation/research,
Tourism/recreation

■ Birds

Species		Season	Year	Pop min	Pop max	Acc	Criteria
Phalacrocorax carbo	Cormorant	R	1994	2,123	3,022	A	A4i, B1i
Phalacrocorax aristotelis	Shag	R	—	6,000	—	—	A4i, B1i, B3
[1] *Anser anser*	Greylag Goose	B	1997	1,700	1,700	—	A4i, B1i
[2] *Anser anser*	Greylag Goose	N	—	2,000	3,000	C	A4i, B1i
Branta bernicla	Brent Goose	P	—	—	10,000	—	A4i, B1i
Somateria mollissima	Eider	R	—	40,000	50,000	—	A4i, B1i
Calidris canutus	Knot	P	—	200,000	—	—	A4i, B1i
Larus hyperboreus	Glaucous Gull	R	1989	4,500	5,000	A	A4i, B1i
Larus marinus	Great Black-backed Gull	R	1973	12,000	18,000	—	A4i, B1i, B3
Rissa tridactyla	Kittiwake	B	—	23,000	—	—	A4i, B1i
[3] *Cepphus grylle*	Black Guillemot	R	—	530	—	—	B1ii, B2
[4] *Fratercula arctica*	Puffin	B	—	Abundant		—	A4ii, B1ii, B2

1. Large increase.
2. Moulting (c.1,700 pairs breed).
3. Flatey only; actual total much higher (up to 50% of national population).
4. "Hundreds of thousands" of pairs breed (believed to exceed threshold).

The site supports huge numbers of breeding seabirds; *Fulmarus
glacialis* is common but does not meet criteria.

■ Protection status
National High **International** None
100 ha of IBA covered by Nature Reserve (Flatey, 100 ha). 40 ha of
IBA covered by Nature Reserve (Hrisey, 40 ha). 9 ha of IBA covered
by Nature Reserve (Melrakkaey, 9 ha). 20,000 ha of IBA covered by
Nature Reserve (Landscape) (Vatnsfjördur, 20,000 ha). 300,000 ha of
IBA covered by Conservation Area (Breidafjördur, 300,000 ha).

■ Conservation issues

Threats Aquaculture/fisheries (U), Consequences of animal/plant introductions (U),
Disturbance to birds (U), Infrastructure (U), Recreation/tourism (U), Unsustainable
exploitation (U)

Predation by introduced American mink *Mustela vison* and net-fishing
for lumpfish both pose threats. Human activities such as tourism, hunting, seaweed-harvesting and eider husbandry (*Somateria mollissima*)
cause disturbance to birds. Gilsfjördur was formerly a mudflat but this
was ruined by road-construction (it is now a brackish lagoon), and
further road-building in other firths is a threat. A management plan is
being developed and is expected to be completed in 1998.

Álftafjördur–Hofsstadavogur A4i, B1i 007

Admin region Snæfellsnes og Hnappadalssýsla
Coordinates 65°00'N 22°40'W
Altitude 0–24 m **Area** 3,000 ha

■ Site description
A complex of coastal bays, small offshore islands, beaches and
intertidal flats, south of the Breidafjördur area.

Habitats Wetland (20%; tidal river/enclosed tidal water; mudflat/sandflat), Marine areas
(70%; sea inlet/coastal features), Rocky areas (10%; sea cliff/rocky shore; rock stacks/islets)
Land-use Agriculture, Fisheries/aquaculture

■ Birds

Species		Season	Year	Pop min	Pop max	Acc	Criteria
[1] *Cygnus cygnus*	Whooper Swan	P	1993	—	1,100	—	A4i, B1i
Branta bernicla	Brent Goose	P	—	1,200	3,200	—	B1i
Calidris canutus	Knot	P	1990	9,000	—	—	A4i, B1i

1. Several hundred moult.

An important staging area for wildfowl and waders.

■ Protection status
National High **International** None
3,000 ha of IBA covered by Conservation Area (Breidafjördur,
300,000 ha).

Löngufjörur A1, A4i, B1i 008

Admin region Mýrasýsla, Snæfellsnes og Hnappadalssýsla
Coordinates 64°45'N 22°30'W
Altitude 0–0 m **Area** 17,000 ha

■ Site description
An extensive stretch of estuarine coast with a variety of habitats
including bays, offshore islands, rock and cliff areas, beaches, intertidal
flats, brackish lakes, marshes and saltmarshes. The area extends from
Akrar at Mýrar to Glámsflói and Sauratjörn on Snæfellsnes. Minor
land-uses include eider husbandry (*Somateria mollissima*) ('Other'
land-use) and recreation.

Habitats Wetland (50%; tidal river/enclosed tidal water; mudflat/sandflat; standing fresh
water; standing brackish and salt water), Marine areas (40%; sea inlet/coastal features),
Rocky areas (10%; rock stacks/islets)
Land-use Agriculture, Other

■ Birds

Species		Season	Year	Pop min	Pop max	Acc	Criteria
[1] *Somateria mollissima*	Eider	N	—	—	80,000	—	A4i, B1i
Calidris canutus	Knot	P	1990	12,000	—	—	A4i, B1i

1. Moulting.

Other notable species are breeding *Phalacrocorax carbo* and *Sterna
paradisaea* (hundreds of pairs each), staging *Anser albifrons* (a few
hundred), *Branta bernicla*, *Calidris alpina* and *Tringa totanus*, and
wintering *Haematopus ostralegus*.

■ Protection status
National None **International** None

■ Conservation issues

Threats Recreation/tourism (U)

The area is on the list of sites of conservation interest in the Nature
Conservation Register.

Ferjubakkaflói–Nordurá A4i, B1i 009

Admin region Mýrasýsla
Coordinates 64°36'N 21°40'W
Altitude 6–8 m **Area** 1,500 ha

■ Site description
River flood-plains, c.14 km north-east of the town of Borgarnes, with
pools, marshes and peatbogs. The area extends over Ferjubakkaflóia,
Hóp, the lower parts of Gljúfurá and Nordurá, and Ystatunga south
of Sólheimatunga. Land-uses include hunting, recreation, grazing and
haymaking in some places, and there are some summer cottages.

Habitats Wetland (100%; standing fresh water; river/stream; water-fringe vegetation)
Land-use Agriculture, Tourism/recreation

■ Birds

Species	Season	Year	Pop min	Pop max	Acc	Criteria
Cygnus cygnus Whooper Swan	P	—	—	1,800	—	A4i, B1i
Anser albifrons White-fronted Goose	P	—	1,200	—	—	B1i

Important for staging waterbirds.

■ Protection status
National None **International** None

■ Conservation issues

Threats Drainage (U), Recreation/tourism (U)

Hunting and recreation cause some disturbance to birds, and summer cottages also pose a threat. The area is on the list of sites of conservation interest in the Nature Conservation Register.

Álftanes–Akrar   A4i, B1i, B2 **010**
Admin region Mýrasýsla
Coordinates 64°31′N 22°15′W
Altitude 0–10 m **Area** 13,300 ha

■ Site description
The area covers the shore and islands from Álftanes to Akrar, c.15 km west of Borgarnes town. Habitats comprise extensive intertidal flats (including eel-grass *Zostera* beds), coastal saltmarshes and numerous islands, lagoons, freshwater marshes and standing pools of brackish and salt water. Land-uses are mainly grazing, eider husbandry (*Somateria mollissima*) and egg-collecting ('Other' land-use).

Habitats Grassland (5%), Wetland (20%; tidal river/enclosed tidal water; saltmarsh; standing fresh water), Marine areas (45%; sea inlet/coastal features), Rocky areas (30%; sea cliff/rocky shore; rock stacks/islets)
Land-use Agriculture, Other

■ Birds

Species	Season	Year	Pop min	Pop max	Acc	Criteria
Gavia stellata Red-throated Diver	R	—	200	—	—	B2
Cygnus cygnus Whooper Swan	N	—	—	1,300	—	A4i, B1i
Branta bernicla Brent Goose	P	—	307	10,000	A	A4i, B1i
Calidris canutus Knot	P	1990	8,574	—	—	A4i, B1i
[1] *Calidris maritima* Purple Sandpiper	W	—	—	—	—	A4i, B1i
Arenaria interpres Turnstone	P	1990	426	—	—	A4i, B1i
[1] *Fratercula arctica* Puffin	R	—	—	—	—	B2

1. Believed to exceed threshold.

A rich area for coastal waterbirds. Mýrar is one of the main breeding areas in Iceland for *Gavia stellata*; also common as breeders are *Sterna paradisaea* (a few thousand pairs) and *Fratercula arctica* (the islands of Geldingaey and Lambeyjar hold one of the five largest colonies in Iceland). *Calidris alba* occurs in notable numbers (1,000) on passage.

■ Protection status
National None **International** None

■ Conservation issues
No serious threats are known. The area is on the list of sites of conservation interest in the Nature Conservation Register. The site is an enlarged and re-named version of the IBA 'Hjörsey–Straumfjörður', formerly IS025 in the previous international IBA inventory (Grimmett and Jones 1989).

Borgarfjörður   A4i, B1i **011**
Admin region Borgarfjarðarsýsla, Mýrasýsla
Coordinates 64°30′N 22°00′W
Altitude 0–20 m **Area** 7,000 ha

■ Site description
A large estuary with mudflats, saltmarshes and small offshore islands, near Borgarnes town. The area comprises Borgarvogur, Langárós and the outer part of Borgarfjörður to Álftanes in the Mýrar area. There are large mussel banks (*Mytilus*).

Habitats Wetland (80%; tidal river/enclosed tidal water; mudflat/sandflat; shingle/stony beach), Rocky areas (20%; sea cliff/rocky shore; rock stacks/islets)
Land-use Agriculture, Urban/industrial/transport

■ Birds

Species	Season	Year	Pop min	Pop max	Acc	Criteria
[1] *Somateria mollissima* Eider	N	—	—	100,000	—	A4i, B1i

1. Moulting.

Information on other birdlife in the area is not comprehensive.

■ Protection status
National None **International** None

■ Conservation issues

Threats Construction/impact of dyke/dam/barrage (U), Filling-in of wetlands (U), Industrialization/urbanization (U)

The area is on the list of sites of conservation interest in the Nature Conservation Register.

Innstavogsnes–Grunnafjörður   A4i, B1i **012**
Admin region Borgarfjarðarsýsla
Coordinates 64°22′N 21°55′W
Altitude 0–20 m **Area** 1,900 ha

■ Site description
Estuarine bays lying 10 km north-east of the town of Akranes, with small offshore islands, beaches and intertidal flats. Eider husbandry (*Somateria mollissima*) is practised ('Other' land-use).

Habitats Wetland (80%; mudflat/sandflat), Rocky areas (20%; sea cliff/rocky shore; rock stacks/islets)
Land-use Agriculture, Other

■ Birds

Species	Season	Year	Pop min	Pop max	Acc	Criteria
Branta bernicla Brent Goose	P	—	—	4,983	A	A4i, B1i
Calidris canutus Knot	P	1990	2,600	6,800	B	B1i

There are also notable numbers of staging *Haematopus ostralegus* (1,000–2,000), *Pluvialis apricaria* (a few thousand), *Calidris alpina* and *Charadrius hiaticula*.

■ Protection status
National Partial **International** Partial
1,470 ha of IBA covered by Nature Reserve (Grunnafjörður, 1,470 ha).
1,470 ha of IBA covered by Ramsar Site (Grunnafjörður, 1,470 ha).

■ Conservation issues

Threats Construction/impact of dyke/dam/barrage (U), Filling-in of wetlands (U)

The area was known as Leirárvogar in the previous international IBA inventory (Grimmett and Jones 1989), but the name Grunnafjörður is now preferred.

Hvalfjarðareyri–Laxárvogur   B1i **013**
Admin region Kjósarsýsla
Coordinates 64°19′N 21°40′W
Altitude 0–5 m **Area** 900 ha

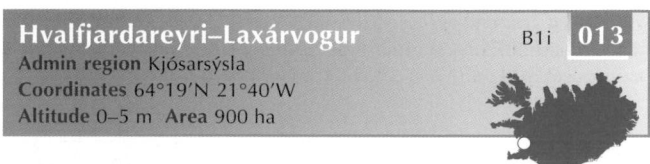

■ Site description
A large embayment of Hvalfjörður, including a bay and estuarine flats from Hvalfjarðareyri to Búðarsandur. There are mussel banks (*Mytilus*) offshore.

Habitats Wetland (20%; mudflat/sandflat), Marine areas (70%; sea inlet/coastal features), Rocky areas (10%; sea cliff/rocky shore)
Land-use Agriculture

■ Birds

Species	Season	Year	Pop min	Pop max	Acc	Criteria
Branta bernicla Brent Goose	P	1996	—	395	A	B1i
Calidris canutus Knot	P	1990	4,400	—	—	B1i

Also notable in winter are *Somateria mollissima* (c.2,000) and *Haematopus ostralegus* (c.500, which is 10% or more of the national total in winter).

■ Protection status
National None **International** None

■ Conservation issues
The area is on the list of sites of conservation interest in the Nature Conservation Register.

Skerjafjördur
A4i, B1i **014**

Admin region Kjósarsýsla, Reykjavík, Gardabær, Kópavogur, Seltjarnarnesbær
Coordinates 64°04′N 22°00′W
Altitude 0–5 m **Area** 3,300 ha

■ Site description
A coastal area in and near the capital, with sea bays, shingle and stony beaches, peninsulas, intertidal flats, brackish lagoons and marshes. The area extends from Bali on Álftanes along the coast, inwards to Skerjafjördur and up to the north part of Seltjarnarnes. Eider husbandry (*Somateria mollissima*) is practised at Bessastadir.

Habitats Grassland (5%), Wetland (20%; mudflat/sandflat; saltmarsh; standing brackish and salt water), Marine areas (70%; sea inlet/coastal features), Rocky areas (5%; sea cliff/rocky shore)
Land-use Agriculture, Tourism/recreation, Urban/industrial/transport

■ Birds

Species	Season	Year	Pop min	Pop max	Acc	Criteria
Branta bernicla Brent Goose	P	—	205	1,334	A	B1i
Somateria mollissima Eider	R	—	3,200	—	—	B1i
Calidris canutus Knot	P	—	3,000	—	—	B1i
Calidris maritima Purple Sandpiper	W	—	1,000	—	B	A4i, B1i
¹ *Arenaria interpres* Turnstone	P	—	200	—	—	A4i, B1i

1. Few hundreds.

An important area for coastal waterbirds. Other species in notable numbers include *Clangula hyemalis* (wintering), *Haematopus ostralegus* (c.60 breeding pairs; 200+ staging on passage), *Calidris alpina* (few hundreds staging on passage), *Tringa totanus* (few hundreds staging on passage), and hundreds to thousands of large gulls in winter (*Larus argentatus*, *L. glaucoides*, *L. hyperboreus* and *L. marinus*).

■ Protection status
National None **International** None
5 ha of IBA covered by unknown type of protected area (Grötta, 5 ha).

■ Conservation issues
Threats Dredging/canalization (U), Filling-in of wetlands (U), Industrialization/urbanization (U), Recreation/tourism (U)

Birds are disturbed by local people and tourists. The area is on the list of sites of conservation interest in the Nature Conservation Register. The site is an enlarged and re-named version of the IBA 'Álftanes', formerly IS020 in the previous international IBA inventory (Grimmett and Jones 1989).

Stafnes–Gardur
A4i, B1i, B3 **015**

Admin region Gullbringusýsla
Coordinates 64°04′N 22°42′W
Altitude 0–5 m **Area** 1,330 ha

■ Site description
A wildlife-rich coastal area with rocky shores, beaches and estuarine intertidal flats on Rosmhvalanes, west and north of Keflavík airport.

The area extends from Hvalnes to the village of Gardur. There are also some dry grasslands by the coast.

Habitats Wetland (10%; tidal river/enclosed tidal water; shingle/stony beach; standing fresh water), Marine areas (70%; sea inlet/coastal features), Rocky areas (20%; sea cliff/rocky shore)
Land-use Tourism/recreation, Urban/industrial/transport

■ Birds

Species	Season	Year	Pop min	Pop max	Acc	Criteria
Cygnus cygnus Whooper Swan	W	1989	101	—	—	B3
Somateria mollissima Eider	W	—	40,000	—	—	A4i, B1i
Calidris alba Sanderling	P	1990	1,176	—	—	A4i, B1i
Calidris maritima Purple Sandpiper	W	1989	1,000	—	B	A4i, B1i
Arenaria interpres Turnstone	W	—	400	1,200	B	A4i, B1i
Arenaria interpres Turnstone	P	1990	900	—	—	A4i, B1i

The area supports important numbers of coastal waterbirds outside the breeding season, including staging waders on passage (max. 4,000 in May). Thousands of large gulls winter in the area (*Larus argentatus*, *L. glaucoides*, *L. hyperboreus* and *L. marinus*). Numbers of breeding species are also notable, including *Somateria mollissima* (over 1,000 pairs) and *Sterna paradisaea* (a few thousand pairs).

■ Protection status
National None **International** None

■ Conservation issues
Threats Filling-in of wetlands (U), Industrialization/urbanization (U), Recreation/tourism (U)

Birds are disturbed by people (tourists, etc.) in some parts of the area. The IBA is on the list of sites of conservation interest in the Nature Conservation Register.

Ósar
A4i, B1i **016**

Admin region Gullbringusýsla
Coordinates 63°57′N 22°42′W
Altitude 0–5 m **Area** 400 ha

■ Site description
A shallow, tidal bay just south of Keflavík airport. The village of Hafnir, on the bay, has a harbour.

Habitats Wetland (10%; mudflat/sandflat), Marine areas (70%; sea inlet/coastal features), Rocky areas (20%; sea cliff/rocky shore)
Land-use Fisheries/aquaculture, Military, Urban/industrial/transport

■ Birds

Species	Season	Year	Pop min	Pop max	Acc	Criteria
Histrionicus histrionicus Harlequin Duck	W	—	50	100	—	A4i, B1i

In winter there is also a wide variety of other coastal waterbirds, including *Aythya marila* (100; one of two flocks in Iceland) and *Calidris maritima* (c.300).

■ Protection status
National None **International** None

■ Conservation issues
Threats Industrialization/urbanization (U)

Dredging, pollution and eutrophication threaten the site, and harbour operations may intensify. The area is on the list of sites of conservation interest in the Nature Conservation Register.

Eldey
A4ii, B1ii, B2 **017**

Admin region Gullbringusýsla
Coordinates 63°43′N 22°58′W
Altitude 0–77 m **Area** 1 ha

■ Site description
A small, rocky island, 14 km south-west of Reykjanes in south-west Iceland.

Habitats Rocky areas (100%; sea cliff/rocky shore; rock stacks/islets)

Land-use Nature conservation/research, Not utilized

■ **Birds**

Species	Season	Year	Pop min	Pop max	Acc	Criteria
Sula bassana Gannet	B	1994	14,100	—	A	A4ii, B1ii, B2

Other common breeding seabirds are *Rissa tridactyla* (3,000 pairs), *Uria aalge* (2,700 pairs) and *Uria lomvia* (510 pairs).

■ **Protection status**

National High **International** None

1 ha of IBA covered by Scientific Reserve (Eldey, 2 ha).

■ **Conservation issues**

No serious threats are known.

Krísuvíkurberg   A4ii, A4iii, B1i, B1ii, B3   018

Admin region Gullbringusýsla

Coordinates 63°52′N 22°04′W

Altitude 0–40 m **Area** 1,200 ha

■ **Site description**

The largest sea cliff in south-west Iceland, 30 km south-west of Reykjavík. The eggs of *Rissa tridactyla* and *Uria aalge* are traditionally collected ('Other' land-use), and livestock are grazed in the area.

Habitats Rocky areas (100%; sea cliff/rocky shore)

Land-use Agriculture, Other, Tourism/recreation

■ **Birds**

Species	Season	Year	Pop min	Pop max	Acc	Criteria
Rissa tridactyla Kittiwake	B	1985	21,100	—	A	B1i
Uria aalge Guillemot	B	1985	20,000	—	A	B1ii
Alca torda Razorbill	B	—	8,700	—	A	A4ii, B1ii, B3

Important for its large numbers of breeding seabirds; other common species include *Fulmarus glacialis*, *Uria lomvia* (c.2,600 pairs), *Cepphus grylle* and *Fratercula arctica*.

■ **Protection status**

National None **International** None

■ **Conservation issues**

Threats Unsustainable exploitation (U)

The area is on the list of sites of conservation interest in the Nature Conservation Register.

Ósasvæði Ölfusár   B1i, B2   019

Admin region Árnessýsla

Coordinates 63°57′N 21°15′W

Altitude 0–19 m **Area** 7,400 ha

■ **Site description**

An extensive area of coastal flood-plain and shallow freshwater marshes by the Ölfusá river, c.35 km south-east of Reykjavík. The area extends over Ölfusforir, Kaldadarnesengjar, Flóagafl and the outlet of the Ölfusá river, and includes a vegetated lava-flow. The area is dominated by sedge *Carex*. Land-uses include angling in rivers and some tourist traffic.

Habitats Grassland (10%), Wetland (90%; tidal river/enclosed tidal water; standing fresh water; river/stream; water-fringe vegetation; fen/transition mire/spring)

Land-use Agriculture, Fisheries/aquaculture, Hunting, Nature conservation/research

■ **Birds**

Many other species of waterbird also breed, and it is one of the most important inland wintering sites for ducks in Iceland.

Species	Season	Year	Pop min	Pop max	Acc	Criteria
[1] *Anser albifrons* White-fronted Goose	P	—	1,000	—	—	B1i
[2] *Calidris alpina* Dunlin	B	—	1,000	—	—	B1i
[3] *Gallinago gallinago* Snipe	P	—	—	10,000	—	B1i
[2,4] *Limosa limosa* Black-tailed Godwit	B	1995	200	—	—	B2

1. c.1,000 in spring, 500+ in autumn.
2. Highest recorded breeding density in Iceland.
3. Autumn; 1,000+ pairs breed.
4. "A few hundred" pairs.

■ **Protection status**

National Partial **International** None

About 3,000 ha of IBA covered by Nature Reserve (name not known, c.3,000 ha).

■ **Conservation issues**

Threats Agricultural intensification/expansion (U), Aquaculture/fisheries (U), Consequences of animal/plant introductions (U), Construction/impact of dyke/dam/barrage (U), Disturbance to birds (U), Drainage (U), Unsustainable exploitation (U)

Hunting disturbs birds and is a problem in some places, particularly in winter when the wildfowl are concentrated at ice-free areas. Horses also cause disturbance and their grazing is a threat in parts of the area. Water-borne pollution from nearby urbanized and industrial areas is a problem, and introduced American mink *Mustela vison* also pose a threat. The area is on the list of sites of conservation interest in the Nature Conservation Register. Part of the area, on the west bank of the Ölfusá river, has been declared a bird reserve.

Stokkseyri–Eyrarbakki   A4i, B1i   020

Admin region Árnessýsla

Coordinates 63°52′N 21°07′W

Altitude 0–5 m **Area** 4,300 ha

■ **Site description**

A coastal wetland in southern Iceland, by the villages of Stokkseyri and Eyrabakki, which extends from the river outlet of Ölfusá to Loftsstadir farm. Habitats comprise fresh water, brackish pools, saltmarshes and an adjacent extensive area of beaches and intertidal flats. The shoreline is mainly rocky. Land-use also includes tourism, e.g. kayaking along the coast, lakes and rivers.

Habitats Grassland (10%; mesophile grassland), Wetland (20%; mudflat/sandflat; standing fresh water; standing brackish and salt water; water-fringe vegetation), Marine areas (40%; sea inlet/coastal features), Rocky areas (30%; sea cliff/rocky shore)

Land-use Agriculture, Urban/industrial/transport

■ **Birds**

Species	Season	Year	Pop min	Pop max	Acc	Criteria
Cygnus cygnus Whooper Swan	P	—	250	—	—	B1i
Calidris canutus Knot	P	1990	7,600	—	B	B1i
Calidris maritima Purple Sandpiper	W	1987	255	617	B	A4i, B1i

Thousands of breeding, staging and wintering waterbirds use the area, particularly the coast. In particular, the shore from the mouth of the Ölfusá river to Loftsstadir farm is one of the most important for waterbirds in Iceland. A wide variety of waterbirds breed, including *Sterna paradisaea* (1,000–2,000 pairs). Staging birds in May 1990 included *Calidris alpina* (2,000) and *Arenaria interpres* (200).

■ **Protection status**

National None **International** None

■ **Conservation issues**

Threats Consequences of animal/plant introductions (U), Drainage (U), Dredging/canalization (U), Recreation/tourism (U)

The introduced American mink *Mustela vison* is a threat, and tourism causes disturbance to birds. Part of the area may be threatened by urban development. The area is on the list of sites of conservation interest in the Nature Conservation Register.

Sog
B1i, B2 **021**

Admin region Árnessýsla
Coordinates 64°10'N 21°00'W
Altitude 15–100 m **Area** 500 ha

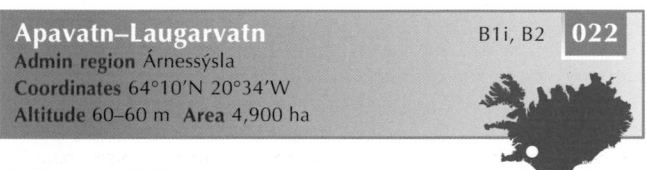

■ Site description
A major freshwater river that drains Lake Thingvallavatn. Land-uses also include angling (salmon fishing), hydroelectric generation and holiday-homes. The area belongs to three communities: Grafningshreppur, Ölfushreppur and Grímsneshreppur.

Habitats Wetland (100%; standing fresh water; river/stream)
Land-use Agriculture

■ Birds

Species	Season	Year	Pop min	Pop max	Acc	Criteria
[1] *Cygnus cygnus* Whooper Swan	P	—	200	—	—	B1i
Bucephala islandica Barrow's Goldeneye	W	—	100	150	B	B2
Mergus merganser Goosander	W	1993	36	—	—	B1i

1. Several hundreds.

One of the few wintering sites for *Bucephala islandica* in Iceland away from Mývatn–Laxá (site 044). Also overwintering, in notable numbers, are *Bucephala clangula* (one of the few wintering sites in Iceland) and *Mergus serrator*.

■ Protection status
National None **International** None

■ Conservation issues

Threats Construction/impact of dyke/dam/barrage (U)

Hydroelectric power-stations have changed the river ecosystem. The area is on the list of sites of conservation interest in the Nature Conservation Register.

Apavatn–Laugarvatn
B1i, B2 **022**

Admin region Árnessýsla
Coordinates 64°10'N 20°34'W
Altitude 60–60 m **Area** 4,900 ha

■ Site description
Apavatn and Laugarvatn lakes and their surrounding marshes/mires lie about 20 km east of Lake Thingvallavatn, in the north-west part of the southern lowlands of Iceland. Marshes are dominated by sedges (*Carex*, *Eriophorum*). There is a wetland with hot-springs at Hjálmstadaengjar. Holiday-homes are present.

Habitats Wetland (100%; standing fresh water; river/stream; water-fringe vegetation; fen/transition mire/spring)
Land-use Agriculture, Fisheries/aquaculture, Tourism/recreation, Urban/industrial/transport

■ Birds

Species	Season	Year	Pop min	Pop max	Acc	Criteria
Bucephala islandica Barrow's Goldeneye	W	—	Common		—	B2
Mergus merganser Goosander	W	1995	10	10	—	B1i

Notable numbers of *Bucephala clangula* (some tens) and *Mergus merganser* (18 in 1988, 46 in 1989) also occur in winter. A wide variety of waterbirds breed, including *Histrionicus histrionicus*, and hundreds of staging *Aythya marila*, *A. fuligula* and *Mergus serrator* use the area on passage.

■ Protection status
National None **International** None

■ Conservation issues

Threats Agricultural intensification/expansion (U), Aquaculture/fisheries (U), Drainage (U), Recreation/tourism (U)

The area is threatened by drainage, and birds are disturbed by traffic, tourists, owners of holiday-homes, boat-traffic on the lakes, windsurfing on Laugarvatn, and by horses. The area is on the list of sites of conservation interest in the Nature Conservation Register.

Brúará
B1i, B2 **023**

Admin region Árnessýsla
Coordinates 64°08'N 20°35'W
Altitude 50–120 m **Area** 2,900 ha

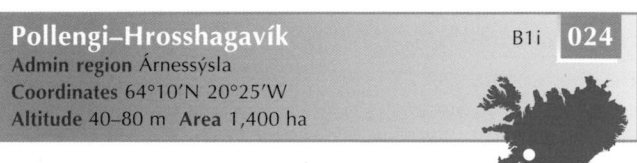

■ Site description
A wetland area, 20 km east of Lake Thingvallavatn, which comprises the Brúará river up to Brúarfoss and adjacent wetlands near the Hvítá river outlet (Selsflód, Reykjanes, Mosar, Skálholtstunga and Höfdaflatir). There are hot-springs at Reykjanes. Anglers fish along parts of the Brúará river.

Habitats Wetland (100%; standing fresh water; river/stream; water-fringe vegetation)
Land-use Agriculture, Hunting, Tourism/recreation

■ Birds

Species	Season	Year	Pop min	Pop max	Acc	Criteria
[1] *Anser anser* Greylag Goose	R	—	200	—	—	B1i
Bucephala islandica Barrow's Goldeneye	W	—	10	50	—	B2

1. Hundreds or even 1,000+ pairs breed (believed to exceed threshold).

An important area for breeding wildfowl and waders, especially *Anser anser* (also moulting, e.g. 550 at Höfdaflatir in 1983), as well as for staging geese and wintering *Bucephala islandica* (one of the few wintering sites away from Mývatn–Laxá (site 044).

■ Protection status
National None **International** None

■ Conservation issues

Threats Agricultural intensification/expansion (U), Disturbance to birds (U), Drainage (U)

Hunting causes disturbance to birds, and parts of the area are threatened with further drainage. Horse-grazing also poses a threat. The IBA is on the list of sites of conservation interest in the Nature Conservation Register. However, it is listed there as a number of individual sites: Brúará; Skálholtstunga and Mosar as one site; Selsflód; Höfdaflatir; and Reykjanes.

Pollengi–Hrosshagavík
B1i **024**

Admin region Árnessýsla
Coordinates 64°10'N 20°25'W
Altitude 40–80 m **Area** 1,400 ha

■ Site description
A large area of rivers, streams, lakes, pools and extensive riparian marshes/mires of sedge (*Carex*, *Eriophorum*), c.18 km south of the Geysir hot-spring area. Tunguey is an island. Pond-weed *Potamogeton* is common in pools, and *Salix* bushes are common on land in the drier areas.

Habitats Grassland (5%), Wetland (95%; standing fresh water; river/stream; water-fringe vegetation; fen/transition mire/spring)
Land-use Agriculture, Nature conservation/research

■ Birds

Species	Season	Year	Pop min	Pop max	Acc	Criteria
Cygnus cygnus Whooper Swan	P	—	150	300	B	B1i
Anser albifrons White-fronted Goose	P	1990	1,300	—	—	B1i

Hrosshagavík is important for staging waterbirds in spring and autumn. A wide variety of waterbirds breed in the area.

■ Protection status
National Partial **International** None
684 ha of IBA covered by Nature Reserve (Pollengi og Tunguey, 684 ha).

■ Conservation issues

Threats Consequences of animal/plant introductions (U), Disturbance to birds (U), Drainage (U)

Predation by introduced American mink *Mustela vison* poses a problem, and hunting causes disturbance to birds. The Tungufljót river, which flows into Hrosshagavík, has changed from a glacial to a freshwater river, after its glacial tributary, the Farid, was dammed in the highlands. Sediment deposition in Hrosshagavík and Pollengi has thus probably been sharply reduced, with unknown ecological consequences. Most of the IBA is protected, but important parts of the area, such as the northern parts of Pollengi and Hrosshagavík, are not protected.

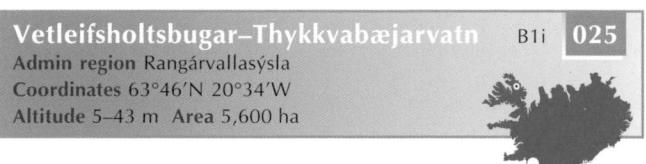

Vetleifsholtsbugar–Thykkvabæjarvatn — B1i — 025
Admin region Rangárvallasýsla
Coordinates 63°46′N 20°34′W
Altitude 5–43 m **Area** 5,600 ha

■ Site description
An extensive marsh/mire, dominated by sedge (*Carex, Eriophorum*), with lakes and pools, 10 km south of the town of Hella in southern Iceland. It stretches from Thykkvabæjarvatn (with surrounding marshes) to Kringlutjörn and Frakkavatn (with surrounding marshes), and includes Andalækur and the area from Vetleifsholtbugaur to Hrútsvatn. This is the southern and western part of Safamýri, formerly one of the richest *Carex–Eriophorum* marshes in Iceland before its drainage and the damming of the Thverá and Ytri-Rangá rivers. Pond-weed *Potamogeton* is abundant in Frakkavatn.

Habitats Wetland (100%; standing fresh water; river/stream; water-fringe vegetation; fen/transition mire/spring)
Land-use Agriculture, Hunting

■ Birds

Species	Season	Year	Pop min	Pop max	Acc	Criteria
Cygnus cygnus Whooper Swan	P	1989	200	—	—	B1i
[1] ***Anser albifrons*** White-fronted Goose	P	1991	1,000	—	—	B1i

1. Roosting and feeding area.

A wide variety of wildfowl and waders breed in the area, and *Anas penelope* moults on Frakkavatn and Andalækur.

■ Protection status
National None **International** None

■ Conservation issues

Threats Disturbance to birds (U), Drainage (U)

Parts of the site have been severely damaged by drainage and the area is also threatened by further drainage for agricultural purposes. Hunting causes excessive disturbance at the roost sites of *Anser albifrons*. Only a part of this area is in the Nature Conservation Register. The site is an enlarged and re-named version of the IBA 'Safamýri', formerly site 009 in the previous international IBA inventory (Grimmett and Jones 1989).

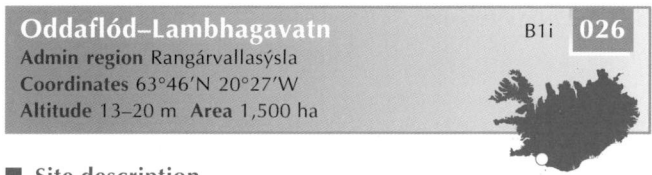

Oddaflód–Lambhagavatn — B1i — 026
Admin region Rangárvallasýsla
Coordinates 63°46′N 20°27′W
Altitude 13–20 m **Area** 1,500 ha

■ Site description
A complex of freshwater rivers, streams, pools and extensive riparian marshes/mires, c.7 km south of the town of Hella. The area extends from Langanes on the east side of the Eystri-Rangá river (including Lambhagavatn lake and surrounding marshes), along the Eystri-Rangá, Thverá and Ytri-Rangá rivers, to Selalækur farm. The marshes are dominated by sedges (*Carex, Eriophorum*). The main land-use is non-intensive grazing.

Habitats Wetland (100%; standing fresh water; river/stream; water-fringe vegetation; fen/transition mire/spring)
Land-use Agriculture, Nature conservation/research

■ Birds

Species	Season	Year	Pop min	Pop max	Acc	Criteria
Anser albifrons White-fronted Goose	P	1990	900	—		B1i

The area is particularly important for waterbirds staging in spring, including *Pluvialis apricaria* (hundreds) and *Limosa limosa* (730 in 1990). A wide variety of wildfowl, waders and other waterbirds breed in the area.

■ Protection status
National Partial **International** None
540 ha of IBA covered by Nature Reserve (Oddaflód, 540 ha).

■ Conservation issues

Threats Agricultural intensification/expansion (U), Disturbance to birds (U), Drainage (U)

Hunting causes disturbance to birds, drainage ditches carry silt into Lake Lambhagavatn, and horse-grazing and fish-farming also have detrimental effects. The northern part of the Oddaflód area is not protected but is included in the IBA, and a northern part of the IBA has been drained.

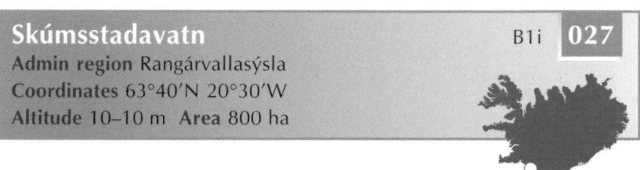

Skúmsstadavatn — B1i — 027
Admin region Rangárvallasýsla
Coordinates 63°40′N 20°30′W
Altitude 10–10 m **Area** 800 ha

■ Site description
A shallow freshwater lake, pools and extensive marshes/mires of sedge (*Carex, Eriophorum*), 14 km south of the town of Hella in southern Iceland. Grazing in the marshes is considerable.

Habitats Wetland (100%; standing fresh water; water-fringe vegetation; fen/transition mire/spring)
Land-use Agriculture, Hunting

■ Birds

Species	Season	Year	Pop min	Pop max	Acc	Criteria
Cygnus cygnus Whooper Swan	P	—	—	200	—	B1i
Anser albifrons White-fronted Goose	P	—	—	1,000	—	B1i
Limosa limosa Black-tailed Godwit	P	—	—	900	—	B1i

The lake is important for staging waterbirds. Breeding birds include *Gavia stellata*, *Cygnus cygnus*, *Anas acuta* and several other duck species, *Limosa limosa* and *Numenius phaeopus*.

■ Protection status
National None **International** None

■ Conservation issues

Threats Agricultural intensification/expansion (U), Disturbance to birds (U), Drainage (U)

Drainage is a major threat to this wetland, and has severely affected the lake. Excessive horse-grazing is also a threat. The effects on birds of disturbance caused by shooting are not known. The area is on the list of sites of conservation interest in the Nature Conservation Register.

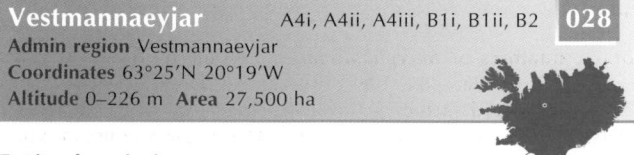

Vestmannaeyjar — A4i, A4ii, A4iii, B1i, B1ii, B2 — 028
Admin region Vestmannaeyjar
Coordinates 63°25′N 20°19′W
Altitude 0–226 m **Area** 27,500 ha

■ Site description
The site comprises all of the islands (and surrounding waters) in this offshore archipelago. Traditional harvesting of seabirds takes place ('Other' land-use): the eggs of *Fulmarus glacialis* and auks; the young, mainly of *Sula bassana*; and adults of *Fratercula arctica*.

Habitats Grassland (20%), Marine areas (60%; open sea; sea inlet/coastal features), Rocky areas (20%; sea cliff/rocky shore; rock stacks/islets)
Land-use Nature conservation/research, Other, Tourism/recreation

Birds

Species		Season	Year	Pop min	Pop max	Acc	Criteria
Fulmarus glacialis	Fulmar	B	1984	65,000	—	—	A4ii, B1ii
Puffinus puffinus	Manx Shearwater	B	1991	8,000	10,000	—	A4ii, B1ii, B2
Hydrobates pelagicus	Storm Petrel	B	1991	50,000	100,000	B	A4ii, B1ii, B2
Oceanodroma leucorhoa	Leach's Petrel	B	1991	80,000	150,000	B	A4ii, B1ii, B2
Sula bassana	Gannet	B	1994	9,000	9,000	A	A4ii, B1ii, B2
Rissa tridactyla	Kittiwake	B	1984	32,000	32,000	—	A4i, B1i
Uria aalge	Guillemot	B	1984	52,900	61,000	A	B1ii
Fratercula arctica	Puffin	B	—	1,000,000	1,000,000	—	A4ii, B1ii, B2

More than one million pairs of seabirds breed here, including the largest congregation of breeding *Oceanodroma leucorhoa* in Europe, more than 90% of breeding *Hydrobates pelagicus* in Iceland, and 100% of breeding *Puffinus puffinus* in Iceland.

Protection status

National Low **International** None
270 ha of IBA covered by Scientific Reserve (Surtsey, 270 ha).

Conservation issues

Threats Recreation/tourism (U)

The islands are not protected, except Surtsey, but Ystiklettur and three islands, Ellidaey, Súlnasker and Hellisey, are on the list of sites of conservation interest in the Nature Conservation Register.

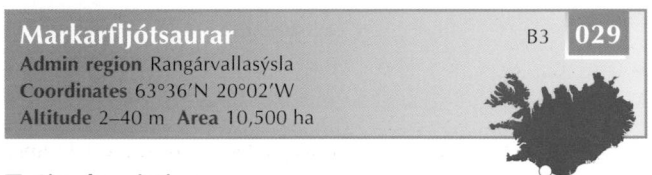

Markarfljótsaurar
Admin region Rangárvallasýsla
Coordinates 63°36'N 20°02'W
Altitude 2–40 m **Area** 10,500 ha
B3 029

Site description
A glacial outwash plain formed by the Markarfljót river. Habitats include small marshes of sedge (*Carex, Eriophorum*), sandy areas with rushes *Juncus*, and flat areas of glacial outwash gravel that are partly vegetated. The native vegetation cover has been increasing since barriers were built to prevent the Markarfljót river from changing its course. Land-uses include grazing.

Habitats Scrub (30%; heathland), Wetland (20%; standing fresh water; river/stream; fen/transition mire/spring), Rocky areas (50%)
Land-use Agriculture, Fisheries/aquaculture, Hunting

Birds

Species		Season	Year	Pop min	Pop max	Acc	Criteria
Numenius phaeopus	Whimbrel	B	—		Abundant	—	B3

Numenius phaeopus occurs at the highest density recorded in Iceland, or possibly in the world (42 pairs/km^2). Not much information on birds is available for the area, but the breeding avifauna includes a good variety of ducks, waders and other waterbirds.

Protection status
National None **International** None

Conservation issues

Threats Aquaculture/fisheries (U), Consequences of animal/plant introductions (A)

An introduced and invasive plant (Nootka lupin *Lupinus nootkatensis*) has spread over extensive areas and is a big threat.

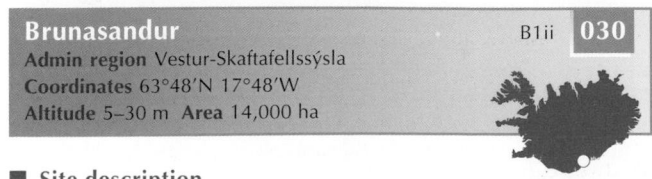

Brunasandur
Admin region Vestur-Skaftafellssýsla
Coordinates 63°48'N 17°48'W
Altitude 5–30 m **Area** 14,000 ha
B1ii 030

Site description

Habitats Wetland (30%; standing fresh water; river/stream; water-fringe vegetation; fen/transition mire/spring), Rocky areas (70%)
Land-use Agriculture

A wetland area on an extensive gravel plain, 13 km east of the town Kirkjubæjarklaustur. Habitats include springs, large and small flood-marshes of sedge (*Carex, Eriophorum*), sandy areas with rushes *Juncus*, and flat areas of gravel that are partly or completely vegetated. Land-uses include grazing.

Birds

Species		Season	Year	Pop min	Pop max	Acc	Criteria
[1] *Stercorarius parasiticus*	Arctic Skua	B	—	200	—	—	B1ii

1. "Several hundred" pairs breed.

Little information on birds is available for the area.

Protection status
National None **International** None

Conservation issues

Threats Consequences of animal/plant introductions (U), Unsustainable exploitation (U)

Hunting is a problem. Nootka lupin *Lupinus nootkatensis*, an introduced plant which is highly invasive, could be a potential threat to the habitat.

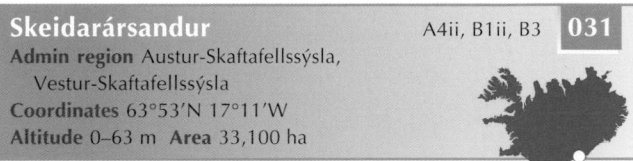

Skeidarársandur
Admin region Austur-Skaftafellssýsla, Vestur-Skaftafellssýsla
Coordinates 63°53'N 17°11'W
Altitude 0–63 m **Area** 33,100 ha
A4ii, B1ii, B3 031

Site description
A very large glacial outwash plain formed by the Skeidará river, on the south-east coast by Vatnajökull glacier, and including Ingólfshöfdi and its vicinity. There are some small marshes of sedge (*Carex, Eriophorum*), sandy areas with rushes *Juncus*, and flat, gravel areas that are partly or completely vegetated.

Habitats Wetland (20%; standing fresh water; river/stream; fen/transition mire/spring), Rocky areas (80%)
Land-use Tourism/recreation

Birds

Species		Season	Year	Pop min	Pop max	Acc	Criteria
Stercorarius skua	Great Skua	B	1985	1,275	1,560	—	A4ii, B1ii, B3
Alca torda	Razorbill	B	1986	4,500	—	—	A4ii, B1ii, B3

Not much information on birds is available for the area apart from Ingólfshöfdi, but the breeding avifauna also includes a good variety of waders and other waterbirds.

Protection status
National Low **International** None
90 ha of IBA covered by Nature Reserve (Landscape) (Ingólfshöfdi, 90 ha).

Conservation issues

Threats Consequences of animal/plant introductions (U)

Nootka lupin *Lupinus nootkatensis*, an introduced plant which is highly invasive, may pose a potential threat to the habitat.

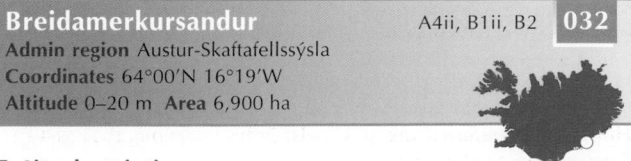

Breidamerkursandur
Admin region Austur-Skaftafellssýsla
Coordinates 64°00'N 16°19'W
Altitude 0–20 m **Area** 6,900 ha
A4ii, B1ii, B2 032

Site description
A wetland area on a glacial outwash plain, formed by a number of rivers running from the Vatnajökull glacier on the south-east coast of Iceland. There are small marshes (dominated by *Carex* and *Eriophorum*), glacial lagoons, sandy areas with rushes *Juncus*, and flat

areas of glacial outwash gravel, partly or completely vegetated with moss and other vegetation. Land-uses may include hunting.

Habitats Wetland (30%; standing fresh water; river/stream; fen/transition mire/spring), Rocky areas (70%)
Land-use Tourism/recreation

■ **Birds**

Species		Season	Year	Pop min	Pop max	Acc	Criteria
Gavia stellata	Red-throated Diver	R	—	20	25	—	B2
Stercorarius skua	Great Skua	B	—	4,000	4,650	B	A4ii, B1ii

A good diversity of waders also breed here.

■ **Protection status**
National None **International** None

■ **Conservation issues**

Threats Consequences of animal/plant introductions (U)

Nootka lupin *Lupinus nootkatensis*, an introduced plant which is highly invasive, may pose a potential threat to the natural vegetation of the habitat.

Hestgerdislón–Hornafjardarfljót   B1i 033
Admin region Austur-Skaftafellssýsla
Coordinates 64°12'N 15°37'W
Altitude 0–28 m **Area** 12,700 ha

■ **Site description**
A very large wetland in Sudursveit and Mýrar, south-east Iceland. Habitats comprise extensive sedge marshes (*Carex, Eriophorum*), pools, sandy areas with rushes *Juncus*, mudflats and brackish lagoons. The main land-use is grazing.

Habitats Wetland (100%; tidal river/enclosed tidal water; standing fresh water; standing brackish and salt water; river/stream; water-fringe vegetation; fen/transition mire/spring)
Land-use Agriculture, Fisheries/aquaculture, Hunting

■ **Birds**

Species		Season	Year	Pop min	Pop max	Acc	Criteria
[1] *Cygnus cygnus*	Whooper Swan	B	—	60	80	—	B1i
[2] *Branta leucopsis*	Barnacle Goose	P	—	Common		—	B1i

1. Also moults here.
2. Thousands, mainly in autumn (believed to exceed threshold).

Information on birds is limited, but the area is known to be important for breeding wildfowl and waders as well as for staging waterbirds.

■ **Protection status**
National None **International** None

■ **Conservation issues**

Threats Aquaculture/fisheries (U), Drainage (U), Unsustainable exploitation (U)

Hunting is a problem.

Skardsfjördur   B1i 034
Admin region Austur-Skaftafellssýsla
Coordinates 64°16'N 15°04'W
Altitude 0–14 m **Area** 1,050 ha

■ **Site description**
A brackish coastal lagoon with intertidal mudflats, by the town of Höfn on the western shore of Skardsfjördur and along the coast from Austurfjörur to Hornsvík.

Habitats Wetland (100%; mudflat/sandflat; standing brackish and salt water)
Land-use Fisheries/aquaculture, Military, Nature conservation/research, Urban/industrial/transport

■ **Birds**

Species		Season	Year	Pop min	Pop max	Acc	Criteria
Somateria mollissima	Eider	N	1992	10,000	—	—	B1i
Calidris alpina	Dunlin	P	—	5,000	10,000	C	B1i

Other notable waders on passage include *Haematopus ostralegus* (hundreds), *Charadrius hiaticula* (1,000), *Calidris canutus* (min. 2,000) and *Limosa limosa* (hundreds).

■ **Protection status**
National Low **International** None
15 ha of IBA covered by Country Park (Osland, 15 ha).

■ **Conservation issues**

Threats Aquaculture/fisheries (U), Filling-in of wetlands (U), Industrialization/urbanization (U)

The area is on the list of sites of conservation interest in the Nature Conservation Register.

Lónsfjördur   A4i, B1i, B3 035
Admin region Austur-Skaftafellssýsla
Coordinates 64°25'N 14°40'W
Altitude 0–10 m **Area** 2,700 ha

■ **Site description**
A brackish coastal lagoon with intertidal mudflats about 30 km north-east of Hornafjardarbær (Höfn) town, south-east Iceland. There are extensive beds of aquatic plants (*Ruppia*, eel-grass *Zostera* and algae). The area is surrounded by farms, grasslands and marshes. The marshes are grazed, and there is fishing in the lagoon (nets and traps).

Habitats Wetland (100%; standing brackish and salt water)
Land-use Agriculture

■ **Birds**

Species		Season	Year	Pop min	Pop max	Acc	Criteria
Cygnus cygnus	Whooper Swan	P	1995	7,000	8,000	—	A4i, B1i
[1] *Cygnus cygnus*	Whooper Swan	N	—	2,000	4,000	B	A4i, B1i, B3

1. Moulting.

Over 3,000 staging waders were recorded here during an aerial survey in May 1990. There has been no regular counting of birds at the site, apart from moulting *Cygnus cygnus* (annually since 1992).

■ **Protection status**
National None **International** None

■ **Conservation issues**

Threats Agricultural intensification/expansion (U)

Nutrient run-off from adjacent hayfields, which are fertilized on a regular basis, could affect the water quality in the lagoon. The area is on the list of sites of conservation interest in the Nature Conservation Register.

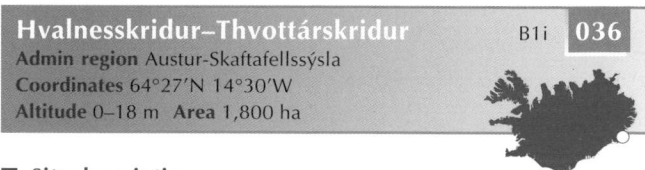

Hvalnesskridur–Thvottárskridur   B1i 036
Admin region Austur-Skaftafellssýsla
Coordinates 64°27'N 14°30'W
Altitude 0–18 m **Area** 1,800 ha

■ **Site description**
A rocky seashore, about 20 km south-east of Djúpivogur.

Habitats Marine areas (80%), Rocky areas (20%; sea cliff/rocky shore)
Land-use Not utilized

■ **Birds**

Species		Season	Year	Pop min	Pop max	Acc	Criteria
[1] *Somateria mollissima*	Eider	N	—	5,000	10,000	—	B1i

1. Moulting.

■ **Protection status**
National None **International** None

■ **Conservation issues**
There are no known threats to the site.

Álftafjördur–Hamarsfjördur A4i, B1i 037

Admin region Sudur-Múlasýsla
Coordinates 64°34′N 14°30′W
Altitude 0–20 m **Area** 3,500 ha

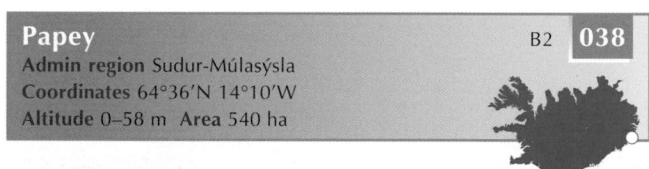

■ **Site description**
A complex coastal area of shallow bays, brackish lagoons and intertidal flats, south-east of the town of Djúpivogur.

Habitats Wetland (20%; tidal river/enclosed tidal water; saltmarsh; standing brackish and salt water), Marine areas (70%; sea inlet/coastal features), Rocky areas (10%; rock stacks/islets)
Land-use Agriculture

■ **Birds**

Species	Season	Year	Pop min	Pop max	Acc	Criteria
Cygnus cygnus Whooper Swan	P	1997	200	—	B	B1i
[1] *Anser anser* Greylag Goose	N	—	1,000	10,000	—	A4i, B1i

1. Moulting.

Notable numbers of migrating waders stage here on passage (over 2,700 in May 1990).

■ **Protection status**
National None **International** None

■ **Conservation issues**
No serious threats are known. The area is on the list of sites of conservation interest in the Nature Conservation Register.

Papey B2 038

Admin region Sudur-Múlasýsla
Coordinates 64°36′N 14°10′W
Altitude 0–58 m **Area** 540 ha

■ **Site description**
A low offshore island of boggy grassland, with low cliffs. Neighbouring islands in surrounding waters are also included. Land-uses include summer-homes, some grazing, tourism, collection of *Uria aalge* eggs, and traditional harvesting of adult *Fratercula arctica* ('Other' land-use).

Habitats Grassland (50%), Marine areas (40%; sea inlet/coastal features), Rocky areas (10%; sea cliff/rocky shore; rock stacks/islets)
Land-use Other, Tourism/recreation

■ **Birds**

Species	Season	Year	Pop min	Pop max	Acc	Criteria
Fratercula arctica Puffin	B	—	20,000	—	—	B2

■ **Protection status**
National None **International** None

■ **Conservation issues**
No serious threats are known. The area is on the list of sites of conservation interest in the Nature Conservation Register.

Skrúdur B2 039

Admin region Sudur-Múlasýsla
Coordinates 64°54′N 13°37′W
Altitude 0–160 m **Area** 92 ha

■ **Site description**
An uninhabited offshore island with cliffs, off the Fáskrúdsfjördur

firth. The defined area does not include the surrounding sea. Land-uses include some grazing, recreation, collection of *Uria aalge* eggs, and traditional harvesting of adult *Fratercula arctica* ('Other' land-use).

Habitats Grassland (20%), Marine areas (50%), Rocky areas (30%; sea cliff/rocky shore)
Land-use Other

■ **Birds**

Species	Season	Year	Pop min	Pop max	Acc	Criteria
Sula bassana Gannet	B	1994	1,337	1,337	A	B2
[1] *Fratercula arctica* Puffin	B	—	2,000	—	—	B2

1. "Thousands" of pairs breed (believed to exceed threshold).

■ **Protection status**
National High **International** None
92 ha of IBA covered by Nature Reserve (Skrúdur, 92 ha).

■ **Conservation issues**
Part of the harvest of *Fratercula arctica* is exported to the Faeroes.

Úthérad A4i, B1i, B1ii, B2 040

Admin region Nordur-Múlasýsla
Coordinates 65°30′N 14°19′W
Altitude 5–30 m **Area** 36,200 ha

■ **Site description**
Lowlands by Héradsflói bay, 40 km north of the town of Egilsstadir, including Héradssandur, Hjaltastadathinghá and the northern part of Hróarstunga. There are riparian marshes with streams, lakes and freshwater pools, and extensive mires dominated by sedges (*Carex*, *Eriophorum*).

Habitats Scrub (10%; heathland), Grassland (20%), Wetland (70%; sand-dunes/sand beach; standing fresh water; river/stream; water-fringe vegetation; fen/transition mire/spring)
Land-use Agriculture

■ **Birds**

Species	Season	Year	Pop min	Pop max	Acc	Criteria
Gavia stellata Red-throated Diver	B	—	—	200	—	B2
Podiceps auritus Slavonian Grebe	B	—	20	—	—	B1i
Anser anser Greylag Goose	B	1996	1,230	—	—	A4i, B1i
[1] *Anser anser* Greylag Goose	N	1997	5,311	5,500	—	A4i, B1i
Stercorarius parasiticus Arctic Skua	B	—	1,200	—	C	B1ii

1. Moulting.

The area supports a rich variety of breeding waterbirds.

■ **Protection status**
National None **International** None

■ **Conservation issues**

Threats Drainage (U), Unsustainable exploitation (U)

Hunting and shooting pose a threat: *Stercorarius parasiticus* and *S. skua* are shot illegally in the area. The area is on the list of sites of conservation interest in the Nature Conservation Register. The site is an enlarged and re-named version of the IBA 'Héradssandur–Hjaltastadathinghá', formerly IS050 in the previous international IBA inventory (Grimmett and Jones 1989).

Skoruvík–Skálabjarg A4i, A4ii, A4iii, B1i, B1ii, B3 041

Admin region Nordur-Thingeyjarsýsla
Coordinates 66°22′N 14°46′W
Altitude 0–80 m **Area** 5,300 ha

■ **Site description**
Sea cliffs in the far north-east of mainland Iceland, c.25 km north-east of the town of Thórshöfn. Land-uses include grazing,

tourism, and the collection of eggs of *Uria aalge* from the cliffs every spring.

Habitats Rocky areas (100%; sea cliff/rocky shore)
Land-use Agriculture, Tourism/recreation

■ Birds

Species	Season	Year	Pop min	Pop max	Acc	Criteria
Rissa tridactyla Kittiwake	B	1984	139,100	139,100	A	A4i, B1i
Uria aalge Guillemot	B	—	44,600	76,400	A	B1ii
Alca torda Razorbill	B	1984	14,830	22,010	A	A4ii, B1ii, B3

The site supports huge numbers of breeding seabirds, including *Uria lomvia* (12,000 pairs).

■ Protection status
National None **International** None

■ Conservation issues

Threats Disturbance to birds (U)

The area is on the list of sites of conservation interest in the Nature Conservation Register. The site results from the merging of two sites identified in the previous pan-European IBA inventory (Grimmett and Jones 1989), 'Skoruvík' (former site IS048) and 'Langanes' (former site IS049).

Melrakkaslétta
A4i, B1i, B3 042
Admin region Nordur-Thingeyjarsýsla
Coordinates 66°29′N 16°15′W
Altitude 0–60 m **Area** 24,600 ha

■ Site description
A peninsula in the north-east part of Iceland. The IBA extends from Presthólahraun, south of the town of Kópasker along the coast to Sveinungsvík, south-east of the town of Raufarhöfn. Habitats include an extensive and species-rich intertidal zone, coastal brackish lakes, cliffs, marshes, freshwater lakes, extensive heathland, and eroded gravel areas. Land-uses include eider husbandry (*Somateria mollissima*), grazing and fishing.

Habitats Scrub (30%; heathland), Grassland (5%; alpine/subalpine/boreal grassland; mesophile grassland), Wetland (30%; standing fresh water; standing brackish and salt water; river/stream; water-fringe vegetation; fen/transition mire/spring), Marine areas (30%; sea inlet/coastal features), Rocky areas (5%; sea cliff/rocky shore)
Land-use Agriculture

■ Birds

Species	Season	Year	Pop min	Pop max	Acc	Criteria
Gavia immer Great Northern Diver	B	—	15	20	—	A4i, B1i
Anser anser Greylag Goose	N	—	1,000	—	—	B1i
Somateria mollissima Eider	R	—	11,000	—	—	B1i
Calidris canutus Knot	P	1990	7,280	7,280	B	B1i
Calidris maritima Purple Sandpiper	R	—	Abundant		—	B3
Arenaria interpres Turnstone	P	1990	2,220	2,220	B	A4i, B1i

The area is relatively rich in breeding species of waterfowl, raptors and waders. *Calidris maritima* occurs at one of its highest breeding densities in Iceland, as does *Lagopus mutus*. The area is also important for staging waders and for moulting *Anser anser*. There are four seabird-nesting cliffs in the area (Snartastadanúpur, Raudinúpur, Ormarslónshöfdi and Súlur), of which Raudinúpur is the largest, and breeding species include *Rissa tridactyla* (c.15,000 pairs).

■ Protection status
National None **International** None

■ Conservation issues

Threats Consequences of animal/plant introductions (U)

Predation by introduced American mink *Mustela vison* is a threat. The area is on the list of sites of conservation interest in the Nature Conservation Register.

Öxarfjördur
A4i, A4ii, B1i, B1ii 043
Admin region Nordur-Thingeyjarsýsla
Coordinates 66°07′N 16°45′W
Altitude 0–15 m **Area** 2,500 ha

■ Site description
An extensive wetland by Öxarfjördur bay, comprising rivers (fed by cold and thermal springs), freshwater and brackish marshes, streams, lakes and pools. The freshwater marshes are dominated by sedges (*Carex, Eriophorum*). Land-uses include grazing, fishing and fish-farming.

Habitats Wetland (100%; sand-dunes/sand beach; standing fresh water; river/stream; water-fringe vegetation; fen/transition mire/spring)
Land-use Agriculture, Fisheries/aquaculture, Tourism/recreation, Urban/industrial/transport

■ Birds

Species	Season	Year	Pop min	Pop max	Acc	Criteria
Podiceps auritus Slavonian Grebe	R	—	20	40	—	B1i
Cygnus cygnus Whooper Swan	N	1996	141	141	A	B1i
[1] *Anser anser* Greylag Goose	N	—	4,000	—	—	A4i, B1i
Stercorarius skua Great Skua	B	1984	210	240	A	A4ii, B1ii

1. Moulting.

There is a good variety of other breeding waterfowl and waders.

■ Protection status
National None **International** None

■ Conservation issues

Threats Aquaculture/fisheries (U), Consequences of animal/plant introductions (U)

Predation by introduced American mink *Mustela vison* threatens waterbird populations. Nootka lupin *Lupinus nootkatensis*, an introduced plant which is highly invasive, is a threat to the natural vegetation of the habitat. The pollution and development caused by fish-farming are potential problems, as is a plan to build a geothermal power-station. The area is on the list of sites of conservation interest in the Nature Conservation Register.

Mývatn–Laxá
A4i, A4iii, B1i, B2, B3 044
Admin region Sudur-Thingeyjarsýsla
Coordinates 65°36′N 17°00′W
Altitude 0–310 m **Area** 10,200 ha

■ Site description
A shallow eutrophic lake (Mývatn) with many islands and fed by cold and thermal springs. There are numerous small lakes, pools, bogs and sedge marshes (*Carex, Eriophorum*) in the surrounding area. The Laxá river drains the lake into Skjálfandi bay. 'Rocky areas' here are lava. Land-uses include farming, fishing, energy production (hydroelectric and geothermal), mining and tourism.

Habitats Scrub (30%; scrub; heathland), Grassland (10%), Wetland (50%; standing fresh water; river/stream; water-fringe vegetation; fen/transition mire/spring), Rocky areas (10%)
Land-use Agriculture, Nature conservation/research, Tourism/recreation, Urban/industrial/transport

■ Birds

Species	Season	Year	Pop min	Pop max	Acc	Criteria
Podiceps auritus Slavonian Grebe	B	1990	140	140	A	A4i, B1i
Cygnus cygnus Whooper Swan	W	—	223	223	A	B1i, B3
Cygnus cygnus Whooper Swan	N	—	500	700	—	A4i, B1i
[1] *Aythya marila* Scaup	B	1989	3,275	3,275	A	B1i
Histrionicus histrionicus Harlequin Duck	B	—	222	222	A	A4i, B1i, B2
Bucephala islandica Barrow's Goldeneye	B	—	1,110	1,110	A	B2
Mergus merganser Goosander	W	1986	99	99	—	B1i

1. Individuals in spring, 1975–1989 mean (mean 2,434 moulting males in same period).

The site holds 20,000 or more waterbirds on a regular basis. Some duck species—*Anas penelope, Aythya fuligula* and *Aythya marila*—breed at higher densities than anywhere else in Europe. Other notable birds include diverse breeding waterbirds, raptors and passerines, and, outside the breeding season, moulting *Mergus merganser* (365 birds; mean 1975–1989).

■ Protection status
National High **International** High
10,200 ha of IBA covered by Conservation Area (Mývatn–Laxá, 440,000 ha). 10,200 ha of IBA covered by Ramsar Site (Mývatn–Laxá, 20,000 ha).

■ Conservation issues

Threats Aquaculture/fisheries (U), Dredging/canalization (U), Industrialization/ urbanization (U), Recreation/tourism (U)

The lake is threatened by commercial dredging for diatomite, by power-generation operations, and by urbanization. Fishing and tourism disturb birds and diving waterbirds are also killed in fishing nets. Erosion in the area is excessive. There is a research station at Skútustadir run by the Ministry of Environment.

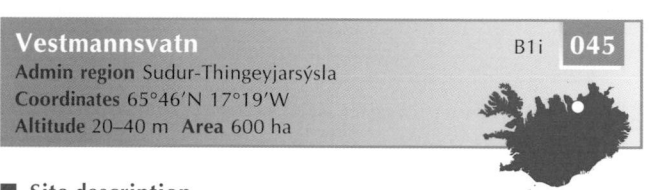

Vestmannsvatn
B1i 045
Admin region Sudur-Thingeyjarsýsla
Coordinates 65°46′N 17°19′W
Altitude 20–40 m **Area** 600 ha

■ Site description
A complex of shallow riparian lakes, 30 km south of the town of Húsavík, and including rivers, streams, pools and freshwater marshes, surrounded by *Betula* wood and cultivated land. 'Rocky areas' are vegetated lava and eroded gravel areas. Land-uses include grazing and fishing.

Habitats Scrub (10%; scrub; heathland), Grassland (10%), Wetland (70%; standing fresh water; river/stream; water-fringe vegetation), Rocky areas (20%)
Land-use Agriculture, Nature conservation/research, Other

■ Birds

Species	Season	Year	Pop min	Pop max	Acc	Criteria
Podiceps auritus Slavonian Grebe	B	—	10	15	—	B1i

The area also supports a wide variety of wildfowl including notable numbers of breeding (200–400 pairs) and staging duck (Anatidae).

■ Protection status
National High **International** None
600 ha of IBA covered by Nature Reserve (Vestmannsvatn, 600 ha).

■ Conservation issues

Threats Aquaculture/fisheries (U), Consequences of animal/plant introductions (U)

Predation by introduced American mink *Mustela vison* is a threat, as is the impact of net-fishing.

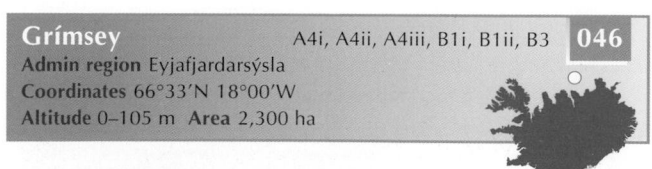

Grímsey
A4i, A4ii, A4iii, B1i, B1ii, B3 046
Admin region Eyjafjardarsýsla
Coordinates 66°33′N 18°00′W
Altitude 0–105 m **Area** 2,300 ha

■ Site description
An offshore island with sea cliffs and grasslands. Land-uses include sheep farming, fishing, tourism, collection of eggs of *Uria aalge*, and traditional harvesting of adult puffins *Fratercula arctica*.

Habitats Grassland (20%), Marine areas (60%; open sea), Rocky areas (20%; sea cliff/ rocky shore)
Land-use Agriculture, Hunting, Tourism/recreation

■ Birds
Huge numbers of seabird breed; other common species include *Fulmarus glacialis*, *Uria lomvia* (c.7,100 pairs) and *Sterna paradisaea* (hundreds of pairs).

Species	Season	Year	Pop min	Pop max	Acc	Criteria
Rissa tridactyla Kittiwake	B	1983	54,400	54,400	A	A4i, B1i
Uria aalge Guillemot	B	1985	54,400	69,600	—	B1ii
Alca torda Razorbill	B	—	26,300	38,800	A	A4ii, B1ii, B3
[1] *Fratercula arctica* Puffin	B	—	10,000	—	—	B1ii

1. "Some tens of thousands" of pairs breed (believed to exceed threshold).

■ Protection status
National None **International** None

■ Conservation issues

Threats Recreation/tourism (U), Unsustainable exploitation (U)

Disturbance of birds by tourists and hunters is a threat, as is egg-collecting. The area is on the list of sites of conservation interest in the Nature Conservation Register.

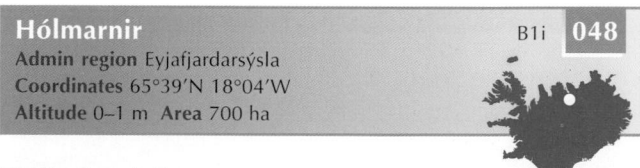

Höfdahverfi
A4i, B1i 047
Admin region Sudur-Thingeyjarsýsla
Coordinates 65°54′N 18°10′W
Altitude 0–20 m **Area** 60 ha

■ Site description
A wetland extending from the outlet of the Fnjóská river to Bárdartjörn near the village of Grenivík. Habitats comprise large and small riparian marshes of sedge (*Carex*, *Eriophorum*), pools, river and streams, river islets with willow *Salix*, and saltmarshes. Land-uses include grazing and eider husbandry (*Somateria mollissima*).

Habitats Wetland (100%; saltmarsh; standing fresh water; river/stream; water-fringe vegetation)
Land-use Agriculture

■ Birds

Species	Season	Year	Pop min	Pop max	Acc	Criteria
Somateria mollissima Eider	R	—	10,000	—	—	A4i, B1i

Not much information is available on birds, but other breeding species include a good variety of ducks and waders.

■ Protection status
National None **International** None

■ Conservation issues
The area on the list of sites of conservation interest in the Nature Conservation Register.

Hólmarnir
B1i 048
Admin region Eyjafjardarsýsla
Coordinates 65°39′N 18°04′W
Altitude 0–1 m **Area** 700 ha

■ Site description
A slow-flowing river with associated estuary and seasonally flooded marshes (dominated by sedge *Carex*) by Akureyri airport.

Habitats Wetland (100%; tidal river/enclosed tidal water; river/stream; water-fringe vegetation)
Land-use Agriculture, Hunting, Urban/industrial/transport

■ Birds

Species	Season	Year	Pop min	Pop max	Acc	Criteria
Limosa limosa Black-tailed Godwit	P	—	600	800	B	B1i

The area supports hundreds of migrating ducks in spring, as well as a wide variety of breeding waterfowl and waders.

■ Protection status
National None **International** None

■ Conservation issues

Threats Disturbance to birds (U), Filling-in of wetlands (U), Industrialization/urbanization (U), Recreation/tourism (U)

Development of the airport poses a threat, and birds are disturbed by hunters, horse-riders and dog-walkers. The area is on the list of sites of conservation interest in the Nature Conservation Register.

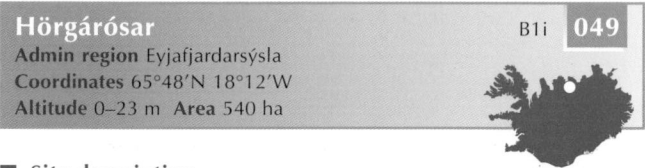

Hörgárósar — B1i 049
Admin region Eyjafjardarsýsla
Coordinates 65°48'N 18°12'W
Altitude 0–23 m **Area** 540 ha

■ Site description
A shallow estuary, located 9 km north-west of the town of Akureyri. It is flanked by meadows and bogs, with some eroded gravel areas. Other land-uses include angling and eider husbandry (*Somateria mollissima*).

Habitats Grassland (30%), Wetland (60%; tidal river/enclosed tidal water; standing fresh water; standing brackish and salt water; river/stream), Rocky areas (10%)
Land-use Agriculture, Hunting

■ Birds

Species	Season	Year	Pop min	Pop max	Acc	Criteria
[1] *Anser anser* Greylag Goose	N	—	—	2,000	—	B1i

1. Moulting; some tens of pairs breed.

The site supports about 30 breeding waterbird species. The estuary is one of few in the Eyjafjördur area and supports notable numbers of foraging waders.

■ Protection status
National None **International** None

■ Conservation issues

Threats Unsustainable exploitation (U)

Hunting is a threat. The area is on the list of sites of conservation interest in the Nature Conservation Register.

Hrísey — A4i, B1i 050
Admin region Eyjafjardarsýsla
Coordinates 66°00'N 18°23'W
Altitude 0–110 m **Area** 767 ha

■ Site description
An inshore island in the Eyjafjördur firth, opposite the town of Dalvík. There is a village on the island. Land-uses include eider husbandry (*Somateria mollissima*). No grazing is allowed.

Habitats Scrub (70%; heathland), Grassland (30%)
Land-use Tourism/recreation

■ Birds

Species	Season	Year	Pop min	Pop max	Acc	Criteria
Somateria mollissima Eider	R	—	3,000	4,000	—	B1i
Sterna paradisaea Arctic Tern	B	—	25,000	—	—	A4i, B1i

Lagopus mutus occurs at high density (up to 40 males/km²), and a variety of waders also breed.

■ Protection status
National None **International** None

■ Conservation issues

Threats Consequences of animal/plant introductions (U)

The native heathland vegetation is being replaced by the introduced and invasive Nootka lupin *Lupinus nootkatensis*, and by afforestation with *Picea*, *Larix* and *Pinus*. The area is on the list of sites of conservation interest in the Nature Conservation Register.

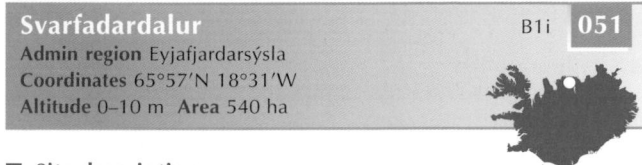

Svarfadardalur — B1i 051
Admin region Eyjafjardarsýsla
Coordinates 65°57'N 18°31'W
Altitude 0–10 m **Area** 540 ha

■ Site description
A complex of river flood-plains, marshes, small lakes and flood-meadows near the town of Dalvík. Land-uses are mainly grazing and haymaking.

Habitats Grassland (10%; humid grassland), Wetland (90%; standing fresh water; river/stream; water-fringe vegetation)
Land-use Agriculture, Nature conservation/research

■ Birds

Species	Season	Year	Pop min	Pop max	Acc	Criteria
Branta leucopsis Barnacle Goose	P	1992	400	600	—	B1i

Notable breeding species include *Podiceps auritus* and various duck species; hundreds of *Anas penelope* moult here.

■ Protection status
National High **International** None
540 ha of IBA covered by Nature Reserve (Svarfadardalur, 540 ha).

■ Conservation issues

Threats Aquaculture/fisheries (U), Consequences of animal/plant introductions (U), Recreation/tourism (U)

Predation by introduced American mink *Mustela vison* is a threat, as is tourism.

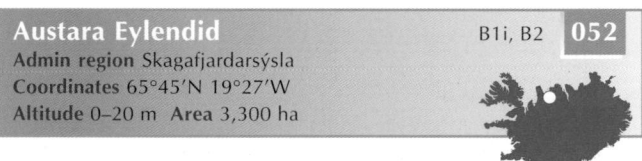

Austara Eylendid — B1i, B2 052
Admin region Skagafjardarsýsla
Coordinates 65°45'N 19°27'W
Altitude 0–20 m **Area** 3,300 ha

■ Site description
Riparian marshes, pools and lakes, c.10 km east and south-east of Saudárkrókur town. The site includes the Austari-Héradsvötn delta and lakes in that area, from Gardsvatn to Borgarey, as well as lakes in Hegranes and their neighbouring marshes, Ásvatn, Svanavatn, Hendilkotsvatn, Hólmavatn and Urridavatn. Marshes are dominated by sedge *Carex*. Land-uses include grazing and fishing.

Habitats Grassland (10%), Wetland (90%; standing fresh water; river/stream; water-fringe vegetation; fen/transition mire/spring)
Land-use Agriculture

■ Birds

Species	Season	Year	Pop min	Pop max	Acc	Criteria
Podiceps auritus Slavonian Grebe	B	—	20	—	—	B1i
[1] *Anser anser* Greylag Goose	B	—	Common	—	—	B1i
[1] *Limosa limosa* Black-tailed Godwit	B	—	Common	—	—	B1i, B2

1. Believed to exceed threshold.

The site supports a diverse community of breeding waterbirds, and hundreds of migrating *Branta leucopsis* stage here in spring.

■ Protection status
National None **International** None

■ Conservation issues

Threats Consequences of animal/plant introductions (U), Drainage (U)

Predation by the introduced American mink *Mustela vison* is a threat, as may be grazing. The area is on the list of sites of conservation interest in the Nature Conservation Register.

Miklavatn–Skógar B1i 053

Admin region Skagafjardarsýsla
Coordinates 65°42′N 19°34′W
Altitude 0–5 m **Area** 2,100 ha

■ Site description

A river flood-plain near Saudárkrókur town, comprising lakes, pools and extensive, seasonally flooded marshes/mires, dominated by sedges (*Carex, Eriophorum*). The area includes the lakes and marshes by Miklavatn, Áshildarholtsvatn, Tjarnartjörn and the Skógar area. Land-uses include grazing and fishing.

Habitats Wetland (100%; standing fresh water; river/stream; water-fringe vegetation; fen/transition mire/spring)
Land-use Agriculture, Nature conservation/research

■ Birds

Species	Season	Year	Pop min	Pop max	Acc	Criteria
Cygnus cygnus Whooper Swan	N	—	150	—	—	B1i
Anser anser Greylag Goose	N	—	3,000	—	—	B1i
Aythya marila Scaup	N	—	300	—	—	B1i

An important moulting area which also supports a wide diversity of breeding wildfowl, waders and other waterbirds.

■ Protection status

National Partial **International** None
1,550 ha of IBA covered by Nature Reserve (Miklavatn, 1,550 ha).

■ Conservation issues

Threats Drainage (U), Industrialization/urbanization (U)

Drangey A4iii 054

Admin region Skagafjardarsýsla
Coordinates 65°57′N 19°40′W
Altitude 0–140 m **Area** 1,500 ha

■ Site description

An inshore rocky island with sea cliffs and grassland. Eggs are collected from *Uria aalge* at places along the cliff every spring, and adult puffins *Fratercula arctica* are also harvested traditionally. Tourists regularly visit the island in summer.

Habitats Rocky areas (100%; sea cliff/rocky shore)
Land-use Tourism/recreation

■ Birds

The site holds more than 10,000 pairs of breeding seabirds on a regular basis, including abundant *Fratercula arctica* and more than 1% of the Icelandic population of *Rissa tridactyla* (c.9,000 pairs). *Uria aalge* seems to be increasing and *Uria lomvia* decreasing.

■ Protection status

National None **International** None

■ Conservation issues

No serious threats are known. The area is on the list of sites of conservation interest in the Nature Conservation Register.

Hóp–Vatnsdalur A4i, B1i 055

Admin region Austur-Húnavatnssýsla
Coordinates 65°31′N 20°19′W
Altitude 0–20 m **Area** 12,000 ha

■ Site description

An extensive complex of rivers, associated marshes/mires (*Carex, Eriophorum*), and grassland, 12 km south-west of the town of Blönduós. The area covers Hóp and Húnavatn and neighbouring areas, Eylendi, and along Hnausakvísl and Flódid, as well as the area to the south along Vatnsdalsá to Hof farm in the Vatnsdalur valley. Land-uses include grazing and angling.

Habitats Grassland (20%), Wetland (80%; standing fresh water; river/stream; water-fringe vegetation; fen/transition mire/spring)
Land-use Agriculture, Fisheries/aquaculture, Hunting

■ Birds

Species	Season	Year	Pop min	Pop max	Acc	Criteria
[1] *Cygnus cygnus* Whooper Swan	P	—	100	300	C	B1i
[2] *Anser anser* Greylag Goose	N	—	300	—	—	B1i
Branta leucopsis Barnacle Goose	P	—	10,000	15,000	—	A4i, B1i

1. Several hundred staging; 100–200 moulting.
2. Several hundred moulting on Flódid.

The site also supports a good diversity of breeding waterbirds.

■ Protection status

National None **International** None

■ Conservation issues

Threats Aquaculture/fisheries (U), Drainage (U), Unsustainable exploitation (U)

Hunting causes problems. The area is on the list of sites of conservation interest in the Nature Conservation Register. The site is an enlarged and re-named version of the IBA 'Eylendid', formerly site IS037 in the previous international IBA inventory (Grimmett and Jones 1989).

Arnarvatnsheidi–Tvídægra A4i, B1i 056

Admin region Mýrasýsla, Vestur-Húnavatnssýsla
Coordinates 65°00′N 20°30′W
Altitude 400–550 m **Area** 60,000 ha

■ Site description

A vast wetland area in the highlands, c.30 km north and west of Langjökull glacier, with extensive flat, eroded areas of gravel. Ownership of the highlands has not been resolved, but farmers hold grazing and fishing rights.

Habitats Scrub (10%; heathland), Wetland (50%; standing fresh water; river/stream; blanket bog; fen/transition mire/spring), Rocky areas (40%)
Land-use Agriculture, Tourism/recreation

■ Birds

Species	Season	Year	Pop min	Pop max	Acc	Criteria
[1] *Gavia immer* Great Northern Diver	B	—	Common	—	—	A4i, B1i
[2] *Cygnus cygnus* Whooper Swan	B	—	200	—	—	B1i

1. Believed to exceed threshold.
2. At least a few hundred pairs.

One of the main breeding areas of *Cygnus cygnus* in Iceland (e.g. 286 moulting on two lakes in Arnarvatnsheidi in 1976).

■ Protection status

National None **International** None

■ Conservation issues

Threats Consequences of animal/plant introductions (U), Infrastructure (U)

Road construction, and predation by introduced American mink *Mustela vison*, pose threats. The area is on the list of sites of conservation interest in the Nature Conservation Register.

Eyjavatn–Fridmundarvötn B1i 057

Admin region Austur-Húnavatnssýsla
Coordinates 65°15′N 19°42′W
Altitude 434–499 m **Area** 7,500 ha

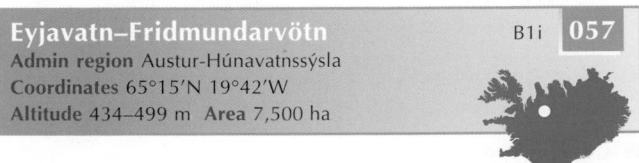

■ Site description

Lakes and associated extensive freshwater marshes dominated by sedges (*Carex, Eriophorum*), covering Fridmundarvötn, Eyjavatn og Mjóavatn and neighbouring areas south to Áfangafell mountain.

There are eroded, flat gravel areas. Ownership of the highlands is not resolved, but farmers have grazing and fishing rights.

Habitats Wetland (80%; standing fresh water; river/stream; water-fringe vegetation; fen/transition mire/spring), Rocky areas (20%)
Land-use Agriculture

■ **Birds**

Species	Season	Year	Pop min	Pop max	Acc	Criteria
Cygnus cygnus Whooper Swan	N	1988	260	—	—	B1i

No birdwatcher or ornithologist is known to have visited Lake Eyjavatn by land, and very little recent information is thus available, but the site is believed to support important numbers of moulting *Cygnus cygnus* at least. Numerous duck species (Anatidae) breed in large numbers and at high density, but have only been surveyed from the air and no detailed information is available.

■ **Protection status**
National None **International** None

■ **Conservation issues**

Threats Consequences of animal/plant introductions (U)

Predation by the introduced American mink *Mustela vison* poses a threat. Austara–Fridmundarvatn is now a part of the water supply for Blanda hydroelectric power-station, with water from the glacial Blanda river running through. The area is on the list of sites of conservation interest in the Nature Conservation Register.

Gudlaugstungur–Álfgeirstungur
A4i, B1i **058**
Admin region Austur-Húnavatnssýsla
Coordinates 64°59'N 19°24'W
Altitude 520–620 m **Area** 11,500 ha

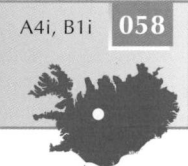

■ **Site description**
A wetland to the north of the Kjölur area, in the central highlands of Iceland. There are extensive marshes/mires of sedge (*Carex, Eriophorum*) overlying permafrost, and eroded gravel areas. The ownership of the highlands is not resolved, but farmers hold grazing and fishing rights. The main land-use is grazing.

Habitats Scrub (30%; heathland), Wetland (40%; standing fresh water; river/stream; water-fringe vegetation; fen/transition mire/spring), Rocky areas (30%)
Land-use Agriculture

■ **Birds**

Species	Season	Year	Pop min	Pop max	Acc	Criteria
[1] *Anser brachyrhynchus* Pink-footed Goose	B	—	500	—	—	A4i, B1i

1. Hundreds or a few thousands of pairs.

Hundreds of *Anser brachyrhynchus* moult in Álfgeirstungur. Not much information on birds is available for the area.

■ **Protection status**
National None **International** None

■ **Conservation issues**
No threats are known.

Thjórsárver
A4i, B1i, B3 **059**
Admin region Rangárvallasýsla, Árnessýsla
Coordinates 64°34'N 18°40'W
Altitude 580–1,140 m **Area** 37,500 ha

■ **Site description**
A tract of wetland in the tundra-like central highlands, south of the Hofsjökull glacier, with rivers, lakes, ponds, extensive marshes/ mires of sedge (*Eriophorum, Carex*), and flat, eroded gravel areas. Ownership of the highlands has not been resolved, but farmers have grazing rights.

Habitats Scrub (20%; heathland), Wetland (70%; standing fresh water; river/stream; water-fringe vegetation; fen/transition mire/spring), Rocky areas (10%)
Land-use Agriculture

■ **Birds**

Species	Season	Year	Pop min	Pop max	Acc	Criteria
Anser brachyrhynchus Pink-footed Goose	B	—	6,000	10,000	A	A4i, B1i, B3

■ **Protection status**
National High **International** High
37,500 ha of IBA covered by Nature Reserve (Thjórsárver, 37,500 ha).
37,500 ha of IBA covered by Ramsar Site (Thjórsárver, 37,500 ha).

■ **Conservation issues**

Threats Construction/impact of dyke/dam/barrage (U), Other (U), Recreation/tourism (U)

Excessive erosion ('Other' threat) is a problem. Traffic by people in the area is increasing as a result of more roads being constructed in and around the site—the roads lead to hydroelectric power-stations and to the Kvíslavötn reservoir (which lies partly within the IBA). The national energy authority is planning a reservoir (for hydroelectric power generation) in the southern part of the reserve that would put 62 km^2 of the reserve under water.

Veidivötn
A4i, B1i, B2 **060**
Admin region Rangárvallasýsla
Coordinates 64°08'N 18°49'W
Altitude 560–930 m **Area** 7,600 ha

■ **Site description**
A complex of crater-lakes in the southern highlands of Iceland, c.30 km south-west of the Vatnajökull glacier. Many lakes have some surrounding vegetation (marshes and grassy areas), and lava-fields have some moss-cover, but otherwise, away from the lakes, there are large, flat expanses of eroded gravel with little or no vegetation. The area is used for sheep-grazing, tourism and trout-fishing (one of Iceland's most popular areas).

Habitats Wetland (50%; standing fresh water; river/stream; fen/transition mire/spring), Rocky areas (50%)
Land-use Agriculture, Tourism/recreation

■ **Birds**

Species	Season	Year	Pop min	Pop max	Acc	Criteria
Gavia immer Great Northern Diver	B	1996	10	15	B	A4i, B1i
Bucephala islandica Barrow's Goldeneye	W	—	—	50	—	B2

Other breeding birds include some *Aythya marila* and *Histrionicus histrionicus*, and *A. marila* also moults in the area (c.200 birds).

■ **Protection status**
National None **International** None

■ **Conservation issues**

Threats Consequences of animal/plant introductions (U), Other (U), Recreation/tourism (U)

Anglers, hunting, introduced American mink *Mustela vison*, and excessive erosion ('Other' threat) are all potential threats. Ownership of the highlands has not been resolved, but farmers have grazing and fishing rights. The area is on the list of sites of conservation interest in the Nature Conservation Register.

Eyjabakkar
A4i, B1i **061**
Admin region Nordur-Múlasýsla
Coordinates 64°44'N 15°31'W
Altitude 620–700 m **Area** 6,800 ha

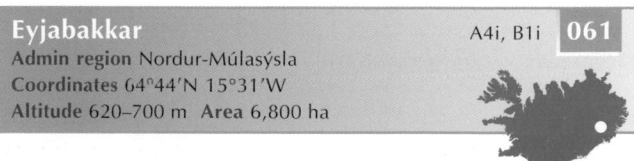

■ **Site description**
A wetland in the highlands, by Eyjabakkajökull in Vatnajökul glacier, with extensive sedge marshes (*Carex, Eriophorum*). The ownership of

the highlands is not resolved, but farmers hold grazing and fishing rights in the area.

Habitats Wetland (100%; standing fresh water; river/stream; water-fringe vegetation; fen/transition mire/spring)
Land-use Not utilized

■ **Birds**

Species	Season	Year	Pop min	Pop max	Acc	Criteria
¹ *Anser brachyrhynchus* Pink-footed Goose	N	—	5,505	5,505	A	A4i, B1i
1. Moulting.						

■ **Protection status**
National None **International** None

■ **Conservation issues**

Threats Construction/impact of dyke/dam/barrage (U)

The area is under serious threat of submersion; the planned construction of a hydroelectric power-station in Jökulsá á Fljótsdal has already been approved by the Althingi (national legislature), and this will require a reservoir that will completely cover the Eyjabakki IBA. The IBA is on the list of sites of conservation interest in the Nature Conservation Register.

REFERENCES

BJÖRNSSON, H. (1976) [The bird life in the Öræfi area, south-east Iceland.] *Náttúrufræðingurinn* 46: 56–104. (In Icelandic, with English summary.)

BJÖRNSSON, H. (1982) Fuglar. [Birds in the western part of Eyjafjördur.] Pp. 119–129 in H. Hallgrímsson, ed. Skýrsla um könnun á náttúrufari og minjum á vesturströnd Eyjafjarðar. Unpublished report to Staðarvalsnefnd. (In Icelandic.)

EINARSSON, Á. (1985) Botn Mývatns: Fortíð, nútíð og framtíð. *Náttúrufræðingurinn* 55: 153–173. (In Icelandic, with English summary.)

EINARSSON, Á. (1994) Mývatn-Laxá Ramsar site—a case of integrated monitoring. Pp. 211-219 in G. Aubrecht, G. Dick and C. Prentice, eds. *Monitoring of ecological change in wetlands of Middle Europe. Proceedings of an International Workshop in Linz, Austria, October 1993.* Slimbridge, U.K.: International Waterfowl and Wetlands and Research Bureau (IWRB Publ. 30).

FJELDSÅ, J. (1975) Recent changes in the waterfowl situation in the lakes Myvatn and Vikingavatn, Iceland. *Dansk Orn. Foren. Tidsskr.* 69: 89–102.

GARÐARSSON, A. (1973) Fuglastofnar og selir á Breiðafirði. [Populations of birds and seals at Breiðafjörður.] Icelandic Insititute of Natural History. Unpublished report. 27 pp. (In Icelandic.)

GARÐARSSON, A. ED. (1975) Votlendi. [Wetlands.] Rit Landverndar 4. Reykjavik: Landvernd. 238 pp. (In Icelandic, with English summary.)

GARÐARSSON, A. (1979) Íslenski húsandarstofnin. [Distribution and numbers of the Barrow's Goldeneye (*Bucephala islandica*) in Iceland.] *Náttúrufræðingurinn* 48: 162–191. (In Icelandic, with English summary.)

GARÐARSSON, A. (1979) Skarfatal 1975. [A census of breeding Cormorants (*Phalacrocorax carbo*) and Shags (*Phalacrocorax aristotelis*) in Iceland 1975.] *Náttúrufræðingurinn* 49: 126–154. (In Icelandic, with English summary.)

GARÐARSSON, A. (1985) The huge bird-cliff, Látrabjarg, in western Iceland. *Environ. Conserv.* 12: 83–84.

GARÐARSSON, A. (1991) Fuglalíf vid Mývatn og Laxá. [The birdlife of Mývatn and Laxá.] Pp. 278–319 in A. Garðarsson and A. Einarsson, eds. *Náttúra Mývatns.* Reykjavík: Hið íslenska Náttúrufræðifélag. (In Icelandic.)

GARÐARSSON, A. (1992) Andfuglar og aðrir vatnafuglar. Pp. 77–116 in A. Garðarsson, ed. *Fuglar, rit Landverndar.* Reykjavik: Landvernd.

GARÐARSSON, A. (1995) Svartfugl í íslenskum fuglabjorgum. [Numbers and distribution of Common Murre *Uria aalge*, Thick-billed Murre *U. lomvia* and Razorbill *Alca torda* in Iceland.] *Bliki* 16: 47–65. (In Icelandic, with English summary.)

GARÐARSSON, A. (1995) Fjöldi súlu við Ísland 1989–1994. [Numbers of Gannets *Sula bassana* in Iceland 1984–94.] *Náttúrufræðingurinn* 64: 203–208. (In Icelandic, with English summary.)

GARÐARSSON, A. (1996) Ritubyggðir. [Numbers and distribution of breeding Kittiwake *Rissa tridactyla* in Iceland.] *Bliki* 17: 1–16. (In Icelandic, with English summary.)

GARÐARSSON, A. AND EINARSSON, A. (1994) Responses of breeding duck populations to changes in food supply. *Hydrobiologia* 279/280: 15–27.

GARÐARSSON, A. AND GUÐMUNDSSON, G. A. (1991) Yfirlit um gildi einstakra fjörusvæða fyrir vaðfugla. [Important shores for waders in Iceland.] Unpublished report. 45 pp. (In Icelandic.)

GARÐARSSON, A. AND GUDMUNDSSON, G. A. (1996) Numbers of Light-bellied Brent Geese (*Branta bernicla hrota*) staging in Iceland bird spring. *Wildfowl* 47: 68–72.

GARÐARSSON, A. AND NIELSEN, Ó. K. (1989) Fuglalíf á tveimur leirum við Reykjavík. I. Vaðfuglar. [Seasonal variation in numbers of birds on two tidal mudflats in south-west Iceland. Part I. Shorebirds.] *Náttúrufræðingurinn* 59: 59–84. (In Icelandic, with English summary.)

GARÐARSSON, A. AND SIGURÐSSON, J. B. (1971) *Skýrsla um rannsóknir á heiðagæs í Þjórsárverum sumarið 1971.* [Report on studies of Pink-footed Geese at Thjórsárver the summer of 1971.] Orkustofnun, raforkudeild. 100 pp. (In Icelandic, with English summary.)

GARÐARSSON A. AND SKARPHÉDINSSON, K. H. (1984) A census of the Icelandic Whooper Swan population. *Wildfowl* 35: 37–47.

GARÐARSSON, A. AND SKARPHÉDINSSON, K. H. (1985) Veturseta álftar. [The wintering of Whooper Swans (*Cygnus cygnus*) in Iceland.] *Bliki* 4: 45–56. (In Icelandic, with English summary.)

GARÐARSSON, A., INGÓLFSSON, A. AND ELDON, J. (1976) Lokaskýrsla um rannsóknir á ósólmasvæði Eyjafjarðarár 1974. [Report on natural history of the delta of Eyjafjardará river.] Líffræðistofnun háskólans. Fjölrit 7. (In Icelandic.)

GERRITSEN, G. J. AND GROEN, N. M. (1995) *Icelandic Black-tailed Godwit project 1993.* Zeist, Netherlands: WIWO (Foundation working group for international waterbird and wetland research) (Report 51). 44 pp. (In English, with Icelandic summary.)

GRIMMETT, R. F. A. AND JONES, T. A. (1989) *Important Bird Areas in Europe.* Cambridge, U.K.: International Council for Bird Preservation (Techn. Publ. 9). 888 pp.

GUÐMUNDSSON, F. (1971) Straumendur á Íslandi. [The Harlequin Duck *Histrionicus histrionicus* in Iceland.] *Náttúrufræðingurinn* 41: 1–28. (In Icelandic, with English summary.)

GUDMUNDSSON, G. A. AND GARÐARSSON, A. (1993) Numbers, geographic distribution and habitat utilization of waders (Charadrii) in spring on the shores of Iceland. *Ecography* 16: 82–93.

HALLGRÍMSSON, H. (1984) Landnám lifs í Skjálftavötnum í Kelduhverfi. [Development of life in Skjálftavötn, in a lake in NE-Iceland.] *Náttúrufræðingurinn* 53: 149–159. (In Icelandic, with English summary.)

HEATH, M. F. AND BORGGREVE, C. (2000) *BirdLife International/EBCC European Bird Database 1998.* Cambridge, UK: BirdLife International.

HILMARSSON, J. Ó. (1991) *Um fuglalíf og mikilvægustu fuglasvæði í Flóa.* [Report on birds and the most important bird areas in Flói.] Samvinnunefnd um svæðisskipulag í Flóa. 34 pp. (In Icelandic.)

HILMARSSON, J. Ó. (1998) Fuglalíf og votlendi við Ölfusárós. [Birdlife and wetlands by Ölfusár river.] Pp. 185–191 in J. S. Ólafsson, ed. *Íslensk votlendi—verndun og nýting.* [Icelandic wetlands—conservation and utilisation.] Reykjavik: Háskólaútgáfan. (In Icelandic.)

HILMARSSON, J. Ó. AND ÞORLEIFSSON, E. (1991) Ölfusforir—Sunnlensk náttuúruperla sem sótt er að. [Ölfusforir—a threatened wetland in the southern lowlands of Iceland.] *Áfangar* 41: 17–23. (In Icelandic.)

HILMARSSON, J. Ó., ÞORLEIFSSON, E. Ó. AND GUÐNASSON, I. (1990) Votlendi á Suðurlandi. Fuglar. [Wetlands in the southern lowlands of Iceland. Birds.] Skýrsla til Landverndar. Unpublished report. 50 pp. (In Icelandic.)

HILMARSSON, J. Ó., ÞORLEIFSSON, E. Ó. AND GUÐNASON, I. (1991) Könnun á votlendum á Suðurlandi 1990. Fuglar. [A survey of wetlands and their birds in the southern lowlands of Iceland.] Skýrsla til Pokasjóðs Landverndar. 50 pp. Unpublished report. (In Icelandic.)

HJÁLMARSSON, Á.W. (1979) Fuglalíf í Snæfellsnes- og Hnappadalssýslu. [Bird life in Snæfellsnes- and Hnappadalssýslu.] *Náttúrufræðingurinn* 49: 112–125. (In Icelandic, with English summary.)

INGÓLFSSON, A. (1990) Sjávarlón á Íslandi. [Brackish lagoons in Iceland.] Fjölrit nr. 21. Náttúruverndarráð. 64 pp. (In Icelandic.)

INGÓLFSSON, A., KJARTANSDÓTTIR, A. AND GARÐARSSON, A. (1980) Athuganir á fuglum og smádýralífi í Skarðsfirði. [A survey of bird and invertebrates at Skarðsfjördur.] Líffræðistofnun Háskólans. Fjölrit 13. 21 pp. (In Icelandic.)

JÓNASSON, P., ED. (1979) Ecology of eutrophic subarctic lake Mývatn and the river Laxá. *Oikos* 32: 1–308.

KERBES, R. H., OGILVIE, M. A. AND BOYD, H. (1971) Pink-footed Geese of Iceland and Greenland: a population review base on aerial survey of Þjórsárver in June, 1970. *Wildfowl* 22: 5–17.

LUND-HANSEN, L. C. AND LANGE, P. (1991) The numbers and distribution of the Great Skua (*Stercorarius skua*) breeding in Iceland 1984–1985. *Acta Naturalia Islandica* 34: 1–16.

NÁTTÚRUFRÆÐISTOFNUN ÍSLANDS (1996) *Válisti 1, plöntur.* [The Icelandic Red data book 1, plants.] 82 pp. (In Icelandic.)

NÁTTÚRUVERNDARRÁÐ (1996) *Náttúruminjaskrá.* [The Nature Conservation Register] no. 7. 64 pp. (In Icelandic, with English summary.)

NIELSEN, Ó. K. (1998) Hrun flórgoðastofnins á Íslandi. [The population decline of the Slavonian Grebe in Iceland.] Pp. 197–205 in J. S. Ólafsson, ed. *Íslensk votlendi—verndun og nýting.* [Icelandic wetlands—conservation and utilisation.] Reykjavik: Háskólaútgáfan. (In Icelandic, with English summary.)

ÓLAFSSON, J. S., ED. (1998) *Íslensk votlendi—verndun og nýting.* [Icelandic wetlands—conservation and utilisation.] Reykjavik: Háskólaútgáfan. 283 pp. (In Icelandic, with English summary.)

PETERSEN, Æ. (1970) Fuglalif í Skógum á óshólmasvæði Héraðsvatna í Skagafirði. [Birdlife at Skógar in the Heraðsvötn river delta, northern Iceland.] *Náttúrufræðingurinn* 40: 26–46. (In Icelandic, with English summary.)

PETERSEN, Æ. (1979) Varpfuglar Flateyjar á Breiðafirði og nokkurra nærliggjandi eyja. [The breeding birds of Flatey and some adjoining islets in Breiðafjördur, north-west Iceland.] *Náttúrufræðingurinn* 49: 229–256. (In Icelandic, with English summary.)

PETERSEN, Æ. (1981) The breeding biology and feeding ecology of Black Guillemots. Unpublished D.Phil. thesis. University of Oxford.

PETERSEN, Æ. (1989) Náttúrufar í Breiðafjarðareyjum. [The fauna of islands in Breiðafjörður.] In: Ferðafélag Íslands árbók 1989. Breiðafjardaeyjar. 62: 17–52. (In Icelandic.)

PETERSEN, Æ. AND HJARTARSON, G. (1989) Vetrarfuglatalningar: Skipulag og árangur 1987. [The Icelandic Christmas Bird Counts: some general points, and results for 1987.] Fjölrit Náttúrufræðistofnunar 11. 42 pp. (In Icelandic, with English summary.)

PETERSEN, Æ. AND HJARTARSON, G. (1991) Vetrarfuglatalningar: Árangur 1988. [The Icelandic Christmas Bird Counts: results for 1988.] Fjölrit Náttúrufræðistofnunar 18. 42 pp. (In Icelandic, with English summary.)

PETERSEN, Æ. AND HJARTARSON, G. (1993) Vetrarfuglatalningar: Árangur 1989. [The Icelandic Christmas Bird Counts: results for 1989.] Fjölrit Náttúrufræðistofnunar 18. 43 pp. (In Icelandic with English summary.)

PETERSEN, Æ. AND THORSTENSEN, S. (1990) Fuglalif við Akureyrarflugvöll og grennd 1987. [Birdlife at Akureyri airport and surrounding wetlands, north Iceland 1987.] *Bliki* 9: 7–20. (In Icelandic, with English summary.)

PETERSEN, Æ. AND THORSTENSEN, S. (1993) Hettumáfsvörp í Eyjafirði 1990. [The distribution and numbers of Black-headed Gulls in Eyjafjörður 1990.] *Bliki* 13: 45–59. (In Icelandic, with English summary.)

SKARPHÉÐINSSON, K. H. (1997) *Fuglalif í Mýrarsýslu.* [Birdlife in the county of Mýrarsýsla.] Náttúrufræðistofnun Íslands. 24 pp. (In Icelandic.)

SKARPHÉÐINSSON, K. H. AND GUÐMUNDSSON, G. A. (1987) Fuglalíf í Skógum, Skagafirði, og nágrenni, 1987. [The birdlife of Skógar and vicinity, north Iceland.] *Bliki* 9: 49–66. (In Icelandic, with English summary.)

SKARPHÉÐINSSON, K. H. AND ÞÓRISSON, S. (1993) Fuglalíf. [Birdlife in the highlands of east Iceland in areas of potential hydroelectric power-plants] Pp. 63–88 in K. Þórarinsson, ed. Samanburður á umhverfisáhrifum nokkurra tilhagana á stórvikjun á Austurlandi (Austurlandsvirkjun). [A comparison of environmental impacts of hydroelectrical power stations in the eastern highlands of Iceland.] SINO. [Ministry of Industry and Nature Conservancy Council co-operative committee.] 119 pp. (In Icelandic.)

SKARPHÉÐINSSON, K. H., PÉTURSSON, G. AND HILMARSSON, J. Ó. (1994) *Útbreiðsla varpfugla á Suðvesturlandi, könnun 1987–1992.* [Atlas of breeding birds in south-western Iceland: a survey 1987–1992.] Fjölrit Náttúrufræðistofnunar 25. 126 pp. (In Icelandic, with English summary.)

THORSTEINSSON, I. (1985) Eyðing gróðurs og endurheimt landgæða á Íslandi [Vegetation erosion and restoration of land quality in Iceland]. In *Náttúra Íslands* [*The nature of Iceland*], second edition. Reykjavík: Almenna Bókafélagið. 475 pp. (In Icelandic.)

TIEDEMAN, R. (1990) *Athugun á fari vaðfugla um Skarðsfjörð og Hornafjörð vorið 1988.* [A study of the migration of waders at Skarðsfjördur and Hornafjördur.] Háskóli Íslands, Líffræðiskor. 5e verkefni. 33 pp. (In Icelandic, with English summary.)

TUCKER, G. M. AND HEATH, M. F. (1994) *Birds in Europe: their conservation status.* Cambridge, U.K.: BirdLife International (BirdLife Conservation Series no. 3). 600 pp.

ÞORLEIFSSON, E. Ó. (1995) *Útbreiðsla og fjöldi nokkurra votlendisfugla á Suðurlandsundirlendi ásamt Votlendisskrá.* [The distribution and number of wetland birds in the southern lowlands of Iceland, including a list of wetland areas.] Háskóli Íslands, Jarðfræði og Landafræðiskor. 61 pp. (In Icelandic.)

ÞORLEIFSSON, E. Ó. AND HILMARSSON, J. Ó. (1990) Fuglalíf í Ölfusforum. [Birds in the Ölfusforir wetland]. Skýrsla til Landverndar. Unpublished report. 18 pp. (In Icelandic.)

ÞORLEIFSSON, E. Ó. AND HILMARSSON, J. Ó. (1992) Pollengissvæðið. Merk votlendi viðármót Hvitar og Tungufljóts. [Pollengissvædid. An important wetland where Hvítá and Tunguflót rivers merge.] *Útivist* 18: 83–96. (In Icelandic.)

ÞORSTEINSSON, Þ. (1995) Fuglarannsóknir í Hrísey. [Birdlife in Hrísey.] Unpublished manuscript. (In Icelandic.)

REPUBLIC OF
IRELAND

JACKIE HUNT, JOHN DERWIN, JOHN COVENEY AND STEPHEN NEWTON

Sheskinmore (IBA 020), County Donegal. (PHOTO: ALYN WALSH)

GENERAL INTRODUCTION

The island of Ireland is located on the western edge of Europe, extending from about 51°N to 55°N and from 5°W to 10°W. It has a total area of 84,421 km², of which 70,282 km² form the Republic of Ireland (hereafter referred to as 'Ireland'). A total of 140 Important Bird Areas (IBAs) are identified in this inventory (Table 1, Map 1), covering an area of about 4,309 km², equivalent to c.6% of the land area of the country. These 140 sites include 48 newly identified IBAs. In the previous pan-European inventory (Grimmett and Jones 1989), 110 IBAs were identified. During the current review, 91 of these original sites were found to still qualify under the current

(revised) IBA criteria. One of these sites (former site IE110) has been split into two IBAs for this inventory, and a number of the others have been expanded in size. Seven out of the 110 original sites did not meet criteria and do not feature in this inventory (they are listed in Table 1). The remaining 12 of the 110 original sites have been amalgamated with six of the 91 qualifying sites to form enlarged IBAs.

The long coastline of Ireland extends over 7,100 km (EPA 1996) and has a wide variety of habitats. About 60% of the IBAs are coastal, with islands and cliffs being important for breeding seabirds and estuaries for wintering wildfowl. The interior of Ireland is dominated by a low-lying limestone plain, surrounded by mountains

Table 1. Summary of Important Bird Areas in the Republic of Ireland.   140 IBAs covering 4,309 km² *

IBA code	1989 code	International/National name	Administrative region	Area (ha)	Criteria (see p. 11)
001	IE001	Inishtrahull	Donegal	315	B2, B3, C7
002	—	Malin Head	Donegal	750	C2, C6
003	IE002	Trawbreaga Bay	Donegal	1,100	B1i, B2, C2, C3
004	—	Lough Foyle	Donegal	21,803	A4i, A4iii, B1i, B2, B3, C2, C3, C4
005	IE004	Lough Swilly including Blanket Nook and Inch Lake	Donegal	9,000	A4i, A4iii, B1i, B2, B3, C2, C3, C4, C6
006	IE003	River Foyle: Carrigans and Swilly Burn valleys	Donegal	2,300	B1i, B3, C2, C3
007	—	Fanad Head peninsula	Donegal	8,600	C6
008	IE005	Greer's Island (Massmount), Mulroy Bay	Donegal	19	C7
009	—	Lough Fern	Donegal	185	C7
010	IE006	Horn Head cliffs	Donegal	176	A4iii, B3, C3, C4
011	—	Dunfanaghy New Lake	Donegal	626	C7
012	IE007	Tory Island	Donegal	607	A1, C1, C6
013	IE008	Inishbofin, Inisdooey and Inisbeg	Donegal	604	A1, B1i, C1, C2, C6
014	—	Falcarragh to Min an Chladaigh	Donegal	4,700	A1, C1, C6
015	—	Inishsirrer and Inishmeane	Donegal	140	B1i, B2, C2
016	—	Glenveagh National Park	Donegal	9,593	C7
017	—	Lough Barra bog	Donegal	739	C7

Table 1 ... continued. Summary of Important Bird Areas in the Republic of Ireland.   140 IBAs covering 4,309 km² *

IBA code	1989 code	International/National name	Administrative region	Area (ha)	Criteria (see p.11)
018	IE009, IE010	Inishkeeragh and Illancrone	Donegal	25	B2, C2, C6
019	IE011	Roaninish	Donegal	144	B2, C7
020	IE012	Sheskinmore Lough	Donegal	944	B1i, C7
021	—	Inishkeel	Donegal	126	B1i, C2
022	—	Lough Nillan bog	Donegal	4,168	C7
023	—	Tormore Island	Donegal	30	C7
024	—	West Donegal coast	Donegal	4,050	B2, C6
025	IE013	Rathlin O'Birne	Donegal	154	B1i, B2, C2
026	IE014	Inishduff	Donegal	47	B3
027	IE016	Moors west and north-west of Lough Derg, Brownhall bogs around Loughs Golagh and Dunragh (includes Pettigo Plateau)	Donegal	691	C7
028	—	Lough Derg	Donegal	888	C7
029	IE015	Durnesh Lough	Donegal	365	B1i, B2, B3, C2
030	—	Donegal Bay	Donegal	40,000	A4i, B1i, C2
031	IE017	Inishmurray	North West	260	B1i, B2, B3, C2
032	IE019	Ardboline Island and Horse Island	North West	25	B1i, C2
033	IE018	Drumcliff Bay and Ballintemple	North West	3,000	B1i, B2, C2
034	IE020	Cummeen Strand (Sligo Harbour)	North West	1,865	B1i, B2, C3
035	—	Ballysadare Bay	North West	2,146	B1i, B2, C3, C6
036	IE022	Lough Gara	North West	1,788	B1i, B3, C3
037	IE021	Aughris Head	North West	18	C7
038	IE023	Killala Bay	West, North West	4,294	B1i, B2, C3
039	IE025	Illaunmaistir (Oilean Maistir)	West	165	A4ii, A4iii, B1ii, B2, C2, C4, C6
040	IE026	Stags of Broadhaven	West	136	C6
041	IE028, IE029, IE033	Broadhaven, Blacksod and Tullaghan Bays and parts of the Mullet peninsula	West	10,852	A4i, B1i, B2, B3, C2, C3, C6
042	IE030	Inishglora and Inishkeeragh	West	337	A4ii, A4iii, B1ii, B2, B3, C2, C4, C6
043	IE031	Inishkea Islands	West	592	A4i, B1i, B2, C2
044	IE032	Duvillaun Islands	West	446	B1i, B2, B3, C2
045	IE027	Carrowmore Lake	West	967	B2, C7
046	—	Owenduff river catchment and Nephin Beg	West	25,622	C7
047	IE024	Lough Conn and Lough Cullin (including Moy valley)	West	7,227	B3, C7
048	IE037	Clare Island cliffs	West	800	B2
049	—	Lough Carra	West	1,595	C7
050	IE038	Cross Lough (Killadoon)	West	1	C6
051	—	Lough Mask	West	8,529	C7
052	IE039	Inishbofin and Inishshark (including Davillaun)	West	1,015	B1i, B2, C2
053	IE040	High Island	West	169	B2, B3, C7
054	IE041–IE043, IE045–IE048	Connemara Islands	West	20,000	B1i, B2, C2, C6
055	IE044	Roundstone bog	West	7,000	A4iii, C4, C6
056	IE049	Lough Corrib	West	18,240	A4iii, B1i, C3, C4
057	IE050	Inner Galway Bay	West	11,905	B1i, B2, C3, C6
058	IE051	Rahasane turlough	West	257	B1i, B2, B3, C2, C3
059	—	Lough Rea	West	200	B1i, C3
060	—	Coole Park and Garryland complex	West	389	C7
061	IE052	Aran Islands (parts)	West	4,300	C6
062	IE054	Lough Cutra	West	390	C7
063	IE053	Cliffs of Moher	Mid West	140	A4iii, B2, B3, C4
064	IE055	Ballyallia lake	Mid West	308	B1i, C3
065	IE056, IE057	Mid Clare coast including Mutton and Mattle Islands	Mid West	7,000	A4i, B1i, C2, C3
066	—	Illaunonearaun	Mid West	46	C2
067	—	Loop Head	Mid West	401	A4iii, C4
068	IE058	Shannon and Fergus estuary	Mid West	16,718	A4i, A4iii, B1i, B2, B3, C2, C3, C4
069	IE062, IE059	Tralee Bay and Barrow Harbour	South West	3,290	B1i, B2, C3, C6
070	IE060	Magharee Islands, Mucklaghmore and Illaunbarnagh	South West	370	B2, B3, C6
071	IE061	Lough Gill	South West	157	B2, B3, C7
072	—	Dingle peninsula	Mid West	3,500	A4iii, B2, C4, C6
073	IE064	Blasket Islands	South West	750	A4ii, A4iii, B1ii, B2, B3, C2, C3, C4, C6
074	IE063	Castlemaine Harbour	South West	11,374	A4i, A4iii, B1i, B2, C2, C3, C4
075	IE065	Puffin Island	South West	53	A4ii, A4iii, B1ii, B2, C2, C3, C4, C6
076	IE067	The Skelligs: Great Skellig and Little Skellig	South West	31	A4ii, A4iii, B1ii, B2, C2, C3, C4, C6
077	—	Iveragh peninsula	South West	4,000	B2, C6
078	—	Eirk bog	South West	13	C7
079	—	Killarney National Park	South West	10,329	C7

Table 1 ... continued. Summary of Important Bird Areas in the Republic of Ireland.   140 IBAs covering 4,309 km² *

IBA code	1989 code	International/National name	Administrative region	Area (ha)	Criteria (see p. 11)
080	IE068	Bull and Cow Rocks	South West	336	A4ii, B1ii, B2, B3, C2, C6
081	—	Beara peninsula	South West	3,250	B2, C6
082	—	Sheeps Head and Mizen Head peninsulas	South West	5,500	B2, C6
083	IE071	Inner Clonakilty Bay	South West	588	B1i, B2, C3
084	—	The Gearagh and the Iniscarra reservoir	South West	323	C7
085	—	Kilcolman bog	South West	63	C7
086	—	Old Head of Kinsale	South West	15	C7
087	IE072	Sovereign Islands	South West	2	A4iii, C4
088	IE073	Cork Harbour	South West	5,950	A4iii, B1i, B2, C3, C4, C6
089	IE074	Ballycotton, Ballynamona and Shanagarry	South West	200	B2, C7
090	IE075	Ballymacoda	South West	602	B1i, B2, C3
091	IE076	Blackwater estuary	South East, South West	500	B1i, B2, C3
092	IE077	River Blackwater callows	South East	1,053	B1i, B2, B3, C2, C3
093	—	Helvick Head	South East	78	C7
094	IE078	Dungarvan Harbour	South East	1,300	A4i, B1i, B2, C2, C3
095	IE079	Tramore Backstrand	South East	1,557	B1i, B2, C3, C6
096	IE080	Bannow Bay	South East	958	B1i, B2, C3
097	IE081	Keeragh Islands	South East	22	C7
098	IE082	The Cull/Killag	South East	896	A4i, B1i, B2, C2, C3
099	IE083	Saltee Islands	South East	126	B2, B3, C7
100	IE084	Tacumshin lake	South East	528	B1i, B2, C7
101	IE085	Lady's Island Lake	South East	466	A4i, A4iii, B1i, B2, C2, C4, C6
102	IE086	Wexford Harbour and Slobs	South East	5,000	A4i, A4iii, B1i, B2, B3, C2, C3, C4
103	—	Cahore marshes	South East	450	B1i, B2, C2, C3
104	—	Wicklow Head	East	134	C7
105	IE088	North Wicklow coastal marshes	East	670	B1i, B2, C3, C6
106	IE110	Wicklow Mountains	East	30,000	B2, C6
107	IE110	Poulaphouca reservoir	East	1,949	C7
108	—	Upper Barrow flood-plain	East	1,000	A4i, A4iii, B1i, B2, B3, C2, C4
109	IE090, IE089	Dublin Bay	East	3,000	A4i, A4iii, B1i, B2, C2, C3, C4, C6
110	—	Howth Head	East	102	B2, C7
111	—	Ireland's Eye	East	90	C7
112	IE091	Baldoyle Bay	East	203	B1i, B2, C3
113	IE092	Malahide/Broadmeadow estuary	East	606	A4iii, B1i, B2, C3, C4
114	IE093	Lambay Island	East	612	A4i, A4iii, B1i, B1ii, B3, C2, C3, C4
115	IE095	Rogerstown estuary	East	368	B1i, B2, C3
116	—	Skerries Islands	East	62	B1i, B3, C3
117	IE094	Rockabill	East	1	A4i, B1i, B2, C2, C6
118	—	Nanny estuary and shoreline	East	150	B2
119	IE107	Boyne estuary	East, North East	404	B1i, B2, C3, C6
120	IE106	Stabannan–Braganstown	North East	491	A4iii, B1i, B2, B3, C3, C4
121	IE108	Dundalk Bay	North East	4,920	A4i, A4iii, B1i, B2, C2, C3, C4
122	IE109	Carlingford Lough	North East	4,660	B1i, B2, C3
123	IE105	Lough Oughter	North East	1,464	B1i, B3, C2
124	—	Lough Kinale and Lough Derragh	North East, Midlands	281	B1i, C7
125	IE104	Loughs Kilglass and Forbes, and Ballykenny/Fishertown bogs	Midlands	1,352	C7
126	—	Lough Arrow	Midlands, North West	1,266	C7
127	—	Bellanagare bog	Midlands	1,243	C7
128	—	Lough Ree	Midlands	10,788	C7
129	IE099	River Suck callows: Shannon Bridge–Castlecoote	Midlands, West	4,000	A4i, B1i, B2, B3, C2, C3
130	IE096	Lough Derg	West	11,989	A4iii, B1i, C3, C4
131	IE097	River Shannon callows: Portumna–Athlone	Mid West, Midlands, West	5,788	A1, A4i, A4iii, B1i, B2, B3, C1, C2, C3, C4, C6
132	IE098	River Little Brosna callows: New Bridge–River Shannon	South East, Midlands	1,154	A4i, A4iii, B1i, B2, B3, C2, C3, C4
133	—	All Saints bog	Midlands	326	B1i, C3
134	—	Mongan bog	Midlands	129	C7
135	IE102	Lough Iron–Glen Lough	Midlands	263	B1i, B2, B3, C2, C3
136	—	Garriskil bog	Midlands	324	B1i, C3
137	—	Lough Sheelin	East, North East, Midlands	1,885	C7
138	IE103	Lough Derravaragh	Midlands	1,120	B1i, B3, C3
139	IE101	Lough Owel	Midlands	1,032	B1i, C3
140	IE100	Lough Ennell	Midlands	1,404	B1i, C3

* This figure includes the total area of two cross-border IBAs (sites 004 and 122), thus including (very approximately) c.120 km² of United Kingdom territory.

Sites identified in the previous inventory of IBAs in Europe (Grimmett and Jones 1989) but no longer considered to be IBAs
IE034 Moynish Beg; IE035 Inishraher Islet; IE036 Dorinish Bar; IE066 Moylaun Island; IE069 Whiddy Island; IE070 Roaringwater Bay Islands; IE087 Thurles Sugar Factory Lagoons.

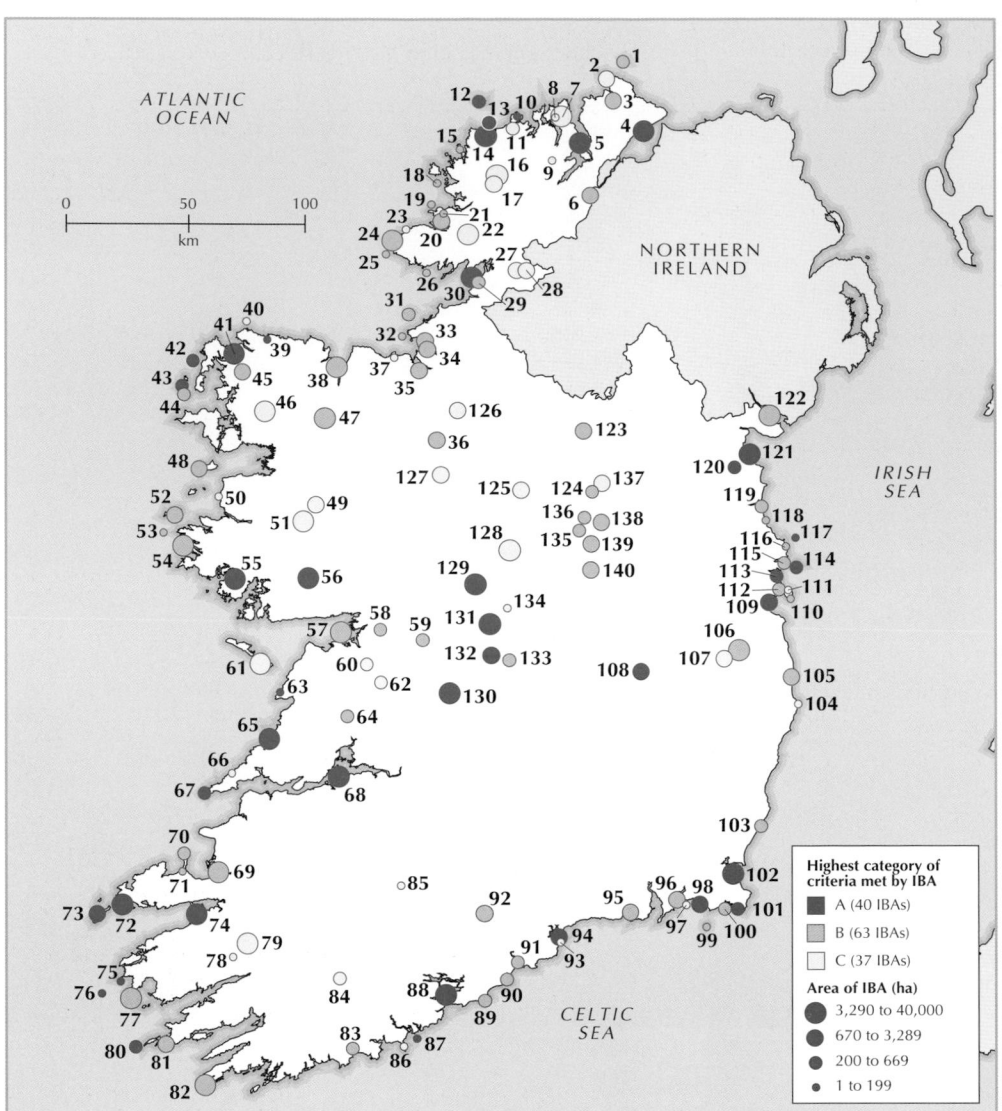

Map 1. Location, area and criteria category of Important Bird Areas in the Republic of Ireland.

Highest category of criteria met by IBA

- A (40 IBAs)
- B (63 IBAs)
- C (37 IBAs)

Area of IBA (ha)

- 3,290 to 40,000
- 670 to 3,289
- 200 to 669
- 1 to 199

ATLANTIC OCEAN

NORTHERN IRELAND

IRISH SEA

CELTIC SEA

(up to 1,000 m above sea-level). Lakes and inland loughs are plentiful, covering c.6% of the land area and predominating at c.20% of the IBAs. There are numerous peatlands in the country, with raised bogs in the midlands and blanket bogs in the uplands, especially in the west, and c.10% of the IBAs are predominantly bogland.

ORNITHOLOGICAL IMPORTANCE

Map 1 shows that 40 of the 140 IBAs are of global importance (qualifying under 'A' criteria) and 63 are of European importance ('B' criteria being the highest met). The remaining 37 IBAs qualify under EU criteria ('C') only.

The 48 newly identified IBAs comprise upland areas (seven are mainly blanket bog, four raised bog), coastal sites (six are mainly coastal islands, ten cliffs), wetlands identified by the Irish Wetland Bird Survey (four estuaries, 11 lakes, one coastal lake, two wet-grassland sites) and sites important for species of global conservation concern (three agricultural grasslands). Of these new sites, 24 meet IBA criteria for particular bird species (three for *Crex crex*, five for *Pyrrhocorax pyrrhocorax*, four for *Anser albifrons flavirostris*, three for *Branta bernicla hrota*, four for *Branta leucopsis* and the remainder for other waterfowl). The other 24 new sites are designated or soon-to-be-designated as Special Protection Areas (SPAs) under the EC Birds Directive (thus meeting C7 criteria).

There are 67 species of European conservation concern (SPEC) which breed regularly in Ireland (Tucker and Heath 1994). Of these, the only species of global conservation concern is *Crex crex*. A further 33 of these 67 breeding species have an unfavourable conservation status in Europe, including a number of seabirds for which Ireland holds important breeding congregations.

Eight IBAs have been selected to cover the most important breeding sites for *Crex crex*. Four of the sites are globally important, meeting the A1 criterion (Table 2), of which River Shannon callows (site 131) holds the largest number of breeding birds in the country, while the other four sites are important in the EU context (meeting C criteria).

On a European and global level, Ireland is particularly important for breeding seabirds and has 13 such SPECs, nine of which have an unfavourable conservation status in Europe (Tucker and Heath 1994). Of Ireland's 84 coastal IBAs, 34 are of international importance for breeding seabirds. Nine IBAs hold (individually) at least 1% of the global breeding population of a seabird species (meeting the A4i/ii criteria), for the following five species: *Puffinus puffinus*, *Hydrobates pelagicus*, *Sula bassana*, *Phalacrocorax aristotelis* and *Sterna dougallii* (Table 3). A further three IBAs support 1% or more of a distinct breeding population of a seabird species (thus meeting the B1i/ii criteria), for four species: *Puffinus puffinus*, *Sterna sandvicensis*, *Uria aalge* and *Fratercula arctica* (Table 3). The Blasket Islands (site 073) and The Skelligs (site 076) are of particular note, supporting a wide diversity of breeding seabirds in numbers of international importance.

A total of 71 IBAs support particular species of wintering wildfowl or waders in numbers that are important at the global or European level—in total, 24 such species meet such criteria (A4i, B1i, B2, B3). Of these species and sites, Table 3 lists those species that meet the A4i/B1i criteria (at 66 out of the 71 sites). Regarding those species/sites meeting B2/B3 criteria outside the breeding season, eight SPECs overwinter at Irish IBAs in numbers of international importance (out of the total of 14 'winter SPECs' identified in Europe by Tucker and Heath [1994]): *Cygnus columbianus*, *Cygnus cygnus*, *Branta leucopsis*, *Aythya marila*, *Calidris canutus*, *Calidris alpina*, *Limosa lapponica* and *Numenius arquata*. Thirty-six coastal IBAs are important for wintering waterfowl (31 estuaries, four coastal lakes and one coastal shore), along with peatlands, river wetlands and lakes.

'Wetlands of international importance' in the sense of the Ramsar Convention, i.e. those regularly holding 20,000 or more wintering waterfowl, include Lough Swilly (site 005), Cork Harbour (site 088), Wexford Harbour and Slobs (site 102), Dublin Bay (site 109) and Dundalk Bay (site 121). The River Shannon catchment, when taken as a whole (including sites 068, 129, 131 and 132), is the most important site for wintering waterfowl in Ireland, with particularly high numbers of *Cygnus cygnus*, *Anser albifrons flavirostris*, *Pluvialis apricaria* and *Limosa limosa*. Although *Anser albifrons* is not a species of European conservation concern, the subspecies *A. a. flavirostris* (which breeds in Greenland) is listed on Annex I of the EC Birds Directive and there are especially important sites for the subspecies at sites 102 (where over a third of the Irish population winter), 005 and 132. The traditional habitat for this species is bog and this is

Table 2. Important Bird Areas in the Republic of Ireland that are important for species of global conservation concern (meeting criterion A1).

Species	IBA code
Crex crex Corncrake	012, 013, 014, 131

Table 3. Important Bird Areas in the Republic of Ireland that support important numbers of one or more congregatory species (i.e. meeting criteria A4 and/or B1). IBAs meeting both criteria A4 and B1 for the species are shown in **bold**. IBAs meeting only criterion B1 for the species concerned, and not A4, are shown in normal type. For key to 'Season', see p. 7.

Species	Season	IBA code
Gavia immer Great Northern Diver	W	**030, 041**
Puffinus puffinus Manx Shearwater	B	**073, 075, 076**, 114
Hydrobates pelagicus Storm Petrel	B	**039, 042, 073, 075, 076, 080**
Sula bassana Gannet	B	**076**
Phalacrocorax aristotelis Shag	B	**114**
Cygnus olor Mute Swan	R	113, 124
	W	029, 101, 140
	N	100, 101
Cygnus columbianus Bewick's Swan	W	**004, 098, 108, 129, 132**
Cygnus cygnus Whooper Swan	W	**004**, 005, 006, 029, 058, 068, 092, 123, **131**, 132, 135
	P	005
Anser albifrons White-fronted Goose	W	004, 005, 006, 036, 102, 103, 129, 132, 133, 135, 136, 138, 139, 140
Anser anser Greylag Goose	W	005, 120, 121
Branta leucopsis Barnacle Goose	W	003, 013, 015, 021, 025, 031, 032, 033, 041, **043**, 044, 052, 054, 065
Branta bernicla Brent Goose	W	003, **004**, 034, 035, 038, 041, 057, 068, 069, 074, 094, 095, 096, 098, 102, 105, 109, 112, 113, 115, 116, 119, 121, 122
Anas penelope Wigeon	W	004, 132
Anas crecca Teal	W	064, 132
Anas clypeata Shoveler	W	059, 064
Aythya ferina Pochard	W	056, 138
Mergus serrator Red-breasted Merganser	W	057
Fulica atra Coot	P	056
Pluvialis apricaria Golden Plover	W	068, 103, 131
Pluvialis squatarola Grey Plover	W	**102**
Calidris canutus Knot	W	109, 115, **121**
Calidris alpina Dunlin	W	068, 088
Limosa limosa Black-tailed Godwit	W	058, 068, 083, 088, 090, 091, 092, 098, **102**, 130, 131, **132**
Limosa lapponica Bar-tailed Godwit	W	**004, 074, 094**, 102, **109, 121**
Numenius phaeopus Whimbrel	P	**131**
Tringa totanus Redshank	W	005, **068**, 088, 109, 121
Arenaria interpres Turnstone	W	**065**
Sterna sandvicensis Sandwich Tern	B	101
Sterna dougallii Roseate Tern	B	**101**, 117
	P	109
Uria aalge Guillemot	B	114
Fratercula arctica Puffin	B	075

Table 4. Species of European conservation concern and species listed on Annex I of the EC Birds Directive with significant breeding populations at IBAs in the Republic of Ireland (meeting any IBA criteria).

Species [1]	Minimum national breeding population (pairs) [2]	Proportion (%) of national population breeding at all IBAs in the Republic of Ireland
Puffinus puffinus Manx Shearwater	30,000	58
Hydrobates pelagicus Storm Petrel	50,000	100 [3]
Oceanodroma leucorhoa Leach's Petrel	200	100
Sula bassana Gannet	25,000	100 [3]
Phalacrocorax aristotelis Shag	8,300	36
Falco columbarius Merlin	200	12
Falco peregrinus Peregrine	350	7
Crex crex Corncrake	183	80
Pluvialis apricaria Golden Plover	300	7
Tringa totanus Redshank	4,000	10
Phalaropus lobatus Red-necked Phalarope	3	67
Larus canus Common Gull	3,000	14
Larus fuscus Lesser Black-backed Gull	3,200	36
Larus marinus Great Black-backed Gull	3,100	36
Sterna sandvicensis Sandwich Tern	1,800	100 [3]
Sterna dougallii Roseate Tern	454	100 [3]
Sterna hirundo Common Tern	1,700	83
Sterna paradisaea Arctic Tern	2,100	91
Sterna albifrons Little Tern	174	86
Alca torda Razorbill	11,000	100 [3]
Cepphus grylle Black Guillemot	1,200	12
Fratercula arctica Puffin	8,000	100 [3]
Pyrrhocorax pyrrhocorax Chough	219	100 [3]

1. Only those species of European conservation concern (see Box 1, p. 12) that meet IBA criteria in the Republic of Ireland are listed, together with those species listed on Annex I of the EC Birds Directive that fulfil criterion C6 in IBAs in the Republic of Ireland.
2. Data are taken from the BirdLife/EBCC European Bird Database 1998 (Heath and Borggreve 2000).
3. The percentage of the national population in IBAs exceeds 100%. Usually this is because the national population estimate has not been updated recently whilst the IBA population estimate has been recently updated with new data as a result of comprehensive surveys of IBAs themselves. Also, the individual site count for a species may be the maximum or average over recent years, and summing these may record more birds than are present nationally in any single year.

still used by some flocks in Ireland. Ireland also supports, almost exclusively, the wintering population of *Branta bernicla hrota*, which breeds in the central Canadian Arctic.

A total of 50 IBAs are important for breeding SPECs, meeting B2/B3 criteria (Table 4). The IBA network does not adequately cover a number of dispersed, scarce and data-deficient breeding species, in particular *Pluvialis apricaria* and several species of raptor (Table 4), as well as *Gavia stellata* and *Melanitta nigra*.

HABITATS

Ireland is dominated by agricultural habitat, which comprises 68% of the land area, and this is predominantly pasture with arable crops in the more productive areas of the south and east. Peatlands are widespread, as both blanket and raised bogs, although their area

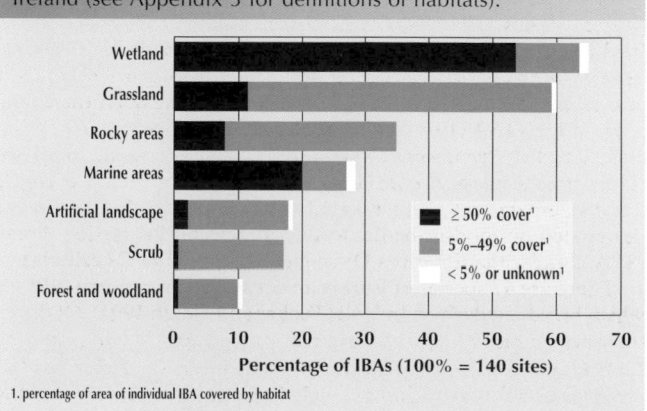

Figure 1. Habitats at Important Bird Areas in the Republic of Ireland (see Appendix 3 for definitions of habitats).

1. percentage of area of individual IBA covered by habitat

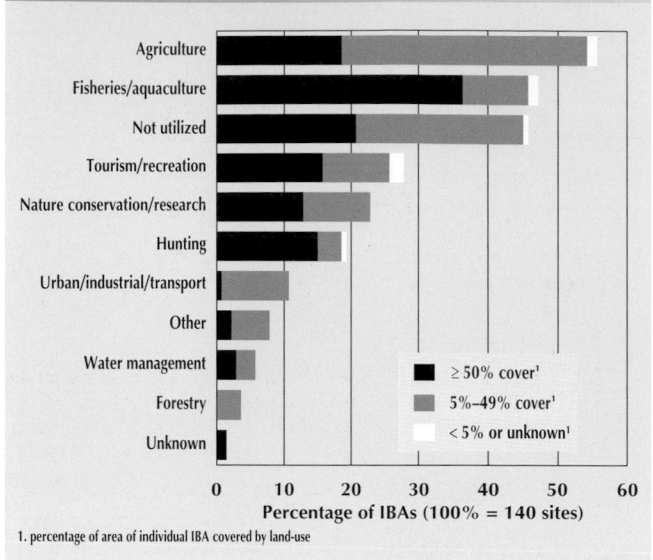

Figure 2. Land-uses at Important Bird Areas in the Republic of Ireland (see Appendix 3 for definitions of land-uses).

Percentage of IBAs (100% = 140 sites)

■ ≥ 50% cover[1]
■ 5%–49% cover[1]
□ < 5% or unknown[1]

1. percentage of area of individual IBA covered by land-use

has been substantially reduced by peat extraction and afforestation. The area of wooded land is small, with plantations (mainly of non-native conifers) occupying 5% of the country and native deciduous woodland less than 1% (EPA 1996).

Wetlands occupy 14% of Ireland and open water 3% (EPA 1996). Wetlands are the dominant habitat-type (by area) at 75 of the 140 IBAs and cover a significant area at a further 14 IBAs (Figure 1). This includes estuaries, coastal lagoons, rivers, lakes and bogs and reflects the importance of Ireland for wintering waterbirds. Twenty-seven IBAs include inland lakes, while nine peatland IBAs contain large tracts of blanket bog and five are mainly raised bogs. Together, the peatland IBAs cover c.20% of the total IBA area. They are important for breeding waders such as *Pluvialis apricaria* and for wintering *Anser albifrons flavirostris*.

Islands and coastal cliffs account for most of the 'rocky areas' found at 49 of the 140 IBAs (Figure 1). Marine habitats are often associated with these sites and dominate (by area) at 28 IBAs, while covering a significant proportion at a further ten. These coastal and marine IBAs reflect Ireland's importance for breeding seabirds.

Grassland is the dominant habitat at 16 of the IBAs. Two major types of grassland can be identified, wet grassland and agricultural grassland. Extensive wet grasslands occur at Wexford Slobs (site 102) and the callows of the rivers Shannon and Little Brosna (sites 129, 131 and 132). As well as their significance for wintering wildfowl, some of these grasslands are important for breeding *Crex*

crex, *Vanellus vanellus* and *Tringa totanus*. Agricultural grasslands are important for *Crex crex* and *Pyrrhocorax pyrrhocorax*.

Native deciduous woodland covers less than 1% of the country and is correspondingly scarce at IBAs, being mostly confined to National Parks (e.g. sites 079 and 106). Other forested habitat is dominated by non-native conifer plantations.

IMPACTS ON IBAs – LAND-USE AND THREATS

Figure 2 shows the land-uses recorded at IBAs in Ireland. The most widespread land-use at IBAs is agriculture, predominantly livestock farming, which occurs at 78 of the 140 IBAs and is the dominant land-use (by area) at 26 sites (Figure 2). Correspondingly, the most widespread threat to IBAs is agricultural intensification. This threat is considered to have a high impact at 11 IBAs, primarily sites where the maintenance of non-intensive farming practices are crucial for the persistence of breeding *Crex crex* (sites 002, 007, 012–014, 041 and 131), sites which have suffered severe overgrazing such as at Owenduff–Nephin Beg (site 046) and water-bodies threatened by nutrient pollution as a result of agricultural run-off (e.g. sites 123 and 138). At a further 57 IBAs, the threat is considered to have a low to medium impact and mainly relates to nutrient pollution of estuarine and lake sites, overgrazing of bogs, and drainage of wetlands.

Fisheries and/or aquaculture are the second most frequent economic activity at IBAs, recorded at 66 IBAs and the main activity at 51 IBAs (Figure 2). Fishery activities, including intertidal shellfish cultivation, are considered to be a potential economic use for marine and estuarine habitats, but may not yet occur at all suitable sites. Intertidal shellfish cultivation is a serious threat at a number of IBAs, including Trawbreaga Bay (site 003), Drumcliff Bay (site 033) and Dungarvan Harbour (site 094). It potentially causes a loss of mudflat habitat and also disturbance to wintering waterbirds.

Recreation/tourism activities and developments pose a threat at 63 IBAs, although they usually have a medium or low impact. In coastal IBAs, such developments include caravan sites (site 069), marinas (site 131) and golf courses (sites 038 and 086), while at inland lakes, problems are posed at some sites by boating, angling and holiday-home developments (e.g. site 130).

The other main land-uses within IBAs are tourism/recreation and nature conservation/research, which occur at 39 and 32 IBAs respectively and dominate by area at 22 and 18 IBAs. Hunting is allowed for certain bird species during the open season and occurs within at least 27 IBAs—at 21 IBAs, the majority of the site is open to this activity. Industrial activities occur within 15 sites, though cover most of the area at only one IBA (site 109). Forestry and water management are marginal land-uses within Ireland's IBAs.

Significant disturbance to birds' essential activities, e.g. nesting and feeding, occurs at a minimum of 44 IBAs, mainly due to visitor pressure and hunting activities. Visitor pressure is particularly

Figure 3. Threats at Important Bird Areas in the Republic of Ireland (see Appendix 3 for definitions of threat types and impact categories).

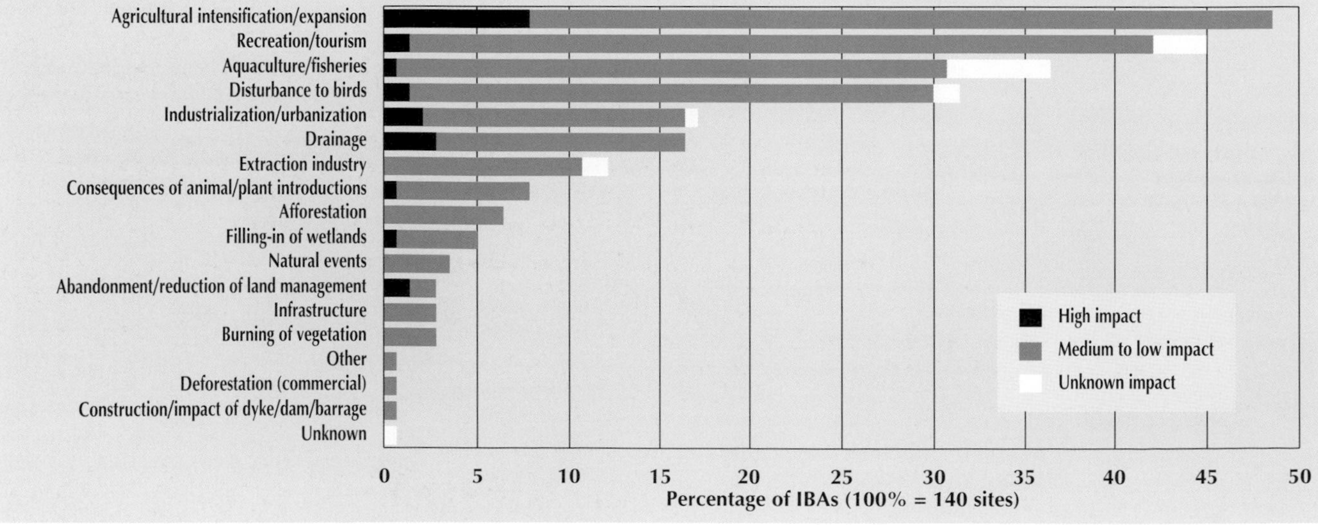

■ High impact
■ Medium to low impact
□ Unknown impact

Percentage of IBAs (100% = 140 sites)

threatening to sites which are important for ground-nesting seabirds or nesting waders. Hunting can lead to widespread disturbance within IBAs, particularly of wintering waterfowl, and it is generally considered to be of medium impact.

Drainage and industrialization/urbanization both threaten over 15% of IBAs. Within Ireland, large-scale drainage programmes were carried out in the 1960s and 1970s, causing significant destruction to bog and wetland habitats (EPA 1996). While such drainage programmes are not as extensive at present, local drainage schemes, often linked to agricultural intensification, still threaten IBAs, such as at sites 058, 089 and 102. Bogs, such as sites 085 and 127, are also threatened. Industrialization and urbanization have a particularly high impact at Cork Harbour (site 088), due to recent, extensive road development and land-claim projects. A number of other, mainly estuarine, sites are also threatened by this activity, with a medium or low impact.

From Figure 3 it can be seen that infrastructure is one of the least frequent threats at IBAs. However, individual projects can have a marked effect on specific IBAs, such as road developments within Cork Harbour (site 088), Malahide/Swords (site 113) and planned road development within Dublin Bay (site 109), while port development threatens the Boyne estuary (site 119). The filling-in of wetlands is another serious threat, often linked to infrastructural or urban development, which is causing irreversible damage to wetlands such as Rogerstown estuary (site 115).

The alteration of habitat structure at IBAs by introduced (non-native) plant species, e.g. cord-grass *Spartina* on mudflats in estuaries and *Rhododendron* shrubs in native woodlands, poses a threat at 11 IBAs. Other important threats, which affect an approximately similar number of sites, are extraction industries and the abandonment of land. Land abandonment is an important threat at IBAs where breeding *Crex crex* are present (e.g. site 013), since suitable habitat may be lost if agricultural land is not managed appropriately. This threat is also linked to agricultural intensification, since specifically non-intensive farming practices are required to maintain suitable habitat.

PROTECTION STATUS

The National Parks and Wildlife section of Dúchas, The Heritage Service, is the principal state agency involved in nature conservation. It is responsible for the implementation of the Wildlife Act (1976), the Conservation of Wild Birds Regulations (S.I. 291 of 1985) which implements the EC Birds Directive and the European Communities (Natural Habitats) Regulations (S.I. 94 of 1997) which implements the EC Habitats Directive. Table 5 shows the overlap between IBAs and areas that are protected by national and international law.

■ National protection
The national protected-area system for nature conservation is as follows.

1. Statutory Nature Reserve
Nature Reserves are designated and protected from damaging activities under the 1976 Wildlife Act. They are regarded as the most rigorous system in Ireland for the protection of ecosystems and species of flora and fauna. State ownership is not necessary.

2. National Park
These sites are owned and managed by Dúchas, The Heritage Service for nature conservation, public use and appreciation. Except for Killarney National Park, they have no legal protection. However, damaging activities are prevented as a result of state ownership and through management agreements where turbary or grazing rights exist.

3. Refuge for Fauna
These are designated under the 1976 Wildlife Act for the protection of one or more species, where they require special measures to protect their habitat. This designation has, so far, only been used to protect inaccessible sites where development threats are unlikely. State ownership is not necessary.

4. Wildfowl Sanctuary
These are designated under the 1976 Wildlife Act to protect certain ducks, geese and waders from hunting. Land within them can only be protected by other measures. State ownership is not necessary.

Natural Heritage Areas are a proposed designation for sites of national importance for nature conservation. There are no legal powers to prevent damaging activities within these sites, but the 1999 Wildlife (Amendment) Bill has now been published and, with its enactment, this situation should change. At present, the proposal of a site for designation may already affect grant aid and planning permissions. Natural Heritage Areas will provide a national framework for the protection of natural habitats within Ireland.

Out of the 140 IBAs identified, 20 are protected by national legislation as a result of overlapping with Nature Reserves, while

Table 5. Protection status of Important Bird Areas in the Republic of Ireland. A tick (✔) indicates that an IBA overlaps with a protected area (to any extent).

IBA code	International name	Statutory Nature Reserve	National Park	Refuge for Fauna	Wildfowl Sanctuary	Ramsar Site	Biosphere Reserve	Special Protection Area	Biogenetic Reserve
			National				International		
001	Inishtrahull							✔	
002	Malin Head								
003	Trawbreaga Bay				✔	✔		✔	
004	Lough Foyle							✔	
005	Lough Swilly including Blanket Nook and Inch Lake				✔	✔		✔	
006	River Foyle: Carrigans and Swilly Burn valleys								
007	Fanad Head peninsula								
008	Greer's Island (Massmount), Mulroy Bay							✔	
009	Lough Fern				✔			✔	
010	Horn Head cliffs			✔				✔	
011	Dunfanaghy New Lake							✔	
012	Tory Island							✔	
013	Inishbofin, Inisdooey and Inisbeg							✔	
014	Falcarragh to Min an Chladaigh								
015	Inishsirrer and Inishmeane								
016	Glenveagh National Park		✔					✔	
Subtotal of IBAs		**0**	**1**	**1**	**3**	**2**	**0**	**11**	**0**

IBA code	International name	Statutory Nature Reserve	National Park	Refuge for Fauna	Wildfowl Sanctuary	Ramsar Site	Biosphere Reserve	Special Protection Area	Biogenetic Reserve
			National				International		
017	Lough Barra bog	✔					✔	✔	
018	Inishkeeragh and Illancrone								
019	Roaninish								
020	Sheskinmore Lough				✔			✔	
021	Inishkeel								
022	Lough Nillan bog							✔	
023	Tormore Island								
024	West Donegal coast								
025	Rathlin O'Birne								
026	Inishduff								
027	Moors west and north-west of Lough Derg, Brownhall bogs around Loughs Golagh and Dunragh (includes Pettigo Plateau)	✔					✔	✔	
028	Lough Derg				✔			✔	
029	Durnesh Lough								
030	Donegal Bay								
031	Inishmurray							✔	
032	Ardboline Island and Horse Island								
Subtotal of IBAs		**2**	**1**	**1**	**5**	**4**	**0**	**17**	**0**

Table 5 ... continued. Protection status of Important Bird Areas in the Republic of Ireland. A tick (✔) indicates that an IBA overlaps with a protected area (to any extent).

IBA code	International name	Statutory Nature Reserve	National Park	Refuge for Fauna	Wildfowl Sanctuary	Ramsar Site	Biosphere Reserve	Special Protection Area	Biogenetic Reserve
033	Drumcliff Bay and Ballintemple	✔						✔	
034	Cummeen Strand (Sligo Harbour)					✔		✔	
035	Ballysadare Bay								
036	Lough Gara				✔	✔		✔	
037	Aughris Head								
038	Killala Bay					✔		✔	
039	Illaunmaistir (Oilean Maistir)							✔	
040	Stags of Broadhaven							✔	
041	Broadhaven, Blacksod and Tullaghan Bays and parts of the Mullet peninsula					✔		✔	
042	Inishglora and Inishkeeragh							✔	
043	Inishkea Islands				✔			✔	
044	Duvillaun Islands							✔	
045	Carrowmore Lake				✔			✔	
046	Owenduff river catchment and Nephin Beg					✔		✔	
047	Lough Conn and Lough Cullin (including Moy valley)				✔			✔	
048	Clare Island cliffs								
049	Lough Carra				✔			✔	
050	Cross Lough (Killadoon)								
051	Lough Mask				✔			✔	
052	Inishbofin and Inishshark (including Davillaun)								
053	High Island							✔	
054	Connemara Islands								
055	Roundstone bog							✔	
056	Lough Corrib					✔		✔	
057	Inner Galway Bay					✔		✔	
058	Rahasane turlough							✔	
059	Lough Rea								
060	Coole Park and Garryland complex	✔			✔	✔		✔	✔
061	Aran Island (parts)								
062	Lough Cutra							✔	
063	Cliffs of Moher			✔				✔	
064	Ballyallia lake				✔	✔		✔	
065	Mid Clare coast including Mutton and Mattle Islands				✔			✔	
066	Illaunonearaun								
067	Loop Head								
068	Shannon and Fergus estuary							✔	
069	Tralee Bay and Barrow Harbour	✔				✔		✔	
070	Magharee Islands, Mucklaghmore and Illaunbarnagh								
071	Lough Gill				✔			✔	
072	Dingle peninsula								
073	Blasket Islands	✔						✔	
074	Castlemaine Harbour	✔			✔	✔		✔	
075	Puffin Island	✔						✔	
076	The Skelligs: Great Skellig and Little Skellig	✔						✔	
077	Iveragh peninsula								
078	Eirk bog	✔						✔	
079	Killarney National Park		✔				✔	✔	
080	Bull and Cow Rocks			✔					
081	Beara peninsula								
082	Sheeps Head and Mizen Head peninsulas								
083	Inner Clonakilty Bay								
084	The Gearagh and the Iniscarra reservoir	✔			✔	✔		✔	✔
085	Kilcolman bog	✔			✔			✔	
Subtotal of IBAs		**12**	**2**	**3**	**18**	**16**	**1**	**52**	**2**
086	Old Head of Kinsale			✔				✔	
087	Sovereign Islands								
088	Cork Harbour				✔	✔		✔	
089	Ballycotton, Ballynamona and Shanagarry				✔	✔		✔	
090	Ballymacoda					✔		✔	
091	Blackwater estuary					✔		✔	
092	River Blackwater callows				✔			✔	
093	Helvick Head								
094	Dungarvan Harbour					✔		✔	
095	Tramore Backstrand					✔		✔	
096	Bannow Bay				✔	✔		✔	
097	Keeragh Islands								
098	The Cull/Killag	✔						✔	
099	Saltee Islands	✔						✔	
100	Tacumshin lake				✔			✔	
101	Lady's Island Lake			✔				✔	
102	Wexford Harbour and Slobs	✔			✔	✔		✔	
103	Cahore marshes								
104	Wicklow Head								
105	North Wicklow coastal marshes				✔			✔	
106	Wicklow Mountains	✔	✔					✔	
107	Poulaphouca reservoir							✔	
108	Upper Barrow flood-plain								
109	Dublin Bay	✔			✔	✔	✔	✔	
110	Howth Head								
111	Ireland's Eye								
112	Baldoyle Bay	✔				✔		✔	
113	Malahide/Broadmeadow estuary					✔		✔	
114	Lambay Island							✔	
115	Rogerstown estuary	✔			✔	✔		✔	
116	Skerries Islands								
117	Rockabill			✔				✔	
118	Nanny estuary and shoreline								
119	Boyne estuary				✔			✔	
120	Stabannan–Braganstown							✔	
121	Dundalk Bay				✔	✔		✔	
122	Carlingford Lough							✔	
123	Lough Oughter				✔	✔		✔	
124	Lough Kinale and Lough Derragh							✔	
125	Loughs Kilglass and Forbes, and Ballykenny/Fishertown bogs							✔	
126	Lough Arrow							✔	
127	Bellanagare bog							✔	
128	Lough Ree							✔	
129	River Suck callows: Shannon Bridge–Castlecoote	✔						✔	
130	Lough Derg							✔	
131	River Shannon callows: Portumna–Athlone							✔	
132	River Little Brosna callows: New Bridge–River Shannon							✔	
133	All Saints bog							✔	
134	Mongan bog				✔	✔		✔	✔
135	Lough Iron–Glen Lough				✔	✔		✔	
136	Garriskil bog					✔		✔	
137	Lough Sheelin							✔	
138	Lough Derravaragh					✔		✔	
139	Lough Owel					✔		✔	
140	Lough Ennell					✔		✔	
Total number of IBAs		**20**	**3**	**6**	**31**	**36**	**2**	**97**	**3**

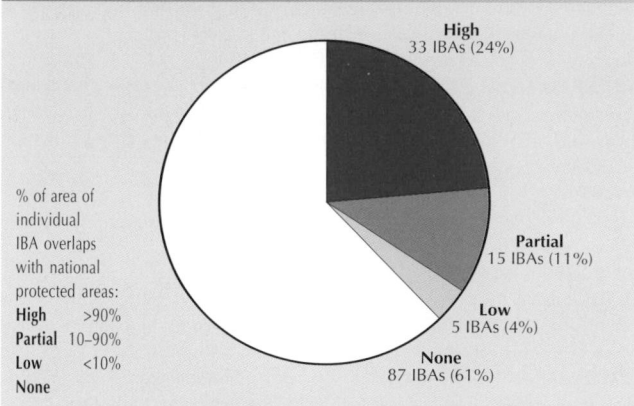

Figure 4. The national protection status of Important Bird Areas in the Republic of Ireland.

High
33 IBAs (24%)

% of area of individual IBA overlaps with national protected areas:
High >90%
Partial 10–90%
Low <10%
None

Partial
15 IBAs (11%)

Low
5 IBAs (4%)

None
87 IBAs (61%)

Total area of overlap between IBA network in the Republic of Ireland and national protected-area system (see Table 5 for categories) = 518–554 km² (12–13% of total IBA area).

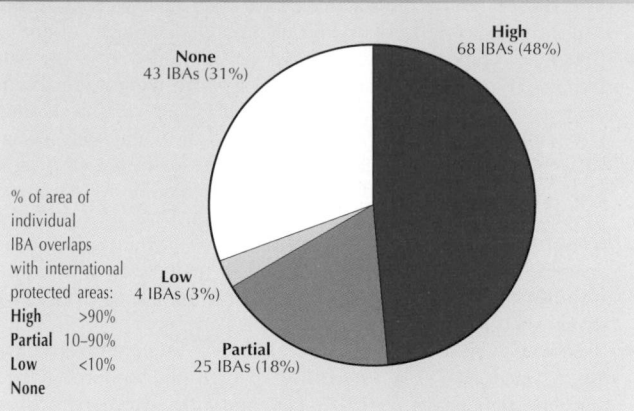

Figure 5. The international protection status of Important Bird Areas in the Republic of Ireland.

High
68 IBAs (48%)

None
43 IBAs (31%)

% of area of individual IBA overlaps with international protected areas:
High >90%
Partial 10–90%
Low <10%
None

Low
4 IBAs (3%)

Partial
25 IBAs (18%)

Total area of overlap between IBA network in the Republic of Ireland and international protected-area system (see Table 5 for categories) = 2,301–2,335 km² (55% of total IBA area).

<table>
<tr><td>Box 1. International legislation and initiatives that are relevant to site conservation in the Republic of Ireland (see Appendix 1 for a general description of these agreements).</td><td>Global
Biodiversity Convention ✔
Ramsar Convention ✔
Bonn Convention ✔
World Heritage Convention ✔
MAB Programme ✔

Pan-European
Bern Convention ✔

Regional
EC Birds Directive ✔
EC Habitats Directive ✔

✔ Convention ratified/initiative supported
(✔) Convention signed</td></tr>
</table>

three overlap with National Parks, 31 with Wildfowl Sanctuaries and six with Refuges for Fauna (Table 5). The National Parks cover 39,722 ha of the total IBA area (9%). About 25% of the IBAs overlap to a high degree with protected areas, but about 60% do not overlap at all (Figure 4).

■ International protection

The Irish Government has ratified all of the international conventions and initiatives relevant to site-based conservation of nature (Box 1). Thirty-six IBAs overlap with Ramsar Sites, of which all are Special Protection Areas (SPAs) and of which 10 are also Nature Reserves (Table 5). Out of the 140 IBAs identified, 97 are protected by overlap with SPAs. A further 20 IBAs are protected by proposed SPAs. The remaining 23 IBAs do not overlap with proposed or designated SPAs and are mainly new sites identified during the current IBA review.

Of the 97 IBAs which overlap with SPAs, about two-thirds overlap to a high degree, and these latter sites include 16 offshore island IBAs, 15 IBAs which meet the C7 criterion as SPAs and two IBAs which are National Parks. Designation of the whole IBA area as an SPA has not been problematic for the island sites since they are mainly uninhabited and state-owned. The National Parks are also state-owned, and the C7 sites qualify as IBAs primarily because of their SPA status and so match the SPA area.

The remaining one-third of the 97 IBAs do not overlap to such a high extent with SPAs (see Figure 5). At a number of these IBAs, a significant and integral part of the IBA lies outside the designated boundary of the SPA, e.g. at Dublin Bay (site 109) and Cork Harbour (site 088). Within other IBAs, only the state-owned foreshore has been designated as an SPA, leaving important parts unprotected (Magee and Coveney 1995). Where this has happened, the SPA boundary needs to be increased to include all parts of the IBA. Proposed SPAs should be designated at the 20 IBAs with which they overlap, and the remaining 23 IBAs without any SPA protection should be considered for SPA designation. Proposed candidate Special Areas for Conservation overlap with 52 IBAs. The exact areas and boundaries of these sites are unknown as they have yet to be designated.

CONSERVATION

- BirdWatch Ireland has 14 reserves, which are contained within IBAs (Kilcolman Bog, Cuskinny Marsh, Lough Beg, Sheskinmore Lough, Rogerstown Estuary, Little Skellig, Puffin Island, Termoncarragh Lake, Annagh Marsh, Illaunmaistir, Bullock Island, Bishops Island, Wexford Wildfowl Reserve and Kilcoole Reserve). BirdWatch Ireland is preparing management plans for a number of its reserves which lie within IBAs. These reserves have been acquired for the protection of habitats important for birds and cover a total area of 409 ha, c.1% of the total IBA area.

- Research and conservation projects for *Crex crex* and terns *Sterna* are ongoing. The Corncrake Conservation Project operates in the Shannon callows (site 131), north Donegal and north-west Mayo. It promotes non-intensive farming practices for the conservation of breeding habitat for *Crex crex*, and an annual census of population numbers and distribution is undertaken. Tern conservation projects operate on Rockabill island (site 117), Lady's Island Lake (site 101) and at Kilcoole marshes (site 105). These projects aim to protect breeding sites through habitat management and to continue research on population demography. Annual data on population numbers is collected. The INTERREG Programme of the EU funds research and monitoring of the colonies of *Sterna dougallii* at Rockabill island and Lady's Island Lake.

- The Irish Wetland Bird Survey (I-WeBS) monitors the numbers and distribution of waterfowl in the Republic of Ireland during the non-breeding season. All wintering sites are monitored for *Anser albifrons flavirostris*, *Anser anser*, *Branta bernicla hrota* and *Branta leucopsis*. The Countryside Bird Survey (CBS) monitors the numbers and distribution of common countryside birds during the breeding season. The former survey has been in operation since 1994 and the latter since 1998. These surveys aim to provide an indication of species' population trends at wintering sites and in the wider countryside.

- Annual monitoring of seabird colonies is carried out at key breeding colonies (e.g. sites 076 and 099). The last seabird population census for the Republic of Ireland occurred in 1987. Seabird 2000, a joint project between the Republic and the United Kingdom, will census Ireland's coastal areas, including islands and inland breeding sites, to provide data on breeding seabird numbers and distribution. This project will start in 1999 and continue until 2001. A census of *Cepphus grylle*, on the east coast of Ireland, was completed in 1998.

- Conservation plans for SPAs and SACs are being prepared by Dúchas, The Heritage Service. These areas overlap with IBAs and the plans should provide specific objectives to maintain the conservation importance of each site. The Rural Environment Protection Scheme—Ireland's implementation of the EU's agri-environment regulations—should ensure that environmentally sensitive farming takes place within IBAs with agricultural land-uses.

ANALYTICAL METHODS

- This IBA review was completed in 1997 using available literature and through consultation with Dúchas, The Heritage Service.
- Breeding numbers of terns *Sterna* were obtained from the All-Ireland Tern Survey completed in 1995 and from more recent counts at specific sites (e.g. sites 101 and 117). Waterfowl counts were obtained from the 1995/96 I-WeBS Report and from special surveys of particular species (e.g. *Branta bernicla* and *Branta leucopsis*). The 1992 survey of *Pyrrhocorax pyrrhocorax* was used to identify sites important for this species. Data on *Crex crex* from 1995 and 1996 were used to identify important sites for the species. No new breeding seabird data were available, so population figures from the previous pan-European IBA inventory (Grimmett and Jones 1989) were used.
- To obtain habitat information, site synopses for Natural Heritage Areas were used (NPW 1996) and, where available, more detailed site reports (e.g. for sites 101, 114, and 117). However, neither the site synopses nor specific site reports provided detailed information on habitat cover, so for most IBAs the percentage cover has been estimated.
- The lack of specific site information was also a problem for assessing land-use cover and threat status at IBAs. Wherever possible, local knowledge was used to gain this information, together with Natural Heritage Area site synopses (NPW 1996). The SPA and SAC management plans, when completed, should provide more accurate information.
- Three cross-border sites were identified: Lough Foyle (site 004), Pettigo Plateau (site 027) and Carlingford Lough (site 122). Data presented is for the Republic-side only, except that the areas quoted for sites 004 and 122 refer to the whole of each cross-border site, i.e. the figures include UK territory. A similar approach has been followed for these sites in the chapter for the United Kingdom.
- The primary administrative regions listed in the site accounts (and Table 1) are the eight EU NUTS regions for the Republic of Ireland. The secondary administrative regions (not listed) are the 26 counties of the Republic. Neither of these is satisfactory for use as an 'EU region' for the application of the C6 criterion, due to the small total area of the country. Thus, for applying the C6 criterion, the relevant EU region was considered to be the whole country.

GLOSSARY

callows flood-meadows traditionally used for producing hay.

drumlin a mound of glacial deposits (sand and gravel).

esker a ridge of glacial deposits (sand and gravel).

INTERREG a source of funding, partly financed by the European Regional Development Fund of the EU, aimed at encouraging cross-border development, in this case maritime and general economic developments between eastern Ireland and western Wales.

I-WeBS Irish Wetland Bird Survey.

karst a limestone region with underground drainage and many cavities and passages caused by the dissolution of the rock.

lough a lake or narrow sea inlet.

NUTS Nomenclature des Unités Territoriales Statistiques—the administrative regions of the European Union are called NUTS regions, and are designated by the EC Statistical Office.

NPW National Parks and Wildlife (formerly National Parks and Wildlife Service), part of Dúchas, The Heritage Service, which is part of the Department of Arts, Heritage, Gaeltacht and the Islands.

polder a flat area of land, often below sea-level, with an artificially regulated water-regime, having been claimed from the sea or from a lake or river.

SAC Special Area for Conservation (to be designated under the EC Habitats Directive).

SPA Special Protection Area (designated under Article 4 of the EC Birds Directive).

turlough a deep, grassy depression on limestone, which fills with water in wet weather, especially in winter.

ACKNOWLEDGEMENTS

We would like to thank the following for their help and advice in compiling the IBA database and this chapter: BirdLife International Secretariat; Dúchas, The Heritage Service, especially Oscar Merne; Simon Delany and Kendrew Colhoun (I-WeBS coordinators), Ann Marie McDerritt (Corncrake Project Officer), Catherine Casey (Habitat Management Officer), Oran O'Sullivan (General Manager, BirdWatch Ireland); Shelley Hackett and Mark Kavanagh, both of whom contributed directly to the preparation of the IBA Review, and numerous members of BirdWatch Ireland, to whom we are very grateful.

■ SITE ACCOUNTS

Inishtrahull — B2, B3, C7 — 001
Admin region Donegal
Coordinates 55°26'N 7°14'W
Altitude 0–43 m **Area** 315 ha

■ **Site description**
A formerly inhabited marine island with an automated lighthouse located 5 km north of Malin Head, in County Donegal. The site also includes Tor Rocks, c.1 km to the north, and the intervening sea area. The island is predominantly grassland, which until recently was grazed by red deer *Cervus elaphus*. Low-intensity fishing takes place between the main island and Tor Rocks.

Habitats Grassland (12%; dry siliceous grassland), Marine areas (88%; sea inlet/coastal features)
Land-use Agriculture, Fisheries/aquaculture (60%), Not utilized (40%)

■ **Birds**

Species	Season	Year	Pop min	Pop max	Acc	Criteria
Phalacrocorax aristotelis Shag	B	1987	300	300	B	B3
Larus fuscus Lesser Black-backed Gull	B	1991	100	—	—	B3
Cepphus grylle Black Guillemot	B	1991	20	—	—	B2

The cliffs and rocks support important colonies of breeding seabirds. Other breeding species present in nationally important numbers (1991–1992) include *Fulmarus glacialis* (250 pairs), *Larus argentatus* (500 pairs), *Larus canus* (30 pairs) and *Larus marinus* (50 pairs). Additionally Inishtrahull is a nationally important winter feeding site for *Branta leucopsis* (153 birds, 1987) and is a breeding site for *Somateria mollissima* (over 200 pairs, 1992).

■ **Protection status**
National None **International** High
315 ha of IBA covered by Special Protection Area (Inistrahull, 315 ha).

■ **Conservation issues**

Threats Aquaculture/fisheries (C), Disturbance to birds (C), Recreation/tourism (C)

Until their recent removal, overgrazing by deer was a potential threat to the site. There may be some disturbance to birds due to rock-angling and scuba-diving activities.

Malin Head — C2, C6 — 002
Admin region Donegal
Coordinates 55°22'N 7°21'W
Altitude 10–110 m **Area** 750 ha

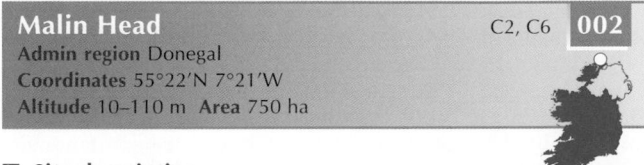

■ **Site description**
A long stretch of unspoilt coastline in northern County Donegal, extending from just north of Ballygorman village around Malin Head to White Strand Bay on its southern side. Mixed farmland is the main habitat, with meadow and grazing pasture.

Habitats Grassland (100%; mesophile grassland)
Land-use Agriculture (100%)

■ Birds

Species	Season	Year	Pop min	Pop max	Acc	Criteria
[1] *Branta leucopsis* Barnacle Goose	W	1996	80	80	—	C2
Crex crex Corncrake	B	1996	8	8	A	C6

1. Regular visitor from neighbouring islands.

Pyrrhocorax pyrrhocorax and *Somateria mollissima* also breed.

■ Protection status
National None **International** None

■ Conservation issues

Threats Agricultural intensification/expansion (A)

Crex crex is highly sensitive to changes in agricultural practice and the late cutting of hay-meadows is essential to its survival at this site. However, the site is threatened by agricultural intensification, including an increase in silage production which leads to earlier cutting, and loss of hay-meadows due to conversion to pasture. BirdWatch Ireland, supported by NPW and RSPB, operates a grant scheme in this area, to try to ensure continued farming practices that favour *Crex crex*.

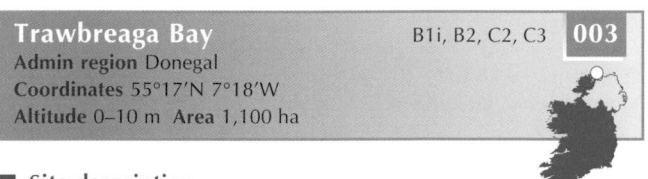

Trawbreaga Bay   B1i, B2, C2, C3   003
Admin region Donegal
Coordinates 55°17′N 7°18′W
Altitude 0–10 m **Area** 1,100 ha

■ Site description
An almost land-locked bay, situated next to Malin Head on the north County Donegal coast. At its mouth Doagh Isle on the western shore encloses most of the bay, which at low tide is largely exposed mud- and sandflats, with some rocky substrate. The Isle consists of machair and sand-dunes, the latter also being present on the eastern shore of the bay, again at its mouth. Feeding fields for geese *Branta*, adjacent to the bay, are included. Land-uses include intertidal shellfish cultivation, and recreation.

Habitats Grassland (20%; humid grassland; machair), Wetland (80%; tidal river/enclosed tidal water; mudflat/sandflat; sand-dunes/sand beach; shingle/stony beach)
Land-use Agriculture (20%), Fisheries/aquaculture (50%), Not utilized (30%)

■ Birds

Species	Season	Year	Pop min	Pop max	Acc	Criteria
Branta leucopsis Barnacle Goose	W	1996	740	740	A	B1i, B2, C2
Branta bernicla Brent Goose	W	1995	319	319	A	B1i, C3

Trawbreaga Bay is the most northerly wetland in Ireland and is important for a diversity of wintering waders and wildfowl.

■ Protection status
National High **International** High
IBA overlaps with Wildfowl Sanctuary (Trawbreaga Bay; area not known). 1,003 ha of IBA covered by Ramsar Site (Trawbreaga Bay, 1,003 ha). 1,003 ha of IBA covered by Special Protection Area (Trawbreaga Bay, 1,003 ha).

■ Conservation issues

Threats Aquaculture/fisheries (B), Disturbance to birds (B), Extraction industry (C)

There may be some disturbance to wintering birds due to wildfowling and water-sports, while intertidal shellfish cultivation may negatively affect habitat quality. The level of sand and gravel extraction which took place in the past is now much reduced.

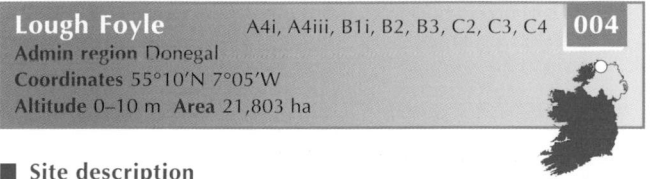

Lough Foyle   A4i, A4iii, B1i, B2, B3, C2, C3, C4   004
Admin region Donegal
Coordinates 55°10′N 7°05′W
Altitude 0–10 m **Area** 21,803 ha

■ Site description
A large, shallow sea inlet and estuary of the River Foyle, with extensive mudflat, especially along its eastern shore. This site lies immediately north of Derry city, on the north County Donegal/Derry coast. It is a cross-border IBA, with most of the site falling within County Derry in Northern Ireland (UK site 278)—the stated area of 21,803 ha refers to the whole site (on both sides of the border) but other data given here (on habitats, land-uses, threats and birds) are specific to the Republic of Ireland side.

Habitats Grassland (mesophile grassland), Wetland (tidal river/enclosed tidal water; mudflat/sandflat; sand-dunes/sand beach; river/stream), Marine areas (sea inlet/coastal features), Artificial landscape (highly improved reseeded grassland)
Land-use Agriculture, Fisheries/aquaculture, Not utilized

■ Birds

Species	Season	Year	Pop min	Pop max	Acc	Criteria
Cygnus columbianus Bewick's Swan	W	1989	163	181	A	A4i, B1i, B2, C2
Cygnus cygnus Whooper Swan	W	1989	1,072	1,607	A	A4i, B1i, B3, C2
[1] *Anser albifrons* White-fronted Goose	W	1994	510	510	A	B1i, C3
Branta bernicla Brent Goose	W	1996	4,500	4,500	A	A4i, B1i, C3
Anas penelope Wigeon	W	1989	16,959	17,704	A	B1i, C3
Limosa lapponica Bar-tailed Godwit	W	1989	1,987	2,833	A	A4i, B1i, B2, C2
Numenius arquata Curlew	W	1989	2,360	2,832	A	B2

1. Mean 1992–1996; same flock uses site 005.

This site is of international importance for wintering waterfowl. Most of the birds use the Northern Ireland section of the site, but notable concentrations of *Anas crecca*, *Calidris canutus* and, increasingly, *Branta bernicla* use the Donegal section.

■ Protection status
National None **International** Low
347 ha of IBA covered by Special Protection Area (Lough Foyle, 347 ha).

■ Conservation issues

Threats Agricultural intensification/expansion (C), Industrialization/urbanization (C)

For many years, expansion of rubbish-dumping activities has threatened mudflats in County Donegal. There is currently a proposal to extend Derry city airport which would result in a significant adverse impact on the site (loss of mudflat).

Lough Swilly including Blanket Nook and Inch Lake   A4i, A4iii, B1i, B2, B3, C2, C3, C4, C6   005
Admin region Donegal
Coordinates 55°07′N 7°32′W
Altitude 0–5 m **Area** 9,000 ha

■ Site description
This site encompasses a large part of Lough Swilly between Letterkenny and Buncrana, in County Donegal. It is a long, narrow sea inlet with extensive banks of mud and shingle between Letterkenny and Inch, including Inch Island. There is some empoldered land at Big Isle and Blanket Nook and an embanked sea channel between Inch Island and the mainland. The boundaries of the IBA have been redrawn to cover a smaller area compared to that in the previous European inventory (Grimmett and Jones 1989).

Habitats Grassland (10%; humid grassland; mesophile grassland), Wetland (80%; tidal river/enclosed tidal water; mudflat/sandflat), Artificial landscape (10%; highly improved reseeded grassland; arable land)
Land-use Agriculture (20%), Fisheries/aquaculture (80%), Hunting (95%)

■ Birds
This is a key wetland for birds in Ireland, important for the richness and abundance of its wintering and breeding species. Wintering waterbirds regularly occur in total numbers of international importance (22,750–26,600 birds in 1995 and 1996). Up to 14 other wintering species also occur in numbers of national importance, including *Tadorna tadorna* (793 birds, 1996), *Anas penelope* (1,861 birds, 1995), *Anas crecca* (1,669 birds, 1996) and *Charadrius hiaticula* (167 birds, 1996).

Species	Season	Year	Pop min	Pop max	Acc	Criteria
Cygnus columbianus Bewick's Swan	W	1996	48	48	A	B2

Species ... continued	Season	Year	Pop min	Pop max	Acc	Criteria
Cygnus cygnus Whooper Swan	W	1996	653	653	A	B1i, B3, C2
[1] *Cygnus cygnus* Whooper Swan	P	1996	2,000	—	—	A4i, B1i, C2
[2] *Anser albifrons* White-fronted Goose	W	1996	500	500	A	B1i, C3
Anser anser Greylag Goose	W	1996	1,203	1,203	A	B1i, C3
Calidris alpina Dunlin	W	1995	9,151	9,151	A	B2
Numenius arquata Curlew	W	1995	2,350	2,350	A	B2
Tringa totanus Redshank	W	1996	1,472	1,472	A	B1i, C3
[3] *Sterna sandvicensis* Sandwich Tern	B	1995	222	222	B	B2, C6

1. Autumn.
2. Mean 1992–1996.
3. May be the same birds that used to breed at Greer's Island (site 008).

■ Protection status

National Low **International** Partial
Part of IBA covered by Wildfowl Sanctuary (Blanket Nook, 48 ha). IBA overlaps with Ramsar Site (Lough Swilly; area not known). 3,107 ha of IBA covered by Special Protection Area (Lough Swilly, 3,107 ha). 278 ha of IBA covered by Special Protection Area (Inch Lough, 278 ha).

■ Conservation issues

Threats Agricultural intensification/expansion (B), Disturbance to birds (B), Filling-in of wetlands (B)

Parts of the site are threatened by nutrient pollution due to agricultural run-off. Changes in agricultural practice could threaten the feeding fields of swans *Cygnus* and geese *Anser* at Inch Lough and Blanket Nook. Use of the site for water-sports and aquaculture (intertidal and subtidal shellfish cultivation) is increasing and may threaten habitat quality. In 1998 land-claim, apparently unauthorized, for the construction of a marina at Fahan on the site's east shore, damaged intertidal sandflat. Inch Island, where *Sterna sandvicensis* breeds, lies within the Lough Swilly SPA.

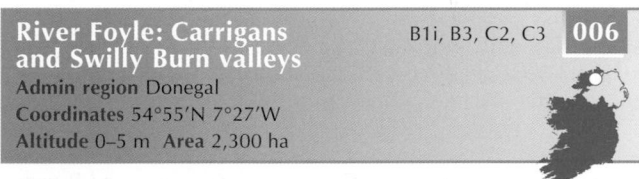

River Foyle: Carrigans and Swilly Burn valleys
B1i, B3, C2, C3 — 006

Admin region Donegal
Coordinates 54°55′N 7°27′W
Altitude 0–5 m **Area** 2,300 ha

■ Site description

This site encompasses an 8-km estuarine stretch of the River Foyle, with mudflat and saltmarsh habitat and two contiguous river valleys, with wet meadow, arable fields and improved pasture. It is located south of Derry city in Northern Ireland, while its eastern boundary is the County Donegal/Tyrone border. Nearby Lough Foyle, located north of Derry city, is a separate site (site 004).

Habitats Scrub (10%; scrub), Wetland (50%; tidal river/enclosed tidal water; mudflat/sandflat; river/stream; water-fringe vegetation), Artificial landscape (50%; highly improved reseeded grassland; arable land)
Land-use Agriculture (50%), Hunting (70%), Not utilized (10%)

■ Birds

Species	Season	Year	Pop min	Pop max	Acc	Criteria
Cygnus cygnus Whooper Swan	W	1995	452	452	A	B1i, B3, C2
[1] *Anser albifrons* White-fronted Goose	W	1987	236	254	A	B1i, C3

1. Mean 1982–1987.

This is an important site for wintering wildfowl. Species occurring in nationally important numbers include *Anas crecca* (657 birds, 1995), *Bucephala clangula* (115 birds, 1996) and *Mergus serrator* (42 birds, 1996).

■ Protection status

National None **International** None

■ Conservation issues

Threats Disturbance to birds (B), Industrialization/urbanization (C)

Wildfowling causes disturbance to birds, and the proximity of Derry city may also adversely affect the site.

Fanad Head Peninsula
C6 — 007

Admin region Donegal
Coordinates 55°13′N 7°40′W
Altitude 0–100 m **Area** 8,600 ha

■ Site description

A peninsula west of Malin Head, of mainly mixed farmland habitat. The site boundary extends from Saldanha Head, south of Portsalon on the east side of the peninsula, around to Marks Point at Broad Water in Mulroy Bay, on the west side. The major water-bodies are excluded from the IBA.

Habitats Grassland (100%; mesophile grassland)
Land-use Agriculture (100%)

■ Birds

Species	Season	Year	Pop min	Pop max	Acc	Criteria
Crex crex Corncrake	B	1996	7	7	A	C6

The Fanad coast, adjacent to but outside the IBA, is also notable for wintering seaduck, with *Somateria mollissima* (420 birds, 1995) and *Clangula hyemalis* (38 birds, 1995) occurring in numbers of national importance.

■ Protection status

National None **International** None

■ Conservation issues

Threats Agricultural intensification/expansion (A)

Crex crex is highly sensitive to changes in agricultural practice and the late cutting of hay-meadows is essential to its survival at this site. However, the site is threatened by agricultural intensification, including the expansion of silage production which leads to earlier cutting, and loss of hay-meadows for conversion to pasture. BirdWatch Ireland, with support from NPW and RSPB, operates a grant scheme in this area, to try to ensure the continuation of farming practices that favour *Crex crex*.

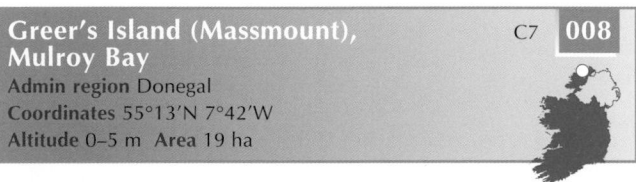

Greer's Island (Massmount), Mulroy Bay
C7 — 008

Admin region Donegal
Coordinates 55°13′N 7°42′W
Altitude 0–5 m **Area** 19 ha

■ Site description

A small island and surrounding waters in Mulroy Bay, County Donegal. The site has been extended since the previous pan-European inventory (Grimmett and Jones 1989) to include 18 ha of surrounding waters.

Habitats Grassland (5%), Wetland (95%; tidal river/enclosed tidal water)
Land-use Fisheries/aquaculture (95%), Not utilized (5%)

■ Birds

This site was formerly of importance for *Sterna sandvicensis*, holding the second-largest breeding colony in Ireland (180 pairs) in 1984, although more recently numbers have declined (with none breeding in 1995). The species may yet recolonize—the birds that used to nest at the site are now believed to breed at Inch Lake (site 005). There are also breeding *Sterna paradisaea* (20 pairs, 1984) and a nationally important colony of *Larus ridibundus* (180 birds, 1984).

■ Protection status

National None **International** High
19 ha of IBA covered by Special Protection Area (Greer's Island, 19 ha).

■ Conservation issues

Threats Aquaculture/fisheries (C), Disturbance to birds (C), Recreation/tourism (C)

Recreation may cause some disturbance to nesting terns *Sterna*, and fisheries may deplete their prey stock, with implications for their breeding success. The site retains its conservation status as an IBA due to its designation as a Special Protection Area and beacause of the potential for recolonization by *Sterna sandvicensis*.

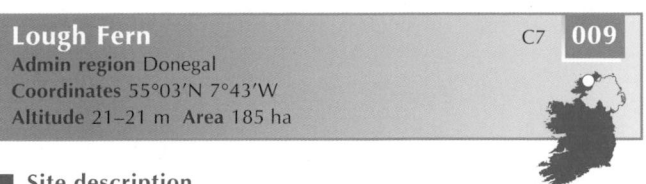

Lough Fern   C7 009
Admin region Donegal
Coordinates 55°03′N 7°43′W
Altitude 21–21 m **Area** 185 ha

■ Site description
Lough Fern is situated south of Mulroy Bay in County Donegal. There are wetlands at its south and north ends, with marsh, reedbed and wet woodland. The lake is used by anglers.

Habitats Wetland (100%; standing fresh water; river/stream; water-fringe vegetation)
Land-use Hunting, Not utilized (100%), Tourism/recreation

■ Birds
Lough Fern was designated as a Special Protection Area on the basis of migratory waterfowl populations. It is one of the most important wintering sites in Ireland for *Aythya ferina*, (1,208 birds, 1996).

■ Protection status
National High **International** High
IBA overlaps with Wildfowl Sanctuary (Lough Fern; area not known). 185 ha of IBA covered by Special Protection Area (Lough Fern, 185 ha).

■ Conservation issues

Threats Disturbance to birds (U), Recreation/tourism (C)

There is little information available in relation to threats. However, use of the site by anglers, together with wildfowling, is likely to cause disturbance to wintering birds.

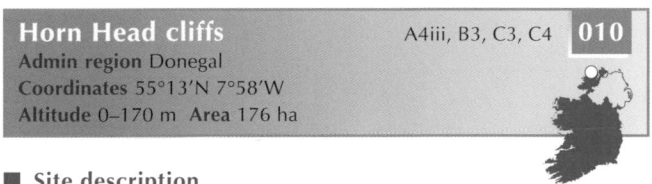

Horn Head cliffs   A4iii, B3, C3, C4 010
Admin region Donegal
Coordinates 55°13′N 7°58′W
Altitude 0–170 m **Area** 176 ha

■ Site description
High, rocky quartzite cliffs on a well-defined peninsula to the north of Dunfanaghy, on the County Donegal coast.

Habitats Rocky areas (100%; sea cliff/rocky shore)
Land-use Not utilized (100%)

■ Birds

Species	Season	Year	Pop min	Pop max	Acc	Criteria
Phalacrocorax aristotelis Shag	B	1987	75	200	A	B3
[1] *Alca torda* Razorbill	B	1987	4,000	6,000	B	B3, C3

1. Individuals.

This site contains an internationally important colony of breeding seabirds. Other species breeding in numbers of national importance include *Fulmarus glacialis* (1,000 pairs), *Rissa tridactyla* (4,500 pairs), *Uria aalge* (5,000 birds) and *Cepphus grylle* (25 birds).

■ Protection status
National High **International** High
176 ha of IBA covered by Refuge for Fauna (Horn Head; area not known). 176 ha of IBA covered by Special Protection Area (Horn Head cliffs, 176 ha).

■ Conservation issues

Threats Aquaculture/fisheries (C), Recreation/tourism (U)

Disturbance to breeding seabirds is limited by the inaccessibility of the cliffs. However, an increase in tourist activity could pose a threat. Offshore fishing may deplete the prey stock of seabirds, with implications for their breeding success. The site lies within a proposed candidate Special Area for Conservation (Horn Head and Ringclevan; area not known).

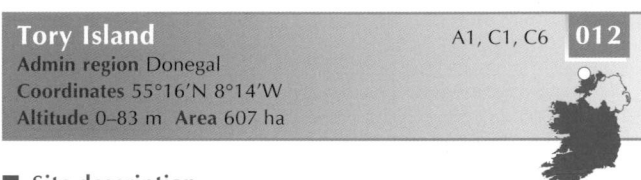

Dunfanaghy New Lake   C7 011
Admin region Donegal
Coordinates 55°10′N 8°00′W
Altitude 0–10 m **Area** 626 ha

■ Site description
A coastal lagoon, with large sand-dunes and surrounding grassland, south of Dunfanaghy in County Donegal.

Habitats Grassland (10%; mesophile grassland), Wetland (80%; sand-dunes/sand beach; standing fresh water; water-fringe vegetation), Artificial landscape (10%; forestry plantation)
Land-use Agriculture (40%), Forestry (10%), Not utilized (50%)

■ Birds
This site has been designated as a Special Protection Area on the basis of its migratory birds, especially wintering *Anser albifrons flavirostris* (174 birds, 1996) and *Branta leucopsis* (232 birds, 1995), which occur here in nationally important numbers.

■ Protection status
National None **International** High
626 ha of IBA covered by Special Protection Area (Dunfanaghy New Lake, 626 ha).

■ Conservation issues

Threats Afforestation (C), Agricultural intensification/expansion (C)

Part of the site has been damaged by afforestation and there has been some modification of the dunes through agricultural usage. The site lies within a proposed candidate Special Area for Conservation (Horn Head and Ringclevan; area not known).

Tory Island   A1, C1, C6 012
Admin region Donegal
Coordinates 55°16′N 8°14′W
Altitude 0–83 m **Area** 607 ha

■ Site description
A large, inhabited marine island and surrounding waters, situated 11 km north of Bloody Foreland in County Donegal. The island is mainly low-lying but high cliffs occur along the northern side, and at the east end rise to 90 m. Back from the cliffs maritime heath dominates. Farming is largely low intensity with hay meadows and grazing by cattle and sheep. However, there has been some improvement of land for arable crops. There is an unmanned lighthouse at the west end.

Habitats Grassland (20%; humid grassland), Wetland (5%; standing fresh water), Marine areas (35%; open sea; sea inlet/coastal features), Rocky areas (25%; sea cliff/rocky shore; rock stacks/islets), Artificial landscape (15%; arable land; other urban/industrial areas; ruderal land)
Land-use Agriculture (20%), Fisheries/aquaculture (40%), Nature conservation/research (100%), Urban/industrial/transport (10%), Water management (10%)

■ Birds

Species	Season	Year	Pop min	Pop max	Acc	Criteria
Crex crex Corncrake	B	1996	21	21	A	A1, C1, C6

This is an internationally important site for the globally threatened *Crex crex*. It is also of national importance for a diversity of breeding seabirds, including *Fulmarus glacialis* (260 pairs, 1987), *Rissa tridactyla* (530 pairs, 1987), *Uria aalge* (650 birds, 1987), *Alca torda* (630 birds, 1987) and *Fratercula arctica* (>1,000 birds, 1994).

■ Protection status
National None **International** High
607 ha of IBA covered by Special Protection Area (Tory Island, 607 ha).

■ Conservation issues

Threats Abandonment/reduction of land management (A), Agricultural intensification/expansion (B), Recreation/tourism (B)

Crex crex is highly sensitive to changes in agricultural practices and the late cutting of hay-meadows is essential to its survival at this site.

However, the site is threatened by the intensification of farming, mainly the extension of winter grazing into the summer, preventing meadow growth. BirdWatch Ireland, with support from NPW and RSPB, operates a grant scheme on the island to encourage farming practices that favour *Crex crex*. Predation may also threaten *Crex crex* on this island. Other threats include erosion of maritime heath due to its extreme exposure together with grazing by domestic stock and rabbits, and localized peat-cutting. The site overlaps with a proposed candidate Special Area for Conservation (Tory Island; area not known).

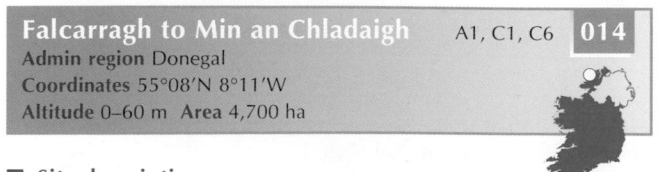

Inishbofin, Inisdooey and Inisbeg — A1, B1i, C1, C2, C6 — 013
Admin region Donegal
Coordinates 55°11'N 8°10'W
Altitude 0–38 m **Area** 604 ha

■ Site description
The site comprises three islands, Inishbofin, Inishdooey and Inishbeg and is located 2 km off the Donegal coast, 5 km north-west of Falcarragh. The largest island, Inishbofin, comprises mainly dry grassland which, although farmed in the past, is now largely abandoned. In the previous European inventory (Grimmett and Jones 1989) the site included just one island, but the nearby islands of Inishdooey and Inishbeg, together with the surrounding waters, have now been added. Inishbofin is inhabited during the summer months.

Habitats Scrub (5%; scrub), Grassland (5%; mesophile grassland), Wetland (5%; shingle/stony beach), Marine areas (80%; sea inlet/coastal features), Artificial landscape (5%; other urban/industrial areas)
Land-use Agriculture (5%), Fisheries/aquaculture (80%), Nature conservation/research (20%), Not utilized (10%), Urban/industrial/transport (5%)

■ Birds

Species		Season	Year	Pop min	Pop max	Acc	Criteria
Branta leucopsis	Barnacle Goose	W	1996	400	400	A	B1i, C2
Crex crex	Corncrake	B	1996	15	27	A	A1, C1, C6

Together with Tory Island (site 012), these islands held 20% of the national population of *Crex crex* in 1996 (numbers are calling males, 1995–1996). The site was also nationally important for breeding terns *Sterna*. Recently only *Sterna paradisaea* has bred (72 pairs, 1995).

■ Protection status
National None **International** High
604 ha of IBA covered by Special Protection Area (Inishbofin, Inishdooey and Inishbeg, 604 ha).

■ Conservation issues

Threats Abandonment/reduction of land management (A), Agricultural intensification/expansion (B), Disturbance to birds (C)

This site is threatened mainly by agricultural abandonment. *Crex crex* is highly sensitive to changes in agricultural practice, and the late cutting of hay-meadows is essential to its survival at the site. However, most of the land is managed for conservation by BirdWatch Ireland, with support from NPW and RSPB, to maintain hay-meadows, the late cutting of hay and early cover.

Falcarragh to Min an Chladaigh — A1, C1, C6 — 014
Admin region Donegal
Coordinates 55°08'N 8°11'W
Altitude 0–60 m **Area** 4,700 ha

■ Site description
This large site follows the coastline from Falcarragh to Min an Chladaigh in north County Donegal. It encompasses a large area inland, much of which is small, extensively managed farms, and it excludes the estuary at Ballyness Bay.

Habitats Grassland (100%; mesophile grassland)
Land-use Agriculture (100%)

■ Birds

Species		Season	Year	Pop min	Pop max	Acc	Criteria
Crex crex	Corncrake	B	1996	26	26	A	A1, C1, C6

This site is an important breeding area for *Crex crex* and is the closest mainland site to Inishbofin (site 013) and, further out to sea, Tory Island (site 012), two islands which together held 20% of the national population of this species in 1996.

■ Protection status
National None **International** None

■ Conservation issues

Threats Agricultural intensification/expansion (A)

The late cutting of hay-meadows is essential to the survival of *Crex crex* at this site. However, the site is threatened by agricultural intensification, including an increase in silage production which leads to earlier cutting, and loss of hay-meadows for conversion to pasture. BirdWatch Ireland, with support from NPW and RSPB, operates a grant scheme in this area, to try to ensure farming practices that continue to favour *Crex crex*.

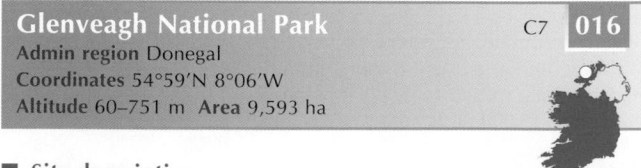

Inishsirrer and Inishmeane — B1i, B2, C2 — 015
Admin region Donegal
Coordinates 55°05'N 8°21'W
Altitude 0–33 m **Area** 140 ha

■ Site description
Two formerly inhabited islands, lying 1–2 km offshore and 6 km north of Bunbeg in County Donegal. Information on land-use and threats is incomplete. The site does not include surrounding waters, and lies adjacent to Gola Island (site 024).

Habitats Grassland (100%)
Land-use Unknown (100%)

■ Birds

Species		Season	Year	Pop min	Pop max	Acc	Criteria
Branta leucopsis	Barnacle Goose	W	1995	300	400	B	B1i, B2, C2

■ Protection status
National None **International** None

■ Conservation issues

Threats Unknown (U)

The site lies within a proposed candidate Special Area for Conservation (Gweedore Bay and Islands; area not known).

Glenveagh National Park — C7 — 016
Admin region Donegal
Coordinates 54°59'N 8°06'W
Altitude 60–751 m **Area** 9,593 ha

■ Site description
Glenveagh National Park is situated 15 km west of Letterkenny in north-west County Donegal. This is a mountainous area, dominated by Atlantic blanket bog, with lakes, rivers, woodland and heath. Grazing and peat-cutting ('Other' land-use) take place within the site. The National Park Visitor Centre and Glenveagh Castle attract visitors.

Habitats Wetland (80%; standing fresh water; river/stream; blanket bog), Rocky areas (20%; scree/boulders; inland cliff)
Land-use Agriculture (50%), Nature conservation/research (100%), Not utilized (20%), Other (50%), Tourism/recreation (100%)

■ Birds
The site was designated as a Special Protection Area on the basis of breeding *Gavia stellata*, *Pluvialis apricaria*, *Falco peregrinus* and

F. columbarius, and wintering *Anser albifrons flavirostris* (all species listed on Annex I of the EC Birds Directive).

■ Protection status

National High **International** High

9,593 ha of IBA covered by National Park (Glenveagh, 9,737 ha). 9,593 ha of IBA covered by Special Protection Area (Glenveagh National Park, 9,593 ha).

■ Conservation issues

Threats Afforestation (B), Agricultural intensification/expansion (C), Consequences of animal/plant introductions (B), Extraction industry (B)

Trampling and overgrazing by sheep and deer have caused damage to some areas of bog, while other areas are threatened by peat-cutting, erosion and burning. Introduced (non-native) *Rhododendron* scrub has invaded and choked some areas of woodland and covered adjacent hillsides, but a removal programme is now nearing completion. The site lies within a proposed candidate Special Area for Conservation (Glenveagh National Park; area not known).

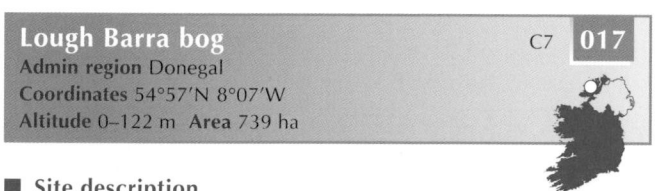

Lough Barra bog — C7 — 017
Admin region Donegal
Coordinates 54°57'N 8°07'W
Altitude 0–122 m **Area** 739 ha

■ Site description

Lough Barra bog is a lowland blanket bog situated in the upper part of the Gweebarra river valley. It lies adjacent to the southern boundary of Glenveagh National Park (site 016) in County Donegal.

Habitats Wetland (100%; blanket bog)
Land-use Agriculture (25%), Nature conservation/research (50%), Other (25%)

■ Birds

This site provides valuable feeding habitat for a small flock of wintering *Anser albifrons flavirostris* (10 birds, 1994). The IBA was designated as a Special Protection Area for this species and for its breeding numbers of four other species that are also listed on Annex I of the EC Birds Directive: *Gavia stellata*, *Falco columbarius*, *Falco peregrinus* and *Pluvialis apricaria*.

■ Protection status

National Partial **International** High

176 ha of IBA covered by Nature Reserve (Lough Barra bog, 176 ha). 176 ha of IBA covered by Ramsar Site (Lough Barra bog, 176 ha). 739 ha of IBA covered by Special Protection Area (Lough Barra bog, 739 ha).

■ Conservation issues

Threats Agricultural intensification/expansion (C), Extraction industry (C)

Major threats to the site are peat-cutting, overgrazing and trampling by sheep and deer. There are annual deer culls to control numbers and the main herd is kept within the National Park. The IBA overlaps with a proposed candidate Special Area for Conservation (Lough Barra Bog; area not known).

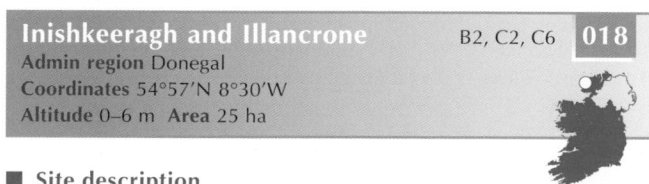

Inishkeeragh and Illancrone — B2, C2, C6 — 018
Admin region Donegal
Coordinates 54°57'N 8°30'W
Altitude 0–6 m **Area** 25 ha

■ Site description

The site comprises two uninhabited marine islands: Inishkeeragh, located 2.5 km from the mainland and comprising unimproved dry grassland, and Illancrone (former site IE010), a small island on a stony reef, 1.5 km from the mainland. The only land-use is sheep-grazing (intensity not known).

Habitats Grassland (70%), Rocky areas (30%; sea cliff/rocky shore)
Land-use Agriculture (70%), Not utilized (30%)

■ Birds

Species		Season	Year	Pop min	Pop max	Acc	Criteria
Branta leucopsis	Barnacle Goose	W	1994	235	235	A	B2, C2
Larus canus	Common Gull	B	1984	50	50	—	B2
Sterna paradisaea	Arctic Tern	B	1995	224	224	A	C6
Sterna albifrons	Little Tern	B	1995	13	13	A	B2, C6

This is an important site for wintering *Branta leucopsis* and breeding seabirds, particularly terns *Sterna*. Historically, five tern species bred on these islands, but in recent years (1994–1995) *Sterna dougallii* has not bred, and the number of *Sterna sandvicensis* has been small (1 pair, 1995). *Sterna hirundo* continues to breed, and the islands are one of the top five breeding sites in the Republic of Ireland for *Sterna paradisaea* and *Sterna albifrons*.

■ Protection status

National None **International** None

■ Conservation issues

Threats Agricultural intensification/expansion (C)

The site is under consideration by NPW for designation as a Special Protection Area. Nesting terns are disturbed by sheep grazing.

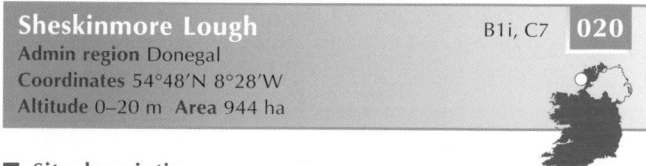

Roaninish — B2, C7 — 019
Admin region Donegal
Coordinates 54°52'N 8°32'W
Altitude 0–10 m **Area** 144 ha

■ Site description

A tight group of small, flat, uninhabited islets, located 3.5 km off Dawros Head in County Donegal. Much of the site is sparsely vegetated with the exception of the main island Roaninish, which is covered in lush maritime grassland, and has two small ponds.

Habitats Grassland (5%; mesophile grassland), Marine areas (85%; sea inlet/coastal features), Rocky areas (10%; sea cliff/rocky shore; rock stacks/islets)
Land-use Fisheries/aquaculture (85%), Not utilized (15%)

■ Birds

Species		Season	Year	Pop min	Pop max	Acc	Criteria
Hydrobates pelagicus	Storm Petrel	B	1987	1,000	1,000	C	B2

This is an important site for breeding seabirds; species present in numbers of national importance are *Larus marinus* (60 birds, 1984) and *Larus argentatus* (200 birds, 1984). In the past the site has been important for wintering *Branta leucopsis* (250 birds, pre-1987) but not in recent years.

■ Protection status

National None **International** None

■ Conservation issues

Threats Aquaculture/fisheries (U)

There is no precise information on threats, although fishing in surrounding waters may deplete the prey stock of seabirds, with implications for their breeding success. The site is a proposed (by NPW) Special Protection Area (Roaninish, 144 ha).

Sheskinmore Lough — B1i, C7 — 020
Admin region Donegal
Coordinates 54°48'N 8°28'W
Altitude 0–20 m **Area** 944 ha

■ Site description

Habitats Grassland (10%; machair), Wetland (90%; mudflat/sandflat; sand-dunes/sand beach; coastal lagoon; standing fresh water)
Land-use Agriculture (20%), Nature conservation/research (75%), Tourism/recreation (5%)

Sheskinmore Lough is situated approximately 6 km north-west of Ardara in County Donegal. The site comprises intertidal mud- and sandflats, together with sand-dunes, machair and extensive marshes. Of particular ecological interest is Sheskinmore Lough itself, which is a partially sand-filled lagoon. The site is grazed, although a large part of it is managed for nature conservation. A caravan site lies within a relatively small section of the dunes.

■ Birds
This site supports a diversity of wintering and breeding bird species. The number of wintering *Branta leucopsis* has fallen just below the B1i criterion threshold in recent years, but in view of high numbers during the 1980s (1,123 birds in 1981, and an average of 556 birds in the mid-1980s) the site has been retained as an IBA.

■ Protection status
National High **International** High
IBA overlaps with Wildfowl Sanctuary (Sheskinmore Lough; area not known). 944 ha of IBA covered by Special Protection Area (Sheskinmore Lough, 944 ha).

■ Conservation issues
Threats Agricultural intensification/expansion (C), Drainage (C)

Past attempts at drainage of the lake and marsh have caused damage. NPW now own 365 ha of the site and there are plans to reverse the drainage. Parts of the site are threatened by overgrazing (mainly by rabbits), agricultural improvement and recreational use. 15.8 ha of the site is owned by BirdWatch Ireland as a reserve. The IBA lies within a proposed candidate Special Area for Conservation (Sheskinmore Lough; area not known).

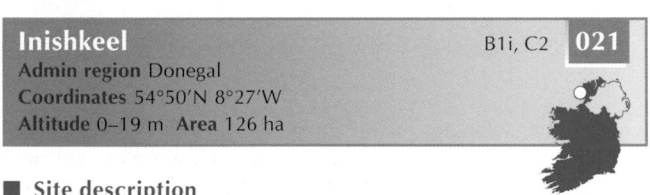

Inishkeel
B1i, C2 **021**
Admin region Donegal
Coordinates 54°50′N 8°27′W
Altitude 0–19 m **Area** 126 ha

■ Site description
A small island and surrounding waters in Gweebarra Bay, 0.5 km offshore from Portnoo in west County Donegal. There is an old church on the island and it can be accessed by foot at low tide. It is mainly grass covered with a rocky shoreline.

Habitats Grassland (10%; mesophile grassland), Marine areas (80%; sea inlet/coastal features), Rocky areas (10%; rock stacks/islets)
Land-use Fisheries/aquaculture (80%), Not utilized (20%)

■ Birds

Species	Season	Year	Pop min	Pop max	Acc	Criteria
Branta leucopsis Barnacle Goose	W	1994	337	337	A	B1i, C2

In the winter this site provides feeding habitat for internationally important numbers of *Branta leucopsis*, which also use Sheskinmore Lough (site 020). A nationally important flock of *Somateria mollissima* (500 birds, 1987/88) winter around the island.

■ Protection status
National None **International** None

■ Conservation issues
Threats Aquaculture/fisheries (C)

This site has been proposed as a Special Protection Area (Iniskeel, 126 ha) by NPW and should be designated in the near future.

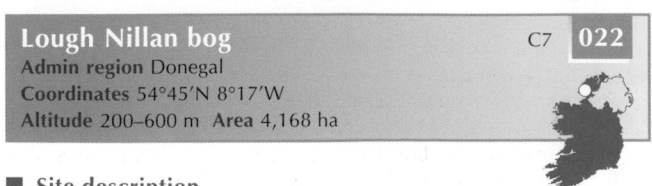

Lough Nillan bog
C7 **022**
Admin region Donegal
Coordinates 54°45′N 8°17′W
Altitude 200–600 m **Area** 4,168 ha

■ Site description
A large blanket bog complex in the range of hills immediately south of Glenties, County Donegal. Upland areas support drier heathland

vegetation, while in the lower parts of the site there are pools and on some of the slopes, flushes. There are numerous lakes and rivers. Three areas of conifer plantations are excluded from the IBA. Land-use includes peat-cutting ('Other' land-use).

Habitats Wetland (90%; standing fresh water; river/stream; blanket bog), Rocky areas (10%; inland cliff)
Land-use Agriculture (80%), Other (20%)

■ Birds
The site was designated as a Special Protection Area on the basis of its wintering *Anser albifrons flavirostris* (72 birds, 1992), and breeding *Pluvialis apricaria* (13–15 pairs) and *Falco columbarius*, all species listed on Annex I of the EC Birds Directive.

■ Protection status
National None **International** High
4,168 ha of IBA covered by Special Protection Area (Lough Nillan Bog, 4,168 ha).

■ Conservation issues
Threats Afforestation (B), Agricultural intensification/expansion (B), Extraction industry (B)

Overgrazing combined with peat-cutting is causing erosion in some parts of the site. Afforestation within the bog complex has resulted in habitat fragmentation, degrading the value of the site for conservation. The IBA lies within a proposed candidate Special Area for Conservation (Lough Nillan Bog; area not known).

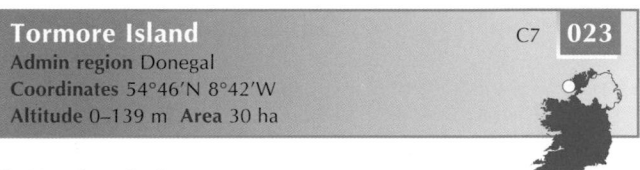

Tormore Island
C7 **023**
Admin region Donegal
Coordinates 54°46′N 8°42′W
Altitude 0–139 m **Area** 30 ha

■ Site description
A small island just offshore of the Slieve Tooey area, a wild and remote part of County Donegal, 15 km west of Ardara. The site includes the surrounding waters and the mainland cliffs 1 km to either side of the island.

Habitats Grassland (10%), Marine areas (80%; open sea), Rocky areas (10%; sea cliff/rocky shore)
Land-use Fisheries/aquaculture (80%), Not utilized (20%)

■ Birds
On the island and the mainland cliffs 1 km on either side there are nationally important numbers of breeding seabirds, including *Rissa tridactyla* (600 pairs, 1987), *Fratercula arctica* (3,000 birds, 1970) and *Alca torda* (362 birds, 1987). Smaller numbers of *Fulmarus glacialis* (155 pairs, 1987), *Phalacrocorax aristotelis* (11 pairs, 1987) and *Uria aalge* (50 birds, 1987) also breed at this site.

■ Protection status
National None **International** None

■ Conservation issues
Threats Aquaculture/fisheries (C)

On the basis of its breeding seabirds (especially *Fratercula arctica*), this site has been proposed as a Special Protection Area (Tormore Island, 30 ha) by NPW and should be designated in the near future. The site lies within a proposed candidate Special Area for Conservation (Slieve Tooey/Tormore Island/Loughros Beg Bay; area not known).

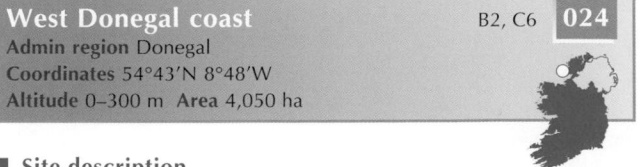

West Donegal coast
B2, C6 **024**
Admin region Donegal
Coordinates 54°43′N 8°48′W
Altitude 0–300 m **Area** 4,050 ha

■ Site description
An extended coastal site in County Donegal, which covers the mainland coastline from Dunmore Head in the north to Muckross

Head in the south, and also includes Aranmore Island and Gola Island, lying 15 and 25 km north of this coastal stretch respectively. A number of other IBAs occur within this area but are treated separately. Information on land-use and threats is incomplete.

Habitats Scrub (15%; heathland), Grassland (50%; mesophile grassland), Rocky areas (35%; sea cliff/rocky shore)
Land-use Agriculture (65%), Not utilized (35%)

■ Birds

Species		Season	Year	Pop min	Pop max	Acc	Criteria
[1] *Pyrrhocorax pyrrhocorax*	Chough	R	1992	53	53	A	B2, C6

1. Figure is sum of possible, probable and definite breeding pairs.

This area is important for *Pyrrhocorax pyrrhocorax*, and good numbers of breeding seabirds and wintering geese also occur.

■ Protection status
National None **International** None

■ Conservation issues

Threats Agricultural intensification/expansion (C), Disturbance to birds (U)

For the survival of *Pyrrhocorax pyrrhocorax* at this site, it is vital that low-intensity farming along the cliff-tops is maintained. The site overlaps with three proposed candidate Special Areas for Conservation (Slieve League; Slieve Tooey/Tormore Island/Loughros Beg Bay; West of Ardara/Maas road; areas not known).

Rathlin O'Birne
Admin region Donegal
Coordinates 54°40′N 8°50′W
Altitude 0–26 m **Area** 154 ha
B1i, B2, C2 | 025

■ Site description
A medium-sized, rocky, marine island with an automated lighthouse, located 2 km off the west coast of County Donegal, and 9 km south-west of Glencolumbkille.

Habitats Grassland (20%; mesophile grassland), Marine areas (70%; sea inlet/coastal features), Rocky areas (10%; rock stacks/islets)
Land-use Fisheries/aquaculture (70%), Not utilized (30%)

■ Birds

Species		Season	Year	Pop min	Pop max	Acc	Criteria
Hydrobates pelagicus	Storm Petrel	B	1987	1,000	1,000	C	B2
Branta leucopsis	Barnacle Goose	W	1993	345	345	A	B1i, B2, C2

This is an important site for wintering wildfowl and breeding seabirds. Seabirds breeding in nationally important numbers include *Larus argentatus* (460–550 pairs, 1987) and *Larus marinus* (45–60 pairs, 1987).

■ Protection status
National None **International** None

■ Conservation issues

Threats Aquaculture/fisheries (C)

Fishing in surrounding waters may deplete the prey stock of seabirds, with implications for their breeding success. The site is a proposed (by NPW) Special Protection Area (Rathlin O'Birne, 154 ha).

Inishduff
Admin region Donegal
Coordinates 54°36′N 8°33′W
Altitude 0–5 m **Area** 47 ha
B3 | 026

■ Site description
A small, uninhabited, rocky, marine island and surrounding sea, situated 8 km south-west of Killybegs and 2 km off the County

Donegal coast. The island is low-lying and flat-topped with short grassland vegetation.

Habitats Grassland (5%; mesophile grassland), Marine areas (80%; sea inlet/coastal features), Rocky areas (15%; rock stacks/islets)
Land-use Fisheries/aquaculture (80%), Not utilized (20%)

■ Birds

Species		Season	Year	Pop min	Pop max	Acc	Criteria
Phalacrocorax aristotelis	Shag	B	1987	116	116	A	B3
Larus marinus	Great Black-backed Gull	B	1987	150	150	—	B3

The island is important for breeding seabirds.

■ Protection status
National None **International** None

■ Conservation issues

Threats Aquaculture/fisheries (C)

Fishing in surrounding waters may deplete the prey stock of seabirds, with implications for their breeding success. The site is a proposed (by NPW) Special Protection Area (Inishduff, 47 ha).

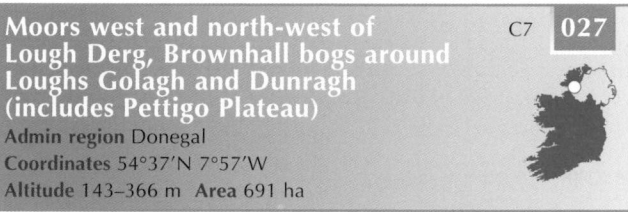

Moors west and north-west of Lough Derg, Brownhall bogs around Loughs Golagh and Dunragh (includes Pettigo Plateau)
Admin region Donegal
Coordinates 54°37′N 7°57′W
Altitude 143–366 m **Area** 691 ha
C7 | 027

■ Site description
Located in County Donegal 10 km east-south-east of Donegal town, this is an extensive complex of blanket bog, wet heath, lakes and pools covering an area of low hills and broad basins. There is grassland within the Brownhall estate, which lies adjacent to the bog and forms part of the site. This complex is also known as the Pettigo Plateau and extends across the border into Northern Ireland (County Fermanagh) where it is covered by an immediately adjacent IBA (UK site 282; 'Pettigoe Plateau'). Land-uses include peat-cutting ('Other' land-use).

Habitats Scrub (10%; scrub), Grassland (10%; humid grassland), Wetland (80%; standing fresh water; blanket bog; water-fringe vegetation)
Land-use Agriculture (60%), Hunting (100%), Nature conservation/research (25%), Other (20%)

■ Birds
This site has been designated as a Special Protection Area due to the presence of breeding *Pluvialis apricaria* and *Gavia stellata* and of wintering *Anser albifrons flavirostris* (average 113 during 1992–1996), all of which are listed under Annex I of the EC Birds Directive. This is also a notable breeding site for the nationally scarce *Lagopus lagopus*.

■ Protection status
National High **International** High
691 ha of IBA covered by Nature Reserve (Pettigo Plateau, 900 ha). 691 ha of IBA covered by Ramsar Site (Pettigo Plateau, 900 ha). 691 ha of IBA covered by Special Protection Area (Pettigo Plateau, 691 ha).

■ Conservation issues

Threats Agricultural intensification/expansion (B), Afforestation (B), Burning of vegetation (B), Disturbance to birds (C)

Restricted access to Brownhall estate limits disturbance to this goose-feeding site. However, a deterioration since 1989 in the suitability of Brownhall grasslands for *Anser albifrons flavirostris* (following agricultural improvement) may be the reason for a decline in numbers of this species. Alternative feeding sites, such as Durnesh Lough, are limited and more disturbed. In the past, afforestation caused serious degradation of blanket bog and is now the subject of an action against Ireland in the European Court. The site overlaps with a proposed candidate Special Area for Conservation (Pettigo Plateau; area not known).

Lough Derg   C7   028
Admin region Donegal
Coordinates 54°37′N 7°53′W
Altitude 143–143 m   **Area** 888 ha

■ Site description
Lough Derg is a large lake, situated approximately 6 km north of Pettigo in County Donegal. The lake is naturally nutrient-poor (oligotrophic). It is surrounded by extensive conifer plantations; good examples of wetland scrub occur on the lakeshore and islands.

Habitats Scrub (5%; scrub), Wetland (95%; standing fresh water; water-fringe vegetation)
Land-use Not utilized (100%)

■ Birds
The site was designated as a Special Protection Area on the basis of migratory waterfowl populations. An island within the lough is regularly used as a winter feeding site by small numbers of *Anser albifrons flavirostris*. The main flock uses site 027, immediately east of Lough Derg and separated by conifer plantations. There is also a nationally important breeding colony of *Larus fuscus* (800 birds, 1990).

■ Protection status
National High   **International** High
IBA overlaps with Wildfowl Sanctuary (Lough Derg (Donegal); area not known). 888 ha of IBA covered by Special Protection Area (Lough Derg (Donegal), 888 ha).

■ Conservation issues
Threats Deforestation (commercial) (C)

Felling of the surrounding conifer plantation may lead to pollution of the lake, which is already acidic.

Durnesh Lough   B1i, B2, B3, C2   029
Admin region Donegal
Coordinates 54°34′N 8°12′W
Altitude 0–10 m   **Area** 365 ha

■ Site description
A large freshwater lake adjacent to Donegal Bay and situated 10 km north of Ballyshannon in County Donegal. The lake is separated from the sea by sand-dunes, is fringed by extensive reedbeds and large areas of wet grassland, and is surrounded by drumlins.

Habitats Grassland (10%; humid grassland), Wetland (90%; sand-dunes/sand beach; standing fresh water; water-fringe vegetation; fen/transition mire/spring)
Land-use Agriculture (10%), Hunting (100%)

■ Birds

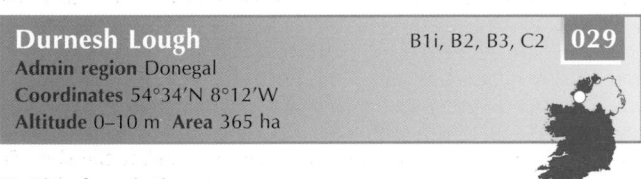

Species		Season	Year	Pop min	Pop max	Acc	Criteria
Cygnus olor	Mute Swan	W	1995	109	109	—	B1i
Cygnus columbianus	Bewick's Swan	W	—	—	40	—	B2
Cygnus cygnus	Whooper Swan	W	1997	226	226	A	B1i, B3, C2

This is an important wintering site for waterfowl, particularly swans *Cygnus*. Formerly, *Aythya marila* was also recorded in internationally important numbers. The fields around Durnesh Lough are an alternative feeding site for *Anser albifrons flavirostris* from Pettigo plateau (site 027).

■ Protection status
National None   **International** None

■ Conservation issues
Threats Agricultural intensification/expansion (C), Disturbance to birds (C), Drainage (C)

Wildfowling causes disturbance to birds, and agricultural intensification of surrounding farmland may threaten water quality due to nutrient pollution.

Donegal Bay   A4i, B1i, C2   030
Admin region Donegal
Coordinates 54°35′N 8°15′W
Altitude 0–20 m   **Area** 40,000 ha

■ Site description
A large sea bay, extending from Doorin Point in the north to Kildoney Point in the south, directly west of Donegal town, County Donegal. The innermost part of the bay, a tidal area behind sand-dune systems, is not included as it is surprisingly poor for waterfowl.

Habitats Marine areas (100%; open sea; sea inlet/coastal features)
Land-use Fisheries/aquaculture (100%)

■ Birds

Species		Season	Year	Pop min	Pop max	Acc	Criteria
Gavia immer	Great Northern Diver	W	1996	79	316	B	A4i, B1i, C2

This is one of the most important wintering sites in Ireland for *Melanitta nigra* (1,150 birds, 1996), which occur in nationally important numbers, together with *Cygnus olor* (109 birds, 1995), *Clangula hyemalis* (32 birds, 1996) and *Mergus serrator* (50 birds, 1996). The shores of Donegal Bay support nationally important numbers of *Calidris alba* (100 birds, 1996).

■ Protection status
National None   **International** None

■ Conservation issues
Threats Aquaculture/fisheries (U), Recreation/tourism (U)

The sand shores which border this site are under considerable recreational pressure. Use of the bay for water-sports may cause some disturbance to birds. There is intertidal shellfish cultivation within the inner bay.

Inishmurray   B1i, B2, B3, C2   031
Admin region North West
Coordinates 54°26′N 8°40′W
Altitude 0–20 m   **Area** 260 ha

■ Site description
A low, flat marine island, with rocky coastline and several small lakes, situated 6 km north-west of Streedagh Point in County Sligo. The main habitat is wet acidic grassland. The island has been uninhabited since the 1950s and is an important archaeological site. The IBA has been expanded since the previous European inventory (Grimmett and Jones 1989) to include the surrounding sea area.

Habitats Grassland (20%; humid grassland), Marine areas (65%; open sea), Rocky areas (15%; sea cliff/rocky shore; rock stacks/islets)
Land-use Fisheries/aquaculture (65%), Other (20%), Tourism/recreation (20%)

■ Birds

Species		Season	Year	Pop min	Pop max	Acc	Criteria
[1] *Hydrobates pelagicus*	Storm Petrel	B	1987	100	1,000	C	B2
Phalacrocorax aristotelis	Shag	B	1987	237	237	A	B3
Branta leucopsis	Barnacle Goose	W	1994	473	473	A	B1i, B2, C2

1. Probably closer to 1,000 pairs.

An important site for breeding seabirds and for wintering wildfowl, as well as a nationally important breeding site for *Somateria mollissima*.

■ Protection status
National None   **International** High
260 ha of IBA covered by Special Protection Area (Inishmurray, 260 ha).

■ Conservation issues
Threats Aquaculture/fisheries (C), Disturbance to birds (C), Recreation/tourism (C)

The main threat to birds is disturbance from visitors to the island; access and visitor numbers should be controlled during the breeding season.

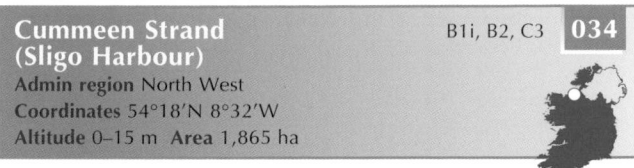

Ardboline Island and Horse Island

B1i, C2 | **032**

Admin region North West
Coordinates 54°21'N 8°42'W
Altitude 0–10 m **Area** 25 ha

■ Site description

Ardboline and Horse Island lie 1 km apart and 15 km north-west of Sligo town in County Sligo. Both islands are uninhabited and grass-covered with a rocky shoreline. The surrounding waters are not included within the site.

Habitats Grassland (100%)
Land-use Unknown (100%)

■ Birds

Species	Season	Year	Pop min	Pop max	Acc	Criteria
Branta leucopsis Barnacle Goose	W	1996	—	500	A	B1i, C2

This is an alternative feeding site for *Branta leucopsis* from Drumcliff Bay and Ballintemple (site 033). Breeding seabirds also occur on both islands, with Ardboline Island supporting nationally important numbers of *Phalacrocorax carbo* (205 pairs, 1985).

■ Protection status

National None **International** None

■ Conservation issues

Threats Aquaculture/fisheries (C)

Little information is available on this site.

Drumcliff Bay and Ballintemple

B1i, B2, C2 | **033**

Admin region North West
Coordinates 54°20'N 8°33'W
Altitude 0–10 m **Area** 3,000 ha

■ Site description

Drumcliff Bay is the most northern section of Sligo Bay's three estuaries. The main habitats are extensive mud- and sandflats together with goose-feeding fields at Ballintemple, Lissadell and Balgilgan. The site previously included goose-feeding fields at Lissadell and has been considerably enlarged since the previous pan-European inventory (Grimmett and Jones 1989) to include Drumcliff Bay itself. There is intertidal shellfish cultivation (aquaculture).

Habitats Wetland (40%; tidal river/enclosed tidal water; mudflat/sandflat; saltmarsh; sand-dunes/sand beach), Marine areas (40%; sea inlet/coastal features), Artificial landscape (20%; highly improved reseeded grassland)
Land-use Agriculture (20%), Fisheries/aquaculture (20%), Nature conservation/research (5%), Not utilized (60%)

■ Birds

Species	Season	Year	Pop min	Pop max	Acc	Criteria
Branta leucopsis Barnacle Goose	W	1994	1,774	1,774	A	B1i, B2, C2

The site supports large numbers of wintering wildfowl and waders. In particular, the improved grassland at Ballintemple and Lissadell provides feeding habitat for internationally important numbers of *Branta leucopsis*, as well as *Anser albifrons flavirostris* and *Cygnus cygnus*. Wintering waders include nationally important numbers of *Tringa totanus* (593 birds, 1995).

■ Protection status

National Low **International** Partial
29 ha of IBA covered by Nature Reserve (Balgilgan/Lissadell, 29 ha). 1,575 ha of IBA covered by Special Protection Area (Drumcliff Bay, 1,575 ha).

■ Conservation issues

Threats Aquaculture/fisheries (B)

NPW manage Balgilgan/Lissadell Nature Reserve for the geese (*Anser/Branta*). Intertidal shellfish cultivation may threaten habitat quality. Feeding fields for geese at Ballintemple are not protected. The site overlaps with a proposed candidate Special Area for Conservation (Lissadell and Drumcliff Bay; area not known).

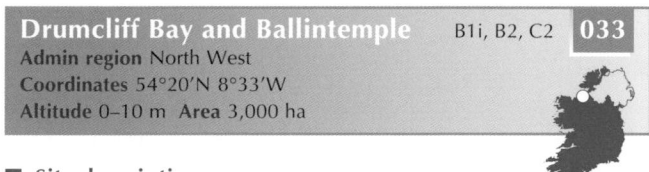

Cummeen Strand (Sligo Harbour)

B1i, B2, C3 | **034**

Admin region North West
Coordinates 54°18'N 8°32'W
Altitude 0–15 m **Area** 1,865 ha

■ Site description

Cummeen Strand is the middle of Sligo Bay's three discrete estuarine areas. It lies at the mouth of the River Garavogue and stretches west from Sligo town. Intertidal mud- and sandflats are the dominant habitat, with sand-dunes at Killaspug and Coney Island, and a shingle spit at Standalone Point. The estuary has been modified with the construction of a training wall. There is intertidal shellfish cultivation.

Habitats Grassland (20%; mesophile grassland; machair), Wetland (80%; tidal river/enclosed tidal water; mudflat/sandflat; sand-dunes/sand beach; sea inlet/coastal features)
Land-use Agriculture (20%), Fisheries/aquaculture (10%), Not utilized (60%), Urban/industrial/transport (10%)

■ Birds

Species	Season	Year	Pop min	Pop max	Acc	Criteria
Branta bernicla Brent Goose	W	1996	608	608	B	B1i, C3
Limosa lapponica Bar-tailed Godwit	W	1996	333	333	B	B2

An important wintering and passage site for wildfowl and waders.

■ Protection status

National None **International** Partial
1,491 ha of IBA covered by Ramsar Site (Cummeen Strand, 1,491 ha). 1,491 ha of IBA covered by Special Protection Area (Cummeen Strand, 1,491 ha).

■ Conservation issues

Threats Aquaculture/fisheries (B), Industrialization/urbanization (C)

The proximity of Sligo town may negatively affect the site. The feasibility of completing Capital Dredging Works is currently being considered, including the disposal of dredge spoil on mudflat. Habitat quality may be reduced by intertidal shellfish cultivation and increasing recreational use.

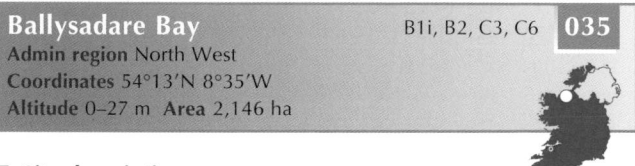

Ballysadare Bay

B1i, B2, C3, C6 | **035**

Admin region North West
Coordinates 54°13'N 8°35'W
Altitude 0–27 m **Area** 2,146 ha

■ Site description

Ballysadare Bay, located 7 km south of Sligo town, is the most southern of the three estuarine areas which comprise Sligo Bay. The site encompasses extensive areas of mudflat, with well-developed saltmarsh in places. It extends as far as the spit at Strandhill dunes, where it opens out to the sea. Shooting is permitted in the marshes at the upper reaches of the bay.

Habitats Forest and woodland, Grassland (10%), Wetland (90%; tidal river/enclosed tidal water; mudflat/sandflat; saltmarsh; sand-dunes/sand beach)
Land-use Agriculture (10%), Fisheries/aquaculture (20%), Hunting (10%), Not utilized (60%)

■ Birds

Species	Season	Year	Pop min	Pop max	Acc	Criteria
[1] *Branta bernicla* Brent Goose	W	1996	200	—	—	B1i, C3
Limosa lapponica Bar-tailed Godwit	W	1996	333	333	A	B2, C6

1. Number needs confirmation.

This site supports a range of waterfowl species in winter.

■ Protection status
National None **International** None

■ Conservation issues

Threats Disturbance to birds (C), Extraction industry (B), Recreation/tourism (C)

Adjacent to the site there is pressure from industrial development; however, a proposed asphalt factory was recently refused consent. This site has been proposed as a Special Protection Area (Ballysadare Bay, 2,146 ha) by NPW and should be designated in the near future. It also lies within a proposed candidate Special Area for Conservation (Ballysadare Bay; area not known).

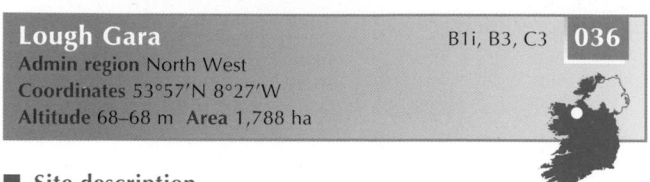

Lough Gara   B1i, B3, C3   036
Admin region North West
Coordinates 53°57′N 8°27′W
Altitude 68–68 m **Area** 1,788 ha

■ Site description
Lough Gara, in Counties Sligo and Roscommon, is situated 7 km west of Boyle at its northern end and 7 km north-east of Ballaghadereen at its southern margin. It is a shallow limestone lake, with a maximum depth of 16 m. To the south it is fed by the Lunge and Breedoge rivers, while in the north it drains into the River Shannon via the River Boyle. The lakeshore comprises reedbed and marsh, which extend along the River Boyle and within the lake are low-lying islands. Adjoining the lake is raised bog. Land-uses include peat-cutting ('Other' land-use).

Habitats Scrub (10%), Grassland (10%; humid grassland), Wetland (80%; standing fresh water; river/stream; raised bog; water-fringe vegetation; fen/transition mire/spring), Artificial landscape (10%; highly improved reseeded grassland)
Land-use Agriculture (20%), Fisheries/aquaculture (80%), Hunting (40%), Other (10%)

■ Birds

Species		Season	Year	Pop min	Pop max	Acc	Criteria
Cygnus cygnus	Whooper Swan	W	1996	110	110	A	B3
¹ *Anser albifrons*	White-fronted Goose	W	1994	503	503	A	B1i, C3

1. Mean 1990–1994.

This is an important site for wintering wildfowl.

■ Protection status
National Partial **International** High
800 ha of IBA covered by Wildfowl Sanctuary (Lough Gara, 800 ha). 1,742 ha of IBA covered by Ramsar Site (Lough Gara, 1,742 ha). 1,742 ha of IBA covered by Special Protection Area (Lough Gara, 1,742 ha).

■ Conservation issues

Threats Agricultural intensification/expansion (C), Disturbance to birds (B), Extraction industry (C)

The lake has been subject to various drainage schemes since the mid-nineteenth century and water-levels are now permanently lowered. Threats include siltation due to peat-cutting and further drainage, while wildfowling causes some disturbance to geese.

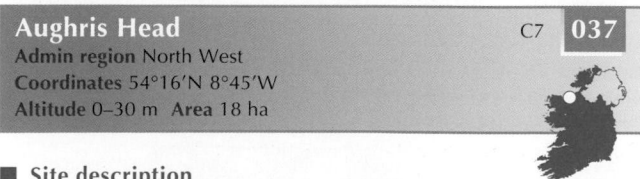

Aughris Head   C7   037
Admin region North West
Coordinates 54°16′N 8°45′W
Altitude 0–30 m **Area** 18 ha

■ Site description
A stretch of mainland cliff, c.1.5 km long, situated on the north-facing County Sligo coastline, approximately 20 km west of Ballysadare. The cliffs, reaching 30 m in height, are near-vertical and horizontally stratified.

Habitats Marine areas (10%; open sea), Rocky areas (90%; sea cliff/rocky shore)
Land-use Fisheries/aquaculture (10%), Not utilized (90%)

■ Birds
This is a notable site for breeding seabirds: there are nationally important numbers of *Rissa tridactyla* (742 pairs, 1997) and *Uria aalge*

(1,211 pairs, 1997). Other species include *Alca torda* (at least 87 birds, 1997), *Fulmarus glacialis* (94 pairs, 1997) and *Phalacrocorax aristotelis* (9 pairs, 1997).

■ Protection status
National None **International** None

■ Conservation issues

Threats Aquaculture/fisheries (C)

Although the numbers of breeding seabirds have fallen below the thresholds of international IBA criteria, the site is retained as an IBA since it was included in the previous pan-European inventory (Grimmett and Jones 1989) and is now being considered for designation as a Special Protection Area by NPW (on the basis of its breeding seabirds).

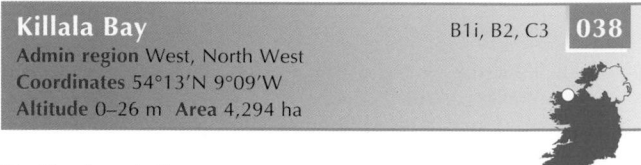

Killala Bay   B1i, B2, C3   038
Admin region West, North West
Coordinates 54°13′N 9°09′W
Altitude 0–26 m **Area** 4,294 ha

■ Site description
A north-facing triangular bay, on the county borders of Mayo and Sligo and at the mouth of the Moy river. A long, sand island, Bartragh Island, separates the south-west side of the bay from open water. Most of the inner region is intertidal, with extensive sand- and mudflats. The main land-uses are for amenity, and the Moy estuary is renowned for salmon fishing.

Habitats Wetland (100%; tidal river/enclosed tidal water; mudflat/sandflat; saltmarsh; sand-dunes/sand beach; shingle/stony beach)
Land-use Fisheries/aquaculture (80%), Hunting (100%), Tourism/recreation (50%)

■ Birds

Species		Season	Year	Pop min	Pop max	Acc	Criteria
Branta bernicla	Brent Goose	W	1996	229	229	A	B1i, C3
Calidris canutus	Knot	W	1996	802	802	A	B2
Limosa lapponica	Bar-tailed Godwit	W	1996	413	413	A	B2

Other wintering species occurring in numbers of national importance include *Mergus serrator* (31 birds, 1996), *Charadrius hiaticula* (140 birds, 1995), *Pluvialis squatarola* (237 birds, 1996), *Calidris alba* (57 birds, 1996) and *Calidris alpina* (2,131 birds, 1996).

■ Protection status
National None **International** Partial
1,061 ha of IBA covered by Ramsar Site (Killala Bay, 1,061 ha). 1,061 ha of IBA covered by Special Protection Area (Killala Bay, 1,061 ha).

■ Conservation issues

Threats Aquaculture/fisheries (C), Industrialization/urbanization (C), Recreation/tourism (B)

The main threats to the site are uncontrolled or accidental emissions into the estuary and bay from Ballina sewage plant and, until recently, from the chemical plant (Asahi) at Killala (now closed). Other threats include intensive holiday-village developments adjacent to the bay, and golf-course expansion and development on the dunes at Inishcrone and Bartragh Island. There is damage to saltmarsh due to grazing and tractors. The site lies within a proposed candidate Special Area for Conservation (Killala Bay; area not known).

Illaunmaistir (Oilean Maistir)   A4ii, A4iii, B1ii, B2,   039
Admin region West   C2, C4, C6
Coordinates 54°19′N 9°38′W
Altitude 0–100 m **Area** 165 ha

■ Site description
A small, steep-sided, inaccessible rocky island (rising to 100 m) and surrounding waters, located just off the cliff-dominated north coast of County Mayo, 19 km west of Ballycastle.

Habitats Marine areas (95%; sea inlet/coastal features), Rocky areas (5%; sea cliff/rocky shore)
Land-use Fisheries/aquaculture (95%), Nature conservation/research (5%)

■ Birds

Species	Season	Year	Pop min	Pop max	Acc	Criteria
Hydrobates pelagicus Storm Petrel	B	1987	7,500	10,000	C	A4ii,B1ii,B2,C2,C6
Fratercula arctica Puffin	B	1989	2,000	—	B	B2

This is an important site for breeding seabirds; additional species include *Fulmarus glacialis* (10 pairs), *Puffinus puffinus* (10–100 pairs), *Phalacrocorax aristotelis* (>10 pairs) and *Cepphus grylle* (5 pairs).

■ Protection status
National None **International** High
165 ha of IBA covered by Special Protection Area (Illaunmaistir, 165 ha).

■ Conservation issues

Threats Aquaculture/fisheries (C)

The island (5 ha) is a reserve owned by BirdWatch Ireland. Fishing in surrounding waters may deplete the prey stock of seabirds, with implications for their breeding success.

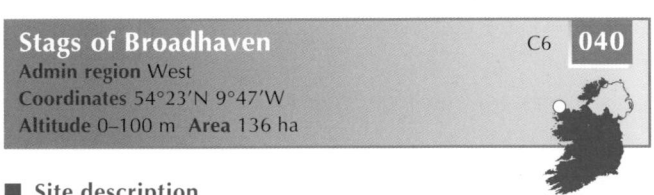

Stags of Broadhaven   C6   040
Admin region West
Coordinates 54°23′N 9°47′W
Altitude 0–100 m **Area** 136 ha

■ Site description
A group of four precipitous rocky islets (totalling 4 ha and rising to 100 m) and the surrounding sea area, located off the cliff-dominated north coast of County Mayo and 2 km north of Benwee Head.

Habitats Marine areas (95%; sea inlet/coastal features), Rocky areas (5%; sea cliff/rocky shore)
Land-use Not utilized (100%)

■ Birds

Species	Season	Year	Pop min	Pop max	Acc	Criteria
[1] *Oceanodroma leucorhoa* Leach's Petrel	B	1982	200	200	B	C6

1. The only proven Irish breeding site.

An important site for breeding seabirds; additional species include *Hydrobates pelagicus* (no recent data; <100 pairs, 1966), *Fulmarus glacialis* (100 pairs, 1982), *Larus argentatus* (c.25 pairs, 1971), *Rissa tridactyla* (c.25 pairs, 1969), *Alca torda* (9 pairs, 1971) and *Fratercula arctica* (no recent data; one of the most densely populated colonies in 1966).

■ Protection status
National None **International** High
136 ha of IBA covered by Special Protection Area (Stags of Broadhaven, 136 ha).

■ Conservation issues

Threats Aquaculture/fisheries (C)

Fishing in surrounding waters may deplete the prey stock of seabirds, with implications for their breeding success.

Broadhaven, Blacksod and Tullaghan Bays and parts of the Mullet peninsula   A4i, B1i, B2, B3, C2, C3, C6   041
Admin region West
Coordinates 54°15′N 9°52′W
Altitude 0–30 m **Area** 10,852 ha

■ Site description
A very large coastal complex, next to Belmullet in County Mayo. This site includes the intertidal mudflats, sandflats and saltmarsh of several bays as well as parts of the Mullet peninsula and mainland, with machair, lake, marsh and non-intensive farmland. This site is an

amalgamation of three sites which were listed as separate IBAs in the previous European inventory (Grimmett and Jones 1989): Broadhaven Bay (formerly IE028), Termoncarragh Lake (formerly IE029) and Blacksod Bay (formerly IE033).

Habitats Grassland (30%; mesophile grassland; machair), Wetland (70%; tidal river/enclosed tidal water; mudflat/sandflat; saltmarsh; sand-dunes/sand beach; coastal lagoon)
Land-use Agriculture (30%), Fisheries/aquaculture (20%), Hunting (70%)

■ Birds

Species	Season	Year	Pop min	Pop max	Acc	Criteria
Gavia immer Great Northern Diver	W	1996	37	65	A	A4i, B1i, C2
Cygnus cygnus Whooper Swan	W	1996	107	124	B	B3
[1] *Branta leucopsis* Barnacle Goose	W	1996	230	780	A	B1i, B2, C2
Branta bernicla Brent Goose	W	1996	194	277	A	B1i, C3
Crex crex Corncrake	B	1996	10	10	A	C6
Limosa lapponica Bar-tailed Godwit	W	1996	241	563	A	B2
[2] *Phalaropus lobatus* Red-necked Phalarope	B	1966	0	2	A	C6
Sterna sandvicensis Sandwich Tern	B	1995	81	81	A	B2, C6

1. Part of flock from site 042.
2. The only regular site over past decades, although not every year in recent years.

The bays and other coastal, lake and intertidal habitats support a wide diversity of wintering and breeding birds. In winter, there are internationally important numbers of several waterbirds. In addition, there are nationally important numbers of *Anser albifrons flavirostris*, *Mergus serrator* (43 birds, 1996), *Pluvialis squatarola* (61 birds, 1995), *Charadrius hiaticula*, *Calidris alba* (65 birds, 1995), *Calidris alpina* (2,465 birds, 1996) and *Limosa limosa* (136 birds, 1996).

■ Protection status
National None **International** Partial
683 ha of IBA covered by Ramsar Site (Blacksod/Broadhaven Bay, 683 ha). 7,493 ha of IBA covered by Special Protection Area (Blacksod and Broadhaven Bays, 7,493 ha). 109 ha of IBA covered by Special Protection Area (Cross Lough (The Mullet), 109 ha). 377 ha of IBA covered by Special Protection Area (Termoncarragh Lake, 377 ha).

■ Conservation issues

Threats Agricultural intensification/expansion (B), Aquaculture/fisheries (U)

Onshore, the site is threatened by overgrazing, increased fencing and increased use of fertilizer, while pressure to develop intertidal shellfish cultivation is increasing within the bays. The breeding habitat of *Crex crex*, in particular, is threatened by changes in agricultural practice, with earlier cutting of hay and silage, and the replacement of meadow with sheep-grazing pasture. Farming practices that favour *Crex crex* are being encouraged within the area through a grant scheme. There are plans to attract *Phalaropus lobatus* back to Annagh marsh on the Mullet peninsula, through habitat-restoration measures. A 24 ha reserve owned by BirdWatch Ireland lies within the site. The IBA overlaps with a proposed candidate Special Area for Conservation (Blacksod/Mullet; area not known).

Inishglora and Inishkeeragh   A4ii, A4iii, B1ii, B2, B3, C2, C4, C6   042
Admin region West
Coordinates 54°13′N 10°09′W
Altitude 0–22 m **Area** 337 ha

■ Site description
Two low-lying offshore islands, 1 km west of Corraun Point on the Mullet peninsula, County Mayo. This site includes Carricknaronty Rocks, Duffar Rocks and the surrounding sea area.

Habitats Grassland (10%; humid grassland), Marine areas (85%; sea inlet/coastal features), Rocky areas (5%; sea cliff/rocky shore; rock stacks/islets)
Land-use Fisheries/aquaculture (85%), Not utilized (15%)

■ Birds
These islands are important for their breeding colonies of seabirds, and are also notable for wintering *Branta leucopsis* (265 birds, 1994; birds also use sites 043 and 044), and for breeding *Sterna paradisaea* (105 pairs, 1995). There are also small numbers of *Sterna albifrons*. Other breeding seabirds in numbers of national importance are

Phalacrocorax carbo (57 pairs), *Larus marinus* (75 pairs) and *Larus fuscus* (min. 20 pairs).

Species	Season	Year	Pop min	Pop max	Acc	Criteria
[1] *Hydrobates pelagicus* Storm Petrel	B	1987	10,000	20,000	C	A4ii,B1ii,B2,C2,C6
Phalacrocorax aristotelis Shag	B	1987	175	175	A	B3
Larus canus Common Gull	B	1989	55	65	—	B2

1. One of the largest colonies in Ireland.

■ Protection status

National None **International** High

337 ha of IBA covered by Special Protection Area (Inishglora and Inishkeeragh, 337 ha).

■ Conservation issues

Threats	Aquaculture/fisheries (U)

Fishing may deplete the prey stock of seabirds, with implications for their breeding success.

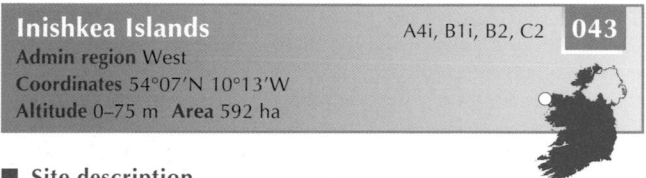

Inishkea Islands
A4i, B1i, B2, C2   **043**
Admin region West
Coordinates 54°07′N 10°13′W
Altitude 0–75 m   **Area** 592 ha

■ Site description

Two large islands and surrounding rocks, 4 km west of the Mullet peninsula in County Mayo. The northern island is dominated by machair and has a small lake. The southern island is machair-covered in the northern part, with a heath-covered hill and ridge dominating to the south. The islands have been uninhabited since 1932, but there is still grazing of cattle and sheep.

Habitats Scrub (30%; heathland), Grassland (70%; machair)
Land-use Agriculture (100%)

■ Birds

Species	Season	Year	Pop min	Pop max	Acc	Criteria
[1] *Branta leucopsis* Barnacle Goose	W	1993	2,681	2,681	A	A4i, B1i, B2, C2

1. Birds also use sites 042 and 044.

This is the most important wintering site for *Branta leucopsis* in Ireland (birds also use sites 042 and 044). Other wintering birds of national importance (no more recent data) include *Pluvialis apricaria* (1,500, 1987), *Calidris alba* (200, 1987), *Calidris maritima* (175, 1987) and *Arenaria interpres* (400, 1987). After an absence from the islands since the 1960s, *Crex crex* have returned to breed (2 birds, 1998). The islands comprise one of the top sites in Ireland for shorebirds breeding on machair, e.g. *Haematopus ostralegus*, *Vanellus vanellus* and *Calidris alpina*.

■ Protection status

National Partial **International** Partial

IBA overlaps with Wildfowl Sanctuary (Inishkea Islands; area not known). 272 ha of IBA covered by Special Protection Area (Inishkea Islands, 272 ha).

■ Conservation issues

Threats	Agricultural intensification/expansion (C)

Day-trippers may cause disturbance to nesting birds. The site overlaps with a proposed candidate Special Area for Conservation by 272 ha (Inishkea Islands; area not known).

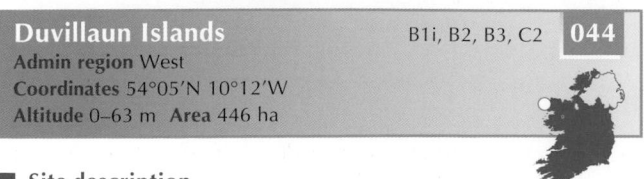

Duvillaun Islands
B1i, B2, B3, C2   **044**
Admin region West
Coordinates 54°05′N 10°12′W
Altitude 0–63 m   **Area** 446 ha

■ Site description

This is a group of five offshore islands with outlying rocks and reefs, 3 km south-west of the Mullet peninsula in County Mayo.

Habitats Grassland (10%; mesophile grassland), Marine areas (75%; sea inlet/coastal features), Rocky areas (15%; sea cliff/rocky shore; rock stacks/islets)
Land-use Fisheries/aquaculture (75%), Not utilized (25%)

■ Birds

Species	Season	Year	Pop min	Pop max	Acc	Criteria
[1] *Branta leucopsis* Barnacle Goose	W	1994	200	500	A	B1i, B2, C2
Larus marinus Great Black-backed Gull	B	1987	210	210	A	B3
Cepphus grylle Black Guillemot	B	1981	25	30	—	B2

1. Birds also use sites 042 and 043.

These islands support important numbers of wintering geese and breeding seabirds. Seabirds breeding in numbers of national importance are *Phalacrocorax carbo* (185 pairs, 1981), *Fulmarus glacialis* (500 pairs, 1981), *Larus canus* (20–50 pairs, 1981) and *Larus argentatus* (300–400 pairs, 1981).

■ Protection status

National None **International** None

■ Conservation issues

Threats	Aquaculture/fisheries (U)

The site is a proposed (by NPW) Special Protection Area (Duvillaun Island, 446 ha), and should be designated in the near future.

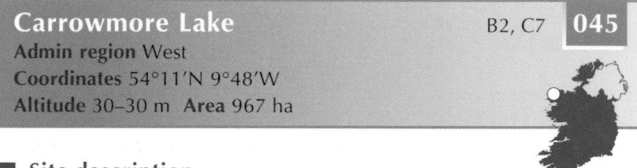

Carrowmore Lake
B2, C7   **045**
Admin region West
Coordinates 54°11′N 9°48′W
Altitude 30–30 m   **Area** 967 ha

■ Site description

Carrowmore lake is situated 2.5 km north-west of Bangor, in north-west County Mayo. It is a medium-sized, fairly shallow lake, originally with low to moderate nutrient-levels (oligotrophic–mesotrophic), and is surrounded by blanket bog and some new forestry plantations. The IBA is considerably larger than in the previous European inventory (Grimmett and Jones 1989), when it comprised solely Darreen's Island, a low-lying grassy island in the north-western part of the lake. The lake is used for angling.

Habitats Wetland (100%; standing fresh water; water-fringe vegetation)
Land-use Fisheries/aquaculture (100%)

■ Birds

Species	Season	Year	Pop min	Pop max	Acc	Criteria
Larus canus Common Gull	B	1993	300	—	—	B2

At Darreen's Island, in Carrowmore lake, there is a long-established colony of gulls *Larus*. Formerly the site was also important for breeding terns *Sterna*, particularly *Sterna sandvicensis* (164 pairs, 1984) and *Sterna paradisaea* (18 pairs, 1984). However, in recent years neither of these species, nor *Larus ridibundus* (1,500 pairs, 1987), have bred here. It is believed that the terns switched to Inishderry Island in Broadhaven Bay (site 041) and that they may interchange between the two sites. *Anser albifrons flavirostris* winters in numbers of national importance (146, 1994); this flock also uses sites 046 and 041.

■ Protection status

National High **International** High

IBA overlaps with Wildfowl Sanctuary (Carrowmore Lough; area not known). 967 ha of IBA covered by Special Protection Area (Carrowmore Lake, 967 ha).

■ Conservation issues

Threats	Agricultural intensification/expansion (C), Aquaculture/fisheries (C), Recreation/tourism (C)

Water quality is threatened by the intensification of agriculture and the effects of nutrient pollution. It is not known why terns stopped breeding on Darreen's Island, which was designated as a Special Protection Area on account of them, but they may return to breed in future. The site lies within a proposed candidate Special Area for Conservation (Carrowmore Lake; area not known).

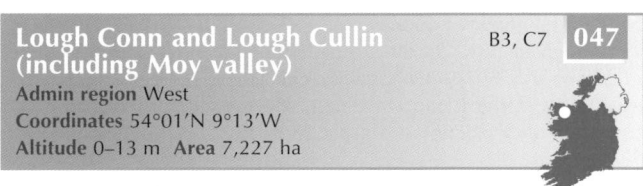

Owenduff river catchment and Nephin Beg C7 046
Admin region West
Coordinates 54°02′N 9°38′W
Altitude 0–721 m **Area** 25,622 ha

■ Site description
A large area of relatively intact blanket bog in north-west County Mayo, bounded by Bangor to the north, Mullranny in the south-west and Lough Feeagh to the east. The site is one of the best examples of an Atlantic blanket-bog system in Europe and supports a diversity of other habitats, including upland grassland, mountainous terrain, lakes and rivers. Sheep graze the area.

Habitats Grassland (20%; humid grassland), Wetland (70%; standing fresh water; river/stream; blanket bog; fen/transition mire/spring), Rocky areas (10%; inland cliff)
Land-use Agriculture (80%), Fisheries/aquaculture (10%), Hunting (20%), Nature conservation/research (5%), Tourism/recreation (50%)

■ Birds
This site was designated as a Special Protection Area based on its high number of wintering *Anser albifrons flavirostris* (146 birds, 1994), together with breeding *Pluvialis apricaria*, both of which are Annex I species under the EC Birds Directive.

■ Protection status
National None **International** High
1,382 ha of IBA covered by Ramsar Site (Owenduff catchment, 1,382 ha). 25,622 ha of IBA covered by Special Protection Area (Owenduff/Nephin Complex, 25,622 ha).

■ Conservation issues

Threats Agricultural intensification/expansion (A), Disturbance to birds (B), Extraction industry (B)

The severity of overgrazing by sheep within this site is the subject of a legal action against Ireland by the European Commission. It is believed to have contributed to a decline in wintering *Anser albifrons flavirostris* and breeding *Pluvialis apricaria*. Other pressures on this site are wildfowling (causing disturbance to geese) and peat extraction. The IBA lies within a proposed candidate Special Area for Conservation (Owenduff/Nephin Complex; area not known).

Lough Conn and Lough Cullin (including Moy valley) B3, C7 047
Admin region West
Coordinates 54°01′N 9°13′W
Altitude 0–13 m **Area** 7,227 ha

■ Site description
A wetland complex, 2 km east of Foxford in County Mayo and comprising two large lakes, with islands, and a diversity of shoreline habitats including fens, marshes, wet grasslands, rocky shorelines and deciduous woodland. The lakes are drained by the Moy river and the site also includes grasslands which surround this river to the east and north-east of Lough Cullin (Moy valley). The site has been extended since the previous European inventory (Grimmett and Jones 1989) to include the Moy valley. The Moy river was drained in the 1960s and its adjacent grasslands no longer flood. The lakes are popular for angling.

Habitats Grassland (10%; humid grassland), Wetland (80%; shingle/stony beach; standing fresh water; water-fringe vegetation; fen/transition mire/spring), Artificial landscape (10%; highly improved reseeded grassland)
Land-use Agriculture (30%), Fisheries/aquaculture (70%), Nature conservation/research (5%), Tourism/recreation (5%)

■ Birds
Loughs Conn and Cullin are important for their waterfowl populations, and the Moy valley is notable for breeding *Crex crex*

(5 pairs, 1996). Wintering species of national importance are *Anser albifrons flavirostris* (146 birds, 1994), *Aythya ferina* (431 birds, 1995), *Fulica atra* (1,500 birds, 1996), *Cygnus olor* (284 birds, 1996), *Aythya fuligula* (694 birds, 1996) and *Bucephala clangula* (102 birds, 1996). This is also one of three regular breeding sites for *Melanitta nigra* in Ireland.

Species		Season	Year	Pop min	Pop max	Acc	Criteria
Cygnus cygnus	Whooper Swan	W	1987	132	132	—	B3

■ Protection status
National Partial **International** Partial
2,600 ha of IBA covered by Wildfowl Sanctuary (Lough Conn, 2,600 ha). 1,135 ha of IBA covered by Wildfowl Sanctuary (Lough Cullin, 1,135 ha). 5,291 ha of IBA covered by Special Protection Area (Lough Conn, 5,291 ha). 1,136 ha of IBA covered by Special Protection Area (Lough Cullin, 1,136 ha).

■ Conservation issues

Threats Agricultural intensification/expansion (A), Aquaculture/fisheries (C), Extraction industry (U), Recreation/tourism (C)

Previously the herb-rich grasslands alongside the Moy river provided breeding habitat for large concentrations of *Crex crex*. However, drainage of the river in the 1960s dried out the land, allowing more intensive farming with earlier cutting of meadow and increased use of fertilizer. This is likely to have caused the reduction in numbers of *Crex crex*. BirdWatch Ireland, with support from NPW and RSPB, operate a grant scheme in the area to encourage farming practices that favour *Crex crex*. The main threat to the lake is nutrient pollution, due partly to agricultural intensification within the catchment and partly to increased siltation (probably a consequence of large-scale mechanical peat extraction taking place upstream). There is also increasing pressure from lake shore developments (holiday homes/marinas) which cause habitat loss, and increase the problem of nutrient pollution due to inputs of domestic waste.

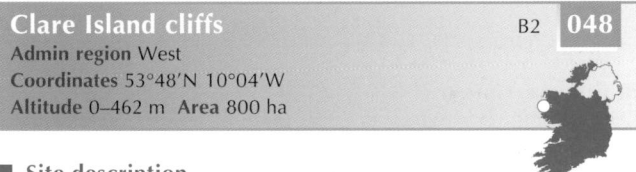

Clare Island cliffs B2 048
Admin region West
Coordinates 53°48′N 10°04′W
Altitude 0–462 m **Area** 800 ha

■ Site description
Clare Island is situated at the entrance of Clew Bay, 5 km from the mainland in County Mayo. The sea cliffs extend for 8 km along the north-western side of the island; the site boundary runs parallel to, and 100 m inland from, the cliff-edge.

Habitats Marine areas (10%; sea inlet/coastal features), Rocky areas (90%; sea cliff/rocky shore)
Land-use Agriculture (25%), Not utilized (75%)

■ Birds

Species		Season	Year	Pop min	Pop max	Acc	Criteria
Cepphus grylle	Black Guillemot	B	1987	15	15	—	B2

The cliffs hold notable seabird colonies, including one of the largest colonies of *Fulmarus glacialis* (1,898 pairs, 1990) in Ireland, and nationally important numbers of *Larus argentatus* (min. 550 pairs, 1987) and *Rissa tridactyla* (1,712 pairs, 1990). This is also a notable breeding site for *Pyrrhocorax pyrrhocorax*.

■ Protection status
National None **International** None

■ Conservation issues

Threats Agricultural intensification/expansion (C), Aquaculture/fisheries (C)

This site is being considered by NPW for designation as a Special Protection Area, and it overlaps with a proposed candidate Special Area for Conservation (Clare Island Cliffs; area not known). The cliffs are listed as an area of international scientific importance, on account of their rare Arctic-alpine plant communities and seabird colonies.

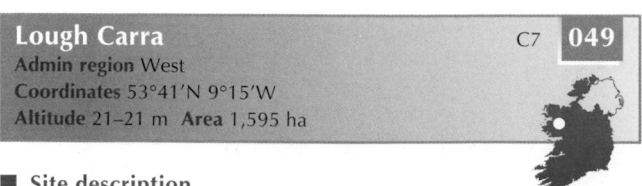

Lough Carra

Admin region West
Coordinates 53°41′N 9°15′W
Altitude 21–21 m **Area** 1,595 ha

C7 049

■ Site description
Lough Carra is situated south of Castlebar, in County Mayo. It is a large, clear, calcareous lake with many bays, and islands, and is predominantly spring-fed. There are areas of wet woodland, marsh and reedbed on the lakeshore. The lake is linked hydrologically to Lough Mask (site 051), immediately to its south.

Habitats Wetland (100%; standing fresh water; water-fringe vegetation; fen/transition mire/spring)
Land-use Fisheries/aquaculture (100%), Water management (100%)

■ Birds
The site was designated as a Special Protection Area on the basis of migratory waterfowl populations, including nationally important numbers of *Aythya fuligula* (438 birds, 1995).

■ Protection status
National High **International** High
IBA overlaps with Wildfowl Sanctuary (Lough Carra; area not known). 1,595 ha of IBA covered by Special Protection Area (Lough Carra, 1,595 ha).

■ Conservation issues

Threats Drainage (B)

Reduced water-levels may have led to a decline in diving duck populations. The site lies within a proposed candidate Special Area for Conservation (Lough Carra/Mask complex; area not known).

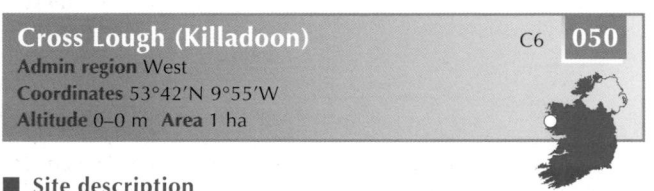

Cross Lough (Killadoon)

Admin region West
Coordinates 53°42′N 9°55′W
Altitude 0–0 m **Area** 1 ha

C6 050

■ Site description
Cross Lough is situated near Killadoon village, south-west of Louisburgh in County Mayo. The lough is a coastal lagoon separated from the sea by a shingle ridge, within which there is a small islet.

Habitats Grassland (100%; mesophile grassland)
Land-use Not utilized (100%)

■ Birds

Species		Season	Year	Pop min	Pop max	Acc	Criteria
Sterna sandvicensis	Sandwich Tern	B	1995	70	70	A	C6

The islet is the site of a long-established breeding colony of *Sterna sandvicensis*.

■ Protection status
National None **International** None

■ Conservation issues

Threats Natural events (B)

The breaching of the shingle bar may lead to erosion of the islet. The colony of terns *Sterna* has declined in recent years, possibly due to predation by American mink *Mustela vison*.

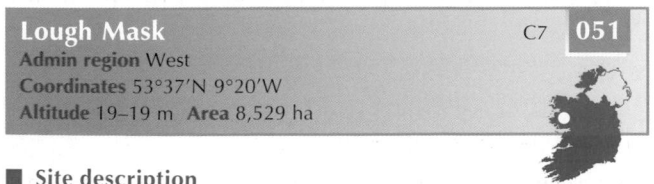

Lough Mask

Admin region West
Coordinates 53°37′N 9°20′W
Altitude 19–19 m **Area** 8,529 ha

C7 051

■ Site description
Located in County Mayo, Lough Mask is situated south of Lough Carra (site 049), which drains into it, and north of Lough Corrib (site 056), into which it drains. It is one of the deepest lakes in the country and is calcareous. It is fed by the Owenbrin river which deposits large amounts of sandy sediment at its entrance forming an extensive delta.

Habitats Wetland (100%; standing fresh water; river/stream; water-fringe vegetation)
Land-use Fisheries/aquaculture (90%), Not utilized (10%)

■ Birds
The site was designated as a Special Protection Area on the basis of its migratory waterfowl populations, with *Aythya fuligula* occurring in numbers of national importance (684 birds, 1996). There are also nationally important colonies of breeding gulls, with *Larus fuscus* (722 birds, 1993), *L. canus* (742 birds, 1993) and *L. ridibundus* (2,650 birds, 1993). It is also a probable breeding site for the nationally scarce *Melanitta nigra*.

■ Protection status
National High **International** High
IBA overlaps with Wildfowl Sanctuary (Lough Mask; area not known). 8,529 ha of IBA covered by Special Protection Area (Lough Mask, 8,529 ha).

■ Conservation issues

Threats Agricultural intensification/expansion (B)

Nutrient pollution may threaten the lake, due to intensification of agriculture on surrounding farmland. The site lies within a proposed candidate Special Area for Conservation (Lough Carra/Mask complex; area not known).

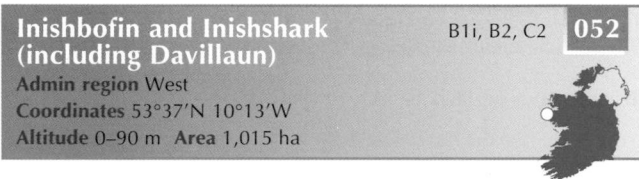

Inishbofin and Inishshark (including Davillaun)

Admin region West
Coordinates 53°37′N 10°13′W
Altitude 0–90 m **Area** 1,015 ha

B1i, B2, C2 052

■ Site description
A group of marine islands situated approximately 5.5 km off the west County Galway coast. Inishbofin, the largest island, is inhabited year-round by approximately 250 people. Two-thirds of this island is commonage and the main habitat-type is heathland, the other third is used for agriculture, mainly sheep-grazing, with small areas of meadow. Sheer cliffs and two very large stacks are present at its western end. Inishark is situated less that 1 km south-west of Inishbofin, and has been uninhabited since 1960. Its main habitat-types are heathland with rough pasture. The much smaller Davillaun Island lies 2 km east of Inishbofin, it is uninhabited. The IBA has been expanded to encompass Inishark and Davillaun, which were not included within this site in the previous pan-European inventory (Grimmett and Jones 1989).

Habitats Scrub (50%; heathland), Grassland (30%; humid grassland; mesophile grassland), Wetland (10%; shingle/stony beach), Rocky areas (10%; sea cliff/rocky shore)
Land-use Agriculture (50%), Not utilized (45%), Urban/industrial/transport (5%)

■ Birds

Species		Season	Year	Pop min	Pop max	Acc	Criteria
Puffinus puffinus	Manx Shearwater	B	1987	200	300	B	B2
Branta leucopsis	Barnacle Goose	W	1993	400	400	B	B1i, B2, C2

Breeding *Puffinus puffinus* and wintering *Branta leucopsis* occur on both Inishark and Inishbofin, the latter species occurring also on Davillaun. Other seabirds breeding in numbers of national importance are *Fulmarus glacialis* (824 pairs, 1990) and *Hydrobates pelagicus* (>30 pairs, 1965). Inishbofin was formerly a stronghold of the globally threatened *Crex crex*, but breeding numbers are now small (3 calling males, 1998), though still of national importance. *Pyrrhocorax pyrrhocorax* breed in low numbers on the two main islands.

■ Protection status
National None **International** None

■ Conservation issues

Threats Abandonment/reduction of land management (B), Agricultural intensification/expansion (B), Extraction industry (C)

With changes in farm practice on both islands, mainly the replacement of meadow with sheep-grazing pasture, there has been a stark decline in breeding numbers of *Crex crex* and a total disappearance of breeding *Miliaria calandra*. To try to reverse this trend, farming practices that favour *Crex crex* are being encouraged through a grant scheme. Other threats to Inishbofin in particular include peat-cutting and drainage.

High Island   B2, B3, C7   **053**
Admin region West
Coordinates 53°33′N 10°17′W
Altitude 0–60 m   Area 169 ha

■ Site description

A small, uninhabited marine island lying 3 km west of Aughris Point, off the west coast of County Galway. The island, with a largely sheer cliff coastline, rises to 60 m in height. It is of archaeological interest for its ancient monastic settlements.

Habitats Grassland (10%; mesophile grassland), Marine areas (80%; sea inlet/coastal features), Rocky areas (10%; sea cliff/rocky shore; rock stacks/islets)
Land-use Fisheries/aquaculture (80%), Not utilized (20%)

■ Birds

Species	Season	Year	Pop min	Pop max	Acc	Criteria
Hydrobates pelagicus Storm Petrel	B	1996	1,000	1,000	—	B2
Larus marinus Great Black-backed Gull	B	1987	200	200	B	B3

The cliffs and undisturbed coastal grasslands of High Island provide an important site for breeding seabirds. *Fulmarus glacialis* also breeds in nationally important numbers (350 pairs, 1987).

■ Protection status

National None **International** High
169 ha of IBA covered by Special Protection Area (High Island, 169 ha).

■ Conservation issues

Threats Aquaculture/fisheries (C)

The isolation and difficulty of landing on this island have so far secured it from serious human disturbance. Fishing in surrounding waters may deplete the prey stock of seabirds, with implications for their breeding success.

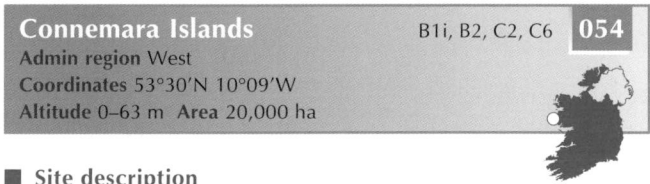

Connemara Islands   B1i, B2, C2, C6   **054**
Admin region West
Coordinates 53°30′N 10°09′W
Altitude 0–63 m   Area 20,000 ha

■ Site description

This very large site encompasses many small islands and islets stretching from Slyne Head (Illaunamid Island) south-eastwards via Ballyconneely, Bertraghboy and Kilkieran Bay as far as Greatman's Bay. Several IBAs which were treated separately in the previous pan-European inventory (Grimmett and Jones 1989) have been combined to form this site, including Eeshal Island (formerly IE041), Horse Island (formerly IE042), Hen Island (formerly IE043), Oilean Geabhrog (formerly IE045), Oilean nan Geabhrog (formerly IE046), Duck Island (formerly IE047) and Geabhrog Island (formerly IE048). The site also includes surrounding waters, covering a sea area up to 5 km off the mainland, along a coast of 40 km in length.

Habitats Grassland (10%), Wetland (5%; sand-dunes/sand beach; coastal lagoon), Marine areas (80%; sea inlet/coastal features), Rocky areas (5%; rock stacks/islets)
Land-use Agriculture (10%), Fisheries/aquaculture (80%), Not utilized (10%)

■ Birds

Species	Season	Year	Pop min	Pop max	Acc	Criteria
Branta leucopsis Barnacle Goose	W	1994	225	370	—	B1i, C2
Sterna sandvicensis Sandwich Tern	B	1995	223	223	A	B2, C6
Sterna hirundo Common Tern	B	1995	139	139	A	C6
Sterna paradisaea Arctic Tern	B	1995	666	666	A	C6
Sterna albifrons Little Tern	B	1995	41	41	A	B2, C6

This group of islands supports some of the most important colonies of breeding terns *Sterna*, especially *Sterna paradisaea*, in Ireland and is also an important winter feeding site for *Branta leucopsis*, particularly on St Macdara's Island and more recently in Inishmuskerry. A detailed review of tern usage from surveys in 1969–1970, 1984 and 1995 is required to clarify which are the most important islands. In the absence of such a review, a single such IBA is considered a better approach as terns appear to be very mobile within this area.

■ Protection status

National None **International** None

■ Conservation issues

Threats Aquaculture/fisheries (U), Recreation/tourism (B)

Fishing in surrounding waters may deplete the prey stock of seabirds, with implications for their breeding success, while increasing tourism (trips to the islands) may lead to disturbance of nesting terns. The site overlaps with a proposed Special Protection Area (Slyne Head, 1,514 ha).

Roundstone bog   A4iii, C4, C6   **055**
Admin region West
Coordinates 53°23′N 9°47′W
Altitude 20–300 m   Area 7,000 ha

■ Site description

Roundstone bog is a complex of lakes, rocky outcrops and lowland Atlantic blanket bog. Rocky outcrops and variations in topography have resulted in a complexity of peatland plant communities, making the site of particular conservation interest. The site includes Lough Scannive (83 ha) which was treated as an IBA (formerly IE044) in the previous pan-European inventory (Grimmett and Jones 1989).

Habitats Wetland (80%; standing fresh water; blanket bog), Rocky areas (20%).
Land-use Agriculture (60%), Not utilized (30%), Other (10%)

■ Birds

Species	Season	Year	Pop min	Pop max	Acc	Criteria
Falco columbarius Merlin	B	—	4	—	—	C6
[1] *Pluvialis apricaria* Golden Plover	B	—	20	—	—	C6
[2] *Sterna sandvicensis* Sandwich Tern	B	—	31	—	—	C6

1. >6% national breeding population.
2. 2% national breeding population.

An important site for breeding *Pluvialis apricaria*, *Falco columbarius* and *Sterna sandvicensis*. Lough Scannive, within this site, was designated as a Special Protection Area on account of its nationally important numbers of breeding *Phalacrocorax carbo* (218 pairs, 1986). In winter the site also supports nationally important numbers of *Anser albifrons flavirostris* (30 birds) which are particularly significant since they utilize the natural bog habitat.

■ Protection status

National None **International** Low
49 ha of IBA covered by Special Protection Area (Lough Scannive, 49 ha).

■ Conservation issues

Threats Afforestation (C), Agricultural intensification/expansion (C), Drainage (C), Extraction industry (B), Industrialization/urbanization (A)

A development proposal for an airstrip within the western margin of the bog is a significant threat. Other hazards to the site include large-scale mechanical peat-cutting and, in the surrounding area, afforestation and overgrazing by sheep and cattle, resulting in peat erosion. Part of the site overlaps with a proposed candidate Special Area for Conservation (Connemara Bog Complex; 6,000 ha).

Lough Corrib   A4iii, B1i, C3, C4   056
Admin region West
Coordinates 53°24′N 9°17′W
Altitude 0–25 m   **Area** 18,240 ha

■ Site description
Lough Corrib is situated north of Galway city, and is the second-largest lake in Ireland. It consists of two parts: a smaller, shallower basin to the south and a large, deeper basin to the north, connected by a relatively narrow channel. It supports one of the largest areas of wetland vegetation in the country, with extensive submerged beds of stonewort *Chara*, as well as reed-swamp, marsh, fen and wet grassland. The lakeshore includes woodland, raised bog, callow, and limestone pavement. Apart from raised bog these habitats are also present on the many lake islands. The lake is used for trout fishing.

Habitats Forest and woodland (5%; broadleaved deciduous forest), Grassland (10%; humid grassland; mesophile grassland), Wetland (85%; standing fresh water; river/stream; water-fringe vegetation; fen/transition mire/spring)
Land-use Agriculture (20%), Fisheries/aquaculture (80%), Hunting (100%)

■ Birds

Species		Season	Year	Pop min	Pop max	Acc	Criteria
Aythya ferina	Pochard	W	1996	8,050	8,050	A	B1i, C3
Fulica atra	Coot	P	1996	25,100	25,100	A	B1i, C3

This is an important site for wintering waterfowl. Several additional species occur in numbers of national importance, including *Anser albifrons flavirostris* (140 birds, 1996), *Anas penelope* (1,000 birds, 1995), *Anas strepera* (35 birds, 1996), *Anas clypeata* (84 birds, 1996), *Aythya fuligula* (2,676 birds, 1996), *Bucephala clangula* (145 birds, 1996), *Vanellus vanellus* (4,050 birds, 1995) and *Pluvialis apricaria* (7,000 birds, 1995). Lough Corrib is one of only three regular breeding sites known for *Melanitta nigra* in Ireland, and numbers are of national importance (30 pairs, 1995).

■ Protection status
National None   **International** High
17,728 ha of IBA covered by Ramsar Site (Lough Corrib, 17,728 ha). 17,728 ha of IBA covered by Special Protection Area (Lough Corrib, 17,728 ha).

■ Conservation issues

Threats Agricultural intensification/expansion (B), Aquaculture/fisheries (C), Disturbance to birds (B), Industrialization/urbanization (B)

The uncontrolled discharge of sewage, particularly into the southern part of the lake, is causing nutrient pollution. Other threats to habitat quality are wildfowling (causing disturbance to birds) and increasing pressure from fishing and from lakeshore developments such as hotels, holiday homes and marinas.

Inner Galway Bay   B1i, B2, C3, C6   057
Admin region West
Coordinates 53°12′N 9°03′W
Altitude 0–5 m   **Area** 11,905 ha

■ Site description
Situated on the west County Clare/Galway coast, this is the shallow, more sheltered part of a large sea bay, which is partly protected from the open sea by the Aran Islands. On the eastern and southern sides of the site there are numerous shallow tidal inlets including the smaller bays of Kinvara, Aughinish, Corranroo and Ballyvaughan. The southern side is fringed with limestone pavement while a number of small, low islands composed of glacial deposits are located along the eastern side. Intertidal shellfish cultivation takes place mainly on the southern and eastern shores of the site, while the northern shore, where Galway city is located, is subject to greater human pressure, due to amenity and recreation use.

Habitats Wetland (30%; mudflat/sandflat; sand-dunes/sand beach; shingle/stony beach), Marine areas (70%; sea inlet/coastal features)
Land-use Fisheries/aquaculture (90%), Urban/industrial/transport (10%)

■ Birds

Species		Season	Year	Pop min	Pop max	Acc	Criteria
Gavia arctica	Black-throated Diver	W	1996	39	49	A	C6
Branta bernicla	Brent Goose	W	1996	525	525	A	B1i, C3
Mergus serrator	Red-breasted Merganser	W	1996	244	244	A	B1i, C3
Limosa lapponica	Bar-tailed Godwit	W	1996	277	277	B	B2
[1] *Sterna sandvicensis*	Sandwich Tern	B	—	81	81	A	B2, C6

1. Nesting on an islet in Inner Corranroo Bay.

This is an important site for wintering waterfowl and breeding seabirds. Several other species occur at this site in numbers of national importance, including wintering *Anas penelope* (1,413 birds, 1995), *Clangula hyemalis* (71 birds, 1996), *Charadrius hiaticula* (449 birds, 1996), *Pluvialis squatarola* (86 birds, 1996), *Pluvialis apricaria* (2,275 birds, 1996) and *Calidris alpina* (1,835 birds, 1996), as well as breeding *Phalacrocorax carbo* (min. 220 pairs, 1987) and *Sterna hirundo* (98 pairs, 1995).

■ Protection status
National None   **International** High
11,905 ha of IBA covered by Ramsar Site (Inner Galway Bay, 11,905 ha). 11,905 ha of IBA covered by Special Protection Area (Inner Galway Bay, 11,905 ha).

■ Conservation issues

Threats Aquaculture/fisheries (C), Industrialization/urbanization (B), Other (C), Recreation/tourism (C)

An ongoing problem is the discharge of untreated sewage from Galway city into the sea bay ('Other' threat). A proposal for the construction of a causeway across intertidal mudflats, to carry a pipeline to a sewage-treatment plant on Mutton Island, has met with controversy. However, this solution is now being implemented despite opposition and lack of favour from the European Commission. Effects on the inner bay in terms of changes to sediment patterns are unknown. Other threats to habitat quality include intertidal shellfish cultivation and development of the recreational and amenity potential of the site. The IBA overlaps with a proposed candidate Special Area for Conservation (Inner Galway Bay; area not known).

Rahasane turlough   B1i, B2, B3, C2, C3   058
Admin region West
Coordinates 53°13′N 8°47′W
Altitude 10–30 m   **Area** 257 ha

■ Site description
Situated on the Dunkellin river, west of Craughwell in south-west Galway, this is the last large turlough (karst lake) remaining in Ireland. The site comprises marshes, seasonally flooded wet meadows, with limestone outcrops and scrub at its margins. In the summer the site is grazed by cattle and sheep.

Habitats Scrub (5%; scrub), Grassland (75%; steppe/dry calcareous grassland; humid grassland), Wetland (20%; standing fresh water; river/stream; water-fringe vegetation)
Land-use Agriculture (75%), Hunting (100%)

■ Birds

Species		Season	Year	Pop min	Pop max	Acc	Criteria
Cygnus columbianus	Bewick's Swan	W	1996	24	24	A	B2
Cygnus cygnus	Whooper Swan	W	1996	248	248	A	B1i, B3, C2
Limosa limosa	Black-tailed Godwit	W	1989	100	1,100	—	B1i, C3

This is an important site for wintering waterfowl. Species wintering in nationally important numbers include *Anser albifrons flavirostris* (139 birds, 1995) and *Anas penelope* (5,570 birds, 1996).

■ **Protection status**
National None **International** Partial
221 ha of IBA covered by Special Protection Area (Rahasane Turlough, 221 ha).

■ **Conservation issues**

> **Threats** Agricultural intensification/expansion (B), Disturbance to birds (B), Drainage (B)

Drainage of the site has been a long-standing threat. However, its designation as a Special Protection Area and its status as a proposed candidate Special Area for Conservation (Rahasane Turlough; area not known) should reduce this threat. Disturbance to wintering birds is caused by wildfowling. There has been some clearance of limestone pavement next to the lake, with implications for water quality and disturbance to birds.

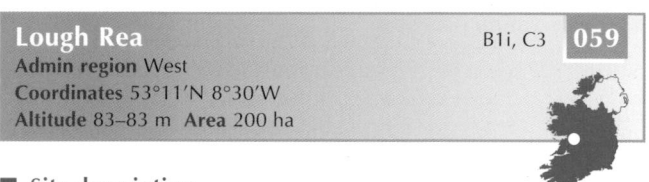

Lough Rea   B1i, C3   059
Admin region West
Coordinates 53°11′N 8°30′W
Altitude 83–83 m **Area** 200 ha

■ **Site description**
A small lake with islands and some reed-swamp, situated just south of the town of Loughrea in County Galway. There is improved farmland around the lake, and it is used by anglers.

> **Habitats** Wetland (100%; standing fresh water; water-fringe vegetation)
> **Land-use** Tourism/recreation (100%)

■ **Birds**

Species	Season	Year	Pop min	Pop max	Acc	Criteria
[1] *Anas clypeata* Shoveler	W	1996	467	681	A	B1i, C3

1. Maximum is mean peak in mid-1980s (minimum 1996).

This is one of the most important wintering sites in Ireland for *Fulica atra* (1,700 birds, 1980s). *Aythya fuligula* (452 birds, 1986), and *Pluvialis apricaria* (1,000 birds, 1995) also occur in numbers of national importance.

■ **Protection status**
National None **International** None

■ **Conservation issues**

> **Threats** Recreation/tourism (C)

The main threat to the lake is nutrient pollution from agricultural run-off, as many of the surrounding fields have been fertilized.

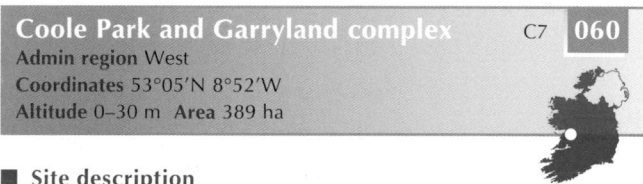

Coole Park and Garryland complex   C7   060
Admin region West
Coordinates 53°05′N 8°52′W
Altitude 0–30 m **Area** 389 ha

■ **Site description**
A site comprising a range of habitats including turloughs, Lough Coole, grassland and mixed deciduous woodland, situated north-west of Gort in County Galway. It is a popular public amenity area.

> **Habitats** Forest and woodland (60%; broadleaved deciduous forest), Grassland (15%; mesophile grassland), Wetland (25%; standing fresh water; river/stream; fen/transition mire/spring)
> **Land-use** Agriculture (15%), Tourism/recreation (85%)

■ **Birds**
The site was designated a Special Protection Area on the basis of its migratory waterfowl, particularly *Cygnus cygnus* which is an Annex I species under the EC Birds Directive.

■ **Protection status**
National High **International** High
363 ha of IBA covered by Nature Reserve (Coole–Garryland, 363 ha). Part of IBA covered by Wildfowl Sanctuary (Coole Lough, 363 ha).

364 ha of IBA covered by Ramsar Site (Coole Lough and Garryland Complex, 364 ha). 389 ha of IBA covered by Special Protection Area (Coole Park and Garryland Complex, 389 ha). 363 ha of IBA covered by Biogenetic Reserve (Coole Park and Garryland Complex, 363 ha).

■ **Conservation issues**

> **Threats** Disturbance to birds (C)

Shooting on adjacent lands causes disturbance to birds. A large part of the site is owned by NPW. A proposed candidate Special Area for Conservation (Coole Park and Garryland Complex; 363 ha) lies within the IBA.

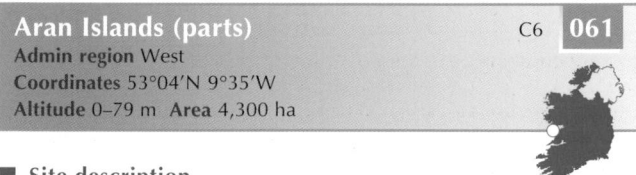

Aran Islands (parts)   C6   061
Admin region West
Coordinates 53°04′N 9°35′W
Altitude 0–79 m **Area** 4,300 ha

■ **Site description**
Inishmaan is the middle of the three Aran Islands situated approximately 15 km off the west coast of County Clare. The island is an extension of the karstic Carboniferous limestone region of the Burren. It consists of dry calcareous grassland, coastal dune and machair habitats. Inishmore, and a group of small islands (Brannock Islands, including Rock Island) lying to its west, have been added to this site since its listing in the previous pan-European inventory (Grimmett and Jones 1989). Low-intensity farming methods have maintained the species-richness and diversity of the flora.

> **Habitats** Grassland (45%; steppe/dry calcareous grassland; machair), Wetland (15%; sand-dunes/sand beach; shingle/stony beach), Rocky areas (40%)
> **Land-use** Agriculture (45%), Not utilized (55%)

■ **Birds**

Species	Season	Year	Pop min	Pop max	Acc	Criteria
[1] *Sterna paradisaea* Arctic Tern	B	1995	345	345	A	C6

1. 338 pairs on Rock Island, the most westerly of a group of small islands west of Inishmore; the remainder on Inishmaan.

This area supports the largest discrete breeding colony of *Sterna paradisaea* in Ireland, most of which occur on Rock Island. Low numbers of *Sterna albifrons* (3 pairs, 1995) breed on Inishmaan. Other breeding seabirds at this site include *Phalacrocorax carbo*, *Phalacrocorax aristotelis*, *Fulmarus glacialis* and *Cepphus grylle* (140 birds on Inishmore, 1999).

■ **Protection status**
National None **International** None

■ **Conservation issues**

> **Threats** Agricultural intensification/expansion (C), Recreation/tourism (C)

Agricultural intensification would have a significant negative effect upon this site. Tourism is an important industry on the Aran Islands, especially Inishmore, and needs to be controlled to minimize the impact to the environment. Terns *Sterna* on Inishmaan are vulnerable to disturbance. Two proposed candidate Special Areas for Conservation (Inishmaan, 928 ha; Inishmore, 20 ha) lie within the IBA.

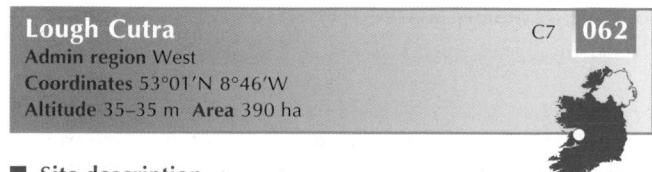

Lough Cutra   C7   062
Admin region West
Coordinates 53°01′N 8°46′W
Altitude 35–35 m **Area** 390 ha

■ **Site description**
A freshwater lake, with low to moderate nutrient levels, lying on limestone 4 km south-east of Gort in County Galway. The lake supports aquatic vegetation, with reedbeds in sheltered bays.

> **Habitats** Wetland (100%; standing fresh water; water-fringe vegetation)
> **Land-use** Tourism/recreation (100%)

■ **Birds**

Lough Cutra was designated as a Special Protection Area on the basis of important numbers of breeding *Phalacrocorax carbo* (166 pairs, 1985; up to 300 birds in winter).

■ **Protection status**

National None **International** High
390 ha of IBA covered by Special Protection Area (Lough Cutra, 390 ha).

■ **Conservation issues**

| Threats | Agricultural intensification/expansion (C), Recreation/tourism (C) |

Agricultural intensification, including excessive use of fertilizer and slurry-spreading, is leading to nutrient pollution of the lake.

Cliffs of Moher   A4iii, B2, B3, C4 063
Admin region Mid West
Coordinates 52°58′N 9°26′W
Altitude 0–230 m **Area** 140 ha

■ **Site description**

Vertical sea cliffs up to 230 m in height, stretching 7 km along the County Clare coast, 10 km west of Ennistymon. The cliffs are mainly horizontally layered and unvegetated, with some wide vegetated slopes. The cliffs are a major tourist attraction with visitor centre and car park.

Habitats Rocky areas (100%; sea cliff/rocky shore)
Land-use Not utilized (80%), Tourism/recreation (20%)

■ **Birds**

Species		Season	Year	Pop min	Pop max	Acc	Criteria
Alca torda	Razorbill	B	1987	2,300	2,300	A	B3
[1] *Fratercula arctica*	Puffin	B	1987	700	1,000	B	B2

1. Minimum 1980, maximum 1987.

This is the largest colony of breeding seabirds in County Clare. Additional species that breed in numbers of national importance are *Fulmarus glacialis* (min. 3,000 birds, 1987), *Rissa tridactyla* (4,300 birds, 1987) and *Uria aalge* (12,800 birds, 1987).

■ **Protection status**

National High **International** High
140 ha of IBA covered by Refuge for Fauna (Cliffs of Moher; area not known). 140 ha of IBA covered by Special Protection Area (Cliffs of Moher, 140 ha).

■ **Conservation issues**

| Threats | Recreation/tourism (C) |

The high visitor numbers to this site do not seem to have an undue effect on nesting seabirds.

Ballyallia lake   B1i, C3 064
Admin region Mid West
Coordinates 52°53′N 8°59′W
Altitude 20–20 m **Area** 308 ha

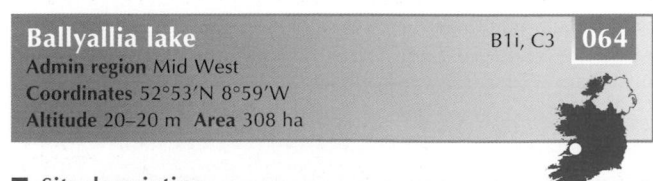

■ **Site description**

Habitats Forest and woodland (10%; broadleaved deciduous forest), Grassland (25%; humid grassland), Wetland (40%; standing fresh water; fen/transition mire/spring), Artificial landscape (25%; highly improved reseeded grassland)
Land-use Agriculture (50%), Nature conservation/research (50%)

This is a small, shallow lake situated on the River Fergus, approximately 4 km north of Ennis town, in County Clare. The lake is fringed by reedbeds and surrounded by farmland to the north and south, with a low-lying flood-plain of wet grassland and rough grazing to the west. The lake is used for fishing and tourism. The site boundaries have been extended since the previous pan-European inventory (Grimmett and Jones 1989).

■ **Birds**

Species		Season	Year	Pop min	Pop max	Acc	Criteria
Anas crecca	Teal	W	—	—	4,000	—	B1i, C3
Anas clypeata	Shoveler	W	1996	120	496	—	B1i, C3

An important wintering site for waterfowl. Additional species which occur in numbers of national importance are *Tachybaptus ruficollis* (38 birds, 1996), *Anas penelope* (1,200 birds, 1995), *A. platyrhynchos* (600 birds, 1996), *A. strepera* (76 birds, 1996), *A. acuta* (35 birds, 1995), *Aythya marila* (64 birds, 1996) and *Fulica atra* (300 birds, 1996).

■ **Protection status**

National High **International** High
308 ha of IBA covered by Wildfowl Sanctuary (Ballyalia lake, 308 ha). 308 ha of IBA covered by Ramsar Site (Ballyalia lake, 308 ha). 308 ha of IBA covered by Special Protection Area (Ballyalia lake, 308 ha).

■ **Conservation issues**

| Threats | Agricultural intensification/expansion (B), Recreation/tourism (C) |

Intensification of farming adjacent to the lake threatens its water quality, due to increased fertilizer run-off. The site has been managed as a Wildfowl Sanctuary for the last twenty years.

Mid Clare coast including Mutton and Mattle Islands   A4i, B1i, C2, C3 065
Admin region Mid West
Coordinates 52°47′N 9°30′W
Altitude 0–30 m **Area** 7,000 ha

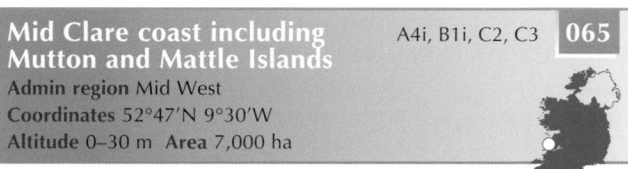

■ **Site description**

The site encompasses Mutton and Mattle Islands, lying approximately 3.5 km west of Quilty, County Clare. The site boundaries have been extended since the previous pan-European inventory (Grimmett and Jones 1989) to include the mainland coastline between Rinnamyrall Point (on the western edge of Doonbeg Bay) and Spanish Point to the north, as well as the sea area between the coast and the islands. Mattle Island, previously treated as a separate IBA (former site IE057), is now also included within this site. Mutton Island is a small, rocky, uninhabited island, covered by maritime grass and grazed by goats year-round; Mattle Island is also small and rocky, but is not grazed.

Habitats Grassland (5%; mesophile grassland), Marine areas (40%; sea inlet/coastal features), Rocky areas (55%; sea cliff/rocky shore; rock stacks/islets)
Land-use Agriculture (5%), Fisheries/aquaculture (40%), Not utilized (55%)

■ **Birds**

Species		Season	Year	Pop min	Pop max	Acc	Criteria
[1] *Branta leucopsis*	Barnacle Goose	W	1994	350	350	A	B1i, C2
[2] *Arenaria interpres*	Turnstone	W	1996	400	700	B	A4i, B1i, C3

1. Mainly on Mutton Island.
2. Minimum figures, as only mainland counted.

This site is important for wintering shorebirds and wildfowl. Also along the coast are nationally important numbers of wintering *Charadrius hiaticula* (180 birds, 1996), *Calidris maritima* (134 birds, 1995), *C. alpina* (2,200 birds, 1996) and *C. alba* (170 birds, 1996), as well as breeding *Hydrobates pelagicus*, *Phalacrocorax carbo* (60 pairs, 1987) and *Larus marinus* (50 pairs, 1987).

■ **Protection status**

National Low **International** Low
IBA overlaps with Wildfowl Sanctuary (Mutton Island; area not known). 54 ha of IBA covered by Special Protection Area (Mattle Island, 54 ha). 516 ha of IBA covered by Special Protection Area (Mutton Island, 516 ha).

■ **Conservation issues**

| Threats | Agricultural intensification/expansion (C), Aquaculture/fisheries (U), Recreation/tourism (C) |

Overgrazing by goats, made worse by the presence of rabbits, is a problem on Mutton Island. Additionally, the area is visited by large numbers of tourists, which need to be regulated. The site overlaps with two proposed candidate Special Areas for Conservation (White Strand/Carrowmore marsh; Carrowmore Point to Spanish Point and Islands; areas not known).

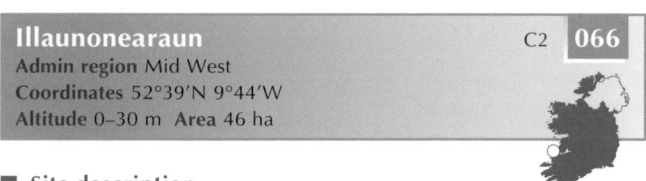

Illaunonearaun
C2 066
Admin region Mid West
Coordinates 52°39'N 9°44'W
Altitude 0–30 m **Area** 46 ha

■ Site description
A small island and surrounding sea, situated 500 m off the County Clare coast, and about 7 km south-west of Kilkee.

Habitats Grassland (15%; mesophile grassland), Marine areas (80%; sea inlet/coastal features), Rocky areas (5%; rock stacks/islets)
Land-use Fisheries/aquaculture (80%), Not utilized (20%)

■ Birds

Species	Season	Year	Pop min	Pop max	Acc	Criteria
Branta leucopsis Barnacle Goose	W	1997	108	108	A	C2

Branta leucopsis winter here in notable numbers—probably the same flock as use Mutton Island on the Mid Clare coast (site 065). Breeding seabirds include *Phalacrocorax carbo* (60 birds, 1995) and *Larus marinus*.

■ Protection status
National None **International** None

■ Conservation issues

Threats Aquaculture/fisheries (C)

Fishing in surrounding waters may deplete the prey stock of seabirds, with implications for their breeding success. On the basis of wintering *Branta leucopsis*, this site has been proposed as a Special Protection Area (Illaunonearaun, 46 ha) by NPW and should be designated in the near future.

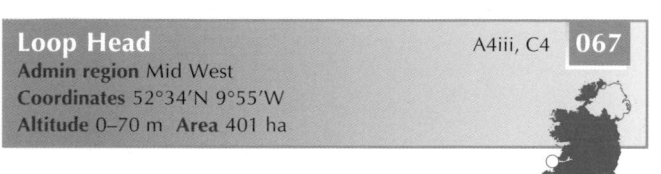

Loop Head
A4iii, C4 067
Admin region Mid West
Coordinates 52°34'N 9°55'W
Altitude 0–70 m **Area** 401 ha

■ Site description
Loop Head is the most westerly point in County Clare, approximately 20 km south-west of Kilkee. The site comprises horizontally stratified vertical sea cliffs with stacks, rising up to 60 m, and the surrounding sea area. There is a lighthouse on the headland.

Habitats Scrub (20%; heathland), Marine areas (75%; sea inlet/coastal features), Rocky areas (5%; sea cliff/rocky shore)
Land-use Agriculture (15%), Fisheries/aquaculture (75%), Not utilized (10%)

■ Birds
Breeding seabirds include nationally important numbers of *Rissa tridactyla* (690 pairs, 1987) and *Uria aalge* (4,010 birds, 1987). This is a good site for sea-watching, with a large passage of skuas *Stercorarius* and shearwaters *Puffinus* in late summer and autumn.

■ Protection status
National None **International** None

■ Conservation issues

Threats Agricultural intensification/expansion (B), Aquaculture/fisheries (C), Recreation/tourism (C)

Above the cliffs, grazing and trampling pressure has severely degraded the heathland, causing erosion. Parts of the cliffs used by nesting birds are vulnerable to human disturbance. On the basis of its breeding seabirds, the site has been proposed as a Special Protection Area (Loop Head, 401 ha) by NPW and should be designated in the near future.

Shannon and Fergus estuary
A4i, A4iii, B1i, B2, B3, C2, C3, C4 068
Admin region Mid West
Coordinates 52°40'N 9°04'W
Altitude 0–10 m **Area** 16,718 ha

■ Site description
A large estuarine complex with islands, saltmarshes, mudflats, raised saltmarsh and wet meadows. The site encompasses the Fergus river estuary from Clarecastle (where it becomes tidal) to the junction with the Shannon estuary, and includes the estuary inland as far as Limerick city. The estuary lies within Counties Clare, Limerick and Kerry, and contains the largest port and most extensive areas of industrial development in mid-west Ireland.

Habitats Grassland (20%; humid grassland), Wetland (80%; tidal river/enclosed tidal water; mudflat/sandflat; saltmarsh; river/stream; water-fringe vegetation)
Land-use Agriculture (20%), Fisheries/aquaculture (50%), Hunting (50%), Tourism/recreation (50%), Urban/industrial/transport (20%)

■ Birds

Species	Season	Year	Pop min	Pop max	Acc	Criteria
Cygnus cygnus Whooper Swan	W	1996	256	256	A	B1i, B3, C2
Branta bernicla Brent Goose	W	1995	318	318	A	B1i, C3
Aythya marila Scaup	W	1996	201	201	A	B2
Pluvialis apricaria Golden Plover	W	1995	11,067	11,067	A	B1i, C2
Calidris canutus Knot	W	1996	800	800	A	B2
Calidris alpina Dunlin	W	1996	19,335	19,335	A	B1i, B2, C3
Limosa limosa Black-tailed Godwit	W	1996	1,987	1,987	A	B1i, C3
Limosa lapponica Bar-tailed Godwit	W	1996	511	511	A	B2
Numenius arquata Curlew	W	1995	2,896	2,896	A	B2
Tringa totanus Redshank	W	1995	3,494	3,494	A	A4i, B1i, C3

This is one of the most important sites in Ireland for wintering and migrating waterfowl, supporting 10 species in numbers of international importance. A further 13 species occur in numbers of national importance, including *Anser anser* (216 birds, 1996), *Tadorna tadorna* (1,060 birds, 1996), *Anas penelope* (6,935 birds, 1996), *Anas crecca* (2,590 birds, 1995), *Anas acuta* (48 birds, 1995), *Anas clypeata* (84 birds, 1996), *Vanellus vanellus* (28,194 birds, 1995), *Numenius arquata* (2,896 birds, 1995) and *Tringa nebularia* (36 birds, 1996).

■ Protection status
National None **International** High
16,718 ha of IBA covered by Special Protection Area (Shannon and Fergus Estuary, 16,718 ha).

■ Conservation issues

Threats Aquaculture/fisheries (C), Consequences of animal/plant introductions (B), Disturbance to birds (B), Filling-in of wetlands (B), Industrialization/urbanization (B), Recreation/tourism (U)

Threats to the site include industrial and urban development, the spread of non-native cord-grass *Spartina* over intertidal mudflats, marina developments and increased boating activities, pollution from industry, and increasing intertidal shellfish cultivation. The effects of these pressures on the site include habitat loss and disturbance and lead to a general degradation of habitat quality.

Tralee Bay and Barrow Harbour
B1i, B2, C3, C6 069
Admin region South West
Coordinates 52°16'N 9°48'W
Altitude 0–10 m **Area** 3,290 ha

■ Site description
A large, shallow sea bay on the north coast of County Kerry, including intertidal areas at the mouth of the River Lee (where the town of Tralee is located) and at Barrow Harbour. Some protection is given to the River Lee estuary by Derrymore Island, a spit formed of shingle ridges, while Barrow Harbour is protected by land with only a small inlet open to the sea. North of Barrow Harbour the site encompasses a large, sandy intertidal inlet, sand-dunes and beach

which extend as far as Akeragh Lough. The site has been extended since the previous pan-European inventory (Grimmett and Jones 1989) to include Akeragh Lough and intervening coastal habitats (former site IE059).

Habitats Grassland (10%; mesophile grassland), Wetland (80%; mudflat/sandflat; saltmarsh; sand-dunes/sand beach; shingle/stony beach), Rocky areas (10%; sea cliff/rocky shore)
Land-use Agriculture (10%), Fisheries/aquaculture (50%), Hunting (80%), Nature conservation/research (20%)

■ Birds

Species		Season	Year	Pop min	Pop max	Acc	Criteria
Gavia immer	Great Northern Diver	W	1995	43	43	A	C6
Branta bernicla	Brent Goose	W	1995	535	535	A	B1i, C3
Aythya marila	Scaup	W	1995	1,560	1,560	A	B2
Calidris alpina	Dunlin	W	1996	4,112	4,112	A	B2
Limosa lapponica	Bar-tailed Godwit	W	1996	903	903	A	B2

This is an important wetland, with internationally important numbers of wintering waterfowl. Several other species occur in numbers of national importance including *Anas crecca* (860 birds, 1995), *Melanitta nigra* (620 birds, 1995), *Pluvialis apricaria* (3,053 birds, 1995) and *Vanellus vanellus* (5,700 birds, 1995).

■ Protection status
National Partial **International** Partial
106 ha of IBA covered by Nature Reserve (Derrymore Island, 106 ha). 755 ha of IBA covered by Nature Reserve (Tralee Bay, 755 ha). 861 ha of IBA covered by Ramsar Site (Tralee Bay, 861 ha). 1,199 ha of IBA covered by Special Protection Area (Akeragh, Lough Banna and Barrow Harbour, 1,199 ha). 754 ha of IBA covered by Special Protection Area (Tralee Bay, 754 ha).

■ Conservation issues

Threats Consequences of animal/plant introductions (B), Industrialization/urbanization (C), Recreation/tourism (C)

Akeragh Lough has been seriously degraded by siltation, drainage and nutrient pollution, the latter as a result of effluent discharge from the adjacent caravan site. Habitat quality within the intertidal zone is threatened by the spread of non-native cord-grass *Spartina* with further possible adverse effects due to the proximity of Tralee town. The IBA overlaps with a proposed candidate Special Area for Conservation (Tralee Bay and Magherees peninsula, West to Cloghane; area not known).

Magharee Islands, Mucklaghmore and Illaunbarnagh   B2, B3, C6   070
Admin region South West
Coordinates 52°20′N 10°02′W
Altitude 0–22 m   **Area** 370 ha

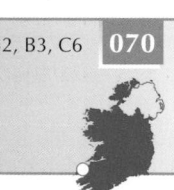

■ Site description
The Magharee Islands, comprising a group of six islands and several additional islets and shallow reefs, are situated 2 km off the northern end of the Castlegregory peninsula in County Kerry. They are uninhabited, except for holiday visitors. The largest islands, Illauntannig and Illaunimmil, were inhabited in the past and are still grazed by sheep and cattle. The site has been extended since the previous European inventory (Grimmett and Jones 1989) to encompass the surrounding waters.

Habitats Grassland (5%; mesophile grassland), Marine areas (85%; sea inlet/coastal features), Rocky areas (10%; sea cliff/rocky shore)
Land-use Agriculture (15%), Fisheries/aquaculture (85%)

■ Birds
The Magharee Islands are of international importance for their breeding seabird colonies. Other species occurring in numbers of national importance are breeding *Phalacrocorax carbo* (100 pairs, 1987) and *Larus marinus* (100 pairs, 1987), and on Illauntannig wintering *Branta leucopsis* (267 birds, 1993).

Species		Season	Year	Pop min	Pop max	Acc	Criteria
Phalacrocorax aristotelis	Shag	B	1987	135	135	A	B3
Larus fuscus	Lesser Black-backed Gull	B	1987	32	47	A	B3
Sterna paradisaea	Arctic Tern	B	1995	232	232	A	C6
Sterna albifrons	Little Tern	B	1995	36	36	A	B2, C6

■ Protection status
National None **International** None

■ Conservation issues

Threats Aquaculture/fisheries (C), Disturbance to birds (B), Recreation/tourism (C)

Disturbance is a possible threat to the site. However, visitor pressure so far seems to be controlled. Overgrazing by livestock on Illauntannig and Ilaunamil may affect *Branta leucopsis*. The IBA overlaps with a proposed Special Protection Area (Magheree Islands, 288 ha).

Lough Gill   B2, B3, C7   071
Admin region South West
Coordinates 52°16′N 10°02′W
Altitude 3–3 m   **Area** 157 ha

■ Site description
Lough Gill is situated on the Magharees peninsula in Tralee Bay, on the north coast of County Kerry. It is a very shallow coastal lagoon, with a modified inlet and sluice gate, draining into Tralee Bay. The lagoon is fringed by extensive reedbeds and bordered by dunes, dune grassland and machair on its northern side, while intensive farmland borders most of its southern side. The dune system has been modified by golf-course development. The lagoon is used for fishing and boating.

Habitats Wetland (100%; sand-dunes/sand beach; standing fresh water; river/stream; water-fringe vegetation)
Land-use Agriculture (20%), Hunting (100%), Water management (5%)

■ Birds

Species		Season	Year	Pop min	Pop max	Acc	Criteria
Cygnus columbianus	Bewick's Swan	W	—	—	100	—	B2
Cygnus cygnus	Whooper Swan	W	1995	52	104	B	B3

This is an important wintering site for swans *Cygnus*.

■ Protection status
National High **International** High
IBA overlaps with Wildfowl Sanctuary (Lough Gill; area not known). 157 ha of IBA covered by Special Protection Area (Lough Gill, 157 ha).

■ Conservation issues

Threats Agricultural intensification/expansion (C), Disturbance to birds (C), Drainage (C), Recreation/tourism (C)

Nutrient pollution of Lough Gill, due to run-off from agriculture and probably forestry, is a serious threat to water and habitat quality. There is increasing pressure on the site from fishing and amenity interests. Recent extraction of sand from the lake has been stopped, for the present. The site lies within a proposed candidate Special Area for Conservation (Tralee Bay and Magherees peninsula, West to Cloghane; area not known).

Dingle peninsula   A4iii, B2, C4, C6   072
Admin region Mid West
Coordinates 52°08′N 10°27′W
Altitude 0–240 m   **Area** 3,500 ha

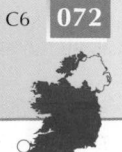

■ Site description
The most northerly of five peninsulas in south-west County Kerry. This linear coastal site stretches from Brandon Point in the north

around the coast as far as Annascaul in the south. Information on land-use and threats is incomplete.

Habitats Scrub (20%; heathland), Grassland (30%; mesophile grassland), Rocky areas (50%; sea cliff/rocky shore)
Land-use Agriculture (50%), Not utilized (50%)

■ Birds

Species	Season	Year	Pop min	Pop max	Acc	Criteria
[1] *Pyrrhocorax pyrrhocorax* Chough	R	1992	73	73	A	B2, C6

1. Figure is sum of possible, probable and definite breeding pairs.

This is an important site for breeding *Pyrrhocorax pyrrhocorax*.

■ Protection status
National None International None

■ Conservation issues

Threats Agricultural intensification/expansion (C), Disturbance to birds (C)

For the survival of *Pyrrhocorax pyrrhocorax* at this site, it is vital that low-intensity farming on the cliff-tops is maintained. The site overlaps with a proposed candidate Special Area for Conservation (Mount Brandon; area not known).

Blasket Islands
A4ii, A4iii, B1ii, B2, B3, C2, C3, C4, C6 **073**
Admin region South West
Coordinates 52°05′N 10°35′W
Altitude 0–183 m Area 750 ha

■ Site description
This is the largest group of islands on the south-west coast, lying a few kilometres off the Dingle peninsula in County Kerry. The group includes Great Blasket Island, with steep cliffs on its northern side, and the five smaller, exposed rocky islands of Inistooskert, Inisvickillaun, Inisnabro, Tearaght and Beginish. Great Blasket Island was once inhabited and now has a visitor centre at its northern end. A small herd of feral red deer *Cervus elaphus* are present on Inishvickillaun. The islands are visited by tourists.

Habitats Grassland (50%; dry siliceous grassland), Rocky areas (50%; sea cliff/rocky shore; rock stacks/islets)
Land-use Not utilized (80%), Tourism/recreation (20%)

■ Birds

Species	Season	Year	Pop min	Pop max	Acc	Criteria
[1] *Puffinus puffinus* Manx Shearwater	B	1988	2,000	5,000	B	A4ii, B1ii, B2, C3
[1] *Hydrobates pelagicus* Storm Petrel	B	1988	40,000	100,000	B	A4ii, B1ii, B2, C2, C6
Phalacrocorax aristotelis Shag	B	1988	350	350	A	B3
Larus fuscus Lesser Black-backed Gull	B	1988	425	425	A	B3
Larus marinus Great Black-backed Gull	B	1988	375	425	A	B3
Cepphus grylle Black Guillemot	B	1988	22	22	A	B2
Fratercula arctica Puffin	B	1988	4,472	5,321	A	B2

1. Difficult to census accurately.

This site is of particular importance for its seabird colonies. Additional species occurring in numbers of national importance are *Fulmarus glacialis* (2,200 pairs, 1988), *Rissa tridactyla* (750 pairs, 1988) and *Alca torda* (450 birds, 1988).

■ Protection status
National Low International Partial
27 ha of IBA covered by Nature Reserve (Tearaght Island, 27 ha). 19 ha of IBA covered by [Marine] Nature Reserve (Terraght Island, 19 ha). 287 ha of IBA covered by Special Protection Area (Blasket Islands, 287 ha).

■ Conservation issues

Threats Recreation/tourism (C)

Human disturbance from visitors to Great Blasket is a possible threat. However, isolation protects the islands from most threats.

Castlemaine Harbour
A4i, A4iii, B1i, B2, C2, C3, C4 **074**
Admin region South West
Coordinates 52°07′N 9°55′W
Altitude 0–10 m Area 11,374 ha

■ Site description
A large, shallow, tidal estuary at the head of Dingle Bay in County Kerry. Sheltered from the open sea by sand- and shingle-spits on the north and south sides, the estuary supports extensive intertidal mudflats with beds of eelgrass *Zostera* and fringes of saltmarsh. Inch spit on the north side supports the most extensive and intact dunes in the region, while on the south side, a smaller spit with a dune system occurs. Since the previous IBA inventory (Grimmett and Jones 1989), the site has been extended to include the feeding areas of *Melanitta nigra* in the open part of the Bay immediately to the west of the sand-spits.

Habitats Grassland (20%; humid grassland), Wetland (80%; tidal river/enclosed tidal water; mudflat/sandflat; saltmarsh; sand-dunes/sand beach; shingle/stony beach)
Land-use Agriculture (20%), Fisheries/aquaculture (60%), Not utilized (20%)

■ Birds

Species	Season	Year	Pop min	Pop max	Acc	Criteria
Branta bernicla Brent Goose	W	1996	1,062	1,062	A	B1i, C3
Calidris canutus Knot	W	1989	—	3,000	—	B2
Limosa lapponica Bar-tailed Godwit	W	1996	967	1,007	A	A4i, B1i, B2, C2

An important wetland for wintering birds, with numbers exceeding 20,000 individuals in most years. It is also the most important wintering site in Ireland for *Gavia stellata* (230 birds, 1996) and *Melanitta nigra* (5,000 birds, 1996). Many other species occur in numbers of national importance, including *Anas penelope* (4,093 birds, 1996), *Haematopus ostralegus* (1,173 birds, 1995), *Pluvialis apricaria* (2,300 birds, 1995), *Calidris alpina* (1,350 birds, 1995) and *Tringa totanus* (270 birds, 1995).

■ Protection status
National Partial International Partial
927 ha of IBA covered by Nature Reserve (Castlemaine Harbour, 927 ha). IBA overlaps with Wildfowl Sanctuary (Castlemaine Harbour; area not known). 923 ha of IBA covered by Ramsar Site (Castlemaine Harbour, 923 ha). 2,973 ha of IBA covered by Special Protection Area (Castlemaine Harbour, 2,973 ha).

■ Conservation issues

Threats Agricultural intensification/expansion (C), Aquaculture/fisheries (C), Natural events (C)

Potential threats to the site are pollution of the wetland due to agricultural run-off, degradation of the dunes by a possible golf-course development, and erosion of the dunes by natural processes. The site overlaps with a proposed candidate Special Area for Conservation (Castlemaine Harbour; area not known).

Puffin Island
A4ii, A4iii, B1ii, B2, C2, C3, C4, C6 **075**
Admin region South West
Coordinates 51°50′N 10°24′W
Altitude 0–160 m Area 53 ha

■ Site description
A long, narrow and grassy, uninhabited island, lying 0.5 km off the northern side of St Finan's Bay in south-west County Kerry. It is steep-sided with a long narrow twin-peaked ridge rising to 145 m. The island is owned by BirdWatch Ireland and permission is required for access.

Habitats Grassland (80%; mesophile grassland), Rocky areas (20%; sea cliff/rocky shore; rock stacks/islets)
Land-use Agriculture (80%), Nature conservation/research (100%)

■ Birds

Species	Season	Year	Pop min	Pop max	Acc	Criteria
Puffinus puffinus Manx Shearwater	B	1987	10,000	20,000	C	A4ii, B1ii, B2, C3
Hydrobates pelagicus Storm Petrel	B	1987	4,000	4,000	C	A4ii, B1ii, B2, C2, C6
Fratercula arctica Puffin	B	1987	8,000	10,000	A	B1ii, B2, C3

An important site for breeding seabirds. Additional species occurring in numbers of national importance include *Fulmarus glacialis* (700 pairs, 1987), *Larus marinus* (150 pairs, 1987) and *Alca torda* (800 birds, 1987).

■ Protection status
National High **International** High
53 ha of IBA covered by Nature Reserve (Puffin Island, 53 ha). 53 ha of IBA covered by Special Protection Area (Puffin Island, 53 ha).

■ Conservation issues

Threats Agricultural intensification/expansion (B)

Unauthorized grazing which may cause erosion, occurs on the site.

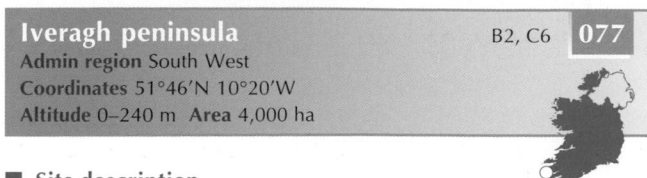

The Skelligs: Great Skellig and Little Skellig
A4ii, A4iii, B1ii, B2, C2, C3, C4, C6 **076**
Admin region South West
Coordinates 51°47'N 10°31'W
Altitude 0–240 m **Area** 31 ha

■ Site description
Two precipitous, rocky, uninhabited islands, situated 16 km west of Bolus Head on the Iveragh peninsula in County Kerry. Great Skellig reaches a height of 240 m and is the site of an old Celtic monastery. Little Skellig lies 1 km to its north-east and reaches 134 m in height. Great Skellig is popular with day-trippers. Landing on Little Skellig is prohibited.

Habitats Marine areas (20%; sea inlet/coastal features), Rocky areas (80%; sea cliff/rocky shore; rock stacks/islets; scree/boulders)
Land-use Not utilized (40%), Tourism/recreation (60%)

■ Birds

Species		Season	Year	Pop min	Pop max	Acc	Criteria
Puffinus puffinus	Manx Shearwater	B	1987	5,000	5,000	C	A4ii, B1ii, B2, C3
Hydrobates pelagicus	Storm Petrel	B	1987	10,000	10,000	C	A4ii, B1ii, B2, C2, C6
Sula bassana	Gannet	B	1993	22,500	22,500	A	A4ii, B1ii, B2, C3
Fratercula arctica	Puffin	B	1993	1,000	1,000	A	B2

The Skellig Islands are of international importance for breeding seabirds. In particular, the colony of *Sula bassana* on Little Skellig is the largest in Ireland. Other species breeding in numbers of national importance are *Fulmarus glacialis* (>800 pairs, 1993), *Rissa tridactyla* (>2,000 pairs, 1993), *Alca torda* (>300 birds, 1993) and *Uria aalge* (1,500 birds, 1993).

■ Protection status
National High **International** Partial
23 ha of IBA covered by Nature Reserve (Great Skellig, 23 ha). 8 ha of IBA covered by Nature Reserve (Little Skellig, 8 ha). 25 ha of IBA covered by Special Protection Area (The Skelligs: Great Skellig and Little Skellig, 25 ha).

■ Conservation issues

Threats Disturbance to birds (C), Recreation/tourism (C)

It is important to ensure that visitors to Great Skellig use the paths, to prevent erosion of the fragile soils where many of the birds have their nest-burrows. BirdWatch Ireland has a long-term lease on Little Skellig.

Iveragh peninsula
B2, C6 **077**
Admin region South West
Coordinates 51°46'N 10°20'W
Altitude 0–240 m **Area** 4,000 ha

■ Site description
The Iveragh peninsula is situated in south-west Kerry, south of the Dingle peninsula. The site extends from 5 km west of Glenbeigh on the northern side of the peninsula around the coast to Lamb's Head on the southern side, and includes Valentia Island. This linear site comprises sea cliff, grassland and heath habitats. Information on land-use and threats is incomplete.

Habitats Scrub (10%; heathland), Grassland (40%; mesophile grassland), Rocky areas (50%; sea cliff/rocky shore)
Land-use Agriculture (50%), Not utilized (50%)

■ Birds

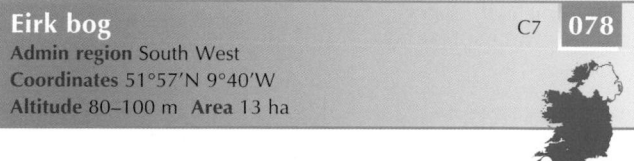

Species		Season	Year	Pop min	Pop max	Acc	Criteria
[1] *Pyrrhocorax pyrrhocorax*	Chough	R	1992	111	111	A	B2, C6

1. Figure is sum of possible, probable and definite breeding pairs.

This is an important site for breeding *Pyrrhocorax pyrrhocorax*.

■ Protection status
National None **International** None

■ Conservation issues

Threats Agricultural intensification/expansion (C), Disturbance to birds (C)

For the survival of *Pyrrhocorax pyrrhocorax* at this site, it is vital that low-intensity farming on the cliff-tops is maintained.

Eirk bog
C7 **078**
Admin region South West
Coordinates 51°57'N 9°40'W
Altitude 80–100 m **Area** 13 ha

■ Site description
Eirk bog is situated in the Owenreagh valley, 1 km north of Moll's Gap and 3 km south-west of Killarney National Park (site 079) in County Kerry. It is a classical example of an intermediate bog, between blanket and raised bog.

Habitats Wetland (100%; raised bog; blanket bog)
Land-use Nature conservation/research (100%)

■ Birds
Eirk bog provides wintering habitat for a small flock of *Anser albifrons flavirostris*, which is now the only regular flock of this species in the south-west of the country, and that is the basis for the designation of the site as a Special Protection Area.

■ Protection status
National High **International** High
13 ha of IBA covered by Nature Reserve (Eirk Bog, 16 ha). 13 ha of IBA covered by Special Protection Area (Eirk Bog, 13 ha).

■ Conservation issues

Threats Agricultural intensification/expansion (C), Burning of vegetation (C)

Overgrazing by sheep and deer pose a potential threat to the site. The IBA lies within a proposed candidate Special Area for Conservation (Eirk Bog; area not known).

Killarney National Park
C7 **079**
Admin region South West
Coordinates 52°00'N 9°35'W
Altitude 0–832 m **Area** 10,329 ha

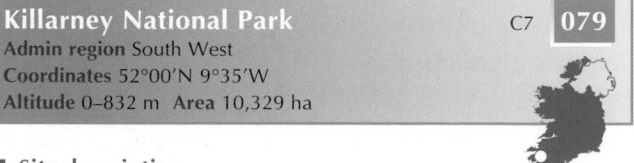

■ Site description
Killarney National Park extends south-west from Killarney town in County Kerry. It supports a diversity of habitats, from blanket bog and heath, to lakes which include the extensive Lough Leane and smaller Muckross lake. Parts of the lake shores are bordered by conifer plantations, and deciduous woodland occurs on the southern shore of Muckross lake; both are popular for angling and recreational boating.

Habitats Forest and woodland (5%; broadleaved deciduous forest), Grassland (10%; humid grassland), Wetland (70%; standing fresh water; river/stream; blanket bog; fen/transition mire/spring), Rocky areas (10%; inland cliff), Artificial landscape (5%; forestry plantation)
Land-use Agriculture (25%), Forestry (10%), Nature conservation/research (100%), Tourism/recreation (100%)

■ Birds

Killarney National Park was designated as a Special Protection Area on the basis of breeding *Falco peregrinus*, *F. columbarius* and *Pyrrhocorax pyrrhocorax*, and wintering *Anser albifrons flavirostris* (43 birds, 1994), all listed on Annex I of the EC Birds Directive.

■ Protection status

National High **International** High

10,129 ha of IBA covered by National Park (Killarney National Park, 10,129 ha). 8,308 ha of IBA covered by Biosphere Reserve (Killarney National Park, 8,308 ha). 10,329 ha of IBA covered by Special Protection Area (Killarney National Park, 10,329 ha).

■ Conservation issues

Threats Afforestation (C), Agricultural intensification/expansion (B), Consequences of animal/plant introductions (C), Extraction industry (C)

The main threats to the site include overgrazing by sheep and deer, turf-cutting and peat extraction. The spread of non-native *Rhododendron* scrub is causing major damage to woodland habitat quality. However coniferous forestry is gradually being replaced by native tree species. Nutrient pollution of Lough Leane, due to agricultural intensification, is a serious problem. The site lies within a proposed candidate Special Area for Conservation (Killarney National Park; area not known).

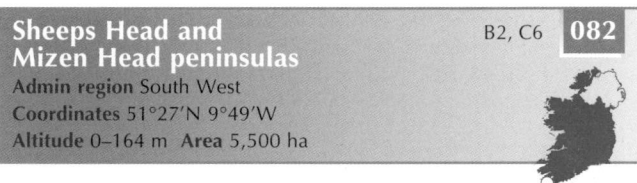

Bull and Cow Rocks   A4ii, B1ii, B2, B3, C2, C6   080
Admin region South West
Coordinates 51°35′N 10°17′W
Altitude 0–60 m **Area** 336 ha

■ Site description

Two uninhabited rocky islets and surrounding waters, 6 km west of the Beara peninsula in south-west County Cork. There is a lighthouse on Bull Rock which is owned by Commissioners of Irish Lights. Cow Rock is publicly-owned.

Habitats Marine areas (95%; open sea), Rocky areas (5%; sea cliff/rocky shore; rock stacks/islets)
Land-use Fisheries/aquaculture (95%), Not utilized (5%)

■ Birds

Species		Season	Year	Pop min	Pop max	Acc	Criteria
Hydrobates pelagicus	Storm Petrel	B	1987	2,000	5,000	B	A4ii, B1ii, B2, C2, C6
Sula bassana	Gannet	B	1994	1,815	1,815	A	B2
Alca torda	Razorbill	B	1987	900	900	A	B3

This site supports important breeding seabird colonies. Additional seabirds breeding in nationally important numbers include *Phalacrocorax carbo* (50 pairs, 1987), *Rissa tridactyla* (590 pairs, 1987) and *Uria aalge* (2,000 pairs, 1987).

■ Protection status

National High **International** None

IBA overlaps with Refuge for Fauna (Bull; area not known). IBA overlaps with Refuge for Fauna (Cow; area not known).

■ Conservation issues

Threats Aquaculture/fisheries (C)

Fishing in surrounding waters may deplete the prey stock of seabirds, with implications for their breeding success. Isolation protects these islands from most threats. The site is a proposed Special Protection Area (Bull and Cow Rocks, 336 ha).

Beara peninsula   B2, C6   081
Admin region South West
Coordinates 51°37′N 10°04′W
Altitude 0–150 m **Area** 3,250 ha

■ Site description

A linear coastal site in County Cork, which extends from Kenmare

Bay south around the peninsula into Bantry Harbour and includes Dursey Island. Coastal habitats include sea cliff, grassland and heath. Information on land-use and threats is incomplete.

Habitats Scrub (20%; heathland), Grassland (50%; mesophile grassland), Rocky areas (30%; sea cliff/rocky shore)
Land-use Agriculture (70%), Not utilized (30%)

■ Birds

Species		Season	Year	Pop min	Pop max	Acc	Criteria
[1] *Pyrrhocorax pyrrhocorax*	Chough	R	1992	65	65	A	B2, C6

1. Figure is sum of possible, probable and definite breeding pairs.

This is an important site for breeding *Pyrrhocorax pyrrhocorax*.

■ Protection status

National None **International** None

■ Conservation issues

Threats Agricultural intensification/expansion (C), Disturbance to birds (C)

For the survival of *Pyrrhocorax pyrrhocorax* at this site, it is vital that low-intensity farming on the cliff-tops is maintained.

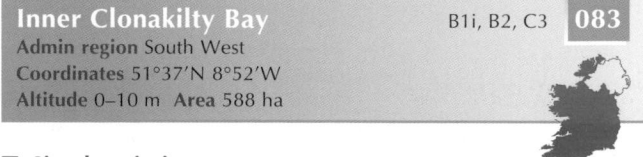

Sheeps Head and Mizen Head peninsulas   B2, C6   082
Admin region South West
Coordinates 51°27′N 9°49′W
Altitude 0–164 m **Area** 5,500 ha

■ Site description

A linear coastal site encompassing two south-westerly peninsulas in County Cork as well as Cape Clear and Sherkin Islands. Information on land-use and threats is incomplete.

Habitats Scrub (5%; heathland), Grassland (60%; mesophile grassland), Rocky areas (35%; sea cliff/rocky shore)
Land-use Agriculture (65%), Not utilized (35%)

■ Birds

Species		Season	Year	Pop min	Pop max	Acc	Criteria
[1] *Pyrrhocorax pyrrhocorax*	Chough	R	1992	129	129	A	B2, C6

1. Figure is sum of possible, probable and definite breeding pairs.

This is an important site for breeding *Pyrrhocorax pyrrhocorax*.

■ Protection status

National None **International** None

■ Conservation issues

Threats Agricultural intensification/expansion (C), Recreation/tourism (C)

For the survival of *Pyrrhocorax pyrrhocorax* at this site, it is vital that low-intensity farming on the cliff-tops is maintained. The site overlaps with a proposed candidate Special Area for Conservation (Barleycove to Ballyrisode Point; area not known).

Inner Clonakilty Bay   B1i, B2, C3   083
Admin region South West
Coordinates 51°37′N 8°52′W
Altitude 0–10 m **Area** 588 ha

■ Site description

A tidal bay stretching from Clonakilty in west County Cork to the open sea, and comprising two small estuaries, separated by Inchydoney Island. Most of the intertidal area is sandflats, although mudflats occur at the sheltered upper end of each estuary, with adjacent sand-dunes and inland marshes. At the head of the western estuary there is an extensive wetland, the Cloheen Strand Intake, which comprises saline lagoons, brackish grasslands, open freshwater marsh and stands of alder *Alnus*.

Habitats Scrub (15%; scrub), Grassland (15%; humid grassland), Wetland (60%; mudflat/sandflat; standing brackish and salt water), Marine areas (10%; sea inlet/coastal features)
Land-use Agriculture (15%), Not utilized (85%)

■ **Birds**

Species	Season	Year	Pop min	Pop max	Acc	Criteria
Limosa limosa Black-tailed Godwit	W	1995	945	945	A	B1i, C3
Numenius arquata Curlew	W	1995	1,844	1,844	A	B2

This is an important wetland for wintering waterfowl. Additional species that occur in numbers of national importance include *Tadorna tadorna* (160 birds, 1996), *Pluvialis squatarola* (86 birds, 1995), *Vanellus vanellus* (4,146 birds, 1995), *Calidris alpina* (1,827 birds, 1995) and *Tringa totanus* (309 birds, 1995).

■ **Protection status**
National None **International** None

■ **Conservation issues**

Threats Agricultural intensification/expansion (C), Construction/impact of dyke/dam/barrage (B), Recreation/tourism (B)

From 1992 to 1996, the Cloheen Strand Intake was threatened by plans to develop a golf course. However, following court action by BirdWatch Ireland and NPW, this threat has been averted. The area has now been purchased by NPW which should ensure its long-term protection. The site is a proposed Special Protection Area (Clonakilty Bay, 588 ha) and lies within a proposed candidate Special Area for Conservation (Clonakility Bay; area not known).

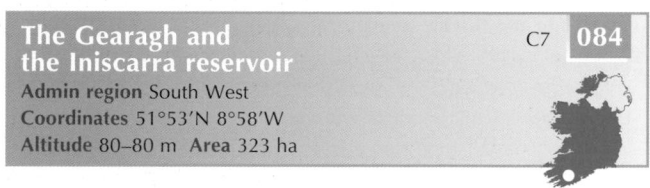

The Gearagh and the Iniscarra reservoir C7 084
Admin region South West
Coordinates 51°53'N 8°58'W
Altitude 80–80 m **Area** 323 ha

■ **Site description**
The Gearagh valley is located 3 km south of Macroom, County Cork, and forms part of the channel of the Lee river. In the 1950s the valley was dammed, trees felled and 60% of it flooded for a hydroelectric scheme. Some of the original alluvial woodland remains. The site also encompasses the upper part of the Iniscarra reservoir as far as the Carrigadrohid Dam.

Habitats Forest and woodland (15%; alluvial/very wet forest), Grassland (10%; humid grassland), Wetland (75%; standing fresh water; water-fringe vegetation)
Land-use Agriculture (20%), Hunting (100%), Water management (100%)

■ **Birds**
The site was designated as a Special Protection Area on the basis of its migratory waterfowl, notably those species wintering in numbers of national importance: *Anas penelope* (2,000 birds, 1996), *Anas crecca* (1,600 birds, 1996), *Anas platyrhynchos* (1,750 birds, 1985), *Fulica atra* (312 birds, 1995) and *Pluvialis apricaria* (1,500 birds, 1985).

■ **Protection status**
National High **International** High
300 ha of IBA covered by Nature Reserve (The Gearagh, 300 ha). IBA overlaps with Wildfowl Sanctuary (Lee Reservoir; area not known). 307 ha of IBA covered by Ramsar Site (The Gearagh, 307 ha). 323 ha of IBA covered by Special Protection Area (The Gearagh, 323 ha). 300 ha of IBA covered by Biogenetic Reserve (The Gearagh, 300 ha).

■ **Conservation issues**

Threats Agricultural intensification/expansion (C), Disturbance to birds (B)

Wildfowling causes disturbance to birds and is a problem at this site. The site overlaps with a proposed candidate Special Area for Conservation (The Gearagh; area not known).

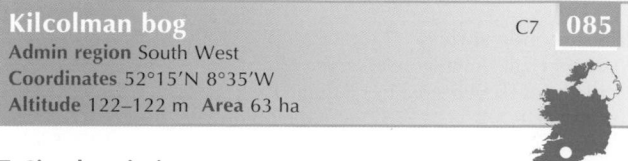

Kilcolman bog C7 085
Admin region South West
Coordinates 52°15'N 8°35'W
Altitude 122–122 m **Area** 63 ha

■ **Site description**
Kilcolman bog, situated 4 km north-east of Buttevant in County Cork, is an area of reed-swamp, floating fen and open water. It is the site of a former lake and water-levels are currently managed for conservation using sluice gates.

Habitats Wetland (100%; standing fresh water; water-fringe vegetation; fen/transition mire/spring)
Land-use Nature conservation/research (100%)

■ **Birds**
This site was designated as a Special Protection Area based on its migratory waterfowl populations, particularly for *Cygnus cygnus* which is an Annex I species under the EC Birds Directive. Additionally, *Anas crecca* (950 birds, 1996) and *A. clypeata* (126 birds, 1996) winter in numbers of national importance.

■ **Protection status**
National High **International** High
51 ha of IBA covered by Nature Reserve (Kilcolman Bog, 51 ha). IBA overlaps with Wildfowl Sanctuary (Kilcolman Bog; area not known). 63 ha of IBA covered by Special Protection Area (Kilcolman Bog, 63 ha).

■ **Conservation issues**

Threats Agricultural intensification/expansion (B), Drainage (B)

The main threats are agricultural improvements and drainage on nearby land. Part of the site (21 ha) is a BirdWatch Ireland reserve.

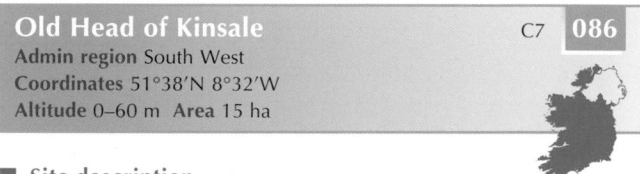

Old Head of Kinsale C7 086
Admin region South West
Coordinates 51°38'N 8°32'W
Altitude 0–60 m **Area** 15 ha

■ **Site description**
A 5-km long headland situated on the south County Cork coast, approximately 5 km from Kinsale.

Habitats Rocky areas (100%; sea cliff/rocky shore)
Land-use Not utilized (100%)

■ **Birds**
The site was designated as a Special Protection Area on the basis of its breeding seabirds. Old Head is a major seabird colony, the largest on the south coast apart from the Saltee Islands. Breeding seabirds recorded in nationally important numbers in 1987 include *Uria aalge* (4,500 birds), *Alca torda* (320 birds) and *Rissa tridactyla* (1,259 pairs). In addition, *Falco peregrinus* and *Falco tinnunculus* breed and there are cliff-nesting *Delichon urbica*. It is a moderately important breeding site for *Pyrrhocorax pyrrhocorax* and large non-breeding flocks (35–50 birds) have been seen.

■ **Protection status**
National High **International** High
15 ha of IBA covered by Refuge for Fauna (Old Head of Kinsale, 15 ha). 15 ha of IBA covered by Special Protection Area (Old Head of Kinsale, 15 ha).

■ **Conservation issues**

Threats Recreation/tourism (C)

The area above the sea cliffs has been developed as a golf course, which could pose a threat to *Pyrrhocorax pyrrhocorax*.

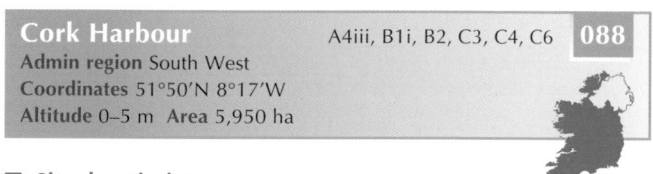

Sovereign Islands — A4iii, C4 — 087

Admin region South West
Coordinates 51°40'N 8°27'W
Altitude 0–32 m **Area** 2 ha

■ Site description
Two small, flat-topped islands (less that 30 m high) and surrounding waters, 1.5 km offshore from Oysterhaven in County Cork.

Habitats Grassland (1%), Marine areas (98%; sea inlet/coastal features), Rocky areas (1%; sea cliff/rocky shore)
Land-use Fisheries/aquaculture (98%), Not utilized (2%)

■ Birds
This site supports breeding seabirds, including *Fulmarus glacialis*, *Phalacrocorax carbo* and *Larus marinus*.

■ Protection status
National None **International** None

■ Conservation issues

Threats Aquaculture/fisheries (C)

Fishing in surrounding waters may deplete the prey stock of seabirds, with implications for their breeding success. On the basis of its breeding seabirds, the area and its surrounding waters have been proposed as a Special Protection Area (Sovereign Island, 125 ha).

Cork Harbour — A4iii, B1i, B2, C3, C4, C6 — 088

Admin region South West
Coordinates 51°50'N 8°17'W
Altitude 0–5 m **Area** 5,950 ha

■ Site description
A large, very sheltered sea bay with several river estuaries situated in County Cork. Intertidal mudflats are extensive with some areas of saltmarsh. There are three to four adjoining small freshwater or brackish lagoons and two large areas of open water, Lough Mahon and Lower Harbour, which are separated by Great Island. Large centres of human habitation lie adjacent to this site, including Cork city, which is a major port. Cork harbour and port form the largest industrial area on Ireland's south coast.

Habitats Forest and woodland (5%; alluvial/very wet forest), Grassland (10%; humid grassland), Wetland (80%; tidal river/enclosed tidal water; mudflat/sandflat; saltmarsh; standing brackish and salt water; water-fringe vegetation), Artificial landscape (5%; other urban/industrial areas)
Land-use Agriculture (20%), Fisheries/aquaculture (50%), Nature conservation/research (5%), Tourism/recreation (20%), Urban/industrial/transport (20%)

■ Birds

Species		Season	Year	Pop min	Pop max	Acc	Criteria
Calidris alpina	Dunlin	W	1995	12,050	12,050	A	B1i, B2, C3
Limosa limosa	Black-tailed Godwit	W	1996	1,399	1,399	A	B1i, C3
Limosa lapponica	Bar-tailed Godwit	W	1996	456	456	A	B2
Numenius arquata	Curlew	W	1995	1,669	1,669	A	B2
Tringa totanus	Redshank	W	1996	1,344	1,344	A	B1i, C3
Sterna hirundo	Common Tern	B	1995	102	102	A	C6

Cork Harbour regularly supports over 20,000 waterfowl. It is one of the most important sites in Ireland for breeding *Sterna hirundo* and for wintering *Podiceps cristatus* (286 birds, 1996), *Mergus serrator* (133 birds, 1996), *Haematopus ostralegus* (1,364 birds, 1995) and *Vanellus vanellus* (15,400 birds, 1995), as well as for staging *Numenius phaeopus* (3,304 birds, 1979). Several other species also occur in numbers of national importance, including *Phalacrocorax carbo* (991 birds, 1996), *Tadorna tadorna* (2,167 birds, 1986), *Anas penelope* (2,601 birds, 1995), *Anas crecca* (1,418 birds, 1996) and *Pluvialis apricaria* (4,431 birds, 1995).

■ Protection status
National Partial **International** Partial
IBA overlaps with Wildfowl Sanctuary (Douglas Estuary; area not known). 1,436 ha of IBA covered by Ramsar Site (Cork Harbour, 1,436 ha). 1,436 ha of IBA covered by Special Protection Area (Cork Harbour, 1,436 ha).

■ Conservation issues

Threats Abandonment/reduction of land management (C), Agricultural intensification/ expansion (B), Aquaculture/fisheries (B), Consequences of animal/plant introductions (A), Extraction industry (C), Filling-in of wetlands (A), Industrialization/urbanization (A), Infrastructure (B), Natural events (C), Recreation/tourism (C)

Ongoing road, urban and industrial development has led to considerable loss of intertidal habitat, including mudflat. Additional threats to habitat quality are infestation of mudflats by non-native cord-grass *Spartina*, intertidal shellfish cultivation, and pressure from recreation and amenity interests. Whitegate oil refinery poses an ongoing pollution threat. Given the damage to this site and ongoing pressures from development, the inclusion of unprotected wetland areas within the Special Protection Area is critical.

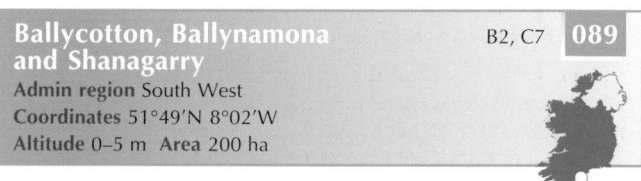

Ballycotton, Ballynamona and Shanagarry — B2, C7 — 089

Admin region South West
Coordinates 51°49'N 8°02'W
Altitude 0–5 m **Area** 200 ha

■ Site description
A composite coastal system, stretching northwards from Ballycotton towards Garrvroe in County Cork. The site consists of brackish and freshwater lagoons saltwater marshes, mudflats, sandflats, dunes and wet meadows. The main lagoon was an inlet of the sea until the 1930s when it was cut off by the development of a shingle-bank. The bank was breached only from time to time until 1991 when a new breach was created which has remained open, changing the lake back to a tidal inlet.

Habitats Grassland (20%; humid grassland), Wetland (80%; tidal river/enclosed tidal water; mudflat/sandflat; saltmarsh; sand-dunes/sand beach; shingle/stony beach; coastal lagoon)
Land-use Agriculture (20%), Not utilized (60%), Tourism/recreation (20%)

■ Birds

Species		Season	Year	Pop min	Pop max	Acc	Criteria
Cygnus columbianus	Bewick's Swan	W	1996	27	125	A	B2

The site is of particular importance for *Cygnus columbianus*. However, due to loss of the main lagoon, numbers have declined drastically over the last ten years. This is also one of the most important sites in Ireland for wintering *Arenaria interpres* (275 birds, 1996) which, along with several other species, including *Anas crecca* (1,109 birds, 1996), *Charadrius hiaticula* (182 birds, 1996) and *Pluvialis apricaria* (3,755 birds, 1995), occur in numbers of national importance.

■ Protection status
National Partial **International** Partial
IBA overlaps with Wildfowl Sanctuary (Ballycotton, Ballynamona, and Shanagarry; area not known). 92 ha of IBA covered by Ramsar Site (Ballycotton, Ballynamona, and Shanagarry, 92 ha). 92 ha of IBA covered by Special Protection Area (Ballycotton, Ballynamona, and Shanagarry, 92 ha).

■ Conservation issues

Threats Agricultural intensification/expansion (B), Drainage (A), Natural events (C), Recreation/tourism (B)

Past drainage, land-claim and breaching of the shingle-bar have damaged this wetland site. Visitor pressure may cause disturbance to wintering birds, and the natural erosion of intertidal habitats is a threat. The site lies within a proposed candidate Special Area for Conservation (Ballycotton, Ballynamona and Shanagarry; area not known).

Ballymacoda

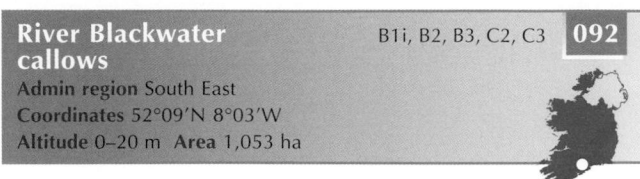

B1i, B2, C3 **090**

Admin region South West
Coordinates 51°54'N 7°54'W
Altitude 0–5 m **Area** 602 ha

■ Site description

A coastal site situated north-east of Ballymacoda in County Cork and encompassing the Womanagh river estuary, comprising a winding channel flanked by marshy fields, saltmarsh and mudflats. The estuary is sheltered from the open sea by a stabilized shingle-bar and extensive sand beach. Much of the land adjacent to the estuary has been claimed for agricultural use, mainly cattle-grazing and silage, but most fields remain marshy.

Habitats Grassland (20%; humid grassland), Wetland (80%; tidal river/enclosed tidal water; mudflat/sandflat; saltmarsh; sand-dunes/sand beach)
Land-use Agriculture (20%), Not utilized (80%)

■ Birds

Species		Season	Year	Pop min	Pop max	Acc	Criteria
Calidris alpina	Dunlin	W	1995	3,750	3,750	A	B2
Limosa limosa	Black-tailed Godwit	W	1996	181	700	A	B1i, C3
Limosa lapponica	Bar-tailed Godwit	W	1996	441	441	A	B2
Numenius arquata	Curlew	W	1995	2,150	2,150	A	B2

This is an important wetland site, which in the past has regularly held over 20,000 waterfowl, but in recent years numbers have not reached this threshold. Additional species present in nationally important numbers include *Pluvialis apricaria* (8,850 birds, 1996), *Pluvialis squatarola* (514 birds, 1995), *Vanellus vanellus* (3,050 birds, 1996), *Calidris alba* (131 birds, 1996) and *Arenaria interpres* (142 birds, 1996).

■ Protection status

National None **International** Partial
375 ha of IBA covered by Ramsar Site (Ballymacoda, 375 ha). 375 ha of IBA covered by Special Protection Area (Ballymacoda, 375 ha).

■ Conservation issues

Threats Agricultural intensification/expansion (B), Aquaculture/fisheries (B)

Water quality is adversely affected by run-off from slurry spreading. Intertidal shellfish cultivation is a recent development within the site, which may threaten habitat quality.

Blackwater estuary

B1i, B2, C3 **091**

Admin region South East, South West
Coordinates 51°58'N 7°50'W
Altitude 0–5 m **Area** 500 ha

■ Site description

A small estuary of the Blackwater river with a narrow opening to the sea. This site includes areas of intertidal mudflat and saltmarsh within the main Blackwater estuary and the smaller adjoining Tourig estuary. An intertidal pool at Foxhole, where the embankment has been breached is also within the site. The estuary is used for recreational boating activities.

Habitats Grassland (25%; humid grassland), Wetland (75%; tidal river/enclosed tidal water; mudflat/sandflat; saltmarsh)
Land-use Agriculture (25%), Fisheries/aquaculture (75%)

■ Birds

Species		Season	Year	Pop min	Pop max	Acc	Criteria
Limosa limosa	Black-tailed Godwit	W	1996	845	845	A	B1i, C3
Numenius arquata	Curlew	W	1995	1,544	1,544	A	B2

Several other wintering species occur in numbers of national importance, including *Anas penelope* (1,001 birds, 1995), *Pluvialis squatarola* (77 birds, 1996) and *Calidris alpina* (2,537 birds, 1996).

■ Protection status

National None **International** High

468 ha of IBA covered by Ramsar Site (Blackwater Estuary, 468 ha). 468 ha of IBA covered by Special Protection Area (Blackwater Estuary, 468 ha).

■ Conservation issues

Threats Aquaculture/fisheries (C), Industrialization/urbanization (C), Infrastructure (B), Recreation/tourism (C)

Permission is currently being sought for construction of a bypass around Youghal town, which will cross the Tourig estuary. Subsequent to consultation, the route of least damage to the estuary was taken; however, some loss of intertidal habitat will occur and increased disturbance to the site is likely.

River Blackwater callows

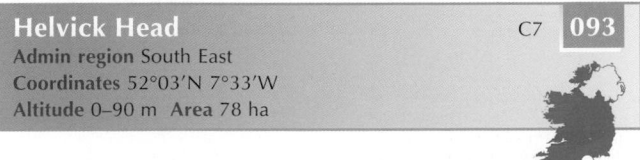

B1i, B2, B3, C2, C3 **092**

Admin region South East
Coordinates 52°09'N 8°03'W
Altitude 0–20 m **Area** 1,053 ha

■ Site description

A narrow flood-plain of the River Blackwater surrounded by parallel sandstone ridges and extending 29 km along the river from Fermoy east to Cappoquin. The site comprises the river itself and adjacent wet grassland along either side.

Habitats Forest and woodland (10%; broadleaved deciduous forest; alluvial/very wet forest), Grassland (40%; humid grassland), Wetland (50%; river/stream; water-fringe vegetation; fen/transition mire/spring)
Land-use Agriculture (50%), Fisheries/aquaculture (50%)

■ Birds

Species		Season	Year	Pop min	Pop max	Acc	Criteria
Cygnus columbianus	Bewick's Swan	W	1995	36	36	A	B2
Cygnus cygnus	Whooper Swan	W	1996	213	213	A	B1i, B3, C2
Limosa limosa	Black-tailed Godwit	W	1996	1,000	1,000	A	B1i, C3

The river flood-plain supports important numbers of wintering waterfowl. Additional species wintering in numbers of national importance are *Anas penelope* (4,217 birds, 1996), *Anas crecca* (1,844 birds, 1996), *Anas platyrhynchos* (844 birds, 1996) and *Anas clypeata* (50 birds, 1996).

■ Protection status

National High **International** High
IBA overlaps with Wildfowl Sanctuary (River Blackwater Callows; area not known). 1,053 ha of IBA covered by Special Protection Area (River Blackwater Callows, 1,053 ha).

■ Conservation issues

Threats Agricultural intensification/expansion (B), Drainage (B)

A potential threat to the site is loss of wet meadows due to the deepening of drains.

Helvick Head

C7 **093**

Admin region South East
Coordinates 52°03'N 7°33'W
Altitude 0–90 m **Area** 78 ha

■ Site description

Helvick Head is situated on the southern tip of Dungarvan Harbour in County Waterford. Steep sandstone cliffs provide nesting sites for seabirds. The adjacent sea area is included within the site.

Habitats Scrub (10%; heathland), Marine areas (70%; sea inlet/coastal features), Rocky areas (20%; sea cliff/rocky shore)
Land-use Fisheries/aquaculture (70%), Not utilized (30%)

■ Birds

Breeding seabirds include nationally important numbers of *Rissa tridactyla* (1,000–1,500 pairs, 1987), as well as *Uria aalge* (1,000 birds, 1987).

■ Protection status
National None **International** None

■ Conservation issues

Threats Aquaculture/fisheries (C)

The inaccessibility of the cliffs prevents significant disturbance. On the basis of its breeding seabirds, this site has been proposed as a Special Protection Area (Helvick Head, 78 ha) by NPW and will be designated in the near future.

Dungarvan Harbour   A4i, B1i, B2, C2, C3   094
Admin region South East
Coordinates 52°04′N 7°34′W
Altitude 0–10 m **Area** 1,300 ha

■ Site description
A large, east-facing sea bay on the south coast in County Waterford. The extensive intertidal sand- and mudflats at this site are sheltered by Helvick Head to the south and Ballynacourty Point to the north. The linear Cunnigar shingle-spit extends far into the bay, providing further shelter to the inner mudflats.

Habitats Wetland (80%; mudflat/sandflat; saltmarsh; sand-dunes/sand beach), Marine areas (20%; sea inlet/coastal features; other urban/industrial areas)
Land-use Fisheries/aquaculture (30%), Not utilized (50%), Tourism/recreation (20%)

■ Birds

Species		Season	Year	Pop min	Pop max	Acc	Criteria
Branta bernicla	Brent Goose	W	1995	616	616	A	B1i, C3
Calidris canutus	Knot	W	1996	996	996	A	B2
Calidris alpina	Dunlin	W	1996	6,100	6,100	A	B2
Limosa limosa	Black-tailed Godwit	W	1996	331	952	A	B1i, C3
Limosa lapponica	Bar-tailed Godwit	W	1996	1,593	1,593	A	A4i, B1i, B2, C2

An important site for wintering waterbirds. Several additional species occur in numbers of national importance including *Tadorna tadorna* (995 birds, 1995), *Pluvialis apricaria* (6,100 birds, 1996), *Vanellus vanellus* (3,775 birds, 1996) and *Tringa totanus* (910 birds, 1996).

■ Protection status
National None **International** Partial
1,041 ha of IBA covered by Ramsar Site (Dungarvan Harbour, 1,041 ha). 1,041 ha of IBA covered by Special Protection Area (Dungarvan Harbour, 1,041 ha).

■ Conservation issues

Threats Aquaculture/fisheries (A), Recreation/tourism (U)

The southern side of this bay has been extensively developed for intertidal shellfish cultivation. Possible implications are loss of, and changes to, the intertidal habitat, and increased disturbance to wintering birds. The beach and harbour are also of high recreational importance with further implications in terms of disturbance to the site.

Tramore Backstrand   B1i, B2, C3, C6   095
Admin region South East
Coordinates 52°10′N 7°06′W
Altitude 0–20 m **Area** 1,557 ha

■ Site description
A small, shallow bay next to Tramore village in County Waterford, comprising mainly intertidal mudflat with some saltmarsh. It is sheltered from the sea by a long, shingle spit with sand-dunes, leaving only a narrow opening out to sea. The site has been extended since the last pan-European inventory (Grimmett and Jones 1989) to include Tramore Bay, outside of the shingle spit, between Great Newtown and Brownstone Head.

Habitats Wetland (100%; mudflat/sandflat; saltmarsh; sand-dunes/sand beach)
Land-use Not utilized (80%), Tourism/recreation (20%)

■ Birds

Species		Season	Year	Pop min	Pop max	Acc	Criteria
[1] *Gavia stellata*	Red-throated Diver	W	1996	107	107	—	C6
Branta bernicla	Brent Goose	W	1996	591	591	A	B1i, C3
Limosa lapponica	Bar-tailed Godwit	W	1996	576	576	A	B2

1. Tramore Bay.

This wetland supports several wintering waterfowl in numbers of international importance. Additional species wintering in nationally important numbers include *Calidris alpina* (2,721 birds, 1996), *Pluvialis apricaria* (3,600 birds, 1996), *Pluvialis squatarola* (258 birds, 1996), *Calidris alba* (71 birds, 1995) and *Limosa limosa* (250 birds, 1995).

■ Protection status
National None **International** Partial
367 ha of IBA covered by Ramsar Site (Tramore Backstrand, 367 ha). 367 ha of IBA covered by Special Protection Area (Tramore Backstrand, 367 ha).

■ Conservation issues

Threats Consequences of animal/plant introductions (B), Filling-in of wetlands (B), Industrialization/urbanization (C), Natural events (B), Recreation/tourism (C)

A municipal dump adjacent to the site threatens habitat quality due to the effects of pollution. Other threats include erosion of the dune system and the spread of non-native cord-grass *Spartina* across the mudflats. The site overlaps with a proposed candidate Special Area for Conservation (Tramore Backstrand; area not known).

Bannow Bay   B1i, B2, C3   096
Admin region South East
Coordinates 52°13′N 6°48′W
Altitude 0–10 m **Area** 958 ha

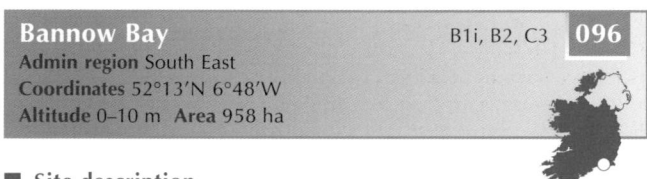

■ Site description
An extensive, sheltered sea bay and estuary, situated in County Wexford, 20 km east of Waterford city. At low tide over 75% of the bay is exposed mud and sand with some saltmarsh. The Ownduff and Corock rivers discharge into the head of the bay which is constricted at its mouth by sandbars and a dune system on either side. There is intertidal shellfish cultivation.

Habitats Wetland (100%; tidal river/enclosed tidal water; mudflat/sandflat; saltmarsh; sand-dunes/sand beach; shingle/stony beach)
Land-use Fisheries/aquaculture (20%), Hunting (20%), Not utilized (60%)

■ Birds

Species		Season	Year	Pop min	Pop max	Acc	Criteria
Branta bernicla	Brent Goose	W	1995	1,161	1,161	A	B1i, C3
Calidris alpina	Dunlin	W	1995	5,520	5,520	A	B2
Limosa lapponica	Bar-tailed Godwit	W	1996	570	570	A	B2

This wetland supports a wide range of wintering waterfowl. Several additional species occur in numbers of national importance including *Tadorna tadorna* (491 birds, 1996), *Pluvialis apricaria* (7,480 birds, 1995), *Pluvialis squatarola* (280 birds, 1996), *Vanellus vanellus* (3,450 birds, 1995) and *Tringa totanus* (485 birds, 1996).

■ Protection status
National High **International** High
IBA overlaps with Wildfowl Sanctuary (Bannow Bay; area not known). 958 ha of IBA covered by Ramsar Site (Bannow Bay, 958 ha). 900 ha of IBA covered by Special Protection Area (Bannow Bay, 900 ha).

■ Conservation issues

Threats Aquaculture/fisheries (B), Consequences of animal/plant introductions (C), Disturbance to birds (B), Recreation/tourism (B)

Intertidal shellfish cultivation is a possible threat to habitat quality, while wildfowling causes disturbance to birds. Habitat quality is reduced by the spread of non-native cord-grass *Spartina*. In 1997 unauthorized mechanical cockle-harvesting caused damage to the intertidal mudflats.

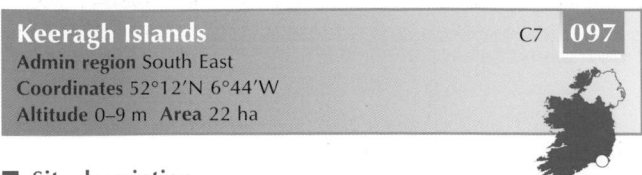

Keeragh Islands — C7 097

Admin region South East
Coordinates 52°12'N 6°44'W
Altitude 0–9 m **Area** 22 ha

■ Site description

The Keeraghs are two low-lying islets located approximately 2 km offshore to the west of Ballyteigue Bay in County Wexford. The vegetation is mainly maritime in character and there are surrounding reefs.

Habitats Grassland (5%; mesophile grassland), Marine areas (90%; sea inlet/coastal features), Rocky areas (5%; rock stacks/islets)
Land-use Fisheries/aquaculture (90%), Not utilized (10%)

■ Birds

The number of breeding *Phalacrocorax carbo* (239 pairs, 1987) comprises about 5% of the Irish population; also notable were the numbers of breeding *Sterna paradisaea* (12 pairs, 1984) which, however, have ceased to breed at the site despite an attempted restoration programme.

■ Protection status

National None **International** None

■ Conservation issues

Threats Aquaculture/fisheries (U), Disturbance to birds (B)

Fishing in surrounding waters may deplete the prey stock of seabirds, with implications for their breeding success. Day-trippers to the site may lead to disturbance. On the basis of its numbers of breeding *Phalacrocorax carbo* and *Sterna paradisaea*, this site was proposed as a Special Protection Area (Keeragh Islands, 22 ha) by NPW and should be designated in the near future.

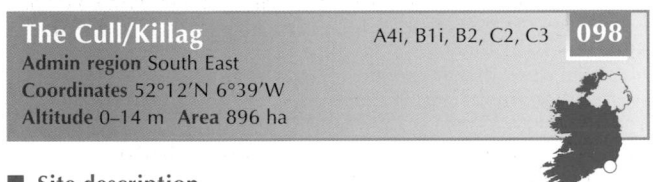

The Cull/Killag — A4i, B1i, B2, C2, C3 098

Admin region South East
Coordinates 52°12'N 6°39'W
Altitude 0–14 m **Area** 896 ha

■ Site description

Situated next to Kilmore quay in County Wexford, the western part of this site (the Cull) is a long, narrow sea inlet and estuary, protected from the open sea by a shingle-spit with dunes. The eastern part of this intertidal system (Killag) was claimed in the last century by construction of the Cull bank and is now polderland, most of which is intensively farmed grassland and arable land.

Habitats Wetland (50%; tidal river/enclosed tidal water; mudflat/sandflat; sand-dunes/sand beach; shingle/stony beach), Marine areas (30%; sea inlet/coastal features), Artificial landscape (20%; highly improved reseeded grassland; arable land)
Land-use Agriculture (20%), Nature conservation/research (80%)

■ Birds

Species	Season	Year	Pop min	Pop max	Acc	Criteria
[1] *Cygnus columbianus* Bewick's Swan	W	1996	312	555	A	A4i, B1i, B2, C2
Branta bernicla Brent Goose	W	1995	695	695	A	B1i, C3
Limosa limosa Black-tailed Godwit	W	1996	550	770	A	B1i, C3
Numenius arquata Curlew	W	1995	1,415	1,415	A	B2
1. Feeding on improved grasslands.						

This is an important site for wintering waterbirds; additional species occurring in numbers of national importance are *Anas crecca* (520 birds, 1996), *Anas acuta* (55 birds, 1996), *Mergus serrator*

(41 birds, 1996), *Pluvialis apricaria* (4,100 birds, 1995), *Vanellus vanellus* (6,210 birds, 1995) and *Calidris alpina* (1,275 birds, 1996).

■ Protection status

National Partial **International** Partial
531 ha of IBA covered by Nature Reserve (Ballyteigue Burrow, 531 ha).
8 ha of IBA covered by Nature Reserve (Ballyteigue Burrow, 8 ha).
526 ha of IBA covered by Special Protection Area (Ballyteigue Burrow, 526 ha).

■ Conservation issues

Threats Agricultural intensification/expansion (C), Disturbance to birds (B), Industrialization/urbanization (C), Recreation/tourism (C)

There is a proposal for a wind-farm at Killag, which may cause displacement of *Cygnus columbianus* from parts of the site. Changes in agricultural practice threaten the feeding sites of swans *Cygnus*. The site lies within a proposed candidate Special Area for Conservation (Ballyteigue Burrow; area not known).

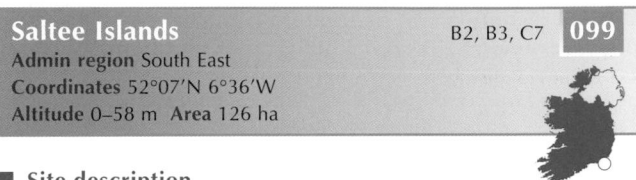

Saltee Islands — B2, B3, C7 099

Admin region South East
Coordinates 52°07'N 6°36'W
Altitude 0–58 m **Area** 126 ha

■ Site description

The Saltee Islands (Great Saltee and Little Saltee) lie 5 km offshore from Kilmore Quay in County Wexford. Both islands have exposed rocky cliffs and boulder beaches. The islands have not been farmed since the 1940s.

Habitats Rocky areas (50%; sea cliff/rocky shore), Artificial landscape (50%; ruderal land)
Land-use Nature conservation/research (100%), Tourism/recreation (50%)

■ Birds

Species	Season	Year	Pop min	Pop max	Acc	Criteria
[1] *Sula bassana* Gannet	B	1996	1,530	1,530	A	B2
[2] *Phalacrocorax aristotelis* Shag	B	1996	225	—	A	B3
Larus fuscus Lesser Black-backed Gull	B	1996	600	600	A	B3
Larus marinus Great Black-backed Gull	B	1996	100	100	A	B3
Alca torda Razorbill	B	1996	3,200	3,200	A	B3
Fratercula arctica Puffin	B	1996	1,300	1,300	A	B2
1. Great Saltee.						
2. Both islands.						

The Saltees are internationally important for breeding seabird colonies. Species occurring in numbers of national importance are: *Fulmarus glacialis* (350 pairs, 1996), *Larus argentatus* (500 pairs, 1996), *Rissa tridactyla* (2,500 pairs, 1996) and *Uria aalge* (15,000 birds, 1996). Great Saltee is also a notable site for spring and autumn passerine migration.

■ Protection status

National High **International** High
126 ha of IBA covered by Nature Reserve (Saltee Islands, 126 ha). 126 ha of IBA covered by Special Protection Area (Saltee Islands, 126 ha).

■ Conservation issues

Threats Recreation/tourism (C)

Day-trippers, mainly to Great Saltee, may cause some disturbance to seabird colonies. NPW runs a long-term seabird population monitoring and ringing programme on the islands, which are a private bird sanctuary.

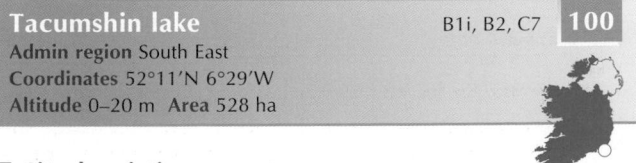

Tacumshin lake — B1i, B2, C7 100

Admin region South East
Coordinates 52°11'N 6°29'W
Altitude 0–20 m **Area** 528 ha

■ Site description

A shallow, coastal lagoon situated on the south coast of County Wexford, 15 km south of Wexford town. The lagoon was formerly a shallow sea bay which over time has been separated from the sea by a spit of shingle and sand. A drainage pipe reduces the water-level in the lagoon during the summer months, but in the winter, inflow exceeds outflow and the lake floods.

Habitats Grassland (25%; humid grassland), Wetland (75%; sand-dunes/sand beach; shingle/stony beach; coastal lagoon; standing fresh water; standing brackish and salt water; water-fringe vegetation; fen/transition mire/spring)
Land-use Agriculture (15%), Hunting (100%), Tourism/recreation (25%)

■ Birds

Species	Season	Year	Pop min	Pop max	Acc	Criteria
[1] *Cygnus olor* Mute Swan	N	—	300	400	—	B1i
Cygnus columbianus Bewick's Swan	W	1996	145	145	A	B2
Aythya marila Scaup	W	1996	55	55	A	B2
Numenius arquata Curlew	W	1995	1,740	1,740	A	B2

1. One of the largest moulting congregations in Ireland.

The waterfowl population of this lagoon is exceptionally diverse and the area supports large numbers of birds throughout the year, which is unusual among Irish wetlands. Additional species occurring in numbers of national importance include *Anas penelope* (4,980 birds, 1996), *Anas acuta* (440 birds, 1996), *Anas clypeata* (111 birds, 1996), *Fulica atra* (2,100 birds, 1996), *Pluvialis apricaria* (7,860 birds, 1995) and *Vanellus vanellus* (5,660 birds, 1995).

■ Protection status
National High **International** High
IBA overlaps with Wildfowl Sanctuary (Tacumshin Lake; area not known). 528 ha of IBA covered by Special Protection Area (Tacumshin Lake, 528 ha).

■ Conservation issues

Threats Agricultural intensification/expansion (B), Disturbance to birds (B), Drainage (B)

Plans are underway for the construction of a sluice at the shingle-bar, to control water-levels. Wildfowling is regulated by NPW. The site overlaps with a proposed candidate Special Area for Conservation (Tacumshin Lake; area not known).

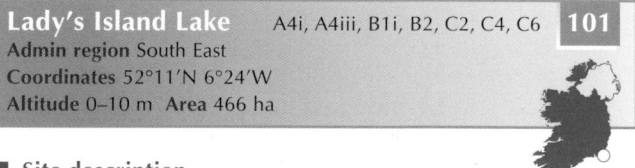

Lady's Island Lake   A4i, A4iii, B1i, B2, C2, C4, C6   101
Admin region South East
Coordinates 52°11′N 6°24′W
Altitude 0–10 m **Area** 466 ha

■ Site description
A shallow coastal lagoon, separated from the sea by a barrier of sand and shingle, and situated 3 km west of Carnsore Point in County Wexford. The lake has three islands, Lady's Island (now connected to the mainland by a causeway and included within the IBA), Inish and Sgarbheen.

Habitats Grassland (20%; humid grassland), Wetland (80%; shingle/stony beach; coastal lagoon; water-fringe vegetation)
Land-use Agriculture (10%), Nature conservation/research (20%), Not utilized (40%), Tourism/recreation (30%)

■ Birds

Species	Season	Year	Pop min	Pop max	Acc	Criteria
Cygnus olor Mute Swan	W	—	600	600	—	B1i
[1] *Cygnus olor* Mute Swan	N	—	300	400	—	B1i
Sterna sandvicensis Sandwich Tern	B	1996	1,358	1,358	A	B1i, B2, C2, C6
[2] *Sterna dougallii* Roseate Tern	B	1996	124	124	A	A4i, B1i, B2, C2, C6
Sterna hirundo Common Tern	B	1996	386	386	A	C6
Sterna paradisaea Arctic Tern	B	1995	151	151	A	C6

1. Moulting.
2. One of two regular breeding sites in Ireland.

This is an internationally important site for breeding terns, with colonies of four species (formerly five) present. The site was formerly of international importance for wintering waterfowl and still holds nationally important numbers of *Aythya ferina* (639 birds, 1995), *Aythya marila* (140 birds, 1996), *Anas penelope* (1,850 birds, 1996),

Anas crecca (72 birds, 1996), *Aythya fuligula* (231 birds, 1995) and *Vanellus vanellus* (2,230 birds, 1995).

■ Protection status
National Low **International** Partial
4 ha of IBA covered by Refuge for Fauna (Lady's Island Lake (Inish and Sgarbheen), 4 ha). 356 ha of IBA covered by Special Protection Area (Lady's Island Lake, 356 ha). 4 ha of IBA covered by Special Protection Area (Lady's Island Lake (Inish and Sgarbheen), 4 ha).

■ Conservation issues

Threats Drainage (A), Recreation/tourism (A)

The lake is used by recreational windsurfers and boats, which can cause disturbance to nesting terns. In most years a channel is cut in the barrier to relieve flooding; however, this reduction in water-level can permit predators to reach nesting terns. Construction of a sluice to control water-levels is likely in the near future. There is nutrient pollution of the lake due to agricultural run-off. The terns have been studied on the islands since 1960, and BirdWatch Ireland have co-managed the colonies with NPW since 1993. The site lies within a proposed candidate Special Area for Conservation (Lady's Island Lake; area not known).

Wexford Harbour and Slobs   A4i, A4iii, B1i, B2, B3, C2, C3, C4   102
Admin region South East
Coordinates 52°19′N 6°26′W
Altitude 0–10 m **Area** 5,000 ha

■ Site description
An extensive shallow estuary at the mouth of the Slaney river, next to Wexford town, County Wexford. The site includes intertidal mud- and sandflats which are protected by Raven and Rosslare Points and behind which lie the north and south 'slobs'. These are two flat areas of farmland, mainly arable and pasture, empoldered behind 19th century sea-walls. There are partially afforested dunes at Raven and Rosslare Points. The main remaining intertidal areas are at Hopeland on the south shore and between Ferrybank and Ferrycarrig on the inner north shore. There is bottom culture of mussels *Mytilus* within the estuary. Parts of the site are heavily used for recreation. Compared to its listing in the previous pan-European inventory (Grimmett and Jones 1989), the site has now been extended to include the waters offshore from Raven Point.

Habitats Forest and woodland (10%; mixed forest), Wetland (55%; tidal river/enclosed tidal water; mudflat/sandflat; saltmarsh; sand-dunes/sand beach), Artificial landscape (35%; highly improved reseeded grassland; arable land; forestry plantation)
Land-use Agriculture (35%), Fisheries/aquaculture (50%), Forestry (5%), Nature conservation/research (20%), Urban/industrial/transport (10%)

■ Birds

Species	Season	Year	Pop min	Pop max	Acc	Criteria
Cygnus cygnus Whooper Swan	W	1996	147	147	A	B3
Anser albifrons White-fronted Goose	W	1996	9,793	9,793	A	B1i, C3
Branta bernicla Brent Goose	W	1995	2,609	2,609	A	B1i, C3
Aythya marila Scaup	W	1996	432	432	A	B2
Pluvialis squatarola Grey Plover	W	1996	2,200	2,200	A	A4i, B1i, C3
Calidris canutus Knot	W	1996	640	640	A	B2
Calidris alpina Dunlin	W	1995	9,265	9,265	A	B2
Limosa limosa Black-tailed Godwit	W	1995	2,340	2,340	A	A4i, B1i, C3
Limosa lapponica Bar-tailed Godwit	W	1996	2,126	2,126	A	B1i, B2, C2
Numenius arquata Curlew	W	1996	2,431	2,431	A	B2

This is a wetland of international importance for several species of waterfowl, regularly holding over 20,000 wintering birds. It is one of the two most important sites in the world for wintering *Anser albifrons flavirostris*. The sea off Raven Point holds nationally important numbers of *Melanitta nigra* (1,260 birds, 1997; one of the top wintering sites in Ireland) and divers *Gavia*. Many other species also occur in numbers of national importance, including wintering *Anas penelope* (5,125 birds, 1995), *Anas crecca* (690 birds, 1995), *Anas platyrhynchos* (2,521 birds, 1995), *Haematopus ostralegus* (2,205 birds, 1996) and *Vanellus vanellus* (12,080 birds, 1996).

■ Protection status
National Partial **International** Partial
589 ha of IBA covered by Nature Reserve (The Raven, 589 ha). 110 ha of IBA covered by Nature Reserve (Wexford Wildfowl Reserve, 110 ha). IBA overlaps with Wildfowl Sanctuary (Rosslare Point; area not known). 589 ha of IBA covered by Ramsar Site (The Raven, 589 ha). 194 ha of IBA covered by Ramsar Site (Wexford Wildfowl Reserve, 194 ha). 589 ha of IBA covered by Special Protection Area (The Raven, 589 ha). 110 ha of IBA covered by Special Protection Area (Wexford Wildfowl Reserve, 110 ha). 2,734 ha of IBA covered by Special Protection Area (Wexford Harbour, 2,734 ha).

■ Conservation issues

> **Threats** Agricultural intensification/expansion (C), Aquaculture/fisheries (C), Disturbance to birds (B), Drainage (A), Recreation/tourism (B)

The site has been damaged due to the filling-in of 8 ha of intertidal mudflat at Ferrybank on the north shore, which was the subject of an official complaint to the European Commission from BirdWatch Ireland. Drainage and land-claim at Hopeland, a key part of this wetland and still not included within the Special Protection Area, is another threat.

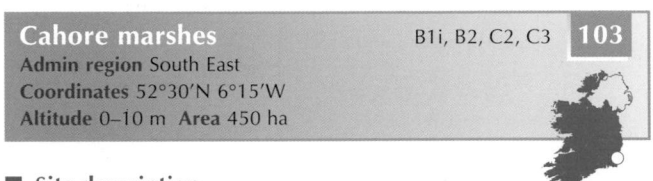

Cahore marshes   B1i, B2, C2, C3   **103**
Admin region South East
Coordinates 52°30'N 6°15'W
Altitude 0–10 m   **Area** 450 ha

■ Site description
Located just south of Cahore Point in County Wexford, this site comprises a large area of polder, which is separated from the sea by a ridge of sand-dunes. The polder was formerly a wetland, which was drained to provide agriculturally improved grassland for grazing.

> **Habitats** Grassland (40%; mesophile grassland), Wetland (60%; sand-dunes/sand beach; fen/transition mire/spring)
> **Land-use** Agriculture (40%), Not utilized (60%)

■ Birds

Species	Season	Year	Pop min	Pop max	Acc	Criteria
Cygnus columbianus Bewick's Swan	W	1996	26	26	A	B2
[1] *Anser albifrons* White-fronted Goose	W	1996	307	307	A	B1i, C3
Pluvialis apricaria Golden Plover	W	1996	10,250	10,250	A	B1i, C2

1. Mean 1995–1996.

This is an important site for wintering waterfowl, including nationally important numbers of *Anas penelope* (1,400 birds, 1996), *Anas acuta* (22 birds, 1996), and *Vanellus vanellus* (6,800 birds, 1996).

■ Protection status
National None **International** None

■ Conservation issues

> **Threats** Agricultural intensification/expansion (C), Drainage (C)

Although the site has no formal protection, the landowner is sympathetic to waterbird conservation. However, damage to the adjacent dunes for a caravan site has recently taken place.

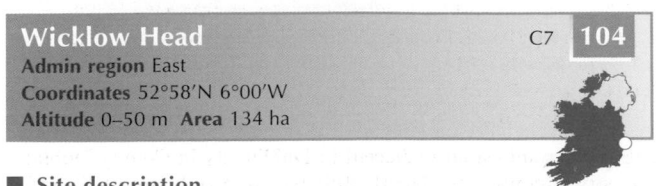

Wicklow Head   C7   **104**
Admin region East
Coordinates 52°58'N 6°00'W
Altitude 0–50 m   **Area** 134 ha

■ Site description
Wicklow Head, situated a mile south of Wicklow town, is a rocky headland with sheer cliffs and inlets. The site includes the adjacent waters. There is a coastguard station and lighthouse on the headland.

> **Habitats** Scrub (20%; heathland), Marine areas (70%), Rocky areas (10%; sea cliff/rocky shore)
> **Land-use** Fisheries/aquaculture (70%), Tourism/recreation (30%)

■ Birds
There are nationally important colonies of breeding seabirds, mostly *Rissa tridactyla* (1,125 pairs, 1994), with smaller numbers of *Alca torda* (191 birds, 1994), *Uria aalge* (244 birds, 1994), *Fulmarus glacialis* and *Phalacrocorax aristotelis*.

■ Protection status
National None **International** None

■ Conservation issues

> **Threats** Aquaculture/fisheries (C), Recreation/tourism (C)

Walkers may cause some disturbance to birds, while fishing in surrounding waters may deplete the prey stock of seabirds, with implications for their breeding success. On the basis of its breeding seabirds, this site has been proposed as a Special Protection Area (Wicklow Head, 134 ha) by NPW and should be designated in the near future.

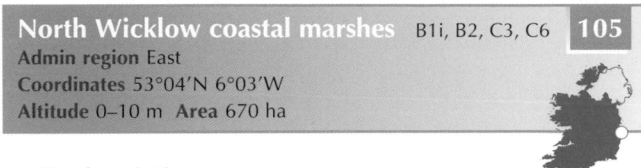

North Wicklow coastal marshes   B1i, B2, C3, C6   **105**
Admin region East
Coordinates 53°04'N 6°03'W
Altitude 0–10 m   **Area** 670 ha

■ Site description
A coastal wetland complex, extending for 18 km between Greystones and Wicklow in County Wicklow. A shingle barrier extends the length of the site, protecting brackish and freshwater marsh, estuary fen and wet grassland. Two key wetland areas are Broadlough estuary to the south and Kilcoole marshes to the north. These marshes were empoldered in the late 1980s. A mainline railway track runs along the length of the ridge. This is also an important amenity area.

> **Habitats** Grassland (45%; humid grassland), Wetland (45%; sand-dunes/sand beach; shingle/stony beach; coastal lagoon; standing fresh water; standing brackish and salt water), Artificial landscape (10%)
> **Land-use** Agriculture (50%), Hunting (50%), Nature conservation/research (10%), Urban/industrial/transport (10%)

■ Birds

Species	Season	Year	Pop min	Pop max	Acc	Criteria
Cygnus columbianus Bewick's Swan	W	—	—	140	—	B2
[1] *Branta bernicla* Brent Goose	W	1995	1,000	1,000	A	B1i, C3
Sterna albifrons Little Tern	B	1995	36	36	A	B2, C6

1. Birds commute daily from site 109.

An important site for wintering waterfowl and for breeding terns *Sterna*. Following empolderment, Kilcoole marshes are now a prime feeding area for *Branta bernicla*. Other species wintering in numbers of national importance are *Anser anser* (250 birds, 1997), *Anas penelope* (1,084 birds, 1996), *Anas crecca* (500 birds, 1996), *Melanitta nigra* (200 birds, 1996) and *Vanellus vanellus* (2,800 birds, 1996).

■ Protection status
National High **International** Partial
IBA overlaps with Wildfowl Sanctuary (Coast, Greystones–Wicklow; area not known). 237 ha of IBA covered by Special Protection Area (Broad Lough, 237 ha). 150 ha of IBA covered by Special Protection Area (Kilcoole Marshes, 150 ha).

■ Conservation issues

> **Threats** Disturbance to birds (B), Drainage (B), Industrialization/urbanization (B), Recreation/tourism (C)

Drainage of the marshes is reducing habitat quality. There is disturbance to wintering birds due to wildfowling while the amenity importance of the area results in some disturbance to the colony of *Sterna albifrons* and to wintering birds. Proposals for an industrial jetty will lead to habitat loss and fragmentation, with implications for coastal erosion. BirdWatch Ireland and NPW have operated a Little Tern Protection Scheme at Kilcoole since 1985. The site overlaps with a proposed candidate Special Area for Conservation (Coast, Greystones–Wicklow; area not known).

Wicklow Mountains
B2, C6 106

Admin region East
Coordinates 53°10′N 6°24′W
Altitude 100–925 m **Area** 30,000 ha

■ Site description
Located 20 km south of Dublin city, this site encompasses the upland areas of Counties Wicklow and Dublin. It comprises broad granite domes interspersed with pinnacled tops, rocky foothills, deep glens, numerous rivers and streams, and several lakes. Much of the area is a mosaic of heath, blanket bog and upland grassland, with stands of bracken and pockets of woodland. Poulaphouca reservoir, included within this site in the previous pan-European inventory (Grimmett and Jones 1989), is now treated separately (site 107). Land-uses include peat-cutting (which is also a potential threat), forestry and recreation (due to the close proximity of Dublin).

> **Habitats** Forest and woodland (5%; broadleaved deciduous forest), Scrub (15%; heathland), Grassland (10%; humid grassland), Wetland (50%; standing fresh water; river/stream; blanket bog), Artificial landscape (20%; highly improved reseeded grassland; forestry plantation)
> **Land-use** Agriculture (40%), Forestry (20%), Nature conservation/research (50%), Other (10%), Tourism/recreation (70%)

■ Birds

Species	Season	Year	Pop min	Pop max	Acc	Criteria
[1] *Falco columbarius* Merlin	B	1996	20	30	A	C6
Falco peregrinus Peregrine	B	—	26	—	—	B2, C6

1. The only well studied population in the country.

The nationally scarce *Falco columbarius* and *F. peregrinus* as well as *Lagopus lagopus* breed within the extensive areas of bog and moorland. This is also one of the most important sites in Ireland for *Phoenicurus phoenicurus* (50 pairs, 1996), which breed in the *Quercus* woodlands, and for *Turdus torquatus* (20 pairs, 1996), which breed in open, rocky areas.

■ Protection status
National Partial **International** Partial
20,000 ha of IBA covered by National Park (Wicklow Mountains, 20,000 ha). 157 ha of IBA covered by Nature Reserve (Glendalough, 157 ha). 1,958 ha of IBA covered by Nature Reserve (Glenealo Valley, 1,958 ha). 15,399 ha of IBA covered by Special Protection Area (Wicklow Mountains, 15,399 ha).

■ Conservation issues

> **Threats** Afforestation (B), Disturbance to birds (B), Extraction industry (C), Recreation/tourism (B)

NPW own large areas of the site which they manage for nature conservation by, for example, maintaining traditional sheep-grazing methods. However, conflict between farming and the implementation of conservation management measures is yet to be fully resolved. Due to the proximity of Dublin city, careful management of visitors is required to ensure amenity use and conservation management objectives are also not in conflict. The site overlaps with a proposed candidate Special Area for Conservation (Wicklow Mountains National Park; area not known).

Poulaphouca reservoir
C7 107

Admin region East
Coordinates 53°08′N 6°30′W
Altitude 180–180 m **Area** 1,949 ha

■ Site description
Poulaphouca reservoir, the largest inland water-body in south-east Ireland, is located south-east of Blessington, in County Dublin. It was created in 1944 by damming the River Liffey for the purpose of generating electricity from hydro-power, and also supplies water to Dublin city. Wet grassland and sandy shores surround the lake, and some of its perimeter has been planted with conifers to stabilize eroding banks and reduce pollution.

> **Habitats** Grassland (45%), Wetland (55%; standing fresh water)
> **Land-use** Agriculture (45%), Water management (55%)

■ Birds
The site was designated as a Special Protection Area on the basis of its migratory waterfowl, particularly *Anser anser* (655 birds, 1996).

■ Protection status
National None **International** High
1,949 ha of IBA covered by Special Protection Area (Poulaphouca Reservoir, 1,949 ha).

■ Conservation issues

> **Threats** Agricultural intensification/expansion (B), Recreation/tourism (C)

The lake is an important amenity area for Dublin city and careful management is required to ensure its conservation importance is maintained. There are some problems between farming interests and the use of improved fields for grazing by geese. Wildfowling leading to disturbance to birds is also likely.

Upper Barrow flood-plain
A4i, A4iii, B1i, B2, B3, C2, C4 108

Admin region East
Coordinates 53°05′N 7°03′W
Altitude 20–30 m **Area** 1,000 ha

■ Site description
A large river and flood-plain, confined within a narrow valley and extending from Monasterevin, 16 km south to Athy on the County Kildare/County Laois border.

> **Habitats** Grassland (50%; humid grassland), Wetland (50%; river/stream; water-fringe vegetation)
> **Land-use** Agriculture (50%), Not utilized (50%)

■ Birds

Species	Season	Year	Pop min	Pop max	Acc	Criteria
Cygnus columbianus Bewick's Swan	W	1987	180	180	A	A4i, B1i, B2, C2
Cygnus cygnus Whooper Swan	W	1996	100	100	A	B3

An important site for wintering waterfowl.

■ Protection status
National None **International** None

■ Conservation issues

> **Threats** Drainage (C)

With the intensification of agriculture, this site may be threatened by drainage of the flood-meadows.

Dublin Bay
A4i, A4iii, B1i, B2, C2, C3, C4, C6 109

Admin region East
Coordinates 53°21′N 6°12′W
Altitude 0–10 m **Area** 3,000 ha

■ Site description

> **Habitats** Wetland (90%; tidal river/enclosed tidal water; mudflat/sandflat; saltmarsh; sand-dunes/sand beach), Artificial landscape (10%; highly improved reseeded grassland; other urban/industrial areas)
> **Land-use** Nature conservation/research (30%), Not utilized (40%), Tourism/recreation, Urban/industrial/transport (60%)

A large bay and estuary adjacent to Dublin city in County Dublin. This site encompasses North Bull Island, Sandymount Strand, Tolka estuary, Dalkey Island area (a number of islands and surrounding waters), and part of Dublin docks. Dublin docks was treated as a separate IBA (former site IE089) in the previous pan-European inventory (Grimmett and Jones 1989). There are extensive sand- and mudflats, saltmarsh, and sand-dunes and beaches. North Bull Island is Dublin's main recreational beach, and its two main land-uses are conservation and recreation. There is high amenity use of Dublin Bay as a whole.

■ Birds

Species	Season	Year	Pop min	Pop max	Acc	Criteria
Branta bernicla Brent Goose	W	1995	1,800	1,800	A	B1i, C3
Haematopus ostralegus Oystercatcher	W	1995	1,067	1,067	A	C6
Calidris canutus Knot	W	1995	4,380	4,380	A	B1i, B2, C3
Calidris alpina Dunlin	W	1995	6,416	6,416	A	B2
Limosa lapponica Bar-tailed Godwit	W	1997	492	1,000	A	A4i, B1i, B2, C2
Numenius arquata Curlew	W	1995	1,007	1,007	A	B2
Tringa totanus Redshank	W	1995	1,900	1,900	A	B1i, C3
[1] *Sterna dougallii* Roseate Tern	P	1996	100	200	C	A4i, B1i, C2
[2] *Sterna hirundo* Common Tern	B	1997	120	120	A	C6

1. Turnover at Dalkey difficult to estimate and numbers may be much larger.
2. Colonies in Dublin Port area and at Dalkey.

This is a wetland of international importance for waterfowl, regularly supporting over 20,000 wintering birds. Species wintering in numbers of national importance include *Tadorna tadorna* (1,119 birds, 1995), *Anas penelope* (1,270 birds, 1995), *Anas crecca* (1,490 birds, 1995), *Anas acuta* (414 birds, 1995), *Anas clypeata* (370 birds, 1995), *Pluvialis squatarola* (914 birds, 1995), *Calidris alba* (450 birds, 1995) and *Limosa limosa* (466 birds, 1995). During August, large numbers of terns *Sterna* (typically about 5,000 and occasionally up to 30,000 birds) use Sandymount Strand as an evening roost.

■ Protection status
National Partial **International** Partial
1,436 ha of IBA covered by Nature Reserve (North Bull Island, 1,436 ha). IBA overlaps with Wildfowl Sanctuary (North Bull Island; area not known). 1,436 ha of IBA covered by Ramsar Site (North Bull Island, 1,436 ha). 500 ha of IBA covered by Biosphere Reserve (North Bull Island, 500 ha). 1,396 ha of IBA covered by Special Protection Area (Bull Island, 1,396 ha). 654 ha of IBA covered by Special Protection Area (Sandymount Strand and the Tolka estuary, 654 ha).

■ Conservation issues

Threats Disturbance to birds (A), Industrialization/urbanization (B), Infrastructure (B), Recreation/tourism (A)

Ongoing and proposed infrastructural developments (roads, port expansion, pipelines), to meet urban and industrial demands, continue to threaten this site, together with pressure from amenity users. The tern colony at Dublin port has been studied since 1950. In view of the pressures on this site, given its proximity to Dublin city, the need to complete its protection as a Special Protection Area is critical. The site overlaps with a proposed candidate Special Area for Conservation (North Bull Island; area not known).

Howth Head · B2, C7 · 110
Admin region East
Coordinates 53°22'N 6°03'W
Altitude 0–50 m **Area** 102 ha

■ Site description
A rocky headland, sea cliffs and adjacent sea area, situated on the northern side of Dublin Bay. On the slopes above the cliffs there is a mosaic of heathland vegetation. The sewage outflow for north Dublin is off Howth Head ('Other' land-use). The area is very popular for walkers and horse-riders.

Habitats Scrub (10%; heathland), Marine areas (80%; sea inlet/coastal features), Rocky areas (10%; sea cliff/rocky shore)
Land-use Fisheries/aquaculture (80%), Other (80%), Tourism/recreation (10%)

■ Birds

Species	Season	Year	Pop min	Pop max	Acc	Criteria
Cepphus grylle Black Guillemot	B	1990	21	—	—	B2

The sea cliffs are important for breeding seabirds, with nationally important numbers of *Rissa tridactyla* (c.1,700 pairs, 1987) and *Alca torda* (280 birds, 1987).

■ Protection status
National None **International** None

■ Conservation issues

Threats Aquaculture/fisheries (C), Industrialization/urbanization (B)

Sewage disposal is a threat but plans for a new sewage-treatment plant are now underway. The site has been proposed as a Special Protection Area (Howth Head, 102 ha) by NPW and should be designated in the near future.

Ireland's Eye · C7 · 111
Admin region East
Coordinates 53°24'N 6°04'W
Altitude 0–69 m **Area** 90 ha

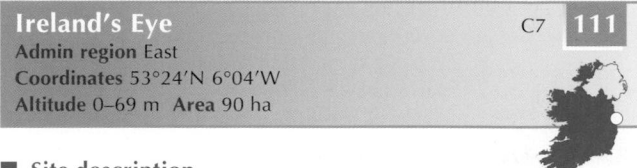

■ Site description
An uninhabited island and surrounding waters, located 1.5 km north of Howth, in County Dublin. The island is mainly rough grassland with steep sea cliffs on the north-east side. The island receives quite high numbers of visitors in the summer months given its proximity to Dublin.

Habitats Grassland (20%; mesophile grassland), Marine areas (50%; sea inlet/coastal features), Rocky areas (30%; sea cliff/rocky shore; rock stacks/islets)
Land-use Fisheries/aquaculture (50%), Tourism/recreation (50%)

■ Birds
Seabirds breeding in nationally important numbers include *Sula bassana* (106 pairs, 1996), *Phalacrocorax carbo* (217 pairs, 1994), *Rissa tridactyla* (1,079 pairs, 1994), *Uria aalge* (1,498 birds, 1994) and *Alca torda* (428 birds, 1994).

■ Protection status
National None **International** None

■ Conservation issues

Threats Aquaculture/fisheries (C), Recreation/tourism (C)

Control and management of visitors to the island is important to ensure there is no disturbance to nesting seabirds. On the basis of its breeding seabirds, this site has been proposed as a Special Protection Area (Ireland's Eye, 90 ha) by NPW and should be designated in the near future.

Baldoyle Bay · B1i, B2, C3 · 112
Admin region East
Coordinates 53°24'N 6°08'W
Altitude 0–5 m **Area** 203 ha

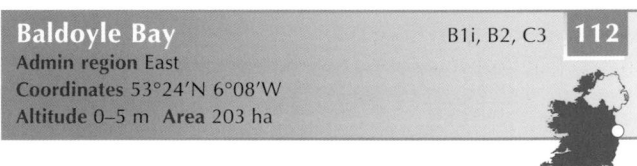

■ Site description
A coastal site extending from just south of Portmarnock village to the west pier at Howth in County Dublin. This tidal bay is located 5 km north of Dublin and is protected from the open sea by a large sand-dune system. It comprises the estuary of the Sluice and Mayne rivers and includes the marsh adjacent to the Mayne river. Up to 95% of the estuary is exposed at low tide. The site is used for recreational boating.

Habitats Wetland (100%; tidal river/enclosed tidal water; mudflat/sandflat; sand-dunes/sand beach; fen/transition mire/spring)
Land-use Fisheries/aquaculture (20%), Not utilized (60%), Tourism/recreation (20%)

■ Birds

Species	Season	Year	Pop min	Pop max	Acc	Criteria
Branta bernicla Brent Goose	W	1995	480	480	A	B1i, C3
Limosa lapponica Bar-tailed Godwit	W	1996	348	348	A	B2

This is an important site for wintering waterfowl. Further species wintering in numbers of national importance include *Tadorna tadorna* (214 birds, 1996), *Anas acuta* (68 birds, 1996), *Melanitta nigra* (150 birds, 1996), *Pluvialis apricaria* (2,150 birds, 1996), *Pluvialis squatarola* (533 birds, 1996) and *Calidris alba* (70 birds, 1996).

■ Protection status
National High **International** High
203 ha of IBA covered by Nature Reserve (Baldoyle Bay, 203 ha). 203 ha of IBA covered by Ramsar Site (Baldoyle Bay, 203 ha). 203 ha of IBA covered by Special Protection Area (Baldoyle Bay, 203 ha).

■ Conservation issues

Threats Consequences of animal/plant introductions (C), Industrialization/urbanization (C), Recreation/tourism (B)

The infestation of intertidal mudflats by non-native cord-grass *Spartina* threatens habitat quality. The site is of educational value due to its close proximity to Dublin.

Malahide/Broadmeadow estuary	A4iii, B1i, B2, C3, C4	113

Admin region East
Coordinates 53°27′N 6°09′W
Altitude 0–5 m **Area** 606 ha

■ Site description
The Broadmeadow river estuary is situated immediately north of Malahide and east of Swords in County Dublin. The site is divided by a railway viaduct and protected from the sea by a large sand-spit. There are sand- and mudflats within the outer estuary. However, inland of the viaduct, only the extreme inner part of the estuary drains at low tide; saltmarsh is present here.

Habitats Wetland (85%; mudflat/sandflat; saltmarsh; sand-dunes/sand beach; shingle/stony beach; standing brackish and salt water; water-fringe vegetation), Artificial landscape (15%; highly improved reseeded grassland; other urban/industrial areas)
Land-use Not utilized (35%), Tourism/recreation (50%), Urban/industrial/transport (15%)

■ Birds

Species		Season	Year	Pop min	Pop max	Acc	Criteria
Cygnus olor	Mute Swan	R	1995	40	99	A	B1i
Branta bernicla	Brent Goose	W	1996	1,200	1,200	A	B1i, C3
Calidris canutus	Knot	W	1996	2,000	2,000	A	B2

This is an important site for wintering waterfowl. Many other species occur in numbers of national importance, including *Tadorna tadorna* (534 birds, 1995), *Bucephala clangula* (390 birds, 1996), *Mergus serrator* (171 birds, 1996), *Haematopus ostralegus* (1,343 birds, 1995), *Pluvialis apricaria* (4,000 birds, 1996) and *Calidris alpina* (1,850 birds, 1996).

■ Protection status
National None **International** High
IBA overlaps with Ramsar Site (Malahide Estuary; area not known). 546 ha of IBA covered by Special Protection Area (Broadmeadow/Swords Estuary, 546 ha).

■ Conservation issues

Threats Consequences of animal/plant introductions (B), Disturbance to birds (B), Industrialization/urbanization (A), Infrastructure (C), Recreation/tourism (B)

Permission has been granted for the construction of a motorway bridge across the most sensitive extreme inner part of the estuary. Infestation of mudflats by non-native cord-grass *Spartina* threatens habitat quality. The inner estuary is used for water-sports, which may cause disturbance. Housing and marina developments have claimed parts of the outer estuary. The site lies within a proposed candidate Special Area for Conservation (Malahide Estuary; area not known).

Lambay Island	A4i, A4iii, B1i, B1ii, B3, C2, C3, C4	114

Admin region East
Coordinates 53°29′N 6°01′W
Altitude 0–127 m **Area** 612 ha

■ Site description
Situated 4 km off the north coast of County Dublin, this site includes Lambay Island and surrounding waters. About a third of the island on the lower western shore comprises managed pasture, with much of the rest being used as rough grazing for cattle and sheep.

Habitats Forest and woodland (5%; mixed forest), Scrub (5%; scrub), Grassland (10%; mesophile grassland; machair), Wetland (10%; mudflat/sandflat; sand-dunes/sand beach; shingle/stony beach), Marine areas (55%; sea inlet/coastal features), Rocky areas (10%; sea cliff/rocky shore), Artificial landscape (5%; ruderal land)
Land-use Agriculture (35%), Fisheries/aquaculture (60%), Urban/industrial/transport (5%)

■ Birds

Species		Season	Year	Pop min	Pop max	Acc	Criteria
Puffinus puffinus	Manx Shearwater	B	1987	50	100	A	B1ii, C3
Phalacrocorax aristotelis	Shag	B	1995	1,164	1,164	A	A4i, B1i, B3, C2
Uria aalge	Guillemot	B	1995	51,777	51,777	A	B1ii, C3
Alca torda	Razorbill	B	1995	3,646	3,646	A	B3

Lambay Island is internationally important for breeding seabirds. Several other seabird species breed in nationally important numbers, including *Fulmarus glacialis* (573 pairs, 1995), *Phalacrocorax carbo* (605 pairs, 1995) and *Rissa tridactyla* (5,102 pairs, 1995). This site also supports nationally important numbers of wintering *Anser anser* (437 birds, 1995) and is one of the top sites for this species in Ireland.

■ Protection status
National None **International** High
612 ha of IBA covered by Special Protection Area (Lambay Island, 612 ha).

■ Conservation issues

Threats Industrialization/urbanization (U), Recreation/tourism (C)

Under the present management, the island's bird populations are secure and little disturbed. The NPW and BirdWatch Ireland have an ongoing population monitoring programme for seabirds and geese.

Rogerstown estuary	B1i, B2, C3	115

Admin region East
Coordinates 53°30′N 6°06′W
Altitude 0–5 m **Area** 368 ha

■ Site description
Situated 2 km north of Donabate, this is a relatively small, narrow estuary separated from the sea by a sand/shingle-bar and divided by the Dublin–Belfast railway line. The estuary drains almost completely at low tide, exposing extensive mudflats with some saltmarsh. The largest municipal dump in Ireland is situated on the north-east shore of the site.

Habitats Grassland (10%; humid grassland), Wetland (75%; tidal river/enclosed tidal water; mudflat/sandflat; saltmarsh; shingle/stony beach), Artificial landscape (15%; other urban/industrial areas)
Land-use Agriculture (10%), Nature conservation/research (5%), Not utilized (70%), Urban/industrial/transport (15%)

■ Birds

Species		Season	Year	Pop min	Pop max	Acc	Criteria
Branta bernicla	Brent Goose	W	1996	1,804	1,804	A	B1i, C3
Calidris canutus	Knot	W	1996	4,096	4,095	A	B1i, B2, C3

This is an important site for wintering waterfowl. Additional species wintering in numbers of national importance include *Tadorna tadorna* (827 birds, 1996), *Anas crecca* (677 birds, 1995), *Pluvialis apricaria* (4,000 birds, 1996), *Vanellus vanellus* (7,735 birds, 1996) and *Tringa totanus* (861 birds, 1996).

■ Protection status
National High **International** Partial
196 ha of IBA covered by Nature Reserve (Rogerstown Estuary, 196 ha). 368 ha of IBA covered by Wildfowl Sanctuary (Rogerstown Estuary, 368 ha). 195 ha of IBA covered by Ramsar Site (Rogerstown Estuary, 195 ha). 196 ha of IBA covered by Special Protection Area (Rogerstown Estuary, 196 ha).

■ Conservation issues

Threats Consequences of animal/plant introductions (B), Disturbance to birds (B), Filling-in of wetlands (B)

Since starting in 1970, municipal rubbish-dumping has destroyed 44 ha of intertidal mudflat. Infestation of remaining mudflat by non-native cord-grass *Spartina* threatens habitat quality, and there is increasing pressure on the site from recreation, amenity and adjacent urban development. BirdWatch Ireland owns a 24 ha reserve of wet grassland, bordering the inner part of the estuary, and, with support from the local authority, have recently constructed a hide on the estuary's south shore. The site lies within a proposed candidate Special Area for Conservation (Rogerstown estuary; area not known).

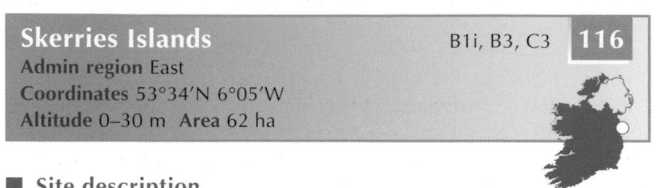

Skerries Islands · B1i, B3, C3 · 116
Admin region East
Coordinates 53°34'N 6°05'W
Altitude 0–30 m **Area** 62 ha

■ Site description
A group of three small islands (Shenicks, St Patricks and Colt) and surrounding sea, situated 1–2 km east of Skerries, in north County Dublin.

Habitats Grassland (10%; mesophile grassland), Marine areas (70%; sea inlet/coastal features), Rocky areas (20%; sea cliff/rocky shore; rock stacks/islets)
Land-use Fisheries/aquaculture (70%), Nature conservation/research (20%), Not utilized (30%)

■ Birds

Species		Season	Year	Pop min	Pop max	Acc	Criteria
Phalacrocorax aristotelis	Shag	B	1986	112	—	A	B3
Branta bernicla	Brent Goose	W	1996	215	215	A	B1i, C3

The site is important for waterfowl and shorebirds. *Phalacrocorax carbo* breeds in numbers of national importance (350 pairs, 1996).

■ Protection status
National None **International** None

■ Conservation issues

Threats Aquaculture/fisheries (C), Recreation/tourism (B)

Day-trippers from Skerries can cause disturbance to birds. Shenick Isle (6.3 ha) is a bird reserve managed by BirdWatch Ireland. The site is a proposed Special Protection Area (Skerries Islands, 62 ha).

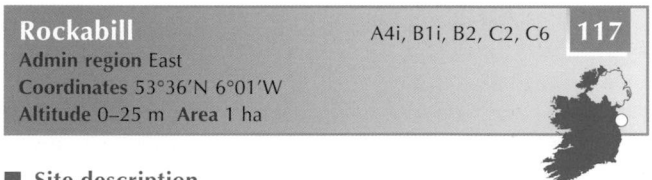

Rockabill · A4i, B1i, B2, C2, C6 · 117
Admin region East
Coordinates 53°36'N 6°01'W
Altitude 0–25 m **Area** 1 ha

■ Site description
Two small, rocky islands approximately 7 km off the north coast of County Dublin. The lighthouse present on one island has been unmanned since 1989.

Habitats Scrub (10%; scrub), Marine areas (30%; sea inlet/coastal features), Rocky areas (40%; rock stacks/islets), Artificial landscape (20%; other urban/industrial areas)
Land-use Nature conservation/research (80%), Urban/industrial/transport (20%)

■ Birds

Species		Season	Year	Pop min	Pop max	Acc	Criteria
[1] *Sterna dougallii*	Roseate Tern	B	1996	563	563	A	A4i, B1i, B2, C2, C6
Sterna hirundo	Common Tern	B	1996	387	387	A	C6
Cepphus grylle	Black Guillemot	B	1998	30	—	B	B2

1. One of two regular breeding sites in Ireland.

Rockabill is important for breeding seabirds and supports the largest breeding colony of *Sterna dougallii* in the north-east Atlantic and, thus, in Europe.

■ Protection status
National High **International** High
1 ha of IBA covered by Refuge for Fauna (Rockabill Island; area not known). 1 ha of IBA covered by Special Protection Area (Rockabill, 1 ha).

■ Conservation issues

Threats Disturbance to birds (A), Recreation/tourism (B)

Since 1989 BirdWatch Ireland have, with NPW, managed the tern colony and there is presently very little disturbance.

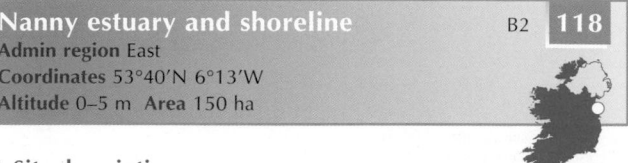

Nanny estuary and shoreline · B2 · 118
Admin region East
Coordinates 53°40'N 6°13'W
Altitude 0–5 m **Area** 150 ha

■ Site description
Situated in County Meath this is a 3 km long and approximately 500 m wide stretch of shoreline, extending between Laytown and Benhead on the east coast. This site includes the muddy estuarine channel of the River Nanny, which opens out into a wide, exposed sand beach. This is an important recreation and amenity area.

Habitats Wetland (100%; sand-dunes/sand beach)
Land-use Not utilized (50%), Tourism/recreation (50%)

■ Birds

Species		Season	Year	Pop min	Pop max	Acc	Criteria
Calidris canutus	Knot	W	1996	800	800	A	B2

Additional species which winter in nationally important numbers include *Melanitta nigra*, *Pluvialis apricaria*, *Pluvialis squatarola*, *Charadrius hiaticula* and *Calidris alba*.

■ Protection status
National None **International** None

■ Conservation issues

Threats Recreation/tourism (C)

Beach-users may cause some disturbance to wintering waterfowl.

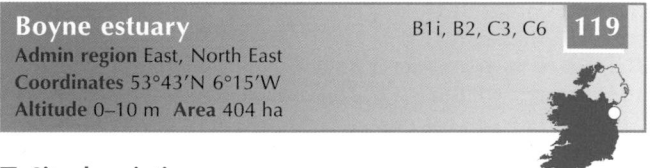

Boyne estuary · B1i, B2, C3, C6 · 119
Admin region East, North East
Coordinates 53°43'N 6°15'W
Altitude 0–10 m **Area** 404 ha

■ Site description
A rather narrow estuary, which widens at its mouth and comprises intertidal mudflat and saltmarsh habitats. It is situated on the east coast, at the border between Counties Louth and Meath and is the port for the town of Drogheda. The estuary has been modified by the construction of training walls on either side, to facilitate deep water access to the port.

Habitats Wetland (100%; tidal river/enclosed tidal water; mudflat/sandflat; saltmarsh; sand-dunes/sand beach)
Land-use Fisheries/aquaculture (80%), Hunting (100%), Urban/industrial/transport (20%)

■ Birds

Species		Season	Year	Pop min	Pop max	Acc	Criteria
Branta bernicla	Brent Goose	W	1996	210	210	A	B1i, C3
Calidris canutus	Knot	W	1996	1,777	1,777	A	B2
[1] *Sterna albifrons*	Little Tern	B	1995	14	14	A	B2, C6

1. On sand-spit in outer estuary.

An important site for wintering waterfowl; additional species that winter in numbers of national importance include *Pluvialis apricaria* (6,000 birds, 1995), *Pluvialis squatarola* (255 birds, 1996), *Vanellus*

vanellus (7,500 birds, 1996), *Calidris alba* (163 birds, 1996), *Limosa limosa* (287 birds, 1996) and *Arenaria interpres* (444 birds, 1995).

■ Protection status

National High **International** High

IBA overlaps with Wildfowl Sanctuary (Boyne Estuary; area not known). 404 ha of IBA covered by Special Protection Area (Boyne Estuary, 404 ha).

■ Conservation issues

Threats Filling-in of wetlands (B), Industrialization/urbanization (B), Recreation/tourism (B)

This estuary is threatened with urban and particularly industrial expansion, including dredging and land-claim of wetlands.

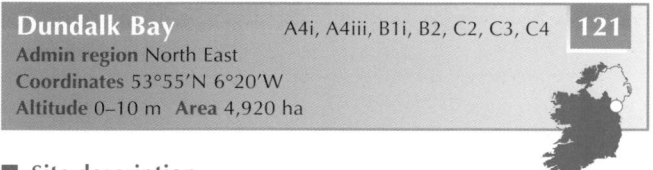

Stabannan–Braganstown 120
A4iii, B1i, B2, B3, C3, C4
Admin region North East
Coordinates 53°52′N 6°26′W
Altitude 15–15 m **Area** 491 ha

■ Site description

Situated between Ardee and Castlebellingham in County Louth, this site consists of drained wetlands on the River Glyde flood-plain which are now predominantly improved grassland and tillage.

Habitats Grassland (20%; humid grassland; mesophile grassland), Artificial landscape (80%; highly improved reseeded grassland; arable land)
Land-use Agriculture (100%)

■ Birds

Species	Season	Year	Pop min	Pop max	Acc	Criteria
Cygnus columbianus Bewick's Swan	W	1989	—	26	—	B2
Cygnus cygnus Whooper Swan	W	1995	120	120	A	B3
[1] *Anser anser* Greylag Goose	W	1996	1,661	1,661	A	B1i, C3

1. Birds roost at site 121.

This site is an important winter feeding area for waterfowl. Additionally, *Pluvialis apricaria* (3,000 birds, 1995) occur in numbers of national importance.

■ Protection status

National None **International** High

491 ha of IBA covered by Special Protection Area (Stabannan–Braganstown, 491 ha).

■ Conservation issues

Threats Agricultural intensification/expansion (C)

Disturbance to wintering wildfowl is limited, as access to this private estate is limited and no shooting is allowed. However, changes in agricultural practice, which could alter the feeding habitat of geese, is a possible threat.

Dundalk Bay 121
A4i, A4iii, B1i, B2, C2, C3, C4
Admin region North East
Coordinates 53°55′N 6°20′W
Altitude 0–10 m **Area** 4,920 ha

■ Site description

A very large, open, shallow sea bay on the east coast, extending east from Dundalk town in County Louth. This site encompasses extensive sand- and mudflats, which at low tide are up to 3 km wide, as well as saltmarshes, shingle-beaches and tidal rivers. The estuaries of the rivers Dee, Glyde, Fane and Castletown are all included in the site. There is intertidal shellfish cultivation. Saltmarshes at Lurgangreen and Marsh South are partially fenced and used for grazing sheep.

Habitats Grassland (10%; humid grassland), Wetland (90%; tidal river/enclosed tidal water; mudflat/sandflat; saltmarsh; sand-dunes/sand beach; shingle/stony beach)
Land-use Agriculture (10%), Fisheries/aquaculture (50%), Hunting (80%)

■ Birds

Species	Season	Year	Pop min	Pop max	Acc	Criteria
[1] *Anser anser* Greylag Goose	W	1996	1,661	1,661	A	B1i, C3
Branta bernicla Brent Goose	W	1996	447	447	A	B1i, C3
Calidris canutus Knot	W	1995	15,545	15,545	A	A4i, B1i, B2, C3
Calidris alpina Dunlin	W	1996	5,834	5,834	A	B2
Limosa lapponica Bar-tailed Godwit	W	1995	1,660	1,660	A	A4i, B1i, B2, C2
Numenius arquata Curlew	W	1995	2,278	2,278	A	B2
Tringa totanus Redshank	W	1995	1,857	1,857	A	B1i, C3

1. Birds roost here but feed at site 120.

This wetland is of international importance for its waterfowl, regularly holding over 20,000 wintering birds. Several other species occur in numbers of national importance including *Tadorna tadorna* (391 birds, 1996), *Anas penelope* (1,026 birds, 1995), *Anas acuta* (112 birds, 1996), *Haematopus ostralegus* (6,605 birds, 1995), *Pluvialis apricaria* (7,240 birds, 1996) and *Limosa limosa* (360 birds, 1995).

■ Protection status

National Partial **International** High

IBA overlaps with Wildfowl Sanctuary (Ballymascanlon; area not known). IBA overlaps with Wildfowl Sanctuary (Lurgan Green; area not known). 4,768 ha of IBA covered by Ramsar Site (Dundalk Bay, 4,768 ha). 4,768 ha of IBA covered by Special Protection Area (Dundalk Bay, 4,768 ha).

■ Conservation issues

Threats Agricultural intensification/expansion (C), Aquaculture/fisheries (C), Consequences of animal/plant introductions (C), Industrialization/urbanization (B)

Pressure from housing development is leading to loss of saltmarsh. Further habitat loss, due to the proximity of Dundalk town, may impact on the site. Habitat quality may be reduced by intertidal shellfish cultivation and by the spread of non-native cord-grass *Spartina*.

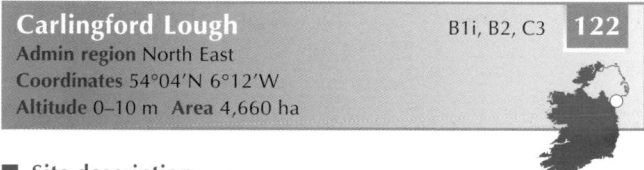

Carlingford Lough 122
B1i, B2, C3
Admin region North East
Coordinates 54°04′N 6°12′W
Altitude 0–10 m **Area** 4,660 ha

■ Site description

A 15 km long, narrow sea lough, surrounded by mountains. The southern shore lies in County Louth, while the rest of the site is in Northern Ireland (UK site 274), this being a cross-border site—the stated area of 4,660 ha covers the entire site on both sides of the border but other data given here (on habitats, land-uses, threats and birds) are specific to the Republic of Ireland side. Much of the lough is relatively deep. However, there are intertidal mudflats in the south-east and north-east and pockets of saltmarsh. There is intertidal shellfish cultivation and the lough is used for boating.

Habitats Wetland (mudflat/sandflat; saltmarsh; sand-dunes/sand beach; shingle/stony beach), Marine areas (sea inlet/coastal features)
Land-use Fisheries/aquaculture, Tourism/recreation

■ Birds

Species	Season	Year	Pop min	Pop max	Acc	Criteria
Branta bernicla Brent Goose	W	1995	315	315	A	B1i, C3
Aythya marila Scaup	W	1996	640	640	A	B2

This is an important site for wintering waterfowl. Other waterbirds which winter in numbers of national importance are *Podiceps cristatus* (40 birds, 1996), *Phalacrocorax carbo* (106 birds, 1995) and *Charadrius hiaticula* (126 birds, 1995).

■ Protection status

National None **International** Low

172 ha of IBA covered by Special Protection Area (Carlingford Lough, 172 ha).

■ Conservation issues

Threats Aquaculture/fisheries (B), Recreation/tourism (B)

Habitat quality may be threatened by intertidal shellfish cultivation and increasing pressure from recreation interests.

Lough Oughter | B1i, B3, C2 | 123

Admin region North East
Coordinates 54°00′N 7°28′W
Altitude 50–50 m **Area** 1,464 ha

Site description
A complicated system of inter-drumlin lakes, basins and islands on the River Erne, County Cavan. Sheltered shores support swamp and marsh habitat and the site also includes adjacent fields which occasionally flood. The site is a southward extension of Upper Lough Erne (UK site 287) in Northern Ireland.

Habitats Forest and woodland (10%; broadleaved deciduous forest), Grassland (10%; humid grassland), Wetland (70%; standing fresh water; water-fringe vegetation), Artificial landscape (10%; highly improved reseeded grassland)
Land-use Agriculture (20%), Fisheries/aquaculture (70%), Not utilized (10%)

Birds

Species	Season	Year	Pop min	Pop max	Acc	Criteria
Cygnus cygnus Whooper Swan	W	1995	174	174	A	B1i, B3, C2

This site is important for its wintering birds. Other species wintering in numbers of national importance are *Podiceps cristatus* (40 birds, 1996), *Phalacrocorax carbo* (139 birds, 1996), *Cygnus olor* (137 birds, 1996) and *Anas penelope* (1,544 birds, 1995).

Protection status
National High **International** High
IBA overlaps with Wildfowl Sanctuary (Lough Oughter; area not known). 1,464 ha of IBA covered by Ramsar Site (Lough Oughter, 1,464 ha). 1,464 ha of IBA covered by Special Protection Area (Lough Oughter, 1,464 ha).

Conservation issues

Threats Agricultural intensification/expansion (A), Drainage (C), Recreation/tourism (C)

The deepening of drains and excessive use of fertilizer are resulting in nutrient pollution of the lake.

Lough Kinale and Lough Derragh | B1i, C7 | 124

Admin region North East, Midlands
Coordinates 53°46′N 7°24′W
Altitude 64–64 m **Area** 281 ha

Site description
Located east of Longford town mainly within County Longford, this site comprises the larger Lough Kinale and, to its south-east, Lough Derragh. Lough Kinale has two main basins which are almost separated by swamp formations. The main input of water comes from Lough Sheelin via the River Inny. Both lakes are linked by a short channel and are used for fishing.

Habitats Wetland (100%; standing fresh water; river/stream; raised bog; water-fringe vegetation)
Land-use Hunting (100%), Tourism/recreation (100%)

Birds

Species	Season	Year	Pop min	Pop max	Acc	Criteria
[1] *Cygnus olor* Mute Swan	R	1987	—	100	A	B1i

1. Five counts over 1985–1987.

Loughs Kinale and Derragh are important for waterfowl. Species occurring in nationally important numbers are *Aythya ferina* (1,639 birds, 1996), *Aythya fuligula* (873 birds, 1996) and *Fulica atra* (552 birds, 1996).

Protection status
National None **International** High

---

281 ha of IBA covered by Special Protection Area (Lough Kinale and Derragh Lough, 281 ha).

Conservation issues

Threats Afforestation (B), Disturbance to birds (B), Recreation/tourism (B)

There is some disturbance to birds due to wildfowling and boating. The site is state-owned, allowing shooting pressure to be regulated by NPW. Pollution of the lake due to adjacent conifer plantations, causing siltation and fertilizer run-off, is likely.

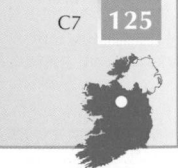

Loughs Kilglass and Forbes, and Ballykenny/Fishertown bogs | C7 | 125

Admin region Midlands
Coordinates 53°46′N 7°53′W
Altitude 40–42 m **Area** 1,352 ha

Site description
This site, situated north-west of Longford, has been expanded since the previous European inventory (Grimmett and Jones 1989) when it only included the Castles Forbes complex (comprising the Camlin river flood-plain and two adjacent raised bogs). The revised site extends north to include Lough Forbes. Adjacent callows are also included.

Habitats Forest and woodland (5%; broadleaved deciduous forest), Grassland (20%; humid grassland), Wetland (75%; standing fresh water; raised bog; water-fringe vegetation; fen/transition mire/spring)
Land-use Agriculture (20%), Tourism/recreation (80%)

Birds
This site has been designated as a Special Protection Area as it supports nationally important numbers of *Anser albifrons flavirostris* in winter. A flock (217 birds, 1994) uses 20 known feeding sites, mainly callows, marsh and improved grassland within and to the north of this site, and is likely to use the lakes and bogs for roosting. Fieldwork is required to establish details of site use.

Protection status
National None **International** High
1,352 ha of IBA covered by Special Protection Area (Lough Forbes and Ballykenny/Fishertown Bog Complex, 1,352 ha).

Conservation issues

Threats Agricultural intensification/expansion (C), Disturbance to birds (B), Recreation/tourism (B)

Wildfowl numbers have declined recently and this could be due to an increase in cruisers and other pleasure boats on the site. The site overlaps with a proposed candidate Special Area for Conservation (Lough Forbes Complex; area not known).

Lough Arrow | C7 | 126

Admin region Midlands, North West
Coordinates 54°04′N 8°19′W
Altitude 55–55 m **Area** 1,266 ha

Site description
Lough Arrow is a large, limestone lake with wooded islands and reedbeds. It is situated north of Ballinafad in Counties Sligo and Roscommon. Historically, the nutrient-levels in the lake-water have been moderate (mesotrophic). There is trout- and eel-fishing and boating. Information on land-uses is incomplete.

Habitats Wetland (100%; standing fresh water; water-fringe vegetation)
Land-use Tourism/recreation (100%)

Birds
The site was designated as a Special Protection Area on the basis of migratory waterfowl, with the following number of individuals recorded during the period 1986–1987: *Tachybaptus ruficollis* (35),

Anas penelope (87), *Anas platyrhynchos* (27), *Aythya ferina* (36), *Aythya fuligula* (226), *Bucephala clangula* (49) and *Fulica atra* (325).

■ **Protection status**
National None **International** High
1,266 ha of IBA covered by Special Protection Area (Lough Arrow, 1,266 ha).

■ **Conservation issues**

> Threats Agricultural intensification/expansion (B)

Little information is available on threats but it is believed that nutrient pollution of the lake due to fertilizer run-off from adjacent farmland may be a problem.

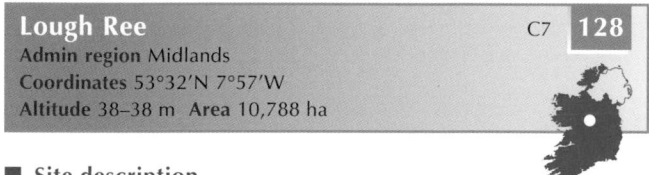

Bellanagare bog C7 127
Admin region Midlands
Coordinates 53°49′N 8°25′W
Altitude 90–140 m **Area** 1,243 ha

■ **Site description**
A large, upland bog situated 6 km north-east of Castlerea in County Roscommon. The bog consists of ridges and flushes and several streams rise within the site. Peat-cutting takes place within the site ('Other' land-use).

> Habitats Wetland (100%; river/stream; raised bog; blanket bog; fen/transition mire/spring)
> Land-use Other (50%), Water management (50%)

■ **Birds**
The site was designated as a Special Protection Area on the basis of breeding *Pluvialis apricaria*, a species listed under Annex I of the EC Birds Directive.

■ **Protection status**
National None **International** High
1,243 ha of IBA covered by Special Protection Area (Bellanagare Bog, 1,243 ha).

■ **Conservation issues**

> Threats Burning of vegetation (B), Drainage (B), Extraction industry (B)

The site is vulnerable to water loss, as it has an extensive drainage network in its northern half, and peat is actively cut in places all around the site. As the bog has become quite dry it is now vulnerable to burning to improve it for grazing. The site lies within a proposed candidate Special Area for Conservation (Bellangare Bog; area not known).

Lough Ree C7 128
Admin region Midlands
Coordinates 53°32′N 7°57′W
Altitude 38–38 m **Area** 10,788 ha

■ **Site description**
Lough Ree is the third-largest lake in Ireland, and is situated on the River Shannon system between Lanesborough and Athlone. The shoreline, with many indented bays, has extensive reedbeds, callow and lowland wet grassland. Land-uses include low-intensity grazing on the grasslands, angling and other recreational uses.

> Habitats Grassland (10%; humid grassland), Wetland (90%; standing fresh water; river/stream; water-fringe vegetation)
> Land-use Agriculture (10%), Hunting (50%), Tourism/recreation (50%)

■ **Birds**
This site was designated a Special Protection Area on the basis of its migratory waterfowl, with nationally important numbers of *Tachybaptus ruficollis* (145 birds, 1985), *Anas penelope* (1,306 birds, 1985), *Anas crecca* (584 birds, 1985), *Aythya fuligula* (1,317 birds, 1985) and *Fulica atra* (798 birds, 1985). This is also one of only three regular breeding sites in Ireland for *Melanitta nigra* (37 birds, 1995).

■ **Protection status**
National None **International** High
10,788 ha of IBA covered by Special Protection Area (Lough Ree, 10,788 ha).

■ **Conservation issues**

> Threats Agricultural intensification/expansion (A), Disturbance to birds (C), Recreation/tourism (C)

The lake is threatened by nutrient pollution, with organic enrichment coming from agricultural and probably domestic sources. There is increasing pressure on the lake, from leisure developments, such as lakeshore holiday homes, marinas and hotels as well as cruiser traffic. The site lies within a proposed candidate Special Area for Conservation (Lough Ree; area not known).

River Suck callows: A4i, B1i, B2, B3, C2, C3 129
Shannon Bridge–Castlecoote
Admin region Midlands, West
Coordinates 53°24′N 8°10′W
Altitude 33–45 m **Area** 4,000 ha

■ **Site description**
A long, sinuous stretch of semi-natural, lowland wet grassland (callows) alongside the River Suck, in Counties Galway and Roscommon. This site extends for 50 km from Castlecoote in the north to Shannonbridge in the south where it meets the River Shannon callows (site 131). The callows are seasonally flooded between October and April. The area is flanked by raised bogs, many of which have been converted to agricultural use following peat extraction.

> Habitats Grassland (20%; humid grassland), Wetland (60%; river/stream; raised bog; water-fringe vegetation), Artificial landscape (20%; highly improved reseeded grassland)
> Land-use Agriculture (40%), Fisheries/aquaculture (60%), Hunting (100%)

■ **Birds**

Species		Season	Year	Pop min	Pop max	Acc	Criteria
Cygnus columbianus	Bewick's Swan	W	1982	180	180	—	A4i, B1i, B2, C2
Cygnus cygnus	Whooper Swan	W	1995	116	116	A	B3
[1] *Anser albifrons*	White-fronted Goose	W	1994	377	377	A	B1i, C3

1. Mean 1990–1994.

This is an important site for wintering waterfowl. Additional species wintering in numbers of national importance include *Anas penelope* (1,351 birds, 1995) and *Vanellus vanellus* (3,282 birds, 1995). *Crex crex* was breeding until recently (1 pair, 1993).

■ **Protection status**
National Partial **International** Partial
1,100 ha of IBA covered by Nature Reserve (Muckanagh Wildfowl Sanctuary, 1,100 ha). 3,225 ha of IBA covered by Special Protection Area (River Suck Callows: Shannon Bridge–Athleague, 3,225 ha).

■ **Conservation issues**

> Threats Agricultural intensification/expansion (B), Disturbance to birds (B), Drainage (B), Extraction industry (C), Filling-in of wetlands (B), Recreation/tourism (C)

Crex crex is highly sensitive to changes in farming practice. Agricultural intensification is likely to have caused the decline and eventual loss of breeding *Crex crex* at this site. Water and habitat quality are threatened by siltation due to mechanical peat extraction in surrounding areas. Wildfowling is likely to cause disturbance to wintering birds.

Lough Derg A4iii, B1i, C3, C4 130
Admin region West
Coordinates 52°59′N 8°19′W
Altitude 33–57 m **Area** 11,989 ha

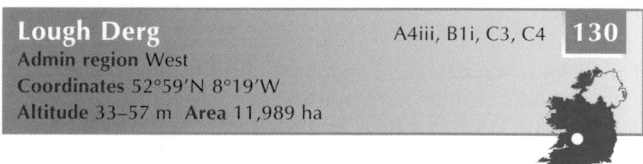

■ **Site description**
An extensive lake system, extending from Portumna south to Killaloe in Counties Tipperary, Clare, Offaly and Galway. In the previous

European inventory (Grimmett and Jones 1989) the site included only Church Island, but the area has been expanded to incorporate the whole of Lough Derg and its islands. Lough Derg is used by anglers and for recreational boating.

Habitats Grassland (5%), Wetland (95%; standing fresh water; water-fringe vegetation)
Land-use Agriculture (5%), Tourism/recreation (95%)

■ Birds

Species	Season	Year	Pop min	Pop max	Acc	Criteria
Limosa limosa Black-tailed Godwit	W	1995	1,200	1,200	B	B1i, C3

Cygnus olor winters in numbers of national importance (327 birds, 1995).

■ Protection status
National None International High
11,989 ha of IBA covered by Special Protection Area (Lough Derg [River Shannon], 11,989 ha).

■ Conservation issues

Threats Agricultural intensification/expansion (A), Industrialization/urbanization (B), Recreation/tourism (C)

The main threat to the lake is nutrient pollution, due to increasing input from adjacent farmland and from adjoining towns. The lake is also under increasing pressure from amenity development, with the construction of lakeshore holiday homes, hotels, marinas and jetties.

River Shannon callows: Portumna–Athlone   131
A1, A4i, A4iii, B1i, B2, B3, C1, C2, C3, C4, C6
Admin region Mid West, Midlands, West
Coordinates 53°15'N 8°04'W
Altitude 33–38 m Area 5,788 ha

■ Site description
The flood-plain of the River Shannon, the longest waterway in Ireland with a catchment that drains more than 20% of the country. The area lies between Lough Ree in the north (site 128) and Lough Derg in the south (site 130) and is contiguous with the Little Brosna callows (site 132) and the Suck callows (site 129), both of which are tributaries. This complex is one of the few relatively unmodified flood-plains within the European Union. Beside the river are extensive areas of callow (seasonally flooded, semi-natural wet grassland) which is used for permanent hay or silage or for summer grazing, mainly by cattle. The river is used for coarse angling and leisure-boat cruising. The callows were once flanked by raised bog, which is now largely lost due to mechanical peat-cutting.

Habitats Grassland (40%; humid grassland), Wetland (60%; river/stream; raised bog; water-fringe vegetation)
Land-use Agriculture (40%), Fisheries/aquaculture (40%), Nature conservation/research (100%), Water management (10%)

■ Birds

Species	Season	Year	Pop min	Pop max	Acc	Criteria
Cygnus columbianus Bewick's Swan	W	1995	31	31	A	B2
Cygnus cygnus Whooper Swan	W	1995	901	901	A	A4i, B1i, B3, C2
Crex crex Corncrake	B	1996	54	54	A	A1, C1, C2, C6
Pluvialis apricaria Golden Plover	W	1995	10,000	10,000	A	B1i, C2
Limosa limosa Black-tailed Godwit	W	1995	1,150	1,150	A	B1i, C3
[1] *Numenius phaeopus* Whimbrel	P	1995	5,000	—	—	A4i, B1i, C3
Tringa totanus Redshank	B	1987	400	400	A	B2

1. One of the most important staging sites in Ireland and Europe.

This site is of international importance for wintering waterfowl and regularly supports over 20,000 wintering birds. The Shannon callows are one of the last strongholds for the globally threatened *Crex crex* in Ireland and are also of importance for breeding waders, particularly *Tringa totanus*. Additional wintering species that occur in numbers of national importance, include *Cygnus olor* (575 birds, 1995), *Anas penelope* (3,135 birds, 1996), *Anas crecca* (576 birds, 1995), *Aythya*

fuligula (200 birds, 1995), *Vanellus vanellus* (15,400 birds, 1995) and *Calidris alpina* (1,250 birds, 1996).

■ Protection status
National None International High
5,788 ha of IBA covered by Special Protection Area (River Shannon Callows: Portumna to Athlone, 5,788 ha).

■ Conservation issues

Threats Agricultural intensification/expansion (A), Disturbance to birds (B), Drainage (C), Extraction industry (U), Industrialization/urbanization (B), Recreation/tourism (C)

The callows are threatened by changes in farming practice, mainly intensification, with serious implications for breeding birds, particularly *Crex crex*. BirdWatch Ireland, with support from NPW and RSPB, operates a grant scheme to encourage farming practices that favour *Crex crex*, and breeding numbers have recently stabilized. However, problems remain due to earlier mowing of hay and the replacement of hay with silage (which involves earlier mowing, increased use of fertilizer, and multiple cuts per year). Further, an extension of the grazing season and higher stocking rates have increased the risk of disturbance to breeding waders. The River Shannon is of high recreational value, being used by anglers, water- and jet-skiers, and for boating holidays (motor-cruisers), all of which may cause some disturbance to birds. Pressure to develop the recreation potential of the river has increased, with particular pressure for marina developments away from existing towns. Siltation of the river due to extensive mechanical peat extraction within the surrounding area is a further threat. Athlone town is expanding, with increasing pressure for drainage of callow habitat. BirdWatch Ireland own a reserve at Bullock and Bishops Island on the callows (3 ha).

River Little Brosna callows: New Bridge–River Shannon   132
A4i, A4iii, B1i, B2, B3, C2, C3, C4
Admin region South East, Midlands
Coordinates 53°08'N 8°03'W
Altitude 33–38 m Area 1,154 ha

■ Site description
This site follows the Little Brosna river from its junction with the River Shannon callows (site 131) for 9 km south-eastwards to just beyond New Bridge. It is situated 6 km north-west of Birr, in Counties Offaly and Tipperary. The main habitat is callow (low-lying, semi-natural, wet grassland), which is seasonally flooded between October and April.

Habitats Grassland (60%; humid grassland; mesophile grassland), Wetland (40%; standing fresh water; river/stream; raised bog; water-fringe vegetation; fen/transition mire/spring)
Land-use Agriculture (60%), Fisheries/aquaculture (20%), Hunting (60%), Nature conservation/research (100%)

■ Birds

Species	Season	Year	Pop min	Pop max	Acc	Criteria
Cygnus columbianus Bewick's Swan	W	—	100	250	—	A4i, B1i, B2, C2
Cygnus cygnus Whooper Swan	W	1995	178	178	A	B1i, B3, C2
[1] *Anser albifrons* White-fronted Goose	W	1996	566	566	A	B1i, C3
Anas penelope Wigeon	W	1996	14,000	14,000	A	B1i, C3
Anas crecca Teal	W	1996	4,000	4,000	A	B1i, C3
Limosa limosa Black-tailed Godwit	W	1995	4,300	4,300	A	A4i, B1i, C3

1. Mean 1992–1996.

This is an internationally important wetland, regularly supporting over 20,000 wintering waterfowl. Additional species wintering in numbers of national importance include *Anas platyrhynchos* (700 birds, 1996), *Anas acuta* (250 birds, 1996), *Anas clypeata* (200 birds, 1996), *Pluvialis apricaria* (8,100 birds, 1996), *Vanellus vanellus* (6,500 birds, 1995) and *Calidris alpina* (1,250 birds, 1995). Until recently *Crex crex* were breeding (2 pairs, 1993).

■ Protection status
National None International High

1,154 ha of IBA covered by Special Protection Area (River Little Brosna Callows: New Bridge–River Shannon, 1,154 ha).

■ Conservation issues

Threats Agricultural intensification/expansion (B), Disturbance to birds (B), Drainage (C)

Crex crex is highly sensitive to changes in farming practice. The intensification of farming, with earlier mowing and the replacement of hay with silage (involving earlier mowing, increased use of fertilizer, and multiple silage cuts), is likely to have caused the decline and eventual absence of breeding *Crex crex* from this site. Further, an extension of the grazing season and higher stocking rates have increased the risk of disturbance to breeding waders. Disturbance to wintering birds is minimized by the bogland to the south of the site, which serves to isolate it. However, wildfowling on parts of the site is likely to cause disturbance.

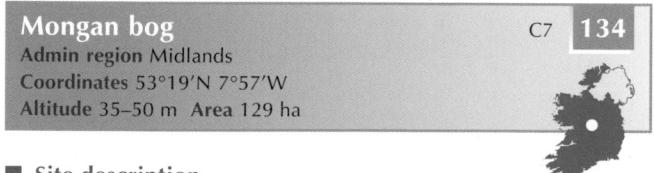

All Saints bog
B1i, C3 **133**
Admin region Midlands
Coordinates 53°07′N 7°56′W
Altitude 50–50 m Area 326 ha

■ Site description

All Saints bog is a lowland raised bog lying about 5 km north-west of Birr, County Offaly. It includes a wooded section with birch *Betula* and also areas of cutaway and drained bog. Peat-cutting ('Other' land-use) takes place in parts of the site.

Habitats Scrub (5%; scrub), Wetland (95%; raised bog)
Land-use Nature conservation/research (100%), Other (20%)

■ Birds

Species	Season	Year	Pop min	Pop max	Acc	Criteria
Anser albifrons White-fronted Goose	W	1994	555	555	A	B1i, C3

Anser albifrons flavirostris uses this site as a refuge from the adjacent Little Brosna callows (site 132).

■ Protection status

National None **International** High
326 ha of IBA covered by Special Protection Area (All Saints bog, 326 ha).

■ Conservation issues

Threats Disturbance to birds (C), Extraction industry (B)

The site has been damaged by continuing commercial peat extraction. The site lies within a proposed candidate Special Area for Conservation (All Saints Bog; area not known).

Mongan bog
C7 **134**
Admin region Midlands
Coordinates 53°19′N 7°57′W
Altitude 35–50 m Area 129 ha

■ Site description

Mongan bog is a raised bog situated immediately east of the monastic site of Clonmacnoise and 12 km south of Athlone in County Offaly. Lying in a basin, it is surrounded mainly by high ground, including an esker ridge, and comprises a well-developed system of hummocks, pools and *Sphagnum* lawns.

Habitats Wetland (100%; raised bog)
Land-use Nature conservation/research (100%)

■ Birds

This site was formerly important for wintering *Anser albifrons flavirostris*, although it is now only occasionally visited by this species. Other breeding species which are listed on Annex I of the EC Birds Directive are *Falco peregrinus*, *Falco columbarius* and *Circus cyaneus*.

■ Protection status

National High **International** High
119 ha of IBA covered by Reserve (Mongan Bog, 119 ha). 129 ha of IBA covered by Ramsar Site (Mongan Bog, 129 ha). 129 ha of IBA covered by Special Protection Area (Mongan Bog, 129 ha). 117 ha of IBA covered by Biogenetic Reserve (Mongan Bog, 117 ha).

■ Conservation issues

No threats are known. This site is almost entirely privately-owned by An Taisce (it is a private, non-statutory reserve) and has been intensively researched since 1972. The area lies within a proposed candidate Special Area for Conservation (Mongan Bog; area not known).

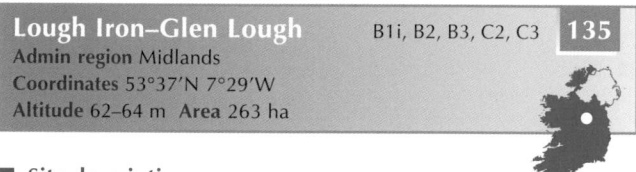

Lough Iron–Glen Lough
B1i, B2, B3, C2, C3 **135**
Admin region Midlands
Coordinates 53°37′N 7°29′W
Altitude 62–64 m Area 263 ha

■ Site description

Glen Lough is situated approximately 5 km north-west of Lough Iron, and is connected to it via the Black River. Both lakes are located in County Westmeath and have suffered drastic drops in water-level subsequent to drainage in the 1960s. As a result both lakes are now occupied by freshwater marsh, with little surface water except when winter flooding occurs. Parts of both lakes have also suffered from the planting of conifers and both are surrounded by farmland. Reedbed fringes, and is encroaching further into, Lough Iron, while Glen Lough supports *Salix* scrub, reed-swamp, dry grassland, cutaway bog and fen. Wildfowling occurs at both sites.

Habitats Scrub (10%; scrub), Grassland (20%; humid grassland), Wetland (40%; standing fresh water; river/stream; water-fringe vegetation; fen/transition mire/spring), Artificial landscape (30%; highly improved reseeded grassland; forestry plantation)
Land-use Agriculture (60%), Forestry (10%), Hunting (30%)

■ Birds

Species	Season	Year	Pop min	Pop max	Acc	Criteria
Cygnus columbianus Bewick's Swan	W	1989	10	20	—	B2
Cygnus cygnus Whooper Swan	W	1995	248	248	A	B1i, B3, C2
[1] *Anser albifrons* White-fronted Goose	W	1996	408	408	A	B1i, C3

1. Mean 1992–1996.

In recent years numbers of wintering swans *Cygnus* and *Anser albifrons flavirostris* have declined at Glen Lough. Birds of the latter species also use Lough Ennell (site 140), Lough Owel (site 139), Lough Derravaragh (site 138) and Garriskil bog (site 136). Dabbling duck occur in large numbers and this is one of the most important sites in Ireland for wintering *Anas clypeata* (159 birds, 1996). Other species occurring in numbers of national importance are *Anas penelope* (3,118 birds, 1995), *Anas crecca* (950 birds, 1995), *Aythya fuligula* (350 birds, 1995), *Fulica atra* (370 birds, 1996), *Pluvialis apricaria* (5,300 birds, 1996) and *Vanellus vanellus* (7,000 birds, 1995).

■ Protection status

National Partial **International** High
182 ha of IBA covered by Wildfowl Sanctuary (Lough Iron, 182 ha). 263 ha of IBA covered by Ramsar Site (Lough Iron–Glen Lough, 263 ha). 81 ha of IBA covered by Special Protection Area (Glen Lough, 81 ha). 82 ha of IBA covered by Special Protection Area (Lough Iron, 182 ha).

■ Conservation issues

Threats Afforestation (C), Disturbance to birds (C), Drainage (A)

In 1997 the Office of Public Works completed maintenance drainage at Glen Lough which resulted in less frequent winter flooding over shorter periods. A complaint in relation to this damage was made to the European Commission. Restoration measures are now in place, though their success is yet to be determined. Also within Glen Lough the area where *Anser albifrons flavirostris* used to feed has been planted with conifers. At both lakes disturbance to birds is likely due to wildfowling.

Garriskil bog
B1i, C3 **136**

Admin region Midlands
Coordinates 53°40'N 7°27'W
Altitude 64–64 m **Area** 324 ha

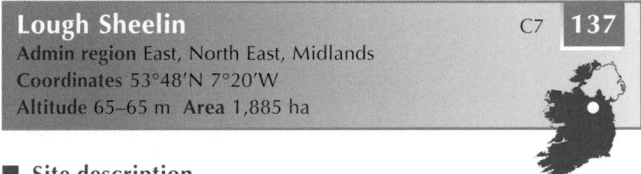

■ Site description
A raised bog situated 3 km west of Lough Derravaragh (site 138) and 3 km east of the village of Rathowen, in County Westmeath. It is bounded to the south-west by the Inny and Riffey rivers. The site comprises a well-developed system of pools and hummocks and there are some areas of cutaway bog which have drier heathland vegetation. Human use of the site is low.

Habitats Wetland (100%; raised bog)
Land-use Nature conservation/research (80%), Water management (20%)

■ Birds

Species	Season	Year	Pop min	Pop max	Acc	Criteria
[1] *Anser albifrons* White-fronted Goose	W	1996	408	408	A	B1i, C3

1. Mean 1992–1996.

This site was designated as a Special Protection Area based on its use by *Anser albifrons flavirostris*—the same flock that uses Lough Iron–Glen Lough (site 135), Lough Derravaragh (site 138), Lough Owel (site 139) and Lough Ennel (site 140).

■ Protection status
National None **International** High
324 ha of IBA covered by Ramsar Site (Garriskil bog; area not known). 324 ha of IBA covered by Special Protection Area (Garriskil Bog, 324 ha).

■ Conservation issues

Threats Burning of vegetation (C), Drainage (C)

This site has been damaged in the past by peat-cutting and burning. Further damage by drainage has been reduced as the drains have now been blocked. Most of the site is now owned by NPW and managed for nature conservation. The area lies within a proposed candidate Special Area for Conservation (Garriskil Bog; area not known).

Lough Sheelin
C7 **137**

Admin region East, North East, Midlands
Coordinates 53°48'N 7°20'W
Altitude 65–65 m **Area** 1,885 ha

■ Site description
Situated south of Cavan town, Lough Sheelin is part of the Inny sub-catchment of the Shannon system, lying north-east of Loughs Kinale/Derragh (site 124) into which it drains. Raised bogs surround the lake and there are two wooded islands. The lake is used for angling.

Habitats Forest and woodland (5%; broadleaved deciduous forest), Wetland (95%; standing fresh water; river/stream; raised bog; water-fringe vegetation)
Land-use Tourism/recreation (100%)

■ Birds
Lough Sheelin is one of the most important wintering sites in Ireland for *Podiceps cristatus* (140 birds, 1996), *Aythya ferina* (635 birds, 1985), *Aythya fuligula* (1,125 birds, 1996) and *Bucephala clangula* (219 birds, 1996), which all occur in nationally important numbers.

■ Protection status
National None **International** High
1,885 ha of IBA covered by Special Protection Area (Lough Sheelin, 1,885 ha).

■ Conservation issues

Threats Agricultural intensification/expansion (A)

Since the 1970s the lake has suffered periodic heavy agricultural pollution, although water quality is now approaching its natural nutrient-poor status.

Lough Derravaragh
B1i, B3, C3 **138**

Admin region Midlands
Coordinates 53°39'N 7°20'W
Altitude 64–64 m **Area** 1,120 ha

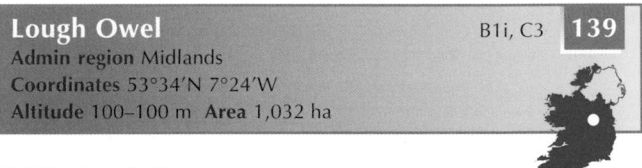

■ Site description
Lough Derravaragh is located approximately 12 km north of Mullingar town, in County Westmeath. The River Inny flows into and out of the north-west end of the lake, which is wide and shallow with extensive reedbed and swamp, backed by small areas of raised bog. The south-east arm of the lake is long and narrow, with freshwater marsh and fen. The lake is important for fishing and is used for water-sports.

Habitats Wetland (100%; standing fresh water; river/stream; water-fringe vegetation; fen/transition mire/spring)
Land-use Fisheries/aquaculture (100%), Hunting (100%), Tourism/recreation (100%)

■ Birds

Species	Season	Year	Pop min	Pop max	Acc	Criteria
Cygnus cygnus Whooper Swan	W	1996	108	108	A	B3
[1] *Anser albifrons* White-fronted Goose	W	1996	408	408	A	B1i, C3
Aythya ferina Pochard	W	1996	3,701	3,701	A	B1i, C3

1. Mean 1992–1996.

The same flock of *Anser albifrons flavirostris* also uses sites 135, 136, 139 and 140. Other species which occur in numbers of national importance are *Tachybaptus ruficollis* (34 birds, 1996), *Cygnus olor* (128 birds, 1996), *Aythya fuligula* (1,800 birds, 1996) and *Fulica atra* (643 birds, 1996).

■ Protection status
National None **International** High
1,120 ha of IBA covered by Ramsar Site (Lough Derravaragh, 1,120 ha). 1,120 ha of IBA covered by Special Protection Area (Lough Derravaragh, 1,120 ha).

■ Conservation issues

Threats Agricultural intensification/expansion (A), Recreation/tourism (B)

Nutrient pollution, due to agricultural intensification, threatens habitat quality. There is increasing pressure on the site due to recreation activities and wildfowling may cause some disturbance to birds.

Lough Owel
B1i, C3 **139**

Admin region Midlands
Coordinates 53°34'N 7°24'W
Altitude 100–100 m **Area** 1,032 ha

■ Site description
Lough Owel is a large calcareous lake located north-west of Mullingar in County Westmeath. It is relatively shallow with a rocky, marl-covered bottom, and a rocky shoreline with patchy vegetation. Marsh and fen areas are present in the south-western and northern corners of the lake, and the surrounding farmland is used by geese *Anser*. Fishing, especially for trout, is popular at this site.

Habitats Wetland (100%; standing fresh water; water-fringe vegetation; fen/transition mire/spring)
Land-use Fisheries/aquaculture (100%)

■ Birds

Species	Season	Year	Pop min	Pop max	Acc	Criteria
[1] *Anser albifrons* White-fronted Goose	W	1996	408	408	A	B1i, C3

1. Mean 1992–1996.

Anser albifrons flavirostris occurs in numbers of international importance; the birds also use Lough Ennell (site 140), Lough Iron–Glen Lough (site 135), Lough Derravaragh (site 138) and Garriskil bog (site 136). Other waterfowl species which winter in numbers of national importance are *Anas clypeata* (268 birds, 1996), *Aythya fuligula* (500 birds, 1995), *Aythya ferina* (500 birds, 1995), *Bucephala clangula* (195 birds, 1995) and *Fulica atra* (2,500 birds, 1996).

■ Protection status
National None **International** High

1,032 ha of IBA covered by Ramsar Site (Lough Owel, 1,032 ha). 1,032 ha of IBA covered by Special Protection Area (Lough Owel, 1,032 ha).

■ Conservation issues

Threats Agricultural intensification/expansion (B), Aquaculture/fisheries (B), Drainage (B), Recreation/tourism (C)

Possible threats include increasing abstraction for water-supply to Mullingar, resulting in a lowering of the lake's water-level. Nutrient pollution due to agricultural intensification and pressure from recreational boating and fishing may also adversely impact on the site.

Habitats Forest and woodland (10%; broadleaved deciduous forest), Scrub (10%; scrub), Wetland (80%; standing fresh water; river/stream; water-fringe vegetation)
Land-use Agriculture (20%), Fisheries/aquaculture (60%), Tourism/recreation (60%)

■ Birds

Species		Season	Year	Pop min	Pop max	Acc	Criteria
[1] *Cygnus olor*	Mute Swan	W	1987	424	424	—	B1i
[2] *Anser albifrons*	White-fronted Goose	W	1996	408	408	A	B1i, C3

1. Mean 1984–1987.
2. Mean 1992–1996.

This site supports internationally important numbers of *Anser albifrons flavirostris*, which also use Lough Owel (site 139), Lough Iron–Glen Lough (site 135), Lough Derravaragh (site 138) and Garriskil bog (site 136).

■ Protection status
National None **International** High

1,404 ha of IBA covered by Ramsar Site (Lough Ennell, 1,404 ha). 1,404 ha of IBA covered by Special Protection Area (Lough Ennell, 1,404 ha).

■ Conservation issues

Threats Agricultural intensification/expansion (B), Industrialization/urbanization (B), Recreation/tourism (C)

Past discharge of effluent from the Mullingar sewage-treatment plant (now upgraded), together with fertilizer input from surrounding farmland, have had a negative impact on water quality.

Lough Ennell   B1i, C3   **140**
Admin region Midlands
Coordinates 53°28'N 7°24'W
Altitude 84–84 m   **Area** 1,404 ha

■ Site description
A large open, steep-sided but shallow limestone lake, situated 3 km south of Mullingar in County Westmeath. The Brosna river flows into the lake from the north. There are limited areas of reedbed and scrub and a number of small wooded islands. Calcareous grassland has colonized parts of the former lake bed. The site is used for angling, boating and camping, and some sections are managed for visitor access.

REFERENCES

AN FORAS FORBARTHA (1981) *Areas of Scientific Interest in Ireland.* Dublin: An Foras Forbartha.

ANON. (1992) *The Office of Public Works Wildlife Service Report for 1990.* Dublin: Government Stationery Office.

ARCHER, E. (1996) The Dalkey Island Tern Project 1996. Dublin: BirdWatch Ireland. Unpublished report.

ASPEY. N., WALLACE, E. AND NEWTON, S. (1997) Lady's Island Tern Report, 1997. Dublin: BirdWatch Ireland. Unpublished report.

BERROW, S. D., MACKIE, K. L., O'SULLIVAN, O., SHEPHERD, K. B., MELLON, C. AND COVENEY, J. A. (1992) The Second International Chough Survey in Ireland. *Irish Birds* 5(1): 1–10.

BRAZIER, H. AND MERNE, O. (1988) The Blasket Islands Expedition 1988. Dublin: Irish Wildbird Conservancy and Irish National Parks and Wildlife Service. Unpublished report.

CAIRNS, R. P. S. (1997) *Wicklow Mountains National Park Study.* Dublin: Government Stationery Office.

CARRUTHERS, T. AND LARNER, J. (1993) *The birds of Killarney National Park.* Dublin: Government Stationery Office.

CASEY, C. (1996) BirdWatch Ireland Proposal for Funding of Corncrake conservation in Ireland under LIFE II. Dublin: BirdWatch Ireland. Unpublished.

CASEY, C. AND HUNT, J. (1997) Corncrake fieldwork in the Shannon Callows, 1997. Dublin: BirdWatch Ireland. Unpublished report.

CASEY, S., MOORE, N., RYAN, L., MERNE, O. J., COVENEY, J. A. AND DEL NEVO, A. (1995) The Roseate Tern Conservation Project on Rockabill, Co. Dublin: a six year review 1989–1994. *Irish Birds* 5: 251–264.

COLHOUN, K. (1998) *I-WeBS Report 1996–97: results of the third winter of the Irish Wetland Bird Survey.* Dublin: BirdWatch Ireland.

COVENEY, J. (1991) Cork Harbour counts 1991–1992: an interim report. Pp. 70–75 in Anon. *Cork Bird Report 1991.* Dublin: Irish Wildbird Conservancy.

COVENEY, J. (1995) Initial IWC submission on draft management plan for the Wicklow Mountains in the context of a nature conservation strategy for the Wicklow Mountains. Dublin: Irish Wildbird Conservancy. Unpublished.

CRAMP, S., BOURNE, W. R. P. AND SAUNDERS, D. (1974) *The seabirds of Britain and Ireland.* London: Collins.

CRANSWICK, P., BOWLER, J. M., DELANY, S. N., EINARSSON, O., GARDARSSON, A., MCELWAINE, J. G., MERNE, O. J., REES, E. C. AND WELLS, J. H. (1996) Numbers of Whooper Swans *Cygnus cygnus* in Iceland, Ireland and Britain in January 1995: results of international Whooper Swan census. *Wildfowl* 47: 17–30.

DELANY, S. (1996) *I-WeBS Report 1994–95: results of the first winter of the Irish Wetland Bird Survey.* Dublin: BirdWatch Ireland.

DELANY, S. (1997) *I-WeBS Report 1995–96: results of the second winter of the Irish Wetland Bird Survey.* Dublin: BirdWatch Ireland.

DELANY, S. AND GITTINGS, T. (1996) Survey of Common Scoters at known Irish breeding sites, May 1996. Unpublished report.

DELANY, S. AND GITTINGS, T. (1996) A pre-breeding census of Common Scoters in Ireland in 1995. *Irish Birds* 5(4): 413–422.

DERWIN, J. (1996) Corncrake fieldwork in the Shannon Callows. Dublin: BirdWatch Ireland. Unpublished report.

DERWIN, J. (1997) Corncrake fieldwork in north Donegal, 1997. Dublin: BirdWatch Ireland. Unpublished report.

DROMEY, M. AND KELEMAN, J.(1996) Conservation plan for Natura 2000 site: Coole Garryland pSAC, Co. Galway. Dublin: National Parks and Wildlife Service.

EPA (ENVIRONMENTAL PROTECTION AGENCY) (1996) *State of the Environment in Ireland.* Dublin: Environmental Protection Agency.

FOX, A. D., NORRISS, D. W., STROUD, D. A. AND WILSON, H. J. (1994) *Greenland White-fronted Geese in Britain and Ireland 1982/83–1993/94.* Dublin: Irish National Parks and Wildlife Service (Greenland White-fronted Goose Study Research Rep. No. 8).

GIBBONS, D. W., REID, J. B. AND CHAPMAN, R. A. (1993) *The new atlas of breeding birds in Britain and Ireland, 1988–91.* London: T. and A. D. Poyser.

GITTINGS, T. AND DELANY, S. (1996) A pre-breeding census of Common Scoters in Ireland in 1995. *Irish Birds* 5(4): 413–422.

GORDON, T. (1996) Corncrake fieldwork in Mayo and west Connaught. Dublin: BirdWatch Ireland. Unpublished report.

GORDON, T. (1997) Corncrake fieldwork in Mayo and west Connaught, 1997. Dublin: BirdWatch Ireland. Unpublished report.

GRIMMETT, R. AND JONES, T. A. (1989) *Important Bird Areas in Europe.* Cambridge, UK: International Council for Bird Preservation (Techn. Publ. 9).

HANNON, C., BERROW, S. AND NEWTON, S. F. (1997) The status and distribution of breeding terns in Ireland in 1995. *Irish Birds* 6(1): 1–22.

HANNON, C. (1997) The 1995 all-Ireland tern survey. Dublin: BirdWatch Ireland. Unpublished report.

HEATH, M. F. AND BORGGREVE, C. (2000) *BirdLife International/ EBCC European Bird Database 1998.* Cambridge, UK: BirdLife International.

HEERY, D. (1993) *The Shannon floodlands: a natural history.* Kinvara, Ireland: Tir Eolas.

HEERY, S. (1996) Birds in central Ireland. In Anon. *Mid-Shannon Bird Report 1992-1995.* Dublin: BirdWatch Ireland.

HEFFERNAN, M. L. (1995) Shellfish farming and Special Protection Areas for birds in Ireland. Dublin: Trinity College (M.Sc. thesis).

HICKIE, D. (1996) *Evaluation of environmental designations in Ireland*. Dublin: The Heritage Council.

HURLEY, J. (1994) *The South Wexford coast: a natural heritage coastline*. Kilmore, Ireland: SWC Promotions.

HURLEY, J. (1997) *Water levels at Lady's Island Lake 1984–1996*. Kilmore, Ireland: SWC Promotions.

HUTCHINSON, C. D. (1994) *Where to watch birds in Ireland*. London: Christopher Helm.

HUTCHINSON, C. D. AND O'HALLORAN, J. (1994) The ecology of Black-tailed Godwits at an Irish south coast estuary. *Irish Birds* 5(2): 165–172.

KIRBY, J. S., REES, E. C., MERNE, O. J. AND GARDARSSON, A. (1992) International census of Whooper Swans *Cygnus cygnus* in Britain, Ireland and Iceland–January 1991. *Wildfowl* 43: 20–26.

LEANE, K. AND PHALAN, B. (1997) The Little Tern protection scheme at Kilcoole/Newcastle, Co. Wicklow. Dublin: BirdWatch Ireland. Unpublished report.

LLOYD, C., TASKER, M. L. AND PARTRIDGE, K. (1991) *The status of seabirds in Britain and Ireland*. London: Poyser.

MADDEN, B. (1987) The birds of Mongan Bog, Co. Offaly. *Irish Birds* 3: 441–448.

MADDEN, B. AND MERNE, O. J. (1995) A survey of breeding birds on Lambay Island, May 1995. Dublin: National Parks and Wildlife. Unpublished report.

MAGEE, E. (1996) Corncrake fieldwork in north Donegal. Dublin: BirdWatch Ireland. Unpublished report.

MAGEE, E. AND COVENEY, J. (1995) Important Bird Areas (IBAs): threats and protection status. Dublin: Irish Wildbird Conservancy. Unpublished report.

McMANUS, F., McNALLY, J. M. AND COONEY, T. (1992) Wildfowl and waders of Rogerstown estuary. P. 66 in *Irish East Coast Bird Report 1992*. Dublin: Irish Wildbird Conservancy.

McMILLAN, A. (1988) The wintering birds of Kilcoole/Newcastle Marshes 1987/88. Pp. 61–68 in *Irish East Coast Bird Report 1987*. Dublin: Irish Wildbird Conservancy.

MERNE, O. J. AND WALSH, A. (1994) Barnacle Geese in Ireland, spring 1993 and 1994. *Irish Birds* 5: 151–156.

MERNE, O. J., NORRISS, D., WILSON, H. J., SHEPPARD, R. AND NAIRN, R. (1989) Ireland. Pp. 341–374 in R. F. A. Grimmett and T. A. Jones, eds. *Important Bird Areas in Europe*. Cambridge, UK: International Council for Bird Preservation (Techn. Publ. 9).

MUNDY, R. AND HANNON, C. (1996) Rockabill Tern Report 1996. Dublin: BirdWatch Ireland. Unpublished report.

MUNDY, R. AND MILLETT, J. (1997) Rockabill Tern Report, 1997. Dublin: BirdWatch Ireland. Unpublished report.

NPW (NATIONAL PARKS AND WILDLIFE) (1996) NHA Site Synopses. Dublin: National Parks and Wildlife. Unpublished reports.

NPWS (NATIONAL PARKS AND WILDLIFE SERVICE) (1997) *Proposed candidate Special Areas of Conservation, Ireland*. Dublin: Department of Arts, Culture and the Gaeltacht.

NEWTON, A. V. AND WALLACE, E. (1996) Lady's Island Tern Report 1996. Dublin: BirdWatch Ireland. Unpublished report.

OGILVIE, M. A. (1983) The numbers of Greenland Barnacle Geese in Britain and Ireland. *Wildfowl* 34: 77–88.

PHALAN, B. (1996) The Little Tern Protection Scheme at Kilcoole/Newcastle, Co. Wicklow, 1996 with a summary from the Little Tern colony at Baltray, Co. Louth. Dublin: BirdWatch Ireland. Unpublished report.

PIERCE, S. AND WILSON, J. (1980) Spring migration of Whimbrels over Cork Harbour. *Irish Birds* 1: 514–516.

ROCHE, R. AND MERNE, O. (1977) *The Saltees: islands of birds and legends*. Dublin: O'Brien Press.

ROWE, D. AND WILSON, C. J. (1996) *High skies and lowlands: an anthology of the Wexford Slobs and harbour*. Enniscorthy, Ireland: Duffry Press.

RYAN, C. (1992) Red Grouse at Liffey Head Bog, Co. Wicklow. In *Irish East Coast Bird Report 1992*. Dublin: Irish Wildbird Conservancy.

SHEPPARD, R. (1993) *Ireland's wetland wealth—the report of the Winter Wetlands Survey 1984/85 to 1986/87*. Dublin: Irish Wildbird Conservancy.

SMIDDY, P. (1981) The waterfowl of Ballymacoda, Co. Cork. *Irish Birds* 4: 525–548.

SMIDDY, P. (1996) The waterfowl of the Blackwater Estuary (Youghal Harbour), Cos Waterford and Cork. *Irish Naturalists' Journal* 25: 157–165.

THOMPSON, K. R., BRINDLEY, E. AND HEUBECK, M. (1996) *Seabird numbers and breeding success in Britain and Ireland, 1995*. Peterborough, UK: Joint Nature Conservation Committee.

THOMPSON, K. R., BRINDLEY, E. AND HEUBECK, M. (1997) *Seabird numbers and breeding success in Britain and Ireland, 1996*. Peterborough, UK: Joint Nature Conservation Committee.

TUCKER, G. M. AND EVANS, M. I., EDS. (1997) *Habitats for birds in Europe: a conservation strategy for the wider environment*. Cambridge, UK: BirdLife International (BirdLife Conservation Series No. 6).

TUCKER, G. M. AND HEATH, M. F. (1994) *Birds in Europe: their conservation status*. Cambridge, UK: BirdLife International (BirdLife Conservation Series No. 3).

WARING, M. AND DAVIS, S. (1983) Rediscovery of Leach's Petrels breeding in Ireland. *Irish Birds* 2: 360–363.

WALSH, A. AND MERNE, O. J. (1988) Barnacle Geese in Ireland, spring 1988. *Irish Birds* 3: 539–550.

WHILDE, A. (1985) The 1984 all-Ireland tern survey. *Irish Birds* 3: 1–32.

WHILDE, A. (1990) *Birds of Galway. A review of recent records and field studies.*

LATVIA

EDMUNDS RAČINSKIS

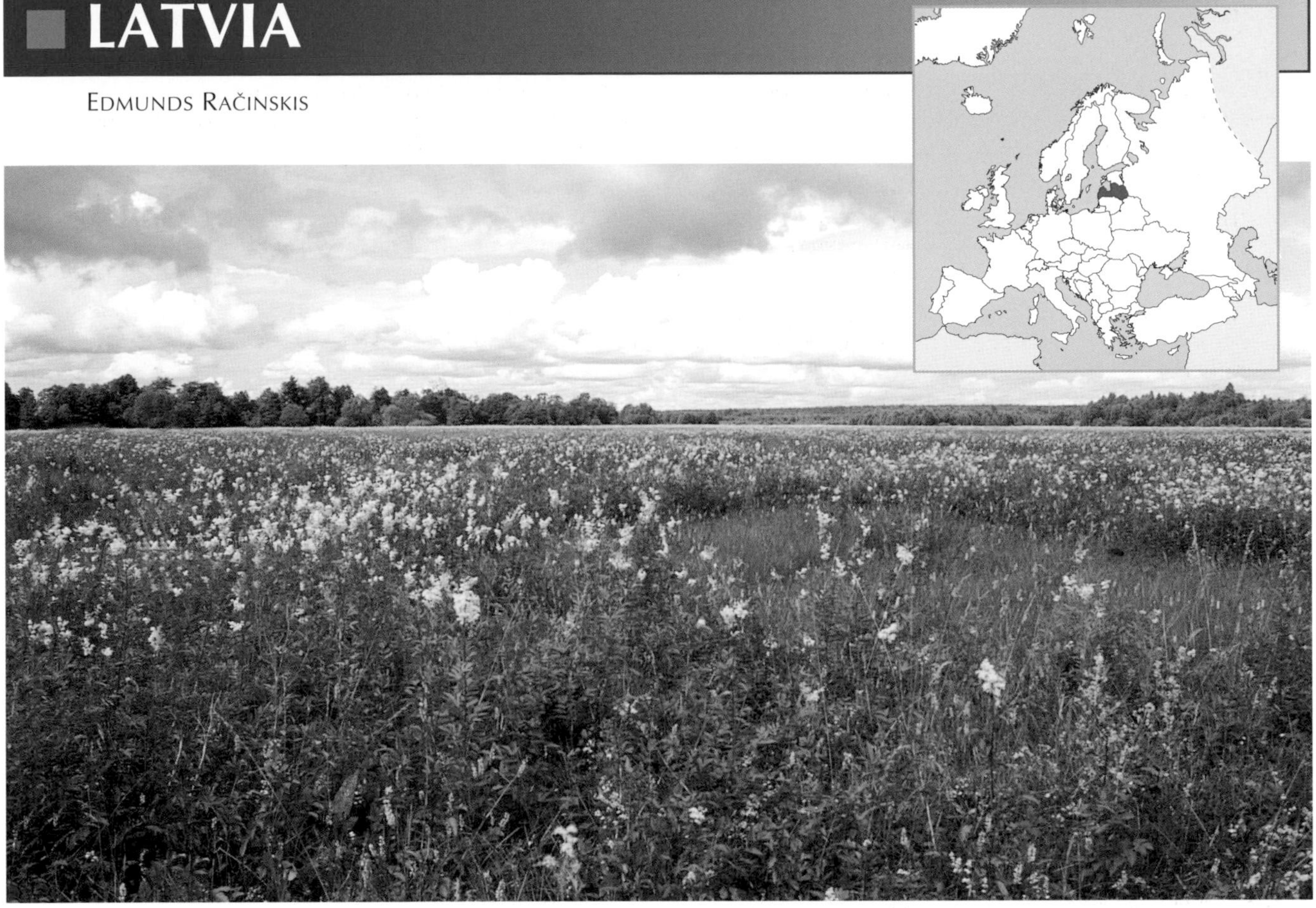

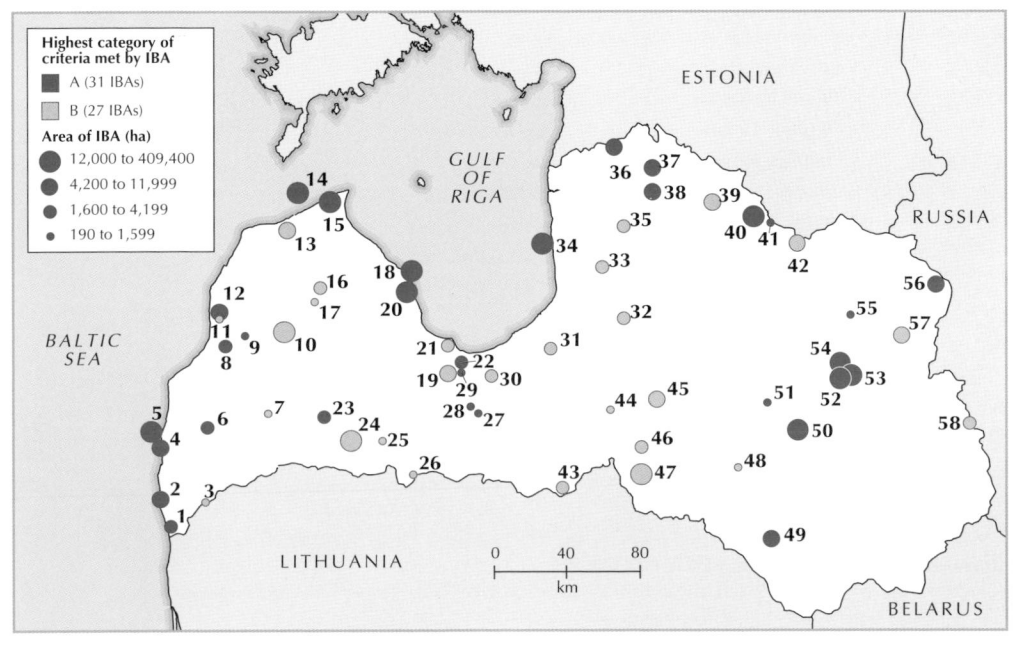

Uzava river meadows (IBA 008). (PHOTO: EDMUNDS RAČINSKIS)

GENERAL INTRODUCTION

A total of 58 Important Bird Areas (IBAs) have been identified in Latvia as of 1998 (Table 1). Of these, 54 are non-marine IBAs, covering 319,799 ha or nearly 5% of the total land-surface area of Latvia (64,589 km²), while the remaining four IBAs are marine with a total area of 766,700 ha.

Latvia has a Baltic Sea coastline of c.500 km, and is bordered by Estonia to the north, by Russia and Belarus to the east and south-east, and by Lithuania to the south. Almost all of the country (97.5% of the area) lies below 200 m elevation. There are two main

landscape-types (Anon. 1998a, 1998b): forest (covering 44.6% of Latvia) and agricultural land (38.8%). Mires cover 5.6% nationally, whilst inland waters cover 3.7%.

Forests are mainly mixed, and are dominated by Scots pine *Pinus sylvestris* (dominant over 39% of forest area), silver birch *Betula* (28%) and Norway spruce *Picea abies* (21%), yet are very diverse. Roughly half of the forest area lies on wet soils. Stands of old forest (over 100 years old) constitute c.9% of the forest area. Forty-two percent of the area of mire in Latvia is raised bog, 9% is transitional mire and 49% is fen; 9.8% of the mire area is protected. Semi-natural grasslands occupy less than 1% of Latvia.

Map 1. Location, area and criteria category of Important Bird Areas in Latvia.

Highest category of criteria met by IBA
- A (31 IBAs)
- B (27 IBAs)

Area of IBA (ha)
- 12,000 to 409,400
- 4,200 to 11,999
- 1,600 to 4,199
- 190 to 1,599

417

Table 1. Summary of Important Bird Areas in Latvia.   58 IBAs covering 10,865 km²

IBA code	National code	1989 code	International name	National name	Administrative region	Area (ha)	Criteria (see p. 11)
001	LV001	—	Nida bog	Nidas purvs	Liepaja	2,500	A4i, B1i
002	LV002	SU019	Pape lake	Papes ezers	Liepaja	4,400	A4iii, B1i, B2, B3
003	LV003	—	Dunika bog	Dunikas tirelis	Liepaja	1,400	B1i
004	LV004	SU018	Liepaja lake	Liepajas ezers	Liepaja	5,200	A1, B1i, B2
005	—	—	Latvia, west coast	Jura no Nidas lidz Pavilostai	Liepaja	409,400	A4i, A4iii, B1i
006	—	—	Durbe lake	Durbes ezers	Liepaja	2,500	A1, B1i
007	LV012	—	Skrunda fish-ponds	Skrundas zivju diki	Kuldiga	720	B1i
008	—	—	Uzava river meadows	Uzavas augsteces plavas	Kuldiga	3,700	A1, B2
009	—	—	Kamburi meadows	Kamburu plavas	Kuldiga	850	A1
010	LV011	—	Kuldiga forest area	Mezi pie Kuldigas	Kuldiga	13,000	B2
011	LV006	—	Sarnate bogs	Sarnates purvi	Ventspils	1,500	B1i
012	—	—	Uzava lowland	Uzavas lejtece	Ventspils	4,200	A1, B2
013	LV008	—	Irbe river valley and Lielais Ances bog	Irbes ieleja un Lielais Ances purvs	Ventspils	6,000	B1i
014	—	—	Irbe strait	Irbes saurums	Ventspils, Talsi	165,500	A4i, A4ii, A4iii, B1i, B1ii, B2
015	LV009	SU016	Slitere Nature Reserve	Sliteres Valsts rezervâts	Talsi	15,517	A4iv, B1iv, B2
016	—	—	Ilini	Ilini	Ventspils, Talsi	3,600	B1i
017	—	—	Spare lake	Spares ezers	Talsi	1,100	B1i
018	LV014	—	Gulf of Riga, west coast	Rigas lica R piekraste	Talsi, Tukums	102,800	A4i, A4iii, B1i, B2
019	LV017	SU017	Lielais Kemeru bog	Lielais Kemeru tirelis	Riga, Tukums, Jelgava	6,800	B1i, B2
020	LV015	SU015	Lake Engure	Engures ezers	Talsi, Tukums	18,100	A4i, A4iii, B1i, B2, B3
021	LV016	SU014	Lake Kanieris	Kanieris	Tukums	2,400	B1i
022	LV020	SU013	Babite lake	Babites ezers	Riga	3,100	A4i, A4iii, B1i, B3
023	LV013	—	Satini fish-ponds	Satinu zivju diki	Saldus	2,642	A4i, B1i, B2
024	—	—	Zvarde forest area	Zvardes mezi	Saldus	12,000	B2
025	—	—	Lielauce lake	Lielauces ezers	Dobele	1,400	B1i
026	LV018	—	Ukri forest area	Mezi pie Ukriem	Dobele	1,200	B2
027	—	—	Lielupe river flood-plain meadows	Lielupes palienes plavas	Jelgava	190	A1
028	—	—	Svete river mouth	Svetes griva	Jelgava	1,100	A1, A4i, A4iii, B1i
029	LV019	—	Kalnciems meadows and wet forest	Plavas un mitrie mezi pie Kalnciema	Jelgava	1,000	A1
030	LV021	—	Cena bog	Cenas tirelis	Riga	3,700	B1i, B2
031	—	—	Liela Jugla river mouth	Lielas Juglas griva	Riga, Riga municipality	1,600	B1i
032	LV028	—	Sudas bog	Sudas purvs	Cesis	2,600	B1i
033	LV027	—	Lielais and Pemmas bogs	Lielais un Pemmas purvs	Limbazi	4,000	B1i
034	LV024	—	Gulf of Riga, east coast	Rigas lica A piekraste	Riga, Limbazi	89,000	A4i, B1i
035	LV026	—	Madiesenu bog and Augstroze	Madiesenu purvs	Limbazi, Valmiera	3,000	B1i
036	LV025	SU010	Kapzemes, Ollu and Pirtsmeza bogs	Kapzemes, Ollu un Pirtsmeza purvi	Limbazi, Valmiera	11,000	A4i, B1i
037	—	—	Ruja fish-ponds	Rujas zivju diki	Valmiera	4,350	A1, B1i
038	—	—	Burtnieks lake	Burtnieks	Valmiera	10,000	A1, B1i
039	—	—	Seda marsh	Sedas tirelis	Valka	7,500	B1i, B2
040	LV031	—	Zile forest area	Mezi pie Ziles	Valka	13,000	A1, B2
041	—	—	Cirgali meadows	Cirgalu plavas	Valka	650	A1
042	LV033	—	Gaujiena bogs and forests	Purvi un mezi pie Gaujienas	Aluksne	7,500	B1i
043	—	—	Panemune forest area	Panemunes mezi	Bauska	2,000	B2
044	—	—	Daugava river at Kaibala	Daugava pie Kaibalas	Ogre	850	B1i
045	LV029	—	Lobe lake area	Lobes ezers un apkartne	Ogre, Aizkraukle	7,300	B2
046	LV030	—	Daudzeva bog and fish-ponds	Daudzevas purvs un zivju diki	Aizkraukle	2,900	B1i, B2
047	—	—	Zalve forest area	Zalves mezi	Aizkraukle	12,800	B2
048	LV034	—	Abeli forest area	Mezi pie Abeliem	Jekabpils	1,330	B2
049	—	—	Dviete area	Dviete	Jekabpils, Daugavpils	4,800	A1, B1i
050	LV035	SU011	Teici and Pelecare bogs	Teicu un Pelecares purvi	Jekabpils, Preili, Madona	24,000	A4i, B1i, B2
051	—	—	Aiv19.ekste river flood-plain meadows	Aiviekstes palienes plavas pie Laudonas	Madona	600	A1, B1i, B2
052	LV036	—	Lubans lake and fish-ponds	Lubans un zivju diki	Rezekne, Madona	22,000	A1, A4iii, B1i
053	—	SU012	Baltie Klani marshes and adjoining bogs	Baltie klani un apkartejie purvi	Balvi, Rezekne, Madona	19,000	A1, A4i, B1i, B2
054	—	—	Pededze river forests and Parabaine	Pededzes lejteces mezi un Parabaine	Gulbene, Balvi, Madona	12,000	A1, B2
055	—	—	Pededze and Sita flood-plain	Pededzes un Sitas palienes	Gulbene	1,200	A1
056	—	—	Katlesi forest area	Katlesi	Aluksne, Balvi	10,000	A1, B2
057	LV037	—	Stampaku, Murnieku and Orlovas bogs	Stampaku, Murnieku un Orlovas purvi	Balvi	10,000	B1i
058	LV038	—	Zabolotje bog	Zabolotjes purvs	Ludza	4,000	B1i

Sites identified in the inventory of IBAs in Latvia (Viksne 1994) but no longer considered to be IBAs
LV005 Ziemupe–Akmenrags sea coast; LV007 Ovisi–River Irbe mouth sea coast; LV010 Lake Usma and Plucu-Novadu bogs; LV022 Daugavgriva wetland; LV023 Vecdaugava wetland; LV032 Mezole forest area.

The average population density in Latvia (39 persons/km²) is relatively low in European terms.

The distribution of IBAs across Latvia is rather even (Map 1). However, no sites are situated above 150 m elevation, therefore there are fewer IBAs in the higher parts of the central-east and south-east. As a result, most non-marine IBAs relate mainly to coastal lagoons, river flood-plains in the lowlands, the largest bogs, and fish-pond areas.

In comparison with the 10 sites identified in Latvia in the 'original' IBA inventory in Europe (Grimmett and Jones 1989)—all retained in the current inventory—and the 38 sites documented in the national IBA inventory (Viksne 1994), 58 sites have been identified under the current review, up to 1998 (Table 1). A few more IBAs have been identified since the completion of this review and cannot be included in this book. For instance, Sturu bog (Saldus district) and Ozolu bog with Graudupe fields (Kuldiga district) are both important for their regular autumn congregations of more than 1,000 *Grus grus* (meeting criterion B1i), to name just two of the most prominent candidate sites. This illustrates that the identification of IBAs in Latvia is not yet complete and that the list could grow to an estimated 65–70 sites before the year 2000.

ORNITHOLOGICAL IMPORTANCE

Altogether there are 109 species of European conservation concern (SPECs) which breed in Latvia (Tucker and Heath 1994). Three of these are globally threatened, i.e. *Aquila clanga*, *Crex crex* and *Acrocephalus paludicola*, although *Crex crex* is the only one to have a Latvian breeding population that is significant at the European scale, therefore most of the IBAs qualifying under criterion A1 (17 out of 19) are identified particularly for this species (Table 2). Two sites are important for breeding *Aquila clanga*, although neither has more than one certainly identified breeding pair (Table 2). No sites were identified for *Acrocephalus paludicola* because of a lack of data on its occurrence in Latvia. In addition, the near-threatened *Haliaeetus albicilla* and *Gallinago media* breed at several IBAs but numbers are too low to meet any IBA criteria.

Only five sites qualify as IBAs solely under the A1 criterion (all for *Crex crex*)—most other A1 IBAs also meet other criteria, mainly A4i or B1i as important stop-over sites for migrating geese *Anser* and yellow-billed swans *Cygnus cygnus/C. columbianus*. Both sites qualifying under A1 for *Aquila clanga* also qualify under B2 for *Aquila pomarina*. Altogether, 31 out of the 58 IBAs are important on a global scale (19 meet A1, 12 meet A4i, one meets A4ii, eight meet A4iii, and one meets A4iv).

The majority (40) of IBAs in Latvia meet criterion B1i, through supporting significant numbers of waterbirds (mainly staging), especially *Anser albifrons*, *A. fabalis*, *Cygnus cygnus* and *Grus grus* (Table 3). Twelve of these 40 sites also meet criterion A4i. Nearly half (26) of all IBAs qualify under criterion B2, being among the most important breeding sites in Latvia for numerous bird species that have an unfavourable conservation status in Europe, such as *Botaurus stellaris*, *Ciconia nigra*, *Aythya ferina*, *Aquila pomarina*, *Pandion haliaetus*, *Tetrao tetrix*, *Crex crex*, *Grus grus*, *Larus minutus*, *Chlidonias niger*, *Caprimulgus europaeus* and *Picoides tridactylus* (Table 4). Other criteria (A4ii, B1ii, B1iv and B3) are met at only a few sites (1, 1, 1 and 3 respectively), based on current knowledge.

Most IBAs in Latvia meet a total of one to three criteria. Five sites qualify under four criteria each (Table 1), while only one site qualifies under either five or six criteria (020 and 014 respectively), out of the total of 10 different criteria that are met in Latvia. Four out of these latter seven IBAs, together with 050, also form the 'Top Five' list for the maximum number of qualifying species per site: Lake Engure (020; eight species), Baltie Klani marshes and adjoining bogs (053; seven species), Teici and Pelecare bogs (050; five species), Irbe strait (014; five species), and Gulf of Riga, west coast (018; five species). However, this kind of ranking alone does not provide a full indication of the value of each area, as the importance of a site is multifaceted and constituted by many factors.

Even though IBAs have been identified for a number of breeding species of European conservation concern (under B2/B3 criteria), such as *Ciconia nigra*, *Aquila pomarina*, *Pandion haliaetus*, *Caprimulgus europaeus* and *Picoides tridactylus* (Table 4), these and

Table 2. Important Bird Areas in Latvia that are important for species of global conservation concern (meeting criterion A1).

Species	IBA code
Aquila clanga Greater Spotted Eagle	054, 056
Crex crex Corncrake	004, 006, 008, 009, 012, 027, 028, 029, 037, 038, 040, 041, 049, 051, 052, 053, 055

Table 3. Important Bird Areas in Latvia that support important numbers of one or more congregatory species (i.e. meeting criteria A4 and/or B1). IBAs meeting both criteria A4 and B1 for the species are shown in **bold**. IBAs meeting only criterion B1 for the species concerned, and not A4, are shown in normal type. For key to 'Season', see p. 7.

Species	Season	IBA code
Gavia stellata Red-throated Diver	W	**014**
Gavia arctica Black-throated Diver	W	**014**, **034**
Podiceps grisegena	B	**020**
Red-necked Grebe	W	018
Cygnus olor Mute Swan	W	004
Cygnus columbianus Bewick's Swan	P	**022**
Cygnus cygnus Whooper Swan	P	002, 004, 006, 007, 021, 022, **023**, **028**, 031, 037, 038, 039, 044, 046, 051, 052, **053**
	N	007
Anser fabalis Bean Goose	P	**001**, 003, 006, 011, 013, 017, 019, 025, 028, 030, 032, 033, 035, **036**, 042, 049, **050**, 052, **053**, 057, 058
Anser albifrons White-fronted Goose	P	001, 013, 019, 028, 030, 033, 035, 036, 042, 049, 050, 052, 053, 057, 058
Aythya ferina Pochard	B	020
Clangula hyemalis Long-tailed Duck	W	**014**, **018**
Melanitta fusca Velvet Scoter	W	**014**, **018**
Bucephala clangula Goldeneye	N	**018**, **034**
Mergus serrator	W	018
Red-breasted Merganser		
Mergus merganser Goosander	W	**005**
Grus grus Crane	P	002, 011, 016, 032, 035, 050, 053
	N	019, 020, 036, 050
Larus minutus Little Gull	B	**053**
Chlidonias niger Black Tern	B	**053**
Cepphus grylle Black Guillemot	W	**014**

Table 4. Species of European conservation concern with significant breeding populations at Important Bird Areas in Latvia (meeting any IBA criteria).

Species [1]	Minimum national breeding population (pairs) [2]	Proportion (%) of national population breeding at all IBAs in Latvia
Botaurus stellaris Bittern	200	25
Ciconia nigra Black Stork	900	6
Aythya ferina Pochard	2,500	48
Aquila pomarina Lesser Spotted Eagle	2,000	5
Aquila clanga Greater Spotted Eagle	1	100 [3]
Pandion haliaetus Osprey	100	27
Tetrao tetrix Black Grouse	5,000	11
Crex crex Corncrake	26,000	2
Grus grus Crane	300	25
Larus minutus Little Gull	700	100 [3]
Chlidonias niger Black Tern	2,000	90
Caprimulgus europaeus Nightjar	3,000	10
Alcedo atthis Kingfisher	300	7
Picoides tridactylus Three-toed Woodpecker	1,000	2
Acrocephalus schoenobaenus Sedge Warbler	80,000	3
Acrocephalus scirpaceus Reed Warbler	20,000	8

1. Only those species of European conservation concern (see Box 1, p. 12) that meet IBA criteria in Latvia are listed.
2. Data are taken from the BirdLife/EBCC European Bird Database 1998 (Heath and Borggreve 2000).
3. The percentage of the national population in IBAs exceeds 100%. Usually this is because the national population estimate has not been updated recently whilst the IBA population estimate has been recently updated with new data as a result of comprehensive surveys of IBAs themselves. Also, the individual site count for a species may be the maximum or average over recent years, and summing these may record more birds than are present nationally in any single year.

other non-congregatory breeding species are not and cannot be adequately conserved in Latvia by the IBA network alone, and measures to protect these dispersed species must therefore be targeted at the whole habitat or, where appropriate, at the species itself. Much the same is true for *Crex crex*, a globally threatened species that is dependent on low-intensity agricultural land-use practices in the wider countryside, and which is still highly dispersed across the landscape—only 2.2–2.5% of the national population, or 575–940 calling males, occur in the IBAs that qualify for this species (Table 4). It is also difficult to assess the importance of the sites identified for migrating waterbirds (under A4i/B1i criteria) because neither the exact population size of the flyway crossing Latvia, nor the precise numbers at sites, nor even the identity of all of the important stop-over sites, are known.

HABITATS

Open habitats are predominant in IBAs (Figure 1), especially wetlands, grassland and agricultural land. Forty-four of the IBAs in Latvia are either wetlands (32 sites) or grassland/agricultural land (12 sites) according to the dominant habitat. Bogs, marshes and fens are the main types of wetland in IBAs, since they cover the majority of 17 IBAs and at least 5% of the area of 30 sites. River flood-plains, meadows and agricultural land constitute the greater part of 12 IBAs (with at least 5% cover at 24 sites). Lakes and reservoirs are the main habitat at 11 sites (and occur at 22 sites), while fish-ponds are the core habitat for four sites (and are contained by a total of six). Only 10 IBAs are predominantly forested, while the majority of IBAs (44 sites) have more than 5% forest-cover (Figure 1), reflecting the dominance of forest across the country (44% cover overall). Finally, four marine IBAs have been identified in the Baltic Sea and Gulf of Riga, covering mainly shallow coastal waters.

The key bird species at mires, which are mainly raised bogs, are staging *Anser albifrons* and *Anser fabalis* and local or staging *Grus grus* that rest, feed and roost here (criteria A4i, B1i). Less common are bogs that qualify for their high numbers of breeding *Grus grus* and *Tetrao tetrix* (criterion B2; Table 4). River flood-plains and other types of grassland or agricultural land are also frequented by significant numbers of geese *Anser* and *Grus grus* during migration (A4i, B1i), although the key species here are breeding *Crex crex* (A1) and staging *Cygnus cygnus* (A4i, B1i). Staging *Cygnus cygnus*, sometimes with *C. columbianus*, as well as *Anser albifrons* and *A. fabalis*, are the key qualifying species at lakes and reservoirs and also at fish-ponds, where important concentrations also occur of breeding *Botaurus stellaris*, *Larus minutus*, *Chlidonias niger* (all B2 species), and *Aythya ferina*, *Acrocephalus schoenobaenus* and *Acrocephalus scirpaceus* (B3 species). Another B2 species associated with fish-ponds and other wetlands is *Pandion haliaetus*.

Although most forests in Latvia do not qualify as IBAs, because their birds tend to be distributed in a highly dispersed manner, a number of particularly rich and diverse forest sites have been identified as IBAs. These areas hold notably high breeding densities of *Aquila pomarina*, *Ciconia nigra*, *Picoides tridactylus* and *Caprimulgus europaeus* (all B2 species) or even support breeding *Aquila clanga* (A1 species; two sites). The four large marine IBAs are identified on the basis of their wintering, moulting and migrating seabirds and waterbirds, such as *Gavia arctica*, *Podiceps grisegena*,

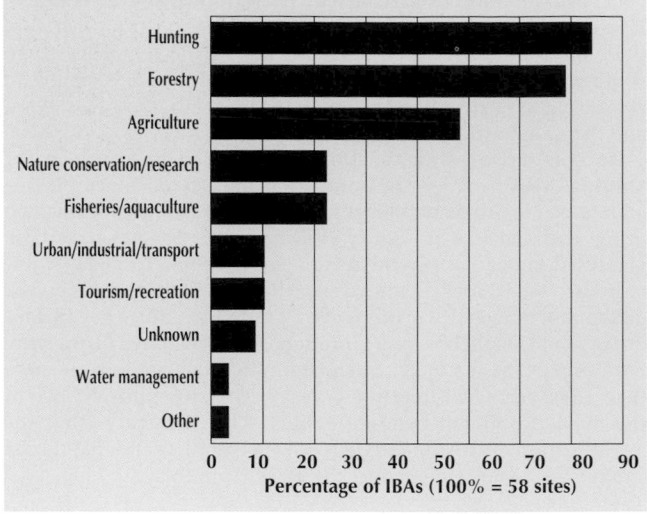

Figure 2. Occurence of land-uses at Important Bird Areas in Latvia (see Appendix 3 for definitions of land-uses).

Mergus merganser, *Mergus serrator*, *Bucephala clangula*, *Clangula hyemalis*, *Melanitta fusca* (all A4i, B1i) and *Cepphus grylle* (A4ii, B1ii).

As expected, forest and agricultural land are 'under-represented' in terms of the proportion of IBAs dominated by these habitats compared to the national land-cover statistics, because they either do not usually host distinct congregations of birds, or they are much more difficult to protect, even if such congregations temporarily occur (e.g. geese *Anser* and *Grus grus* feeding on fields).

IMPACTS ON IBAs – LAND-USE AND THREATS

Traditionally, forestry and agriculture are the two main types of land-use, together covering 83% of the country's area, in almost equal proportions. Both of these land-uses occur in nearly all IBAs in Latvia—forestry occurs in at least 69% of IBAs and agriculture in 48% (Figure 2). Only hunting (of mammals and gamebirds) is more widespread across IBAs as a human activity (74%, Figure 2). Despite the considerable number of designated protected areas in the country, only a minority of IBAs (22%) are the subject of nature conservation activities and/or regular research projects (Figure 2). Fishing, and fish-farming to a lesser extent (normally confined to fish-pond areas), also occurs at 22% of IBAs (Figure 2), at both inland wetlands and marine areas. Around 10% or less of sites are known to be used for other types of activities, such as peat extraction in bogs (12.5% of mire habitat in Latvia is used for peat extraction). All four marine areas are affected by shipping and recreation activities.

Every one of the above-mentioned land-uses causes some disturbance of birds' essential activities, such as breeding or foraging. Most sites, irrespective of their size, location or protection status, are subject to such disturbance (Figure 3). However, there are three major threat-types that not only disturb birds' essential activities but can also dramatically affect and change their habitat and resource supplies. The most widespread threat currently is intensified forest management, which affects about half of all IBAs (Figure 3).

Interestingly, both abandonment/reduction of land management, and agricultural intensification and expansion, each threaten about 30% of IBAs (Figure 3). It may seem contradictory that these threats could be equally common. The reasons lie in recent trends in land-use and ownership changes. The state's transition to a growing market economy has been accompanied by a dramatic decrease in agricultural output in many areas. Large expanses of agricultural land have been set aside or abandoned. In the short term, this land is of increased importance for some birds, for instance *Crex crex*, but it soon loses its suitability for such 'open-country' species as the ground vegetation becomes too dense and the land becomes overgrown with bushes and small trees. Similarly, the abandonment of meadows and semi-natural grasslands, through the cessation of traditional stock-grazing and mowing, has already

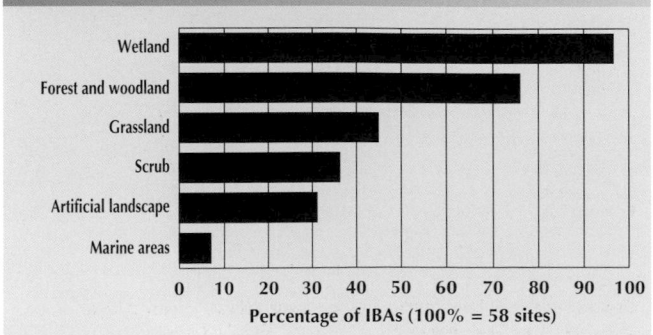

Figure 1. Occurrence of habitats at Important Bird Areas in Latvia (see Appendix 3 for definitions of habitats).

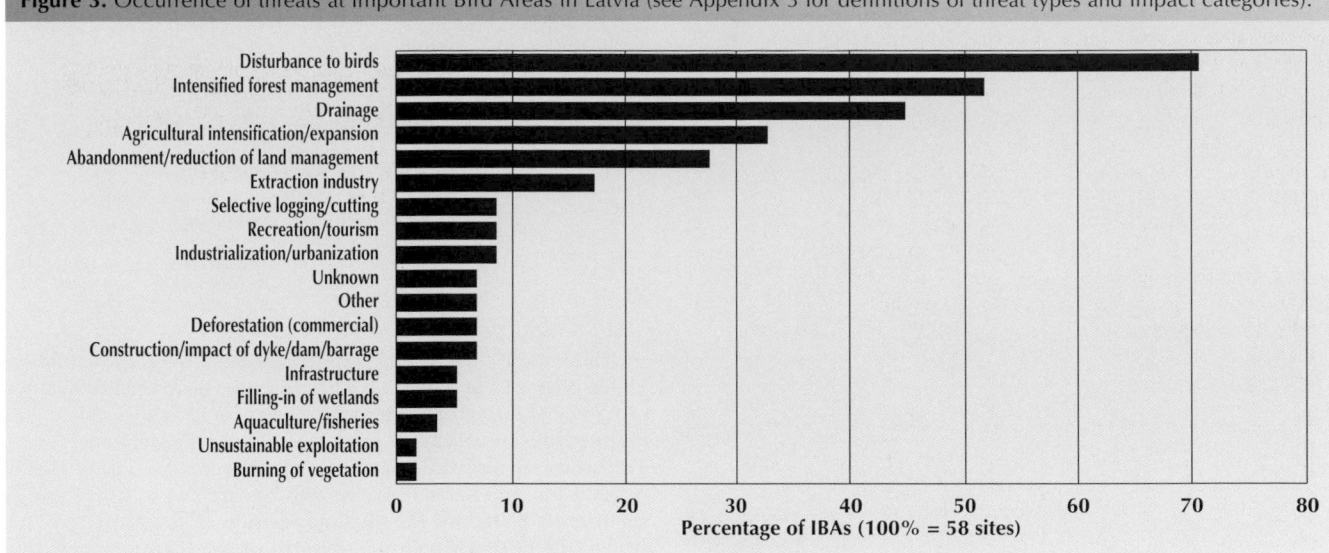

Figure 3. Occurrence of threats at Important Bird Areas in Latvia (see Appendix 3 for definitions of threat types and impact categories).

reduced breeding densities of meadow birds at several sites. At the same time, farming practices are intensifying in other areas of the country, at least locally, and are potentially more hazardous to birds. Such agricultural intensification is likely to increase in extent in the future.

Forestry in Latvia is intensifying and has grown to be the major state export; felling activity has doubled since 1990/1991. Year-round harvesting is causing critical disturbance to sensitive bird species, such as *Ciconia nigra* and *Aquila pomarina*, countrywide. The structure of forest stands is changing towards a much lower percentage of older and less disturbed stands. Moreover, a considerable proportion of forest in Latvia has been privatized and thereafter it has become hard if not impossible to influence management for conservation.

The extraction industry (peat mining) has remained a constant threat to most peatland IBAs in Latvia (Figure 3). The potentially high threat to IBAs of drainage (Figure 3) is hopefully over-estimated (it is a costly process), whilst that posed by industrialization, urbanization and growing infrastructure may well increase markedly in (potential) impact in the near future. Hunting pressure has generally increased since 1990, partly due to illegal hunting, and is causing regular disturbance to birds at most IBAs. The use of the coastal zone for recreation and development, as well as the intensification of marine transportation and the offshore industry, are together leading to serious degradation of coastal and marine habitats. Although pollution from Butinge oil terminal in Lithuania is thought to pose a major potential threat to two marine IBAs (005 and 014) in the future, developments in domestic industry are also a serious risk to the very high bird numbers which winter or moult at, or migrate through, these marine sites.

PROTECTION STATUS

■ National protection

Thirty-four IBAs (59% of the total number) have a partial or high overlap with the national protected-area system in Latvia (Figure 4, Table 5). Twenty-four IBAs (41% of the total), including the four marine areas, overlap only to a small extent, or not at all (Figure 4, Table 5).

The law on Specially Protected Nature Territories (1993) provides for the following types of protected area (former IUCN category in brackets): [State] Nature Reserves (I), National Parks (II), Restricted Nature Territories (IV), Nature Parks (V), Protected Landscape Territories (V), Natural Monuments (III) (e.g. trees, ravines and waterfalls), and Biosphere Reserves (IX).

At least 11% of the total non-marine area of IBAs is covered by Nature Reserves, at least 4% by National Parks and at least 36% by Restricted Nature Territories (Table 5). Altogether, 1,332–1,560 km² of the total IBA area (up to 50% of their total non-marine area) are nationally protected (Figure 4). Most of the unprotected sites were only recently identified as IBAs; only two sites out of 19 unprotected had already been listed in the national IBA inventory of 1994 (Viksne 1994).

Also, most of these unprotected sites are dominated by habitats that are difficult to protect: (1) forest (five sites), (2) agricultural land/grassland (nine sites), and (3) marine areas (four sites). The most important IBAs that still have little or no overlap with the national protected-area system are Skrunda fish-ponds (007), Uzava river meadows (008), Uzava lowland (012), Zvarde forest area (024), Svete river mouth (028), Cirgali meadows (041), Dviete area (049), and Pededze and Sita flood-plain (055).

Figure 4. The national protection status of Important Bird Areas in Latvia.

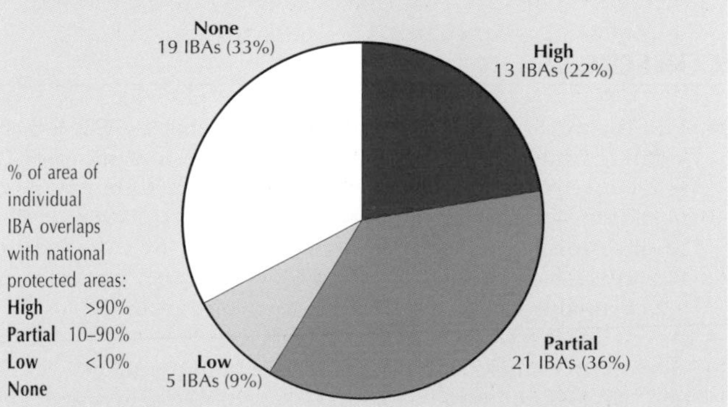

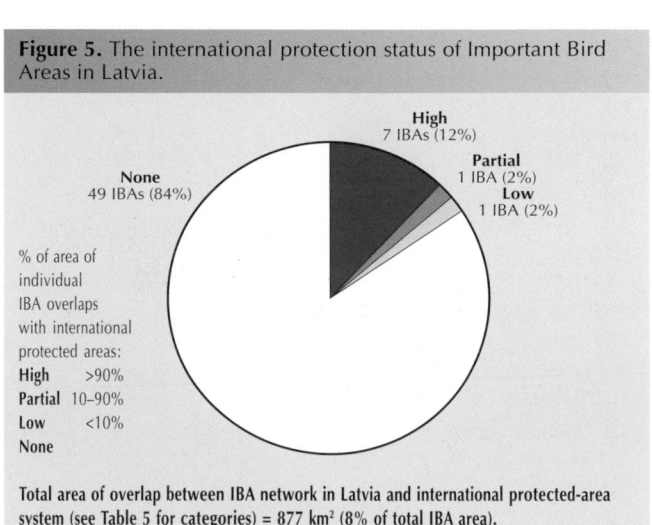

None
19 IBAs (33%)

High
13 IBAs (22%)

% of area of individual IBA overlaps with national protected areas:
High   >90%
Partial 10–90%
Low   <10%
None

Low
5 IBAs (9%)

Partial
21 IBAs (36%)

Total area of overlap between IBA network in Latvia and national protected-area system (see Table 5 for categories) = 1,332–1,557 km² (12–14% of total IBA area).

Figure 5. The international protection status of Important Bird Areas in Latvia.

High
7 IBAs (12%)

Partial
1 IBA (2%)
Low
1 IBA (2%)

None
49 IBAs (84%)

% of area of individual IBA overlaps with international protected areas:
High   >90%
Partial 10–90%
Low   <10%
None

Total area of overlap between IBA network in Latvia and international protected-area system (see Table 5 for categories) = 877 km² (8% of total IBA area).

421

Table 5. Protection status of Important Bird Areas in Latvia. A tick (✔) indicates that an IBA overlaps with a protected area (to any extent).

IBA code	International name	Nature Reserve	National Park	Restricted Nature Territory	Ramsar Site	Biosphere Reserve
		National			International	
001	Nida bog			✔		
002	Pape lake			✔		
003	Dunika bog			✔		
004	Liepaja lake			✔		
005	Latvia, west coast					
006	Durbe lake					
007	Skrunda fish-ponds					
008	Uzava river meadows			✔		
009	Kamburi meadows					
010	Kuldiga forest area			✔		
011	Sarnate bogs			✔		
012	Uzava lowland					
013	Irbe river valley and Lielais Ances bog			✔		
014	Irbe strait					
015	Slitere Nature Reserve	✔				
016	Ilini			✔		
017	Spare lake					
018	Gulf of Riga, west coast					
019	Lielais Kemeru bog		✔	✔		
020	Lake Engure			✔	✔	
021	Lake Kanieris		✔	✔	✔	
022	Babite lake			✔		
023	Satini fish-ponds			✔		
024	Zvarde forest area			✔		
025	Lielauce lake			✔		
026	Ukri forest area			✔		
027	Lielupe river flood-plain meadows			✔		
028	Svete river mouth					
029	Kalnciems meadows and wet forest		✔			
030	Cena bog			✔		
031	Liela Jugla river mouth					
032	Sudas bog	✔	✔			
033	Lielais and Pemmas bogs			✔		
034	Gulf of Riga, east coast					✔
035	Madiesenu bog and Augstroze			✔		✔
036	Kapzemes, Ollu and Pirtsmeza bogs			✔		✔
037	Ruja fish-ponds					✔
038	Burtnieks lake			✔		✔
039	Seda marsh			✔		✔
040	Zile forest area			✔		
041	Cirgali meadows					
042	Gaujiena bogs and forests			✔		
043	Panemune forest area					
044	Daugava river at Kaibala					
045	Lobe lake area			✔		
046	Daudzeva bog and fish-ponds			✔		
047	Zalve forest area			✔		
048	Abeli forest area			✔		
049	Dviete area					
050	Teici and Pelecare bogs	✔		✔	✔	
051	Aiviekste river flood-plain meadows					
052	Lubans lake and fish-ponds			✔		
053	Baltie Klani marshes and adjoining bogs			✔		
054	Pededze river forests and Parabaine			✔		
055	Pededze and Sita flood-plain					
056	Katlesi forest area					
057	Stampaku, Murnieku and Orlovas bogs			✔		
058	Zabolotje bog			✔		
Total number of IBAs		3	4	36	3	6

Box 1. International legislation and initiatives that are relevant to site conservation in Latvia (see Appendix 1 for a general description of these agreements).

Global	
Biodiversity Convention	✔
Ramsar Convention	✔
Bonn Convention	✔
World Heritage Convention	✔
MAB Programme	✔
Pan-European	
Bern Convention	✔
Regional	
Helsinki Convention	✔

✔ Convention ratified/initiative supported
(✔) Convention signed

Under the 1993 law, five Nature Reserves, two National Parks, 11 Nature Parks and one Biosphere Reserve have been designated in Latvia so far. The exact number of other currently existing or planned designations is not clear. Many Restricted Nature Territories are new and not yet officially designated. The full list of protected nature areas in Latvia will be enforced by a new law in summer 1998. Before the ongoing revision of the protected-area system, in 1991, there were 189 sites of the 'Restricted Nature Territory' type, six 'Landscape Territories' and 271 'Natural Monuments'. Protected areas (all types of designations) are said to cover 6.2–6.8% of the total territory of Latvia, according to various sources. In any case, the percentage ranks as the lowest among the three Baltic states.

For the purpose of this review, 'draft' protected areas (not yet designated) have been included in the site accounts (and not distinguished from designated areas), although some changes in size or even status may yet occur. If this had not been done, the overall national protection status of IBAs in Latvia would have been greatly underestimated.

Protected areas were traditionally owned by the state or by local government. However, large proportions of land within these areas have been privatized in recent years, with ownership transferred to physical persons or legal entities. These privately-owned areas pose major problems for conservation and management. To date, no nature-conservation areas are owned by non-governmental bodies.

The responsibility for nature conservation at the state level lies with the Nature Protection Division of the Ministry of Environmental Protection and Regional Development. Supervision and enforcement is a task of the State Environmental Inspectorate, the Flora and Fauna Division, and eight Regional Environmental Boards.

■ International protection

Latvia has ratified a number of international conventions (see Box 1). There are three designated Ramsar Sites, with a further nine on a 'shadow list' of potential sites. Four marine Baltic Sea Protection Areas (BSPAs) have been identified under the Helsinki Convention but still have no legal status.

Three IBAs overlap fully with the designated Ramsar Sites, covering a total area of 43,300 ha, or about 14% of the total non-marine area of IBAs (Figure 5, Table 5). An approximately similar proportion of the IBA area also has some international status through overlap with Biosphere Reserves (Figure 5, Table 5).

CONSERVATION

- Few IBAs are covered by bird-monitoring schemes. The longest running and most comprehensive research and monitoring scheme is run at Lake Engure (020) by the Laboratory of Ornithology of the Institute of Biology (Viksne 1997). Monitoring is a duty of the scientific staff at state Nature Reserves (three IBAs: 015, 032 and 050). The four marine IBAs are covered by regular mid-winter waterbird counts.
- About 30 sites (mostly protected IBAs) have been covered by short-term faunistic surveys. There are only irregular visits to, and casual observation data for, the rest of the sites (nearly one third of all IBAs).
- The concept of individual site-management plans for protected areas is still new in Latvia, though developing. Only

26% of IBAs (15 sites, or at least their protected parts) have management plans.

ANALYTICAL METHODS

- The present IBA project took the existing national IBA inventory (Viksne 1994) and protected areas network, and improved the knowledge base through literature and map searches, requests for data, and fieldwork. New sites were thus identified, and visited in the field so as to make counts of relevant species (e.g. *Crex crex*), check boundaries, threats, etc. Countrywide bird counts and requests for information were organized, so as to obtain additional data on spring congregations of staging *Cygnus cygnus* and *Cygnus columbianus*, and on gathering points for *Grus grus* and on the stop-over sites of *Anser fabalis* and *Anser albifrons* in autumn.

- Except where otherwise stated, counts of staging birds on migration (such as swans *Cygnus*, geese *Anser*, etc.) are given as the average number of individuals (minimum/maximum) that have been counted using the site at any one time, i.e. during one day or over a longer period, and counts are not given as seasonal totals.

- It should be noted that the protection status of the IBAs has been assigned only provisionally, since it is based on a new draft list of protected areas that has not yet been officially ratified.

ACKNOWLEDGEMENTS

Providing data, advice and valuable comments to the IBA project were Dr Janis Viksne, Antra Stipniece (Laboratory of Ornithology of the Institute of Biology), Dr Janis Priednieks, Dr Otars Opermanis, Aivars Petrins, Elga Strazdina (Faculty of Biology of the University of Latvia, and Latvian Fund for Nature) and Maris Strazds (Latvian Ornithological Society). The outcome of the project is also a credit to many more experts and fieldworkers: Ainars Aunins, Andris Avotins, Ilmars Bauga, Dr Janis Baumanis, Ugis Bergmanis, Arnis Berzins, D. Grundulis, Rudite Hahele, Dr Mara Janaus, Zigrida Jansone, Martins Kalnins, Aigars Kalvans, Juris Kazubiernis, Oskars Keiss, Maris Kreilis, Janis Kuze, Viesturs Larmanis, Rolands Lebuss, A. Leilands, Andis Liepa, Dr Juris Lipsbergs, Maris Maskalans, Ruslans Matrozis, Gints Malkalnietis, K. Millers, Inga Poznaka, Janis Stomers, Agris Strazds, Gvido Sviklis, M. Upeniece, Gundars Vaverins, Ilze Vilka, Viesturs Vintulis, N. Zeidaks and Normunds Zommers.

The IBA project was financially supported by the Swedish Ornithological Society (SOF; the BirdLife Partner in Sweden) and in part by the BirdLife Secretariat, owing to voluntary coordination by Lars Lindell, Lennart Carlsson and Hakan Ortman (SOF). The tireless efforts of Melanie Heath, Zoltan Waliczky and their colleagues at the BirdLife Secretariat, both through correspondence and through organization of valuable workshops, have helped the Latvian IBA project to strengthen its organizational and theoretical basis. And finally, many thanks to Maris Strazds for work guidance and continuous help, as well as for commenting on and correcting the text of the overview.

■ SITE ACCOUNTS

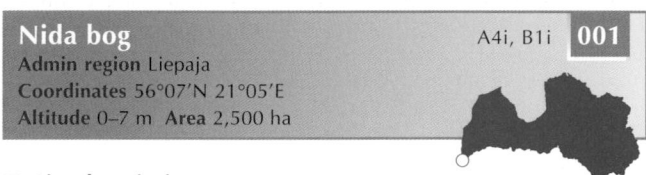

Nida bog   A4i, B1i 001
Admin region Liepaja
Coordinates 56°07′N 21°05′E
Altitude 0–7 m **Area** 2,500 ha

■ Site description
An open raised bog, surrounded by transitional mire, fen and wet forest, and separated from the Baltic Sea by a narrow strip of sand-dunes overgrown with pines *Pinus*. Land-uses are cranberry *Vaccinium* collection, hunting and peat extraction in part of the bog.

Habitats Forest and woodland (alluvial/very wet forest), Wetland (sand-dunes/sand beach; raised bog; fen/transition mire/spring)
Land-use Forestry, Hunting, Nature conservation/research, Urban/industrial/transport

■ Birds

Species	Season	Year	Pop min	Pop max	Acc	Criteria
Anser fabalis Bean Goose	P	—	Abundant		—	A4i, B1i
Anser albifrons White-fronted Goose	P	—	Abundant		—	B1i

Millions of birds migrate through a narrow belt along the sea coast each autumn and the site is a crucial staging spot for geese before they cross the Baltic Sea. Thousands of *Anser fabalis* and *A. albifrons* occur in mixed flocks in autumn and numbers are thought to exceed, by a wide margin, 1% or more of flyway population size for both species, and also probably to exceed 1% or more of biogeographic population size for *A. fabalis*, although targeted counts are needed. A survey of *Acrocephalus paludicola* is planned.

■ Protection status
National Partial **International** None
1,970 ha of IBA covered by Restricted Nature Territory (Nida Bog, 1,970 ha).

■ Conservation issues

Threats Disturbance to birds (U), Drainage (U), Extraction industry (U), Intensified forest management (U)

Peat extraction and drainage are the main threats. Hunting of migratory birds (geese) in autumn causes disturbance to birds, but may be banned. Coastal-zone regulations protect the shoreline from development to some extent. This IBA and the nearby Pape lake (site 002) are included on the national 'shadow list' of Ramsar Sites, and WWF produced a management plan for this combined area in 1996.

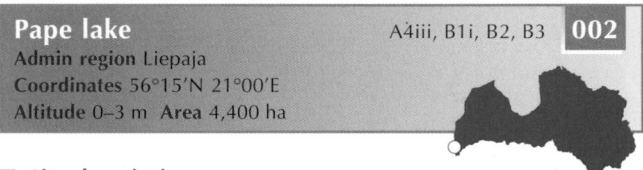

Pape lake   A4iii, B1i, B2, B3 002
Admin region Liepaja
Coordinates 56°15′N 21°00′E
Altitude 0–3 m **Area** 4,400 ha

■ Site description
A shallow coastal lake, richly overgrown with *Phragmites*, *Typha*, *Scirpus* and surrounded by *Carex* meadows. An artificial channel connects the lake with the Baltic Sea. The lake is used for fishing and hunting.

Habitats Forest and woodland (mixed forest), Scrub (scrub), Grassland (humid grassland; mesophile grassland), Wetland (sand-dunes/sand beach; standing fresh water)
Land-use Agriculture, Forestry, Hunting, Nature conservation/research

■ Birds

Species	Season	Year	Pop min	Pop max	Acc	Criteria
Botaurus stellaris Bittern	B	—	8	20	—	B2
Cygnus cygnus Whooper Swan	P	—	500	500	A	B1i
Grus grus Crane	P	—	300	500	B	B1i
Acrocephalus scirpaceus Reed Warbler	B	—	300	500	—	B3

The site holds 20,000 or more waterbirds on a regular basis, and hundreds of thousands (perhaps millions) of landbirds (diurnal raptors, owls, pigeons and passerines) migrate through the area in a narrow and well-defined stream (between the east coast of the lake and the seashore), mainly in autumn. Mixed flocks of up to 1,000 *Anser fabalis/A. albifrons* occur on autumn passage. Species of global conservation concern that do not meet IBA criteria: *Anser erythropus* (on passage), *Haliaeetus albicilla* (non-breeding), *Crex crex* (breeding), *Acrocephalus paludicola* (status unknown).

■ Protection status
National Partial **International** None
1,205 ha of IBA covered by Restricted Nature Territory (Pape, 1,205 ha).

■ Conservation issues

Threats Abandonment/reduction of land management (U), Disturbance to birds (U), Recreation/tourism (U)

Coastal-zone regulations protect the shoreline from development to some extent. Pape Reserve was established in 1977. This IBA and the nearby Nida bog (site 001) are included on the national 'shadow list' of Ramsar Sites, and WWF produced a management plan for this combined area in 1996.

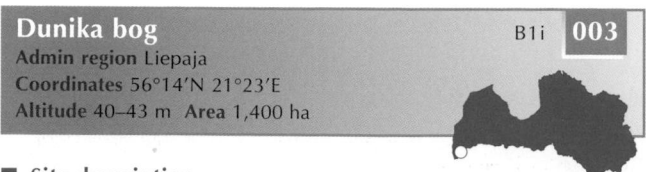

Dunika bog
Admin region Liepaja
Coordinates 56°14′N 21°23′E
Altitude 40–43 m **Area** 1,400 ha

B1i 003

■ Site description

A large, open raised bog with natural forest, small lakes and several islands. Unaffected by drainage, the bog is used for cranberry *Vaccinium* collection and for hunting.

Habitats Forest and woodland (mixed forest), Wetland (raised bog)
Land-use Forestry, Hunting

■ Birds

Species	Season	Year	Pop min	Pop max	Acc	Criteria
[1] *Anser fabalis* Bean Goose	P	—	—	—	—	B1i

1. See main text.

The area is thought to be an important stop-over and resting site for migrating geese *Anser fabalis/A. albifrons* and *Grus grus* in autumn. However, there are no recent counts, and further surveys are needed.

■ Protection status

National High **International** None
1,400 ha of IBA covered by Restricted Nature Territory (Dunika, c.1,500 ha).

■ Conservation issues

Threats Disturbance to birds (U), Drainage (U), Extraction industry (U), Intensified forest management (U)

The main threat is peat extraction. The site was first designated as a protected area in 1977.

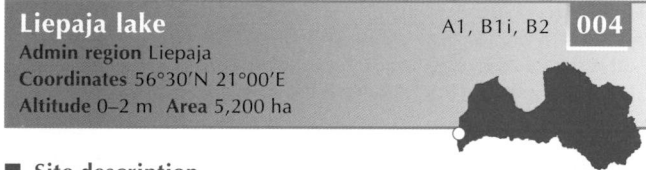

Liepaja lake
Admin region Liepaja
Coordinates 56°30′N 21°00′E
Altitude 0–2 m **Area** 5,200 ha

A1, B1i, B2 004

■ Site description

A shallow eutrophic coastal lake with extensive areas of emergent vegetation (*Phragmites*, *Typha*, *Scirpus*, *Sparganium*), surrounded by seasonally-flooded meadows and arable land. The lake is used for yachting, commercial and leisure fishing, and hunting.

Habitats Scrub (scrub), Grassland (humid grassland; mesophile grassland), Wetland (standing fresh water; water-fringe vegetation; fen/transition mire/spring), Artificial landscape (arable land)
Land-use Agriculture, Fisheries/aquaculture, Hunting, Tourism/recreation

■ Birds

Species	Season	Year	Pop min	Pop max	Acc	Criteria
Cygnus olor Mute Swan	W	1990	—	2,400	—	B1i
[1] *Cygnus cygnus* Whooper Swan	P	—	Common		—	B1i
Crex crex Corncrake	B	—	20	50	—	A1
Chlidonias niger Black Tern	B	—	100	100	C	B2

1. Hundreds in spring.

An important breeding site for *Crex crex* and for breeding and migrating waterbirds, as well as for thousands of moulting dabbling ducks, and up to 2,400 *Cygnus olor* in mild winters. The IBA supports the only remaining breeding population of *Calidris alpina schinzii* in Latvia, and the globally near-threatened *Gallinago media* also breeds.

■ Protection status

National Partial **International** None
About 4,500 ha of IBA covered by Restricted Nature Territory (Liepaja Lake, c.4,500 ha).

■ Conservation issues

Threats Agricultural intensification/expansion (U), Disturbance to birds (U), Drainage (U), Filling-in of wetlands (U), Industrialization/urbanization (U), Recreation/tourism (U)

The area is threatened by urban development (from Liepaja town) along the coast, downgrading of protection status, increased human disturbance, and pollution by industrial effluent, sewage and agricultural run-off. It is included on the national 'shadow list' of Ramsar Sites.

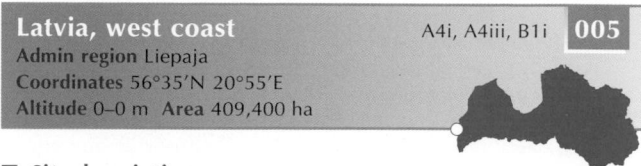

Latvia, west coast
Admin region Liepaja
Coordinates 56°35′N 20°55′E
Altitude 0–0 m **Area** 409,400 ha

A4i, A4iii, B1i 005

■ Site description

Coastal waters of the Baltic Sea from Nida (on the Lithuanian border) to Pavilosta, extending offshore up to 30 m depth.

Habitats Wetland (sand-dunes/sand beach), Marine areas (open sea; sea inlet/coastal features)
Land-use Urban/industrial/transport, Unknown

■ Birds

Species	Season	Year	Pop min	Pop max	Acc	Criteria
Mergus merganser Goosander	W	—	10,000	—	—	A4i, B1i

The site holds 20,000 or more waterbirds on a regular basis, and is an important wintering area for *Mergus merganser* and for divers *Gavia*, and possibly for *Clangula hyemalis* and *Mergus serrator*. Concentrated streams of migrating seabirds and waterbirds fly non-stop along the coast in spring and can be counted from the shore. A total of c.130,000 birds were counted at sea in spring 1989, including (seasonal totals in brackets) *Gavia stellata* (2,480), *G. arctica* (1,176), *Gavia* sp. (3,027), *Anas crecca* (9,072), *Aythya marila* (13,952; up to 2,139 passing per day), *Melanitta fusca* (21,385; up to 3,342 per day), *Clangula hyemalis* (45,140; up to 6,520 per day) and *Mergus serrator* (1,349).

■ Protection status

National None **International** None

■ Conservation issues

Threats Disturbance to birds (U), Industrialization/urbanization (U), Other (U)

The area is mainly threatened by disturbance and pollution from marine traffic ('Other' threat, above) and coastal sources, such as the expanding Butinge oil terminal just across the border in Lithuania. Coastal-zone regulations protect the shoreline from development to some extent. The site includes a proposed/prospective Baltic Sea Protection Area (the Pape–Perkone stretch).

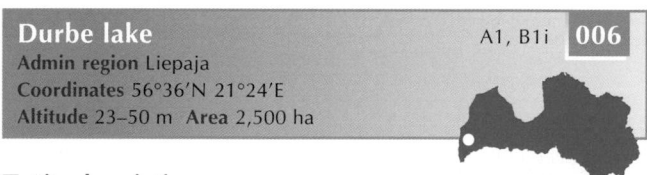

Durbe lake
Admin region Liepaja
Coordinates 56°36′N 21°24′E
Altitude 23–50 m **Area** 2,500 ha

A1, B1i 006

■ Site description

Durbe lake (area 670 ha, mean depth 1.5 m) is rich in emergent vegetation, being eutrophic and with low banks. The IBA extends to meadows along the tributaries of the Lanupe and Trumpe rivers and includes several fish-ponds (20–50 ha). Natural habitat diversity is high. The lake lies near Durbe town and is surrounded by several small villages and numerous farmsteads, with land mostly used for agriculture and pasture. The lake is rich in fish and is used for fishing and recreation.

Habitats Scrub (scrub), Grassland (humid grassland; mesophile grassland), Wetland (standing fresh water; river/stream; water-fringe vegetation), Artificial landscape (arable land)
Land-use Agriculture, Fisheries/aquaculture, Hunting

■ Birds

Species	Season	Year	Pop min	Pop max	Acc	Criteria
[1] *Cygnus cygnus* Whooper Swan	P	1997	300	500	—	B1i
[2] *Anser fabalis* Bean Goose	P	—	Abundant		—	B1i
Crex crex Corncrake	B	—	20	—	—	A1

1. May include some *C. columbianus*.
2. 2,500 in autumn 1996 (may include some *A. albifrons*).

An important resting place for migrating waterbirds, especially for geese in autumn (reported to be regular; mostly *Anser fabalis* but possibly mixed with *A. albifrons*) and for *Cygnus cygnus* in spring. Migrating ducks, *Grus grus*, waders and gulls also rest in good numbers on passage, and the meadows hold breeding *Crex crex*.

■ Protection status
National None **International** None

■ Conservation issues

Threats Agricultural intensification/expansion (U), Disturbance to birds (U)

The mean water-level of Durbe lake was lowered (from 3.9 m) around 1930. The site has been little investigated.

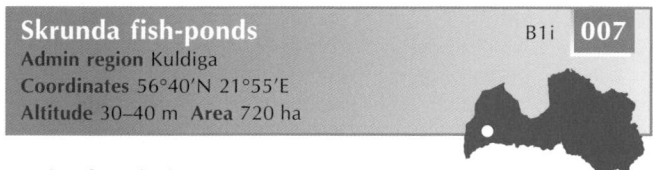

Skrunda fish-ponds
B1i 007
Admin region Kuldiga
Coordinates 56°40'N 21°55'E
Altitude 30–40 m **Area** 720 ha

■ Site description
Fish-ponds set in an open landscape with mixed forest. The area is used for fish-farming, agriculture, forestry, and hunting.

Habitats Forest and woodland (mixed forest), Scrub (scrub), Wetland (standing fresh water; water-fringe vegetation), Artificial landscape (arable land)
Land-use Agriculture, Fisheries/aquaculture, Forestry, Hunting

■ Birds

Species	Season	Year	Pop min	Pop max	Acc	Criteria
[1] *Cygnus cygnus* Whooper Swan	P	—	Abundant		—	B1i
[2] *Cygnus cygnus* Whooper Swan	N	1995	—	500	—	B1i

1. Hundreds in spring.
2. Post-breeding congregation.

The site is important for migrating waterbirds, especially *Cygnus cygnus*, and also supports a wide variety of breeding and migratory waterbirds. Species of global conservation concern that do not meet IBA criteria: *Haliaeetus albicilla* (non-breeding), *Crex crex* (breeding).

■ Protection status
National None **International** None

■ Conservation issues

Threats Disturbance to birds (U), Filling-in of wetlands (U)

Disturbance to birds is a threat. The site is listed as data-deficient in a recent review of actual and potential Ramsar Sites in Latvia.

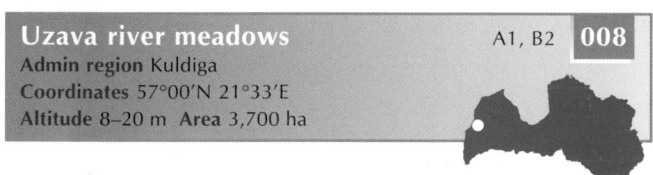

Uzava river meadows
A1, B2 008
Admin region Kuldiga
Coordinates 57°00'N 21°33'E
Altitude 8–20 m **Area** 3,700 ha

■ Site description
A rather narrow (up to 3 km) and elongated (22 km) belt of both natural and managed (cultivated) flood-plain meadows along the Uzava river. The area is bordered by extensive forests, and is used for low-intensity agriculture (arable, grass meadows and grazing).

Habitats Scrub (scrub), Grassland (humid grassland; mesophile grassland), Wetland (river/stream)
Land-use Agriculture, Hunting

■ Birds

Species	Season	Year	Pop min	Pop max	Acc	Criteria
Crex crex Corncrake	B	1996	20	50	—	A1, B2

The meadows are important for breeding *Crex crex*.

■ Protection status
National Low **International** None

140 ha of IBA covered by Restricted Nature Territory (Dillu meadows, 140 ha).

■ Conservation issues

Threats Abandonment/reduction of land management (U), Agricultural intensification/expansion (U), Drainage (U)

The site has been visited by ornithologists since 1996.

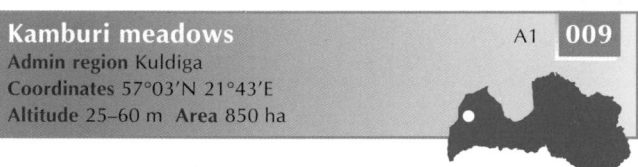

Kamburi meadows
A1 009
Admin region Kuldiga
Coordinates 57°03'N 21°43'E
Altitude 25–60 m **Area** 850 ha

■ Site description
An area of drained fen, now managed as meadows, with small channelized streams, and surrounded by forest. The land is privately owned, and used mainly for low-intensity grazing and haymaking.

Habitats Forest and woodland (mixed forest), Grassland (mesophile grassland), Wetland (river/stream)
Land-use Agriculture

■ Birds

Species	Season	Year	Pop min	Pop max	Acc	Criteria
Crex crex Corncrake	B	1996	25	30	—	A1

Conditions are favourable for breeding *Crex crex*.

■ Protection status
National None **International** None

■ Conservation issues

Threats Abandonment/reduction of land management (U), Agricultural intensification/expansion (U)

Human activities have been reduced in some areas in recent years, leading to overgrowth of meadows by scrub.

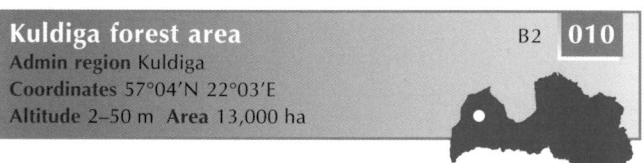

Kuldiga forest area
B2 010
Admin region Kuldiga
Coordinates 57°04'N 22°03'E
Altitude 2–50 m **Area** 13,000 ha

■ Site description
A vast area of mixed forests, mainly *Pinus* and *Picea* with *Populus tremula* and *Betula*, and with several small mires. Due to the high density of Eurasian beavers *Castor fiber*, even formerly drained stands of forest are now wetter than before. The area is bordered by the Venta river and its tributary the Abava to the west and north.

Habitats Forest and woodland (mixed forest; alluvial/very wet forest), Wetland (river/stream; fen/transition mire/spring)
Land-use Forestry, Hunting

■ Birds

Species	Season	Year	Pop min	Pop max	Acc	Criteria
Ciconia nigra Black Stork	B	1993	10	10	—	B2
Aquila pomarina Lesser Spotted Eagle	B	—	5	10	—	B2
Pandion haliaetus Osprey	B	1993	3	4	—	B2
Alcedo atthis Kingfisher	B	1994	20	—	—	B2

The area supports a high diversity of breeding species of forest and mire, with important numbers of several species. *Alcedo atthis* breeds at particularly high density on the bordering rivers.

■ Protection status
National Partial **International** None
1,800 ha of IBA covered by Restricted Nature Territory (Mangene forest, 1,800 ha).

Conservation issues

Threats Disturbance to birds (U), Drainage (U), Intensified forest management (U)

The site is threatened by the felling of older forest stands. A management plan will be produced by the Latvian Ornithological Society in 1998.

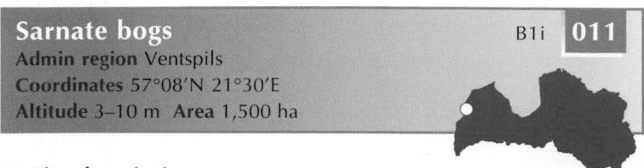

Sarnate bogs   B1i **011**
Admin region Ventspils
Coordinates 57°08'N 21°30'E
Altitude 3–10 m **Area** 1,500 ha

Site description
Two raised bogs and a shallow, overgrown lake with wet coastal meadows. The area includes mixed woodland with *Juniperus* bushes.

Habitats Forest and woodland (mixed forest), Grassland (humid grassland), Wetland (standing fresh water; raised bog; water-fringe vegetation)
Land-use Forestry, Hunting, Nature conservation/research

Birds

Species	Season	Year	Pop min	Pop max	Acc	Criteria
Anser fabalis Bean Goose	P	—	Common		—	B1i
¹ **Grus grus** Crane	P	—	—	—	—	B1i

1. Hundreds gather in autumn.

An important site for migrating geese and *Grus grus*. Species of global conservation concern that do not meet IBA criteria: *Crex crex* (breeding), *Acrocephalus paludicola* (status unknown).

Protection status
National Partial **International** None
About 1,100 ha of IBA covered by Restricted Nature Territory (Sarnate bogs, c.1,100 ha).

Conservation issues

Threats Drainage (U)

The adjoining land has been drained for agriculture and forestry. The reserve was designated in 1987. WWF produced a management plan for the Jurkalne area, which includes this IBA, in 1996.

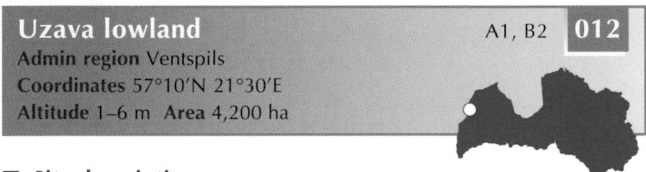

Uzava lowland   A1, B2 **012**
Admin region Ventspils
Coordinates 57°10'N 21°30'E
Altitude 1–6 m **Area** 4,200 ha

Site description
The flood-plain of the Uzava river, once a vast area of fen and water-meadows, but now considerably modified due to drainage projects. Among the fields and embankments are wet grasslands with shrub-lined ditches and remaining oxbow lakes, which overall still provide important breeding habitat for meadow birds. The area floods in spring.

Habitats Grassland (humid grassland), Wetland (standing fresh water)
Land-use Agriculture

Birds

Species	Season	Year	Pop min	Pop max	Acc	Criteria
Crex crex Corncrake	B	1996	40	60	B	A1, B2

One of the best areas for breeding *Crex crex* in Latvia. Before the area was drained, the Uzava lowlands were of outstanding importance for migrating *Grus grus*, which used to gather in flocks of thousands in autumn. A few hundred *Grus grus* still stop over in autumn, together with migrating geese, ducks and swans (including *Cygnus cygnus* and *C. columbianus*).

Protection status
National None **International** None

Conservation issues

Threats Abandonment/reduction of land management (U), Agricultural intensification/expansion (U)

The site is listed as data-deficient in a recent review of actual and potential Ramsar Sites in Latvia. A detailed ornithological survey is needed.

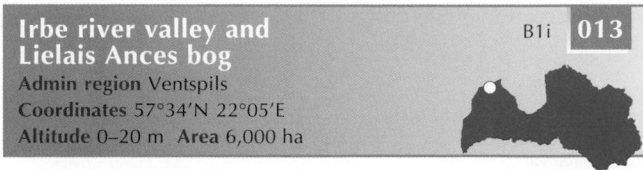

Irbe river valley and   B1i **013**
Lielais Ances bog
Admin region Ventspils
Coordinates 57°34'N 22°05'E
Altitude 0–20 m **Area** 6,000 ha

Site description
A raised bog with forested sandy islands and peninsulas, surrounded by vast *Pinus* forests. There are several long and narrow lakes among forested sand-dunes. The valley of the Irbe river has many oxbow lakes, broadleaved forests and meadows with a natural flooding regime. Land-uses were strictly controlled by the Soviet military regime in former decades (since the IBA lay near the border of the USSR), and thus the habitats have been relatively unaffected by man.

Habitats Forest and woodland (broadleaved deciduous forest; mixed forest; alluvial/very wet forest), Scrub (scrub), Grassland (mesophile grassland), Wetland (sand-dunes/sand beach; river/stream; raised bog; fen/transition mire/spring)
Land-use Forestry, Hunting, Nature conservation/research

Birds

Species	Season	Year	Pop min	Pop max	Acc	Criteria
¹ **Anser fabalis** Bean Goose	P	—	—	—	—	B1i
¹ **Anser albifrons** White-fronted Goose	P	—	—	—	—	B1i

1. No counts, but numbers thought to be significant.

The site is an important staging area for migrating geese (*Anser fabalis* and *A. albifrons*) and probably for *Grus grus* and ducks. The breeding avifauna is rich, including *Ciconia nigra*, *Aquila pomarina*, *Pandion haliaetus*, *Grus grus*, *Tetrao urogallus* (at high density), *Dendrocopos leucotos*, *Picoides tridactylus* and *Bucephala clangula*. There are unverified reports (without supporting counts) of concentrations of *Grus grus* in the area in autumn, and of high numbers of waterbirds (mainly ducks) gathering on the flood-plain during spring migration. Species of global conservation concern that do not meet IBA criteria: *Gallinago media* (status unknown).

Protection status
National Partial **International** None
About 5,000 ha of IBA covered by Restricted Nature Territory (name not known, c.5,000 ha).

Conservation issues

Threats Abandonment/reduction of land management (U), Disturbance to birds (U), Intensified forest management (U)

The main threat is the logging of forests. It is planned to convert this site, together with Slitere Nature Reserve (015), into a National Park with Restricted Nature Territories as core areas. The site was investigated by biologists in 1993–1994 and has been visited almost annually since then.

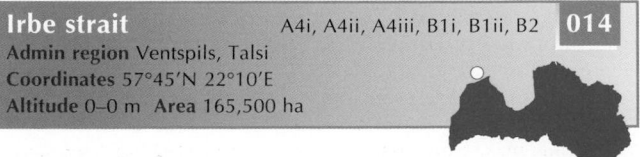

Irbe strait   A4i, A4ii, A4iii, B1i, B1ii, B2 **014**
Admin region Ventspils, Talsi
Coordinates 57°45'N 22°10'E
Altitude 0–0 m **Area** 165,500 ha

Site description
The strait connects the Gulf of Riga to the open Baltic Sea. It comprises the coastal waters lying between Ovisi village and Cape Kolka, and extending from the shore of Kurzeme county to the offshore border with Estonia. Sand and gravel are the main bottom sediments. The benthic fauna is dominated by shellfish *Macoma*. The main marine-

traffic routes from the Baltic Sea to Estonian and Latvian ports in the Gulf of Riga pass through the strait.

Habitats Wetland (sand-dunes/sand beach), Marine areas (open sea; sea inlet/coastal features)
Land-use Urban/industrial/transport, Unknown

■ Birds

Species	Season	Year	Pop min	Pop max	Acc	Criteria
[1] *Gavia stellata* Red-throated Diver	W	—	—	—	—	A4i, B1i
[1] *Gavia arctica* Black-throated Diver	W	—	—	—	—	A4i, B1i
Clangula hyemalis Long-tailed Duck	W	—	Abundant	—	A4i, B1i
Melanitta fusca Velvet Scoter	W	—	Abundant	—	A4i, B1i, B2
[1] *Cepphus grylle* Black Guillemot	W	—	—	—	—	A4ii, B1ii

1. See main text.

The strait supports internationally important concentrations of several seabirds in winter, e.g. *Gavia stellata*, *G. arctica*, *Clangula hyemalis*, *Melanitta fusca* and *Cepphus grylle*. There are also large concentrations of *Mergus serrator* and *M. merganser*. Species of global conservation concern that do not meet IBA criteria: *Haliaeetus albicilla* (wintering).

■ Protection status
National None **International** None

■ Conservation issues

Threats Disturbance to birds (U), Industrialization/urbanization (U), Other (U)

The area is threatened by disturbance and pollution from marine traffic ('Other' threat, above) and coastal sources, since prevailing currents reach from as far as the expanding Butinge oil terminal just across the border in Lithuania, or even from Kaliningrad (Russia). Coastal-zone regulations protect the shoreline from development to some extent. Part of this site (from Lielirbe to Kolka) has been proposed as a Baltic Sea Protection Area. The site should be managed as an integral part of the entire Irbe strait, not as an area separate from the Estonian part.

Slitere Nature Reserve
A4iv, B1iv, B2 **015**
Admin region Talsi
Coordinates 57°42′N 22°27′E
Altitude 0–120 m **Area** 15,517 ha

■ Site description
There is a wide variety of habitats, including sand beach, sand-dunes, a mosaic of *Pinus* woodland and fens, a raised bog (Bazu), and rich broadleaved forest (*Fraxinus*, *Acer*, *Ulmus*, *Tilia*) on the ancient raised coast and inland plain.

Habitats Forest and woodland (native coniferous forest; mixed forest; alluvial/very wet forest), Grassland (humid grassland; mesophile grassland), Wetland (sand-dunes/sand beach; river/stream; raised bog; fen/transition mire/spring)
Land-use Forestry, Hunting, Nature conservation/research, Tourism/recreation

■ Birds

Species	Season	Year	Pop min	Pop max	Acc	Criteria
Caprimulgus europaeus Nightjar	B	—	200	300	—	B2

One of the most important areas for bird conservation in Latvia, and the most distinct bottleneck site for migrating birds in the country, both in spring and autumn. A unique diversity of breeding birds occur at high densities, including waterbirds, raptors, and characteristic species of forest, mire and coast. The Irbe strait and Cape Kolka form a migratory bottleneck site with seasonal concentrations of waterbirds and over 20,000 raptors, c.22,000 *Columba palumbus*, and hundreds of thousands of passerines passing in total. Species of global conservation concern that do not meet IBA criteria: *Haliaeetus albicilla* (wintering; max. 5 on passage), *Aquila clanga* (1–2 breeding pairs in the past, but no recent records of breeding), *Crex crex* (6–10 breeding pairs), *Gallinago media* (on passage).

■ Protection status
National High **International** None
15,037 ha of IBA covered by Nature Reserve (Slitere, 15,037 ha).

■ Conservation issues

Threats Disturbance to birds (U), Infrastructure (U), Intensified forest management (U), Recreation/tourism (U)

The main threat is posed by the likely downgrading of the nature reserve to the level of national park, which may result in the development of recreation, tourism and related infrastructure. The area has been a reserve since 1921 and has experienced almost no human activities for 70 years; it is covered by a management plan. It is considered one of the richest areas for nature conservation in Latvia or even in the entire Baltic region, with high scientific, historical, and landscape value. The fauna and flora have been well investigated.

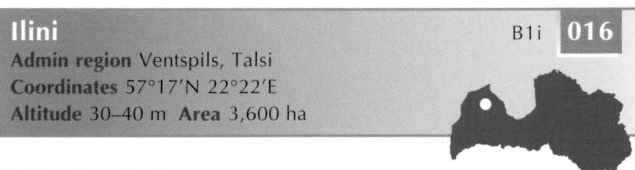

Ilini
B1i **016**
Admin region Ventspils, Talsi
Coordinates 57°17′N 22°22′E
Altitude 30–40 m **Area** 3,600 ha

■ Site description
This remote and little-populated area is situated at the edge of a vast tract of forest and bog. Habitats in the IBA include agricultural land, forest and a small raised bog.

Habitats Forest and woodland (mixed forest), Wetland (river/stream; raised bog), Artificial landscape (arable land)
Land-use Agriculture, Forestry, Hunting

■ Birds

Species	Season	Year	Pop min	Pop max	Acc	Criteria
[1] *Grus grus* Crane	P	1984	1,000	1,000	—	B1i

1. Reported to stage regularly in autumn.

An important area for *Grus grus* staging on migration and for breeding *Crex crex*. After recent land-use changes (fields abandoned or set aside), the number of *Crex crex* may now exceed 30–50 pairs, while *Grus grus* may have temporarily shifted its staging grounds elsewhere.

■ Protection status
National Partial **International** None
About 700 ha of IBA covered by Restricted Nature Territory (Stiklu bogs, c.7,000 ha).

■ Conservation issues

Threats Abandonment/reduction of land management (U), Agricultural intensification/expansion (U), Disturbance to birds (U), Drainage (U), Extraction industry (U), Intensified forest management (U)

The site requires further detailed ornithological studies, together with the adjacent Restricted Nature Territory.

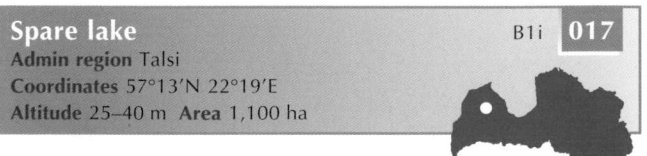

Spare lake
B1i **017**
Admin region Talsi
Coordinates 57°13′N 22°19′E
Altitude 25–40 m **Area** 1,100 ha

■ Site description
A lake near Spare village with adjoining forests and agricultural land. The lake is rich in emergent vegetation.

Habitats Forest and woodland (mixed forest), Wetland (standing fresh water; river/stream), Artificial landscape (arable land)
Land-use Agriculture, Forestry, Hunting

■ Birds

Species	Season	Year	Pop min	Pop max	Acc	Criteria
Anser fabalis Bean Goose	P	1996	Abundant	—	B1i

The lake is reported to be a regular roosting site for thousands of geese (*Anser fabalis* and *A. albifrons*) on autumn passage.

■ **Protection status**
National None **International** None

■ **Conservation issues**

Threats Disturbance to birds (U)

The site needs further ornithological survey.

Gulf of Riga, west coast — A4i, A4iii, B1i, B2 | 018
Admin region Talsi, Tukums
Coordinates 57°22′N 23°09′E
Altitude 0–0 m **Area** 102,800 ha

■ **Site description**
A stretch of coastal waters within the Gulf of Riga, from Cape Kolka to the village of Lapmezciems, and extending offshore to 30 m depth. Bottom sediments are sandy with many shellfish, especially bivalves *Macoma*, while in deeper waters (>40 m depth) beyond the IBA the seabed has more gravel and mud. The site includes the sand beach (dominated by shingle and cobbles in places) and coastal meadows, although the latter constitute probably less than 5% of the total area.

Habitats Wetland (sand-dunes/sand beach), Marine areas (sea inlet/coastal features)
Land-use Fisheries/aquaculture, Tourism/recreation

■ **Birds**

Species	Season	Year	Pop min	Pop max	Acc	Criteria
Podiceps grisegena Red-necked Grebe	W	—	550	550	—	B1i
Clangula hyemalis Long-tailed Duck	W	1990	220,000	—	—	A4i, B1i
Melanitta fusca Velvet Scoter	W	1990	100,000	140,000	—	A4i, B1i, B2
Bucephala clangula Goldeneye	N	1990	13,000	13,000	—	A4i, B1i
Mergus serrator Red-breasted Merganser	W	1990	1,890	—	—	A4i, B1i

The Gulf of Riga is internationally important for several waterbirds in winter, and for moulting *Bucephala clangula* after the breeding season. This part of the gulf holds 20,000 or more waterbirds on a regular basis.

■ **Protection status**
National None **International** None

■ **Conservation issues**

Threats Disturbance to birds (U), Aquaculture/fisheries (U), Other (U)

There are various threats to the area from pollution ('Other' threat, above), seabird mortality in fishing nets, and disturbance to birds by industrial/recreational marine traffic. Coastal-zone regulations protect the shoreline from development to some extent. A stretch of this coast, from Kaltene to Engure, has been proposed as a Baltic Sea Protection Area, and an area of c.134,000 ha (including part or all of the IBA) is included on the national 'shadow list' of potential Ramsar Sites.

Lielais Kemeru bog — B1i, B2 | 019
Admin region Riga, Tukums, Jelgava
Coordinates 56°52′N 23°28′E
Altitude 5–25 m **Area** 6,800 ha

■ **Site description**
A raised bog with many small lakes, surrounded by mixed forests (*Pinus*, *Picea*, *Betula*). Land-uses includes cranberry *Vaccinium* collecting, hunting and forestry.

Habitats Forest and woodland (mixed forest; alluvial/very wet forest), Wetland (raised bog)
Land-use Forestry, Hunting, Nature conservation/research

■ **Birds**

An important staging site for migrating geese and *Grus grus*. Species of global conservation concern that do not meet IBA criteria: *Crex crex* (breeding).

Species	Season	Year	Pop min	Pop max	Acc	Criteria
[1] *Anser fabalis* Bean Goose	P	—	Abundant	—	B1i
[1] *Anser albifrons* White-fronted Goose	P	—	Abundant	—	B1i
Grus grus Crane	N	1984	200	500	B	B1i
Picoides tridactylus Three-toed Woodpecker	R	—	5	10	—	B2

1. Thousands roost at site.

■ **Protection status**
National High **International** None
5,762 ha of IBA covered by Restricted Nature Reserve (Lielais Kemeru tirelis, 5,762 ha). 6,800 ha of IBA covered by National Park (Kemeri, 42,790 ha).

■ **Conservation issues**

Threats Disturbance to birds (U), Unknown

The site was considered data-deficient under a recent review of Latvian Ramsar Sites (actual and potential). The area is covered by a management plan.

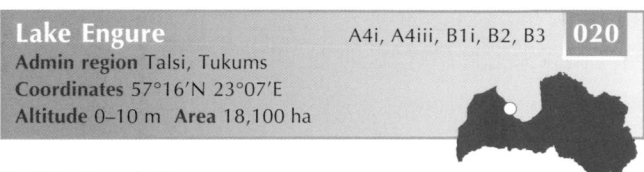

Lake Engure — A4i, A4iii, B1i, B2, B3 | 020
Admin region Talsi, Tukums
Coordinates 57°16′N 23°07′E
Altitude 0–10 m **Area** 18,100 ha

■ **Site description**
A freshwater lake with seven islands, separated from the Gulf of Riga by a narrow (1.5–2.5 km) strip of land. About 30% of the lake is covered with emergent vegetation, mainly *Phragmites*, *Typha* and *Scirpus*. The silty lake-bottom is covered with algae (stonewort *Chara*). To the west of the lake, there is a 1–3-km-wide zone of wet, mixed forest. To the east, there are *Pinus* forests between the lake and the sea and a 3-km-wide zone of shallow waters offshore. Human activities at the lake include forestry, haymaking, grazing, hunting and fishing.

Habitats Forest and woodland (mixed forest; alluvial/very wet forest), Scrub (scrub), Grassland (humid grassland), Wetland (standing fresh water; river/stream; water-fringe vegetation; fen/transition mire/spring)
Land-use Forestry, Hunting, Nature conservation/research

■ **Birds**

Species	Season	Year	Pop min	Pop max	Acc	Criteria
Podiceps grisegena Red-necked Grebe	B	1995	600	600	A	A4i, B1i
[1] *Botaurus stellaris* Bittern	B	1995	30	30	A	B2
Aythya ferina Pochard	B	—	1,000	1,300	A	B1i, B3
Grus grus Crane	B	1995	5	10	A	B2
Grus grus Crane	N	1994	800	800	—	B1i
Larus minutus Little Gull	B	1995	150	150	—	B2
Chlidonias niger Black Tern	B	—	70	70	—	B2
Acrocephalus schoenobaenus Sedge Warbler	B	1995	1,500	1,500	—	B3
Acrocephalus scirpaceus Reed Warbler	B	1995	1,200	1,200	—	B3

1. The best site in Latvia.

The lake is one of the most important sites for breeding waterbirds in the Baltic area. The site holds 20,000 or more waterbirds on a regular basis: besides the vast numbers of breeding wildfowl (Anatidae), in the post-breeding season the area regularly supports 13,000 wildfowl, 12,000 *Fulica atra* and 800 *Grus grus*, and about 5,500 *Bucephala clangula* also gather offshore to moult. Occasionally a stop-over site for geese *Anser* and yellow-billed swans *Cygnus columbianus*/*C. cygnus*. Species of global conservation concern that do not meet IBA criteria: *Anser erythropus* (three records on passage), *Aythya nyroca* (max. 5 pairs), *Haliaeetus albicilla* (one pair), *Crex crex* (max. 10 pairs).

■ **Protection status**
National Partial **International** High
About 4,000 ha of IBA covered by Restricted Nature Territory (Engure, c.4,000 ha). 18,100 ha of IBA covered by Ramsar Site (Lake Engure, 18,100 ha).

■ Conservation issues

Threats Abandonment/reduction of land management (U), Disturbance to birds (U), Intensified forest management (U)

The main threats are posed by attempts to downgrade the protection status, increased human disturbance, and overgrowth of vegetation due to abandonment and lack of management. A management plan is under development.

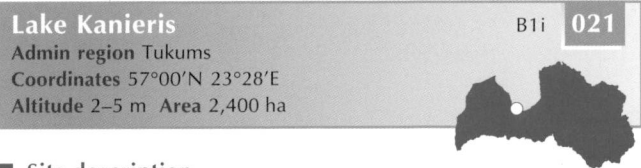

Lake Kanieris | B1i | 021
Admin region Tukums
Coordinates 57°00′N 23°28′E
Altitude 2–5 m **Area** 2,400 ha

■ Site description
A shallow (<1.5 m) coastal freshwater lake, rich in emergent vegetation, with several natural islands, two of them covered with broadleaved forest, and five artificial islands for nesting waterfowl. Human activities include fishing and hunting.

Habitats Forest and woodland (alluvial/very wet forest), Wetland (standing fresh water; water-fringe vegetation)
Land-use Fisheries/aquaculture, Hunting, Nature conservation/research

■ Birds

Species	Season	Year	Pop min	Pop max	Acc	Criteria
Cygnus cygnus Whooper Swan	P	1993	250	250	—	B1i

One of the richest lakes for breeding birds in Latvia and an important passage site for swans and ducks. The area also supports about 2,000 moulting ducks. Species of global conservation concern that do not meet IBA criteria: *Anser erythropus* (probable passage visitor), *Haliaeetus albicilla* (breeding).

■ Protection status
National High **International** Partial
1,128 ha of IBA covered by Restricted Nature Territory (Kanieris, 1,128 ha). 2,400 ha of IBA covered by National Park (Kemeri, 42,790 ha). 1,200 ha of IBA covered by Ramsar Site (Lake Kanieris, 1,200 ha).

■ Conservation issues

Threats Agricultural intensification/expansion (U), Disturbance to birds (U), Industrialization/urbanization (U), Unsustainable exploitation (U)

The lake is polluted by agricultural run-off and industrial sewage entering from the Slocene river. The main threat is disturbance to birds by increased fishing and hunting. The site is covered by a management plan.

Babite lake | A4i, A4iii, B1i, B3 | 022
Admin region Riga
Coordinates 56°55′N 23°35′E
Altitude 0–2 m **Area** 3,100 ha

■ Site description
A eutrophic freshwater lake, rich in emergent vegetation and surrounded by farmland and wet meadows. The lake is used for fishing and hunting.

Habitats Scrub (scrub), Grassland (humid grassland), Wetland (standing fresh water; water-fringe vegetation)
Land-use Fisheries/aquaculture, Hunting

■ Birds

Species	Season	Year	Pop min	Pop max	Acc	Criteria
¹*Cygnus columbianus* Bewick's Swan	P	1990	—	—	—	A4i, B1i
¹*Cygnus cygnus* Whooper Swan	P	—	—	—	—	B1i
Aythya ferina Pochard	B	—	200	200	—	B3
1. Hundreds occur.						

There is a rich assemblage of breeding waterbirds, and the area is important for migrating wildfowl in spring and autumn, especially *Cygnus columbianus* and *Cygnus cygnus*. During the post-breeding period the lake supports about 20,000 waterbirds (mainly *Fulica atra*, ducks and *Cygnus olor*). Species of global conservation concern that do not meet IBA criteria: *Anser erythropus* (two records on passage).

■ Protection status
National Partial **International** None
About 2,600 ha of IBA covered by Restricted Nature Territory (Babite lake, c.2,600 ha).

■ Conservation issues

Threats Disturbance to birds (U)

The lake is polluted by agricultural run-off and industrial sewage. It has been a protected area since 1957, and is included on the national 'shadow list' of Ramsar Sites. The Latvian Fund for Nature launched an investigation of the area in 1998, aimed at producing a management plan.

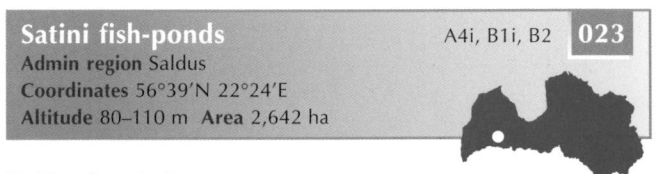

Satini fish-ponds | A4i, B1i, B2 | 023
Admin region Saldus
Coordinates 56°39′N 22°24′E
Altitude 80–110 m **Area** 2,642 ha

■ Site description
The area comprises about 30 fish-ponds, some with small islands and extensive emergent vegetation, set in a landscape of mixed forests, small fens and extensively used agricultural land (mainly pasture and hay-meadows). Land-uses include fish-farming, forestry, and low-intensity farming.

Habitats Forest and woodland (mixed forest; alluvial/very wet forest), Scrub (scrub), Wetland (standing fresh water; water-fringe vegetation; fen/transition mire/spring), Artificial landscape (arable land)
Land-use Agriculture, Fisheries/aquaculture, Forestry, Hunting, Nature conservation/research

■ Birds

Species	Season	Year	Pop min	Pop max	Acc	Criteria
Cygnus cygnus Whooper Swan	P	1996	500	1,000	—	A4i, B1i
Aquila pomarina Lesser Spotted Eagle	B	1996	9	9	—	B2
Pandion haliaetus Osprey	B	1996	7	7	—	B2

The site supports a diverse avifauna of wetland and forest during the breeding and migration seasons. Breeding species of global conservation concern that do not meet IBA criteria: *Haliaeetus albicilla* (1–2 pairs), *Crex crex* (min. 7 pairs).

■ Protection status
National High **International** None
2,600 ha of IBA covered by Restricted Nature Territory (name not known, 2,600 ha).

■ Conservation issues

Threats Disturbance to birds (U), Intensified forest management (U)

The IBA is threatened by drainage and intensification in all land-uses. It is part of a 3,500 ha site included on the national 'shadow list' of Ramsar Sites, and a management plan exists.

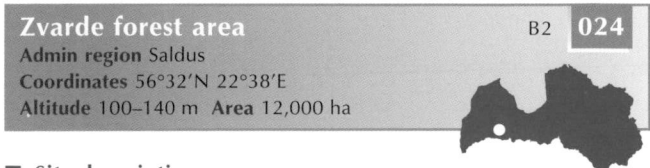

Zvarde forest area | B2 | 024
Admin region Saldus
Coordinates 56°32′N 22°38′E
Altitude 100–140 m **Area** 12,000 ha

■ Site description
A vast forest area, largely unaffected by drainage and comparatively little managed until recently as it was a Soviet military firing range.

The site includes smaller areas of bog and fen, and two small lakes. The forests are dominated by *Alnus* and *Pinus*, with many beaver-ponds on the small natural streams. The main form of present land-use is intensive forestry.

Habitats Forest and woodland (broadleaved deciduous forest; mixed forest; alluvial/very wet forest), Wetland (standing fresh water; raised bog; fen/transition mire/spring), Artificial landscape (arable land)
Land-use Agriculture, Forestry, Hunting, Nature conservation/research

■ Birds

Species		Season	Year	Pop min	Pop max	Acc	Criteria
Aquila pomarina	Lesser Spotted Eagle	B	1996	10	10	B	B2
Pandion haliaetus	Osprey	B	1996	5	5	A	B2

The area holds high densities of breeding *Aquila pomarina* and *Pandion haliaetus*, and *Ciconia nigra* (6–7 pairs) also breeds in good numbers. Species of global conservation concern that do not meet IBA criteria: *Haliaeetus albicilla* (status unknown), *Crex crex* (breeding).

■ Protection status
National Low **International** None
About 400 ha of IBA covered by Restricted Nature Territory (Zwarde, c.2,000 ha).

■ Conservation issues

Threats Deforestation (commercial) (U), Disturbance to birds (U), Drainage (U), Intensified forest management (U), Selective logging/cutting (U)

The forest area and its biological value is heavily disturbed and seriously threatened by intensified forestry, commercial deforestation and the creation of associated infrastructure, on state-owned and particularly on private land where it is almost impossible to apply protection regulations.

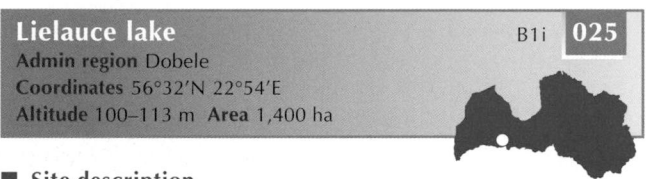

Lielauce lake
B1i 025
Admin region Dobele
Coordinates 56°32′N 22°54′E
Altitude 100–113 m **Area** 1,400 ha

■ Site description
A shallow (1.5 m) eutrophic lake surrounded by fens and wet forests, with a silt bottom, low banks and a high (40%) cover of emergent vegetation. Land-uses include fishing, hunting, and cranberry *Vaccinium* collection ('Other' land-use, below).

Habitats Forest and woodland (mixed forest; alluvial/very wet forest), Wetland (standing fresh water; water-fringe vegetation; fen/transition mire/spring)
Land-use Fisheries/aquaculture, Forestry, Hunting, Other

■ Birds

Species		Season	Year	Pop min	Pop max	Acc	Criteria
Anser fabalis	Bean Goose	P	1996	Abundant		—	B1i

The lake is used during autumn migration by up to 4,000 roosting geese, mainly comprising *Anser fabalis* and *A. albifrons* (the less common of the two). Species of global conservation concern that do not meet IBA criteria: *Aquila clanga* (1 pair was breeding in 1961, but the species most probably no longer breeds).

■ Protection status
National Partial **International** None
388 ha of IBA covered by Restricted Nature Territory (Viki, 388 ha).

■ Conservation issues

Threats Unknown

The Restricted Nature Territory covers part of the shore while the lake itself remains unprotected. The avifauna of the lake and its surroundings was studied briefly in the 1960s. The importance of the site for roosting geese was discovered in autumn 1996.

Ukri forest area
B2 026
Admin region Dobele
Coordinates 56°22′N 23°10′E
Altitude 65–90 m **Area** 1,200 ha

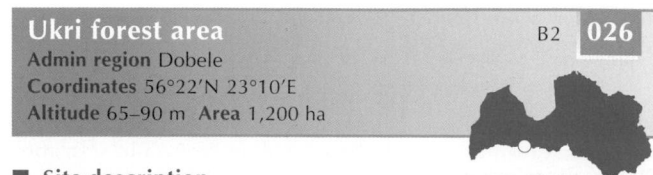

■ Site description
A tract of partly drained broadleaved forest, dominated by *Fraxinus*, with large numbers of old oak *Quercus* trees and rich undergrowth.

Habitats Forest and woodland (broadleaved deciduous forest; mixed forest; alluvial/very wet forest)
Land-use Forestry, Hunting

■ Birds

Species		Season	Year	Pop min	Pop max	Acc	Criteria
Aquila pomarina	Lesser Spotted Eagle	B	1993	9	9	—	B2

An important site for breeding *Aquila pomarina*.

■ Protection status
National High **International** None
About 1,150 ha of IBA covered by Restricted Nature Territory (Ukru Garsa, c.1,150 ha).

■ Conservation issues

Threats Agricultural intensification/expansion (U), Drainage (U), Intensified forest management (U)

The IBA is threatened by additional drainage and by degradation of forest quality as a result of the removal of dead and damaged trees. The site is monitored as a sample plot for studies on *Aquila pomarina* and *Dendrocopos leucotos*.

Lielupe river flood-plain meadows
A1 027
Admin region Jelgava
Coordinates 56°40′N 23°44′E
Altitude 0–3 m **Area** 190 ha

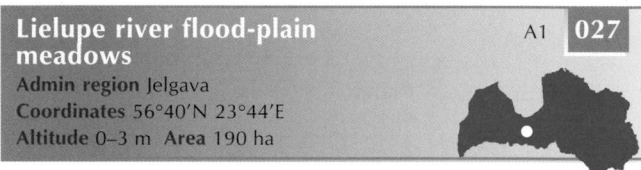

■ Site description
Natural and cultivated flood-plain meadows of the Lielupe river, situated within the territory of Jelgava town. The main land-uses are mowing and grazing, although land within the reserve is no longer mowed or grazed, and the site is often visited by people for fishing and recreation.

Habitats Scrub (scrub), Grassland (mesophile grassland), Wetland (river/stream)
Land-use Agriculture, Tourism/recreation

■ Birds

Species		Season	Year	Pop min	Pop max	Acc	Criteria
Crex crex	Corncrake	B	1996	30	45	—	A1

The area supports a rich assemblage of breeding birds of flood-plain meadows, notably *Crex crex*. Species of global conservation concern that do not meet IBA criteria: *Gallinago media* (breeding).

■ Protection status
National High **International** None
About 190 ha of IBA covered by a Restricted Nature Territory (c.190 ha).

■ Conservation issues

Threats Abandonment/reduction of land management (U), Disturbance to birds (U), Infrastructure (U), Recreation/tourism (U)

The main threats are changes in traditional land-use and disturbance to birds. The site has been studied by ornithologists since the end of the 1980s, and the Latvian Ornithological Society has made recommendations for management. The site is of high botanical and habitat interest as one of the last unaltered flood-plain meadows to remain in Latvia.

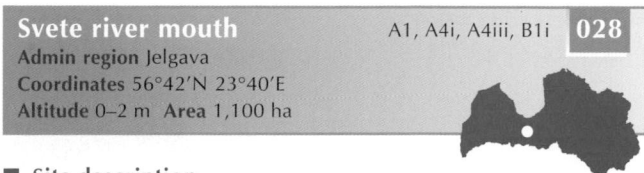

Svete river mouth — A1, A4i, A4iii, B1i — 028
Admin region Jelgava
Coordinates 56°42'N 23°40'E
Altitude 0–2 m **Area** 1,100 ha

■ Site description
The flood-plain of the Svete and Lielupe rivers, near the mouth of the Svete. Most of the area floods in spring. The land is used for agriculture, including arable farming and haymaking.

Habitats Scrub (scrub), Grassland (mesophile grassland), Wetland (river/stream; water-fringe vegetation), Artificial landscape (arable land)
Land-use Agriculture, Water management

■ Birds

Species	Season	Year	Pop min	Pop max	Acc	Criteria
Cygnus cygnus Whooper Swan	P	1996	500	1,000	—	A4i, B1i
Anser fabalis Bean Goose	P	1996	500	1,500	—	B1i
Anser albifrons White-fronted Goose	P	1997	1,000	3,000	—	B1i
Crex crex Corncrake	B	1996	25	40	—	A1

The area is important for breeding *Crex crex*, and there is a lek of the globally near-threatened *Gallinago media*. Spring floods provide excellent feeding and resting conditions for migrating waterbirds, of which the site holds 20,000 or more on a regular basis, including thousands of geese (*Anser albifrons*, *A. fabalis*; daily max. 4,500–6,000) and hundreds of yellow-billed swans (*Cygnus cygnus*, *C. columbianus*).

■ Protection status
National None **International** None

■ Conservation issues

Threats Abandonment/reduction of land management (U), Agricultural intensification/expansion (U), Construction/impact of dyke/dam/barrage (U), Disturbance to birds (U), Drainage (U)

Ornithological research has been carried out annually since 1990.

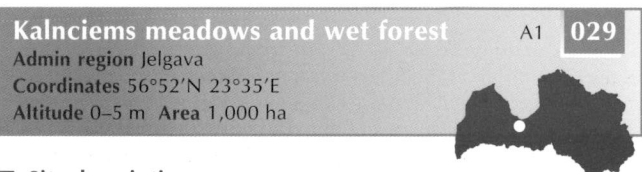

Kalnciems meadows and wet forest — A1 — 029
Admin region Jelgava
Coordinates 56°52'N 23°35'E
Altitude 0–5 m **Area** 1,000 ha

■ Site description
One of the largest tracts of wet *Alnus* forest in Latvia, with relatively intact flood-plain meadows, on the left side of the lower reaches of the Lielupe river. Some trees are more than 100 years old and there are many fallen trunks. Part of the area, including the natural and cultivated flood-plain meadows, used to flood in spring.

Habitats Forest and woodland (alluvial/very wet forest), Scrub (scrub), Grassland (humid grassland; mesophile grassland), Wetland (standing fresh water)
Land-use Agriculture, Forestry, Urban/industrial/transport

■ Birds

Species	Season	Year	Pop min	Pop max	Acc	Criteria
Crex crex Corncrake	B	—	20	35	—	A1

Important numbers of *Crex crex* breed in the meadows, and several woodpecker species breed in the forests.

■ Protection status
National High **International** None
1,000 ha of IBA covered by National Park (Kemeri, 42,790 ha).

■ Conservation issues

Threats Abandonment/reduction of land management (U), Agricultural intensification/expansion (U), Disturbance to birds (U), Intensified forest management (U)

The meadows have been traditionally used for haymaking, but are now threatened by drainage, changes in land-use, and abandonment.

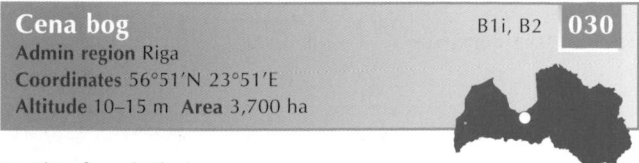

Cena bog — B1i, B2 — 030
Admin region Riga
Coordinates 56°51'N 23°51'E
Altitude 10–15 m **Area** 3,700 ha

■ Site description
One of the largest raised bogs in Latvia, with many small lakes, a zone of transitional mire in the centre, and many peninsulas covered by mixed forest. The southern part of the bog is used for peat extraction, and other land-uses include hunting and cranberry *Vaccinium* collecting.

Habitats Forest and woodland (mixed forest), Wetland (raised bog)
Land-use Forestry, Hunting, Urban/industrial/transport

■ Birds

Species	Season	Year	Pop min	Pop max	Acc	Criteria
Anser fabalis Bean Goose	P	—	800	—	—	B1i
[1] *Anser albifrons* White-fronted Goose	P	—	—	—	—	B1i
[2] *Grus grus* Crane	B	—	15	20	—	B2

1. See main text.
2. Among highest densities in Latvia.

Thousands of geese occur on passage, mainly *Anser fabalis* and *A. albifrons*, and the site is also important for breeding and migrating *Grus grus*.

■ Protection status
National Partial **International** None
About 2,300 ha of IBA covered by Restricted Nature Territory (c.2,300 ha).

■ Conservation issues

Threats Extraction industry (U)

Peat extraction is the main threat. The site is listed as data-deficient in a recent review of actual and potential Ramsar Sites in Latvia.

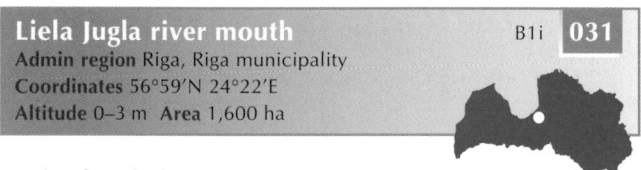

Liela Jugla river mouth — B1i — 031
Admin region Riga, Riga municipality
Coordinates 56°59'N 24°22'E
Altitude 0–3 m **Area** 1,600 ha

■ Site description
The site comprises flood-plain meadows along the lower reaches of the Liela Jugla and Maza Jugla rivers, which flow into Jugla lake, and a set of small ponds and lakes. The area usually floods in spring. The area is close to the city of Riga, being partly within its administrative boundaries, and consequently includes many houses and gardens.

Habitats Forest and woodland (mixed forest), Scrub (scrub), Grassland (mesophile grassland), Wetland (standing fresh water; river/stream; water-fringe vegetation), Artificial landscape (other urban/industrial areas)
Land-use Agriculture, Unknown

■ Birds

Species	Season	Year	Pop min	Pop max	Acc	Criteria
Cygnus cygnus Whooper Swan	P	1997	420	—	—	B1i

According to reports, the flooded areas serve as a regular staging site for migrating waterbirds in spring, and *Cygnus cygnus* has been confirmed in important numbers. Species of global conservation concern that do not meet IBA criteria: *Haliaeetus albicilla* (status unknown), *Crex crex* (breeding possible but not verified).

■ Protection status
National None **International** None

■ Conservation issues

Threats Disturbance to birds (U), Filling-in of wetlands (U), Industrialization/urbanization (U), Infrastructure (U)

The site was identified very recently and has only been visited during spring counts of migrating waterbirds.

Sudas bog

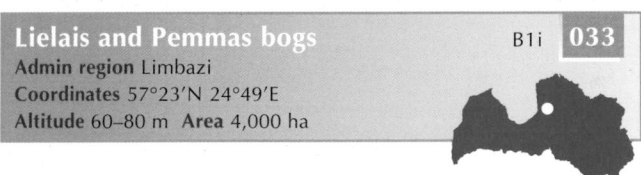

B1i **032**

Admin region Cesis
Coordinates 57°08'N 25°00'E
Altitude 105–120 m **Area** 2,600 ha

■ Site description

The site is mainly a raised bog, with some transitional mire, fen and lakes. There are several islands with old stands of mixed forest (*Picea*, *Quercus*, *Tilia*, *Populus*). Sulphurous springs and the source of the Suda river are situated in the southern part.

Habitats Forest and woodland (mixed forest; alluvial/very wet forest), Wetland (standing fresh water; raised bog; fen/transition mire/spring)
Land-use Forestry, Hunting, Nature conservation/research

■ Birds

Species	Season	Year	Pop min	Pop max	Acc	Criteria
¹ *Anser fabalis* Bean Goose	P	—	Common		—	B1i
² *Grus grus* Crane	P	1996	300	1,000	—	B1i

1. No counts.
2. Regular staging in autumn.

Thousands of migrating geese gather at the bog in autumn, especially *Anser fabalis*, as well as hundreds of *Grus grus*. Species of global conservation concern that do not meet IBA criteria: *Haliaeetus albicilla* (status unknown), *Aquila clanga* (status unknown). Breeding bird species include *Ciconia nigra*, *Grus grus*, *Pluvialis apricaria* and *Picoides tridactylus*.

■ Protection status

National High **International** None
1,581 ha of IBA covered by Nature Reserve (name not known, 1,581 ha). 2,600 ha of IBA covered by National Park (Gauja, 92,048 ha).

■ Conservation issues

Threats Disturbance to birds (U), Drainage (U), Intensified forest management (U)

The part of the bog within the Nature Reserve is protected and almost unaffected by human activities, but other parts of the IBA are threatened by the drainage of adjacent agricultural land. The site is listed as data-deficient in a recent review of actual and potential Ramsar Sites in Latvia. The area is being surveyed as part of the Gauja National Park breeding bird atlas project (1995–1997).

Lielais and Pemmas bogs

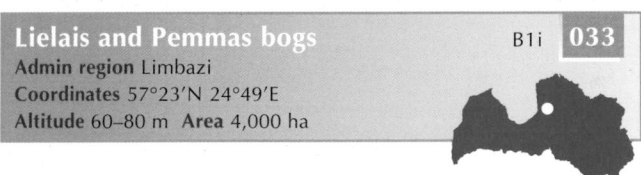

B1i **033**

Admin region Limbazi
Coordinates 57°23'N 24°49'E
Altitude 60–80 m **Area** 4,000 ha

■ Site description

Two large and open raised bogs with many small and several big lakes and some forested islands. The bogs are surrounded by forests of different types, from *Pinus* to mixed stands, with many old *Quercus* trees. Land-uses include cranberry *Vaccinium* collecting, hunting and forestry.

Habitats Forest and woodland (mixed forest; alluvial/very wet forest), Wetland (raised bog)
Land-use Forestry, Hunting

■ Birds

Species	Season	Year	Pop min	Pop max	Acc	Criteria
¹ *Anser fabalis* Bean Goose	P	—	—	—	—	B1i
¹ *Anser albifrons* White-fronted Goose	P	—	—	—	—	B1i

1. See main text.

Thousands of migrating geese (*Anser fabalis* and *A. albifrons*) stop to roost at the bog in autumn. Breeding birds include *Gavia arctica*, *Ciconia nigra*, *Circaetus gallicus*, *Aquila chrysaetos*, *Pandion haliaetus*, *Grus grus*, *Pluvialis apricaria*, *Tringa glareola*, *Numenius arquata* and *N. phaeopus*.

■ Protection status

National Partial **International** None
About 3,000 ha of IBA covered by Restricted Nature Territory (c.3,000 ha).

■ Conservation issues

Threats Intensified forest management (U), Unknown

The area is threatened by peat extraction, drainage and intensive forestry. It is listed as data-deficient in a recent review of actual and potential Ramsar Sites in Latvia.

Gulf of Riga, east coast

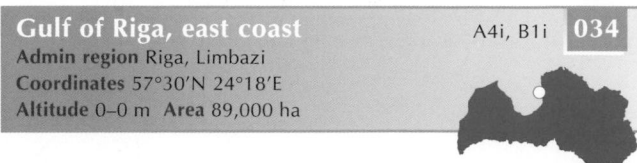

A4i, B1i **034**

Admin region Riga, Limbazi
Coordinates 57°30'N 24°18'E
Altitude 0–0 m **Area** 89,000 ha

■ Site description

A stretch of coastal waters in the Gulf of Riga, from the Estonian border to the mouth of the Gauja river, extending offshore up to 30 m depth. Bottom sediments are sand-dominated and inhabited by shellfish, especially bivalves *Macoma*. Beyond the IBA in deeper areas (>40 m), substrates are also sandy but mixed with more gravel and mud.

Habitats Wetland (sand-dunes/sand beach), Marine areas (sea inlet/coastal features)
Land-use Fisheries/aquaculture, Tourism/recreation

■ Birds

Species	Season	Year	Pop min	Pop max	Acc	Criteria
Gavia arctica Black-throated Diver	W	—	—	3,800	—	A4i, B1i
¹ *Bucephala clangula* Goldeneye	N	—	5,000	8,000	—	A4i, B1i

1. Moulting.

The site supports important concentrations of wintering *Gavia arctica* and moulting *Bucephala clangula*.

■ Protection status

National None **International** Low
About 8,500 ha of IBA covered by Biosphere Reserve (Ziemelvidzeme, 450,000 ha).

■ Conservation issues

Threats Disturbance to birds (U), Aquaculture/fisheries (U), Other (U)

There are various threats to the area from pollution ('Other' threat, above), seabird mortality in fishing nets, and disturbance to birds by industrial/recreational marine traffic. Coastal-zone regulations protect the shoreline from development to some extent. A stretch of this coast (Estonian border–Dzeni) has been proposed as a Baltic Sea Protection Area, and a part of the IBA is included on the national 'shadow list' of potential Ramsar Sites.

Madiesenu bog and Augstroze

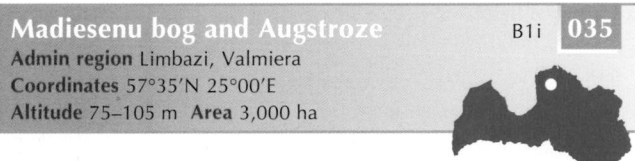

B1i **035**

Admin region Limbazi, Valmiera
Coordinates 57°35'N 25°00'E
Altitude 75–105 m **Area** 3,000 ha

■ Site description

A vast, open raised bog with two large and many small lakes. Several islands and peninsulas are covered by different forest-types (from *Pinus* to deciduous). The Briede river flows through the bog. Land-uses include cranberry *Vaccinium* collecting, hunting and forestry.

Habitats Forest and woodland (mixed forest), Wetland (standing fresh water; raised bog)
Land-use Forestry, Hunting

■ Birds

Species	Season	Year	Pop min	Pop max	Acc	Criteria
¹ *Anser fabalis* Bean Goose	P	—	—	—	—	B1i
¹ *Anser albifrons* White-fronted Goose	P	—	—	—	—	B1i
Grus grus Crane	P	—	200	—	—	B1i

1. No counts, but numbers thought to be significant.

The area is important for staging *Grus grus* and geese on migration.

Protection status

National High **International** High
3,000 ha of IBA covered by Restricted Nature Territory (Augstroze, c.3,500 ha). 3,000 ha of IBA covered by Biosphere Reserve (Ziemelvidzeme, 450,000 ha).

Conservation issues

> **Threats** Disturbance to birds (U), Drainage (U), Intensified forest management (U)

The site is threatened by the drainage of adjacent areas. It was first designated as (part of) a protected area in 1977.

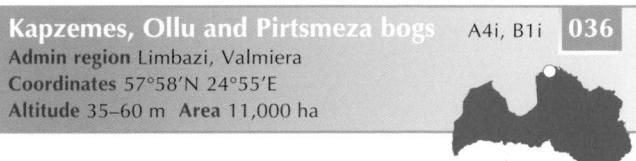

Kapzemes, Ollu and Pirtsmeza bogs — A4i, B1i — 036
Admin region Limbazi, Valmiera
Coordinates 57°58'N 24°55'E
Altitude 35–60 m **Area** 11,000 ha

Site description

This site, together with the Estonian IBA 'Nigula Reserve' (031) across the border, is one of the largest and least disturbed areas of bog in the Baltic region. The site comprises three large raised bogs, with transitional mire in some parts and with many small lakes. The largest bog contains islands of woodland which have remained relatively untouched by forestry. Forests around the bogs are mixed and still largely unaffected by drainage.

> **Habitats** Forest and woodland (mixed forest; alluvial/very wet forest), Wetland (raised bog; fen/transition mire/spring), Artificial landscape (arable land)
> **Land-use** Forestry, Hunting, Nature conservation/research

Birds

Species	Season	Year	Pop min	Pop max	Acc	Criteria
Anser fabalis Bean Goose	P	1996	Abundant		—	A4i, B1i
Anser albifrons White-fronted Goose	P	1996	Abundant		—	B1i
Grus grus Crane	N	1996	200		—	— B1i

An area of outstanding value for migrating geese in autumn, with at least 10,000 roosting *Anser fabalis* and *A. albifrons*. The globally threatened *Aquila clanga* has occurred during the breeding season (one pair in 1997, but breeding not confirmed). The site is also important for non-breeding/migrating *Grus grus* (much more than 200 may occur, e.g. 800 seen across border at Nigula in autumn 1997) and for its diverse assemblage of breeding species.

Protection status

National Partial **International** High
About 5,500 ha of IBA covered by two Restricted Nature Territories (totalling c.5,500 ha). 11,000 ha of IBA covered by Biosphere Reserve (Ziemelvidzeme, 450,000 ha).

Conservation issues

> **Threats** Disturbance to birds (U), Drainage (U), Extraction industry (U), Intensified forest management (U)

The IBA forms part of a transboundary bog complex with Nigula Reserve in Estonia. The Latvian Fund for Nature commenced a research project in 1997, with the support of the Regional Environment Center. The site is included on the national 'shadow list' of Ramsar Sites.

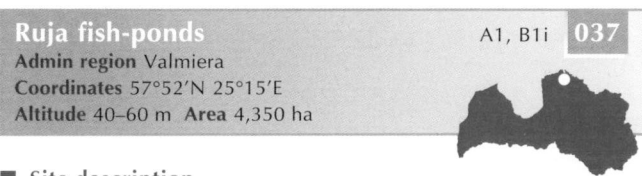

Ruja fish-ponds — A1, B1i — 037
Admin region Valmiera
Coordinates 57°52'N 25°15'E
Altitude 40–60 m **Area** 4,350 ha

Site description

The area comprises a complex of fish-ponds, the flood-plain of the Ruja river, and adjoining forests.

> **Habitats** Forest and woodland (mixed forest), Scrub, Grassland, Wetland (standing fresh water; river/stream)
> **Land-use** Fisheries/aquaculture, Forestry, Hunting

Birds

Species	Season	Year	Pop min	Pop max	Acc	Criteria
[1] *Cygnus cygnus* Whooper Swan	P	—	—	—	—	B1i
Crex crex Corncrake	B	1996	20		—	— A1

1. Several hundreds occur in spring (no exact counts).

The flood-plain supports breeding *Crex crex*, and the fish-ponds provide suitable breeding conditions for a wide range of waterbird species, as well as serving as resting and feeding grounds for passage birds. Species of global conservation concern that do not meet IBA criteria: *Haliaeetus albicilla* (status unknown).

Protection status

National None **International** High
4,350 ha of IBA covered by Biosphere Reserve (Ziemelvidzeme, 450,000 ha).

Conservation issues

> **Threats** Agricultural intensification/expansion (U), Disturbance to birds (U), Intensified forest management (U)

The site is listed as data-deficient in a recent review of actual and potential Ramsar Sites in Latvia. A detailed ornithological survey is needed.

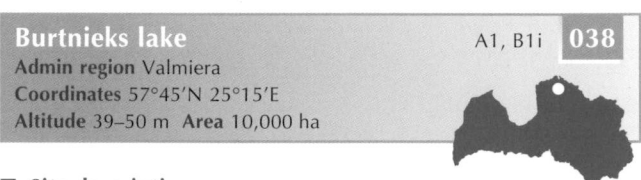

Burtnieks lake — A1, B1i — 038
Admin region Valmiera
Coordinates 57°45'N 25°15'E
Altitude 39–50 m **Area** 10,000 ha

Site description

The area includes Burtnieks lake (4,007 ha), meadows, arable land and forests around the Seda and Ruja tributaries.

> **Habitats** Forest and woodland (mixed forest; alluvial/very wet forest), Scrub (scrub), Grassland (mesophile grassland), Wetland (standing fresh water; river/stream; water-fringe vegetation; fen/transition mire/spring), Artificial landscape (arable land)
> **Land-use** Agriculture, Fisheries/aquaculture, Forestry, Hunting

Birds

Species	Season	Year	Pop min	Pop max	Acc	Criteria
[1] *Cygnus cygnus* Whooper Swan	P	—	—	—	—	B1i
Crex crex Corncrake	B	1996	30	60	B	A1

1. Hundreds thought to occur in spring, possibly mixed with *C. columbianus* (no recent counts).

The lake itself is believed to be important for migrating waterbirds, especially *Cygnus cygnus*. The meadows and other agricultural land around the lake support important numbers of breeding *Crex crex*. The area includes the biggest and northernmost colony of *Ciconia ciconia* in Latvia (about 35 nests), and most of these birds probably forage within the IBA. Species of global conservation concern that do not meet IBA criteria: *Haliaeetus albicilla* (status unknown).

Protection status

National Low **International** High
700 ha of IBA covered by Restricted Nature Territory (Vidusburtnieks, 700 ha). 10,000 ha of IBA covered by Biosphere Reserve (Ziemelvidzeme, 450,000 ha).

Conservation issues

> **Threats** Agricultural intensification/expansion (U), Drainage (U)

The site has been relatively little investigated and is listed as data-deficient in a recent review of actual and potential Ramsar Sites in Latvia.

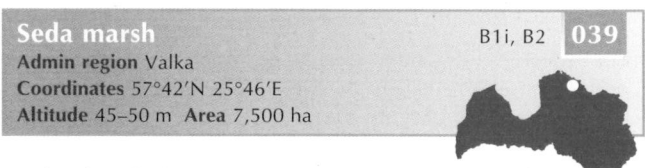

Seda marsh — B1i, B2 — 039
Admin region Valka
Coordinates 57°42'N 25°46'E
Altitude 45–50 m **Area** 7,500 ha

Site description

Seda marsh is a mire (both fen and bog) which has been and continues to be used intensively for commercial peat extraction, thus most of the original habitat has been destroyed. However, the excavated areas fill with water and are colonized by vegetation, forming many ponds of different sizes and depths, with diverse habitat features. Some ponds have become reedbeds, while fen and marshland have regenerated in other areas. Flood-plain meadows and wet forests (some being old) dominate the northern part of the site. Extracted peat is used for fuel and is also exported.

Habitats Forest and woodland (mixed forest; alluvial/very wet forest), Grassland (humid grassland), Wetland (river/stream; raised bog; fen/transition mire/spring)
Land-use Forestry, Hunting, Urban/industrial/transport

■ Birds

Species	Season	Year	Pop min	Pop max	Acc	Criteria
[1] *Cygnus cygnus* Whooper Swan	P	—	Abundant	—	—	B1i
Chlidonias niger Black Tern	B	—	20	—	—	B2

1. Regular in spring.

The area is important for migrating *Cygnus cygnus* (about 500 *Cygnus* counted, mostly this species) and for breeding *Chlidonias niger*. It supports a high overall diversity of breeding and migrating species of wetland and forest. Species of global conservation concern that do not meet IBA criteria: *Haliaeetus albicilla* (breeding), *Crex crex* (breeding in the meadows). At least 1,000 (and up to several thousand) roosting geese were observed and hunted at the site during autumn 1996, and hundreds of migrant *Grus grus* gather here in autumn.

■ Protection status
National Partial **International** High
About 6,500 ha of IBA covered by Restricted Nature Territory (c.6,500 ha). 7,500 ha of IBA is covered by Biosphere Reserve (Ziemelvidzeme, 450,000 ha).

■ Conservation issues

Threats Abandonment/reduction of land management (U), Drainage (U), Intensified forest management (U)

Peat extraction should be stopped and further drainage of the area should be prevented. The flood-plain meadows are threatened by overgrowth if management is abandoned. The IBA contains two short-term 'Forest Sanctuaries' (434 ha), set up by the forestry authorities to protect particular nest-sites. About 7,000 ha of the IBA is included as a site on the national 'shadow list' of potential Ramsar Sites. The IBA has been visited by several ornithologists during the 1990s.

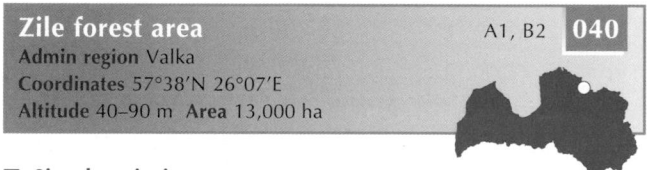

Zile forest area   A1, B2   040
Admin region Valka
Coordinates 57°38′N 26°07′E
Altitude 40–90 m **Area** 13,000 ha

■ Site description
A vast *Pinus* forest, the majority of which burnt down in 1911 and was later restored by planting. About 1,000 ha have not been cut since then. Ground conditions vary widely, from dry areas to wet depressions. In the north, the area borders the Gauja river, where there are many oxbow lakes and natural flood-plain meadows on terraces. The Gauja valley is rich in stands of old broadleaved forest. Human activities include forestry and hunting.

Habitats Forest and woodland (broadleaved deciduous forest; mixed forest; alluvial/very wet forest), Grassland (mesophile grassland), Wetland (river/stream)
Land-use Agriculture, Forestry, Hunting

■ Birds

Species	Season	Year	Pop min	Pop max	Acc	Criteria
Crex crex Corncrake	B	1995	50	50	A	A1, B2
[1] *Caprimulgus europaeus* Nightjar	B	1995	110	110	B	B2

1. Up to 200–300 pairs.

The most important site for *Caprimulgus europaeus* in Latvia. The IBA also supports a diverse assemblage of breeding birds of open and closed forest and of riverine wetlands.

■ Protection status
National Low **International** None
About 350 ha of IBA covered by two Restricted Nature Territories (totalling 350 ha).

■ Conservation issues

Threats Intensified forest management (U)

No conservation activities took place before 1996, when parts of the area were proposed for protection as Nature Reserves (201 ha) and 'Forest Sanctuaries' (263 ha; set up by the forestry authorities to protect particular nest-sites).

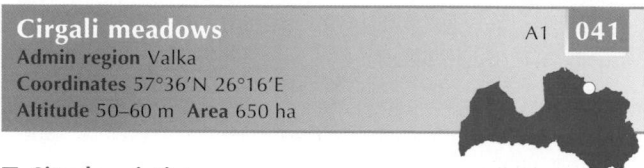

Cirgali meadows   A1   041
Admin region Valka
Coordinates 57°36′N 26°16′E
Altitude 50–60 m **Area** 650 ha

■ Site description
Flood-plain meadows on the left side of the Gauja river, bordering Estonia. Conditions are very diverse, ranging from wet (many oxbow lakes in all stages of succession) to dry (poor sandy soils). Plant species-richness and diversity are high. The meadows have been used extensively for grass-mowing and grazing. The area supports a diverse fauna and flora, and is also important for its geological and landscape value.

Habitats Forest and woodland (alluvial/very wet forest), Scrub (scrub), Grassland (dry siliceous grassland; humid grassland; mesophile grassland), Wetland (standing fresh water; river/stream)
Land-use Agriculture, Tourism/recreation

■ Birds

Species	Season	Year	Pop min	Pop max	Acc	Criteria
Crex crex Corncrake	B	1996	20	—	—	A1

The site supports a high density of breeding *Crex crex*.

■ Protection status
National None **International** None

■ Conservation issues

Threats Abandonment/reduction of land management (U), Agricultural intensification/expansion (U), Burning of vegetation (U), Drainage (U), Recreation/tourism (U)

Although visited by ornithologists in 1996, the site has otherwise been very little investigated. Despite the high diversity of plant species, no botanical survey data is available.

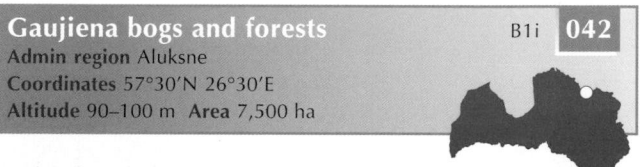

Gaujiena bogs and forests   B1i   042
Admin region Aluksne
Coordinates 57°30′N 26°30′E
Altitude 90–100 m **Area** 7,500 ha

■ Site description
Several raised bogs, separated and surrounded by vast, mixed, mainly wet forests, near the Estonian border. The area is relatively unaffected by human activities, which include forestry, hunting and cranberry *Vaccinium* collecting.

Habitats Forest and woodland (mixed forest), Wetland (raised bog)
Land-use Forestry, Hunting

■ Birds

Species	Season	Year	Pop min	Pop max	Acc	Criteria
[1] *Anser fabalis* Bean Goose	P	—	—	—	—	B1i
[1] *Anser albifrons* White-fronted Goose	P	—	—	—	—	B1i

1. See main text.

The site is an important staging area for migrating geese (*Anser fabalis*, *A. albifrons*), although no precise counts have been made. There is a diverse assemblage of breeding birds of forest and bog.

■ **Protection status**
National Partial **International** None
About 1,500 ha of IBA covered by four Restricted Nature Territories (totalling c.1,500 ha).

■ **Conservation issues**

Threats Drainage (U), Intensified forest management (U)

The protected areas cover bogs.

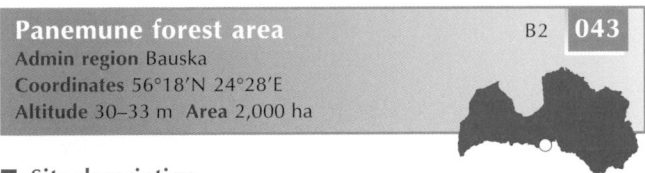

Panemune forest area   B2   043
Admin region Bauska
Coordinates 56°18'N 24°28'E
Altitude 30–33 m **Area** 2,000 ha

■ **Site description**
A tract of mixed and broadleaved forest near the Lithuanian border, with large numbers of old oak *Quercus* trees and rich undergrowth. The area has been partially drained.

Habitats Forest and woodland (broadleaved deciduous forest; mixed forest), Artificial landscape (arable land)
Land-use Agriculture, Forestry, Hunting

■ **Birds**

Species	Season	Year	Pop min	Pop max	Acc	Criteria
Aquila pomarina Lesser Spotted Eagle	B	1988	10	10	B	B2

The area is particularly important for breeding *Aquila pomarina*.

■ **Protection status**
National None **International** None

■ **Conservation issues**

Threats Deforestation (commercial) (U), Disturbance to birds (U), Intensified forest management (U), Selective logging/cutting (U)

Three short-term 'Forest Sanctuaries' (totalling 46 ha) have been established by the forestry authorities, to protect nest-sites of *Ciconia nigra* and *Aquila pomarina*.

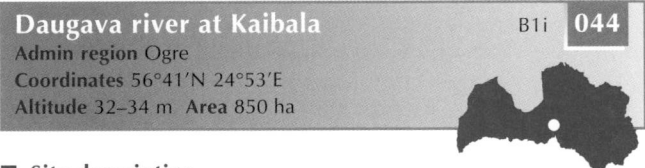

Daugava river at Kaibala   B1i   044
Admin region Ogre
Coordinates 56°41'N 24°53'E
Altitude 32–34 m **Area** 850 ha

■ **Site description**
A stretch of the Daugava river above the Kegums hydroelectric-power barrage (built in 1939), usually 600–850 m across, with several islands and with banks that are either steep or low and easily flooded. About 10% of the area is overgrown with emergent vegetation.

Habitats Wetland (river/stream)
Land-use Unknown

■ **Birds**

Species	Season	Year	Pop min	Pop max	Acc	Criteria
Cygnus cygnus Whooper Swan	P	1995	530	800	A	B1i

Large numbers of migratory waterbirds stage here in spring (daily max. 3,000 birds). The site is especially important for *Cygnus cygnus*, but *C. columbianus* is also present in smaller numbers.

■ **Protection status**
National None **International** None

■ **Conservation issues**

Threats Disturbance to birds (U)

The site was only recently identified but its ornithological importance is already rather well documented. Further investigations on other fauna are needed, however.

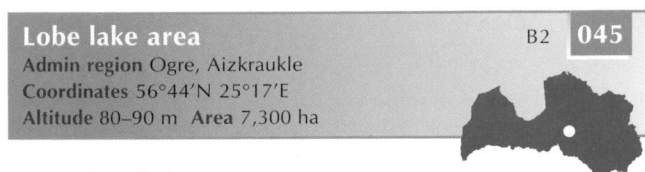

Lobe lake area   B2   045
Admin region Ogre, Aizkraukle
Coordinates 56°44'N 25°17'E
Altitude 80–90 m **Area** 7,300 ha

■ **Site description**
Habitats include a shallow lake (520 ha), rich in emergent vegetation, several raised bogs, wet broadleaved forests and agricultural land. Land-uses include forestry, hunting, cranberry *Vaccinium* collecting ('Other' land-use, below), agriculture, fishing and peat extraction, although habitats have been relatively unaffected so far.

Habitats Forest and woodland (mixed forest; alluvial/very wet forest), Wetland (standing fresh water; river/stream; raised bog; water-fringe vegetation; fen/transition mire/spring)
Land-use Forestry, Hunting, Other

■ **Birds**

Species	Season	Year	Pop min	Pop max	Acc	Criteria
Pandion haliaetus Osprey	B	—	6	6	—	B2

Pandion haliaetus breeds at probably its highest density in Latvia, and the site is possibly important for migrating geese although no data are available to confirm this. Species of global conservation concern that do not meet IBA criteria: *Crex crex* (breeding).

■ **Protection status**
National Partial **International** None
About 1,500 ha of IBA covered by three Restricted Nature Territories (totalling c.1,500 ha).

■ **Conservation issues**

Threats Disturbance to birds (U), Extraction industry (U), Intensified forest management (U)

Potential major threats to the site include planned drainage, extraction of curative mud (sapropel), and forest clearance. The protected areas cover bogs, whilst the lake and a proportion of the forest remain unprotected. The site is listed as data-deficient in a recent review of actual and potential Ramsar Sites in Latvia.

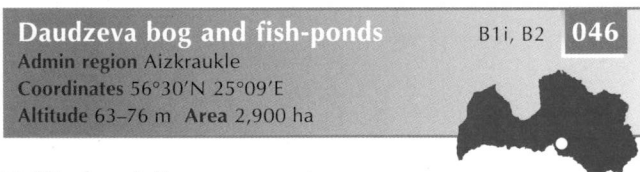

Daudzeva bog and fish-ponds   B1i, B2   046
Admin region Aizkraukle
Coordinates 56°30'N 25°09'E
Altitude 63–76 m **Area** 2,900 ha

■ **Site description**
A raised bog (1,055 ha) with forested peninsulas, several small lakes, surrounding forest stands (*Pinus*, *Picea*), and fish-ponds. Human activities include cranberry *Vaccinium* collecting, hunting, fishing, forestry and agriculture.

Habitats Forest and woodland (mixed forest; alluvial/very wet forest), Wetland (standing fresh water; raised bog), Artificial landscape (arable land)
Land-use Agriculture, Fisheries/aquaculture, Forestry, Hunting

■ **Birds**

Species	Season	Year	Pop min	Pop max	Acc	Criteria
[1] *Cygnus cygnus* Whooper Swan	P	—	Abundant		—	B1i
Pandion haliaetus Osprey	B	—	5	5	—	B2

1. Regular and numerous (at least 500 *C. columbianus/C. cygnus* in spring).

The area is important for migrant *Cygnus cygnus* (at least 500, possibly mixed with *C. columbianus*, recorded in spring) and for breeding *Pandion haliaetus*. Other migrating waterbirds are thought to occur at the fish-ponds in significant numbers, and *Tetrao urogallus* is said to breed at high density.

■ **Protection status**
National Partial **International** None
1,900 ha of IBA covered by Restricted Nature Territory (Aklais bog, 1,900 ha).

■ **Conservation issues**

> **Threats** Disturbance to birds (U), Drainage (U), Intensified forest management (U)

The area is threatened by forestry and associated drainage. The fish-ponds and a proportion of forest remain unprotected.

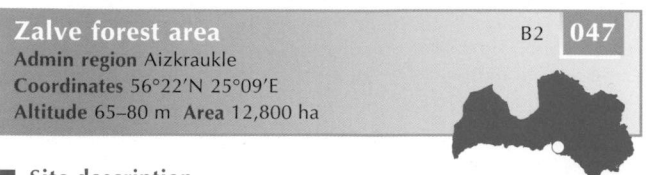

Zalve forest area · B2 · 047
Admin region Aizkraukle
Coordinates 56°22′N 25°09′E
Altitude 65–80 m **Area** 12,800 ha

■ **Site description**
Part of an extensive forest area, the site comprises partly drained stands of mixed and deciduous forest, with a significant proportion of oak *Quercus* and other hardwood trees. There are several small raised bogs, and two unregulated rivers and their streams run through the area.

> **Habitats** Forest and woodland (broadleaved deciduous forest; mixed forest; alluvial/very wet forest), Wetland (river/stream; raised bog), Artificial landscape (arable land)
> **Land-use** Agriculture, Forestry, Hunting

■ **Birds**

Species	Season	Year	Pop min	Pop max	Acc	Criteria
Aquila pomarina Lesser Spotted Eagle	B	—	10	20	C	B2

The area is important for breeding *Aquila pomarina*.

■ **Protection status**
National Low **International** None
230 ha of IBA covered by Restricted Nature Territory (230 ha).

■ **Conservation issues**

> **Threats** Deforestation (commercial) (U), Disturbance to birds (U), Drainage (U), Intensified forest management (U), Selective logging/cutting (U)

Nine short-term 'Forest Sanctuaries' (totalling 243 ha) have been proposed by the forestry authorities, to protect important nest-sites.

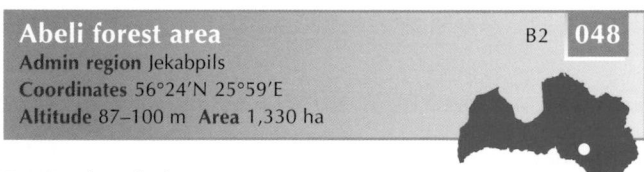

Abeli forest area · B2 · 048
Admin region Jekabpils
Coordinates 56°24′N 25°59′E
Altitude 87–100 m **Area** 1,330 ha

■ **Site description**
An area of deciduous and mixed forests, dominated by *Populus tremula*, with a good proportion of old stands and of swamp-forest. There is a high diversity of forest-types, with *Alnus*, *Betula*, *Picea*, *Fraxinus* and *Tilia* trees common in places. The small, unregulated Ziemelsuseja river flows through the large area of swamp-forests, and natural flood-plain meadows occur along the riverbanks.

> **Habitats** Forest and woodland (broadleaved deciduous forest; mixed forest; alluvial/very wet forest), Grassland (mesophile grassland), Wetland (river/stream)
> **Land-use** Forestry, Unknown

■ **Birds**

Species	Season	Year	Pop min	Pop max	Acc	Criteria
Picoides tridactylus Three-toed Woodpecker	B	1993	12	16	—	B2

An area with an diverse forest avifauna, being notably important for *Picoides tridactylus*. Species of global conservation concern that do not meet IBA criteria: *Crex crex* (breeding).

■ **Protection status**
National High **International** None
1,330 ha of IBA covered by Restricted Nature Territory (Abeli, c.2,140 ha).

■ **Conservation issues**

> **Threats** Drainage (U), Intensified forest management (U)

Monitoring of key species would be highly desirable.

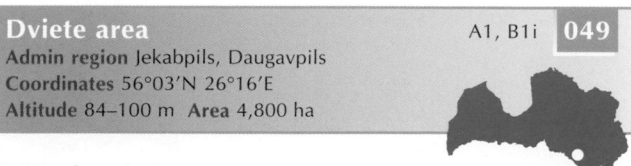

Dviete area · A1, B1i · 049
Admin region Jekabpils, Daugavpils
Coordinates 56°03′N 26°16′E
Altitude 84–100 m **Area** 4,800 ha

■ **Site description**
Scrubby coastal and flood-plain meadows of the Daugava river and its tributary the Dviete, also including two shallow lakes along the Dviete and small areas of fen. The main land-use is agriculture (grass-mowing, pasture and arable).

> **Habitats** Scrub (scrub), Grassland (humid grassland; mesophile grassland), Wetland (standing fresh water; river/stream), Artificial landscape (arable land)
> **Land-use** Agriculture

■ **Birds**

Species	Season	Year	Pop min	Pop max	Acc	Criteria
[1] *Anser fabalis* Bean Goose	P	—		Abundant	—	B1i
[1] *Anser albifrons* White-fronted Goose	P	—		Abundant	—	B1i
Crex crex Corncrake	B	1996	30		—	A1

1. Numbers thought to be significant.

An important stop-over site for migrating waterbirds when the area is flooded in spring. Thousands of ducks and geese are said by local people to occur, and one count in spring 1997 produced c.500 *Anser fabalis* and c.1,500 *A. albifrons*. The meadows are important for breeding *Crex crex*.

■ **Protection status**
National None **International** None

■ **Conservation issues**

> **Threats** Abandonment/reduction of land management (U), Agricultural intensification/expansion (U), Disturbance to birds (U), Drainage (U)

A little-studied area.

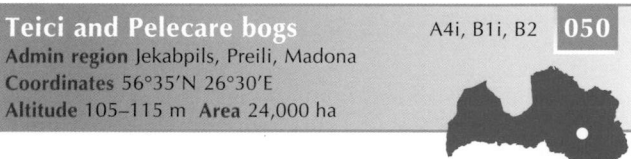

Teici and Pelecare bogs · A4i, B1i, B2 · 050
Admin region Jekabpils, Preili, Madona
Coordinates 56°35′N 26°30′E
Altitude 105–115 m **Area** 24,000 ha

■ **Site description**
These are large raised bogs (Teici is the largest in Latvia), transitional mires and fens, with 'islands' and 'peninsulas' of forest, and small and large lakes. Surrounding forests vary from dry *Pinus* stands to mixed forest, with a significant proportion of broadleaved trees. Land-uses include cranberry *Vaccinium* collecting, and hunting (in forested areas).

> **Habitats** Forest and woodland (mixed forest; alluvial/very wet forest), Wetland (standing fresh water; raised bog; fen/transition mire/spring)
> **Land-use** Forestry, Hunting, Nature conservation/research

■ **Birds**

Species	Season	Year	Pop min	Pop max	Acc	Criteria
Anser fabalis Bean Goose	P	—	4,000	4,000	B	A4i, B1i
Anser albifrons White-fronted Goose	P	—	4,000	4,000	B	B1i
Aquila pomarina Lesser Spotted Eagle	B	1990	8	10	A	B2

Species ... continued	Season	Year	Pop min	Pop max	Acc	Criteria
[1] *Tetrao tetrix* Black Grouse	B	—	550	—	A	B2
Grus grus Crane	B	1990	20	25	A	B2
Grus grus Crane	P	—	500	800	A	B1i
[2] *Grus grus* Crane	N	1990	200	300	A	B1i

1. Lekking males.
2. Birds gather in summer.

This is the best site in Latvia for some breeding species of mire and/or forest, such as *Tetrao tetrix*, *Grus grus*, *Pluvialis apricaria* (70–90 pairs) and *Numenius phaeopus* (20–50 pairs). The site is also very important for non-breeding and migrating *Grus grus*, as well as for up to 8,000 geese (*Anser fabalis* and *A. albifrons*) which roost on the bogs during autumn migration. Species of global conservation concern that do not meet IBA criteria: *Anser erythropus* (one record on passage), *Haliaeetus albicilla* (non-breeding), *Aquila clanga* (status unknown), *Crex crex* (breeding).

■ **Protection status**
National High **International** High
19,047 ha of IBA covered by Nature Reserve (Teici, 19,047 ha). 4,546 ha of IBA covered by Restricted Nature Territory (Pelecare, 4,546 ha). 24,000 ha of IBA covered by Ramsar Site (Teici and Pelecare bogs, 24,000 ha).

■ **Conservation issues**

Threats Disturbance to birds (U), Unknown

Pelecare bog lies outside Teici Nature Reserve and is threatened by peat extraction and the cutting of old forest stands. An increase in agricultural activities in adjoining areas, due to land privatization, is a serious threat to the whole area. About 25% of the Nature Reserve is strictly protected, where no human activity is allowed apart from scientific research. The site is covered by a management plan. Ornithological expeditions first visited the area in 1953, since when the site has been investigated regularly by ornithologists.

Aiviekste river flood-plain meadows — A1, B1i, B2 — 051

Admin region Madona
Coordinates 56°43′N 26°14′E
Altitude 80–90 m **Area** 600 ha

■ **Site description**
A narrow belt (about 14 km long and up to 1 km broad) of relatively unmanaged flood-plain meadows (a rare habitat in Latvia) along the Aiviekste river, in the lowlands around Lubans lake. The meadows regularly flood each spring.

Habitats Scrub (scrub), Grassland (mesophile grassland), Wetland (river/stream)
Land-use Agriculture

■ **Birds**

Species	Season	Year	Pop min	Pop max	Acc	Criteria
[1] *Cygnus cygnus* Whooper Swan	P	—	—	—	—	B1i
Crex crex Corncrake	B	1996	55	65	A	A1, B2

1. See main text.

The meadows support a rich assemblage of breeding birds, including one of the highest breeding densities of *Crex crex* in Latvia, and are also important for migrating waterbirds during spring floods, especially *Cygnus cygnus* and *Cygnus columbianus* (several hundreds of yellow-billed swans are thought to use the site) and ducks.

■ **Protection status**
National None **International** None

■ **Conservation issues**

Threats Abandonment/reduction of land management (U), Agricultural intensification/ expansion (U)

Ornithological research commenced mainly in 1996, supported in part by the Latvian IBA programme.

Lubans lake and fish-ponds — A1, A4iii, B1i — 052

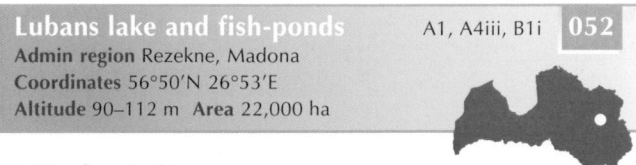

Admin region Rezekne, Madona
Coordinates 56°50′N 26°53′E
Altitude 90–112 m **Area** 22,000 ha

■ **Site description**
The area includes Lubans lake, a shallow water-body, now regulated and surrounded by embankments, and a large fish-pond area, as well as bogs, flood-plain meadows and different types of forest. Although the area is seriously affected by hydrological management, it still has a high diversity of natural habitats. The main land-uses are fish-farming, fishing, forestry, hunting, peat extraction, cranberry *Vaccinium* collecting, and agriculture.

Habitats Forest and woodland (mixed forest; alluvial/very wet forest), Scrub (scrub), Grassland (humid grassland; mesophile grassland), Wetland (standing fresh water; river/ stream; raised bog; water-fringe vegetation; fen/transition mire/spring), Artificial landscape (arable land)
Land-use Agriculture, Fisheries/aquaculture, Forestry, Hunting, Water management

■ **Birds**

Species	Season	Year	Pop min	Pop max	Acc	Criteria
Cygnus cygnus Whooper Swan	P	1997	500	—	—	B1i
[1] *Anser fabalis* Bean Goose	P	—	—	—	—	B1i
[1] *Anser albifrons* White-fronted Goose	P	—	—	—	—	B1i
Crex crex Corncrake	B	—	Common		—	A1

1. 100s–1,000s occur.

This is one of the richest bird areas in Latvia. The fish-ponds, lake and meadows support thousands of moulting ducks and migrating geese, swans and waders. The site regularly supports 20,000 or more waterbirds in breeding, moulting and migration seasons, including grebes, wildfowl and *Fulica atra*. Species of global conservation concern which do not meet IBA criteria: *Haliaeetus albicilla* (breeding and non-breeding birds), *Aquila clanga* (status unknown), *Gallinago media* (status unknown).

■ **Protection status**
National Partial **International** None
About 11,000 ha of IBA covered by two Restricted Nature Territories (c.11,000 ha).

■ **Conservation issues**

Threats Agricultural intensification/expansion (U), Construction/impact of dyke/dam/ barrage (U), Disturbance to birds (U), Drainage (U), Extraction industry (U), Intensified forest management (U)

The site is threatened by further drainage, unfavourable water management, and peat extraction. A wider area of the Lubana lowlands, including this IBA, is included on the national 'shadow list' of Ramsar Sites.

Baltie Klani marshes and adjoining bogs — A1, A4i, B1i, B2 — 053

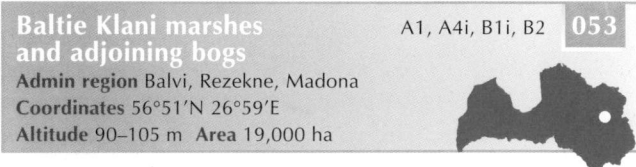

Admin region Balvi, Rezekne, Madona
Coordinates 56°51′N 26°59′E
Altitude 90–105 m **Area** 19,000 ha

■ **Site description**
A vast and diverse complex of lowland wetlands to the north and north-east of Lubans lake (site 052) that includes several marshes (e.g. Baltie Klani), large bogs (Salas, Berzpils and Snitkas), flood-plain meadows (e.g. Ica and Aiviekste) and forests. The area adjoins another IBA (054, Pededze river forests and Parabaine) which lies to the west and north-west. The site was called 'Gomelis marsh' (former site SU012) in the previous pan-European IBA inventory (Grimmett and Jones 1989), and was much smaller.

Habitats Forest and woodland (mixed forest; alluvial/very wet forest), Scrub (scrub), Grassland (humid grassland; mesophile grassland), Wetland (river/stream; raised bog; fen/transition mire/spring)
Land-use Agriculture, Forestry, Hunting

■ Birds

Species	Season	Year	Pop min	Pop max	Acc	Criteria
Cygnus cygnus Whooper Swan	P	—	600	1,000	—	A4i, B1i
[1] *Anser fabalis* Bean Goose	P	—	—	—	—	A4i, B1i
[1] *Anser albifrons* White-fronted Goose	P	—	—	—	—	B1i
Crex crex Corncrake	B	1996	100	200	—	A1
[1] *Grus grus* Crane	P	—	—	—	—	B1i
Larus minutus Little Gull	B	1987	2,000	2,000	—	A4i, B1i, B2
Chlidonias niger Black Tern	B	1987	1,500	2,000	—	A4i, B1i, B2

1. 100s–1,000s occur regularly.

One of the largest and most important bird areas in Latvia, supporting good numbers of rare and threatened breeding species of wetland and hosting large numbers of *Grus grus*, geese and other waterbirds on passage. The meadows are important for breeding *Crex crex*, and Gomelis marsh holds the largest colonies of *Chlidonias niger* and *C. leucopterus* in Latvia. Species of global conservation concern that do not meet IBA criteria: *Haliaeetus albicilla* (breeding), *Aquila clanga* (one pair probably nests, having shifted from site 054; birds from two nearby pairs also visit the area to feed), *Gallinago media* (breeding in meadows).

■ Protection status
National High **International** None
About 4,000 ha of IBA covered by Restricted Nature Territory (Salas, c.4,000 ha). About 3,700 ha of IBA covered by Restricted Nature Territory (Lagazas-Snitku bog, c.3,700 ha). About 4,500 ha of IBA covered by Restricted Nature Territory (Berzpils, c.4,500 ha). About 5,000 ha of IBA covered by Restricted Nature Territory (Parabaine, c.10,000 ha).

■ Conservation issues

Threats Abandonment/reduction of land management (U), Agricultural intensification/ expansion (U), Construction/impact of dyke/dam/barrage (U), Drainage (U), Extraction industry (U)

The whole IBA, along with the adjacent Lubans lake, has been widely and seriously affected by large-scale hydrological projects and drainage, but it remains a large tract of highly diverse natural wetland. The Lubans lake complex (Lubana lowlands; c.78,000 ha), of which this IBA forms a part, is included on the national 'shadow list' of Ramsar Sites.

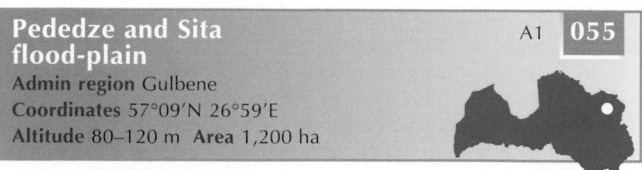

Pededze river forests and Parabaine
A1, B2   054
Admin region Gulbene, Balvi, Madona
Coordinates 56°55'N 26°53'E
Altitude 90–100 m **Area** 12,000 ha

■ Site description
Wet flood-plain forests of the Pededze and Aiviekste rivers, forming part of the complex of IBAs in the Lubans lowlands. There are also streams, meadows and several raised bogs.

Habitats Forest and woodland (broadleaved deciduous forest; mixed forest; alluvial/very wet forest), Wetland (river/stream; raised bog)
Land-use Forestry, Hunting

■ Birds

Species	Season	Year	Pop min	Pop max	Acc	Criteria
Aquila pomarina Lesser Spotted Eagle	B	1996	15	20	B	B2
Aquila clanga Greater Spotted Eagle	B	1995	1	2	A	A1

The area supports an outstandingly rich and diverse breeding bird fauna, including important numbers of *Aquila pomarina* and *A. clanga*, as well as *Ciconia nigra* (5–8 pairs) and eight woodpecker species (all those in Latvia apart from *Picus viridis*). Breeding species of global conservation concern that do not meet IBA criteria: *Haliaeetus albicilla* (1 pair), *Crex crex*.

■ Protection status
National Partial **International** None
About 4,000 ha of IBA covered by Restricted Nature Territory (Pededze River Lower Reaches, c.4,000 ha). About 5,000 ha of IBA covered by Restricted Nature Territory (Parabaine, c.10,000 ha).

■ Conservation issues

Threats Disturbance to birds (U), Intensified forest management (U), Selective logging/ cutting (U)

There is a remarkable richness and diversity of plants, rare and threatened species, and rare and natural habitats.

Pededze and Sita flood-plain
A1   055
Admin region Gulbene
Coordinates 57°09'N 26°59'E
Altitude 80–120 m **Area** 1,200 ha

■ Site description
The area includes wet flood-plain meadows of the Pededze river and its tributary, the Sita, which are flooded in spring. Among the meadows there are stands of wet forest, overgrown oxbow lakes and scattered old oak *Quercus* trees.

Habitats Forest and woodland (alluvial/very wet forest), Scrub (scrub), Grassland (humid grassland; mesophile grassland), Wetland (river/stream)
Land-use Agriculture, Forestry, Hunting

■ Birds

Species	Season	Year	Pop min	Pop max	Acc	Criteria
[1] *Crex crex* Corncrake	B	—	Abundant		—	A1

1. Tens of pairs.

The site is important for breeding *Crex crex*. Congregations of migrant waterbirds occur (over 1,000 individuals per day). Species of global conservation concern that do not meet IBA criteria: *Haliaeetus albicilla* (non-breeding).

■ Protection status
National None **International** None

■ Conservation issues

Threats Abandonment/reduction of land management (U), Agricultural intensification/ expansion (U), Construction/impact of dyke/dam/barrage (U), Disturbance to birds (U), Intensified forest management (U)

Up till now the meadows have been traditionally mown, but due to land privatization there is a high risk of land abandonment, which will lead to overgrowth of the meadows by bushes and trees. Potentially, conversion of part of the area to arable land is also a threat, together with illegal hunting and fishing. The site is listed as data-deficient in a recent review of actual and potential Ramsar Sites in Latvia. The site has been visited by ornithologists since 1992, while entomologists and hydrobiologists surveyed the site in 1996. No botanical survey has been carried out.

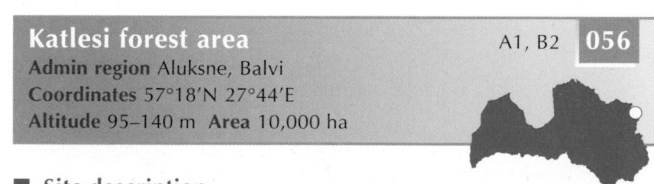

Katlesi forest area
A1, B2   056
Admin region Aluksne, Balvi
Coordinates 57°18'N 27°44'E
Altitude 95–140 m **Area** 10,000 ha

■ Site description
A large tract of forest near the Russian border, dominated by *Pinus* stands, with alluvial *Alnus* forests extending along several unregulated or partly regulated streams.

Habitats Forest and woodland (mixed forest; alluvial/very wet forest), Wetland (river/ stream), Artificial landscape (arable land)
Land-use Agriculture, Forestry, Hunting

■ Birds

Species	Season	Year	Pop min	Pop max	Acc	Criteria
Aquila pomarina Lesser Spotted Eagle	B	1996	10	10	B	B2
[1] *Aquila clanga* Greater Spotted Eagle	B	—	—	—	C	A1

1. See main text.

The site is important for breeding *Aquila pomarina*, and *Aquila clanga* may breed (birds are present, possibly representing a breeding pair).

■ **Protection status**
National None **International** None

■ **Conservation issues**

Threats Deforestation (commercial) (U), Disturbance to birds (U), Drainage (U), Intensified forest management (U), Selective logging/cutting (U)

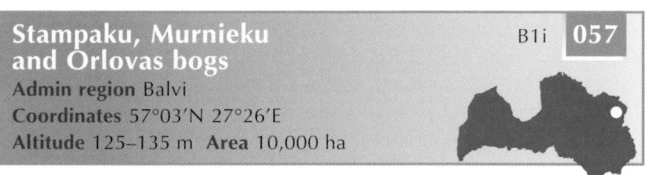

Stampaku, Murnieku and Orlovas bogs   B1i 057
Admin region Balvi
Coordinates 57°03′N 27°26′E
Altitude 125–135 m **Area** 10,000 ha

■ **Site description**
Three open raised bogs, separated and surrounded by vast mixed forests (*Pinus, Picea, Betula, Populus*), and with lakes and several forested islands. Land-uses include forestry, cranberry *Vaccinium* collecting, hunting, and sport-fishing on one of the lakes.

Habitats Forest and woodland (mixed forest; alluvial/very wet forest), Wetland (standing fresh water; raised bog; fen/transition mire/spring), Artificial landscape (arable land)
Land-use Agriculture, Forestry, Hunting

■ **Birds**

Species	Season	Year	Pop min	Pop max	Acc	Criteria
¹ *Anser fabalis* Bean Goose	P	—	—	—	—	B1i
¹ *Anser albifrons* White-fronted Goose	P	—	—	—	—	B1i
1. See main text.						

Anser fabalis and *A. albifrons* are numerous on passage, although no precise counts have been made. There is a very diverse assemblage of breeding birds of forest, lakes and bog. Species of global conservation concern that do not meet IBA criteria: *Haliaeetus albicilla* (status unknown).

■ **Protection status**
National Partial **International** None
About 6,600 ha of IBA covered by two Restricted Nature Territories (totalling c.6,600 ha).

■ **Conservation issues**
Threats include the intensification of human activities, especially forestry and drainage. The protected areas cover bogs. The site is listed

as data-deficient in a recent review of actual and potential Ramsar Sites in Latvia.

Threats Agricultural intensification/expansion (U), Disturbance to birds (U), Drainage (U), Extraction industry (U), Intensified forest management (U)

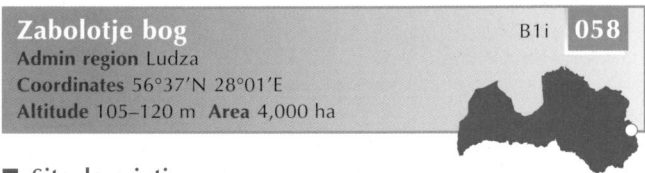

Zabolotje bog   B1i 058
Admin region Ludza
Coordinates 56°37′N 28°01′E
Altitude 105–120 m **Area** 4,000 ha

■ **Site description**
A large area of raised bog with adjacent forests near the Russian border (the major part of the bog lies within Russian territory). The bog is comparatively open, with many small lakes and one bigger lake, Pitelis. Mixed, wet forests (*Pinus, Betula, Alnus*) surround most of the bog, with some stands more than 100 years old. The area is little affected by human activities, which include forestry, cranberry *Vaccinium* collecting, and hunting.

Habitats Forest and woodland (mixed forest; alluvial/very wet forest), Wetland (standing fresh water; raised bog; fen/transition mire/spring)
Land-use Forestry, Hunting

■ **Birds**

Species	Season	Year	Pop min	Pop max	Acc	Criteria
¹ *Anser fabalis* Bean Goose	P	—	—	—	—	B1i
¹ *Anser albifrons* White-fronted Goose	P	—	—	—	—	B1i
1. See main text.						

Anser fabalis and *A. albifrons* are numerous on passage, although no precise counts have been made. There is a diverse assemblage of breeding birds of forest and bog. Species of global conservation concern that do not meet IBA criteria: *Gallinago media* (breeding).

■ **Protection status**
National Partial **International** None
1,736 ha of IBA covered by Restricted Nature Territory (Klesniku bog, 1,736 ha). 1,771 ha of IBA covered by Restricted Nature Territory (Gulbju-Platpirovas bog, 1,771 ha).

■ **Conservation issues**

Threats Drainage (U), Extraction industry (U), Intensified forest management (U)

The site is threatened by increased tree-felling, drainage and possibly peat extraction. It is listed as data-deficient in a recent review of actual and potential Ramsar Sites in Latvia.

REFERENCES

ANON. (1992) *WWF Project 4568: Conservation Plan for Latvia, final report.* Riga: LU Ekologiskais centrs.

ANON. (1997) *Latvian environment in figures, a collection of statistical data.* Riga: Central Statistical Bureau of Latvia.

ANON. (1998a) *Baltic state of the environment report, based on environmental indicators.* Riga: Baltic Environmental Forum.

ANON. (1998b) *National report on biological diversity, Latvia.* Riga: Ministry of Environmental Protection and Regional Development/United Nations Development Programme.

AVOTINS, A. (1996) [Aiviekste river floodplain meadows.] P. 4 in *'IBA review', Newsletter of IBA project of Latvian Ornithological Society.* (In Latvian.)

AVOTINS, A. (1996) [Black-throated Diver *Gavia arctica* at Teichi Bog.]. *Putni daba* 6(2): 2–11. (In Latvian, with English summary.)

BAUMANIS, J. (1980) [Changes in bird fauna of Cenas bog over a ten-year period (1969–1978).] *Retie augi un dzivnieki:* Pp. 29–33. (In Latvian.)

BERGMANIS, U. AND AVOTINS, A. (1990) [Avifauna of the Teici Reserve and its surroundings.] *Putni daba* 3: 71–87. (In Latvian, with English summary.)

CELMINS, A., BAUMANIS, J. AND MEDNIS, A. (1993) List of Latvian bird species. Riga. Unpublished.

CELMINS, A., BAUMANIS, J. AND ROZE, V. (1995) [Spring migration of waterfowl in the sea near Pape in 1989.] *Putni daba* 5(1): 17–29. (In Latvian, with English summary.)

DURINCK, J., SKOV, H., JENSEN, F. P. AND PIHL, S. (1994) *Important marine areas for wintering birds in the Baltic Sea.* Copenhagen: Ornis Consult.

GRIMMETT, R. F. A. AND JONES, T. A. (1989) *Important Bird Areas in Europe.* Cambridge, UK: International Council for Bird Preservation (Techn. Publ. 9).

GROSSE, A. AND TRANSEHE, N. (1929) Verzeichnis der Wirbeltiere des Ostbaltischen Gebietes. *Arbeiten Naturf.-Ver. Riga* 18: 1–75.

HEATH, M. F. AND BORGGREVE, C. (2000) *BirdLife International/EBCC European Bird Database 1998.* Cambridge, UK: BirdLife International.

JAUNZEMIS, M. (1994) Ipasi aizsargajamas putnu sugas Ances Dizpurva un ta apkartne. [Particularly protected bird species in the Bog Ances Dizpurvs and its surroundings.] Bachelor's degree thesis, Riga: University of Latvia. (In Latvian.)

KASPARSONS, G. (1961) Lielauces ezera putni. [Birds of Lielauce lake.] *Mednieks un makskernieks* 3. (In Latvian.)

KEISS, O. (1997) Results of a randomised Corncrake *Crex crex* survey in Latvia (1996): population estimate and habitat selection. *Vogelwelt* 118: 231–235.

KUMARI, E. (1987) [Migrations and stop-overs of the Common Crane in the Baltic area.] In I. A. Neufeldt and J. Keskpaik, eds. [*Crane study in the USSR. Communications of the Baltic Commission for the Study of Bird Migration no. 19.*] (In Russian, with English summary.)

LIPSBERGS, J. AND BERGMANIS, U. (1987) [Premigratory concentrations ot the Common Crane in Latvia in 1984.] In I. A. Neufeldt and J. Keskpaik, eds. [*Crane study in the USSR. Communications of the Baltic Commission for the Study of Bird Migration no. 19.*] (In Russian, with English summary.)

LIPSBERGS, J. (1989) Par meza zoss—*Anser anser* (L.)—perejumiem 1988. gada Liepajas un Papes ezeros. *Retie augi un dzivnieki.*

MEDNIS, A. *Anser erythropus.* In Viksne, J. ed. (1983) *Birds of Latvia, territorial distribution and number.* Riga.

MICHANEK, G. AND BLUMBERGA, U. (1998) *Environmental legal system in Latvia.* Riga: Ministry of Environmental Protection and Regional Development of the Republic of Latvia/Swedish Environmental Protection Agency.

OPERMANIS, O. (1998) *Wetlands and the Ramsar Convention in Latvia.* Riga: Latvian Ornithological Society.

PETERHOFS, E. (1983) Sliteres Valsts rezervata ornitofaunas sistematiskais saraksts. *Mezsaimnieciba un mezrupnieciba* 4: 12–18.

PETERHOFS, E. (1984) Papildinajumi Sliteres Valsts rezervata ornitofaunas sistematiskaja saraksta. *Mezsaimnieciba un mezrupnieciba* 3: 13.

PETERSONS, J. (1938) Maza zoss *Anser erythropus* (L.). *Daba un zinatne*: 29.

PETRINS, A. (1982) Liela Kemeru tirela ornitofauna. *Retie augi un dzivnieki*: 26–33.

SCOTT, D. A. AND ROSE, P. M. (1996) *Atlas of Anatidae populations in Africa and western Eurasia.* Wageningen, The Netherlands: Wetlands International (Publ. no. 41).

STRAZDS, M., MEIERS, H. AND PETRINS, A. (1996) Analysis of ecological conditions of breeding habitat of *Ciconia nigra* in Latvia. Pp. 62–63 in *II International Conference on* Ciconia nigra, *Trujillo (Extremadura, Spain), Abstracts.*

TIDRIKIS, A. (1995) Durbes ezers. In Kavacs, G. (1995) *Latvijas daba. Enciklopçdija, 2.* daïa. Riga.

TUCKER, G. M. AND HEATH, M. F. (1994) *Birds in Europe: their conservation status.* Cambridge, UK: BirdLife International (BirdLife Conservation Series no. 3).

VIKSNE, J. (1991) Results of restoration of water level on lake Kanieris, Latvia. Pp. 123–127 in C. M. Finlayson and T. Larsson, eds. *Wetland Management and Restoration. Proc. Workshop, Sweden 1990.* Stockholm: Swedish Environmental Protection Agency.

VIKSNE, J. (1994) *Putniem nozimigas vietas Latvija.* [Important Bird Areas in Europe. Latvia.] Riga: Latvijas Ornitologijas Biedriba. (In Latvian.)

VIKSNE, J. (1997) [*The birds of lake Engure*]. Riga: Jana Seta. (In Latvian.)

VIKSNE, J. AND JANAUS, M. (1989) [Colonies of gulls, terns and the Grey Heron in Latvia in 1986.] *Putni daba* 2: 55–71. (In Latvian, with English summary.)

WWF (1996) *Management Plan for Lake Pape Project Area.* Copenhagen: WWF-Denmark.

■ LIECHTENSTEIN

Georg Willi

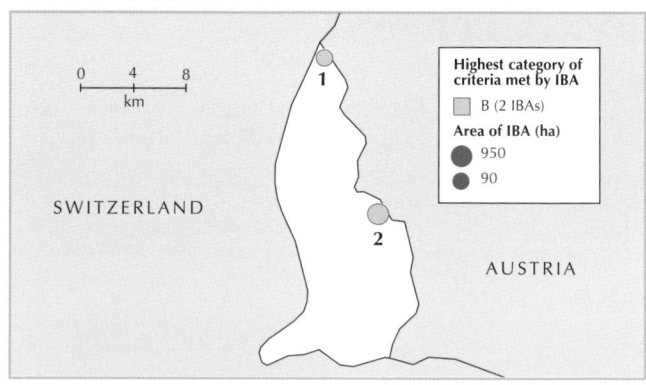

Garselli-Zigerberg, Alpengebeit (IBA 002), a mountainous area of semi-natural forests and alpine pastures. (PHOTO: GEORG WILLI)

GENERAL INTRODUCTION

The Principality of Liechtenstein, situated between Switzerland and Austria, has an area of 160 km² and a population (in 1998) of 31,000 (an average population density of 194 people per km²). One third of the country lies in the Rhine valley and the rest is mountainous, the altitude varying between 430–2,600 m.

Three main landscape types exist: the alluvial flood-plain of the Rhine; the slopes of the Rhine valley; and the high mountainous area, which covers a third of the country, and is characterized by north–south running mountain ridges and valleys.

Two Important Bird Areas (IBAs) have been identified, one in the Rhine valley (001) and the other in the mountains (002), with a combined total area of 1,040 ha or 6.5% of the country's surface area (Table 1, Map 1).

ORNITHOLOGICAL IMPORTANCE

Fifty-seven species of European conservation concern (SPECs) breed in Liechtenstein, and two, *Circus cyaneus* and *Circus pygargus*, winter and occur on passage respectively (Tucker and Heath 1994). The globally threatened *Crex crex* breeds at one site (001), thereby fulfilling IBA criterion B2 (Table 2).

The breeding populations of some lowland SPECs, including *Saxicola rubetra* and *Locustella naevia*, are important for the Rhine valley. These species occur in Ruggeller Riet, Talgebiet (001), alongside breeding *Coturnix coturnix* and *Acrocephalus palustris*.

The Rhine valley is also nationally important for migratory birds including ducks and waders.

The slopes of the Rhine valley and the high montane areas support noteworthy breeding populations of several SPECs (*Aquila chrysaetos*, *Tetrao tetrix* and *Picoides tridactylus*) and non-SPECs (*Bonasa bonasia*, *Tetrao urogallus*, *Glaucidium passerinum*, *Aegolius funereus* and *Dendrocopos leucotos*). Garselli-Zigerberg, Alpengebiet (002) supports all of these except for *A. chrysaetos*. Breeding *Serinus citrinella* are sufficiently numerous at the site as to qualify it as an IBA under the B3 criterion (Table 2).

Map 1. Location, area and criteria category of Important Bird Areas in Liechtenstein.

Table 1. Summary of Important Bird Areas in Liechtenstein.				2 IBAs covering 10 km²	
IBA code	1989 code	International/national name	Administrative region	Area (ha)	Criteria (see p. 11)
001	LI001	Ruggeller Riet, Talgebiet	Ruggell, Schellenberg	90	B2
002	LI002	Garselli-Zigerberg, Alpengebiet	Triesenberg, Planken, Balzers, Schaan	950	B3

Table 2. Species of European conservation concern with significant breeding populations at Important Bird Areas in Liechtenstein (meeting any IBA criteria).

Species [1]	Minimum national breeding population (pairs) [2]	Proportion (%) of national population breeding at all IBAs in Liechtenstein
Crex crex Corncrake	2	100
Serinus citrinella Citril Finch	200	20

1. Only those species of European conservation concern (see Box 1, p. 12) that meet IBA criteria in Liechtenstein are listed.
2. Data are taken from the BirdLife/EBCC European Bird Database 1998 (Heath and Borggreve 2000).

Table 3. Protection status of Important Bird Areas in Liechtenstein. A tick (✔) indicates that an IBA overlaps with a protected area (to any extent).

IBA code	International name	National Nature Reserve	International Ramsar Site
001	Ruggeller Riet, Talgebiet	✔	✔
002	Garselli-Zigerberg, Alpengebiet		
Total number of IBAs		1	1

Box 1. International legislation and initiatives that are relevant to site conservation in Liechtenstein (see Appendix 1 for a general description of these agreements).

Global	
Biodiversity Convention	✔
Ramsar Convention	✔
Bonn Convention	✔
World Heritage Convention	
MAB Programme	
Pan-European	
Bern Convention	✔

✔ Convention ratified/initiative supported
(✔) Convention signed

HABITATS

There has been a major loss of wetland on the Rhine flood-plain as a result of drainage for agriculture. Dry grasslands have also disappeared because of agricultural intensification and urban expansion. Up until at least 1927 much of the valley was often inundated, but now only remnants of marshes and wooded swamps remain.

Over 40% of the slopes of the Rhine valley are wooded. Native deciduous woodland formerly dominated, but coniferous forests now occupy a larger area. The high mountains also support forest and alpine pastures, and it is this landscape type that is included within Garselli-Zigerberg, Alpengebiet (002).

IMPACTS ON IBAs – LAND-USE AND THREATS

The Rhine flood-plain is used for agriculture and human settlements, whilst forestry is the main land-use on the slopes, alongside human habitations. The mountains are used for intensive livestock-grazing, forestry and tourism.

Agricultural intensification poses a threat to the flood-plain, whilst intensive forestry management practices present a problem at higher altitudes.

PROTECTION STATUS

■ National protection

There are seven Nature Reserves (Naturschutzgebiet) in Liechtenstein, including Ruggeller Riet, which overlaps entirely with

IBA 001 (Table 3). It is prohibited to intensify agricultural practices at these sites, and visitors are not allowed to leave the reserve paths during the breeding season. The Ministry of Agriculture, Forestry and Environment is responsible for nature conservation.

■ International protection

Liechtenstein has ratified the Bern, Bonn and Ramsar Conventions (Box 1). There is one Ramsar Site in Liechtenstein, Ruggeller Riet, which encompasses IBA 001 (Table 3).

ANALYTICAL METHODS

- Bird data were collected over the period 1976–1996.

ACKNOWLEDGEMENTS

The following accounts have been compiled from information provided by the author, G. Willi (Botanisch-Zoologische Gesellschaft).

■ SITE ACCOUNTS

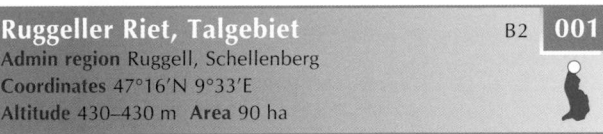

Ruggeller Riet, Talgebiet — B2 — 001
Admin region Ruggell, Schellenberg
Coordinates 47°16′N 9°33′E
Altitude 430–430 m **Area** 90 ha

■ Site description
An area of wet grassland and arable land with drainage ditches, scrub and a small expanse of open water, situated in the Rhine valley.

Habitats Scrub (6%; scrub), Grassland (67%; humid grassland), Artificial landscape (27%; highly improved reseeded grassland)
Land-use Agriculture (55%), Nature conservation/research (30%), Not utilized (15%)

■ Birds

Species	Season	Year	Pop min	Pop max	Acc	Criteria
[1] *Crex crex* Corncrake	B	1996	2	2	A	B2

1. Up to 8 breeding pairs in recent years. Only breeding population in Liechtenstein.

Supports the only breeding population of the globally threatened *Crex crex* in Liechtenstein, as well as breeding *Coturnix coturnix*, *Saxicola rubetra* and *Lanius collurio*. *Circus cyaneus* winters, and both *Circus aeruginosus* and *Circus pygargus* occur on passage.

■ Protection status
National High **International** High

90 ha of IBA covered by Nature Reserve (Ruggeller Riet, 90 ha). 90 ha of IBA covered by Ramsar Site (Ruggeller Riet, 101 ha).

■ Conservation issues

Threats Abandonment/reduction of land management (U), Agricultural intensification/ expansion (C), Consequences of animal/plant introductions (B), Disturbance to birds (C), Drainage (B), Groundwater abstraction (B), Recreation/tourism (C)

The main threat to the IBA is posed by agricultural intensification on land adjacent to the Nature Reserve and, to a lesser extent and in spite of it being protected, within the reserve itself. The plant *Solidago virgaurea* has been introduced and is a problem. Human access is controlled during the breeding season, and there is a management plan for the site.

Garselli-Zigerberg, Alpengebiet — B3 — 002
Admin region Triesenberg, Planken, Balzers, Schaan
Coordinates 47°10′N 9°36′E
Altitude 950–2,120 m **Area** 950 ha

■ Site description
A mountainous area supporting natural forests and alpine pastures. Human activities include stock-grazing and other forms of agriculture.

Habitats Forest and woodland (50%; mixed forest), Grassland (25%; alpine/subalpine/boreal grassland), Rocky areas (25%; scree/boulders)
Land-use Agriculture (5%), Forestry (20%), Not utilized (75%)

■ Birds

Species	Season	Year	Pop min	Pop max	Acc	Criteria
Serinus citrinella Citril Finch	B	1995	40	—	—	B3

Important for breeding *Serinus citrinella* and forest species such as *Dryocopus martius*, *Dendrocopos leucotos* and *Picoides tridactylus*.

Upland species are also present, with *Bonasa bonasia*, *Tetrao tetrix*, *Tetrao urogallus* and *Turdus torquatus* breeding.

■ Protection status
National None **International** None

■ Conservation issues

Threats Intensified forest management (C), Recreation/tourism (C)

The area is threatened by development for tourism.

REFERENCES

HEATH, M. F. AND BORGGREVE, C. (2000) *BirdLife International/EBCC European Bird Database 1998*. Cambridge, UK: BirdLife International.

TUCKER, G. M. AND HEATH, M. F. (1994) *Birds in Europe: their conservation status*. Cambridge, UK: BirdLife International (BirdLife Conservation Series no. 3).

WILLI, G. (1984) *Die Brutvögel des liechtensteinischen Alpenraumes*. Vaduz (Naturkdl. Forschung im Fürstentum Liechtenstein 4).

WILLI, G. (1990) Die Vogelwelt des Ruggeller Rietes [The birds of the Ruggeller Riet]. *Berichte der Bot.-Zool. Gesellschaft Liechtenstein-Sargans-Werdenberg* 18: 177–211.

WILLI, G. (1996) Vorkommen von Wiesenvögeln im Gebiet Bangs-Matschels [Presence of birds of meadows in Bangs-Matschels]. *Vorarlberger Naturschau* 2: 101–118.

WILLI, G. AND BROGGI, M. F. (1983, 1985, 1986) Die Vogelwelt des Fürstentums Liechtenstein unter Berücksichtigung der benachbarten Gebiete. Teile I, II, III. *Ber. Bot.-Zool. Ges. Liechtenstein-Sargans-Werdenberg* 12: 61–117, 14: 103–143, 15: 37–92.

LITHUANIA

L. RAUDONIKIS, P. KURLAVIČIUS AND G. MATIUKAS

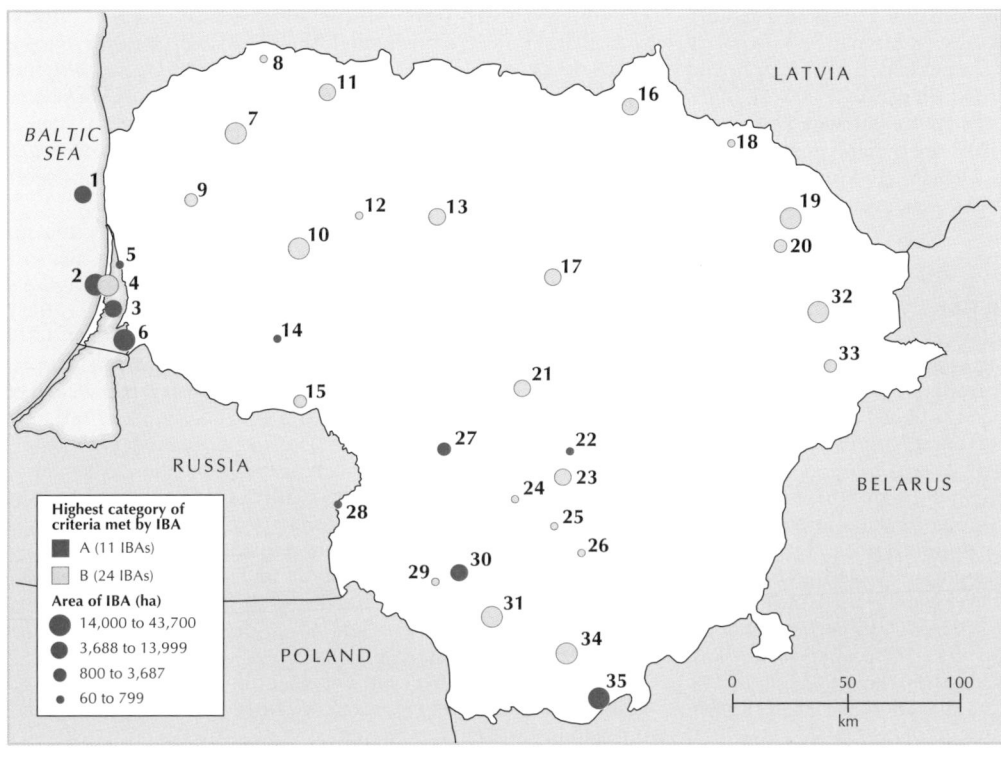

Wetland and forest are the predominant habitats at IBAs in Lithuania. (PHOTO: MINDAUGAS MACIULIS)

GENERAL INTRODUCTION

Lithuania, covering 65,300 km², is bounded in the north by Latvia, in the west by the Baltic Sea, in the east by Belarus and in the south by Russia (Kaliningrad region) and Poland. It is the largest and the southernmost of the three Baltic republics, and is generally flat with some hilly landscapes, the highest reaching 293 m.

Just over half (54%) of the land area is used for agriculture, whilst 30% is covered by forest, mostly Scot's pine *Pinus sylvestris* (38%) and Norway spruce *Picea abies* (20%) stands, and 4% is inland water. About 10.8 % of the territory falls within protected areas.

Lithuania has 35 Important Bird Areas (IBAs) covering 3,177 km², about 5% of the country's land area (Table 1, Map 1).

Map 1. Location, area and criteria category of Important Bird Areas in Lithuania.

Highest category of criteria met by IBA

- ■ A (11 IBAs)
- □ B (24 IBAs)

Area of IBA (ha)

- ● 14,000 to 43,700
- ● 3,688 to 13,999
- ● 800 to 3,687
- • 60 to 799

Table 1. Summary of Important Bird Areas in Lithuania.   35 IBAs covering 3,177 km²

IBA code	National code	1989 code	International name	National name	Administrative region	Area (ha)	Criteria (see p. 11)
001	23	—	Seashore at Palanga	Baltijos jūra prie Palangos	Klaipėda	8,000	A1, A4i, A4iii, B1i
002	20	—	Seashore at Nida	Baltijos jūra prie Nidos	Klaipėda	20,000	A4i, A4iii, B1i, B2
003	15	SU023	Kuronian lagoon	Kuršių įlanka	Klaipėda	6,000	A4i, A4iii, B1i
004	16	SU023	Kuronian spit	Kuršių nerija	Klaipėda	26,394	B1iv
005	30	—	Tyras	Tyras	Klaipėda	600	A1, B2
006	21	SU022	Nemunas delta	Nemuno delta	Klaipėda	26,625	A1, A4iii, B2
007	38	—	Žemaitija National Park	Žemaitijos nacionalinis parkas	Telšiai	20,120	B3
008	32	—	Varduva	Varduva	Telšiai	600	B2
009	19	SU020	Minija	Minija	Klaipėda and Telšiai	800	B2
010	33	—	Varniai	Varniai	Telšiai	16,495	B2
011	9	—	Kamanos	Kamanos	Šiauliai	6,468	B2
012	25	—	Pavėžupis fish-ponds	Pavėžupio tvenkiniai	Šiauliai	400	B2
013	31	—	Tyruliai	Tyruliai	Šiauliai	3,688	B3
014	8	—	Jūra river valley	Jūros upės slėnis	Tauragė	200	A1, B2
015	36	—	Viešvilė Reserve	Viešvilės rezervatas	Tauragė	3,216	B2
016	2	SU021	Biržai forest	Biržų giria	Panevėžys	10,000	B2
017	12	—	Krekenava	Krekenava	Panevėžys	8,680	B2
018	3	—	Čedasai	Čedasai	Panevėžys	100	B2
019	27	—	Sartai	Sartai	Panevėžys and Utena	14,000	B2
020	34	—	Vasaknos fish-ponds	Vasaknų tvenkiniai	Utena	800	B2
021	17	—	Labūnava forest	Labūnavos miškas	Kaunas	9,515	B2
022	28	—	Šešuva river valley	Šešuvos slėnis	Kaunas	60	A1, B2
023	11	—	Kauno Marios Regional Park	Kauno marių regioninis parkas	Kaunas	10,173	B2
024	7	—	Išaužas fish-ponds	Išlaužo tvenkiniai	Kaunas	300	B2
025	10	—	Kašonys	Kašonys	Kaunas	100	B2
026	35	—	Verknė river valley (middle part)	Verknės slėnis	Kaunas	600	B3
027	22	—	Novaraistis	Novaraistis	Kaunas, Marijampolė	827	A4i, B1i, B3
028	29	—	Širvinta river valley	Širvintos slėnis	Marijampolė	300	A1, B2
029	37	—	Žaltytis	Žaltytis	Marijampolė	392	B2, B3
030	39	SU024	Žuvintas	Žuvintas	Alytus	6,570	A1, B2, B3
031	18	—	Meteliai Regional Park	Metelių regioninis parkas	Alytus	15,299	B1i, B2, B3
032	1	—	Aukštaitija National Park	Aukštaitijos nacionalinis parkas	Utena and Vilnius	40,570	B2
033	13	SU026	Kretuonas	Kretuonas	Vilnius	1,260	B2
034	6	—	Dzūkija forest	Dzūkijos miškai	Alytus	43,700	B2
035	4	SU025	Čepkeliai	Čepkeliai	Alytus	14,800	A1, B2

Seven IBAs were identified in the previous pan-European inventory (Grimmett and Jones 1989). One of these, Kuronian Spit (formerly SU023) was a transboundary site shared between Lithuania and Kaliningrad in Russia, but currently is smaller (site 004) and falls within Lithuania only (Table 1). Twenty-eight new IBAs were identified during 1995–1996. Most IBAs are wetland sites, including 12 sites in western Lithuania, six of which fall within the coastal zone or near the sea coast. All other sites are distributed quite equally throughout Lithuania.

ORNITHOLOGICAL IMPORTANCE

There are more than 100 species of European conservation concern (SPECs; Tucker and Heath 1994) breeding in Lithuania including the globally threatened *Crex crex*, *Acrocephalus paludicola* and *Aythya nyroca*; and the near-threatened *Gallinago media* and *Haliaeetus albicilla*.

IBAs holding important breeding numbers of these species are listed in Table 2. Tyras bog (005) is a particularly important area for protection of the Lithuanian population of *Acrocephalus paludicola*. Žuvintas (030) is also an important area for *Acrocephalus paludicola*. Čepkeliai raised bog (035) supports the largest known local breeding population of *Gallinago media*. Important numbers of *Acrocephalus paludicola, Crex crex, Gallinago media* and *Haliaeetus albicilla* breed in the Nemunas delta (006). Jūra (014), Šešuva (022) and Širvinta (028) river valleys hold the largest known local breeding populations of *Crex crex*.

Non-breeding populations of other species of global conservation concern present in Lithuania include *Anser erythropus* which occurs during migration. The status of *Branta ruficollis* and *Aquila clanga* are insufficiently known: both species are considered as occasional visitors during migration (Kurlavicius 1995). There is one internationally important wintering place for *Polysticta stelleri* in Lithuania (Palanga, 001) with up to 1,000 birds present every winter.

SPECs with significant breeding populations at IBAs in Lithuania are shown in Table 4. These include *Botaurus stellaris* (at sites 010, 012, 023, 024, 030, 031), *Ciconia nigra* (016, 017, 021), *Circus pygargus* (013, 026), *Aquila pomarina* (017, 021), *Tetrao tetrix* (011, 035), *Porzana porzana* (007, 027, 029, 030), *Porzana parva* (029, 030, 031), *Grus grus* (015, 027, 035), *Larus minutus* (010, 012), *Sterna albifrons* (008, 024, 033), *Chlidonias niger* (006, 010, 018, 019, 020, 025, 029, 031, 033), *Caprimulgus europaeus* (032, 034), *Alcedo atthis* (008, 009, 023, 032), *Coracias garrulus* (032, 034) and *Lullula arborea* (034).

Three Lithuanian IBAs qualify based on populations of wintering waterbirds (Table 3): Palanga (001) with *Polysticta stelleri* and more than 20,000 waterbirds regularly wintering; Nida (002) with up to 6–10 % of the Palearctic wintering population of *Melanitta fusca* and up to 10,000 *Clangula hyemalis;* and Kuronian lagoon (003) with more than 1% of the north-west European population of wintering *Mergus merganser* and *M. albellus*. Two sites qualify for passage birds (027, 031) (Table 3).

Kuronian spit (004) is an important bottleneck site with large numbers of migrating passerines, storks and raptors passing through in spring and autumn.

Table 2. Important Bird Areas in Lithuania that are important for species of global conservation concern (meeting criterion A1).

Species	IBA code
Polysticta stelleri Steller's Eider	001
Haliaeetus albicilla White-tailed Eagle	006
Crex crex Corncrake	006, 014, 022, 028
Gallinago media Great Snipe	006, 035
Acrocephalus paludicola Aquatic Warbler	005, 006, 030

Table 3. Important Bird Areas in Lithuania that support important numbers of one or more congregatory species (i.e. meeting criteria A4 and/or B1). IBAs meeting both criteria A4 and B1 for the species are shown in **bold**. IBAs meeting only criterion B1 for the species concerned, and not A4, are shown in normal type. For key to 'Season', see p. 7.

Species	Season	IBA code
Polysticta stelleri Steller's Eider	W	**001**
Melanitta fusca Velvet Scoter	W	**002**
Mergus albellus Smew	W	**003**
Mergus merganser Goosander	W	**003**
Fulica atra Coot	P	031
Grus grus Crane	P	**027**

Table 4. Species of European conservation concern with significant breeding populations at Important Bird Areas in Lithuania (meeting any IBA criteria).

Species [1]	Minimum national breeding population (pairs) [2]	Proportion (%) of national population breeding at all IBAs in Lithuania
Botaurus stellaris Bittern	400	17
Ciconia nigra Black Stork	450	4
Haliaeetus albicilla White-tailed Eagle	30	27
Circus pygargus Montagu's Harrier	300	7
Aquila pomarina Lesser Spotted Eagle	700	4
Tetrao tetrix Black Grouse	2,000	9
Porzana porzana Spotted Crake	800	16
Porzana parva Little Crake	150	36
Crex crex Corncrake	25,000	1
Grus grus Crane	600	8
Gallinago media Great Snipe	50	60
Larus minutus Little Gull	200	32
Sterna albifrons Little Tern	400	22
Chlidonias niger Black Tern	2,000	18
Caprimulgus europaeus Nightjar	4,000	5
Alcedo atthis Kingfisher	700	7
Coracias garrulus Roller	250	2
Lullula arborea Woodlark	15,000	1
Acrocephalus paludicola Aquatic Warbler	250	92

1. Only those species of European conservation concern (see Box 1, p. 12) that meet IBA criteria in Lithuania are listed.
2. Data are taken from the BirdLife/EBCC European Bird Database 1998 (Heath and Borggreve 2000).

The most important Lithuanian IBA, Nemunas delta (006) in western Lithuania, supports several species of global conservation concern, most of the SPECs breeding in Lithuania and wintering and migrating birds.

HABITATS

Most IBAs in Lithuania support complexes of different habitat-types. This is the case within the regional and national parks although, overall, forest is dominant. Over 80% of IBAs (30 sites) support forest, with eight of these sites having more than 50% forest cover (Figure 1)

More than 80% of IBAs contain wetland habitat, and at 40% of sites this covers more than 50% of the IBA area. Much of this wetland coverage is raised bog such as at Kamanos (011) and Čepkeliai (035), or transitional and/or mixed mires such as Viešvile

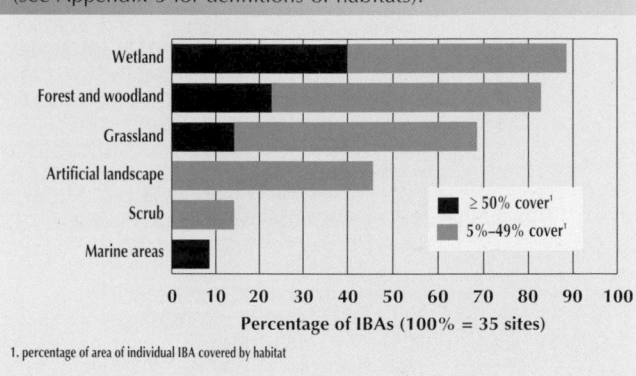

Figure 1. Habitats at Important Bird Areas in Lithuania (see Appendix 3 for definitions of habitats).

1. percentage of area of individual IBA covered by habitat

reserve (015). Novaraistis (027) is an exploited and partly regenerating peatbog. Žuvintas (030) contains flooded and swamp forest, a rare habitat-type in Lithuanian IBAs.

Several IBAs hold meadows and grasslands, which provide important habitat for *Crex crex*. Two sites are predominantly marine, Palanga (001) and Nida (002).

IMPACTS ON IBAs – LAND-USE AND THREATS

Most IBAs have mixed ownership, although some are privately owned (largely land within regional and national parks and fish-ponds) and others state-owned, such as strict reserves (Žuvintas (030), Čepkeliai (035), Kamanos (011), Viešvile (015)), marine sites and most smaller wetlands and meadows.

More than 70% of IBAs are used for recreation and tourism, but only a small part of each site is used exclusively for these purposes. A significant proportion of IBAs are used for forestry and agriculture. All forest in Lithuania, with the exception of strict nature reserves, is used for some forestry activities. Marine sites and fish-ponds are used for fisheries and aquaculture. Strictly protected reserves and some parts of national and regional parks are used for nature conservation and research only.

Human disturbance of birds, caused mainly by recreation, forestry, and agricultural activities, and direct threats to forests from forestry activities (including selective logging/cutting, commercial deforestation and intensified forest management) are currently the most serious factors affecting IBAs in Lithuania.

The abandonment of meadows, previously used for haymaking and grazing, is also detrimental to many birds. The decline of fisheries due to the privatization of fish-ponds affects several IBAs. Currently afforestation and drainage have a low impact only, in some unprotected meadows and wetland areas. The construction of an oil terminal at Butingė on the coast will seriously threaten the Palanga IBA (001).

Figure 2. Land-uses at Important Bird Areas in Lithuania (see Appendix 3 for definitions of land-uses).

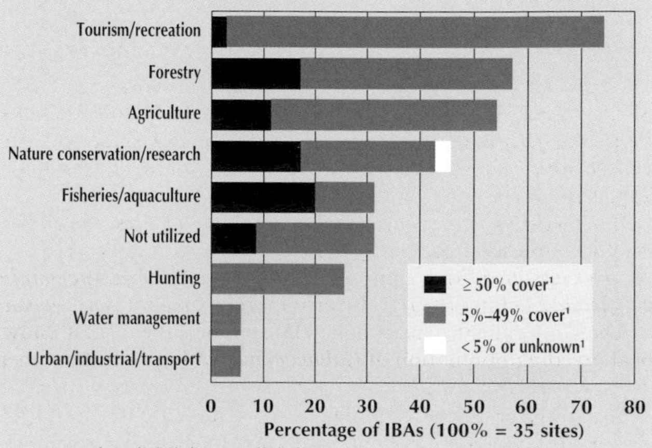

[Bar chart: Percentage of IBAs (100% = 35 sites), categories: Tourism/recreation, Forestry, Agriculture, Nature conservation/research, Fisheries/aquaculture, Not utilized, Hunting, Water management, Urban/industrial/transport. Legend: ≥50% cover[1], 5%–49% cover[1], <5% or unknown[1]]

1. percentage of area of individual IBA covered by land-use

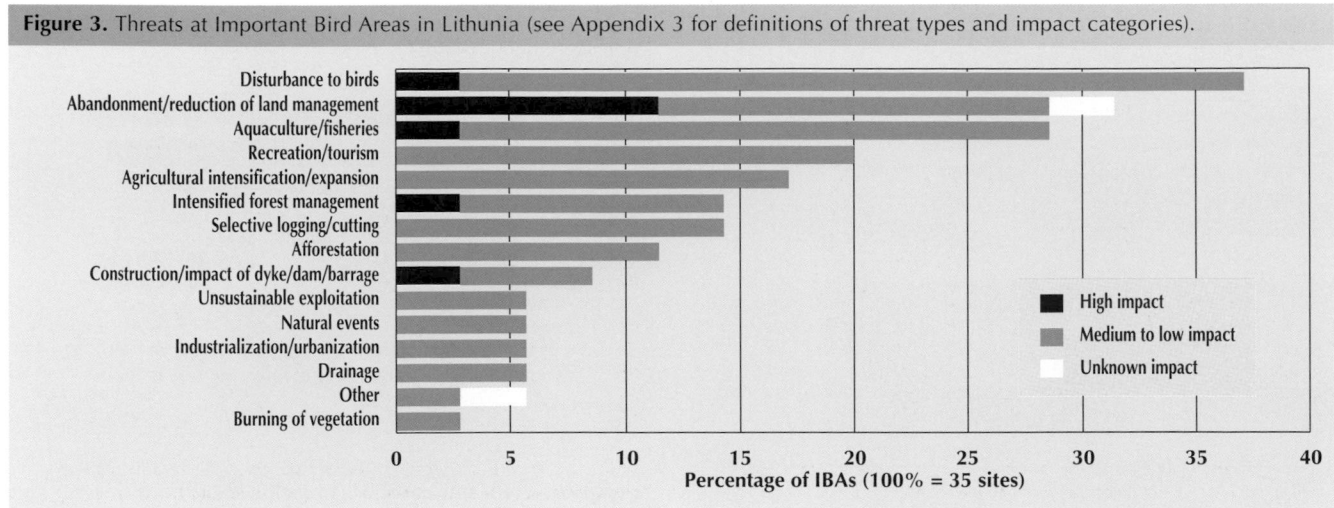

Figure 3. Threats at Important Bird Areas in Lithunia (see Appendix 3 for definitions of threat types and impact categories).

PROTECTION STATUS

■ National protection

The following principal categories of protected areas are recognized in Lithuania (links to IBAs are shown in Table 5).

1. Nature Reserve

Strictly protected areas with very little or no management.

2. National Park

All the National Parks have their own Nature Reserves and partially protected zones. Parts of these parks may be intensively managed, used for forestry or agriculture, and include urban areas.

3. Partial nature reserves

There are several types of protected areas within this category including Ornithological Reserves (these offer the best protection for birds), Botanical/Zoological Reserves, Landscape Reserves and Ichthyological Reserves (the latter protects rivers and streams only).

4. Regional Parks

These are a complex of Nature Reserves, Partial nature reserves, managed areas, recreational zones and buffer zones.

Of the 35 IBAs, nine are totally unprotected and a further 10 IBAs have less than 90% protective cover (Figure 4).

■ International protection

International legislation and initiatives that are relevant to site conservation in Lithuania are shown in Box 1. In total, 50,000 ha of IBAs in Lithuania are included in Ramsar Sites, encompassing the five largest wetland IBAs (Table 5, Figure 5).

Box 1. International legislation and initiatives that are relevant to site conservation in Lithuania (see Appendix 1 for a general description of these agreements).

Global	
Biodiversity Convention	✔
Ramsar Convention	✔
Bonn Convention	
World Heritage Convention	✔
MAB Programme	(✔)

Pan-European	
Bern Convention	✔

Regional	
Helsinki Convention	✔

✔ Convention ratified/initiative supported
(✔) Convention signed

Table 5. Protection status of Important Bird Areas in Lithuania.
A tick (✔) indicates that an IBA overlaps with a protected area (to any extent).

IBA code	International name	Nature Reserve	National Park	Ornithological Reserve	Botanical/Zoological Reserve	Landscape Reserve	Ichthyological Reserve	Regional Park	Ramsar Site
001	Seashore at Palanga							✔	
002	Seashore at Nida		✔						
003	Kuronian lagoon								
004	Kuronian spit		✔						
005	Tyras			✔					
006	Nemunas delta							✔	✔
007	Žemaitija National Park		✔						
008	Varduva					✔			
009	Minija						✔		
010	Varniai							✔	
011	Kamanos	✔						✔	
012	Pavėžupis fish-ponds								
013	Tyruliai			✔					
014	Jūra river valley						✔		
015	Viešvilė Reserve	✔						✔	
016	Biržai forest			✔					
017	Krekenava							✔	
018	Čedasai								
Subtotal of IBAs		**2**	**3**	**0**	**3**	**1**	**2**	**4**	**3**

IBA code	International name	Nature Reserve	National Park	Ornithological Reserve	Botanical/Zoological Reserve	Landscape Reserve	Ichthyological Reserve	Regional Park	Ramsar Site
019	Sartai							✔	
020	Vasaknos fish-ponds								
021	Labūnava forest								
022	Šešuva river valley								
023	Kauno Marios Regional Park							✔	
024	Išaužas fish-ponds								
025	Kašonys								
026	Verknė river valley (middle part)								
027	Novaraistis			✔					
028	Širvinta river valley					✔			
029	Žaltytis			✔					
030	Žuvintas	✔							✔
031	Meteliai Regional Park							✔	
032	Aukštaitija National Park		✔						
033	Kretuonas			✔					
034	Dzūkija forest		✔						
035	Čepkeliai	✔							✔
Total number of IBAs		**4**	**5**	**3**	**3**	**2**	**2**	**7**	**5**

Figure 4. The national protection status of Important Bird Areas in Lithuania.

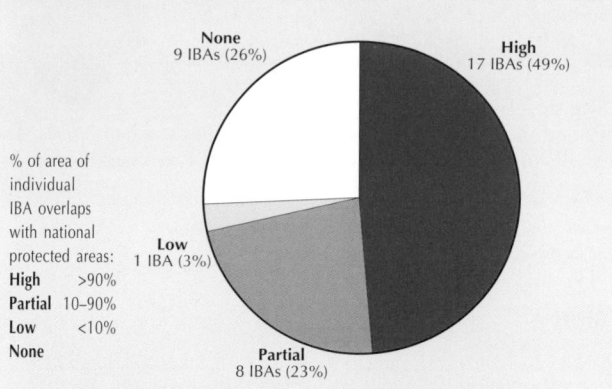

% of area of individual IBA overlaps with national protected areas:
High >90%
Partial 10–90%
Low <10%
None

Total area of overlap between IBA network in Lithuania and national protected-area system (see Table 5 for categories) = 2,720 km² (86% of total IBA area).

Figure 5. The international protection status of Important Bird Areas in Lithuania.

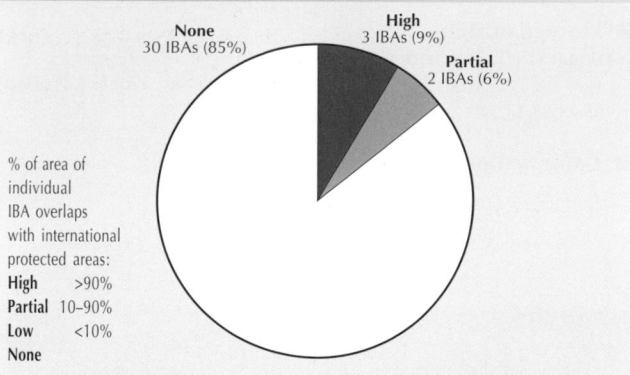

% of area of individual IBA overlaps with international protected areas:
High >90%
Partial 10–90%
Low <10%
None

Total area of overlap between IBA network in Lithuania and international protected-area system (see Table 5 for categories) = 484 km² (15% of total IBA area).

CONSERVATION ISSUES

- Management plans have been produced for Nemunas delta (006) and are in preparation for Varniai (010) and Meteliai Regional Parks (031).
- Permanent scientific monitoring studies are carried out in seven IBAs, and 16 are totally or partially covered by field workers within the IBA monitoring network.

ANALYTICAL METHODS

- Most of the bird data were collected during 1995–1996, being provided by the IBA network of field workers and the coordinator of the project.
- The land-use, threat and habitat data were assessed in 1996.
- All protected areas (with the exception of some Ichthyological Reserves) have good quality evaluations of area, habitats and land-use. Some IBAs which are unprotected have low quality area evaluation.

ACKNOWLEDGEMENTS

The funds for IBA work in Lithuania were provided by the Swedish Ornithological Society, with support from the Swiss Association for the Protection of Birds. Some data have been collected within different ornithological and nature protection projects with support from the Ministries of Environment, Agriculture and Forest Husbandry of Lithuania. Some projects were financed by local municipalities (Prienai, Kaišiadorys, Rokiškis, Pasvalys).

The bird data on marine and brackish areas were provided by the Institute of Ecology (G. Vaitkus, S. Švažas). The Nemunas Delta area and Tyras bird data were provided by the Ornithological Society of Klaipėda Region (a branch of the Lithuanian Ornithological Society). The most active field workers within the IBA network were: A. Aleknonis, D. Anuškevičius, J. Auglys, R. Barauskas, A. Butleris, E. Drobelis, M. Jankauskienė, V. Jusys, M. Kirstukas, V. Logminas, V. Lopeta, M. Mačiulis, A. Mačikūnas, D. Makavičius, V. Malinauskas, R. Mečionis, V. Naruševičius, Vl. Naruševičius, V. Pareigis, A. Pranaitis, Ž. Preikša, B. Šablevičius, S. Skuja, V. Stanevičius. The national IBA coordinator during the main field work was G. Matiukas.

SITE ACCOUNTS

Seashore at Palanga   A1, A4i, A4iii, B1i   001
Admin region Klaipėda
Coordinates 55°50'N 20°55'E
Altitude 0–0 m   **Area** 8,000 ha

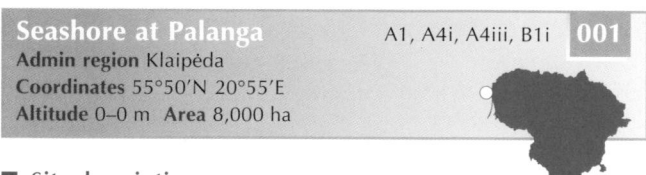

Site description
An offshore area in the Baltic Sea between 55°50'N and 55°55'N.

Habitats Marine areas (100%; open sea)
Land-use Fisheries/aquaculture (60%), Nature conservation/research (40%), Tourism/recreation (20%)

Birds

Species	Season	Year	Pop min	Pop max	Acc	Criteria
Polysticta stelleri Steller's Eider	W	1995	800	1,000	B	A1, A4i, B1i

The site is important for wintering and migrating waterbirds, especially wintering seaduck (including important numbers of *Clangula hyemalis*, *Gavia arctica* and *Alca torda*), totalling more than 20,000 individuals on a regular basis. The number of wintering *Polysticta stelleri* varies according to different sources (300–1,200), but 800–1,000 individuals is the most recent estimate.

Protection status
National Partial **International** None
The southern part of the IBA falls within a marine strict nature reserve (Pajūris Regional Park).

Conservation issues

Threats Disturbance to birds (C), Industrialization/urbanization (B)

In the near future, the Butingė oil terminal will be constructed near Palanga and oil pollution is therefore a potential threat.

Seashore at Nida   A4i, A4iii, B1i, B2   002
Admin region Klaipėda
Coordinates 55°30'N 21°02'E
Altitude 0–0 m   **Area** 20,000 ha

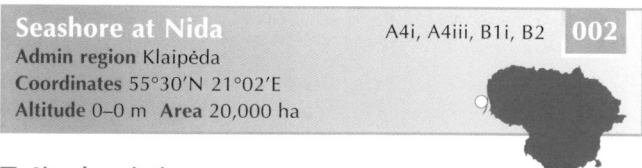

Site description
An offshore area (extending up to 40 km in length) in the Baltic Sea near the Kuronian spit.

Habitats Marine areas (100%; open sea)
Land-use Fisheries/aquaculture (70%), Not utilized (20%), Tourism/recreation (10%)

Birds

Species	Season	Year	Pop min	Pop max	Acc	Criteria
Melanitta fusca Velvet Scoter	W	1994	15,000	40,000	B	A4i, B1i, B2

In winter the area supports 6–10% of the western Palearctic population of *Melanitta fusca* (at densities of up to 1,000 birds/km²) as well as large numbers of other seaduck, e.g. *Clangula hyemalis* (up to

10,000 birds). The site holds more than 20,000 waterbirds on a regular basis.

■ Protection status
National High **International** None
20,000 ha of IBA covered by National Park (Kuršių Nerijos, 26,394 ha).

■ Conservation issues

Threats Industrialization/urbanization (C)

The site is covered by the national IBA monitoring network.

Kuronian lagoon
A4i, A4iii, B1i **003**
Admin region Klaipėda
Coordinates 55°25′N 21°10′E
Altitude 0–0 m **Area** 6,000 ha

■ Site description
The coastline and adjacent brackish water area (up to 2 km offshore) of a shallow marine bay. The area is used for shipping and industrial fishing.

Habitats Marine areas (100%; open sea; sea inlet/coastal features)
Land-use Fisheries/aquaculture (90%), Tourism/recreation (20%)

■ Birds

Species		Season	Year	Pop min	Pop max	Acc	Criteria
Mergus albellus	Smew	W	1994	1,100	—	B	A4i, B1i
Mergus merganser	Goosander	W	1993	3,000	19,000	B	A4i, B1i

An important area for staging and wintering waterbirds, supporting more than 20,000 birds in total, especially ducks and swans. The site is very important for wintering *Mergus albellus* and *M. merganser*.

■ Protection status
National None **International** None

■ Conservation issues

Threats Aquaculture/fisheries (B)

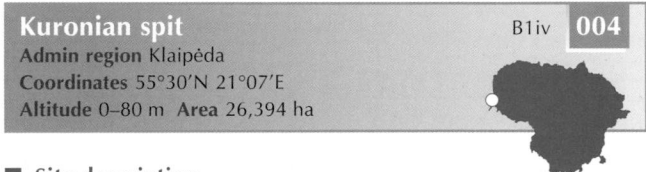

Kuronian spit
B1iv **004**
Admin region Klaipėda
Coordinates 55°30′N 21°07′E
Altitude 0–80 m **Area** 26,394 ha

■ Site description
A narrow sand-spit covered with *Pinus* woodland, located between the Kuronian lagoon and the Baltic Sea. Most of the area is used for recreation, and some for forestry. There are few villages.

Habitats Forest and woodland (70%; native coniferous forest), Wetland (25%; sand-dunes/sand beach), Artificial landscape (5%; other urban/industrial areas)
Land-use Forestry (20%), Nature conservation/research (20%), Tourism/recreation (60%)

■ Birds
Storks, birds of prey and passerines migrate through the area in large numbers, although no exact counts have been made.

■ Protection status
National High **International** None
26,394 ha of IBA covered by National Park (Kuršių Nerija, 26,394 ha).

■ Conservation issues

Threats Recreation/tourism (C)

There is a management plan for the National Park, which includes components on nature conservation and visitor management.

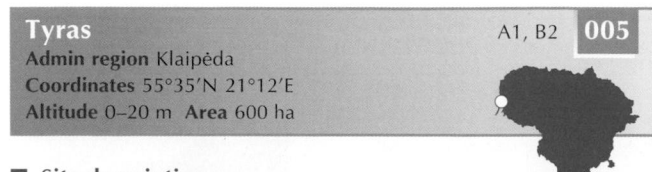

Tyras
A1, B2 **005**
Admin region Klaipėda
Coordinates 55°35′N 21°12′E
Altitude 0–20 m **Area** 600 ha

■ Site description
Wet flood-meadows, mostly dominated by *Carex*, some ponds, and marshes with mixed forests, near the shores of Kuronian lagoon.

Habitats Forest and woodland (10%; mixed forest), Grassland (80%; humid grassland), Wetland (10%; standing fresh water; water-fringe vegetation)
Land-use Agriculture (60%), Forestry (5%), Not utilized (30%), Tourism/recreation (10%)

■ Birds

Species		Season	Year	Pop min	Pop max	Acc	Criteria
Acrocephalus paludicola	Aquatic Warbler	B	1996	200	—	B	A1, B2

This is the main breeding area for *Acrocephalus paludicola* in Lithuania. Breeding species of global conservation concern that do not meet IBA criteria: *Crex crex* and *Haliaetus albicilla* (1 pair).

■ Protection status
National Partial **International** None
313 ha of IBA covered by Botanical/Zoological Reserve (Tyras, 313 ha).

■ Conservation issues

Threats Other

The area is covered by the national IBA monitoring network. Open habitats are threatened by natural succession to forests ('Other' threat).

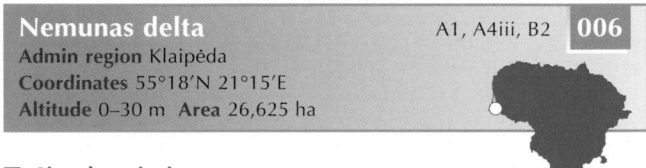

Nemunas delta
A1, A4iii, B2 **006**
Admin region Klaipėda
Coordinates 55°18′N 21°15′E
Altitude 0–30 m **Area** 26,625 ha

■ Site description
Flood-meadows, reedbeds, rivers, lakes and forests in the Nemunas delta. Most of the IBA is protected, with the remainder being used for haymaking, pasture and cultivation. Krokų Lanka lake (55°25′N 21°24′E) is used for fishing.

Habitats Forest and woodland (15%; broadleaved deciduous forest; mixed forest; alluvial/very wet forest), Grassland (60%; humid grassland), Wetland (20%; fen/transition mire/spring; sand-dunes/sand beach; standing fresh water; river/stream; raised bog; water-fringe vegetation), Artificial landscape (5%; urban parks/gardens; other urban/industrial areas)
Land-use Agriculture (30%), Forestry (10%), Nature conservation/research (50%), Tourism/recreation (20%)

■ Birds

Species		Season	Year	Pop min	Pop max	Acc	Criteria
Botaurus stellaris	Bittern	B	1996	15	20	A	B2
Haliaeetus albicilla	White-tailed Eagle	B	1996	4	5	A	A1
Crex crex	Corncrake	B	1996	170	200	A	A1, B2
Gallinago media	Great Snipe	B	1996	20	25	A	A1
Chlidonias niger	Black Tern	B	1998	—	200	A	B2
Acrocephalus paludicola	Aquatic Warbler	B	1996	20	30	A	A1, B2

The most important bird area in Lithuania. Very large numbers of waterbirds congregate at the site on passage (autumn and spring) and during the moulting season, including *Cygnus columbianus*, *Anser fabalis*, *A. albifrons*, *A. anser*, *Aythya fuligula* and *Mergus albellus*. A very rich and diverse assemblage of wetland, meadow and forest species breed (often in large numbers), including four breeding species of global conservation concern and numerous waterbirds and raptors. Large populations of gulls and terns also breed at the site, and include *Larus minutus*, *Sterna albifrons* and *Chlidonias niger*. The large colonies of *Larus ridibundus* disappeared in the 1980s.

■ Protection status

National High **International** High
26,625 ha of IBA covered by Regional Park (Nemunas delta, 26,625 ha).
23,950 ha of IBA covered by Ramsar Site (Nemunas delta, 23,950 ha).

■ Conservation issues

Threats Abandonment/reduction of land management (C), Agricultural intensification/ expansion (B), Disturbance to birds (B)

Haymaking has been abandoned on many meadows, although these currently still provide good habitat for migratory waterbirds and breeding waders. Krokų Lanka lake and adjoining meadows are covered by the national IBA monitoring network. A management plan is currently being prepared with the support of the Worldwide Fund for Nature and Euronatur.

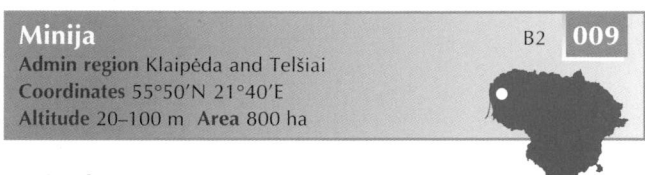

Species		Season	Year	Pop min	Pop max	Acc	Criteria
¹ *Sterna albifrons*	Little Tern	B	1996	—	—	—	B2
Alcedo atthis	Kingfisher	R	1996	10	—	A	B2

1. No population estimate (see main text).

■ Protection status

National Partial **International** None
470 ha of IBA covered by Landscape Reserve (Varduva, 470 ha).

■ Conservation issues

Threats Construction/impact of dyke/dam/barrage (B), Disturbance to birds (C), Recreation/tourism (C), Selective logging/cutting (C)

The area is covered by the national IBA monitoring network.

Žemaitija National Park B3 007

Admin region Telšiai
Coordinates 56°05′N 21°57′E
Altitude 70–200 m **Area** 20,120 ha

■ Site description

The majority of the area is covered by hemi-boreal forest (mostly dominated by *Picea*), and there are also bogs, marshes, several lakes with islands, meadows, and agricultural land. Land-uses are many and varied, including agriculture, forestry, and recreation.

Habitats Forest and woodland (45%; broadleaved deciduous forest; native coniferous forest; mixed forest), Grassland (20%; humid grassland), Wetland (25%; standing fresh water; raised bog), Artificial landscape (10%)
Land-use Agriculture (20%), Forestry (40%), Nature conservation/research (60%), Tourism/recreation (20%)

■ Birds

Species		Season	Year	Pop min	Pop max	Acc	Criteria
Porzana porzana	Spotted Crake	B	1996	25	—	—	B3

An important breeding area for *Porzana porzana*. Breeding species of global conservation concern that do not meet IBA criteria: *Crex crex*. This is the main breeding site for *Mergus merganser* (10–18 pairs) in Lithuania and is also important for breeding *Ciconia ciconia* (more than 70 pairs) and *Tetrao tetrix*.

■ Protection status

National High **International** None
20,120 ha of IBA covered by National Park (Žemaitija, 20,120 ha).

■ Conservation issues

Threats Disturbance to birds (A), Selective logging/cutting (C)

The biggest threats are posed by land privatization and forestry.

Varduva B2 008

Admin region Telšiai
Coordinates 56°22′N 22°08′E
Altitude 60–120 m **Area** 600 ha

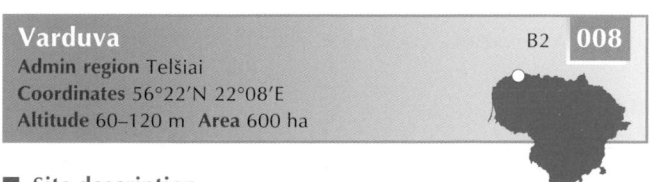

■ Site description

A variety of habitats in the Varduva valley, including a 274 ha reservoir with small islets covering in total c.3 ha.

Habitats Forest and woodland (15%; native coniferous forest; mixed forest), Grassland (25%; humid grassland; mesophile grassland), Wetland (40%; standing fresh water; river/stream), Artificial landscape (20%; highly improved reseeded grassland)
Land-use Agriculture (20%), Forestry (10%), Hunting (20%), Tourism/recreation (30%), Water management (20%)

■ Birds

An important breeding area for *Alcedo atthis* and *Sterna albifrons*. Species of global conservation concern that do not meet IBA criteria: *Aythya nyroca* (on passage).

Minija B2 009

Admin region Klaipėda and Telšiai
Coordinates 55°50′N 21°40′E
Altitude 20–100 m **Area** 800 ha

■ Site description

The area comprises the Minija and Babrungas valleys, and includes deciduous forests and meadows. The riverbanks are high.

Habitats Forest and woodland (65%; broadleaved deciduous forest; mixed forest), Grassland (15%), Wetland (25%; standing fresh water; river/stream; water-fringe vegetation)
Land-use Forestry (60%), Nature conservation/research (20%), Not utilized (10%), Tourism/recreation (20%)

■ Birds

Species		Season	Year	Pop min	Pop max	Acc	Criteria
Alcedo atthis	Kingfisher	R	1996	15	—	—	B2

Important numbers of *Alcedo atthis* breed. Breeding species of global conservation concern that do not meet IBA criteria: *Crex crex* (a few pairs).

■ Protection status

National Partial **International** None
300 ha of IBA covered by Ichthyological Reserve (Minija, 1,976 ha).

■ Conservation issues

Threats Recreation/tourism (C)

The Ichthyological Reserve protects only the river itself and a narrow zone along the banks, which is enough for *Alcedo atthis*, but does not provide real protection to the wider river valley.

Varniai B2 010

Admin region Telšiai
Coordinates 55°40′N 22°25′E
Altitude 60–120 m **Area** 16,495 ha

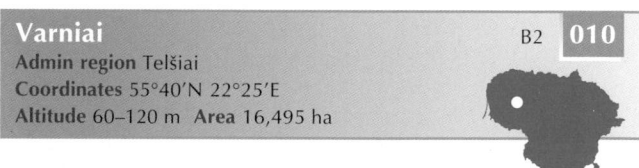

■ Site description

A large, swampy wetland of reedbeds, lakes, forests, and meadows. Biržulis lake is very shallow and surrounded by reedbeds. Sterva lake is surrounded by bogs. This IBA was previously known as 'Lakes Biržulis and Styrvas' in the previous pan-European inventory (Grimmett and Jones 1989).

Habitats Forest and woodland (40%; broadleaved deciduous forest; native coniferous forest; mixed forest), Grassland (10%; humid grassland), Wetland (50%; standing fresh water; river/stream; raised bog; water-fringe vegetation)
Land-use Agriculture (30%), Forestry (20%), Nature conservation/research (40%), Tourism/recreation (20%)

■ Birds

Species		Season	Year	Pop min	Pop max	Acc	Criteria
Botaurus stellaris	Bittern	B	1996	6	10	—	B2

Species ... continued	Season	Year	Pop min	Pop max	Acc	Criteria
Larus minutus Little Gull	B	1996	10	—	B	B2
Chlidonias niger Black Tern	B	1996	25	30	B	B2

An important breeding site for *Botaurus stellaris* and *Larus minutus*. Breeding species of global conservation concern that do not meet IBA criteria: *Crex crex* (a few calling males).

■ Protection status
National High **International** None
16,495 ha of IBA covered by Regional Park (Varniai, 16,495 ha).

■ Conservation issues

Threats Abandonment/reduction of land management (C)

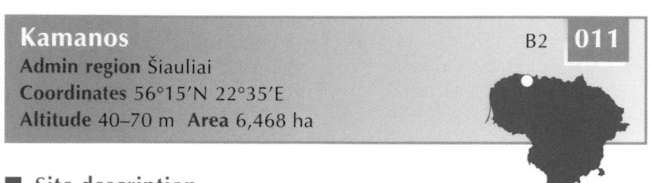

Kamanos
B2 011
Admin region Šiauliai
Coordinates 56°15′N 22°35′E
Altitude 40–70 m **Area** 6,468 ha

■ Site description
A large raised bog with some small lakes, surrounded by predominantly coniferous forests (mainly spruce *Picea* with some pine *Pinus*).

Habitats Artificial landscape (10%), Forest and woodland (40%; native coniferous forest), Wetland (60%; raised bog; fen/transition mire/spring)
Land-use Nature conservation/research (100%)

■ Birds

Species	Season	Year	Pop min	Pop max	Acc	Criteria
¹ *Tetrao tetrix* Black Grouse	R	1995	40	50	A	B2

1. Displaying males.

The site is important for mire-breeding species including *Tetrao tetrix* (with more than 50 displaying males, the largest concentration in Lithuania) and *Pluvialis apricaria* (min. 7 pairs), and supports large numbers of *Grus grus* on passage (up to 200 birds in autumn migration, 1995–1996).

■ Protection status
National Partial **International** High
4,300 ha of IBA covered by Strict Nature Reserve (Kamanos, 4,300 ha). 5,195 ha of IBA covered by Ramsar Site (Kamanos, 5,195 ha).

■ Conservation issues

Threats Afforestation (C), Natural events (C)

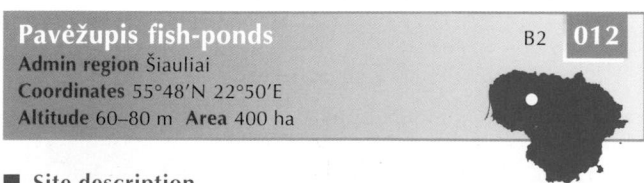

Pavėžupis fish-ponds
B2 012
Admin region Šiauliai
Coordinates 55°48′N 22°50′E
Altitude 60–80 m **Area** 400 ha

■ Site description
A system of intensively farmed fish-ponds with scattered trees.

Habitats Forest and woodland (5%), Grassland (10%; humid grassland), Wetland (80%; standing fresh water; water-fringe vegetation), Artificial landscape (5%)
Land-use Fisheries/aquaculture (80%), Hunting (20%), Tourism/recreation (5%), Urban/industrial/transport (5%)

■ Birds

Species	Season	Year	Pop min	Pop max	Acc	Criteria
Botaurus stellaris Bittern	B	1996	7	13	A	B2
Larus minutus Little Gull	B	1996	20	—	A	B2

An important breeding area for *Botaurus stellaris* and *Larus minutus*, and notable also for *Podiceps grisegena* (up to 20 pairs). Breeding species of global conservation concern that do not meet IBA criteria: *Haliaeetus albicilla* (irregular), *Crex crex* (a few pairs).

■ Protection status
National None **International** None

■ Conservation issues

Threats Aquaculture/fisheries (C)

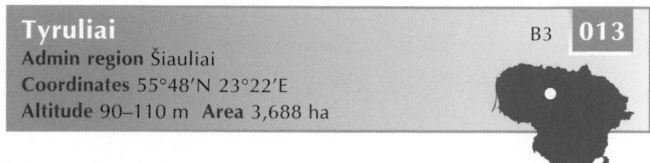

Tyruliai
B3 013
Admin region Šiauliai
Coordinates 55°48′N 23°22′E
Altitude 90–110 m **Area** 3,688 ha

■ Site description
An exploited peatbog and abandoned system of ponds with scrub, mixed woodland, meadows and reedbeds, and surrounded by agricultural areas. The majority of the area is not utilized by man.

Habitats Forest and woodland (40%; broadleaved deciduous forest; mixed forest; alluvial/very wet forest), Grassland (15%; humid grassland; mesophile grassland), Wetland (45%; standing fresh water; raised bog; water-fringe vegetation)
Land-use Agriculture (10%), Forestry (30%), Hunting (20%), Not utilized (50%)

■ Birds

Species	Season	Year	Pop min	Pop max	Acc	Criteria
Circus pygargus Montagu's Harrier	B	1996	6	7	B	B3

The most important breeding site for *Circus pygargus* in Lithuania. Breeding species of global conservation concern that do not meet IBA criteria: *Crex crex* (a few calling males).

■ Protection status
National High **International** None
3,688 ha of IBA covered by Botanical/Zoological Reserve (Tyruliai, 3,688 ha).

■ Conservation issues

Threats Abandonment/reduction of land management (C), Agricultural intensification/expansion (C)

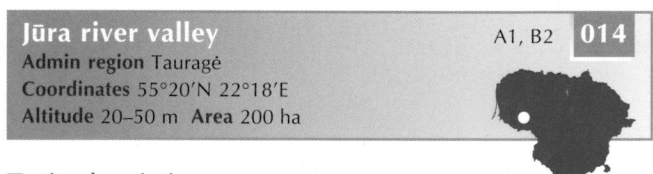

Jūra river valley
A1, B2 014
Admin region Tauragė
Coordinates 55°20′N 22°18′E
Altitude 20–50 m **Area** 200 ha

■ Site description
Wet and semi-dry meadows in the Jūra valley.

Habitats Scrub (10%; scrub), Grassland (50%; humid grassland; mesophile grassland), Wetland (20%; standing fresh water; raised bog; water-fringe vegetation), Artificial landscape (20%; highly improved reseeded grassland)
Land-use Agriculture (70%), Tourism/recreation (30%)

■ Birds

Species	Season	Year	Pop min	Pop max	Acc	Criteria
Crex crex Corncrake	B	1996	30	—	B	A1, B2

The site is important for breeding *Crex crex*.

■ Protection status
National Partial **International** None
130 ha of IBA covered by Ichthyological Reserve (Jūra, 114 km long).

■ Conservation issues

Threats Abandonment/reduction of land management (C), Agricultural intensification/expansion (C)

The Ichthyological Reserve protects only the river itself and a narrow zone along the banks, and does not provide real protection to the wider river valley, especially the meadows.

Viešvilė Reserve B2 015

Admin region Tauragė
Coordinates 55°06'N 22°28'E
Altitude 30–70 m **Area** 3,216 ha

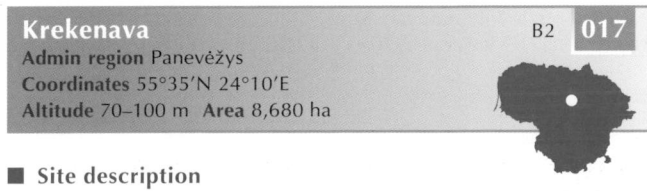

■ Site description
An area of boreal forest (60% pine *Pinus*, 20% alder *Alnus* and 10% birch *Betula* stands) with large bogs (covering 40% of total area).

Habitats Forest and woodland (65%; native coniferous forest; mixed forest), Wetland (60%; standing fresh water; raised bog; water-fringe vegetation)
Land-use Forestry (10%), Nature conservation/research (100%)

■ Birds

Species	Season	Year	Pop min	Pop max	Acc	Criteria
Grus grus Crane	B	1996	10	13	A	B2

An important breeding area for *Grus grus* (the highest density in Lithuania). Breeding species of global conservation concern that do not meet IBA criteria: *Crex crex*.

■ Protection status
National High **International** High
3,216 ha of IBA covered by Strict Nature Reserve (Viešvilė, 3,216 ha).
3,216 ha of IBA covered by Ramsar Site (Viešvilė, 3,216 ha).

■ Conservation issues

Threats Disturbance to birds (B)

The site is covered by the national IBA monitoring network.

Biržai forest B2 016

Admin region Panevėžys
Coordinates 56°13'N 24°42'E
Altitude 70–120 m **Area** 10,000 ha

■ Site description
An area of deciduous and mixed wet woodland which is under intensive forest management.

Habitats Forest and woodland (90%; broadleaved deciduous forest; mixed forest; alluvial/very wet forest), Grassland (10%)
Land-use Forestry (90%), Nature conservation/research (5%), Tourism/recreation (10%)

■ Birds

Species	Season	Year	Pop min	Pop max	Acc	Criteria
Ciconia nigra Black Stork	B	1996	—	6	B	B2

Apart from important numbers of breeding *Ciconia nigra*, the area is also rich in breeding woodpecker species, and rare species of owl may breed as well.

■ Protection status
National Low **International** None
144 ha of IBA covered by Botanical Reserve (Biržų Giria, 144 ha).

■ Conservation issues

Threats Intensified forest management (B)

Krekenava B2 017

Admin region Panevėžys
Coordinates 55°35'N 24°10'E
Altitude 70–100 m **Area** 8,680 ha

■ Site description

Habitats Forest and woodland (50%; broadleaved deciduous forest; mixed forest), Grassland (15%), Wetland (10%; river/stream), Artificial landscape (25%; arable land; urban parks/gardens)
Land-use Agriculture (40%), Forestry (50%), Hunting (10%)

A tract of mixed and deciduous forest, in central Lithuania, most of which is managed.

■ Birds

Species	Season	Year	Pop min	Pop max	Acc	Criteria
Aquila pomarina Lesser Spotted Eagle	B	1996	1	10	—	B2

An important site for breeding birds of prey (especially *Aquila pomarina*), *Ciconia nigra* (no population estimate), and rare woodpecker species in Lithuania. Species of global conservation concern that do not meet IBA criteria: *Haliaeetus albicilla* (on passage), *Crex crex* (5–6 calling males).

■ Protection status
National High **International** None
8,680 ha of IBA covered by Regional Park (Krekenava, 11,929 ha).

■ Conservation issues

Threats Abandonment/reduction of land management (A), Aquaculture/fisheries (B), Intensified forest management (A)

Forest management causes disturbance to birds.

Čedasai B2 018

Admin region Panevėžys
Coordinates 56°05'N 25°25'E
Altitude 40–60 m **Area** 100 ha

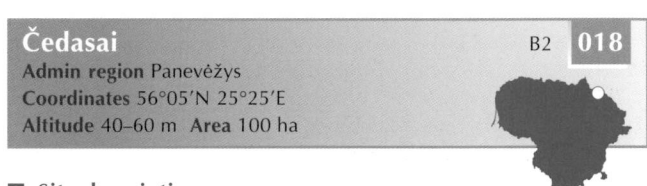

■ Site description
A very shallow, nutrient-rich lake.

Habitats Forest and woodland (10%), Wetland (90%; standing fresh water; water-fringe vegetation; fen/transition mire/spring)
Land-use Agriculture (10%), Not utilized (60%), Tourism/recreation (30%)

■ Birds

Species	Season	Year	Pop min	Pop max	Acc	Criteria
Chlidonias niger Black Tern	B	1996	30	40	B	B2

An important breeding site for *Chlidonias niger*. Species of global conservation concern that do not meet IBA criteria: *Haliaeetus albicilla* (non-breeding), *Crex crex* (breeding).

■ Protection status
National None **International** None

■ Conservation issues

Threats Disturbance to birds (B)

The site is covered by the national IBA monitoring network. There are plans to extract curative mud from the lake bed.

Sartai B2 019

Admin region Panevėžys and Utena
Coordinates 55°48'N 25°49'E
Altitude 50–100 m **Area** 14,000 ha

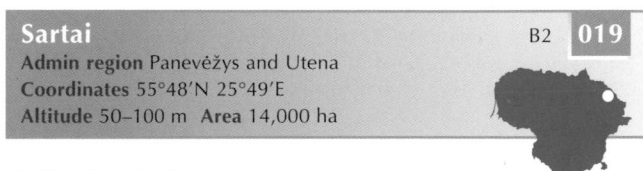

■ Site description
Sartai lake is adjacent to the Rokiškis fish-ponds. The lake is large and long, with reedbeds, and is surrounded by mixed forests.

Habitats Forest and woodland (40%; native coniferous forest; mixed forest), Grassland (15%; humid grassland; mesophile grassland), Wetland (35%; standing fresh water), Artificial landscape (10%; highly improved reseeded grassland; other urban/industrial areas)
Land-use Fisheries/aquaculture (25%), Forestry (25%), Hunting (15%), Nature conservation/research (10%), Tourism/recreation (25%)

■ Birds

Species	Season	Year	Pop min	Pop max	Acc	Criteria
Chlidonias niger Black Tern	B	1996	50	—	B	B2

An important site for *Chlidonias niger*. Breeding species of global conservation concern that do not meet IBA criteria: *Haliaeetus albicilla* (1–2 pairs), *Crex crex* (more than 10 pairs).

■ Protection status
National High **International** None
12,565 ha of IBA covered by Regional Park (Sartai, 12,565 ha).

■ Conservation issues

Threats Aquaculture/fisheries (C), Recreation/tourism (C), Selective logging/cutting (C)

Threats are varied. The fish-ponds are used intensively which poses a threat through drastic changes in habitat, e.g. ponds may be drained at the time of year when they are most important for birds.

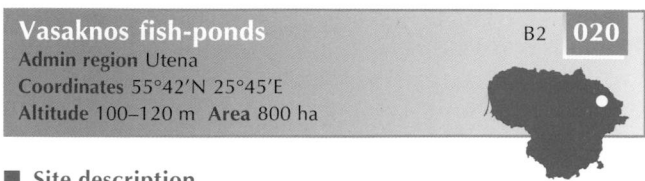

Vasaknos fish-ponds — B2 020
Admin region Utena
Coordinates 55°42′N 25°45′E
Altitude 100–120 m **Area** 800 ha

■ Site description
A large system of intensively farmed fish-ponds.

Habitats Forest and woodland (20%; native coniferous forest), Wetland (50%; standing fresh water; water-fringe vegetation), Artificial landscape (30%; other urban/industrial areas)
Land-use Fisheries/aquaculture (80%), Hunting (10%), Tourism/recreation (15%), Urban/industrial/transport (5%)

■ Birds

Species	Season	Year	Pop min	Pop max	Acc	Criteria
Chlidonias niger Black Tern	B	1996	100	—	B	B2

An important breeding site for *Chlidonias niger*. Species of global conservation concern that do not meet IBA criteria: *Aythya nyroca* (status unknown), *Haliaeetus albicilla* (1 pair), *Crex crex* (breeding).

■ Protection status
National None **International** None

■ Conservation issues

Threats Aquaculture/fisheries (B), Recreation/tourism (C), Unsustainable exploitation (B)

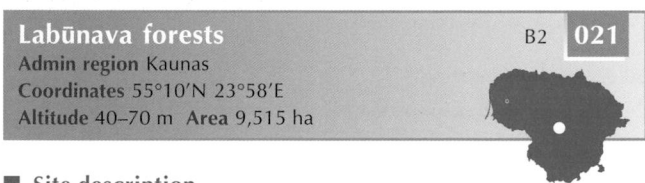

Labūnava forests — B2 021
Admin region Kaunas
Coordinates 55°10′N 23°58′E
Altitude 40–70 m **Area** 9,515 ha

■ Site description
Deciduous forests, mostly wet, that are intensively managed.

Habitats Forest and woodland (75%; broadleaved deciduous forest; mixed forest), Grassland (5%), Wetland (10%; standing fresh water; raised bog), Artificial landscape (5%; arable land; urban parks/gardens; other urban/industrial areas)
Land-use Agriculture (10%), Forestry (90%)

■ Birds

Species	Season	Year	Pop min	Pop max	Acc	Criteria
Ciconia nigra Black Stork	B	1996	5	8	A	B2
Aquila pomarina Lesser Spotted Eagle	B	1996	12	—	—	B2

The best site in Lithuania for breeding *Aquila pomarina* and some other birds of prey. Species of global conservation concern that do not meet IBA criteria: *Haliaeetus albicilla* (on passage), *Crex crex* (breeding).

■ Protection status
National None **International** None

■ Conservation issues

Threats Disturbance to birds (C), Selective logging/cutting (B)

The site is covered by the national IBA monitoring network.

Šešuva river valley — A1, B2 022
Admin region Kaunas
Coordinates 54°56′N 24°18′E
Altitude 40–60 m **Area** 60 ha

■ Site description
Semi-natural wet meadows in a river valley (100–500 m wide) with some *Salix* bushes and small ponds. Floods are seasonal but irregular and the meadows have varied water regimes. Grazing and haymaking take place at low intensity.

Habitats Forest and woodland (10%; broadleaved deciduous forest), Grassland (75%; humid grassland), Wetland (15%; standing fresh water; raised bog)
Land-use Agriculture (75%), Not utilized (10%), Tourism/recreation (20%)

■ Birds

Species	Season	Year	Pop min	Pop max	Acc	Criteria
Crex crex Corncrake	B	1996	25	40	A	A1, B2

The area supports one of the highest breeding densities of *Crex crex* in Lithuania, with the meadows in the Kaišiadorys district providing particularly suitable habitat.

■ Protection status
National None **International** None

■ Conservation issues

Threats Abandonment/reduction of land management (U), Afforestation (C), Agricultural intensification/expansion (C)

The site is covered by the national IBA monitoring network, and there is an annual census of *Crex crex*. Currently, there are no major threats.

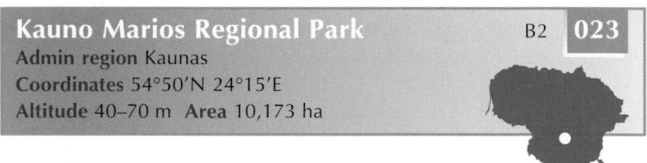

Kauno Marios Regional Park — B2 023
Admin region Kaunas
Coordinates 54°50′N 24°15′E
Altitude 40–70 m **Area** 10,173 ha

■ Site description
This site covers the upper part of a reservoir used for generating hydroelectric power, and includes some islands as well as surrounding forests, swamps and meadows.

Habitats Forest and woodland (20%; broadleaved deciduous forest; native coniferous forest; mixed forest; alluvial/very wet forest), Scrub (5%; scrub), Grassland (10%; humid grassland; mesophile grassland), Wetland (65%; standing fresh water; river/stream; water-fringe vegetation)
Land-use Fisheries/aquaculture (40%), Forestry (20%), Tourism/recreation (40%), Water management (30%)

■ Birds

Species	Season	Year	Pop min	Pop max	Acc	Criteria
Botaurus stellaris Bittern	B	1996	10	—	B	B2
Alcedo atthis Kingfisher	B	1996	15	20	B	B2

There are important numbers of breeding *Botaurus stellaris* and *Alcedo atthis*. Breeding species of global conservation concern that do not meet IBA criteria: *Haliaeetus albicilla* (1–2 pairs) and *Crex crex* (a few calling males). Other notable breeding species include *Aythya ferina* (min. 20 pairs) and *Dendrocopos medius* (min. 6 pairs).

■ Protection status
National High **International** None
10,173 ha of IBA covered by Regional Park (Kauno Marios, 10,173 ha).

■ Conservation issues

Threats Abandonment/reduction of land management (A), Construction/impact of dyke/dam/barrage (B), Intensified forest management (C), Recreation/tourism (B)

Due to hydropower generation, the water-levels of the reservoir fluctuate between day and night by as much as 0.5 m, although by less in summer. A serious impact on birds is predicted, although this has not yet been investigated.

Išlaužas fish-ponds

B2 024

Admin region Kaunas
Coordinates 54°45'N 23°56'E
Altitude 50–80 m **Area** 300 ha

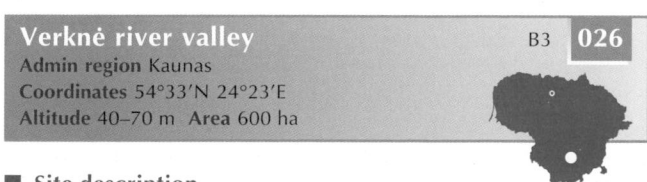

■ Site description
A complex of intensively farmed fish-ponds.

Habitats Forest and woodland (5%), Grassland (5%), Wetland (75%; standing fresh water; water-fringe vegetation), Artificial landscape (15%; highly improved reseeded grassland; other urban/industrial areas)
Land-use Fisheries/aquaculture (80%), Tourism/recreation (20%)

■ Birds

Species		Season	Year	Pop min	Pop max	Acc	Criteria
Botaurus stellaris	Bittern	B	1998	4	6	—	B2
¹ *Sterna albifrons*	Little Tern	B	1996	—	10	B	B2

1. 2–4 pairs only in 1997 and 1998.

During the period 1995–1996 up to 10 pairs of breeding *Sterna albifrons* were found breeding in the area. Breeding species of global conservation concern that do not meet IBA criteria: *Crex crex* (a few calling males).

■ Protection status
National None **International** None

■ Conservation issues

Threats Aquaculture/fisheries (B), Disturbance to birds (B), Unsustainable exploitation (B)

Intensive aquaculture poses a threat through drastic changes in habitat, e.g. ponds may be drained at the time of year when they are most important for birds.

Kašonys

B2 025

Admin region Kaunas
Coordinates 54°39'N 24°12'E
Altitude 50–70 m **Area** 100 ha

■ Site description
A complex of four lakes and ponds with surrounding meadows. The area is used intensively for fishing and recreation.

Habitats Scrub (5%; scrub), Grassland (10%; humid grassland), Wetland (70%; standing fresh water; water-fringe vegetation), Artificial landscape (15%; highly improved reseeded grassland)
Land-use Agriculture (20%), Fisheries/aquaculture (30%), Not utilized (20%), Tourism/recreation (40%)

■ Birds

Species		Season	Year	Pop min	Pop max	Acc	Criteria
Chlidonias niger	Black Tern	B	1996	30	35	A	B2

A rich area for breeding waterbirds, especially *Chlidonias niger* but also including, for example, three grebe species (*Podiceps cristatus*, *P. nigricollis* and *Tachybaptus ruficollis*).

■ Protection status
National None **International** None

■ Conservation issues

Threats Aquaculture/fisheries (A), Disturbance to birds (B)

Verknė river valley

B3 026

Admin region Kaunas
Coordinates 54°33'N 24°23'E
Altitude 40–70 m **Area** 600 ha

■ Site description
Semi-natural wet meadows, scrub and deciduous forests in the Verknė river valley. Abandoned land is being overgrown by scrub.

Habitats Forest and woodland (20%; mixed forest; alluvial/very wet forest), Scrub (10%; scrub), Grassland (30%; humid grassland), Wetland (30%; river/stream; water-fringe vegetation; fen/transition mire/spring), Artificial landscape (10%; highly improved reseeded grassland)
Land-use Agriculture (40%), Forestry (10%), Hunting (20%), Not utilized (30%)

■ Birds

Species		Season	Year	Pop min	Pop max	Acc	Criteria
Circus pygargus	Montagu's Harrier	B	1996	4	6	B	B3

An important breeding area for *Circus pygargus*. Breeding species of global conservation concern that do not meet IBA criteria: *Crex crex* (up to 10 calling males).

■ Protection status
National None **International** None

■ Conservation issues

Threats Afforestation (C), Burning of vegetation (B), Drainage (C)

Novaraistis

A4i, B1i, B3 027

Admin region Kaunas, Marijampolė
Coordinates 54°56'N 23°27'E
Altitude 30–50 m **Area** 827 ha

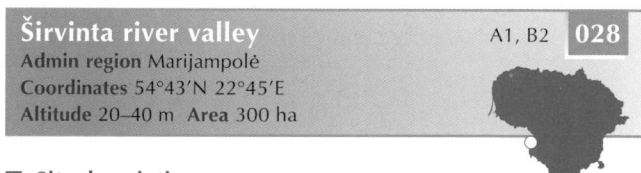

■ Site description
A bog which was formerly exploited for peat and then abandoned without any restorative measures being taken. It has now undergone some natural recovery, aided by the dam-creating activities of Eurasian beavers *Castor fiber* which are very common in the area.

Habitats Forest and woodland (20%; mixed forest), Wetland (80%; raised bog)
Land-use Forestry (20%), Not utilized (80%), Tourism/recreation (10%)

■ Birds

Species		Season	Year	Pop min	Pop max	Acc	Criteria
Porzana porzana	Spotted Crake	B	1996	20	20	A	B3
Grus grus	Crane	P	1996	700	1,200	—	A4i, B1i

The area is important for breeding *Porzana porzana*, for migrating *Grus grus*, and for moulting birds. Breeding species of global conservation concern that do not meet IBA criteria: *Crex crex* (a few calling males).

■ Protection status
National High **International** None
827 ha of IBA covered by Ornithological Reserve (Novaraistis, 827 ha).

■ Conservation issues

Threats Abandonment/reduction of land management (C)

The site is covered by the national IBA monitoring network.

Širvinta river valley

A1, B2 028

Admin region Marijampolė
Coordinates 54°43'N 22°45'E
Altitude 20–40 m **Area** 300 ha

■ Site description
A river valley (50–100 m wide) with flood-meadows, scrub, swamps, streams and ponds. The whole valley is used for haymaking and grazing.

Habitats Scrub (10%; scrub), Grassland (70%; humid grassland; mesophile grassland), Wetland (20%; standing fresh water; water-fringe vegetation)
Land-use Agriculture (60%), Not utilized (30%), Tourism/recreation (10%)

■ Birds

Species		Season	Year	Pop min	Pop max	Acc	Criteria
Crex crex	Corncrake	B	1996	34	34	A	A1, B2

This is a particularly good site in Lithuania for *Crex crex*.

■ **Protection status**
National High **International** None
300 ha of IBA covered by Landscape Reserve.

■ **Conservation issues**

> **Threats** Agricultural intensification/expansion (C), Disturbance to birds (C), Drainage (C)

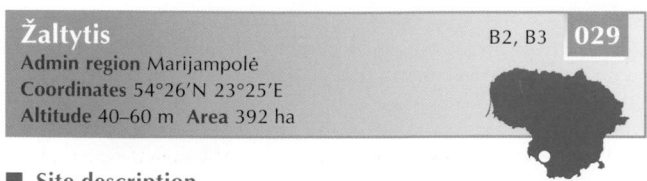

Žaltytis

Admin region Marijampolė
Coordinates 54°26'N 23°25'E
Altitude 40–60 m **Area** 392 ha

B2, B3 029

■ **Site description**
A lake surrounded by bogs and swamps.

> **Habitats** Forest and woodland (20%; mixed forest), Wetland (80%; standing fresh water; raised bog; water-fringe vegetation)
> **Land-use** Agriculture (10%), Forestry (10%), Hunting (10%), Nature conservation/research (70%)

■ **Birds**

Species	Season	Year	Pop min	Pop max	Acc	Criteria
Porzana porzana Spotted Crake	B	1995	10	—	C	B3
[1] *Porzana parva* Little Crake	B	1996	Frequent		—	B3
Chlidonias niger Black Tern	B	1996	30	35	C	B2

1. 13–19 pairs during 1984–1986.

An important area for breeding crakes *Porzana*.

■ **Protection status**
National High **International** None
392 ha of IBA covered by Ornithological Reserve (Žaltytis, 392 ha).

■ **Conservation issues**

> **Threats** Abandonment/reduction of land management (C), Aquaculture/fisheries (C)

The area is covered by the national IBA monitoring network.

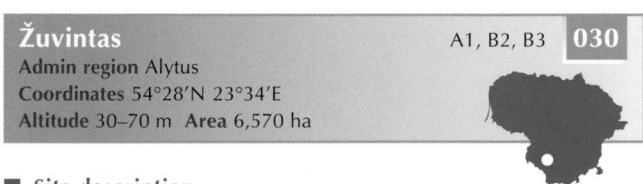

Žuvintas

Admin region Alytus
Coordinates 54°28'N 23°34'E
Altitude 30–70 m **Area** 6,570 ha

A1, B2, B3 030

■ **Site description**
A complex of raised bogs, marshes, forests, meadows and a large, shallow, overgrown, nutrient-rich lake.

> **Habitats** Forest and woodland (20%; broadleaved deciduous forest; mixed forest; alluvial/very wet forest), Grassland (5%), Wetland (75%; standing fresh water; river/stream; raised bog)
> **Land-use** Nature conservation/research (100%)

■ **Birds**

Species	Season	Year	Pop min	Pop max	Acc	Criteria
Botaurus stellaris Bittern	B	1995	10	15	B	B2
Porzana porzana Spotted Crake	B	1995	20	30	B	B3
Porzana parva Little Crake	B	1995	40	60	B	B3
Acrocephalus paludicola Aquatic Warbler	B	1995	10	15	B	A1, B2

An important wetland for a wide variety of breeding and migrating waterbirds (including good numbers of *Anser fabalis* and *A. albifrons* on passage). *Acrocephalus paludicola* has greatly decreased since 1980, when there were 25–30 pairs. This is the best breeding site for *Porzana parva* and *P. porzana* in Lithuania. Breeding species of global conservation concern that do not meet IBA criteria: *Crex crex* (3–5 calling males), *Gallinago media*. More than 10 pairs of *Aythya nyroca* bred in the 1970s but no recent data are available.

■ **Protection status**
National Partial **International** Partial
5,442 ha of IBA covered by Strict Nature Reserve (Žuvintas, 5,442 ha).
5,442 ha of IBA covered by Ramsar Site (Žuvintas, 5,442 ha).

■ **Conservation issues**

> **Threats** Abandonment/reduction of land management (A), Afforestation (C), Construction/impact of dyke/dam/barrage (A), Other (B)

The abundance of breeding ducks and waders has declined due to nutrient pollution of the wetland by human activities ('Other' threat).

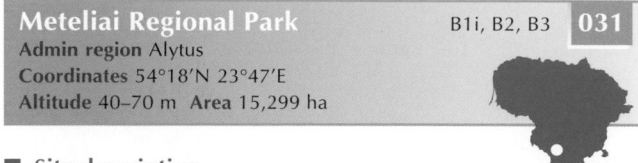

Meteliai Regional Park

Admin region Alytus
Coordinates 54°18'N 23°47'E
Altitude 40–70 m **Area** 15,299 ha

B1i, B2, B3 031

■ **Site description**
Three large lakes with differing habitat conditions. Dusia lake is mesotrophic, while Meteliai and Obelija lakes are eutrophic and have numerous reedbeds. Forests, meadows and marshes adjoin the lakes. Land-uses are varied, and include agriculture, fishing, forestry, recreation and human habitation.

> **Habitats** Forest and woodland (40%; broadleaved deciduous forest; native coniferous forest; mixed forest), Grassland (10%), Wetland (40%; standing fresh water; river/stream; water-fringe vegetation), Artificial landscape (10%; highly improved reseeded grassland; arable land; other urban/industrial areas)
> **Land-use** Agriculture (10%), Fisheries/aquaculture (30%), Forestry (40%), Tourism/recreation (30%)

■ **Birds**

Species	Season	Year	Pop min	Pop max	Acc	Criteria
Botaurus stellaris Bittern	B	1996	6	8	B	B2
Porzana porzana Spotted Crake	B	1996	30	—	A	B3
[1] *Porzana parva* Little Crake	B	1996	Uncommon		—	B3
Fulica atra Coot	P	1996	15,000	—	A	B1i
Chlidonias niger Black Tern	B	1996	25	30	A	B2

1. 9–12 pairs during 1984–1986.

The site is important for breeding *Botaurus stellaris* and crakes *Porzana*, and for moulting and migrating congregations of other waterbirds, especially *Fulica atra*. Breeding species of global conservation concern that do not meet IBA criteria: *Aythya nyroca* (6-8 pairs), *Crex crex*.

■ **Protection status**
National High **International** None
15,299 ha of IBA covered by Regional Park (Meteliai, 15,299 ha).

■ **Conservation issues**

> **Threats** Agricultural intensification/expansion (C), Aquaculture/fisheries (B), Disturbance to birds (B), Intensified forest management (C)

Dusia, Metelys and Obelija lakes are covered by the national IBA monitoring network.

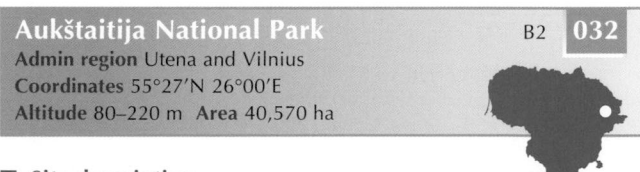

Aukštaitija National Park

Admin region Utena and Vilnius
Coordinates 55°27'N 26°00'E
Altitude 80–220 m **Area** 40,570 ha

B2 032

■ **Site description**
A complex of woodlands (mostly pine *Pinus*-dominated), lakes, rivers and meadows. The majority of the area is under forest management and is used for recreation.

> **Habitats** Forest and woodland (70%; native coniferous forest; mixed forest), Grassland (5%; humid grassland; mesophile grassland), Wetland (25%; standing fresh water; raised bog; water-fringe vegetation), Artificial landscape (10%; highly improved reseeded grassland; arable land; urban parks/gardens)
> **Land-use** Agriculture (10%), Forestry (50%), Hunting (10%), Nature conservation/research (30%), Tourism/recreation (30%)

■ **Birds**
This is one of the most important sites in Lithuania for *Coracias garrulus*, and *Caprimulgus europaeus*; *Tetrao tetrix* and *Alcedo atthis* are also common. Species of global conservation concern that do not meet IBA criteria: *Haliaeetus albicilla* (non-breeding) and *Crex crex* (breeding).

Species	Season	Year	Pop min	Pop max	Acc	Criteria
[1] *Tetrao tetrix* Black Grouse	R	1996	—	—	—	B2
[1] *Caprimulgus europaeus* Nightjar	B	1996	—	—	—	B2
[1] *Alcedo atthis* Kingfisher	R	1996	—	—	—	B2
[1] *Coracias garrulus* Roller	B	1996	—	—	—	B2

1. No population estimate (see main text).

■ Protection status
National High **International** None
40,570 ha of IBA covered by National Park (Aukštaitija, 40,570 ha). 800 ha of IBA covered by Strict Nature Reserve (800 ha).

■ Conservation issues

Threats Disturbance to birds (B), Intensified forest management (C), Recreation/tourism (C)

Some parts of the IBA are covered by the national IBA monitoring network. Part of the IBA has been managed to stop forest succession.

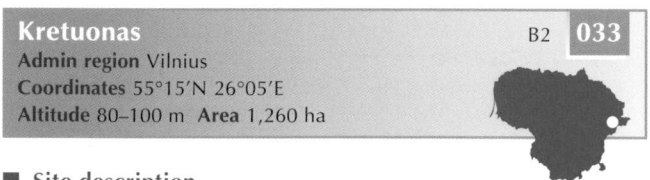

Kretuonas — B2 033
Admin region Vilnius
Coordinates 55°15′N 26°05′E
Altitude 80–100 m **Area** 1,260 ha

■ Site description
A shallow nutrient-rich lake with six islands, surrounded by wet meadows, mires, reedbeds and woodland.

Habitats Forest and woodland (10%; native coniferous forest; mixed forest), Grassland (10%; humid grassland), Wetland (80%; standing fresh water; river/stream; raised bog; water-fringe vegetation)
Land-use Agriculture (5%), Fisheries/aquaculture (60%), Nature conservation/research (20%), Not utilized (10%), Tourism/recreation (20%)

■ Birds

Species	Season	Year	Pop min	Pop max	Acc	Criteria
Sterna albifrons Little Tern	B	1996	—	10	B	B2
Chlidonias niger Black Tern	B	1988	40	40	—	B2

The lake (and particularly the islands) are important for breeding waterbirds, notably *Sterna albifrons* and *Chlidonias niger*. Breeding species of global conservation concern that do not meet IBA criteria: *Aythya nyroca* (possibly an irregular breeder), *Crex crex* (up to 3 calling males), *Gallinago media* (1 known pair).

■ Protection status
National High **International** None
1,260 ha of IBA covered by Ornithological Reserve (Kretuonas, 1,260 ha).

■ Conservation issues

Threats Abandonment/reduction of land management (A), Aquaculture/fisheries (B)

Overgrowth by shrubs has reduced the extent of some open habitats and has thus reduced the numbers of some bird species, especially breeding waders. Bird observations are made every year.

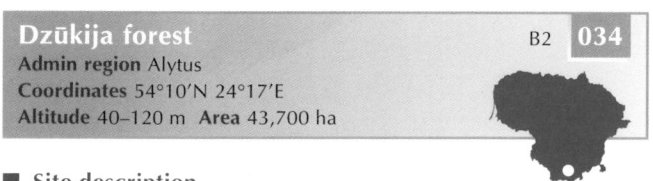

Dzūkija forest — B2 034
Admin region Alytus
Coordinates 54°10′N 24°17′E
Altitude 40–120 m **Area** 43,700 ha

■ Site description
A large tract of *Pinus*-dominated dry forest, traversed by rivers and with patches of deciduous woodland. The majority of the forest is managed.

Habitats Forest and woodland (95%; native coniferous forest; mixed forest), Grassland (5%), Wetland (10%; fen/transition mire/spring; standing fresh water; river/stream)
Land-use Agriculture (5%), Forestry (80%), Nature conservation/research (20%), Tourism/recreation (10%)

■ Birds

Species	Season	Year	Pop min	Pop max	Acc	Criteria
[1] *Caprimulgus europaeus* Nightjar	B	1996	—	—	—	B2
[1] *Coracias garrulus* Roller	B	1996	—	—	—	B2
[1] *Lullula arborea* Woodlark	B	1996	—	—	—	B2

1. No population estimate (see main text).

The forest supports important numbers of breeding *Coracias garrulus*, *Caprimulgus europaeus* and *Lullula arborea*, although there have been no specific counts.

■ Protection status
National High **International** None
43,700 ha of IBA covered by National Park (Dzūkija, 55,880 ha).

■ Conservation issues

Threats Disturbance to birds (B), Selective logging/cutting (B)

About 400 ha within the IBA/National Park is strictly protected.

Čepkeliai — A1, B2 035
Admin region Alytus
Coordinates 54°00′N 24°30′E
Altitude 80–100 m **Area** 14,800 ha

■ Site description
The site encompasses the largest raised bog in Lithuania (5,858 ha) with many forest 'islands', small lakes and marshes, and surrounded by mostly dry *Pinus* forests on sand-dunes. The bog is the source of two of the cleanest rivers in the country, the Ūla and Katra. There is a very low level of land-use.

Habitats Forest and woodland (40%; native coniferous forest; mixed forest), Wetland (60%; standing fresh water; river/stream; raised bog)
Land-use Nature conservation/research

■ Birds

Species	Season	Year	Pop min	Pop max	Acc	Criteria
Tetrao tetrix Black Grouse	B	1996	50	—	—	B2
Grus grus Crane	B	1996	10	13	A	B2
Gallinago media Great Snipe	B	1996	10	20	B	A1

A nationally important site for breeding waders (*Pluvialis apricaria* and *Tringa glareola*), woodpeckers (*Picus canus*, *P. viridis* and *Picoides tridactylus*) and *Grus grus*, and the most important site in Lithuania for *Gallinago media* and for *Tetrao tetrix* (more than 50 pairs). Breeding species of global conservation concern that do not meet IBA criteria: *Haliaeetus albicilla*, *Crex crex*.

■ Protection status
National Partial **International** Partial
10,590 ha of IBA covered by Strict Nature Reserve (Čepkeliai, 10,590 ha). 10,590 ha of IBA covered by Ramsar Site (Čepkeliai, 10,590 ha).

■ Conservation issues

Threats Natural events (C)

The reserve is strictly protected and there are no real threats other than the natural colonization of the raised bog by trees, and the event of natural fire. The whole site is covered by the national IBA monitoring network.

REFERENCES

ALEKNONIS, A. (1993) Novaraistis—a bird sanctuary of national importance. *Acta Ornith. Lit.* 7–8: 123.

DROBELIS, E. AND MATIUKAS, G. (1996) [The census of Black Storks in Lithuania in 1995.] *Ciconia* 4: 16–21. (In Lithuanian.)

457

GRIMMETT, R. F. A. AND JONES T. A. (1989) *Important Bird Areas in Europe*. Cambridge, UK: International Council for Bird Preservation (Tech. Publ. 9).

HEATH, M. F. AND BORGGREVE, C. (2000) *BirdLife International/EBCC European Bird Database 1998*. Cambridge, UK: BirdLife International.

JUSYS, V., POSKUS, A., MECIONIS, R. AND MAČIULIS, M. (1995) Nemunas Delta—Important Bird Area. *Baltasis Gandras (The White Stork)* 1995/1: 14–16.

LOGMINAS, V., ED. (1974) [*Kretuonas ornithological reserve.*] 148 pp. Periodika Publisher (In Lithuanian.)

LOPETA, V. (1994) The birds of Pavezupis. *Ciconia* 2(1/2): 110–115.

LOPETA, V. (1996) [The ornithological observations in Kelme and Siauliai districts.] *Ciconia* 4: 37–40. (In Lithuanian.)

MAČIKŪNAS, A. (1994) [A changes of Kauno mariu ornithofauna ...]. Doctoral thesis, Insitute of Ecology, Vilnius. (In Lithuanian.)

MAKAVIČIUS, D. (1994) The observations of birds of prey in Kamanos Reserve in 1991–1992. *Ciconia* 2(1/2): 95–100.

MAKAVIČIUS, D. (1994) The observations of *Mergus merganser* in the Mazeikiai district. *Ciconia* 2(1/2): 66.

MALINAUSKAS, V. (1993) Bird species of the Red Data Book of Lithuania detected in the Kaisiadorys. *Acta Ornith. Lit.* 7/8: 115–116.

MALINAUSKAS, V. (1996) [The rare plants and animals in Kaisiadorys district.] *Baltasis Gandras (The White Stork)* 1(2). (In Lithuanian.)

MALINAUSKAS, V. (1996) The best places for Corncrake (four years evaluations). Unpublished report.

MATIUKAS, G. (1994) The breeding bird atlas (Zemaitija National Park). Unpublished report.

MATIUKAS, G. AND MALINAUSKAS, V. (1996) The inventory of not protected nature values in Prienai district. Unpublished report.

MEČIONIS, R. (1996) Avocet—a new breeding bird species in Lithuania. *Ciconia* 4: 55–56.

NARUŠEVIČIUS, V. (1996) [The birds of the Labunava forestry and surroundings.] *Ciconia* 4: 40–43. (In Lithuanian.)

NEDZINSKAS, V. (1984) [Current situation of waterfowl in the Zuvintas Strict Nature Reserve.] In: *Proc. of Seminar. Moscow*. (In Russian.)

NEDZINSKAS, V. (1987) [The present state of Zuvintas Strict Nature Reserve.] In: *Ecology of birds in Lithuanian SSR*. (In Russian.)

NEDZINSKAS, V. (1993) [Birds of Zuvintas Nature Reserve In. *The Zuvintas Nature Reserve*.] (In Russian.)

PRANAITIS, A. (1992) Avifauna of Zuvintas Nature Reserve, 1980–1990. *Acta Ornithologica Lituanica* 5/6: 64–71.

PRANAITIS, A. (1996) The Zuvintas lake and swamp—important IBA. *Baltasis Gandras (The White Stork)* 2(3): 16–17.

PRANAITIS, A. AND BAUBLYS, G. (1996) The Red-footed Falcons in the surroundings of Zuvintas. *Ciconia* 4: 56.

STANEVIČIUS, V. (1992) Abundance, stucture and spatial distribution of ornithological complexes of lakes in south Lithuania. BSc thesis. (In Russian.)

STANEVIČIUS, V. (1995) Recent changes in lake's nonbreeding avifauna in Lithuania. *Abstr. of International Conference and 13th Meeting of the EBCC*.

SVAZAS, S. (1992) The significance of Lithuanian marine waters for the wintering population of the Velvet Scoter. *Acta Ornith. Lit.* 5/6: 39–41.

SVAZAS, S. (1993) Seabird numbers and distribution in Lithuanian marine waters. *Acta Ornith. Lit.* 7/8: 44–56.

SVAZAS, S. AND VAITKUS, G. (1992) Numbers and distribution of wintering waterfowl in Lithuanian coastal areas in 1987–1992. *Acta Ornith. Lit./IWRB Seaduck Bull.* 2: 10–19.

TUCKER, G. M. AND HEATH, M. F. (1994) *Birds in Europe: their conservation status*. Cambridge, UK: BirdLife International (BirdLife Conservation Series no. 3).

VAITKEVICIUS, A. P. AND PETRAITIS, A. K. (1964) [The ornithofauna of Nemunas river delta.] *Works of Lithuanian Academy of Sciences* 1(33). (In Russian.)

ZALAKEVICIUS, M., SVAZAS, S., STANEVIČIUS, V. AND VAITKUS, G. (1995) *Bird migration and wintering in Lithuania*. Vilnius. (Acta Zoologica Lituanica. Ornithologia. Vol. 2).

LUXEMBOURG

Patric Lorgé

Black Stork *Ciconia nigra*, an important species at IBAs in Luxembourg. (PHOTO: LNVL)

GENERAL INTRODUCTION

Luxembourg is one of Europe's smallest sovereign states, with a surface area of 2,586 km². It borders Belgium to the west and north, Germany to the east, and France to the south. Luxembourg has no mountains, no moorland and very little standing water.

There are four main land divisions: a small area of iron-ore deposits in the south, with a declining but still important iron and steel industry; a small area of lowland farmland in the remainder of the south and the centre; a strip of very steep, heavily wooded valleys (part of the Eifel/Ardennes massif); and remnants of marshes and bogs in the north-west on an otherwise cultivated plateau.

Luxembourg has nine Important Bird Areas (IBAs), as compared to three in the previous pan-European inventory (Grimmett and Jones 1989). These nine sites are much smaller and, with the exception of two sites, fall within the previous larger IBAs (Table 1, Map 1).

ORNITHOLOGICAL IMPORTANCE

Luxembourg holds one breeding species of global conservation concern, *Crex crex*, but this does not occur in sufficient numbers

Map 1. Location, area and criteria category of Important Bird Areas in Luxembourg.

BELGIUM

GERMANY

0   10   25
km

FRANCE

Highest category of criteria met by IBA
- B (1 IBA)
- C (8 IBAs)

Area of IBA (ha)
- 3,200 to 3,646
- 1,300 to 3,199
- 150 to 1,299
- 60 to 149

Table 1. Summary of Important Bird Areas in Luxembourg. 9 IBAs covering 113 km²

IBA code	National code	1989 Code	International name	National name	Administrative region	Area (ha)	Criteria (see p. 11)
001	LU001	LU001	Wiltzer and Trattenerbach	Reste der Oeslinger Feuchtegebiete	Canton de Clervaux	1,300	C6
002	LU002	LU001	Our	Our	Canton de Clervaux	1,700	C6
003	LU003	LU001	Pont Misere	Pont Misere	Canton de Wiltz	3,646	C6
004	LU004	—	Weisse Ernz	Tal der Weissen Ernz	Canton de Mersch	60	C6
005	LU005	—	Syre	Syre	Canton de Luxembourg	90	C6
006	LU006	LU003	Haff Réimech	Haff Réimech	Canton de Réimech	150	C6
007	LU007	LU002	Weiler-la-tour, Kessel	Weiler-la-tour, Kessel	Canton de Luxembourg	80	B1i
008	LU008	LU002	Roeserbann	Roeserbann	Canton d'Esch/Alzette	1,067	C6
009	LU009	LU002	Minières	Minières	Canton d'Esch/Alzette	3,200	C6

Table 2. Important Bird Areas in Luxembourg that support important numbers of one or more congregatory species (i.e. meeting criteria A4 and/or B1). IBAs meeting both criteria A4 and B1 for the species are shown in **bold**. IBAs meeting only criterion B1 for the species concerned, and not A4, are shown in normal type. For key to 'Season', see p. 7.

Species		Season	IBA code
Grus grus	Crane	P	007

Figure 1. Habitats at Important Bird Areas in Luxembourg (see Appendix 3 for definitions of habitats).

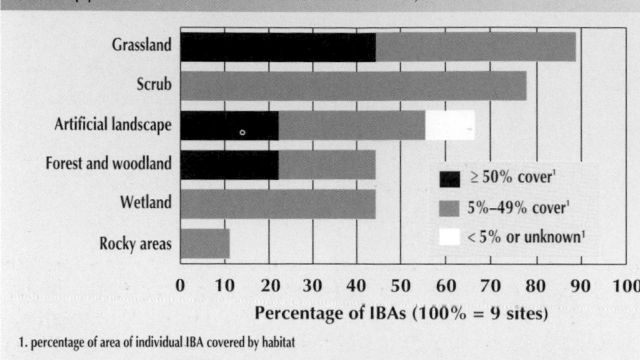

1. percentage of area of individual IBA covered by habitat

Figure 2. Land-uses at Important Bird Areas in Luxembourg (see Appendix 3 for definitions of land-uses).

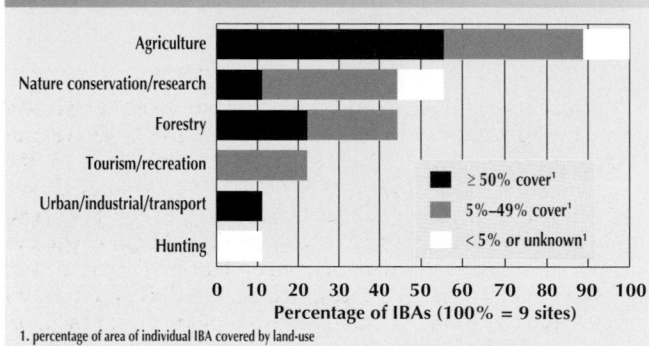

1. percentage of area of individual IBA covered by land-use

to meet the A1 criterion threshold at any site. An additional 83 species of European conservation concern (SPECs) also occur: five (three breeding, two occurring) of which have more than 50% of their global ranges in Europe and have an unfavourable conservation status in Europe (SPEC category 2); 36 (21 breeding, 15 occurring) of which have an unfavourable conservation status but less than 50% of their global population in Europe (SPEC category 3); 42 (37 breeding, 5 occurring) of which have more than 50% of their population in Europe but have a favourable conservation status (SPEC category 4). Several IBAs support important breeding populations of SPECs and species listed on Annex I of the EC

Birds Directive, including *Ixobrychus minutus* (IBA 006), *Ciconia nigra* (002, 003), *Pernis apivorus* (002, 003), *Milvus milvus* (002, 003), *Bonasa bonasia* (002, 003), *Crex crex* (004, 006), *Aegolius funereus* (001), *Dryocopus martius* (003), *Dendrocopos medius* (003) and *Lullula arborea* (009).

There are few wetland sites in Luxembourg but Weiler-la-tour (007) is an important roosting place for *Grus grus* with up to 1,200 birds observed here on autumn migration (Table 2). The nearest other roosting sites in the region are found some 200 km away in the Meuse valley in northern France.

HABITATS

Agriculture dominates the Luxembourg landscape with nearly 50% of the country being arable land. In the Oesling region in the north, which covers one third of the country, agriculture is partly dominated by grassland cultivation. Overall, agriculture is part pastoral, part arable, with grazing-, hay- and silage-meadows predominating (the main product being milk). Vines are grown for wine along the Moselle and some of its tributaries. This high agricultural coverage is reflected in habitats within IBAs, with 89% of IBAs holding some grassland, and 67% some artificial habitat of one sort or another (Figure 1).

Forests cover a third of the land surface, and of this area one-third is coniferous and two-thirds deciduous, although all is almost entirely modified. A large amount of reforestation has been carried out in the last 30 years with *Picea* plantations expanding at the expense of native hardwoods. Forty-four percent of IBAs have some forest and woodland, although plantations are classified as artificial landscapes (Figure 1). The Luxembourg landscape is extremely poor in standing freshwater and moorlands; wetlands, once abundant, have been much reduced by modern agriculture, as have hedgerows. Four IBAs hold some wetlands. A small part of country, the so-called Minette, is dominated by abandoned open-cast (iron-ore) mines.

IMPACTS ON IBAs – LAND-USE AND THREATS

Since the mid-1960s, farming in Luxembourg has been undergoing a dramatic transition from family-run mixed farms to highly specialized units. As the trend to increased agricultural production persists, so too is there a shift towards intensive, highly mechanized farming methods. Agriculture is a land-use in all IBAs (Figure 2). The result of these intensive agricultural practices is a decline of almost all farmland and grassland breeding birds, including *Crex crex*. Agricultural intensification and drainage are major threats to IBAs 001, 004, 005, 007 and 008.

Coppiced *Quercus* was once use commercially for its bark at Pont Misère (003), providing highly suitable habitat for *Bonasa bonasia*. However, the bark is no longer used commercially and the *Quercus* coppice is developing into forest and becoming less attractive to *Bonasa bonasia*.

Figure 3. Threats at Important Bird Areas in Luxembourg (see Appendix 3 for definitions of threat types and impact categories).

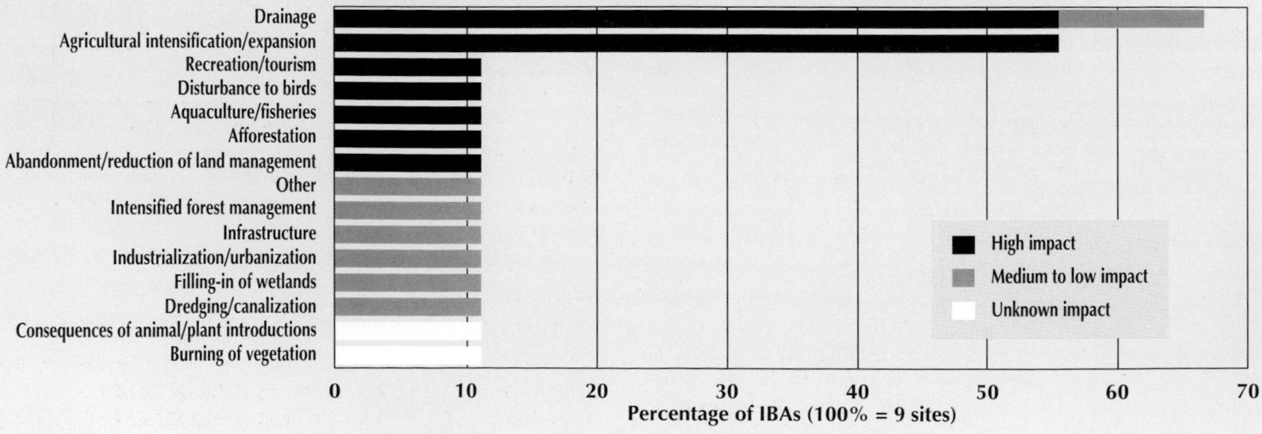

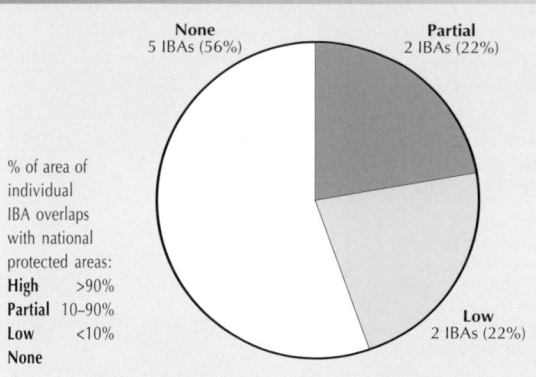

Figure 4. The national protection status of Important Bird Areas in Luxembourg.

None
5 IBAs (56%)

Partial
2 IBAs (22%)

% of area of
individual
IBA overlaps
with national
protected areas:
High >90%
Partial 10–90%
Low <10%
None

Low
2 IBAs (22%)

Total area of overlap between IBA network in Luxembourg and national protected-area system (see Table 5 for categories) = 6 km² (5% of total IBA area).

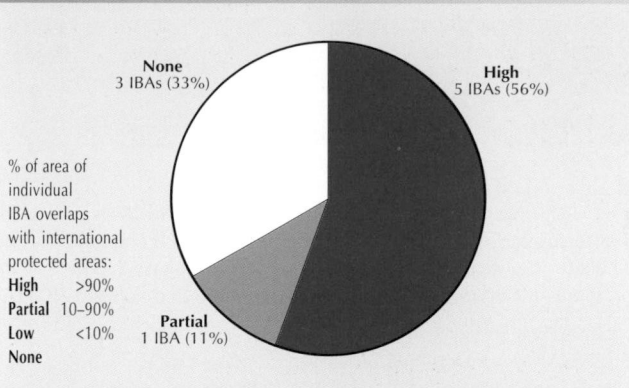

Figure 5. The international protection status of Important Bird Areas in Luxembourg.

None
3 IBAs (33%)

High
5 IBAs (56%)

% of area of
individual
IBA overlaps
with international
protected areas:
High >90%
Partial 10–90%
Low <10%
None

Partial
1 IBA (11%)

Total area of overlap between IBA network in Luxembourg and international protected-area system (see Table 5 for categories) = 100 km² (89% of total IBA area).

Tourism and recreation is a land-use at 22% of IBAs (Figure 2) and causes considerable disturbance to Haff Réimech (006), since the surrounding area is heavily frequented by tourists.

The major threat for Minières (009) is vegetational succession, with large areas changing from barren ground, with sparse vegetation and only a few bushes, to forest.

PROTECTION STATUS

■ National protection

The Ministry of Environment and the Service Conservation de la Nature are the responsible authorities for nature conservation at the national level. The commonest form of protected areas are Natural Reserves, which are designated by the Ministry of Environment, and which overlap with four IBAs (Table 3, Figure 4).

■ International protection

The international instruments that Luxembourg is party to are shown in Box 1. It is only during the last few years that the national

authorities have started to designate protection areas required by the Birds and Habitat Directives of the European Commission. With the exception of sites 004, 005 and 007, all IBAs are totally or at least partially designated as Special Protection Areas (SPAs), under the EC Birds Directive. One IBA is a designated Ramsar Site, Haff Réimech (site 006). International protection status is summarized in Table 3 and Figure 5.

CONSERVATION

- Luxembourg is one of the EU countries where the designation of SPAs has taken a very long time. Even in 1999, the year of the 20th anniversary of the EC Birds Directive, not all the important areas have been designated as SPAs. However, during the last two years and under the pressure of the European Commission, great efforts have been made in the designation of protected areas, under the Birds and the Habitat Directives. For some of the designated areas, management plans have been compiled, and it remains necessary to compile management plans for the other IBAs too. However, at least three IBAs considered to be of international importance are still not protected under any legislation.

ANALYTICAL METHODS

- All information on populations and distribution were provided by the ornithological database of LNVL or taken from the atlas of breeding birds in Luxembourg (Melchior *et al.* 1987). Most of the rarer species are well covered by ornithological surveys (*Falco peregrinus*, *Bubo bubo*, *Ciconia nigra*), made by the Ornithological Working Group of LNVL.
- Bird population data are from the period 1995–1998.

GLOSSARY

Foundation Hëllef fir d'Natur Luxembourg Nature Conservation Trust.
Gutland southern part of Luxembourg .
LNVL Lëtzebuerger Natur- a Vulleschutzliga (Luxembourg League for the Protection of Birds and Nature), the BirdLife International Partner in Luxembourg.
Oesling northern part of Luxembourg.
SPA Special Protection Area (designated under Article 4 of the EC Birds Directive).

Table 3. Protection status of Important Bird Areas in Luxembourg. A tick (✔) indicates that an IBA overlaps with a protected area (to any extent).

IBA code	International name	National — Natural Reserve	International — Ramsar Site	International — Special Protection Area
001	Wiltzer and Trattenerbach	✔		✔
002	Our			✔
003	Pont Misere			✔
004	Weisse Ernz			
005	Syre			
006	Haff Réimech	✔	✔	✔
007	Weiler-la-tour, Kessel			
008	Roeserbann	✔		✔
009	Minières	✔		✔
Total number of IBAs		**4**	**1**	**6**

Box 1. International legislation and initiatives that are relevant to site conservation in Luxembourg (see Appendix 1 for a general description of these agreements).

Global	
Biodiversity Convention	✔
Ramsar Convention	✔
Bonn Convention	✔
World Heritage Convention	✔
MAB Programme	
Pan-European	
Bern Convention	✔
Regional	
EC Birds Directive	✔
EC Habitats Directive	✔

✔ Convention ratified/initiative supported
(✔) Convention signed

ACKNOWLEDGEMENTS

The site accounts were compiled with information from the ornithological database of the LNVL and written by P. Lorgé. Special thanks to Marie-Paule Kremer, Ministère de l'Environnement, to Birgit Gödert-Jakoby from LNVL and to the BirdLife Secretariat IBA team for their help.

■ SITE ACCOUNTS

Wiltzer and Trattenerbach C6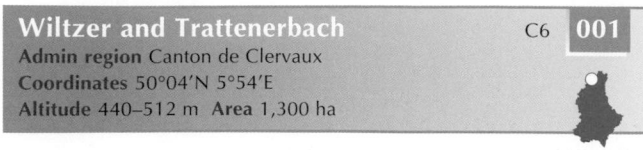

Admin region Canton de Clervaux
Coordinates 50°04′N 5°54′E
Altitude 440–512 m **Area** 1,300 ha

■ Site description

The catchment area of two small rivers, the Wiltz and the Trattenerbach, with adjacent wet meadows, wetlands and small forests. The site was included within a larger IBA (formerly LU001) in the previous international IBA inventory (Grimmett and Jones 1989).

Habitats Forest and woodland (20%; broadleaved deciduous forest; native coniferous forest), Scrub (10%; scrub), Grassland (20%; humid grassland), Wetland (3%; standing fresh water), Artificial landscape (50%; highly improved reseeded grassland; arable land)
Land-use Agriculture (75%), Forestry (15%), Nature conservation/research (8%), Fisheries/aquaculture (2%)

■ Birds

Species	Season	Year	Pop min	Pop max	Acc	Criteria
[1] *Ciconia nigra* Black Stork	N	1998	1	3	—	C6
Aegolius funereus Tengmalm's Owl	B	1998	1	2	—	C6
1. Pairs.						

The most important site in Luxembourg for *Ciconia nigra;* three pairs nest in large forests up to 20 km away but feed almost exclusively in this area. The IBA is also the only breeding site in the country for *Aegolius funereus.* Both species are listed on Annex I of the EC Birds Directive.

■ Protection status

National Low **International** High
63 ha of IBA covered by Natural Reserve (Wincrange 'Ramescher', 63 ha). 63 ha of IBA covered by Special Protection Area (Wincrange Ramerscher, 63 ha). 467 ha of IBA covered by Special Protection Area (Ramescher et vallee de la Tratterbach, 467 ha). 291 ha of IBA covered by Special Protection Area (Troisvierges Cornelysmillen, 291 ha). 90 ha of IBA covered by Special Protection Area (Hoffelt Kaleburen, 90 ha). 67 ha of IBA covered by Special Protection Area (Troine/ Hoffelt Sporbach, 67 ha).

■ Conservation issues

Threats Agricultural intensification/expansion (A), Drainage (A), Filling-in of wetlands (B)

Adjacent to the IBA are several remaining wetland areas, some of which are owned by Foundation Hëllef fir d'Natur.

Our C6 002

Admin region Canton de Clervaux
Coordinates 50°08′N 6°07′E
Altitude 400–505 m **Area** 1,700 ha

■ Site description

An area of deciduous and coniferous forest, adjacent to the Our stream on the Luxembourg–Germany border. The site was included within a larger IBA (formerly LU001) in the previous international IBA inventory (Grimmett and Jones 1989).

Habitats Forest and woodland (95%; broadleaved deciduous forest; native coniferous forest), Grassland (5%; humid grassland)
Land-use Agriculture (5%), Forestry (95%)

■ Birds

Species	Season	Year	Pop min	Pop max	Acc	Criteria
Ciconia nigra Black Stork	B	1998	1	2	—	C6
Pernis apivorus Honey Buzzard	B	1998	3	5	—	C6
Milvus milvus Red Kite	B	1998	1	2	—	C6
Bonasa bonasia Hazel Grouse	B	1998	1	3	—	C6

One of the most important areas in Luxembourg for breeding *Ciconia nigra*, *Pernis apivorus*, *Milvus milvus* and *Bonasa bonasia,* all listed on Annex I of the EC Birds Directive.

■ Protection status

National None **International** High
IBA entirely covered by Special Protection Area.

■ Conservation issues

Threats Intensified forest management (B), Other (B)

'Other' threat is water pollution from camping sites and villages, as sewage plants have not been constructed.

Pont Misere C6 003

Admin region Canton de Wiltz
Coordinates 49°51′N 5°48′E
Altitude 325–511 m **Area** 3,646 ha

■ Site description

The largest water reservoir in Luxembourg, with adjacent forests. The site was included within a larger IBA (formerly LU001) in the previous international IBA inventory (Grimmett and Jones 1989).

Habitats Forest and woodland (71%; broadleaved deciduous forest; native coniferous forest), Scrub (5%; scrub), Grassland (9%; mesophile grassland), Wetland (3%; tidal river/enclosed tidal water), Artificial landscape (5%; arable land), Unknown (2%)
Land-use Agriculture (20%), Forestry (80%), Hunting, Nature conservation/research

■ Birds

Species	Season	Year	Pop min	Pop max	Acc	Criteria
Ciconia nigra Black Stork	B	1998	1	2	—	C6
Pernis apivorus Honey Buzzard	B	1998	1	5	—	C6
Milvus milvus Red Kite	B	1998	1	1	—	C6
Bonasa bonasia Hazel Grouse	R	1998	3	10	—	C6
Dryocopus martius Black Woodpecker	R	1998	10	15	—	C6
Dendrocopos medius	R	1998	5	10	—	C6
Middle Spotted Woodpecker						

These forests are the most important area in Luxembourg for breeding *Ciconia nigra, Pernis apivorus, Milvus milvus, Bonasa bonasia, Dryocopus martius* and *Dendrocopos medius,* all listed on Annex I of the Birds Directive. The coppiced *Quercus* woodland, with an abundance of undergrowth, particularly favours *Bonasa bonasia.*

■ Protection status

National None **International** High
IBA entirely covered by Special Protection Area.

■ Conservation issues

Threats Abandonment/reduction of land management (A), Burning of vegetation (U), Consequences of animal/plant introductions (U), Drainage (A)

Weisse Ernz C6 004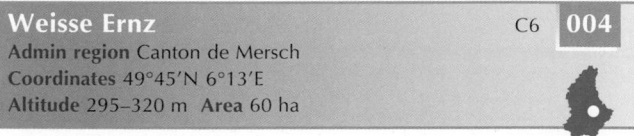

Admin region Canton de Mersch
Coordinates 49°45′N 6°13′E
Altitude 295–320 m **Area** 60 ha

■ Site description

A farm and grassland area, adjacent to the Weisse Ernz stream.

Habitats Scrub (10%; scrub), Grassland (85%; humid grassland), Wetland (5%; water-fringe vegetation)
Land-use Agriculture (100%)

■ Birds

The third most important site for *Crex crex* in Luxembourg. Breeding birds include *Alcedo atthis* and *Lanius collurio*. *Milvus milvus* breeds in the nearby forests. The wet grasslands also provide important roosting habitat for *Philomachus pugnax* and *Pluvialis apricaria*.

Species		Season	Year	Pop min	Pop max	Acc	Criteria
Crex crex	Corncrake	B	1998	—	1	—	C6

■ Protection status
National None **International** None

■ Conservation issues

Threats Agricultural intensification/expansion (A), Drainage (A)

LNVL is proposing this site as a Special Protection Area to the Ministry of Environment.

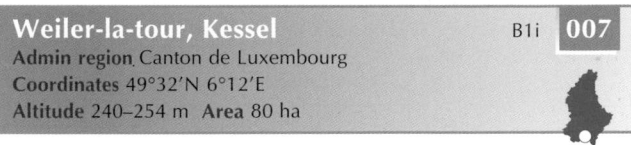

Syre
C6 005

Admin region Canton de Luxembourg
Coordinates 49°40'N 6°18'E
Altitude 240–260 m **Area** 90 ha

■ Site description
A valley with grassland and small wetlands (ponds and reedbeds) along the Syre stream.

Habitats Scrub (10%; scrub), Grassland (70%; humid grassland), Wetland (10%; standing fresh water; river/stream), Artificial landscape (10%; arable land)
Land-use Agriculture (70%), Nature conservation/research (30%)

■ Birds

Species		Season	Year	Pop min	Pop max	Acc	Criteria
Ciconia ciconia	White Stork	N	1998	—	—	—	C6

An important area for *Ciconia ciconia* with several birds summering in the area. Other species listed on Annex I of the EC Birds Directive and breeding at the site include *Lanius collurio* and *Alcedo atthis*. Species occurring on passage include *Luscinia svecica*, *Philomachus pugnax* and *Tringa glareola*.

■ Protection status
National None **International** None

■ Conservation issues

Threats Agricultural intensification/expansion (A), Drainage (A)

Thirty percent of the area is owned by the Foundation Hëllef fir d'Natur.

Haff Réimech
C6 006

Admin region Canton de Réimech
Coordinates 49°30'N 6°21'E
Altitude 140–140 m **Area** 150 ha

■ Site description
This is the largest wetland area in Luxembourg, and includes the Moselle valley and gravel-pits. The site was included within a larger IBA (formerly LU002) in the previous international IBA inventory (Grimmett and Jones 1989).

Habitats Scrub (35%; scrub; heathland), Grassland (15%; humid grassland; mesophile grassland), Wetland (45%; standing fresh water), Artificial landscape (5%; highly improved reseeded grassland; perennial crops/orchards/groves)
Land-use Agriculture, Nature conservation/research (65%), Tourism/recreation (35%)

■ Birds

Species		Season	Year	Pop min	Pop max	Acc	Criteria
Ixobrychus minutus	Little Bittern	B	1998	1	2	—	C6

The most important wetland in Luxembourg with records of over 230 bird species, including the only breeding site for *Ixobrychus minutus*. The site also holds breeding populations of *Picus canus, Alcedo atthis*

and *Lanius collurio*, all listed on Annex I of the EC Birds Directive. The site is also of national importance for wintering birds including *Botaurus stellaris*, *Mergus albellus* and *Falco peregrinus*.

■ Protection status
National Partial **International** High
100 ha of IBA overlap with Natural Reserve (Haff Réimech). 68 ha of IBA covered by Ramsar Site (Haff Réimech, 313 ha). 150 ha of IBA covered by Special Protection Area.

■ Conservation issues

Threats Aquaculture/fisheries (A), Recreation/tourism (A)

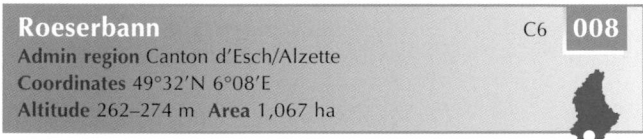

Weiler-la-tour, Kessel
B1i 007

Admin region Canton de Luxembourg
Coordinates 49°32'N 6°12'E
Altitude 240–254 m **Area** 80 ha

■ Site description
An area of grassland which is flooded in winter, and cut for silage in the spring and summer. The site was included within a larger IBA (formerly LU002) in the previous international IBA inventory (Grimmett and Jones 1989).

Habitats Scrub (5%; scrub), Grassland (90%; humid grassland), Wetland (5%; standing fresh water)
Land-use Agriculture (90%), Nature conservation/research (10%)

■ Birds

Species		Season	Year	Pop min	Pop max	Acc	Criteria
Grus grus	Crane	P	1997	300	1,200	A	B1i

An important autumn roosting site for *Grus grus*, the only site within a 200 km range. The area is also nationally important for migrating waterbirds, although numbers are small, including wintering *Anser fabalis* (100–150 birds). Species of global conservation concern that do not meet IBA criteria: *Crex crex* (breeding).

■ Protection status
National None **International** None

■ Conservation issues

Threats Agricultural intensification/expansion (A), Disturbance to birds (A), Drainage (B), Dredging/canalization (C)

11 ha of IBA covered by proposed Natural Reserve (Lannebur, 11 ha).

Roeserbann
C6 008

Admin region Canton d'Esch/Alzette
Coordinates 49°32'N 6°08'E
Altitude 262–274 m **Area** 1,067 ha

■ Site description
Lowland hay-meadows that are flooded in winter, along a small stream with natural eutrophic lakes. The site was included within a larger IBA (formerly LU002) in the previous international IBA inventory (Grimmett and Jones 1989).

Habitats Grassland (100%; humid grassland; mesophile grassland), Artificial landscape (forestry plantation; other urban/industrial areas)
Land-use Agriculture (100%)

■ Birds

Species		Season	Year	Pop min	Pop max	Acc	Criteria
Crex crex	Corncrake	B	1998	1	5	—	C6

This is the most important site for *Crex crex* in Luxembourg. *Milvus migrans, Alcedo atthis* and *Lanius collurio*, listed on Annex I of the Bird Directive, also breed.

■ **Protection status**

National Low **International** Partial

20 ha of IBA covered by Natural Reserve (Schifflange-Brill, 20 ha). 353 ha of IBA covered by Special Protection Area (Roeser–Roeserbann, 353 ha). 20 ha of IBA covered by Special Protection Area (Schifflange-Brill, 20 ha).

■ **Conservation issues**

Threats Agricultural intensification/expansion (A), Drainage (A), Infrastructure (B)

An LIFE programme to conserve *Crex crex* has been funded by the EU.

Minières · C6 · 009

Admin region Canton d'Esch/Alzette
Coordinates 49°29′N 6°05′E
Altitude 290–479 m **Area** 3,200 ha

■ **Site description**
Abandoned open-cast iron mines in south-west Luxembourg. The site was included within a larger IBA (formerly LU002) in the previous international IBA inventory (Grimmett and Jones 1989).

Habitats Forest and woodland (15%; broadleaved deciduous forest), Scrub (15%, scrub), Rocky areas (10%; inland cliff), Artificial landscape (60%; ruderal land; arable land)
Land-use Agriculture (15%), Forestry (20%), Tourism/recreation (5%), Urban/industrial/transport (60%)

■ **Birds**

Species	Season	Year	Pop min	Pop max	Acc	Criteria
Lullula arborea Woodlark	B	1998	5	20	—	C6

This is the last site with breeding *Lullula arborea* in the country. Other breeding species include *Bubo bubo, Pernis apivorus, Milvus milvus, Picus canus, Dryocopus martius* and *Lanius collurio.*

■ **Protection status**
National Partial **International** High

100 ha of IBA covered by Natural Reserve (Ellergronn, 110 ha). 165 ha of IBA covered by Natural Reserve (Pètange-Prënzebierg, 165 ha). 110 ha of IBA covered by Natural Reserve (Dudelange Haard, 110 ha). IBA covered by Special Protection Area.

■ **Conservation issues**

Threats Afforestation (A), Industrialization/urbanization (B)

REFERENCES

GRIMMETT, R. F. A. AND JONES, T. A. (1989) *Important Bird Areas in Europe.* Cambridge, UK: International Council for Bird Preservation (Techn. Publ. 9).

HULTEN, M. AND WASSENICH, V. (1960/61) *Die vogelfauna Luxemburgs.* Inst. Gr.- D. Lux. XXVII: 285–422, XXVII: 339–488.

MELCHIOR, E., MENTGEN, E., PELTZER, R., SCHMITT, J. AND WEISS, J. (1987) [*Atlas of breeding birds in Luxembourg.*] Luxembourg: Lëtzebuerger Natur-a Vulleschutzliga. (In German, French and English.)

THE NETHERLANDS

EDUARD OSIECK

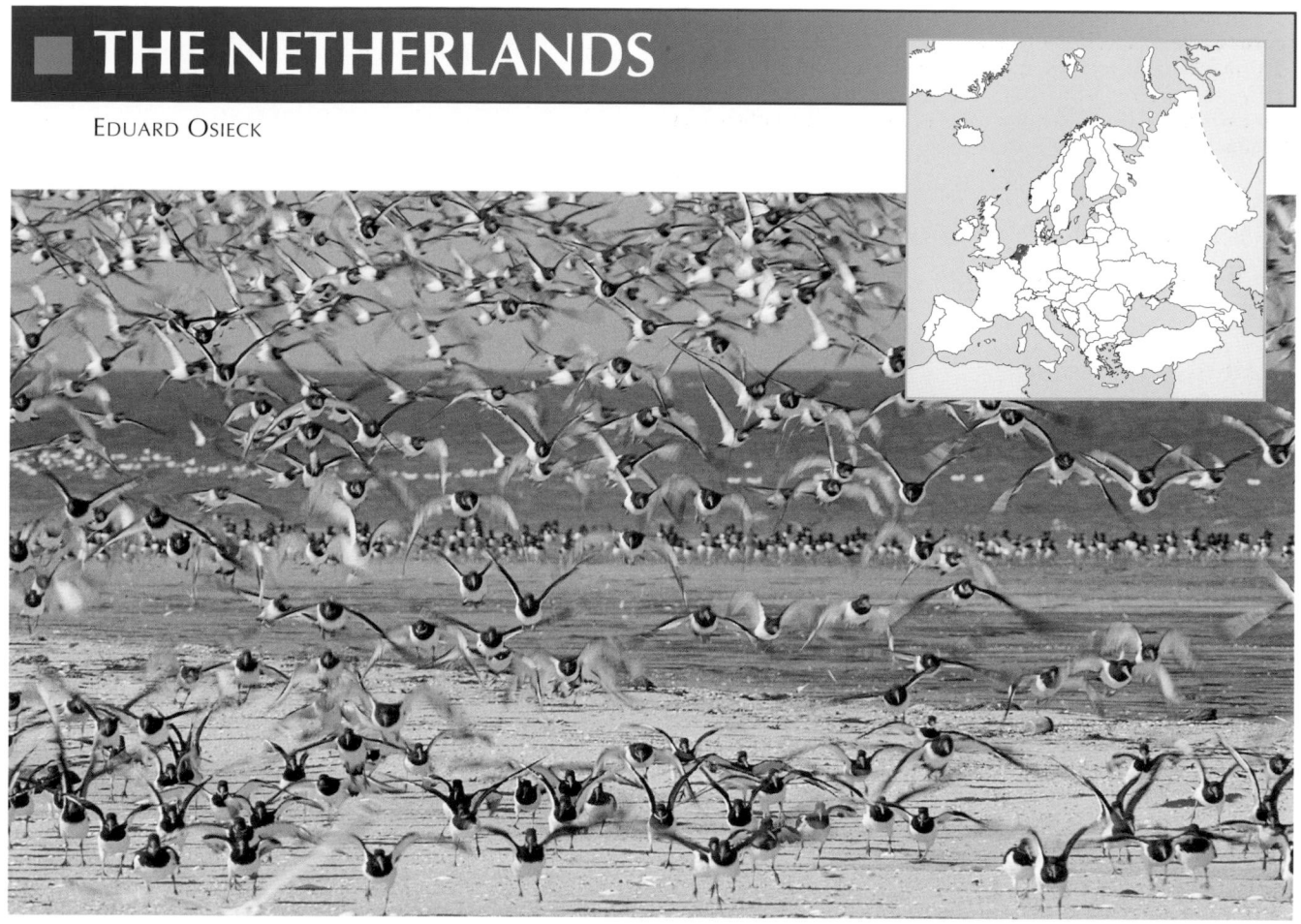

Oystercatcher *Haematopus ostralegus*, a key species at coastal IBAs in the Netherlands. (PHOTO: RSPB)

GENERAL INTRODUCTION

The Netherlands are situated at the delta of the rivers Rhine (Rijn), Maas and Schelde, forming much of the North Sea coast of continental Europe. The country covers 49,443 km² of which 15% comprises open water (inshore waters, lakes and rivers). The area excluding territoral sea (i.e. sea within 12 nautical miles) is 40,588 km². About half of the country consists of embanked polders

situated below sea-level, which are drained by a dense network of ditches, canals, reservoirs and pumping engines. Coastal defence consists of coastal dunes, sea walls (dykes) and barrages. The Netherlands has 106 Important Bird Areas (IBAs), covering 11,600 km² and equalling 24% of the country's total area although only 8% of the total land surface is covered by IBAs (Table 1, Map 1).

The 'original' pan-European IBA inventory (Grimmett and Jones 1989) identified 70 IBAs in the Netherlands, of which six

Table 1. Summary of Important Bird Areas in the Netherlands.   106 IBAs covering 11,600 km²

IBA code	National code[1]	1989 code	International name	National name	Administrative region	Area (ha)	Criteria (see p. 11)
001	NL0010	NL001	Wadden Sea	Waddenzee	Groningen, Friesland, Noord-Holland	233,855	A4i, A4iii, B1i, C2, C3, C4
002	NL0021	NL002	Texel: Schorren and Zeeburg	Texel: De Schorren en Zeeburg	Noord-Holland	1,600	A4i, A4iii, B1i, B2, C2, C3, C4, C6
003	NL0022	NL002	Texel: Dunes and Hors	Texel: Duinen en De Hors	Noord-Holland	3,850	A4i, B1i, B2, B3, C2, C6
004	NL0030	NL003	Vlieland	Vlieland	Friesland	2,740	A4i, A4iii, B1i, B2, B3, C2, C3, C4, C6
005	NL0040	NL004	Griend	Griend	Friesland	100	A4i, A4iii, B1i, B2, C2, C3, C4, C6
006	NL0051	NL005	Terschelling: De Boschplaat	Terschelling: De Boschplaat	Friesland	4,400	A4i, A4iii, B1i, B2, B3, C2, C3, C4, C6
007	NL0052	NL005	Terschelling: Dunes and Noordvaarder	Terschelling: Duinen en Noordvaarder	Friesland	4,320	C6
008	NL0060	NL006	Ameland: Duinen-Oerd	Ameland: Duinen-Oerd	Friesland	3,150	A4i, A4iii, B1i, B2, C2, C3, C4, C6
009	NL0070	NL007	Engelsmanplaat	Engelsmanplaat	Friesland	720	A4i, A4iii, B1i, C3, C4
010	NL0080	NL008	Schiermonnikoog	Schiermonnikoog	Friesland	2,800	A4i, A4iii, B1i, B2, B3, C2, C3, C4, C6
011	NL0091	NL009	Rottumerplaat	Rottumerplaat	Groningen	782	A4i, A4iii, B1i, C3, C4, C6
012	NL0092	NL009	Rottumeroog	Rottumeroog	Groningen	311	A4i, A4iii, B1i, B2, C3, C4, C6
013	NL0100	NL013	Balgzand	Balgzand	Noord-Holland	6,000	A4i, A4iii, B1i, B2, B3, C2, C3, C4, C6
014	NL0110	NL012	Frisian Wadden Sea coast	Friese waddenkust	Friesland	9,310	A4i, A4iii, B1i, B2, B3, C2, C3, C4, C6
015	NL0120	NL011	Lauwersmeer	Lauwersmeer	Groningen, Friesland	7,820	A4i, B1i, B2, B3, C2, C3, C6
016	NL0130	NL010	Groningen Wadden Sea coast	Groningse waddenkust	Groningen	4,600	A4i, A4iii, B1i, B2, B3, C2, C3, C4, C6
017	NL0140	NL014	Dollard	Dollard	Groningen	6,400	A4i, A4iii, B1i, B2, B3, C2, C3, C4, C6
018	NL0150	—	North Sea north of the Wadden Sea	Noordzee benoorden de Wadden	Groningen, Friesland, Noord-Holland	187,000	A4i, A4iii, B1i, C2, C3, C4, C6
019	NL0160	NL039	Zwanenwater	Zwanenwater	Noord-Holland	600	B1i, B2, C2
020	NL0171	NL046	Voordelta	Voordelta	Zuid-Holland, Zeeland	107,000	A4i, A4iii, B1i, B2, C3, C4

465

Table 1 ... continued. Summary of Important Bird Areas in the Netherlands. 106 IBAs covering 11,600 km²

IBA code	National code[1]	1989 code	International name	National name	Administrative region	Area (ha)	Criteria (see p. 11)
021	NL0172	—	Westplaat	Westplaat	Zuid-Holland	350	B1i, B3, C3, C6
022	NL0173	NL046	Voornes Duin	Voornes Duin	Zuid-Holland	1,130	B1i, B2, C2, C3
023	NL0174	NL046	Kwade Hoek	Kwade Hoek	Zuid-Holland	430	B1i, B2, C2, C6
024	NL0180	NL047	Haringvliet	Haringvliet	Zuid-Holland	10,900	A4i, A4iii, B1i, B2, B3, C2, C3, C4, C6
025	NL0190	NL047	Hollands Diep	Hollands Diep	Noord-Brabant, Zuid-Holland	4,300	A4iii, B1i, B2, C3, C4
026	NL0200	NL048	Lake Volkerak	Volkerakmeer	Noord-Brabant, Zuid-Holland, Zeeland	6,300	A4i, A4iii, B1i, B2, B3, C2, C3, C4, C6
027	NL0210	NL049	Grevelingen	Grevelingen	Zuid-Holland, Zeeland	13,580	A4i, A4iii, B1i, B2, B3, C2, C3, C4, C6
028	NL0220	NL050	Oosterschelde	Oosterschelde, incl. inlagen	Zeeland	36,880	A4i, A4iii, B1i, B2, B3, C2, C3, C4, C6
029	NL0230	NL050	Zoommeer	Zoommeer	Noord-Brabant, Zeeland	930	B1i, B3, C2, C3, C6
030	NL0240	NL050	Markiezaat	Markiezaat	Noord-Brabant, Zeeland	2,030	B1i, B2, B3, C2, C3, C6
031	NL0250	NL051	Lake Veersemeer	Veerse Meer	Zeeland	3,010	A4i, A4iii, B1i, B2, C2, C3, C4, C6
032	NL0260	NL052	Westerschelde and Saeftinghe	Westerschelde en Saeftinghe	Zeeland	50,800	A4i, A4iii, B1i, B2, B3, C2, C3, C4, C6
033	NL0270	NL053	Zwin (Dutch part)	Het Zwin (excl. Belgische deel)	Zeeland	128	C7
034	NL0280	NL030	Lake IJsselmeer	IJsselmeer	Friesland, Flevoland, Noord-Holland	109,000	A4i, A4iii, B1i, B2, C2, C3, C4, C6
035	NL0281	NL016	Makkumer- and Kooiwaard	Makkumer- en Kooiwaard	Friesland	1,740	A4i, A4iii, B1i, B2, C2, C3, C4
036	NL0282	NL016	Workumerwaard	Workumerwaard	Friesland	1,320	A4i, A4iii, B1i, C2, C3, C4, C6
037	NL0283	NL019	Steile Bank and Mokkebank	Steile Bank en Mokkebank	Friesland	4,270	A4i, A4iii, B1i, B2, C3, C4
038	NL0290	NL030	Lake Markermeer	Markermeer	Flevoland, Noord-Holland	69,700	A4i, A4iii, B1i, B2, C2, C3, C4, C6
039	NL0300	—	Lake Ketelmeer	Ketelmeer	Overijssel, Flevoland	3,750	A4iii, B1i, C3, C4
040	NL0310	NL028	Lake Zwartemeer	Zwarte Meer	Overijssel, Flevoland	2,180	A4iii, B1i, C2, C4, C6
041	NL0320	—	Lake Drontermeer	Drontermeer	Overijssel, Gelderland, Flevoland	640	A4i, B1i, B2, C2
042	NL0330	NL032	Lake Veluwemeer	Veluwemeer	Gelderland, Flevoland	3,390	A4i, A4iii, B1i, B2, C2, C4, C6
043	NL0340	NL032	Lake Wolderwijd	Wolderwijd en Nuldernauw	Gelderland, Flevoland	2,750	A4i, B1i, B2, C2
044	NL0351	NL037	Lake Gooimeer	Gooimeer	Flevoland, Noord-Holland	2,670	A4i, A4iii, B1i, B2, C2, C3, C4, C6
045	NL0352	NL033	Lake Eemmeer	Eemmeer	Flevoland, Utrecht, Noord-Holland	1,340	A4i, B1i, B2, C2, C3, C6
046	NL0361	NL067	IJssel: Deventer–Zwolle	IJssel: Deventer-Zwolle	Overijssel	3,000	A4i, A4iii, B1i, B2, B3, C2, C4, C6
047	NL0362	NL028	IJssel: Zwolle–Ketelmeer	IJssel: Zwolle-Ketelmeer	Overijssel	1,350	A4i, B1i, B2, B3, C2, C6
048	NL0370	NL044	Gelderse Poort	Gelderse Poort	Gelderland	6,460	A4i, A4iii, B1i, B2, B3, C2, C3, C4, C6
049	NL0380	NL066	Rijn: Heteren–Amerongen	Rijn: Heteren–Amerongen	Gelderland, Utrecht	2,480	A4i, A4iii, B1i, B2, C2, C4, C6
050	NL0390	NL043	Waal: Ewijk–Waardenburg	Waal: Ewijk-Waardenburg	Gelderland	5,940	A4i, A4iii, B1i, B2, C2, C3, C4, C6
051	NL0400	NL045	Biesbosch	Biesbosch	Noord-Brabant, Zuid-Holland	9,050	A4i, A4iii, B1i, B2, C2, C3, C4, C6
052	NL0410	NL059	Lake Leekstermeer	Leekstermeer	Groningen, Drenthe	850	A4i, A4iii, B1i, C3, C4
053	NL0420	NL061	Lake Zuidlaardermeer and Onnerpolder	Zuidlaardermeer en Onnerpolder	Groningen, Drenthe	1,950	A4i, B1i, B2, C2
054	NL0430	NL015	Groote Wielen	Groote Wielen (Grutte Wielen)	Friesland	580	A4i, A4iii, B1i, B2, C2, C3, C4, C6
055	NL0440	NL023	Oude Venen	Oude Venen (Alde Feanen)	Friesland	2,500	A4i, A4iii, B1i, B2, C2, C3, C4, C6
056	NL0450	NL023	De Deelen	De Deelen	Friesland	1,260	A4i, A4iii, B1i, B2, C2, C3, C4, C6
057	NL0460	NL024	Van Oordt's Mersken	Van Oordt's Mersken	Friesland	670	A4i, A4iii, B1i, B2, C3, C4
058	NL0471	NL022	Lake Sneekermeer and Goingarijp	Sneekermeer en Goingarijpsterpoelen	Friesland	1,670	A4i, B1i, B2, C2, C3
059	NL0472	NL022	Terkaplesterpoelen and Akmarijp	Terkaplesterpoelen en Akmarijp	Friesland	770	A4i, A4iii, B1i, B2, C2, C3, C4, C6
060	NL0480	NL021	Lake Witte and Zwarte Brekken	Witte en Zwarte Brekken, en Oudhof	Friesland	460	A4i, A4iii, B1i, B2, C2, C3, C4
061	NL0490	NL017	Lake Oudegaasterbrekken	Oudegaasterbrekken	Friesland	1,760	A4i, B1i, C3
062	NL0500	NL017	Lake Fluessen, Vogelhoek and Morra	Fluessen, Vogelhoek en Morra	Friesland	2,160	A4i, A4iii, B1i, B2, C2, C3, C4
063	NL0510	NL020	Rottige Meenthe and Brandemeer	Rottige Meenthe en Brandemeer	Friesland	1,920	A4i, B1i, B2, C2
064	NL0520	NL027	De Weerribben	De Weerribben	Overijssel	3,470	B2, C6
065	NL0530	NL027	De Wieden	De Wieden	Overijssel	8,440	B1i, B2, C2, C3, C6
066	NL0540	NL031	Oostvaardersplassen	Oostvaardersplassen	Flevoland	5,600	A4i, A4iii, B1i, B2, B3, C2, C3, C4, C6
067	NL0550	NL031	Lepelaarplassen	Lepelaarplassen	Flevoland	510	A4i, B1i, B2, C2, C3, C6
068	NL0560	NL038	Eilandspolder	Eilandspolder	Noord-Holland	2,040	B1i, C2
069	NL0570	—	Polder Zeevang	Zeevang	Noord-Holland	1,250	A4iii, B1i, C3, C4
070	NL0580	NL038	Wormer- and Jisperveld	Wormer- en Jisperveld	Noord-Holland	1,940	A4i, B1i, C2, C3, C6
071	NL0591	NL038	Ilperveld, Varkensland and Twiske	Ilperveld, Varkensland en Twiske	Noord-Holland	1,960	A4i, A4iii, B1i, B2, C3, C4, C6
072	NL0592	NL038	Oostzanerveld	Oostzanerveld	Noord-Holland	750	A4i, B1i, C3, C6
073	NL0600	NL034	Oostelijke Vechtplassen	Oostelijke Vechtplassen	Utrecht, Noord-Holland	7,040	B2, C2, C6
074	NL0610	NL036	Naardermeer	Naardermeer	Noord-Netherlands	1,120	A4i, B1i, B2, C2, C3, C6
075	NL0620	NL033	Polder Arkemheen	Arkemheen	Gelderland	1,460	A4i, B1i, B2, C2, C6
076	NL0630	NL040	Nieuwkoopse Plassen	Nieuwkoopse Plassen	Zuid-Holland	2,000	B2, C2, C6
077	NL0640	NL041	Reeuwijkse Plassen	Reeuwijkse Plassen	Zuid-Holland	1,650	A4i, A4iii, B1i, B2, C2, C3, C4
078	NL0650	NL042	Zouweboezem	Zouweboezem	Zuid-Holland	140	C6
079	NL0660	—	Donkse Laagten	Donkse Laagten	Zuid-Holland	180	B1i, C3
080	NL0670	NL042	Banks of River Linge	Linge-Oevers, Nieuw Zuider Lingedijk	Gelderland, Zuid-Holland	610	C6
081	NL0680	NL054	Yersekse and Kapelse Moer	Yersekse en Kapelse Moer	Zeeland	490	B1i, C3

Table 1 ... continued. Summary of Important Bird Areas in the Netherlands.

106 IBAs covering 11,600 km²

IBA code	National code[1]	1989 code	International name	National name	Administrative region	Area (ha)	Criteria (see p. 11)
082	NL0690	NL060	Fochteloërveen and Lake Esmeer	Fochteloërveen en Esmeer	Friesland, Drenthe	3,830	A4i, B1i, C3
083	NL0700	NL025	Dwingelderveld	Dwingelderveld	Drenthe	3,800	B1i, C3
084	NL0710	NL026	Bargerveen	Bargerveen	Drenthe	2,200	B2, C6
085	NL0720	NL063	Engbertsdijksvenen	Engbertsdijksvenen	Overijssel	1,030	C6
086	NL0730	NL056	Mariapeel and Deurnesepeel	Mariapeel en Deurnesepeel	Noord-Brabant, Limburg	2,560	C6
087	NL0740	NL056	Groote Peel	Groote Peel	Noord-Brabant, Limburg	1,350	B1i, C3, C6
088	NL0750	NL056	Strabrechtse Heide and Beuven	Strabrechtse Heide en Beuven	Noord-Brabant	1,630	C6
089	NL1010	—	De Wilck	De Wilck	Zuid-Holland	770	A4i, B1i, B2, C2, C6
090	NL1020	—	Zwarte Water and Overijsselse Vecht	Zwarte Water en Overijsselse Vecht	Overijssel	1,480	A4i, B1i, C2, C3
091	NL1030	NL047	Oudeland van Strijen	Oudeland van Strijen	Zuid-Holland	1,070	A4i, B1i, B2, C2, C3
092	NL1040	—	Dunes of Schoorl	Schoorlse Duinen	Noord-Holland	2,500	B2
093	NL2010	—	Drents–Friese Wold	Drents–Friese Wold	Friesland, Drenthe	7,100	C6
094	NL2020	—	Veluwe	Veluwe	Gelderland	91,800	C6
095	NL2030	NL068	Sallandse Heuvelrug	Sallandse Heuvelrug	Overijssel	4,100	C6
096	NL2040	—	Loonse and Drunense Duinen	Loonse en Drunense Duinen	Noord-Brabant	4,090	C6
097	NL2050	NL069	Regte Heide	Regte Heide	Noord-Brabant	410	C6
098	NL2060	NL070	Oirschotse Heide	Oirschotse Heide	Noord-Brabant	1,190	C6
099	NL2070	NL057	De Hamert/Bergbossen	De Hamert/Bergbossen	Limburg	4,030	C6
100	NL2080	—	De Utrecht	De Utrecht	Noord-Brabant	3,870	C6
101	NL2090	—	Weerter- and Budelerbergen	Weerter- en Budelerbergen	Noord-Brabant, Limburg	2,890	C6
102	NL2100	—	Leudal	Leudal	Limburg	720	C6
103	NL2110	—	Leenderbos and Groote Heide	Leenderbos en Groote Heide	Noord-Brabant	2,270	C6
104	NL2120	NL058	Meinweg	Meinweg	Limburg	1,990	C7
105	NL2130	—	Brabantse Wal	Brabantse Wal	Noord-Brabant	5,800	C6
106	NL3010	NL064	Kampina	Kampina	Noord-Brabant	1,150	C7

1. van den Tempel and Osieck 1994

Sites identified in the previous inventory of IBAs in Europe (Grimmett and Jones 1989) but no longer considered to be IBAs

NL018 Slotermeer; NL029 Noordoostpolder-West; NL035 Botshol and Ronde Hoep; NL055 Putting – Groot Eiland; NL062 Tjeukemeer; NL065 Maas: Vierlingsbeek – Grave and Ohé – Beesel.

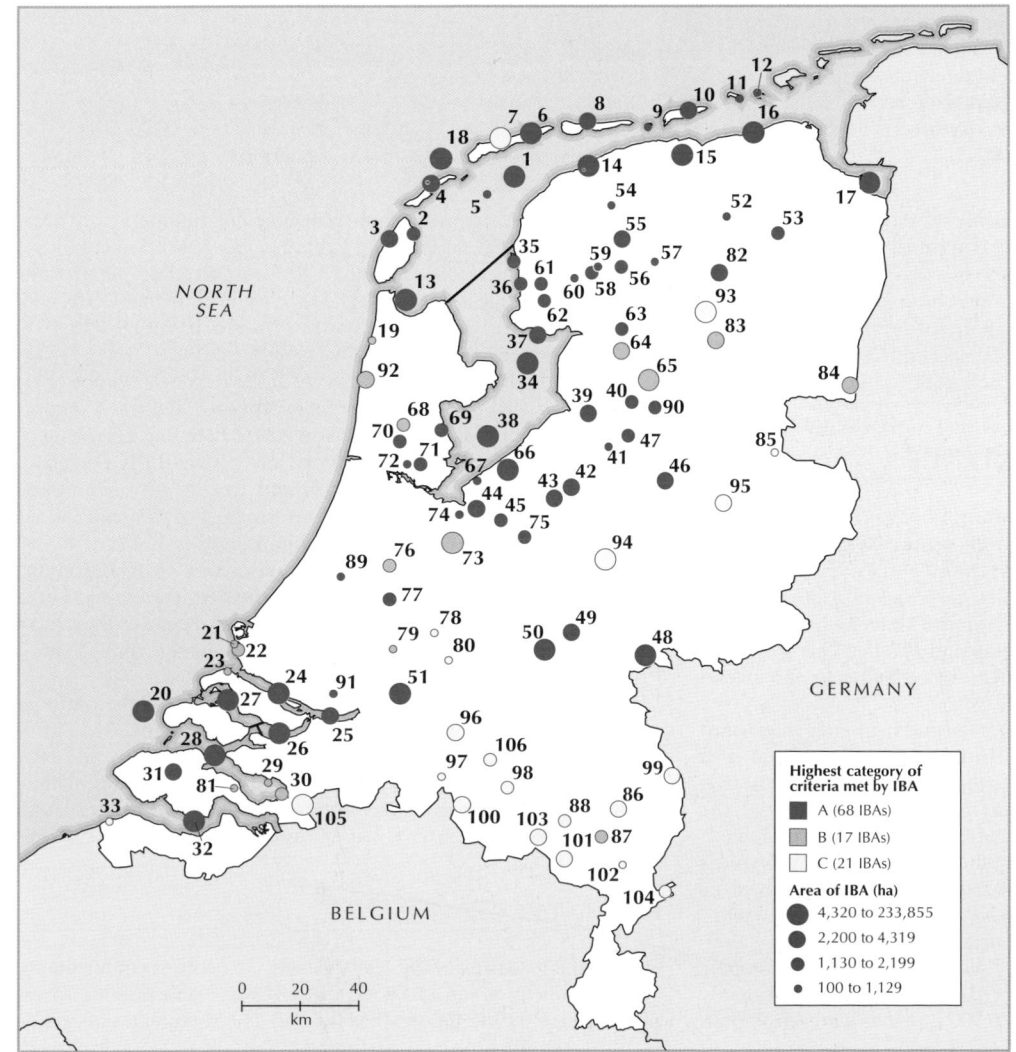

Map 1. Location, area and criteria category of Important Bird Areas in the Netherlands.

Highest category of criteria met by IBA

- A (68 IBAs)
- B (17 IBAs)
- C (21 IBAs)

Area of IBA (ha)

- 4,320 to 233,855
- 2,200 to 4,319
- 1,130 to 2,199
- 100 to 1,129

Table 2. Important Bird Areas in the Netherlands that support important numbers of one or more congregatory species (i.e. meeting criteria A4 and/or B1). IBAs meeting both criteria A4 and B1 for the species are shown in **bold**. IBAs meeting only criterion B1 for the species concerned, and not A4, are shown in normal type. For key to 'Season', see p. 7.

Species	Season	IBA code
Gavia stellata Red-throated Diver	W	**018**
Podiceps cristatus Great Crested Grebe	N	034, 037
Phalacrocorax carbo Cormorant	B	022, 065, **066**, **067**, **074**
	N	001, 027, **034**, **037**, **066**, 067
Platalea leucorodia Spoonbill	B	**002**, **003**, 004, 006, 019, 022, **066**, 067, 074
	P	035, 040, 051
	N	002, 003, 006, 013, **015**, 023, 027, 032, **066**, 068, 070
Cygnus columbianus Bewick's Swan	W	**015**, **027**, **028**, **031**, **041**, **042**, **043**, **044**, **045**, **046**, **047**, **049**, **050**, **051**, **053**, **063**, **075**, **077**, **089**, **090**
Cygnus cygnus Whooper Swan	W	046, 066
Anser fabalis Bean Goose	W	**017**, **048**, **082**, 083, 087
Anser brachyrhynchus Pink-footed Goose	W	**060**, **061**
Anser albifrons White-fronted Goose	W	**015**, **017**, 032, **048**, **050**, 051, **052**, **054**, **055**, **056**, **057**, **058**, **059**, **060**, 062, 066, 079, 081, **090**, 091
Anser anser Greylag Goose	N	**015**, **017**, **024**, **032**, **066**
Branta leucopsis Barnacle Goose	W	**001**, **010**, **014**, **015**, **016**, **017**, **024**, **026**, **027**, **031**, 051, **054**, **055**, **056**, **058**, **059**, **060**, **062**, **066**, 091
Branta bernicla Brent Goose	N	**001**, **002**, **006**, **008**, **014**, **016**, **027**, **028**
Tadorna tadorna Shelduck	N	**001**, **006**, **008**, **010**, **013**, **014**, **016**, 028, **032**
Anas penelope Wigeon	W	**001**, **014**, 015, 024, 026, 028, **032**, 034, **038**, 045, **054**, **055**, 058, 069, 070, **071**, 077
Anas strepera Gadwall	N	**015**, 024, 025, 026, 030, 034, 044, 051, 055, 066
Anas crecca Teal	N	001, 015, 017, **066**
Anas acuta Pintail	N	001, 006, 010, 013, 015, 026, 027, 028, 032, 066
Anas clypeata Shoveler	N	001, 015, 026, 028, 029, 030, 044, 045, 048, 054, 055, 057, 058, 066
Aythya ferina Pochard	N	034, **038**, 039, 050
Aythya fuligula Tufted Duck	N	034, **038**, 039, **067**
Aythya marila Scaup	W	**001**, **020**, **034**, **035**, **037**, **038**
Somateria mollissima Eider	N	**001**, 018

Species	Season	IBA code
Melanitta nigra Common Scoter	W	**018**
Bucephala clangula Goldeneye	W	026, **027**
Mergus albellus Smew	W	034, 038, 067
Mergus serrator Red-breasted Merganser	W	**027**, 031
Mergus merganser Goosander	W	**034**, **037**
Fulica atra Coot	N	031, 034
Haematopus ostralegus Oystercatcher	N	**001**, **004**, **005**, **006**, **008**, **010**, **011**, **012**, **013**, **014**, **016**, **028**, **032**
Recurvirostra avosetta Avocet	B	**013**, **014**, **016**, **026**, **027**, **028**, 029, 030
	N	**001**, **006**, **008**, **013**, **014**, **016**, **017**, **026**, **032**, **036**, **066**
Charadrius hiaticula Ringed Plover	N	**032**
Charadrius alexandrinus Kentish Plover	N	**032**
Pluvialis squatarola Grey Plover	N	**001**, **005**, **006**, **008**, **009**, **010**, **011**, **012**, **014**, **016**, **028**, **032**
Calidris canutus Knot	W	**001**, **004**, **005**, 006, **013**, **028**
	P	**001**, **004**, **005**, **010**, **011**, **028**
Calidris alpina Dunlin	W	**001**, **028**, 032
	N	**001**, **005**, 006, **008**, **010**, **011**, **012**, **013**, **014**, **016**, **017**, **028**, **032**
Limosa limosa Black-tailed Godwit	N	**036**, **055**, **057**, **066**, **070**, **071**, **072**
Limosa lapponica Bar-tailed Godwit	W	**001**, **004**, **006**, 010, **013**, **028**, **032**
	P	**001**, **002**, **004**, **005**, **008**, **014**, **016**, **017**, **028**
Numenius arquata Curlew	W	**001**, **005**, **006**, **008**, **012**, **014**, **016**, **028**
	N	**001**, **004**, **005**, **006**, **008**, **009**, **010**, **011**, **012**, **013**, **014**, **016**, **028**, **032**
Tringa erythropus Spotted Redshank	N	**001**, **013**, **014**, **017**, **028**, **032**
Tringa totanus Redshank	N	**001**, **006**, **013**, **014**, 016, **021**, **028**, **032**
Tringa nebularia Greenshank	N	**001**
Arenaria interpres Turnstone	W	**001**
	N	**013**, **028**
Larus fuscus Lesser Black-backed Gull	B	**006**, 010
Sterna sandvicensis Sandwich Tern	B	**005**, **027**, 032
Sterna albifrons Little Tern	B	032
Chlidonias niger Black Tern	P	**013**, **034**, **066**

have not been confirmed as IBAs during the current review process as they no longer meet the qualifying criteria (Table 1). A further 19 of the original IBAs have been split into two to four IBAs each during the current review, and 17 new IBAs have been identified since 1989 (of which six since 1994). This current inventory is based mainly on the national IBA inventory (van den Tempel and Osieck 1994), which includes 87 sites (13 'splits' plus six new sites, totalling 106 sites).

ORNITHOLOGICAL IMPORTANCE

There are 99 species of European conservation concern (SPECs) that breed in the Netherlands, as well as 11 'winter' SPECs that winter regularly in the country (Tucker and Heath 1994). Of the 99 breeding SPECs, two are globally threatened (*Crex crex* and *Aythya nyroca*, the latter breeding irregularly) and a further 52 have an unfavourable conservation status in Europe (Tucker and Heath 1994). No IBAs meet the A1 criterion for globally threatened and near-threatened species.

The majority of IBAs in the Netherlands support important congregations of migratory waterbirds (Table 1), with 64 sites meeting the A4i criterion and a further 16 sites meeting the B1i criterion (Table 2). These wetlands hold more than 1% of the biogeographic or flyway populations of those species listed in Table 2. The country is particularly important for migratory waterbirds during the migration seasons and during winter, for species such as (top sites listed in brackets) *Cygnus columbianus* (015), *Anser anser* (066, major moulting site), *Branta leucopsis* (014), *Aythya marila* (034), *Haematopus ostralegus* (001), *Limosa lapponica* (001), *Calidris canutus* (001) and *Chlidonias niger* (034). Of these internationally important wetlands, 49 also hold 20,000 or more waterbirds on a regular basis, meeting criterion A4iii (Table 1).

Sixty-six IBAs support important breeding numbers of SPECs, meeting criteria B2 and/or B3 (Table 1). The Netherlands holds a very significant proportion of the European breeding populations of the following species: *Platalea leucorodia* (sites 002–004, 006, 066, recent increase at 022), *Recurvirostra avosetta* (014, 016, 026, 027) and *Sterna sandvicensis* (005, 027).

All IBAs in the Netherlands qualify under European Union (EU) criteria ('C criteria'), with the current exception of Dunes of Schoorl (092), which qualifies under criterion B2 for breeding *Larus canus*, which species is not listed in Annex I of the EC Birds Directive. Twenty-one of the IBAs in the Netherlands qualify only under these EU criteria, of which 18 under criterion C6 for Annex I species such as *Ardea purpurea* (where the minimum threshold for B2/B3 is not met), *Pernis apivorus*, *Circus cyaneus*, *Grus grus* on passage (small numbers), *Tetrao tetrix*, and *Caprimulgus europaeus*. Three further sites meet only criterion C7, simply because they have already been designated by the Netherlands government as Special Protection Areas under the EC Birds Directive.

For 13 SPECs and Annex I species, over 75% of the national population breeds within the IBA network (Table 3). Those breeding species which are not adequately covered by the IBA network due to the dispersed nature of their distribution include *Ciconia ciconia*, *Anas querquedula*, *Limosa limosa*, *Alcedo atthis* and most passerines (see 'Analytical methods', below).

HABITATS

Of the total land area of the Netherlands, 70% consists of farmland, 14% of built-up areas and roads, 9% of woodland (mainly forest plantations), 4% of 'natural' areas and 2% of recreational areas. Natural areas include coastal dunes (21% of the total), saltmarshes

Table 3. Species of European conservation concern and species listed on Annex I of the EC Birds Directive with significant breeding populations at IBAs in the Netherlands.

Species [1]	Minimum national breeding population (pairs) [2]	Proportion (%) of national population breeding at all IBAs in the Netherlands
Botaurus stellaris Bittern	215	52
Ixobrychus minutus Little Bittern	10	50
Ardea purpurea Purple Heron	210	95
Platalea leucorodia Spoonbill	400	100[3]
Pernis apivorus Honey Buzzard	700	30
Circus aeruginosus Marsh Harrier	800	30
Circus cyaneus Hen Harrier	80	100[3]
Circus pygargus Montagu's Harrier	20	15
Tetrao tetrix Black Grouse	29	100[3]
Porzana porzana Spotted Crake	150	45
Crex crex Corncrake	80	30
Recurvirostra avosetta Avocet	8,400	81
Charadrius alexandrinus Kentish Plover	425	82
Philomachus pugnax Ruff	400	39
Larus melanocephalus Mediterranean Gull	90	44
Larus canus Common Gull	7,000	77
Larus fuscus Lesser Black-backed Gull	24,000	67
Sterna sandvicensis Sandwich Tern	10,000	100[3]
Sterna hirundo Common Tern	14,000	91
Sterna paradisaea Arctic Tern	850	98
Sterna albifrons Little Tern	275	100[3]
Chlidonias niger Black Tern	1,100	71
Asio flammeus Short-eared Owl	100	62
Caprimulgus europaeus Nightjar	450	80
Alcedo atthis Kingfisher	125	22
Dryocopus martius Black Woodpecker	2,300	38
Lullula arborea Woodlark	2,700	64
Anthus campestris Tawny Pipit	60	100[3]
Luscinia svecica Bluethroat	5,500	59
Lanius collurio Red-backed Shrike	150	72

1. Only those species of European conservation concern (see Box 1, p. 12) that meet IBA criteria in the Netherlands are listed, together with those species listed on Annex I of the EC Birds Directive that fulfil criterion C6 in IBAs in the Netherlands.
2. Data are taken from the BirdLife/EBCC European Bird Database 1998 (Heath and Borggreve 2000).
3. The percentage of the national population in IBAs exceeds 100%. Usually this is because the national population estimate has not been updated recently whilst the IBA population estimate has been recently updated with new data as a result of comprehensive surveys of IBAs themselves. Also, the individual site count for a species may be the maximum or average over recent years, and summing these may record more birds than are present nationally in any single year.

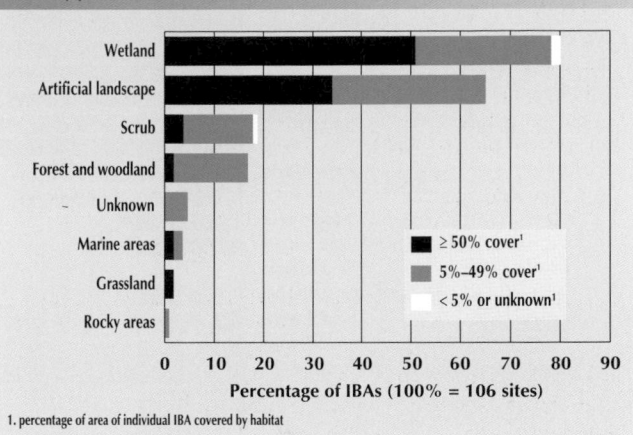

Figure 1. Habitats at Important Bird Areas in the Netherlands (see Appendix 3 for definitions of habitats).

1. percentage of area of individual IBA covered by habitat

and *Mergus serrator*. The largest freshwater lakes (16% of total IBA area) IJsselmeer (034) and Markermeer (038) hold huge numbers of both piscivorous species (*Podiceps cristatus*, *Phalacrocorax carbo*, *Mergus albellus*, *Chlidonias niger*) and mussel *Mytilus*-eating species (*Aythya fuligula*, *A. marila*, *A. ferina*). Inland lakes and the major rivers are important roosts for geese (*Anser/Branta*) and *Anas penelope*. If aquatic vegetation (e.g. pondweed *Potamogeton*) is present, then *Cygnus columbianus* feeds on these lakes in autumn, e.g. Veluwemeer (042).

Two vast marine IBAs (25% of the total IBA area) have been identified, holding large numbers of *Gavia stellata* and *Melanitta nigra*. Of the extensive area of agricultural grassland that is used for feeding by swans *Cygnus*, geese and *Anas penelope*, only small proportions (5–10%) have been included in the inventory (see 'Analytical methods', below). Two special types of wetland are wet heathland and peatbogs, which are of importance for such breeding species as *Luscinia svecica* and *Lanius collurio*, i.e. Bargerveen (site 084), for *Grus grus* on passage, and for *Anser fabalis fabalis* when roosting. Twelve IBAs consist mainly of woodland and heathland (11% of total IBA area), and have been selected under criterion C6 for *Pernis apivorus*, *Tetrao tetrix*, *Caprimulgus europaeus*, *Dryocopus martius*, *Lullula arborea* and *Anthus campestris* (sites 093–103,105).

IMPACTS ON IBAs – LAND-USE AND THREATS

The Netherlands is a densely populated country (470 persons/km² on average) although the majority of the population is urban. Consequently the human pressure on most IBAs is high. Nearly 90% of all IBAs are used for recreation, and most wetlands support (commercial) fisheries (Figure 2). Hunting is allowed in many

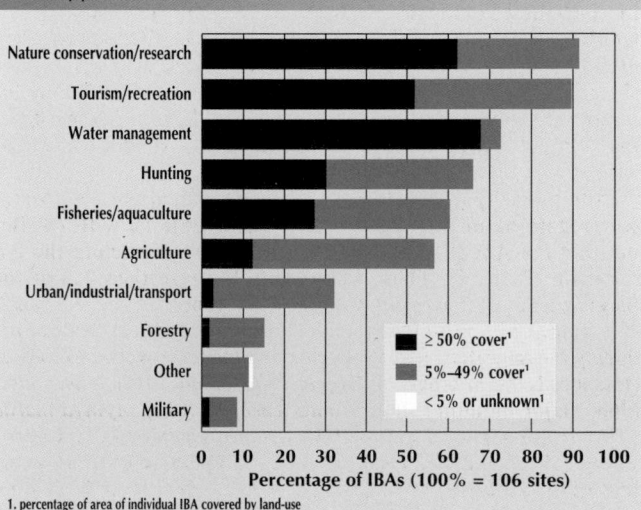

Figure 2. Land-uses at Important Bird Areas in the Netherlands (see Appendix 3 for definitions of land-uses).

1. percentage of area of individual IBA covered by land-use

(7%), marshland (32%) and heathland (21%). Seven IBAs consist mainly of coastal dunes (covering about half of the national area of this habitat) which are important breeding areas for *Platalea leucorodia*, *Circus cyaneus*, *Larus canus* and *Asio flammeus*. The majority of the saltmarshes and (isolated) sandflats are included within the IBA network. They are of great importance for breeding *Platalea leucorodia*, *Recurvirostra avosetta*, *Charadrius alexandrinus*, *Larus fuscus*, *Sterna sandvicensis*, *S. hirundo* and *S. albifrons*, as feeding areas for *Anser anser* (site 032, in winter), *Branta leucopsis* and *B. bernicla*, and as high-tide roosts for large numbers of waders and gulls. Another major wetland habitat is marshland (56% of national area covered by IBAs), of which reedbeds and swamp-forest are an important breeding habitat for *Botaurus stellaris*, *Ardea purpurea*, *Phalacrocorax carbo*, *Platalea leucorodia* (site 066), *Circus aeruginosus* and *Luscinia svecica*. During May and June, tens of thousands of non-breeding *Anser anser* moult in the Oostvaardersplassen (066) while feeding in the extensive reedbeds.

The main habitat within IBAs is wetland: over half of the IBAs (51%) are predominantly wetland, and a further 27% of the total have a lower proportion of wetland (Figure 1). Apart from the wetland types mentioned previously, the other main types are inshore (coastal) waters and lakes. The first category concerns permanent (shallow sub-tidal) water and intertidal mudflats (comprising 30% of the total area of IBAs in the country), which are mainly found in the Wadden Sea (site 001), Oosterschelde (028) and Westerschelde (032). These are the main coastal wetlands used by large numbers of waterbirds and, in particular, waders on passage and during winter.

Lakes (20% of the total IBA area) include the two saline (dammed) lakes Grevelingen (site 027) and Veerse Meer (031), which are especially important for piscivorous species such as *Podiceps cristatus*

Figure 3. Threats at Important Bird Areas in the Netherlands (see Appendix 3 for definitions of threat types and impact categories).

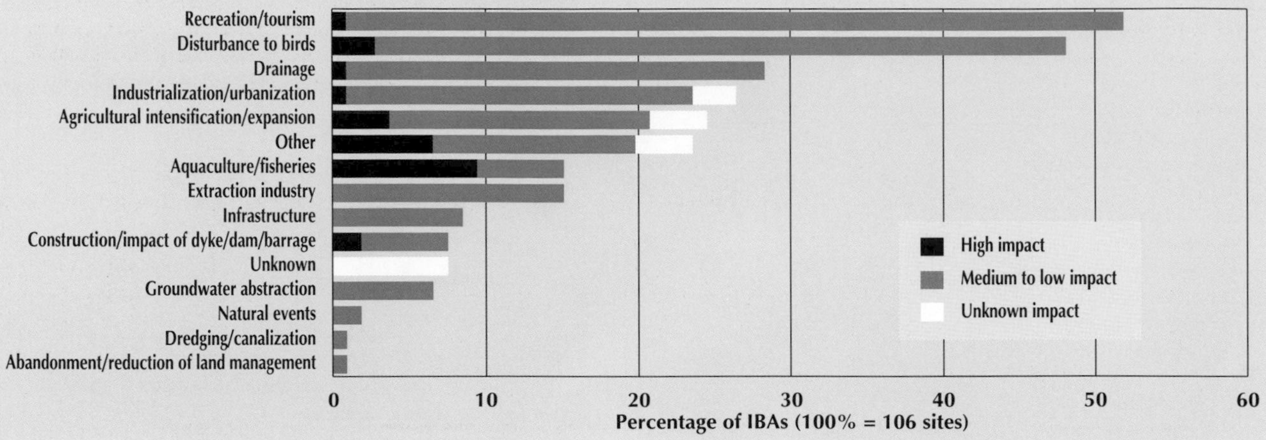

Recreation/tourism
Disturbance to birds
Drainage
Industrialization/urbanization
Agricultural intensification/expansion
Other
Aquaculture/fisheries
Extraction industry
Infrastructure
Construction/impact of dyke/dam/barrage
Unknown
Groundwater abstraction
Natural events
Dredging/canalization
Abandonment/reduction of land management

■ High impact
■ Medium to low impact
□ Unknown impact

Percentage of IBAs (100% = 106 sites)

wetlands (but many coastal sites are closed for hunting), although the number of quarry species is limited (only one waterbird species: *Anas platyrhynchos*). Dairy farming occurs in over half of the IBAs, but agriculture affects most IBAs in direct or indirect ways (through drainage, groundwater extraction and nutrient pollution). The land-use category 'urban/industrial/transport', which applies to one third of the IBAs (Figure 2), refers mainly to shipping (25% of IBAs), roads, and the extraction of sand and groundwater.

Most threats to IBAs in the Netherlands do not involve the large-scale destruction of habitat but rather such factors as the regular disturbance of birds by human activities, and the gradual deterioration of habitat quality due to, for example, nutrient pollution (often from sources remote from the IBA), drainage, scrub encroachment and unnatural water management (i.e. high level in summer and low in winter). Recreation and disturbance are considered to be threats in about half of the IBAs, although rated as 'high impact' in only a few areas (Figure 3). Commercial fisheries are a threat at 15% of the IBAs, and at nearly 10% the threat is rated as 'high impact', all other categories having a much lower score. This specifically refers to shellfish fisheries on intertidal mudflats (which cause habitat destruction and food shortage for birds) and to over-fishing on the IJsselmeer and Markermeer (034, 038).

PROTECTION STATUS

■ National protection

Nature conservation is administered by the Directorate Nature Management of the Ministry of Agriculture, Nature Management and Fisheries. Policies are determined by the Nature Policy Plan (Ministry of Agriculture, Nature Management and Fisheries 1990) and the Policy Memorandum on 'Green Space' (1993) which aim primarily at the establishment of an Ecological Network (EHS)

consisting of core areas (i.e. nature reserves of at least 250 ha extent), restoration areas, water-bodies, woodland, farmland with management restrictions, and ecological corridors. All areas within the network of about 7,000 km² (land) and 70,000 km² (water) enjoy basic protection from human interference which affects the natural features of the area concerned. Derogation can be allowed in favour of serious national interests. All IBAs are part of this network, apart from two which are situated at the border (sites 061 and 089). Core areas receive the highest level of protection and are managed as Protected Natural Monuments, Nature Reserves and/or National Parks. Through their overlap with these protected areas, most IBAs have some protection (Table 4), but only about one third of the IBAs overlap to a high degree (Figure 4).

1. Protected Natural Monuments

Protected Natural Monuments (Beschermde Natuurmonumenten) are sites which, because of their high natural values, have been designated under the Nature Conservation Act. In principle, no human interference is allowed, but permits can be issued if the natural features of the site are not at stake. However, human activities which were already taking place before the designation can often be continued so long as they are not intensified. Through their overlap with Natural Monuments, about 316,000 ha of IBAs are protected under this Act, including large parts of the Wadden Sea, Oosterschelde, Haringvliet, Volkerakmeer, Friese IJsselmeerkust (sites 035–037), Zwartemeer, Eemmeer, Oostvaardersplassen, Mariapeel, Deurnese Peel, Bargerveen and Groote Peel (Table 4). Except for the two first-mentioned areas, most other Natural Monuments overlap with existing Nature Reserves.

2. Nature Reserves

The Netherlands has an extensive system of Nature Reserves owned and managed by the State (National Service for Nature and Landscape, SBB), or by private nature conservation bodies

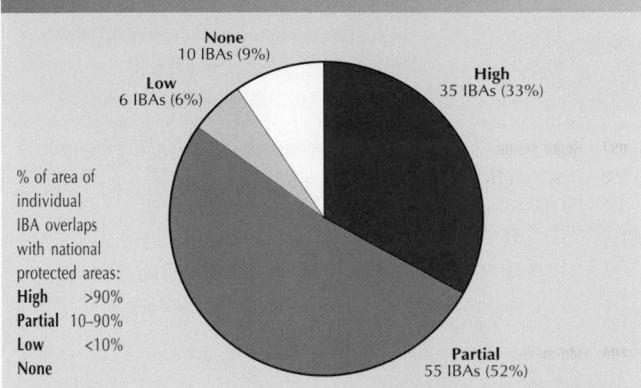

Figure 4. The national protection status of Important Bird Areas in the Netherlands.

None
10 IBAs (9%)

Low
6 IBAs (6%)

High
35 IBAs (33%)

% of area of individual IBA overlaps with national protected areas:
High >90%
Partial 10–90%
Low <10%
None

Partial
55 IBAs (52%)

Total area of overlap between IBA network in the Netherlands and national protected-area system (see Table 5 for categories) = 2,682–4,221 km² (23–36% of total IBA area).

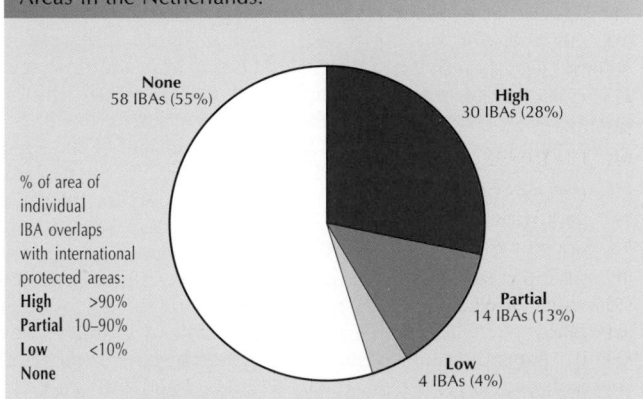

Figure 5. The international protection status of Important Bird Areas in the Netherlands.

None
58 IBAs (55%)

High
30 IBAs (28%)

% of area of individual IBA overlaps with international protected areas:
High >90%
Partial 10–90%
Low <10%
None

Partial
14 IBAs (13%)

Low
4 IBAs (4%)

Total area of overlap between IBA network in the Netherlands and international protected-area system (see Table 5 for categories) = 3,696 km² (32% of total IBA area).

(Natuurmonumenten, Provincial Landscapes) which receive an annual contribution from the government towards the management costs. The total area of Nature Reserves in 1997 was about 2,000 km², of which about 70% is situated within IBAs (Table 4, Figure 4). The total area of Nature Reserves (and restoration areas) should increase by another 1,500 km² by 2018, in the framework of the establishment of the Ecological Network.

3. National Parks
National Parks are areas of over 1,000 ha in size with special natural features and good opportunities for recreational activities. There are ten such parks, of which nine overlap with IBAs (Table 4, Figure 4). Four more are planned which overlap with IBAs: Duinen Texel (site 003), Lauwersmeer (015), Oosterschelde (028) and Oude Venen (055).

Table 4. Protection status of Important Bird Areas in the Netherlands.
A tick (✔) indicates that an IBA overlaps with a protected area (to any extent); a plus sign (+) indicates that designation is expected in 1999.

IBA code	International name	National Natural Monument	National Nature Reserve	National National Park	National Private Reserve	International Ramsar Site	International Biosphere Reserve	International Special Protection Area
001	Wadden Sea	✔				✔	✔	✔
002	Texel: Schorren and Zeeburg	✔	✔			✔		✔
003	Texel: Dunes and Hors	✔	✔			+		+
004	Vlieland	✔	✔			✔		✔
005	Griend	✔	✔			✔		✔
006	Terschelling: De Boschplaat	✔	✔			✔		✔
007	Terschelling: Dunes and Noordvaarder	✔	✔			+		+
008	Ameland: Duinen-Oerd	✔	✔			✔		✔
009	Engelsmanplaat	✔				✔		✔
010	Schiermonnikoog	✔	✔	✔		✔		✔
011	Rottumerplaat	✔				✔		✔
012	Rottumeroog	✔				✔		✔
013	Balgzand	✔				✔		✔
014	Frisian Wadden Sea coast	✔	✔			✔		✔
015	Lauwersmeer	✔	✔			+		+
016	Groningen Wadden Sea coast	✔	✔			✔		✔
017	Dollard	✔	✔			✔		✔
018	North Sea north of the Wadden Sea					+		+
019	Zwanenwater		✔			✔		✔
020	Voordelta					+		✔
021	Westplaat					+		+
022	Voornes Duin		✔			+		+
023	Kwade Hoek		✔					✔
024	Haringvliet	✔	✔			+		+
025	Hollands Diep	✔	✔			+		+
026	Lake Volkerak	✔	✔			✔		✔
027	Grevelingen					+		+
028	Oosterschelde	✔	✔			✔		✔
029	Zoommeer	✔				+		+
030	Markiezaat	✔	✔			✔		✔
031	Lake Veersemeer		✔			+		+
032	Westerschelde and Saeftinghe	✔	✔			✔		✔
033	Zwin (Dutch part)							✔
034	Lake IJsselmeer	✔	✔			+		+
035	Makkumer- and Kooiwaard	✔	✔			+		✔
036	Workumerwaard	✔				+		✔
037	Steile Bank and Mokkebank	✔	✔			+		✔
038	Lake Markermeer	✔	✔			+		✔
039	Lake Ketelmeer					+		+
040	Lake Zwartemeer	✔				✔		✔
041	Lake Drontermeer					+		+
042	Lake Veluwemeer		✔			+		+
043	Lake Wolderwijd					+		+
044	Lake Gooimeer	✔	✔					✔
045	Lake Eemmeer	✔	✔					✔
046	IJssel: Deventer–Zwolle	✔	✔					+
047	IJssel: Zwolle–Ketelmeer	✔	✔					+
048	Gelderse Poort	✔	✔					+
049	Rijn: Heteren–Amerongen		✔					+
050	Waal: Ewijk–Waardenburg	✔	✔					✔
051	Biesbosch		✔	✔		✔		✔
052	Lake Leekstermeer		✔			+		+
053	Lake Zuidlaardermeer and Onnerpolder		✔			+		+
	Subtotal number of IBAs	36	37	2	0	21	1	31

IBA code	International name	National Natural Monument	National Nature Reserve	National National Park	National Private Reserve	International Ramsar Site	International Biosphere Reserve	International Special Protection Area
054	Groote Wielen		✔					+
055	Oude Venen	✔	✔			✔		✔
056	De Deelen		✔			✔		✔
057	Van Oordt's Mersken		✔					+
058	Lake Sneekermeer and Goingarijp		✔			+		+
059	Terkaplesterpoelen and Akmarijp		✔			+		+
060	Lake Witte and Zwarte Brekken		✔					+
061	Lake Oudegaasterbrekken		✔			+		+
062	Lake Fluessen, Vogelhoek and Morra		✔			+		+
063	Rottige Meenthe and Brandemeer		✔			+		+
064	De Weerribben		✔	✔		✔		✔
065	De Wieden		✔			+		+
066	Oostvaardersplassen	✔	✔			✔		✔
067	Lepelaarplassen	✔	✔					✔
068	Eilandspolder		✔					+
069	Polder Zeevang		✔					+
070	Wormer- and Jisperveld		✔			+		+
071	Ilperveld, Varkensland and Twiske	✔	✔					+
072	Oostzanerveld		✔					+
073	Oostelijke Vechtplassen	✔	✔			+		+
074	Naardermeer		✔			✔		✔
075	Polder Arkemheen		✔					+
076	Nieuwkoopse Plassen	✔	✔					✔
077	Reeuwijkse Plassen		✔			+		+
078	Zouweboezem		✔					✔
079	Donkse Laagten		✔					+
080	Banks of River Linge	✔	✔					+
081	Yersekse and Kapelse Moer		✔					+
082	Fochteloërveen and Lake Esmeer		✔					+
083	Dwingelderveld		✔	✔				✔
084	Bargerveen	✔	✔			✔		✔
085	Engbertsdijksvenen	✔	✔			✔		✔
086	Mariapeel and Deurnesepeel	✔	✔			✔		✔
087	Groote Peel	✔	✔	✔		✔		✔
088	Strabrechtse Heide and Beuven	✔	✔					+
089	De Wilck		✔					+
090	Zwarte Water and Overijsselse Vecht	✔	✔					+
091	Oudeland van Strijen		✔					+
092	Dunes of Schoorl	✔	✔					+
093	Drents–Friese Wold		✔	✔				+
094	Veluwe		✔		✔			+
095	Sallandse Heuvelrug		✔					+
096	Loonse and Drunense Duinen		✔	✔				+
097	Regte Heide		✔					
098	Oirschotse Heide							
099	De Hamert/Bergerbossen	✔	✔	✔				✔
100	De Utrecht	✔	✔					+
101	Weerter- and Budelerbergen		✔					+
102	Leudal		✔					+
103	Leenderbos and Groote Heide		✔					+
104	Meinweg		✔	✔				✔
105	Brabantse Wal							+
106	Kampina		✔					✔
	Total number of IBAs	52	88	9	1	30	1	47

Box 1. International legislation and initiatives that are relevant to site conservation in the Netherlands (see Appendix 1 for a general description of these agreements).

Global	
Biodiversity Convention	✔
Ramsar Convention	✔
Bonn Convention	✔
World Heritage Convention	✔
MAB Programme	✔
Pan-European	
Bern Convention	✔
Regional	
EC Birds Directive	✔
EC Habitats Directive	✔

✔ Convention ratified/initiative supported
(✔) Convention signed

- Vereniging SOVON and specialized institutes run comprehensive bird-monitoring schemes, including annual counts of rare and colonial breeding species, integrated censuses of breeding birds at reserves, common bird censuses, monthly counts of waterbirds on the large water-bodies, and monthly national counts of swans and geese. Midwinter counts cover all waterbirds nationwide.

- Many wetland IBAs are now covered by a network of IBA-caretakers that monitor threats in these sites and undertake local conservation actions. Their efforts are being coordinated by the BirdLife Partner in the Netherlands (Vogelbescherming Nederland), which also undertakes national and international conservation actions when appropriate.

■ International protection

Figure 5 summarizes the international protection status of IBAs in the Netherlands. The Netherlands is a member state of the European Union, and the EC Birds and Habitats Directives have applied from the dates that these legal instruments entered into force (1981 and 1994 respectively). A total of 30 Special Protection Areas have been designated under the Birds Directive; these are contained by or overlap with 47 IBAs (Table 4): Wadden Sea (contains 10 IBAs, overlaps with five others), Zwanenwater, Kwade Hoek (contains site 023, overlaps with 020), Volkerakmeer, Oosterschelde (including 030), Verdronken Land van Saeftinghe (part of 032), Zwingebied (033), Friese IJsselmeerkust (contains 034–037), Zwartemeer, 'Eemmeer, Gooimeer en IJmeer' (parts of 044–045, 038), Kil van Hurwenen (part of 050), De Biesbosch, Oude Venen, De Deelen, De Weerribben, Oostvaardersplassen, Lepelaarsplassen, Naardermeer, Nieuwkoopse Plassen, Zouweboezem, Dwingelderveld, Fochteloërveen, Bargerveen, Engbertsdijkvenen, Mariapeel, Deurnesepeel, Groote Peel, Landgoed De Hamert (part of 099), Meinweg, and Kampina. As a consequence of a judgement by the European Court of Justice on 19 May 1998, the Netherlands intends to designate most of the other IBAs (or incompletely designated IBAs) as Special Protection Areas in 1999.

In December 1996 and July 1998, lists of proposed Sites of Community Interest under the Habitats Directive were submitted to the European Commission. These lists include 63 IBAs in total. Future designation as Special Areas for Conservation will provide protection aimed at natural habitats and (non-bird) species for which the area has been designated.

The Netherlands is also party to the Ramsar Convention (since 1980), Bern Convention (1980) and Bonn Convention (Box 1). A total of 18 sites have been designated under the Ramsar Convention, which are contained by or overlap with 30 IBAs: Wadden Sea (contains nine IBAs, overlaps with six others), Zwanenwater, Krammer-Volkerak (site 026), Oosterschelde (including 030), Verdronken Land van Saeftinghe, Zwartemeer, Biesbosch Zuidwaard, Oude Venen, De Deelen, De Weerribben, Oostvaardersplassen, Naardermeer, Groote Peel, Bargerveen, Engbertsdijkvenen, and Deurnesepeel. The latter three were designated under the Convention's non-bird criteria. The designations of Griend (1981) and Boschplaat (1981) have been incorporated in the Wadden Sea designation since 1984. The designation as Ramsar Sites of 34 other IBAs is currently (1999) being considered (003, 004, 007, 008, 010, 015, 018, 020, 021, 022, 024, 025, 027, 029, 031, 034, 038, 039, 041, 042, 043, 052, 053, 058, 059, 061, 062, 063, 065, 068, 070, 073, 077). The Wadden Sea has been designated as a Biosphere Reserve (the same area as the SPA designation).

CONSERVATION

- Protected areas are usually covered by management plans. Integral management plans do not exist for most other areas, although separate policy plans are often in force for various human activities (e.g. water management, recreation, sand extraction). The following seven IBAs are not covered at all by any management plans (or only a minor part is covered): Engelsmanplaat (009), North Sea north of the Wadden Sea (018), Hollands Diep (025), Lake Oudegaasterbrekken (061), Oudeland van Strijen (091), Oirschotse Heide (098), De Utrecht (100).

ANALYTICAL METHODS

- This inventory is based mainly on the partly government-commissioned national IBA inventory (van den Tempel and Osieck 1994), which covered all bird species listed on Annex I of the EC Birds Directive, all waterbird species meeting 1% threshold levels, and *Charadrius alexandrinus*. For the current inventory, only one more SPEC was included in the analysis (*Larus canus*), because the addition of other SPECs would probably not have revealed any new IBAs. The differences between this inventory and the previous pan-European IBA inventory (Grimmett and Jones 1989), which itself was an update of the 1981 IBA list (Osieck and Mörzer Bruyns 1981), are caused by (1) an increase in the number of bird species covered (in particular, species added to Annex I of the Birds Directive in 1985); (2) the splitting of sites; (3) the fact that agricultural grassland has been included to a limited extent only (100 ha criterion, see below); and (4) the use of more recent bird data.

- Quoted population estimates for colonial and rare breeding species are based mainly on three or more counts during the period 1987–1992. Population data that are quoted for dispersed species or species that are difficult to census, such as *Pernis apivorus*, *Porzana porzana*, *Dryocopus martius*, *Caprimulgus europaeus*, *Lullula arborea* and *Luscinia svecica*, refer usually to single counts or to careful estimates. Quoted numbers for waterbirds refer generally to mean seasonal maxima, based on monthly counts or counts during peak months (1987–1992). Unless otherwise stated, the quoted numbers of pairs/individuals of a bird species are mean seasonal figures derived over several years (2–5 years). Most commonly (87% of all figures quoted in the tables of key species in the main site accounts), the mean is based on a 5-, 4- or 3-year series. The end-year of the series is quoted in the table for each mean figure, and is most commonly 1991, 1990 or 1992 (87% of all figures quoted). Quoted numbers of individuals at nocturnal roosts of geese are in some cases based on rough estimates from the 1980s (in particular sites 054–062). Most bird data were provided by Bird Census Work SOVON, which organization coordinates all national bird census-work through volunteers and which incorporates most of the census data collected by professionals.

- Huge numbers of swans, geese, *Anas penelope* and *Pluvialis apricaria* feed in winter on agricultural grassland and arable land. Sometimes *Sterna hirundo* nests in unusual places such as sand-filled areas intended for industrial use. Such artificial habitats have hardly any other conservation values, except for wet grasslands which may hold appreciable densities of breeding waders such as *Limosa limosa*, and which also sometimes serve as feeding areas for *Ardea purpurea* and *Platalea leucorodia* during the breeding season. Such sites were considered to be only eligible as IBAs if at least 100 ha was owned and managed as a nature reserve. This additional criterion can be considered as a national interpretation of the rule that an IBA must exist as an actual or potential protected area which can be managed in some way for nature conservation (Grimmett and Jones 1989: 13). This site criterion is also considered in line with Article 4 of the EC Birds Directive, because such sites are considered more 'suitable' from a conservation point of view than areas without such protected sites. In this respect, it should be noted that land areas with a more or less natural vegetation hardly occur outside protected areas in the Netherlands.

- For the application of European Union criterion C6, the Netherlands was treated as a single NUTS region. In principle this criterion has been applied for all Dutch species listed on Annex I of the Birds Directive, including dispersed breeding species (e.g. *Pernis apivorus*), birds on passage (e.g. *Sterna caspia*), and wintering birds (e.g. *Haliaeetus albicilla*).

- Data on the legal protection status of sites have been extracted from official publications and statutory documents (situation as of 1 June 1999). It should be noted that the official area sizes of site designations are always given, even if these are incorrect (e.g. Ramsar and SPA designations of the Wadden Sea give an area size of 250,000 ha, although the actual sizes are 271,000 ha and 272,100 ha respectively). The ownership and areal extent of Nature Reserves (including forestry plantations) managed by conservation bodies have been taken from *Complete gids Natuur- en Wandelgebieden in Nederland* published by Vereniging Natuurmonumenten (1996); updates were made available).

- Site boundaries were digitized using official topographical maps (scale 1:50,000) and stored in a geographical information system held by the IKC Nature Management of the Ministry of Agriculture, Nature Management and Fisheries (Wageningen).

GLOSSARY

EHS Ecological Network.
NUTS Nomenclature des Unités Territoriales Statistiques – the administrative regions of the European Union are called NUTS regions, and are designated by the EC Statistical Office (Eurostat).

polder a flat area of land, often below sea-level, with an artificially regulated water-regime, having been claimed from the sea or from a lake or river.
SOVON Samenwerkende Organisaties Vogelonderzoek Nederland.
SPA Special Protection Area (designated under Article 4 of the EC Birds Directive).

ACKNOWLEDGEMENTS

The review of the national IBA list (Van den Tempel & Osieck 1994) was commissioned, and co-financed, by the Centre for Information and Knowledge on Nature Management (IKC natuurbeheer) of the Ministry of Agriculture, Nature Management and Fisheries. The majority of the bird data was collected by Bird Census Work SOVON. A large number of birdwatchers, local bird clubs, (government) institutions and other organisations made the results of their bird counts available for this purpose. A number of individuals and institutions deserve a special mention, considering the relatively large quantity of unpublished data which they have provided: L. M. J. van den Bergh, J. H. Cronau, M. R. van Eerden, R. ter Horst and C. Witkamp, P. L. Meininger, C. J. G. Scharringa and C. J. Smit. F. Hustings (SOVON) provided information regarding numbers of bird species not bound to wetlands. Additional bird data was obtained from A. J. Dijksen, R. van Dongen, W. B. van Eijk, G. J. Gerritsen, M. F. Leopold, C. N. de Vries, F. J. J. Niewold, B. van Noorden, H. Sierdsema, J. B. M. Thissen, B. Voslamber, and D. Woets. In collecting other data many individuals and institutions contributed, including J. B. M. Thissen and R. Zollinger, Vereniging Natuurmonumenten, National Forest Service (SBB) and provincial associations. A commission appointed by the IKC natuurbeheer, consisting of A. J. Binsbergen, G. C. Boere, J. Kooijman, G. J. Post, J. B. M. Thissen, J. H. Cronau, E. C. L. Marteijn and P. L. Meininger, provided worthwhile comments on the 1994 review.

■ SITE ACCOUNTS

Wadden Sea   A4i, A4iii, B1i, C2, C3, C4   001
Admin region Groningen, Friesland, Noord-Holland
Coordinates 53°18′N 5°23′E
Altitude (-20)–0 m   **Area** 233,855 ha

■ Site description
Together with the Danish and German sections, the Wadden Sea (Waddenzee) is the largest intertidal area in Europe. Important habitats of the ecosystem include mudflats, sandflats, saltmarshes, shallowly submerged sandbanks, and estuaries. The Dutch section is bounded by the Waddeneilanden and the mainland. It was separated from Lake IJsselmeer (site 034) in 1932 and from the Lauwerszee (015) in 1969. The Wadden Sea IBA includes the main part of the intertidal system but the main isles (005, 009), the bays (013, 017) and the saltmarshes/forelands (002–004, 006–008, 010–014, 016) have been considered as separate sites. The area covered by the Wadden Sea Memorandum (national policy paper), of which the boundary is determined by the mean of the annual maximum high-water mark, overlaps with these sites and has a total area of 272,100 ha. Human activities include extraction of natural gas and of sand, and shellfish fisheries.

Habitats Wetland (100%; tidal river/enclosed tidal water; mudflat/sandflat)
Land-use Fisheries/aquaculture (90%), Military (18%), Nature conservation/research (85%), Tourism/recreation (100%), Urban/industrial/transport (11%)

■ Birds

Species		Season	Year	Pop min	Pop max	Acc	Criteria
[1] *Phalacrocorax carbo*	Cormorant	N	1991	2,811	2,811	B	B1i, C3
[1] *Branta leucopsis*	Barnacle Goose	W	1991	28,491	28,491	A	A4i, B1i, C2
[1] *Branta bernicla*	Brent Goose	N	1990	56,080	56,080	A	A4i, B1i, C3
[1] *Tadorna tadorna*	Shelduck	N	1990	45,236	45,236	A	A4i, B1i, C3
[1] *Anas penelope*	Wigeon	W	1991	61,350	61,350	A	A4i, B1i, C3
[1] *Anas crecca*	Teal	N	1991	4,153	4,153	A	B1i, C3
[1] *Anas acuta*	Pintail	N	1991	5,384	5,384	A	B1i, C3
[1] *Anas clypeata*	Shoveler	N	1991	1,249	1,249	A	B1i, C3
[1] *Aythya marila*	Scaup	W	1990	21,319	21,319	A	A4i, B1i, C3
[1] *Somateria mollissima*	Eider	N	1994	79,545	79,545	B	A4i, B1i, C3
[1] *Haematopus ostralegus*	Oystercatcher	N	1990	255,916	255,916	A	A4i, B1i, C3
[1] *Recurvirostra avosetta*	Avocet	N	1991	15,557	15,557	A	A4i, B1i, C2
[1] *Pluvialis squatarola*	Grey Plover	N	1990	29,265	29,265	A	A4i, B1i, C3

Species ... continued		Season	Year	Pop min	Pop max	Acc	Criteria
[2] *Calidris canutus*	Knot	W	1991	41,117	41,117	A	A4i, B1i, C3
[1] *Calidris canutus*	Knot	P	1991	46,732	46,732	A	A4i, B1i, C3
[2] *Calidris alpina*	Dunlin	W	1991	56,985	56,985	A	A4i, B1i, C3
[1] *Calidris alpina*	Dunlin	N	1990	182,674	182,674	A	A4i, B1i, C3
[1] *Limosa lapponica*	Bar-tailed Godwit	W	1991	17,045	17,045	A	A4i, B1i, C2
[1] *Limosa lapponica*	Bar-tailed Godwit	P	1991	84,388	84,388	A	A4i, B1i, C2
[1] *Numenius arquata*	Curlew	W	1991	57,693	57,693	A	A4i, B1i, C3
[1] *Numenius arquata*	Curlew	N	1990	92,462	92,462	A	A4i, B1i, C3
[1] *Tringa erythropus*	Spotted Redshank	N	1991	1,914	1,914	A	A4i, B1i, C3
[1] *Tringa totanus*	Redshank	N	1990	12,694	12,694	A	A4i, B1i, C3
[1] *Tringa nebularia*	Greenshank	N	1990	2,120	2,120	B	A4i, B1i, C3
[1] *Arenaria interpres*	Turnstone	W	1990	2,341	2,341	B	A4i, B1i, C3

1. Sites 002–014 and 016–017 included.
2. January mean.

The Wadden Sea is a major breeding, staging, wintering, feeding and moulting area for huge numbers of many duck, goose, wader, gull and tern species. No numbers are given for breeding birds as most nest in immediately adjacent IBAs. This complex site was not taken into account for the application of C6 criterion ('five most important sites in NUTS region'), because of its close proximity to adjacent sites (002–014, 016–017).

■ Protection status
National Partial   **International** High
About 108,000 ha of IBA covered by Natural Monument (Waddenzee I, 125,000 ha). 79,700 ha of IBA covered by Natural Monument (Waddenzee II, 80,000 ha). 233,855 ha of IBA covered by Special Protection Area (Waddenzee, '250,000 ha' [official, incorrect figure]). 233,855 ha of IBA covered by Ramsar Site (Waddenzee, '250,000 ha' [official, incorrect figure]). 233,855 ha of IBA covered by Biosphere Reserve (Waddenzee, 260,000 ha).

■ Conservation issues

Threats Aquaculture/fisheries (A), Disturbance to birds (B), Extraction industry (C), Recreation/tourism (B)

Mechanical fishing of cockles *Cardium* by suction dredging, military training, recreation, and gas extraction are the main threats to the area. Cockle fishing affects the food resources of birds such as *Somateria mollissima* and *Haematopus ostralegus* and destroys the sediment structure, while all long-established banks of mussels *Mytilus* have been removed, and the recovery of eel-grass *Zostera* is hindered. The Special Protection Area and the Ramsar designation cover the whole of this site although the area-sizes given in the designation orders are much less. The two Natural Monuments together cover about 85% of the area, including all of the saltmarshes and most of the intertidal flats. The current management plan covers the period 1996–2001.

Texel: Schorren and Zeeburg   A4i, A4iii, B1i, B2, C2, C3, C4, C6 **002**
Admin region Noord-Holland
Coordinates 53°08'N 4°54'E
Altitude 0–10 m **Area** 1,600 ha

■ Site description
The site comprises a saltmarsh (De Schorren), adjacent intertidal mudflats (contiguous to site 001), cord-grass *Spartina* swards, and inland farmland managed for *Branta bernicla* (Zeeburg) on the north-eastern side of Texel, the Wadden Sea island. The saltmarsh is protected against erosion by 30 longitudinal levees. This site, together with site 003, formed part of a single, larger site (former site NL002) in the previous international IBA inventory (Grimmett and Jones 1989).

Habitats Wetland (78%; mudflat/sandflat), Artificial landscape (22%; highly improved reseeded grassland)
Land-use Agriculture (20%), Fisheries/aquaculture (70%), Nature conservation/research (85%), Tourism/recreation (90%), Water management (20%)

■ Birds

Species		Season	Year	Pop min	Pop max	Acc	Criteria
Platalea leucorodia	Spoonbill	B	1991	55	55	A	A4i,B1i,B2,C2,C6
Platalea leucorodia	Spoonbill	N	1991	84	84	A	B1i, C2, C6
Branta bernicla	Brent Goose	N	1991	8,013	8,013	A	A4i, B1i, C3
Calidris canutus	Knot	W	1991	1,283	1,283	A	B2
Limosa lapponica	Bar-tailed Godwit	W	1990	430	430	B	B2
Limosa lapponica	Bar-tailed Godwit	P	1990	11,043	11,043	A	A4i, B1i, C2, C6
[1] *Numenius arquata*	Curlew	W	1991	2,002	2,002	A	B2
Sterna sandvicensis	Sandwich Tern	B	1991	386	386	A	B2, C6
Sterna paradisaea	Arctic Tern	B	1992	77	77	B	C6

1. January mean.

De Schorren is an important high-water roost for waders and ducks feeding in the Wadden Sea. The saltmarsh holds important breeding colonies of *Platalea leucorodia*, *Sterna paradisaea* and *S. sandvicensis* (until 1992). In spring *Branta bernicla* feeding inland are concentrated at Zeeburg to alleviate agricultural damage elsewhere on the island. Average seasonal peak number of waterbirds during 1992–1996 was over 20,000.

■ Protection status
National Partial **International** Partial
970 ha of IBA covered by Natural Monument (Schorren van de Eendracht, 970 ha). 286 ha of IBA covered by Natural Monument (Waddenzee I, 125,000 ha). 1,256 ha of IBA covered by Nature Reserve (De Schorren, 1,256 ha). 111 ha of IBA covered by Nature Reserve (Zeeburg, 111 ha). 1,256 ha of IBA covered by Special Protection Area (Waddenzee, '250,000 ha' [official, incorrect figure]). 1,256 ha of IBA covered by Ramsar Site (Waddenzee, '250,000 ha' [official, incorrect figure]).

■ Conservation issues

Threats Aquaculture/fisheries (A), Disturbance to birds (B), Drainage (B), Industrialization/urbanization (C), Recreation/tourism (B)

The main threats are shellfish fisheries (see site 001) and disturbance of birds on the mudflats by anglers, worm-diggers, military training flights to and from the Vliehors (004), and by small aircraft. The saltmarsh and mudflats are included in the SPA- and Ramsar-designated Wadden Sea. The saltmarsh and the inland farmland are managed as Nature Reserves and closed to the public, although the area can be overlooked from the dyke. Although the mudflats are legally protected as a Natural Monument they are not closed to shellfish fisheries and only partly closed to recreational activities.

Texel: Dunes and Hors   A4i, B1i, B2, B3, C2, C6 **003**
Admin region Noord-Holland
Coordinates 53°07'N 4°47'E
Altitude 0–25 m **Area** 3,850 ha

■ Site description
An extensive area of sand-dunes that stretches along 25 km of the North Sea side of Texel island; the width of the site varies from 200 m (near De Koog village) to 2 km. Important habitats include small lakes and dune-slacks (e.g. De Muy, De Geul), sea inlets with saltmarshes (De Slufter, De Mok), sandflats (De Hors), shifting and fixed dunes, and cord-grass *Spartina* swards. Parts of the inner dunes are covered by forestry plantations (largely excluded from the site). Hunting is allowed but with restrictions on quarry species. Other land-uses include scattered houses, recreational facilities, and groundwater abstraction. This site, together with site 002, formed part of a single, larger site (former site NL002) in the previous pan-European IBA inventory (Grimmett and Jones 1989).

Habitats Wetland (96%; saltmarsh; sand-dunes/sand beach)
Land-use Hunting (90%), Nature conservation/research (84%), Tourism/recreation (95%)

■ Birds

Species		Season	Year	Pop min	Pop max	Acc	Criteria
Platalea leucorodia	Spoonbill	B	1991	54	54	A	A4i,B1i,B2,C2,C6
Platalea leucorodia	Spoonbill	N	1991	31	31	A	B1i, C2
Circus cyaneus	Hen Harrier	B	1991	16	16	A	C6
[1] *Limosa lapponica*	Bar-tailed Godwit	W	1995	856	856	A	B2
Larus canus	Common Gull	B	1991	1,262	1,262	A	B2
Larus fuscus	Lesser Black-backed Gull	B	1991	990	990	A	B3
Sterna albifrons	Little Tern	B	1991	33	33	A	B2, C6
Asio flammeus	Short-eared Owl	B	1991	8	8	A	C6

1. January mean.

The area is important for its two traditional breeding sites of *Platalea leucorodia*.

■ Protection status
National Partial **International** None
70 ha of IBA covered by Natural Monument (Hanenplas, 70 ha). 5 ha of IBA covered by Natural Monument (Hanenplas II, 5 ha). 51 ha of IBA covered by Natural Monument (Korverskooi, 51 ha). 60 ha of IBA covered by Natural Monument (Waddenzee I, 125,000 ha). 300 ha of IBA covered by Natural Monument (Waddenzee II, 80,000 ha). 9 ha covered by Nature Reserve ('t Stoar, 9 ha). 4 ha of IBA covered by Nature Reserve (De Petten, 4 ha). 800 ha of IBA covered by Nature Reserve (Duinen Midden, Texel, 1,284 ha). 1,370 ha of IBA covered by Nature Reserve (Duinen Noord, Texel, 1,370 ha). 1,092 ha of IBA covered by Nature Reserve (Duinen Zuid, Texel, 1,092 ha).

■ Conservation issues

Threats Disturbance to birds (B), Recreation/tourism (B)

Threats include military training (De Hors) and increasing tourism, although large areas are closed to the public during the breeding season. The site is largely owned and managed as Nature Reserves by the National Forestry Service. The saltmarsh and mudflats are included in the SPA- and Ramsar-designated Wadden Sea.

Vlieland   A4i, A4iii, B1i, B2, B3, C2, C3, C4, C6 **004**
Admin region Friesland
Coordinates 53°17'N 4°59'E
Altitude 0–30 m **Area** 2,740 ha

■ Site description
The site is 17 km long and covers 85% of this barrier island in the Wadden Sea, lying between Texel and Terschelling (the village and the main tourist facilities on the east side have been excluded). The western half of the island (Vliehors) is an extensive sandflat (adjacent to the Wadden Sea, site 001). The eastern part consists of an extensive area of both shifting and fixed sand-dunes (the width of which varies

from 300 to 1,700 m), forestry plantations, some embanked brackish lagoons (Kroonpolders) and mudflats (Posthuiswad). The western part of the island (Vliehors) is an air-force training area. Other land-uses include scattered houses, recreational facilities, hunting, and groundwater abstraction.

Habitats Wetland (94%; mudflat/sandflat; sand-dunes/sand beach; standing brackish and salt water), Artificial landscape (6%; forestry plantation)
Land-use Fisheries/aquaculture (7%), Hunting (100%), Military (6%), Nature conservation/research (57%), Tourism/recreation (57%), Urban/industrial/transport (5%)

■ **Birds**

Species	Season	Year	Pop min	Pop max	Acc	Criteria
Platalea leucorodia Spoonbill	B	1991	34	34	A	B1i, B2, C2, C6
Circus cyaneus Hen Harrier	B	1991	6	6	A	C6
Haematopus ostralegus Oystercatcher	N	1992	12,608	12,608	A	A4i, B1i, C3
Calidris canutus Knot	W	1992	20,250	20,250	A	A4i, B1i, B2, C3
Calidris canutus Knot	P	1990	16,850	16,850	B	A4i, B1i, C3
Limosa lapponica Bar-tailed Godwit	W	1992	5,320	5,320	A	B1i, B2, C2, C6
Limosa lapponica Bar-tailed Godwit	P	1992	19,012	19,012	A	A4i, B1i, C2
Numenius arquata Curlew	N	1992	4,460	4,460	A	A4i, B1i, C3
Larus canus Common Gull	B	1991	608	608	A	B2
Larus fuscus Lesser Black-backed Gull	B	1992	905	905	B	B3

The dunes hold a recently-established breeding colony of *Platalea leucorodia*. The island also has a large number of *Somateria mollissima* (2,500 nests) and a large breeding colony of *Larus argentatus*. The mudflats south of the island are an important feeding area for tens of thousands of waterbirds that have high-tide roosts in the polders and on the Vliehors (count data for this sandflat hardly exist).

■ **Protection status**
National Partial **International** Partial
200 ha of IBA covered by Natural Monument (Waddenzee I, 125,000 ha). 1,350 ha of IBA covered by Nature Reserve (Vlieland, 1,840 ha). 367 ha of IBA covered by Special Protection Area (Waddenzee, '250,000 ha' [official, incorrect figure]). 367 ha of IBA covered by Ramsar Site (Waddenzee, '250,000 ha' [official, incorrect figure]).

■ **Conservation issues**

Threats Disturbance to birds (B), Groundwater abstraction (B), Recreation/tourism (B)

Threats include shellfish fisheries (Wadden Sea), air-force training on the Vliehors, and increasing tourism (although a large part of the area is closed to the public during the breeding season). The dune area and Kroonpolders are managed as a Nature Reserve by the National Forestry Service. Only the mudflats of the Wadden Sea (of which c.100 ha are included in this site) and the Vliehors have been included in the Ramsar and SPA designations.

Griend   A4i, A4iii, B1i, B2, C2, C3, C4, C6   005
Admin region Friesland
Coordinates 53°15'N 5°15'E
Altitude 0–2 m Area 100 ha

■ **Site description**
A small, crescent-shaped island in the western part of the Wadden Sea (site 001 encloses the entire site) with beaches, intertidal mudflats and sandflats, and raised saltmarshes. The island was reinforced by building a 2.5 km long dyke on the northern side in 1987 with sand supplementation in 1988 to enlarge the breeding area for terns *Sterna*.

Habitats Wetland (100%; mudflat/sandflat; saltmarsh; sand-dunes/sand beach)
Land-use Fisheries/aquaculture (50%), Nature conservation/research (100%)

■ **Birds**

Species	Season	Year	Pop min	Pop max	Acc	Criteria
Haematopus ostralegus Oystercatcher	N	1991	13,600	13,600	A	A4i, B1i, C3
Pluvialis squatarola Grey Plover	N	1989	2,042	2,042	A	A4i, B1i, C3
Calidris canutus Knot	W	1991	31,833	31,833	A	A4i, B1i, B2, C3

Species ... continued	Season	Year	Pop min	Pop max	Acc	Criteria
Calidris canutus Knot	P	1991	23,194	23,194	A	A4i, B1i, C3
Calidris alpina Dunlin	N	1989	30,118	30,118	A	A4i, B1i, C3
Limosa lapponica Bar-tailed Godwit	W	1991	159	159	A	B2
Limosa lapponica Bar-tailed Godwit	P	1992	19,012	19,012	A	A4i, B1i, C2, C6
[1] *Numenius arquata* Curlew	W	1993	4,067	4,067	B	A4i, B1i, B2, C3
Numenius arquata Curlew	N	1991	6,238	6,238	A	A4i, B1i, C3
Sterna sandvicensis Sandwich Tern	B	1991	7,360	7,360	A	A4i, B1i, B2, C2, C6
Sterna hirundo Common Tern	B	1991	1,600	1,600	A	C2, C6
Sterna paradisaea Arctic Tern	B	1991	528	528	A	C6

1. January mean.

The area is important as a breeding site for terns *Sterna*, and as a high-tide roost for tens of thousands of waders which feed on the surrounding mudflats.

■ **Protection status**
National High **International** High
100 ha of IBA covered by Natural Monument (Waddenzee I, 125,000 ha). 100 ha of IBA covered by Nature Reserve (Griend, 100 ha). 100 ha of IBA covered by Special Protection Area (Waddenzee, '250,000 ha' [official, incorrect figure]). 100 ha of IBA covered by Ramsar Site (Waddenzee, '250,000 ha' [official, incorrect figure]).

■ **Conservation issues**

Threats Aquaculture/fisheries (A)

The main threat is the mechanical cockle *Cardium* fisheries on the surrounding mudflats (see Wadden Sea, site 001). The island (leased to Natuurmonumenten) is closed to the public, with wardens/research teams present during the breeding season. The site has been designated twice under the Ramsar Convention: in 1980 (23 ha), and in 1984 as part of the Wadden Sea. The role of the island as the main breeding site for terns *Sterna* in the Dutch Wadden Sea has been safeguarded by the recent dyke construction.

Terschelling: De Boschplaat   A4i, A4iii, B1i, B2, B3, C2, C3, C4, C6   006
Admin region Friesland
Coordinates 53°26'N 5°28'E
Altitude 0–20 m Area 4,400 ha

■ **Site description**
This site, comprising the eastern half of Terschelling island in the Wadden Sea, and being contiguous with site 007, consists of an extensive area of intertidal mudflats, raised saltmarshes, sand-dunes, and cord-grass *Spartina* swards, and lies adjacent to site 001. The area is protected from the North Sea by a sand dyke, built at the beginning of the twentieth century. This site, together with site 007, formed part of a single, larger site (Terschelling, former site NL005) in the previous pan-European IBA inventory (Grimmett and Jones 1989).

Habitats Wetland (100%; mudflat/sandflat; saltmarsh; sand-dunes/sand beach)
Land-use Agriculture (5%), Hunting (100%), Nature conservation/research (100%), Tourism/recreation (50%)

■ **Birds**

Species	Season	Year	Pop min	Pop max	Acc	Criteria
Platalea leucorodia Spoonbill	B	1991	41	41	A	B1i, B2, C2, C6
Platalea leucorodia Spoonbill	N	1990	38	38	B	B1i, C2
Branta bernicla Brent Goose	N	1992	6,730	6,730	A	A4i, B1i, C3
Tadorna tadorna Shelduck	N	1992	5,363	5,363	A	A4i, B1i, C3
Anas acuta Pintail	N	1991	2,114	2,114	A	B1i, C3
Haematopus ostralegus Oystercatcher	N	1992	12,961	12,961	A	A4i, B1i, C3
Recurvirostra avosetta Avocet	N	1990	783	783	A	B1i, C2
Pluvialis squatarola Grey Plover	N	1992	2,278	2,278	A	A4i, B1i, C3
Calidris canutus Knot	W	1991	5,465	5,465	A	B1i, B2, C3
Calidris alpina Dunlin	N	1992	20,392	20,392	A	B1i, C3
[1] *Limosa lapponica* Bar-tailed Godwit	W	1992	9,601	9,601	A	A4i, B1i, B2, C2, C6
[1] *Numenius arquata* Curlew	W	1992	3,851	3,851	A	A4i, B1i, B2, C3
Numenius arquata Curlew	N	1991	5,384	5,384	A	A4i, B1i, C3
Tringa totanus Redshank	N	1992	1,617	1,617	A	B1i, C3

Species ... continued		Season	Year	Pop min	Pop max	Acc	Criteria
Larus fuscus Lesser Black-backed Gull	B	1991	12,060	12,060	A	A4i, B1i, B3, C3

1. January mean.

The area is an important feeding area in spring for *Branta bernicla* and is used as a high-tide roost by waterbirds that feed in the Wadden Sea. *Platalea leucorodia* and *Larus fuscus* breed in important numbers.

■ Protection status
National High **International** High
4,400 ha of IBA covered by Natural Monument (De Boschplaat, 4,400 ha). 4,400 ha of IBA covered by Nature Reserve (De Boschplaat, 4,400 ha). 3,500 ha of IBA covered by Special Protection Area (Waddenzee, '250,000 ha' [official, incorrect figure]). 3,500 ha of IBA covered by Ramsar Site (De Boschplaat, 4,400 ha).

■ Conservation issues

Threats Disturbance to birds (B), Extraction industry (C)

The main threat is gas extraction in the Wadden Sea; collecting of gull *Larus* eggs causes disturbance. The site was designated in 1980 as a Ramsar Site, and again in 1984 as part of the Wadden Sea designation. The Nature Reserve is managed by the National Forestry Service, and is closed to the public during the breeding season (apart from a bicycle track along the sand dyke). The mudflats south of the island have been closed to cockle *Cardium* and mussel *Mytilus* fishing since 1993. Hunting is restricted to rabbits.

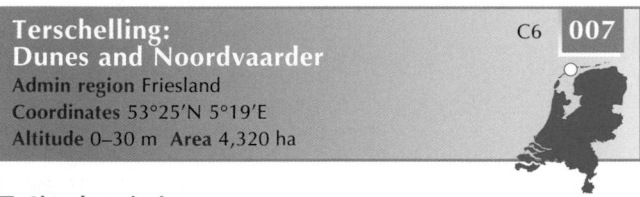

Terschelling: Dunes and Noordvaarder   C6   007
Admin region Friesland
Coordinates 53°25'N 5°19'E
Altitude 0–30 m **Area** 4,320 ha

■ Site description
This site comprises the sand-dunes of the barrier island Terschelling in the Wadden Sea, from an extensive sandflat in the west (Noordvaarder) up to De Boschplaat (006) in the east. In the south it is bordered by villages, grassland polders and conifer plantations. There are shifting and fixed dunes, with the latter covered in herbaceous vegetation or crowberry *Empetrum nigrum*, as well as humid dune-slacks. Land-uses include scattered holiday-houses, recreational facilities, hunting, and groundwater abstraction. This site, together with site 006, formed part of a single, larger site (Terschelling, former site NL005) in the previous international IBA inventory (Grimmett and Jones 1989).

Habitats Wetland (92%; sand-dunes/sand beach), Artificial landscape (8%; forestry plantation)
Land-use Agriculture (5%), Hunting (100%), Nature conservation/research (100%), Tourism/recreation (50%)

■ Birds

Species		Season	Year	Pop min	Pop max	Acc	Criteria
Circus aeruginosus Marsh Harrier	B	1991	33	33	A	C6
Circus cyaneus Hen Harrier	B	1991	36	36	B	C6
Asio flammeus Short-eared Owl	B	1991	6	6	A	C6
Lanius collurio Red-backed Shrike	B	1994	5	5	B	C6

■ Protection status
National High **International** None
150 ha of IBA covered by Natural Monument (Waddenzee II, 80,000 ha). 4,320 ha of IBA covered by Nature Reserve (Terschelling [excluding Boschplaat], 4,938 ha).

■ Conservation issues

Threats Disturbance to birds (B), Extraction industry (C), Groundwater abstraction (B), Recreation/tourism (B)

Threats include increasing tourism, although part of the area is closed to the public during the breeding season. The Nature Reserve is managed by the National Forestry Service.

Ameland: Duinen-Oerd   A4i, A4iii, B1i, B2, C2, C3, C4, C6   008
Admin region Friesland
Coordinates 53°28'N 5°45'E
Altitude 0–15 m **Area** 3,150 ha

■ Site description
A 22-km long area of sand-dunes on the eastern side of this barrier island in the Wadden Sea (adjacent to site 001). The width of the dunes varies from 100 m (near the main village) to 1.5 km. Other habitats include saltmarshes (Neerlands Reid), sandflats (De Hon), and intertidal mudflats. The site does not include the villages, extensive touristic facilities, or the grassland polders that are intensively used for dairy farming. Land-uses include natural-gas extraction, groundwater abstraction, hunting (restricted to rabbits), and reed-harvesting. The area lies close to an airfield.

Habitats Wetland (89%; mudflat/sandflat; saltmarsh; sand-dunes/sand beach), Artificial landscape (11%; highly improved reseeded grassland; forestry plantation)
Land-use Fisheries/aquaculture (8%), Forestry (5%), Hunting (100%), Nature conservation/research (20%), Tourism/recreation (58%)

■ Birds

Species		Season	Year	Pop min	Pop max	Acc	Criteria
Botaurus stellaris Bittern	R	1989	6	6	B	B2, C6
Branta bernicla Brent Goose	N	1991	9,327	9,327	A	A4i, B1i, C3
Tadorna tadorna Shelduck	N	1990	6,727	6,727	A	A4i, B1i, C3
Circus aeruginosus Marsh Harrier	B	1992	28	28	A	C6
Circus cyaneus Hen Harrier	B	1991	20	20	A	C6
Haematopus ostralegus Oystercatcher	N	1991	54,916	54,916	A	A4i, B1i, C3
Recurvirostra avosetta Avocet	N	1990	797	797	B	B1i, C2
Pluvialis squatarola Grey Plover	N	1990	2,066	2,066	A	A4i, B1i, C3
Calidris canutus Knot	W	1991	2,050	2,050	B	B2
[1] *Calidris alpina* Dunlin	W	1990	10,314	10,314	A	B2
Calidris alpina Dunlin	N	1990	20,463	20,463	A	B1i, C3
Limosa lapponica Bar-tailed Godwit	W	1991	134	134	A	B2
Limosa lapponica Bar-tailed Godwit	P	1991	13,025	13,025	B	A4i, B1i, C2, C6
[1] *Numenius arquata* Curlew	W	1990	6,331	6,331	A	A4i, B1i, B2, C3
Numenius arquata Curlew	N	1991	13,036	13,036	A	A4i, B1i, C3
Asio flammeus Short-eared Owl	B	1991	28	28	A	C6
Lanius collurio Red-backed Shrike	B	1989	16	16	B	C6

1. January mean.

The raised saltmarshes are an important spring feeding area for *Branta bernicla*, and the area is also important as a high-tide roost for tens of thousands of waterbirds which feed in the Wadden Sea.

■ Protection status
National Partial **International** Partial
265 ha of IBA covered by Natural Monument (Neerlands Reid, 265 ha). 50 ha of IBA covered by Nature Reserve (De Vleijen en Nesserbos, 50 ha). 48 ha of IBA covered by Nature Reserve (Grauwe Duin e.o., 48 ha). 116 ha of IBA covered by Nature Reserve (Hagedorenveld, 116 ha). 33 ha of IBA covered by Nature Reserve (Jan Roepeheide, 33 ha). 22 ha of IBA covered by Nature Reserve (Kievitspolle, 22 ha). 12 ha of IBA covered by Nature Reserve (Oostbosje en landschapselementen, 12 ha). 83 ha of IBA covered by Nature Reserve (Roosduinen, 83 ha). 950 ha of IBA covered by Special Protection Area (Waddenzee, '250,000 ha' [official, incorrect figure]). 950 ha of IBA covered by Ramsar Site (Waddenzee, '250,000 ha' [official, incorrect figure]).

■ Conservation issues

Threats Aquaculture/fisheries (B), Disturbance to birds (B), Extraction industry (B), Groundwater abstraction (B), Recreation/tourism (B)

Threats include shellfish fisheries (Wadden Sea), gas extraction, disturbance by small aircraft (the local airfield was extended recently), reed-harvesting, and an increase in tourism (although part of the dune area is closed to the public during the breeding season). The dune area and the eastern part of the island are managed as Nature Reserves, although only small parts are actually owned by conservation bodies. The saltmarshes and mudflats are included in the SPA- and Ramsar-designated Wadden Sea.

Engelsmanplaat   A4i, A4iii, B1i, C3, C4   009

Admin region Friesland
Coordinates 53°27'N 6°03'E
Altitude 0–1 m **Area** 720 ha

■ Site description

An eroded islet in the Wadden Sea (site 001 encloses the entire site) between Schiermonnikoog, Ameland, and the mainland. The site consists of bare intertidal sandbanks and mudflats.

Habitats Wetland (100%; mudflat/sandflat)
Land-use Fisheries/aquaculture (50%), Nature conservation/research (100%), Tourism/recreation (100%)

■ Birds

Species	Season	Year	Pop min	Pop max	Acc	Criteria
Pluvialis squatarola Grey Plover	N	1992	2,104	2,104	A	A4i, B1i, C3
Numenius arquata Curlew	N	1992	5,441	5,441	A	A4i, B1i, C3

An important high-water roost for numerous waders, especially *Pluvialis squatarola* and *Numenius arquata*. The average seasonal peak number of waterbirds during 1992–1996 exceeded 20,000. The site lost its breeding colony of terns *Sterna* during the early 1980s as a result of leveling by erosion.

■ Protection status

National High **International** High
720 ha of IBA covered by Natural Monument (Waddenzee I, 125,000 ha). 720 ha of IBA covered by Special Protection Area (Waddenzee, '250,000 ha' [official, incorrect figure]). 720 ha of IBA covered by Ramsar Site (Waddenzee, '250,000 ha' [official, incorrect figure]).

■ Conservation issues

Threats Disturbance to birds (A), Extraction industry (B), Recreation/tourism (B)

Monitoring during the breeding season was stopped in the late 1980s after the islet had lost its importance for breeding birds.

Schiermonnikoog   A4i, A4iii, B1i, B2, B3,   010
    C2, C3, C4, C6

Admin region Friesland
Coordinates 53°30'N 6°15'E
Altitude 0–15 m **Area** 2,800 ha

■ Site description

The site comprises the main part of the easternmost of the five inhabited barrier islands in the Wadden Sea (adjacent to site 001), but excludes the village and the adjoining part of grassland polder. The total length is 14 km, with a maximum width of 2,500 m. Habitats include beaches, shifting and fixed sand-dunes with herbaceous vegetation or crowberry *Empetrum nigrum*, humid dune-slacks, cord-grass *Spartina* swards, saltmarshes, mudflats, freshwater marsh and improved grassland. Land-uses include scattered houses, recreational facilities, dairy farming and groundwater abstraction.

Habitats Wetland (88%; saltmarsh; sand-dunes/sand beach), Artificial landscape (8%; highly improved reseeded grassland)
Land-use Agriculture (8%), Fisheries/aquaculture (5%), Hunting (35%), Nature conservation/research (67%), Tourism/recreation (50%), Water management (8%)

■ Birds

Species	Season	Year	Pop min	Pop max	Acc	Criteria
Branta leucopsis Barnacle Goose	W	1990	4,883	4,883	B	A4i, B1i, B2, C2
Tadorna tadorna Shelduck	N	1991	3,202	3,202	A	B1i, C3
Anas acuta Pintail	N	1991	606	606	A	B1i, C3
Circus cyaneus Hen Harrier	B	1992	14	14	B	C6
Haematopus ostralegus Oystercatcher	N	1991	28,279	28,279	A	A4i, B1i, C3
Pluvialis squatarola Grey Plover	N	1991	3,136	3,136	A	A4i, B1i, C3
Calidris canutus Knot	W	1990	2,590	2,590	B	B2
Calidris canutus Knot	P	1991	24,936	24,936	A	A4i, B1i, C3
Calidris alpina Dunlin	N	1991	23,237	23,237	A	A4i, B1i, C3

Species ... continued	Season	Year	Pop min	Pop max	Acc	Criteria
[1] *Limosa lapponica* Bar-tailed Godwit	W	1991	1,348	1,348	A	B1i, B2, C2, C6
[1] *Numenius arquata* Curlew	W	1991	2,788	2,788	A	B2
Numenius arquata Curlew	N	1991	6,856	6,856	A	A4i, B1i, C3
Larus canus Common Gull	B	1992	463	463	B	B2
Larus fuscus Lesser Black-backed Gull	B	1992	1,561	1,561	B	B1i, B3, C3
Asio flammeus Short-eared Owl	B	1992	3	3	B	C6
Lanius collurio Red-backed Shrike	B	1992	5	5	B	C6

1. January mean.

The raised saltmarshes are an important spring feeding area for *Branta bernicla* and the grassland polder is also a feeding area for *Branta leucopsis*. The area is an important high-tide roost for tens of thousands of waterbirds that feed in the Wadden Sea. *Platalea leucorodia* established a breeding colony in 1994.

■ Protection status

National High **International** Partial
1,500 ha of IBA covered by Natural Monument (Waddenzee I, 125,000 ha). 1,889 ha of IBA covered by Nature Reserve (Schiermonnikoog, 1,889 ha). 2,800 ha of IBA covered by National Park (Schiermonnikoog, 5,400 ha). 855 ha of IBA covered by Special Protection Area (Waddenzee, '250,000 ha' [official, incorrect figure]). 855 ha of IBA covered by Ramsar Site (Waddenzee, '250,000 ha' [official, incorrect figure]).

■ Conservation issues

Threats Extraction industry (C), Groundwater abstraction (B), Recreation/tourism (B)

Threats include gas extraction and increasing tourism, although part of the dune area is closed to the public during the breeding season. The dune area and saltmarshes are managed as a Nature Reserve by Natuurmonumenten. The saltmarshes and part of the dunes fall within the boundaries of the Ramsar- and SPA-designated Wadden Sea.

Rottumerplaat   A4i, A4iii, B1i, C3, C4, C6   011

Admin region Groningen
Coordinates 53°32'N 6°30'E
Altitude 0–6 m **Area** 782 ha

■ Site description

A small, uninhabited barrier island in the Wadden Sea between Schiermonnikoog and Rottumeroog, with beaches, shifting and fixed sand-dunes, saltmarshes, cord-grass *Spartina* swards, and mudflats (the entire site is enclosed by site 001). The accretion of the island was promoted by the building of a sand dyke, which was reinforced in the 1970s. There are a small number of guided excursions, otherwise the island is closed to the public. Hunting is restricted to rabbits. The site (all of the mudflats south of the island) has been entirely closed to cockle *Cardium* and mussel *Mytilus* fishing since 1993. Coastal defence measures have been reduced since 1988. This site, together with site 012, formed part of a single, larger site (former site NL009) in the previous pan-European IBA inventory (Grimmett and Jones 1989).

Habitats Wetland (100%; mudflat/sandflat; saltmarsh; sand-dunes/sand beach)
Land-use Hunting (5%), Nature conservation/research (100%), Tourism/recreation (100%)

■ Birds

Species	Season	Year	Pop min	Pop max	Acc	Criteria
Haematopus ostralegus Oystercatcher	N	1992	16,640	16,640	B	A4i, B1i, C3
Pluvialis squatarola Grey Plover	N	1991	2,686	2,686	A	A4i, B1i, C3
Calidris canutus Knot	P	1991	12,556	12,556	A	A4i, B1i, C3
Calidris alpina Dunlin	N	1991	37,977	37,977	A	A4i, B1i, C3
Numenius arquata Curlew	N	1992	6,351	6,351	B	A4i, B1i, C3
Sterna paradisaea Arctic Tern	B	1991	103	103	A	C6

An important high-tide roost for waterbirds that feed in the Wadden Sea.

■ Protection status

National High **International** High
782 ha of IBA covered by Natural Monument (Waddenzee I, 125,000 ha). 782 ha of IBA covered by Special Protection Area

(Waddenzee, '250,000 ha' [official, incorrect figure]). 782 ha of IBA covered by Ramsar Site (Waddenzee, '250,000 ha' [official, incorrect figure]).

■ **Conservation issues**

Threats Abandonment/reduction of land management (C), Extraction industry (C)

Gas extraction in the Wadden Sea (resulting in subsidence) is a threat.

Rottumeroog   A4i, A4iii, B1i, B2, C3, C4, C6   012
Admin region Groningen
Coordinates 53°33′N 6°35′E
Altitude 0–9 m **Area** 311 ha

■ **Site description**
A small, uninhabited barrier island in the Wadden Sea (entirely enclosed by site 001), between Rottumeroog and the Eems/Dollard estuary. The site includes the Zuiderduintjes, a isolated dune area, 2 km south of the main island. The island, which was located at the present position of Rottumerplaat 350 years ago, is being reduced by erosion. Habitats include sandflats and mudflats, shifting and fixed sand-dunes, saltmarshes, and cord-grass *Spartina* swards. The island is closed to the public; hunting taking place to reduce rabbit numbers. The site (all the mudflats south of the island) has been entirely closed to cockle *Cardium* and mussel *Mytilus* fishing since 1993. This site, together with site 011, formed part of a single, larger site (former site NL009) in the previous international IBA inventory (Grimmett and Jones 1989).

Habitats Wetland (100%; mudflat/sandflat; saltmarsh; sand-dunes/sand beach)
Land-use Hunting (100%), Nature conservation/research (100%), Tourism/recreation (10%)

■ **Birds**

Species	Season	Year	Pop min	Pop max	Acc	Criteria
Haematopus ostralegus Oystercatcher	N	1992	19,180	19,180	B	A4i, B1i, C3
Pluvialis squatarola Grey Plover	N	1992	3,069	3,069	B	A4i, B1i, C3
[1] *Calidris alpina* Dunlin	W	1992	6,254	6,254	A	B2
Calidris alpina Dunlin	N	1992	29,120	29,120	B	A4i, B1i, C3
[1] *Numenius arquata* Curlew	W	1992	5,578	5,578	B	A4i, B1i, B2, C3
Numenius arquata Curlew	N	1991	6,854	6,854	A	A4i, B1i, C3
Sterna paradisaea Arctic Tern	B	1991	60	60	A	C6
Sterna albifrons Little Tern	B	1991	25	25	A	B2, C6

1. January mean.

An important high-tide roost for waterbirds that feed in the Wadden Sea.

■ **Protection status**
National High **International** High
311 ha of IBA covered by Natural Monument (Waddenzee I, 125,000 ha). 311 ha of IBA covered by Special Protection Area (Waddenzee, '250,000 ha' [official, incorrect figure]). 311 ha of IBA covered by Ramsar Site (Waddenzee, '250,000 ha' [official, incorrect figure]).

■ **Conservation issues**

Threats Extraction industry (C)

Gas extraction in the Wadden Sea (resulting in subsidence) is a threat.

Balgzand   A4i, A4iii, B1i, B2, B3, C2, C3, C4, C6   013
Admin region Noord-Holland
Coordinates 52°55′N 4°46′E
Altitude (-10)–0 m **Area** 6,000 ha

■ **Site description**
An extensive area of intertidal mudflats and sandflats in the western part of the Wadden Sea, between the harbour area of Den Helder and the Amsteldiep gully (site 001 is contiguous with this site). Along the dyke are some small saltmarshes, partly extended in the late 1980s to compensate for habitat loss due to dyke reinforcement. Stock farming

is restricted to dyke slopes and (occasionally) saltmarsh. The site has been entirely closed to cockle *Cardium* and mussel *Mytilus* fishing since 1993.

Habitats Wetland (100%; tidal river/enclosed tidal water; mudflat/sandflat)
Land-use Agriculture (5%), Fisheries/aquaculture (5%), Nature conservation/research (100%), Tourism/recreation (10%)

■ **Birds**

Species	Season	Year	Pop min	Pop max	Acc	Criteria
Platalea leucorodia Spoonbill	N	1991	144	144	A	B1i, C2, C6
Tadorna tadorna Shelduck	N	1991	5,201	5,201	A	A4i, B1i, C3
Anas acuta Pintail	N	1991	871	871	A	B1i, C3
Haematopus ostralegus Oystercatcher	N	1991	31,037	31,037	A	A4i, B1i, C3
Recurvirostra avosetta Avocet	B	1991	384	384	A	A4i,B1i,B3,C2,C6
Recurvirostra avosetta Avocet	N	1991	1,215	1,215	A	A4i, B1i, C2
Calidris canutus Knot	W	1991	32,560	32,560	A	A4i, B1i, B2, C3
Calidris alpina Dunlin	N	1991	34,995	34,995	A	A4i, B1i, C3
[1] *Limosa lapponica* Bar-tailed Godwit	W	1991	1,027	1,027	A	A4i, B1i, B2, C2
Numenius arquata Curlew	N	1991	13,348	13,348	A	A4i, B1i, C3
Tringa erythropus Spotted Redshank	N	1991	1,177	1,177	A	A4i, B1i, C3
Tringa totanus Redshank	N	1991	2,652	2,652	A	B1i, C3
Arenaria interpres Turnstone	N	1991	832	832	A	A4i, B1i, C3
Sterna hirundo Common Tern	B	1991	1,035	1,035	A	C2, C6
Chlidonias niger Black Tern	P	1991	90,367	90,367	B	A4i, B1i, C2, C6

1. November–January mean.

The site is an important high-tide roost for tens of thousands of waterbirds, and huge numbers of *Chlidonias niger* roost here at night in late summer, after feeding during the day on the IJsselmeer (034). It holds important breeding numbers of *Recurvirostra avosetta* and *Sterna hirundo*; the small areas of saltmarsh are the only available breeding sites for these species in this part of the Wadden Sea.

■ **Protection status**
National High **International** High
6,000 ha of IBA covered by Natural Monument (Waddenzee I, 125,000 ha). 6,000 ha of IBA covered by Special Protection Area (Waddenzee, '250,000 ha' [official, incorrect figure]). 6,000 ha of IBA covered by Ramsar Site (Waddenzee, '250,000 ha' [official, incorrect figure]).

■ **Conservation issues**

Threats Disturbance to birds (B), Recreation/tourism (B)

Disturbance by the public, planes and helicopters (air-force base near Den Helder) and the (illegal) taking of eggs are problems. The saltmarshes are managed as a nature reserve (but not owned) by Noordhollands Landschap.

Frisian Wadden Sea coast   A4i, A4iii, B1i, B2, B3, C2, C3, C4, C6   014
Admin region Friesland
Coordinates 53°20′N 5°45′E
Altitude 1–2 m **Area** 9,310 ha

■ **Site description**
An extensive area of intertidal mudflats, saltmarshes, and grassland polders outside the Wadden Sea dyke of Friesland (total length 40 km). The site is contiguous with the Wadden Sea IBA (site 001), and adjacent to Lauwersmeer (015) in the east. Land reclamation by the furthering of natural accretion (intensified since the 1930s) has ended, but the existing system of dams and ditches will be maintained to reduce erosion.

Habitats Wetland (87%; mudflat/sandflat; saltmarsh), Artificial landscape (13%; highly improved reseeded grassland)
Land-use Agriculture (13%), Fisheries/aquaculture (65%), Hunting (50%), Nature conservation/research (91%), Tourism/recreation (25%)

■ **Birds**
This is the main feeding site for *Branta leucopsis* and *B. bernicla* in winter, in the Netherlands at least, and possibly over a much greater area. The saltmarshes and polders are an important high-tide

Species	Season	Year	Pop min	Pop max	Acc	Criteria
Branta leucopsis Barnacle Goose	W	1990	35,636	35,636	B	A4i,B1i,B2,C2,C6
Branta bernicla Brent Goose	N	1990	30,423	30,423	A	A4i, B1i, C3
Tadorna tadorna Shelduck	N	1990	14,545	14,545	A	A4i, B1i, C3
Anas penelope Wigeon	W	1990	18,984	18,984	A	A4i, B1i, C3
Haematopus ostralegus Oystercatcher	N	1990	41,373	41,373	A	A4i, B1i, C3
Recurvirostra avosetta Avocet	B	1993	2,241	2,241	B	A4i,B1i,B3,C2,C6
Recurvirostra avosetta Avocet	N	1990	4,618	4,618	A	A4i, B1i, C2, C6
Pluvialis squatarola Grey Plover	N	1990	6,616	6,616	A	A4i, B1i, C3
[1] *Calidris alpina* Dunlin	W	1990	9,161	9,161	A	B2
Calidris alpina Dunlin	N	1990	42,094	42,094	A	A4i, B1i, C3
Limosa lapponica Bar-tailed Godwit	P	1990	14,521	14,521	B	A4i, B1i, C2, C6
[1] *Numenius arquata* Curlew	W	1990	15,054	15,054	A	A4i, B1i, B2, C3
Numenius arquata Curlew	N	1990	24,764	24,764	A	A4i, B1i, C3
Tringa erythropus Spotted Redshank	N	1990	729	729	B	A4i, B1i, C3
Tringa totanus Redshank	N	1990	5,653	5,653	A	A4i, B1i, C3

1. January mean.

roost for waterbirds that feed in the Wadden Sea. This is also the most important breeding site for *Recurvirostra avosetta* in the Netherlands.

■ Protection status
National High **International** High
2,270 ha of IBA covered by Natural Monument (Waddenzee I, 125,000 ha). 4,800 ha of IBA covered by Natural Monument (Noord-Friesland buitendijks, 4,800 ha). 700 ha of IBA covered by Natural Monument (Noord-Friesland buitendijks II, 700 ha). 670 ha of IBA covered by Natural Monument (Kwelder langs de noordkust van Friesland, 670 ha). 964 ha of IBA covered by Nature Reserve (Noord Friesland buitendijks, 940 ha). 9,310 ha of IBA covered by Special Protection Area (Waddenzee, '250,000 ha' [official, incorrect figure]). 8,360 ha of IBA covered by Ramsar Site (Waddenzee, '250,000 ha' [official, incorrect figure]).

■ Conservation issues

Threats Agricultural intensification/expansion (B), Aquaculture/fisheries (B), Disturbance to birds (C), Extraction industry (C), Industrialization/urbanization (C)

Apart from about 1,000 ha of summer polders, the site is largely included in the Ramsar-designated Wadden Sea.

Lauwersmeer A4i, B1i, B2, B3, C2, C3, C6 015
Admin region Groningen, Friesland
Coordinates 53°22′N 6°13′E
Altitude (-13)–(-2) m **Area** 7,820 ha

■ Site description
A dammed estuary, formerly part of the Wadden Sea (closed off in 1969), which has become freshwater, though the estuary structure remains. The surrounding area is mainly open grassland and arable land with scattered farms. The site is adjacent to the Wadden Sea (site 001) in the north, the Frisian Wadden Sea coast (014) in the west and the Groningen Wadden Sea coast (016) in the east. Hunting is allowed but with restrictions on quarry species (and will be terminated in the near future).

Habitats Wetland (44%; standing fresh water; water-fringe vegetation), Artificial landscape (51%; highly improved reseeded grassland; arable land; forestry plantation), Unknown (5%)
Land-use Agriculture (10%), Fisheries/aquaculture (25%), Hunting (10%), Military (35%), Nature conservation/research (73%), Tourism/recreation (65%), Urban/industrial/transport (26%), Water management (100%)

■ Birds

Species	Season	Year	Pop min	Pop max	Acc	Criteria
Platalea leucorodia Spoonbill	N	1990	164	164	A	A4i, B1i, C2, C6
Cygnus columbianus Bewick's Swan	W	1990	3,053	3,053	A	A4i,B1i,B2,C2,C6
Cygnus cygnus Whooper Swan	W	1990	65	65	A	B3, C6
Anser albifrons White-fronted Goose	W	1991	7,508	7,508	A	B1i, C3
Anser anser Greylag Goose	N	1991	9,445	9,445	A	A4i, B1i, C3
Branta leucopsis Barnacle Goose	W	1990	18,080	18,080	A	A4i,B1i,B2,C2,C6
Anas penelope Wigeon	W	1991	17,850	17,850	A	B1i, C3

Species ... continued	Season	Year	Pop min	Pop max	Acc	Criteria
Anas strepera Gadwall	N	1990	1,396	1,396	A	A4i, B1i, C3
Anas crecca Teal	N	1991	12,783	12,783	A	B1i, C3
Anas acuta Pintail	N	1991	11,702	11,702	A	B1i, C3
Anas clypeata Shoveler	N	1991	2,740	2,740	A	B1i, C3
Circus aeruginosus Marsh Harrier	B	1991	50	50	A	C6
Circus pygargus Montagu's Harrier	B	1991	3	3	A	C6
Recurvirostra avosetta Avocet	B	1991	116	116	A	B3
Philomachus pugnax Ruff	B	1991	89	89	A	C6
Sterna paradisaea Arctic Tern	B	1991	63	63	A	C6
Asio flammeus Short-eared Owl	B	1991	9	9	A	C6

An important area for non-breeding *Platalea leucorodia* and a wide variety of waterfowl.

■ Protection status
National Partial **International** None
5,504 ha of IBA covered by Natural Monument (Lauwersmeer I, 5,504 ha). 196 ha of IBA covered by Natural Monument (Lauwersmeer II, 196 ha). 113 ha of IBA covered by Nature Reserve (Bantpolder, 113 ha). 49 ha of IBA covered by Nature Reserve (Bochtjesplaat, 49 ha). 4,617 ha of IBA covered by Nature Reserve (Lauwersmeer, 4,617 ha).

■ Conservation issues

Threats Agricultural intensification/expansion (U), Disturbance to birds (B), Extraction industry (C), Other (B), Recreation/tourism (B)

The main threats include increasing tourism and boating, military training (artillery practice), gas extraction in the Wadden Sea, commercial reed-harvesting since 1996/1997 ('Other' threat, above), and nutrient pollution (mainly from agriculture). The importance of the area for breeding and feeding birds is decreasing due to the natural succession of vegetation and the desalinization of the soil after reclamation.

Groningen Wadden Sea coast A4i, A4iii, B1i, B2, B3, C2, C3, C4, C6 016
Admin region Groningen
Coordinates 53°26′N 6°34′E
Altitude 0–2 m **Area** 4,600 ha

■ Site description
An extensive area of intertidal mudflats, saltmarshes and grassland polders outside the Wadden Sea dyke of Groningen (total length 34 km), contiguous with the Wadden Sea itself (site 001). The site is adjacent in the east to Lauwersmeer (015) and to the Eems/Dollard estuary together with the port and industrial area of Eemshaven. Land reclamation by the furthering of natural accretion (intensified since the 1930s) has been ended, but the existing system of dams and ditches will be maintained to reduce erosion. One-third of the mudflats have been closed to shellfish fisheries.

Habitats Wetland (100%; mudflat/sandflat; saltmarsh)
Land-use Agriculture (10%), Fisheries/aquaculture (66%), Hunting (30%), Nature conservation/research (100%), Tourism/recreation (100%)

■ Birds

Species	Season	Year	Pop min	Pop max	Acc	Criteria
Branta leucopsis Barnacle Goose	W	1990	8,221	8,221	B	A4i, B1i, B2, C2
Branta bernicla Brent Goose	N	1990	7,789	7,789	B	A4i, B1i, C3
Tadorna tadorna Shelduck	N	1990	9,349	9,349	B	A4i, B1i, C3
Haematopus ostralegus Oystercatcher	N	1991	41,446	41,446	B	A4i, B1i, C3
Recurvirostra avosetta Avocet	B	1991	1,263	1,263	A	A4i,B1i,B3,C2,C6
Recurvirostra avosetta Avocet	N	1990	4,091	4,091	B	A4i, B1i, C2, C6
Pluvialis squatarola Grey Plover	N	1990	8,968	8,968	B	A4i, B1i, C3
Calidris canutus Knot	W	1990	889	889	B	B2
Calidris alpina Dunlin	N	1990	26,474	26,474	B	A4i, B1i, C3
Limosa lapponica Bar-tailed Godwit	P	1990	12,330	12,330	B	A4i, B1i, C2, C6
[1] *Numenius arquata* Curlew	W	1990	14,693	14,693	B	A4i, B1i, B2, C3
Numenius arquata Curlew	N	1990	15,788	15,788	B	A4i, B1i, C3
Tringa totanus Redshank	N	1990	2,445	2,445	B	B1i, C3

1. January mean.

The saltmarshes and polders form an important high-tide roost for waterbirds that feed in the Wadden Sea and are an important feeding area for *Branta bernicla* and *B. leucopsis*. This is the second most important breeding site for *Recurvirostra avosetta* in the Netherlands.

■ **Protection status**

National High **International** High

3,380 ha of IBA covered by Natural Monument (Waddenzee I, 125,000 ha). 1,220 ha of IBA covered by Natural Monument (Kwelders langs de noordkust van Groningen, 1,220 ha). 90 ha of IBA covered by Nature Reserve (Kwelders Groninger Noordkust, 90 ha). 43 ha of IBA covered by Nature Reserve (Uithuizerwad, 43 ha). 4,600 ha of IBA covered by Special Protection Area (Waddenzee, '250,000 ha' [official, incorrect figure]). 4,600 ha of IBA covered by Ramsar Site (Waddenzee, '250,000 ha' [official, incorrect figure]).

■ **Conservation issues**

Threats Agricultural intensification/expansion (B), Aquaculture/fisheries (B), Disturbance to birds (B), Extraction industry (C), Industrialization/urbanization (C)

Dollard   A4i, A4iii, B1i, B2, B3, C2, C3, C4, C6   017

Admin region Groningen
Coordinates 53°17′N 7°08′E
Altitude (-2)–2 m **Area** 6,400 ha

■ **Site description**

An estuary with saltmarshes and intertidal mudflats; the site includes a small artificial lagoon located just at the inland side of the dyke (Polder Breebaert). The Dollard estuary is partly located in Germany, and this site lies adjacent to the Wadden Sea (site 001) and to Emden Harbour in the German part of the Dollard.

Habitats Wetland (100%; tidal river/enclosed tidal water; mudflat/sandflat; saltmarsh)
Land-use Fisheries/aquaculture (20%), Hunting (20%), Nature conservation/research (100%), Tourism/recreation (50%), Urban/industrial/transport (10%)

■ **Birds**

Species		Season	Year	Pop min	Pop max	Acc	Criteria
Anser fabalis	Bean Goose	W	1991	9,960	9,960	A	A4i, B1i, C3
Anser albifrons	White-fronted Goose	W	1991	37,292	37,292	A	A4i, B1i, C3
Anser anser	Greylag Goose	N	1990	9,188	9,188	A	A4i, B1i, C3
Branta leucopsis	Barnacle Goose	W	1991	2,807	2,807	A	A4i, B1i, B2
Anas crecca	Teal	N	1991	4,639	4,639	A	B1i, C3
Recurvirostra avosetta	Avocet	B	1991	207	207	A	B3
Recurvirostra avosetta	Avocet	N	1990	1,844	1,844	B	A4i, B1i, C2, C6
Calidris alpina	Dunlin	N	1991	21,465	21,465	A	B1i, C3
Limosa lapponica	Bar-tailed Godwit	P	1990	8,864	8,864	—	A4i, B1i, C2
Tringa erythropus	Spotted Redshank	N	1990	1,414	1,414	B	A4i, B1i, C3

An important feeding and roosting area for ducks and waders. Four species of geese fly in to roost during winter from an extensive feeding area in Germany and the Netherlands. Large numbers of *Recurvirostra avosetta* nest inland, but the young are often not able to move to the feeding areas of the Dollard.

■ **Protection status**

National High **International** High

4,900 ha of IBA covered by Natural Monument (Dollard, 4,900 ha). 96 ha of IBA covered by Natural Monument (Dollard II, 96 ha). 1,341 ha of IBA covered by Natural Monument (Waddenzee I, 125,000 ha). 63 ha of IBA covered by Nature Reserve (Breebaert, 63 ha). 345 ha of IBA covered by Nature Reserve (Dollard GRL, 345 ha). 3,844 ha of IBA covered by Nature Reserve (Dollard NM, 3,844 ha). 6,337 ha of IBA covered by Special Protection Area (Waddenzee, '250,000 ha' [official, incorrect figure]). 6,337 ha of IBA covered by Ramsar Site (Waddenzee, '250,000 ha' [official, incorrect figure]).

■ **Conservation issues**

Threats Disturbance to birds (C), Extraction industry (C)

North Sea north of the Wadden Sea   A4i, A4iii, B1i, C2, C3, C4, C6   018

Admin region Groningen, Friesland, Noord-Holland
Coordinates 53°20′N 5°00′E
Altitude (-20)–0 m **Area** 187,000 ha

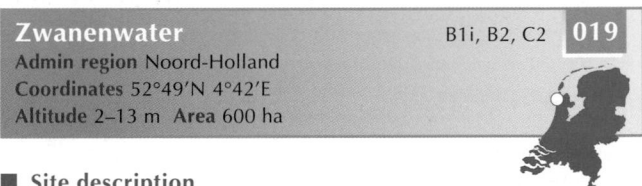

■ **Site description**

An extensive area of coastal waters, extending from the Eems/Dollard estuary and German border in the east across to Groet (Noord-Holland) in the south. The area is adjacent to 11 IBAs (001, 003–004, 006–012, 019). The outer boundary follows roughly the line of 20 metres depth. Important habitats include shallowly submerged sandbanks.

Habitats Marine areas (100%; open sea)
Land-use Fisheries/aquaculture (100%), Tourism/recreation (20%), Urban/industrial/transport (20%)

■ **Birds**

Species		Season	Year	Pop min	Pop max	Acc	Criteria
[1] *Gavia stellata*	Red-throated Diver	W	1990	7,000	7,000	B	A4i, B1i, C2, C6
[1,2] *Gavia arctica*	Black-throated Diver	W	1990	750	750	B	C6
Somateria mollissima	Eider	N	1993	22,125	22,125	A	B1i, C3
Melanitta nigra	Common Scoter	W	1993	94,250	94,250	A	A4i, B1i, C3

1. Number estimated from boat counts.
2. Majority of Dutch wintering population.

The number of *Somateria mollissima* increased during the winters of 1992/93 and 1993/94 due to food shortage in the Wadden Sea.

■ **Protection status**

National None **International** None

■ **Conservation issues**

Threats Aquaculture/fisheries (A), Disturbance to birds (B)

The zone lying up to three nautical miles offshore from islands is included in the Trilateral Cooperation Area between Denmark, Germany and Netherlands with regard to the protection of the Wadden Sea. The ecological target for this zone is a "favourable food availability for birds" (as agreed upon in 1994).

Zwanenwater   B1i, B2, C2   019

Admin region Noord-Holland
Coordinates 52°49′N 4°42′E
Altitude 2–13 m **Area** 600 ha

■ **Site description**

An area of shifting and fixed sand-dunes along the mainland coast, with humid dune-slacks, two lakes, coastal marshes, and woodland.

Habitats Wetland (100%; sand-dunes/sand beach; standing fresh water)
Land-use Nature conservation/research (98%), Water management (100%)

■ **Birds**

Species		Season	Year	Pop min	Pop max	Acc	Criteria
Platalea leucorodia	Spoonbill	B	1991	30	30	A	B1i, B2, C2
Larus canus	Common Gull	B	1991	397	397	A	B2

A traditional breeding colony of *Platalea leucorodia*.

■ **Protection status**

National High **International** High

586 ha of IBA covered by Nature Reserve (Zwanenwater, 600 ha). 600 ha of IBA covered by Special Protection Area (Zwanenwater, 600 ha). 600 ha of IBA covered by Ramsar Site (Zwanenwater, 600 ha).

■ **Conservation issues**

Threats Disturbance to birds (B)

Disturbance is caused by a shooting range to the south of the site.

Voordelta   A4i, A4iii, B1i, B2, C3, C4   020

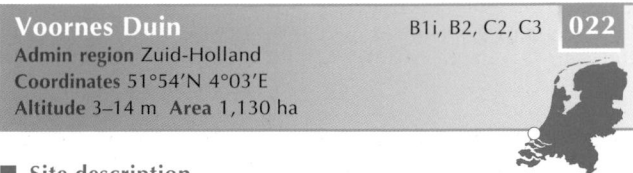

Admin region Zuid-Holland, Zeeland
Coordinates 51°43′N 3°35′E
Altitude (-20)–0 m   **Area** 107,000 ha

■ Site description
An extensive area of coastal waters of the North Sea, extending from Rotterdam in the north up to the Westerschelde estuary (032) in the south. The site also adjoins the closed-off delta area of the Rhine/Maas river system, which includes seven other IBAs (021–024, 027–029), and is close to Vlaamse Banken in Belgium. Important habitats include shallowly submerged sandbanks and intertidal mud- and sandflats. This site, together with sites 022 and 023, formed part of a single, larger site (former site NL046) in the previous pan-European IBA inventory (Grimmett and Jones 1989).

Habitats Marine areas (96%; open sea)
Land-use Fisheries/aquaculture (96%), Military (30%), Tourism/recreation (22%), Urban/industrial/transport (5%)

■ Birds

Species	Season	Year	Pop min	Pop max	Acc	Criteria
[1] *Aythya marila* Scaup	W	1995	3,460	3,460	A	A4i, B1i, B2, C3

1. Seasonal peak number probably underestimated and exceeds A4i threshold.

In winter this area holds fluctuating numbers of *Aythya marila* (max. 5,550, 1992/93), *Somateria mollissima* (max. 9,968, 1992/93) and *Melanitta nigra* (max. 20,000, 1986/87). The mean total of waterbirds in February (1992/93–1994/95) exceeds 20,000.

■ Protection status
National None **International** Low
395 ha of IBA covered by Special Protection Area (Kwade Hoek, 825 ha).

■ Conservation issues

Threats Aquaculture/fisheries (A), Construction/impact of dyke/dam/barrage (C), Recreation/tourism (B)

The main threats concern shellfish fisheries and pollution. Sedimentation has increased due to the hydrological works on the Rhine/Maas delta, which have involved the closing of several sea arms, i.e. Haringvliet, Grevelingen and Oosterschelde (024, 027, 028). The SPA-designated Kwade Hoek (see site 023) also includes a small part of this area.

Westplaat   B1i, B3, C3, C6   021

Admin region Zuid-Holland
Coordinates 51°55′N 4°02′E
Altitude 0–0 m   **Area** 350 ha

■ Site description
A shallow bay between the old coast (Voornes Duin, site 022) and the harbour extension of Rotterdam (Maasvlakte), bordered by the Voordelta (020) on the seaward side. It is part of the former mouth of the River Maas, which was closed off in 1966.

Habitats Wetland (90%; mudflat/sandflat; saltmarsh), Marine areas (10%; open sea)
Land-use Fisheries/aquaculture (10%), Nature conservation/research (100%), Tourism/recreation (10%)

■ Birds

Species	Season	Year	Pop min	Pop max	Acc	Criteria
Recurvirostra avosetta Avocet	B	1991	174	174	A	B3
Tringa totanus Redshank	N	1991	2,275	2,275	B	B1i, C3
Sterna sandvicensis Sandwich Tern	B	1991	88	88	A	C6

A recently built small islet holds breeding terns *Sterna*, *Recurvirostra avosetta* and *Charadrius alexandrinus*. The mudflats are attractive to waders on passage.

■ Protection status
National None **International** None

■ Conservation issues

Threats Aquaculture/fisheries (A), Construction/impact of dyke/dam/barrage (B), Disturbance to birds (B)

The main threats concern shellfish fisheries, the planned extension of the industrial area of Rotterdam (Maasvlakte), and leisure aircraft causing disturbance.

Voornes Duin   B1i, B2, C2, C3   022

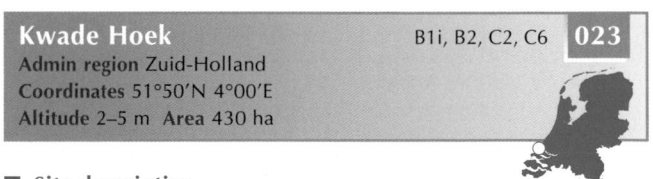

Admin region Zuid-Holland
Coordinates 51°54′N 4°03′E
Altitude 3–14 m   **Area** 1,130 ha

■ Site description
The least spoiled dune area in the Netherlands, located between Oostvoorne (close to 021) and Haringvliet (024). The area includes two lakes (Breedewater, Quackjeswater) and mesotrophic dune-slacks surrounded by *Alnus* woodland and wet dune-valleys. Hunting does not include wildfowl. This site, together with sites 020 and 023, formed part of a single, larger site (former site NL046) in the previous pan-European IBA inventory (Grimmett and Jones 1989).

Habitats Wetland (100%; sand-dunes/sand beach)
Land-use Hunting (5%), Nature conservation/research (98%), Tourism/recreation (52%), Water management (100%)

■ Birds

Species	Season	Year	Pop min	Pop max	Acc	Criteria
Phalacrocorax carbo Cormorant	B	1991	1,055	1,055	A	B1i, C3
Platalea leucorodia Spoonbill	B	1991	10	10	A	B1i, B2, C2

A small dune-slack holds breeding *Platalea leucorodia* and *Phalacrocorax carbo*.

■ Protection status
National High **International** None
312 ha of IBA covered by Nature Reserve (Duinen van Oostvoorne, 312 ha). 800 ha of IBA covered by Nature Reserve (Voornes Duin, 800 ha).

■ Conservation issues

Threats Construction/impact of dyke/dam/barrage (C), Disturbance to birds (A), Recreation/tourism (B)

The planned extension of the industrial area of Rotterdam (Maasvlakte), recreation, and leisure aircraft causing disturbance are the main threats.

Kwade Hoek   B1i, B2, C2, C6   023

Admin region Zuid-Holland
Coordinates 51°50′N 4°00′E
Altitude 2–5 m   **Area** 430 ha

■ Site description
A small area of dunes, saltmarshes and mudflats between Haringvliet (024) and the Voordelta (020). This site, together with sites 020 and 022, formed part of a single, larger site (former site NL046) in the previous pan-European IBA inventory (Grimmett and Jones 1989).

Habitats Wetland (100%; mudflat/sandflat; saltmarsh; sand-dunes/sand beach)
Land-use Agriculture (10%), Fisheries/aquaculture (5%), Nature conservation/research (100%), Tourism/recreation (50%)

■ Birds

Species	Season	Year	Pop min	Pop max	Acc	Criteria
Platalea leucorodia Spoonbill	N	1992	127	127	B	B1i, C2, C6
Branta leucopsis Barnacle Goose	W	1992	1,246	1,246	A	B2

An important feeding and roosting site for *Platalea leucorodia*, particularly those from the Voornes Duin colony (022).

■ Protection status
National Low **International** High

27 ha of IBA covered by Nature Reserve (Kop van Goeree, 27 ha). 5 ha of IBA covered by Nature Reserve (Kwade Hoek, 5 ha). 430 ha of IBA covered by Special Protection Area (Kwade Hoek, 825 ha).

■ **Conservation issues**

Threats Industrialization/urbanization (C), Recreation/tourism (B)

The SPA-designation also includes a small part of Voordelta (020).

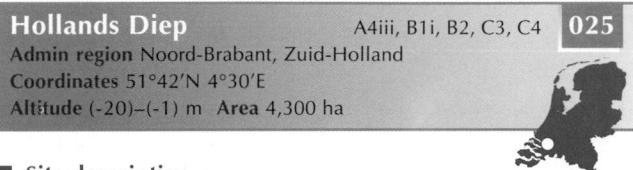

Haringvliet A4i, A4iii, B1i, B2, B3, C2, C3, C4, C6 024
Admin region Zuid-Holland
Coordinates 51°46'N 4°15'E
Altitude (-22)–(-1) m **Area** 10,900 ha

■ **Site description**
Together with the adjoining Hollands Diep (025), this is one of the former estuaries of the Rhine/Maas river system, closed from the sea in 1970. Essentially a 27-km long stagnant freshwater lake, bordered by reedbeds, willow *Salix* scrub and wet meadows. The water-level varies, depending on the river supply. The site is separated at the west end from the Hollands Diep by a bridge and from Lake Volkerak (026) by a dam. This site, together with site 025, formed part of a single, larger site (former site NL047) in the previous pan-European IBA inventory (Grimmett and Jones 1989).

Habitats Wetland (87%; standing fresh water; water-fringe vegetation), Artificial landscape (13%; highly improved reseeded grassland)
Land-use Agriculture (5%), Fisheries/aquaculture (65%), Hunting (80%), Nature conservation/research (32%), Other (5%), Tourism/recreation (80%), Urban/industrial/transport (51%), Water management (100%)

■ **Birds**

Species	Season	Year	Pop min	Pop max	Acc	Criteria
Anser anser Greylag Goose	N	1992	4,001	4,001	A	A4i, B1i, C3
Branta leucopsis Barnacle Goose	W	1991	15,818	15,818	A	A4i,B1i,B2,C2,C6
Anas penelope Wigeon	W	1992	15,623	15,623	A	B1i, C3
Anas strepera Gadwall	N	1992	484	484	A	B1i, C3
Recurvirostra avosetta Avocet	B	1991	86	86	A	B3
Sterna hirundo Common Tern	B	1991	864	864	A	C2, C6
Sterna albifrons Little Tern	B	1991	24	24	A	B2, C6

The open water and sandbanks are used as a roost by large numbers of geese *Anser* from the surrounding arable and grassland polders (no counts are available). The grassland bordering the Haringvliet is important as a feeding site for *Branta leucopsis* and as a breeding area for waders and marsh species. The area holds two breeding colonies of *Sterna hirundo* (one also in use by *Sterna albifrons*). The mean total of waterbirds in January exceeds 20,000.

■ **Protection status**
National Partial **International** None
190 ha of IBA covered by Natural Monument (Slijkplaat, 190 ha). 900 ha of IBA covered by Natural Monument (Ventjagersplaten ten noorden van de Hellegatsdam, 900 ha). 60 ha of IBA covered by Natural Monument (Westerse Laagjes, 60 ha). 70 ha of IBA covered by Natural Monument (Westplaat buitengronden en Meneersche Plaat, 70 ha). 24 ha of IBA covered by Natural Monument (Quackgors I, 24 ha). 45 ha of IBA covered by Natural Monument (Riet-en grasgorzen II Quackgors, 45 ha). 10 ha of IBA covered by Natural Monument (Riet-en grasgorzen II Quackgors, 10 ha). 5 ha of IBA covered by Natural Monument (Riet- en grasgorzen II Westerse Laagjes, 5 ha). 5 ha of IBA covered by Natural Monument (Rietgorzen Oosterse Laagjes, 5 ha). 60 ha of IBA covered by Natural Monument (Rietgorzen Stad a/h Haringvliet-Den Bommel, 60 ha). 380 ha of IBA covered by Natural Monument (Scheelhoek, 380 ha). 130 ha of IBA covered by Natural Monument ('s Lands bekade Gorzen, 130 ha). 380 ha of IBA covered by Natural Monument (Beninger Slikken, 380 ha). 20 ha of IBA covered by Natural Monument (Beninger Slikken, 20 ha). 54 ha of IBA covered by Natural Monument (Blanke Slikken, 54 ha). 200 ha of IBA covered by Natural Monument (Blanke Slikken, 200 ha). 55 ha of IBA covered by Natural Monument (Gorzen Oosterse Laagjes, 55 ha). 18 ha of IBA covered by Natural Monument (Grasgorzen Griendweipolder, 18 ha). 60 ha of IBA covered by Natural Monument (Grasgorzen Stad a/h Haringvliet-Den Bomm, 60 ha). 70 ha of IBA covered by Natural Monument (Grasgorzen tussen Den Bommel en de Hellegatsdam, 70 ha). 13 ha of IBA covered by Natural Monument (Kleiput in de Tiendgorzen, 13 ha). 400 ha of IBA covered by Natural Monument (Korendijkse Slikken, 400 ha). 14 ha of IBA covered by Natural Monument (Leenheren Buitengorzen, 14 ha). 30 ha of IBA covered by Natural Monument (Oosterse Laagjes, 30 ha). 461 ha of IBA covered by Nature Reserve (Korendijkse Slikken, 461 ha). 322 ha of IBA covered by Nature Reserve (Grasgorzen Haringvliet, 322 ha). 275 ha of IBA covered by Nature Reserve (Blanke Slikken, 275 ha). 377 ha of IBA covered by Nature Reserve (Beningerslikken, 377 ha). 26 ha of IBA covered by Nature Reserve (Quackgors, 26 ha). 30 ha of IBA covered by Nature Reserve (Scheelhoek, 30 ha).

■ **Conservation issues**

Threats Disturbance to birds (C), Industrialization/urbanization (B), Other (A), Recreation/tourism (B)

The main problems are heavily polluted sediments and nutrient pollution ('Other' threat, above).

Hollands Diep A4iii, B1i, B2, C3, C4 025
Admin region Noord-Brabant, Zuid-Holland
Coordinates 51°42'N 4°30'E
Altitude (-20)–(-1) m **Area** 4,300 ha

■ **Site description**
A stagnant 17-km long freshwater lake, located between Haringvliet (024) and Biesbosch (051), bordered by reedbeds and grassland polders. The water-level varies, depending on the river supply. This site, together with site 024, formed part of a single, larger site (former site NL047) in the previous international IBA inventory (Grimmett and Jones 1989).

Habitats Wetland (90%; standing fresh water), Artificial landscape (10%; highly improved reseeded grassland)
Land-use Agriculture (5%), Fisheries/aquaculture (80%), Hunting (30%), Nature conservation/research (8%), Tourism/recreation (90%), Urban/industrial/transport (10%), Water management (100%)

■ **Birds**

Species	Season	Year	Pop min	Pop max	Acc	Criteria
Branta leucopsis Barnacle Goose	W	1991	1,032	1,032	A	B2
Anas strepera Gadwall	N	1992	326	326	A	B1i, C3

The site is especially important for roosting geese from surrounding feeding areas, although there have been few counts of numbers. The average seasonal peak number of waterbirds during 1992–1996 exceeded 20,000.

■ **Protection status**
National Low **International** None
235 ha of IBA covered by Natural Monument (Esscheplaat, Zeehondenplaat en Sasseplaat, 235 ha). 30 ha of IBA covered by Natural Monument (Esscheplaat, Zeehondenplaat en Sasseplaat II, 30 ha). 40 ha of IBA covered by Natural Monument (Hoogezandse Gorzen, 40 ha). 55 ha of IBA covered by Natural Monument (Oosterse Slobbegorzen, 55 ha). 97 ha of IBA covered by Nature Reserve (Esscheplaat, 97 ha).

■ **Conservation issues**

Threats Industrialization/urbanization (B), Recreation/tourism (B)

The main problems are heavily polluted sediments and nutrient pollution.

Lake Volkerak A4i, A4iii, B1i, B2, B3, C2, C3, C4, C6 026
Admin region Noord-Brabant, Zuid-Holland, Zeeland
Coordinates 51°39'N 4°15'E
Altitude (-15)–(-1) m **Area** 6,300 ha

■ **Site description**
A former tidal estuary of the Rhine/Maas river sytem, closed off from the Oosterschelde (028) in 1987. It also adjoins Grevelingen (027) in

the west, Haringvliet/Hollands Diep (024/025) in the north, and is linked with the Zoommeer (029) via the Schelde–Rhine river connection (shipping lane to Antwerp). The 20-km long stagnant freshwater lake includes some islets. Hunting is allowed but with restrictions as to quarry species.

Habitats Wetland (100%; standing fresh water; water-fringe vegetation)
Land-use Fisheries/aquaculture (60%), Hunting (100%), Nature conservation/research (54%), Tourism/recreation (60%), Urban/industrial/transport (10%), Water management (100%)

■ **Birds**

Species	Season	Year	Pop min	Pop max	Acc	Criteria
Branta leucopsis Barnacle Goose	W	1991	2,872	2,872	A	A4i, B1i, B2, C2
Anas penelope Wigeon	W	1991	12,515	12,515	A	B1i, C3
Anas strepera Gadwall	N	1991	424	424	A	B1i, C3
Anas acuta Pintail	N	1991	601	601	A	B1i, C3
Anas clypeata Shoveler	N	1991	1,251	1,251	A	B1i, C3
Bucephala clangula Goldeneye	W	1991	3,187	3,187	A	B1i, C3
Recurvirostra avosetta Avocet	B	1991	532	532	A	A4i,B1i,B3,C2,C6
Recurvirostra avosetta Avocet	N	1991	1,833	1,833	A	A4i, B1i, C2, C6
Charadrius alexandrinus Kentish Plover	B	1991	105	105	A	B2
Larus melanocephalus Mediterranean Gull	B	1991	15	15	A	C6
Sterna albifrons Little Tern	B	1991	36	36	A	B2, C6

An important site for breeding *Recurvirostra avosetta*, *Charadrius alexandrinus* (max. 184 pairs, 1989) and *Sterna albifrons*, but numbers are decreasing due to vegetation succession. The best breeding site for *Larus melanocephalus* in the Netherlands (e.g. 143 pairs in 1993). The mean total number of waterbirds in January exceeds 20,000.

■ **Protection status**
National Partial **International** High
3,300 ha of IBA covered by Natural Monument (Krammer-Volkerak I, 3,300 ha). 130 ha of IBA covered by Natural Monument (Krammer-Volkerak II, 130 ha). 295 ha of IBA covered by Nature Reserve (Krammersche Slikken, 295 ha). 15 ha of IBA covered by Nature Reserve (Schorren bij Ooltgensplaat, 15 ha). 4 ha of IBA covered by Nature Reserve (Slikken van de Heen, 4 ha). 193 ha of IBA covered by Nature Reserve (Slikken van de Heen II, 193 ha). 600 ha of IBA covered by Nature Reserve (Slikken van de Heen en Plaat van de Vliet, 600 ha). 12 ha of IBA covered by Nature Reserve (Dintelse Gorzen, 12 ha). 493 ha of IBA covered by Nature Reserve (Dintelse Gorzen II, 493 ha). 420 ha of IBA covered by Nature Reserve (Hellegatsplaten, 420 ha). 18 ha of IBA covered by Nature Reserve (Inlaag 1887, 18 ha). 6,300 ha of IBA covered by Special Protection Area (Krammer-Volkerak, 6,450 ha). 6,300 ha of IBA covered by Ramsar Site (Krammer-Volkerak, 6,450 ha).

■ **Conservation issues**

Threats Other (U)

The main problem is nutrient pollution ('Other' threat, above). The bird-species composition outside the breeding season is much affected by the ongoing change from a salt- to a freshwater ecosystem.

Grevelingen A4i, A4iii, B1i, B2, B3, C2, C3, C4, C6 **027**
Admin region Zuid-Holland, Zeeland
Coordinates 51°45′N 4°00′E
Altitude (-18)–0 m **Area** 13,580 ha

■ **Site description**
A former estuary, 18 km in length, which was closed from the sea in 1971. It is now a stagnant saline lake, mostly bordered by dykes with islets, sand-dunes and wet meadows. It adjoins the Voordelta (020) to the west, and Lake Volkerak (026) and Oosterschelde (028) to the east. Hunting does not include waterbirds.

Habitats Wetland (80%; standing brackish and salt water), Artificial landscape (20%; highly improved reseeded grassland)
Land-use Agriculture (5%), Fisheries/aquaculture (80%), Hunting (20%), Nature conservation/research (100%), Tourism/recreation (90%), Water management (100%)

■ **Birds**

Species	Season	Year	Pop min	Pop max	Acc	Criteria
Phalacrocorax carbo Cormorant	N	1990	3,013	3,013	A	B1i, C3
Platalea leucorodia Spoonbill	N	1993	34	34	A	B1i, C2
Cygnus columbianus Bewick's Swan	W	1991	222	222	A	A4i, B1i, B2, C2
Branta leucopsis Barnacle Goose	W	1991	11,053	11,053	A	A4i,B1i,B2,C2,C6
Branta bernicla Brent Goose	N	1991	3,752	3,752	A	A4i, B1i, C3
Anas acuta Pintail	N	1991	1,635	1,635	A	B1i, C3
Bucephala clangula Goldeneye	W	1991	4,823	4,823	A	A4i, B1i, C3
Mergus serrator Red-breasted Merganser	W	1990	3,883	3,883	A	A4i, B1i, C3
Recurvirostra avosetta Avocet	B	1991	420	420	A	A4i,B1i,B3,C2,C6
Charadrius alexandrinus Kentish Plover	B	1991	103	103	A	B2
Sterna sandvicensis Sandwich Tern	B	1991	2,850	2,850	A	A4i,B1i,B2,C2,C6

This clear, saline lake is especially attractive to piscivorous waterbirds, and the grassland bordering the northern shores (Slikken van Flakkee) is one of the main feeding sites of *Branta leucopsis* in south-west Netherlands. The site holds important roosts of geese. The mean total number of waterbirds in January exceeds 20,000.

■ **Protection status**
National None **International** None

■ **Conservation issues**

Threats Industrialization/urbanization (C), Recreation/tourism (B)

Numbers of herbivorous bird species such as *Cygnus olor* and *Aythya ferina* have been much reduced due to the near-disappearance of eel-grass *Zostera*.

Oosterschelde A4i, A4iii, B1i, B2, B3, C2, C3, C4, C6 **028**
Admin region Zeeland
Coordinates 51°35′N 3°56′E
Altitude (-44)–0 m **Area** 36,880 ha

■ **Site description**
This 40-km long water-body was formerly an estuary of the Rhine/Maas river system, via Hollands Diep (025) and Lake Volkerak (026), but has been closed off from the sea since 1986 by a storm-surge barrier which allows the tidal regime to continue with some restrictions. The sea can be completely shut out during storms or high tides. Two freshwater lakes have developed on the eastern side following the construction of secondary dams (Markiezaat and Zoommeer, 029 and 030). South of this area, Lake Veersemeer (031) came into being following the closing of the Veerse Gat in 1961. This site, together with sites 029 and 030, formed part of a single, larger site (former site NL050) in the previous pan-European IBA inventory (Grimmett and Jones 1989).

Habitats Wetland (100%; tidal river/enclosed tidal water; mudflat/sandflat)
Land-use Fisheries/aquaculture (80%), Nature conservation/research (65%), Tourism/recreation (80%), Urban/industrial/transport (21%), Water management (100%)

■ **Birds**

Species	Season	Year	Pop min	Pop max	Acc	Criteria
Cygnus columbianus Bewick's Swan	W	1990	443	443	A	A4i, B1i, B2, C2
Branta leucopsis Barnacle Goose	W	1991	1,645	1,645	A	B2
Branta bernicla Brent Goose	N	1990	13,175	13,175	A	A4i, B1i, C3
Tadorna tadorna Shelduck	N	1991	3,572	3,572	A	B1i, C3
Anas penelope Wigeon	W	1991	16,344	16,344	A	B1i, C3
Anas acuta Pintail	N	1990	3,440	3,440	A	B1i, C3
Anas clypeata Shoveler	N	1990	858	858	A	B1i, C3
Haematopus ostralegus Oystercatcher	N	1990	94,595	94,595	A	A4i, B1i, C3
Recurvirostra avosetta Avocet	B	1991	361	361	A	A4i, B1i, B3, C2
Charadrius alexandrinus Kentish Plover	B	1991	40	40	A	B2
Pluvialis squatarola Grey Plover	N	1991	7,974	7,974	A	A4i, B1i, C3
Calidris canutus Knot	W	1991	9,424	9,424	A	A4i, B1i, B2, C3
Calidris canutus Knot	P	1990	14,128	14,128	A	A4i, B1i, C3
[1] *Calidris alpina* Dunlin	W	1991	25,361	25,361	A	A4i, B1i, B2, C3
Calidris alpina Dunlin	N	1990	39,459	39,459	A	A4i, B1i, C3
Limosa lapponica Bar-tailed Godwit	W	1991	5,109	5,109	A	B1i, B2, C2, C6
Limosa lapponica Bar-tailed Godwit	P	1991	9,170	9,170	A	A4i, B1i, C2
[1] *Numenius arquata* Curlew	W	1991	6,084	6,084	A	A4i, B1i, B2, C3
Numenius arquata Curlew	N	1990	13,115	13,115	A	A4i, B1i, C3

Species ... continued		Season	Year	Pop min	Pop max	Acc	Criteria
Tringa erythropus	Spotted Redshank	N	1990	1,319	1,319	A	A4i, B1i, C3
Tringa totanus	Redshank	N	1991	2,743	2,743	A	B1i, C3
Arenaria interpres	Turnstone	N	1991	1,334	1,334	A	A4i, B1i, C3

1. January mean.

This is the most important intertidal staging area for ducks and waders in south-west Netherlands. Thousands of geese *Anser*, feeding in adjacent farmland polders, use the area as roost. *Recurvirostra avosetta* and *Charadrius alexandrinus* breed in small lagoons ('inlagen', inland of the dyke) and at Neeltje Jans (building site of storm-surge barrier).

■ Protection status
National Partial **International** High
340 ha of IBA covered by Natural Monument (Oosterschelde-binnendijks, 340 ha). 240 ha of IBA covered by Natural Monument (Oosterschelde-binnendijks, 240 ha). 1,230 ha of IBA covered by Natural Monument (Oosterschelde-buitendijks, 1,230 ha). 22,000 ha of IBA covered by Natural Monument (Oosterschelde-buitendijks, 22,000 ha). 224 ha of IBA covered by Nature Reserve (Schelphoek, 224 ha). 149 ha of IBA covered by Nature Reserve (Thoolse Schorren en Slikken, 149 ha). 10 ha of IBA covered by Nature Reserve (Inlagen Anna Friso, 10 ha). 45 ha of IBA covered by Nature Reserve (Inlagen Noord-Beveland, 45 ha). 752 ha of IBA covered by Nature Reserve (Oosterschelde Buitendijks, 752 ha). 36,160 ha of IBA covered by Special Protection Area (Oosterschelde, 38,000 ha). 36,160 ha of IBA covered by Ramsar Site (Oosterschelde en Markiezaat, 38,000 ha).

■ Conservation issues
Threats Aquaculture/fisheries (A), Construction/impact of dyke/dam/barrage (A), Disturbance to birds (B), Extraction industry (B), Recreation/tourism (A)

The main problems are: the reduction of tidal volume and flow-speed by 30% due to the building of the storm-surge barrier; cockle *Cardium* fisheries and shellfish farming; disturbance by ultra-light aircraft and by the air force; and the expansion of recreation (boating). The SPA and Ramsar designations also include Markiezaat (030).

Zoommeer   B1i, B3, C2, C3, C6   029
Admin region Noord-Brabant, Zeeland
Coordinates 51°30'N 4°12'E
Altitude (-10)–(-1) m **Area** 930 ha

■ Site description
A stagnant freshwater lake to the west and east of the Schelde–Rhine river connection (shipping lane), which developed after the building of the Oesterdam at the eastern end of the Oosterschelde (028) in 1986. In the south-east the site is adjacent to Lake Markiezaat (030). This site, together with sites 028 and 030, formed part of a single, larger site (former site NL050) in the previous pan-European IBA inventory (Grimmett and Jones 1989).

Habitats Wetland (82%; standing fresh water), Artificial landscape (18%; highly improved reseeded grassland)
Land-use Agriculture (5%), Fisheries/aquaculture (70%), Hunting (20%), Nature conservation/research (24%), Tourism/recreation (80%), Urban/industrial/transport (20%), Water management (100%)

■ Birds

Species		Season	Year	Pop min	Pop max	Acc	Criteria
Anas clypeata	Shoveler	N	1990	708	708	A	B1i, C3
Recurvirostra avosetta	Avocet	B	1991	262	262	A	B1i, B3, C2
Larus melanocephalus Mediterranean Gull		B	1991	6	6	A	C6

The site is a roost for geese *Anser* from surrounding feeding areas, but no counts are available.

■ Protection status
National Partial **International** None
218 ha of IBA covered by Natural Monument (Zoommeer-Eendracht, 218 ha).

■ Conservation issues
Threats Agricultural intensification/expansion (B)

The main problems are nutrient pollution and intensive grazing.

Markiezaat   B1i, B2, B3, C2, C3, C6   030
Admin region Noord-Brabant, Zeeland
Coordinates 51°28'N 4°16'E
Altitude 0–0 m **Area** 2,030 ha

■ Site description
A stagnant shallow freshwater lake with reedbeds and wet meadows, which was cut off from the Oosterschelde (028) in 1983. It is adjacent to the Zoommeer (029) in the north-west, with the city of Bergen op Zoom at the north-eastern border, and the Schelde–Rhine river connection at the west side. This site, together with sites 028 and 029, formed part of a single, larger site (former site NL050) in the previous pan-European IBA inventory (Grimmett and Jones 1989).

Habitats Wetland (82%; standing fresh water; water-fringe vegetation), Artificial landscape (18%; highly improved reseeded grassland)
Land-use Agriculture (10%), Hunting (10%), Nature conservation/research (92%)

■ Birds

Species		Season	Year	Pop min	Pop max	Acc	Criteria
Anas strepera	Gadwall	N	1990	916	916	A	B1i, C3
Anas clypeata	Shoveler	N	1990	455	455	A	B1i, C3
Recurvirostra avosetta	Avocet	B	1991	265	265	A	B1i, B3, C2
Charadrius alexandrinus	Kentish Plover	B	1991	30	30	A	B2
Larus melanocephalus Mediterranean Gull		B	1991	14	14	A	C6

The site is a roost for geese *Anser* from surrounding feeding areas, but no counts are available.

■ Protection status
National High **International** High
1,700 ha of IBA covered by Natural Monument (Markiezaatsmeer-Zuid, 1,700 ha). 160 ha of IBA covered by Natural Monument (Markiezaatsmeer-Zuid II, 160 ha). 107 ha of IBA covered by Nature Reserve (Molenplaat, 107 ha). 1,300 ha of IBA covered by Nature Reserve (Markiezaat, 1,300 ha). 1,840 ha of IBA covered by Special Protection Area (Oosterschelde, 38,000 ha). 1,840 ha of IBA covered by Ramsar Site (Oosterschelde en Markiezaat, 38,000 ha).

■ Conservation issues
Threats Agricultural intensification/expansion (B), Industrialization/urbanization (B), Infrastructure (C)

The main problems are nutrient pollution and waste-water discharge. The Ramsar and SPA designations also include the Oosterschelde (028).

Lake Veersemeer   A4i, A4iii, B1i, B2, C2, C3, C4, C6   031
Admin region Zeeland
Coordinates 51°32'N 3°44'E
Altitude (-23)–(-2) m **Area** 3,010 ha

■ Site description
A 20-km long brackish lake (formerly part of the Oosterschelde estuary, closed off in 1961) with sandbanks and small islands, and surrounded by wet meadows, improved grassland, arable land and some forestry plantations.

Habitats Wetland (74%; standing brackish and salt water), Artificial landscape (26%; highly improved reseeded grassland; forestry plantation)
Land-use Agriculture (8%), Fisheries/aquaculture (74%), Hunting (10%), Nature conservation/research (13%), Tourism/recreation (84%), Water management (100%)

■ Birds
An important roost for tens of thousands of geese *Anser* (although there are few counts), and for thousands of waders from Oosterschelde (028) at high water.

Species	Season	Year	Pop min	Pop max	Acc	Criteria
Cygnus columbianus Bewick's Swan	W	1991	173	173	A	A4i, B1i, B2, C2
Branta leucopsis Barnacle Goose	W	1990	2,175	2,175	A	B1i, B2, C2
Mergus serrator Red-breasted Merganser	W	1991	1,383	1,383	A	B1i, C3
Fulica atra Coot	N	1991	22,783	22,783	A	B1i, C3
Larus melanocephalus Mediterranean Gull	B	1991	2	2	A	C6

■ Protection status
National Partial **International** None
108 ha of IBA covered by Nature Reserve (Goudplaat, 108 ha). 286 ha of IBA covered by Nature Reserve (Middelplaten, 286 ha).

■ Conservation issues

Threats Construction/impact of dyke/dam/barrage (A), Other (A), Recreation/tourism (B)

The main problems are nutrient pollution ('Other' threat, above), insufficient exchange with Oosterschelde water, and recreational pressure.

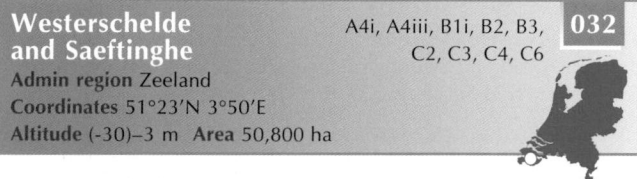

Westerschelde and Saeftinghe — 032
A4i, A4iii, B1i, B2, B3, C2, C3, C4, C6
Admin region Zeeland
Coordinates 51°23'N 3°50'E
Altitude (-30)–3 m **Area** 50,800 ha

■ Site description
A tidal estuary of the River Schelde with mudflats, sandbanks and raised saltmarsh (Verdronken Land van Saeftinghe, 3,500 ha), and the only estuary in south-west Netherlands which will be allowed to remain open to the sea. The estuary is 60 km long from the Belgian border up to the North Sea, and is adjacent to the Voordelta (020) in the west.

Habitats Wetland (100%; tidal river/enclosed tidal water; mudflat/sandflat; saltmarsh)
Land-use Agriculture (5%), Fisheries/aquaculture (50%), Hunting (25%), Nature conservation/research (11%), Tourism/recreation (80%), Urban/industrial/transport (50%)

■ Birds

Species	Season	Year	Pop min	Pop max	Acc	Criteria
Platalea leucorodia Spoonbill	N	1991	57	57	A	B1i, C2
Anser albifrons White-fronted Goose	W	1991	7,782	7,782	A	B1i, C3
Anser anser Greylag Goose	N	1991	14,921	14,921	A	A4i, B1i, C3
[1] *Tadorna tadorna* Shelduck	N	1991	4,728	4,728	A	A4i, B1i, C3
Anas penelope Wigeon	W	1990	23,385	23,385	A	A4i, B1i, C3
Anas acuta Pintail	N	1991	3,343	3,343	A	B1i, C3
Haematopus ostralegus Oystercatcher	N	1991	14,427	14,427	A	A4i, B1i, C3
Recurvirostra avosetta Avocet	B	1991	180	180	A	B3
Recurvirostra avosetta Avocet	N	1992	1,207	1,207	A	A4i, B1i, C2
Charadrius hiaticula Ringed Plover	N	1990	4,153	4,153	A	A4i, B1i, C3
Charadrius alexandrinus Kentish Plover	B	1991	70	70	A	B2
Charadrius alexandrinus Kentish Plover	N	1990	752	752	A	B1i, C3
Pluvialis squatarola Grey Plover	N	1991	3,542	3,542	A	A4i, B1i, C3
Calidris canutus Knot	W	1991	1,083	1,083	A	B2
[2] *Calidris alpina* Dunlin	W	1991	21,960	21,960	A	B1i, B2, C3
Calidris alpina Dunlin	N	1990	28,236	28,236	A	A4i, B1i, C3
Limosa lapponica Bar-tailed Godwit	W	1991	1,078	1,078	A	B1i, B2, C2, C6
[2] *Numenius arquata* Curlew	W	1991	3,185	3,185	A	B2
Numenius arquata Curlew	N	1991	6,122	6,122	A	A4i, B1i, C3
Tringa erythropus Spotted Redshank	N	1990	906	906	A	A4i, B1i, C3
Tringa totanus Redshank	N	1991	2,029	2,029	A	B1i, C3
Larus melanocephalus Mediterranean Gull	B	1991	3	3	A	C6
Sterna sandvicensis Sandwich Tern	B	1991	537	537	A	B1i, B2, C2, C6
Sterna hirundo Common Tern	B	1991	1,580	1,580	A	C2, C6
Sterna albifrons Little Tern	B	1991	136	136	A	B1i, B2, C2, C6

1. Moulting.
2. January mean.

An important roost for tens of thousands of geese *Anser* from Zeeuws-Vlaanderen, but numbers of *Anser albifrons* in particular have been poorly covered by counts.

■ Protection status
National Low **International** Low

2,400 ha of IBA covered by Natural Monument (Verdronken Land van Saeftinge I, 2,400 ha). 1,100 ha of IBA covered by Natural Monument (Verdronken Land van Saeftinge II, 1,100 ha). 28 ha of IBA covered by Natural Monument (Zwarte Polder, 28 ha). 92 ha of IBA covered by Natural Monument (Zwarte Polder II, 92 ha). 99 ha of IBA covered by Natural Monument (Schor van Waarde, 99 ha). 1 ha of IBA covered by Natural Monument (Schor van Waarde, 1 ha). 189 ha of IBA covered by Nature Reserve (Braakman, 189 ha). 18 ha of IBA covered by Nature Reserve (Inlaag 1887, 18 ha). 14 ha of IBA covered by Nature Reserve (Kapelle Bank, 14 ha). 69 ha of IBA covered by Nature Reserve (Rammekens, 69 ha). 544 ha of IBA covered by Nature Reserve (Saeftinghe, 544 ha). 248 ha of IBA covered by Nature Reserve (Schor bij Bath, 248 ha). 34 ha of IBA covered by Nature Reserve (Schor bij Ossendrecht, 53 ha). 163 ha of IBA covered by Nature Reserve (Zuidgors, 163 ha). 76 ha of IBA covered by Nature Reserve (Schor van Waarde, 76 ha). 3,500 ha of IBA covered by Special Protection Area (Verdronken Land van Saeftinge, 3,500 ha). 3,500 ha of IBA covered by Ramsar Site (Verdronken Land van Saeftinge, 3,500 ha).

■ Conservation issues

Threats Agricultural intensification/expansion (B), Aquaculture/fisheries (A), Disturbance to birds (C), Dredging/canalization (B), Extraction industry (C), Industrialization/urbanization (A), Infrastructure (C), Recreation/tourism (B)

The main problems are the further deepening of the shipping lane (erosion causes loss of mudflats and saltmarsh), nutrient pollution through discharge of polder water, and industrial discharges. The SPA and Ramsar designations concern the saltmarsh area.

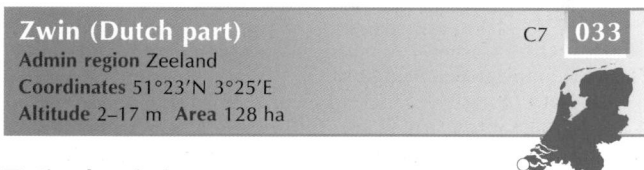

Zwin (Dutch part) — C7 — 033
Admin region Zeeland
Coordinates 51°23'N 3°25'E
Altitude 2–17 m **Area** 128 ha

■ Site description
A small coastal wetland, consisting of a former estuary, which lies adjacent to a Belgian IBA of the same name (Het Zwin) and also to Westerschelde (site 032).

Habitats Wetland (38%; saltmarsh; sand-dunes/sand beach), Marine areas (40%; open sea), Artificial landscape (22%; highly improved reseeded grassland)
Land-use Agriculture (15%), Hunting (100%), Nature conservation/research (39%), Tourism/recreation (10%)

■ Protection status
National None **International** High
128 ha of IBA covered by Special Protection Area (Nederlandse Zwingebied, 128 ha).

■ Conservation issues

Threats Recreation/tourism (B)

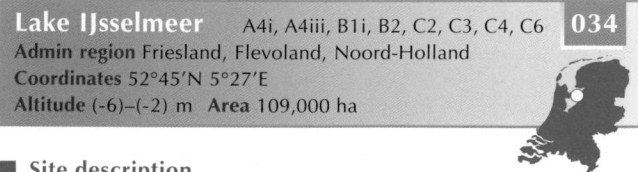

Lake IJsselmeer — A4i, A4iii, B1i, B2, C2, C3, C4, C6 — 034
Admin region Friesland, Flevoland, Noord-Holland
Coordinates 52°45'N 5°27'E
Altitude (-6)–(-2) m **Area** 109,000 ha

■ Site description
Previously the Zuiderzee, this area is now a vast shallow freshwater lake, having been cut off from the Wadden Sea (001) by the Afsluitdijk (in 1932) and with 45% of its extent having been reclaimed. The original IJsselmeer was then bisected by a dyke in 1975, which separated it from the southern part now called Markermeer (038). This site adjoins three subsites 035, 036 and 037 (the figure for the area of this site excludes these subsites) which are located along the Frisian coast. The lake receives Rhine water through the IJssel river (046 and 047) via Lake Ketelmeer (039). The wetland habitat in the subsites is not included in the percentage cover for this site (to avoid overlap). Extraction of sand and water occurs, and natural-gas extraction is

planned. Military training (artillery) occurs at Breezanddijk (Afsluitdijk). The lake has been locally deepened to over 25 m by sand extraction. This site, together with site 038, formed part of a single, larger site (former site NL030) in the previous pan-European IBA inventory (Grimmett and Jones 1989).

Habitats Wetland (95%; standing fresh water)
Land-use Fisheries/aquaculture (100%), Military (12%), Tourism/recreation (100%), Urban/industrial/transport (15%), Water management (100%)

■ Birds

Species		Season	Year	Pop min	Pop max	Acc	Criteria
Podiceps cristatus	Great Crested Grebe	N	1990	8,669	8,669	A	B1i, C3
Phalacrocorax carbo	Cormorant	N	1990	10,438	10,438	A	A4i, B1i, C3
Anas penelope	Wigeon	W	1991	14,040	14,040	A	B1i, C3
Anas strepera	Gadwall	N	1991	480	480	A	B1i, C3
Aythya ferina	Pochard	N	1991	6,038	6,038	A	B1i, C3
Aythya fuligula	Tufted Duck	N	1990	28,842	28,842	A	A4i, B1i, C3
Aythya marila	Scaup	W	1991	134,121	134,121	A	A4i, B1i, B2, C3
Mergus albellus	Smew	W	1990	361	361	A	B1i, C2, C6
Mergus merganser	Goosander	W	1991	5,524	5,524	A	A4i, B1i, C3
Fulica atra	Coot	N	1991	15,378	15,378	A	B1i, C3
Chlidonias niger	Black Tern	P	1991	90,367	90,367	B	A4i, B1i, C2, C6

Numbers are based on aerial counts, which tend to underestimate those species with a scattered occurrence. This is the main moulting area for subadult *Cygnus olor* in the Netherlands, and the main feeding area for *Phalacrocorax carbo* from Oostvaardersplassen (066), although the actual numbers are poorly represented by the aerial counts. The number of *Chlidonias niger* is based on numbers flying to roost at Balgzand (013). Other species which do not fulfil IBA criteria include non-breeding *Larus minutus* (5,100 in January 1983).

■ Protection status
National Low **International** Low
88 ha of IBA covered by Natural Monument (Friese IJsselmeerkust I, 4,800 ha). 12 ha of IBA covered by Natural Monument (Friese IJsselmeerkust II, 120 ha). 45 ha of IBA covered by Natural Monument (De Ven, 45 ha). 40 ha of IBA covered by Natural Monument (Stoenckherne, 40 ha). 100 ha of IBA covered by Natural Monument (Stoenckherne II, 100 ha). 17 ha of IBA covered by Nature Reserve (De Ven, 17 ha). 100 ha of IBA covered by Nature Reserve (Onderdijken, 100 ha). 240 ha of IBA covered by Special Protection Area (Friese IJsselmeerkust, 5,130 ha).

■ Conservation issues

Threats Agricultural intensification/expansion (B), Aquaculture/fisheries (A), Industrialization/urbanization (C), Other (B), Recreation/tourism (B)

The main problems are over-fishing, water management (level deliberately kept high during summer to supply water for farming), pollution by nutrients from the River Rhine/IJssel and by trace pollutants such as cadmium, mercury and DDT ('Other' threat, above), entanglement in fishing nets (involving thousands of birds), and recreation (leisure boating).

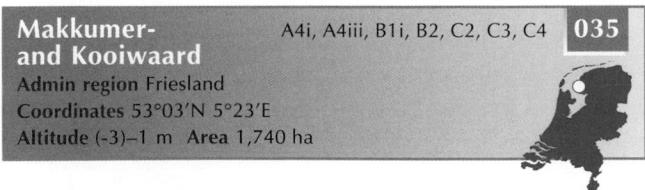

Makkumer- and Kooiwaard A4i, A4iii, B1i, B2, C2, C3, C4 **035**
Admin region Friesland
Coordinates 53°03′N 5°23′E
Altitude (-3)–1 m **Area** 1,740 ha

■ Site description
A foreshore area of sandbanks, reedbeds and shallow waters along the Frisian west coast. It is a subsite of Lake IJsselmeer (034), and lies adjacent to the Workumerwaard (036) in the south. The northern border is formed by the Afsluitdijk which separates the IJsselmeer from the Wadden Sea (001). This site, together with site 036, formed part of a single, larger site (former site NL016) in the previous pan-European IBA inventory (Grimmett and Jones 1989).

Habitats Wetland (94%; standing fresh water; water-fringe vegetation)
Land-use Fisheries/aquaculture (77%), Hunting (10%), Nature conservation/research (70%), Other (5%), Tourism/recreation (78%), Water management (100%)

■ Birds

Species		Season	Year	Pop min	Pop max	Acc	Criteria
Platalea leucorodia	Spoonbill	P	1992	37	37	A	B1i, C2
[1] *Aythya marila*	Scaup	W	1990	30,640	30,640	A	A4i, B1i, B2, C3

1. Number also included in figure for site 034.

Non-breeding numbers are based on aerial counts, which tend to underestimate species with a scattered occurrence. The site is an important roost for geese *Anser*, but actual roosting numbers are poorly reflected by counts.

■ Protection status
National High **International** High
1,582 ha of IBA covered by Natural Monument (Friese IJsselmeerkust I, 4,800 ha). 62 ha of IBA covered by Natural Monument (Friese IJsselmeerkust II, 120 ha). 48 ha of IBA covered by Nature Reserve (Makkumer- en Kooiwaard, 51 ha). About 1,600 ha of IBA covered by Special Protection Area (Friese IJsselmeerkust, 5,130 ha).

■ Conservation issues

Threats Agricultural intensification/expansion (A), Industrialization/urbanization (B), Recreation/tourism (B), Other (B)

The main problems are water management (the water-level is deliberately kept high during summer), the building of a new harbour, commercial reed-harvesting ('Other' threat, above), and recreation (leisure boating).

Workumerwaard A4i, A4iii, B1i, C2, C3, C4, C6 **036**
Admin region Friesland
Coordinates 52°59′N 5°25′E
Altitude (-2)–0 m **Area** 1,320 ha

■ Site description
An area of shallow waters, wet meadows and (landward of the dyke) improved grassland along the Frisian west coast. It is a subsite of Lake IJsselmeer (034), and lies adjacent to the Makkumer- and Kooiwaard (035) in the north. This site, together with site 035, formed part of a single, larger site (former site NL016) in the previous pan-European IBA inventory (Grimmett and Jones 1989).

Habitats Wetland (39%; standing fresh water), Artificial landscape (61%; highly improved reseeded grassland)
Land-use Agriculture (35%), Fisheries/aquaculture (39%), Nature conservation/research (36%), Other (5%), Tourism/recreation (54%), Water management (100%)

■ Birds

Species		Season	Year	Pop min	Pop max	Acc	Criteria
[1] *Recurvirostra avosetta*	Avocet	N	1988	1,500	1,500	C	A4i, B1i, C2
Philomachus pugnax	Ruff	B	1991	13	13	A	C6
[1] *Philomachus pugnax*	Ruff	N	1986	7,000	7,000	C	C6
Limosa limosa	Black-tailed Godwit	N	1986	9,000	9,000	B	A4i, B1i, C3
Sterna hirundo	Common Tern	B	1991	1,680	1,680	A	C2, C6

1. Only one recent count available.

Non-breeding numbers are based on aerial counts which tend to underestimate species with a scattered occurrence. The site is an important roost for geese and waders, but actual roosting numbers are poorly reflected by counts. The average seasonal peak number of waterbirds during 1992–1996 exceeded 20,000.

■ Protection status
National Partial **International** Partial
550 ha of IBA covered by Natural Monument (Friese IJsselmeerkust I, 4,800 ha). 2 ha of IBA covered by Natural Monument (Friese IJsselmeerkust II, 120 ha). 550 ha of IBA covered by Special Protection Area (Friese IJsselmeerkust, 5,130 ha).

■ Conservation issues

Threats Agricultural intensification/expansion (B), Other (B), Recreation/tourism (B)

The main problems are water management (the water-level is deliberately kept high during summer), agricultural intensification, and commercial reed-harvesting ('Other' threat, above). The foreshore is legally protected under the Nature Conservation Act.

Steile Bank and Mokkebank

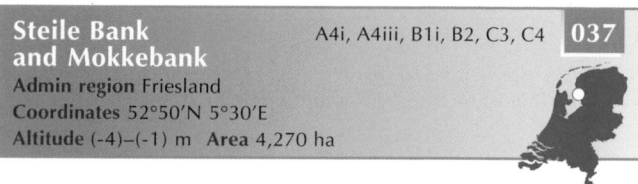

A4i, A4iii, B1i, B2, C3, C4 · **037**

Admin region Friesland
Coordinates 52°50'N 5°30'E
Altitude (-4)–(-1) m · **Area** 4,270 ha

■ Site description

An area of sandbanks and shallow waters, with a small reedbed and an embanked grassland polder, along the Frisian south coast. It is a subsite of Lake IJsselmeer (034).

Habitats Wetland (100%; standing fresh water)
Land-use Fisheries/aquaculture (100%), Nature conservation/research (60%), Tourism/recreation (100%), Water management (100%)

■ Birds

Species	Season	Year	Pop min	Pop max	Acc	Criteria
1 *Podiceps cristatus* Great Crested Grebe	N	1990	7,896	7,896	A	B1i, C3
1 *Phalacrocorax carbo* Cormorant	N	1990	6,916	6,916	A	A4i, B1i, C3
1 *Aythya marila* Scaup	W	1991	9,549	9,549	A	A4i, B1i, B2, C3
1 *Mergus merganser* Goosander	W	1990	2,576	2,576	A	A4i, B1i, C3

1. Number also included in figure for site 034.

The site is an important roost for geese *Anser* (from Noordoostpolder) and waders, but no recent counts are available. Non-breeding numbers are based on aerial counts which tend to underestimate species with a scattered occurrence. This is the main moulting area for *Podiceps cristatus* in the Netherlands (up to 20,000). The mean total number of wintering waterbirds exceeds 20,000.

■ Protection status

National Partial **International** Partial
2,580 ha of IBA covered by Natural Monument (Friese IJsselmeerkust I, 4,800 ha). 44 ha of IBA covered by Natural Monument (Friese IJsselmeerkust II, 120 ha). 41 ha of IBA covered by Nature Reserve (Huitebuersterbutenpolder, 41 ha). 2,624 ha of IBA covered by Special Protection Area (Friese IJsselmeerkust, 5,130 ha).

■ Conservation issues

Threats Agricultural intensification/expansion (A), Recreation/tourism (B), Other (C)

The main problems are water management (the water-level is deliberately kept high during summer), disturbance by boating, and excessive reed-harvesting ('Other' threat, above).

Lake Markermeer

A4i, A4iii, B1i, B2, C2, C3, C4, C6 · **038**

Admin region Flevoland, Noord-Holland
Coordinates 52°32'N 5°15'E
Altitude (-8)–(-1) m · **Area** 69,700 ha

■ Site description

A stagnant freshwater lake, separated from Lake IJsselmeer (034) by the closing of the Houtribdijk in 1975, and bordered to the east by the polders Oostelijk and Zuidelijk Flevoland (reclaimed in 1957 and 1968). The lake is connected to Lake Gooimeer (044) in the south-east, and is also adjacent to Oostvaardersplassen (066) and Lepelaarsplassen (067) in the east, via the Zuidelijk Flevoland polder. The lake has been locally deepened to more than 30 m by sand extraction. This site, together with site 034, formed part of a single, larger site (former site NL030) in the previous international IBA inventory (Grimmett and Jones 1989).

Habitats Wetland (100%; standing fresh water)
Land-use Fisheries/aquaculture (90%), Hunting (5%), Tourism/recreation (100%), Urban/industrial/transport (40%), Water management (100%)

■ Birds

Numbers are based on aerial counts which tend to underestimate species with a scattered occurrence (e.g. *Chlidonias niger*). This is the

Species	Season	Year	Pop min	Pop max	Acc	Criteria
Anas penelope Wigeon	W	1991	29,500	29,500	A	A4i, B1i, C3
Aythya ferina Pochard	N	1990	26,192	26,192	A	A4i, B1i, C3
Aythya fuligula Tufted Duck	N	1991	64,390	64,390	A	A4i, B1i, C3
Aythya marila Scaup	W	1991	15,226	15,226	A	A4i, B1i, B2, C3
Mergus albellus Smew	W	1991	625	625	A	B1i, C2, C6
Chlidonias niger Black Tern	P	1990	871	871	A	C6

main feeding area of the *Phalacrocorax carbo* that breed at Lepelaarsplassen (067) and Naardermeer (074), and is an important moulting area for (subadult) *Cygnus olor*, *Aythya fuligula* and *Aythya ferina*.

■ Protection status

National Low **International** Low
110 ha of IBA covered by Natural Monument (Kustzone Muiden, 110 ha). 15 ha of IBA covered by Nature Reserve (De Drost, Hooft, Warenar, 15 ha). 67 ha of IBA covered by Nature Reserve (IJdoorn, 67 ha). 110 ha of IBA covered by Nature Reserve (Kogen, 110 ha). 19 ha of IBA covered by Nature Reserve (Uiterdijken, 19 ha). 110 ha of IBA covered by Special Protection Area (Eemmeer, Gooimeer en IJmeer, 1,800 ha).

■ Conservation issues

Threats Agricultural intensification/expansion (B), Aquaculture/fisheries (A), Disturbance to birds (B), Extraction industry (C), Industrialization/urbanization (B), Recreation/tourism (B), Other (B)

The main problems are over-fishing, water management (the water-level is deliberately kept high during summer), land reclamation for building IJburg (660 ha will be reclaimed near Amsterdam), pollution by nutrients and by trace pollutants such as cadmium, mercury and DDT ('Other' threat, above), entanglement in fishing nets, and disturbance caused by wildfowl hunting and recreation (leisure navigation). A small part of the area lies in the 'Eemmeer, Gooimeer en IJmeer' SPA (as part of the IJmeer).

Lake Ketelmeer

A4iii, B1i, C3, C4 · **039**

Admin region Overijssel, Flevoland
Coordinates 52°36'N 5°45'E
Altitude (-5)–(-1) m · **Area** 3,750 ha

■ Site description

A freshwater lake, bounded in the north by the dyke of Noordoostpolder (reclaimed in 1942), in the south by the dyke of Oostelijk Flevoland (1957), in the east by the delta of the IJssel river (047), and in the west by Lake IJsselmeer (034). Only the IJssel delta has some reedbeds along the foreshore. Sand extraction occurs, as well as extensive dredging to clean heavily polluted sediments.

Habitats Wetland (100%; standing fresh water)
Land-use Fisheries/aquaculture (90%), Hunting (50%), Tourism/recreation (90%), Urban/industrial/transport (20%), Water management (100%)

■ Birds

Species	Season	Year	Pop min	Pop max	Acc	Criteria
Aythya ferina Pochard	N	1992	5,507	5,507	A	B1i, C3
Aythya fuligula Tufted Duck	N	1991	15,599	15,599	A	B1i, C3

The mean total number of wintering waterbirds in January exceeds 20,000.

■ Protection status

National None **International** None

■ Conservation issues

Threats Agricultural intensification/expansion (B), Aquaculture/fisheries (B), Disturbance to birds (B), Industrialization/urbanization (B), Recreation/tourism (B), Other (B)

The main problems are water management (the water-level of the IJsselmeer is deliberately kept high during summer), nutrient pollution (from the River Rhine/IJssel and by trace pollutants such as cadmium, mercury and DDT), over-fishing, wildfowl hunting (mainly on the east side), recreation (leisure boating), and reed-harvesting along the eastern foreshore ('Other' threat, above). An island is under construction (as of 1998) for the storage of polluted sediments, but this will be beneficial to birds in the long-term.

Lake Zwartemeer — A4iii, B1i, C2, C4, C6 — 040
Admin region Overijssel, Flevoland
Coordinates 52°38′N 5°58′E
Altitude (-3)–(-1) m **Area** 2,180 ha

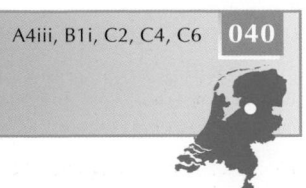

■ Site description
A freshwater lake with extensive reedbeds, bounded in the north by the dyke of Noordoostpolder (reclaimed in 1942) and in the south by the mainland (province of Overijssel). The Zwarte Water river (090) flows into the lake in the north-east corner, and the site is adjacent to Lake Ketelmeer (039) in the west (Ramspol). The north-eastern border is close to De Wieden (065). There is a shipping lane (dredged). This site, together with site 047, formed part of a single, larger site (former site NL028) in the previous pan-European IBA inventory (Grimmett and Jones 1989).

Habitats Wetland (96%; standing fresh water; water-fringe vegetation)
Land-use Fisheries/aquaculture (86%), Nature conservation/research (81%), Tourism/recreation (86%), Urban/industrial/transport (30%), Water management (100%)

■ Birds

Species	Season	Year	Pop min	Pop max	Acc	Criteria
Ardea purpurea Purple Heron	B	1991	24	24	A	C6
Platalea leucorodia Spoonbill	P	1991	44	44	A	B1i, C2

This is an important roost for geese *Anser* from surrounding feeding areas, but counts underestimate numbers. The average seasonal peak number of waterbirds during 1992–1996 exceeded 20,000.

■ Protection status
National Partial **International** High
1,650 ha of IBA covered by Natural Monument (Zwarte Meer, 1,650 ha). 206 ha of IBA covered by Natural Monument (Zwarte Meer II, 206 ha). 2,050 ha of IBA covered by Special Protection Area (Zwarte Meer, 2,050 ha). 2,050 ha of IBA covered by Ramsar Site (Zwarte Meer, 2,050 ha).

■ Conservation issues

Threats Agricultural intensification/expansion (A), Construction/impact of dyke/dam/barrage (B), Disturbance to birds (B), Other (B)

The main threats are nutrient pollution (as at site 039, but problems are greater here as the lake is shallower), commercial reed-harvesting ('Other' threat, above), disturbance caused by wildfowl hunting, and the construction of a storm-surge barrier on the west side at Ramspol.

Lake Drontermeer — A4i, B1i, B2, C2 — 041
Admin region Overijssel, Gelderland, Flevoland
Coordinates 52°30′N 5°51′E
Altitude (-3)–(-1) m **Area** 640 ha

■ Site description
A freshwater lake, bounded in the west by the dyke of the Oostelijk Flevoland polder (reclaimed in 1957) and in the east by the mainland. It is connected to Lake Ketelmeer (039) via Lake Vossemeer in the north, and lies adjacent to Lake Veluwemeer (042) in the south (separated by sluices). Sand extraction occurs.

Habitats Wetland (96%; standing fresh water)
Land-use Fisheries/aquaculture (93%), Tourism/recreation (98%), Urban/industrial/transport (50%), Water management (100%)

■ Birds

Species	Season	Year	Pop min	Pop max	Acc	Criteria
Cygnus columbianus Bewick's Swan	W	1992	253	253	A	A4i, B1i, B2, C2

■ Protection status
National None **International** None

■ Conservation issues

Threats Recreation/tourism (C)

The main problems are disturbance by recreation and nutrient pollution (but water quality is improving).

Lake Veluwemeer — A4i, A4iii, B1i, B2, C2, C4, C6 — 042
Admin region Gelderland, Flevoland
Coordinates 52°23′N 5°40′E
Altitude (-4)–(-1) m **Area** 3,390 ha

■ Site description
A freshwater lake, bounded in the north-west by the dyke of Oostelijk Flevoland polder (reclaimed in 1957) and in the south-east by the mainland. There are extensive though narrow reedbeds along the mainland coast. The site lies adjacent to Lake Drontermeer (041) in the north and to Lake Wolderwijd (043) in the south-east (with sluices at both sides). Sand extraction occurs. This site, together with site 043, formed part of a single, larger site (former site NL032) in the previous pan-European IBA inventory (Grimmett and Jones 1989).

Habitats Wetland (97%; standing fresh water; water-fringe vegetation)
Land-use Fisheries/aquaculture (80%), Hunting (20%), Tourism/recreation (85%), Urban/industrial/transport (30%), Water management (100%)

■ Birds

Species	Season	Year	Pop min	Pop max	Acc	Criteria
Cygnus columbianus Bewick's Swan	W	1992	1,220	1,220	A	A4i,B1i,B2,C2,C6

The site is a roost for geese *Anser* from surrounding feeding areas, but numbers are poorly covered by counts. The average seasonal peak number of waterbirds during 1992–1996 was more than 20,000.

■ Protection status
National Low **International** None
26 ha of IBA covered by Nature Reserve (Veluwerandmeren, 26 ha).

■ Conservation issues

Threats Recreation/tourism (B)

The main problems are disturbance by recreation and nutrient pollution (but water quality is improving).

Lake Wolderwijd — A4i, B1i, B2, C2 — 043
Admin region Gelderland, Flevoland
Coordinates 52°21′N 5°35′E
Altitude (-8)–(-1) m **Area** 2,750 ha

■ Site description
A freshwater lake, bounded on the northern and western sides by the dykes of the polders Oostelijk and Zuidelijk Flevoland (reclaimed in 1957 and 1968), and in the south-east by the mainland. The site lies adjacent to Lake Veluwemeer (042) in the north-east, and to Lake Nijkerkernauw (connected to Eemmeer, 045) in the south (with sluices at both sides), and is also adjacent to Polder Arkemheen (075) in the south. Sand extraction occurs. This site, together with site 042, formed part of a single, larger site (former site NL032) in the previous pan-European IBA inventory (Grimmett and Jones 1989).

Habitats Wetland (97%; standing fresh water)
Land-use Fisheries/aquaculture (90%), Tourism/recreation (28%), Urban/industrial/transport (20%), Water management (100%)

■ Birds

Species	Season	Year	Pop min	Pop max	Acc	Criteria
Cygnus columbianus Bewick's Swan	W	1992	205	205	A	A4i, B1i, B2, C2

Protection status
National None **International** None

Conservation issues

Threats Recreation/tourism (B)

The main problems are disturbance (by recreation) and nutrient pollution (but water quality is improving).

Lake Gooimeer   A4i, A4iii, B1i, B2, C2, C3, C4, C6   **044**
Admin region Flevoland, Noord-Holland
Coordinates 52°19′N 5°12′E
Altitude (-28)–(-1) m   **Area** 2,670 ha

Site description
A freshwater lake, bounded in the north by the dyke of Zuidelijk Flevoland polder (reclaimed in 1968) and in the south by the mainland. The site is connected to Lake Markermeer (038) in the west and to Lake Eemmeer (045) in the east. There are extensive though narrow reedbeds along the mainland coast. The site includes a grassland polder east of the city of Naarden.

Habitats Wetland (97%; standing fresh water)
Land-use Fisheries/aquaculture (20%), Nature conservation/research (18%), Tourism/recreation (80%), Urban/industrial/transport (30%), Water management (100%)

Birds

Species	Season	Year	Pop min	Pop max	Acc	Criteria
Cygnus columbianus Bewick's Swan	W	1991	193	193	A	A4i, B1i, B2, C2
Anas strepera Gadwall	N	1992	419	419	A	B1i, C3
Anas clypeata Shoveler	N	1992	697	697	A	B1i, C3
Chlidonias niger Black Tern	P	1992	334	334	A	C6

The average seasonal peak number of waterbirds during 1992–1996 was more than 20,000.

Protection status
National Partial **International** Partial
15 ha of IBA covered by Natural Monument (Gooikust bij Naarden, 15 ha). 65 ha of IBA covered by Natural Monument (Gooikust bij Naarden II, 65 ha). 400 ha of IBA covered by Natural Monument (Gooimeer, 400 ha). 178 ha of IBA covered by Nature Reserve (Gooimeer, 178 ha). 490 ha of IBA covered by Special Protection Area (Eemmeer, Gooimeer en IJmeer, 1,800 ha).

Conservation issues

Threats Aquaculture/fisheries (B), Industrialization/urbanization (C), Recreation/tourism (B)

The main problems are over-fishing and entanglement in fishing nets, disturbance (by recreation), and nutrient pollution (but water quality is improving). The SPA also includes Eemmeer (045) and a minor part of Markermeer (038).

Lake Eemmeer   A4i, B1i, B2, C2, C3, C6   **045**
Admin region Flevoland, Utrecht, Noord-Holland
Coordinates 52°17′N 5°19′E
Altitude (-5)–(-1) m   **Area** 1,340 ha

Site description
A freshwater lake, bounded in the north by the dyke of Zuidelijk Flevoland polder (reclaimed in 1968) and in the south by the mainland. The site is connected to Lake Gooimeer (044) in the north-west and to Lake Nijkerkernauw (adjacent to Lake Wolderwijd, 043) in the south-east. There is an extensive reedbed along the mainland in the western corner. The site includes part of a grassland polder on the southern side. There is a shipping lane (dredged). This site, together with site 075, formed part of a single, larger site (former site NL033) in the previous pan-European IBA inventory (Grimmett and Jones 1989).

Habitats Wetland (75%; standing fresh water; water-fringe vegetation), Artificial landscape (24%; highly improved reseeded grassland)

Land-use Agriculture (20%), Fisheries/aquaculture (20%), Hunting (10%), Nature conservation/research (100%), Tourism/recreation (20%), Urban/industrial/transport (30%), Water management (100%)

Birds

Species	Season	Year	Pop min	Pop max	Acc	Criteria
Cygnus columbianus Bewick's Swan	W	1990	1,197	1,197	B	A4i,B1i,B2,C2,C6
Anas penelope Wigeon	W	1992	13,878	13,878	A	B1i, C3
Anas clypeata Shoveler	N	1992	440	440	A	B1i, C3

This is a roost for large numbers of *Cygnus columbianus* which come from feeding areas in nearby grassland polders (e.g. Arkemheen), but count data are not available.

Protection status
National High **International** Partial
1,200 ha of IBA covered by Natural Monument (Eemmeer, 1,200 ha). 146 ha of IBA covered by Nature Reserve (Eemland, 177 ha). 137 ha of IBA covered by Nature Reserve (Eemmeer, 137 ha). 1,200 ha of IBA covered by Special Protection Area (Eemmeer, Gooimeer en IJmeer, 1,800 ha).

Conservation issues

Threats Aquaculture/fisheries (B), Industrialization/urbanization (B), Recreation/tourism (B)

The main problems are nutrient pollution (but water quality is improving), over-fishing, and disturbance by recreation. A scheme to compensate for restrictions on agricultural practices applies to part of this site. The entire lake (but not the landward polder) has been designated as an SPA; the designation also includes Gooimeer (044) and a small part of Markermeer (038).

IJssel: Deventer–Zwolle   A4i, A4iii, B1i, B2, B3, C2, C4, C6   **046**
Admin region Overijssel
Coordinates 52°24′N 6°08′E
Altitude 1–0 m   **Area** 3,000 ha

Site description
A 30-km long section of the IJssel river between the cities of Deventer and Zwolle, which lies adjacent to site 047. The site includes the riverbed and the flood-plain (mainly used for dairy farming), and is bounded by the winter dykes. Economic activities include sand and clay extraction.

Habitats Wetland (27%; river/stream; water-fringe vegetation), Artificial landscape (69%; highly improved reseeded grassland)
Land-use Agriculture (65%), Fisheries/aquaculture (17%), Hunting (70%), Nature conservation/research (20%), Tourism/recreation (17%), Urban/industrial/transport (11%), Water management (70%)

Birds

Species	Season	Year	Pop min	Pop max	Acc	Criteria
Cygnus columbianus Bewick's Swan	W	1991	713	713	A	A4i,B1i,B2,C2,C6
Cygnus cygnus Whooper Swan	W	1991	418	418	A	B1i, B3, C2, C6
Mergus albellus Smew	W	1991	110	110	A	C6
Crex crex Corncrake	B	1991	5	5	A	C6
Alcedo atthis Kingfisher	R	1991	2	2	A	C6

An important roost for geese *Anser*, but numbers are poorly covered by counts. The mean count of waterbirds in January exceeds 20,000 in total.

Protection status
National Partial **International** None
495 ha of IBA covered by Natural Monument (IJsseluiterwaarden, 615 ha). 15 ha of IBA covered by Nature Reserve (Dorperwaarden, 15 ha). 303 ha of IBA covered by Nature Reserve (Fortmond: Duursche Waarden, Buitenwaarden, 303 ha). 102 ha of IBA covered by Nature Reserve (Hengforder Waarden, 102 ha). 18 ha of IBA covered by Nature Reserve (Oldeneel, 18 ha). 41 ha of IBA covered by Nature Reserve (Veeserwaarden, 41 ha). 38 ha of IBA covered by

Nature Reserve (Vorchterwaarden, 38 ha). 45 ha of IBA covered by Nature Reserve (Welsumer Waarden, 45 ha). 121 ha of IBA covered by Nature Reserve (Windesheim, 121 ha).

■ Conservation issues

Threats Agricultural intensification/expansion (B), Disturbance to birds (B), Industrialization/urbanization (B)

The main problems are agricultural intensification (on the river forelands), and pollution by nutrients and other chemicals discharged by industry and agriculture. A scheme to compensate for restrictions on agricultural practices applies to part of this site.

IJssel: Zwolle–Ketelmeer A4i, B1i, B2, B3, C2, C6 047
Admin region Overijssel
Coordinates 52°32'N 5°57'E
Altitude 0–3 m **Area** 1,350 ha

■ Site description
A 20-km long section of the River IJssel between the city of Zwolle and Lake Ketelmeer (039), which lies adjacent to site 046. The site includes the riverbed and the flood-plain (used for dairy farming), and is bounded by the winter dykes. Economic activities include sand and clay extraction. This site, together with site 040, formed part of a single, larger site (former site NL028) in the previous pan-European IBA inventory (Grimmett and Jones 1989).

Habitats Wetland (30%; river/stream; water-fringe vegetation), Artificial landscape (70%; highly improved reseeded grassland)
Land-use Agriculture (65%), Fisheries/aquaculture (20%), Hunting (5%), Nature conservation/research (13%), Tourism/recreation (20%), Urban/industrial/transport (10%), Water management (100%)

■ Birds

Species	Season	Year	Pop min	Pop max	Acc	Criteria
Cygnus columbianus Bewick's Swan	W	1991	210	210	A	A4i, B1i, B2, C2
Cygnus cygnus Whooper Swan	W	1991	52	52	A	B3, C6

■ Protection status
National Partial **International** None
120 ha of IBA covered by Natural Monument (IJsseluiterwaarden, 615 ha). 30 ha of IBA covered by Nature Reserve (Engelse Werk, 30 ha). 41 ha of IBA covered by Nature Reserve (Vreugderijkerwaard, 41 ha). 137 ha of IBA covered by Nature Reserve (Zalk-Wilsum, 137 ha).

■ Conservation issues

Threats Agricultural intensification/expansion (B), Disturbance to birds (C), Industrialization/urbanization (B)

The main problems are agricultural intensification (on the river forelands), and pollution by nutrients and chemicals discharged by industry and agriculture. A scheme to compensate for restrictions on agricultural practices applies to part of the site.

Gelderse Poort A4i, A4iii, B1i, B2, B3, C2, C3, C4, C6 048
Admin region Gelderland
Coordinates 51°53'N 6°02'E
Altitude 10–13 m **Area** 6,460 ha

■ Site description

Habitats Wetland (20%; standing fresh water; river/stream; water-fringe vegetation), Artificial landscape (80%; highly improved reseeded grassland)
Land-use Agriculture (60%), Fisheries/aquaculture (10%), Hunting (80%), Nature conservation/research (15%), Tourism/recreation (30%), Urban/industrial/transport (5%), Water management (100%)

A 20-km long section of the River Rhine between Tolkamer (near the German border) and Arnhem (close to site 049) and a 12-km section of the River Waal between the branch of the Rhine and the city of

Nijmegen (close to site 050). The site includes the riverbed, flood-plain, clay pits, and the inland subsites Oude Rijnstrangen (1,090 ha) and Ooijpolder (1,575 ha). Elsewhere the site is bounded by the winter dykes. Clay extraction occurs.

■ Birds

Species	Season	Year	Pop min	Pop max	Acc	Criteria
Botaurus stellaris Bittern	R	1992	24	24	B	B2, C2, C6
Ixobrychus minutus Little Bittern	B	1991	2	2	A	C6
Cygnus columbianus Bewick's Swan	W	1991	143	143	A	B2
Cygnus cygnus Whooper Swan	W	1991	110	110	A	B3, C6
Anser fabalis Bean Goose	W	1991	6,482	6,482	A	A4i, B1i, C3
Anser albifrons White-fronted Goose	W	1991	35,933	35,933	A	A4i, B1i, C3
Anas clypeata Shoveler	N	1991	803	803	A	B1i, C3
Mergus albellus Smew	W	1991	194	194	A	C6
Crex crex Corncrake	B	1992	6	6	A	C6
Chlidonias niger Black Tern	B	1993	136	136	A	B2, C2, C6

There are large roosts of *Anser albifrons*, the birds arriving from German and Dutch feeding areas (max. 100,000), but available counts underestimate the actual numbers.

■ Protection status
National Partial **International** None
82 ha of IBA covered by Natural Monument (Oude Waal, 82 ha). 2 ha of IBA covered by Natural Monument (Weide Oude Rijnstrangen, 2 ha). 108 ha of IBA covered by Nature Reserve (Bemmelse, Gendtse en Klompenwaard, 108 ha). 17 ha of IBA covered by Nature Reserve (Oooijpolder, 17 ha). 410 ha of IBA covered by Nature Reserve (Ooijpolder en Millingerwaard, 485 ha). 348 ha of IBA covered by Nature Reserve (Oude Rijnstrangen, 348 ha).

■ Conservation issues

Threats Agricultural intensification/expansion (A), Disturbance to birds (B), Drainage (B), Industrialization/urbanization (B), Infrastructure (B), Recreation/tourism (C)

The main problems are agricultural intensification (on the river forelands), disturbance (wildfowl hunting), the extension of the A15 motorway, and pollution by agricultural and industrial discharges. A scheme to compensate for restrictions on agricultural practices applies to part of the site.

Rijn: Heteren–Amerongen A4i, A4iii, B1i, B2, C2, C4, C6 049
Admin region Gelderland, Utrecht
Coordinates 51°57'N 5°40'E
Altitude 8–10 m **Area** 2,480 ha

■ Site description
A 22-km long stretch of the River Rhine (Rijn), close to Gelderse Poort (048), between the villages of Heteren and Amerongen (industry plants excluded). The site includes the river channel and surrounding flood-plain, the latter being mainly used for dairy farming, and is bounded by the winter dykes.

Habitats Wetland (26%; river/stream; water-fringe vegetation), Artificial landscape (72%; highly improved reseeded grassland)
Land-use Agriculture (65%), Fisheries/aquaculture (10%), Hunting (25%), Nature conservation/research (18%), Tourism/recreation (20%), Urban/industrial/transport (20%), Water management (100%)

■ Birds

Species	Season	Year	Pop min	Pop max	Acc	Criteria
Cygnus columbianus Bewick's Swan	W	1988	320	320	B	A4i, B1i, B2, C2
Crex crex Corncrake	B	1991	3	3	A	C6

The average seasonal peak number of waterbirds during 1992–1996 was more than 20,000.

■ Protection status
National Partial **International** None
120 ha of IBA covered by Nature Reserve (Amerongse Bovenpolder, 120 ha). 110 ha of IBA covered by Nature Reserve (Blauwe Kamer, 110 ha). 39 ha of IBA covered by Nature Reserve (Plassewaard, 39 ha).

214 ha of IBA covered by Nature Reserve (Wageningse Uiterwaarden, 214 ha).

■ **Conservation issues**

Threats Agricultural intensification/expansion (B), Disturbance to birds (C), Industrialization/urbanization (B)

The main threats are agricultural intensification (on the river forelands) and pollution by agricultural and industrial discharges.

Waal: Ewijk–Waardenburg
A4i, A4iii, B1i, B2, C2, C3, C4, C6 050

Admin region Gelderland
Coordinates 51°54′N 5°32′E
Altitude 3–10 m **Area** 5,940 ha

■ **Site description**
A 39-km long stretch of the River Waal, close to Gelderse Poort (048), between the villages of Ewijk and Waardenburg. The site comprises the river channel, surrounding flood-plain (used mainly for dairy farming) and clay pits, and is bounded by winter dykes.

Habitats Wetland (28%; river/stream), Artificial landscape (72%; highly improved reseeded grassland)
Land-use Agriculture (45%), Fisheries/aquaculture (15%), Hunting (5%), Nature conservation/research (11%), Tourism/recreation (20%), Urban/industrial/transport (11%), Water management (100%)

■ **Birds**

Species	Season	Year	Pop min	Pop max	Acc	Criteria
Cygnus columbianus Bewick's Swan	W	1991	378	378	A	A4i, B1i, B2, C2
Anser albifrons White-fronted Goose	W	1991	15,029	15,029	A	A4i, B1i, C3
Aythya ferina Pochard	N	1991	4,540	4,540	A	B1i, C3
Crex crex Corncrake	B	1991	5	5	A	C6

There are two roosts of geese *Anser*, which come from surrounding feeding areas, but counts underestimate actual numbers. The mean total number of waterbirds in January exceeds 20,000.

■ **Protection status**
National Partial **International** Partial
48 ha of IBA covered by Natural Monument (Kil van Hurwenen, 48 ha). 97 ha of IBA covered by Nature Reserve (Afferdense en Deestse Waard, 97 ha). 43 ha of IBA covered by Nature Reserve (Bandijk Winssen, 43 ha). 146 ha of IBA covered by Nature Reserve (Hurwenensche Uiterwaarden, 146 ha). 220 ha of IBA covered by Nature Reserve (Neerijnen, 293 ha). 65 ha of IBA covered by Nature Reserve (Sint Andries, 65 ha). 45 ha of IBA covered by Nature Reserve (Waarden bij Heeselt, 45 ha). 9 ha of IBA covered by Nature Reserve (Waarden bij Wamel, 9 ha). 1,005 ha of IBA covered by Special Protection Area (Kil van Hurwenen e.o, 1,005 ha).

■ **Conservation issues**

Threats Agricultural intensification/expansion (B), Construction/impact of dyke/dam/barrage (B), Disturbance to birds (C), Industrialization/urbanization (B), Infrastructure (C)

The SPA designation covers some river forelands in the western part of the site. A compensation scheme is in place for those farmers affected by restrictions on agricultural practices. Clay extraction is combined with restoration of river forelands.

Biesbosch
A4i, A4iii, B1i, B2, C2, C3, C4, C6 051

Admin region Noord-Brabant, Zuid-Holland
Coordinates 51°46′N 4°50′E
Altitude 0–3 m **Area** 9,050 ha

■ **Site description**
A former tidal estuary in the Rhine/Maas river system, sealed off from the sea in 1970 (see Haringvliet, 024) and no longer subject to marine influence. The site consists of a flood-plain, polders, marshland and swamp-forest, and is intersected by many formerly tidal creeks. The

site is adjacent to Hollands Diep (025) in the west; it does not include three drinking-water reservoirs within its boundary. Human activities include reed-harvesting ('Other' land-use, below).

Habitats Forest and woodland (16%; alluvial/very wet forest), Wetland (45%; standing fresh water; river/stream; water-fringe vegetation), Artificial landscape (39%; highly improved reseeded grassland)
Land-use Agriculture (30%), Fisheries/aquaculture (30%), Hunting (50%), Nature conservation/research (49%), Other, Tourism/recreation (35%), Urban/industrial/transport (16%), Water management (6%)

■ **Birds**

Species	Season	Year	Pop min	Pop max	Acc	Criteria
Platalea leucorodia Spoonbill	P	1990	60	60	A	B1i, C2
Cygnus columbianus Bewick's Swan	W	1992	290	290	A	A4i, B1i, B2, C2
Anser albifrons White-fronted Goose	W	1992	7,878	7,878	A	B1i, C3
Branta leucopsis Barnacle Goose	W	1992	2,179	2,179	A	B1i, B2, C2
Anas strepera Gadwall	N	1992	607	607	A	B1i, C3
Circus aeruginosus Marsh Harrier	B	1993	55	55	B	C6
Crex crex Corncrake	B	1991	5	5	A	C6
Alcedo atthis Kingfisher	R	1991	2	2	A	C6
Luscinia svecica Bluethroat	B	1992	1,783	1,783	B	C6

An important roost for geese *Anser* which come from surrounding feeding areas, but counts underestimate actual numbers. The mean total number of waterbirds in January exceeds 20,000.

■ **Protection status**
National High **International** High
2,691 ha of IBA covered by Nature Reserve (Brabantse Biesbosch, 2,691 ha). 806 ha of IBA covered by Nature Reserve (Dordtse Biesbosch, 806 ha). 797 ha of IBA covered by Nature Reserve (Sliedrechtse Biesbosch, 797 ha). 7,100 ha of IBA covered by National Park (De Biesbosch, 7,100 ha). 8,850 ha of IBA covered by Special Protection Area (De Biesbosch, 8,850 ha). 1,700 ha of IBA covered by Ramsar Site (De Biesbosch Zuidwaard, 1,700 ha).

■ **Conservation issues**

Threats Industrialization/urbanization (B), Recreation/tourism (B)

The main threats are the pollution of bottom sediments by industrial chemicals, and recreation. Clay extraction will result in marsh restoration in the north of the area.

Lake Leekstermeer
A4i, A4iii, B1i, C3, C4 052

Admin region Groningen, Drenthe
Coordinates 53°11′N 6°26′E
Altitude (-3)–(-1) m **Area** 850 ha

■ **Site description**
A freshwater lake located south-west of the city of Groningen, surrounded by reedbeds, peat-bogs and pastures.

Habitats Wetland (31%; standing fresh water; water-fringe vegetation), Artificial landscape (65%; highly improved reseeded grassland)
Land-use Fisheries/aquaculture (26%), Nature conservation/research (97%), Tourism/recreation (31%), Water management (100%)

■ **Birds**

Species	Season	Year	Pop min	Pop max	Acc	Criteria
Anser albifrons White-fronted Goose	W	1990	20,415	20,415	A	A4i, B1i, C3

■ **Protection status**
National High **International** None
587 ha of IBA covered by Nature Reserve (Leekstermeer (Dr), 587 ha). 37 ha of IBA covered by Nature Reserve (Leekstermeer (Gr), 37 ha). 150 ha of IBA covered by Nature Reserve (Leekstermeer GRL, 150 ha).

■ **Conservation issues**

Threats Disturbance to birds (B), Drainage (C), Infrastructure (C)

The hunting of geese *Anser* during the winter, and recreational activities during summer and autumn, disturb birds. A compensation scheme is in place for those farmers affected by restrictions on agricultural practices.

Lake Zuidlaardermeer and Onnerpolder — A4i, B1i, B2, C2 — 053

Admin region Groningen, Drenthe
Coordinates 53°08'N 6°41'E
Altitude 0–1 m Area 1,950 ha

■ Site description

A freshwater lake located south-east of the city of Groningen, with reedbeds and an extensive area of wet pasture. Human activities include reed-harvesting.

Habitats Wetland (34%; standing fresh water), Artificial landscape (66%; highly improved reseeded grassland)

Land-use Agriculture (50%), Fisheries/aquaculture (30%), Hunting (25%), Nature conservation/research (63%), Tourism/recreation (70%), Water management (100%)

■ Birds

Species	Season	Year	Pop min	Pop max	Acc	Criteria
Cygnus columbianus Bewick's Swan	W	1991	282	282	A	A4i, B1i, B2, C2

Lake Zuidlaardermeer is used as a roost by swans *Cygnus* and geese *Anser*.

■ Protection status

National Partial **International** None
261 ha of IBA covered by Nature Reserve (Onnerpolder, 261 ha). 171 ha of IBA covered by Nature Reserve (Zuidlaardermeer, 171 ha). 330 ha of IBA covered by Nature Reserve (Zuidlaardermeer II, 330 ha).

■ Conservation issues

Threats Disturbance to birds (C), Drainage (B), Extraction industry (B), Other (B), Recreation/tourism (C)

Nutrient pollution of the lake is a problem ('Other' threat, above). A compensation scheme is in place for those farmers affected by restrictions on agricultural practices.

Groote Wielen — A4i, A4iii, B1i, B2, C2, C3, C4, C6 — 054

Admin region Friesland
Coordinates 53°13'N 5°52'E
Altitude 0–1 m Area 580 ha

■ Site description

A complex of freshwater lakes (resulting partly from peat diggings), reedbeds and wet meadows, located to the east of the city of Leeuwarden. Human activities include reed-harvesting ('Other' land-use, below), and the site includes two duck decoys.

Habitats Wetland (40%; standing fresh water; water-fringe vegetation), Artificial landscape (60%; highly improved reseeded grassland)

Land-use Agriculture (6%), Fisheries/aquaculture (10%), Hunting (5%), Nature conservation/research (85%), Other (5%), Tourism/recreation (50%), Water management (100%)

■ Birds

Species	Season	Year	Pop min	Pop max	Acc	Criteria
Anser albifrons White-fronted Goose	W	1989	40,000	40,000	A	A4i, B1i, C3
Branta leucopsis Barnacle Goose	W	1990	4,000	4,000	A	A4i, B1i, B2, C2
Anas penelope Wigeon	W	1990	20,000	20,000	A	A4i, B1i, C3
Anas clypeata Shoveler	N	1989	1,000	1,000	A	B1i, C3
Philomachus pugnax Ruff	N	1989	4,000	4,000	A	C6

An important roost for geese *Anser* which come from surrounding feeding areas.

■ Protection status

National Partial **International** None
462 ha of IBA covered by Nature Reserve (Ryptsjerkster- en Binnemiedepolder, 462 ha).

■ Conservation issues

Threats Disturbance to birds (C), Drainage (B), Recreation/tourism (B)

A compensation scheme is in place for those farmers affected by restrictions on agricultural practices.

Oude Venen — A4i, A4iii, B1i, B2, C2, C3, C4, C6 — 055

Admin region Friesland
Coordinates 53°07'N 5°55'E
Altitude (-1)–0 m Area 2,500 ha

■ Site description

An area of lakes (resulting partly from peat-diggings), reedbeds, wet meadows and woodland, located south-east of the city of Leeuwarden. Human activities include reed-harvesting ('Other' land-use, below) and natural-gas extraction. This site, together with site 056, formed part of a single, larger site (former site NL023) in the previous pan-European IBA inventory (Grimmett and Jones 1989).

Habitats Forest and woodland (10%; alluvial/very wet forest), Wetland (40%; standing fresh water; water-fringe vegetation), Artificial landscape (50%; highly improved reseeded grassland)

Land-use Agriculture (25%), Fisheries/aquaculture (10%), Hunting (17%), Nature conservation/research (63%), Other (5%), Tourism/recreation (45%), Water management (100%)

■ Birds

Species	Season	Year	Pop min	Pop max	Acc	Criteria
Anser albifrons White-fronted Goose	W	1989	30,000	30,000	A	A4i, B1i, C3
Branta leucopsis Barnacle Goose	W	1989	10,000	10,000	A	A4i, B1i, B2, C2, C6
Anas penelope Wigeon	W	1989	35,000	35,000	A	A4i, B1i, C3
Anas strepera Gadwall	N	1989	500	500	A	B1i, C3
Anas clypeata Shoveler	N	1989	1,500	1,500	A	B1i, C3
Porzana porzana Spotted Crake	B	1995	8	8	A	C6
Philomachus pugnax Ruff	N	1989	25,000	25,000	A	C6
Limosa limosa Black-tailed Godwit	N	1989	10,000	10,000	A	A4i, B1i, C3

This is an important roost for geese *Anser* and waders from surrounding feeding areas. Waterbird numbers quoted are rough estimates.

■ Protection status

National Partial **International** High
95 ha of IBA covered by Natural Monument (Tuskensleatten, 95 ha). 2,140 ha of IBA covered by Nature Reserve (Oude Venen, 2,140 ha). 2,500 ha of IBA covered by Special Protection Area (Oude Venen, 2,500 ha). 2,500 ha of IBA covered by Ramsar Site (Oude Venen, 2,500 ha).

■ Conservation issues

Threats Disturbance to birds (C), Drainage (B), Other (A), Recreation/tourism (B)

Nutrient pollution is a problem ('Other' threat, above). A compensation scheme is in place for those farmers affected by restrictions on agricultural practices.

De Deelen — A4i, A4iii, B1i, B2, C2, C3, C4, C6 — 056

Admin region Friesland
Coordinates 53°02'N 5°55'E
Altitude (-1)–0 m Area 1,260 ha

■ Site description

An area of former peat-workings comprising open water, reedbeds, shrubs and wet meadows, located to the north of the city of Heerenveen. Human activities include reed-harvesting ('Other' land-use, below). This site, together with site 055, formed part of a single, larger site (former site NL023) in the previous pan-European IBA inventory (Grimmett and Jones 1989).

Habitats Forest and woodland (10%; alluvial/very wet forest), Wetland (90%; standing fresh water; water-fringe vegetation)

Land-use Agriculture (5%), Fisheries/aquaculture (50%), Hunting (20%), Nature conservation/research (92%), Other (5%), Tourism/recreation (20%), Water management (100%)

■ Birds

Species		Season	Year	Pop min	Pop max	Acc	Criteria
Anser albifrons	White-fronted Goose	W	1994	35,173	35,173	A	A4i, B1i, C3
Branta leucopsis	Barnacle Goose	W	1994	3,430	3,430	A	A4i, B1i, B2, C2
Chlidonias niger	Black Tern	B	1993	62	62	B	B2, C2, C6

An important roost for geese *Anser* from surrounding feeding areas.

■ Protection status

National High **International** Partial
1,158 ha of IBA covered by Nature Reserve (De Deelen, 1,158 ha).
520 ha of IBA covered by Special Protection Area (De Deelen, 520 ha).
520 ha of IBA covered by Ramsar Site (De Deelen, 520 ha).

■ Conservation issues

Threats Drainage (B), Other (A)

Nutrient pollution of wetlands is a problem ('Other' threat, above).

Van Oordt's Mersken   A4i, A4iii, B1i, B2, C3, C4   057
Admin region Friesland
Coordinates 53°03'N 6°05'E
Altitude (-1)–0 m **Area** 670 ha

■ Site description
Flood-plain meadows of the River Koningsdiep, situated in the eastern part of Friesland.

Habitats Wetland (river/stream), Artificial landscape (96%; highly improved reseeded grassland)
Land-use Agriculture (90%), Hunting (50%), Nature conservation/research (58%), Urban/industrial/transport (6%), Water management (100%)

■ Birds

Species		Season	Year	Pop min	Pop max	Acc	Criteria
Anser albifrons	White-fronted Goose	W	1989	30,000	30,000	A	A4i, B1i, C3
Branta leucopsis	Barnacle Goose	W	1989	1,500	1,500	A	B2
Anas clypeata	Shoveler	N	1989	400	400	A	B1i, C3
Limosa limosa	Black-tailed Godwit	N	1989	5,000	5,000	A	A4i, B1i, C3

This is an important roost for geese *Anser* from surrounding feeding areas. Waterbird numbers quoted are rough estimates.

■ Protection status
National Partial **International** None
388 ha of IBA covered by Nature Reserve (Van Oordt's Mersken, 388 ha).

■ Conservation issues

Threats Disturbance to birds (B), Drainage (B)

The hunting of geese disturbs birds. A compensation scheme is in place for those farmers affected by restrictions on agricultural practices.

Lake Sneekermeer and Goingarijp   A4i, B1i, B2, C2, C3   058
Admin region Friesland
Coordinates 53°01'N 5°46'E
Altitude (-2)–(-1) m **Area** 1,670 ha

■ Site description
A complex of freshwater lakes (former peat-workings), wet meadows and marshland, located east of the city of Sneek. The site is adjacent to Terkaplesterpoelen and Akmarijp (059), and belongs to the same water-management unit as Lake Witte and Zwarte Brekken (060). This site, together with site 059, formed part of a larger site (former site NL022) in the previous pan-European IBA inventory (Grimmett and Jones 1989).

Habitats Wetland (70%; standing fresh water; water-fringe vegetation), Artificial landscape (30%; highly improved reseeded grassland)
Land-use Agriculture (30%), Fisheries/aquaculture (65%), Hunting (5%), Nature conservation/research (34%), Tourism/recreation (90%), Water management (100%)

■ Birds

Species		Season	Year	Pop min	Pop max	Acc	Criteria
Anser albifrons	White-fronted Goose	W	1989	15,000	15,000	A	A4i, B1i, C3
Branta leucopsis	Barnacle Goose	W	1989	5,000	5,000	A	A4i, B1i, B2, C2
Anas penelope	Wigeon	W	1989	15,000	15,000	A	B1i, C3
Anas clypeata	Shoveler	N	1989	500	500	A	B1i, C3

This is an important roost for geese *Anser* from surrounding feeding areas. Waterbird numbers quoted are rough estimates.

■ Protection status
National Partial **International** None
564 ha of IBA covered by Nature Reserve (Sneekermeer, 564 ha).

■ Conservation issues

Threats Disturbance to birds (C), Recreation/tourism (B)

Terkaplesterpoelen and Akmarijp   A4i, A4iii, B1i, B2, C2, C3, C4, C6   059
Admin region Friesland
Coordinates 53°02'N 5°48'E
Altitude (-2)–0 m **Area** 770 ha

■ Site description
A freshwater lake (former peat-workings) and extensive wet meadows (Akmarijp) located to the east of the city of Sneek. The site is adjacent to Lake Sneekermeer and Goingarijp (058). This site, together with site 058, formed part of a single, larger site (former site NL022) in the previous pan-European IBA inventory (Grimmett and Jones 1989).

Habitats Wetland (39%; standing fresh water; water-fringe vegetation), Artificial landscape (61%; highly improved reseeded grassland)
Land-use Agriculture (50%), Fisheries/aquaculture (29%), Hunting (50%), Nature conservation/research (55%), Tourism/recreation (31%), Water management (100%)

■ Birds

Species		Season	Year	Pop min	Pop max	Acc	Criteria
Anser albifrons	White-fronted Goose	W	1989	25,000	25,000	A	A4i, B1i, C3
Branta leucopsis	Barnacle Goose	W	1989	10,000	10,000	A	A4i, B1i, B2, C2, C6

This is an important roost for geese *Anser* from surrounding feeding areas. Waterbird numbers quoted are rough estimates.

■ Protection status
National Partial **International** None
420 ha of IBA covered by Nature Reserve (De Terkaplesterpuollen, 420 ha).

■ Conservation issues

Threats Disturbance to birds (B), Drainage (B)

Wildfowl hunting disturbs birds. A compensation scheme is in place for those farmers affected by restrictions on agricultural practices.

Lake Witte and Zwarte Brekken   A4i, A4iii, B1i, B2, C2, C3, C4   060
Admin region Friesland
Coordinates 53°00'N 5°41'E
Altitude (-3)–(-1) m **Area** 460 ha

■ Site description
A freshwater lake (former peat-workings) surrounded by marshland and wet meadows that partly flood in winter, and located to the south of the city of Sneek. The site belongs to the same water management unit as Lake Sneekermeer (058). Human activities include reed-harvesting ('Other' land-use, below).

Habitats Wetland (45%; standing fresh water; water-fringe vegetation), Artificial landscape (55%; highly improved reseeded grassland)
Land-use Agriculture (25%), Fisheries/aquaculture (30%), Hunting (10%), Nature conservation/research (57%), Other (5%), Tourism/recreation (35%), Water management (100%)

■ Birds

Species	Season	Year	Pop min	Pop max	Acc	Criteria
Anser brachyrhynchus Pink-footed Goose	W	1989	10,000	10,000	A	A4i, B1i, C3
Anser albifrons White-fronted Goose	W	1989	15,000	15,000	A	A4i, B1i, C3
Branta leucopsis Barnacle Goose	W	1989	5,000	5,000	A	A4i, B1i, B2, C2

This is an important roost for geese *Anser* from surrounding feeding areas. The mean total number of waterbirds in winter exceeds 20,000. Waterbird numbers quoted are rough estimates.

■ Protection status

National Partial **International** None
262 ha of IBA covered by Nature Reserve (Witte en Zwarte Brekken, 285 ha).

■ Conservation issues

Threats Disturbance to birds (B), Drainage (B), Industrialization/urbanization (C), Infrastructure (B)

Wildfowl hunting disturbs birds.

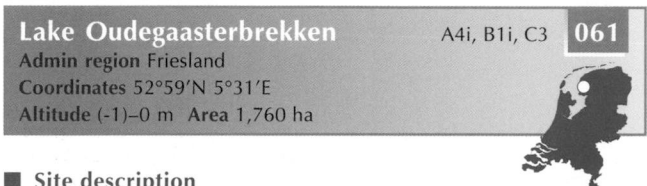

Lake Oudegaasterbrekken
A4i, B1i, C3 **061**
Admin region Friesland
Coordinates 52°59′N 5°31′E
Altitude (-1)–0 m **Area** 1,760 ha

■ Site description

A complex of freshwater lakes and improved grassland situated to the south-west of the city of Sneek. This site, together with site 062, formed part of a single, larger site (former site NL017) in the previous pan-European IBA inventory (Grimmett and Jones 1989).

Habitats Wetland (48%; standing fresh water), Artificial landscape (45%; highly improved reseeded grassland), Unknown (7%)
Land-use Agriculture (40%), Fisheries/aquaculture (45%), Hunting (20%), Nature conservation/research (10%), Tourism/recreation (55%), Water management (100%)

■ Birds

Species	Season	Year	Pop min	Pop max	Acc	Criteria
Anser brachyrhynchus Pink-footed Goose	W	1989	15,000	15,000	A	A4i, B1i, C3

This is an important roost for geese *Anser* from surrounding feeding areas. Waterbird numbers quoted are rough estimates.

■ Protection status

National Partial **International** None
162 ha of IBA covered by Nature Reserve (Blauhuester Puollen, 167 ha).
16 ha of IBA covered by Nature Reserve (Grons, Sanmar, Gaastmar, 83 ha).

■ Conservation issues

Threats Disturbance to birds (B), Drainage (B), Recreation/tourism (C)

A compensation scheme is in place for those farmers affected by restrictions on agricultural practices.

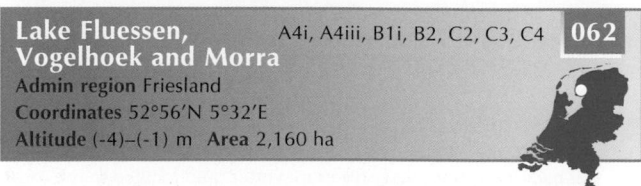

Lake Fluessen, Vogelhoek and Morra
A4i, A4iii, B1i, B2, C2, C3, C4 **062**
Admin region Friesland
Coordinates 52°56′N 5°32′E
Altitude (-4)–(-1) m **Area** 2,160 ha

■ Site description

Habitats Wetland (82%; standing fresh water; water-fringe vegetation), Artificial landscape (18%; highly improved reseeded grassland)
Land-use Agriculture (15%), Fisheries/aquaculture (77%), Hunting (50%), Nature conservation/research (12%), Tourism/recreation (87%), Water management (100%)

A large freshwater lake with sparse water-fringe vegetation and surrounding wet meadows, located to the south-west of the city of

Sneek, and close to Lake Oudegaasterbrekken (061). This site, together with site 061, formed part of a single, larger site (former site NL017) in the previous pan-European IBA inventory (Grimmett and Jones 1989).

■ Birds

Species	Season	Year	Pop min	Pop max	Acc	Criteria
Anser albifrons White-fronted Goose	W	1989	25,000	25,000	A	A4i, B1i, C3
Branta leucopsis Barnacle Goose	W	1989	7,500	7,500	A	A4i, B1i, B2, C2

This is an important roost for geese *Anser* from surrounding feeding areas. Waterbird numbers quoted are rough estimates.

■ Protection status

National Partial **International** None
124 ha of IBA covered by Nature Reserve (De Samenvoeging, 124 ha).
30 ha of IBA covered by Nature Reserve (It Skar en Feandyk, 83 ha).
126 ha of IBA covered by Nature Reserve (Vogelhoek, Buitenlanden en Eilanden Fluessen, 126 ha).

■ Conservation issues

Threats Disturbance to birds (B), Drainage (B), Recreation/tourism (C)

The hunting of wildfowl, particularly geese, disturbs birds. A compensation scheme is in place for those farmers affected by restrictions on agricultural practices.

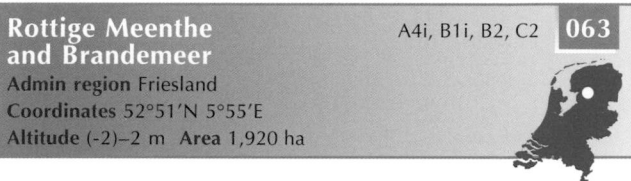

Rottige Meenthe and Brandemeer
A4i, B1i, B2, C2 **063**
Admin region Friesland
Coordinates 52°51′N 5°55′E
Altitude (-2)–2 m **Area** 1,920 ha

■ Site description

An area of small ponds and canals (former peat-workings) interspersed with fens, reedbeds, swampy woodland and wet meadows, and located south of the city of Heerenveen, near to De Weerribben (064). Human activities include reed-harvesting ('Other' land-use, below).

Habitats Forest and woodland (5%; alluvial/very wet forest), Wetland (70%; standing fresh water; water-fringe vegetation), Artificial landscape (25%; highly improved reseeded grassland)
Land-use Agriculture (25%), Fisheries/aquaculture (5%), Hunting (40%), Nature conservation/research (65%), Other (25%), Tourism/recreation (10%), Urban/industrial/ transport (5%), Water management (100%)

■ Birds

Species	Season	Year	Pop min	Pop max	Acc	Criteria
Cygnus columbianus Bewick's Swan	W	1989	200	200	A	A4i, B1i, B2, C2

A roost for geese *Anser* from surrounding feeding areas. Waterbird numbers quoted are rough estimates.

■ Protection status

National Partial **International** None
459 ha of IBA covered by Nature Reserve (Brandemeer, 459 ha).
798 ha of IBA covered by Nature Reserve (Rottige Meenthe, 798 ha).

■ Conservation issues

Threats Drainage (B)

The drainage of neighbouring farmland poses a threat. A compensation scheme is in place for those farmers affected by restrictions on agricultural practices.

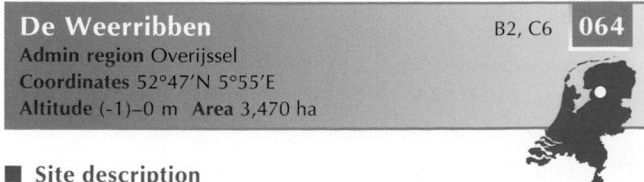

De Weerribben
B2, C6 **064**
Admin region Overijssel
Coordinates 52°47′N 5°55′E
Altitude (-1)–0 m **Area** 3,470 ha

■ Site description

An area of ponds and canals (former peat-workings), fens, reedbeds, swampy woodland and wet meadows, located to the west of the city of Steenwijk. The site is situated close to site 063, and lies adjacent to De Wieden (065) with which it formed a single site (the former site NL027) in the previous pan-European IBA inventory (Grimmett and Jones 1989). Human activities include tourism and commercial reed-harvesting ('Other' land-use, below).

Habitats Forest and woodland (33%; alluvial/very wet forest), Wetland (47%; standing fresh water; water-fringe vegetation), Artificial landscape (20%; highly improved reseeded grassland)
Land-use Agriculture (5%), Fisheries/aquaculture (30%), Hunting (60%), Nature conservation/research (90%), Other (25%), Tourism/recreation (32%), Water management (100%)

■ **Birds**

Species	Season	Year	Pop min	Pop max	Acc	Criteria
Botaurus stellaris Bittern	R	1991	12	12	A	B2, C6
Porzana porzana Spotted Crake	B	1994	2	2	A	C6

■ **Protection status**
National High **International** High
3,115 ha of IBA covered by Nature Reserve (De Weerribben, 3,115 ha). 3,450 ha of IBA covered by National Park (De Weerribben, 3,450 ha). 3,400 ha of IBA covered by Special Protection Area (De Weerribben, 3,400 ha). 3,400 ha of IBA covered by Ramsar Site (De Weerribben, 3,400 ha).

■ **Conservation issues**

Threats Agricultural intensification/expansion (U), Disturbance to birds (C), Drainage (B), Industrialization/urbanization (U), Other (A)

The main threats are posed by commercial reed-harvesting ('Other' threat, above), and by nutrient pollution of wetlands by agricultural and industrial/urban discharges. A compensation scheme is in place for those farmers affected by restrictions on agricultural practices.

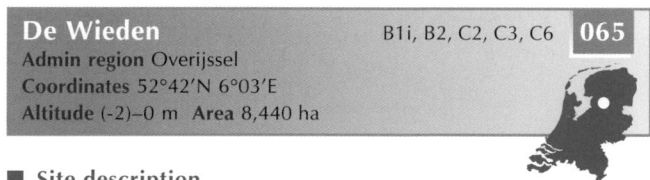

De Wieden B1i, B2, C2, C3, C6 **065**
Admin region Overijssel
Coordinates 52°42′N 6°03′E
Altitude (-2)–0 m **Area** 8,440 ha

■ **Site description**
An area of shallow lakes and canals (former peat-workings) with fens, reedbeds, swampy woodland and wet meadows, located to the north of the city of Zwolle. The IBA is adjacent to De Weerribben (064), with which it formed a single site ('De Wieden and De Weerribben', the former site NL027) in the previous pan-European IBA inventory (Grimmett and Jones 1989). Human activities include water-sports, tourism and reed-harvesting ('Other' land-use, below).

Habitats Forest and woodland (12%; alluvial/very wet forest), Wetland (73%; standing fresh water; water-fringe vegetation), Artificial landscape (14%; highly improved reseeded grassland)
Land-use Agriculture (10%), Fisheries/aquaculture (44%), Nature conservation/research (62%), Other (9%), Tourism/recreation (90%), Water management (100%)

■ **Birds**

Species	Season	Year	Pop min	Pop max	Acc	Criteria
Phalacrocorax carbo Cormorant	B	1991	864	864	A	B1i, C3
Porzana porzana Spotted Crake	B	1995	5	5	A	C6
Chlidonias niger Black Tern	B	1984	128	128	B	B2, C2, C6

A roost for geese *Anser* from surrounding feeding areas, but no counts are available.

■ **Protection status**
National Partial **International** None
4,991 ha of IBA covered by Nature Reserve (De Wieden, 4,991 ha). 285 ha of IBA covered by Nature Reserve (De Wieden II, 285 ha).

■ **Conservation issues**

Threats Agricultural intensification/expansion (U), Disturbance to birds (C), Drainage (A), Industrialization/urbanization (U), Other (B)

The site is threatened by the drainage of surrounding polders, commercial reed-harvesting ('Other' threat, above), and by nutrient pollution of wetlands by agricultural and industrial/urban discharges.

A compensation scheme is in place for those farmers affected by restrictions on agricultural practices.

Oostvaardersplassen A4i, A4iii, B1i, B2, B3, **066**
Admin region Flevoland C2, C3, C4, C6
Coordinates 52°26′N 5°21′E
Altitude (-5)–(-3) m **Area** 5,600 ha

■ **Site description**
An extensive area of shallow lakes, pools, reedbeds, *Salix* woodland and grassland which has developed on a polder (Zuidelijk Flevoland, reclaimed in 1968), having been spared from cultivation. It is situated south of the city of Lelystad, and adjoins Markermeer (038) in the north. This site, together with site 067, formed part of a single, larger site (former site NL031) in the previous pan-European IBA inventory (Grimmett and Jones 1989).

Habitats Forest and woodland (8%; broadleaved deciduous forest; alluvial/very wet forest), Wetland (69%; standing fresh water; water-fringe vegetation), Artificial landscape (23%; ruderal land)
Land-use Nature conservation/research (100%), Water management (100%)

■ **Birds**

Species	Season	Year	Pop min	Pop max	Acc	Criteria
Phalacrocorax carbo Cormorant	B	1991	6,246	6,246	A	A4i, B1i, C3
Phalacrocorax carbo Cormorant	N	1991	4,247	4,247	A	A4i, B1i, C3
Botaurus stellaris Bittern	R	1991	7	7	A	B2, C6
[1] *Platalea leucorodia* Spoonbill	B	1991	192	192	A	A4i,B1i,B2,C2,C6
Platalea leucorodia Spoonbill	N	1991	582	582	A	A4i, B1i, C2, C6
Cygnus cygnus Whooper Swan	W	1991	475	475	A	B1i, B3, C2, C6
Anser albifrons White-fronted Goose	W	1991	6,723	6,723	A	B1i, C3
Anser anser Greylag Goose	N	1990	50,375	50,375	A	A4i, B1i, C3
Branta leucopsis Barnacle Goose	W	1991	2,911	2,911	A	A4i, B1i, B2, C2
Anas strepera Gadwall	N	1991	598	598	A	B1i, C3
Anas crecca Teal	N	1990	52,580	52,580	A	A4i, B1i, C3
Anas acuta Pintail	N	1991	5,013	5,013	A	B1i, C3
Anas clypeata Shoveler	N	1991	3,916	3,916	A	B1i, C3
Circus aeruginosus Marsh Harrier	B	1991	58	58	A	C6
Porzana porzana Spotted Crake	B	1995	28	28	A	C6
Recurvirostra avosetta Avocet	N	1990	4,281	4,281	A	A4i, B1i, C2, C6
Limosa limosa Black-tailed Godwit	N	1990	5,596	5,596	A	A4i, B1i, C3
Chlidonias niger Black Tern	P	1991	2,336	2,336	A	A4i, B1i, C2, C6
Luscinia svecica Bluethroat	B	1991	750	750	A	C6

1. No nesting occurred in 1996–1997 (water level too low).

The site is the main roost for geese *Anser* from feeding areas in Flevoland, and is the most important moulting area for *Anser anser* in north-west Europe.

■ **Protection status**
National High **International** High
5,600 ha of IBA covered by Natural Monument (Oostvaardersplassen, 5,600 ha). 5,600 ha of IBA covered by Nature Reserve (Oostvaardersplassen, 5,600 ha). 5,600 ha of IBA covered by Special Protection Area (Oostvaardersplassen, 5,600 ha). 5,600 ha of IBA covered by Ramsar Site (Oostvaardersplassen, 5,600 ha).

■ **Conservation issues**

Threats Disturbance to birds (C), Natural events (B), Other (B), Recreation/tourism (C)

The main problems affecting the area are the natural succession of vegetation and the effects of botulism on wild birds ('Other' threat, above). In 1997 the area was reconnected with Lepelaarplassen (067) by a 250-m-wide stretch of marshland.

Lepelaarplassen A4i, B1i, B2, C2, C3, C6 **067**
Admin region Flevoland
Coordinates 52°24′N 5°12′E
Altitude (-5)–(-3) m **Area** 510 ha

■ **Site description**
An area of shallow lakes, pools, reedbeds, and *Salix* woodland that has developed on a polder (Zuidelijk Flevoland, reclaimed in 1968),

having been spared from cultivation. The site is located to the west of the city of Almere, and adjoins Markermeer (038) in the north. This site, together with site 066, formed part of a single, larger site (former site NL031) in the previous pan-European IBA inventory (Grimmett and Jones 1989).

Habitats Forest and woodland (23%; alluvial/very wet forest), Wetland (74%; standing fresh water; water-fringe vegetation)
Land-use Nature conservation/research (100%), Tourism/recreation (5%), Water management (100%)

■ **Birds**

Species	Season	Year	Pop min	Pop max	Acc	Criteria
Phalacrocorax carbo Cormorant	B	1991	2,990	2,990	A	A4i, B1i, C3
Phalacrocorax carbo Cormorant	N	1990	2,305	2,305	A	B1i, C3
Platalea leucorodia Spoonbill	B	1991	25	25	A	B1i, B2, C2
Aythya fuligula Tufted Duck	N	1991	16,810	16,810	A	A4i, B1i, C3
Mergus albellus Smew	W	1990	588	588	A	B1i, C2, C6
[1] *Luscinia svecica* Bluethroat	B	1993	150	150	C	C6

1. Only one recent count available.

■ **Protection status**
National High **International** Partial
350 ha of IBA covered by Natural Monument (Lepelaarplassen, 350 ha). 470 ha of IBA covered by Nature Reserve (Lepelaarplassen, 470 ha). 90 ha of IBA covered by Nature Reserve (Wilgenbos, 90 ha). 350 ha of IBA covered by Special Protection Area (Lepelaarplassen, 350 ha).

■ **Conservation issues**

Threats Industrialization/urbanization (B), Natural events (B), Other (B)

The buffer zone that separates the site from Almere is under pressure from urban development, and the effects of the natural succession of vegetation and of botulism on wild birds ('Other' threat) pose additional problems. In 1997 the site was reconnected with Oostvaardersplassen (066) by a 250-m-wide stretch of marshland.

Eilandspolder   B1i, C2   068
Admin region Noord-Holland
Coordinates 52°34'N 4°51'E
Altitude (-2)–(-2) m **Area** 2,040 ha

■ **Site description**
A polder complex consisting of pools, marshland, wet meadows and ditches, located to the east of the city of Alkmaar. Human activities include reed-harvesting ('Other' land-use). This site, together with sites 070–072, formed part of a single, larger site (former site NL038) in the previous pan-European IBA inventory (Grimmett and Jones 1989).

Habitats Wetland (10%; standing fresh water; water-fringe vegetation), Artificial landscape (85%; highly improved reseeded grassland), Unknown (5%)
Land-use Agriculture (30%), Fisheries/aquaculture (5%), Hunting (10%), Nature conservation/research (59%), Other (5%), Tourism/recreation (20%), Water management (100%)

■ **Birds**

Species	Season	Year	Pop min	Pop max	Acc	Criteria
Platalea leucorodia Spoonbill	N	1991	32	32	A	B1i, C2

■ **Protection status**
National Partial **International** None
671 ha of IBA covered by Nature Reserve (Eilandspolder Oost, 671 ha). 323 ha of IBA covered by Nature Reserve (Eilandspolder West, 323 ha). 214 ha of IBA covered by Nature Reserve (Polder Mijzen, 214 ha).

■ **Conservation issues**

Threats Recreation/tourism (B)

A compensation scheme is in place for those farmers affected by restrictions on agricultural practices.

Polder Zeevang   A4iii, B1i, C3, C4   069
Admin region Noord-Holland
Coordinates 52°33'N 5°02'E
Altitude (-2)–(-1) m **Area** 1,250 ha

■ **Site description**
A polder complex comprising improved grassland, wet meadows and ditches with some water-fringe vegetation, adjoining Markermeer (038) in the east.

Habitats Wetland (water-fringe vegetation), Artificial landscape (98%; highly improved reseeded grassland)
Land-use Agriculture (25%), Hunting (15%), Nature conservation/research (17%), Urban/industrial/transport (7%), Water management (100%)

■ **Birds**

Species	Season	Year	Pop min	Pop max	Acc	Criteria
Anas penelope Wigeon	W	1993	15,256	15,256	A	B1i, C3

The mean total number of waterbirds in January exceeds 20,000.

■ **Protection status**
National Partial **International** None
10 ha of IBA covered by Nature Reserve (Groote Braak (Braken IJsselmeerdijk), 14 ha). 202 ha of IBA covered by Nature Reserve (Zeevang, 202 ha).

■ **Conservation issues**

Threats Drainage (B)

A compensation scheme is in place for those farmers affected by restrictions on agricultural practices.

Wormer- and Jisperveld   A4i, B1i, C2, C3, C6   070
Admin region Noord-Holland
Coordinates 52°31'N 4°50'E
Altitude (-2)–(-1) m **Area** 1,940 ha

■ **Site description**
A polder landscape including a shallow lake, ditches, wet meadows and marshland, situated to the north of the city of Zaandam. This site, together with sites 068, 071 and 072, formed part of a single, larger site (former site NL038) in the previous pan-European IBA inventory (Grimmett and Jones 1989).

Habitats Wetland (17%; standing fresh water; water-fringe vegetation), Artificial landscape (83%; highly improved reseeded grassland)
Land-use Agriculture (25%), Fisheries/aquaculture (10%), Hunting (10%), Nature conservation/research (32%), Tourism/recreation (11%), Water management (100%)

■ **Birds**

Species	Season	Year	Pop min	Pop max	Acc	Criteria
Platalea leucorodia Spoonbill	N	1991	38	38	A	B1i, C2
Anas penelope Wigeon	W	1991	17,410	17,410	A	B1i, C3
Philomachus pugnax Ruff	B	1993	19	19	B	C6
Limosa limosa Black-tailed Godwit	N	1992	5,500	5,500	B	A4i, B1i, C3

■ **Protection status**
National Partial **International** None
618 ha of IBA covered by Nature Reserve (Wormer- en Jisperveld, 618 ha).

■ **Conservation issues**

Threats Disturbance to birds (B), Drainage (B), Industrialization/urbanization (B), Other (A), Recreation/tourism (B)

The main problems are the nutrient pollution of wetlands ('Other' threat, above), disturbance caused by ultra-light planes, and the effects of urbanization. A compensation scheme is in place for those farmers affected by restrictions on agricultural practices.

Ilperveld, Varkensland and Twiske   A4i, A4iii, B1i, B2, C3, C4, C6   071

Admin region Noord-Holland
Coordinates 52°27'N 4°56'E
Altitude (-2)–(-1) m **Area** 1,960 ha

■ Site description
A polder complex comprising pools, ditches, marshland, wet meadows, improved grassland and a recreational area (Twiske). The IBA is located to the north of the city of Amsterdam, adjacent to Oostzanerveld (072). This site, together with sites 068, 070 and 072, formed part of a single, larger site (former site NL038) in the previous pan-European IBA inventory (Grimmett and Jones 1989).

Habitats Forest and woodland (5%; mixed forest), Wetland (22%; standing fresh water; water-fringe vegetation), Artificial landscape (70%; highly improved reseeded grassland)
Land-use Agriculture (40%), Fisheries/aquaculture (5%), Hunting (70%), Nature conservation/research (100%), Tourism/recreation (8%), Water management (100%)

■ Birds

Species	Season	Year	Pop min	Pop max	Acc	Criteria
Botaurus stellaris Bittern	R	1991	7	7	A	B2, C6
Anas penelope Wigeon	W	1993	21,526	21,526	B	A4i, B1i, C3
Philomachus pugnax Ruff	B	1991	20	20	A	C6
Limosa limosa Black-tailed Godwit	N	1992	9,850	9,850	B	A4i, B1i, C3

■ Protection status
National Partial **International** None
315 ha of IBA covered by Natural Monument (Waterland Varkensland, 315 ha). 531 ha of IBA covered by Nature Reserve (Varkensland, 531 ha).

■ Conservation issues

Threats Disturbance to birds (B), Drainage (B), Other, Recreation/tourism (B)

The main threats to the site are nutrient pollution of wetlands ('Other' threat), recreation (on water and land), and disturbance caused by aircraft. A compensation scheme is in place for those farmers affected by restrictions on agricultural practices.

Oostzanerveld   A4i, B1i, C3, C6   072

Admin region Noord-Holland
Coordinates 52°27'N 4°52'E
Altitude (-2)–1 m **Area** 750 ha

■ Site description
The IBA comprises a polder landscape with wet meadows and ditches. It is located to the north of the city of Amsterdam and adjoins Ilperveld, Varkensland and Twiske (071). This site, together with sites 068, 070 and 071, formed part of a single, larger site (former site NL038) in the previous pan-European IBA inventory (Grimmett and Jones 1989).

Habitats Wetland (20%; standing fresh water; water-fringe vegetation), Artificial landscape (80%; highly improved reseeded grassland)
Land-use Agriculture (75%), Fisheries/aquaculture (10%), Hunting (70%), Nature conservation/research (38%), Tourism/recreation (25%), Water management (100%)

■ Birds

Species	Season	Year	Pop min	Pop max	Acc	Criteria
Philomachus pugnax Ruff	B	1991	14	14	A	C6
Limosa limosa Black-tailed Godwit	N	1992	6,000	6,000	B	A4i, B1i, C3

■ Protection status
National Partial **International** None
279 ha of IBA covered by Nature Reserve (Oostzanerveld, 279 ha).

■ Conservation issues

Threats Recreation/tourism (B)

A compensation scheme is in place for those farmers affected by restrictions on agricultural practices.

Oostelijke Vechtplassen   B2, C2, C6   073

Admin region Utrecht, Noord-Holland
Coordinates 52°13'N 5°05'E
Altitude (-5)–0 m **Area** 7,040 ha

■ Site description
An extensive area of shallow lakes and canals (former peat-workings), fens, reedbeds, swampy woodland, and wet meadows. The site is located to the west of the city of Hilversum, close to the River Vecht. Human activities include water-sports and reed-harvesting.

Habitats Forest and woodland (20%; alluvial/very wet forest), Wetland (75%; standing fresh water; water-fringe vegetation), Artificial landscape (5%; highly improved reseeded grassland)
Land-use Agriculture (5%), Fisheries/aquaculture (60%), Hunting (80%), Nature conservation/research (27%), Tourism/recreation (65%), Urban/industrial/transport (8%), Water management (100%)

■ Birds

Species	Season	Year	Pop min	Pop max	Acc	Criteria
Ixobrychus minutus Little Bittern	B	1991	3	3	B	C6
Chlidonias niger Black Tern	B	1992	66	66	A	B2, C2, C6

An important roost for geese *Anser* from surrounding feeding areas, but no counts are available.

■ Protection status
National Partial **International** None
80 ha of IBA covered by Natural Monument (Moerasterrein Loosdrecht, 80 ha). 598 ha of IBA covered by Nature Reserve (Ankeveense Plassen, 598 ha). 176 ha of IBA covered by Nature Reserve (Het Hol, Kortenhoef, 176 ha). 50 ha of IBA covered by Nature Reserve (Horstermeerpolder, 50 ha). 51 ha of IBA covered by Nature Reserve (Horstermeerpolder II, 51 ha). 328 ha of IBA covered by Nature Reserve (Kortenhoefse Plassen, 328 ha). 445 ha of IBA covered by Nature Reserve (Loosdrechtse Plassen, 445 ha). 62 ha of IBA covered by Nature Reserve (Polder Mijnden, 62 ha). 1 ha of IBA covered by Nature Reserve (Spiegelplas, 1 ha). 203 ha of IBA covered by Nature Reserve (Tienhovense Plassen, 203 ha). 16 ha of IBA covered by Nature Reserve (Wijde Blik, 16 ha).

■ Conservation issues

Threats Agricultural intensification/expansion (U), Disturbance to birds (C), Drainage (B), Industrialization/urbanization (U), Other (B), Recreation/tourism (B)

The main problems affecting the site are the drainage of water to surrounding low-lying polders, nutrient pollution of wetlands, disturbance to birds caused by boating, and reed-harvesting ('Other' threat). A compensation scheme is in place for those farmers affected by restrictions on agricultural practices.

Naardermeer   A4i, B1i, B2, C2, C3, C6   074

Admin region Noord-Holland
Coordinates 52°18'N 5°07'E
Altitude (-2)–0 m **Area** 1,120 ha

■ Site description
A complex of shallow freshwater lakes, pools and canals (former peat-workings), fens, reedbeds and swamp-forest, surrounded by improved grassland which is being converted to wet meadows and marshland. The site is located alongside the Amsterdam to Bussum railway.

Habitats Forest and woodland (17%; alluvial/very wet forest), Wetland (43%; standing fresh water; water-fringe vegetation), Artificial landscape (40%; highly improved reseeded grassland)
Land-use Agriculture (20%), Nature conservation/research (94%), Water management (100%)

■ Birds

Species	Season	Year	Pop min	Pop max	Acc	Criteria
Phalacrocorax carbo Cormorant	B	1991	3,414	3,414	A	A4i, B1i, C3
Ardea purpurea Purple Heron	B	1991	31	31	A	C6
Platalea leucorodia Spoonbill	B	1991	32	32	A	B1i, B2, C2

■ Protection status
National High **International** Partial
1,049 ha of IBA covered by Nature Reserve (Naardermeer, 1,049 ha). 750 ha of IBA covered by Special Protection Area (Naardermeer, 750 ha). 752 ha of IBA covered by Ramsar Site (Naardermeer, 752 ha).

■ Conservation issues

Threats Groundwater abstraction (B), Other (U)

Nutrient pollution of wetlands is a problem ('Other' threat), as is the abstraction of water to supply lower-lying agricultural polders. The restoration of marshland (formerly agricultural grassland) will enable a link to be made between this site and the Ankeveense Plassen marsh area (the northern part of site 073) in the near future.

Polder Arkemheen A4i, B1i, B2, C2, C6 075
Admin region Gelderland
Coordinates 52°14′N 5°26′E
Altitude (-1)–0 m **Area** 1,460 ha

■ Site description
A polder of wet grassland, located to the north-east of the city of Amersfoort. The site adjoins Lake Wolderwijd (043) in the east and is close to Lake Eemmeer (045) in the west. This site, together with site 045, formed part of a single, larger site (former site NL033) in the previous pan-European IBA inventory (Grimmett and Jones 1989).

Habitats Artificial landscape (100%; highly improved reseeded grassland)
Land-use Agriculture (65%), Hunting (90%), Nature conservation/research (12%), Tourism/recreation (5%), Water management (100%)

■ Birds

Species	Season	Year	Pop min	Pop max	Acc	Criteria
Cygnus columbianus Bewick's Swan	W	1991	2,808	2,808	A	A4i,B1i,B2,C2,C6

■ Protection status
National Partial **International** None
170 ha of IBA covered by Nature Reserve (Arkemheen, 170 ha).

■ Conservation issues

Threats Agricultural intensification/expansion (B), Drainage (B), Industrialization/urbanization (C)

The main threats in the long term are posed by (further) drainage and the expansion of the city of Amersfoort and nearby villages. A compensation scheme is in place for those farmers affected by restrictions on agricultural practices.

Nieuwkoopse Plassen B2, C2, C6 076
Admin region Zuid-Holland
Coordinates 52°09′N 4°47′E
Altitude (-5)–(-1) m **Area** 2,000 ha

■ Site description
A complex of shallow freshwater lakes, pools, canals, reedbeds, wet meadows and swamp-forest, located 15 km north-west of the city of Utrecht.

Habitats Wetland (69%; standing fresh water; water-fringe vegetation), Artificial landscape (27%; highly improved reseeded grassland)
Land-use Fisheries/aquaculture (30%), Hunting (25%), Nature conservation/research (59%), Tourism/recreation (27%), Water management (100%)

■ Birds

Species	Season	Year	Pop min	Pop max	Acc	Criteria
Ardea purpurea Purple Heron	B	1991	107	107	A	B2, C2, C6
Chlidonias niger Black Tern	B	1991	88	88	A	B2, C2, C6

■ Protection status
National Partial **International** High
60 ha of IBA covered by Natural Monument (De Haak, 60 ha). 10 ha of IBA covered by Nature Reserve (De Haeck, 10 ha). 39 ha of IBA covered by Nature Reserve (De Meije, 39 ha). 1,127 ha of IBA covered by Nature Reserve (Nieuwkoopse Plassen, 1,127 ha). 2,000 ha of IBA covered by Special Protection Area (Nieuwkoopse Plassen, 2,000 ha).

■ Conservation issues

Threats Disturbance to birds (C), Drainage (B), Other (U), Recreation/tourism (B)

The main problems affecting the site include drainage of water to lower-lying polders, and nutrient pollution of wetlands ('Other' threat). A compensation scheme is in place for those farmers affected by restrictions on agricultural practices.

Reeuwijkse Plassen A4i, A4iii, B1i, B2, C2, C3, C4 077
Admin region Zuid-Holland
Coordinates 52°03′N 4°47′E
Altitude (-5)–(-1) m **Area** 1,650 ha

■ Site description
A complex of shallow lakes interspersed with strips of land, reed margins, wet meadows and improved grassland, located to the north-east of the city of Gouda.

Habitats Wetland (51%; standing fresh water; water-fringe vegetation), Artificial landscape (45%; highly improved reseeded grassland)
Land-use Agriculture (20%), Fisheries/aquaculture (45%), Hunting (50%), Nature conservation/research (14%), Tourism/recreation (55%), Water management (100%)

■ Birds

Species	Season	Year	Pop min	Pop max	Acc	Criteria
Cygnus columbianus Bewick's Swan	W	1992	193	193	A	A4i, B1i, B2, C2
Anas penelope Wigeon	W	1992	14,976	14,976	A	B1i, C3

The average seasonal peak number of waterbirds during 1992–1996 was more than 20,000.

■ Protection status
National Partial **International** None
227 ha of IBA covered by Nature Reserve (Reeuwijkse Plassen, 227 ha).

■ Conservation issues

Threats Disturbance to birds (B), Recreation/tourism (B)

Hunting in the southern part of the site causes disturbance to birds. A compensation scheme is in place for those farmers affected by restrictions on agricultural practices.

Zouweboezem C6 078
Admin region Zuid-Holland
Coordinates 51°57′N 5°00′E
Altitude (-1)–1 m **Area** 140 ha

■ Site description
The site comprises reedbeds, scrub and wet meadows alongside a canal, and adjoins the River Lek (an arm of the Rhine) south-west of the city of Utrecht. Human activities include reed-harvesting ('Other' land-use). This site, together with site 080, formed part of a single, larger site (former site NL042) in the previous pan-European IBA inventory (Grimmett and Jones 1989).

Habitats Wetland (80%; standing fresh water; water-fringe vegetation), Artificial landscape (20%; highly improved reseeded grassland)
Land-use Agriculture (20%), Fisheries/aquaculture (20%), Hunting (36%), Nature conservation/research (51%), Other (5%), Tourism/recreation (30%), Water management (100%)

■ Birds

Species	Season	Year	Pop min	Pop max	Acc	Criteria
Ardea purpurea Purple Heron	B	1991	19	19	A	C6

■ Protection status

National Partial **International** High

71 ha of IBA covered by Nature Reserve (Zouweboezem, 71 ha). 140 ha of IBA covered by Special Protection Area (Zouweboezem, 140 ha).

■ Conservation issues

Threats Other (A)

The main threat is commercial reed-harvesting ('Other' threat). A compensation scheme is in place for those farmers affected by restrictions on agricultural practices.

Donkse Laagten
B1i, C3 | 079

Admin region Zuid-Holland
Coordinates 51°54′N 4°48′E
Altitude (-2)–1 m **Area** 180 ha

■ Site description

The IBA is situated in the Alblasserwaard polder, east of Rotterdam, and is covered by wet meadows. There are three duck decoys.

Habitats Artificial landscape (100%; highly improved reseeded grassland)
Land-use Agriculture (50%), Hunting (25%), Nature conservation/research (95%), Water management (100%)

■ Birds

Species	Season	Year	Pop min	Pop max	Acc	Criteria
Anser albifrons White-fronted Goose	W	1993	8,419	8,419	B	B1i, C3

■ Protection status

National High **International** None
171 ha of IBA covered by Nature Reserve (Donkse Laagten, 171 ha).

■ Conservation issues

Threats Unknown

Banks of River Linge
C6 | 080

Admin region Gelderland, Zuid-Holland
Coordinates 51°52′N 5°04′E
Altitude 0–1 m **Area** 610 ha

■ Site description

The site is located to the north-east of the city of Gorinchem and consists of the channel of the River Linge, its narrow flood-plain and excavations along the Nieuwe Zuider Lingedijk dyke, as well as associated wet meadows, marshland and swampy woodland. This site, together with site 078, formed part of a single, larger site (former site NL042) in the previous pan-European IBA inventory (Grimmett and Jones 1989).

Habitats Forest and woodland (19%; mixed forest; alluvial/very wet forest), Wetland (33%; standing fresh water; water-fringe vegetation), Artificial landscape (48%; highly improved reseeded grassland)
Land-use Agriculture (30%), Fisheries/aquaculture (10%), Nature conservation/research (58%), Tourism/recreation (25%), Water management (100%)

■ Birds

Species	Season	Year	Pop min	Pop max	Acc	Criteria
Ardea purpurea Purple Heron	B	1991	19	19	A	C6

■ Protection status

National Partial **International** None

60 ha of IBA covered by Natural Monument (Oeverlanden langs de Linge, 170 ha). 4 ha of IBA covered by Natural Monument (Oeverlanden langs de Linge, 95 ha). 60 ha of IBA covered by Nature Reserve (Linge Oevers, 60 ha). 219 ha of IBA covered by Nature Reserve (Nieuwe Zuider Lingedijk, 219 ha).

■ Conservation issues

Threats Recreation/tourism (B)

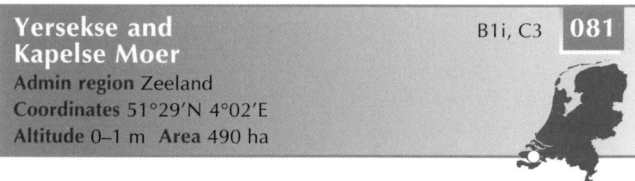

Yersekse and Kapelse Moer
B1i, C3 | 081

Admin region Zeeland
Coordinates 51°29′N 4°02′E
Altitude 0–1 m **Area** 490 ha

■ Site description

A complex of wet grassland, hedges and woodland patches situated on both sides of the Kanaal door Zuid-Beveland Canal that connects Oosterschelde (028) and Westerschelde and Saeftinghe (032). The site is located east of the city of Goes.

Habitats Artificial landscape (100%; highly improved reseeded grassland)
Land-use Agriculture (20%), Hunting (50%), Nature conservation/research (66%), Tourism/recreation (30%), Water management (100%)

■ Birds

Species	Season	Year	Pop min	Pop max	Acc	Criteria
Anser albifrons White-fronted Goose	W	1991	16,112	16,112	A	B1i, C3

■ Protection status

National Partial **International** None
117 ha of IBA covered by Nature Reserve (Kapelse Moer, 117 ha). 205 ha of IBA covered by Nature Reserve (Yerseke Moer, 205 ha).

■ Conservation issues

Threats Drainage (B)

A compensation scheme is in place for those farmers affected by restrictions on agricultural practices.

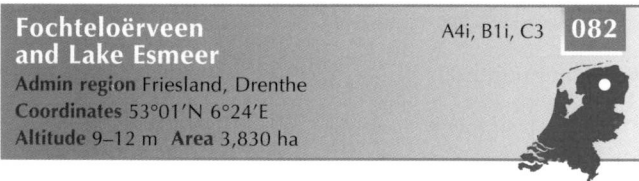

Fochteloërveen and Lake Esmeer
A4i, B1i, C3 | 082

Admin region Friesland, Drenthe
Coordinates 53°01′N 6°24′E
Altitude 9–12 m **Area** 3,830 ha

■ Site description

A complex of raised bogs, heathland, open water, forested areas and some improved grasslands. The site is located west of the city of Assen.

Habitats Forest and woodland (20%; mixed forest), Scrub (10%; heathland), Wetland (45%; raised bog), Artificial landscape (25%; highly improved reseeded grassland)
Land-use Agriculture (10%), Forestry (10%), Hunting (20%), Nature conservation/research (62%), Water management (100%)

■ Birds

Species	Season	Year	Pop min	Pop max	Acc	Criteria
[1] *Anser fabalis* Bean Goose	W	1991	5,193	5,193	A	A4i, B1i, C3

1. *A. f. rossicus.*

An important roost for geese *Anser* from surrounding feeding areas, but no counts are available.

■ Protection status

National Partial **International** None
2,302 ha of IBA covered by Nature Reserve (Fochteloërveen, 2,302 ha). 57 ha of IBA covered by Nature Reserve (Huis ter Heide, 57 ha). 2,500 ha of IBA covered by Special Protection Area (Fochteloërveen, 2,500 ha).

■ Conservation issues

Threats Disturbance to birds (B)

Goose hunting disturbs birds.

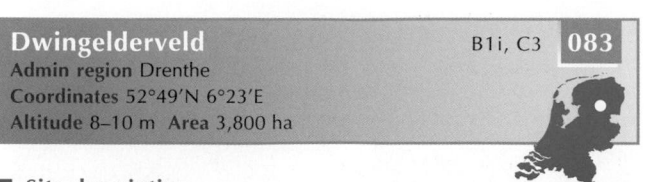

Dwingelderveld B1i, C3 083
Admin region Drenthe
Coordinates 52°49′N 6°23′E
Altitude 8–10 m Area 3,800 ha

■ Site description
An area of heathland and fen containing c.40 freshwater bodies of various sizes, surrounded by predominantly coniferous forest. The site is located to the north-west of the city of Hoogeveen.

Habitats Forest and woodland (50%; mixed forest), Scrub (45%; heathland)
Land-use Forestry (12%), Hunting (75%), Nature conservation/research (85%), Tourism/recreation (50%), Water management (100%)

■ Birds

Species	Season	Year	Pop min	Pop max	Acc	Criteria
¹ *Anser fabalis* Bean Goose	W	1991	812	812	A	B1i, C3

1. *A. f. fabalis.*

■ Protection status
National High **International** High
1,366 ha of IBA covered by Nature Reserve (Dwingelderveld, 1,366 ha). 1 ha of IBA covered by Nature Reserve (Dwingelderveld II, 1 ha). 1,849 ha of IBA covered by Nature Reserve (Kraloerheide en Dwingelo, 1,849 ha). 3,600 ha of IBA covered by National Park (Dwingelderveld, 3,600 ha). 3,692 ha of IBA covered by Special Protection Area (Dwingelderveld, 3,692 ha).

■ Conservation issues

Threats Drainage (C)

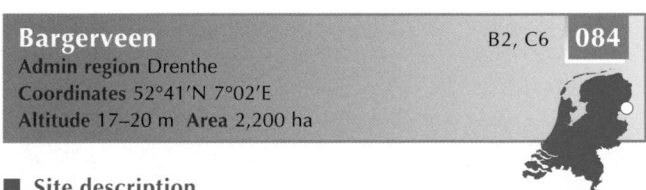

Bargerveen B2, C6 084
Admin region Drenthe
Coordinates 52°41′N 7°02′E
Altitude 17–20 m Area 2,200 ha

■ Site description
An area of peatland and pools located in the south-eastern corner of Drenthe province near to the German border, which includes one of the last remaining raised bogs in the Netherlands. The majority of the site has been cut for peat but some parts remain intact.

Habitats Scrub (50%; heathland), Wetland (36%; raised bog), Artificial landscape (10%; highly improved reseeded grassland)
Land-use Nature conservation/research (92%), Tourism/recreation (30%), Water management (100%)

■ Birds

Species	Season	Year	Pop min	Pop max	Acc	Criteria
Porzana porzana Spotted Crake	B	1995	10	10	A	C6
Lanius collurio Red-backed Shrike	B	1990	64	64	B	B2, C6

■ Protection status
National High **International** High
66 ha of IBA covered by Natural Monument (Meerstalblok, 66 ha). 2,100 ha of IBA covered by Nature Reserve (Bargerveen, 2,100 ha). 2,100 ha of IBA covered by Special Protection Area (Bargerveen, 2,100 ha). 2,100 ha of IBA covered by Ramsar Site (Bargerveen, 2,100 ha).

■ Conservation issues

Threats Disturbance to birds (C), Drainage (B)

Hunting of geese *Anser* disturbs birds.

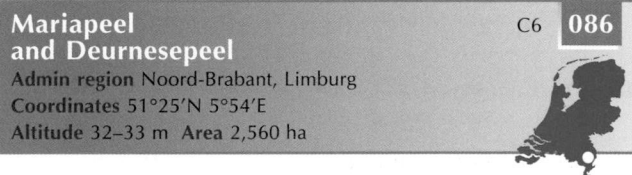

Engbertsdijksvenen C6 085
Admin region Overijssel
Coordinates 52°29′N 6°40′E
Altitude 14–16 m Area 1,030 ha

■ Site description
One of the last remaining raised bogs in the Netherlands, c.10 ha of which has not been cut for peat. The site is located to the north of the city of Almelo, and is surrounded by arable land.

Habitats Forest and woodland (5%; mixed forest), Scrub (50%; heathland), Wetland (45%; raised bog)
Land-use Nature conservation/research (95%), Tourism/recreation (20%), Water management (100%)

■ Birds

Species	Season	Year	Pop min	Pop max	Acc	Criteria
Grus grus Crane	P	1991	46	46	A	C6

■ Protection status
National High **International** High
865 ha of IBA covered by Natural Monument (Engbertsdijkvenen I, 865 ha). 110 ha of IBA covered by Natural Monument (Engbertsdijkvenen II, 110 ha). 954 ha of IBA covered by Nature Reserve (Engbertsdijkvenen, 954 ha). 975 ha of IBA covered by Special Protection Area (Engbertsdijkvenen, 975 ha). 975 ha of IBA covered by Ramsar Site (Engbertsdijkvenen, 975 ha).

■ Conservation issues

Threats Drainage (B)

Mariapeel and Deurnesepeel C6 086
Admin region Noord-Brabant, Limburg
Coordinates 51°25′N 5°54′E
Altitude 32–33 m Area 2,560 ha

■ Site description
The site comprises two adjacent areas that contain remnant fragments of a raised bog (formerly 30,000 ha in extent), and includes pools, peatlands, marshes, swampy *Betula* forest, heathland and grassland. The area is located between the cities of Helmond and Venlo. This site, together with sites 087 and 088, formed part of a single, larger site (former site NL056) in the previous pan-European IBA inventory (Grimmett and Jones 1989).

Habitats Forest and woodland (41%; mixed forest), Scrub (9%; heathland), Wetland (50%; raised bog)
Land-use Forestry (5%), Hunting (20%), Nature conservation/research (89%), Tourism/recreation (50%), Water management (100%)

■ Birds

Species	Season	Year	Pop min	Pop max	Acc	Criteria
Grus grus Crane	P	1992	100	100	A	C6
¹ *Luscinia svecica* Bluethroat	B	1990	176	176	C	C6

1. Only one recent count available.

■ Protection status
National High **International** High
500 ha of IBA covered by Natural Monument (Deurnese Peel, 500 ha). 1,000 ha of IBA covered by Natural Monument (Deurnese Peel, 1,000 ha). 1,100 ha of IBA covered by Natural Monument (Mariapeel, 1,100 ha). 449 ha of IBA covered by Nature Reserve (Deurnese Peel, 449 ha). 1,142 ha of IBA covered by Nature Reserve (Mariapeel, 1,142 ha). 1,450 ha of IBA covered by Special Protection Area (Deurnese Peelgebieden, 1,450 ha). 1,060 ha of IBA covered by Special Protection Area (Mariapeel, 1,060 ha). 1,450 ha of IBA covered by Ramsar Site (Deurnese Peelgebieden, 1,450 ha).

■ Conservation issues

> **Threats** Agricultural intensification/expansion (B), Drainage (B), Infrastructure (B), Recreation/tourism (B)

Threats include acidification from surrounding farms, the construction of roads, cycle-paths, bridges and tracks, and the succession of vegetation that is attendant upon drainage (scrub encroachment in the northern part of the site has not been fully suppressed).

Groote Peel   B1i, C3, C6   087

Admin region Noord-Brabant, Limburg
Coordinates 51°20'N 5°49'E
Altitude 27–29 m **Area** 1,350 ha

■ Site description

The area contains remnant fragments of a raised bog (formerly 30,000 ha in extent), and includes pools, peatlands, marshes, swampy *Betula* forest and *Molinia* heathland. The site is situated near to Mariapeel en Deurnesepeel (086), north-east of the city of Weert. This site, together with sites 086 and 088, formed part of a single, larger site (former site NL056) in the previous pan-European IBA inventory (Grimmett and Jones 1989).

> **Habitats** Forest and woodland (10%; mixed forest), Scrub (30%; heathland), Wetland (60%; raised bog)
> **Land-use** Forestry (5%), Hunting (10%), Nature conservation/research (99%), Tourism/recreation (30%), Water management (100%)

■ Birds

Species	Season	Year	Pop min	Pop max	Acc	Criteria
[1] *Anser fabalis* Bean Goose	W	1991	3,262	3,262	A	B1i, C3
Luscinia svecica Bluethroat	B	1993	313	313	B	C6

1. *A. f. rossicus*.

The site is a roost for *Anser fabalis*, but counts probably underestimate actual numbers.

■ Protection status

National High **International** High
900 ha of IBA covered by Natural Monument (De Groote Peel I, 900 ha). 440 ha of IBA covered by Natural Monument (De Groote Peel II, 440 ha). 1,024 ha of IBA covered by Nature Reserve (De Groote Peel, 1,024 ha). 1,300 ha of IBA covered by National Park (De Groote Peel, 1,300 ha). 1,320 ha of IBA covered by Special Protection Area (De Groote Peel, 1,320 ha). 1,320 ha of IBA covered by Ramsar Site (De Groote Peel, 1,320 ha).

■ Conservation issues

> **Threats** Agricultural intensification/expansion (B), Drainage (B)

Threats include drainage and acidification from surrounding farms.

Strabrechtse Heide and Beuven   C6   088

Admin region Noord-Brabant
Coordinates 51°23'N 5°38'E
Altitude 22–26 m **Area** 1,630 ha

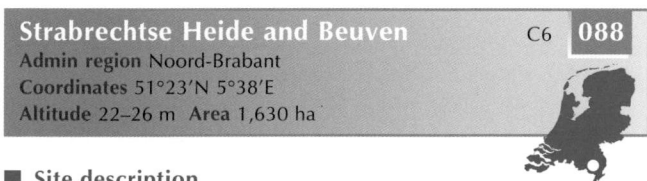

■ Site description

Tracts of heathland and fen interspersed with forestry plantations (mixed woodland), arable land and a shallow freshwater lake (Beuven). The site is located to the south-east of the city of Eindhoven. This site, together with sites 086 and 087, formed part of a single, larger site (former site NL056) in the previous pan-European IBA inventory (Grimmett and Jones 1989).

> **Habitats** Scrub (72%; heathland), Wetland (5%; standing fresh water), Artificial landscape (23%; highly improved reseeded grassland; forestry plantation)
> **Land-use** Agriculture (10%), Hunting (15%), Nature conservation/research (77%), Tourism/recreation (50%), Water management (100%)

■ Birds

Species	Season	Year	Pop min	Pop max	Acc	Criteria
Grus grus Crane	P	1991	87	87	A	C6

■ Protection status

National Partial **International** None
375 ha of IBA covered by Natural Monument (Beuven, 375 ha). 876 ha of IBA covered by Nature Reserve (Strabrechtse Heide, 876 ha).

■ Conservation issues

> **Threats** Agricultural intensification/expansion (B), Drainage (B)

De Wilck   A4i, B1i, B2, C2, C6   089

Admin region Zuid-Holland
Coordinates 52°07'N 4°33'E
Altitude (-2)–(-1) m **Area** 770 ha

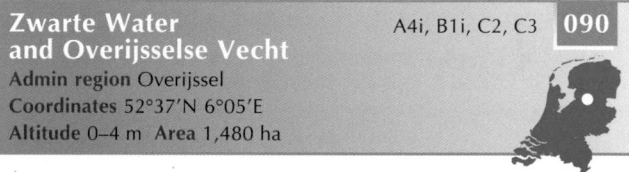

■ Site description

An area of wet meadows and improved grassland located to the south-east of the city of Leiden.

> **Habitats** Artificial landscape (99%; highly improved reseeded grassland)
> **Land-use** Agriculture (100%), Nature conservation/research (17%), Tourism/recreation (10%)

■ Birds

Species	Season	Year	Pop min	Pop max	Acc	Criteria
Cygnus columbianus Bewick's Swan	W	1993	248	248	A	A4i,B1i,B2,C2,C6

■ Protection status

National Partial **International** None
127 ha of IBA covered by Nature Reserve (De Wilck, 127 ha).

■ Conservation issues

> **Threats** Drainage (B), Recreation/tourism (C)

Zwarte Water and Overijsselse Vecht   A4i, B1i, C2, C3   090

Admin region Overijssel
Coordinates 52°37'N 6°05'E
Altitude 0–4 m **Area** 1,480 ha

■ Site description

The site covers the channels and flood-plain of these two small rivers, and contains wet meadows, water-fringe vegetation and pools. The site is adjacent to Zwartemeer (040) and is situated to the north of the city of Zwolle. Human activities include reed-harvesting.

> **Habitats** Grassland (74%; humid grassland; mesophile grassland), Wetland (21%; river/stream; water-fringe vegetation), Artificial landscape (5%; highly improved reseeded grassland)
> **Land-use** Agriculture (81%), Hunting (80%), Nature conservation/research (25%), Tourism/recreation (10%), Urban/industrial/transport (10%), Water management (100%)

■ Birds

Species	Season	Year	Pop min	Pop max	Acc	Criteria
Cygnus columbianus Bewick's Swan	W	1993	363	363	A	A4i, B1i, C2
Anser albifrons White-fronted Goose	W	1993	12,800	12,800	A	A4i, B1i, C3

■ Protection status

National Partial **International** None
41 ha of IBA covered by Natural Monument (Kievitsbloemterreinen Ov Vecht en Zwarte Water, 41 ha). 85 ha of IBA covered by Natural Monument (Kievitsbloemterreinen Zwarte Water, 85 ha). 123 ha of IBA covered by Natural Monument (Kievitsbloemterreinen langs de Overijsselse Vecht, 123 ha). 115 ha of IBA covered by Nature Reserve (Buitenlanden Langenholte, 115 ha). 132 ha of IBA covered by Nature

Reserve (Oeverlanden langs de Vecht, 132 ha). 176 ha of IBA covered by Nature Reserve (Uiterwaarden Zwarte Water, 176 ha).

■ Conservation issues

Threats Agricultural intensification/expansion (B), Construction/impact of dyke/dam/barrage (B), Disturbance to birds (B), Drainage (B), Other (B)

The main problems affecting the site are the excessive harvesting and burning of reedbeds ('Other' threat), disturbance caused by wildfowl hunting, and the construction of a storm-surge barrier (see Lake Zwartemeer [site 040]).

Oudeland van Strijen A4i, B1i, B2, C2, C3 091
Admin region Zuid-Holland
Coordinates 51°46′N 4°31′E
Altitude (-2)–(-2) m **Area** 1,070 ha

■ Site description
An expanse of wet grassland overlying a clay polder to the south of the city of Rotterdam.

Habitats Grassland (96%; humid grassland)
Land-use Agriculture (90%), Nature conservation/research (96%), Water management (100%)

■ Birds

Species	Season	Year	Pop min	Pop max	Acc	Criteria
Anser albifrons White-fronted Goose	W	1993	9,709	9,709	A	B1i, C3
Branta leucopsis Barnacle Goose	W	1993	2,318	2,318	A	A4i, B1i, B2, C2

The site is well known for its wintering geese *Anser* and breeding waders. Geese from this feeding area roost in the Haringvliet (024).

■ Protection status
National Partial **International** None
380 ha of IBA covered by Nature Reserve (Oudeland van Strijen, 380 ha).

■ Conservation issues
No serious threats are known. The core of the area was recently acquired for conservation as part of a programme of land consolidation.

Dunes of Schoorl B2 092
Admin region Noord-Holland
Coordinates 52°42′N 4°40′E
Altitude 0–30 m **Area** 2,500 ha

■ Site description
The northern part of an extensive, contiguous dune system, bounded on its northern side by the Hondsbossche Zeewering (sea dyke) and on its southern side by the road to Bergen aan Zee. The dunes include an artificial lake and the majority of the woodland consists of planted conifers.

Habitats Wetland (50%; sand-dunes/sand beach; standing fresh water), Artificial landscape (50%; forestry plantation)
Land-use Forestry (25%), Hunting (30%), Nature conservation/research (100%), Tourism/recreation (100%)

■ Birds

Species	Season	Year	Pop min	Pop max	Acc	Criteria
Larus canus Common Gull	B	1991	2,415	2,415	A	B2

■ Protection status
National High **International** None
648 ha of IBA covered by Natural Monument (Duinen bij Bergen, 1,250 ha). 1,760 ha of IBA covered by Natural Monument (Schoorlse Duinen, 1,760 ha). 1,852 ha of IBA covered by Nature Reserve (Schoorlse Duinen, 1,852 ha).

■ Conservation issues

Threats Groundwater abstraction (C)

Groundwater abstraction takes place just outside the site, and as a result the groundwater-level has dropped by several decimetres within a radius of 500 m.

Drents–Friese Wold C6 093
Admin region Friesland, Drenthe
Coordinates 52°54′N 6°20′E
Altitude 9–11 m **Area** 7,100 ha

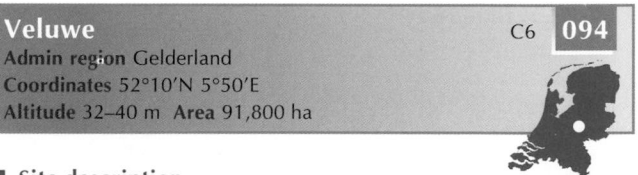

■ Site description
An extensive area of forestry plantations (85% of the IBA area), located 20 km south-west of the city of Assen. Forest stands are mainly of conifers but also include some deciduous/mixed woodlands. They are of various ages and under various forestry regimes, and are interspersed with patches of heathland and fen.

Habitats Scrub (10%; heathland), Artificial landscape (90%; highly improved reseeded grassland; forestry plantation)
Land-use Forestry (30%), Hunting (100%), Nature conservation/research (84%), Tourism/recreation (50%), Water management (100%)

■ Birds

Species	Season	Year	Pop min	Pop max	Acc	Criteria
[1] *Pernis apivorus* Honey Buzzard	B	1989	17	17	C	C6
[1] *Dryocopus martius* Black Woodpecker	R	1990	60	60	C	C6

1. Only one recent count available.

■ Protection status
National High **International** None
1,000 ha of IBA covered by Nature Reserve (Berkenheuvel, 1,000 ha). 1,849 ha of IBA covered by Nature Reserve (Boswachterij Appelscha, 1,849 ha). 2,471 ha of IBA covered by Nature Reserve (Boswachterij Smilde, 2,471 ha). 63 ha of IBA covered by Nature Reserve (Bouwersveld, 63 ha). 426 ha of IBA covered by Nature Reserve (Doldersummer Veld, 426 ha). 119 ha of IBA covered by Nature Reserve (Kern Boswachterij Vledderveld, 119 ha). 108 ha of IBA covered by Nature Reserve (Vledderhof, 108 ha). 6,130 ha of IBA covered by National Park (Drents-Friese Woud, 6,130 ha).

■ Conservation issues

Threats Recreation/tourism (C)

Veluwe C6 094
Admin region Gelderland
Coordinates 52°10′N 5°50′E
Altitude 32–40 m **Area** 91,800 ha

■ Site description
An extensive area of forestry plantations, heathland, fen and sand-drifts, situated in the centre of the country. Forest stands consist mainly of conifers but with some deciduous/mixed woodland, and are of various ages and under various forestry regimes. The site is bordered in the south by the River Rhine and in the east by the valley of the River IJssel. Small villages are excluded from the site.

Habitats Scrub (26%; heathland), Artificial landscape (72%; forestry plantation)
Land-use Forestry (40%), Military (7%), Nature conservation/research (41%), Tourism/recreation (30%), Urban/industrial/transport (8%), Water management (100%)

■ Birds

Species	Season	Year	Pop min	Pop max	Acc	Criteria
[1] *Pernis apivorus* Honey Buzzard	B	1990	165	165	C	C6
[2] *Caprimulgus europaeus* Nightjar	B	1995	191	191	B	C6
Alcedo atthis Kingfisher	R	1992	19	19	B	C6
[1] *Dryocopus martius* Black Woodpecker	R	1990	700	700	C	C6

Species ... continued	Season	Year	Pop min	Pop max	Acc	Criteria
Lullula arborea Woodlark	B	1992	1,375	1,375	B	C6
Anthus campestris Tawny Pipit	B	1991	63	63	B	C6
Lanius collurio Red-backed Shrike	B	1990	17	17	B	C6

1. Only one recent estimate available.
2. Mean for central and southern part of area.

■ Protection status
National Partial **International** None
35 ha of IBA covered by Nature Reserve ('t Sol, 35 ha). 69 ha of IBA covered by Nature Reserve (Beekbergerwoud, 69 ha). 28 ha of IBA covered by Nature Reserve (Bergsham, 28 ha). 448 ha of IBA covered by Nature Reserve (Bruggelen, 448 ha). 463 ha of IBA covered by Nature Reserve (De Dellen en Ambtsbos, 463 ha). 285 ha of IBA covered by Nature Reserve (De Haere, 285 ha). 1,173 ha of IBA covered by Nature Reserve (Deelerwoud, 1,173 ha). 52 ha of IBA covered by Nature Reserve (Deelerwoud II, 52 ha). 2,014 ha of IBA covered by Nature Reserve (Garderen, 2,014 ha). 1,293 ha of IBA covered by Nature Reserve (Hoenderloo, 1,293 ha). 244 ha of IBA covered by Nature Reserve (Hoeve Delle, 244 ha). 155 ha of IBA covered by Nature Reserve (Hoog Buurlose Heide, 155 ha). 3,537 ha of IBA covered by Nature Reserve (Kootwijk, 3,537 ha). 1,425 ha of IBA covered by Nature Reserve (Leuvenhorst, 1,425 ha). 837 ha of IBA covered by Nature Reserve (Leuvenumse Bos, 837 ha). 1,157 ha of IBA covered by Nature Reserve (Loenermark en Loener Bos, 1,157 ha). 135 ha of IBA covered by Nature Reserve (Majuba, 135 ha). 4,904 ha of IBA covered by Nature Reserve (Nationaal Park Veluwezoom, 4,904 ha). 2,125 ha of IBA covered by Nature Reserve (Nunspeet, 2,125 ha). 172 ha of IBA covered by Nature Reserve (Orderbos, 172 ha). 104 ha of IBA covered by Nature Reserve (Otterlose Bos, 104 ha). 224 ha of IBA covered by Nature Reserve (Oud-Groevenbeek, 224 ha). 1,965 ha of IBA covered by Nature Reserve (Planken Wambuis, 1,965 ha). 143 ha of IBA covered by Nature Reserve (Ramenberg, 143 ha). 162 ha of IBA covered by Nature Reserve (Reeënberg, 162 ha). 447 ha of IBA covered by Nature Reserve (Rozendaal, 447 ha). 168 ha of IBA covered by Nature Reserve (Scherpenberg en Morena, 168 ha). 2,535 ha of IBA covered by Nature Reserve (Speulder- en Sprielderbos, 2,535 ha). 40 ha of IBA covered by Nature Reserve (Steilhul, 40 ha). 350 ha of IBA covered by Nature Reserve (Sysselt, 350 ha). 210 ha of IBA covered by Nature Reserve (Tongerense heide, 210 ha). 1,442 ha of IBA covered by Nature Reserve (Ugchelen, 1,442 ha). 429 ha of IBA covered by Nature Reserve (Varenna, 429 ha). 509 ha of IBA covered by Nature Reserve (Wekeromse Zand, 509 ha). 38 ha of IBA covered by Nature Reserve (Wilde Kamp, 38 ha). 104 ha of IBA covered by Nature Reserve (Zandhegge, 104 ha). 5,400 ha of IBA covered by Private Reserve (De Hoge Veluwe, 5,400 ha).

■ Conservation issues

Threats Infrastructure (B), Recreation/tourism (B)

The main problems are scrub encroachment (which is reducing the extent of heathland), infrastructural development (an expanding network of roads, cycle-paths and footpaths), and recreation (including hot-air balloons and mountain bikes).

Sallandse Heuvelrug   C6 095
Admin region Overijssel
Coordinates 52°20'N 6°25'E
Altitude 10–74 m **Area** 4,100 ha

■ Site description
An area of forestry plantations and dry heathland, located between the villages of Nijverdal and Holten. Forest stands consist of deciduous/mixed woodlands and conifer plantations of various ages and under varying management regimes.

Habitats Scrub (25%; heathland), Artificial landscape (75%; forestry plantation)
Land-use Forestry (40%), Nature conservation/research (79%), Tourism/recreation (50%)

■ Birds
The site holds the only viable population of *Tetrao tetrix* in the country.

Species	Season	Year	Pop min	Pop max	Acc	Criteria
Tetrao tetrix Black Grouse	R	1991	19	19	A	C6
[1] *Dryocopus martius* Black Woodpecker	R	1992	26	26	C	C6

1. Only one recent count available.

■ Protection status
National Partial **International** None
2,321 ha of IBA covered by Nature Reserve (Sallandse Heuvelrug, 2,321 ha). 907 ha of IBA covered by Nature Reserve (Sprengenberg, 907 ha).

■ Conservation issues

Threats Disturbance to birds (B), Infrastructure (B), Recreation/tourism (B)

Blocks of conifer plantations have been felled in order to increase the area of heathland, thereby benefiting *Tetrao tetrix*.

Loonse and Drunense Duinen   C6 096
Admin region Noord-Brabant
Coordinates 51°39'N 5°06'E
Altitude 9–21 m **Area** 4,090 ha

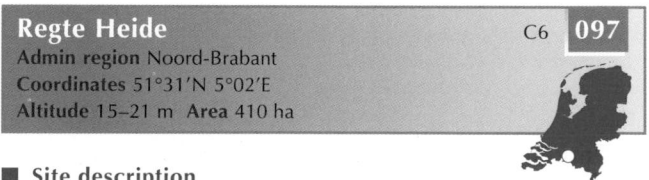

■ Site description
The largest area of inland sand-drifts in Europe, surrounded by forest and located west of the city of 's Hertogenbosch. Forest stands consist of deciduous/mixed woodlands and conifer plantations of various ages and under varying management regimes.

Habitats Scrub (6%; heathland), Rocky areas (15%; inland sand-dunes), Artificial landscape (79%; highly improved reseeded grassland; forestry plantation)
Land-use Nature conservation/research (70%), Tourism/recreation (50%)

■ Birds

Species	Season	Year	Pop min	Pop max	Acc	Criteria
Tetrao tetrix Black Grouse	R	1991	4	4	A	C6
Lullula arborea Woodlark	B	1991	49	49	A	C6

■ Protection status
National High **International** None
410 ha of IBA covered by Nature Reserve (De Brand, 410 ha). 2,211 ha of IBA covered by Nature Reserve (Loonse en Drunense Duinen, 2,211 ha). 262 ha of IBA covered by Nature Reserve (Plantloon, 262 ha). 3,400 ha of IBA covered by National Park (Loonse en Drunense Duinen, 3,400 ha).

■ Conservation issues

Threats Recreation/tourism (B)

Regte Heide   C6 097
Admin region Noord-Brabant
Coordinates 51°31'N 5°02'E
Altitude 15–21 m **Area** 410 ha

■ Site description
A small area of heathland situated on a sand ridge running between two stream valleys. The site is located to the south-west of the city of Tilburg, and contains scattered trees and some woodland (deciduous/mixed and coniferous).

Habitats Scrub (60%; heathland), Artificial landscape (35%; highly improved reseeded grassland; forestry plantation), Unknown (5%)
Land-use Nature conservation/research (100%)

■ Birds

Species	Season	Year	Pop min	Pop max	Acc	Criteria
Tetrao tetrix Black Grouse	R	1991	5	5	A	C6

503

■ Protection status
National Partial **International** None
340 ha of IBA covered by Nature Reserve (Regte Heide en Ooijevaarsnest, 474 ha).

■ Conservation issues

Threats Unknown

The main problem is scrub encroachment, which is reducing the extent of heathland.

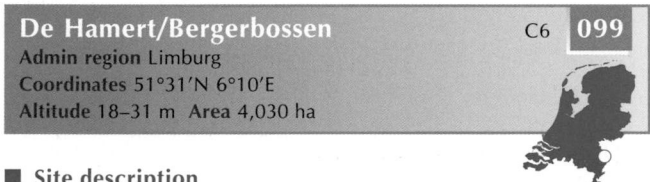

Oirschotse Heide — C6 098
Admin region Noord-Brabant
Coordinates 51°29'N 5°21'E
Altitude 20–22 m **Area** 1,190 ha

■ Site description
A military training area comprising dry heathland and forest, located to the north-west of the city of Eindhoven. Forest stands consist of conifer plantations and deciduous/mixed woodlands of various ages and under varying management regimes.

Habitats Scrub (44%; heathland), Artificial landscape (50%; forestry plantation), Unknown (6%)
Land-use Military (80%), Tourism/recreation (50%)

■ Birds

Species	Season	Year	Pop min	Pop max	Acc	Criteria
Tetrao tetrix Black Grouse	R	1991	8	8	A	C6

The site holds a remnant population of *Tetrao tetrix*.

■ Protection status
National None **International** None

■ Conservation issues

Threats Disturbance to birds (A)

De Hamert/Bergerbossen — C6 099
Admin region Limburg
Coordinates 51°31'N 6°10'E
Altitude 18–31 m **Area** 4,030 ha

■ Site description
A 20-km-long area of heathland and forest with scrub, fen, hedges and some cultivated land. Forest stands consist of conifer plantations and deciduous/mixed woodlands of various ages and under varying management regimes. The site is situated on the east bank of the River Maas (also known as 'Maasduinen'), between the villages of Heijen and Arcen.

Habitats Scrub (27%; heathland), Artificial landscape (67%; forestry plantation)
Land-use Forestry (45%), Hunting (65%), Nature conservation/research (44%), Tourism/recreation (50%), Water management (5%)

■ Birds

Species	Season	Year	Pop min	Pop max	Acc	Criteria
Caprimulgus europaeus Nightjar	B	1993	43	43	B	C6
[1] *Dryocopus martius* Black Woodpecker	R	1993	29	29	C	C6
Lullula arborea Woodlark	B	1993	151	151	B	C6

1. Only one recent count available.

■ Protection status
National Partial **International** Partial
444 ha of IBA covered by Natural Monument (Heideterreinen Bergen, 444 ha). 598 ha of IBA covered by Nature Reserve (Bergerbos, 598 ha). 113 ha of IBA covered by Nature Reserve (Bosserheide, 113 ha). 123 ha of IBA covered by Nature Reserve (Eckeltse Bergen, 123 ha). 824 ha of IBA covered by Nature Reserve (Landgoed de Hamert, 824 ha). 137 ha

of IBA covered by Nature Reserve (Rode Hoek, 137 ha). 1,460 ha of IBA covered by National Park (De Hamert, 1,460 ha). 1,460 ha of IBA covered by Special Protection Area (De Hamert, 1,460 ha).

■ Conservation issues

Threats Unknown

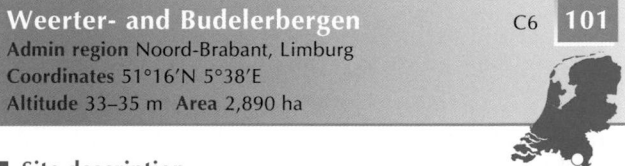

De Utrecht — C6 100
Admin region Noord-Brabant
Coordinates 51°26'N 5°08'E
Altitude 20–32 m **Area** 3,870 ha

■ Site description
The site is adjacent to the De Utrecht estate, and consists of wet heathland, fen, woodland and some cultivated land. Forest stands consist of deciduous/mixed woodlands and conifer plantations of various ages and under varying management regimes. The site is located along the Belgian border, south-east of the city of Tilburg.

Habitats Scrub (10%; heathland), Artificial landscape (90%; highly improved reseeded grassland; forestry plantation)
Land-use Agriculture (10%), Forestry (40%), Nature conservation/research (23%), Tourism/recreation (50%), Water management (100%)

■ Birds

Species	Season	Year	Pop min	Pop max	Acc	Criteria
Caprimulgus europaeus Nightjar	B	1988	26	26	B	C6

■ Protection status
National Partial **International** None
900 ha of IBA covered by Natural Monument (Mispeleindse en Neterselse Heide, 900 ha). 471 ha of IBA covered by Nature Reserve (Rovertse Heide, 471 ha).

■ Conservation issues

Threats Unknown

Weerter- and Budelerbergen — C6 101
Admin region Noord-Brabant, Limburg
Coordinates 51°16'N 5°38'E
Altitude 33–35 m **Area** 2,890 ha

■ Site description
An area of woodland and dry heathland located to the north-west of the city of Weert. Forest stands consist of deciduous/mixed woodlands and conifer plantations of various ages and under varying management regimes.

Habitats Scrub (20%; heathland), Artificial landscape (80%; forestry plantation)
Land-use Forestry (30%), Military (50%), Nature conservation/research (28%), Tourism/recreation (50%), Urban/industrial/transport (6%), Water management (100%)

■ Birds

Species	Season	Year	Pop min	Pop max	Acc	Criteria
[1] *Lullula arborea* Woodlark	B	1992	49	49	C	C6
[1] *Anthus campestris* Tawny Pipit	B	1992	3	3	C	C6

1. Only one recent count available.

■ Protection status
National Partial **International** None
547 ha of IBA covered by Nature Reserve (Het Weerterbos, 547 ha). 232 ha of IBA covered by Nature Reserve (Hugterheide, 232 ha). 21 ha of IBA covered by Nature Reserve (Weerterheide, 21 ha).

■ Conservation issues

Threats Unknown

Leudal   C6   102
Admin region Limburg
Coordinates 51°15′N 5°55′E
Altitude 23–28 m   Area 720 ha

■ Site description
A small area of mixed woodland alongside two streams, located to the north-west of the city of Roermond.

Habitats Artificial landscape (95%; highly improved reseeded grassland, forestry plantation)
Land-use Agriculture (5%), Forestry (25%), Hunting (100%), Nature conservation/research (65%), Tourism/recreation (15%), Water management (100%)

■ Birds

Species	Season	Year	Pop min	Pop max	Acc	Criteria
¹ *Alcedo atthis* Kingfisher	R	1992	4	4	C	C6

1. Only one recent count available.

■ Protection status
National Partial   **International** None
470 ha of IBA covered by Nature Reserve (Leudal, 470 ha).

■ Conservation issues

Threats Unknown

Leenderbos and Groote Heide   C6   103
Admin region Noord-Brabant
Coordinates 51°20′N 5°30′E
Altitude 26–29 m   Area 2,270 ha

■ Site description
An area of dry heathland, fen and forestry plantations (mixed woodland and conifers) located to the south-east of the city of Eindhoven.

Habitats Scrub (22%; heathland), Artificial landscape (75%; highly improved reseeded grassland; forestry plantation)
Land-use Agriculture (5%), Forestry (50%), Hunting (97%), Nature conservation/research (97%), Tourism/recreation (95%), Water management (100%)

■ Birds

Species	Season	Year	Pop min	Pop max	Acc	Criteria
Caprimulgus europaeus Nightjar	B	1995	17	18	A	C6
¹ *Lullula arborea* Woodlark	B	1991	50	50	C	C6

1. Only one recent count available.

■ Protection status
National High   **International** None
2,055 ha of IBA covered by Nature Reserve (Leende I, 2,055 ha).
158 ha of IBA covered by Nature Reserve (Leende II, 258 ha).

■ Conservation issues

Threats Unknown

Meinweg   C7   104
Admin region Limburg
Coordinates 51°10′N 6°08′E
Altitude 26–72 m   Area 1,990 ha

■ Site description

Habitats Scrub (23%; heathland), Artificial landscape (76%; highly improved reseeded grassland; forestry plantation)
Land-use Forestry (45%), Hunting (80%), Nature conservation/research (53%), Tourism/recreation (25%), Water management (20%)

An area of partly wet heathland and fen, with two valleys which support woodland. Woodland stands consist of deciduous/mixed woodlands and conifer plantations of various ages and under varying management regimes. The site is situated along the German border, east of the city of Roermond.

■ Birds
This site has been included because it concerns a designated Special Protection Area. In the national IBA review this site was included as the fifth most important site nationally for *Caprimulgus europaeus* but it has now lost this position, after the addition of Brabantse Wal (105) as an IBA.

■ Protection status
National High   **International** Partial
1,051 ha of IBA covered by Nature Reserve (De Meinweg, 1,051 ha).
1,600 ha of IBA covered by National Park (De Meinweg, 1,600 ha).
1,600 ha of IBA covered by Special Protection Area (De Meinweg, 1,600 ha).

■ Conservation issues

Threats Unknown

Brabantse Wal   C6   105
Admin region Noord-Brabant
Coordinates 51°26′N 4°22′E
Altitude 10–26 m   Area 5,800 ha

■ Site description
An area of woodland and heathland, located south of the city of Bergen op Zoom. The site is adjacent to the Belgian IBA of Kalmhoutsche Heide. Forest stands consist of deciduous/mixed woodlands and conifer plantations of various ages and under varying management regimes.

Habitats Scrub (heathland), Artificial landscape (97%; highly improved reseeded grassland; forestry plantation)
Land-use Agriculture (5%), Forestry (50%), Hunting (90%), Military (6%), Nature conservation/research (24%), Tourism/recreation (80%)

■ Birds

Species	Season	Year	Pop min	Pop max	Acc	Criteria
Caprimulgus europaeus Nightjar	B	1994	68	68	A	C6
Dryocopus martius Black Woodpecker	R	1994	48	48	A	C6
Lullula arborea Woodlark	B	1994	63	63	A	C6

This site is important at the EU level for *Caprimulgus europaeus*, *Dryocopus martius* and *Lullula arborea*.

■ Protection status
National None   **International** None

■ Conservation issues

Threats Groundwater abstraction (B), Recreation/tourism (C)

Groundwater abstraction is a major problem.

Kampina   C7   106
Admin region Noord-Brabant
Coordinates 51°34′N 5°16′E
Altitude 8–11 m   Area 1,150 ha

■ Site description
An area of heathland and fen, intersected by streams and surrounded by woodland, situated to the east of the city of Tilburg.

Habitats Forest and woodland (50%; mixed forest), Scrub (40%; heathland), Wetland (10%; fen/transition mire/spring)
Land-use Nature conservation/research (100%), Tourism/recreation (50%)

■ Birds
Until 1989 the site held a small population of *Tetrao tetrix* (and was considered fifth in order of national importance for this species,

505

together with two other nearby sites). Eight other species, listed in Annex I of the EC Birds Directive, breed at the site although not in appreciable numbers. The fens in the area are used for roosting by wintering geese, but counts are not available.

■ **Protection status**
National High **International** High

1,150 ha of IBA covered by Nature Reserve (Kampina, 1,213 ha). 1,150 ha of IBA covered by Special Protection Area (Kampina, 1,150 ha).

■ **Conservation issues**
The site was designated as an SPA in 1986 but the basis for the designation is not available.

REFERENCES

ALTENBURG, W. *et al.* (1986) *Witte en Zwarte Brekken.* Leeuwarden, Netherlands: Fryske Foriening foar Fjildbiology.

ARTS, F. A. AND MEININGER, P. L. (1994) *Kustbroedvogels langs de Westerschelde 1900–1993: een reconstructie.* Middelburg, Netherlands: Rijkswaterstaat.

ARTS, F. A. AND MEININGER, P. L. (1994) *Watervogels in de Westerschelde 1900–1990: een reconstructie.* Middelburg, Netherlands: Rijkswaterstaat.

BAKKER, T. (1995) *Broedvogelinventarisatie Schiermonnikoog 1992.* 's-Graveland, Netherlands: Natuurmonumenten.

BAPTIST, H. (1984) Changes in the Oosterschelde and their impact on waders. *Wader Study Group Bull.* 40: 33–34.

BAPTIST, H. J. M., AND MEININGER, P. L. (1996) *Vogels van de Voordelta.* Middelburg, Netherlands: Rijksinstituut voor Kust en Zee (Rapport RIKZ 96.018).

BEEMSTER, N. (1996) Dynamisch waterpeil in rietmoerassen en effecten op vegetatie en vogels. *Limosa* 69: 80–81.

BEEMSTER, N. J., DROST, H. J. AND VAN EERDEN, M. R. (1989) *Evaluatie van het beheer in het Lauwersmeer in de periode 1982–1987.* Lelystad, Netherlands: Rijkswaterstaat (Flevobericht 303).

VAN DEN BERGH, L. M. J. (1983) *De betekenis van het Nederlands-Westduitse grensgebied langs de Nederrijn als pleisterplaats voor wilde ganzen.* Leersum, Netherlands: Rijksinstituut voor Natuurbeheer.

BEUKEMA, J. J. (1995) Het belang van het Balgzand als foerageergebied voor vogels: 25 jaar een vinger aan de pols. *Graspieper* 15: 146–152.

BIJLSMA, R. G. (1992) *De broedvogels van het Leenderbos en omgeving in 1991.* Beek, Netherlands: Samenwerkende Organisaties Vogelonderzoek Nederland (SOVON Rapport 92/01).

BOUDEWIJN, T. J. AND DIRKSEN, S. (1995) Impact of contaminants on the breeding success of the Cormorant *Phalacrocorax carbo sinensis* in the Netherlands. *Ardea* 83: 325–338.

BOUDEWIJN, T. J. AND MES, R. G. (1986) *De ontwikkeling van de vogelstand in het Hollands Diep/Haringvliet gebied in de periode '72–'84 en de invloed van het peilbeheer op watervogels.* Leeuwarden, Netherlands: Ecoland.

VAN DEN BRINK, H. (1989) *De vogels van Rottumeroog en Rottumerplaat in 1978–89.* Beek, Netherlands: Samenwerkende Organisaties Vogelonderzoek Nederland (SOVON Rapport 89/7).

BROUWER, P. *et al.* (1986) *Vogels van de Ooypolder.* Nijmegen, Netherlands: Van Hoorn.

VAN DER COELEN, J. AND VAN SEGGELEN, C. (1993) *De broedvogels van het Zuidelijk Peelgebied. Avifaunakartering Limburg, Deelgebied II, 1991.* Maastricht, Netherlands: Huisdrukkerij Provincie Limburg.

CRUYSBERG, W. P. (1984) *Avifauna van de Mariapeel.* Helenaveen, Netherlands: Staatsbosbeheer.

VAN DIJK, A. J. AND KOOPMAN, E. V. (1988) *Dwingelderveld Avifauna.* 's-Graveland, Netherlands: Natuurmonumenten.

DIJKSEN, A. J. (1996) *Vogels op het Gouwe Boltje: Een overzicht van de avifauna van Texel.* Den Burg, Netherlands: Langeveld and de Rooy.

DIRKSEN, S. (1987) *Oeververdediging en vogels in het Haringvliet.* Utrecht, Netherlands: Bureau Ecoland.

VAN EERDEN, M. R. AND ZIJLSTRA, M. (1986) *Natuurwaarden van het IJsselmeergebied.* Lelystad, Netherlands: Rijksdienst voor de IJsselmeerpolders (Flevobericht 273).

ENGELMOER, M., KUIPERS, R., GARTNER, H. AND FERWEDA, A. (1996) *Vogeltellingen langs de Friese Waddenkust 1990–1995.* Ferwerd, Netherlands: Fryske Foriening foar Fjildbiology.

ERHART, F. AND BEKHUIS, J. (1996) *Broedvogels van de Gelderse Poort 1989–1994.* Arnhem, Netherlands: Vogelwerkgroep Arnhem.

ESSINK, K. AND BOSCH, J. G. (1993) On the Conservation of the Island of Griend, Dutch Wadden Sea. *Wadden Sea Newsl.* 93(1): 5–7.

EUVERMAN G. (1988) *Hoogwater in het hoogveen. Veranderingen in vegetatie en avifauna en het beheer in de Engbertsdijkvenen, 1978–1988.* Sine loco, Netherlands: Staatsbosbeheer Twente.

GEBUIS, H. *et al.* (1987) *Avifauna Dordtse Biesbosch.* Dordrecht, Netherlands: Natuur- en Vogelwacht Dordrecht.

DE GELDER, A. (1986) *Broedvogels in SBB-objecten Noord-Holland 1970–1985.* Haarlem, Netherlands: Staatsbosbeheer.

GERDES, K. (1991) Zum Einfluß der Wattenjagd auf die Vogelwelt des Dollart. *Vogelk. Ber. Niedersachsens* 23: 25–30.

GERDES, K. (1994) [Long-term and short-term changes of geese numbers *Anser fabalis, Anser albifrons, Anser anser* and *Branta leucopsis* near the Dollart and their ecological correlations]. *Vogelwarte* 37: 157–178. (In German.)

GERRITSEN, G. J. *et al.* (1986) *Flora en fauna van de IJsseluiterwaarden.* Zwolle, Netherlands: Provinciale Planologische Dienst.

GRIMMETT, R. F. A. AND JONES, T. A., EDS. (1989) *Important bird areas in Europe.* Cambridge, UK: International Council for Bird Preservation (Techn. Publ. no. 3).

HEATH, M. F. AND BORGGREVE, C. (2000) *BirdLife International/EBCC European Bird Database 1998.* Cambridge, UK: BirdLife International.

HUIJSER, M. P., DROST, H. J. AND RÖLING, Y. J. B. (1995) Vegetatieontwikkeling en cyclisch waterpeilbeheer in de Oostvaardersplassen. *Levende Nat.* 96: 213–222.

IEDEMA, C. W. AND KIK, P. (1989) *Het zoetwatermoeras de Oostvaardersplassen.* Lelystad, Netherlands: Rijksdienst voor de IJsselmeerpolders (Flevobericht 259).

DE JONG, F., BAKKER, J. F., DANKERS N. AND DAHL K. (1993) *Quality Status Report of the North Sea: Subregion 10. The Wadden Sea.* Wilhelmshaven, Germany: Common Wadden Sea Secretariat.

JOOSTEN, J. H. J. AND BAKKER, T. W. M. (1987) *De Groote Peel in verleden, heden en toekomst.* Utrecht, Netherlands: Staatsbosbeheer.

DE KRAKER, K. (1994) *De Grevelingen geteld: Watervogeltellingen en broedvogelinventarisaties 1986–1993.* Goes, Netherlands: Staatsbosbeheer.

KWINT, N. D. (1994) *De betekenis van het Nationaal Park Veluwezoom voor vogels.* Beek-Ubbergen, Netherlands: Vereniging SOVON (SOVON onderzoekrapport 94/02).

LAMBECK, R. H. D., SANDEE, A. J. J. AND DE WOLF, L. (1989) Long-term patterns in the wader usage of an intertidal flat in the Oosterschelde (SW Netherlands) and the impact of the closure of an adjacent estuary. *J. Appl. Ecol.* 26: 419–431.

MEIJER, R. (1995) *Broedvogels van de Biesbosch: Ontwikkelingen van de broedvogelbevolking 25 jaar na een nieuwe start.* Werkendam, Netherlands: Staatsbosbeheer.

MEININGER, P. L. (1990) *Kustbroedvogels in het Deltagebied in 1994 met een samenvatting van zestien jaar monitoring 1979–1994* Middelburg, Netherlands: Rijkswaterstaat.

MEIRE, P. AND KUYKEN, E. (1984) Relations between the distribution of waders and the intertidal benthic fauna of the Oosterschelde, Netherlands. Pp. 57–68 in P. R. Evans, J. D. Goss-Custard and W. Hale, eds. *Coastal waders and wildfowl in winter.* Cambridge, UK: Cambridge University Press.

MELTOFTE, H., BLEW, J., FRIKKE, J., ROSNER, H. U. AND SMIT, C. J. (1994) Numbers and distribution of waterbirds in the Wadden Sea: Results and evaluation of 36 simultaneous counts in the Dutch German Danish Wadden Sea 1980–1991. *Wader Study Group Bull.* 74 Suppl.

MES, R. *et al.* (1980) *Flora en fauna van de Engelsmanplaat.* Leiden, Netherlands: Stichting Veth.

MINISTRY OF AGRICULTURE, NATURE MANAGEMENT AND FISHERIES (1990) *Nature Policy Plan.* The Hague: Ministry of Agriculture, Nature Management and Fisheries (abridged version of original in Dutch).

VAN NES, E. H. AND MARTEIJN, E. C. L. (1991) Watervogels in het Volkerakmeer–Zoommeer; ontwikkelingen in de eerste twee jaar na afsluiting (1987–89). *Limosa* 64: 155–164.

NIEWOLD, F. J. J. (1993) *Raamplan voor behoud en herstel van leefgebieden van korhoenders T. t. in Midden-Brabant.* Wageningen, Netherlands: IBN-DLO.

NIEWOLD, F. J. J. AND NIJLAND, H. (1988) *De Sallandse Heuvelrug als reservaat voor het Westeuropese heidekorhoen.* Arnhem, Netherlands: Rijksinstituut voor Natuurbeheer (RIN rapport 88/59).

NIJLAND, F. AND TIMMERMAN, A. (1986) De betekenis van de Groote Wielen en omgeving voor vogels. *Limosa* 59: 115–117.

OOSTENBRINK, W. T., DIRKSEN, S. AND BOUDEWIJN, T. J. (1993) *Wind op water: Overzicht bestaande kennis van watervogels op het IJsselmeer ten noorden van Medemblik.* Culemborg, Netherlands: Bureau Waardenburg.

OSIECK, E. AND MÖRZER BRUYNS, M. F. (1981) *Important bird areas in the European Community*. Cambridge, UK: International Council for Bird Preservation.

PLATTEEUW, M. (1996) *Watervogels in het IJmeer en zuidelijk Markermeer: Beschrijving van de situatie in de seizoenen 1990/91–1993/94*. Lelystad, Netherlands: RIZA (RIZA Nota 96.007).

PLATTEEUW, M. AND BEEKMAN, J. H. (1994) Verstoring van watervogels door scheepvaart op Ketelmeer en IJsselmeer. *Limosa* 67: 27–33.

POOT, M., RASMUSSEN, L. M., VAN ROOMEN, M., RÖSNER, H. U. AND SÜDBECK, P. (1996) *Migratory Waterbirds in the Wadden Sea 1993/94*. Wilhelmshaven, Germany: Common Wadden Sea Secretariat (Wadden Sea Ecosystem 5).

PROP, D. AND VELDKAMP, R. (1987) *Broedvogels van De Weerribben*. Utrecht, Netherlands: Staatsbosbeheer.

SARIS, F. *et al.* (1987) *Avifauna van de Biesbosch: Een beschrijving van de veranderingen en de dynamiek van een unieke vogelgemeenschap*. Tilburg, Netherlands: Staatsbosbeheer.

SCHEKKERMAN, H., MEININGER, P. L. AND MEIRE, P. M. (1994) Changes in the waterbird populations of the Oosterschelde (SW Netherlands) as a result of large-scale coastal engineering works. *Hydrobiologia* 282/283: 509–524.

SLOB, G. J. (1989) *15 jaar vogelontwikkelingen in het afgesloten Grevelingenbekken*. Goes, Netherlands: Staatsbosbeheer.

SMIT, C. J. AND WOLFF, W. J. (1980) *Birds of the Wadden Sea*. Rotterdam, Netherlands: Balkema.

SPAANS, B. (1994) De broedvogels van het Volkerak–Zoommeer in de eerste vijf jaar na de afsluiting. *Limosa* 67: 15–26.

SPONSELEE, G. M. P. (1979) *Het Verdronken Land van Saeftinghe*. Kloosterzand, Netherlands: Duerinck Krachten.

STOOKER, G. (1988) *Inventarisatie van biologische waarden op de Strabrechtse Heide*. Tilburg, Netherlands: Staatsbosbeheer.

STUART, J. J. (1988) *Voorkomen en voedsel van watervogels in het Veerse Meer*. Middelburg, Netherlands: Rijkswaterstaat.

STUART, J. J., MEININGER, P. L. AND MEIRE, P. M. (1990) *Watervogels van de Westerschelde. Deel 1: Tekst*. Middelburg, Netherlands: Rijkswaterstaat.

VAN DEN TEMPEL, R. AND OSIECK, E. R. (1994) *Areas important for birds in the Netherlands*. Zeist, Netherlands: Vogelbescherming Nederland (Technisch Rapport 13E).

TUCKER, G. M. AND HEATH, M. F. (1994) *Birds in Europe: their conservation status*. Cambridge, UK: BirdLife International (BirdLife Conservation Series no. 3).

VEEN, J. AND VAN DE KAM, J. (1988) *Griend vogeleiland in de Waddenzee*. 's-Graveland, Netherlands: Natuurmonumenten.

VELDKAMP, R. (1985) *Broedvogels van De Wieden*. 's-Graveland, Netherlands: Natuurmonumenten.

VENEMA, P. (1989) *Ganzen in het Leekstermeergebied: Overwintering en trek*. Groningen, Netherlands: Provincie Groningen.

VISSER, G. (1994) *De Bosplaat: Terschellingers scheppen Europees natuurreservaat*. Assen, Netherlands: Van Gorcum.

VOGEL, R. L. (1996) De Veluwe als laatste strohalm van warmteminnende broedvogelsoorten in Nederland: ontwikkelingen op de voet gevolgd. *Limosa* 69: 186–187.

WOETS, D. (1985) *Vogelleven in de Weerribben*. Steenwijk, Netherlands: Stichting Vrienden van de Weerribben.

WOLFF, W. J. AND SMIT, C. J. (1984) The Dutch Wadden Sea. Pp. 238–252 in P. R. Evans, J. D. Goss-Custard and W. Hale, eds. *Coastal waders and wildfowl in winter*. Cambridge, UK: Cambridge University Press.

WOUTERSEN, K. (1992) De Stormmeeuw *Larus canus* in de Schoorlse Duinen. *Sula* 6: 81–92.

WYMENGA, E. AND ALTENBURG, W. (1993) *Natuurontwikkeling in de Alde Feanen: Ontwikkelingen in vegetatie en broedvogels in 1990–1992*. Veenwouden, Netherlands: Bureau Altenburg & Wymenga.

ZIJLSTRA, M., LOONEN, M. J. J. A., VAN EERDEN, M. R. AND DUBBELDAM, W. (1991) The Oostvaardersplassen as a key moulting site for Greylag Geese *Anser anser* in western Europe. *Wildfowl* 42: 45–52.

ZWART, F. (1985) *Broedvogels van Terschelling*. Assen, Netherlands: Van Gorcum.

■ NORWAY

TERJE LISLEVAND, ASBJØRN FOLVIK AND INGAR JOSTEIN ØIEN

Øvre Pasvik Nature Reserve (IBA 001), the largest virgin forest in Norway. (PHOTO: INGAR JOSTEIN ØIEN)

GENERAL INTRODUCTION

Norway is situated in the north-western corner of Europe, between the latitudes of 58°N and 71°N. It borders the North-east Atlantic Ocean, from the Skagerrak channel in the south to the Arctic Ocean in the north. The coastline, at 21,465 km, is very long, with many fjords and a vast number of islands, islets and skerries. Norway is very mountainous, covering an area of 323,759 km², and is divided into 18 counties. In 1998, the human population numbered about 4,400,000 inhabitants, giving a density of about 13 persons/km², the lowest in continental Europe.

A total of 52 Important Bird Areas (IBAs) are identified in mainland Norway in this inventory (Table 1, Map 1), covering

9,307 km², equivalent to c.3% of the national land surface. This total does not include one offshore marine IBA in the Skagerrak which is shared with Denmark, 61% of its area lying within Norwegian territory. This marine IBA does not feature further in this chapter; see Box 4 in the introductory chapter 'Overview of results' for further discussion of marine IBAs identified in Europe, and for further explanation of their treatment in this book. The Arctic territories of Svalbard, Jan Mayen and Bjørnøya (Bear Island) are also parts of Norwegian territory, but are covered by a separate chapter within this inventory (see p. 533).

The first pan-European IBA inventory (Grimmett and Jones 1989) identified 49 IBAs in mainland Norway, of which 11 no longer meet the current (revised) IBA criteria (they are listed in Table 1).

Table 1. Summary of Important Bird Areas in Norway.   52 IBAs covering 9,307 km²

IBA code	1989 code	International name	National name	Administrative region	Area (ha)	Criteria (see p. 11)
001	NO001	Øvre Pasvik	Øvre Pasvik	Finnmark	20,000	A3, B2
002	NO002	Neiden and Munkefjord	Neiden and Munkefjord	Finnmark	1,180	B1i
003	NO003	Varangerfjord	Varangerfjord	Finnmark	60,000	A1, A3, A4i, A4iii, B1i
004	NO004	Hornøy and Reinøy	Hornøy and Reinøy	Finnmark	200	A4i, A4iii, B1i, B1ii, B3
005	NO005	Makkaurhalvøya (Syltefjordstauran)	Makkaurhalvøya (Syltefjordstauran)	Finnmark	11,600	A4i, A4iii, B1i, B1ii, B2
006	NO006	Kongsøy	Kongsøy	Finnmark	280	A4iii, B1i, B3
007	NO007	Tanamunningen	Tanamunningen	Finnmark	3,450	A4i, A4iii, B1i
008	NO008	Omgangsstauran	Omgangsstauran	Finnmark	780	A4i, A4iii, B1i
009	NO009	Sværholtklubben	Sværholtklubben	Finnmark	220	A4i, A4iii, B1i
010	NO011	Gjesværstappan	Gjesværstappan	Finnmark	720	A4i, A4iii, B1i, B2, B3
011	NO012	Hjelmsøy	Hjelmsøy	Finnmark	430	A4i, A4ii, A4iii, B1i, B1ii, B2, B3
012	NO010	Inner part of Porsanger Fjord	Indre Porsangerfjord	Finnmark	2,000	A1, A4i, A4iii, B1i, B3
013	NO013	Alta-Kautokeino watercourse	Alta-Kautokeino watercourse	Finnmark	30,000	B2
014	NO014	Loppa	Loppa	Finnmark	720	A4iii, B1ii, B2, B3
015	NO015	Nord-Fugløy	Nord-Fugløy	Troms	2,130	A4iii, B1ii, B2
016	NO016	Sør-Fugløy	Sør-Fugløy	Troms	125	A1, A4ii, A4iii, B1ii, B2, B3
017	NO017	Sørkjosen	Sørkjosen	Troms	433	A4i, A4iii, B1i

Table 1 ... continued. Summary of Important Bird Areas in Norway. 52 IBAs covering 9,307 km²

IBA code	1989 code	International name	National name	Administrative region	Area (ha)	Criteria (see p. 11)
018	NO018	Bleiksøy	Bleiksøy	Nordland	20	A4ii, A4iii, B1ii, B2
019	NO019	Skogvoll (including Skarvklakken)	Skogvoll (including Skarvklakken)	Nordland	2,800	A1, B1i, B2
020	—	Andøya	Andøya	Nordland	17,000	A4i, B1i
021	NO020	Anda	Anda	Nordland	10	A4iii, B2
022	—	Langøya	Langøya	Nordland	20,000	A4i, B1i
023	NO021	Nykvåg	Nykvåg	Nordland	20	A4ii, A4iii, B1ii, B2
024	NO024	Værøy	Værøy	Nordland	500	A4ii, A4iii, B1ii, B2
025	NO025	Røst	Røst	Nordland	1,750	A4i, A4ii, A4iii, B1i, B1ii, B2, B3
026	NO026	Saltstraumen	Saltstraumen	Nordland	200	A1
027	—	Fugløya	Fugløya	Nordland	—	A4iii
028	NO028	Svenningen–Risvær	Svenningen–Risvær	Nordland	15,000	A1
029	NO027	Lovunden	Lovunden	Nordland	—	A1, A4iii, B1ii, B2
030	NO029	Vega archipelago	Vega archipelago	Nordland	50,000	A1, A4i, A4iii, B1i, B1ii, B2, B3
031	—	Sklinna	Sklinna	Nord-Trøndelag	106	A4i, B1i, B1ii, B2, B3
032	NO034	Froan	Froan	Sør-Trøndelag	60,000	A1, A4i, B1i, B1ii, B2, B3
033	NO033	Ørland wetland system	Ørland Våtmarkssystem	Sør-Trøndelag	2,920	A4i, B1i, B2
034	NO030	Inner Trondheimsfjord wetland system	Indre Trondheimsfjord Våtmarkssystem	Nord-Trøndelag	9,500	A4i, A4iii, B1i
035	—	Lake Leksdalsvatn	Leksdalsvatn	Nord-Trøndelag	2,200	A4i, B1i
036	—	Stjørdals Fjord	Stjørdalsfjorden	Nord-Trøndelag, Sør-Trøndelag	2,500	A4i, A4iii, B1i, B2
037	NO035	Gaulosen	Gaulosen	Sør-Trøndelag	330	A4i, B1i
038	NO036	Havmyran	Havmyran	Sør-Trøndelag	3,960	A1
039	NO037	Smøla archipelago	Smøla archipelago	Møre og Romsdal	27,400	A1, A4i, B1i, B1ii, B2
040	NO039	Runde	Runde	Møre og Romsdal	640	A4i, A4ii, A4iii, B1i, B1ii, B2, B3
041	NO040	Dovrefjell	Dovrefjell	Oppland, Sør-Trøndelag	50,000	A1, B2
042	NO041	Hardangervidda	Hardangervidda	Buskerud, Hordaland, Telemark	427,200	A1, A4i, B1i, B2, B3
043	—	Kjørholmane seabird reserve	Kjørholmane sjøfuglreservat	Rogaland	600	A4i, B1i, B3
044	NO042	Jæren wetland system	Jæren wetland system	Rogaland	13,500	A1, B1i
045	—	Lista wetland system	Lista våtmarkssystem	Vest-Agder	1,189	A4i, B1i, B2, B3
046	—	Skjernøy, South Skerries	Skjernøy, sør skjærgården	Vest-Agder	100	A4i, B1i, B3
047	—	Setesdal valley (southern part)	Nedre Setesdal	Aust-Agder	30,000	B2
048	—	Lake Vannsjø	Vannsjø	Østfold	15,000	B2
049	—	Aukerfjella	Aukerfjella	Østfold	30,000	B2
050	NO046	Nordre Øyeren and Sørumsneset	Nordre Øyeren og Sørumsneset	Akershus	7,504	A1, A4i, B1i, B2
051	—	Vorma–Andelva	Vorma–Andelva	Akershus	40	A4i, B1i
052	—	Lake Storsjøen	Storsjøen i Odalen	Hedmark	4,400	A4i, B1i

Sites identified in the previous inventory of IBAs in Europe (Grimmett and Jones 1989) but no longer considered to be IBAs
NO022 Grunnfjorden; NO023 Hovsflesa; NO031 Forramyrene; NO032 Tautra and Svaet; NO038 Sandblåstvågen/Gaustadvågen; NO043 Ilene and Presterødkilen wetland system; NO044 Kurefjorden; NO045 Øra; NO047 Dokkadeltaet; NO048 Akersvika; NO049 Lågendeltaet.

Two of the original sites (former sites NO010 and NO030) have been merged with new IBAs, of which 16 have been identified (Table 1). Overall, the IBAs are situated mainly along the coast, especially in the northern part of the country (Map 1). In the southern part, two relatively large mountain areas (sites 041 and 042) have been identified, together with a few less extensive wetland sites and three larger wetland systems.

ORNITHOLOGICAL IMPORTANCE

The list of Norwegian IBAs is dominated by seabird cliffs and other seabird colonies, and to a lesser degree by important staging areas for migrating geese from the Svalbard populations (particularly *Branta leucopsis* and *Anser brachyrhynchus*). Fifteen sites hold significant numbers of five species of global conservation concern, thus qualifying as IBAs under criterion A1 (Table 2). A total of

Table 2. Important Bird Areas in Norway that are important for species of global conservation concern (meeting criterion A1).

Species	IBA code
Anser erythropus Lesser White-fronted Goose	003, 012
Polysticta stelleri Steller's Eider	003
Haliaeetus albicilla White-tailed Eagle	016, 019, 026, 028, 029, 030, 032, 038, 039
Crex crex Corncrake	044
Gallinago media Great Snipe	041, 042, 050

41 sites support 1% or more of the global, flyway or biogeographic populations of 28 congregatory species, thus qualifying under criteria A4/B1 (Table 3), and two areas meet criterion A3 as biome-restricted assemblages of species (Table 1).

A total of 108 species of European conservation concern (SPECs) breed regularly in Norway (Tucker and Heath 1994). Of these, four are of global conservation concern (*Anser erythropus*, *Haliaeetus albicilla*, *Crex crex* and *Gallinago media*) and 56 more have an unfavourable conservation status in Europe (Tucker and Heath 1994). The SPECs with a significant breeding population in Norway (on a European scale) are listed in Table 4, as well as the proportion that breed within the IBA network. A smaller number of bird species regularly stage in Norway on migration, or winter, but do not breed, there, including eight SPECs, of which *Polysticta stelleri* is the only one considered to be of global conservation concern. Norway has no endemic bird species.

Norway is especially important, in a European context, for two species of global conservation concern: the number of breeding *Haliaeetus albicilla* (c.1,500 pairs) and the number of wintering *Polysticta stelleri* (8,000–15,000 birds) are the largest in any European country. Congregations of *Haliaeetus albicilla* are scattered all along the coast of northern Norway, and many more sites are likely to support significant numbers of birds than the nine IBAs listed here (Table 2). Therefore, while further data are collected to identify these sites, wide-scale measures are needed to protect and conserve this species across the whole landscape, not just in protected areas (Tucker and Evans 1997).

Apart from Øvre Pasvik (site 001), and three of the four sites chosen on the basis of the breeding numbers of *Pandion haliaetus*

Map 1. Location, area and criteria category of Important Bird Areas in Norway.

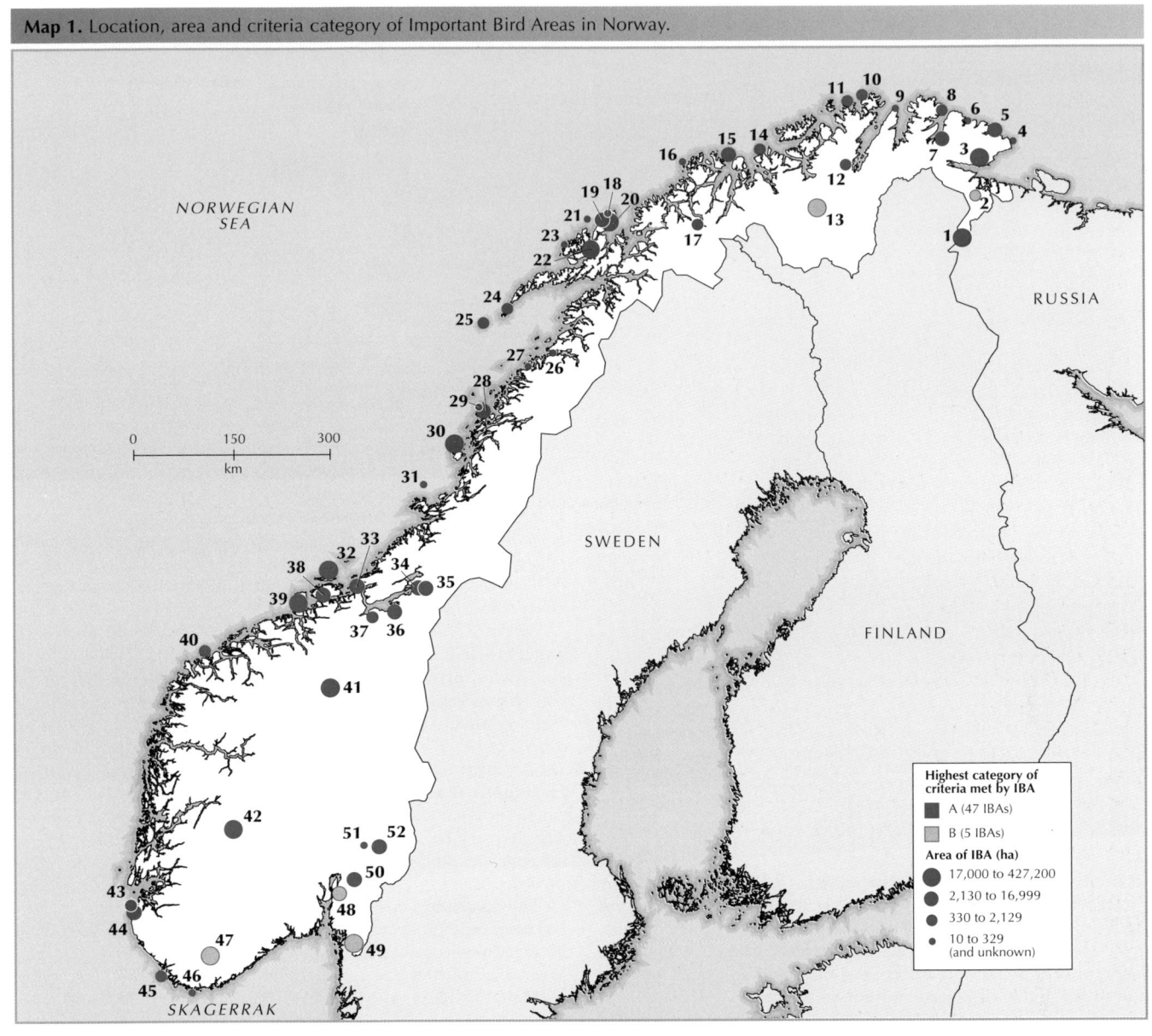

Table 3. Important Bird Areas in Norway that support important numbers of one or more congregatory species (i.e. meeting criteria A4 and/or B1). IBAs meeting both criteria A4 and B1 for the species are shown in **bold**. IBAs meeting only criterion B1 for the species concerned, and not A4, are shown in normal type. For key to 'Season', see p. 7.

Species	Season	IBA code
Gavia immer Great Northern Diver	W	**030, 039**
Podiceps grisegena Red-necked Grebe	W	**039**
Podiceps auritus Slavonian Grebe	B	035
	W	044, 045
	P	017, 034
Sula bassana Gannet	B	040
Phalacrocorax carbo Cormorant	R	**032**
	B	006, 008, **030**
	W	033
Phalacrocorax aristotelis Shag	R	**032, 043**
	B	**025, 031, 040**
Cygnus cygnus Whooper Swan	W	**050, 051**
	P	**035, 052**
Anser brachyrhynchus Pink-footed Goose	P	019, **020, 022, 034, 035, 037**, 050
Anser anser Greylag Goose	P	**045**
	N	030, 039
Branta leucopsis Barnacle Goose	P	**030**
Anas crecca Teal	P	050
Somateria mollissima Eider	R	012, 036
	B	030
	W	002, 003, 007, **030**, 033, 039
	P	034, 036
	N	030, **032**, 033

Species	Season	IBA code
Somateria spectabilis King Eider	W	**003, 004**,
Polysticha stelleri Steller's Eider	W	**003**
Mergus serrator Red-breasted Merganser	W	**033, 039**
	P	007
	N	**032**
Mergus merganser Goosander	P	012
	N	007
Charadrius morinellus Dotterel	B	**042**
Calidris canutus Knot	P	012, 017
Calidris maritima Purple Sandpiper	W	003, 030
Limosa lapponica Bar-tailed Godwit	P	012
Tringa totanus Redshank	P	034
Larus canus Common Gull	B	036
Larus fuscus Lesser Black-backed Gull	B	**045, 046**
Larus argentatus Herring Gull	R	**004**
Rissa tridactyla Kittiwake	B	**005, 008, 009, 011, 040**
Alca torda Razorbill	B	004, 005, 010, **011**, 014, 015, 016, 023, 024, 025, 040
Cepphus grylle Black Guillemot	R	014, 016, 030, 031
	B	025, 029, 039
	N	032
Fratercula arctica Puffin	B	**010, 011**, 014, **015, 016, 018, 023, 024, 025, 040**

Table 4. Species of European conservation concern with significant breeding populations at Important Bird Areas in Norway (meeting any IBA criteria).

Species [1]	Minimum national breeding population (pairs) [2]	Proportion (%) of national population breeding at all IBAs in Norway
Gavia stellata Red-throated Diver	2,000	1
Sula bassana Gannet	3,500	100[3]
Phalacrocorax aristotelis Shag	16,000	38
Mergus albellus Smew	10	50
Haliaeetus albicilla White-tailed Eagle	1,600	3
Pandion haliaetus Osprey	150	20
Falco rusticolus Gyrfalcon	300	8
Crex crex Corncrake	70	23
Pluvialis apricaria Golden Plover	50,000	10
Limicola falcinellus Broad-billed Sandpiper	1,500	<1
Philomachus pugnax Ruff	10,000	3
Gallinago media Great Snipe	5,000	9
Numenius phaeopus Whimbrel	10,000	3
Tringa totanus Redshank	40,000	2
Larus canus Common Gull	100,000	7
Larus fuscus Lesser Black-backed Gull	25,000	28
Larus marinus Great Black-backed Gull	30,000	4
Alca torda Razorbill	20,000	100[3]
Cepphus grylle Black Guillemot	20,000	23
Fratercula arctica Puffin	2,000,000	92
Perisoreus infaustus Siberian Jay	10,000	1

1. Only those species of European conservation concern (see Box 1, p. 12) that meet IBA criteria in Norway are listed.
2. Data are taken from the BirdLife/EBCC European Bird Database 1998 (Heath and Borggreve 2000).
3. The percentage of the national population in IBAs exceeds 100%. Usually this is because the national population estimate has not been updated recently whilst the IBA population estimate has been recently updated with new data as a result of comprehensive surveys of IBAs themselves. Also, the individual site count for a species may be the maximum or average over recent years, and summing these may record more birds than are present nationally in any single year.

(B2 criterion; sites 047–049), Norwegian IBAs hardly cover any productive forest. Norway supports good numbers, significant at the European level, of several boreal species, among them raptors, grouse, owls, woodpeckers and other typical forest birds which are scarce or of conservation concern in a European context. However, due to the highly dispersed and non-overlapping distributions of these species, the identification of particularly important sites for individual species, or for species-rich assemblages of them, is difficult in the absence of a great deal of detailed and locality-specific data. The same also applies to several species of breeding wildfowl (Anatidae) and wader (Scolopacidae).

HABITATS

Norway possesses a wide range of habitats. Hemi-boreal forests and shallow, nutrient-rich lakes are found in the south, while tundra and taiga (boreal forest) exist in the north. However, more than 70% of the terrain in Norway is mountainous (of which 50% is exposed bedrock) or is otherwise of low productivity. The high mountain areas, even in the southern part of the country, are in many respects comparable ecologically with the tundra in the far north. Key bird species in such habitats include *Pluvialis apricaria*, *Charadrius morinellus*, *Calidris maritima*, *Lagopus lagopus*, *Lagopus mutus*, *Plectrophenax nivalis* and *Calcarius lapponicus*.

The abundance of islands and islets along the coast provide suitable habitat for numerous seabird colonies. In the south, gulls (*Larus canus*, *L. marinus*, *L. fuscus* and *L. argentatus*) and terns (*Sterna hirundo* and *S. paradisaea*) are the most numerous species in such colonies. In the north, *Fratercula arctica*, *Uria aalge* and *Rissa tridactyla* are the most numerous species, but the colonies are often larger and more localized to huge cliffs.

Of the various estuaries and other types of wetland, the deep fjords along the western coastline are less important for birdlife. However, the productive fjords of the Trøndelag counties and northern Norway, as well as the shallow seas along this coast, are very important for divers (Gaviidae)—on a global scale the

Figure 1. Habitats at Important Bird Areas in Norway (see Appendix 3 for definitions of habitats).

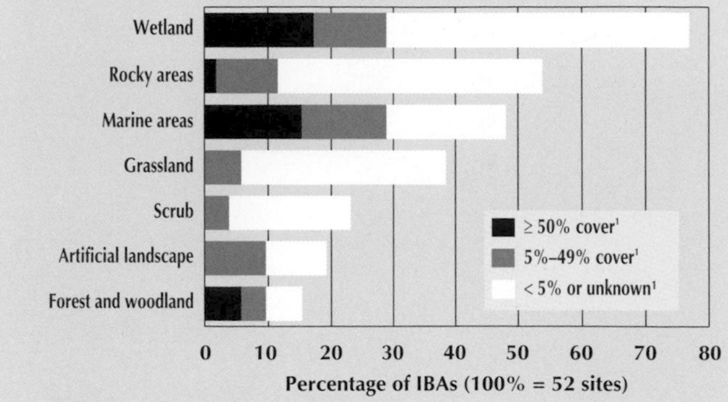

Percentage of IBAs (100% = 52 sites)

1. percentage of area of individual IBA covered by habitat

Norwegian coast is particularly important for *Gavia adamsii*—as well as *Podiceps auritus*, *P. grisegena* and several wildfowl species (Anatidae). In wetlands in forested and mountainous areas, breeding waders are numerous (e.g. *Calidris temminckii*, *Tringa nebularia*, *T. totanus*, *T. glareola*, *Philomachus pugnax*, *Numenius phaeopus* and *Phalaropus lobatus*). Bogs and marshes cover about 4.8% of the national land area, while freshwater lakes and ponds cover 5.4%.

About 37% of Norway (119,000 km²) is covered by forest, concentrated mainly in the south, of which 66,450 km² was considered productive (in 1982). In the south-east, evergreen coniferous forest of spruce *Picea* and pine *Pinus* predominates. Here, relatively common bird species include *Aquila chrysaetos*, *Tetrao tetrix*, *T. urogallus*, *Aegolius funereus*, *Picoides tridactylus*, *Dendrocopos major*, *Dryocopus martius* and *Perisoreus infaustus*. Deciduous woodlands of birch *Betula* are widespread in the subalpine zone above the coniferous belt, where *Cuculus canorus*, *Luscinia svecica*, *Fringilla montifringilla* and *Emberiza schoeniclus* are common. In total, 79% of the forest area in Norway is privately owned.

The percentage cover of different habitats at Norwegian IBAs has been only moderately well recorded (Figure 1), as a result of inexact knowledge of the situation on the ground. Wetlands, rocky areas and marine areas are the habitat-types most frequently registered at IBAs, at more than 70%, more than 50% and more than 40% of the sites respectively.

IMPACTS ON IBAs – LAND-USE AND THREATS

The dominant land-use in Norway is forestry. Large-scale agriculture is limited and restricted to the south-west and south-east. Only about 3.6% of the national land area is arable but grazing, by sheep in the south and by domesticated reindeer in the north, is widespread in forest and mountain areas. The long coastline makes an ideal base for fisheries, both near-shore and pelagic, which are indeed some of the most important industries in the country.

Another offshore enterprise, but one which also has a significant influence on the land, is the oil industry. Mostly located off the south-western and western coasts of the country, oil and gas extraction is very important for the Norwegian economy. Recently, plans have been launched for expanding this industry to the northernmost sea areas. Potentially, this could have a negative effect on the many seabird colonies in this region.

Figure 2 shows the land-uses recorded within Norwegian IBAs. Nature conservation/research is the most frequently recorded use (occurring in 46% of the IBAs). Other frequent uses are fisheries/aquaculture and recreation/tourism (both at c.33% of the sites), as well as agriculture (at 31%).

From Figure 3 it is evident that disturbance to birds, recreation/tourism, and the extraction industry are the three most widespread or frequent threats (potential and actual) at Norwegian IBAs. Disturbance and tourism/recreation are often correlated and would be difficult to separate in any detailed consideration of threats. Because a high proportion of Norwegian IBAs are seabird colonies,

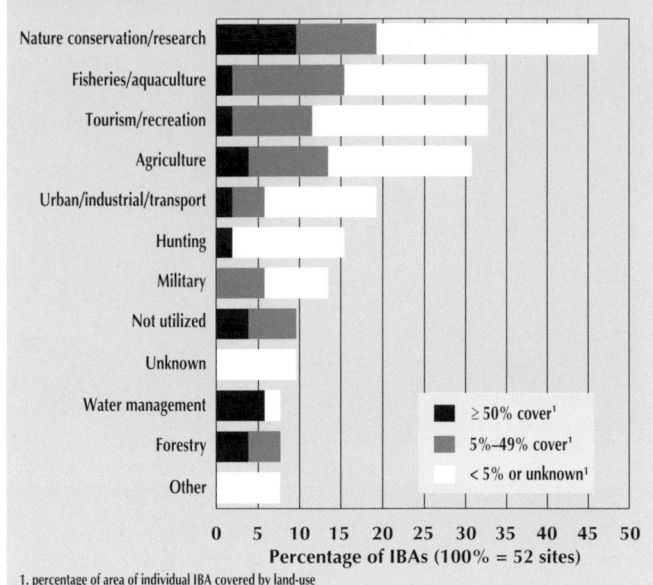

Figure 2. Land-uses at Important Bird Areas in Norway (see Appendix 3 for definitions of land-uses).

Nature conservation/research
Fisheries/aquaculture
Tourism/recreation
Agriculture
Urban/industrial/transport
Hunting
Military
Not utilized
Unknown
Water management
Forestry
Other

≥ 50% cover[1]
5%–49% cover[1]
< 5% or unknown[1]

Percentage of IBAs (100% = 52 sites)
0 5 10 15 20 25 30 35 40 45 50

1. percentage of area of individual IBA covered by land-use

fisheries may perhaps be the most serious threat at these areas. In the past, over-exploitation of fish stocks has caused dramatic declines in several seabird populations along the coast of northern Norway, especially *Uria aalge* and *Fratercula arctica*. On the other hand, industrial fishing has probably had positive effects (through the production of discards) on some seabird populations, e.g. *Fulmarus glacialis* and *Sula bassana*, which have shown marked population increases in the last few decades. Nevertheless, sustainable management of the fish stocks is crucial for most of the seabird colonies listed in this inventory.

Aquaculture is a widespread industry along the Norwegian coast. Because of newly established national regulations which aim to prevent the escape of farmed fish into the wild fish population, the fish farms now have to be equipped with extra nets outside the farm itself. Recent information indicates that this may cause some bycatch of seabirds, especially seaduck such as *Somateria mollissima*. If so, aquaculture may have a direct impact on the key birds at several IBAs along the Norwegian coast. Thus, reliable and detailed information on this potential threat is clearly needed.

Introduced animals have not been commonly reported as posing a significant threat to birds in Norway or at IBAs, but American mink *Mustela lutreola* (originally escaped from fur-farms)

is known to be a significant predator at many seabird colonies and may thus be a threat in some cases. A rather common bird in most of southern Norway is *Branta canadensis*, introduced from North America between 1960 and 1980 for hunting purposes. Little is known about this species' influence on native birds. Today, the deliberate introduction of new species to Norway is strictly prohibited by law.

PROTECTION STATUS

Table 5 and Figures 4 and 5 summarize the national and international protection status of Norwegian IBAs.

■ National protection

The Ministry of Environment (Miljøverndepartementet) is the highest authority in questions concerning nature protection in Norway, but active responsibility is delegated largely to the Directorate for Nature Management (Direktoratet for Naturforvaltning).

Nature conservation areas in Norway are legally protected by three Nature Conservation Acts (in 1910, 1953 and 1970). They fall mainly into the following three categories (Anon. 1995):

1. National Parks
These are relatively large, natural areas, little influenced by human activities, normally situated on land originally owned by the state (can sometimes include areas of adjacent privately-owned land). All parts of the environment and landscape are protected against human disturbance, pollution and other human operations. At present, 18 National Parks have been established in Norway, covering an area of 13,788 km² (4.3% of the total land area).

2. Nature Reserves
These are normally relatively small, untouched areas established to protect special types of nature or animals. Examples are forest reserves, wetland reserves and bird sanctuaries. This is the highest level of protection under the Nature Conservation Act, and may often involve strict restrictions on human activities. There are 1,293 Nature Reserves, covering 2,289 km² (0.7% of total land area).

3. Landscape Protection Areas
These are mainly areas with natural and cultural landscapes where the landscape itself is the reason for the protection status. Traditional use of the landscape is not prohibited, as long as this do not significantly change the character of the landscape. This is the lowest form of protection under the Nature Conservation Act. There are 82 Landscape Protection Areas, covering 4,671 km² (1.4% of total land area).

Figure 3. Threats at Important Bird Areas in Norway (see Appendix 3 for definitions of threat types and impact categories).

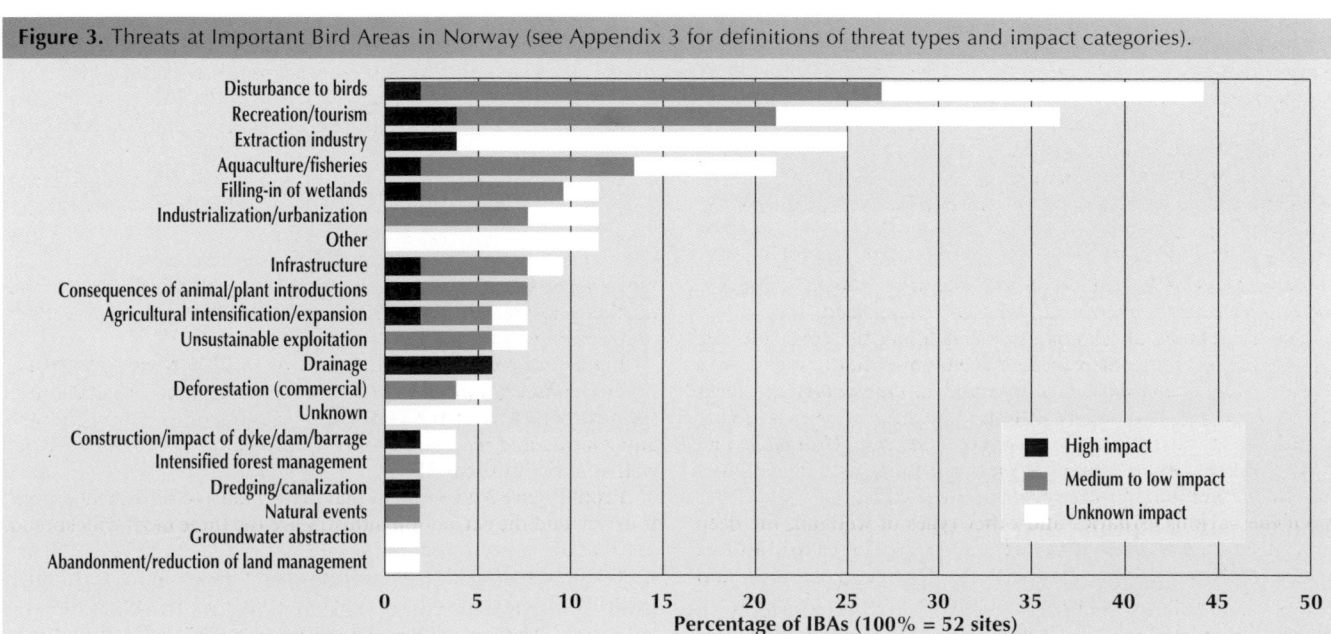

Disturbance to birds
Recreation/tourism
Extraction industry
Aquaculture/fisheries
Filling-in of wetlands
Industrialization/urbanization
Other
Infrastructure
Consequences of animal/plant introductions
Agricultural intensification/expansion
Unsustainable exploitation
Drainage
Deforestation (commercial)
Unknown
Construction/impact of dyke/dam/barrage
Intensified forest management
Dredging/canalization
Natural events
Groundwater abstraction
Abandonment/reduction of land management

High impact
Medium to low impact
Unknown impact

Percentage of IBAs (100% = 52 sites)
0   5   10   15   20   25   30   35   40   45   50

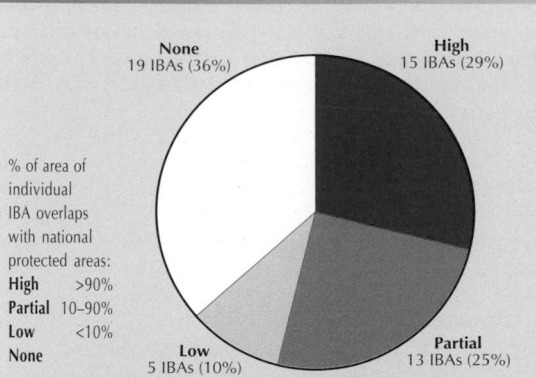

Figure 4. The national protection status of Important Bird Areas in Norway.

None
19 IBAs (36%)

High
15 IBAs (29%)

% of area of individual IBA overlaps with national protected areas:
High >90%
Partial 10–90%
Low <10%
None

Low
5 IBAs (10%)

Partial
13 IBAs (25%)

Total area of overlap between IBA network in Norway and national protected-area system (see Table 5 for categories) = 4,584–4,912 km² (49–53% of total IBA area).

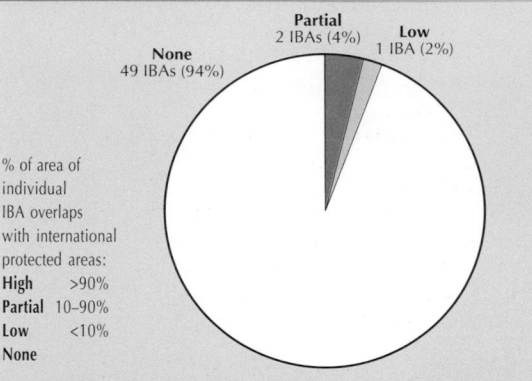

Figure 5. The international protection status of Important Bird Areas in Norway.

Partial
2 IBAs (4%)

Low
1 IBA (2%)

None
49 IBAs (94%)

% of area of individual IBA overlaps with international protected areas:
High >90%
Partial 10–90%
Low <10%
None

Total area of overlap between IBA network in Norway and international protected-area system (see Table 5 for categories) = 83 km² (1% of total IBA area).

Table 5. Protection status of Important Bird Areas in Norway.
A tick (✔) indicates that an IBA overlaps with a protected area (to any extent).

		National				Inter-national			National				Inter-national
IBA code	International name	National Park	Nature Reserve	Flora and Fauna Protection Area	Landscape Protection Area	Ramsar Site	IBA code	International name	National Park	Nature Reserve	Flora and Fauna Protection Area	Landscape Protection Area	Ramsar Site
001	Øvre Pasvik	✔	✔				027	Fugløya					
002	Neiden and Munkefjord		✔				028	Svenningen–Risvær					
003	Varangerfjord		✔				029	Lovunden					
004	Hornøy and Reinøy		✔				030	Vega archipelago		✔			
005	Makkaurhalvøya (Syltefjordstauran)		✔				031	Sklinna					
006	Kongsøy		✔				032	Froan		✔	✔	✔	
007	Tanamunningen		✔				033	Ørland wetland system		✔	✔		
008	Omgangsstauran		✔				034	Inner Trondheimsfjord wetland system		✔	✔		
009	Sværholtklubben		✔				035	Lake Leksdalsvatn		✔	✔		
010	Gjesværstappan		✔				036	Stjørdals Fjord					
011	Hjelmsøy		✔				037	Gaulosen		✔		✔	
012	Inner part of Porsanger fjord		✔			✔	038	Havmyran		✔			
013	Alta-Kautokeino watercourse						039	Smøla archipelago					
014	Loppa		✔				040	Runde		✔			
015	Nord-Fugløy		✔				041	Dovrefjell	✔	✔		✔	
016	Sør-Fugløy						042	Hardangervidda	✔				
017	Sørkjosen						043	Kjørholmane seabird reserve		✔			
018	Bleiksøy						044	Jæren wetland system		✔		✔	✔
019	Skogvoll (including Skarvklakken)		✔				045	Lista wetland system		✔	✔	✔	
020	Andøya						046	Skjernøy, South Skerries		✔			
021	Anda						047	Setesdal valley (southern part)					
022	Langøya						048	Lake Vannsjø		✔			
023	Nykvåg						049	Aukerfjella		✔			
024	Værøy						050	Nordre Øyeren and Sørumsneset		✔			✔
025	Røst		✔				051	Vorma–Andelva					
026	Saltstraumen						052	Lake Storsjøen					
Subtotal of IBAs		1	16	0	0	1	**Total number of IBAs**		**3**	**32**	**5**	**5**	**3**

A network of wardens has been established in all of the Norwegian National Parks, as well as in many of the mountain areas owned by the state; other protected areas are also under varying degrees of direct supervision.

There are no privately-owned nature reserves in Norway. The protection of Norwegian IBAs, through their overlap with areas protected by national law, is shown in Figure 4. A substantial minority of the IBAs (36%) have no such protection.

■ International protection

Norway is party to all of the international agreements that are relevant to the protection of sites for nature conservation (Box 1). Table 5 and Figure 5 summarize the situation with respect to the IBAs. In general, few of the IBAs overlap with sites protected under

Box 1. International legislation and initiatives that are relevant to site conservation in Norway (see Appendix 1 for a general description of these agreements).

Global
Biodiversity Convention ✔
Ramsar Convention ✔
Bonn Convention ✔
World Heritage Convention ✔
MAB Programme ✔

Pan-European
Bern Convention ✔

✔ Convention ratified/initiative supported
(✔) Convention signed

such international legislation (Figure 5). Three Norwegian IBAs overlap with Ramsar Sites (Table 5), while two IBAs lie within the European network of Biogenetic Reserves (020 and 041).

CONSERVATION

- The national populations of several bird species are monitored annually in Norway through projects conducted by the Norwegian Ornithological Society (NOF)—a yearly census of passerines since 1994, conservation projects on *Anser erythropus* since 1990, on *Haliaeetus albicilla* since 1974, and on *Crex crex* since 1995. Additionally, in cooperation with NOF, the Norwegian Institute for Nature Research (NINA) performs annual monitoring surveys of many seabird populations, and has recently also started a programme to monitor several species of bird and other organisms in different habitats.
- At present, the Directorate for Nature Management (*in litt.*) is considering several new areas for inclusion in the national List of Ramsar Sites, and NOF has encouraged this work with a request to include all the relevant IBAs.
- The Norwegian government is presently considering plans for extending the system of nature-protection areas (Anon. 1997), and will before 2008 evaluate 17 new sites for National Park status, 17 sites for Landscape Protection Area status, and one (large) site for Nature Reserve status. In addition, an expansion in area will be considered for 14 established National Parks. In total, these proposals could increase the protected-area system in Norway to cover 10–15% of the national land area.
- Most existing protected areas in Norway have a management plan.

ANALYTICAL METHODS

- All estimates of the national population size of bird species are taken from Gjershaug *et al.* (1994), and are of variable quality.
- Data for breeding seabirds are of good quality and refer to data from censuses performed mostly by NINA and NOF personnel. Several species are surveyed annually in this way.
- The inventory has focused little on marine (non-land) sites because the data on bird numbers and distribution at sea are not easily available. However, several marine sites will probably meet the IBA criteria, and analyzing the data to identify important offshore concentrations of seabirds should be given high priority in the future.
- Except for *Gallinago media*, population data for the species of global conservation concern are very reliable and are based on information from special projects performed by NOF.
- Where IBAs are selected due to the particularly high abundance of some species, these numbers are reliable and are based on recent counts, unless otherwise stated.

- A lack of data/time has prevented a full analysis and identification of sites that hold significant numbers of species of European conservation concern (thus meeting the B2/B3 criteria). Exceptions are *Falco rusticolus* and *Pandion haliaetus*, which have been reasonably well covered by this inventory, as well as some species that are already well covered by other criteria, such as *Sula bassana*, *Aythya marila* (winter), *Polysticta stelleri* (winter), *Haliaeetus albicilla* and *Fratercula arctica*. The detailed breeding distributions of *Gallinago media* and *Limicola falcinellus* are not yet known well enough to identify B2 sites for them, but it is important that further work is done to map such sites. The majority of other species that could potentially meet B2/B3 criteria in Norway, for example *Gavia stellata*, *Tringa totanus* and *Perisoreus infaustus*, have such widespread or scattered distributions that identification of qualifying sites (on the basis of current information) would be difficult.

GLOSSARY

fjord a steep-sided coastal valley, created by the erosive action of glaciers and then subsequently flooded with seawater.
NINA Norsk Institutt for Naturforskning (Norwegian Institute for Nature Research).
NOF Norsk Ornitologisk Forening (Norwegian Ornithological Society), the BirdLife Partner for Norway and Svalbard.
øy an island.
skjær (skerry) a small islet or rocky reef in the sea, exposed at low tide.

ACKNOWLEDGEMENTS

We thank all the persons who in different ways have helped us with the data-collection during the work on the Norwegian IBA inventory. A special thanks to the following local IBA coordinators: Jon Bekken, Knut Eie, Alv Ottar Folkestad, Roar Frølandshagen, Karl-Otto Jacobsen, Magne Myklebust, Knut S. Olsen, Tormod Røed, Morten Stokke, Per Inge Værnesbranden and Arve Østlyngen. In addition, Odd Frydenlund Steen, Jan E. Gunnersen, Roy Nordbakke and Jo Ranke provided important information about *Pandion haliaetus* in Norway, making it possible to select the B2 sites for that species. Odd Frydenlund Steen also kindly provided the population estimate for *Falco rusticolus* at Hardangervidda. Information provided by Jon Atle Kålås made it clear that selection of B2 sites for *Gallinago media* would be premature. Finally Tycho Anker-Nilssen, Morten Ekker and Trond Haugskott all made important contributions by providing various sorts of information about the sites that have been selected. The work was financially supported by the Norwegian Directorate for Nature Management and by the environmental departments at the County Governorates.

SITE ACCOUNTS

Øvre Pasvik

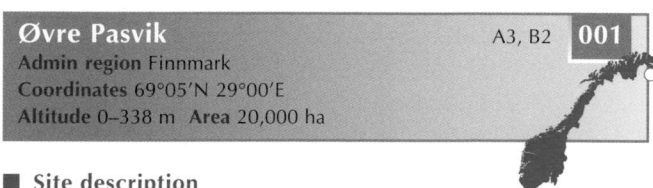

A3, B2 **001**

Admin region Finnmark
Coordinates 69°05′N 29°00′E
Altitude 0–338 m Area 20,000 ha

■ Site description

This is the largest virgin forest in Norway, close to the border with Russia and Finland. The landscape is flat, with some ridges, and is covered by boreal coniferous forest (this being the westernmost limit of the Siberian taiga) and mires, with numerous fish-rich lakes.

Habitats Forest and woodland (80%; native coniferous forest), Wetland (standing fresh water; river/stream; raised bog)
Land-use Forestry (20%), Hunting, Military (10%), Nature conservation/research (10%), Tourism/recreation (10%)

■ Birds

Breeding species include at least 10 of the 15 species in Europe that are restricted to the boreal biome (when breeding)—an eleventh such species, *Emberiza rustica*, may also breed irregularly—as well as a wide variety of wildfowl and waders, and *Haliaeetus albicilla* (a species of

global conservation concern which, however, does not meet IBA criteria).

Species		Season	Year	Pop min	Pop max	Acc	Criteria
[1] *Mergus albellus* Smew		B	1998	5	10	—	A3
[2] *Limicola falcinellus* Broad-billed Sandpiper		B	—	—	—	—	B2
Lymnocryptes minimus Jack Snipe		B	1998	Uncommon		—	A3
[3] *Surnia ulula* Hawk Owl		B	1998	Frequent		—	A3
[3] *Strix nebulosa* Great Grey Owl		B	1998	1	5	C	A3
Bombycilla garrulus Waxwing		B	1998	Frequent		—	A3
[4] *Phylloscopus borealis* Arctic Warbler		B	1998	Rare		—	A3
Parus cinctus Siberian Tit		R	1998	Common		—	A3
Perisoreus infaustus Siberian Jay		R	1998	50		—	A3
Fringilla montifringilla Brambling		B	1998	Common		—	A3
Pinicola enucleator Pine Grosbeak		B	1998	Uncommon		—	A3

1. Along the Pasvik river.
2. Occasionally seen; probably breeding.
3. Breeds especially in years when small rodents are abundant.
4. May breed every year in small numbers.

■ Protection status

National Partial **International** None

6,660 ha of IBA covered by National Park (Øvre Pasvik, 6,660 ha). 1,910 ha of IBA covered by Nature Reserve (Pasvik, 1,910 ha).

■ Conservation issues

Threats Disturbance to birds (U), Infrastructure (B), Intensified forest management (B), Recreation/tourism (U)

There is some logging and re-afforestation. Plans for a road in the area, cutting through the Pasvik valley to Finland, are currently shelved. Two administratively-protected forest areas (state-owned) lie within the IBA. Plans to extend the National Park exist. The Nature Reserve is adjacent to the Pasvik Zapovednik across the border in Russia, and the Norwegian and Russian authorities have cooperated in planning these protected areas.

Neiden and Munkefjord   B1i 002
Admin region Finnmark
Coordinates 69°40′N 29°35′E
Altitude 0–0 m **Area** 1,180 ha

■ Site description
The estuaries of the Neidenelva and Munkelva rivers. The Neidenelva river is broad and calm, and the estuary has high terraces and numerous sandbanks. Munkefjorden is a shallow bay (mostly <10 m deep), lying south of the Neiden estuary. Huge intertidal flats are exposed at low tide. Other habitats include coastal meadows, saltmarshes and farms.

Habitats Forest and woodland, Wetland (tidal river/enclosed tidal water; mudflat/ sandflat; saltmarsh)
Land-use Fisheries/aquaculture, Tourism/recreation

■ Birds

Species	Season	Year	Pop min	Pop max	Acc	Criteria
Somateria mollissima Eider	W	1998	3,000	—	—	B1i

Several species of seaduck sometimes occur in large concentrations, e.g. *Clangula hyemalis* (max. 4,000 in spring) and *Mergus merganser* (max. 2,000 in August). In spring there are high numbers of staging waders, especially *Limosa lapponica* (max. 500) and *Calidris canutus* (max. 2,500), and about 200 *Calidris maritima* winter in the area. The area supports one of the largest concentrations of divers in Norway, especially during spring, with up to 100 *Gavia stellata* and up to 400 *Gavia arctica*.

■ Protection status
National High **International** None
1,180 ha of IBA covered by Nature Reserve (Neiden and Munkefjord, 1,180 ha).

■ Conservation issues

Threats Unknown

Threat status is not known.

Varangerfjord   A1, A3, A4i, A4iii, B1i 003
Admin region Finnmark
Coordinates 70°12′N 29°52′E
Altitude 0–53 m **Area** 60,000 ha

■ Site description
The site is an Arctic shoreline, and includes a relatively small proportion of shallow sea offshore. A main road runs along the coast, and two towns, Vadsø and Vardø, lie in the area. Important localities within the IBA are (1) Nesseby (treated as subsite NO003-1 in the previous pan-European IBA inventory of Grimmett and Jones 1989; 70°10′N 28°50′E; 74 ha), (2) Vadsøy and Vadsøysundet (former subsite NO003-2; 70°05′N 29°45′E; 120 ha), (3) Ekkerøy (former subsite NO003-3; 70°05′N 30°10′E; 160 ha), and (4) Skjåholmen (71°20′N 28°45′E; 1,500 ha). Nesseby is a broad tidal bay with shallow water. 'Vadsøy and Vadsøysundet' consist of the eastern part of Vadsøy island and the bay (with extensive intertidal flats and shallow subtidal water) between the

island and the mainland. Ekkerøy comprises the southern and eastern half of the Store Ekkerøy peninsula, just east of Vadsø, and includes steep 50 m high cliffs. On the north side of the peninsula, the peaty ground slopes less steeply towards the sea and is covered in heathland. There is some sheep-grazing and collecting of gulls' eggs on the peninsula. Skjåholmen is a small island in the innermost part of the Varangerfjord. It is c.3 km long and 500–600 m wide, and is surrounded by sandy beaches and large expanses of shallow water. Skjåholmen is used for hunting, recreation, egg-collection and reindeer-herding.

Habitats Scrub (heathland), Wetland (shingle/stony beach), Marine areas (sea inlet/ coastal features), Rocky areas (sea cliff/rocky shore)
Land-use Agriculture, Fisheries/aquaculture, Tourism/recreation, Urban/industrial/transport

■ Birds

Species	Season	Year	Pop min	Pop max	Acc	Criteria
[1] *Anser erythropus*	P	1998	—	60	—	A1
Lesser White-fronted Goose						
Somateria mollissima Eider	W	1989	5,000	6,000	—	B1i
Somateria spectabilis King Eider	W	—	1,500	7,500	—	A4i, B1i
Polysticta stelleri Steller's Eider	W	—	10,000	112,000	—	A1, A4i, B1i
Buteo lagopus Rough-legged Buzzard	B	—	—	—	—	A3
Falco rusticolus Gyrfalcon	R	—	—	—	—	A3
Calidris minuta Little Stint	B	—	—	—	—	A3
Calidris temminckii Temminck's Stint	B	—	—	—	—	A3
Calidris maritima Purple Sandpiper	W	1989	1,000	1,000	—	A4i, B1i
Limosa lapponica Bar-tailed Godwit	B	—	—	—	—	A3
Stercorarius longicaudus	B	—	—	—	—	A3
Long-tailed Skua						
Anthus cervinus Red-throated Pipit	B	—	—	—	—	A3
Carduelis hornemanni Arctic Redpoll	B	—	—	—	—	A3
Calcarius lapponicus Lapland Bunting	B	—	—	—	—	A3
Plectrophenax nivalis Snow Bunting	B	—	—	—	—	A3

1. At Skjåholmen in spring and autumn (one of the most important passage sites in Norway).

About 80–90% of the European wintering population of *Polysticta stelleri* gathers offshore, some on the fjord off Nesseby but mostly further east. Even in summer up to 1,000 birds remain in the area. *Somateria spectabilis* and *Somateria mollissima* also winter in important numbers, as does *Calidris maritima* in the tidal zone. Breeding species include at least 10 of the 32 species in Europe that are restricted to the Arctic/ tundra biome (when breeding)—an eleventh such species, *Aythya marila*, may also breed. In spring, the area is an important staging ground for migrating waders, especially *Calidris canutus*, and there are also good numbers of waders in autumn, e.g. *Calidris alpina* (max. 10,000 birds). *Haliaeetus albicilla* (a species of global conservation concern) is resident in the Ekkerøy area (although in numbers too small to meet IBA criteria), and breeding colonies of *Rissa tridactyla* are also notable on Ekkerøy (c.20,000 pairs) and Ranvika (c.10,000 pairs).

■ Protection status
National Low **International** None
160 ha of IBA covered by Nature Reserve (Ekkerøya, 160 ha).

■ Conservation issues

Threats Aquaculture/fisheries (U), Disturbance to birds (U), Extraction industry (U), Recreation/tourism (U)

Bycatch of *Polysticta stelleri* and other seaduck by commercial fisheries has been suspected, but good data on this issue are lacking from the area. Careful examination of this possible problem should be given priority. Planned oil production in the Barents Sea may have a negative impact on coastal and marine birds. From 1996 Skjåholmen was included in a study by NOF on *Anser erythropus*.

Hornøy and Reinøy   A4i, A4iii, B1i, B1ii, B3 004
Admin region Finnmark
Coordinates 70°24′N 31°10′E
Altitude 0–65 m **Area** 200 ha

■ Site description
The site comprises the grass-covered islands of Hornøya and Reinøya and islets of Prestholmen and Lille Avløysinga (totalling c.150 ha of land) plus c.50 ha of intervening sea. The western part of Hornøya is 65 m high, with steep cliffs facing westward, while the eastern part is

flat. Reinøya has no steep cliffs. Hornøya is the easternmost point of Norway at 31°10'E; there is a lighthouse at its northern end. About 10,000–30,000 eggs of *Larus argentatus* are collected per year. Hornøya is owned by Vardø municipality and the Lighthouse Department, while Prestholmen belongs to the vicar in Vardø.

Habitats Scrub (heathland), Grassland (alpine/subalpine/boreal grassland), Wetland (shingle/stony beach), Marine areas (25%; sea inlet/coastal features), Rocky areas (sea cliff/rocky shore)
Land-use Nature conservation/research, Other

■ Birds

Species	Season	Year	Pop min	Pop max	Acc	Criteria
[1] *Somateria spectabilis* King Eider	W	1990	2,000	3,000	—	A4i, B1i
[2] *Larus argentatus* Herring Gull	R	1989	50,000	50,000	—	A4i, B1i
Larus marinus Great Black-backed Gull	R	1997	600	700	—	B3
Alca torda Razorbill	B	1997	250	250	—	B1ii

1. Maximum February–April.
2. The largest colony in Europe.

The islands hold the largest colony of *Larus argentatus* in Europe, as well as many thousands of pairs of a wide range of other breeding seabirds, e.g. *Rissa tridactyla* (at least 20,000 pairs). *Polysticta stelleri* is common from January to April in large, dense flocks (totalling more than 400 birds).

■ Protection status
National High **International** None
200 ha of IBA covered by Nature Reserve (Hornøya and Reinøya, 800 ha).

■ Conservation issues

Threats Extraction industry (U)

Planned oil production in the Barents Sea may have a negative impact on coastal and marine birds. Entry to the Nature Reserve is not allowed between 1 April and 15 August.

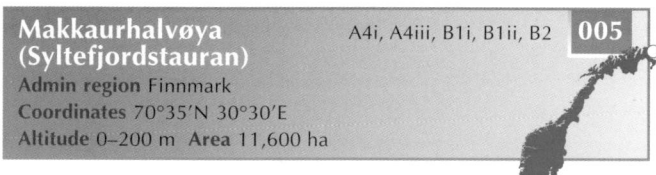

Makkaurhalvøya (Syltefjordstauran) — A4i, A4iii, B1i, B1ii, B2 — 005
Admin region Finnmark
Coordinates 70°35'N 30°30'E
Altitude 0–200 m **Area** 11,600 ha

■ Site description
This is a coastline with steep cliffs and several rocky pillars, plunging 200 m into the sea from a montane plateau. About 250 ha of the IBA area is sea, the rest is land. Four salmon fisheries (aquaculture) are situated in the area.

Habitats Scrub (heathland), Grassland (alpine/subalpine/boreal grassland), Wetland (shingle/stony beach), Marine areas (2%; sea inlet/coastal features), Rocky areas (sea cliff/rocky shore)
Land-use Fisheries/aquaculture

■ Birds

Species	Season	Year	Pop min	Pop max	Acc	Criteria
[1] *Sula bassana* Gannet	B	1990	450	450	A	B2
[2] *Rissa tridactyla* Kittiwake	B	1997	140,000	140,000	A	A4i, B1i
Alca torda Razorbill	B	1985	1,200	1,200	A	B1ii

1. The northernmost colony in the world and the only one in Finnmark.
2. The largest colony in Norway.

Together with Hjelmsøya, these cliffs support the largest, most varied and most important seabird colonies in Finnmark. This is the largest colony in Norway of *Uria aalge* (formerly 12,000 pairs in 1985 but had declined to 2,500 pairs by 1997). Good numbers of seaduck occur offshore in winter.

■ Protection status
National High **International** None
11,600 ha of IBA covered by Nature Reserve (Makkaurhalvøya, 11,600 ha).

■ Conservation issues

Threats Aquaculture/fisheries (U), Extraction industry (U)

Planned oil production in the Barents Sea may have a negative impact on coastal and marine birds.

Kongsøy — A4iii, B1i, B3 — 006
Admin region Finnmark
Coordinates 70°44'N 29°30'E
Altitude 0–99 m **Area** 280 ha

■ Site description
Kongsøy is a large, grass-covered island with steep cliffs. Helløy and Skarvholmen are low-lying islands with minimal vegetation. This site comprises 75 ha of land and 205 ha of sea. Gulls' eggs are collected by people from Kongsfjord and Berlevåg.

Habitats Grassland (alpine/subalpine/boreal grassland), Wetland (shingle/stony beach), Marine areas (73%; sea inlet/coastal features), Rocky areas (sea cliff/rocky shore)
Land-use Other

■ Birds

Species	Season	Year	Pop min	Pop max	Acc	Criteria
Phalacrocorax carbo Cormorant	B	1989	600	600	A	B1i
Phalacrocorax aristotelis Shag	B	1989	400	400	A	B3

A breeding colony of *Rissa tridactyla* (c.18,000 pairs) is nationally important.

■ Protection status
National High **International** None
280 ha of IBA covered by Nature Reserve (Kongsøyene, 280 ha).

■ Conservation issues

Threats Extraction industry (U)

Planned oil production in the Barents Sea may have a negative impact on coastal and marine birds.

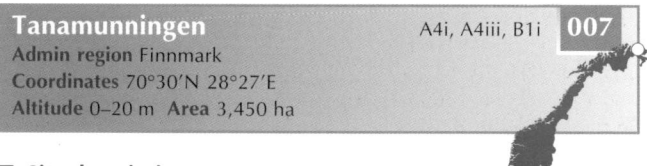

Tanamunningen — A4i, A4iii, B1i — 007
Admin region Finnmark
Coordinates 70°30'N 28°27'E
Altitude 0–20 m **Area** 3,450 ha

■ Site description
The large estuary of the Tana river in the Tanafjord, with extensive areas of shallow water, intertidal sand and gravel-banks, and subarctic coastal meadows. The biggest banks and meadows are east of the main river course. Høyholmen is a grass-covered islet in the estuary. Leirpollen is a small cove to the east.

Habitats Grassland (5%; alpine/subalpine/boreal grassland), Wetland (95%; tidal river/enclosed tidal water; mudflat/sandflat)
Land-use Hunting

■ Birds

Species	Season	Year	Pop min	Pop max	Acc	Criteria
Somateria mollissima Eider	W	1989	4,000	—	—	B1i
[1] *Mergus serrator* Red-breasted Merganser	P	1989	1,500	—	—	B1i
[2] *Mergus merganser* Goosander	N	1989	27,000	27,000	—	A4i, B1i

1. Daily maximum.
2. Moulting (mainly males).

A very important site for seaduck outside the breeding season. Most males of the north-western European population of *Mergus merganser* gather to moult here, or move here after moulting at fjords in Finnmark, in August–September. Unfortunately no reliable counts of this species have been made since the late 1980s. The number may be much lower now, possibly below 10,000 individuals. Species of global conservation concern which do not meet IBA criteria: *Haliaeetus albicilla* (common non-breeder in spring and summer; max. 7 on passage). The delta is also a notable staging ground for migrating geese (especially *Anser fabalis*), ducks and waders; other notable species are *Falco rusticolus* (frequently seen in spring and summer) and *Calidris maritima* (up to 500 in winter).

■ Protection status
National High **International** None
3,360 ha of IBA covered by Nature Reserve (Tanamunningen, 3,360 ha).

■ Conservation issues

Threats Disturbance to birds (U), Extraction industry (U), Infrastructure (U)

Reasons for any possible decline in moulting *Mergus merganser* are not known, and a new census of the birds in the area is urgently needed. A planned harbour (for the mining industry) adjacent to the Nature Reserve may have a negative impact on birds and habitats in the area, but may also reduce the existing boat traffic at the site (which currently may cause disturbance to birds). The area is proposed as a Ramsar Site.

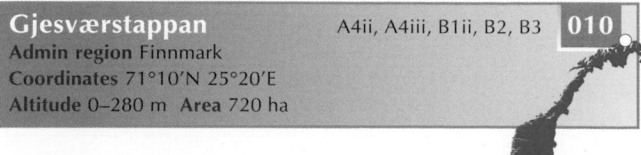

Omgangsstauran   A4i, A4iii, B1i 008
Admin region Finnmark
Coordinates 70°55′N 28°30′E
Altitude 0–278 m **Area** 780 ha

■ Site description
A stretch of coastline with steep cliffs. Land covers 390 ha of the site, the rest being sea.

Habitats Grassland (alpine/subalpine/boreal grassland), Wetland (shingle/stony beach), Marine areas (50%; sea inlet/coastal features), Rocky areas (sea cliff/rocky shore)
Land-use Nature conservation/research

■ Birds

Species	Season	Year	Pop min	Pop max	Acc	Criteria
Phalacrocorax carbo Cormorant	B	1989	100	1,000	A	B1i
[1] *Rissa tridactyla* Kittiwake	B	1997	35,000	35,000	A	A4i, B1i

1. 74,000 pairs in 1985.

The cliffs are important for breeding seabirds.

■ Protection status
National High **International** None
780 ha of IBA covered by Nature Reserve (Omgangsstauran, 780 ha).

■ Conservation issues

Threats Extraction industry (U)

Planned oil production in the Barents Sea may have a negative impact on coastal and marine birds.

Sværholtklubben   A4i, A4iii, B1i 009
Admin region Finnmark
Coordinates 70°58′N 26°40′E
Altitude 0–170 m **Area** 220 ha

■ Site description
A peninsula jutting into the sea, with steep cliffs. Land covers 70 ha of the site, the rest being sea.

Habitats Grassland (alpine/subalpine/boreal grassland), Wetland (shingle/stony beach), Marine areas (68%; sea inlet/coastal features), Rocky areas (sea cliff/rocky shore)
Land-use Nature conservation/research

■ Birds

Species	Season	Year	Pop min	Pop max	Acc	Criteria
[1] *Rissa tridactyla* Kittiwake	B	1997	20,000	25,000	A	A4i, B1i

1. 48,000 pairs in 1985.

The cliffs are important for breeding seabirds.

■ Protection status
National High **International** None
220 ha of IBA covered by Nature Reserve (Sværholtklubben, 220 ha).

■ Conservation issues

Threats Extraction industry (U)

Planned oil production in the Barents Sea may have a negative impact on coastal and marine birds.

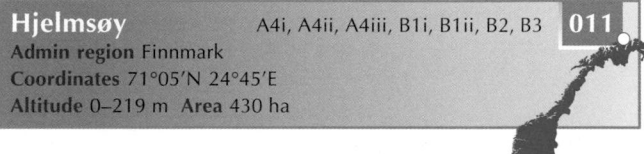

Gjesværstappan   A4ii, A4iii, B1ii, B2, B3 010
Admin region Finnmark
Coordinates 71°10′N 25°20′E
Altitude 0–280 m **Area** 720 ha

■ Site description
Three steep, grass-covered islands: Storstappen, Kjerkestappen and Bukkstappen. Land covers 170 ha of the site, the rest being sea.

Habitats Grassland (alpine/subalpine/boreal grassland), Marine areas (76%; sea inlet/coastal features), Rocky areas (sea cliff/rocky shore)
Land-use Nature conservation/research

■ Birds

Species	Season	Year	Pop min	Pop max	Acc	Criteria
[1] *Sula bassana* Gannet	B	1997	350	500	A	B2
[2] *Alca torda* Razorbill	B	—	4,500	4,500	A	B1ii, B3
[3] *Fratercula arctica* Puffin	B	1990	400,000	400,000	A	A4ii, B1ii, B2

1. Breeding since 1988.
2. 2,500 pairs in 1980s.
3. The second-largest colony in Norway (most are on Storstappen).

Cliff-breeding seabirds nest mainly on Storstappen.

■ Protection status
National High **International** None
720 ha of IBA covered by Nature Reserve (Gjesværstappan, 720 ha).

■ Conservation issues

Threats Extraction industry (U)

Planned oil production in the Barents Sea may have a negative impact on coastal and marine birds.

Hjelmsøy   A4i, A4ii, A4iii, B1i, B1ii, B2, B3 011
Admin region Finnmark
Coordinates 71°05′N 24°45′E
Altitude 0–219 m **Area** 430 ha

■ Site description
A large island with steep cliffs on its northernmost peninsula. Land covers 220 ha of the site, the rest being sea.

Habitats Scrub (heathland), Grassland (alpine/subalpine/boreal grassland), Wetland (shingle/stony beach), Marine areas (49%; sea inlet/coastal features), Rocky areas (sea cliff/rocky shore)
Land-use Nature conservation/research

■ Birds

Species	Season	Year	Pop min	Pop max	Acc	Criteria
Rissa tridactyla Kittiwake	B	—	50,000	50,000	A	A4i, B1i
[1] *Alca torda* Razorbill	B	1995	10,000	10,000	A	A4ii, B1ii, B3
[2] *Fratercula arctica* Puffin	B	1996	60,000	60,000	A	A4ii, B1ii, B2

1. Second largest colony in Norway; 7,000 in 1980s.
2. 20,000 in 1980s.

An important site for breeding seabirds.

■ Protection status
National High **International** None
430 ha of IBA covered by Nature Reserve (Hjelmsøystauran, 430 ha).

■ Conservation issues

Threats Extraction industry (U)

Planned oil production in the Barents Sea may have a negative impact on coastal and marine birds.

Inner part of Porsanger Fjord

A1, A4i, A4iii, B1i, B3 — 012

Admin region Finnmark
Coordinates 70°10′N 24°40′E
Altitude 0–50 m **Area** 2,000 ha

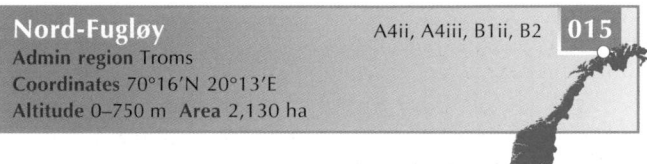

■ Site description

An area of huge mudflats, grassy shorelines, saltmarshes, mires and birch *Betula* forest, close to Stabbursneset headland. Heathland dominates on the islands. There is some traditional egg-collecting by local inhabitants, and harvesting of cloudberries *Rubus chamaemorus* on the islands. Goose hunting takes place, mainly of *Anser fabalis*. The area includes 'Stabbursneset', a site (the former NO010) in the previous pan-European IBA inventory (Grimmett and Jones 1989).

Habitats Scrub (heathland), Wetland (tidal river/enclosed tidal water; mudflat/sandflat; raised bog)
Land-use Hunting, Nature conservation/research, Other

■ Birds

Species	Season	Year	Pop min	Pop max	Acc	Criteria
Anser erythropus Lesser White-fronted Goose	N	1996	50	70	A	A1
[1] *Somateria mollissima* Eider	R	1998	2,500	5,000	A	B1i
[2] *Mergus merganser* Goosander	P	1998	3,000	4,000	A	A4i, B1i
[2,3] *Calidris canutus* Knot	P	1989	25,000	60,000	A	A4i, B1i
Philomachus pugnax Ruff	B	1998	200	—	A	B3
[2] *Limosa lapponica* Bar-tailed Godwit	P	1998	1,000	4,000	A	A4i, B1i
Numenius phaeopus Whimbrel	B	1998	300	—	A	B3

1. 10,000 in winter.
2. Spring.
3. Numbers fluctuate from year to year.

Valdakmyra is an important staging ground for almost the entire Norwegian breeding population of *Anser erythropus*, both in spring (May–June) and autumn (July–September), the species having declined dramatically in Fennoscandia since the 1940s. The huge flocks of staging *Calidris canutus* in late May are a spectacular sight, foraging on the sandbanks exposed at low tide before continuing their migration to Greenland and northern Canada. Some of these birds are the same as those staging at Sørkjosen (IBA 017) in Troms. Wildfowl and other waders, both breeding in the area or on migration, are also numerous in spring, e.g. *Limosa lapponica* (up to several hundred on passage). Good numbers of *Somateria mollissima* (10,000) and *Melanitta nigra* (3,000) gather to moult offshore after the breeding season. Species of global conservation concern that do not meet IBA criteria: *Haliaeetus albicilla* (1–2 pairs breed elsewhere but forage in the area in spring and summer).

■ Protection status

National Partial **International** Partial
1,620 ha of IBA covered by Nature Reserve (Stabbursneset, 1,620 ha).
1,620 ha of IBA covered by Ramsar Site (Stabbursneset, 1,620 ha).

■ Conservation issues

Threats Disturbance to birds (U)

Stabbursnes Nature Reserve consists of 14 km² of water/mudflats and c.2.2 km² of land. All human traffic is prohibited at Valdakmyra (part of the Nature Reserve, c.3.5–4.0 km²) between 1 May and 30 June. The staging *Anser erythropus* have been monitored regularly since 1971, and yearly since 1990 by NOF and the Norwegian Institute for Nature Research.

Alta-Kautokeino watercourse

B2 — 013

Admin region Finnmark
Coordinates 69°33′N 23°37′E
Altitude 100–600 m **Area** 30,000 ha

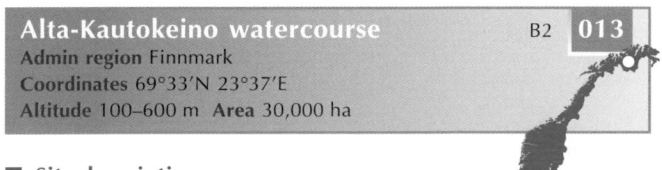

■ Site description

A section of the Alta-Kautokeinoelva valley between Masi and Alta, the northern part being deeper and steeper than the southern part, which is flatter with bogs and lakes.

Habitats Wetland (standing fresh water; river/stream; raised bog)
Land-use Water management

■ Birds

Species	Season	Year	Pop min	Pop max	Acc	Criteria
Falco rusticolus Gyrfalcon	B	1989	0	5	—	B2

The valley is rich in breeding raptors; nine species are present, but no recent estimates of numbers are available.

■ Protection status

National None **International** None

■ Conservation issues

Threats Disturbance to birds (B), Recreation/tourism (U)

The river has been dammed, creating a 20 km long lake which has destroyed a large area of valuable wetland habitat, including broadleaved riverine forest of birch *Betula*.

Loppa

A4iii, B1ii, B2, B3 — 014

Admin region Finnmark
Coordinates 70°22′N 21°24′E
Altitude 0–289 m **Area** 720 ha

■ Site description

An island with cliffs and steep slopes, covered by grassland, bog and heath. The nearest large village is Øksfjord, about 35 km east of Loppa, on the mainland.

Habitats Forest and woodland (5%; broadleaved deciduous forest), Scrub (30%; heathland), Grassland (30%; alpine/subalpine/boreal grassland), Wetland (5%; shingle/stony beach), Marine areas (5%; open sea), Rocky areas (20%; sea cliff/rocky shore), Artificial landscape (5%; urban parks/gardens)
Land-use Agriculture (5%), Fisheries/aquaculture (5%), Nature conservation/research (30%), Not utilized (60%)

■ Birds

Species	Season	Year	Pop min	Pop max	Acc	Criteria
Alca torda Razorbill	B	1997	2,000	3,000	B	B1ii, B3
Cepphus grylle Black Guillemot	R	1993	20	500	B	B1ii, B2
Fratercula arctica Puffin	B	1993	10,000	14,000	A	B1ii

The island has an important seabird colony, which greatly exceeds 10,000 pairs in total.

■ Protection status

National Partial **International** None
245 ha of IBA covered by Nature Reserve (Loppa, 245 ha).

■ Conservation issues

Threats Aquaculture/fisheries (B), Disturbance to birds (B), Extraction industry (U)

Planned oil production in the Barents Sea may have a negative impact on coastal and marine birds. The Nature Reserve includes the steep cliffs on the north-west side.

Nord-Fugløy

A4ii, A4iii, B1ii, B2 — 015

Admin region Troms
Coordinates 70°16′N 20°13′E
Altitude 0–750 m **Area** 2,130 ha

■ Site description

An island with cliffs and steep slopes, rising to a plateau with marshes and small lakes.

Habitats Wetland (standing fresh water; water-fringe vegetation), Rocky areas (sea cliff/rocky shore)
Land-use Nature conservation/research

■ Birds

An important seabird colony. *Uria aalge* has undergone a significant decline in recent years, with 13,000 pairs in 1964, 4,000 pairs in 1974 and less than 100 pairs currently. Species of global conservation concern which do not meet IBA criteria: *Haliaeetus albicilla*.

Species		Season	Year	Pop min	Pop max	Acc	Criteria
Alca torda	Razorbill	B	1989	1,000	2,000	—	B1ii
[1] *Fratercula arctica*	Puffin	B	1967	200,000	—	—	A4ii, B1ii, B2

1. The second-largest colony in Norway.

■ Protection status
National High **International** None
2,130 ha of IBA covered by Nature Reserve (Nord-Fugløy, 2,130 ha).

■ Conservation issues

Threats Aquaculture/fisheries (A)

Sør-Fugløy   A1, A4ii, A4iii, B1ii, B2, B3   016
Admin region Troms
Coordinates 70°07′N 18°30′E
Altitude 0–360 m **Area** 125 ha

■ Site description
A steep island, with slopes partly covered in grass and with boulder scree around the base.

Habitats Grassland (alpine/subalpine/boreal grassland), Rocky areas (100%; sea cliff/rocky shore; scree/boulders)
Land-use Nature conservation/research (100%)

■ Birds

Species		Season	Year	Pop min	Pop max	Acc	Criteria
Haliaeetus albicilla	White-tailed Eagle	N	1995	10	30	B	A1
Alca torda	Razorbill	B	1995	1,000	10,000	B	B1ii, B3
Cepphus grylle	Black Guillemot	R	1994	300	500	B	B1ii, B2
Fratercula arctica	Puffin	B	1990	175,000	175,000	A	A4ii, B1ii, B2

Other breeding seabirds include *Hydrobates pelagicus* (breeding confirmed in 1986; possibly c.100–1,000 pairs).

■ Protection status
National None **International** None

■ Conservation issues

Threats Disturbance to birds (C), Recreation/tourism (C)

The area is proposed as a Nature Reserve with no entrance allowed between 1 April and 31 August.

Sørkjosen   A4i, A4iii, B1i   017
Admin region Troms
Coordinates 69°15′N 19°15′E
Altitude 0–10 m **Area** 433 ha

■ Site description
Sørkjosen is the most important among several large tidal areas in Balsfjord, being the outlet of two rivers at the head of the fjord. The tidal zone stretches from Markenes in the east to Storsteinnes in the west, consisting of large areas of mud, sand and gravel-banks, and extends as far as 700 m out. Along the shoreline there is some woodland of alder *Alnus* and birch *Betula*, a medium-sized coastal meadow, agricultural fields, and some industrial areas. Offshore, outside the IBA, are important fishing areas and spawning grounds for herring *Clupea harengus* and capelin *Mallotus villosus*.

Habitats Wetland (mudflat/sandflat), Marine areas (sea inlet/coastal features)
Land-use Fisheries/aquaculture, Urban/industrial/transport

■ Birds

Species		Season	Year	Pop min	Pop max	Acc	Criteria
[1] *Podiceps auritus*	Slavonian Grebe	P	—	—	260	—	B1i
[2] *Calidris canutus*	Knot	P	1998	10,000	28,000	—	A4i, B1i

1. Spring.
2. Daily maximum on spring passage (28,000 in 1984).

Huge flocks of *Calidris canutus* stage here on the way to their breeding grounds in Greenland and northern Canada, arriving in early May and peaking at several tens of thousands before departing at the end of the month. In late winter, large flocks of seaduck gather in Sørkjosen, feeding on the eggs of capelin and herring. One or two *Falco rusticolus* sometimes hunt in the area.

■ Protection status
National None **International** None

■ Conservation issues

Threats Filling-in of wetlands (C), Industrialization/urbanization (B)

As of 1989, industry was expanding and threatened the tidal area. The area is proposed as a Ramsar Site.

Bleiksøy   A4ii, A4iii, B1ii, B2   018
Admin region Nordland
Coordinates 69°16′N 15°52′E
Altitude 0–160 m **Area** 20 ha

■ Site description
A steep island of grass-covered slopes, with boulder-scree in gullies at the foot of vertical cliffs. Traditional collecting of eggs of *Phalacrocorax aristotelis*, *Rissa tridactyla* and other gulls is permitted until 1 June.

Habitats Marine areas (open sea), Rocky areas (sea cliff/rocky shore; scree/boulders)
Land-use Other

■ Birds

Species		Season	Year	Pop min	Pop max	Acc	Criteria
Fratercula arctica	Puffin	B	1997	80,000	80,000	—	A4ii, B1ii, B2

A seabird colony, with particularly important numbers of *Fratercula arctica*.

■ Protection status
National None **International** None

■ Conservation issues

Threats Disturbance to birds (C), Unsustainable exploitation (C)

It is not known whether there are threats to the site or its birds.

Skogvoll (including Skarvklakken)   A1, B1i, B2   019
Admin region Nordland
Coordinates 69°10′N 15°41′E
Altitude 0–8 m **Area** 2,800 ha

■ Site description
An area of shallow sea with a number of small islands/skerries, including Skarvklakken, and extensive tidal mudflats. Sheep graze in the area.

Habitats Wetland (55%; mudflat/sandflat; saltmarsh; sand-dunes/sand beach), Marine areas (35%; open sea), Rocky areas (10%; rock stacks/islets)
Land-use Agriculture (5%), Nature conservation/research (100%)

■ Birds

Species		Season	Year	Pop min	Pop max	Acc	Criteria
[1] *Sula bassana*	Gannet	B	1989	800	800	—	B2
Anser brachyrhynchus	Pink-footed Goose	P	1989	1,000	—	—	B1i
Haliaeetus albicilla	White-tailed Eagle	U	1997	—	48	—	A1

1. Skarvklakken (one of five colonies in Norway).

There are breeding seabirds, including *Sula bassana* and *Phalacrocorax carbo*, and shorebirds. Ducks and *Anser anser* moult in the area.

■ Protection status
National High **International** None
2,800 ha of IBA covered by Nature Reserve (Skogvoll, 2,800 ha).

■ Conservation issues

Threats Disturbance to birds (C)

Disturbance of nesting birds is a threat. The area is proposed as a Ramsar Site.

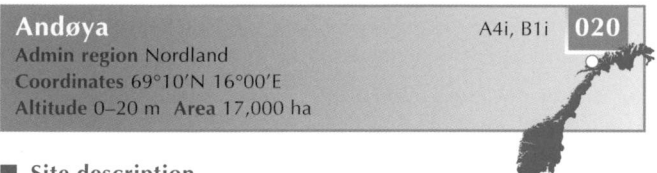

Andøya   A4i, B1i   020
Admin region Nordland
Coordinates 69°10'N 16°00'E
Altitude 0–20 m **Area** 17,000 ha

■ Site description

An area of coastal meadows, pastures and tidal mudflats, stretching from Åse north to Breivik along the eastern part of the island of Andøya. Grassland is mainly sheep-grazed.

Habitats Grassland (alpine/subalpine/boreal grassland), Wetland (mudflat/sandflat)
Land-use Agriculture, Military

■ Birds

Species	Season	Year	Pop min	Pop max	Acc	Criteria
[1] *Anser brachyrhynchus* Pink-footed Goose	P	1998	6,000	7,000	—	A4i, B1i

1. Svalbard population; spring passage (peaks in mid-May).

The site is most important for staging *Anser brachyrhynchus*. *Branta leucopsis* is quite common on passage.

■ Protection status
National None **International** None

■ Conservation issues

Threats Disturbance to birds (U), Other (U)

Grazing geese seem to cause major damage to the crops of local farmers, which may be leading to disturbance of the birds or illegal shooting ('Other' threat).

Anda   A4iii, B2   021
Admin region Nordland
Coordinates 69°10'N 15°10'E
Altitude 0–50 m **Area** 10 ha

■ Site description

A low-lying, grass-covered island, with steep cliffs on the east side.

Habitats Grassland (alpine/subalpine/boreal grassland), Rocky areas (sea cliff/rocky shore)
Land-use Unknown

■ Birds

Species	Season	Year	Pop min	Pop max	Acc	Criteria
Fratercula arctica Puffin	B	1997	20,000	25,000	—	B2

An important colony for *Fratercula arctica*.

■ Protection status
National None **International** None

■ Conservation issues

Threats Unknown

Langøya   A4i, B1i   022
Admin region Nordland
Coordinates 68°45'N 15°25'E
Altitude 0–20 m **Area** 20,000 ha

■ Site description

A 500 m wide strip of coastal meadows, pastures and tidal mudflats

in the east-south-eastern part of the island of Langøya, from Skagen airport (at Stokmarknes) past Sortland to Vikbotn, and then from Vikbotn in a westerly direction to Frøskeland. Grassland is mainly sheep-grazed.

Habitats Grassland (alpine/subalpine/boreal grassland), Wetland (mudflat/sandflat)
Land-use Agriculture

■ Birds

Species	Season	Year	Pop min	Pop max	Acc	Criteria
[1] *Anser brachyrhynchus* Pink-footed Goose	P	1998	6,000	7,000	—	A4i, B1i

1. Svalbard population; spring passage (peaks in mid-May).

The site is most important for staging geese from Svalbard, especially *Anser brachyrhynchus* but also *Branta leucopsis* (quite common).

■ Protection status
National None **International** None

■ Conservation issues

Threats Disturbance to birds (U), Other (U)

Grazing geese seem to cause major damage to the crops of local farmers, which may be leading to disturbance of the birds or illegal shooting ('Other' threat).

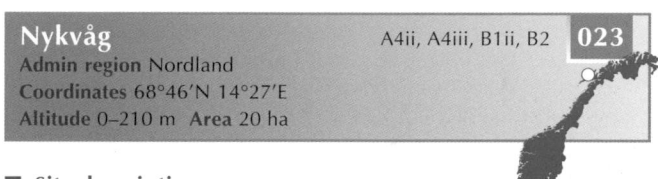

Nykvåg   A4ii, A4iii, B1ii, B2   023
Admin region Nordland
Coordinates 68°46'N 14°27'E
Altitude 0–210 m **Area** 20 ha

■ Site description

Nykvåg is a vertical cliff behind Nykvåg harbour, on the steep, grass-covered island of Fuglenyken. The cliffs of Måsnyken and Frugga are also included in this site.

Habitats Grassland (alpine/subalpine/boreal grassland), Rocky areas (sea cliff/rocky shore)
Land-use Unknown

■ Birds

Species	Season	Year	Pop min	Pop max	Acc	Criteria
Alca torda Razorbill	B	1989	250	250	—	B1ii
Fratercula arctica Puffin	B	1997	200,000	200,000	—	A4ii, B1ii, B2

An important colony for *Fratercula arctica*—the estimate for the colony size is significantly higher than that in 1989 (40,000 pairs).

■ Protection status
National None **International** None

■ Conservation issues

Threats Unknown

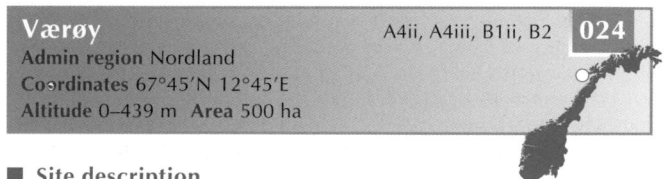

Værøy   A4ii, A4iii, B1ii, B2   024
Admin region Nordland
Coordinates 67°45'N 12°45'E
Altitude 0–439 m **Area** 500 ha

■ Site description

High vertical cliffs and steep grass-covered slopes on the south-west peninsula of Værøy island.

Habitats Grassland (alpine/subalpine/boreal grassland), Marine areas (open sea), Rocky areas (sea cliff/rocky shore)
Land-use Unknown

■ Birds

The breeding colony of *Rissa tridactyla* (15,000–20,000 pairs) is also notable.

Species		Season	Year	Pop min	Pop max	Acc	Criteria
Alca torda	Razorbill	B	1989	800	800	—	B1ii
[1] *Fratercula arctica*	Puffin	B	1989	—	70,000	—	A4ii, B1ii, B2

1. 70,000 pairs in 1974, but considerable decrease since then.

■ Protection status
National None **International** None

■ Conservation issues
No threats are known.

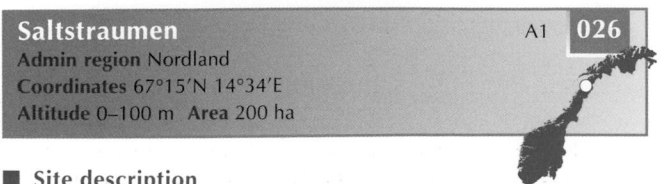

Røst
A4i, A4ii, A4iii, B1i, B1ii, B2, B3 **025**

Admin region Nordland
Coordinates 67°30′N 12°00′E
Altitude 0–259 m **Area** 1,750 ha

■ Site description
Røst is an archipelago consisting of more than 400 islands. The most important seabird colonies are on Vedøy, Storfjellet, Ellefsnyken, Trenyken and Hernyken. These are steep, grass-covered islands (92–259 m high). The island of Røstlandet is inhabited, with numerous ponds, saltmarshes and mires.

Habitats Grassland (alpine/subalpine/boreal grassland), Wetland (saltmarsh; standing fresh water; blanket bog), Rocky areas (sea cliff/rocky shore)
Land-use Nature conservation/research

■ Birds

Species		Season	Year	Pop min	Pop max	Acc	Criteria
Phalacrocorax aristotelis	Shag	B	1997	500	1,000	—	A4i, B1i, B3
[1] *Alca torda*	Razorbill	B	1997	2,000	3,000	—	B1ii, B3
Cepphus grylle	Black Guillemot	B	1997	1,000	1,500	A	B1ii, B2
[2] *Fratercula arctica*	Puffin	B	1997	500,000	660,000	A	A4ii, B1ii, B2

1. Declining (nearly 5,000 pairs in 1964; 2,000–4,000 pairs in 1983).
2. Largest colony in Norway, declining (c.1,400,000 pairs in 1979).

The islands of Røst are famous for one of Europe's largest colonies of *Fratercula arctica*. However, the species has declined severely in abundance during the last 30 years, due to a collapse in the food supply: in the late 1960s the population was estimated as twice as large as it is now. Other breeding seabirds include *Hydrobates pelagicus* and *Oceanodroma leucorhoa* (the largest colonies in Norway), *Alca torda*, *Phalacrocorax aristotelis*, *Uria aalge* (abundance has decreased by 20–30% since the early 1980s), *Fulmarus glacialis* and *Rissa tridactyla* (c.17,500 pairs in 1988; decrease in numbers by more than 30% between 1993 and 1994). Species of global conservation concern that do not meet IBA criteria: *Haliaeetus albicilla* (common).

■ Protection status
National Low **International** None
92 ha of IBA covered by Nature Reserve (Røstlandet, 92 ha).

■ Conservation issues
Threats Aquaculture/fisheries (U)

Following the collapse of the Norwegian herring stock in the late 1960s, the breeding numbers of *Fratercula arctica* have decreased, due to high chick mortality. The only island which is open to the public, apart from Røstlandet, is Vedøy. Access to the bird cliffs is prohibited between 15 April and 15 August, except for daytime excursions to parts of Vedøy. Monitoring and research on the *Fratercula arctica* colony is carried out by the Norwegian Institute for Nature Research.

Saltstraumen
A1 **026**

Admin region Nordland
Coordinates 67°15′N 14°34′E
Altitude 0–100 m **Area** 200 ha

■ Site description
A sea inlet with a very strong and fish-rich tidal river. There is considerable tourist traffic along the river, and some boat traffic through the sea inlet.

Habitats Wetland (tidal river/enclosed tidal water), Marine areas (sea inlet/coastal features)
Land-use Tourism/recreation, Urban/industrial/transport

■ Birds

Species		Season	Year	Pop min	Pop max	Acc	Criteria
Haliaeetus albicilla	White-tailed Eagle	N	—	25	100	—	A1

An important wintering area for *Haliaeetus albicilla*, the abundance of which fluctuates according to the food supply.

■ Protection status
National None **International** None

■ Conservation issues
Threats Recreation/tourism (U)

Traffic causes some disturbance of *Haliaeetus albicilla*, and plans to increase tourist traffic may be a problem.

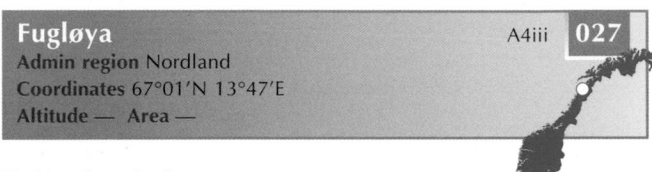

Fugløya
A4iii **027**

Admin region Nordland
Coordinates 67°01′N 13°47′E
Altitude — **Area** —

■ Site description
Gently sloping sides of a south-facing valley, covered with scree.

Land-use Unknown

■ Birds
More than 10,000 pairs of seabird breed here, the commonest species being *Fratercula arctica* (c.10,000 pairs).

■ Protection status
National None **International** None

■ Conservation issues
No threats are known. The site is a proposed Nature Reserve.

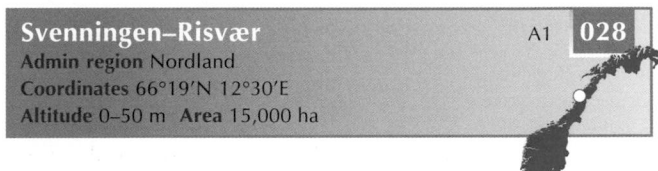

Svenningen–Risvær
A1 **028**

Admin region Nordland
Coordinates 66°19′N 12°30′E
Altitude 0–50 m **Area** 15,000 ha

■ Site description
An archipelago of hundreds of islands (maximum size 300 ha), islets, and skerries. The landscape is undulating with a mosaic of rocks and bogs. Parts of the largest islands are cultivated and inhabited.

Habitats Wetland (raised bog), Rocky areas (rock stacks/islets), Artificial landscape (arable land)
Land-use Agriculture

■ Birds

Species		Season	Year	Pop min	Pop max	Acc	Criteria
Haliaeetus albicilla White-tailed Eagle		W	1989	25	30	—	A1

A very important area for *Haliaeetus albicilla* in winter.

■ Protection status
National None **International** None

■ Conservation issues
Threats Other (U)

The area is very vulnerable to oil pollution ('Other' threat). The site is a proposed Nature Reserve.

Lovunden — 029

A1, A4iii, B1ii, B2

Admin region Nordland
Coordinates 66°21'N 12°19'E
Altitude 0–623 m **Area** —

■ Site description

The island of Lovunden is a steep mountain with scree around the base and numerous islets and skerries offshore. On the north-east side there is a small village where the 300 inhabitants of the island live.

Habitats Marine areas (open sea), Rocky areas (sea cliff/rocky shore; rock stacks/islets; scree/boulders)
Land-use Unknown

■ Birds

Species	Season	Year	Pop min	Pop max	Acc	Criteria
[1] *Haliaeetus albicilla* White-tailed Eagle	R	1995	10	20	—	A1
[2] *Cepphus grylle* Black Guillemot	B	1997	200	—	—	B1ii
[3] *Fratercula arctica* Puffin	B	1997	25,000	25,000	—	B2

1. Individuals (present all year but number of breeding pairs not known).
2. Some hundred pairs breed.
3. Declining: 60,000 pairs in 1957 (250,000 birds in colony); 40,000 pairs in 1977; 25,000 pairs at end of 1980s.

Lovunden is most famous for its huge breeding colony of *Fratercula arctica*, the size of which has, unfortunately, decreased dramatically in recent decades. The colony is occupied between April and mid-September. *Haliaeetus albicilla* is very common throughout the year: one can often see 8–10 birds at the same time, and 15–20 gathered in one flock is not an uncommon sight in spring or early summer.

■ Protection status

National None **International** None

■ Conservation issues

Threats Unknown

Vega archipelago — 030

A1, A4i, A4iii, B1i, B1ii, B2, B3

Admin region Nordland
Coordinates 65°49'N 11°45'E
Altitude 0–800 m **Area** 50,000 ha

■ Site description

Vega is an archipelago of several thousand small islands and islets. Some of the largest islands are partly cultivated and inhabited. The landscape is a mosaic of peatbogs and rocky areas, with scattered brackish tarns between Viksås and Holand, and near Valen, as well as some freshwater ponds. Intertidal areas are extensive, with seaweed beds, nutrient-rich mud, and rock, sand and gravel; the most important mudflats for birds are on the northern side of the main island.

Habitats Wetland (mudflat/sandflat; standing brackish and salt water; blanket bog), Marine areas (open sea; sea inlet/coastal features), Rocky areas (rock stacks/islets), Artificial landscape (arable land)
Land-use Agriculture, Fisheries/aquaculture, Tourism/recreation

■ Birds

Haliaeetus albicilla is common all year-round. *Anser brachyrhynchus* is numerous on passage in spring. A wide variety of waders often breed, and large numbers stage on the island shores in early autumn. Seaduck are the most common wintering waterbirds in the shallow areas west and north of the main island, and include *Somateria spectabilis* (c.500).

Species	Season	Year	Pop min	Pop max	Acc	Criteria
Gavia immer Great Northern Diver	W	1986	200	200	A	A4i, B1i
[1] *Phalacrocorax carbo* Cormorant	B	1989	3,500	3,500	A	A4i, B1i
Phalacrocorax aristotelis Shag	B	1989	300	—	—	B3
[2] *Anser anser* Greylag Goose	N	1989	—	4,000	A	A4i, B1i
[3] *Branta leucopsis* Barnacle Goose	P	1989	—	10,500	A	A4i, B1i
Somateria mollissima Eider	B	1986	5,000	6,000	A	B1i
Somateria mollissima Eider	W	1986	15,000	31,000	A	A4i, B1i
[2] *Somateria mollissima* Eider	N	1986	4,500	5,000	A	B1i

Species ... continued		Season	Year	Pop min	Pop max	Acc	Criteria
[4] *Haliaeetus albicilla* White-tailed Eagle		R	1996	10	—	B	A1, B2
Calidris maritima Purple Sandpiper		W	1989	1,100	1,100	A	A4i, B1i
Cepphus grylle Black Guillemot		R	1986	2,100	2,100	—	B1ii, B2

1. The largest colony north of 60°N in Europe.
2. Moulting.
3. Almost entire Svalbard population stages on spring passage.
4. At least 60 birds in winter.

■ Protection status

National Partial **International** None
Part of IBA covered by Nature Reserve (Kjellerhaugvatn; area unknown). Part of IBA covered by Nature Reserve (Sveavatn; area unknown). Part of IBA covered by Nature Reserve (Vikåsleirene; area unknown).

■ Conservation issues

Threats Abandonment/reduction of land management (U), Extraction industry (U)

The absence since 1980 of sheep-grazing and traditional land management on the outer islands, the preferred staging areas for *Branta leucopsis*, has reduced the availability of suitable plant food for the geese and has forced them to stage on the inner, inhabited islands. Here, through their grazing on crops, the geese are in conflict with farmers. Experiments to scare the geese from some agricultural areas have been carried out. The former staging areas are no longer suitable for *Branta leucopsis* due to domination of the sward by perennial herbs (*Filipendula*) and due to a large increase in the abundance of voles *Microtus*. Oil production in the Norwegian Sea outside Nordland County represents a potential threat to the many seabirds wintering in the waters around Vega. Part of the area is a proposed National Park.

Sklinna — 031

A4i, B1i, B1ii, B2, B3

Admin region Nord-Trøndelag
Coordinates 65°12'N 11°00'E
Altitude 0–31 m **Area** 106 ha

■ Site description

An archipelago, about 20 km from the mainland. The largest island, Heimøya, is 1 km long. Two of the islands are connected with a mole. The largest islands are covered with heathland *Empetrum/Calluna*, mixed with bushes *Rubus/Cornus*. Fishermen lived on Sklinna up to the first half of this century, but now the only settlement is the lighthouse (manned year-round) on Heimøy.

Habitats Scrub (heathland), Marine areas (open sea), Rocky areas (sea cliff/rocky shore; rock stacks/islets)
Land-use Fisheries/aquaculture

■ Birds

Species	Season	Year	Pop min	Pop max	Acc	Criteria
[1] *Phalacrocorax aristotelis* Shag	B	1996	600	1,600	A	A4i, B1i, B3
Larus marinus Great Black-backed Gull	R	1992	341	341	A	B3
Cepphus grylle Black Guillemot	R	1992	526	526	A	B1ii, B2

1. 1987–1996.

The breeding colony of *Phalacrocorax aristotelis* is one of the largest in Norway.

■ Protection status

National None **International** None

■ Conservation issues

Threats Aquaculture/fisheries (C), Recreation/tourism (C)

The breeding seabirds at Sklinna are monitored annually by the Norwegian Institute for Nature Research as part of the National Monitoring Program for Seabirds, and the area is a proposed Nature Reserve. American mink *Mustela vison*, has not been able to reach the archipelago because it is situated so far from the mainland, which is an advantage for the breeding seabirds.

Froan

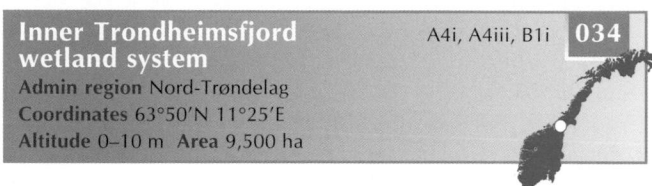

A1, A4i, B1i, B1ii, B2, B3   **032**

Admin region Sør-Trøndelag
Coordinates 63°50′N 8°40′E
Altitude 0–40 m   Area 60,000 ha

■ Site description
The Froan archipelago consists of hundreds of islands, islets and skerries. Most of the islands are low and undulating, with rock outcrops, moorland and small bogs. Only the islands of Sauøya and Sørbuøya are inhabited at present.

Habitats Scrub (heathland), Wetland (5%; mudflat/sandflat; shingle/stony beach), Marine areas (90%; open sea; sea inlet/coastal features), Rocky areas (5%; sea cliff/rocky shore; rock stacks/islets)
Land-use Fisheries/aquaculture (10%), Nature conservation/research (85%), Tourism/recreation (5%)

■ Birds

Species	Season	Year	Pop min	Pop max	Acc	Criteria
Gavia stellata Red-throated Diver	B	1985	—	22	A	B2
Phalacrocorax carbo Cormorant	R	1992	—	2,955	A	A4i, B1i
Phalacrocorax aristotelis Shag	R	1998	—	1,000	A	A4i, B1i, B3
[1] *Somateria mollissima* Eider	N	1998	—	35,000	B	A4i, B1i
Mergus serrator Red-breasted Merganser	N	1985	—	3,000	B	A4i, B1i
[2] *Haliaeetus albicilla* White-tailed Eagle	W	1989	—	20	—	A1
[3] *Cepphus grylle* Black Guillemot	N	1988	—	3,000	B	B1ii

1. Moulting.
2. Three pairs breed.
3. Outside breeding season.

Up to 17 *Gavia adamsii* and eight *Gavia immer* winter in the area.

■ Protection status
National High   **International** None
40,400 ha of IBA covered by Nature Reserve (Froan, 40,400 ha). 12,000 ha of IBA covered by Flora and Fauna Protection Area (Froan Animal Protection Area, 12,000 ha). 8,000 ha of IBA covered by Landscape Protected Area (Froan, 8,000 ha).

■ Conservation issues

Threats Aquaculture/fisheries (B), Consequences of animal/plant introductions (B), Disturbance to birds (B), Extraction industry (A), Recreation/tourism (B)

The large concentrations of moulting and wintering waterbirds in the area are extremely vulnerable to oil pollution.

Ørland wetland system

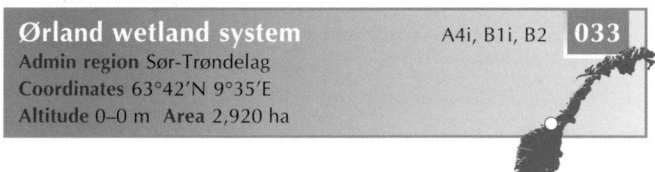

A4i, B1i, B2   **033**

Admin region Sør-Trøndelag
Coordinates 63°42′N 9°35′E
Altitude 0–0 m   Area 2,920 ha

■ Site description
Four wetlands consisting mainly of tidal mudflats and shallow seas, separated from agricultural land by small areas of meadow and saltmarsh.

Habitats Wetland (80%; mudflat/sandflat; saltmarsh; shingle/stony beach), Marine areas (20%; sea inlet/coastal features)
Land-use Fisheries/aquaculture (10%), Nature conservation/research (100%), Tourism/recreation (5%)

■ Birds

Species	Season	Year	Pop min	Pop max	Acc	Criteria
Phalacrocorax carbo Cormorant	W	1992	2,500	2,500	A	B1i
Somateria mollissima Eider	W	1995	3,000	3,000	A	B1i
[1] *Somateria mollissima* Eider	N	1989	6,700	6,700	—	B1i
[2] *Melanitta fusca* Velvet Scoter	W	1995	3,500	3,500	A	B2
Mergus serrator Red-breasted Merganser	W	1995	4,000	4,000	A	A4i, B1i

1. Moulting.
2. Also 7,200 moulting.

Species of global conservation concern which do not meet IBA criteria: *Haliaeetus albicilla* (wintering). The IBA also supports notable numbers of *Podiceps auritus* (49 on passage).

■ Protection status
National High **International** High
1,500 ha of IBA covered by Nature Reserve (Grandefjæra, 1,500 ha). 120 ha of IBA covered by Flora and Fauna Protection Area (Hovsfjæra Bird Sanctuary, 120 ha). 110 ha of IBA covered by Flora and Fauna Protection Area (Innstrandfjæra Bird Sanctuary, 110 ha). 1,190 ha of IBA covered by Flora and Fauna Protection Area (Kråkvågsvaet, 1,190 ha). 2,920 ha of IBA covered by Ramsar Site (Ørlandet, 2,920 ha).

■ Conservation issues

Threats Construction/impact of dyke/dam/barrage (A), Disturbance to birds (B), Drainage (A), Extraction industry (A), Groundwater abstraction (U), Unsustainable exploitation (B)

The meadows and marshes were formerly extensive, but almost all were drained for agriculture during 1960–1990. Threats include sand exploitation, disturbance to birds, airport noise, waste from ships, and agriculture.

Inner Trondheimsfjord wetland system

A4i, A4iii, B1i   **034**

Admin region Nord-Trøndelag
Coordinates 63°50′N 11°25′E
Altitude 0–10 m   Area 9,500 ha

■ Site description
The site comprises a 50 km stretch along the north-eastern side of Trondheimsfjord, the third largest fjord in Norway, from south of Levanger to north of Steinkjer. This is a network of 10–12 key wetlands, some of which would qualify as IBAs individually. The main habitats are extensive shallow subtidal areas, intertidal mudflats and the mouths of two large rivers, Verdalselva and Steinkjerelva, as well as those of several smaller ones. Land surrounding the fjord is mainly cultivated, but semi-natural meadows remain intact in a few places. The site includes 'Gjørv, Borgenfjorden', an IBA that was listed individually (as site NO030) in the previous European IBA inventory (Grimmett and Jones 1989).

Habitats Wetland (15%; tidal river/enclosed tidal water; mudflat/sandflat; saltmarsh), Marine areas (85%; sea inlet/coastal features)
Land-use Hunting, Military, Nature conservation/research, Tourism/recreation, Urban/industrial/transport

■ Birds

Species	Season	Year	Pop min	Pop max	Acc	Criteria
Podiceps auritus Slavonian Grebe	P	—	100	200	—	B1i
[1] *Anser brachyrhynchus* Pink-footed Goose	P	1997	10,000	20,000	A	A4i, B1i
[2] *Somateria mollissima* Eider	P	—	5,000	10,000	A	B1i
Tringa totanus Redshank	P	1996	500	1,500	A	B1i

1. Mainly in spring (Svalbard population).
2. Spring.

Most or all of the Svalbard population of *Anser brachyrhynchus* (30,000 birds) probably stages in the area in May during spring migration, thus this is probably one of the most important stop-over sites in Norway for the species (c.3,000 stage at Gjørv [Borgenfjorden] alone). The geese forage on the mudflats, but spend the nights on the water. The area is notable as a staging area for other seabirds, waders and ducks as well. Seaduck such as *Melanitta nigra*, *M. fusca*, *Bucephala clangula* and *Clangula hyemalis* occur in large numbers on spring migration. The estimated number of geese, ducks, waders and gulls staging in the whole area is 35,000–60,000.

■ Protection status
National Low **International** None
40 ha of IBA covered by Nature Reserve (Hammeren, 40 ha). 210 ha of IBA covered by Nature Reserve (Rinnleiret, 210 ha). 49 ha of IBA covered by Nature Reserve (Ørin, 49 ha). 230 ha of IBA covered by Flora and Fauna Protection Area (Eidsbotn, 230 ha).

■ Conservation issues

Threats Filling-in of wetlands (U), Industrialization/urbanization (U), Recreation/tourism (U), Unsustainable exploitation (U)

Land-claim for industrial development, a horse-racing track and agriculture have destroyed some mudflats in the past. Aquaculture and military activities affect one site each. Local authorities have recently allowed a private land-owner to extract a total of 350,000 m³ of sand and gravel from the sea-bottom at Ørin. This will most probably result in habitat degradation for seaduck, especially for *Melanitta nigra*. Recreation and illegal hunting are also widespread problems. The County Governorate is carrying out a conservation plan for seabird areas (breeding, migrating/moulting and wintering seabirds). In addition to the four areas that are protected already, a further eight areas of mudflat and shallow sea will be protected within a few years. In addition, several islets important for breeding birds will probably be protected by law. There are annual counts of wintering seabirds, as a part of the 'National Monitoring Programme for Seabirds', in the Trondheimsfjord. At two sites there are weekly bird counts between April and October, as part of other projects conducted by NOF.

Lake Leksdalsvatn   A4i, B1i 035
Admin region Nord-Trøndelag
Coordinates 63°50'N 11°37'E
Altitude 70–72 m **Area** 2,200 ha

■ Site description
A large, lowland lake between Verdal and Steinkjer, 12 km long and up to c.20 m deep, with a shoreline of c.35 km. The lake is nutrient-rich with large reedbeds *Phragmites/Schoenoplectus* in shallow areas. Alder *Alnus* and willow *Salix* trees occur along most of the shoreline. Adjacent land is mostly cultivated.

Habitats Forest and woodland (2%; alluvial/very wet forest), Wetland (98%; standing fresh water; water-fringe vegetation)
Land-use Nature conservation/research (10%), Tourism/recreation

■ Birds

Species	Season	Year	Pop min	Pop max	Acc	Criteria
Podiceps auritus Slavonian Grebe	B	1996	20	50	B	B1i
[1] *Cygnus cygnus* Whooper Swan	P	1992	400	982	A	A4i, B1i
[2] *Anser brachyrhynchus* Pink-footed Goose	P	1996	1,000	3,500	A	A4i, B1i

1. Normally 400–600; higher numbers after mild winters when lake is ice-free earlier.
2. Roost site in spring.

The most important site in central Norway for staging *Cygnus cygnus*, and one of the most important for breeding *Podiceps auritus*.

■ Protection status
National Partial **International** None
52 ha of IBA covered by Flora and Fauna Protection Area (Figgaoset, 52 ha). 45 ha of IBA covered by Managed Nature Reserve (Lundselvoset, 45 ha). 237 ha of IBA covered by Flora and Fauna Protection Area (Lyngås-Klinga Bird Sanctuary, 237 ha).

■ Conservation issues

Threats Filling-in of wetlands (C)

The lake is a popular spot for birdwatchers, and the local department of NOF keeps a record of observations.

Stjørdals Fjord   A4i, A4iii, B1i, B2 036
Admin region Nord-Trøndelag, Sør-Trøndelag
Coordinates 63°28'N 10°50'E
Altitude 0–0 m **Area** 2,500 ha

■ Site description

Habitats Wetland (18%; tidal river/enclosed tidal water; mudflat/sandflat), Marine areas (80%; sea inlet/coastal features)
Land-use Fisheries/aquaculture (20%), Urban/industrial/transport (5%)

A 10-km long fjord in the south-eastern part of the Trondheimsfjord, 20–25 km east of Trondheim. At the outlet of the Stjørdalselva river there are meadows, intertidal flats of sand and mud, and shallow subtidal habitat. Further out, on the northern side of the site, there

are fewer mudflats. The sea here is still quite shallow: as far as 1–2 km offshore it is not more than 10–20 m deep.

■ Birds

Species	Season	Year	Pop min	Pop max	Acc	Criteria
Somateria mollissima Eider	R	1993	6,000	9,000	—	B1i
[1] *Somateria mollissima* Eider	P	1993	3,500	4,000	—	B1i
Larus canus Common Gull	B	1993	5,000	10,000	A	A4i, B1i, B2

1. Birds migrating from Trondheimsfjord to the Gulf of Bothnia in spring (total excludes local breeding birds).

This is a notable staging area for congregatory seabirds and waterbirds, especially in spring—for example, in April there are 20,000–30,000 seabirds present. Birds are partly attracted by herring roe, which may be washed ashore in layers up to 0.5 m thick during storms and rough seas (the area is important for spawning herring *Clupea harengus* in spring).

■ Protection status
National None **International** None

■ Conservation issues

Threats Aquaculture/fisheries (B), Filling-in of wetlands (B), Industrialization/urbanization (B), Infrastructure (B), Recreation/tourism (C)

The entanglement and drowning of seabirds in fishing nets is a major problem, especially in spring. Land-claim for industrial development and roads has destroyed mudflats in the inner parts of the fjord. Further road-building is planned, but no final decisions in this respect have yet been made.

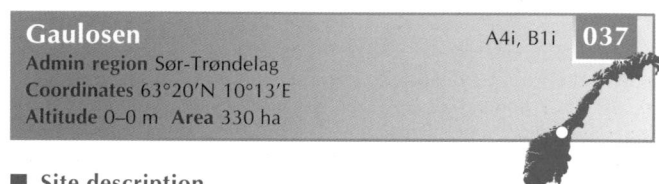

Gaulosen   A4i, B1i 037
Admin region Sør-Trøndelag
Coordinates 63°20'N 10°13'E
Altitude 0–0 m **Area** 330 ha

■ Site description
An estuary of the Gaula river with a small island (Storøra) and extensive tidal mudflats and coastal shallows.

Habitats Wetland (100%; tidal river/enclosed tidal water; mudflat/sandflat; saltmarsh; sand-dunes/sand beach; shingle/stony beach)
Land-use Nature conservation/research (80%), Not utilized (20%)

■ Birds

Species	Season	Year	Pop min	Pop max	Acc	Criteria
Anser brachyrhynchus Pink-footed Goose	P	1991	—	3,250	C	A4i, B1i

The area holds a range of waders and wildfowl in good numbers. Species of global conservation concern which do not meet IBA criteria: *Haliaeetus albicilla* (2 pairs).

■ Protection status
National Partial **International** None
60 ha of IBA covered by Nature Reserve (Gaulosen, 60 ha). 179 ha of IBA covered by Landscape Protected Area (Gaulosen, 179 ha). 5 ha of IBA covered by Nature Reserve (Leinøra, 5 ha).

■ Conservation issues

Threats Disturbance to birds (B), Filling-in of wetlands (A), Infrastructure (A), Unsustainable exploitation (B)

All of the IBA (except Buvikfjæra) is protected. The area is proposed as a Ramsar Site.

Havmyran   A1 038
Admin region Sør-Trøndelag
Coordinates 63°30'N 8°40'E
Altitude 10–70 m **Area** 3,960 ha

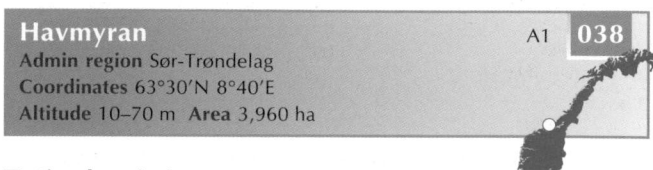

■ Site description
An open mire landscape with many small freshwater lakes.

Habitats Wetland (standing fresh water; fen/transition mire/spring)
Land-use Nature conservation/research

■ Birds

Species	Season	Year	Pop min	Pop max	Acc	Criteria
[1] *Haliaeetus albicilla* White-tailed Eagle	W	—	—	35	—	A1

1. One pair breeds.

The area is also a notable breeding area for waders, mainly *Pluvialis apricaria*, *Calidris alpina* and *Numenius phaeopus*.

■ Protection status
National High **International** None
3,960 ha of IBA covered by Nature Reserve (Havmyran, 3,960 ha).

■ Conservation issues

Threats Other (U)

There are plans to build wind-farms in an adjacent area, which may have an indirect, negative effect on the birds at this site ('Other' threat). The area is proposed as a Ramsar Site.

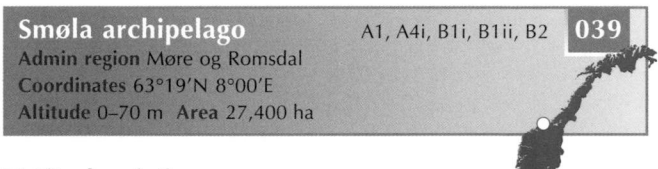

Smøla archipelago   A1, A4i, B1i, B1ii, B2   **039**
Admin region Møre og Romsdal
Coordinates 63°19′N 8°00′E
Altitude 0–70 m **Area** 27,400 ha

■ Site description
An archipelago of 5,847 islands, islets and skerries, with large expanses of intervening shallow sea. The main island, Smøla, is a mosaic of open mire and coastal heathland, with many small lakes, streams, ponds and pools, and is cultivated in places. Its coast is dissected by many inlets and bays. This is one of the largest marine wetlands in Norway, and some of the largest continuous mires in the country are also found here.

Habitats Scrub (heathland), Wetland (standing fresh water; river/stream; fen/transition mire/spring), Marine areas (sea inlet/coastal features), Rocky areas (rock stacks/islets), Artificial landscape
Land-use Agriculture, Fisheries/aquaculture

■ Birds

Species	Season	Year	Pop min	Pop max	Acc	Criteria
Gavia immer Great Northern Diver	W	1989	150	150	—	A4i, B1i
Podiceps grisegena Red-necked Grebe	W	1989	600	600	—	A4i, B1i
[1] *Anser anser* Greylag Goose	N	1989	2,000	2,000	—	B1i
[2] *Somateria mollissima* Eider	W	1989	5,400	5,400	—	B1i
Melanitta fusca Velvet Scoter	W	1989	2,050	2,050	—	B2
Mergus serrator Red-breasted Merganser	W	1989	2,800	2,800	—	A4i, B1i
[3] *Haliaeetus albicilla* White-tailed Eagle	R	1998	30	30	—	A1
Cepphus grylle Black Guillemot	B	1989	250	250	—	B1ii, B2

1. Moulting; 300 pairs breed.
2. 500 pairs breed; 1,700 moulting.
3. 50+ overwinter.

Smøla has one of the highest breeding densities (pairs per hectare of land) of *Haliaeetus albicilla* in the world. The sea areas are important for wintering divers *Gavia*, grebes *Podiceps* and various seaduck. *Cygnus cygnus* winter in notable numbers (up to 300 birds or more). The area has been an important moulting site for flocks of *Anser anser*, causing conflicts with the local farmers. The largest colony of *Ardea cinerea* ever found in Norway was located in the area during the 1970s (200–300 pairs). Some species normally found in the mountains of Norway, or along the coast further north, breed here, e.g. *Pluvialis apricaria*, *Lagopus lagopus* and *Calcarius lapponicus*. Breeding divers (*Gavia stellata* and, to a lesser extent, *G. arctica*) are also relatively common.

■ Protection status
National None **International** None

■ Conservation issues
Current problems include drainage and further cultivation on the largest islands; coastal and marine bird species are very vulnerable to

oil pollution. There are plans to build wind-farms in an area where several pairs of *Haliaeetus albicilla* nest ('Other' threat). Management of *Anser anser* (by shooting), in order to reduce crop damage, is being evaluated by the Norwegian Institute for Nature Research. Protection plans for the area have been prepared by the County Governorate of Møre and Romsdal.

Threats Agricultural intensification/expansion (A), Drainage (A), Industrialization/urbanization (U), Other (U)

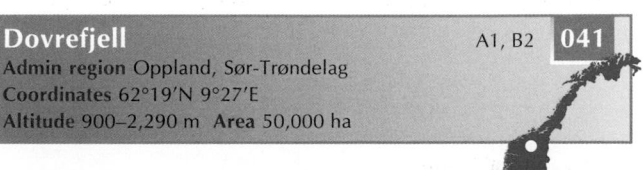

Runde   A4i, A4ii, A4iii, B1i, B1ii, B2, B3   **040**
Admin region Møre og Romsdal
Coordinates 62°24′N 5°36′E
Altitude 0–333 m **Area** 640 ha

■ Site description
An island with cliffs and steep slopes, partly covered with boulders, grassland and heath. There is sheep-grazing.

Habitats Scrub (heathland), Grassland (alpine/subalpine/boreal grassland), Rocky areas (sea cliff/rocky shore; scree/boulders)
Land-use Agriculture, Fisheries/aquaculture, Tourism/recreation

■ Birds

Species	Season	Year	Pop min	Pop max	Acc	Criteria
[1] *Sula bassana* Gannet	B	1998	2,000	—	—	B1ii, B2
[2] *Phalacrocorax aristotelis* Shag	B	1998	1,300	1,300	A	A4i, B1i, B3
[2] *Rissa tridactyla* Kittiwake	B	1998	40,000	50,000	A	A4i, B1i
Alca torda Razorbill	B	1998	3,000	3,000	A	B1ii, B3
Fratercula arctica Puffin	B	1998	100,000	100,000	B	A4ii, B1ii, B2

1. Increasing; the largest colony in Norway.
2. Strongly decreasing.

An important seabird colony, the largest in southern Norway. Breeding numbers of *Stercorarius skua* (15 pairs) and *S. parasiticus* (3 pairs) are also noteworthy. Species of global conservation concern that do not meet IBA criteria: *Haliaeetus albicilla* (non-breeding visitor; probably breeds too).

■ Protection status
National Partial **International** None
265 ha of IBA covered by Nature Reserve (Runde and Grasøyane, 265 ha).

■ Conservation issues

Threats Recreation/tourism (U)

The area is vulnerable to oil pollution. Public access to the Nature Reserve is restricted between 1 April and 31 August. The IBA lies within an area of wildlife protection (comprising 9,000 ha of sea and 700 ha of land).

Dovrefjell   A1, B2   **041**
Admin region Oppland, Sør-Trøndelag
Coordinates 62°19′N 9°27′E
Altitude 900–2,290 m **Area** 50,000 ha

■ Site description
Dovrefjell is the only boreal montane ecosystem in Norway which is still relatively intact and unaffected by man's activities. It is a typical boreal montane area, with broad marshy valleys and forest of birch *Betula*. The National Park is a major recreation area. A railway and a road pass through the Landscape Protection Area.

Habitats Forest and woodland (broadleaved deciduous forest), Grassland (alpine/subalpine/boreal grassland), Wetland (standing fresh water; river/stream; water-fringe vegetation)
Land-use Hunting, Military, Nature conservation/research, Tourism/recreation, Urban/industrial/transport

■ Birds
A notable breeding site for several species of wader, duck and raptor.

Species		Season	Year	Pop min	Pop max	Acc	Criteria
Gallinago media	Great Snipe	B	1989	400	—	—	A1, B2

■ Protection status
National Partial **International** None
25,580 ha of IBA covered by National Park (Dovrefjell, 25,580 ha).
750 ha of IBA covered by Nature Reserve (Fokstumyra, 750 ha).
6,600 ha of IBA covered by Landscape Protected Area (Drivdalen–Kongsvoll–Hjerkinn, 6,600 ha).

■ Conservation issues

> **Threats** Disturbance to birds (B), Recreation/tourism (B)

Access to Fokstumyra Nature Reserve in the breeding season is prohibited except on marked tracks. This reserve is proposed as a Ramsar Site. Studies of *Gallinago media* have been carried out for several years by the Norwegian Institute for Nature Research.

Hardangervidda A1, A4i, B1i, B2, B3 042
Admin region Buskerud, Hordaland, Telemark
Coordinates 60°12′N 7°37′E
Altitude 1,000–1,500 m **Area** 427,200 ha

■ Site description
The largest boreal montane plateau in Europe, dominated by undulating terrain with several large lakes. This is a major sheep-grazing area, and there is also tourism and hunting (of reindeer *Rangifer tarandus* and grouse *Lagopus*).

> **Habitats** Scrub (scrub), Grassland (alpine/subalpine/boreal grassland), Wetland (standing fresh water; river/stream; water-fringe vegetation), Rocky areas (inland cliff)
> **Land-use** Agriculture, Hunting, Nature conservation/research, Tourism/recreation, Urban/industrial/transport

■ Birds

Species		Season	Year	Pop min	Pop max	Acc	Criteria
Falco rusticolus	Gyrfalcon	B	1999	20	20	C	B2
Charadrius morinellus	Dotterel	B	1999	2,500	2,500	A	A4i, B1i
Pluvialis apricaria	Golden Plover	B	1999	5,000	5,000	A	B3
¹ *Gallinago media*	Great Snipe	B	1989	70	100	—	A1, B2

1. Numbers may be increasing; seven leks known with several probably still to be found.

Other breeding species include *Gavia arctica*, *Aquila chrysaetos*, *Calidris temminckii*, *Stercorarius longicaudus* (the southernmost regular breeding area in Europe), *Lagopus lagopus*, *Lagopus mutus*, *Plectrophenax nivalis* and *Calcarius lapponicus*. Hardangervidda was also, until recently, a traditional breeding area for *Nyctea scandiaca*, with up to at least 12–13 pairs in years of high rodent abundance. The last confirmed breeding record was in 1974, and the species appears to have stopped breeding in this area, for unknown reasons (although any records since 1974 may have been kept secret). One hypothesis is that increased tourism and disturbance may have driven the species away, another is that changes in rodent abundance (especially lemmings *Lemmus*) may have altered the food conditions for the owls in an unfavorable way.

■ Protection status
National Partial **International** None
342,200 ha of IBA covered by National Park (Hardangervidda, 342,200 ha).

■ Conservation issues

> **Threats** Disturbance to birds (B), Recreation/tourism (B)

Grazing sheep may have affected the vegetation, and thus altered the habitat requirements of many animals in this very fragile ecosystem. Increasing tourism is a potential problem. Studies in boreal montane ecology (including birds) have been carried out by several research institutions, especially the Universities of Bergen and Oslo and the Norwegian Institute for Nature Research.

Kjørholmane seabird reserve A4i, B1i, B3 043
Admin region Rogaland
Coordinates 58°53′N 5°25′E
Altitude 0–30 m **Area** 600 ha

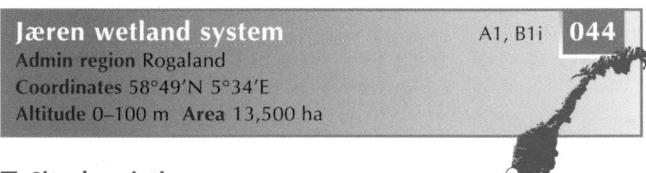

■ Site description
Three larger and several smaller islands and islets, together with surrounding seas. The islands are mainly covered in boulders and scree, intermingled with ponds and vegetated areas. Human activities include fishing and sheep-grazing, both at low intensity.

> **Habitats** Marine areas (94%; open sea; sea inlet/coastal features), Rocky areas (6%; sea cliff/rocky shore; scree/boulders)
> **Land-use** Not utilized (95%)

■ Birds

Species		Season	Year	Pop min	Pop max	Acc	Criteria
¹ *Phalacrocorax aristotelis*	Shag	R	1995	1,910	1,910	A	A4i, B1i, B3
Larus fuscus	Lesser Black-backed Gull	B	1995	500	700	B	B3

1. Increasing.

This is the southernmost seabird colony of notable size in Norway.

■ Protection status
National Low **International** None
44 ha of IBA covered by Nature Reserve (Kjørholmane seabird reserve, 44 ha).

■ Conservation issues

> **Threats** Aquaculture/fisheries (C), Consequences of animal/plant introductions (C), Natural events (C)

Introduced rabbits *Oryctolagus cuniculus* are present. Entrance to the Nature Reserve is prohibited during the breeding season. Breeding seabirds are monitored almost annually by the Norwegian Institute for Nature Research.

Jæren wetland system A1, B1i 044
Admin region Rogaland
Coordinates 58°49′N 5°34′E
Altitude 0–100 m **Area** 13,500 ha

■ Site description
Jæren is one of the main agricultural districts in Norway, lying west and south of the city of Stavanger. The area is defined as the rectangle from Lake Søylandsvatn and Lake Lonavatn in the south (c.5 km apart), stretching about 27 km northwards to Hafrsfjord. The landscape is gently undulating, and the site includes several lakes, sand-dune shores, stone/boulder beaches and some shallow sea. The lakes have a rich aquatic vegetation.

> **Habitats** Wetland (sand-dunes/sand beach; standing fresh water; water-fringe vegetation), Marine areas (sea inlet/coastal features), Rocky areas (sea cliff/rocky shore), Artificial landscape
> **Land-use** Agriculture, Fisheries/aquaculture, Nature conservation/research, Urban/industrial/transport

■ Birds

Species		Season	Year	Pop min	Pop max	Acc	Criteria
Podiceps auritus	Slavonian Grebe	W	1980	55	55	—	B1i
¹ *Crex crex*	Corncrake	B	1999	15	20	A	A1

1. Singing males.

This is the core breeding area for *Crex crex* in Norway, and one of the most important wintering and staging areas for inland waterbirds in Norway, with more than 10,000 occurring in winter. Notable wintering species include *Gavia stellata* (25), *G. arctica* (6), *G. immer* (20), *G. adamsii* (occasional) and *Podiceps grisegena* (110).

■ Protection status
National Partial **International** Low
13 ha of IBA covered by Nature Reserve (Alvevatn, 12 ha). 6 ha of IBA covered by Nature Reserve (Grannesbukta, 6 ha). 74 ha of IBA

covered by Nature Reserve (Grudevatnet, 74 ha). 36 ha of IBA covered by Nature Reserve (Hagavågen, 36 ha). 331 ha of IBA covered by Nature Reserve (Harvalandsvatn, 331 ha). 8 ha of IBA covered by Nature Reserve (Heigremyra, 8 ha). 32 ha of IBA covered by Nature Reserve (Lonavatn, 32 ha). 900 ha of IBA covered by Nature Reserve (Orrevatn, 900 ha). 24 ha of IBA covered by Nature Reserve (Smokkevatn, 24 ha). 13 ha of IBA covered by Nature Reserve (Strandnesvågen, 13 ha). 70 ha of IBA covered by Nature Reserve (Søylandsvatn, 70 ha). 12 ha of IBA covered by Nature Reserve (Øksnevadtjern, 12 ha). 1,608 ha of IBA covered by Landscape Protection Area (Jærstrendene, 1,608 ha). 400 ha of IBA covered by Ramsar Site (Jæren, 400 ha).

■ Conservation issues

Threats Agricultural intensification/expansion (U), Disturbance to birds (U)

The lakes are nutrient-rich, but this is mainly due to agricultural pollution, which has accelerated vegetational succession and which causes blooms of toxic algae. The Grudevatn and Jærstrendene protected areas form part of the existing Ramsar Site. All the other Nature Reserves have been newly designated, and all of them (except Heigremyra) have been proposed for incorporation into the existing Ramsar Site or for designation as new, individual Ramsar Sites.

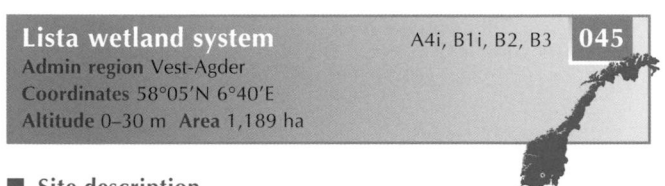

Lista wetland system — A4i, B1i, B2, B3 — 045
Admin region Vest-Agder
Coordinates 58°05′N 6°40′E
Altitude 0–30 m Area 1,189 ha

■ Site description
The area consists of a stretch of coastline and five separate wetlands inland. The latter are remnants following extensive drainage during the twentieth century. The coastline at Lista typically consists of stony and sandy beaches and the site includes a large offshore area of shallow sea. The inland wetlands consist of nutrient-rich lakes, marshes and mudflats.

Habitats Wetland (70%; sand-dunes/sand beach; shingle/stony beach; standing fresh water; blanket bog; fen/transition mire/spring), Marine areas (25%; sea inlet/coastal features), Artificial landscape (5%; arable land; forestry plantation)
Land-use Agriculture (50%), Fisheries/aquaculture (10%), Military (9%), Nature conservation/research (11%), Not utilized (35%), Tourism/recreation (16%)

■ Birds

Species	Season	Year	Pop min	Pop max	Acc	Criteria
Podiceps auritus Slavonian Grebe	W	1995	75	75	A	B1i
¹*Anser anser* Greylag Goose	P	1994	4,000	4,000	A	A4i, B1i
Melanitta fusca Velvet Scoter	W	1995	500	500	A	B2
Tringa totanus Redshank	B	1987	600	600	A	B2
¹*Larus fuscus* Lesser Black-backed Gull	B	1995	2,545	2,545	A	A4i, B1i, B3

1. Increasing.

A notable staging area for waterbirds both in spring and autumn, e.g. for *Calidris alpina* (7,000 on passage). Numerous seabirds, birds of prey and passerines also make use of the wetland system during migration. More than 5,000 pairs of waterbird breed in the area, and 5,000–8,000 waterbirds winter there.

■ Protection status
National High **International** None
147 ha of IBA covered by Nature Reserve (Nesheimvann, 147 ha). 26 ha of IBA covered by Nature Reserve (Rauna, 26 ha). 9 ha of IBA covered by Nature Reserve (Røyrtjern, 9 ha). 11 ha of IBA covered by Flora and Fauna Protection Area (Lundevågen, 11 ha). 37 ha of IBA covered by Flora and Fauna Protection Area (Prestevannet, 37 ha). 257 ha of IBA covered by Landscape Protected Area (Hanangervann og Kråkenesvann, 257 ha).

■ Conservation issues

Threats Agricultural intensification/expansion (B), Consequences of animal/plant introductions (B), Disturbance to birds (B), Drainage (A), Dredging/canalization (A), Filling-in of wetlands (B), Industrialization/urbanization (B), Recreation/tourism (A)

The major part of Lista (c.4,000 ha) was wetland until the Second World War, but the largest amount was drained as late as the 1980s. Although 90% of the site is now protected, birds and habitats in the area are still threatened by agriculture, industrialization (e.g. at Lundevågen) and tourism (e.g. disturbance of birds by sailing at Nordhasselbukta). Nature conservation in general, and conservation of Lista in particular, are treated as a low priority by local politicians and community leaders. These factors are putting great pressure on the existing protected areas. The area that remains unprotected (10% of the total) should be protected, to avoid further habitat destruction. Lista Bird Observatory has conducted standardized studies on migrating birds in the western parts of the area, and is taking part in the European–African Songbird Migration Network project (supported by the European Science Foundation). The local department of the Norwegian Ornithological Society monitors breeding waterbirds and migrating waders and ducks. The colony of *Larus fuscus* at Rauna Nature Reserve is counted and monitored annually, as part of the national seabird research programme, led by the Norwegian Institute for Nature Research (NINA). NINA also conducts annual counts of wintering waterbirds in the area.

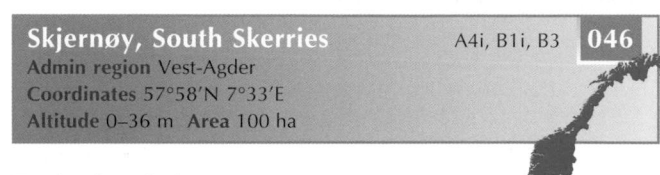

Skjernøy, South Skerries — A4i, B1i, B3 — 046
Admin region Vest-Agder
Coordinates 57°58′N 7°33′E
Altitude 0–36 m Area 100 ha

■ Site description
The southernmost site in Norway: nine islets to the south of Skjernøy, named Store Slettingen, Lille Slettingen, Store Vengelsholmen, Lille Vengelsholmen, Skjøringen, Sandøy, Odden, Hellersøy, and Maurholmen. The islets are jagged, rocky outcrops with minimal vegetation (patches of grass and herbs, with juniper *Juniperus* scrub on some, especially Sandøy). They are surrounded by deep water, but there are many small skerries in the area.

Habitats Scrub (30%; scrub; heathland), Grassland (20%), Marine areas (25%; sea inlet/coastal features), Rocky areas (25%; sea cliff/rocky shore; rock stacks/islets)
Land-use Agriculture (75%), Fisheries/aquaculture (5%), Not utilized (20%), Tourism/recreation (10%)

■ Birds

Species	Season	Year	Pop min	Pop max	Acc	Criteria
¹*Larus fuscus* Lesser Black-backed Gull	B	1995	4,000	4,500	A	A4i, B1i, B3

1. *L. f. intermedius.*

Larus argentatus and *Somateria mollissima* also breed in some numbers at the site.

■ Protection status
National Partial **International** None
6 ha of IBA covered by Nature Reserve (Skjøringen, 6 ha). 11 ha of IBA covered by Nature Reserve (Slettingen, 11 ha). 16 ha of IBA covered by Nature Reserve (Store Vengelsholmen, 16 ha).

■ Conservation issues

Threats Disturbance to birds (B), Recreation/tourism (B)

No great threats to the area are apparent, but disturbance of birds is a problem on the unprotected islands. Slettingen Nature Reserve and Sandøya are covered by the national seabird breeding monitoring project, conducted by the Norwegian Institute for Nature Research.

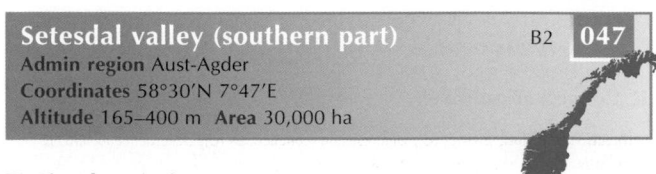

Setesdal valley (southern part) — B2 — 047
Admin region Aust-Agder
Coordinates 58°30′N 7°47′E
Altitude 165–400 m Area 30,000 ha

■ Site description
The site consists of the Otra river and surrounding areas. The river is the largest in the southernmost part of Norway, and has been regulated for hydroelectric purposes to a great extent, although no dams exist

within the site itself. Forests cover most of the surrounding area, mainly consisting of pine *Pinus*.

Habitats Forest and woodland (80%; broadleaved deciduous forest; native coniferous forest), Wetland (10%; standing fresh water; river/stream), Artificial landscape (10%; arable land; forestry plantation; urban parks/gardens; other urban/industrial areas)
Land-use Agriculture (10%), Fisheries/aquaculture (10%), Forestry (50%), Military (10%), Hunting, Tourism/recreation, Urban/industrial/transport (10%)

■ Birds

Species	Season	Year	Pop min	Pop max	Acc	Criteria
Pandion haliaetus Osprey	B	1998	6	10	A	B2

After several decades of very low breeding numbers in Norway, due to the severe influence of acid rain on freshwater ecosystems, *Pandion haliaetus* are now increasing in this area, probably as a result of full national protection of the species in 1962, and re-colonization following the re-introduction of trout *Salmo trutta* and the liming of rivers and streams.

■ Protection status
National None **International** None

■ Conservation issues

Threats Aquaculture/fisheries (B), Deforestation (commercial) (B), Disturbance to birds (A), Industrialization/urbanization (C), Recreation/tourism (A)

Commercial fishing of trout *Salmo trutta* and perch *Perca fluviatilis* utilizes the same fish populations as *Pandion haliaetus*, and should be managed so as to secure the birds' food-supply. Numbers of *Pandion haliaetus* are monitored by local birdwatchers (NOF Aust-Agder), and data on the number of pairs and nesting success exist from about 1980. One nest-site has been protected by the local authorities after it was exposed to disturbance by commercial tourism. Protection includes restrictions on forestry and on public access in the area during the breeding season.

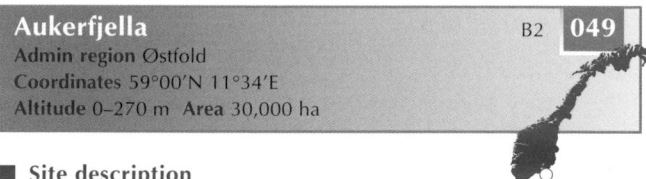

Lake Vannsjø — B2 048
Admin region Østfold
Coordinates 59°40′N 10°50′E
Altitude 25–200 m **Area** 15,000 ha

■ Site description
The site is a large, nutrient-rich freshwater lake, situated near the city of Moss. The lake is connected with the Oslofjord by the Mosse-elva river. Forestry is widespread; military activity mainly comprises low-flying planes from a nearby air base.

Habitats Forest and woodland (broadleaved deciduous forest; native coniferous forest), Wetland (standing fresh water; river/stream; raised bog; water-fringe vegetation; fen/transition mire/spring), Artificial landscape (highly improved reseeded grassland; arable land; forestry plantation)
Land-use Agriculture (10%), Fisheries/aquaculture (90%), Forestry (10%), Military, Nature conservation/research, Tourism/recreation, Water management (90%)

■ Birds

Species	Season	Year	Pop min	Pop max	Acc	Criteria
Pandion haliaetus Osprey	B	1998	9	10	A	B2

This is an important breeding site for *Pandion haliaetus*, with the highest known density of natural nests in Norway.

■ Protection status
National Low **International** None
330 ha of IBA covered by Nature Reserve (Vestre Vannsjø, 330 ha).

■ Conservation issues

Threats Aquaculture/fisheries (U), Deforestation (commercial) (U), Disturbance to birds (U), Intensified forest management (U), Recreation/tourism (U)

Nutrient pollution by agricultural activities is a problem. Forestry may be a problem for *Pandion haliaetus*, since trees are cut close to the nests; such activity should be planned, to avoid nest-sites and to reduce

disturbance to nesting birds. Vannsjo supplies drinking water to Moss, and the local authorities take action to reduce pollution at the lake. Low-flying planes do not seem to affect *Pandion haliaetus* in any way. There is limited tourism in the area, and there are restrictions on motor-boats (maximum 5 knots within 100 m of land). Access to the Nature Reserve is restricted during the breeding season. Local ornithologists ring several bird species in the area, including *Pandion haliaetus*.

Aukerfjella — B2 049
Admin region Østfold
Coordinates 59°00′N 11°34′E
Altitude 0–270 m **Area** 30,000 ha

■ Site description
The site is situated south and east of the town of Halden, in south-eastern Norway. Coniferous forest covers most of the area, and lakes and minor bogs are abundant. Only eight of the lakes are larger than 2 km², with Lake Femsjø being the largest (11 km²). Most of the lakes are nutrient-poor.

Habitats Forest and woodland (65%; native coniferous forest), Wetland (25%; standing fresh water; river/stream; raised bog), Artificial landscape (10%; arable land)
Land-use Forestry (75%)

■ Birds

Species	Season	Year	Pop min	Pop max	Acc	Criteria
Pandion haliaetus Osprey	B	1995	6	10	A	B2

■ Protection status
National Low **International** None
2,500 ha of IBA covered by Nature Reserve (Lundsneset, 5,000 ha).

■ Conservation issues

Threats Deforestation (commercial) (C), Recreation/tourism (C), Other (U)

The 'Other' threat is acid rain. The Nature Reserve lies adjacent to Tresticklan National Park in Sweden, which encloses Lake Søndre Boksjø.

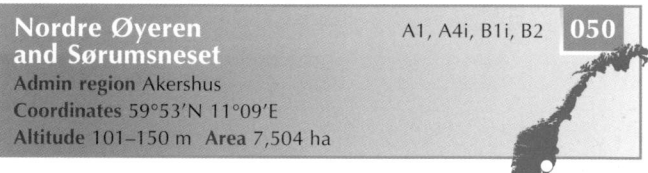

Nordre Øyeren and Sørumsneset — A1, A4i, B1i, B2 050
Admin region Akershus
Coordinates 59°53′N 11°09′E
Altitude 101–150 m **Area** 7,504 ha

■ Site description
The largest inland delta in Scandinavia, formed by the mouths of the Glomma, Leira and Nilelva rivers flowing into Lake Øyeren. The northern part is shallow, with inland areas covered by deciduous forest, scrub, grassland and agricultural land.

Habitats Forest and woodland (5%; broadleaved deciduous forest; native coniferous forest; mixed forest), Wetland (90%; mudflat/sandflat; standing fresh water; river/stream), Artificial landscape (5%; arable land)
Land-use Agriculture (5%), Hunting (50%), Tourism/recreation (90%), Water management (90%)

■ Birds

Species	Season	Year	Pop min	Pop max	Acc	Criteria
Cygnus cygnus Whooper Swan	W	1995	1,500	1,500	A	A4i, B1i
Anser brachyrhynchus Pink-footed Goose	P	1995	400	400	A	B1i
Anas crecca Teal	P	1995	7,600	7,600	A	B1i
Pandion haliaetus Osprey	B	1995	9	9	A	B2
Falco peregrinus Peregrine	P	1995	Frequent	—		B2
Gallinago media Great Snipe	P	1995	Frequent	—		A1

An important area for migrating waterbirds, and for swans *Cygnus* in winter, as well as for breeding *Pandion haliaetus*. Breeding species of global conservation concern which do not meet IBA criteria: *Crex crex* (1–2 pairs).

■ Protection status
National Partial **International** Partial
6,260 ha of IBA covered by Nature Reserve (Nordre Øyeren, 6,260 ha).
6,260 ha of IBA covered by Ramsar Site (Nordre Øyeren, 6,260 ha).

■ Conservation issues

Threats Agricultural intensification/expansion (B), Consequences of animal/plant introductions (A), Disturbance to birds (B), Recreation/tourism (B)

Hunting disrupts and disturbs staging and wintering waterbirds significantly. Nordre Øyeren Bird Observatory has published reports dating back to 1976, and has carried out various projects, including studies of *Dendrocopos leucotos* and systematic waterfowl surveys.

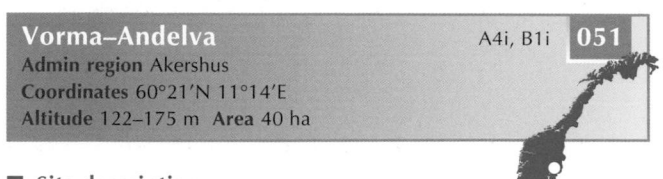

Vorma–Andelva A4i, B1i 051
Admin region Akershus
Coordinates 60°21′N 11°14′E
Altitude 122–175 m **Area** 40 ha

■ Site description
Vorma is the initial stretch of the largest river in Norway, the Glomma, flowing out of Mjøsa, the largest lake in Norway. The most important places for birds at this site are found between the outlet from Mjøsa and Eidsvoll, and along the Andelva river which flows from Lake Aurdal into the Vorma river. The area around the rivers is mostly cultivated. Water is used for electricity generation.

Habitats Wetland (100%; river/stream)
Land-use Urban/industrial/transport (50%), Water management (100%)

■ Birds

Species	Season	Year	Pop min	Pop max	Acc	Criteria
[1] *Cygnus cygnus* Whooper Swan	W	1994	700	700	A	A4i, B1i

1. Increasing.

The best area for *Cygnus cygnus* is up the Vorma river from Eidsvoll Station to Minnesund at the outlet of Lake Mjøsa, an area that does not freeze in winter.

■ Protection status
National None **International** None

■ Conservation issues

Threats Infrastructure (B)

As part of the development of a new main airport in Norway at Gardemoen, there is a railroad planned along the Vorma river upstream from Eidsvoll station. This is the most important area for swans *Cygnus*, and could be critically impacted. Wintering swans and other waterbirds have been counted at Vorma and Glomma since 1988. The Norwegian railroad bureau (NSB) has also initiated studies on wintering waterbirds, related to new railroad projects in the area.

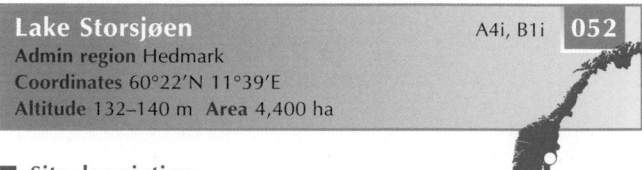

Lake Storsjøen A4i, B1i 052
Admin region Hedmark
Coordinates 60°22′N 11°39′E
Altitude 132–140 m **Area** 4,400 ha

■ Site description
A shallow lake (up to 17 m deep) surrounded by mixed forest, *Alnus* forest and agricultural land. It is normally ice-covered in winter.

Habitats Wetland (100%; standing fresh water)
Land-use Nature conservation/research (7%)

■ Birds

Species	Season	Year	Pop min	Pop max	Acc	Criteria
[1] *Cygnus cygnus* Whooper Swan	P	—	10	1,000	B	A4i, B1i

1. Maximum was in March 1992.

A wide range of waterbirds stage here on passage.

■ Protection status
National None **International** None

■ Conservation issues

Threats Construction/impact of dyke/dam/barrage (U), Disturbance to birds (U), Recreation/tourism (U)

Disturbance to birds occurs, especially in early spring when areas of open water are small and the local people push boats over the ice to these areas and set fishing nets.

REFERENCES

AARVAK, T., ØIEN, I. J., SYROECHKOVSKI, E. E. AND KOSTADINOVA, I. (1997) *The Lesser White-fronted Goose Monitoring Programme. Annual report 1997*. Klæbu, Norway: Norwegian Ornithological Society (NOF Rapportserie. Report No. 5).

ABILDSNES, J. (1998) [*Conservation of biological diversity. Wetland reserves II: the protected areas of Froan.*] Norway: Miljøvernavdelingen, Fylkesmannen i Sør-Trøndelag (Report 2/98). (In Norwegian.)

ANKER-NILSSEN, T. (1997) Bird cliffs in northern Norway. Pp. 458–460 in R. Vik and V. Ree, eds. *Norges Fugleliv*. Fourth edition. Oslo: Det Beste A/S.

ANKER-NILSSEN, T., BAKKEN, V. AND STRANN, K.-B. (1988) [*Analysis of consequences by petroleum activity in the Barents Sea south of 74°30′N.*] Norway: Directorate for Nature Management (Wildlife Report No. 46). (In Norwegian.)

ANKER-NILSSEN, T., BAKKEN, V., BIANKI V., GOLOVKIN, A., STRØM, H. AND TATARINKOVA, I., EDS. (In press) *Status of marine birds breeding in the Barents Sea Region*. Oslo: Norwegian Polar Institute (Report).

ANON. (1981) *Utkast til verneplan for fuglefjell i Finnmark Fylke*. Norway: Fylkesmannen i Finnmark, Environmental Dept.

ANON. (1993) *Verna og verneverdige områder i Finnmark*. Norway: Fylkesmannen i Finnmark (Report No. 2).

ANON. (1993) *Konsekvenser for fugl og vannkvalitet ved utbygging av sjørelatert industriområde i Lundevågen, Farsund*. Norway: Norwegian Institute for Nature Research (Report No. 0–9315).

ANON. (1995) [*Nature Protection Areas in Norway*]. Trondheim, Norway: Direktoratet for Naturforvaltning (DN-report No. 3-1995). 178 pp. (In Norwegian, with English summary.)

ANON. (1997) *Norges Nasjonalparker [National Parks of Norway]*. Trondheim, Norway: Direktoratet for Naturforvaltning. (In Norwegian.)

BARRETT, R. (1996) Number of breeding seabirds in the largest seabird colonies in northern Norway. Unpublished.

BARRETT, R. T. AND STRANN, K.-B. (1987) Two new breeding records of the Storm Petrel *Hydrobates pelagicus* in Norway. *Fauna Norv. Ser. C., Cinclus* 4: 115–116.

BERGAN, M. (1982) Faunistisk report for Oslo og Akershus. *Vår Fuglefauna* 4.

BERGAN, M. (1982) LRSK–rapport nr. 3. *Toppdykker'n* 5: 93–106.

BRUN, E. (1963). Ornithological features of Nord-Fugløy and Sør-Fugløy. *Astorte* 22: 1–13.

BUSTNES, J. O., SYSTAD, G. H. AND STRANN, K.-B. (1993) *Drukning av sjøfugl i laksegarn innenfor reservatet på Loppa*. Norway: Norwegian Institute for Nature Research (NINA Oppdragsmelding 17).

FOLLESTAD, A., LARSEN, B. H. AND NYGÅRD, T. (1989) [*Surveys of seabirds along the coast of Sør- and Nord-Trøndelag and southern parts of Nordland 1983–1986.*] Norway: Norwegian Directorate for Nature Management (Wildlife Rep. No. 41). (In Norwegian, with English summary.)

FREMO, K. E, ANDERSEN, J. E. AND BANGJORD, G. (1994) [*Conservation of biological diversity. Wetland reserves and bird sanctuaries in the county of Sør-Trøndelag.*] Norway: Miljøvernavd, Fylkesmannen i Sør-Trøndelag (Report 7/94). (In Norwegian.)

FREMO, K. E., ANDERSEN, J. E. AND BANGJORD, G. (1994) [*Conservation of biological diversity. National parks, landscape protection areas, plant protection areas and "naturminner" in the county of Sør-Trøndelag.*] Norway: Miljøvernavd, Fylkesmannen i Sør-Trøndelag (Report 10/94). (In Norwegian.)

GJERSHAUG, J. O., THINGSTAD, P. G., ELDØY, S. AND BYRKJELAND, S. (1994) *Norsk Fugleatlas*. Klæbu, Norway: Norsk Ornitologisk Forening. 552 pp. (In Norwegian.)

GRIMMETT, R. F. A. AND JONES, T. A. (1989) *Important Bird Areas in Europe*. Cambridge, UK: International Council for Bird Preservation (Techn. Publ. 9).

HAFTORN, S. (1971) *Norges fugler.* [*Birds of Norway.*] Oslo: Universitetsforlaget. (In Norwegian.)

HAGEN, Y. (1954) *Rovfuglene og viltpleien.* Oslo: Universitetsforlaget.

HÅLAND, A. AND KÅLÅS, J. A. (1980) Spring migration of the Siberian Knot *Calidris canutus*: additional information. *Wader Study Group Bull.* 28: 22–23.

HANSEN, T. O. AND LORENTZEN, N. H. (1987) Trekkfuglstudier på Tjørveneset frem t.o.m. 1986. *Piplerka* 17: 124–156.

HAUGSKOTT, T. (1991) Fuglefaunaen i Falstadbukta, Alfuusfjæra, Eidsbotn, Tynnfjæra, Rinnleiret, Ørin og Tronesbukta, Levanger og Verdal kommuner. (Report written to Fylkesmannen i Nord-Trøndelag.) Unpublished.

HAUGSKOTT, T. (1997) [Inner parts of the Trondheimsfjord: a wetland system of international importance.] *Vår Fuglefauna* 20: 8–13. (In Norwegian, with English summary.)

HEATH, M. F. AND BORGGREVE, C. (2000) *BirdLife International/EBCC European Bird Database 1998.* Cambridge, UK: BirdLife International.

JØRGENSEN, F. (1990) Nesheimsumpen—første rettsrunde. *Piplerka* 20: 145–147.

KÅLÅS, J. A. AND BYRKJEDAL, I. (1981) [The status of breeding waders Charadrii in Norway including Svalbard.] *Proc. Second. Nordic Congr. Ornithol. 1979*: 57–74. (In Norwegian, with English summary.)

KASPERSEN, T. E. AND EINVIK, K. (1997) [*Proposal for a conservation plan for seabird areas in Nord-Trøndelag.*] Norway: The County Governor of Nord-Trøndelag (Environmental Dept. Report No. 3). (In Norwegian.)

KASPERSEN, T. E. AND EINVIK, K. (1994) *Utkast til verneplan for sjøfugler i Nord-Trøndelag.* Norway: Miljøvernavdelingen, Fylkesmannen i Nord-Trøndelag.

KROGSTAD, K. (1978) [Lake Leksdalsvatn, a lowland water with a rich bird fauna.] *Trøndersk Natur* 5: 9–20. (In Norwegian.)

KROGSTAD, K., FRENGEN, O. AND FURUNES, K. A. (1977) [*Ornithological investigations in Lake Leksdalsvatn, Verdal and Steinkjer municipalities, Nord-Trøndelag.*] Trondheim, Norway: DKNVS, The Museum (Report Zoological Series 1977–15). (In Norwegian.)

LORENTSEN, S.-H. AND LARSEN, B. H. (1988) [*Censuses of breeding Eiders and Black Guillemots on Tarva, Været, Tristein and Melstein in Bjugn municipality and Froan in Frøya municipality, Sør-Trøndelag May 1988.*] Norway: Directorate for Nature Management, Viltforskningen (Field Report). (In Norwegian.)

LORENTSEN, S.-H. (1995) *Det nasjonale overvåkningsprogrammet for hekkende sjøfugl. Resultater fra 1995.* Norway: Norwegian Institute for Nature Research (NINA oppdragsmelding 374).

LORENTSEN, S.-H. AND BANGJORD, G. (1982) [Ornithological surveys in Gaulosen, Melhus and Trondheim municipalities 1975–1981.] *Trøndersk Natur Suppl.* 1: 1–43. (In Norwegian.)

LUND, O. AND OLSEN, O. (1979) *Hellesjøvann og Hemnessjøen.* Årsrapport 5.

MOKSNES, A. AND THINGSTAD, P. G. (1980) [The Eider migration from Triondheimsfjorden.] *Vår Fuglefauna* 3: 84–96. (In Norwegian, with English summary.)

MYKLEBUST, M. (1993) [The birds in Gaulosen 1991–1992.] *Trøndersk Natur* 20: 84–96. (In Norwegian.)

MYKLEBUST, M. (1996) [The birds in Gaulosen 1993–1994.] *Trøndersk Natur* 23: 25–35. (In Norwegian.)

NORDBAKKE, R. (1980) [The diet of the population of ospreys *Pandion haliaetus* in south eastern Norway.] *Fauna Norv. Ser. C., Cinclus* 3: 1–8.

NOF/STEINKJER (1991) Lundleiret—artsliste m. kommentarer. Unpublished.

ØIEN, I. J. AND FOLVIK, A. (1996) *Norway.* In: Aulen, G.: *Where to watch birds in Scandinavia.* London: Hamlyn.

ØIEN, I. J., AARVAK, T., LORENTSEN, S.-H. AND BANGJORD, G. (1996) Use of individual differences in belly patches in population monitoring of Lesser White-fronted Goose *Anser erythropus* at a staging ground. *Fauna Norv. Ser. C., Cinclus* 19: 69–76.

OLSEN, K. (1993) Lundevågen Fuglefredningsområde—en viktig del av Lista våtmarkssystem. *Piplerka* 23: 49–50.

OLSEN, K. (1995) Fugleliv og brettseiling—om interessemotsetninger i Nordhasselvika fuglefredningsområde på Lista. *Piplerka* 25: 16–24.

OLSEN, K. S. (1993) Lundevågen—truet av industrien. *Piplerka* 23: 36–48.

OLSEN, K. S. (1993) Nordhasselbukta fuglefredningsområde: Artsliste med kommentarer. *Piplerka* 23: 127–139.

OLSEN, K. S. (1993) Rauna—forandringer i hekkebestanden 1973–92. *Piplerka* 23: 122–130.

OLSEN, K. S. (1994) Fuglelivet i Nesheimvann—en oppsummering. *Piplerka* 24: 5–55.

PEDERSEN, S. (1995) [*Conservation of biological diversity. Wetland reserves I: the protected areas of Gaulosen.*] Norway: Miljøvernavdelingen, Fylkesmannen i Sør-Trøndelag (Report 4/95). (In Norwegian.)

PFAFF, A. AND BENGTSON, R. (1995) *Truete virveldyr i Aust-Agder.* [*Threatened vertebrates in Aust-Agder county.*] Arendal, Norway: Fylkesmannen i Aust-Agder, Miljøvern-avdelingen. 143 pp. (In Norwegian.)

RØER, J. E., ED. (1991) Lista Ornitologiske Stasjon. Årsrapport 1990. Vest-Agder, Norway: Norwegian Ornithological Society.

RØER, J. E., ED. (1992) Lista Ornitologiske Stasjon. Årsrapport 1991. Vest-Agder, Norway: Norwegian Ornithological Society.

RØER, J. E., ED. (1993) Lista Fuglestasjon. Årsrapport 1992. *Piplerka* 23: 2.

RØER, J. E., ED. (1994) Lista Fuglestasjon. Årsrapport 1993. *Piplerka* 24 (suppl. A).

RØER, J. E., ED. (1995) Lista Fuglestasjon. Årsrapport 1994. *Piplerka* 25 (suppl. A).

RØV, N., THOMASSEN, J., ANKER-NILSSEN, T., BARRETT, R., FOLKESTAD, A. O. AND RUNDE, O. J., EDS. (1984) [*The Seabird Project 1979–1984.*] Trondheim, Norway: The Directorate for Game and Freshwater Fish (Wildlife Report No. 35). (In Norwegian, with English summary.)

SCHANDY, T. (1984) [Occurrence and habitat choice of the Great Snipe *Gallinago media* at Hardangervidda.] *Vår Fuglefauna* 7: 205–208. (In Norwegian, with English summary.)

SHIMMINGS, P. (1998) [Changes in use of spring staging areas by Barnacle Geese and the effect of increased use of agricultural areas.] *Vår Fuglefauna* 21: 11–15. (In Norwegian, with English summary.)

STØRKERSEN, Ø. R. (1991) [Bird observations from Gaulosen 1982–1988.] *Trøndersk Natur* 18: 47–56. (In Norwegian.)

STØRKERSEN, Ø. R. AND HAUGSKOTT, T. (1988) [Bird observations from Gaulosen 1982–1983.] *Trøndersk Natur* 15: 98–111. (In Norwegian.)

STRANN, K.-B. (1985) [Spring migration of Knots in northern Norway.] *Vår Fuglefauna* 8: 195–196. (In Norwegian.)

STRANN, K.-B. (1990) [Spring migration of Knots in northern Norway during 1983–1989.] *Vår Fuglefauna* 13: 5–10. (In Norwegian.)

STRANN, K.-B. AND HEGGÅS, J.-H. (1986) [The tidal flats of Sørkjosen, Balsfjord.] *Vår Fuglefauna* 9: 239–242. (In Norwegian.)

SUUL, J. (1975) [Ornithological surveys in Gaulosen, Melhus and Trondheim municipalities, Sør-Trøndelag.] *Det kgl. Norske Vidensk. Selsk. Rapp. Zool. Ser.* 8: 1–43. (In Norwegian.)

THINGSTAD, P. G. AND HOKSTAD, S. (1997) Vannfugl og marin bunndyrfauna i Kråkvågsvaet, Ørland kommune, Sør-Trøndelag. Konsekvenser av eventuell bru og veifylling over Svaet. *Vitenskapsmus. Rapp. Zool. Ser.* 1997, 2: 1–50.

THORSEN, T. (1987) Registrering av teist (*Cepphus grylle*) i Vest-Finnmark 1989. Unpublished.

TUCKER, G. M. AND EVANS, M. I., EDS. (1997) *Habitats for birds in Europe: a conservation strategy for the wider environment.* Cambridge, UK: BirdLife International (BirdLife Conservation Series No. 6).

TUCKER, G. M. AND HEATH, M. F. (1994) *Birds in Europe: their conservation status.* Cambridge, UK: BirdLife International (BirdLife Conservation Series No. 3).

TERJE LISLEVAND, ASBJØRN FOLVIK AND INGAR JOSTEIN ØIEN

Barnacle Goose *Branta leucopsis* at Kongsfjorden (IBA 003). (PHOTO: TERJE LISLEVAND)

GENERAL INTRODUCTION

Svalbard is an Arctic archipelago situated between the latitudes of 74°N and 81°N. The islands constitute one of the northernmost land areas in the world, but due to the influence of the Gulf Stream current the climate is relatively mild (although the average July temperature is only 4.5°C). The surrounding seas (the Greenland and Barents Seas and the Arctic Ocean) are highly productive and provide a rich food supply for numerous organisms, including birds. The sun never sets (midnight sun) between 20 April and 23 August (at the latitude of Longyearbyen), while between 26 October and 15 February the sun stays below the horizon (polar night). The name Spitsbergen is sometimes used in English to refer to the whole

archipelago, but strictly speaking this is only the name of the largest island. In this chapter the two isolated islands of Jan Mayen and Bjørnøya (Bear Island) are also included.

Svalbard has been a part of the Kingdom of Norway since 1925, and the legislation for the area is specified in the Svalbard Act. The population is presently about 3,500 people, mainly situated in the settlements of Longyearbyen, Barentsburg (Russian) and Ny-Ålesund along the west coast of Spitsbergen. The total area of the Svalbard archipelago is c.62,700 km², while that of Bjørnøya is c.178 km² and Jan Mayen is c.380 km². Fourteen Important Bird Areas (IBAs) are identified in this chapter, covering 34,842 km², equivalent to c.55% of the total land surface area under consideration (Table 1, Map 1).

Table 1. Summary of Important Bird Areas in Svalbard.   14 IBAs covering 34,842 km²

IBA code	1989 code	International name	National name	Administrative region	Area (ha)	Criteria (see p. 11)
001	SJ005	North-east Svalbard Nature Reserve	Nord-øst Svalbard Naturreservat	Svalbard	1,903,000	A4i, A4iii, B1i, B2
002	SJ001	North-west Spitsbergen National Park	Nord-vest Spitsbergen Nasjonal Park	Svalbard	328,300	A4i, A4iii, B1i, B2, B3
003	SJ002	Inner parts of Kongsfjorden	Indre deler av Kongsfjorden	Svalbard	140	A3, B1i, B3
004	SJ004	Forlandet National Park	Forlandet Nasjonalpark	Svalbard	64,000	A4iii, B1i, B2, B3
005	SJ013	Daudmannsøyra	Daudmannsøyra	Svalbard	1,000	B1i
006	SJ012	Alkhornet	Alkhornet	Svalbard	100	A4iii
007	SJ011	Fuglefjella	Fuglefjella	Svalbard	500	A4iii
008	SJ014	Nordenskiøldkysten	Nordenskiøldkysten inkludert Kapp Linne Fuglereservat	Svalbard	25,000	A4i, B1i
009	SJ015	Ingeborgfjellet	Ingeborgfjellet	Svalbard	100	A4iii, B1ii
010	SJ007	South Spitsbergen National Park	Sør-Spitsbergen Nasjonalpark	Svalbard	467,300	A4i, A4ii, A4iii, B1i, B1ii, B3
011	SJ006	South-east Svalbard Nature Reserve	Sørøst Svalbard Naturreservat	Svalbard	638,000	A3, A4i, A4iii, B1i, B2, B3
012	SJ016	Hopen island	Hopen	Svalbard	50	A4i, A4ii, A4iii, B1i, B1ii, B2
013	SJ017	Bjørnøya (Bear Island)	Bjørnøya	Svalbard	18,000	A3, A4i, A4ii, A4iii, B1i, B1ii, B2
014	SJ018	Jan Mayen island	Jan Mayen	Svalbard	38,700	A4ii, A4iii, B1ii, B2

Sites identified in the previous inventory of IBAs in Europe (Grimmett and Jones 1989) but no longer considered to be IBAs
SJ003 Hermansenøya Bird Sanctuary; SJ008 Gåsøyane Bird Sanctuary; SJ009 Kongressfjellet; SJ010 Boheman Bird Sanctuary.

Map 1. Location, area and criteria category of Important Bird Areas in Svalbard.

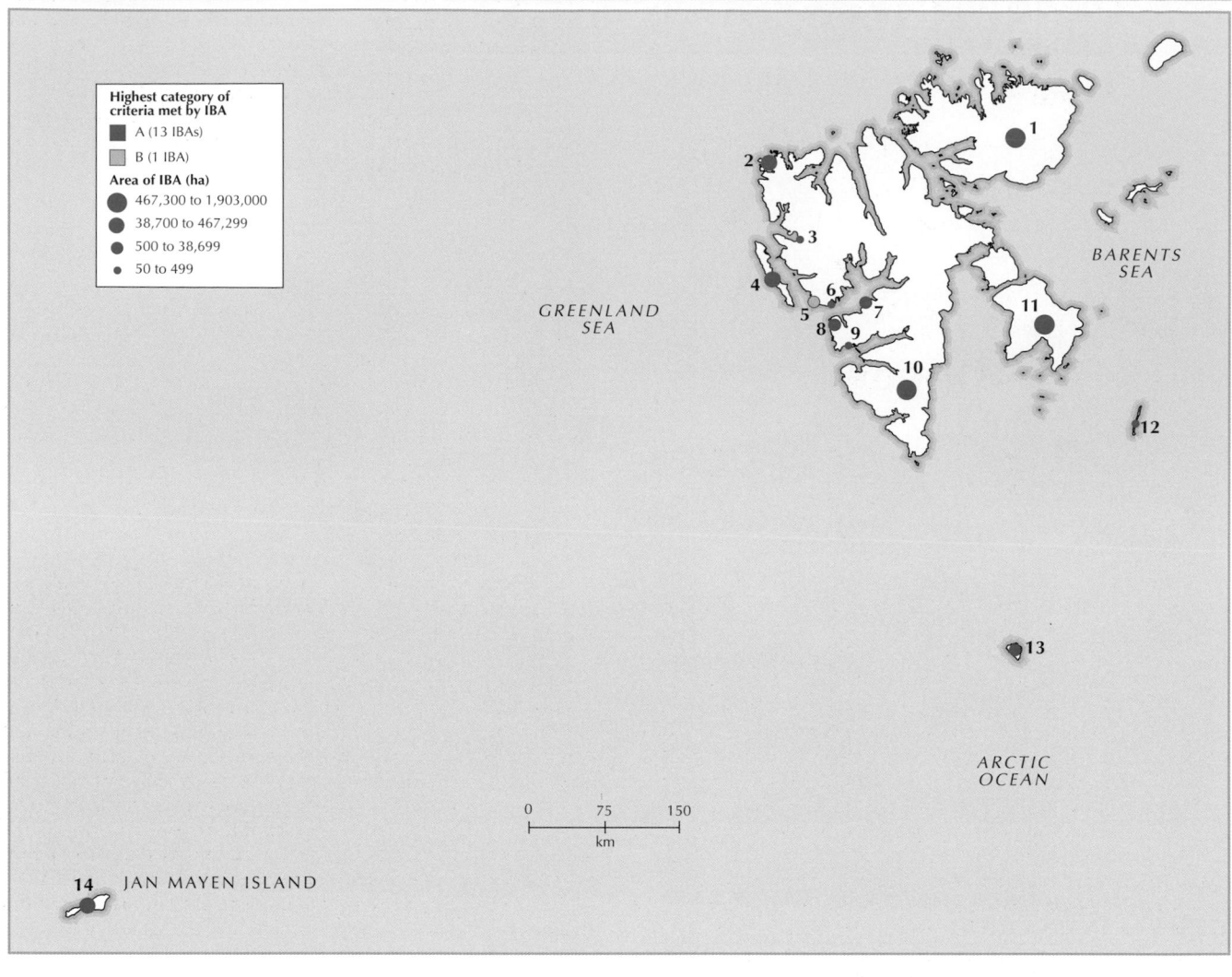

Highest category of criteria met by IBA

■ A (13 IBAs)
■ B (1 IBA)

Area of IBA (ha)

● 467,300 to 1,903,000
● 38,700 to 467,299
● 500 to 38,699
● 50 to 499

GREENLAND SEA

BARENTS SEA

ARCTIC OCEAN

0   75   150
km

14 JAN MAYEN ISLAND

In the previous pan-European IBA inventory (Grimmett and Jones 1989) 18 IBAs were identified in Svalbard, five of which included a number of subsites (up to 16 per site) bringing the total number of different areas described to 53. In the current inventory, no subsites have been distinguished, nor have any new sites, but four of the original 1989 sites have been deleted because they no longer meet the current (revised) IBA criteria (they are listed in Table 1). Of the remaining 14 IBAs, one has been re-named (site 007) and the area of several has been increased or updated in this inventory.

ORNITHOLOGICAL IMPORTANCE

Only about 25–30 bird species breed regularly on Svalbard. Thirteen of these are species of European conservation concern, of which eight have an unfavourable conservation status in Europe (Tucker and Heath 1994). No species of global conservation concern occur in Svalbard in significant numbers. However, the archipelago is extremely important for breeding auks (Alcidae), especially *Uria aalge*, *Uria lomvia* and *Alle alle* (with more than one million breeding pairs of the latter two species), as well as other seabirds such as

Table 2. Important Bird Areas in Svalbard that support important numbers of one or more congregatory species (i.e. meeting criteria A4 and/or B1). IBAs meeting both criteria A4 and B1 for the species are shown in **bold**. IBAs meeting only criterion B1 for the species concerned, and not A4, are shown in normal type. For key to 'Season', see p. 7.

Species	Season	IBA code
Fulmarus glacialis Fulmar	B	**013**, **014**
Anser brachyrhynchus	P	**013**
Pink-footed Goose	N	005
Branta leucopsis Barnacle Goose	B	002, 003, 004, 005, 008, **010**, 011
	P	**013**
	N	005, **008**
Branta bernicla Brent Goose	B	**002**, **011**
Somateria mollissima Eider	B	002, 003, 004, 008, 010
Larus hyperboreus Glaucous Gull	B	**013**
Rissa tridactyla Kittiwake	B	**010**, **012**, **013**
Pagophila eburnea Ivory Gull	B	**001**
Uria aalge Guillemot	B	**013**
Uria lomvia Brünnich's Guillemot	B	**010**, **012**, **013**, **014**
Cepphus grylle Black Guillemot	B	012, **013**, 014
Alle alle Little Auk	B	009, **013**, **014**

Table 3. Species of European conservation concern with significant breeding populations at Important Bird Areas in Svalbard (meeting any IBA criteria).

Species [1]	Minimum national breeding population (pairs) [2]	Proportion (%) of national population breeding at all IBAs in Svalbard
Anser brachyrhynchus Pink-footed Goose	10,000	1
Branta leucopsis Barnacle Goose	2,000	100[3]
Branta bernicla Brent Goose	1,000	100[3]
Calidris maritima Purple Sandpiper	1,000	1
Pagophila eburnea Ivory Gull	237	34
Cepphus grylle Black Guillemot	5,000	49

1. Only those species of European conservation concern (see Box 1, p. 12) that meet IBA criteria in Svalbard are listed.

2. Data are taken from the BirdLife/EBCC European Bird Database 1998 (Heath and Borggreve 2000).

3. The percentage of the national population in IBAs exceeds 100%. Usually this is because the national population estimate has not been updated recently whilst the IBA population estimate has been recently updated with new data as a result of comprehensive surveys of IBAs themselves. Also, the individual site count for a species may be the maximum or average over recent years, and summing these may record more birds than are present nationally in any single year.

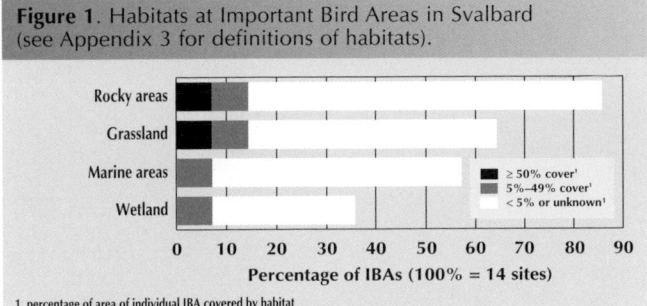

Figure 1. Habitats at Important Bird Areas in Svalbard (see Appendix 3 for definitions of habitats).

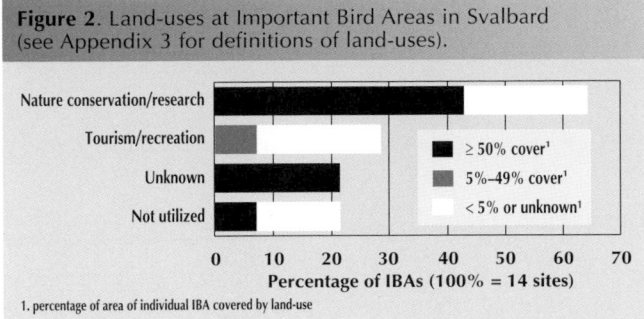

Figure 2. Land-uses at Important Bird Areas in Svalbard (see Appendix 3 for definitions of land-uses).

Fulmarus glacialis (100,000–1,000,000 pairs) and *Rissa tridactyla* (270,000 pairs). The archipelago also holds significant breeding numbers of *Somateria mollissima* (13,500–20,500 pairs), Arctic geese—*Anser brachyrhynchus* (30,000 birds), *Branta leucopsis* (23,000 birds) and *Branta bernicla hrota* (4,000–6,000 birds)—and of *Stercorarius parasiticus*, *Larus hyperboreus* and *Pagophila eburnea* (200–750 pairs). The most numerous breeding wader is *Calidris maritima*, while *Plectrophenax nivalis* is the most common passerine.

Table 2 shows that the IBA network encompasses a large proportion of these important populations, at least for the highly congregatory species such as most of the seabirds. Table 3 lists those species of European conservation concern (Tucker and Heath 1994) that breed in significant numbers on Svalbard (significant at the European level). *Pagophila eburnea* is probably the only such species that is not well covered by the IBA network—the apparent poor coverage for *Anser brachyrhynchus* and *Calidris maritima* (low percentages in Table 3) is because the breeding numbers at IBAs have generally not yet been estimated.

There are no bird species endemic to Svalbard, although the subspecies of *Lagopus mutus* (*L. m. hyperboreus*) is shared only with Franz Josef Land (European Russia). This is also the only sedentary bird species on Svalbard.

HABITATS

Sixty percent of the land area is covered by snow and ice year-round. Of the ice-free land, only about 13% is covered by vegetation, and permafrost is found throughout the area. No trees grow on the archipelago. Habitats for landbirds in Svalbard are therefore marginal and inhospitable. The following crude classification of terrestrial habitats in the area has been made by Norderhaug (1989): (1) islets and skerries, (2) rocks and beaches, (3) tundra, (4) talus scree and mountain slopes, (5) bird cliffs and (6) nunataks (mountain tops rising above ice-sheets). The great majority of terrestrial IBAs in Svalbard are thus dominated by rocky areas and tundra (Figure 1).

The seas surrounding the islands are relatively shallow, averaging 230 m deep. The shallowest areas are found between Spitsbergen and Bjørnøya. The fjords and sea areas north and north-east of Svalbard are covered by ice for 8–9 months of the year, while the fjords on the western side of Spitsbergen may be ice-free for long periods even during the winter. As a result, and since most IBAs in Svalbard are seabird colonies, there is a westerly bias to the IBA distribution (Map 1) and marine habitats are frequently recorded (Figure 1).

IMPACTS ON IBAS – LAND-USE AND THREATS

Human activities are sparse and localized on the islands themselves, as well as at IBAs (Figure 2), but disturbance may still be a serious threat at some seabird-colony IBAs where the level of tourism-related activity is increasing (Figure 3).

Commercial fishing is another activity which may influence the breeding success of seabirds, but so far there is little evidence to show that seabird populations have been reduced because of over-exploitation of the fish stocks. Hunting is not a serious threat to any of the bird species in Svalbard today, but some breeding populations were dramatically reduced in the past by shooting. This was particularly the case for *Branta leucopsis* and *B. bernicla*, which have both recovered in recent years.

Some oil exploration has been conducted on the islands, and there are also some plans for oil production in the Barents Sea. So far, no worthwhile discoveries have been made, either on- or offshore, but any oil extraction in the future could seriously affect some of the seabird populations, for example through accidental oil spills. Chemical pollution is another potential threat to the birdlife of Svalbard. Relatively high concentrations of organochlorine and polychlorinated biphenyl (PCB) chemicals have, for example, been detected in the tissues of carnivores such as *Larus hyperboreus* and polar bear *Ursus maritimus*. This is thought to result from net global transport of such chemicals through the atmosphere towards the polar regions, where they are further concentrated as they rise up the food chain. However, in general, the majority of IBAs in Svalbard do not appear to be severely threatened by man's activities (Figure 3).

PROTECTION STATUS

■ National protection
The Norwegian Ministry of Environment (Miljøverndepartementet) is the highest authority in questions concerning nature protection in both Norway and Svalbard, but the local responsibility is, to a large degree, delegated to the Governor of Svalbard (and for Jan Mayen, to the County Governor of Nordland) and the Norwegian Directorate for Nature Protection (Direktoratet for Natur-forvaltning).

Nature conservation areas in Svalbard are protected legally by the Svalbard Act of 1925, which regulates the management of natural resources on Svalbard. The protected areas fall into the same categories as for mainland Norway (Anon. 1995). About 60% of the land area of Svalbard is protected, mainly as three National Parks (totalling 9,500 km²) as well as two large Nature Reserves (totalling 25,480 km²—much larger than any such reserves on the Norwegian mainland). There are also 15 Bird Sanctuaries, one smaller Nature Reserve, one Botanical Reserve and two areas where the plant species are protected.

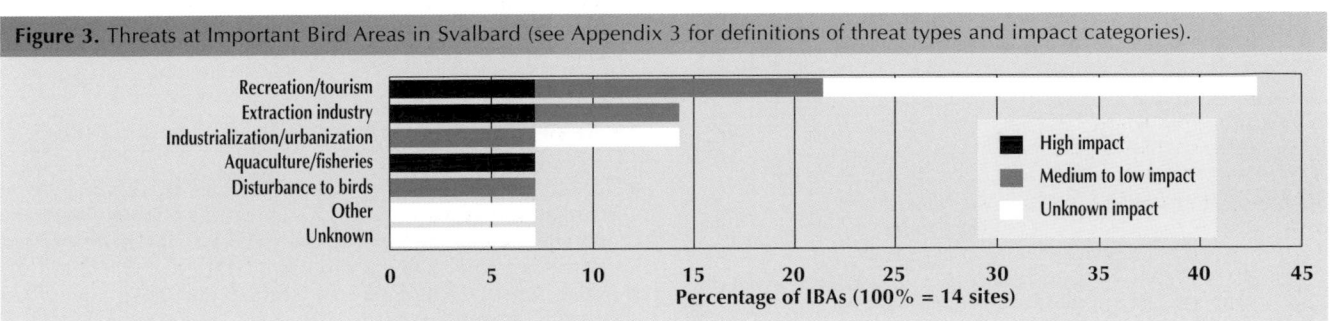

Figure 3. Threats at Important Bird Areas in Svalbard (see Appendix 3 for definitions of threat types and impact categories).

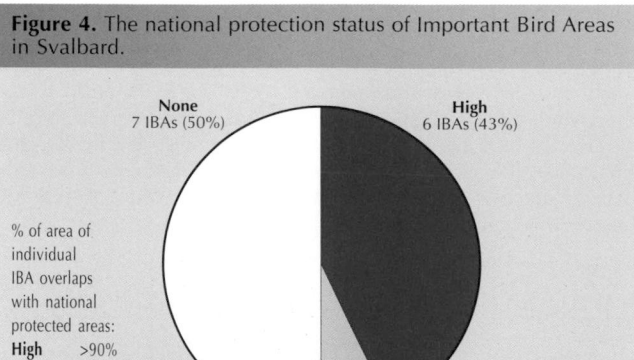

Figure 4. The national protection status of Important Bird Areas in Svalbard.

None
7 IBAs (50%)

High
6 IBAs (43%)

% of area of
individual
IBA overlaps
with national
protected areas:
High   >90%
Partial 10–90%
Low   <10%
None

Low
1 IBA (7%)

Total area of overlap between IBA network in Svalbard and national protected-area system (see Table 4 for categories) = 34,009 km² (98% of total IBA area).

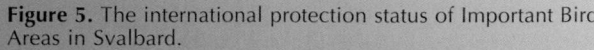
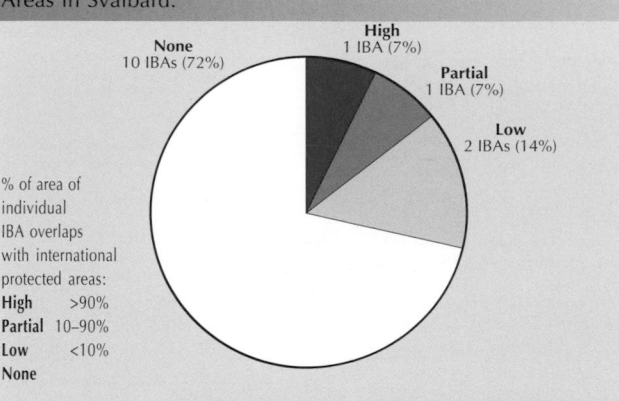

Figure 5. The international protection status of Important Bird Areas in Svalbard.

High
1 IBA (7%)

None
10 IBAs (72%)

Partial
1 IBA (7%)

Low
2 IBAs (14%)

% of area of
individual
IBA overlaps
with international
protected areas:
High   >90%
Partial 10–90%
Low   <10%
None

Total area of overlap between IBA network in Svalbard and international protected-area system (see Table 4 for categories) = 15,554 km² (45% of total IBA area).

The national protection status of the IBAs is shown in Figure 4. Of the 14 IBAs, 50% overlap to some degree with nationally protected areas (Table 4), and thus derive some legal protection. The degree of overlap is high for six IBAs, most of which are very large.

■ International protection

Norway is party to most of the international conservation instruments that are relevant to nature conservation through site protection (Box 1; Anon. 1995). There is one Biosphere Reserve located on Svalbard (North-east Svalbard Nature Reserve), the only one on Norwegian territory. Further, there are five Ramsar Sites in Svalbard, four of which are included in this inventory—the site Gåsøyane was listed in the previous pan-European IBA inventory (Grimmett and Jones 1989) but did not meet the revised IBA criteria and does not appear in the current inventory. Figure 5 and Table 4 characterize the protection status of the IBAs under these international conventions and initiatives.

Table 4. Protection status of Important Bird Areas in Svalbard. A tick (✔) indicates that an IBA overlaps with a protected area (to any extent).

IBA code	International name	National		International	
		National Park	Nature Reserve	Ramsar Site	Biosphere Reserve
001	North-east Svalbard Nature Reserve		✔		✔
002	North-west Spitsbergen National Park	✔	✔		
003	Inner parts of Kongsfjorden		✔	✔	
004	Forlandet National Park	✔	✔	✔	
005	Daudmannsøyra				
006	Alkhornet				
007	Fuglefjella				
008	Nordenskiøldkysten		✔		
009	Ingeborgfjellet				
010	South Spitsbergen National Park	✔	✔	✔	
011	South-east Svalbard Nature Reserve		✔		
012	Hopen island				
013	Bjørnøya (Bear Island)				
014	Jan Mayen island				
Total number of IBAs		**3**	**7**	**3**	**1**

Box 1. International legislation and initiatives that are relevant to site conservation in Svalbard (see Appendix 1 for a general description of these agreements).

Global
Biodiversity Convention	✔
Ramsar Convention	✔
Bonn Convention	✔
World Heritage Convention	
MAB Programme	✔

Pan-European
Bern Convention	✔

✔ Convention ratified/initiative supported
(✔) Convention signed

CONSERVATION

● Permission is needed from the Governorate of Svalbard to enter any protected area in Svalbard (entrance is also prohibited in some areas during some periods).

● Large penalties are normally charged for entering protected areas without permission where entrance is prohibited by law, for example during the breeding season for birds.

● The following activities are generally prohibited within all the protected areas: littering, collection of flowers or fossils, use of motorized vehicles, hunting, landing of helicopters and construction of buildings.

● Currently the protected areas of Svalbard do not cover much of the more biologically productive areas of the islands, and the Norwegian government is therefore planning to extend the protected areas in the year 2000. The Governorate of Svalbard has suggested the establishment of three new Nature Reserves, two National Parks, one Botanical Reserve and three Landscape Protection Areas (totalling 408,800 ha, including both land and sea areas).

● Current or planned protected areas do not yet include any purely marine areas, but the Norwegian Polar Research Institute is currently gathering data in order to be able to identify important pelagic areas of high biological importance so that these may be secured as protected areas in the future.

● Tourism, the mining and oil-extraction industries and commercial fishing are the main sectors which sometimes have conflicting interests with those of nature protection. For example, protection plans for Bjørnøya have been delayed because of the possible need to use the island as a supply base for the offshore oil industry. Likewise, representatives of the mining industry in Svalbard and the Russian authorities have protested against the recently launched conservation plans because of their economic interests in the same areas. Finally, if marine areas are going to be protected in the future, this will definitely cause conflicts with the large fleet of fishing vessels utilizing the rich fish-stocks in the Barents Sea—also a highly important resource for several seabird populations.

● A population monitoring scheme for, at least, the seabirds of Svalbard is required in order to secure the sustainable management of their populations, through revealing any changes in numbers. The methods used so far, e.g. for *Alle alle*, have not proven useful for this purpose, and are unlikely to do so unless drastic changes in bird numbers occur (Isaksen and Gavrilo, in Anker-Nilssen *et al.* [in press]).

ANALYTICAL METHODS

● Data on bird numbers within the different IBAs are estimates and based on those given by Grimmett and Jones (1989) and the seabird database of the Norwegian Polar Institute. The estimates are probably of variable quality.

● New estimates of the numbers of seabirds and shorebirds at IBAs are also taken from Anker-Nilssen *et al.* (in press).

- Where the IBAs presented by Grimmett and Jones (1989) were large protected areas, we have chosen not to split the IBA into smaller areas, even where glaciers make up most of the Nature Reserve/National Park and only a few, concentrated seabird colonies which individually meet the IBA criteria are of ornithological importance.

GLOSSARY

fjord a steep-sided coastal valley, created by the erosive action of glaciers and then subsequently flooded with seawater.
NINA Norsk Institutt for Naturforskning (Norwegian Institute for Nature Research).

NOF Norsk Ornitologisk Forening (Norwegian Ornithological Society), the BirdLife Partner for Norway and Svalbard.
øy an island.
skjær (skerry) a small islet or rocky reef in the sea, exposed at low tide.

ACKNOWLEDGEMENTS

We thank Kjell Isaksen (Norwegian Polar Institute), Fridtjof Mehlum (Norwegian Polar Institute) and Hallvard Strøm (NOF/Norwegian Polar Institute) for providing us with data and information about bird numbers and Important Bird Areas in Svalbard. The work was financially supported by the Norwegian Directorate for Nature Management.

■ SITE ACCOUNTS

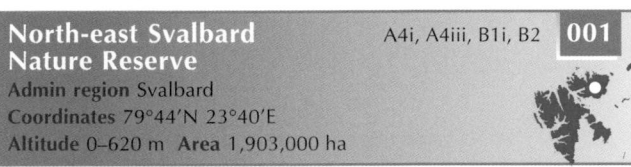

North-east Svalbard Nature Reserve   A4i, A4iii, B1i, B2   **001**
Admin region Svalbard
Coordinates 79°44'N 23°40'E
Altitude 0–620 m   Area 1,903,000 ha

■ Site description
The Nature Reserve covers all of the islands of Nordaustlandet, Kvitøya and Kong Karls Land, as well as the north-east coast of Spitsbergen. Habitats are mainly ice-covered tundra and marsh vegetation; the sea cliffs are the most important habitat for birds.

Habitats Grassland (tundra), Wetland (standing fresh water), Marine areas (open sea; sea inlet/coastal features), Rocky areas (sea cliff/rocky shore; rock stacks/islets)
Land-use Nature conservation/research (100%)

■ Birds

Species	Season	Year	Pop min	Pop max	Acc	Criteria
[1] *Pagophila eburnea* Ivory Gull	B	1989	80	90	—	A4i, B1i, B2
1. Four colonies on Kongsøya.						

Uria lomvia breeds in notable numbers on sea cliffs at Alkefjellet (45,000–50,000 birds) and at Wahlbergøya (8,000 birds).

■ Protection status
National High **International** Partial
1,903,000 ha of IBA covered by Nature Reserve (Nordaust-Svalbard, 1,903,000 ha). 1,555,000 ha of IBA covered by Biosphere Reserve (North-east Svalbard, 1,555,000 ha).

■ Conservation issues

Threats Recreation/tourism (U)

Public access to the islands of Kong Karls Land is prohibited year-round, due to the presence of polar bear *Ursus maritimus*.

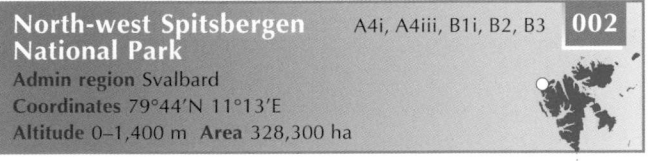

North-west Spitsbergen National Park   A4i, A4iii, B1i, B2, B3   **002**
Admin region Svalbard
Coordinates 79°44'N 11°13'E
Altitude 0–1,400 m   Area 328,300 ha

■ Site description
Bird data are available for the following localities within this huge IBA: Guissezholmen Bird Sanctuary (includes islets near Kapp Guissez; 79°05'N 11°30'E); Casimir–Perierkammen (sea cliffs facing Krossfjorden; 79°08'N 11°52'E); Kongshamaren (headland with cliffs in Kongsfjorden; 79°13'N 11°50'E); Nilsfjellet (sea cliffs facing Krossfjorden; 79°16'N 11°33'E); Knoffberget (sea cliffs on north-west coast of Spitsbergen; 79°22'N 10°52'E); Moseøya Bird Sanctuary (79°40'N 11°00'E); Skorpa Bird Sanctuary (79°40'N 11°00'E); south-west Amsterdamøya (sea cliffs; 79°45'N 10°45'E); north Hakluythovden, Amsterdamøya (sea cliffs; 79°47'N 10°48'E);

Klovningen (small island with sea cliffs at north end of Spitsbergen; 79°53'N 11°30'E); Flathuken (sea cliffs facing Raudfjorden; 79°51'N 11°50'E); Hornbækfjellet (sea cliffs facing Raudfjorden; 79°49'N 11°50'E); Austplana (sea cliffs facing Raudfjorden; 79°47'N 11°53'E); Liefdefjorden (fjord with numerous small islands; 79°40'N 13°00'E); Moffen Nature Reserve (island with lake, off north coast of Spitsbergen; 80°05'N 12°45'E); Nissenfjella (sea cliffs on north-west coast of Spitsbergen; 79°24'N 10°51'E).

Habitats Grassland (tundra), Wetland (standing fresh water), Marine areas (open sea; sea inlet/coastal features), Rocky areas (sea cliff/rocky shore; rock stacks/islets)
Land-use Nature conservation/research (100%)

■ Birds

Species	Season	Year	Pop min	Pop max	Acc	Criteria
[1] *Branta leucopsis* Barnacle Goose	B	1989	115	175	—	B1i, B3
[2] *Branta bernicla* Brent Goose	B	1998	—	—	—	A4i, B1i, B2
Somateria mollissima Eider	B	1989	2,300	2,600	—	B1i
[3] *Cepphus grylle* Black Guillemot	B	1989	130	130	—	B2

1. Moseøya (100–150 pairs) and Skorpa (15–25 pairs).
2. Exact numbers unknown (see main text).
3. Estimate is for Knoffberget only.

There are two breeding concentrations of *Branta leucopsis*, while the number of breeding *Branta bernicla* at Moffen island probably exceeds 1% of the Svalbard population. There are also some large seabird colonies, the most numerous species being *Rissa tridactyla* (10,700 pairs) and *Uria lomvia* (67,700–71,700 breeding birds). The number of *Sterna paradisaea* is also notable (1,500 pairs). Moffen Nature Reserve is the only known breeding site for *Larus sabini* in Svalbard (up to five pairs).

■ Protection status
National High **International** None
328,300 ha of IBA covered by National Park (Nordvest-Spitsbergen, 356,000 ha). 41 ha of IBA covered by Nature Reserve (Guissezholmen [Bird Sanctuary], 41 ha). 1,600 ha of IBA covered by Nature Reserve (Moffen, 1,600 ha). 142 ha of IBA covered by Nature Reserve (Moseøya [Bird Sanctuary], 142 ha). 111 ha of IBA covered by Nature Reserve (Skorpa [Bird Sanctuary], 111 ha).

■ Conservation issues
No threats are known. Access to Moffen Nature Reserve is prohibited between 15 May and 15 September (including the adjacent sea areas and airspace below 500 m).

Inner parts of Kongsfjorden   A3, B1i, B3   **003**
Admin region Svalbard
Coordinates 78°55'N 12°32'E
Altitude 0–200 m   Area 140 ha

■ Site description
The site comprises about ten islands, most with grassy vegetation and some with small freshwater ponds. The fjord is surrounded by steep mountains and cliffs, glaciers and some tundra.

Habitats Grassland (tundra), Marine areas (sea inlet/coastal features), Rocky areas (rock stacks/islets)

Land-use Nature conservation/research (90%), Tourism/recreation (10%)

■ Birds

Species	Season	Year	Pop min	Pop max	Acc	Criteria
Anser brachyrhynchus Pink-footed Goose	B	1989	15	20	—	A3
Branta leucopsis Barnacle Goose	B	1997	329	329	A	A3, B1i, B3
[1] *Somateria mollissima* Eider	B	1995	2,500	4,700	A	B1i
Somateria spectabilis King Eider	B	1999	3,500	3,500	—	A3
Clangula hyemalis Long-tailed Duck	B	1995	Frequent		—	A3
Calidris maritima Purple Sandpiper	B	1995	5	10	—	A3, B3
[2] *Phalaropus fulicarius* Grey Phalarope	B	1995	2	2	—	A3
Stercorarius longicaudus Long-tailed Skua	B	1995	0	2	—	A3
Larus hyperboreus Glaucous Gull	B	1995	Frequent		—	A3
[3] *Pagophila eburnea* Ivory Gull	U	1995	Uncommon		—	A3
Plectrophenax nivalis Snow Bunting	B	1995	Common		—	A3

1. Number varies according to ice cover in spring/early summer.
2. Decline from 15–20 pairs in c.1990.
3. Breeding status uncertain.

The islands and the mainland tundra are relatively species-rich and support at least nine of the 32 species that are restricted in Europe (when breeding) to the Arctic/tundra biome. The first and only instance of *Pluvialis fulva* breeding in the West Palearctic was recorded at Ny Ålesund in 1997 (under consideration by the Norwegian Rarities Committee).

■ Protection status
National High **International** High
140 ha of IBA covered by Nature Reserve (Kongsfjorden [Bird Sanctuary], 140 ha). 140 ha of IBA covered by Ramsar Site (Kongsfjorden, 140 ha).

■ Conservation issues

Threats Disturbance to birds (B), Recreation/tourism (A)

A growing population of reindeer *Rangifer tarandus* may have overgrazed the tundra, possibly reducing the number of suitable nest-sites for some waders (e.g. *Phalaropus fulicarius*, which has declined in number from about 20 pairs to only 2–3 pairs in recent years). The IBA is covered by an 'Area of Plant Protection' (1,140 ha). Population studies (including regular censuses) of *Branta leucopsis* and several seabirds are carried out by the University of Tromsø, the University of Norway at Svalbard (Longyearbyen) and the Norwegian Polar Institute.

Forlandet National Park   A4iii, B1i, B2, B3   004
Admin region Svalbard
Coordinates 78°30'N 11°15'E
Altitude 0–1,084 m **Area** 64,000 ha

■ Site description
The site comprises the whole of the long island of Prins Karls Forland. The habitat is high-Arctic tundra. Bird data are available for three subsites: Forlandsøyene Bird Sanctuary (78°20'N 11°36'E), Plankeholmane Bird Sanctuary (78°12'N 12°00'E) and Fuglehuken (78°53'N 10°30'E). Forlandsøyene covers three islands and a few small skerries; one island is bare, the other two are grassy with small pools. Fuglehuken is an area of sea cliffs at the northern tip of Prins Karls Forland.

Habitats Grassland (tundra), Marine areas (open sea), Rocky areas (sea cliff/rocky shore; rock stacks/islets)

Land-use Nature conservation/research (100%)

■ Birds

Species	Season	Year	Pop min	Pop max	Acc	Criteria
[1] *Branta leucopsis* Barnacle Goose	B	1983	287	415	—	B1i, B3
[1] *Somateria mollissima* Eider	B	1989	750	1,300	—	B1i

Species … continued	Season	Year	Pop min	Pop max	Acc	Criteria
[2] *Cepphus grylle* Black Guillemot	B	1989	200	200	—	B2

1. Forlandsøyene and Plankeholmane.
2. Forlandsøyene.

There are significant numbers of breeding *Branta leucopsis*, and the seabird colonies at Fuglehuken are notable, especially for *Uria lomvia* (40,000 birds).

■ Protection status
National High **International** Low
64,000 ha of IBA covered by National Park (Forlandet, 64,000 ha). 60 ha of IBA covered by Nature Reserve (Forlandsøyene [Bird Sanctuary], 60 ha). 162 ha of IBA covered by Nature Reserve (Plankeholmane, 162 ha). 60 ha of IBA covered by Ramsar Site (Forlandsøyene, 60 ha).

■ Conservation issues

Threats Recreation/tourism (U)

The current situation in the area is not known.

Daudmannsøyra   B1i   005
Admin region Svalbard
Coordinates 78°15'N 13°00'E
Altitude 0–50 m **Area** 1,000 ha

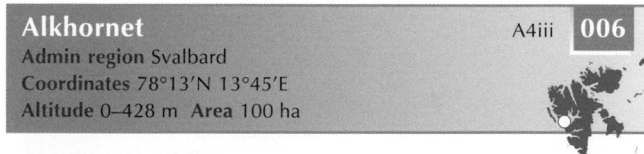

■ Site description
A large flat area with bogs and freshwater ponds.

Habitats Wetland (standing fresh water; raised bog)

Land-use Unknown (100%)

■ Birds

Species	Season	Year	Pop min	Pop max	Acc	Criteria
[1] *Anser brachyrhynchus* Pink-footed Goose	N	1989	200	300	—	B1i
Branta leucopsis Barnacle Goose	B	1989	50	100	—	B1i
[1] *Branta leucopsis* Barnacle Goose	N	1989	500	500	—	B1i

1. Moulting.

An important area for moulting geese.

■ Protection status
National None **International** None

■ Conservation issues
No threats are known.

Alkhornet   A4iii   006
Admin region Svalbard
Coordinates 78°13'N 13°45'E
Altitude 0–428 m **Area** 100 ha

■ Site description
Sea cliffs at the entrance of Isfjorden.

Habitats Rocky areas (100%; sea cliff/rocky shore)

Land-use Unknown (100%)

■ Birds
The area regularly holds more than 10,000 pairs of breeding seabirds, especially *Rissa tridactyla* (5,000 pairs) and *Uria lomvia* (6,300–11,000 pairs).

■ Protection status
National None **International** None

■ Conservation issues
No threats are known. Breeding seabirds are regularly censused by the Norwegian Polar Institute.

Fuglefjella   A4iii   007

Admin region Svalbard
Coordinates 78°13′N 15°15′E
Altitude 0–470 m   **Area** 500 ha

■ Site description
Sea cliffs facing Isfjorden. There is shipping traffic (boats going to and from Longyearbyen). This site was named 'Grumant' in he previous pan-European IBA inventory (Grimmett and Jones 1989).

> **Habitats** Rocky areas (sea cliff/rocky shore)
> **Land-use** Tourism/recreation

■ Birds
Breeding seabirds include *Rissa tridactyla* (10,000 pairs) and *Uria lomvia* (20,000 individuals).

■ Protection status
National None   **International** None

■ Conservation issues

> **Threats** Other (U)

Possible effects of the shipping traffic on seabirds ('Other' threat) have not been investigated.

Nordenskiøldkysten   A4i, B1i   008

Admin region Svalbard
Coordinates 78°00′N 13°50′E
Altitude 0–200 m   **Area** 25,000 ha

■ Site description
A large, flat area, some parts with rich grassy vegetation, and with many freshwater pools.

> **Habitats** Grassland (tundra), Wetland (standing fresh water)
> **Land-use** Nature conservation/research, Tourism/recreation

■ Birds

Species		Season	Year	Pop min	Pop max	Acc	Criteria
Branta leucopsis	Barnacle Goose	B	1989	400	400	—	B1i
¹ *Branta leucopsis*	Barnacle Goose	N	1989	3,000	3,000	—	A4i, B1i
Somateria mollissima	Eider	B	1989	300	300	—	B1i

1. Moulting.

One of the six most important breeding sites for *Phalaropus fulicarius* in Svalbard.

■ Protection status
National Low   **International** None
189 ha of IBA covered by Nature Reserve (Kapp Linné [Bird Sanctuary], 189 ha).

■ Conservation issues

> **Threats** Recreation/tourism (U)

The Norwegian Directorate for Nature Management and the Governor of Svalbard have the authority to impose restrictions on access to the Bird Sanctuary, if necessary, e.g. during the breeding season.

Ingeborgfjellet   A4iii, B1ii   009

Admin region Svalbard
Coordinates 77°46′N 14°25′E
Altitude 0–714 m   **Area** 100 ha

■ Site description
Sea cliffs facing Bellsund.

> **Habitats** Rocky areas (sea cliff/rocky shore)
> **Land-use** Unknown (100%)

■ Birds

Species		Season	Year	Pop min	Pop max	Acc	Criteria
Alle alle	Little Auk	B	1991	55,000	55,000	—	B1ii

An important seabird colony, regularly holding more than 10,000 pairs of breeding seabird; other species include *Rissa tridactyla* (4,600 pairs, 1992) and *Uria lomvia* (21,600 birds, 1992).

■ Protection status
National None   **International** None

■ Conservation issues

> **Threats** Unknown

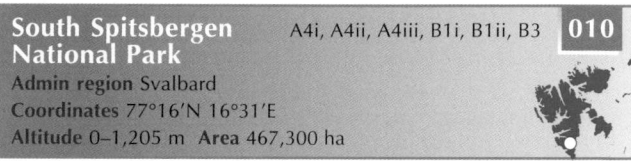

South Spitsbergen National Park   A4i, A4ii, A4iii, B1i, B1ii, B3   010

Admin region Svalbard
Coordinates 77°16′N 16°31′E
Altitude 0–1,205 m   **Area** 467,300 ha

■ Site description
An area of high-Arctic tundra. The Bird Sanctuaries within the National Park are islands and islets with grassy vegetation, freshwater ponds and bare areas. A Polish research station is situated in the southern part of the park.

> **Habitats** Grassland (100%; tundra), Rocky areas (sea cliff/rocky shore)
> **Land-use** Nature conservation/research (100%)

■ Birds

Species		Season	Year	Pop min	Pop max	Acc	Criteria
¹ *Branta leucopsis*	Barnacle Goose	B	1989	850	950	—	A4i, B1i, B3
Somateria mollissima	Eider	B	1989	1,000	1,000	—	B1i
Rissa tridactyla	Kittiwake	B	1989	25,900	25,900	—	A4i, B1i
² *Uria lomvia*	Brünnich's Guillemot	B	1989	208,500	210,000	—	A4ii, B1ii

1. Isøyane (250 pairs) and Dunøyane (600–700 pairs).
2. Individuals; 154,000 at Stellingfjellet; 50,000 at Kovalskifjella; 4,500–6,000 at Sofiekammen.

Sea cliffs at Stellingfjellet and Kovalskifjella (both on the east coast of Torrell Land) and at Sofiekammen (Gnalberget; facing Hornsund) hold important seabird colonies, while the Bird Sanctuaries are important breeding and moulting areas for *Branta leucopsis* and *Somateria mollissima*.

■ Protection status
National High   **International** Low
467,300 ha of IBA covered by National Park (Sør-Spitsbergen, 530,000 ha). 120 ha of IBA covered by Nature Reserve (Dunøyene [Bird Sanctuary], 120 ha). 30 ha of IBA covered by Nature Reserve (Isøyene [Bird Sanctuary], 30 ha). 46 ha of IBA covered by Nature Reserve (Olsholmen [Bird Sanctuary], 46 ha). 3,599 ha of IBA covered by Nature Reserve (Sørkapp [Bird Sanctuary], 3,599 ha). 120 ha of IBA covered by Ramsar Site (Dunøyene, 120 ha). 30 ha of IBA covered by Ramsar Site (Isøyene, 30 ha).

■ Conservation issues
No threats are known.

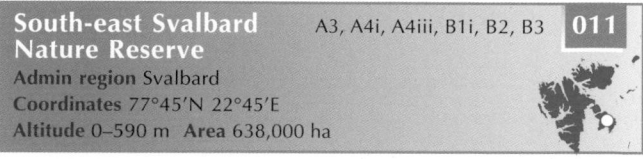

South-east Svalbard Nature Reserve   A3, A4i, A4iii, B1i, B2, B3   011

Admin region Svalbard
Coordinates 77°45′N 22°45′E
Altitude 0–590 m   **Area** 638,000 ha

■ Site description
The Nature Reserve covers the whole of the islands of Barentsøya and Edgeøya, in south-east Svalbard. The habitat is high-Arctic tundra; vegetation is sparse or non-existent over most of the land. Bird data are available for three subsites: Tusenøyane, Negerpynten and Kvalpynten (all on Edgeøya). Tusenøyane (77°05′N 22°00′E;

150,000 ha) is a group of many rocky, low-lying islets (the largest being c.200 ha) in an area of shallow sea, some distance from the south-west coast of Edgeøya. Negerpynten (77°15'N 22°40'E) and Kvalpynten (77°27'N 22°53'E) are sea cliffs at the south-western tip of Edgeøya. There is no settlement in the IBA.

Habitats Grassland (tundra), Marine areas (sea inlet/coastal features), Rocky areas (sea cliff/rocky shore; rock stacks/islets)
Land-use Nature conservation/research (100%), Tourism/recreation

■ Birds

Species	Season	Year	Pop min	Pop max	Acc	Criteria
[1] *Branta leucopsis* Barnacle Goose	B	1989	60	80	—	A3, B1i, B3
[1,2] *Branta bernicla* Brent Goose	B	1989	600	—	—	A3, A4i, B1i, B2
Somateria spectabilis King Eider	B	—	—	—	—	A3
Calidris maritima Purple Sandpiper	B	—	—	—	—	A3
Larus hyperboreus Glaucous Gull	B	—	—	—	—	A3

1. Tusenøyane.
2. See main text.

About 80% of the small and vulnerable Svalbard breeding population of *Branta bernicla* (*B. b. hrota*) breeds at Tusenøyane, as well as four other species that are also restricted in Europe (when breeding) to the Arctic/tundra biome. In late summer and autumn Tusenøyane is also a notable moulting area for *Somateria mollissima* and *Somateria spectabilis*. There are large seabird colonies at Negerpynten and Kvalpynten (e.g. at least 12,000 pairs of *Uria lomvia*).

■ Protection status
National High **International** None
638,000 ha of IBA covered by Nature Reserve (Søraust-Svalbard, 638,000 ha).

■ Conservation issues

Threats Extraction industry (C), Industrialization/urbanization (U), Recreation/tourism (C)

The most serious threat to the birdlife on the islands is an oil spill (there are plans to open the northern Barents Sea to test-drilling for oil and gas). Increased traffic of tourist boats at Tusenøyane may also be a threat, as *Branta bernicla* (especially) are very shy and suffer increased predation of eggs and young if disturbed. Tusenøyane lies within the Nature Reserve. The goose populations are monitored by the Norwegian Polar Institute.

Hopen island
A4i, A4ii, A4iii, B1i, B1ii, B2   **012**
Admin region Svalbard
Coordinates 76°33'N 25°10'E
Altitude 0–370 m **Area** 50 ha

■ Site description
An elongated island in the Barents Sea. There is a radio station, located on the east coast.

Habitats Marine areas (open sea), Rocky areas (sea cliff/rocky shore)
Land-use Nature conservation/research, Not utilized

■ Birds

Species	Season	Year	Pop min	Pop max	Acc	Criteria
Rissa tridactyla Kittiwake	B	1998	40,000	40,000	—	A4i, B1i
[1] *Uria lomvia* Brünnich's Guillemot	B	1998	150,000	150,000	A	A4ii, B1ii
Cepphus grylle Black Guillemot	B	1998	1,000	—	—	B1ii, B2

1. Individuals.

The island is important for its large colonies of breeding seabirds.

■ Protection status
National None **International** None

■ Conservation issues
No threats are known. The radio station causes no disturbance to birds. The area is a proposed Nature Reserve because of its importance for polar bear *Ursus maritimus* (35 winter lairs in 1996).

Bjørnøya (Bear Island)
A3, A4i, A4ii, A4iii, B1i, B1ii, B2   **013**
Admin region Svalbard
Coordinates 74°27'N 19°03'E
Altitude 0–535 m **Area** 18,000 ha

■ Site description
An oceanic island between Spitsbergen and Norway. There are steep sea cliffs at the southern end, while the northern part is flat with numerous lakes and ponds. There is rich vegetation close to the seabird colonies, but tundra is far more sparse in the central and northern parts. The only permanent human settlement on the island is a meteorological station, which does not pose any threat to the birdlife.

Habitats Grassland (35%; tundra), Wetland (20%; standing fresh water), Marine areas (5%; sea inlet/coastal features), Rocky areas (40%)
Land-use Not utilized (100%)

■ Birds

Species	Season	Year	Pop min	Pop max	Acc	Criteria
Fulmarus glacialis Fulmar	B	1981	50,000	60,000	—	A4ii, B1ii
[1] *Anser brachyrhynchus* Pink-footed Goose	P	—	—	—	—	A4i, B1i
[1] *Branta leucopsis* Barnacle Goose	P	—	—	—	—	A4i, B1i
Clangula hyemalis Long-tailed Duck	B	—	—	—	—	A3
Calidris maritima Purple Sandpiper	B	—	—	—	—	A3
Phalaropus fulicarius Grey Phalarope	B	1998	10	—	—	A3
Larus hyperboreus Glaucous Gull	B	1998	2,000	2,000	A	A3, A4i, B1i
Rissa tridactyla Kittiwake	B	1998	100,000	100,000	A	A4i, B1i
Uria aalge Guillemot	B	1998	50,000	50,000	A	A4ii, B1ii
[2] *Uria lomvia* Brünnich's Guillemot	B	1998	190,000	190,000	A	A4ii, B1ii
Cepphus grylle Black Guillemot	B	1998	1,000	1,000	A	B1ii, B2
[3] *Alle alle* Little Auk	B	1985	10,000	100,000	A	B1ii
Plectrophenax nivalis Snow Bunting	B	—	—	—	—	A3

1. Important staging area (see main text).
2. Individuals.
3. Probably in the lower part of the range.

There is a very large seabird colony at the southern end of the island with many tens of thousands of pairs, dominated by *Rissa tridactyla*, *Uria aalge* and *Uria lomvia*. Other notable breeding species include at least five out of the 32 species that are restricted in Europe (when breeding) to the Arctic/tundra biome. The island is an important staging area for an unknown but significant proportion of the Svalbard populations of *Anser brachyrhynchus* (c.30,000 birds in total) and *Branta leucopsis* (c.13,000 birds in total).

■ Protection status
National None **International** None

■ Conservation issues

Threats Aquaculture/fisheries (A), Extraction industry (A), Industrialization/urbanization (B), Recreation/tourism (C)

Bjørnøya may be developed as a supply base for ships and oil rigs, in the event of future activity by the oil industry in the Barents Sea. However, in 1999 the Norwegian government suggested that the whole island might be designated as a Nature Reserve. Representatives of both the Norwegian and the Russian mining industries have protested against this initiative, and the oil industry is also likely to react negatively to such plans. The greatest threats to birds at the island are oil spills and food shortages, the latter partly due to overfishing. The populations of *Fulmarus glacialis*, *Rissa tridactyla*, *Uria aalge* and *Uria lomvia* have been monitored since 1986.

Jan Mayen island
A4ii, A4iii, B1ii, B2   **014**
Admin region Svalbard
Coordinates 71°00'N 8°30'W
Altitude 0–2,277 m **Area** 38,700 ha

■ Site description
A mountain island, situated about 1,000 km west of Bodø on the Norwegian mainland and 450 km east of Greenland. Volcanic ash covers

large parts of the island, and Beerenberg volcano (2,277 m; inactive and covered with a glacier) dominates the rocky tundra landscape. There is very little vegetation. The island was annexed by Norway in 1921.

Habitats Grassland (tundra), Marine areas, Rocky areas
Land-use Nature conservation/research, Not utilized

■ **Birds**

There are large and highly important breeding colonies of seabirds; other notable species include *Rissa tridactyla* (4,000–17,500 pairs), *Sterna paradisaea* (500–1,000 pairs) and *Fratercula arctica* (1,000–10,000 pairs). A total of 96 species have been recorded on the island, mainly as vagrants.

Species	Season	Year	Pop min	Pop max	Acc	Criteria
Fulmarus glacialis Fulmar	B	1998	78,000	160,000	A	A4ii, B1ii
1 *Uria lomvia* Brünnich's Guillemot	B	1986	74,000	147,000	A	A4ii, B1ii
Cepphus grylle Black Guillemot	B	1989	100	1,000	—	B1ii, B2
Alle alle Little Auk	B	1986	10,000	100,000	A	A4ii, B1ii

1. Individuals.

■ **Protection status**

National None **International** None

■ **Conservation issues**

No threats are known.

REFERENCES

ANKER-NILSSEN, T., BAKKEN, V., BIANKI, V., GOLOVKIN, A., STRØM, H. AND TATARINKOVA, I., EDS. (in press) Status of marine birds breeding in the Barents Sea region. Norway: Norwegian Polar Institute.

ANON. (1995) *Nature Protection Areas in Norway*. Trondheim, Norway: Direktoratet for Naturforvaltning (DN-report No. 3-1995). 178 pp. (In Norwegian, with English summary.)

ANON. (1997) *Norges Nasjonalparker (National Parks of Norway)*. Trondheim, Norway: Direktoratet for Naturforvaltning. (In Norwegian.)

BARRETT, R. T. AND MEHLUM, F. (1989) Bird observations and seabird census at Hopen, Svalbard. *Fauna Norv. Ser. C, Cinclus* 12: 21–29.

FJELD, P. E. AND MEHLUM, F. (1988) *Animal life — Svalbard and Jan Mayen*. Oslo: Norwegian Polar Institute. (Map.)

VAN FRANEKER, J. A. AND LUTTIK, R. (1981) *Report on the* Fulmarus glacialis-*expedition, Bear Island, July–August 1980*. Amsterdam: Instituut voor Taxonomische Zoölogie (Verslagen en technische Gegevens No. 32).

VAN FRANEKER, J., CAMPHUIJSEN, K. AND MEHLUM, F. (1986) [The status of the birds of Jan Mayen.] *Vår Fuglefauna* 9: 145–158. (In Norwegian, with English summary.)

VAN FRANEKER, J. A., CAMPHUYSEN, C. J. AND MEHLUM, F. (1998) The birds of Jan Mayen. *Circumpolar Journal* 13: 28-43.

GRIMMETT, R. F. A. AND JONES, T. A. (1989) *Important Bird Areas in Europe*. Cambridge, UK: International Council for Bird Preservation (Techn. Publ. 9).

HEATH, M. F. AND BORGGREVE, C. (2000) *BirdLife International/EBCC European Bird Database 1998*. Cambridge, UK: BirdLife International.

ISAKSEN, K. AND BAKKEN, V. (1995) Breeding populations of seabirds in Svalbard. Pp. 11–36 in K. Isaksen and V. Bakken, eds. *Seabird populations in the Northern Barents Sea*. Oslo: Norwegian Polar Institute (Meddelelser 135).

MEHLUM, F. (1991) Breeding population size of the Common Eider *Somateria mollissima* in Kongsfjorden, Svalbard. *Norsk Polarinstitutt Skrifter* 195: 21–29.

MEHLUM, F. AND BAKKEN, V. (1994) Seabirds in Svalbard, Norway: status, recent changes and management. Pp. 155–171 in D. N. Nettleship, J. Burger and M. Gochfeld, eds. *Seabirds on islands: threats, case studies and action plans*. Cambridge, UK: BirdLife International (BirdLife Conservation Series No. 1).

NORDERHAUG, M. (1989) *Svalbards fugler*. Oslo: Dreyer forlag (in cooperation with the Norwegian Ornithological Society). 101 pp. (In Norwegian.)

THEISEN, F. AND BRUDE, W. (1998) *Evaluering av områdevernet på Svalbard [Evaluation of the protected areas at Svalbard]*. Oslo: Norsk Polarinstitutt (Norwegian Polar Institute). (Meddelelse nr. 153.) 144 pp.

TUCKER, G. M. AND HEATH, M. F. (1994) *Birds in Europe: their conservation status*. Cambridge, UK: BirdLife International (BirdLife Conservation Series No. 3).

■ POLAND

MACIEJ GROMADZKI AND MARIA WIELOCH

Białowieża forest (IBA 031). (PHOTO: PAWEŁ OLAF SIDŁO)

GENERAL INTRODUCTION

Poland covers about 312,700 km² within the temperate forest zone of Europe. It is a low-lying country, with only 9% of its land surface above 300 m, although mountain ranges in the south (dominated by the Western Carpathians) rise up to a maximum of 2,499 m. Poland has a population of 38,612,000 (1996 estimate), with a moderate overall population density of 124 people per km², the highest densities being in the southern upland areas and the lowest in the north-west and north-east.

A total of 77 Important Bird Areas (IBAs) are currently recognised in Poland, covering 19,867 km² or equivalent to about 6.4% of the land surface (Table 1). The IBAs are distributed more or less evenly over the whole country, but with a preponderance in the east and north. The previous pan-European IBA inventory (Grimmett and Jones 1989) listed 126 sites for Poland—thus, a relatively large number of these have since lost their IBA status (see Table 1), especially since 19 of the current 77 sites are completely new IBAs. This is mainly because the IBA criteria have been revised since 1989—only a few of the 1989 sites have lost their IBA status because of actual changes in bird numbers at the site. Apart from amalgamations of previous IBAs (thirteen now form part of current sites 025, 054, 061 and 073), most of the other 54 sites

from 1989 that still meet current IBA criteria are largely unchanged in extent, although the numbering system and many of the site names have been altered.

ORNITHOLOGICAL IMPORTANCE

A total of 128 species of European conservation concern (SPEC) breed regularly in Poland (Tucker and Heath 1994). In addition, 24 SPECs do not breed but are regular visitors to the country on passage or in winter.

Six species of global conservation concern breed in Poland (Table 2)—*Aythya nyroca*, *Haliaeetus albicilla*, *Aquila clanga*, *Crex crex*, *Gallinago media* and *Acrocephalus paludicola*. The most important site for *Aythya nyroca* is the Barycz river valley (site 054), where 20–30% of the national population breed. All of the breeding *Aquila clanga* in Poland nest in the Biebrza river valley (site 025), as do most of the national population of *Acrocephalus paludicola* (Table 2). The number of breeding *Crex crex* in Poland, currently estimated at about 30,000 calling males (1997 survey), represents a major proportion of the European total, and this species played a very important role in identifying IBAs during previous inventories (Grimmett and Jones 1989; Gromadzki *et al.* 1994).

Table 1. Summary of Important Bird Areas in Poland   77 IBAs covering 19,867 km²

IBA code	National code [1]	1989 code	International name	National name	Administrative region	Area (ha)	Criteria (see p. 11)
001	001	PL001	Delta of the Świna river	Delta Świny	zachodnio-pomorskie	4,000	A1, A4i, A4iii, B1i, B2, B3
002	002	PL005	Szczecin lagoon	Zalew Szczeciński	zachodnio-pomorskie	48,000	A1, A4i, A4iii, B1i, B2
003	004	PL007	Rozwarowo marshes	Bagna Rozwarowskie	zachodnio-pomorskie	1,600	A1
004	008	PL009	Świdwie lake	Jezioro Świdwie	zachodnio-pomorskie	900	A4i, B1i
005	010	PL011	Wełtyń lakes	Jeziora Wełtyńskie	zachodnio-pomorskie	4,600	B3
006	009	PL010	Lower Odra river valley	Dolina Dolnej Odry	zachodnio-pomorskie, lubuskie	75,000	A1, A4i, A4iii, B1i, B1iv, B2, B3
007	011	PL012	Miedwie lake	Jezioro Miedwie	zachodnio-pomorskie	3,200	A4i, B1i

543

Table 1 ... continued. Summary of Important Bird Areas in Poland

77 IBAs covering 19,867 km²

IBA code	National code [1]	1989 code	International name	National name	Administrative region	Area (ha)	Criteria (see p. 11)
008	021	PL013	Ińsk Landscape Park	Iński Park Krajobrazowy	zachodnio-pomorskie	17,763	A1, B3
009	013	PL019	Słowiński National Park	Słowiński Park Narodowy	pomorskie	18,247	A4i, B1i
010	023	PL018	Słupia Valley Landscape Park	Park Krajobrazowy Dolina Słupi	pomorskie	37,040	A1
011	025	—	Middle part of Tuchola forest	Wielki Sandr Brdy	pomorskie	38,815	B1i, B2, B3
012	015, 016	PL022	Puck Bay	Zatoka Pucka	pomorskie	56,000	A4i, A4iii, B1i
013	017	PL023	Wisła river mouth	Ujscie Wisły	pomorskie	485	A1, A4i, A4iii, B1i, B2
014	018	PL024	Wisła lagoon	Zalew Wiślany	pomorskie, warmińsko-mazurskie	33,000	A4i, A4iii, B1i
015	019	PL025	Drużno lake	Jezioro Drużno	warmińsko-mazurskie	3,021	A4i, A4iii, B1i, B2
016	027	PL026	Iława forests	Lasy Iławskie	warmińsko-mazurskie	25,279	A1, A4i, B1i, B2, B3
017	047	PL109	Dymerskie meadows	Łąki Dymerskie	warmińsko-mazurskie	300	A4i, B1i
018	045	PL111	Napiwodzko-Ramucka forest	Puszcza Napiwodzko-Ramucka	warmińsko-mazurskie	65,000	A1, B1i, B2, B3
019	020	PL104	Oświn lake	Jezioro Oświn	warmińsko-mazurskie	2,500	B3
020	050	PL103	Borecka forest	Puszcza Borecka	warmińsko-mazurskie	22,000	B2, B3
021	048	PL108	Łuknajno lake	Jezioro Łuknajno	warmińsko-mazurskie	710	A4i, A4iii, B1i, B2, B3
022	051	PL106	Nietlickie marshes	Bagna Nietlickie	warmińsko-mazurskie	1,200	A1, A4i, B1i, B1iv, B2, B3
023	—	—	Pisz forest	Puszcza Piska	warmińsko-mazurskie, podlaskie	163,000	A1, B2
024	053	—	Augustów forest	Puszcza Augustowska	podlaskie	102,000	B2, B3
025	083	PL100–PL102	Biebrza river valley	Dolina Biebrzy	podlaskie	126,047	A1, A4i, B1i, B2, B3
026	084	—	Narew river gaps	Przełomowa Dolina Narwi	podlaskie	4,200	A1, B2
027	085	PL098	Marshy valley of the Narew river	Bagienna Dolina Narwi	podlaskie	9,332	A1, B2, B3
028	086	PL099	Knyszyń forest	Puszcza Knyszyńska	podlaskie	110,000	B2, B3
029	087	—	Gródek—Michałowo basin	Niecka Gródecko—Michałowska	podlaskie	4,700	A1, B2
030	088	—	Upper Narew river valley	Dolina Górnej Narwi	podlaskie	8,400	A1, B2, B3
031	089	PL097	Białowieża forest	Puszcza Białowieska	podlaskie	62,500	A1, B2, B3
032	030	PL039	Warta flood-plain—Słońsk	Rozlewiska Warty—Słońsk	lubuskie	4,244	A1, A4i, A4iii, B1i, B2, B3
033	031	PL035	Noteć river flood-plain	Nadnoteckie Łęgi	wielkopolskie	10,000	A1
034	040	PL033	Obra river flood-plain	Wielki Łęg Obrzański	wielkopolskie	16,000	B2
035	041	PL045	Wonieść reservoir	Zbiornik Wonieść	wielkopolskie	900	B2
036	066	PL031	Middle Warta river valley	Dolina Warty Środkowej	wielkopolskie	32,000	A1, A4iii, B2, B3
037	032	—	Ostrówek and Smogulec ponds	Stawy Ostrówek i Smogulec	kujawsko-pomorskie, wielkopolskie	1,000	B1i
038	033	—	Ślesin and Występ ponds	Stawy Ślesin i Występ	kujawsko-pomorskie	3,200	A4i, B1i
039	—	—	Lower Wisła river	Dolina Dolnej Wisły	pomorskie, kujawsko-pomorskie	32,000	A1, A4i, A4iii, B1i, B2
040	029	—	Marshy valley of the Drwęca river	Bagienna Dolina Drwęcy	kujawsko-pomorskie	3,400	B1i
041	042	PL034	Gopło Millennium Park	Nadgoplański Park Tysiąclecia	kujawsko-pomorskie, wielkopolskie	12,700	A4i, A4iii, B1i, B2
042	044	PL028	Rakutowskie swamps	Blota Rakutowskie	kujawsko-pomorskie	800	A4iii, B1i
043	—	PL029	Ner river valley	Dolina Neru	wielkopolskie, łódzkie	4,800	A1
044	067	—	Jeziorsko reservoir	Zbiornik Jeziorsko	wielkopolskie, łódzkie	4,300	A4i, B1i
045	060	PL122	Kampinos forest	Puszcza Kampinoska	mazowieckie	35,700	A1, B2, B3
046	061	PL086	Middle Wisła river valley	Dolina Środkowej Wisły	lubelskie, mazowieckie	19,000	A1, A4i, A4iii, B1i, B2
047	058	PL120	Zegrzyński reservoir	Zalew Zegrzyński	mazowieckie	12,000	A4iii, B1i
048	—	PL114	Omulew river valley	Dolina Omulwi	mazowieckie	6,000	A1, B2
049	059	PL121	Biała forest	Puszcza Biała	mazowieckie	120,000	A1, B2
050	063	PL094	Liwiec river valley	Dolina Liwca	mazowieckie	11,800	A1, B2
051	065	PL095	Lower Bug river valley	Dolina Dolnego Bugu	lubelskie, mazowieckie, podlaskie	55,000	A1, B2
052	055	PL044	Przemków ponds	Stawy Przemkowskie	dolnośląskie	1,046	A4iii, B2
053	078	PL046	Odra riverine forests	Łęgi Odrzańskie	dolnośląskie	18,000	A1, B2, B3
054	072–077	PL047–PL052	Barycz river valley	Dolina Baryczy	wielkopolskie, dolnośląskie	25,700	A1, A4iii, B1i, B2, B3
055	—	—	Słup reservoir	Zbiornik Słup	dolnośląskie	500	A4i, B1i
056	—	—	Mietków reservoir	Zbiornik Mietkowski	dolnośląskie	920	A4i, B1i
057	079	PL053	Oak-hornbeam forests in the Odra valley	Grądy Odrzanskie	opolskie, dolnośląskie	31,000	B2, B3
058	080	PL057	Turawa reservoir	Jezioro Turawskie	opolskie	2,200	A4iii
·059	101	PL054	Otmuchów reservoir	Jezioro Otmuchowskie	opolskie	2,300	A4i, A4iii, B1i
060	102	PL055	Nysa reservoir	Jezioro Nyskie (Głębinowskie)	opolskie	3,000	A4i, A4iii, B1i
061	108, 109	PL060, PL061	Upper Wisła river valley	Dolina Górnej Wisły	ślaskie, malopolskie	130,000	A4i, A4iii, B1i, B2
062	—	—	Middle Nida flood-plain	Rozlewiska Środkowej Nidy	świętokrzyskie	2,000	A1
063	105	PL085	Małopolska Wisła river gap	Małopolski Przełom Wisły	lubelskie, mazowieckie, świętokrzyskie	1,300	B2
064	092	PL090	Tyśmienica river valley	Dolina Tyśmienicy	lubelskie	14,500	A1, B2, B3
065	093	PL084	Parczew forests	Lasy Parczewskie	lubelskie	8,000	A1, B2

Table 1 ... continued. Summary of Important Bird Areas in Poland

77 IBAs covering 19,867 km²

IBA code	National code [1]	1989 code	International name	National name	Administrative region	Area (ha)	Criteria (see p. 11)
066	097	PL082	Bubnów marshes	Bagno Bubnów	lubelskie	2,104	A1, B2
067	100	—	Middle Bug river valley	Dolina Środkowego Bugu	lubelskie	5,100	A1, B2, B3
068	098	PL081	Chełm calcareous marshes	Chełmskie Torfowiska Węglanowe	lubelskie	1,700	A1, B2, B3
069	099	—	Strzeleckie forests	Lasy Strzeleckie	lubelskie	8,500	B2, B3
070	110	—	Niepołomice forest	Puszcza Niepołomicka	małopolskie	11,000	B3
071	116	PL067	Gorce mountains	Gorce	małopolskie	7,030	B2, B3
072	115	PL065	Tatra mountains	Tatry	małopolskie	21,164	A3, B2, B3
073	111	PL073, PL074	Janów forests	Lasy Janowskie	podkarpackie, lubelskie	50,000	B2
074	—	—	Solska Forest Landscape Park	Park Krajobrazowy Puszczy Solskiej	podkarpackie, lubelskie	28,980	B2
075	—	—	Przemyśl Plateau Landscape Park	Park Krajobrazowy Pogórza Przemyskiego	podkarpackie	62,000	A1, B2, B3
076	112	PL080	Starzawa ponds	Stawy Starzawskie	podkarpackie	950	A4iii, B2
077	118	PL077	Bieszczady mountains	Bieszczady	podkarpackie	114,000	A1, B2, B3

1. Gromadzki *et al.* (1994)

Sites identified in the previous inventory of IBAs in Europe (Grimmett and Jones 1989) but no longer considered to be IBAs

PL002 Zalew Kamieński (Kamień Bay); PL003 Jezioro Liwia Łuża (Lake Liwia Łuża); PL004 Bagna doliny rzek Świniec i Niemicy (Marshes in the valley Świniec and Niemica); PL006 Łąki Skoszewskie (Skoszewo Meadows); PL008 Jezioro Karpino (Lake Karpino); PL014 Drawski Park Krajobrazowy (Drawski Landscape Park); PL015 Jeziora Szczecineckie (Lakes Szczecineckie); PL016 Okolice Żydowa—Białego Boru (Żydowo—Bialy Bór region); PL017 Koszaliński i słupski pas nadmorski (coastal areas of Koszalin and Słupsk); PL020 Jeziora Krępsko–Szczytnieńskie (Lakes Krępsko and Szczytno and surrounding region); PL021 Bielawskie Błota (Bielawskie Bog); PL027 Jezioro Karaś (Lake Karaś); PL030 Kramskie Błota (Kramskie Marshes); PL032 Dolina Warty koło Krajkowa (River Warta valley near Krajkowa); PL036 Jezioro Wielkie (Lake Wielkie); PL037 Dolina Warty koło Santoka (River Warta valley near Santok); PL038 Ujście Noteci (Mouth of the River Noteć); PL040 Dolina Leniwej Obry (Leniwa Obra valley); PL041 Jeziora Chobienickie (Chobienickie Lakes); PL042 Pojezierze Sławskie (Sławskie Lakes); PL043 Stawy rybne Darowa (Darowa fish-ponds); PL056 Stawy rybne w Niemodlinie: zespół Dąbrowa (Niemodlin fish-ponds: Dąbrowa complex); PL058 Stawy rybne Łężczak (Łężczak fish-ponds); PL059 Zbiornik Świerklaniec (Świerklaniec Reservoir); PL062 Zespół stawów rybnych w Przerębie i Spytkowicach (Przeręb and Spytkowice fish-pond complex); PL063 Ojcowski Park Narodowy (Ojców National Park); PL064 Babiogórski Park Narodowy (Babia Góra National Park); PL066 Pieniński Park Narodowy (Pieniny National Park); PL068 Zespół stawów w Górkach (Górki fish-pond complex); PL069 Zespół stawów rybnych w Młodzowie (Młodzowy fish-pond complex); PL070 Zespół stawów rybnych koło Grobli (Fish-pond complex near Grobla); PL071 Stawy rybne w Osieczyskach (Osieczyska fish-ponds); PL072 Zespół stawów rybnych w Budzie Stalowskiej (Buda Stalowska fish-pond complex); PL075 Stawy rybne w Porębach Kupieńskich (Poręby Kupieńskie fish-pond); PL076 Zbiornik Rzeszowski (Rzeszów Reservoir); PL078 Zbiornik Przemyski (Przemyśl brick-pits); PL079 Starorzecze Sanu koło Hurka (Former bed of River San, near Hurko); PL083 Jezioro Uściwierz i przyległe torfowiska (Lake Uściwierz and adjacent marshes); PL087 Dolina Pilicy (River Pilica valley); PL088 Zbiornik Sulejowski (Sulejów Reservoir); PL089 Uroczysko Mosty-Zahajki: zbiornik i lasy (Mosty-Zahajki: reservoirs and forest); PL091 Bagno Całownie/Ub Biel (Całowanie or Biel Fen); PL092 Kompleks leśny Kryńszczak (Kryńszczak forest complex); PL093 Zespół stawów rybnych koło Kotunia (fish-pond complex near Kotuń); PL096 Lasy Łochowskie (Łochów forests); PL105 Jezioro Dobskie (Lake Dobskie); PL107 Półwysep Czarny Róg (Czarny Róg Peninsula); PL110 Bartołty Wielkie; PL112 Lasy Łańskie (Łańskie forests); PL113 Dolina Czarnej (River Czarna valley); PL115 Galwica; PL116 Dolina rzeki Orzyc: część górna (River Orzyc valley: upper part); PL117 Dolina Młławki (River Mławka valley); PL118 Łąki Raczyny (Raczyny Meadows); PL119 Lasy Ościsłowo (Ościsłowo forest complex); PL123 Stawy rybne koło Łowicza/Stawy Mysłaków (Łowicz and Mysłaków fish-ponds); PL124 Stawy rybne Okręt i Rydwan (Okręt and Rydwan fish-ponds); PL125 Stawy rybne Walewice (Walewice fish-ponds); PL126 Stawy rybne Psary (Psary fish-ponds).

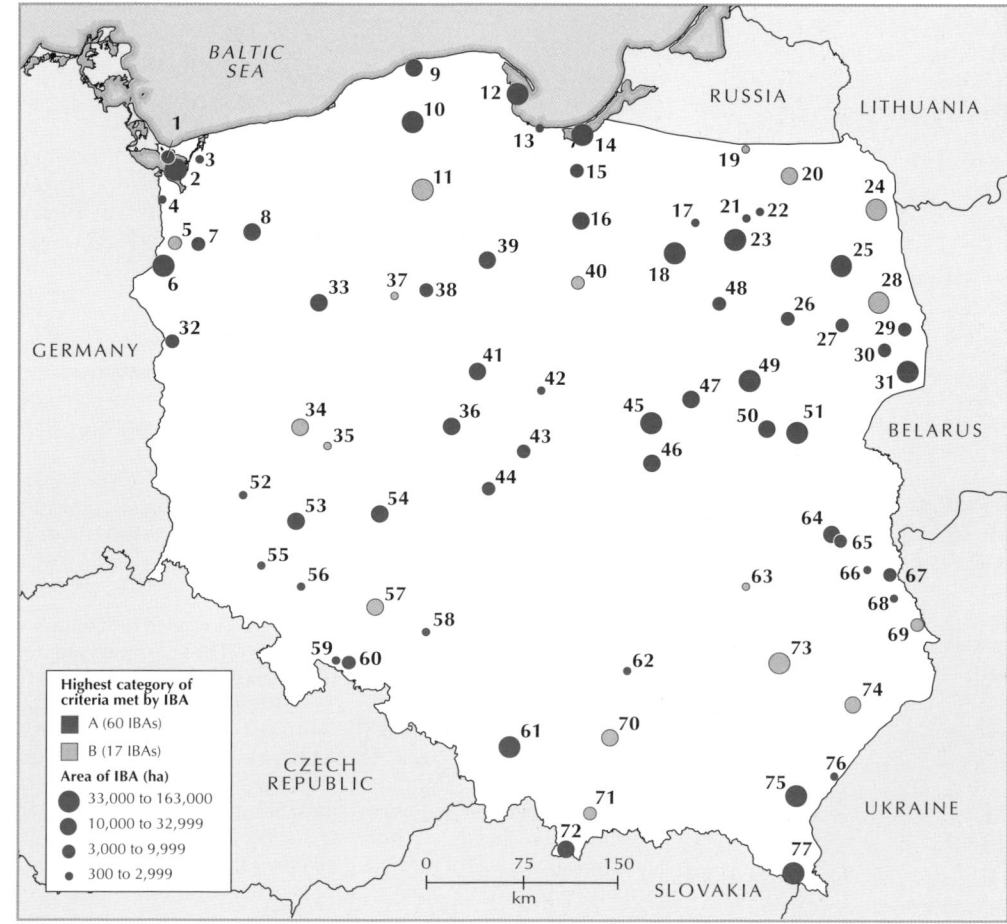

Map 1. Location, area and criteria category of Important Bird Areas in Poland.

Table 2. Important Bird Areas in Poland that are important for species of global conservation concern (meeting criterion A1).

Species	IBA code
Aythya nyroca Ferruginous Duck	054
Haliaeetus albicilla White-tailed Eagle	002, 006, 008, 013, 016, 018, 023, 032, 039, 046, 053, 054, 064
Aquila clanga Greater Spotted Eagle	025
Crex crex Corncrake	006, 010, 016, 018, 022, 023, 027, 030, 031, 032, 033, 036, 039, 043, 045, 048, 049, 050, 051, 062, 064, 065, 067, 075, 077
Gallinago media Great Snipe	025, 026, 029, 030, 051
Acrocephalus paludicola Aquatic Warbler	001, 002, 003, 006, 022, 025, 026, 030, 066, 068

Table 3. Important Bird Areas in Poland that support important numbers of one or more congregatory species (i.e. meeting criteria A4 and/or B1). IBAs meeting both criteria A4 and B1 for the species are shown in **bold**. IBAs meeting only criterion B1 for the species concerned, and not A4, are shown in normal type. For key to 'Season', see p. 7.

Species	Season	IBA code
Podiceps cristatus Great Crested Grebe	W	012
	P	012
Podiceps auritus Slavonian Grebe	P	012
Podiceps nigricollis Black-necked Grebe	B	**061**
Phalacrocorax carbo Cormorant	P	012
Cygnus olor Mute Swan	W	012
	P	021
Cygnus columbianus Bewick's Swan	P	037, **038**
Cygnus cygnus Whooper Swan	W	006, 011
	P	**032**
Anser fabalis Bean Goose	P	**004, 006, 007, 009, 015, 032, 041, 044,** **054, 055, 056, 059, 060**
Anser albifrons White-fronted Goose	P	004, **006,** 007, 009, 013, 014, 015, **032,** 040, 041
Anser anser Greylag Goose	B	032, 054
	W	001
	P	015, 042
Anas strepera Gadwall	B	**006**
	P	**006,** 015
Anas crecca Teal	P	014
Netta rufina Red-crested Pochard	P	**021**
Aythya ferina Pochard	W	006
	P	006, 014
Aythya fuligula Tufted Duck	W	**006, 012, 013**
	P	002, **006**
Aythya marila Scaup	W	**002, 013**
	P	**002**
Bucephala clangula Goldeneye	W	002, 006, 012, **013, 039,** 047
	P	**002,** 014
Mergus albellus Smew	W	**001, 002,** 006, 012, **014**
Mergus merganser Goosander	B	039
	W	**001, 002, 006, 012, 039**
	P	**002,** 009
Grus grus Crane	P	**006, 015, 016, 017,** 018, **022, 032,** 041, 054
	N	004
Gallinago media Great Snipe	B	**025**
Larus minutus Little Gull	P	**013,** 014
Larus canus Common Gull	W	013
	P	013
	N	013
Sterna albifrons Little Tern	B	**046**
Chlidonias hybridus Whiskered Tern	B	061
Chlidonias niger Black Tern	B	**025**
Chlidonias niger Black Tern	P	002, **013**
Chlidonias leucopterus White-winged Black Tern	B	**025**

Table 4. Species of European conservation concern with significant breeding populations at Important Bird Areas in Poland (meeting any IBA criteria).

Species [1]	Minimum national breeding population (pairs) [2]	Proportion (%) of national population breeding at all IBAs in Poland [4]
Botaurus stellaris Bittern	1,100	42
Ixobrychus minutus Little Bittern	400	28
Ciconia nigra Black Stork	950	26
Ciconia ciconia White Stork	30,500	7
Anas strepera Gadwall	1,200	55
Anas querquedula Garganey	2,500	29
Aythya ferina Pochard	40,000	2
Aythya nyroca Ferruginous Duck	250	64
Pernis apivorus Honey Buzzard	1,000	31
Milvus migrans Black Kite	500	17
Milvus milvus Red Kite	400	17
Haliaeetus albicilla White-tailed Eagle	440	25
Circus pygargus Montagu's Harrier	550	56
Aquila pomarina Lesser Spotted Eagle	1,660	29
Aquila clanga Greater Spotted Eagle	15	67
Falco tinnunculus Kestrel	1,500	7
Tetrao tetrix Black Grouse	3,000	14
Coturnix coturnix Quail	5,000	1
Porzana porzana Spotted Crake	2,500	13
Porzana parva Little Crake	700	37
Crex crex Corncrake	6,600	31
Grus grus Crane	2,300	25
Gallinago media Great Snipe	400	100[3]
Limosa limosa Black-tailed Godwit	6,000	57
Tringa totanus Redshank	2,000	56
Larus canus Common Gull	3,500	86
Sterna albifrons Little Tern	1,000	88
Chlidonias hybridus Whiskered Tern	30	100[3]
Chlidonias niger Black Tern	5,000	46
Bubo bubo Eagle Owl	130	64
Asio flammeus Short-eared Owl	30	57
Alcedo atthis Kingfisher	4,000	13
Coracias garrulus Roller	200	15
Picus canus Grey-headed Woodpecker	1,000	10
Dendrocopos medius Middle Spotted Woodpecker	8,000	6
Riparia riparia Sand Martin	150,000	11
Luscinia luscinia Thrush Nightingale	45,000	2
Turdus torquatus Ring Ouzel	3,000	35
Locustella naevia Grasshopper Warbler	7,000	6
Locustella luscinioides Savi's Warbler	8,000	11
Acrocephalus paludicola Aquatic Warbler	2,900	98
Ficedula albicollis Collared Flycatcher	3,000	53
Lanius excubitor Great Grey Shrike	2,000	6

1. Only those species of European conservation concern (see Box 1, p. 12) that meet IBA criteria in Poland are listed.
2. Data are taken from the BirdLife/EBCC European Bird Database 1998 (Heath and Borggreve 2000).
3. The percentage of the national population in IBAs exceeds 100%. Usually this is because the national population estimate has not been updated recently whilst the IBA population estimate has been recently updated with new data as a result of comprehensive surveys of IBAs themselves. Also, the individual site count for a species may be the maximum or average over recent years, and summing these may record more birds than are present nationally in any single year.
4. Figures in this column are not up-to-date for some species, mainly passerines but also, e.g., *Aythya nyroca* (the national population of which is now much smaller). In general, the data are most up-to-date for waterbirds and raptors.

The vast extent of wetlands in Poland is reflected in the country's importance for congregatory waterbirds (Table 3), particularly during the breeding and migration seasons. These IBAs are concentrated along the large rivers and their flood-plains (e.g. Wisła, Odra) and their mouths, and also at the bays, lagoons and coastal lakes along the Baltic coast. These broad corridors form more-or-less clearly defined migratory routes for some waterbirds (east–west along the coast and north–south along the rivers).

Similarly, because there are still relatively large and unfragmented tracts of forest (e.g. Białowieża forest, Borecka forest, Augustów forest), the country supports important populations of some forest species, e.g. raptors, woodpeckers and *Ciconia nigra* (c.1,000 pairs). Poland holds the largest national breeding population of *Ciconia ciconia* in the world, estimated at more than 40,000 pairs, and other species of non-intensive agricultural landscapes, e.g. *Hirundo rustica*, are also very common. The large rivers in Poland have a semi-natural character and hold important numbers of breeding *Larus canus* and *Sterna albifrons*, nesting in their natural habitat (sandy river islands).

Other SPECs that have an unfavourable conservation status in Europe (Tucker and Heath 1994) and that have important breeding populations in Poland include *Botaurus stellaris* (1,100–1,400 pairs), *Aquila pomarina* (1,600–1,800 pairs), *Perdix perdix* (250,000–1,500,000 pairs), *Chlidonias niger* (5,000–7,000 pairs), *Alcedo atthis* (4,000–8,000 pairs), *Alauda arvensis* and *Riparia riparia*. In addition, the following SPECs (which have a favourable status in Europe but are concentrated there on a global scale) also breed in Poland in important numbers: *Aythya ferina*, *Columba palumbus*, *Strix aluco*, *Dendrocopos medius*, *Luscinia luscinia*, *Saxicola rubetra*, *Locustella fluviatilis*, *Locustella luscinioides*, *Acrocephalus palustris*, *Sylvia nisoria*, *Sylvia communis* and *Emberiza citrinella*.

Fourteen out of the 77 IBAs qualify solely under the B2 or B3 criteria (Table 1). Although the national breeding populations of some SPECs are well covered by the IBA network in Poland, those of other SPECs are not (Table 4). The latter group of species (e.g. *Ciconia ciconia*) tend to be well dispersed over the countryside when breeding and, at least during this season, cannot be adequately conserved in Poland by a system of IBAs or protected areas. For these species, habitat conservation measures for the wider countryside are needed (Tucker and Evans 1997).

HABITATS

Before the advent of man, most of Poland was forested and open habitats were limited. Today Poland is an agrarian country, with open agricultural landscapes covering 60% of its area. Small farms of 5–10 ha are the most numerous type of land-holding in many regions, and arable fields are often very small, creating a very diverse mosaic together with other landscape features. In the last decade the amount of abandoned farmland has increased, involving both small farms all over the country as well as large ones (previously state farms) mostly in the north. Part of the abandoned farmland has been afforested, but much has been left fallow and is now in the process of reverting naturally to scrub and woodland. Agricultural habitats are mainly represented in the IBA network by 'Grassland' and 'Artificial landscape' (Figure 1), although not in as high a proportion as the national total.

Forest and woodland currently cover 29% of the country, although only 19% of this growth is older than 80 years. More than 75% of forest is coniferous at present but the deciduous proportion has been increasing in recent decades. In the north-east there are still tracts of natural forest (some large in comparison with other European countries) dominated by broadleaved deciduous species (especially oak *Quercus*, lime *Tilia* and hornbeam *Carpinus*), while in the south there are fragments of more montane forest-types. Forest habitats are well represented within the IBA network (Figure 1).

Mires are still extensive, and cover 1.5 million ha (4.2% of the country). The most widespread are fens, comprising 89% of the total by area, although many have already been drained and are used as hay-meadows and pastures; raised bogs comprise 6.5% and transitional mires 4.5%. Small mires (less than 10 ha) are the norm. The largest intact mires (undrained or incompletely drained) are in the north-east, in the Narew and Biebrza river basins.

Standing water covers about 1.5% of the national surface area. The country is relatively rich in lakes—there are 5,600 over 1 ha in size—which are clustered into a number of 'lakelands', mainly in the north. There are also some large lagoons along the Baltic coast. Several large rivers run through Poland into the Baltic Sea, e.g. the Odra (Oder), the Wisła (Vistula) and its tributaries the Narew and Bug. These rivers are relatively unregulated, being in many areas not isolated from their flood-plains by embankments, and they thus have a diverse physical structure. In a few areas, e.g. along the Odra river, some good-quality tracts of natural flood-plain forest have also been preserved. Wetlands are disproportionately well represented in the IBA network in Poland (Figure 1), due to their

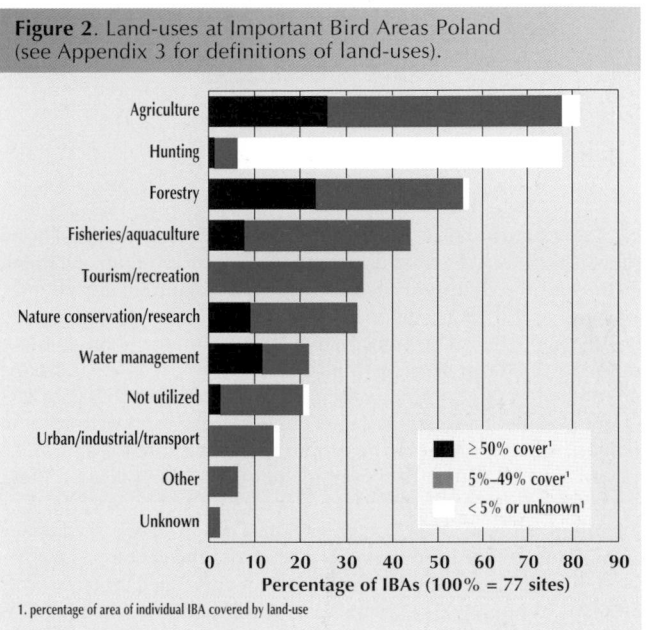

Figure 1. Habitats at Important Bird Areas in Poland (see Appendix 3 for definitions of habitats).

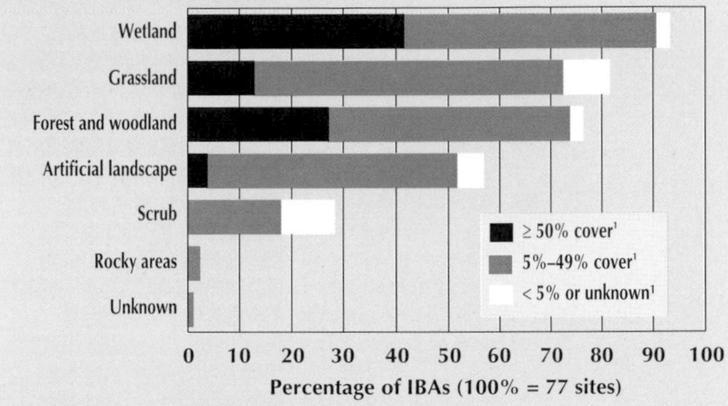

Figure 2. Land-uses at Important Bird Areas Poland (see Appendix 3 for definitions of land-uses).

ease of definition as discrete sites and their great importance for congregatory waterbirds.

IMPACTS ON IBAs – LAND-USE AND THREATS

Agriculture is the most widespread land-use in Poland, covering about 55% of the country, with about five times more land devoted to arable cultivation as to livestock-grazing. Forestry is the second largest sector in terms of national area covered. These two main land-uses also dominate within the Polish IBA network (Figure 2). However, the relatively high preponderance of water-related uses at IBAs does not reflect national land-cover statistics, since wetlands cover a mere c.3% of the country. Thus, the importance of wetlands as IBAs is underlined. Figure 2 shows how widespread hunting is in the IBAs; the only types of land exempted from hunting in Poland are human settlements, Nature Reserves and National Parks.

The threats to birds and habitats at IBAs in Poland are presented in Figure 3. Generally speaking, there are three main threats to riverine sites. First, the current law aimed at the reduction of flooding, which results in the engineering of river channels, dam construction, and clear-felling of riverine forests. Second, the current plans to construct series of large dams on the Wisła and Odra rivers (cascadization). For example, the 'Lower Vistula Cascade' involves the creation of 8–10 dams along the lower Wisła, raising water-levels by the construction of side embankments. Third, the current plan to construct an 'East–West Waterway', for barges of up to 1,500 tonnes, to join Germany with the Dniepr river system via the Noteć, middle Wisła, Narew and Bug rivers. This would completely destroy the natural character of these major Polish rivers or, in the case of the Narew, at least seriously affect it.

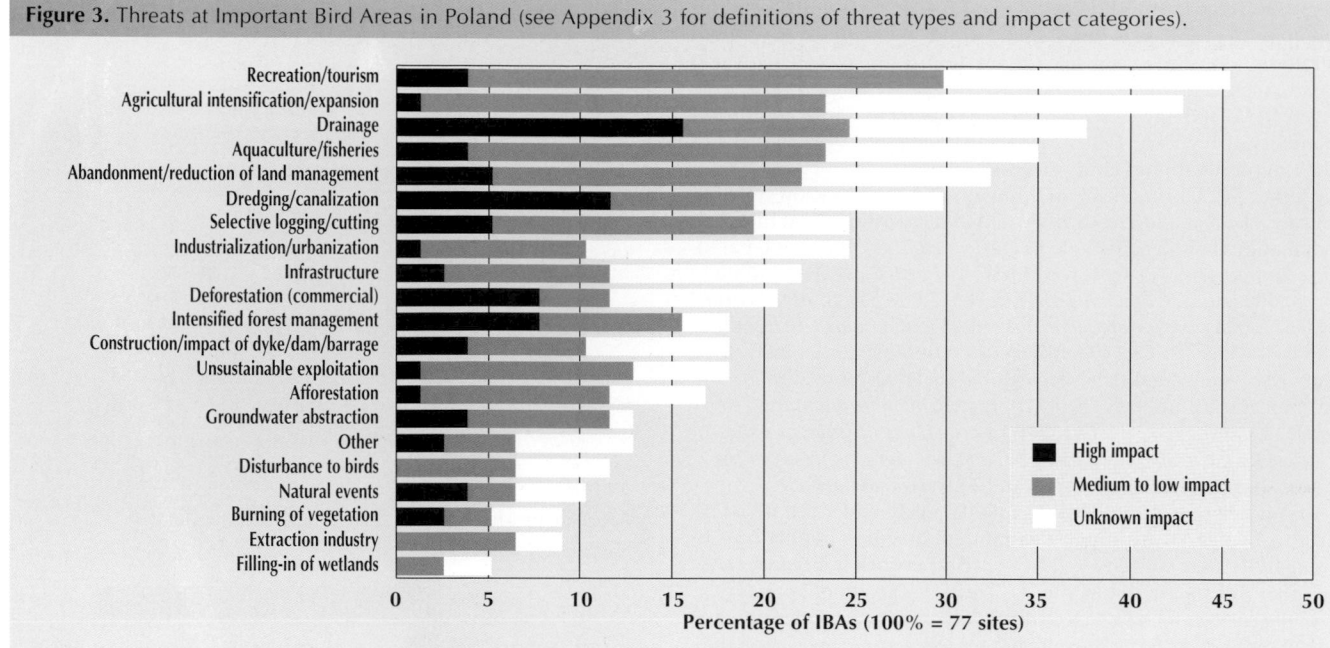

Figure 3. Threats at Important Bird Areas in Poland (see Appendix 3 for definitions of threat types and impact categories).

Legend:
- High impact
- Medium to low impact
- Unknown impact

Percentage of IBAs (100% = 77 sites)

The main threat to birds at fish-pond IBAs is the likelihood that fisheries will be abandoned as a result of economic changes, leading to the disappearance of these man-maintained wetlands. At agricultural IBAs, the main threat is posed by an anticipated change in the Polish farming system, away from the predominance of small, more or less sustainable farms towards a landscape dominated by large, intensive farms. The main threat at forest IBAs is the possible privatization and commercialization of forests in Poland, which continues to be proposed by some lobbies, and which would lead to intensified management including clear-felling, selective felling and afforestation with non-native species. The proposed network of new highways in Poland may also damage some IBAs, of various habitat-types, across the country.

In Figure 3, recreation is the most frequently cited threat to birds at IBAs, although this may be an overestimate since the impact is considered to be high at only three sites. On the other hand, the consequences of introduced animal species to IBAs may have been underestimated—mammalian predators such as American mink *Mustela vison* and racoon-dog *Nyctereutes procyonoides*, introduced to Poland after the Second World War, may be important in determining the breeding numbers of many waterbird species in Poland in the long term.

PROTECTION STATUS

■ National protection
The main piece of national legislation relevant to the protection of sites for nature conservation is the 1991 Law on Nature Conservation which governs the general organization of nature conservation in Poland and which defines eight categories of protected area, listed below.

1. National Park (Park Narodowy)
An area over 1,000 ha in size, with special values for science, nature, social life, culture and education, where the whole of nature and specific characteristics of landscape are protected. National Parks can have strictly protected and/or partially protected zones (Nature Reserves) within them, and have huge buffer zones. National Parks are designated by decision of the Council of Ministries, and each is managed by a board which reports to the Board of National Parks at the Ministry for Environment Protection, Natural Resources and Forestry. Park guards are organized and employed by each park's board.

2. Nature Reserve (Rezerwat Przyrody)
An area preserved for its valuable ecosystem, flora, fauna, vegetation, abiotic elements or landscape, either strictly (no management allowed) or partially (management allowed). Nature Reserves have buffer zones, and are designated by decision of the Minister for Environment Protection, Natural Resources and Forestry (up to 1998) or by a voivode (since 1999). They are administered by the owner (if estate is private) or by a manager (if land is state-owned) and supervised by a voivode. Only in some Nature Reserves are wardens employed by a voivode.

3. Landscape Park (Park Krajobrazowy)
An area protected for its natural, cultural and historical values, under conditions of sustainable development and under prohibition of mineral exploitation, industrial development and urbanisation. Landscape Parks have buffer zones, and are designated by decision of a voivode. Each park is supervised by a board, which organizes and employs park guards.

4. Protected Landscape Area (Obszar Chronionego Krajobrazu)
This is an area valuable for its landscape, designated by a voivode.

5. Site for Geological Documentation (Stanowisko Dokumentacyjne Przyrody Nieożywionej)
A place of interest and importance for science or education, designated by a voivode.

6. Ecological Area (Użytek Ekologiczny)
An area worthy of protection because of its high natural values, e.g. a small water-body, mire, clump of trees, area of dunes, oxbow lake, etc.; designated by a voivode.

7. Natural Landscape Complex
An area protected because of its valuable natural or cultural landscape; designated by a voivode.

8. Nature Monument (Pomnik Przyrody)
A valuable and interesting object or feature, such as a tree, cliff, rock, etc.; designated by a voivode.

'Private reserves', owned by private persons or non-governmental conservation bodies, are not recognised by Polish law unless they are officially designated as Nature Reserves. Sites classed as IBAs, or as other types of site under European conventions, do not have any legal status.

The protection status of IBAs in Poland is shown in Table 5 and in Figures 4 and 5. Those IBAs which are protected as National Parks or Nature Reserves are protected adequately, so long as the legal status of the designation is respected. The same is true for IBAs protected as Landscape Parks, although the application of this designation has only recently commenced in Poland.

Table 5. Protection status of Important Bird Areas in Poland.
A tick (✔) indicates that an IBA overlaps with a protected area (to any extent).

IBA code	International name	National Park	Nature Reserve	Landscape Park	Protected Landscape Area	Ecological Area	Nature Monument	Ramsar Site	World Heritage Site	Biosphere Reserve
		National						**International**		
001	Delta of the Świna river	✔								
002	Szczecin lagoon									
003	Rozwarowo marshes									
004	Świdwie lake		✔					✔		
005	Wełtyń lakes									
006	Lower Odra river valley		✔	✔						
007	Miedwie lake									
008	Ińsk Landscape Park		✔	✔						
009	Słowiński National Park	✔	✔					✔		✔
010	Słupia Valley Landscape Park			✔						
011	Middle part of Tuchola forest	✔	✔	✔						
012	Puck Bay		✔	✔						
013	Wisła river mouth		✔							
014	Wisła lagoon		✔							
015	Drużno lake		✔							
016	Iława forests		✔	✔						
017	Dymerskie meadows					✔				
018	Napiwodzko-Ramucka forest		✔			✔				
019	Oświn lake		✔					✔		
020	Borecka forest		✔							
021	Łuknajno lake		✔					✔		
022	Nietlickie marshes					✔				
023	Pisz forest		✔	✔						
024	Augustów forest	✔	✔							
025	Biebrza river valley	✔						✔		
026	Narew river gaps									
027	Marshy valley of the Narew river	✔								
028	Knyszyn forest		✔	✔						
029	Gródek—Michałowo basin		✔							
030	Upper Narew river valley									
031	Białowieża forest	✔	✔						✔	✔
032	Warta flood-plain—Słońsk		✔	✔				✔		
033	Noteć river flood-plain		✔		✔					
034	Obra river flood-plain									
035	Wonieść reservoir				✔					
036	Middle Warta river valley			✔	✔					
037	Ostrówek and Smogulec ponds									
038	Ślesin and Występ ponds		✔							
039	Lower Wisła river		✔	✔						
040	Marshy valley of the Drwęca river		✔	✔						
041	Gopło Millennium Park		✔	✔						
042	Rakutowskie swamps		✔							
043	Ner river valley				✔					
044	Jeziorsko reservoir									
045	Kampinos forest	✔	✔							
046	Middle Wisła river valley		✔		✔					
047	Zegrzyński reservoir		✔		✔					
048	Omulew river valley									
049	Biała forest		✔							
050	Liwiec river valley			✔	✔					
051	Lower Bug river valley		✔	✔	✔					
052	Przemków ponds		✔	✔						
053	Odra riverine forests		✔		✔	✔				
054	Barycz river valley		✔	✔	✔		✔	✔		
055	Słup reservoir		✔							
056	Mietków reservoir									
057	Oak-hornbeam forests in the Odra valley		✔							
058	Turawa reservoir									
059	Otmuchów reservoir									
060	Nysa reservoir									
061	Upper Wisła river valley		✔							
062	Middle Nida flood-plain			✔	✔					
063	Małopolska Wisła river gap		✔	✔						
064	Tyśmienica river valley									
065	Parczew forests		✔							
066	Bubnów marshes	✔	✔							
067	Middle Bug river valley									
068	Chełm calcareous marshes		✔	✔	✔					
069	Strzeleckie forests			✔						
070	Niepołomice forest		✔							
071	Gorce mountains	✔								
072	Tatra mountains	✔	✔							✔
073	Janów forests		✔	✔	✔					
074	Solska Forest Landscape Park			✔						
075	Przemyśl Plateau Landscape Park		✔	✔						
076	Starzawa ponds									
077	Bieszczady mountains	✔	✔	✔						✔
	Subtotal of IBAs	7	23	11	3	3	0	6	1	4
	Total number of IBAs	**12**	**45**	**25**	**13**	**5**	**1**	**7**	**1**	**4**

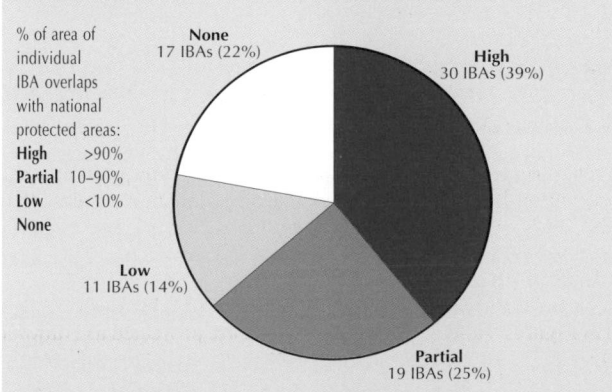

Figure 4. The national protection status of Important Bird Areas in Poland.

% of area of individual IBA overlaps with national protected areas:
High >90%
Partial 10–90%
Low <10%
None

None 17 IBAs (22%)
High 30 IBAs (39%)
Partial 19 IBAs (25%)
Low 11 IBAs (14%)

Total area of overlap between IBA network in Poland and national protected-area system (see Table 5 for categories) = 8,514–9,943 km² (43–50% of total IBA area).

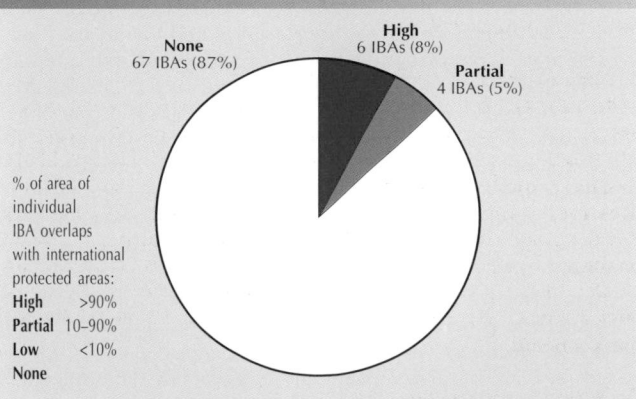

Figure 5. The international protection status of Important Bird Areas in Poland.

% of area of individual IBA overlaps with international protected areas:
High >90%
Partial 10–90%
Low <10%
None

None 67 IBAs (87%)
High 6 IBAs (8%)
Partial 4 IBAs (5%)

Total area of overlap between IBA network in Poland and international protected-area system (see Table 5 for categories) = 2,302 km² (12% of total IBA area).

Box 1. International legislation and initiatives that are relevant to site conservation in Poland (see Appendix 1 for a general description of these agreements).

Global	
Biodiversity Convention	✔
Ramsar Convention	✔
Bonn Convention	✔
World Heritage Convention	✔
MAB Programme	✔
Pan-European	
Bern Convention	✔
Regional	
Helsinki Convention	✔

✔ Convention ratified/initiative supported
(✔) Convention signed

Of the other designations, only Ecological Areas have real meaning and value in protecting IBAs. This designation has been used in two main ways. In the past (although no longer), it was used as a preliminary protection measure, to quickly achieve protection for an area definitely proposed as a Nature Reserve. This was because the bureaucracy at the voivodeship level was less complex than at the ministerial level, and the application could therefore be concluded in a short period. The second, and very important, way in which the designation has been used is to avoid an obligatory duty to economically manage any area of land in the country. For instance, according to regulations any forested peatbog was classed as wasteland, and the forestry authorities were therefore obliged to drain it and then attempt afforestation. By declaring the site as an Ecological Area, the authorities were able to avoid this management obligation and leave the area undamaged.

■ International protection

Poland has ratified all of the international conventions relevant to site protection for nature conservation (Box 1). Such global designations, e.g. Ramsar Sites, World Heritage Sites and Biosphere Reserves, have legal status, although this does not mean that better protection follows such designation (Figure 5, Table 5).

CONSERVATION

- The data in this chapter originate from a variety of mostly local or regional projects, and were not collected specifically for the IBA inventory. An IBA-oriented data-gathering project started in 1998 (run by OTOP) but is limited to the Baltic coast and the adjacent Pomeranian lakeland. In the last decade country-wide censuses were carried out for only a few bird species: for *Ciconia ciconia* by ProNatura (a non-governmental organisation based in Wroclaw) during 1994–1995, for *Acrocephalus paludicola* by OTOP during 1993 and 1997, for *Crex crex* by OTOP during 1997 and 1998, and for *Cygnus olor* by Gdansk Ornithological Station in 1998. Annual censusing of the nests of large raptors and *Ciconia nigra* has been carried out by the Eagle Protection Committee (a non-governmental organisation based in Olsztyn) since the mid-1980s. This is the only country-wide ornithological monitoring project in Poland at the moment. There are many local monitoring projects, oriented towards species or habitats, run by various institutions.
- Management plans exist, or are in preparation, for all National Parks, and some have already been implemented. Such plans are also obligatory for Nature Reserves and Landscape Parks, and many have already been prepared (of which only a few are for Landscape Parks so far), but this process is still in full flow. If the management plan for a Landscape Park is prepared and signed by a voivode, its implementation is obligatory for communes (the administrative unit below the voivode), which means that it may be a very powerful tool for real protection.
- The nest-sites of 11 species of raptor and *Ciconia nigra* are protected efficiently by the designation of protection zones around their nests, and such zones are incorporated into the management plans of forest superintendencies. However, the protection zones declared by law for *Tetrao urogallus*, *Tetrao tetrix*, *Burhinus oedicnemus*, *Merops apiaster* and *Coracias garrulus* are of no practical help in protecting these species. A country-wide nest-protection scheme for *Ciconia ciconia* is run by ProNatura and a similar scheme for *Pandion haliaetus* is run by the Eagle Protection Committee.

- OTOP carries out habitat management at Karsiborska Kępa (part of site 001) for breeding waders and *Acrocephalus paludicola*, and at Beka Nature Reserve (part of site 012) for breeding waders, amongst other sites. A national action plan is being prepared by OTOP for the management of habitat for *Acrocephalus paludicola*.
- OTOP is involved in campaigns, in cooperation with other Polish NGOs, for the designation of the entire Polish part of the Białowieża forest as a National Park; against the construction of a long series of dams along the middle and lower Wisła river (the 'Lower Vistula Cascade'); against a similar series of dams along the Odra river; and against the siting of the Winter Olympic Games 2006 in the Tatra mountains.
- The most urgent tasks in the near future are to prepare and implement management plans for all Nature Reserves and Landscape Parks of importance for birds, to increase the amount of the national IBA network which is covered by officially designated protected areas, to create and implement IBA monitoring and care-taking schemes, and to implement ornithological monitoring over the whole country.

ANALYTICAL METHODS

- The numbers quoted for breeding pairs are yearly maxima (given as a range when there are data for a series of years), those for passage and wintering birds are daily maxima.
- The administrative regions listed are voivodeships (provinces) and refer to the situation as from 1 January 1999; before this date, a different system of regions was in place.
- For some IBAs, the only available information was in Gromadzki *et al.* (1994). In such cases, data are less complete—fewer bird species are listed, and information on the number of pairs or individuals is lacking.
- Most of the original data used in this inventory were gathered during the period 1994–1997. In a few cases only (e.g. sites 021, 025, 047, 049), the data used are mainly from the late 1980s.
- Information on threats is given as provided by contributors, and may therefore depend on subjective judgements in some instances.
- As a rule, the information on threats relates to recent years. For all National Parks, this information is up-to-date.
- In the period during which data were being collected for this inventory, new parks, reserves and other protected areas have been established and the protection status of IBAs has been changing accordingly. This process has not been completed yet, and so the protection status of some IBAs, as stated in this inventory, is likely to change in the next few years.

GLOSSARY

IUCN The World Conservation Union.
OTOP Ogólnopolskie Towarzystwo Ochrony Ptaków—the Polish Society for the Protection of Birds—the Partner Designate of BirdLife International in Poland (a registered charity with headquarters in Gdansk).
voivode the person in charge of a province (voivodeship).
voivodeship a province; the most recent regulation, in 1999, divides Poland into 16 voivodeships.
WCU Wetland Conservation Unit of IUCN.

ACKNOWLEDGEMENTS

We are grateful to the following people, who kindly submitted materials from which the IBA site-accounts were compiled: Artur Adamski, Wiesław Bagiński, Magdalena Bartoszewicz, Piotr Baszanowski, Jan Bednorz, Jacek Betleja, Paweł Bielecki, Wojciech Błoniarz, Grzegorz Bobrowicz, Tomasz Brauze, Alicja Buczek, Tomasz Buczek, Dorota Bukacińska, Dariusz Bukaciński, Stanisław Burdziej, Zdzisław Cenian, Sławomir Chmielewski, Przemysław Chylarecki, Włodzimierz Cichocki, Marian Cieślak, Andrzej Czapulak, Ryszard Czeraszkiewicz, Cezary Ćwikowski, Barbara Diehl, Kazimierz Dobrowolski, Paweł T. Dolata, Andrzej Dombrowski, Andrzej Dyrcz, Jacek Engel, Andrzej Felger, Zbigniew Głowaciński, Blandyna Głuchowska, Andrzej Górski, Tomasz Górski, Wojciech Górski, Jadwiga Gromadzka, Andrzej Grygoruk, Jerzy Grzybek, Sebastian Guentzel, Józef Hordowski, Piotr Indykiewicz, Tomasz Janiszewski, Zbigniew Jaszcz, Stanisław Jażdzyk, Marek Kalisiński, Robert

Kapowicz, Zbigniew Kasprzykowski, Czesław Kawecki, Marek Keller, Grzegorz Kiljan, Janusz Kloskowski, Jarosław Krogulec, Wiesław Król, Alfred Krzyśkowiak, Roman Kucharski, Tomasz Kułakowski, Przemysław Kunysz, Michał Kupczyk, Stanisław Kuźniak, Zenon Lewartowski, Jan Loch, Grzegorz Lorek, Zbigniew Majcher, Izabela Majewska, Michał Maniakowski, Dominik Marchowski, Mateusz Matysiak, Włodzimierz Meissner, Maria Mellin, Sławomir Mielczarek, Marcin Miller, Tomasz Mokwa, Wojciech Mrugowski, Grzegorz Neubauer, Sławomir Niedźwiecki, Czesław Nitecki, Wiesław Nowicki, Czesław Okołów, Bogumiła Olech, Małgorzata Piotrowska, Wojciech Plata, Emil Polubiec, Waldemar Półtorak, Piotr Profus, Mikołaj Pruszyński,

Eugeniusz Pugacewicz, Ewald Ranoszek, Maciej Rodziewicz, Piotr Rydzkowski, Andrzej Ryś, Mirosław Rzępała, Arkadiusz Sikora, Tadeusz Smoleński, Marek Stajszczyk, Wojciech Stasiecek, Artur Staszewski, Tadeusz Stawarczyk, Mateusz Stopiński, Sławomir Studziński, Marian Szymkiewicz, Janusz Tomasiewicz, Maciej Tracz, Magdalena Tracz, Tomasz Uchimiak, Jacek Wasilewski, Jarosław Wawerski, Tomasz Wesołowski, Aleksander Winiecki, Witold Winkowski, Radosław Włodarczyk, Zbigniew Wojciechowski, Cezary Wójcik, Janusz Wójciak, Andrzej Wuczyński, Konrad Wypychowski, Katarzyna Zając, Tadeusz Zając, Dorota Zawadzka, Jarosław Zawadzki, Jerzy Zawadzki, Jacek Zieliński, Marek Zieliński, Piotr Zieliński.

■ SITE ACCOUNTS

Delta of the Świna river   A1, A4i, A4iii, B1i, B2, B3   001
Admin region zachodnio-pomorskie
Coordinates 53°50′N 14°20′E
Altitude 0–10 m **Area** 4,000 ha

■ Site description
A delta (growing in the direction of Szczeciński lagoon) which contains natural and artificial channels of the Świna river, with numerous islands. The site also covers the south-west coast of Wolin island and the south-east part of Uznam island adjoining the Piastowski channel. The plant community is very rich. Most of the forest is old-growth (130–150 years), dominated by alder *Alnus*, mixed birch/oak *Betula/Quercus* and beech/oak *Fagus/Quercus*. Open areas are dominated by saltmarsh, rush *Scirpus* and reedbeds *Phragmites*. The latter completely cover some islets and almost all shores of the other islands. A very small area is used as arable land.

Habitats Forest and woodland (15%; native coniferous forest; alluvial/very wet forest), Grassland (10%; humid grassland), Wetland (70%; saltmarsh; standing fresh water; river/stream; water-fringe vegetation), Artificial landscape (5%; ruderal land)
Land-use Agriculture (30%), Fisheries/aquaculture (30%), Forestry (5%), Nature conservation/research (5%), Not utilized (10%), Other (10%), Tourism/recreation (10%)

■ Birds

Species	Season	Year	Pop min	Pop max	Acc	Criteria
Anser anser Greylag Goose	W	1993	—	2,000	—	B1i
Anas strepera Gadwall	B	1995	49	57	A	B2
Mergus albellus Smew	W	1993	—	1,500	—	A4i, B1i
Mergus merganser Goosander	W	1995	—	6,000	A	A4i, B1i
Locustella luscinioides Savi's Warbler	B	1995	80	80	B	B3
[1] *Acrocephalus paludicola* Aquatic Warbler	B	1997	169	182	A	A1

1. Singing males.

A very attractive area for breeding, migrating and wintering birds with very rich food sources available. Breeding species of global conservation concern that do not meet IBA criteria: *Crex crex* (two pairs). A total of 140 bird species have been recorded breeding.

■ Protection status
National Partial **International** None
2,000 ha of IBA covered by National Park (Woliński, 10,937 ha).

■ Conservation issues

Threats Abandonment/reduction of land management (A), Agricultural intensification/expansion (B), Aquaculture/fisheries (C), Deforestation (commercial) (U), Disturbance to birds (C), Industrialization/urbanization (A), Infrastructure (A), Recreation/tourism (B)

Threats include the expansion of reedbeds onto saltmarsh following reductions in grazing, and unsuitable forestry practices (clear-cutting). Birds are disturbed by fishermen, tourism and forestry. Eggs of *Larus argentatus* are sometimes stolen from the colonies (probably by fox farmers), causing disturbance to birds. A part of the IBA (Karsiborska Kępa, 180 ha) is managed by OTOP (the concept of 'private reserve' does not exist in current Polish law). OTOP projects here are: (1) Distribution, numbers and habitat selection of *Acrocephalus paludicola* (as part of a wider BirdLife International project); (2) action plan for plant community; (3) permanent study of bird numbers and distribution. Projects by the West Pomeranian Ornithological Society include inventory of breeding and migrating birds (June–August 1995).

Szczecin lagoon   A1, A4i, A4iii, B1i, B2   002
Admin region zachodnio-pomorskie
Coordinates 53°46′N 14°28′E
Altitude 20–20 m **Area** 48,000 ha

■ Site description
The Polish part of Szczecin lagoon. The waters are shallow (mean depth 2–3 m) and extremely productive in fish, with high density of benthic organisms. Aquatic plants dominate in places, and shores are covered by reedbeds *Phragmites* and rushes *Scirpus*. The lagoon is used for shipping.

Habitats Grassland (humid grassland), Wetland (100%; standing fresh water; water-fringe vegetation; fen/transition mire/spring)
Land-use Fisheries/aquaculture (50%), Tourism/recreation (40%), Urban/industrial/transport (10%)

■ Birds

Species	Season	Year	Pop min	Pop max	Acc	Criteria
[1] *Aythya fuligula* Tufted Duck	P	1993	10,000	—	—	B1i
Aythya marila Scaup	W	—	40,000	—	—	A4i, B1i
Aythya marila Scaup	P	1993	40,000	70,000	—	A4i, B1i
Bucephala clangula Goldeneye	W	—	6,000	—	—	A4i, B1i
Bucephala clangula Goldeneye	P	—	10,000	—	—	A4i, B1i
Mergus albellus Smew	W	1993	25,000	—	—	A4i, B1i
Mergus merganser Goosander	W	1993	30,000	—	—	A4i, B1i
Mergus merganser Goosander	P	—	50,000	—	—	A4i, B1i
Haliaeetus albicilla White-tailed Eagle	B	1993	8	—	—	A1, B2
Haliaeetus albicilla White-tailed Eagle	W	—	40	50	—	A1
Chlidonias niger Black Tern	P	1993	5,000	—	—	A4i, B1i
Acrocephalus paludicola Aquatic Warbler	B	1993	10	—	—	A1

1. Autumn.

■ Protection status
National None **International** None

■ Conservation issues

Threats Agricultural intensification/expansion (U), Aquaculture/fisheries (U), Industrialization/urbanization (U), Recreation/tourism (U)

The lagoon is heavily polluted by industry, domestic and agricultural sewage.

Rozwarowo marshes   A1   003
Admin region zachodnio-pomorskie
Coordinates 53°52′N 14°45′E
Altitude 20–20 m **Area** 1,600 ha

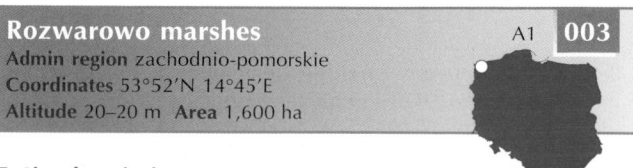

■ Site description
The marshy valley of the Grzybnica and Wołczenica rivers, containing numerous channels. There are considerable areas of fen with large stretches covered with reedbeds *Phragmites* and wet, flooded meadows; bushes of alder *Alnus* are abundant. Land-uses include cattle-farming.

Habitats Scrub (5%; scrub), Grassland (20%; humid grassland), Wetland (75%; standing fresh water; river/stream; fen/transition mire/spring)
Land-use Agriculture (80%), Hunting (10%), Not utilized (10%)

■ Birds

Species	Season	Year	Pop min	Pop max	Acc	Criteria
[1] *Acrocephalus paludicola* Aquatic Warbler	B	1997	28	32	—	A1

1. Singing males.

A total of 151 species have been recorded, 107 as breeders.

■ Protection status
National None **International** None

■ Conservation issues

Threats Agricultural intensification/expansion (U), Drainage (U), Dredging/canalization (U), Infrastructure (U)

Effluent from cattle-farming is a threat. In 1993 part of the marshes were altered by reedbed planting, damaging the habitat for breeding *Acrocephalus paludicola* (immediately before the damage there were 40–60 singing males). New roads are making access to the marshes easier for anglers and poachers.

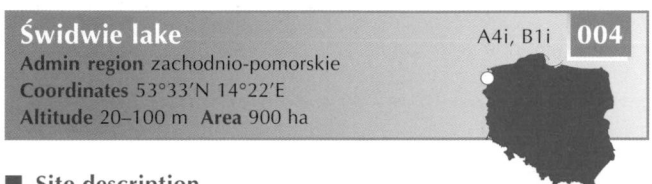

Świdwie lake
A4i, B1i **004**

Admin region zachodnio-pomorskie
Coordinates 53°33′N 14°22′E
Altitude 20–100 m **Area** 900 ha

■ Site description
A nutrient-rich lake surrounded by extensive fens. A large part is occupied by reedbeds (*Phragmites*) and part by meadows and alder *Alnus* forest. Haymaking, grazing and hunting take place around the lake.

Habitats Scrub, Grassland (20%; humid grassland), Wetland (80%; standing fresh water; water-fringe vegetation; fen/transition mire/spring)
Land-use Hunting, Nature conservation/research (100%)

■ Birds

Species	Season	Year	Pop min	Pop max	Acc	Criteria
[1] *Anser fabalis* Bean Goose	P	1993	5,000	—	—	A4i, B1i
[1] *Anser albifrons* White-fronted Goose	P	1993	8,000	—	—	B1i
Grus grus Crane	N	—	110	250	—	B1i

1. Autumn.

Species of global conservation concern that do not meet IBA criteria: *Haliaeetus albicilla* (1 pair feeds in the area, nesting nearby), *Crex crex* (1–3 pairs).

■ Protection status
National High **International** High
900 ha of IBA covered by Nature Reserve (Świdwie, 900 ha). 900 ha of IBA covered by Ramsar Site (Świdwie, 900 ha).

■ Conservation issues
Recent information (March 1998) indicates that all known threats to Swidwie lake have been removed. Previously these had been (1) drainage in the surrounding area in 1976 (40% of water supply lost), (2) agricultural effluent, which had been causing strong nutrient pollution of the lake, and (3) hunting in the surrounding area, which had been disturbing birds within the site. An EU-funded project being implemented in the area involves replacing the water lost in 1976. The new water supply will be stored at Zurawie reservoir, south of the lake, and cleaned there. According to the Nature Conservancy Officer hunting has also been stopped in the surrounding area.

Wełtyń lakes
B3 **005**

Admin region zachodnio-pomorskie
Coordinates 53°15′N 14°35′E
Altitude 24–45 m **Area** 4,600 ha

■ Site description
A complex of small lakes (the largest, Wełtyń, covering 360 ha) which are surrounded by cultivated fields, meadows, pastures and small

---

stands of beech *Fagus*. Some of the lakes have small islands with bushy vegetation and small patches of reed *Phragmites*.

Habitats Forest and woodland (25%; broadleaved deciduous forest; native coniferous forest; mixed forest), Wetland (10%; standing fresh water; river/stream; raised bog; water-fringe vegetation), Artificial landscape (65%; arable land; forestry plantation; urban parks/gardens; other urban/industrial areas; ruderal land)
Land-use Agriculture (50%), Fisheries/aquaculture (10%), Forestry (20%), Hunting, Tourism/recreation (15%), Urban/industrial/transport (5%)

■ Birds

Species	Season	Year	Pop min	Pop max	Acc	Criteria
Cygnus cygnus Whooper Swan	W	1995	20	100	A	B3

Species of global conservation concern that do not meet IBA criteria: *Aythya nyroca* (one breeding pair), *Haliaeetus albicilla* (one pair feeds in the area, nesting nearby).

■ Protection status
National None **International** None

■ Conservation issues

Threats Agricultural intensification/expansion (U), Deforestation (commercial) (C), Drainage (B), Infrastructure (B), Recreation/tourism (C), Selective logging/cutting (C), Unsustainable exploitation (C)

Water pollution from agriculture is a threat, as are drainage and recreation.

Lower Odra river valley
A1, A4i, A4iii, B1i, B1iv, B2, B3 **006**

Admin region zachodnio-pomorskie, lubuskie
Coordinates 53°07′N 14°21′E
Altitude 0–50 m **Area** 75,000 ha

■ Site description
The valley of the Odra river between Kostrzyn town, Szczeciński lagoon (c.150 km long) and Dąbie lake. At its widest part the Odra has two main channels—the Eastern Odra and the Regalica. The area between the main channels is a marshy plain with oxbow lakes and many smaller channels, and is covered by fens, seasonally flooded meadows, swamps and riparian forest. Dąbie lake is a large, shallow delta-lake (5,600 ha, up to 4 m deep). Human activities include boat traffic, cattle-grazing and haymaking, angling, and hunting.

Habitats Forest and woodland (8%; alluvial/very wet forest), Grassland (humid grassland), Wetland (90%; standing fresh water; river/stream; water-fringe vegetation; fen/transition mire/spring), Artificial landscape (other urban/industrial areas; ruderal land)
Land-use Agriculture (30%), Hunting (55%), Tourism/recreation (10%), Urban/industrial/transport (5%)

■ Birds

Species	Season	Year	Pop min	Pop max	Acc	Criteria
[1] *Botaurus stellaris* Bittern	R	1994	18	18	A	B2
Cygnus cygnus Whooper Swan	W	1993	400	500	—	B1i
[1,2] *Anser fabalis* Bean Goose	P	1995	5,000	15,000	A	A4i, B1i
[1,2] *Anser albifrons* White-fronted Goose	P	1995	7,000	20,000	A	A4i, B1i
Anas strepera Gadwall	B	1993	100	130	A	A4i, B1i, B2
Anas strepera Gadwall	P	1993	—	2,000	—	A4i, B1i
Aythya ferina Pochard	W	—	8,000	—	—	B1i
Aythya ferina Pochard	P	1993	10,000	—	—	B1i
Aythya fuligula Tufted Duck	W	1993	50,000	—	—	A4i, B1i
[3] *Aythya fuligula* Tufted Duck	P	—	30,000	—	—	A4i, B1i
Bucephala clangula Goldeneye	W	1993	3,500	—	—	B1i
Mergus albellus Smew	W	—	650	—	—	B1i
Mergus merganser Goosander	W	1993	5,000	10,000	—	A4i, B1i
Haliaeetus albicilla White-tailed Eagle	R	1995	19	20	—	A1, B2
Haliaeetus albicilla White-tailed Eagle	W	—	50	—	—	A1
Crex crex Corncrake	B	1994	20	25	—	A1
[4] *Grus grus* Crane	B	1994	40	50	—	B2

Species ... continued	Season	Year	Pop min	Pop max	Acc	Criteria
Grus grus Crane	P	—	7,000	8,000	—	A4i, B1i
Sterna albifrons Little Tern	B	1993	40	45	—	B2
[5] **Chlidonias niger** Black Tern	B	1994	230	250	A	B2
[1] **Luscinia luscinia** Thrush Nightingale	B	1994	350	400	A	B3
[1] **Locustella luscinioides** Savi's Warbler	B	1994	430	550	A	B3
[6] **Acrocephalus paludicola** Aquatic Warbler	B	1994	60	80	A	A1, B2
[7] **Lanius excubitor** Great Grey Shrike	B	1994	15	20	—	B2

1. Number is for Landscape Park only.
2. 40,000–50,000 *Anser fabalis/Anser albifrons*.
3. Spring.
4. 10–15 pairs in Landscape Park.
5. 90–100 pairs in Landscape Park.
6. Singing males; 15 in Landscape Park.
7. 13–17 pairs in Landscape Park.

One of the most important places in Poland for roosting geese *Anser* and *Grus grus* on autumn passage, with up to 40,000–45,000 *Anser fabalis* and *A. albifrons* in the area.

■ Protection status
National Partial **International** None
31 ha of IBA covered by Nature Reserve (Kurowskie Błota, 31 ha). 30,850 ha of IBA covered by Landscape Park (Cedyński, 30,850 ha). 6,009 ha of IBA covered by Landscape Park (Dolina Dolnej Odry, 6,009 ha).

■ Conservation issues

Threats Abandonment/reduction of land management (U), Agricultural intensification/expansion (U), Burning of vegetation (U), Industrialization/urbanization (U), Infrastructure (B), Recreation/tourism (B)

Heavy water-pollution is a threat, originating from agriculture, industry (chemical, harbour operations, ships and energy) and domestic sewage (from local and upstream sources). Disturbance of birds also occurs.

Miedwie lake — A4i, B1i — 007
Admin region zachodnio-pomorskie
Coordinates 53°16′N 14°52′E
Altitude — **Area** 3,200 ha

■ Site description
A large lake with a moderate level of nutrients, bordered to the south and west by extensive chalk fens and meadows, and to the east by adjoining alder *Alnus* forest. The Płonia river goes through the lake and flows into Dąbie lake. The lake is a drinking water reservoir for the city of Szczecin and also supports a fishery.

Habitats Scrub, Grassland (10%; humid grassland), Wetland (90%; standing fresh water; river/stream; fen/transition mire/spring)
Land-use Agriculture (30%), Fisheries/aquaculture (20%), Hunting, Water management (50%)

■ Birds

Species	Season	Year	Pop min	Pop max	Acc	Criteria
[1] **Anser fabalis** Bean Goose	P	1993	—	—	—	A4i, B1i
[1] **Anser albifrons** White-fronted Goose	P	1993	—	—	—	B1i

1. See text.

Up to 12,000–14,000 *Anser fabalis* and *A. albifrons* stage here in autumn, with up to 1,500 such birds in winter. Breeding species of global conservation concern that do not meet IBA criteria: *Haliaeetus albicilla* (one pair feeds in the area, nesting nearby), *Crex crex* (one pair), *Acrocephalus paludicola* (nine singing males).

■ Protection status
National None **International** None

■ Conservation issues

Threats Agricultural intensification/expansion (U)

Pollution from agricultural sources affects drinking water and poses a threat to the site.

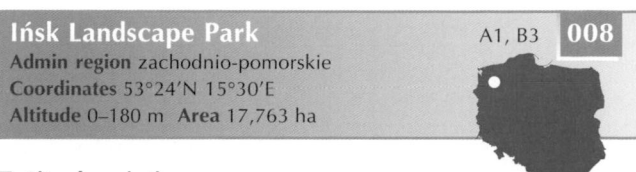

Ińsk Landscape Park — A1, B3 — 008
Admin region zachodnio-pomorskie
Coordinates 53°24′N 15°30′E
Altitude 0–180 m **Area** 17,763 ha

■ Site description
Ińsk Landscape Park protects the moraine landscape of the Ińskie lakeland. The site is drained by the Ina river and its tributaries and partly by the tributaries of the Rega river. There are 63 lakes, most of them flow-lakes. The largest is Ińsko lake with a depth of 42 m and an extensive shoreline. Forest is widely distributed across the park and is dominated by broadleaved forest of *Quercus/Fagus*. In stagnant hollows there are many swamps and cave lakes.

Habitats Forest and woodland (53%; broadleaved deciduous forest; mixed forest), Wetland (9%; standing fresh water; raised bog; water-fringe vegetation), Artificial landscape (38%; arable land)
Land-use Agriculture (38%), Fisheries/aquaculture (9%), Forestry (53%), Hunting

■ Birds

Species	Season	Year	Pop min	Pop max	Acc	Criteria
Milvus milvus Red Kite	B	1996	5	8	—	B3
[1] **Haliaeetus albicilla** White-tailed Eagle	B	1997	6	6	—	A1

1. Daily max. 25 on autumn passage; c.50 winter west of the IBA.

Species of global conservation concern that do not meet IBA criteria: *Crex crex* (3–5 pairs).

■ Protection status
National High **International** None
79 ha of IBA covered by Nature Reserve (Gołowacz, 79 ha). 11 ha of IBA covered by Nature Reserve (Kamienna Buczyna, 11 ha). 17,763 ha of IBA covered by Landscape Park (Iński, 17,763 ha).

■ Conservation issues

Threats Recreation/tourism (U)

There is some erosion of morainal areas by vehicle and foot traffic.

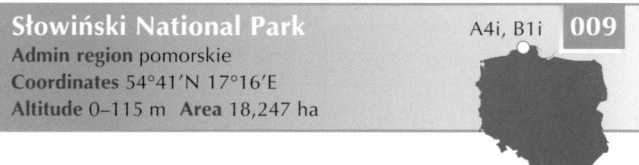

Słowiński National Park — A4i, B1i — 009
Admin region pomorskie
Coordinates 54°41′N 17°16′E
Altitude 0–115 m **Area** 18,247 ha

■ Site description
The site protects a coastal landscape containing one of the largest areas of mobile sand-dunes in Europe (up to 40 m high), and three brackish coastal lakes, the largest being Łebsko (7,140 ha, 5–6 m deep) and the second largest Gardno (2,468 ha, 2–6 m deep). The lakes are surrounded by wet meadows, pastures, and forests of alder *Alnus* and oak *Quercus*, and are bordered by extensive beds of reed *Phragmites* and reed-mace *Typha*. The Łupawa and Łeba rivers flow in to the lakes. Some hollows between dunes are covered by pioneer plant communities and by wet heathland in various stages of development.

Habitats Forest and woodland (24%; native coniferous forest; alluvial/very wet forest), Scrub (heathland), Grassland, Wetland (67%; saltmarsh; sand-dunes/sand beach; standing fresh water; raised bog; water-fringe vegetation), Artificial landscape (9%)
Land-use Fisheries/aquaculture (25%), Forestry (10%), Nature conservation/research (48%), Tourism/recreation (17%)

■ Birds

Species	Season	Year	Pop min	Pop max	Acc	Criteria
[1] **Anser fabalis** Bean Goose	P	1995	—	4,500	—	A4i, B1i
[1] **Anser albifrons** White-fronted Goose	P	1995	—	6,500	—	B1i
[1] **Mergus merganser** Goosander	P	1995	2,500	3,000	—	A4i, B1i

1. 1991–1995.

Breeding species of global conservation concern that do not meet IBA criteria: *Haliaeetus albicilla* (4 pairs), *Crex crex* (10–15 pairs). Other notable breeding species are *Bubo bubo* (4 pairs) and *Circus pygargus* (7–10 pairs).

■ **Protection status**
National High **International** High
18,247 ha of IBA covered by National Park (Słowiński, 18,247 ha).
5,920 ha of IBA covered by 15 Nature Reserves (Bielice; Bory Torfowe; Gackie Lęgi; Gardnieńskie Lęgi; Jezioro Dołgie Małe; Klukowe Buki; Klukowe Lęgi; Mierzeja; Moroszka; Olszyna; Rowokół; Słowińskie Błota; Wyspa Kamienna na jeziorze Gardno; Żarnowisko; Żarnowskie Lęgi; combined area 5,920 ha). 18,247 ha of IBA covered by Ramsar Site (Słowiński, 18,247 ha). 18,247 ha of IBA covered by Biosphere Reserve (Słowiński, 18,247 ha).

■ **Conservation issues**

Threats Abandonment/reduction of land management (U), Agricultural intensification/ expansion (U), Aquaculture/fisheries (U), Drainage (A), Industrialization/urbanization (U)

Heavy water-pollution poses a threat, stemming from agriculture, industry, domestic sewage and fisheries. Reduced cattle-grazing has caused a long-term reduction in the number of breeding waders. Drainage of a large area adjacent to the National Park has destroyed extensive areas of wet meadow and bog within the park.

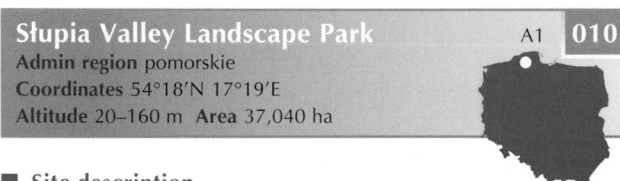

Słupia Valley Landscape Park — A1 — 010
Admin region pomorskie
Coordinates 54°18′N 17°19′E
Altitude 20–160 m **Area** 37,040 ha

■ **Site description**
The site comprises a Landscape Park which protects both the basin of the middle Słupia river (including tributaries: Bytowa, Jutrzenka, Kamienica, Skotawa) as well as many lakes (the largest being Jasień, Głębokie, and Skotowskie). The lakes have low levels of nutrients. There are many ravines. Forest is 40–100 years old, mainly pine *Pinus*, beech *Fagus* and hornbeam *Carpinus* on dry ground, with some mixed *Pinus* and oak *Quercus*. In the swamps there is bog forest of alder *Alnus*, and in the stream valleys there is alder *Alnus* scrub.

Habitats Forest and woodland (72%; broadleaved deciduous forest; native coniferous forest; mixed forest; alluvial/very wet forest), Grassland (8%; steppe/dry calcareous grassland; humid grassland; mesophile grassland), Wetland (6%; standing fresh water; river/stream; raised bog; water-fringe vegetation), Artificial landscape (14%; highly improved reseeded grassland; arable land; ruderal land)
Land-use Agriculture (21%), Forestry (72%), Hunting, Water management (6%)

■ **Birds**

Species	Season	Year	Pop min	Pop max	Acc	Criteria
Crex crex Corncrake	B	1996	15	20	A	A1

A total of 138 species have been recorded breeding, including *Haliaeetus albicilla* (one pair; species is of global conservation concern but does not meet IBA criteria) and *Grus grus* (34–45 pairs).

■ **Protection status**
National High **International** None
31,279 ha of IBA covered by Landscape Park (Zaborski, 31,279 ha).

■ **Conservation issues**

Threats Afforestation (U), Aquaculture/fisheries (U), Construction/impact of dyke/dam/barrage (U), Drainage (U), Filling-in of wetlands (U), Recreation/tourism (B), Selective logging/cutting (U)

There is accidental disturbance to birds by tourism. A project has been underway since 1986 to encourage the breeding of *Mergus merganser* and *Bucephala clangula* on islands in Jasien lake (over 100 nest-boxes).

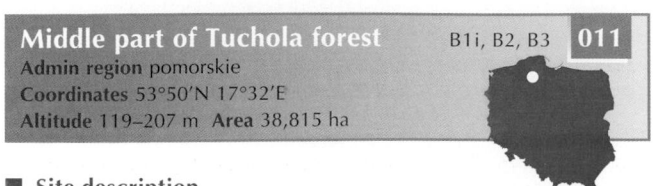

Middle part of Tuchola forest — B1i, B2, B3 — 011
Admin region pomorskie
Coordinates 53°50′N 17°32′E
Altitude 119–207 m **Area** 38,815 ha

■ **Site description**
The area is part of the great Tuchola 'sandr' (outwash plain of glacial origin). The terrain is varied, with elevated plains, extensive hills, many

hummocks, valleys and troughs, and is drained by the Brda river and its many tributaries (the largest being the Zbrzyca). Some of the rivers have steep gradients and strong flows. Of 60 lakes in this area, the largest is Charzykowskie lake (1,363 ha), and the deepest is Ostrowite lake (43 m deep). Many are flow-lakes, being part of the Brda river system, and most have low to moderate levels of nutrients. Forests are dominated by pine *Pinus*. On richer soils there are dry-ground forests of hornbeam *Carpinus*, birch *Betula*, beech *Fagus* and oak *Quercus*, and near watercourses and reservoirs there is riverside carr and forest of alder *Alnus*. There are fens, connected with rivers and lakes, as well as (in hollows) raised bogs and transitional mires.

Habitats Forest and woodland (66%; broadleaved deciduous forest; native coniferous forest; mixed forest; alluvial/very wet forest), Scrub (heathland), Grassland (7%; humid grassland; mesophile grassland), Wetland (12%; standing fresh water; river/stream; raised bog; water-fringe vegetation; fen/transition mire/spring), Artificial landscape (15%; highly improved reseeded grassland; arable land; ruderal land)
Land-use Agriculture (17%), Fisheries/aquaculture (8%), Forestry (57%), Hunting, Nature conservation/research (12%), Urban/industrial/transport (5%)

■ **Birds**

Species	Season	Year	Pop min	Pop max	Acc	Criteria
[1] *Cygnus cygnus* Whooper Swan	W	1995	50	400	A	B1i, B3
Milvus milvus Red Kite	B	1991	—	15	A	B3
[2] *Bubo bubo* Eagle Owl	R	1996	7	10	A	B2

1. 1984–1995.
2. 1984–1996.

An important wintering site for swans *Cygnus* (all three European species), which also holds 10% of the national population of *Pandion haliaetus* on passage. A total of 107 species have been recorded breeding; breeding species of global conservation concern that do not meet IBA criteria: *Haliaeetus albicilla* (three pairs).

■ **Protection status**
National High **International** None
4,789 ha of IBA covered by National Park (Bory Tucholskie, 4,789 ha). 41 ha of IBA covered by Nature Reserve (Bagno Stawek, 41 ha). 70 ha of IBA covered by Nature Reserve (Jezioro Laska, 70 ha). 38 ha of IBA covered by Nature Reserve (Jezioro Małe Łowne, 38 ha). 11 ha of IBA covered by Nature Reserve (Jezioro Nawionek, 11 ha). 31,279 ha of IBA covered by Landscape Park (Zaborski, 31,279 ha).

■ **Conservation issues**

Threats Agricultural intensification/expansion (B), Aquaculture/fisheries (B), Groundwater abstraction (B), Intensified forest management (B), Recreation/tourism (B), Selective logging/cutting (B)

Forestry work close to, or in, buffer zones designated for nesting *Haliaeetus albicilla*, *Bubo bubo* and *Ciconia nigra* disturbs these particular species, as does tourism/recreation.

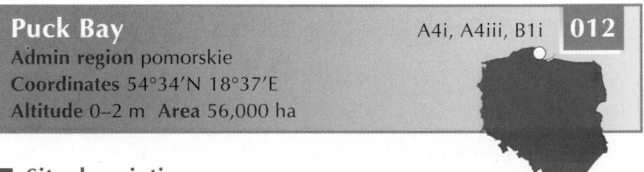

Puck Bay — A4i, A4iii, B1i — 012
Admin region pomorskie
Coordinates 54°34′N 18°37′E
Altitude 0–2 m **Area** 56,000 ha

■ **Site description**
The north-westernmost part of the Gulf of Gdańsk, divided into a shallow western part (also called Puck lagoon; 10,400 ha, average depth 3 m) and a deeper eastern part. The eastern border of this site is the nominal line between the top of Hel peninsula and Gdańsk city. The total length of coastline is c.100 km. Also included in this site are various remnant coastal meadows (totalling 388 ha). Around Puck Bay there are some small fishing harbours and, further to the southwest, there are large harbours at Gdynia and Gdańsk.

Habitats Grassland (humid grassland), Wetland (100%; saltmarsh; sand-dunes/ sand beach; coastal lagoon; standing fresh water; river/stream; water-fringe vegetation)
Land-use Agriculture (5%), Fisheries/aquaculture (45%), Nature conservation/ research (5%), Tourism/recreation (15%), Urban/industrial/transport (30%)

■ Birds

Species	Season	Year	Pop min	Pop max	Acc	Criteria
[1] *Podiceps cristatus* Great Crested Grebe	W	1996	500	3,900	A	B1i
[1] *Podiceps cristatus* Great Crested Grebe	P	1996	500	3,900	A	B1i
[1] *Podiceps auritus* Slavonian Grebe	P	1996	50	300	A	B1i
[1] *Phalacrocorax carbo* Cormorant	P	1996	1,000	6,000	B	B1i
[1] *Cygnus olor* Mute Swan	W	1996	1,800	3,530	A	B1i
[1] *Aythya fuligula* Tufted Duck	W	1996	5,000	31,600	A	A4i, B1i
[1] *Bucephala clangula* Goldeneye	W	1996	1,500	4,000	A	B1i
[1] *Mergus albellus* Smew	W	1996	10	260	A	B1i
[2] *Mergus merganser* Goosander	W	1997	500	4,500	A	A4i, B1i

1. 1991–1996.
2. 1991–1997.

A very important site for wintering and migrating waterbirds, holding well over 20,000 waterbirds during winter, sometimes exceeding 50,000 birds. During severe winters the bay is covered by ice and birds have to move elsewhere. During autumn and spring migration the coastal meadows (sometimes flooded) attract large numbers of waterbirds, particularly waders (up to some thousands), and overhead migration of raptors is pronounced in spring. Beka Nature Reserve supports the largest concentration of breeding *Calidris alpina schinzii* in Poland (c.10–12 pairs) and meadows near Mechelinki support a few additional pairs. More than 300 bird species have been recorded in the area.

■ Protection status

National Partial **International** None
200 ha of IBA covered by Nature Reserve (Beka, 200 ha). About 11,000 ha of IBA covered by Landscape Park (Nadmorski, 17,850 ha).

■ Conservation issues

Threats Aquaculture/fisheries (B), Disturbance to birds (B), Dredging/canalization (A), Natural events (B), Recreation/tourism (B), Unsustainable exploitation (C), Other (B)

Tourism/recreation, hunting and uncontrolled human access along the coast disturb nesting and staging birds. Oil pollution resulting from oil-tanker accidents is a potential hazard. Water-pollution by domestic sewage has been very heavy in the past; discharges are now more purified but still affect submerged vegetation. The coastal salt-meadows have been disappearing due to land-use changes. Many diving birds drown in fishing nets (impact not yet known). Kuling Waterfowl Research Group is carrying out a long-term study of wader migration at the Rewa river mouth and carries out winter waterbird counts.

Wiśła river mouth A1, A4i, A4iii, B1i, B2 013
Admin region pomorskie
Coordinates 54°21′N 18°57′E
Altitude 0–2 m **Area** 485 ha

■ Site description

A 6 km stretch of the lower Wiśła (Vistula) river from Przegalina sluice to the river mouth, including a strip of meadows along the right bank (between Mikoszewo and Drewnica). Habitats include sandy peninsulas, mobile sandflats, small sandy islets, temporary lakes and adjacent dunes, freshwater lakes on either side of the Wiśła channel, and a small patch of coastal forest. The vegetation is very species-rich and at the river mouth shows all stages of natural succession from bare sandflats to bushes and forest on the oldest areas. Willow *Salix* has been planted to stabilize dunes. The meadows are flooded in spring (occasionally at other seasons) and are grazed, mainly by cattle.

Habitats Forest and woodland (10%; broadleaved deciduous forest; native coniferous forest; mixed forest; alluvial/very wet forest), Scrub (5%; scrub), Grassland (25%; steppe/dry calcareous grassland; humid grassland), Wetland (60%; saltmarsh; sand-dunes/sand beach; standing fresh water; river/stream; water-fringe vegetation)
Land-use Agriculture (5%), Fisheries/aquaculture (50%), Forestry (5%), Hunting, Nature conservation/research (35%), Tourism/recreation (5%)

■ Birds

A very important site for wintering, migrating and breeding waterbirds, regularly holding well over 20,000 individuals, sometimes exceeding 150,000 birds. In late summer and early autumn wader passage is

intense, with very high rates of turn-over; *Calidris* species dominate (up to 8,000 waders ringed in a season). When flooded, the meadows near the southern border of the IBA support thousands of ducks and waders. Other waterbirds supported in high numbers include *Clangula hyemalis* (30,000, winter) and non-breeding terns in summer/autumn (max. 1,000 *Sterna sandvicensis*; max. 3,000 *Sterna hirundo*). Overall, at least 22 waterbird species have been recorded breeding, with at least 120 waterbird species recorded in the non-breeding season.

Species	Season	Year	Pop min	Pop max	Acc	Criteria
[1] *Anser albifrons* White-fronted Goose	P	1998	4,000	4,000	A	B1i
[2] *Aythya fuligula* Tufted Duck	W	1996	2,000	17,500	A	A4i, B1i
[2] *Aythya marila* Scaup	W	1996	300	12,500	A	A4i, B1i, B2
[2] *Bucephala clangula* Goldeneye	W	1996	500	12,200	A	A4i, B1i
[3] *Haliaeetus albicilla* White-tailed Eagle	P	1996	—	20	A	A1
[4] *Larus minutus* Little Gull	P	1993	—	40,000	—	A4i, B1i
Larus canus Common Gull	W	1993	—	100,000	—	A4i, B1i
[5] *Larus canus* Common Gull	P	—	—	150,000	—	A4i, B1i
[6] *Larus canus* Common Gull	N	—	—	40,000	—	A4i, B1i
Sterna albifrons Little Tern	B	1997	—	61	A	B2
[4] *Chlidonias niger* Black Tern	P	1993	—	5,000	—	A4i, B1i

1. 1998 only.
2. 1991–1996.
3. Intense spring passage; also a winter visitor.
4. Summer/autumn.
5. Autumn.
6. Individuals; summer.

■ Protection status

National Partial **International** None
150 ha of IBA covered by Nature Reserve (Mewia Łacha, 150 ha).

■ Conservation issues

Threats Aquaculture/fisheries (B), Dredging/canalization (A), Natural events (B), Recreation/tourism (B), Unsustainable exploitation (C), Other (B)

Tourism/recreation, hunting, poaching and uncontrolled human access all lead to significant disturbance of birds. Storms in spring/summer flood the tern *Sterna* colonies on islets, forcing birds to re-nest in less safe areas. Locally increasing populations of gulls *Larus argentatus* and mammalian predators are reducing the number of nesting waders and terns. A proposed series of dams along the lower Wiśła ('cascadization') is potentially a great threat to the area. Gdańsk Ornithological Station is carrying out a long-term study of wader migration.

Wiśła lagoon A4i, A4iii, B1i 014
Admin region pomorskie, warmińsko-mazurskie
Coordinates 54°19′N 19°29′E
Altitude 2–2 m **Area** 33,000 ha

■ Site description

The site comprises the Polish part of this large, shallow coastal lagoon (up to 5 m deep) of brackish water, which is cut off from the Baltic Sea by the Wiśla spit. A narrow channel in the Russian part of the lagoon, through which sea water flows during heavy storms, joins the water-body with the Baltic Sea (Gulf of Gdańsk). There is some river flow to the Polish part of the lagoon from the west, comprising a few branches of the Wiśła (Vistula) river deriving from the uplands. The water-level fluctuates significantly on a daily basis (by up to 1.5 m) because of wind effects. There are extensive reedbeds (*Phragmites*) along the shore, forming one or two belts up to 100 m wide, as well as rich floating and submerged vegetation (*Nymphaea*, *Potamogeton*) which supports a very rich invertebrate and fish fauna. Land-uses include intensive reed-harvesting ('Other').

Habitats Wetland (100%; coastal lagoon; water-fringe vegetation)
Land-use Fisheries/aquaculture (60%), Hunting (10%), Other (10%), Tourism/recreation (20%)

■ Birds

The site regularly supports 20,000 or more waterbirds, mainly wildfowl *Anser/Anas*. Breeding species of global conservation concern that do not meet IBA criteria: *Haliaeetus albicilla* (at least one pair), *Crex crex* (4–10 pairs). The most important parts of the site for birds in general are Elbląg Bay and the Pasłęka mouth. Non-breeding birds occur mainly in the coastal zone, from Przebrno village to the Pasłęka mouth.

Species	Season	Year	Pop min	Pop max	Acc	Criteria
Anser albifrons White-fronted Goose	P	1996	10,000	—	—	B1i
Anas crecca Teal	P	1996	10,000	—	—	B1i
[1] *Aythya ferina* Pochard	P	1996	5,000	—	A	B1i
[2] *Bucephala clangula* Goldeneye	P	1996	3,000	—	A	B1i
[3,4] *Mergus albellus* Smew	W	1996	1,200	3,200	—	A4i, B1i
[3] *Larus minutus* Little Gull	P	1996	1,000	—	—	A4i, B1i

1. Also breeds and moults at site.
2. Up to 2,700 in mild winters.
3. 1989–1996.
4. Meets A4i in mild winters.

■ Protection status
National Low **International** None
420 ha of IBA covered by Nature Reserve (Zatoka Elbląska, 420 ha).

■ Conservation issues

Threats Agricultural intensification/expansion (U), Aquaculture/fisheries (A), Industrialization/urbanization (U), Natural events (U), Recreation/tourism (U), Other (U)

Heavy nutrient pollution from agriculture, industry and domestic sewage is a threat. Birds become trapped in fish-nets. The changes in water-level affect breeding birds. Intensive reed-harvesting is also a problem ('Other'). The entire IBA lies within the buffer zones of two Landscape Parks (Mierzeja Wiślana, 22,390 ha; Wzniesienie Elbląskie, 48,591 ha), approximately equally divided between the two.

Drużno lake   A4i, A4iii, B1i, B2   015
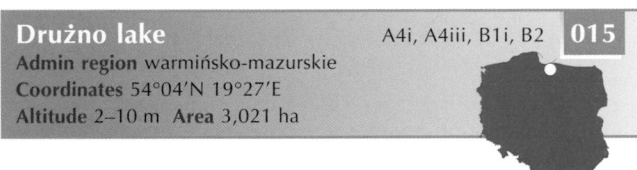
Admin region warmińsko-mazurskie
Coordinates 54°04′N 19°27′E
Altitude 2–10 m **Area** 3,021 ha

■ Site description
A shallow, nutrient-rich lake (up to 1.5 m deep) surrounded by extensive mires and swamp-forest. There is a significant daily fluctuation in water-level, caused by wind-related water-level fluctuation in the Wiślany lagoon, which connects with this site via the Elbląg river. There is a rich vegetation of floating (*Nymphaea*) and submerged (*Potamogeton*) plants, as well as extensive reedbeds *Phragmites*. Alder *Alnus* carr occurs along marshy shores.

Habitats Forest and woodland (10%; alluvial/very wet forest), Scrub (5%; scrub), Grassland (5%; humid grassland), Wetland (80%; standing fresh water; river/stream; water-fringe vegetation; fen/transition mire/spring)
Land-use Agriculture (80%), Fisheries/aquaculture (10%), Hunting, Tourism/recreation (10%)

■ Birds

Species	Season	Year	Pop min	Pop max	Acc	Criteria
[1] *Anser fabalis* Bean Goose	P	1996	5,000	7,000	A	A4i, B1i
Anser albifrons White-fronted Goose	P	1996	—	10,000	A	B1i
Anser anser Greylag Goose	P	—	1,000	2,000	—	B1i
Anas strepera Gadwall	B	—	50	100	A	B2
[1] *Anas strepera* Gadwall	P	1998	800	800	—	B1i
Grus grus Crane	P	1993	—	2,000	A	A4i, B1i
Chlidonias niger Black Tern	B	1996	—	100	A	B2

1. Spring/autumn.

The site regularly supports 20,000 or more waterbirds during spring and autumn migration, mainly wildfowl *Anser/Anas*. Breeding species of global conservation concern that do not meet IBA criteria: *Aythya nyroca* (2–3 pairs), *Crex crex* (2–3 pairs).

■ Protection status
National High **International** None
3,021 ha of IBA covered by Nature Reserve (Jezioro Drużno, 3,021 ha).

■ Conservation issues

Threats Disturbance to birds (B), Recreation/tourism (B), Unsustainable exploitation (A)

Nutrient pollution by agriculture, industry and domestic sewage poses a threat. Hunting in the nature reserve is intense.

Iława forests   A1, A4i, B1i, B2, B3   016
Admin region warmińsko-mazurskie
Coordinates 53°43′N 19°33′E
Altitude 91–126 m **Area** 25,279 ha

■ Site description
Iława Forest Landscape Park is an extensive complex of forests interspersed among 31 lakes (0.5–163 ha), the latter varying widely in nutrient level from rich to poor. Jeziorak, the longest lake in Poland, contains many islands. The site falls mainly within the Drwęca catchment, but part is also drained by the Liwa, Osa and Dzieżgoń rivers. Forest is dominated by pine *Pinus*, beech *Fagus* and alder carr *Alnus*. Lake shores are covered by reedbeds *Phragmites* and bogs.

Habitats Forest and woodland (62%; broadleaved deciduous forest; native coniferous forest; mixed forest; alluvial/very wet forest), Wetland (20%; standing fresh water; river/stream; raised bog; water-fringe vegetation), Artificial landscape (19%; arable land; ruderal land)
Land-use Agriculture (13%), Fisheries/aquaculture (20%), Forestry (62%), Hunting, Not utilized (1%), Tourism/recreation (5%)

■ Birds

Species	Season	Year	Pop min	Pop max	Acc	Criteria
Milvus milvus Red Kite	B	1996	5	8	B	B3
Haliaeetus albicilla White-tailed Eagle	B	1996	7	8	A	A1, B2
Aquila pomarina Lesser Spotted Eagle	B	1996	8	12	A	B2
Crex crex Corncrake	B	1997	100	—	A	A1, B2
[1] *Grus grus* Crane	P	1984	2,000	3,000	—	A4i, B1i

1. 1980–1984; autumn.

■ Protection status
National High **International** None
12 ha of IBA covered by Nature Reserve (Czerwica [Bird Reserve], 12 ha). 106 ha of IBA covered by Nature Reserve (Jasne, 106 ha). 333 ha of IBA covered by Nature Reserve (Jezioro Gaudy [Bird Reserve], 333 ha). 25,045 ha of IBA covered by Landscape Park (Pojezierza Iławskiego, 25,045 ha).

■ Conservation issues

Threats Agricultural intensification/expansion (U), Aquaculture/fisheries (U), Drainage (U), Intensified forest management (U), Recreation/tourism (U)

Birds are disturbed by fishery activities and also accidentally by forestry and tourism. Rare raptors are kept under surveillance each year by the Eagle Protection Committee.

Dymerskie meadows   A4i, B1i   017
Admin region warmińsko-mazurskie
Coordinates 53°46′N 21°00′E
Altitude 150–150 m **Area** 300 ha

■ Site description
An area of wet meadows on the site of a former lake (drained in the 1930s), with a drainage system of channels and ditches, and partly covered with reedbed *Phragmites* and willow *Salix* scrub. Part of the site is cultivated, as is all of the surrounding area. Reed-harvesting is a land-use ('Other').

Habitats Scrub (3%; scrub), Grassland (80%; humid grassland), Wetland (15%; standing fresh water; water-fringe vegetation)
Land-use Agriculture (20%), Hunting, Not utilized (70%), Other (10%)

■ Birds

Species	Season	Year	Pop min	Pop max	Acc	Criteria
[1] *Grus grus* Crane	P	1993	—	2,500	—	A4i, B1i

1. Autumn.

Breeding species of global conservation concern that do not meet IBA criteria: *Crex crex* (7–10 pairs).

■ Protection status
National High **International** None
300 ha of IBA covered by Ecological Area (Łąki Dymerskie, 300 ha).

■ Conservation issues

Threats Drainage (U), Industrialization/urbanization (U), Other (U)

A planned new housing estate nearby poses a threat, as does the intensification of reed-harvesting ('Other').

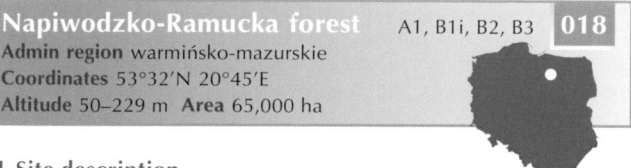

Napiwodzko-Ramucka forest   A1, B1i, B2, B3   018
Admin region warmińsko-mazurskie
Coordinates 53°32′N 20°45′E
Altitude 50–229 m   **Area** 65,000 ha

■ Site description
This varied moraine landscape is drained by the Omulew and Łyna rivers (both rise here). There are many hollows or basins, covering 30% of the site and occupied by lakes, cave-lakes or mires. Thus there are 60 lakes, most of them rather small, with the largest being Łańskie (1,070 ha), Kośno (552 ha) and Omulew (549 ha). The water-bodies are moderate to rich in nutrients, with only a few of the nutrient-poor type. Aquatic vegetation is species-rich and diverse. Lakes are surrounded by reed *Phragmites*, etc., beyond which are periodically flooded sedge-beds. In the wide valley there are fens and transitional mires; raised bogs are scarcer. Forests are mainly coniferous, dominated by pine *Pinus*, and extend onto mires. Broadleaved forest is not common, dominated by hornbeam *Carpinus* on dry ground and by alder *Alnus* trees and willow *Salix* scrub along riversides.

Habitats Forest and woodland (75%; native coniferous forest; mixed forest; alluvial/very wet forest), Scrub (scrub), Grassland (5%; mesophile grassland), Wetland (10%; standing fresh water; river/stream; raised bog; water-fringe vegetation; fen/transition mire/spring), Artificial landscape (10%; highly improved reseeded grassland; arable land; ruderal land)
Land-use Agriculture (15%), Fisheries/aquaculture (5%), Forestry (70%), Hunting, Nature conservation/research (5%), Tourism/recreation (5%)

■ Birds

Species		Season	Year	Pop min	Pop max	Acc	Criteria
Botaurus stellaris	Bittern	B	1995	18	25	—	B2
Ciconia nigra	Black Stork	B	1995	8	10	B	B2
Milvus migrans	Black Kite	B	1995	12	15	B	B2
Milvus milvus	Red Kite	B	1995	10	12	B	B3
[1] *Haliaeetus albicilla*	White-tailed Eagle	R	1996	9	11	A	A1, B2
Aquila pomarina	Lesser Spotted Eagle	B	1996	20	25	A	B2
[2] *Tetrao tetrix*	Black Grouse	R	1995	50	60	—	B2
Crex crex	Corncrake	B	1995	100	120	B	A1, B2
Grus grus	Crane	B	1995	45	55	A	B2
[3] *Grus grus*	Crane	P	—	1,500	—	—	B1i
Coracias garrulus	Roller	B	1996	6	8	B	B2

1. Up to 22 birds at best feeding area (in flocks).
2. Displaying males.
3. Autumn.

About 160 species have been recorded breeding, with particularly high numbers of a variety of raptors. The site is also important for ducks, *Grus grus*, and waders during autumn migration, and is a moulting place for 500–600 *Cygnus olor*.

■ Protection status
National Low **International** None
3,619 ha of IBA covered by 11 Nature Reserves (Bagno Nadrowskie; Dęby Napiwodzkie; Galwica; Jezioro Kośno; Jezioro Orłowo Małe; Koniuszanka I; Koniuszanka II; Las Warminski; Małga; Sołtysek; Źródła Rzeki Łyny; total area 3,619 ha). 192 ha of IBA covered by Ecological Area (Stawy w Tylkówku, 192 ha).

■ Conservation issues

Threats Afforestation (B), Agricultural intensification/expansion (C), Burning of vegetation (A), Drainage (U), Dredging/canalization (U), Infrastructure (B), Intensified forest management (A), Other (U), Recreation/tourism (B), Selective logging/cutting (U), Unsustainable exploitation (U)

Threats include nutrient pollution and subsequent plant encroachment in water-bodies, drainage, poaching and excessive hunting, grass burning in spring, intensive transportation, disturbance of nesting birds, impact of fishery on birds, unsustainably intense forest management (tree-cutting, removal of old trees), and over-collection of wild foodstuffs ('Other'). The site comprises the planned Napiwodzko-Ramucka Forest Landscape Park and its surroundings.

Oświn lake   B3   019
Admin region warmińsko-mazurskie
Coordinates 54°18′N 21°35′E
Altitude 64–80 m   **Area** 2,500 ha

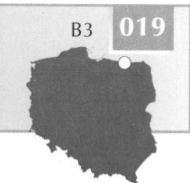

■ Site description
The site encompasses the nutrient-rich lake and adjoining wet forest and open areas with many swamps. Most of the previously pastured areas are no longer used, and have reverted to swamps occupied by young alder *Alnus* wood or sedge meadows. Open water is not extensive, and the greater part of the lake is covered by reedbeds *Phragmites*. There are seven islands (all forested). The Oświnka river (tributary of the Łyna) rises from the lake.

Habitats Forest and woodland (15%; broadleaved deciduous forest; native coniferous forest; mixed forest), Grassland (15%; humid grassland; mesophile grassland), Wetland (40%; standing fresh water; river/stream; raised bog; water-fringe vegetation; fen/transition mire/spring), Artificial landscape (30%; arable land; ruderal land)
Land-use Agriculture (40%), Forestry (12%), Hunting, Nature conservation/research (40%), Not utilized (10%)

■ Birds

Species		Season	Year	Pop min	Pop max	Acc	Criteria
Porzana parva	Little Crake	B	1996	75	80	A	B3

Breeding species of global conservation concern that do not meet IBA criteria: *Haliaeetus albicilla* (one pair), *Crex crex* (four pairs). A total of 126 species have been recorded.

■ Protection status
National Partial **International** Partial
1,007 ha of IBA covered by Nature Reserve (Jezioro Siedmiu Wysp [Bird Reserve], 1,007 ha). 1,007 ha of IBA covered by Ramsar Site (Jezioro Siedmiu Wysp, 1,007 ha).

■ Conservation issues

Threats Agricultural intensification/expansion (B), Aquaculture/fisheries (U), Deforestation (commercial) (B), Drainage (C), Dredging/canalization (C), Infrastructure (C), Intensified forest management (B), Recreation/tourism (C), Unsustainable exploitation (C)

Following drainage operations in 1970 and intensive abstraction of water from the Oświnka river outside the Nature Reserve, the lake-level fell by c.1 m. This caused extensive vegetational changes, and reduced bird numbers. To raise the water-level once more, a dam was built on the Oświnka river in 1993. Hunting is unsustainable, and tourism/recreation causes disturbance to birds. There is a proposal to expand the Nature Reserve boundary, based on studies in 1996.

Borecka forest   B2, B3   020
Admin region warmińsko-mazurskie
Coordinates 54°07′N 22°08′E
Altitude 133–223 m   **Area** 22,000 ha

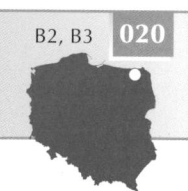

■ Site description
A forest complex, with most stands being broadleaved or mixed. The terrain is varied and is drained by small rivers, mainly of the Ełk catchment (a tributary of the Biebrza) with only a small part drained by the Gołdap (part of the Wielkie Jeziora Mazurskie catchment). There are many water-bodies and a few larger lakes, with a lake complex in the south-eastern part of the site, where the largest lake is Łaźno. Hollows are occupied by wet forest or open swamps. There are large areas of spruce *Picea* forest and, on drier ground, of lime *Tilia* and hornbeam *Carpinus*. Fragments of remnant natural forest are over 150 years old in some places. Many meadows are scattered within the forest, some of them very wet.

Habitats Forest and woodland (90%; broadleaved deciduous forest; native coniferous forest; mixed forest; alluvial/very wet forest), Grassland (humid grassland; mesophile grassland), Wetland (5%; standing fresh water; river/stream; raised bog; water-fringe vegetation; fen/transition mire/spring), Artificial landscape (5%; highly improved reseeded grassland; arable land; urban parks/gardens; other urban/industrial areas; ruderal land)
Land-use Agriculture (5%), Fisheries/aquaculture (5%), Forestry (90%), Hunting

■ Birds

Species		Season	Year	Pop min	Pop max	Acc	Criteria
Ciconia nigra	Black Stork	B	1995	10	15	B	B2
Aquila pomarina	Lesser Spotted Eagle	B	1995	25	30	—	B2
Grus grus	Crane	B	1995	80	100	A	B2
Picus canus		B	1995	15	20	B	B2
Grey-headed Woodpecker							
Ficedula albicollis		B	1995	50	100	C	B3
Collared Flycatcher							

A total of 130 species have been recorded breeding or probably breeding. Breeding species of global conservation concern that do not meet IBA criteria: *Haliaeetus albicilla* (two pairs), *Crex crex* (rare).

■ Protection status
National Low **International** None
232 ha of IBA covered by Nature Reserve (Borki, 232 ha). 49 ha of IBA covered by Nature Reserve (Lipowy Jar, 49 ha). 373 ha of IBA covered by Nature Reserve (Mazury, 373 ha). 3 ha of IBA covered by Nature Reserve (Wyspa Lipowa na Jeziorze Wielki Szwałk, 3 ha).

■ Conservation issues

Threats Afforestation (C), Agricultural intensification/expansion (C), Aquaculture/fisheries (C), Deforestation (commercial) (A), Drainage (B), Dredging/canalization (A), Intensified forest management (A), Recreation/tourism (A), Selective logging/cutting (B)

Tourism/recreation causes disturbance to birds. Intensive tree-felling, and drainage, are also threats.

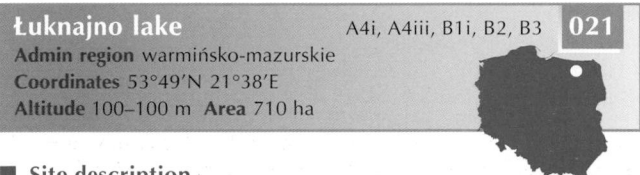

Łuknajno lake A4i, A4iii, B1i, B2, B3 021
Admin region warmińsko-mazurskie
Coordinates 53°49′N 21°38′E
Altitude 100–100 m **Area** 710 ha

■ Site description
A very shallow (up to 3 m deep) nutrient-rich lake, with adjoining sedge-beds, transitional mires, alder *Alnus* woodland and willow *Salix* scrub. The lake shores are covered by beds of bulrush *Scirpus*, reed *Phragmites* and reed-mace *Typha*. Three-quarters of the lake bottom is covered by stonewort *Chara* and pondweed *Potamogeton*. The lake and a surrounding 100-m-wide belt are protected, but the area beyond is cultivated.

Habitats Forest and woodland (3%; alluvial/very wet forest), Scrub (3%; scrub), Grassland (25%; humid grassland; mesophile grassland), Wetland (70%; standing fresh water; water-fringe vegetation; fen/transition mire/spring)
Land-use Fisheries/aquaculture (10%), Nature conservation/research (90%)

■ Birds

Species		Season	Year	Pop min	Pop max	Acc	Criteria
Botaurus stellaris	Bittern	B	1993	25	30	—	B2
Cygnus olor	Mute Swan	P	—	—	2,300	—	B1i
[1] *Netta rufina*	Red-crested Pochard	P	—	900	—	—	A4i, B1i
Porzana parva	Little Crake	B	1993	15	28	—	B3

1. Autumn.

Large concentrations of waterbirds occur, regularly exceeding 20,000 individuals, mainly swans, ducks, *Fulica atra*, and gulls *Larus*. Species of global conservation concern that do not meet IBA criteria: *Haliaeetus albicilla* (1–2 non-breeding birds feed in the IBA, nesting nearby), *Crex crex* (4–6 pairs).

■ Protection status
National High **International** High
710 ha of IBA covered by Nature Reserve (Jezioro Łuknajno, 710 ha). 710 ha of IBA covered by Ramsar Site (Jezioro Łuknajno, 710 ha).

■ Conservation issues

Threats Agricultural intensification/expansion (U), Recreation/tourism (U)

Water overflow from Śniardwy lake threatens the shallow end of this lake with nutrient pollution, following agricultural run-off in the surrounding area.

Nietlickie marshes A1, A4i, B1i, B1iv, B2, B3 022
Admin region warmińsko-mazurskie
Coordinates 53°52′N 21°48′E
Altitude 100–150 m **Area** 1,200 ha

■ Site description
The site is the remnant of the drained Wąż lake, now a fen covered by a system of drainage channels and surrounded by marshy forest of birch *Betula* and alder *Alnus*, willow *Salix* scrub and non-intensively used meadows. The site is drained by the Wężówka river, which flows into Buwełno lake. The Nietlickie marshes are the largest and most intact fens in the whole of the Mazury lakeland, and are covered by sedge-beds, reedbeds *Phragmites* and *Salix* scrub. In 1993 hay harvesting and hunting were stopped there. Because of the large roost of *Grus grus* this area is intensively visited by birdwatchers. Minor land-uses include chalk mining.

Habitats Forest and woodland (5%; alluvial/very wet forest), Grassland (25%; humid grassland), Wetland (70%; river/stream; water-fringe vegetation; fen/transition mire/spring)
Land-use Agriculture (15%), Forestry (5%), Not utilized (75%)

■ Birds

Species		Season	Year	Pop min	Pop max	Acc	Criteria
Porzana porzana	Spotted Crake	B	1994	30	34	A	B3
[1] *Crex crex*	Corncrake	B	1994	22	25	A	A1
[2] *Grus grus*	Crane	P	1994	—	5,000	A	A4i, B1i
Chlidonias niger	Black Tern	B	1994	95	105	A	B2
[3] *Acrocephalus paludicola*		B	1997	5	15	A	A1
Aquatic Warbler							

1. Males.
2. Most important site in autumn (less in spring).
3. 1988–1997.

■ Protection status
National Partial **International** None
546 ha of IBA covered by Ecological Area (Bagna Nietlickie, 546 ha).

■ Conservation issues

Threats Abandonment/reduction of land management (U), Afforestation (U), Agricultural intensification/expansion (U), Burning of vegetation (U), Drainage (A), Extraction industry (U), Industrialization/urbanization (B), Other (U), Recreation/tourism (C)

Any expansion of lake-chalk mining is a threat to the site, as are tourism (birdwatching) and associated bird disturbance, grass burning, the abandonment of cattle-grazing and of grass-mowing at the margins, hunting, and reed-harvesting ('Other' threat).

Pisz forest A1, B2 023
Admin region warmińsko-mazurskie, podlaskie
Coordinates 53°39′N 21°29′E
Altitude 175–200 m **Area** 163,000 ha

■ Site description
Pisz forest lies on the border between the Great Mazury lake region and the Mazury lowlands, and the Pisa and Krutynia rivers flow through this area. The largest lake in Poland—Śniardwy (1,097 km²)—is located in the north-western part of the site, and there are also a dozen other lakes. Many tree species reach the limit of their range here. There are coniferous forests of pine *Pinus* with some smaller areas of spruce *Picea* and broadleaved dry-ground forest of lime *Tilia* and hornbeam *Carpinus*. Around the lakes in wet areas there are alder *Alnus* forests and different kinds of mire.

Habitats Forest and woodland (67%; broadleaved deciduous forest; native coniferous forest; mixed forest; alluvial/very wet forest), Wetland (15%; standing fresh water; river/stream; raised bog; water-fringe vegetation), Artificial landscape (18%; highly improved reseeded grassland; arable land; forestry plantation; urban parks/gardens; other urban/industrial areas; ruderal land)
Land-use Agriculture (18%), Fisheries/aquaculture (13%), Forestry (67%), Hunting, Nature conservation/research (45%)

Birds

Species	Season	Year	Pop min	Pop max	Acc	Criteria
Anas querquedula Garganey	B	1993	Uncommon	—		B2
Haliaeetus albicilla White-tailed Eagle	R	1996	22	26	A	A1, B2
Aquila pomarina Lesser Spotted Eagle	B	1996	80	—	A	B2
Crex crex Corncrake	B	1993	Frequent	—		A1
Bubo bubo Eagle Owl	R	1996	7	10	B	B2

Species of global conservation concern that do not meet IBA criteria: *Aythya nyroca* (rare on passage), *Crex crex* (frequent breeder).

Protection status
National Partial **International** None
5,078 ha of IBA covered by 10 Nature Reserves (Czaplisko-Ławny Lasek [Bird Reserve]; Jezioro Lisiny [Peatbog Reserve]; Jezioro Nidzkie [Landscape Reserve]; Jezioro Pogubie Wielkie [Bird Reserve]; Jezioro Warnołty; Krutynia; Królewska Sosna; Pierwos; Pupy; Strzałowo; total area 5,078 ha). 53,265 ha of IBA covered by Landscape Park (Mazurski, 53,655 ha).

Conservation issues

Threats Afforestation (A), Agricultural intensification/expansion (B), Aquaculture/fisheries (B), Deforestation (commercial) (A), Drainage (A), Dredging/canalization (B), Industrialization/urbanization (B), Intensified forest management (A), Recreation/tourism (B), Selective logging/cutting (B), Unsustainable exploitation (B)

Afforestation with non-native tree species is a threat, and recreation/tourism disturbs birds.

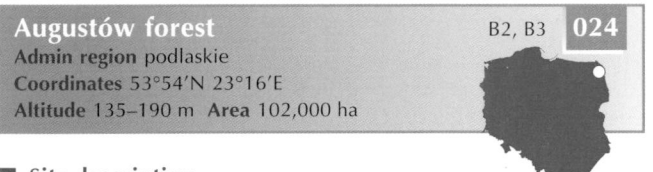

Augustów forest
B2, B3 **024**
Admin region podlaskie
Coordinates 53°54′N 23°16′E
Altitude 135–190 m **Area** 102,000 ha

Site description
The forest is divided into two parts by the Augustów channel, through which the Wołkuszanka river flows into the Niemen river. The northern part is situated on the Augustów plain in the catchment of the Czarna Hańcza and the Marycha rivers (tributaries of the Niemen). The southern part lies along the border between the Augustów plain and the Biebrza valley. The forest is predominantly coniferous (spruce *Picea* and pine *Pinus*), including moist and swampy areas, although large areas are also covered with alder *Alnus* and in some places there is well preserved dry-ground forest of lime *Tilia* and hornbeam *Carpinus*. Many of the forest stands have a natural character. There are several dozen lakes, the largest being Wigry lake (2,187 ha, 73 m in depth). Open areas are occupied by hay meadows and pastures. The National Park in the north-west of the site is used for recreation.

Habitats Forest and woodland (85%; broadleaved deciduous forest; native coniferous forest; mixed forest; alluvial/very wet forest), Wetland (7%; standing fresh water; river/stream; raised bog; water-fringe vegetation), Artificial landscape (8%; highly improved reseeded grassland; arable land; ruderal land)
Land-use Agriculture (8%), Fisheries/aquaculture (5%), Forestry (85%), Hunting, Nature conservation/research (23%)

Birds

Species	Season	Year	Pop min	Pop max	Acc	Criteria
[1] *Botaurus stellaris* Bittern	B	1996	20	—	B	B2
[2] *Ciconia nigra* Black Stork	B	1996	27	39	A	B2
[3] *Pernis apivorus* Honey Buzzard	B	1996	50	75	A	B3
[4] *Aquila pomarina* Lesser Spotted Eagle	B	1996	40	51	A	B2
[5] *Grus grus* Crane	B	1996	90	110	B	B2
[6] *Picus canus* Grey-headed Woodpecker	R	1993	25	30	B	B2

1. In north.
2. 12–14 in south.
3. 30–35 in south.
4. 29–31 in south.
5. 65–70 in south.
6. In south; unknown in north.

Over 200 species have been recorded, c.150 breeding. Breeding species of global conservation concern that do not meet IBA criteria: *Haliaeetus albicilla* (1–2 pairs), *Crex crex* (rare), *Gallinago media*.

Protection status
National Partial **International** None
15,113 ha of IBA covered by National Park (Wigierski, 15,113 ha). 761 ha of IBA covered by Nature Reserve (Kalejty, 761 ha). 314 ha of IBA covered by Nature Reserve (Kukle, 314 ha). 386 ha of IBA covered by 10 Nature Reserves (Jezioro Białe; Jezioro Długie; Kamionka; Maniówka; Ostoja Bobrów Stary Folwark; Suchar Wielki; Suche bagno; Wądołek; Wiatrołuża I & II; total area 386 ha).

Conservation issues

Threats Afforestation (U), Deforestation (commercial) (A), Intensified forest management (C), Recreation/tourism (C), Selective logging/cutting (B)

Afforestation with beech *Fagus* (outside its natural range) poses a threat to *Tetrao urogallus* (its preferred habitat is conifers).

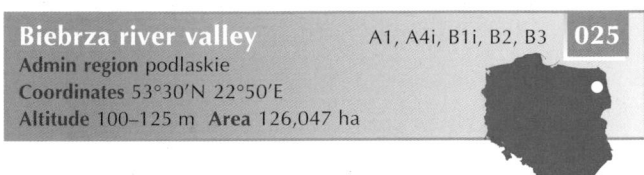

Biebrza river valley
A1, A4i, B1i, B2, B3 **025**
Admin region podlaskie
Coordinates 53°30′N 22°50′E
Altitude 100–125 m **Area** 126,047 ha

Site description
The site comprises the whole of the natural (unregulated) course of the Biebrza river (164 km long) and its valley, along the border of the buffer zone of Biebrza National Park. The valley can be divided into three parts (the upper, middle and lower basin), which differ in physiography, hydrography and ecological character. In the upper basin the river is small and cuts through peat deposits. This area has been partly drained and presently consists of bogs, pastures and meadows, with fragments of marshy pine *Pinus* forest and mixed forest of oak *Quercus* and *Pinus*. The middle basin is dominated by fens, being a mosaic of open and scrub-covered sedge-beds and meadows on alluvial soils. Here there are two extensive areas of natural birch *Betula* forest and some areas are covered with swampy alder *Alnus* forest (admixed with spruce *Picea*) and fragmented *Pinus* forest. The lower basin floods in spring, so is used for haymaking and non-intensive cattle- and horse-grazing. The lower basin is 30 km long and 5–12 km wide. Valley mires here (mainly fens) are natural and have not been modified by man. Along the river are extensive wet meadows (covering c.10% of the lower basin) and many oxbow lakes covered with reeds *Phragmites*. Areas which are regularly and extensively flooded each spring are dominated by sedge-beds. Unflooded areas are covered by variably dense forest of willow *Salix* and *Betula*, as well as sedge-beds. Scrub succession here is proceeding rapidly. Farther away from the river there are extensive young riverside forests *Alnus* in marshy areas and fragments of mixed forest *Quercus/Pinus*.

Habitats Forest and woodland (28%; broadleaved deciduous forest; native coniferous forest; mixed forest; alluvial/very wet forest), Scrub (20%; scrub), Grassland (6%; humid grassland), Wetland (26%; river/stream; raised bog; water-fringe vegetation; fen/transition mire/spring), Artificial landscape (20%; highly improved reseeded grassland; other urban/industrial areas; ruderal land)
Land-use Agriculture (26%), Forestry (28%), Hunting, Nature conservation/research (47%), Not utilized (43%)

Birds
This is the most important breeding place in central and western Europe for some threatened or localized species such as *Gallinago media*, *Crex crex*, *Porzana porzana*, *Aquila clanga* and *Chlidonias leucopterus*, and is also an important site for migrating waders, ducks, geese and *Grus grus*. Breeding species of global conservation concern that do not meet IBA criteria: *Aythya nyroca* (1–3 pairs), *Haliaeetus albicilla* (four pairs), *Crex crex* (common).

Species	Season	Year	Pop min	Pop max	Acc	Criteria
Botaurus stellaris Bittern	B	1990	45	55	A	B2
Ixobrychus minutus Little Bittern	B	1979	20	50	B	B2
Ciconia nigra Black Stork	B	1994	24	26	A	B2
Ciconia ciconia White Stork	B	1991	800	—	A	B2
Circus pygargus Montagu's Harrier	B	1980	72	—	B	B3
Aquila pomarina Lesser Spotted Eagle	B	1992	43	53	A	B2
[1] *Aquila clanga* Greater Spotted Eagle	B	1992	10	13	A	A1, B2
[2] *Tetrao tetrix* Black Grouse	B	1997	185	220	B	B2
[2,3] *Gallinago media* Great Snipe	B	1980	370	—	C	A1, A4i, B1i

Species ... continued	Season	Year	Pop min	Pop max	Acc	Criteria
Limosa limosa Black-tailed Godwit	B	1980	996	—	B	B2
Tringa totanus Redshank	B	1980	195	—	B	B2
Chlidonias niger Black Tern	B	1980	537	905	B	A4i, B1i, B2
[4] *Chlidonias leucopterus* White-winged Black Tern	B	1996	475	1,000	B	A4i, B1i
Bubo bubo Eagle Owl	B	1993	24	25	A	B2
[5] *Acrocephalus paludicola* Aquatic Warbler	B	1997	2,041	2,082	B	A1, B2

1. 1989–1993.
2. Displaying males.
3. 1976–1980.
4. 1979 and 1996.
5. Singing males in 1997.

■ Protection status
National Partial **International** Partial
59,223 ha of IBA covered by National Park (Biebrzański, 59,223 ha).
59,223 ha of IBA covered by Ramsar Site (Biebrzański, 59,223 ha).

■ Conservation issues

> **Threats** Abandonment/reduction of land management (A), Aquaculture/fisheries (B), Recreation/tourism (B), Unsustainable exploitation (B)

Unsustainable exploitation of birds is high. In the upper basin, local people propose further drainage of bogs, and illegal fires are set by land-owners every year. The middle basin was partly drained in the nineteenth century. Fishermen and tourists cause some disturbance to birds. The part of the IBA outside the National Park comprises the buffer zone to the park. The site is an amalgamation of three sites (the former 'PL100'–'PL102') identified in the previous pan-European IBA inventory (Grimmett and Jones 1989).

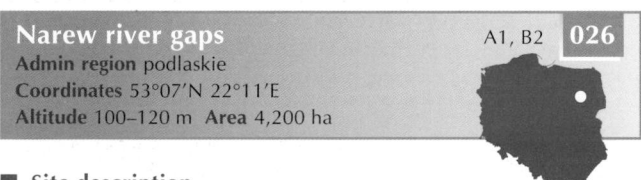

Narew river gaps   A1, B2   026
Admin region podlaskie
Coordinates 53°07′N 22°11′E
Altitude 100–120 m **Area** 4,200 ha

■ Site description
The site comprises the Narew river valley between the drained Wizna marshes and the town of Łomża. The valley is narrow (up to 1.2 km wide) and deeply cut into the plain, with a close to natural character. The valley bottom is covered mainly by peat, to varying depths. There are yearly floods, especially in spring. Flood-plain vegetation includes submerged waterweed (e.g. *Potamogeton*), reedbeds *Phragmites*, meadows, sedge-beds, dry sandy grassland, and fragmented forest of alder *Alnus*. Valley slopes are covered with oak *Quercus* forest, above which is patchy dry-ground forest of lime *Tilia* and hornbeam *Carpinus*.

> **Habitats** Forest and woodland (10%; broadleaved deciduous forest; alluvial/very wet forest), Grassland (15%; steppe/dry calcareous grassland; humid grassland), Wetland (75%; standing fresh water; river/stream; raised bog; water-fringe vegetation; fen/transition mire/spring)
> **Land-use** Agriculture (80%), Forestry (10%), Hunting, Tourism/recreation (10%)

■ Birds

Species	Season	Year	Pop min	Pop max	Acc	Criteria
[1] *Gallinago media* Great Snipe	B	1993	30	—	—	A1
Limosa limosa Black-tailed Godwit	B	1993	78	85	—	B2
[2] *Acrocephalus paludicola* Aquatic Warbler	B	1993	—	43	—	A1, B2

1. Displaying males at four sites.
2. Males.

A total of 178 species have been recorded, including 125 breeders. Breeding species of global conservation concern that do not meet IBA criteria: *Haliaeetus albicilla* (one pair), *Crex crex*.

■ Protection status
National None **International** None

■ Conservation issues

> **Threats** Infrastructure (U)

A new bridge system is planned as part of a new ring road around Łomża and poses a potential threat to the site.

Marshy valley of the Narew river   A1, B2, B3   027
Admin region podlaskie
Coordinates 53°05′N 22°52′E
Altitude 107–122 m **Area** 9,332 ha

■ Site description
A marshy stretch of the Narew valley, spanning 58 km between Suraż town and Żółtki village, and from 300 m to 4 km wide. The valley has a natural character between Suraż and Rzędziny towns and is periodically flooded. The Narew is a braided, meandering river, and creates a system which occupies the whole width of the valley floor in some places. There is a very rich mosaic of plant communities—mainly beds of reed *Phragmites* and sedge *Carex*, alder *Alnus* forest and riverside scrub of willow *Salix*.

> **Habitats** Forest and woodland (5%; broadleaved deciduous forest; native coniferous forest; mixed forest; alluvial/very wet forest), Scrub (3%; scrub), Grassland (10%; steppe/dry calcareous grassland; humid grassland; mesophile grassland), Wetland (67%; standing fresh water; river/stream; raised bog; water-fringe vegetation; fen/transition mire/spring), Artificial landscape (13%; highly improved reseeded grassland; arable land; ruderal land)
> **Land-use** Agriculture (10%), Hunting, Nature conservation/research (78%), Tourism/recreation (5%), Water management (7%)

■ Birds

Species	Season	Year	Pop min	Pop max	Acc	Criteria
Botaurus stellaris Bittern	B	1994	19	45	—	B2
[1] *Porzana porzana* Spotted Crake	B	1994	—	74	—	B3
[2] *Porzana parva* Little Crake	B	1992	10	50	—	B3
[3][4] *Crex crex* Corncrake	B	1994	—	70	—	A1
[5] *Luscinia luscinia* Thrush Nightingale	B	1992	—	400	—	B3
[6] *Locustella luscinioides* Savi's Warbler	B	1994	—	400	B	B3
[3] *Acrocephalus paludicola* Aquatic Warbler	B	1994	—	50	—	B2

1. 200–400 in 1979–1981.
2. 80–250 in 1979–1981.
3. 1988–1994.
4. 150 in 1979–1981.
5. Over 220 in 1979–1981.
6. 1,500–2,000 in 1979–1981.

Breeding species of global conservation concern that do not meet IBA criteria: *Aythya nyroca* (formerly one pair, now extinct here), *Gallinago media* (6–8 pairs).

■ Protection status
National Partial **International** None
7,350 ha of IBA covered by National Park (Narwiański, 7,350 ha).

■ Conservation issues

> **Threats** Agricultural intensification/expansion (U), Dredging/canalization (U)

During 1978–1981 the riverbed between Rędziny and Żółtki towns (8 km long) was straightened, broadened and deepened, and meanders were cut off. This drastically reduced water-levels in the river channels and adjoining areas, and the area became intensively used for agriculture. However, soils became parched, water was lost from wells in the surrounding area, and the vegetation composition changed. There are efforts to stop further degradation by reconstruction of river riffles in the area of Rędziny Dam.

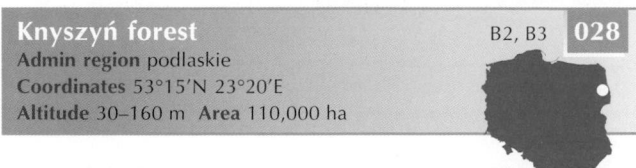

Knyszyń forest   B2, B3   028
Admin region podlaskie
Coordinates 53°15′N 23°20′E
Altitude 30–160 m **Area** 110,000 ha

■ Site description
A fragmented forest, historically divided into the Błudowska, Knyszyń, Malawicka, Odelska and Supraśl forests, with numerous seepages, springs (c.450), clean streams and small rivers. The terrain is varied. River valleys, mainly drained, are occupied by fens and transitional mires covered by reedbeds *Phragmites* and sedge-beds *Carex*. In stagnant hollows there are transitional mires and, more rarely, raised

bogs. Although many stands still have a natural character, most are rather young (40–70 years old). About 80% of the forest is coniferous, dominated by pine *Pinus* and spruce *Picea*. Broadleaved forest is dominated by lime *Tilia* and hornbeam *Carpinus*, with ash *Fraxinus* and alder *Alnus* in riverine habitats and birch *Betula* in marshy areas. Open areas are occupied by fields, meadows, pastures and human settlements.

Habitats Forest and woodland (70%; native coniferous forest; mixed forest; alluvial/very wet forest), Grassland (10%; humid grassland; mesophile grassland), Wetland (10%; standing fresh water; river/stream; raised bog; fen/transition mire/spring), Artificial landscape (10%; arable land; ruderal land)
Land-use Agriculture, Forestry, Hunting

■ Birds

Species		Season	Year	Pop min	Pop max	Acc	Criteria
Ciconia nigra	Black Stork	B	1993	14	16	—	B2
Pernis apivorus	Honey Buzzard	B	1993	60	70	—	B3
Aquila pomarina	Lesser Spotted Eagle	B	1993	48	50	—	B2
[1] *Tetrao tetrix*	Black Grouse	B	1993	—	100	—	B2

1. Displaying males.

A total of 154 species have been recorded, including 139 breeding. Breeding species of global conservation concern that do not meet IBA criteria: *Haliaeetus albicilla* (two pairs), *Crex crex*, *Gallinago media*.

■ Protection status
National Partial **International** None
2,930 ha of IBA covered by 18 Nature Reserves (Bahno w Borkach; Budzisk; Jałówka; Jesionowe Góry; Karczmisko; Krasne; Krzemianka; Krzemienne Góry; Kulikówka; Las Cieliczański; Międzyrzecze; Pieszczana Góra; Stara Dębina; Stare Biele; Starodrzew Szyndzielski; Surażkowo; Wielki Las; Woronicza; combined area 2,930 ha). 73,094 ha of IBA covered by Landscape Park (Puszczy Knyszyńskiej im. Prof. Witolda Sławińskieg, 73,094 ha).

■ Conservation issues
Threats Agricultural intensification/expansion (U), Construction/impact of dyke/dam/barrage (U), Deforestation (commercial) (U), Dredging/canalization (U)

Water pollution from agriculture poses a threat.

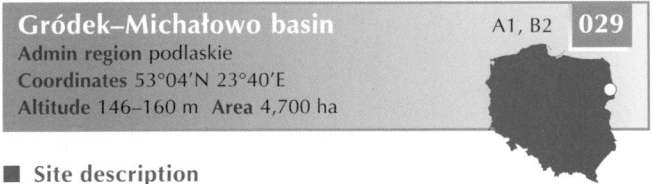

Gródek–Michałowo basin A1, B2 029
Admin region podlaskie
Coordinates 53°04′N 23°40′E
Altitude 146–160 m **Area** 4,700 ha

■ Site description
The site consists of a large basin covered by a thick layer of peat. The basin drains into the upper course of the Supraśl river, which traverses the northern part of the site. Most of the area has been drained by man, but in many places there are still mires. The central part of the basin is occupied by fens (mainly sedge-beds, occasionally reedbeds *Phragmites*), while the southern part is raised bog, with marshy forest and a variety of bog mosses. There are two small lakes, Gorbacz and Wiejki. The marshy forest is dominated by birch *Betula* and pine *Pinus*, with alder *Alnus* scrub also common.

Habitats Forest and woodland (15%; broadleaved deciduous forest; mixed forest; alluvial/very wet forest), Grassland (50%; humid grassland; mesophile grassland), Wetland (30%; standing fresh water; river/stream; raised bog; fen/transition mire/spring), Artificial landscape (5%; highly improved reseeded grassland; arable land)
Land-use Agriculture (55%), Forestry (5%), Hunting, Not utilized (40%)

■ Birds

Species		Season	Year	Pop min	Pop max	Acc	Criteria
[1] *Tetrao tetrix*	Black Grouse	R	1995	35	70	C	B2
[1,2] *Gallinago media*	Great Snipe	B	1995	15	30	C	A1

1. Displaying males.
2. 1986–1995.

A total of 105 species have been recorded breeding. Species of global conservation concern that do not meet IBA criteria: *Haliaeetus albicilla* (one bird on passage), *Crex crex* (20–40 breeding birds).

■ Protection status
National Low **International** None
114 ha of IBA covered by Nature Reserve (Gorbacz [Peatbog Reserve], 114 ha).

■ Conservation issues
Threats Abandonment/reduction of land management (A), Agricultural intensification/expansion (C), Deforestation (commercial) (A), Drainage (B), Dredging/canalization (A), Recreation/tourism (U), Selective logging/cutting (B)

Tourism/recreation causes disturbance to birds.

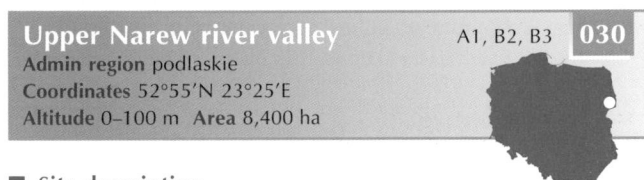

Upper Narew river valley A1, B2, B3 030
Admin region podlaskie
Coordinates 52°55′N 23°25′E
Altitude 0–100 m **Area** 8,400 ha

■ Site description
The site comprises a stretch of the upper Narew valley between the dam at Bondary village and the town of Suraż, as well as the Pietkowo pond complex near Suraż. The Narew river has a natural character, and the valley is up to 3 km wide. Flood-plain plant communities depend on annual river flooding: beds of sedge and reed-grass *Glyceria* dominate, while small patches of reed *Phragmites*, scrub and willow *Salix* woodland occur along the river. Forest covers only 5% of the valley; open areas are mainly pastures and hay meadows. The Pietkowo pond complex adjoins extensive mixed and broadleaved forests. The ponds are densely overgrown with rushes and reeds *Phragmites*, with smaller amounts of sedge, reed-mace *Typha* and bulrush *Scirpus*.

Habitats Forest and woodland (5%; broadleaved deciduous forest; mixed forest; alluvial/very wet forest), Scrub (5%; scrub), Grassland (50%; humid grassland; mesophile grassland), Wetland (15%; standing fresh water; river/stream; water-fringe vegetation), Artificial landscape (10%; arable land; ruderal land), Unknown (15%)
Land-use Agriculture (70%), Fisheries/aquaculture (10%), Forestry (5%), Hunting, Unknown (15%)

■ Birds

Species		Season	Year	Pop min	Pop max	Acc	Criteria
Circus pygargus	Montagu's Harrier	B	1993	42	44	—	B3
Porzana porzana	Spotted Crake	B	1993	30	40	—	B3
Porzana parva	Little Crake	B	1993	35	35	—	B3
Crex crex	Corncrake	B	1993	310	370	—	A1, B2
[1] *Gallinago media*	Great Snipe	B	1993	80	110	—	A1
Limosa limosa	Black-tailed Godwit	B	1993	330	330	—	B2
Tringa totanus	Redshank	B	1993	215	215	—	B2
Asio flammeus	Short-eared Owl	B	1993	2	2	—	B2
Locustella naevia	Grasshopper Warbler	B	1993	100	130	—	B3
Acrocephalus paludicola	Aquatic Warbler	B	1993	18	23	—	A1

1. Displaying males.

A total of 145 species have been recorded breeding (49 at Pietkowo ponds). Species of global conservation concern that do not meet IBA criteria: *Aythya nyroca* (one breeding pair), *Haliaeetus albicilla* (non-breeding visitor).

■ Protection status
National None **International** None

■ Conservation issues
Threats Abandonment/reduction of land management (U), Aquaculture/fisheries (B), Groundwater abstraction (U)

Fish-farming activities include the dredging of ponds and lowering of the water-level in the area of the ponds. Abandonment of management of hay meadows and pasture has reduced the suitability of these habitats for some birds.

Białowieża forest — A1, B2, B3 — 031

Admin region podlaskie
Coordinates 52°46'N 23°43'E
Altitude 135–197 m   **Area** 62,500 ha

Site description

The site comprises the Polish part of the Białowieża forest, one of the largest and best preserved areas of primary lowland temperate forest in Europe, together with small remnants of the Ladzka forest. The forest covers 1,500 km² of flat plain, of which 620 km² are in Poland, the rest in Belarus. Moraine hills rise only c.30 m above the landscape. All rivers which run through the forest have water sources there or on its periphery. Most of the forest lies in the Narew and Bug tributaries of the Wisła (Vistula) catchment. The northern part is drained by tributaries of the Niemen, and the western part is part of the Dniestr catchment. There is an almost total lack of standing water, apart from small bogs. The proportion of forest that can be classed as primeval is not large, but many trees are over 200 years old (old-growth). Most forest is on dry ground, dominated by lime *Tilia* and hornbeam *Carpinus*, while the most interesting ornithologically is dominated by oak *Quercus*. Along valley watercourses there is carr of alder *Alnus* and ash *Fraxinus*, with *Alnus* forest in swampy hollows. There is mixed forest of pine *Pinus* and *Quercus*, as well as coniferous forest (mainly on wet soils) dominated by spruce *Picea* and *Pinus*. As a result of centuries of man's activities there are clearings, forest settlements, hay-meadows along rivers, road systems and trails, narrow-gauge railways, felling sites, hunting areas and gravel-pits.

Habitats Forest and woodland (85%; broadleaved deciduous forest; native coniferous forest; mixed forest; alluvial/very wet forest), Grassland (5%; humid grassland; mesophile grassland), Wetland (5%; standing fresh water; river/stream; raised bog; water-fringe vegetation), Artificial landscape (5%; highly improved reseeded grassland; arable land; urban parks/gardens; other urban/industrial areas; ruderal land)
Land-use Agriculture (5%), Forestry (70%), Hunting, Nature conservation/research (20%), Urban/industrial/transport (5%)

Birds

Species	Season	Year	Pop min	Pop max	Acc	Criteria
Ciconia nigra Black Stork	B	1987	34	34	A	B2
Pernis apivorus Honey Buzzard	B	1986	83	86	A	B3
Aquila pomarina Lesser Spotted Eagle	B	1991	68	68	A	B2
Crex crex Corncrake	B	—	Frequent		—	A1
Dendrocopos medius Middle Spotted Woodpecker	R	—	Abundant		—	B3

A total of 250 species have been recorded, including 177–180 breeding. The site is especially rich in breeding raptors (15 species extant, two extinct), owls (eight species extant, one extinct) and woodpeckers (eight species, out of nine in Europe). Breeding species of global conservation concern that do not meet IBA criteria: *Gallinago media* (rare).

Protection status

National Partial **International** Partial
10,502 ha of IBA covered by National Park (Białowieski, 10,502 ha). 3,463 ha of IBA covered by 20 Nature Reserves (Berezowo; Dolina Waliczówki; Dębowy Grąd; Gnilec; Głęboki Kąt; Kozłowe Borki; Lipiny; Michnówka; Nieznanowo; Olszanka Myśliszcze; Podcerkwia; Podolany; Pogorzelce; Przewłoka; Władysława Szafera; Siemianówka; Sitki; Starzyna; Szczekotowo; Wysokie Bagno; combined area 3,463 ha). 10,502 ha of IBA covered by Biosphere Reserve (Białowieża National Park, 10,502 ha). 10,502 ha of IBA covered by World Heritage Site (Białowieża National Park, 10,502 ha).

Conservation issues

Threats Abandonment/reduction of land management (B), Afforestation (C), Agricultural intensification/expansion (C), Construction/impact of dyke/dam/barrage (B), Deforestation (commercial) (U), Filling-in of wetlands (B), Groundwater abstraction (B), Industrialization/urbanization (C), Intensified forest management (A), Other (A), Recreation/tourism (C), Selective logging/cutting (A)

The greatest threat is from the ongoing replacement of primeval forest by plantations, through intensified forest management, clear-felling, selective logging, and afforestation with conifers. Railway transport of very large quantities of highly toxic chemicals through the forest (more than 100,000 tonnes per year) is a threat ('Other'), and forestry and tourism cause disturbance to birds. Since 1991 efforts have been made to protect the whole of Białowieża forest in Poland, involving OTOP and other nature-conservation organisations. About 80 projects relevant to nature conservation have been carried out in the area.

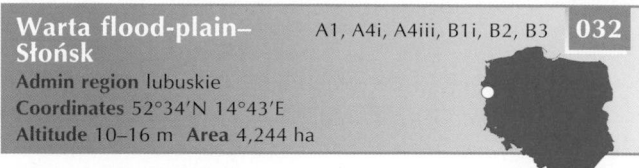

Warta flood-plain– Słońsk — A1, A4i, A4iii, B1i, B2, B3 — 032

Admin region lubuskie
Coordinates 52°34'N 14°43'E
Altitude 10–16 m   **Area** 4,244 ha

Site description

The site includes the flood-plain of the Warta river, where it meets the Odra river, and the lower course of the Postomia river. There are unregulated stretches of river, oxbow lakes, old drainage channels, small lakes, periodically flooded meadows, and pastures. The area floods almost every year, with annual fluctuations in water-level of up to 3.5 m. Highest levels are in March and April. In some years the whole area is underwater all year, in others for only a few months or not at all. Accordingly, the vegetation varies in different years. During heavy floods water-fringe vegetation predominates, mainly reed *Phragmites* and especially reed-grass *Glyceria* and canary-grass *Phalaris*, occupying a few hundred hectares. Large areas that have recently emerged from water are occupied by ruderal herbs *Polygonum/Bidens*. When the flood is limited or does not occur, such vegetation dies and is replaced by dry-ground vegetation and willow *Salix* bushes.

Habitats Forest and woodland (5%; alluvial/very wet forest), Scrub (scrub), Grassland (15%; humid grassland), Wetland (80%; standing fresh water; river/stream; water-fringe vegetation)
Land-use Agriculture (10%), Water management (100%)

Birds

Species	Season	Year	Pop min	Pop max	Acc	Criteria
[1] *Cygnus cygnus* Whooper Swan	P	1997	35	1,600	A	A4i, B1i
[2] *Anser fabalis* Bean Goose	P	1996	—	—	A	A4i, B1i
[2] *Anser albifrons* White-fronted Goose	P	1996	—	—	A	A4i, B1i
[3] *Anser anser* Greylag Goose	B	1996	130	450	—	B1i
Anas strepera Gadwall	B	1996	30	300	A	B2
[4] *Aythya ferina* Pochard	R	1996	40	610	A	B3
[5] *Haliaeetus albicilla* White-tailed Eagle	W	1996	1	31	A	A1
Porzana porzana Spotted Crake	B	1996	14	105	A	B3
[5] *Crex crex* Corncrake	B	1996	10	34	A	A1
[5b] *Grus grus* Crane	P	1996	—	2,450	A	A4i, B1i
Chlidonias niger Black Tern	B	1996	70	620	A	B2

1. 1991–1997.
2. Max. 180,000 *A. fabalis/A. albifrons*, 1991–1996.
3. Also 2,500 moulting birds.
4. 840 on passage
5. 1991–1996.
6. Autumn.

A very important area for moulting, staging, wintering and roosting waterbirds, mainly wildfowl. Up to 33,000 duck (Anatidae) stage here during spring migration, with up to 78,000 in autumn. Over 240 species have been recorded, including 160 breeding species. Data in table are for 1991–1996 unless otherwise stated

Protection status

National High **International** High
4,244 ha of IBA covered by Nature Reserve (Słońsk, 4,244 ha). 4,244 ha of IBA covered by Landscape Park (Ujście Warty, 28,000 ha). 4,244 ha of IBA covered by Ramsar Site (Słońsk, 4,244 ha).

Conservation issues

Threats Abandonment/reduction of land management (B), Dredging/canalization (B), Infrastructure (C)

Threats include a lack of water in some years (due to management of water-levels primarily for human uses), overgrazing by domestic geese and cattle, strong expansion of willow *Salix* scrub (partly due to abandonment of agriculture), disturbance of birds, river dredging, and recreation, tourism and hunting.

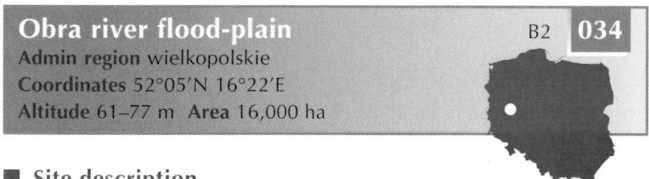

Noteć river flood-plain
Admin region wielkopolskie
Coordinates 52°58'N 16°25'E
Altitude 0–20 m **Area** 10,000 ha
A1 033

■ Site description
The site comprises the stretch of the lower Noteć river valley between the Gwda inflow and Wieleń town. Along the river there are flood-plain terraces and oxbow lakes, with extensive riverine forests, large reedbeds, fens and flooded meadows, and peat workings covered by water-fringe vegetation and scattered trees. Soils range from permanently wet to highly drained, and in some places have been converted to arable land.

Habitats Forest and woodland (alluvial/very wet forest), Scrub (scrub), Grassland (10%; steppe/dry calcareous grassland; humid grassland), Wetland (90%; standing fresh water; river/stream; water-fringe vegetation; fen/transition mire/spring), Artificial landscape (highly improved reseeded grassland; arable land)
Land-use Agriculture (100%), Hunting

■ Birds

Species	Season	Year	Pop min	Pop max	Acc	Criteria
Crex crex Corncrake	B	1987	51	53	—	A1

Species of global conservation concern that do not meet IBA criteria: *Haliaeetus albicilla* (one pair feeds in the area, nesting nearby). Other notable breeding species include *Limosa limosa* (70 pairs) and *Chlidonias niger* (52 pairs).

■ Protection status
National High **International** None
5 ha of IBA covered by Nature Reserve (Czapliniec Kuźnicki, 5 ha). 10,000 ha of IBA covered by Protected Landscape Area (Dolina Noteci, 68,840 ha).

■ Conservation issues

Threats Drainage (U), Selective logging/cutting (U)

Threats include the cutting of trees and shrubs.

Obra river flood-plain
Admin region wielkopolskie
Coordinates 52°05'N 16°22'E
Altitude 61–77 m **Area** 16,000 ha
B2 034

■ Site description
The widest part of the valley of the middle Obra river is characterized by forests and meadows, without larger settlements or a developed road system. The valley is divided up by channels and ditches which drain to the west (two main channels) or to the east to the Warta river via the Mosiński channel. The principal valley habitats are wet fields, marshes, and swamp forests of *Alnus*. Fields are intensively cultivated; wet grassland and scrub are not common. Forest of pine *Pinus* and oak *Quercus* covers the higher elevations.

Habitats Forest and woodland (30%; mixed forest; alluvial/very wet forest), Grassland (10%; humid grassland; mesophile grassland), Wetland (20%; standing fresh water; raised bog; water-fringe vegetation), Artificial landscape (40%; highly improved reseeded grassland; arable land)
Land-use Agriculture (60%), Forestry (30%), Hunting, Urban/industrial/transport (10%)

■ Birds

Species	Season	Year	Pop min	Pop max	Acc	Criteria
Falco tinnunculus Kestrel	B	1985	14	15	A	B2

Other notable breeding species include *Grus grus* (20 pairs) and *Milvus migrans* (six pairs). Breeding species of global conservation concern that do not meet IBA criteria: *Crex crex* (5–6 pairs).

■ Protection status
National None **International** None

■ Conservation issues

Threats Abandonment/reduction of land management (B), Agricultural intensification/expansion (B), Drainage (A), Intensified forest management (A)

The main threats are further drainage and intensification of forest management. The site is adjacent to the Przemęcki Landscape Park (21,400 ha).

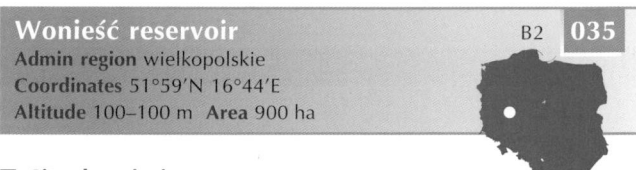

Wonieść reservoir
Admin region wielkopolskie
Coordinates 51°59'N 16°44'E
Altitude 100–100 m **Area** 900 ha
B2 035

■ Site description
A storage reservoir (777 ha) on the Samica river, connected by the Wonieść channel to the Obra river. The reservoir comprises five former lakes (Drzeczkowskie, Witosławskie, Wojnowskie, Jezierzyckie, Wonieść), connected by a narrow channel (c.13 km long, 200–1,300 m wide), with meadows between them. A dam and sluice divide the upper part of the reservoir, where aquatic vegetation is well-developed, from the lower, where such vegetation is very localized. Adjacent there are fish-ponds, forests, meadows and cultivated fields. The reservoir stores water for agriculture and fire-fighting.

Habitats Forest and woodland (5%; broadleaved deciduous forest; native coniferous forest; mixed forest; alluvial/very wet forest), Grassland (mesophile grassland), Wetland (86%; standing fresh water; water-fringe vegetation), Artificial landscape (9%; highly improved reseeded grassland; arable land; ruderal land)
Land-use Agriculture (10%), Fisheries/aquaculture (75%), Forestry (5%), Hunting, Tourism/recreation (15%), Water management (40%)

■ Birds

Species	Season	Year	Pop min	Pop max	Acc	Criteria
[1] *Aythya nyroca* Ferruginous Duck	B	1988	5	11	A	B2

1. Recently extinct, but important site for species's recovery or re-introduction.

The globally threatened *Aythya nyroca* has not bred here since 1995, but the habitat remains and it is believed there is a good chance that it could breed here again, therefore criterion B2 is still applied. Breeding species of global conservation concern that do not meet IBA criteria: *Haliaeetus albicilla* (one pair). Other notable breeding species include *Anas strepera* (22 pairs) and *Chlidonias niger* (20–60 pairs).

■ Protection status
National High **International** None
900 ha of IBA covered by Protected Landscape Area (Krzywińsko–Osiecki, 71,425 ha).

■ Conservation issues

Threats Abandonment/reduction of land management (B), Agricultural intensification/expansion (B), Aquaculture/fisheries (B), Construction/impact of dyke/dam/barrage (C), Recreation/tourism (C)

Birds are disturbed by fisheries, hunting, tourism and angling, and are also threatened by rapid changes in water-level.

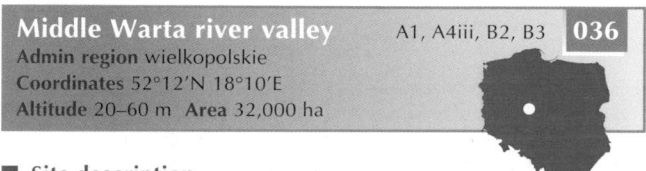

Middle Warta river valley
Admin region wielkopolskie
Coordinates 52°12'N 18°10'E
Altitude 20–60 m **Area** 32,000 ha
A1, A4iii, B2, B3 036

■ Site description
A 120 km stretch of the middle Warta river between Babin village (near Uniejów town) and Pogorzelica village (near Pyzdry town), including the Koło valley (Kotlina Kolska) and the Konin basin (Dolina Konińska). Much of the valley used to flood each spring, but after the construction of Jeziorsko reservoir, spring flooding stopped completely, and habitats changed greatly. As a result of river

embankment, the Koło valley is now a mosaic of cultivated fields, intensively used meadows, pastures, small stands of woodland and settlements. The main land-use is grazing. The Konin basin, however, has a more natural character. Here the river floods onto wet meadows in April and hollows within meadows are permanently flooded and not cultivated. Low-lying oxbow lakes and their surrounding areas are covered mainly with water-fringe vegetation. There are also riverside beds of osier *Salix*, scattered plantations, small areas of carr, and sand-dunes covered with pine *Pinus* forest. Land-use here is mainly non-intensive agriculture, including haymaking in meadows and livestock-grazing on private farms.

Habitats Forest and woodland (native coniferous forest; mixed forest; alluvial/very wet forest), Scrub (scrub), Grassland (steppe/dry calcareous grassland; humid grassland; mesophile grassland), Wetland (sand-dunes/sand beach; standing fresh water; river/stream; raised bog; water-fringe vegetation), Artificial landscape (highly improved reseeded grassland; arable land; ruderal land)
Land-use Agriculture (90%), Hunting, Water management (10%)

■ Birds

Species		Season	Year	Pop min	Pop max	Acc	Criteria
Falco tinnunculus	Kestrel	B	1995	25	35	A	B2
Coturnix coturnix	Quail	B	1995	20	50	A	B2
Porzana porzana	Spotted Crake	B	1995	20	30	—	B3
[1] *Crex crex*	Corncrake	B	1995	55	70	—	A1
[2] *Limosa limosa*	Black-tailed Godwit	B	1995	—	250	A	B2
[3] *Tringa totanus*	Redshank	B	1995	150	180	A	B2
Chlidonias niger	Black Tern	B	1995	100	150	A	B2

1. 1993–1995.
2. 370–500 pairs in 1980s; max. 3,000–4,000 on passage, near B1i threshold.
3. 200–260 pairs in 1980s.

Up to 35,000 or more waterbirds roost here, mainly wildfowl *Anser/Anas* with lesser numbers of waders (Charadrii). Breeding species of global conservation concern that do not meet IBA criteria: *Aythya nyroca* (recently extinct here), *Gallinago media* (two pairs). A total of 153 species have been recorded breeding.

■ Protection status
National Partial **International** None
13,428 ha of IBA covered by Landscape Park (Nadwarciański, 13,428 ha). 10,000 ha of IBA covered by Protected Landscape Area (Pyzdrski, 16,572 ha). 5,000 ha of IBA covered by Protected Landscape Area (Uniejowski, 18,000 ha).

■ Conservation issues

Threats Abandonment/reduction of land management (U), Agricultural intensification/expansion (U), Construction/impact of dyke/dam/barrage (U), Drainage (U), Dredging/canalization (U)

The main threats are posed by changes in the water-regime of the Warta river following the construction of Jeziorsko reservoir upstream, by the abandonment of agricultural management of meadows, by the conversion of meadows to arable land following damming and drainage, and by agricultural intensification locally.

Ostrówek and Smogulec ponds B1i 037
Admin region kujawsko-pomorskie, wielkopolskie
Coordinates 53°05′N 17°20′E
Altitude 80–100 m **Area** 1,000 ha

■ Site description

Habitats Grassland (30%; humid grassland; mesophile grassland), Wetland (60%; standing fresh water; river/stream; water-fringe vegetation), Artificial landscape (10%; ruderal land)
Land-use Agriculture (30%), Fisheries/aquaculture (60%), Hunting, Not utilized (10%)

The Ostrówek and Smogulec fish-pond complexes and adjoining wet meadows (Osieckie) in the Noteć river valley, 45–49 km west of Bydgoszcz. The 35 ponds comprise c.500 ha of water and are full (1 m deep) from April to October when fish (carp *Cyprinus*) are being farmed. Large areas of the ponds are covered with beds of reed *Phragmites* and reed-mace *Typha*. The meadows are covered with canals and ditches; they are not intensively used, and succession to willow *Salix* scrub is occurring in some parts.

■ Birds

Species		Season	Year	Pop min	Pop max	Acc	Criteria
[1] *Cygnus columbianus*	Bewick's Swan	P	1995	—	92	A	B1i

1. 190 in 1993.

A total of 154 species have been recorded, including 38 breeding and 65 migrating waterbirds. Breeding species of global conservation concern that do not meet IBA criteria: *Aythya nyroca* (recently extinct here), *Haliaeetus albicilla* (one pair). A wide variety of raptors, which breed in the surrounding area, forage at the site.

■ Protection status
National None **International** None

■ Conservation issues

Threats Aquaculture/fisheries (U), Disturbance to birds (U), Filling-in of wetlands (U), Unsustainable exploitation (U)

Hunting is a threat, as is disturbance of nesting birds by harvesting activity (reeds and hay).

Ślesin and Występ ponds A4i, B1i 038
Admin region kujawsko-pomorskie
Coordinates 53°08′N 17°42′E
Altitude 60–80 m **Area** 3,200 ha

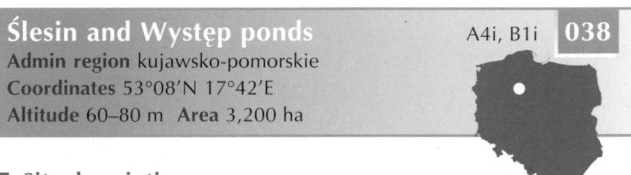

■ Site description
Two fish-pond complexes in the Toruń–Eberswald stream valley. Ślesin fish-pond complex (170 ha) lies c.20 km west of the town of Bydgoszcz, and comprises 14 small ponds of a few hectares each and one large pond (130 ha). Występ fish-pond complex (200 ha) is similar. The ponds are full from April to October, supplied by the Bydgoszcz channel and drainage ditches, and are used for fish-farming (carp *Cyprinus*). Both complexes are surrounded by wet meadows, used for pasture and hay, and areas of mire and wet forest.

Habitats Forest and woodland (10%; broadleaved deciduous forest; native coniferous forest; alluvial/very wet forest), Scrub (5%; scrub), Grassland (65%; steppe/dry calcareous grassland; humid grassland; mesophile grassland), Wetland (18%; standing fresh water; river/stream; raised bog; water-fringe vegetation)
Land-use Agriculture (70%), Fisheries/aquaculture (20%), Forestry (10%), Hunting

■ Birds

Species		Season	Year	Pop min	Pop max	Acc	Criteria
[1] *Cygnus columbianus*	Bewick's Swan	P	1995	178	429	—	A4i, B1i

1. 1988–1995.

The most important place in Poland for *Cygnus columbianus* during migration, and a moulting site for *Cygnus olor*. In summer up to 600 *Remiz pendulinus* and several dozen *Panurus biarmicus* are present. Species of global conservation concern that do not meet IBA criteria: *Haliaeetus albicilla* (one pair resident; up to five birds on passage), *Crex crex* (new breeder).

■ Protection status
National Low **International** None
42 ha of IBA covered by Nature Reserve (Łąki Œlesińskie, 42 ha).

■ Conservation issues

Threats Abandonment/reduction of land management (B), Aquaculture/fisheries (C), Disturbance to birds (C), Dredging/canalization (B), Unsustainable exploitation (B)

Hunting is a problem. Part of the meadows may be converted into arable fields; dry grasslands are slowly reverting to shrubland through lack of grazing/mowing. Numbers of swans *Cygnus* during spring migration have been reduced due to later filling of the ponds, and more efficient drainage of ponds in the autumn means that birds are only able to stay for a shorter period.

Lower Wisła river — A1, A4i, A4iii, B1i, B2 — 039

Admin region pomorskie, kujawsko-pomorskie
Coordinates 53°23′N 18°25′E
Altitude 1–50 m **Area** 32,000 ha

■ Site description
The site comprises a 260-km stretch of the Wisła (Vistula) river flood-plain (of which about 190 km is embanked against floods), between Włocławek town in the south and Przegalina sluice (6 km from the Wisła river mouth) in the north. The terrain is highly varied. Riverbanks or slopes are dozens of metres high in some places, very flat and low-lying in others. The riverbed itself constitutes about quarter of the site's area; the rest consists of meadows, scrub (mainly willow *Salix*), small patches of riverine forest, and numerous oxbow lakes and wetlands. The river passes through some quite large towns (e.g. Toruń, Bydgoszcz, Grudziądz, Tczew).

Habitats Forest and woodland (5%; alluvial/very wet forest), Scrub (20%; scrub), Grassland (30%; humid grassland; mesophile grassland), Wetland (45%; standing fresh water; river/stream; water-fringe vegetation; fen/transition mire/spring), Artificial landscape (5%; other urban/industrial areas)
Land-use Agriculture (20%), Fisheries/aquaculture (25%), Hunting, Tourism/recreation (5%), Urban/industrial/transport (20%), Not utilized (15%), Unknown (15%)

■ Birds

Species		Season	Year	Pop min	Pop max	Acc	Criteria
[1] *Bucephala clangula*	Goldeneye	W	1997	5,024	5,900	A	A4i, B1i
Mergus merganser	Goosander	B	1998	60	60	A	B1i
[2] *Mergus merganser*	Goosander	W	1997	1,356	2,452	A	A4i, B1i
Haliaeetus albicilla	White-tailed Eagle	W	1997	6	45	A	A1
Crex crex	Corncrake	B	1998	153	153	A	A1, B2
Alcedo atthis	Kingfisher	B	1998	46	46	A	B2

1. 1984–1997; 5,054 in 1997 along only 50 km of Wisła.
2. 1984–1997; 20 breeding pairs in 1994 along 50 km of Wisła.

A total of 126 bird species have been recorded breeding or probably breeding at the site, including the largest number of *Crex crex* (153 calling males in 1998) at any site in the Wisła valley. The area also supports significant parts of the national breeding populations of *Charadrius hiaticula*, *Charadrius dubius*, *Sterna hirundo* and *Sterna albifrons*. In 1994 a total of c.37,000 waterbirds were estimated to occur along the river in the late summer post-breeding period, and 46,500 in winter (mainly ducks).

■ Protection status
National Partial **International** None
About 10,000 ha covered by Landscape Park (Zespół Nadwiślańskich, 35,400 ha).

■ Conservation issues

Threats Agricultural intensification/expansion (B), Construction/impact of dyke/dam/barrage (A), Dredging/canalization (A), Industrialization/urbanization (C), Infrastructure (C)

The greatest threat is a potential one: the possible construction of a series of dams along the Wisła river ('cascadization').

Marshy valley of the Drwęca river — B1i — 040

Admin region kujawsko-pomorskie
Coordinates 53°17′N 19°34′E
Altitude 71–132 m **Area** 3,400 ha

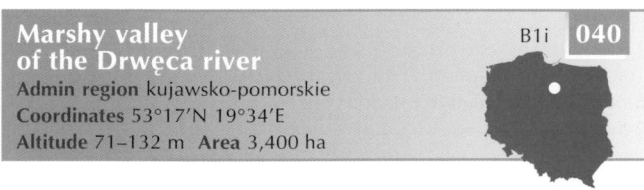

■ Site description
The site lies in the Drwęca river valley between Brodnica town and the road between Jajkowo and Głęboczek villages, and includes the lower parts of the Brynica and Samionka river valleys, Sopień lake and Ostrów lake. The valley is 600 m to 3 km in width and includes a canal system and oxbow lakes. The Drwęca river has a natural character and meanders strongly; overflow in early spring causes extensive flooding. The vegetation is species-rich; besides meadows there are reedbeds *Phragmites*, sedge-beds and small stands of alder *Alnus* woodland.

Habitats Forest and woodland (45%; broadleaved deciduous forest; native coniferous forest; mixed forest; alluvial/very wet forest), Grassland (15%; steppe/dry calcareous grassland; humid grassland; mesophile grassland), Wetland (15%; standing fresh water; river/stream; raised bog; water-fringe vegetation; fen/transition mire/spring), Artificial landscape (25%; highly improved reseeded grassland; arable land; ruderal land)
Land-use Agriculture (30%), Forestry (40%), Hunting, Not utilized (30%)

■ Birds

Species		Season	Year	Pop min	Pop max	Acc	Criteria
[1] *Anser albifrons*	White-fronted Goose	P	1997	6,000	6,000	—	B1i

1. Spring.

Over 200 species have been recorded, 140 of them breeding. Species of global conservation concern that do not meet IBA criteria: *Aythya nyroca* (up to two birds on passage), *Haliaeetus albicilla* (up to five non-breeding birds), *Crex crex* (4–9 breeding pairs).

■ Protection status
National High **International** None
1,287 ha of IBA covered by Nature Reserve (Rzeka Drwęca, 1,287 ha). 3,400 ha of IBA covered by Protected Landscape Area (Dolina Drwęcy, 61,641 ha).

■ Conservation issues

Threats Abandonment/reduction of land management (B), Afforestation (B), Agricultural intensification/expansion (B), Aquaculture/fisheries (C), Deforestation (commercial) (B), Drainage (A), Dredging/canalization (B), Extraction industry (B), Industrialization/urbanization (B), Recreation/tourism (B), Unsustainable exploitation (B)

Threats to birds include the abandonment of land management, disturbance, and hunting and poaching.

Gopło Millennium Park — A4i, A4iii, B1i, B2 — 041

Admin region kujawsko-pomorskie, wielkopolskie
Coordinates 52°36′N 18°25′E
Altitude 20–40 m **Area** 12,700 ha

■ Site description
The park covers Gopło lake and surroundings, as well as the Skulskie lakes (Skulskie, Skulska Wieś, Czartowo) that are part of the Noteć river system. Gopło lake (25 km long) has flat, unforested shores with extensive beds of reed *Phragmites*. There are some islands (25 ha), covered mainly with reed. The surrounding area is covered mainly by wet meadows, fields and small forests.

Habitats Forest and woodland (15%; broadleaved deciduous forest; native coniferous forest), Grassland (30%; humid grassland; mesophile grassland), Wetland (5%; standing fresh water; river/stream; water-fringe vegetation), Artificial landscape (50%; highly improved reseeded grassland; arable land; forestry plantation; urban parks/gardens; ruderal land)
Land-use Agriculture (40%), Fisheries/aquaculture (40%), Hunting (10%), Other (5%), Tourism/recreation (5%)

■ Birds

Species		Season	Year	Pop min	Pop max	Acc	Criteria
[1] *Botaurus stellaris*	Bittern	B	1995	17	17	—	B2
Ixobrychus minutus	Little Bittern	B	1995	7	10	A	B2
[2] *Anser fabalis*	Bean Goose	P	1996	3,000	5,000	—	A4i, B1i
[2] *Anser albifrons*	White-fronted Goose	P	1995	3,000	6,000	—	B1i
[3] *Grus grus*	Crane	P	—	100	1,500	—	B1i

1. 13 pairs at Gopło lake.
2. Also winter visitor.
3. Autumn.

During autumn passage a total of 20,000 or more waterbirds stage regularly at the site, mainly wildfowl, and especially geese *Anser*. Breeding species of global conservation concern that do not meet IBA criteria: *Haliaeetus albicilla* (one pair). A total of 198 species have been recorded, including 74 waterbirds.

■ Protection status
National High **International** None
402 ha of IBA covered by 7 Nature Reserves (Bachorze; Bąbule; Kąty Kickowskie; Potrzymionek; Trzciny Giżewskie; Zatoka Biała Osoba;

Zatoka Sucha; total area 402 ha). 12,684 ha of IBA covered by Landscape Park (Nadgoplański Park Tysiąclecia, 12,684 ha).

■ Conservation issues

> **Threats** Abandonment/reduction of land management (A), Agricultural intensification/expansion (C), Aquaculture/fisheries (A), Other (A), Recreation/tourism (A), Selective logging/cutting (A)

The drainage of adjoining land has resulted in a lower water-level in the lake. Agriculture has resulted in nutrient pollution of the lake, through fertilizer run-off from fields. Reed-harvesting is also a threat ('Other'). Fisheries, angling and sailing cause disturbance to birds, and hunting is a problem.

Rakutowskie swamps
A4iii, B1i   **042**

Admin region kujawsko-pomorskie
Coordinates 52°31′N 19°14′E
Altitude 30–30 m **Area** 800 ha

■ Site description

The site covers Rakutowskie lake (c.300 ha) and the surrounding, periodically flooded sedge meadows, as well as adjoining wet riverine forest and carr. The eastern part of the site includes a wet area of the Kłótnia river with overgrown peat-workings. Rakutowskie lake is rather shallow (average 2.5 m) with a flat shore fringed by a broad belt (100–150 m) of marginal vegetation. Due to (relatively small) water-level fluctuations, the lake area can vary by up to 60–70 ha. Floating and submerged vegetation is rich and a large part of the lake bottom is covered by stonewort *Chara*.

> **Habitats** Forest and woodland (32%; alluvial/very wet forest), Grassland (18%; humid grassland), Wetland (36%; standing fresh water; river/stream; water-fringe vegetation), Artificial landscape (14%; arable land)
> **Land-use** Agriculture (25%), Fisheries/aquaculture (10%), Forestry (35%), Nature conservation/research (30%)

■ Birds

Species		Season	Year	Pop min	Pop max	Acc	Criteria
[1] *Anser anser*	Greylag Goose	P	—	250	600	—	B1i

1. Spring max. 600, autumn max. 250.

More than 20,000 waterbirds use the area in winter, and notable numbers (peak daily counts exceeding 10,000 birds) stage during autumn migration, mainly *Anser*, *Anas*, *Vanellus vanellus*, *Larus* and waders Charadrii. Breeding species of global conservation concern that do not meet IBA criteria: *Haliaeetus albicilla* (one pair), *Crex crex* (1–2 calling males), *Acrocephalus paludicola* (one singing male).

■ Protection status

National Partial **International** None
414 ha of IBA covered by Nature Reserve (Jezioro Rakutowskie, 414 ha). 175 ha of IBA covered by Nature Reserve (Olszyny Rakutowskie, 175 ha).

■ Conservation issues

> **Threats** Groundwater abstraction (A)

The sedge meadows are included in Jezioro Rakutowskie Nature Reserve, and part of the forest/carr is included in Olszyny Rakutowskie Nature Reserve.

Ner river valley
A1   **043**

Admin region łódzkie, wielkopolskie
Coordinates 52°04′N 19°04′E
Altitude 90–100 m **Area** 4,800 ha

■ Site description

The Ner valley is a marshy stretch of the Warszawa–Berlin valley between the towns of Łęczyca and Dąbie, and adjoins the Bzura river valley. Wet meadows dominate the area, but on low-lying land and adjacent to water there are reedbeds *Phragmites* in some places, as well as riverine forest and scrub, on the more elevated, drier ground, dry broadleaved forest. The easternmost part of the valley (around Łęczyca and Błonia towns) was drained in 1980, and is now less attractive to waterbirds. Other parts of the valley flood annually. The most interesting area ornithologically is around Dąbie town.

> **Habitats** Forest and woodland (5%; mixed forest; alluvial/very wet forest), Grassland (45%; humid grassland), Wetland (50%; standing fresh water; river/stream; raised bog; water-fringe vegetation)
> **Land-use** Agriculture (90%), Forestry (5%), Hunting, Not utilized (5%)

■ Birds

Species		Season	Year	Pop min	Pop max	Acc	Criteria
Crex crex	Corncrake	B	1993	20	—	B	A1

The most attractive area in central Poland for staging geese and ducks during spring migration. Breeding species of global conservation concern that do not meet IBA criteria: *Acrocephalus paludicola* (2–3 pairs).

■ Protection status

National Partial **International** None
2,500 ha of IBA covered by Protected Landscape Area (Dolina Bzury, 13,500 ha).

■ Conservation issues

> **Threats** Disturbance to birds (U), Drainage (U), Unsustainable exploitation (U)

Threats include hunting and the collection of eggs of *Anser anser*.

Jeziorsko reservoir
A4i, B1i   **044**

Admin region łódzkie, wielkopolskie
Coordinates 51°47′N 18°41′E
Altitude 90–120 m **Area** 4,300 ha

■ Site description

A storage reservoir (16 km by 3.5 km) in the lowland valley of the unregulated Warta river, between Skęczniew and Warta towns. Meadows and pastures adjoin the reservoir near Proboszczowice and Dzierzążna villages. Its shoreline is formed by natural valley slopes, side dams (which block the mouths of the Teleszyna and Pichna rivers), and also backwater dams, which limit the flooding area when the water-level is at its highest (maximum area is 4,200 ha). The reservoir bottom was not modified before flooding and, when the water-level is low (minimum area 1,700 ha), a varied terrain with scattered small hollows is exposed. The southern part of the reservoir, which floods only during times of high water, is occupied by a mosaic of meadows and willow *Salix* scrub with groups of partly dead trees. Highest water-levels are reached in April and May, followed by a slow fall.

> **Habitats** Grassland (5%; mesophile grassland), Wetland (95%; standing fresh water; raised bog; water-fringe vegetation)
> **Land-use** Agriculture (20%), Water management (80%)

■ Birds

Species		Season	Year	Pop min	Pop max	Acc	Criteria
Anser fabalis	Bean Goose	P	1993	—	7,500	—	A4i, B1i

A notable site for breeding and migrating waterbirds; breeding numbers vary from year to year, depending on the water-level. Breeding species of global conservation concern that do not meet IBA criteria: *Crex crex* (one pair, irregularly).

■ Protection status

National None **International** None

■ Conservation issues

> **Threats** Aquaculture/fisheries (U), Construction/impact of dyke/dam/barrage (U), Recreation/tourism (U)

Birds are disturbed by tourism/recreation. Lowering of the water-level too early in the season destroys many nests. The southern part of reservoir is a 'silence zone', and is planned as a bird reserve (not yet designated).

Kampinos forest A1, B2, B3 045

Admin region mazowieckie
Coordinates 52°20'N 20°35'E
Altitude 70–110 m **Area** 35,700 ha

■ Site description

A highly fragmented forest in the Wisła valley, between the Bzura and Wisła (Vistula) rivers. Coniferous and mixed forests cover banks of sand-dunes along the river terrace, below which lies the marshy valley floor, with watercourses flowing to the Bzura river. Marshy areas are covered with reedbeds *Phragmites*, sedge-beds, meadows, and riverine forest and scrub. Marshy areas higher up the terrace are covered by broadleaved deciduous forest. Former agricultural land, now abandoned (including whole villages), is situated mainly in the centre of the marshy zone, and is reverting to forest, aided by active afforestion.

Habitats Forest and woodland (71%; native coniferous forest; mixed forest; alluvial/very wet forest), Scrub (12%; scrub), Artificial landscape (17%; arable land; other urban/industrial areas; ruderal land)
Land-use Agriculture (10%), Forestry (63%), Nature conservation/research (15%), Not utilized (12%)

■ Birds

Species		Season	Year	Pop min	Pop max	Acc	Criteria
Crex crex	Corncrake	B	1996	255	300	A	A1, B2
Locustella naevia	Grasshopper Warbler	B	1993	80	100	—	B3

The site is very important for breeding *Crex crex*. A total of 133 species have been confirmed breeding. In recent years (1980–1996) 5–7 species stopped breeding compared with the 1950–1979 period. Over the last quarter-century there have been 13 breeding species of raptor and seven non-breeding visitors or winterers. Three raptors (*Falco peregrinus*, *Milvus migrans* and *Circus cyaneus*) stopped breeding in the 1970s, one (*Circaetus gallicus*) in the 1980s, and *Aquila pomarina* is decreasing. Non-raptors which have stopped breeding in recent years at the site include *Tetrao tetrix*, *Burhinus oedicnemus*, *Coracias garrulus* and *Lanius minor*.

■ Protection status

National High **International** None
35,700 ha of IBA covered by National Park (Kampinoski, 35,700 ha). 4,722 ha of IBA covered by 24 Nature Reserves (Biela; Cyganka; Czapliniec Dełby; Czarna Woda im. prof. Aleksandra Kaliszki; Czerwińskie Góry I & II; Granica; Kalisko; Karpaty; Krzywa Góra; Łuże; Nart im. inż. Stanisława Richtera; Niepust; Pożary; Przyćmień; Roztoka; Rybitew; Sieraków im. prof. Romana Kobendzy; Tuszko; Wilków; Zaborów Leśny; Zamczysko; Żurawiowe; together totalling 4,722 ha).

■ Conservation issues

Threats Afforestation (B), Groundwater abstraction (A), Intensified forest management (B), Selective logging/cutting (B)

The purchase of arable land by the National Park and the subsequent abandonment of agricultural management (reversion to forest) has reduced the abundance of wildlife of open, non-forest habitats. The water-level fell by c.2 m over the past few decades as a result of drainage and lower-than-average precipitation. Since 1997 the average water-level has risen somewhat as a result of very high rainfall in summer.

Middle Wisła river valley A1, A4i, A4iii, B1i, B2 046

Admin region lubelskie, mazowieckie
Coordinates 52°03'N 20°37'E
Altitude 50–80 m **Area** 19,000 ha

■ Site description

A large unregulated stretch of the Wisła (Vistula) river, from Gołąb village to Płock town (226 km long), with numerous sand islands. Some islands are bare, others have a herb layer, and high islands have scrub of willow *Salix* and poplar *Populus*. There are sand-dunes. The riverbanks and flood terrace are used mainly for intensive collection of willow *Salix* stems (for planting on riverbanks, dunes, etc., and as

material for crafts), and intensive cattle-grazing on meadows and pastures. The river is used by boat traffic.

Habitats Forest and woodland (20%; alluvial/very wet forest), Grassland (10%; humid grassland; mesophile grassland), Wetland (60%; sand-dunes/sand beach; standing fresh water; river/stream), Rocky areas (5%; inland cliff), Artificial landscape (5%; arable land; ruderal land)
Land-use Agriculture (15%), Fisheries/aquaculture (30%), Hunting, Nature conservation/research (5%), Other (20%), Tourism/recreation (30%), Urban/industrial/transport

■ Birds

Species		Season	Year	Pop min	Pop max	Acc	Criteria
Haliaeetus albicilla	White-tailed Eagle	W	1993	5	15	—	A1
[1] *Larus canus*	Common Gull	R	1993	2,800	2,950	A	B2
Sterna albifrons	Little Tern	B	1993	680	700	A	A4i, B1i, B2
Alcedo atthis	Kingfisher	B	1993	43	52	—	B2

1. 3,400 in winter.

An important site for staging migrants such as waders and passerines, and for wintering waterbirds, of which more than 20,000 occur regularly, mainly ducks. Breeding species of global conservation concern that do not meet IBA criteria: *Aythya nyroca* (two pairs), *Crex crex* (five pairs).

■ Protection status

National High **International** None
5,215 ha of IBA covered by 14 Nature Reserves (Kępa Antonińska; Kępa Rakowska; Kępa Wykowska; Kępy Kazuńskie; Łachy Brzeskie; Ławice Kiełpińskie; Ławice Troszyńskie; Ruska Kępa; Wikliny Wiślane; Wyspy Białobrzeskie; Wyspy Świderskie; Wyspy Zakrzewskie; Wyspy Zawadowskie; Zakole Zakroczymskie; combined area of 5,215 ha). 19,000 ha of IBA covered by Protected Landscape Areas (names not available, total area 220,000 ha).

■ Conservation issues

Threats Abandonment/reduction of land management (C), Agricultural intensification/expansion (B), Construction/impact of dyke/dam/barrage (A), Disturbance to birds (U), Dredging/canalization (A), Extraction industry (U), Natural events (U), Recreation/tourism (C), Unsustainable exploitation (U)

Threats are posed by intensive cattle-grazing on the islands, sand-mining of the riverbed, flooding (natural), felling of riverside trees, unsustainable duck hunting, fish poaching, and disturbance to nesting birds by willow collectors. The greatest threats are potential: there are plans for dredging and canalization of the river, to create a narrow channel without islands, oxbow lakes or meanders, as well as plans for the building of water-storage reservoirs at Płock, Wyszogród, and near Warszawa.

Zegrzyński reservoir A4iii, B1i 047

Admin region mazowieckie
Coordinates 52°31'N 21°03'E
Altitude 100–100 m **Area** 12,000 ha

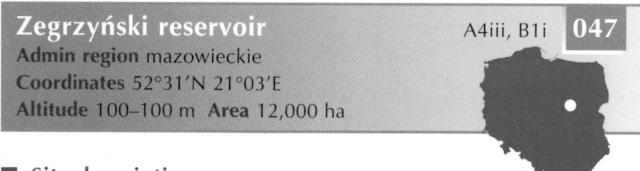

■ Site description

A dammed storage reservoir on the Narew river, with a maximum area of 3,300 ha. To the north the site extends to Koziegłowy village, and includes the mouth of the Bug river. The northern and western shores are high and steep, but along the southern and eastern sides the reservoir is separated by river embankments from extensive cultivated meadows, which cover the former flood terrace. Important bird habitats here include oxbow lakes, islands and willow *Salix* bushes. The reservoir is used for recreation, and there are summer houses.

Habitats Grassland (3%; mesophile grassland), Wetland (95%; standing fresh water; river/stream; water-fringe vegetation)
Land-use Tourism/recreation (20%), Water management (80%)

■ Birds

Species		Season	Year	Pop min	Pop max	Acc	Criteria
[1] *Bucephala clangula*	Goldeneye	W	1998	3,000	4,000	—	B1i

1. 1996–1998.

An important site for migrating waterbirds in autumn (c.20,000 in total, mainly ducks, swans, *Fulica atra* and gulls *Larus*) and also for wintering wildfowl (total 6,800). Breeding species of global conservation concern that do not meet IBA criteria: *Crex crex* (12 pairs).

■ Protection status
National High **International** None
1 ha of IBA covered by Nature Reserve (Dzierżenińska Kępa, 1 ha). 12,000 ha of IBA covered by Protected Landscape Area (Narwiański, 27,111 ha).

■ Conservation issues

Threats Infrastructure (U), Recreation/tourism (U)

Recreation/tourism activity is too intense in summer (all kinds of water-sports), so birds tend to use this area after the tourist season, on migration and in winter. The waterworks for Warszawa lie 3 km beyond Dębe Dam (downstream from the IBA), therefore the water is rather clean.

Omulew river valley
A1, B2 048
Admin region mazowieckie
Coordinates 53°12′N 21°20′E
Altitude 100–125 m **Area** 6,000 ha

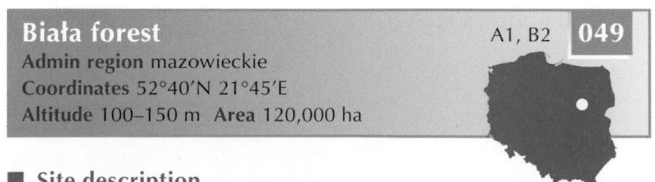

■ Site description
Large areas of fen are located in the middle stretch of this river valley and in flooded parts of the upper river valley. In the lower stretches there is natural old-growth riverine forest, and sandy grasslands.

Habitats Forest and woodland (10%; alluvial/very wet forest), Grassland (55%; steppe/dry calcareous grassland; mesophile grassland), Wetland (30%; river/stream; water-fringe vegetation; fen/transition mire/spring), Artificial landscape (5%; highly improved reseeded grassland; ruderal land)
Land-use Agriculture, Hunting, Not utilized

■ Birds

Species	Season	Year	Pop min	Pop max	Acc	Criteria
¹ *Crex crex* Corncrake	B	1996	80	100	—	A1, B2
Coracias garrulus Roller	B	1992	4	4	—	B2

1. 1992–1996 (extrapolation from smaller plots).

■ Protection status
National None **International** None

■ Conservation issues

Threats Agricultural intensification/expansion (U), Drainage (U), Dredging/canalization (U), Recreation/tourism (U)

Since 1991 the upper river has been regulated, which has influenced the area of flooding. Affected areas have included some areas of marsh, meadow, willow *Salix* scrub and riverside forest.

Biała forest
A1, B2 049
Admin region mazowieckie
Coordinates 52°40′N 21°45′E
Altitude 100–150 m **Area** 120,000 ha

■ Site description
One of the largest remaining complexes of natural forest in the Mazowsze region, situated between the Bug and the Narew rivers, and drained by the Brok, Struga, Truchełka, Turka and Wymakacz rivers. Stands are 40–80 years old, in more or less dense tracts, interspersed with meadows, ponds and willow *Salix* scrub. Seventy percent of the forest is a monoculture of pine *Pinus* or is mixed forest of oak *Quercus* and *Pinus*, 10% is broadleaved dominated by hornbeam *Carpinus*, and the rest is broadleaved riverine forest. Two fish-pond complexes and a dozen or so villages are located in the middle of the site.

Habitats Forest and woodland (80%; native coniferous forest; mixed forest; alluvial/very wet forest), Wetland (10%; standing fresh water; river/stream; water-fringe vegetation), Artificial landscape (10%; arable land; ruderal land)
Land-use Agriculture (25%), Fisheries/aquaculture (5%), Forestry (70%), Hunting

■ Birds

Species	Season	Year	Pop min	Pop max	Acc	Criteria
¹ *Crex crex* Corncrake	B	1997	2	23	—	A1
² *Coracias garrulus* Roller	B	1995	8	12	—	B2

1. 23 calling birds in 100 km² in 1997.
2. 70% decline since 1985–1990.

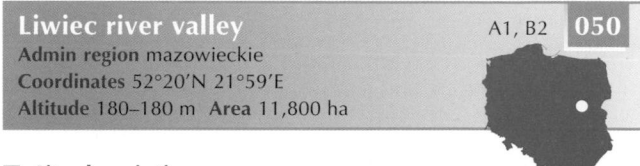

A total of 193 species have been recorded. Breeding species of global conservation concern that do not meet IBA criteria: *Gallinago media*.

■ Protection status
National Low **International** None
15 ha of IBA covered by Nature Reserve (Bartnia [Bird Reserve], 15 ha). 6 ha of IBA covered by Nature Reserve (Popławy, 6 ha). 7 ha of IBA covered by Nature Reserve (Wielgolas, 7 ha).

■ Conservation issues

Threats Deforestation (commercial) (U)

Current forest management poses a threat to birds.

Liwiec river valley
A1, B2 050
Admin region mazowieckie
Coordinates 52°20′N 21°59′E
Altitude 180–180 m **Area** 11,800 ha

■ Site description
A 140 km long stretch of the Liwiec river valley. Some stretches have a natural character, along others the river is regulated. In some places the riverbanks are flat, covered by meadows and wet pastures, in other places they are high. There are fens and transitional mires, used as meadows and pastures, as well as riverine forests. On the riverbanks and some higher areas there are also pine *Pinus* woods. There are two small pond complexes (48 ha, 70 ha).

Habitats Forest and woodland (8%; mixed forest; alluvial/very wet forest), Scrub (10%; scrub), Grassland (50%; humid grassland), Wetland (30%; standing fresh water; river/stream; water-fringe vegetation; fen/transition mire/spring), Artificial landscape (3%)
Land-use Agriculture (60%), Fisheries/aquaculture (5%), Forestry (35%), Hunting

■ Birds

Species	Season	Year	Pop min	Pop max	Acc	Criteria
¹ *Crex crex* Corncrake	B	1993	100	—	—	A1, B2

1. Very good site but not counted in recent years.

A total of 120 species had been recorded breeding by 1980. Breeding species of global conservation concern that do not meet IBA criteria: *Gallinago media* (one pair).

■ Protection status
National Partial **International** None
1,500 ha of IBA covered by Landscape Park (Nadbużański, 53,680 ha). 3,600 ha of IBA covered by Protected Landscape Area (Siedlecko–Węgrowski, 35,840 ha).

■ Conservation issues

Threats Drainage (A)

In 1992 and 1993 the valley was drained, which caused a significant reduction in bird numbers. A Landscape Park ('Dolina Liwca') is planned, as are some Nature Reserves.

Lower Bug river valley
A1, B2 051
Admin region mazowieckie, lubelskie, podlaskie
Coordinates 52°19′N 22°21′E
Altitude 85–116 m **Area** 55,000 ha

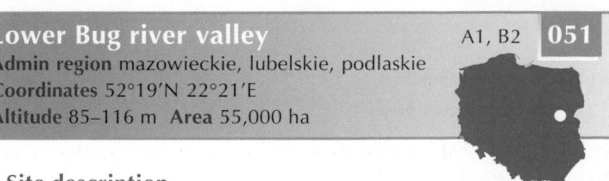

■ Site description
The site contains the channel and valley of the Bug river between the Krzna river tributary and the Zegrzyński reservoir (260 km), with

adjacent extensive dry pastures. The whole area floods in spring. There are some swamps and mires at the mouths of tributaries entering the Bug. The river channel is generally natural, not too modified by man, so there are numerous bare sand islands and others overgrown with ruderal herbs or willow *Salix* scrub. Elsewhere there are also local remnants of willow or poplar *Populus* scrub. On the lowest river terrace there are numerous oxbow lakes, differing in size, depth and extent of aquatic vegetation (*Potamogeton, Lemna*).

Habitats Forest and woodland (5%; alluvial/very wet forest), Scrub (5%; scrub), Grassland (60%; humid grassland; mesophile grassland), Wetland (30%; standing fresh water; river/stream; water-fringe vegetation; fen/transition mire/spring)
Land-use Agriculture, Hunting

■ Birds

Species	Season	Year	Pop min	Pop max	Acc	Criteria
Crex crex Corncrake	B	1993	100	—	—	A1, B2
¹*Gallinago media* Great Snipe	B	1993	50	60	—	A1
Limosa limosa Black-tailed Godwit	B	1993	490	560	—	B2
Tringa totanus Redshank	B	1993	128	205	—	B2
Sterna albifrons Little Tern	B	1993	90	100	—	B2
Chlidonias niger Black Tern	B	1993	350	—	—	B2
Alcedo atthis Kingfisher	B	1993	55	65	—	B2
Coracias garrulus Roller	B	1993	5	8	—	B2

1. Displaying males at 13 sites.

The site supports more breeding *Charadrius hiaticula* than any other inland site in Europe.

■ Protection status
National Partial **International** None
133 ha of IBA covered by Nature Reserve (Łęg Dębowy, 133 ha). 2 ha of IBA covered by Nature Reserve (Skarpa Mołożewska, 2 ha). 64 ha of IBA covered by Nature Reserve (Wydma Mołożewska, 64 ha). 33,000 ha of IBA covered by Landscape Park (Nadbużański, 53,680 ha). 15,000 ha of IBA covered by Landscape Park (Podlaski Przełom Bugu, 30,904 ha). 17,500 ha of IBA covered by Protected Landscape Area (Nadbużański, 55,300 ha).

■ Conservation issues

Threats Abandonment/reduction of land management (U), Construction/impact of dyke/dam/barrage (A), Dredging/canalization (U), Infrastructure (U), Recreation/tourism (U)

Threats include dam-building, conversion of meadows to arable land, building of infrastructure for recreation, and reduced numbers of cattle with consequent reductions in extent of pasture.

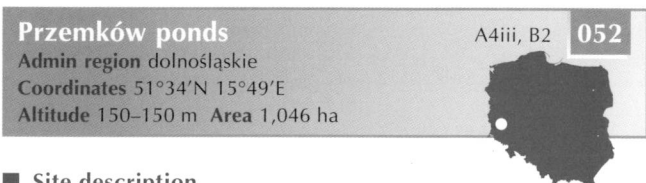

Przemków ponds
Admin region dolnośląskie
Coordinates 51°34′N 15°49′E
Altitude 150–150 m **Area** 1,046 ha
A4iii, B2 · 052

■ Site description
Two pond complexes (769 ha and 179 ha) on the Szprotawa river catchment (a tributary of the Bóbr river), with scattered forest of ash *Fraxinus* and alder *Alnus* (75 ha). Shoreline reedbeds *Phragmites* cover 6% of the ponds' area. Dams are generally treeless. Extensive meadows, sedge-beds and willow *Salix* bushes adjoin this area.

Habitats Forest and woodland (3%; alluvial/very wet forest), Scrub (3%; scrub), Grassland (45%; humid grassland; mesophile grassland), Wetland (45%; standing fresh water; river/stream; water-fringe vegetation), Artificial landscape (3%)
Land-use Fisheries/aquaculture (100%)

■ Birds

Species	Season	Year	Pop min	Pop max	Acc	Criteria
¹*Aythya nyroca* Ferruginous Duck	B	1990	4	6	—	B2

1. No more recent breeding records.

More than 20,000 waterbirds occur regularly on autumn passage, mainly wildfowl and *Fulica atra*. Breeding species of global conservation concern that do not meet IBA criteria: *Haliaeetus albicilla* (one pair), *Crex crex* (one pair).

■ Protection status
National High **International** None
1,046 ha of IBA covered by Nature Reserve (Stawy Przemkowskie [Bird Reserve], 1,046 ha). 1,046 ha of IBA covered by Landscape Park (Przemkowski, 15,466 ha).

■ Conservation issues

Threats Aquaculture/fisheries (U)

High production of organic debris in the ponds leads to a gradual shallowing, sometimes to the extent that the islets used by nesting birds become accessible to mammalian predators. Another problem is that the fish-ponds are rented nowadays, and thus the pressure to reduce bird predation on the fishery has increased. If the ponds are privatized, the presence of waterbirds will be tolerated even less.

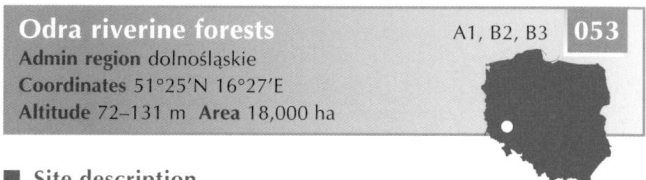

Odra riverine forests
Admin region dolnośląskie
Coordinates 51°25′N 16°27′E
Altitude 72–131 m **Area** 18,000 ha
A1, B2, B3 · 053

■ Site description
The site covers a 105-km-long stretch of the Odra valley from Głoska village (near Brzeg Dolny town) to Głogów town, as well as a 7 km long stretch from the mouth of the Barycz river to the Odra river. The valley is up to 4 km wide, and is bordered by flood embankments. There are broadleaved forests (totalling 5,000 ha) and oxbow lakes. Old-growth forest is common, with trees often over 100 years in age. The oxbow lakes are at different stages of silting up.

Habitats Forest and woodland (30%; broadleaved deciduous forest; native coniferous forest; mixed forest; alluvial/very wet forest), Scrub (6%; scrub), Grassland (39%; humid grassland; mesophile grassland), Wetland (15%; standing fresh water; river/stream; water-fringe vegetation; fen/transition mire/spring), Artificial landscape (10%; highly improved reseeded grassland; arable land; forestry plantation)
Land-use Agriculture (60%), Forestry (35%), Hunting, Water management (6%)

■ Birds

Species	Season	Year	Pop min	Pop max	Acc	Criteria
Milvus migrans Black Kite	B	1996	14	16	A	B2
Milvus milvus Red Kite	B	1996	10	12	A	B3
¹*Haliaeetus albicilla* White-tailed Eagle	W	—	20	—	—	A1
Picus canus Grey-headed Woodpecker	R	1996	20	24	A	B2
Dendrocopos medius Middle Spotted Woodpecker	R	1996	300	400	A	B3
Locustella naevia Grasshopper Warbler	B	1996	100	—	C	B3
Ficedula albicollis Collared Flycatcher	B	1996	160	240	B	B3
Lanius excubitor Great Grey Shrike	R	1996	25	25	B	B2

1. Three pairs breed.

Over 200 species have been recorded, c.150 as breeding species, with more than 60 breeding in riverine forest. Breeding species of global conservation concern that do not meet IBA criteria: *Crex crex* (eight pairs). Other notable breeders are *Pernis apivorus* (12–14 pairs) and *Grus grus* (30 pairs).

■ Protection status
National Low **International** None
5 ha of IBA covered by Nature Reserve (Odrzysko, 5 ha). 1,270 ha of IBA covered by Protected Landscape Area (Dolina Odry, 1,270 ha). 21 ha of IBA covered by Ecological Area (Ścinawskie Bagna, 21 ha).

■ Conservation issues

Threats Abandonment/reduction of land management (B), Construction/impact of dyke/dam/barrage (B), Groundwater abstraction (B), Intensified forest management (B), Selective logging/cutting (U)

Forests are at risk of clear-cutting to improve flood control. Many of the old-growth trees are Nature Monuments. Three Landscape Parks and eight Nature Reserves are planned.

Barycz river valley
A1, A4iii, B1i, B2, B3 **054**

Admin region dolnośląskie, wielkopolskie
Coordinates 51°32'N 17°25'E
Altitude 95–140 m **Area** 25,700 ha

■ Site description
A stretch of the Barycz river valley between Żmigród in the west and the vicinity of Przygodzice in the east. Habitats include five large and five small complexes of fishponds, totalling 130 ponds in all, as well as surrounding meadows, arable fields, marshy areas and forests. Extensive meadows at Odolanów are mainly wet and have a dense drainage system which is cleared every few years with limited effectiveness. Mechanized hay-cutting is carried out in June and July. Some fish-eating birds are controlled (mainly *Ardea cinerea* and *Phalacrocorax carbo*).

Habitats Forest and woodland (23%; broadleaved deciduous forest; native coniferous forest; mixed forest; alluvial/very wet forest), Grassland (23%; steppe/dry calcareous grassland; humid grassland; mesophile grassland), Wetland (26%; standing fresh water; river/stream; raised bog; water-fringe vegetation; fen/transition mire/spring), Artificial landscape (28%; highly improved reseeded grassland; arable land; forestry plantation; urban parks/gardens; other urban/industrial areas; ruderal land)
Land-use Agriculture (47%), Fisheries/aquaculture (25%), Forestry (23%), Hunting, Urban/industrial/transport (5%)

■ Birds

Species	Season	Year	Pop min	Pop max	Acc	Criteria
[1] *Botaurus stellaris* Bittern	B	1994	59	59	A	B2
Ixobrychus minutus Little Bittern	B	1994	2	12	C	B2
Ciconia nigra Black Stork	B	1994	10	—	B	B2
[2] *Anser fabalis* Bean Goose	P	1994	8,100	16,000	B	B1i
[3] *Anser anser* Greylag Goose	B	1994	497	497	B	B1i
Anas strepera Gadwall	B	1994	150	250	B	B2
[4] *Aythya nyroca* Ferruginous Duck	B	1994	40	130	B	A1, B2
Milvus migrans Black Kite	B	1993	10	15	B	B2
[5] *Haliaeetus albicilla* White-tailed Eagle	B	1995	6	6	B	A1
Falco tinnunculus Kestrel	B	1996	17	26	A	B2
[6] *Porzana porzana* Spotted Crake	B	1994	28	28	B	B3
Grus grus Crane	B	1994	40	47	B	B2
Grus grus Crane	P	—	1,500	—	—	B1i
Chlidonias niger Black Tern	B	1994	130	130	A	B2
Alcedo atthis Kingfisher	B	1994	40	50	B	B2
[7] *Riparia riparia* Sand Martin	B	1992	1,345	1,345	A	B2
Locustella luscinioides Savi's Warbler	B	1994	60	120	B	B3

1. Eight-year mean (44–78).
2. Up to 20,000 with other goose species.
3. Seven-year mean (423–561).
4. Three-year mean (40–184); decreasing; 20–30% of national population.
5. Five-year mean.
6. Three-year mean (27–29).
7. Five-year mean (722–1,780).

An important area for breeding, moulting and migrating waterbirds. A total of 276 bird species have been recorded (including 126 waterbirds), of which 166 have bred (including 56 waterbirds).

■ Protection status
National High **International** Partial
5,324 ha of IBA covered by Nature Reserve (Stawy Milickie, 5,324 ha). 49 ha of IBA covered by Nature Reserve (Wydymacz, 49 ha). 25,700 ha of IBA covered by Landscape Park (Dolina Baryczy, 87,040 ha). 1,700 ha of IBA covered by Protected Landscape Area (Wzgórza Ostrzeszowskie i Kotlina Odolanowska, 68,000 ha). 5 ha of IBA covered by Nature Monument (Las Pardoliński, 5 ha). 5,324 ha of IBA covered by Ramsar Site (Stawy Milickie, 5,324 ha).

■ Conservation issues

Threats Abandonment/reduction of land management (B), Afforestation (C), Agricultural intensification/expansion (B), Aquaculture/fisheries (B), Disturbance to birds (B), Drainage (B), Dredging/canalization (B), Extraction industry (C), Groundwater abstraction (B), Infrastructure (C), Intensified forest management (B), Other (B), Recreation/tourism (C), Selective logging/cutting (C), Unsustainable exploitation (B)

Mechanical deepening of the fish-ponds by bulldozers destroys aquatic vegetation and deepens pond margins. Other problems are the disturbance of birds during the breeding season by fish-farming activity and osier harvesting, tree-felling on the pond dams during the breeding season, pollution of the water, air and soil ('Other'), and the drainage of alder woodland. The site is an amalgamation of six sites (the former PL047–PL052) identified in the previous pan-European IBA inventory (Grimmett and Jones 1989).

Słup reservoir
A4i, B1i **055**

Admin region dolnośląskie
Coordinates 51°05'N 16°08'E
Altitude 173–175 m **Area** 500 ha

■ Site description
A storage reservoir on the Nysa Szalona river, 5 km north-west of the town of Jawor, situated in an area of farmland. It consists of two water-bodies joined by a narrow channel, the Gardziel. The larger water-body, Zbiornik Dolny, is adjacent to a dam near the village of Słup and has small patches of willow *Salix* scrub along its eastern and southern banks. The smaller one, Zbiornik Górny, is situated close to a backwater, near Stary Jawor, and has reedbeds *Phragmites*, islands and patches of *Salix* scrub. The whole area floods in spring, creating large expanses of shallow water and silt.

Habitats Grassland (10%; humid grassland; mesophile grassland), Wetland (90%; standing fresh water; river/stream; water-fringe vegetation)
Land-use Agriculture (10%), Hunting, Water management (90%)

■ Birds

Species	Season	Year	Pop min	Pop max	Acc	Criteria
Anser fabalis Bean Goose	P	1996	6,270	6,270	A	A4i, B1i

Breeding species of global conservation concern that do not meet IBA criteria: *Crex crex* (two pairs).

■ Protection status
National High **International** None
500 ha of IBA covered by Landscape Park (Chełmy, 28,461 ha).

■ Conservation issues

Threats Construction/impact of dyke/dam/barrage (B)

Changes in water-level lower the breeding success of some species. Anglers disturb nesting birds, and unsustainable hunting occurs. The site lies in the buffer zone of Chełmy Landscape Park.

Mietków reservoir
A4i, B1i **056**

Admin region dolnośląskie
Coordinates 50°58'N 16°37'E
Altitude 160–165 m **Area** 920 ha

■ Site description
A large storage reservoir situated in a hilly agricultural landscape, used to control water-flow for navigation on the Odra river. It is surrounded by arable land and two small broadleaved forests. Gravel is extracted by mechanical diggers. The area is also used for hunting and angling.

Habitats Wetland (100%; standing fresh water)
Land-use Hunting, Not utilized (10%), Tourism/recreation (10%), Water management (80%)

■ Birds

Species	Season	Year	Pop min	Pop max	Acc	Criteria
Anser fabalis Bean Goose	P	1996	—	64,500	A	A4i, B1i

The largest roosting place for migrating and wintering *Anser fabalis* in Poland.

■ Protection status
National None **International** None

■ Conservation issues

Threats Extraction industry (B), Filling-in of wetlands (B), Recreation/tourism (B)

Birds are disturbed by recreation/tourism (including anglers), by gravel excavators working on the reservoir, and by hunting.

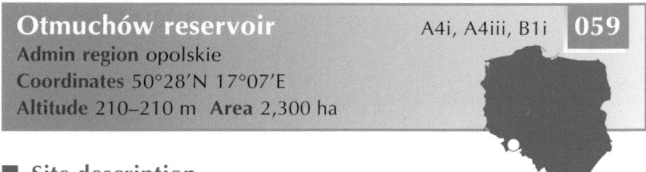

Oak-hornbeam forests in the Odra valley

B2, B3 | 057

Admin region dolnośląskie, opolskie
Coordinates 50°52′N 17°29′E
Altitude 130–146 m **Area** 31,000 ha

■ Site description

The site comprises the 70 km stretch of the Odra valley between Narok town (by Opole town) and Wrocław city. The valley is forested mainly with hornbeam *Carpinus*, but there is also some riverine forest. Much of the site is meadows, pastures and fields. There are also numerous streams, oxbow lakes, areas of shallow water and bare silt remaining from former floods, and fish-ponds.

Habitats Forest and woodland (40%; broadleaved deciduous forest; mixed forest; alluvial/very wet forest), Grassland (30%; humid grassland; mesophile grassland), Wetland (15%; standing fresh water; river/stream; water-fringe vegetation), Artificial landscape (15%; highly improved reseeded grassland; arable land; ruderal land)
Land-use Agriculture (50%), Fisheries/aquaculture (10%), Forestry (40%), Hunting

■ Birds

Species		Season	Year	Pop min	Pop max	Acc	Criteria
Milvus migrans	Black Kite	B	1993	10	12	—	B2
Picus canus	Grey-headed Woodpecker	B	1993	—	25	—	B2
Ficedula albicollis	Collared Flycatcher	B	1993	70	100	—	B3

Breeding species of global conservation concern that do not meet IBA criteria: *Aythya nyroca* (up to two pairs), *Haliaeetus albicilla* (two pairs), *Crex crex* (4–5 pairs).

■ Protection status

National Low **International** None
2 ha of IBA covered by Nature Reserve (Grodzisko Ryczyńskie, 2 ha). 5 ha of IBA covered by Nature Reserve (Kanigóra, 5 ha). 7 ha of IBA covered by Nature Reserve (Łacha Jelcz, 7 ha). 9 ha of IBA covered by Nature Reserve (Zwierzyniec, 9 ha).

■ Conservation issues

Threats Agricultural intensification/expansion (U), Deforestation (commercial) (U)

The area is intensively drained and exploited.

Turawa reservoir

A4iii | 058

Admin region opolskie
Coordinates 50°44′N 18°07′E
Altitude 180–180 m **Area** 2,200 ha

■ Site description

This storage reservoir on the Mała Panew river is used for facilitating navigation on the Odra river. The eastern part of this long reservoir, between the Lubawka river mouth and Szczedrzyk village, is important for birds. The water-body is surrounded mainly by forest. The western and part of the southern shores are embanked, the northern and eastern shores are covered with water-fringe vegetation, mainly reed-grass *Glyceria* and willow *Salix* bushes. There are considerable fluctuations in water-level. At low water a large area of sandy and muddy bottom is exposed at the eastern end. The reservoir is only periodically full.

Habitats Wetland (100%; standing fresh water; water-fringe vegetation)
Land-use Tourism/recreation (20%), Water management (80%)

■ Birds

More than 20,000 ducks and waders occur here on migration or in winter, the main species being *Anas platyrhynchos*, *A. crecca*, *Gallinago gallinago*, *Calidris alpina*, *C. ferruginea*, *C. minuta*, *Tringa nebularia*, *T. glareola*, and *Actitis hypoleucos*. Since 1976 the abundance and species-richness of birds have grown as the vegetation has developed. Breeding species of global conservation concern that do not meet IBA criteria: *Crex crex* (1–2 pairs).

■ Protection status

National None **International** None

■ Conservation issues

Threats Natural events (A)

Rapid filling of the reservoir during floods reduces or eliminates suitable foraging/resting habitat for staging waders on migration.

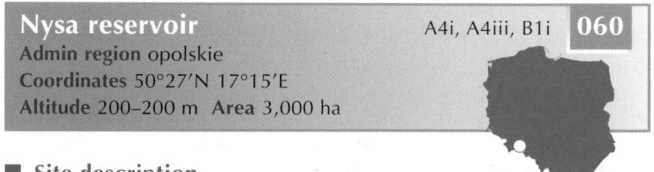

Otmuchów reservoir

A4i, A4iii, B1i | 059

Admin region opolskie
Coordinates 50°28′N 17°07′E
Altitude 210–210 m **Area** 2,300 ha

■ Site description

A large storage reservoir on the Nysa Kłodzka river, situated amongst hills in an agricultural landscape, not far from Nysa reservoir. Broadleaved forest adjoins the embanked eastern side. The western and southern shores have a more natural character, being covered with a wide belt of willow *Salix* bushes. The northern part is used for recreation. The reservoir controls water flow for navigation on the Odra river, and there are considerable fluctuations in water-level. Although some parts of the shore are shingle, the bottom of the reservoir is generally muddy and sandy.

Habitats Forest and woodland (5%; broadleaved deciduous forest; alluvial/very wet forest), Wetland (95%; standing fresh water; water-fringe vegetation)
Land-use Hunting, Tourism/recreation (20%), Water management (80%)

■ Birds

Species		Season	Year	Pop min	Pop max	Acc	Criteria
Anser fabalis	Bean Goose	P	1993	—	6,000	A	A4i, B1i

More than 20,000 migrating and wintering waterbirds occur regularly, mainly geese *Anser*, ducks *Anas*, and *Vanellus vanellus* and other waders.

■ Protection status

National None **International** None

■ Conservation issues

Threats Construction/impact of dyke/dam/barrage (U), Natural events (A)

Rapid filling of the reservoir (during river floods) reduces or eliminates suitable foraging/resting habitat for staging waders on migration.

Nysa reservoir

A4i, A4iii, B1i | 060

Admin region opolskie
Coordinates 50°27′N 17°15′E
Altitude 200–200 m **Area** 3,000 ha

■ Site description

A large storage reservoir on the Nysa Kłodzka river, in a hilly agricultural landscape, near Otmuchów reservoir. At the western end there are artificial islands created as a result of gravel exploitation. Southern and western shores are partly overgrown with willow *Salix* scrub with sparse water-fringe vegetation. Two river mouths (the Widna and the Biała Głuchowska) are important for birds. Land-uses include gravel exploitation.

Habitats Wetland (100%; standing fresh water; water-fringe vegetation)
Land-use Tourism/recreation (10%), Water management (90%)

■ Birds

Species		Season	Year	Pop min	Pop max	Acc	Criteria
Anser fabalis	Bean Goose	P	1993	—	6,000	A	A4i, B1i

Up to 60,000 ducks, geese, gulls and waders occur on migration and in winter.

■ Protection status
National None **International** None

■ Conservation issues

> **Threats** Extraction industry (B), Natural events (A)

Rapid filling of the reservoir (during river floods) reduces or eliminates suitable foraging/resting habitat for staging waders on migration.

Upper Wisła river valley A4i, A4iii, B1i, B2 061
Admin region śląskie, małopolskie
Coordinates 49°57'N 19°11'E
Altitude 219–397 m Area 130,000 ha

■ Site description
This site comprises the Goczałkowice drinking-water reservoir (3,200 ha) and many pond complexes and forest fragments in the valley of the upper Wisła (Vistula) river, from Cieszyn to Spytkowice towns. Valley width is c.12 km. The western and south-western shores of the reservoir are embanked, with the dam forming the eastern shore, but northern and southern parts have a more natural character. Large areas of shore are covered by reed-grass *Glyceria*, and in some places by scrub; wet meadows cover the western part. Water-levels can vary by up to 4 m. The reservoir supports a fishery. The more important pond complexes are Goczałkowice Zdrój (300 ha), Mnich (80 ha), Landek (150 ha), Ligota (170 ha), Pod Borem (150 ha), Dębowiec (400 ha), Przyręb (396 ha) and Spytkowice (350 ha). Mixed forest (80 ha) adjoins the Przeręb ponds, and some ponds are partly covered with reed *Phragmites*. The whole area is used for hunting.

> **Habitats** Forest and woodland (8%; broadleaved deciduous forest; native coniferous forest; mixed forest; alluvial/very wet forest), Grassland (8%; humid grassland; mesophile grassland), Wetland (9%; standing fresh water; river/stream; water-fringe vegetation), Artificial landscape (75%; highly improved reseeded grassland; arable land; other urban/industrial areas; ruderal land)
> **Land-use** Agriculture (74%), Fisheries/aquaculture (5%), Forestry (8%), Hunting, Urban/industrial/transport (8%), Water management (5%)

■ Birds

Species	Season	Year	Pop min	Pop max	Acc	Criteria
[1] *Podiceps nigricollis* Black-necked Grebe	B	1996	936	936	A	A4i, B1i
Botaurus stellaris Bittern	B	1996	55	55	A	B2
Ixobrychus minutus Little Bittern	B	1996	33	—	B	B2
Anas strepera Gadwall	B	1995	50	100	C	B2
Tringa totanus Redshank	B	1996	82	82	A	B2
Chlidonias hybridus Whiskered Tern	B	1996	10	299	A	B1i
Chlidonias niger Black Tern	B	1996	172	198	A	B2

1. 1994–1996.

Breeding species of global conservation concern that do not meet IBA criteria: *Aythya nyroca* (one pair), *Crex crex* (10–20 pairs).

■ Protection status
National Low **International** None
28 ha of IBA covered by Nature Reserve (Rotuz, 28 ha). 16 ha of IBA covered by Nature Reserve (Żaki, 16 ha).

■ Conservation issues

> **Threats** Abandonment/reduction of land management (B), Aquaculture/fisheries (B), Construction/impact of dyke/dam/barrage (C), Drainage (B), Dredging/canalization (A), Extraction industry (B), Industrialization/urbanization (B), Recreation/tourism (A)

Water-fringe vegetation is destroyed when ponds are renovated, and changes in the water-level of the main reservoir cause problems for nesting birds. Abandonment of fish-farming at the ponds is a potential threat. The site is an amalgamation of two sites (the former PL060–PL061) identified in the previous pan-European IBA inventory (Grimmett and Jones 1989).

Middle Nida flood-plain A1 062
Admin region świętokrzyskie
Coordinates 50°34'N 20°30'E
Altitude 190–200 m Area 2,000 ha

■ Site description
The site comprises the stretch of the Nida river valley between the villages of Mostowice and Skowronno Dolne, as well as a wedge of a few square kilometres' area between Umianowice and Skowronno. The valley widens gradually up to 6 km width, to the gorge near the village of Sobowice. The whole of the site is covered by a system of small watercourses, and there are four low hills. There are many oxbow lakes, mires and seasonally flooded areas with aquatic vegetation (e.g. *Potamogeton*) and reed *Phragmites*. Amongst the meadows there are areas of wet alder *Alnus* forest and clumps of willow *Salix*, while the riversides are lined with trees/scrub of *Salix* and poplar *Populus*.

> **Habitats** Forest and woodland (5%; native coniferous forest; alluvial/very wet forest), Grassland (60%; steppe/dry calcareous grassland; humid grassland; mesophile grassland), Wetland (30%; standing fresh water; river/stream; water-fringe vegetation; fen/transition mire/spring), Artificial landscape (5%; highly improved reseeded grassland; arable land)
> **Land-use** Agriculture (70%), Hunting, Not utilized (30%)

■ Birds

Species	Season	Year	Pop min	Pop max	Acc	Criteria
[1] *Crex crex* Corncrake	B	1996	32	48	A	A1

1. Individuals.

A total of 125 species have been recorded breeding, including 47 waterbirds.

■ Protection status
National High **International** None
2,000 ha of IBA covered by Landscape Park (Nadnidziański, 22,850 ha). 300 ha of IBA covered by Ecological Area (Umianowice, 300 ha).

■ Conservation issues

> **Threats** Abandonment/reduction of land management (C), Agricultural intensification/expansion (C), Drainage (A), Dredging/canalization (A)

The main threats are drainage and dredging/canalization. As a result of this and also of agricultural abandonment, open habitats such as the meadows of wet grassland are reverting to scrub and woodland, which is reducing the value of the site for some key bird species.

Małopolska Wisła river gap B2 063
Admin region mazowieckie, lubelskie, świętokrzyskie
Coordinates 51°13'N 21°50'E
Altitude 120–120 m Area 1,300 ha

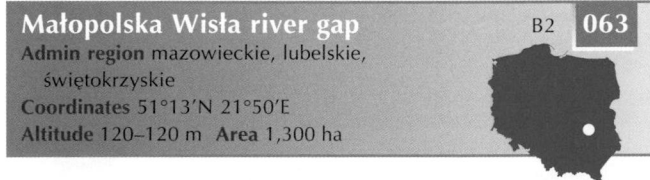

■ Site description
An unmodified part of the Wisła (Vistula) riverbed, 36 km long, with meanders, high banks, numerous islands and sandbars, from Józefów town to Kazimierz Dolny town. The islands vary in character, from low, bare sandy islets to larger, higher islands, covered with willow *Salix* scrub, forest of *Salix* and poplar *Populus*, hay meadows and pasture. The river is extensively used by boat traffic.

> **Habitats** Forest and woodland (3%; alluvial/very wet forest), Scrub (3%; scrub), Grassland (5%; humid grassland), Wetland (80%; river/stream; water-fringe vegetation), Artificial landscape (5%; highly improved reseeded grassland)
> **Land-use** Agriculture (80%), Hunting, Tourism/recreation (20%)

■ Birds

Species	Season	Year	Pop min	Pop max	Acc	Criteria
Larus canus Common Gull	B	1993	40	—	—	B2

Breeding species of global conservation concern that do not meet IBA criteria: *Crex crex* (10 pairs).

■ Protection status
National Partial **International** None
62 ha of IBA covered by Nature Reserve (Krowia Wyspa, 62 ha).
400 ha of IBA covered by Landscape Park (Kazimierski, 13,670 ha).

■ Conservation issues

Threats Construction/impact of dyke/dam/barrage (U), Dredging/canalization (U), Industrialization/urbanization (U)

There is pollution from industrial development. Further canalization of the river is planned.

Tyśmienica river valley   A1, B2, B3 064
Admin region lubelskie
Coordinates 51°36′N 22°49′E
Altitude 132–165 m **Area** 14,500 ha

■ Site description
The site contains the Tyśmienica river valley (right-bank tributary of the Wieprz river) and is covered by wet meadows with some remnant sedge-beds and scrub of willow *Salix* and alder *Alnus* that are used for agriculture. There are eleven small pond complexes, a few hundred peat pits, oxbow lakes, and the large Siemień pond complex (790 ha). In that complex 20% of large ponds and 40–50% of small ones are overgrown with reed *Phragmites* and reed-mace *Typha*. The site is surrounded by agricultural land.

Habitats Forest and woodland (5%; native coniferous forest; mixed forest; alluvial/very wet forest), Scrub (5%; scrub), Grassland (70%; humid grassland; mesophile grassland), Wetland (15%; standing fresh water; water-fringe vegetation; fen/transition mire/spring), Artificial landscape (5%; highly improved reseeded grassland; arable land)
Land-use Agriculture (85%), Fisheries/aquaculture (10%), Forestry (5%), Hunting

■ Birds

Species		Season	Year	Pop min	Pop max	Acc	Criteria
Botaurus stellaris	Bittern	B	1995	25	28	A	B2
Ixobrychus minutus	Little Bittern	B	1995	12	25	B	B2
[1] *Aythya nyroca*	Ferruginous Duck	B	1993	3	8	A	B2
[2] *Haliaeetus albicilla*	White-tailed Eagle	P	1996	—	18	—	A1
Circus pygargus	Montagu's Harrier	B	1995	20	25	A	B3
Falco tinnunculus	Kestrel	B	1995	22	27	B	B2
Porzana parva	Little Crake	B	1992	65	—	B	B3
Crex crex	Corncrake	B	1995	55	150	B	A1, B2
Limosa limosa	Black-tailed Godwit	B	1995	647	668	A	B2
Chlidonias niger	Black Tern	B	1995	90	100	A	B2

1. 1991–1993.
2. On passage at Siemień ponds.

Breeding species of global conservation concern that do not meet IBA criteria: *Gallinago media* (up to five pairs).

■ Protection status
National None **International** None

■ Conservation issues

Threats Abandonment/reduction of land management (C), Afforestation (C), Agricultural intensification/expansion (A), Aquaculture/fisheries (B), Deforestation (commercial) (A), Drainage (A), Groundwater abstraction (B), Selective logging/cutting (B)

Fishermen, and reed burning in spring, cause some disturbance to birds, especially to geese and some ducks. Also, early filling of some ponds reduces breeding numbers of *Charadrius dubius* and *C. hiaticula*, and filling ponds too high destroys nests of gulls and terns.

Parczew forests   A1, B2 065
Admin region lubelskie
Coordinates 51°33′N 22°55′E
Altitude 143–170 m **Area** 8,000 ha

■ Site description
A forest complex in the north-west part of the Łęczyńsko-Włodawskie lakeland, between the Wieprz–Krzna Canal and the Tyśmienica river. The forest is drained by tributaries of the Tyśmienica (Ochoża,

Piwonia-Bobrówka, Konotopa. Forest is mainly pine *Pinus* (stands up to 160 years old in some places) and mixed oak *Quercus*/pine, with some small stands dominated by other broadleaved species. In places there are transitional mires covered by sedge-beds (*Scheuchzeria/Carex*), and there are meadows along the Ochoża.

Habitats Forest and woodland (93%; native coniferous forest; mixed forest; alluvial/very wet forest), Grassland (5%; mesophile grassland), Wetland (2%; standing fresh water; fen/transition mire/spring)
Land-use Agriculture (5%), Forestry (90%), Hunting, Nature conservation/research (5%)

■ Birds

Species		Season	Year	Pop min	Pop max	Acc	Criteria
Crex crex	Corncrake	B	1995	30	—	C	A1
Bubo bubo	Eagle Owl	B	1995	5	6	A	B2

Breeding species of global conservation concern that do not meet IBA criteria: *Aythya nyroca* (2–3 pairs), *Haliaeetus albicilla* (two pairs).

■ Protection status
National Low **International** None
82 ha of IBA covered by Nature Reserve (Jezioro Obradowskie [Peatbog Reserve], 82 ha). 35 ha of IBA covered by Nature Reserve (Królowa Droga, 35 ha). 157 ha of IBA covered by Nature Reserve (Lasy Parczewskie, 157 ha).

■ Conservation issues

Threats Abandonment/reduction of land management (C), Agricultural intensification/expansion (C), Drainage (A), Selective logging/cutting (C)

The greatest threats are drainage, selective logging of the most mature stands in the forest, and the abandonment of agricultural management of meadows (which leads to overgrowth with scrub).

Bubnów marshes   A1, B2 066
Admin region lubelskie
Coordinates 51°22′N 23°17′E
Altitude 175–176 m **Area** 2,104 ha

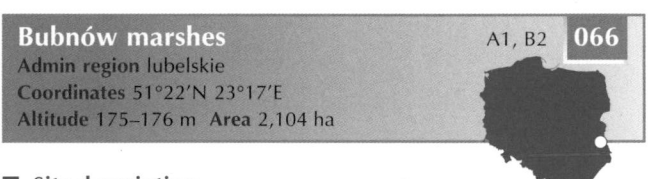

■ Site description
Two marshes—Bubnów and Staw—located in the Łęczyńsko-Włodawskie lakeland. The marshes are separated by a small river, and are drained by a watercourse from the Włodawka catchment. The habitat is mainly fens with sedge-beds. Open areas are covered in some places by sparse reed *Phragmites*. About 10 ha is covered with great fen sedge *Cladium*, and there are characteristic hummocks of dry grassland in the marshes, with small patches of willow *Salix* scrub at the marsh-edges.

Habitats Forest and woodland (18%; alluvial/very wet forest), Grassland (10%; steppe/dry calcareous grassland; humid grassland), Wetland (72%; standing fresh water; water-fringe vegetation; fen/transition mire/spring)
Land-use Nature conservation/research (100%)

■ Birds

Species		Season	Year	Pop min	Pop max	Acc	Criteria
[1] *Acrocephalus paludicola* Aquatic Warbler		B	1997	230	248	A	A1, B2

1. Singing males.

A total of 90 species have been recorded, 50 of them breeding. Breeding species of global conservation concern that do not meet IBA criteria: *Crex crex* (three pairs).

■ Protection status
National High **International** None
2,104 ha of IBA covered by National Park (Poleski, 9,648 ha). 1,469 ha of IBA covered by Nature Reserve (Bagno Bubnów, 1,469 ha).

■ Conservation issues

Threats Burning of vegetation (C), Groundwater abstraction (A)

Reed-burning is a threat to nesting birds.

Middle Bug river valley

A1, B2, B3 **067**

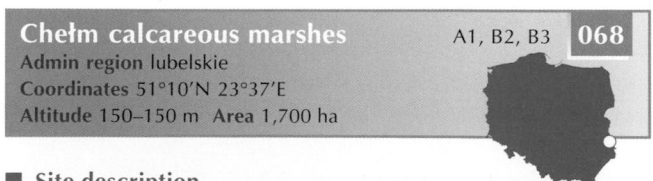

Admin region lubelskie
Coordinates 51°20'N 23°38'E
Altitude 128–179 m Area 5,100 ha

■ Site description

A 340 km long stretch of the Bug river valley along the border with Ukraine and Belarus, from Gołębie village (where the Bug enters Poland) to the mouth of the Krzna tributary. The main tributaries flowing into the Bug along this stretch are (largest first) the Huczwa, Wełnianka, Udal, Uherka, Włodawka and Hanna. This stretch is 2–3 km wide, and includes the Husynne storage reservoir on the Udal tributary. The channel of the Bug is deeply incised and has a natural character (no dredging or regulating work has been undertaken), while the relatively flat valley is covered by meadows with variably wet soils, small areas of degraded riverside forest of alder *Alnus* and willow *Salix* scrub, and arable land. Oxbow lakes are common. Husynne reservoir (112 ha, 2.5 m deep) is half-overgrown with reedbeds *Phragmites* and water-soldier *Pistia*.

> **Habitats** Forest and woodland (5%; broadleaved deciduous forest; native coniferous forest; mixed forest; alluvial/very wet forest), Scrub (10%; scrub), Grassland (65%; steppe/dry calcareous grassland; humid grassland; mesophile grassland), Wetland (10%; standing fresh water; river/stream; water-fringe vegetation; fen/transition mire/spring), Artificial landscape (10%; highly improved reseeded grassland; arable land; other urban/industrial areas; ruderal land)
> **Land-use** Agriculture (75%), Forestry (5%), Hunting, Nature conservation/research (30%), Not utilized (5%), Urban/industrial/transport (5%)

■ Birds

Species		Season	Year	Pop min	Pop max	Acc	Criteria
Ciconia ciconia	White Stork	B	1994	400	430	A	B2
Circus pygargus	Montagu's Harrier	B	1996	40	—	B	B3
[1] *Crex crex*	Corncrake	B	1997	60	—	C	A1
Riparia riparia	Sand Martin	B	1995	10,000	12,000	B	B2

1. 60 calling birds at two 100 km² plots in 1997, so number much higher over whole area.

Other breeding species include *Actitis hypoleucos* and *Alcedo atthis*.

■ Protection status
National None **International** None

■ Conservation issues

> **Threats** Burning of vegetation (B), Drainage (A), Industrialization/urbanization (B), Infrastructure (A)

The enlargement of border crossings in five places poses a threat—some important species no longer breed in these places. Since 1997 a project by IUCN and the Lublin Ornithological Society has investigated status, function and threats in the Bug valley, in cooperation with Ukraine on the right bank.

Chełm calcareous marshes

A1, B2, B3 **068**

Admin region lubelskie
Coordinates 51°10'N 23°37'E
Altitude 150–150 m Area 1,700 ha

■ Site description

> **Habitats** Forest and woodland (3%), Scrub (10%; scrub), Grassland (5%; humid grassland), Wetland (80%; river/stream; water-fringe vegetation; fen/transition mire/spring), Artificial landscape (3%; ruderal land)
> **Land-use** Agriculture (40%), Hunting, Nature conservation/research (50%), Water management (10%)

The site is a complex of calcareous marshes—Gotówka, Brzeźno, Błota Serebryjskie, Rozkosz and Stefanów—situated north-west and west of Chełm town. Fens overlie the chalk, and are dominated by great fen sedge *Cladium*. Wetter areas are covered by beds of reed *Phragmites* and sedge *Carex*. Within the marshes are chalk islands covered with dry grassland and scrub. Surrounding meadows are used by farmers. Most of the marshes are cut by old but still functioning drainage

channels which join the Udal river system (the Bug tributary), the Świerżowski canal system and the Gdolanka river system (the Uherka tributary).

■ Birds

Species		Season	Year	Pop min	Pop max	Acc	Criteria
Circus pygargus	Montagu's Harrier	B	1993	33	45	—	B3
Asio flammeus	Short-eared Owl	B	1993	1	11	—	B2
[1] *Acrocephalus paludicola*	Aquatic Warbler	B	1997	212	241	—	A1, B2

1. Singing males in 1997; in 1980s, 300–350.

Breeding species of global conservation concern that do not meet IBA criteria: *Crex crex* (six pairs), *Gallinago media* (16 displaying males).

■ Protection status
National High **International** None
377 ha of IBA covered by Nature Reserve (Bagno Serebryskie, 377 ha). 165 ha of IBA covered by Nature Reserve (Brzeźno, 165 ha). 473 ha of IBA covered by Nature Reserve (Roskosz, 473 ha). 1,100 ha of IBA covered by Landscape Park (Chełmski, 14,000 ha). 600 ha of IBA covered by Protected Landscape Area (Chełmski, 32,110 ha).

■ Conservation issues

> **Threats** Burning of vegetation (A), Drainage (A), Industrialization/urbanization (U), Infrastructure (U)

In the immediate proximity of Chełm, the cement-works and busy transportation network pose a considerable threat to the marshes. Another threat is infrastructural development associated with a motorway-construction program linking Chełm with the border-crossing at Dorohusk. Only one marsh lies fully within a protected area (Bagno Serebryskie Nature Reserve). There are plans to enlarge the other reserves that partially cover other marshes (Brzeźno and Roskosz). OTOP and IUCN-WCU are carrying out a project to protect and rehabilitate the marshes.

Strzeleckie forests

B2, B3 **069**

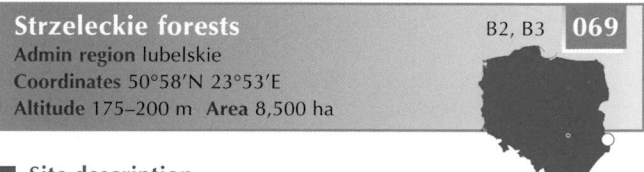

Admin region lubelskie
Coordinates 50°58'N 23°53'E
Altitude 175–200 m Area 8,500 ha

■ Site description

A densely forested area at the confluence of the Bug and Wełnianka rivers. Forest is dominated by dry-ground species, e.g. hornbeam *Carpinus*; riverside forest (alder *Alnus*) and coniferous forest (spruce *Picea*) cover only a small part of the area. The site is surrounded by meadows on almost all sides.

> **Habitats** Forest and woodland (80%; broadleaved deciduous forest; native coniferous forest; alluvial/very wet forest), Grassland (10%; humid grassland; mesophile grassland), Artificial landscape (10%; arable land)
> **Land-use** Agriculture (20%), Forestry (80%), Hunting

■ Birds

Species		Season	Year	Pop min	Pop max	Acc	Criteria
Aquila pomarina	Lesser Spotted Eagle	B	1998	15	20	—	B2
Ficedula albicollis	Collared Flycatcher	B	1993	400	500	—	B3

■ Protection status
National High **International** None
8,500 ha of IBA covered by Landscape Park (Strzelecki, 9,035 ha).

■ Conservation issues

> **Threats** Abandonment/reduction of land management (U), Afforestation (U)

The main threat is the loss of meadows (especially in glades within the forest), due to abandonment of hay harvesting and to afforestation. This is considered to have reduced the number of breeding pairs of *Aquila pomarina* in the forest (from 17–20 pairs at the start of the 1990s to 15 pairs currently).

Niepołomice forest — B3 070

Admin region małopolskie
Coordinates 50°04'N 20°20'E
Altitude 175–200 m **Area** 11,000 ha

■ Site description

Niepołomice forest lies in lightly undulating country at the confluence of the Wisła (Vistula) and Raba rivers (the Karpaty Plateau rapids). The forest is drained by the Drwinka river, which bisects the site. The southern part is densely forested, dominated by pine *Pinus* or mixed oak *Quercus/Pinus*. Dry-ground forest of hornbeam *Carpinus* is dominant in the northern part, but there is also riverine forest of alder *Alnus*, wooded meadows, and oxbow lakes at various stages of silting up. Stands are predominantly young, but in some places there is still some old-growth forest. The forest is surrounded by meadows and arable land, and adjoins a dozen or so villages.

Habitats Forest and woodland (75%; broadleaved deciduous forest; native coniferous forest; mixed forest; alluvial/very wet forest), Grassland (20%; humid grassland; mesophile grassland), Wetland (3%; river/stream), Artificial landscape (3%)
Land-use Agriculture (15%), Forestry (85%), Hunting

■ Birds

Species	Season	Year	Pop min	Pop max	Acc	Criteria
[1] *Ficedula albicollis* Collared Flycatcher	B	1980	500	1,000	—	B3

1. One of the largest populations in Poland.

A total of 180 species have been recorded, including 115 breeders or probable breeders, and 60 migrants.

■ Protection status

National Low **International** None
25 ha of IBA covered by Nature Reserve (Długosz Królewski, 25 ha). 13 ha of IBA covered by Nature Reserve (Dębina, 13 ha). 29 ha of IBA covered by Nature Reserve (Gibiel, 29 ha). 3 ha of IBA covered by Nature Reserve (Koło w Puszczy Niepołomickiej, 3 ha). 25 ha of IBA covered by Nature Reserve (Lipówka, 25 ha). 150 ha of IBA covered by Nature Reserve (Rezerwat hodowlany żubra nizinnego, 150 ha). 7 ha of IBA covered by Nature Reserve (Wiślisko Kobyle, 7 ha).

■ Conservation issues

Threats Deforestation (commercial) (U), Industrialization/urbanization (U)

Air pollution by industry threatens forest trees and other wildlife.

Gorce mountains — B2, B3 071

Admin region małopolskie
Coordinates 49°31'N 20°10'E
Altitude 600–1,288 m **Area** 7,030 ha

■ Site description

A tract of the Gorce mountains (part of the Western Beskidy range), comprising the upper part of the Kamienica river catchment and parts of other catchments. The peaks of Jaworzyna (1,288 m), Kudłoń (1,276 m) and Mostownica (1,251 m) lie within the National Park, which is covered mainly by semi-natural subalpine forest, dominated by spruce *Picea*, oak *Quercus* and fir *Abies*. Mountain pasture occurs at higher elevations.

Habitats Forest and woodland (93%; native coniferous forest; mixed forest), Grassland (6%; alpine/subalpine/boreal grassland), Wetland, Artificial landscape
Land-use Agriculture (2%), Forestry (5%), Nature conservation/research (51%), Not utilized (5%), Tourism/recreation (45%)

■ Birds

Species	Season	Year	Pop min	Pop max	Acc	Criteria
Picus canus Grey-headed Woodpecker	R	1998	10	20	—	B2
Turdus torquatus Ring Ouzel	B	1998	50	100	—	B3

A total of 80 species have been recorded breeding.

■ Protection status

National High **International** None
7,030 ha of IBA covered by National Park (Gorczański, 7,030 ha).

■ Conservation issues

Threats Abandonment/reduction of land management (U), Deforestation (commercial) (U), Disturbance to birds (U), Industrialization/urbanization (U), Infrastructure (U), Recreation/tourism (U)

Some mountain pastures (privately owned) are reverting to forest following the cessation of grazing. Birds are disturbed by the high number of tourists and local people collecting wild foodstuffs. Some privately owned forests along the border of the National Park are being clear-felled. Tree-death from acid rain (air pollution originating from industry upwind) is also a problem. An overhead cable-car to the highest peak (Turbacz) is proposed, which would further increase the number of tourists and the amount of infrastructural development in the region.

Tatra mountains — A3, B2, B3 072

Admin region małopolskie
Coordinates 49°15'N 19°55'E
Altitude 844–2,499 m **Area** 21,164 ha

■ Site description

Tatra National Park covers the whole of the Polish part of the Tatras range (Western Tatras), the youngest and highest mountains in Poland (up to 2,499 m). At lower altitudes there is heavily modified subalpine spruce *Picea* forest, followed by upper subalpine forest, then the mountain pine *Pinus mugo* zone, followed by alpine pastures and rock towers at the highest elevations. There is a great variety of land-forms with many mountain lakes (High Tatras) and karst features (Western Tatras; e.g. caves). The site is contiguous with the 'Tatry' IBA across the border in Slovakia.

Habitats Forest and woodland (71%; native coniferous forest; mixed forest; treeline ecotone), Grassland (5%; alpine/subalpine/boreal grassland), Rocky areas (24%; scree/boulders; inland cliff), Artificial landscape (1%; ruderal land)
Land-use Agriculture (15%), Forestry (5%), Nature conservation/research (70%), Tourism/recreation (10%)

■ Birds

Species	Season	Year	Pop min	Pop max	Acc	Criteria
Tetrao tetrix Black Grouse	B	1986	30	40	—	B2
Bubo bubo Eagle Owl	B	1986	5	6	—	B2
Prunella collaris Alpine Accentor	B	1986	150	300	—	A3
Turdus torquatus Ring Ouzel	B	1986	1,000	2,000	—	B3
Tichodroma muraria Wallcreeper	B	1986	—	10	—	A3

Breeding species include *Crex crex* (of global conservation concern but not meeting IBA criteria) and two of the 10 species in Europe that are restricted to the European high-mountain biome when breeding (*Prunella collaris* in especially good numbers). A total of 200 species have been recorded.

■ Protection status

National High **International** High
21,164 ha of IBA covered by National Park (Tatrzański, 21,164 ha). Over 50% of IBA covered by Nature Reserves (details unavailable; most or all are contiguous). 21,164 ha of IBA covered by Biosphere Reserve (Tatra, 21,164 ha).

■ Conservation issues

Threats Industrialization/urbanization (U), Infrastructure (U), Recreation/tourism (U)

Threats include air and water pollution (air-borne deposits from industry upwind), tourism/recreation, transportation, infrastructure development up to the Park border, and a proposal to hold the Winter Olympic Games here.

Janów forests

B2 073

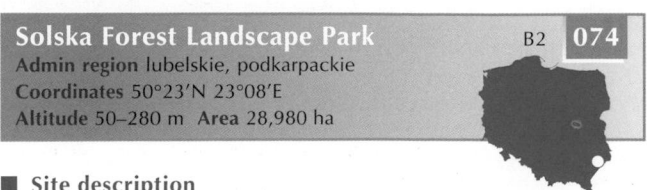

Admin region podkarpackie, lubelskie
Coordinates 50°40'N 22°15'E
Altitude 200–240 m Area 50,000 ha

■ Site description

The north-western part of Solska forest. Wet soils cover half of the area, which is drained by many natural watercourses, channels and ditches. Forest vegetation is dense and species-rich, dominated in places by pine *Pinus*, fir *Abies*, spruce *Picea*, oak *Quercus*, beech *Fagus*, ash *Fraxinus* and alder *Alnus*. Many stands have a natural character with some old-growth trees. Raised bogs and transitional mires occur in areas with little water flow, and were used in the last century for fish-ponds. There are 150 such former ponds, each with an area of 10–50 ha and a varying amount of plant cover.

Habitats Forest and woodland (80%; broadleaved deciduous forest; native coniferous forest; mixed forest; alluvial/very wet forest), Grassland (3%), Wetland (15%; standing fresh water; river/stream; raised bog; water-fringe vegetation), Artificial landscape (3%)
Land-use Fisheries/aquaculture (20%), Forestry (80%), Hunting

■ Birds

Species	Season	Year	Pop min	Pop max	Acc	Criteria
Ciconia nigra Black Stork	B	1993	20	—	—	B2
Aquila pomarina Lesser Spotted Eagle	B	1993	15	—	—	B2

Breeding species of global conservation concern that do not meet IBA criteria: *Aythya nyroca* (2–3 pairs), *Crex crex*.

■ Protection status

National High **International** None
738 ha of IBA covered by Nature Reserve (Imielty Lug, 738 ha). 56 ha of IBA covered by Nature Reserve (Jastkowice, 56 ha). 169 ha of IBA covered by Nature Reserve (Kacze Błota, 169 ha). 2,677 ha of IBA covered by Nature Reserve (Lasy Janowskie, 2,677 ha). 278 ha of IBA covered by Nature Reserve (Szklarnia, 278 ha). 39,150 ha of IBA covered by Landscape Park (Lasy Janowskie, 39,150 ha). 10,500 ha of IBA covered by Protected Landscape Area (Lipsko-Janowski, 60,500 ha).

■ Conservation issues

Threats Aquaculture/fisheries (A), Burning of vegetation (U), Deforestation (commercial) (A), Drainage (A), Natural events (U), Selective logging/cutting (A)

There are 15–20 forest-fires per year, resulting from widespread recreational use of the area, although the fire-fighting response is well organized. Widespread tree-death or damage by infestations of insect pests ('Natural events') can also be a problem, although there is a well-organized monitoring system. In 1994 the area became a 'forest promotion complex', where management (based on ongoing research) aims to re-create approximately natural forest conditions (including hydrology and soils) while allowing some exploitation of forest resources and products to continue, combined with public awareness activities. The site is an amalgamation of two sites (the former PL073–PL074) identified in the previous pan-European IBA inventory (Grimmett and Jones 1989).

Solska Forest Landscape Park

B2 074

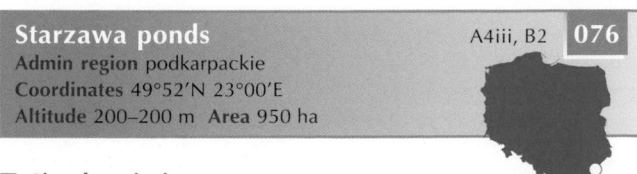

Admin region lubelskie, podkarpackie
Coordinates 50°23'N 23°08'E
Altitude 50–280 m Area 28,980 ha

■ Site description

The site is covered by large expanses of forest, mainly coniferous and dominated by pine *Pinus* and fir *Abies*. There are many fish-ponds, mainly in the area of Ruda Różaniecka village, and wet areas of *Pinus* forest with bilberry *Vaccinium* and small reed-grass *Calamagrostis*.

Habitats Forest and woodland (85%; native coniferous forest), Grassland (10%), Wetland (5%; standing fresh water; river/stream)
Land-use Agriculture (10%), Forestry (85%), Hunting, Water management (5%)

■ Birds

Species	Season	Year	Pop min	Pop max	Acc	Criteria
¹ *Aythya nyroca* Ferruginous Duck	B	1995	4	6	A	B2

1. Decreasing.

Breeding species of global conservation concern that do not meet IBA criteria: *Haliaeetus albicilla* (one pair).

■ Protection status

National High **International** None
28,980 ha of IBA covered by Landscape Park (Puszcza Solska, 28,980 ha).

■ Conservation issues

Threats Aquaculture/fisheries (B), Drainage (B), Groundwater abstraction (B), Selective logging/cutting (B)

Fish-farming involves the cutting of grass and sedge during the breeding season, which disturbs nesting birds.

Przemyśl Plateau Landscape Park

A1, B2, B3 075

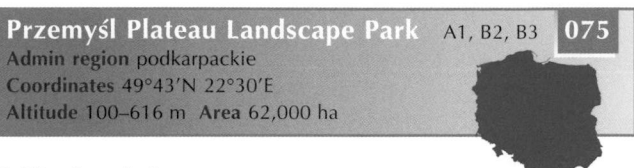

Admin region podkarpackie
Coordinates 49°43'N 22°30'E
Altitude 100–616 m Area 62,000 ha

■ Site description

A varied area of foothills, mainly covered with broadleaved forest of beech *Fagus* and hornbeam *Carpinus* and mixed forest of fir *Abies* and oak *Quercus*. In valley-bottoms there is riverside forest and scrub of alder *Alnus*. Open areas comprise fields and meadows with dry grassland. Some of the area used to be state farms, but has been abandoned and is now used by hunters.

Habitats Forest and woodland (80%; broadleaved deciduous forest; mixed forest), Grassland (10%; steppe/dry calcareous grassland; humid grassland), Wetland (5%; river/stream; raised bog; water-fringe vegetation), Artificial landscape (5%; arable land)
Land-use Agriculture (10%), Forestry (80%), Hunting (5%), Nature conservation/research (5%)

■ Birds

Species	Season	Year	Pop min	Pop max	Acc	Criteria
Ciconia nigra Black Stork	B	1989	8	10	B	B2
Pernis apivorus Honey Buzzard	B	1989	15	20	B	B3
Aquila pomarina Lesser Spotted Eagle	B	1991	15	20	A	B2
Crex crex Corncrake	B	1996	100	200	B	A1, B2

A total of 112 breeding species (and five probable breeders) have been recorded.

■ Protection status

National High **International** None
3 ha of IBA covered by Nature Reserve (Brzoza Czarna w Reczpolu, 3 ha). 138 ha of IBA covered by Nature Reserve (Krępak, 138 ha). 61,862 ha of IBA covered by Landscape Park (Pogórza Przemyskiego, 61,862 ha).

■ Conservation issues

Threats Afforestation (B), Dredging/canalization (A), Intensified forest management (A), Selective logging/cutting (A)

Starzawa ponds

A4iii, B2 076

Admin region podkarpackie
Coordinates 49°52'N 23°00'E
Altitude 200–200 m Area 950 ha

■ Site description

A pond complex with adjacent wet meadows, riverine forests and arable land, situated between the Wisznia river (the San tributary) and the Bucowski Canal near to the Polish–Ukrainian border. Most of the pond area is overgrown with submerged pondweed *Potamogeton*, floating water-lilies *Nymphaea* and fringing belts of reed *Phragmites*. The ponds are intensively used for fish-farming.

Habitats Forest and woodland (15%; alluvial/very wet forest), Grassland (30%; humid grassland), Wetland (50%; standing fresh water; river/stream; water-fringe vegetation), Artificial landscape (5%; arable land; ruderal land)
Land-use Agriculture (70%), Fisheries/aquaculture (30%), Hunting

■ Birds

Species	Season	Year	Pop min	Pop max	Acc	Criteria
[1] *Riparia riparia* Sand Martin	B	1993	2,500	3,000	—	B2

1. One colony by fish-ponds.

An important area for waterbirds migrating along the Wisła (Vistula), San and Dniestr rivers, with up to 10,000–40,000 staging here in autumn, mainly *Anas platyrhynchos*, *Aythya ferina*, *Fulica atra*, *Vanellus vanellus* and *Larus ridibundus*. Species of global conservation concern that do not meet IBA criteria: *Aythya nyroca* (3–4 pairs), *Haliaeetus albicilla* (one non-breeding bird), *Crex crex*.

■ Protection status
National None **International** None

■ Conservation issues

Threats Aquaculture/fisheries (U), Other (U)

Threats include reed-cutting during the breeding season ('Other').

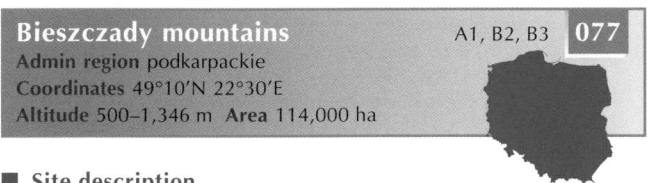

Bieszczady mountains A1, B2, B3 **077**
Admin region podkarpackie
Coordinates 49°10′N 22°30′E
Altitude 500–1,346 m **Area** 114,000 ha

■ Site description
The site covers part of the Western Bieszczady range, the only part of the Eastern Carpathians lying within Poland. The lowest part of the site is mainly deforested, above which is subalpine forest (covering 84% of the site), dominated mainly by beech *Fagus*. Above that are extensive alpine meadows and *Vaccinium* heath, with alder *Alnus* shrubs.

Habitats Forest and woodland (70%; broadleaved deciduous forest; native coniferous forest; mixed forest), Scrub (3%; scrub), Grassland (15%; steppe/dry calcareous grassland; alpine/subalpine/boreal grassland), Wetland (5%; river/stream), Rocky areas (3%), Artificial landscape (3%; arable land; ruderal land)
Land-use Agriculture (15%), Forestry (50%), Hunting, Nature conservation/research (25%), Tourism/recreation (10%)

■ Birds

Species	Season	Year	Pop min	Pop max	Acc	Criteria
[1] *Ciconia nigra* Black Stork	B	1998	20	20	—	B2
[1] *Pernis apivorus* Honey Buzzard	B	1998	25	25	—	B3
[1] *Aquila pomarina* Lesser Spotted Eagle	B	1998	61	61	—	B2
[1] *Crex crex* Corncrake	B	1998	200	200	—	A1, B2
[1] *Bubo bubo* Eagle Owl	B	1998	7	8	—	B2
Ficedula albicollis Collared Flycatcher	B	1998	400	600	—	B3

1. 1995–1998.

A total of 161 species have been recorded. Species of global conservation concern that do not meet IBA criteria: *Aquila clanga* (1–2 non-breeding birds).

■ Protection status
National High **International** High
27,833 ha of IBA covered by National Park (Bieszczadzki, 27,833 ha). 1,876 ha of IBA covered by 17 Nature Reserves (Cisy na Górze Jawor; Dźwiniacz; Gołoborze; Hulskie im. Stefana Myczkowskiego; Krywe; Łokieć; Litmirz; Olsza Kosa w Stężnicy; Olszyna Łęgowa w Kalnicy; Przełom Solinki; Puszcza Bieszczadzka nad Sanem; Sine Wiry; Tarnawa; Wetlina; Woronikówka; Zakole; Zswięzło; combined area of 1,876 ha). 51,146 ha of IBA covered by Landscape Park (Cieśnińsko-Wetliński, 51,146 ha). 34,866 ha of IBA covered by Landscape Park (Doliny Sany, 34,866 ha). 108,924 ha of IBA covered by Biosphere Reserve (East Carpathian/East Beskid, 108,924 ha).

■ Conservation issues

Threats Drainage (U), Industrialization/urbanization (U), Infrastructure (U), Intensified forest management (U)

The main threats are infrastructural and urban development along river valleys and within Landscape Parks (new hotels, pensions, etc.), drainage, loss of suitable habitat features for raptors and hole-nesters, and forest succession in open habitats. Almost the whole area is part of a transboundary Biosphere Reserve shared with Slovakia.

REFERENCES

ADAMSKI, A. (1994) Ekologia rozrodu kani rdzawej *Milvus milvus* w dolinie Odry. [Breeding ecology of the Red Kite *Milvus milvus* in the Middle Odra Valley, south-west Poland.] *Ptaki Śląska* 10: 19–36. (In Polish.)

BAGIŃSKI, W., BRAUZE, T. AND ZIELIŃSKI J. (1996) Rozpoznanie awifaunistyczne doliny Wisły między Solcem Kujawskim a Świeciem na terenach zalewowych w granicach województwa bydgoskiego. Ekspertyza ornitologiczna—część I. Bydgoszcz, Poland: UW. Unpublished. (In Polish.)

BASZANOWSKI, P., SIKORA, A. AND CHYLARECKI, P. (1993) Sieweczka morska (*Charadrius alexandrinus*) nowym gatunkiem lęgowym w awifaunie Polski. [First breeding record of the Kentish Plover (*Charadrius alexandrinus*) in Poland.] *Not. Orn.* 34: 376–378. (In Polish.)

BEDNORZ, J. (1995) Waloryzacja ornitologiczna doliny Noteci i propozycje ochrony jej najwartościowszych odcinków. [Ornithological valorization of the Noteć River valley and proposal of the protection of the most valuable areas.] Pp. 95–119 in J. Bednorz, ed. *Ptaki doliny Noteci.* [*Birds of Noteć River valley.*] Poland: Pr. Zakł. Biol. Ekol. Ptaków, UAM, 4. (In Polish.)

BEDNORZ, J. AND KUPCZYK, M. (1995) Awifauna ptaków doliny Noteci. [Fauna of birds at the Noteć River valley.] Pp. 3–94 in J. Bednorz, ed. *Ptaki doliny Noteci.* [*Birds of Noteć River valley.*] Poland: Pr. Zakł. Biol. Ekol. Ptaków, UAM, 4. (In Polish.)

BOBROWICZ, G. (1995) 'Ścinawskie Bagna'—dokumentacja użytku ekologicznego. Legnica, Poland: UW. Unpublished. (In Polish.)

BOBROWICZ, G. (1996a) Dokumentacja przyrodnicza projektowanego rezerwatu 'Łęg Korea' w dolinie rzeki Odry. Legnica, Poland: UW. Unpublished. (In Polish.)

BOBROWICZ, G. (1996b) Dokumentacja przyrodnicza projektowanego użytku ekologicznego 'Naroczycki łęg' w dolinie rzeki Odry. Legnica, Poland: UW. Unpublished. (In Polish.)

BOBROWICZ, G. (1996c) Projektowane parki krajobrazowe w Dolinie Odry na Dolnym Śląsku. [Projected Oder River Valley landscape parks in Lower Silesia.] *Przeg. Przyr.* 7(1): 3–24. (In Polish.)

BOBROWICZ, G. (1997) Waloryzacja ornitologiczna zbiornika wodnego 'Słup' na Nysie Szalonej. Legnica, Poland: UW. Unpublished. (In Polish.)

BORSUK, S., RAMCZYK, M. A., BAGIŃSKI, W., MIKUSEK, A., BRAUZE, T. AND ZIELIŃSKI, J. (1994) Rezerwat ornitologiczny pn. 'Mała Kępa Ostromecka'. Projekt. Fundacja Centrum Badań i Ochrony Środowiska Człowieka. Bydgoszcz, Poland: UW. Unpublished. (In Polish.)

BUCZEK, A. AND BUCZEK, T. (1988) Projektowany rezerwat faunistyczny Stawy Siemieńskie. [The Siemień Lakes proposed faunistic reserve in Polesie Lubelskie.] *Chrońmy Przyr.* 44(5): 66–70. (In Polish.)

BUCZEK, T. (1992) Lęgi sowy błotnej *Asio flammeus* na torfowiskach węglanowych w okolicach Chełma. [Breeding of the Short-eared Owl (*Asio flammeus*) on carbonate peatlands near Chełm.] *Not. Orn.* 33: 141–144. (In Polish.)

BUCZEK, T. AND BUCZEK, A. (1993) Torfowiska węglanowe w okolicach Chełma—walory przyrodnicze, zagrożenia, ochrona. [Carbonate marshes near Chełm—natural values, threats and conservation.] *Chrońmy Przyr.* 49(3): 76–89.

BUCZEK, T., BUCZEK, A. JASZCZ, Z. AND WÓJCIAK, J. (1996) Ochrona strefowa gniazd: bociana czarnego, orlika krzykliwego, bielika i puchacza w Lasach Parczewskich. [Zone protection of nests: Black Stork (*Ciconia nigra*), Lesser Spotted Eagle (*Aquila pomarina*) and Eagle Owl (*Bubo bubo*) in Parczew Forests.] Report, Biała Podlaska, Poland: UW. (In Polish.)

BUKACIŃSKI, D. AND BUKACIŃSKA, M. (1993) Changes in number and distribution of the Black-headed Gull breeding population on the Vistula river in years 1962–93. *The Ring* 15: 159–164.

BUKACIŃSKI, D. AND JABŁOŃSKI, P. (1992a) Awifauna lęgowa jeziora Łuknajno i terenów przyległych w latach 1982–87. [Breeding avifauna of Lake Łuknajno and surrounding areas in 1982–1987.] *Not. Orn.* 33: 5–45. (In Polish.)

BUKACIŃSKI, D. AND JABŁOŃSKI, P. (1992b) Sezonowa zmienność zespołu ptaków wodno-błotnych na jeziorze Łuknajno w latach 1982–1984. [Seasonal changes in water and marsh bird community on the Łuknajno Lake in 1982–84.] *Not. Orn.* 33: 185–226. (In Polish.)

BUKACIŃSKI, D., CYGAN, P., KELLER, M., PIOTROWSKA, M. AND WÓJCIAK, J. (1994) Liczebność i rozmieszczenie ptaków wodnych gniazdujących na Wiśle Środkowej—zmiany w latach 1973–1993. [Numbers and distribution of waterfowl nesting in the Vistula middle course—fluctuations during 1973–1993.] *Not. Orn.* 35: 5–47. (In Polish.)

CHMIEL, J. AND KUPCZYK, M. (1996) Walory florystyczne i faunistyczne Nadgoplańskiego Parku Tysiąclecia. [Faunistic and floristic values of Gopło Millennium Park.] *Studia Lednickie* 4. Poznań, Poland: PAN IAiE. (In Polish.)

CHYL, A., GÓRSKI, A. (1993) Awifauna doliny Narwi między Rakowem a Łomżą. [Avifauna of Narew valley between Rakowo and Łomża.] *Not. Orn.* 34: 277–286. (In Polish.)

CHYLARECKI, P. AND NOWICKI, W. (1993) Przewidywany wpływ planowanej Drogi Wodnej Wschód–Zachód na awifaunę. [Expected impact of the planned Polish East–West Waterway on the avifauna.] Pp. 121–134 in L. Tomiałojć, ed. *Ochrona przyrody i środowiska w dolinach nizinnych rzek Polski.* [*Nature and environment conservation in the lowland river valleys of Poland.*] Kraków, Poland: IOP PAN. (In Polish.)

CHYLARECKI, P. AND NOWICKI, W. (1993) Wartości przyrodnicze dużych rzek Polski. Zagrożenia i możliwości ochrony. [Natural values of large Polish rivers: threats and possibilities of conservation.] *Chrońmy Przyr.* 49(4): 14–39. (In Polish.)

CHYLARECKI, P., BUKACIŃSKI, D., DOMBROWSKI, A. AND NOWICKI, W. (1993) Charakterystyka ornitofauny Wisły i jej doliny. [The avifauna characteristic of Vistula and its valley.] Warszawa: IUCN-Poland. Unpublished. (In Polish.)

CHYLARECKI, P., WINIECKI, A. AND WYPYCHOWSKI, K. (1992) Awifauna lęgowa doliny Warty na odcinku Uniejów—Spławie. [Birds breeding at the middle Warta valley (Uniejów—Spławie; central Poland.] Pp. 7–55 in A. Winiecki, ed. *Ptaki lęgowe doliny Warty.* [*Breeding birds at the Warta River valley.*] Poland: Pr. Zakł. Biol. Ekol. Ptaków, UAM, 1. (In Polish.)

CIEŚLAK, M., CZAPULAK, A. AND KROGULEC, J. (1991) Ptaki Rezerwatu 'Stawy Przemkowskie' i okolic. [Birds of nature reserve 'Stawy Przemkowskie' and its surroundings.] *Ptaki Śląska* 8: 54–100. (In Polish.)

CZUCHNOWSKI, R. (1993) Ptaki drapieżne Puszczy Niepołomickiej w latach 1987–1990. [Birds of prey in Niepołomicka Forests in 1987–1990]. *Not. Orn.* 34(3/4): 313–318. (In Polish.)

ĆWIKLIŃSKI, C. (1996) Sowy *Strigiformes* Bieszczadów Zachodnich i Gór Sanocko-Turczańskich. [The owls Strigiformes of the western Bieszczady Mountains and Sanocko-Turczańskie Mountains.] *Chrońmy Przyr.* 52(6): 41–55. (In Polish.)

DMOCH, A. AND DOMBROWSKI, A. (1998) Kraska (*Coracias garrulus*) w Puszczy Białej. [The Roller (*Coracias garrulus*) in the Biała Forest.] *Kulon* 3(1): 57–66. (In Polish.)

DOBROWOLSKI, K. A. AND KRZYŚKOWIAK, A. (1989) Świat roślin i zwierząt lasów oraz wód Puszczy Białej. [Flora and fauna of forest and water at Biała Forest] Pp. 458–539 in J. Kazimierski, ed. *Brok i Puszcza Biała—środowisko geograficzne, kulturowe i przyrodnicze.* [*Brok and Biała Forest—geographical, culture and nature environment.*] Ciechanów, Poland: Tow. Przyj. Broku. (In Polish.)

DOLATA, P. T. (1993) Stawy Przygodzickie—zagrożenia środowiska i postulaty ochronne. [The Przygodzickie Ponds—the menace for their habitats and conservation recommendations.] *Przeg. Przyr.* 4(3): 181–192. (In Polish.)

DOMBROWSKI, A., KOT, H. AND RZĘPAŁA, M. (1990) Zgrupowania ptaków Zalewu Zegrzyńskiego. [Concentration of birds at Zegrzyń Reservoir] Pp. 163–180 in Z. Kajak, ed. *Funkcjonowanie ekosystemów wodnych, ich ochrona i rekultywacja. Ekologia zbiorników zaporowych i rzek.* [*Functioning of the water ecosystems, their conservation and reclamation. Ecology of dammed reservoirs and rivers.*] Poland: Pr. SGGW-AR, 50. (In Polish.)

DOMBROWSKI, A., NAWROCKI, P., KROGULEC, J., CHMIELEWSKI, S. AND RZĘPAŁA, M. (1994) Awifauna bocznych odnóg Wisły Środkowej w sezonie lęgowym. [Breeding avifauna of the lateral arms of the Vistula middle course.] *Not. Orn.* 35: 49–78. (In Polish.)

DYRCZ, A. (1994) Pierwsze stwierdzenie lęgu ohara (*Tadorna tadorna*) na Śląsku. [The first breeding record of shelduck (*Tadorna tadorna*) in Silesia.] *Ptaki Śląska* 8: 132–133.

DYRCZ, A. (1995) Ocena wpływu poziomów piętrzenia na Zbiorniku Mietkowskim na siedliska ptaków wodnych i wodno-błotnych. [The effect of water damming on the Mietków on waterfowl and waders habitats.] *Chrońmy Przyr.* 51(6): 26–38.

GŁOWACIŃSKI, Z. , ED. (1992) *Polska czerwona księga zwierząt.* [*Polish Red Data Book for Animals.*] Warszawa: PWRiL. (In Polish.)

GŁOWACIŃSKI, Z. AND PROFUS, P. (1992) Structure and vertical distribution of the breeding bird communities in the Polish Tatra National Park. *Ochrona Przyr.* 50(1): 65–94.

GACKA-GRZESIKIEWICZ, E., ED. (1995) *Korytarz ekologiczny doliny Wisły. Stan, funkcjonowanie, zagrożenia.* [*Vistula as an Ecological Corridor. State—Functioning—Threats.*] Warszawa: IUCN-Poland. (In Polish.)

GÓRSKI, D. (1997) Ptaki wodne i błotne stawów rybnych w Ostrówku. [Waterfowl of fishponds in Ostrówek.] Bydgoszcz, Poland: ART, (MSc. thesis). (In Polish.)

GÓRSKI, W. AND FLOREK, W., ED. (1996) Ocena zasobów przyrodniczych i waloryzacja terenów Parku Krajobrazowego 'Dolina Słupi'. Słupsk, Poland: UW. Unpublished. (In Polish.)

GRIMMETT, R. F. A. AND JONES, T. A. (1989) *Important Bird Areas in Europe.* Cambridge, UK: International Council for Bird Preservation (Tech. Publ. 9).

GROMADZKA, J. AND GROMADZKI, M. (1998) Plan ochrony rezerwatu Mewia Łacha. [Management Plan of Mewia Łacha reserve]. Gdańsk, Poland: UW. Unpublished. (In Polish.)

GROMADZKI, M., DYRCZ, A., GŁOWACIŃSKI, Z. AND WIELOCH, M. (1994) *Ostoje ptaków w Polsce.* [*Important Bird Areas in Poland.*] Gdańsk, Poland: Biblioteka monitoringu środowiska, OTOP. (In Polish.)

GRYGORUK, A. (1996) Narwiański Park Narodowy—22 park narodowy w Polsce. *Białostocczyzna* 4. (In Polish.)

GUENTZEL, S. (1993) Awifauna doliny Drwęcy. Toruń, Poland: UW. Unpublished. (In Polish.)

GUENTZEL, S. (1993) Rozmieszczenie i liczebność tracza nurogęsi (*Mergus merganser*) i gągoła krzykliwego (*Bucephala clangula*) w dolinie Drwęcy na odcinku między Brodnicą a ujściem Brynicy. [Distribution and numbers of Goosander (*Mergus merganser*) and Goldeneye (*Bucephala clangula*) in Drwęca valley between Brodnica and Brynica mouth.] Toruń, Poland: UW. Unpublished. (In Polish.)

HEATH, M. F. AND BORGGREVE, C. (2000) *BirdLife International/EBCC European Bird Database 1998.* Cambridge, UK: BirdLife International.

JANISZEWSKI, T., MARKOWSKI, J., MICHALAK, P., WOJCIECHOWSKI, Z. AND HEJDUK, J. (1991) Rzadkie gatunki ptaków stwierdzone w środkowej Polsce. II. [Rare birds recorded in central Poland. II.] *Not. Orn.* 32: 117–124. (In Polish.)

JANISZEWSKI, T., BARGIEL, R., KALIŃSKI, A,. LESNER, B. AND WŁODARCZYK, W. (1995) Znaczenie zbiornika Jeziorsko dla migrujących ptaków wodno-błotnych. [The role of Jeziorsko Reservoir for migrating waders.] *Streszcz. referatów XVI Zjazdu PTZool, Łódź, Poland.* (In Polish.)

JANISZEWSKI, T., KUCZYŃSKI, L., CHYLARECKI, P. AND WINIECKI, A. 1992 Wyniki wstępnych badań nad awifauną lęgową terenów zbiornika zaporowego Jeziorsko. [Preliminary results of avifaunistic studies on the area of the Jeziorsko Reservoir, central Poland.] Pp. 93–104 in A. Winiecki, ed. *Ptaki lęgowe doliny Warty.* [*Breeding birds at the Warta River valley.*] Poland: Pr. Zakł. Biol. Ekol. Ptaków, UAM, 1. (In Polish.)

JASZCZ, Z. AND WÓJCIAK, J. (1993) Gniazdowanie błotniaków łąkowych (*Circus pygargus*) w zbożach na terenie Lubelszczyzny. [Nesting of Montagu's Harrier (*Circus pygargus*) in corn fields in the Lublin region.] *Not. Orn.* 34: 167–169. (In Polish.)

JERMACZEK, A., CZWOŁGA, T., KRZYŚKÓW, T. AND STAŃKO, R. (1993) Ptaki Kostrzyńskiego Zbiornika Retencyjnego w latach 1990–92. [The birds of the Kostrzyński Retention Reservoir during the breeding season in 1990–92.] *Przeg. Przyr.* 4(2): 21–40. (In Polish.)

JUSZCZAK, K. AND OLECH, B. (1997) Liczebność i rozmieszczenie derkacza, *Crex crex*, na terenach otwartych Kampinoskiego Parku Narodowego [Numbers and distribution of the Corncrake *Crex crex* in the open areas of the Kampinoski National Park and its surroundings in 1996–97] *Not. Orn.* 38: 197–213. (In Polish.)

KORZENIAK, J., ZAJĄC, K. AND ZAJĄC,T. (1995) Delta środkowej Nidy—stan aktualny i perspektywy ochrony. [Delta of the Middle Nida—actual stage and perspective conservation.] *Chrońmy Przyr.* 51(5): 27–46. (In Polish.)

KOSIŃSKI, Z. KUCZYŃSKI, L., OSIEJUK, T. AND WYPYCHOWSKI, K. 1994 Znaczenie zbiornika Jeziorsko dla przelotnych siewkowców (*Charadrii*). [Importance of the Jeziorsko Reservoir for migratory waders (*Charadrii*).] *Przegl. Przyr.* 5(2): 33–45.

KOT, H., ED. (1995) *Przyroda województwa siedleckiego.* [*Nature of Siedlce voivodship.*] Siedlce, Poland: UW. (In Polish.)

KROGULEC, J. (1991) Czynniki warunkujące liczebność błotniaków łąkowych (*Circus pygargus, Aves, Accipitrides*) w rezerwatach torfowiskowych Lubelszczyzny. [Factors effecting numbers of Montagu's Harrier (*Circus pygargus*, Aves, Accipitrides) in peatland reserves at Lublin province.] *Pr. Mat. Muzeum, Prądnik.* 3: 251–254. (In Polish.)

KUŁAKOWSKI, T. (1993) Ptaki Niecki Gródecko-Michałowskiej. [Birds of Gródecko-Michałowska Syncline. Report for PPTOP.] Unpublished. (In Polish.)

KUCHARSKI, R. (1992) Ptaki wodne i błotne stawów rybnych w Ślesinie. [Waterfowl of Ślesin fishponds.] Bydgoszcz, Poland: ART. (MSc. thesis) (In Polish.)

KUCHARSKI, R. (1994) Inwentaryzacja zimujących ptaków jezior i rzek Zaborskiego Parku Krajobrazowego. [Listing of wintering birds on lakes and rivers of Zaborski Landscape Park.] Bydgoszcz, Poland: ART. Unpublished. (In Polish.)

KUNYSZ, P. (1993) Awifauna lęgowa stawów rybnych w Starzawie (1982–1992). [Breeding birds of Starzawa fishponds (1982–1992).] Pp. 15–28 in J. Hordowski, ed. *Badania nad ornitofauną Ziemi Przemyskiej.* [*Study on the avifauna of Przemyœl region.*] Poland: Pr. Zakł. Fizjogr. Arbor. Bolestraszyce. (In Polish.)

KUNYSZ, P. (1994) Awifauna lęgowa Parków Krajobrazowych: Pogórza Przemyskiego, Południoworoztoczańskiego i Puszczy Solskiej. [Breeding birds of Landscape Parks: Przemyśl Plateau, Southern Roztocze and Solska Forest.] *Badania nad ornitofauną Ziemi Przemyskiej* 2: 21–41. (In Polish.)

KUPCZYK, M. (1997) Awifauna Nadgopla—liczebność i rozmieszczenie. [Avifauna of the Gopło area—numbers and distribution.] Pp. 55–116 in M. Kupczyk, ed. *Ptaki wybranych jezior Wielkopolski. [Birds of selected lakes of Wielkopolska.]* Pr. Zakł. Biol. Ekol. Ptaków, UAM, 7. (In Polish.)

KUŹNIAK, S. (1993) Ptaki doliny Obry w okresie lęgowym. [Birds of Obra valley at breeding season.] Unpublished. (In Polish.)

KUŹNIAK, S. AND LOREK, G. (1993) Ptaki Zbiornika Wonieść i terenów sąsiednich. [Birds of Wonieść Reservoir and surrounding areas (western Poland).] *Pr. Zakł. Biol. Ekol. Ptaków, UAM* 2: 1–45. (In Polish.)

LEWARTOWSKI, Z. (1994) Raport o stanie awifauny oraz innych grup kręgowców w NPK. Unpublished. (In Polish.)

LEWARTOWSKI, Z. (1997) Waloryzacja awifauny lęgowej doliny górnej Narwi i konieczność jej ochrony. [Valorization of breeding avifauna of upper Narew valley and need of it protection] *Zeszyty Postępów Nauk Rolniczych,* Falenty k/ Warszawy. (In Polish.)

MACHNIKOWSKI, M., GERSMANOWA, E., JANCZEWSKA, A., KNAPIK, A., MARSZ, A., NARWOJSZ, A., ROSZMAN, H., SAWON, E., SĄGIN, P., SZYMKIEWICZ, M., POSTRACH, K., RUGIEŃ, L., BĄKOWSKI, Z. AND PAMPUCH, T. (1993) *Dokumentacja do powołania Parku Krajobrazowego Puszcza Napiwodzko-Ramucka. [Documentation for creation of Landscape Park of Napiwodzko-Ramucka Forest.]* Gdynia, Poland: IOS. Unpublished. (In Polish.)

MARCHOWSKI, D. (1996) Ptaki lęgowe i zimujące w Parku Krajobrazowym Dolina Dolnej Odry. [Breeding and wintering birds in Landscape Park of Lower Odra valley.] Gryfino, Poland: Dyrekcja PK Dolina Dolnej Odry i Cedyńskiego PK. Unpublished. (In Polish.)

MEISSNER, W., AND KOZAKIEWICZ, M. (1995) Zimowanie ptaków wodnych na Zatoce Gdańskiej w sezonie 1994/95. [Wintering of waterfowl on the Bay of Gdańsk in the 1994/95 season.] *Not. Orn.* 36: 386–390.

MEISSNER, W., KOZAKIEWICZ, M. AND SKAKUJ, M. (1994) Zimowanie ptaków wodnych na Zatoce Gdańskiej w sezonie 1993/94. [Report of wintering waterfowl counts in the Gulf of Gdańsk in 1993/94.] *Not. Orn.* 35: 189–192. (In Polish.)

NOWICKI, W. AND KOT, H. (1993) Awifauna Środkowej Wisły i jej głównych dopływów—unikatowe wartości oraz warunki ich zachowania. [Avifauna of the middle Vistula and its main tributaries: unique features and conditions of their preservation.] Pp. 81–95 in L. Tomiałojć, ed. *Ochrona przyrody i środowiska w dolinach nizinnych rzek Polski.* [*Nature and environment conservation in the lowland river valleys of Poland.*] Kraków, Poland: IOP PAN. (In Polish.)

OLEKSIK, I. (1992) Ptaki Zbiornika Łąka (woj. katowickie). [Birds of Łąka Reservoir (Katowice voiv.).] *Ptaki Śląska* 9: 49–60.

OWCZAREK, S. AND SZLACHETKA, A. (1996) Inwentaryzacja ornitologiczna gminy Rudna. Legnica, Poland : UW. Unpublished. (In Polish.)

PIOTROWSKA, M., WÓJCIAK, J. AND BORCHULSKI, Z. (1990) Bagno Bubnów, projektowany rezerwat faunistyczny w województwie chełmskim. [The Bubnów Bog—a proposed faunistic reserve.] *Chrońmy Przyr.* 46: 54–61. (In Polish.)

PIOTROWSKA, M. (1994) Inwentaryzacja ptaków wodno-błotnych w dolinie Bugu od m. Gołębie w gm. Dołhobyczów do granicy z woj. chełmskim. Zamość, Poland: UW. Unpublished. (In Polish.)

PIOTROWSKA, M. (1995) Awifauna doliny Bugu w granicach województwa chełmskiego. Chełm, Poland: UW. Unpublished. (In Polish.)

PIOTROWSKA, M. (1996) Awifauna doliny Bugu na odcinku Pawluki—Neple w województwie bielskopodlaskim. Biała Podlaska, Poland: UW. Unpublished. (In Polish.)

PRZYBYSZ, J. (1993) Wyniki badań nad ptakami Zaborskiego Parku Krajobrazowego w Borach Tucholskich: Walory przyrodnicze-problemy ochrony-przyszłość. [Results of bird studies at Zaborski Landscape Park in Tuchola Forests: nature value—protection—future.] Toruń, Poland: UMK. (In Polish.)

PUGACEWICZ, E. (1994a) Populacja orlika krzykliwego (*Aquila pomarina*) na Nizinie Północnopodlaskiej. [Population of the Lesser Spotted Eagle (*Aquila pomarina*) in the plain of Nizina Północnopodlaska.] *Not. Orn.* 35: 139–156. (In Polish.)

PUGACEWICZ, E. (1994b) Stan populacji bociana czarnego (*Ciconia nigra*) na Nizinie Północnopodlaskiej w latach 1985–94. [Population of the Black Stork (*Ciconia nigra*) in the Nizina Północnopodlaska lowlands in 1985–1994.] *Not. Orn.* 35: 297–308. (In Polish.)

PUGACEWICZ, E. (1995a) Stan populacji puchacza (*Bubo bubo*) na Nizinie Północnopodlaskiej w latach 1984–94. [Population of the Eagle Owl (*Bubo bubo*) in the Nizina Północnopodlaska lowlands in 1984–1994.] *Not. Orn.* 36: 119–134. (In Polish.)

PUGACEWICZ, E. (1995b) Stan populacji orlika grubodziobego (*Aquila clanga*) w Kotlinie Biebrzańskiej w latach 1989–1993. [Population of the Spotted Eagle (*Aquila clanga*) in the Biebrza Marshes in 1989–1993.] *Not. Orn.* 36: 311–322. (In Polish.)

PUGACEWICZ, E. (1996) Lęgowe ptaki drapieżne Puszczy Białowieskiej. [Birds of prey breeding in the Polish part of the Białowieża Primaeval Forest.] *Not. Orn.* 37: 173–224. (In Polish.)

RANOSZEK, E. AND RANOSZEK, W. (1994) Przyroda Doliny Baryczy— Przewodnik. [Nature of the Barycz Valley—Guide.] Wrocław, Poland: PTPP 'Pro Natura'. (In Polish.)

RODZIEWICZ, A. AND RODZIEWICZ, M. (1995) Walory przyrodnicze Iławskiego Parku Krajobrazowego—założenia do Planu Ochrony Parku. Olsztyn, Poland: BPP. Unpublished. (In Polish.)

SIKORA, A., CENIAN, Z., KAPOWICZ, R., PÓŁTORAK, W. AND RYŚ, A. (1996) Ptaki Jeziora Oświn i terenów przyległych. Propozycja korekty granic rezerwatu. Report for OTOP. Unpublished. (In Polish.)

STAJSZCZYK, M. (1994) Ptaki doliny Odry między Brzegiem a Oławą. [Birds of the valley between Brzeg and Oława.] *Ptaki Śląska* 10: 78–98. (In Polish.)

STAWARCZYK, T. AND KARNAŚ, A. (1992) Sukcesja lęgowych ptaków wodno-błotnych na Zbiorniku Turawskim w latach 1977–1991. [Succession of breeding waterfowl in 1977–1991 on Turawski Reservoir.] *Ptaki Śląska* 9: 1–15. (In Polish.)

STAWARCZYK, T., GRABIŃSKI, W. AND KARNAŚ, A. (1996) Dynamika migracji siewkowych (Charadriiformes) na Zbiornikach Nyskim i Turawskim w latach 1976–94. [Migration of Charadriiformes at Nyski and Turawski Reservoir in 1976–94.] *Ptaki Śląska* 11: 39–80.

SZYMKIEWICZ, M., PIŁAT, G. AND MELLIN, M. (1995) Awifauna Nietlickich Bagien k. Giżycka w 1994. [Avifauna of Nietlice Marshes near Giżycko.] Warszawa: Fundacja IUCN-Poland. (In Polish.)

TOMIAŁOJĆ, L. (1995) The birds of the Białowieża Forests—additional data and summary. *Acta Zool. Crac.* 1(38): 363–397.

TOMIAŁOJĆ, L. AND WESOŁOWSKI, T. (1996) Structure of a primaeval forest bird community during 1970s and 1990s (Białowieża National Park, Poland). *Acta Orn.* 31: 133–154.

TRACZ, M. AND TRACZ, M. (1997) Badania faunistyczne w Ińskim Parku Krajobrazowym. [Faunistic research in the Iński Lanscape Park] *Przeg. Przyr.* 8(3): 105–115. (In Polish.)

TRYJANOWSKI, P. (1991) Godny ochrony fragment doliny Obry w województwie zielonogórskim. [Worthy of protection part of Obra valley in Zielona Góra voivodship.] *Chrońmy Przyr.* 47(5): 112–114.

TUCKER, G. M. AND HEATH, M. F. (1994) *Birds in Europe: their conservation status.* Cambridge, UK: BirdLife International (BirdLife Conservation Series No. 3).

TUCKER, G. M. AND EVANS, M. I., EDS. (1997) *Habitats for birds in Europe: a conservation strategy for the wider environment.* Cambridge, UK: BirdLife International (BirdLife Conservation Series No. 6).

WASILEWSKI, J. (1990) Dynamics of the abundance and consumption of birds of prey in the Niepołomice Forest. *Acta Zool. Crac.* 33(10): 173–213.

WESOŁOWKI, T. AND TOMIAŁOJĆ, L. (1995) Ornithologische Untersuchungen im Urwald von Białowieża—ein Unersicht. *Orn. Beobachter* 92: 111–146.

WINIECKI, A. (1996) Struktura i zmienność zgrupowań ptaków lęgowych w krajobrazie doliny rzecznej oraz możliwości oceny ich wartości. [Structure and variability of breeding bird communities in the river valley landscape and the possibilities of their assessment.] *Pr. Zakł. Biol. Ekol. Ptaków, UAM* 5: 1–135. (In Polish.)

WITKOWSKI, J., ORŁOWSKA, B., RANOSZEK, E. AND STAWARCZYK, T. (1995) Awifauna doliny Baryczy. [The avifauna of the Barycz River valley.] *Not. Orn.* 36: 5–74. (In Polish.)

ZAJĄC, T. (1994) Znaczenie łąk i obszarów podmokłych dla ornitofauny w Polsce—dolina Nidy. [The role of meadows and wet areas for avifauna in Poland—Nida Valley.] Report to IUCN-Poland. Unpublished. (In Polish.)

ZAWADZKA, D. AND ZAWADZKI, J. (1995) Wstępna charakterystyka awifauny Wigierskiego Parku Narodowego. [Preliminary characteristics of the Lake Wigry National Park avifauna.] *Not. Orn.* 36: 297–310. (In Polish.)

ZAWADZKA, D. AND ZAWADZKI, J. (1996) Sprawozdanie z wykonania inwentaryzacji stanowisk lęgowych ptaków, objętych ochroną strefową, w 1996 r. Suwałki, Poland: UW. Unpublished. (In Polish.)

ZIELIŃSKI, J. (1996) Ptaki wodne i błotne stawów rybnych w Ostrówku. [Waterfowl of fishponds in Ostrówek.] Bydgoszcz, Poland: ART (MSc. thesis.)

ZIELIŃSKI, M. AND STUDZIŃSKI, S. (1996) Awifauna Błot Rakutowskich pod Włocławkiem. [Avifauna of the marshland of Błota Rakutowskie near Włocławek.] *Not. Orn.* 37: 259–300. (In Polish.)

■ RUSSIA

Tanya Sviridova

Danilovskoye marshes (IBA 073). (PHOTO: Mikhail Ivanov/RBCU)

GENERAL INTRODUCTION

Russia, covering about 17,075,400 km², spans two continents—Europe and Asia. This account considers only the European part of Russia, which covers about 3,955,800 km² and which is bounded in the east by the Ural mountains, in the south by the Caspian Sea, Caucasus mountains, the Black Sea and Ukraine, in the west by Belarus and the Baltic countries, in the north-west by the Fenno-scandian countries, and in the north by the Arctic Ocean. European Russia straddles the latitudes between 44°N and 82°N (i.e. including Franz Josef Land), and the longitudes between 20°E and 70°E.

European Russia crosses three time-zones as well as eight major biogeographic zones, and contains an enormous diversity of natural, man-altered and artificial environments, which provide habitats for an extraordinarily rich flora and fauna. The biogeographic zones vary from semi-desert in the south-east, passing as one moves northward through steppe, wooded steppe, temperate broadleaved and mixed forest, boreal forest (taiga), wooded tundra, and finally to the tundra proper in the far north. Similar zonation occurs, with increasing altitude, on the main mountain ranges.

Most of the land surface of European Russia lies between sea level and 200 m elevation. There are two high mountain ranges: the Urals (up to c.2,000 m) and the Caucasus (up to c.5,640 m). In addition, the Central Russian Uplands lie in the middle of European Russia. Several large rivers cross European Russia, such as the Volga, Pechora, Severnaya Dvina, Onega, and Don.

European Russia includes 53 out of the 89 administrative regions in the whole country. These incorporate many of the larger centres of human population in Russia, such as Moscow, St Petersburg, Nizhni Novgorod, Saratov, Kazan', Samara, Volgograd, Ufa, Perm', Rostov-na-Donu and Stavropol. Away from these centres, population densities are generally lower than those elsewhere in Europe. Vast areas of mountains and northern forests are sparsely populated.

Out of those sites proposed as Important Bird Areas (IBAs) during the current IBA review, which spanned 1995 to 1997, a total of 218 were confirmed to meet criteria (Table 1). The 218 sites

comprise 154 'new' sites and 64 'original' sites. The previous inventory of IBAs in Europe (Grimmett and Jones 1989) identified 75 sites in European Russia ('original' sites), but 11 of these (listed in Table 1) were excluded from the present review for various reasons. Of these 11, one (former site SU110) was mistakenly classified as lying in Russian territory but was actually in Belarus (see Belarus chapter), four were duplicates of other sites (former site SU098 was the same as former site SU101, and former sites SU131, SU134 and SU135 were the same as SU133), while the other six sites do not meet the current IBA criteria (which have been revised since 1989). Of the remaining 64 'original' sites which are considered to meet the current criteria, 46 were updated with new information and were confirmed to meet the revised criteria, while there was no new information for the remaining 18, for which criteria have been assigned provisionally, based on information in the original 1989 inventory.

Although the 218 IBAs cover about 174,500 km², or about 4.4% of the land area of European Russia, they are not evenly distributed throughout this territory. There are few IBAs on the inland tundra, away from the Arctic shore—identifying such IBAs is difficult because of the lack of infrastructure and because many species breed there in a highly dispersed fashion, meaning that a particular area on its own may not support a significant number of individuals of a species. In addition, there is a large area in the main forest-zone in the north-east of European Russia where very few IBAs have been identified (see Map 1). At the level of individual administrative regions, IBAs tend to be located in the valleys of the larger rivers, as these are important ecological corridors and migration routes; or near to the boundary of the region, where there tends to be less infrastructure and a lower human-population density.

Although the European part is relatively small compared to the whole of Russia, this territory is still vast compared to the rest of Europe, and there are thus many potential IBAs whose importance might be confirmed in the future, once more field surveys have been carried out. A 'shadow' list of such potential IBAs (totalling 151 sites) is presented in Box 2 (at the end of this overview). Field

Map 1. Location, area and criteria category of Important Bird Areas in European Russia (no IBAs were identified in Franz Josef Land).

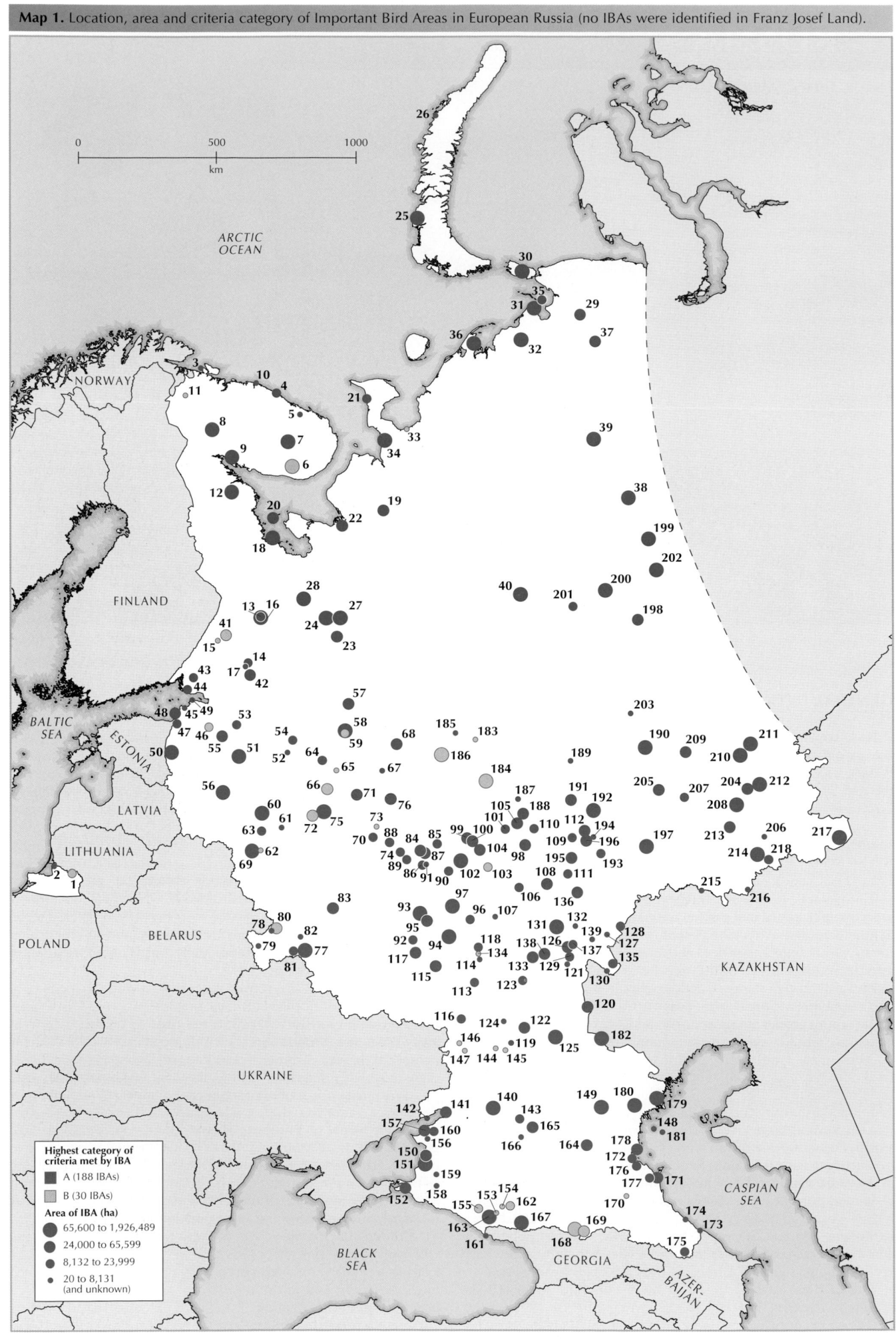

Highest category of
criteria met by IBA

■ A (188 IBAs)

■ B (30 IBAs)

Area of IBA (ha)

● 65,600 to 1,926,489

● 24,000 to 65,599

● 8,132 to 23,999

• 20 to 8,131
(and unknown)

Table 1. Summary of Important Bird Areas in European Russia. 218 IBAs covering 174,519 km²

IBA code	1989 code	International name	National name	Administrative region	Area (ha)	Criteria (see p. 11)
001	—	Nemanski forest	Nemansky Les	Kaliningrad	17,000	B2
002	—	Dal'ni forest	Les Dal'ni	Kaliningrad	4,000	A1
003	SU128	Ainov islands	Ainovy Ostrova	Murmansk	290	A4i, B1i, B3
004	SU129	Sem islands	Sem Ostrovov	Murmansk	10,667	A4iii, B1i, B2, B3
005	SU130	Coastal belt of eastern Murmansk	Vostochnoye poberezh'ye Murmana	Murmansk	260	A4i, B1i
006	SU132	Watershed of the Rivers Strelna and Varzuga	Mezhdurech'ye rek Strelna i Varzuga	Murmansk	250,000	B1i
007	SU133	Middle reaches of the River Ponoy (Zakaznik Ponoyski)	Srednee techeniye reki Ponoy (Zakaznik Ponoyski)	Murmansk	98,600	A1, A3, A4i, B1i, B2
008	SU136	Lapland Biosphere Reserve	Laplandski Zapovednik	Murmansk	278,436	A3, B2, B3
009	SU137	Kandalaksha Bay	Kandalakshski Zaliv	Murmansk	208,000	A1, A4i, A4iii, B1i, B1ii, B2
010	—	Gavrilovski archipelago	Gavrilovski arkhipelag	Murmansk	1,500	A1, A4i, A4iii, B1i, B1ii, B2, B3
011	—	Surroundings of Kiyesh'yaur lake	Okrestnosti ozera Kiyesh'yaur	Murmansk	4,000	B2
012	SU138	Lakes of northern Karelia	Ozera severnoy Karelii	Karelia Republic	1,000,000	A4i, B1i
013	SU141	Kivach Nature Reserve	Zapovednik Kivach	Karelia Republic	10,880	A3, B2, B3
014	SU142	Olonets plain	Olonetskaya ravnina	Karelia Republic	18,000	A1, A4i, A4iii, B1i, B2, B3
015	—	Palinsaari island	Ostrov Palinsaari	Karelia Republic	100	B1i, B3
016	—	Zaonezh'ye	Zaonezh'ye	Karelia Republic	330,000	A1, A3, A4i, A4iii, B1i, B2, B3
017	—	South-eastern coast of Lake Ladoga	Poberezh'ye i ostrova ozera Ladoga yuzhneye ust'ya reki Olonki	Karelia Republic	1,250	A4i, B1i, B2
018	SU140	Onega Bay of White Sea	Onezhskaya Guba Belogo Morya	Arkhangelsk, Karelia Republic	200,000	A4i, A4iii, B1i, B1ii, B2, B3
019	SU127	Pinezhski Nature Reserve	Pinegski Zapovednik	Arkhangelsk	41,244	A1, B2
020	SU139	Solovetski Archipelago	Solovetskiye ostrova	Arkhangelsk	34,700	A1, A4i, B1i, B1ii, B2, B3
021	—	Torna–Shoina watershed	Mezhdurech'e Torny i Shoiny	Arkhangelsk	15,000	A1, A4i, A4iii, B1i, B2, B3
022	—	Delta of River Severnaya Dvina	Delta Severnoy Dviny	Arkhangelsk	50,000	A4i, A4iii, B1i
023	—	Lake Lacha	Ozero Lacha	Arkhangelsk	53,500	A1, A4i, A4iii, B1i, B2
024	—	Kenozer'ye	Kenozer'ye	Arkhangelsk	180,000	A1, A3, A4i, B1i, B2, B3
025	—	Bezymyannaya and Gribovaya Bays and adjoining waters	Guba Bezymyannaya i Gribovaya	Arkhangelsk	140,000	A1, A4i, A4iii, B1i, B1ii, B3
026	—	Arkhangelskaya Bay	Guba Arkhangelskaya	Arkhangelsk	1,000	A4ii, B1ii
027	—	Kargopol' area	Kargopol'skaya sush'	Arkhangelsk	175,000	A1, A4i, A4iii, B1i, B2
028	—	Vodlozero	Vodlozero	Arkhangelsk, Karelia Republic	200,000	A1, B2
029	SU119	Vashutkiny, Padimeyskiye and Khargeyskiye lakes	Vashutkiny, Padimeyskiye i Khargeyskiye Ozera	Arkhangelsk, Nenetski	25,000	A4i, A4iii, B1i
030	SU120	Vaygach island	Ostrov Vaygach	Arkhangelsk, Nenetski	340,000	A3, A4i, B1i, B2, B3
031	SU122	Varandeyskaya Lapta peninsula	Poluostrov Varandeyskaya Lapta	Arkhangelsk, Nenetski	350,000	A4iii
032	SU123	River Chernaya	Reka Chernaya	Arkhangelsk, Nenetski	200,000	A4iii
033	SU125	Southern coast of Cheshskaya Bay	Yuzhnoe poberezh'ye Cheshskoy Guby	Arkhangelsk, Nenetski	—	B1i
034	SU126	Kanin peninsula	Poluostrov Kanin	Arkhangelsk, Nenetski	500,000	A4i, A4iii, B1i
035	SU121	Khaypudyrskaya Bay (islands of B. Zelenets, Dolgi, Matveyev)	Khaypudyrskaya Guba, ostrova B. Zelenets, Dolgi, Matveyev	Nenetski	20,600	A4i, A4iii, B1i
036	SU124	Russki Zavorot peninsula	Poluostrov Russki Zavorot	Nenetski	299,000	A3, A4i, A4iii, B1i, B2
037	—	Middle reaches of Bolshaya Rogovaya river	Sredneye techeniye reki Bolshaya Rogovaya	Nenetski	35,000	A1, A3, B2
038	SU118	Pechoro-Ilychski Nature Reserve	Pechoro-Ilychski Zapovednik	Komi Republic	705,500	A1, B2
039	—	Yugyd Va	Yugyd Va	Komi Republic	1,926,489	A1, A3, B1i, B2
040	—	Valley of Sysola river	Dolina reki Sysoly	Komi Republic	110,000	A1, A3, A4i, B1i, B2
041	SU143	Kilpola island and adjoining waters	Kilpola Ostrov i prilegayushchaya akvatoria	Karelia Republic	30,000	B1i
042	SU144	Mouth of Svir river	Ust'ye reki Svir	Leningrad	65,000	A1, A4i, B1i, B2, B3
043	SU145	Rakovye lakes	Rakovye Ozera	Leningrad	9,700	A1, A4iii, B1i
044	SU146	Berezovye islands of Vyborg Bay	Berezovye ostrova, Vyborgski Zaliv	Leningrad	12,000	A4i, A4iii, B1i
045	SU147	Koporski Bay	Koporskaya Guba	Leningrad	6,000	A1, A4i, A4iii, B1i, B2, B3
046	SU148	Lake Vyalye and adjoining marshes	Ozero Vyal'ye i prilegayushchiye bolota	Leningrad	20,000	B1i
047	SU151	Narva reservoir	Narvskoye Vodokhranilishche	Leningrad	20,000	A4iii
048	—	Kurgalski peninsula	Kurgalski Poluostrov	Leningrad	27,000	A4i, A4iii, B1i
049	—	Swans area (southern shore of Finski Bay)	Lebyazh'ye	Leningrad	6,400	A4i, A4iii, B1i
050	SU152	Chudsko-Pskovski lake and adjacent areas	Pskovsk-Chudskoye Ozero i okrestnosti	Pskov	251,400	A1, A4i, A4iii, A4iv, B1i, B1iv
051	SU150	Lake Ilmen' and adjoining marshy plain	Ozero Ilmen' i okrestnosti	Novgorod	250,000	A1, A4i, A4iii, B1i, B2
052	—	Pereluchski Nature Reserve	Pereluchski Zakaznik	Novgorod	6,425	A1, B2
053	—	Flood-plain of Volkhov river	Volkhovskaya poima	Novgorod	17,650	A1, A4i, B1i
054	—	Redrovski Nature Reserve	Redrovski Zakaznik	Novgorod	16,850	A1
055	SU149	Sources of the River Luga	Verkhov'ya reki Luga	Novgorod, Leningrad	49,600	A1, B1i
056	—	Polisto-Lovatskaya mire system	Polisto-Lovatskaya bolotnaya sistema	Novgorod, Pskov	110,000	A1, A4i, B1i, B2, B3

Table 1 ... continued. Summary of Important Bird Areas in European Russia.   218 IBAs covering 174,519 km²

IBA code	1989 code	International name	National name	Administrative region	Area (ha)	Criteria (see p. 11)
057	—	Sizemski flood-plain of Sheksna reservoir	Sizemski razliv Sheksninskogo vodokhranilische	Vologda	60,000	A1, B2
058	SU114	Rybinsk reservoir	Rybinskoye vodokhranilishche	Vologda, Yaroslavl'	455,000	A1, B1i, B2
059	SU104	Uglichskoy reservoir	Uglichskoe vodokhranilishche	Tver, Yaroslavl'	10,000	B1i
060	SU113	Central Forest Biosphere Reserve and adjacent areas	Tsentralno-Lesnoi Zapovednik i okrestnosti	Tver	63,680	A1, B1i
061	—	Sources of Osuga river	Verkhov'ya reki Osugi	Tver	5,100	A1
062	—	Budnyanski mire	Budnyanski Mokh	Tver	3,156	B1i, B2
063	—	Stakhovski marshes	Stakhovski Mokh	Tver	10,296	A1, B1i
064	—	Upper Mologa river (Verestovo lake)	Verkhov'ye reki Mologi (Ozero Verestovo)	Tver	17,000	A1, B1i, B2
065	—	Savtsinskoye marsh	Boloto "Savtsinskoye"	Tver	4,569	B1i, B2
066	—	Orshinski marshes	Boloto "Orshinski mokh"	Tver	43,200	B1i
067	—	Flood-plain of Kotorosl' and Ust'e rivers	Poima rek Ust'e i Kotorosl'	Yaroslavl'	4,200	A1, A4i, B1i
068	—	Flood-plain of Kostroma river	Kostromskiye razlivy	Yaroslavl', Kostroma	55,125	A4iii, B1i
069	—	Smolenskoye Pohozer'ye	Smolenskoye Pohozer'ye	Smolensk	146,161	A1, B2
070	SU103	Faustovo flood-plains of Moscow river	Faustovskoe rashireniye poimy reki Moskvy	Moscow	9,000	A1, A4i, A4iii, B1i, B2
071	SU105	Homeland of the Crane (Dubna marshes and adjacent areas)	Zhuravlinaya Rodina (Dubnenski bolotny massiv i okrestnosti)	Moscow	38,500	A1, B1i
072	—	Lotoshino crane gathering	Lotoshinskoye zhuravlinoye skopleniye	Moscow, Tver	28,200	B1i
073	—	Danilovskoye marshes	Danilovskoye boloto	Moscow	400	B2
074	—	Dedinivo flood-plain of Oka river	Dedinovskaya poima reki Oki	Moscow	23,120	A1, A4iii, B1i, B2
075	SU107	Zavidovo Nature Reserve, including Lotoshinski, Klinski and Diatlovo fish-ponds	Zavidovski Zapovednik, Lotoshinski i Klinski rybkhozy	Moscow, Tver	133,800	A1, A4i, B1i, B2
076	—	Central Meshchera lake-system	Tsentral'no-Meshcherskaya ozernaya sistema	Moscow, Vladimir, Ryazan'	92,700	A1, B3
077	—	Nerussa–Desna woodland	Nerusso-Desnyanskoe Poles'ye	Bryansk	220,000	A1, B2, B3
078	—	Flood-plain of Iput' river in vicinity of Krutoayr	Poima Iputi mezhdu Krutoyar i Krasnoe	Bryansk	4,000	A4i, A4iii, B1i
079	—	Flood-plain of Iput' river in vicinity of Kholevichami	Poima Iputi mezhdu rekoy Unich' i Kholevicham	Bryansk	6,800	A1, A4i, A4iii, B1i, B2
080	—	Kletnyanski forest	Kletnyanski Les	Bryansk	38,100	B2
081	—	Desna flood-plain near Trubchevsk	Poima Desny mezhdu Trubchevskom i Beloy Berezkoy	Bryansk	17,200	A1, A4i, A4iii, B1i, B2
082	—	Gavan'skiye oak-forest	Gavan'skiye Dubravy	Bryansk	3,000	A1, B3
083	—	Kaluzhskiye Zaseki Nature Reserve	Kaluzhskiye Zaseki	Kaluga	44,613	A1, B2, B3
084	SU101	Oka River Valley Biosphere Reserve	Okski Zapovednik	Ryazan'	55,731	A1
085	—	Valley complex of Moksha and Oka rivers	Dolinny Complex levoberezh'ya reki Oki	Ryazan'	22,400	A1, A4i, A4iii, B1i
086	—	Shilovo flood-plain of Oka river	Shilovskaya poima Oki	Ryazan'	22,000	A1, A4i, A4iii, B1i
087	—	Izhevsk flood-plain of Oka river	Izhevskaya poima Oki	Ryazan'	30,000	A1, A4i, A4iii, B1i
088	—	Solotcha flood-plain of Oka river	Solotchinskaya poima Oki	Ryazan'	12,000	A1, A4i, A4iii, B1i
089	—	Oka valley in vicinity of Murmino	Poima Oki v okrestnostyakh Murmino	Ryazan'	8,400	A4iii, B1i
090	—	Watershed of Tsna and Vysha rivers	Urochische Lepen' (mezhdurech'ye Tsny i Vyshy)	Ryazan'	16,000	A1
091	—	Terekhovski oak-forest	Terekhovskaya poimennaya Dubrava	Ryazan'	5,000	A1
092	—	Kulikovski forest	Kulikovski Les	Lipetsk	18,500	A1
093	—	Upper Voronezh forest	Verkhnevoronezhski lesnoy massiv	Lipetsk, Tambov	92,800	A1, B2
094	—	Watershed of Bityug and Tsna rivers	Bityugo-Tsninski	Tambov	80,000	A1, A4i, B1i
095	—	Zavoronezhski area	Zavoronezhski bolotno-polevoy uchastok	Tambov	48,000	A1, A4i, B1i
096	—	Voroninski Nature Reserve	Voroninski Zapovednik	Tambov	10,320	A1, B1i
097	—	Tsninski forest	Tsninski Lesnoy massiv	Tambov	100,000	A1, B1i, B2
098	SU095	Flood-plain of Sura river	Poima reki Sura, Mordovia	Mordovia Republic	40,000	A4iii, B1i, B2, B3
099	SU096	Mordovian P. G. Smidovich Nature Reserve	Mordovski Zapovednik	Mordovia Republic	32,200	A1, B2
100	SU097	Moksha valley in vicinity of Temnikov	Moksha Dolina v okrestnostyakh Temnikova	Mordovia Republic	28,000	A1, A4i, B1i, B2
101	—	Ichalkovski	Ichalkovski	Mordovia Republic	10,000	A1, B2
102	—	Flood-plain of Vad river	Poima reki Vad	Mordovia Republic	65,600	A1, B2, B3
103	—	Insaro-Kovylkinski	Insaro-Kovylkinsk	Mordovia Republic	22,800	B2, B3
104	—	Moksha flood-plain in vicinity of Krasnoslobodsk	Poima Mokshy v okrestnostyakh Krasnoslobodska	Mordovia Republic	32,400	A1, A4i, B1i, B2
105	—	Flood-plain of Alatyr' river in vicinity of Ardatov	Poima reki Alatyr' v okrestnostyakh Ardatova	Mordovia Republic	38,000	A1, B2
106	—	Surski reservoir	Surskoye vodokhranilische	Penza	11,000	A1, B1i
107	—	Bekovskoye forest	Bekovskoye Lesnichestvo (Serdobski Leskhoz)	Penza	8,000	A1

Table 1 ... continued. Summary of Important Bird Areas in European Russia.   218 IBAs covering 174,519 km²

IBA code	1989 code	International name	National name	Administrative region	Area (ha)	Criteria (see p. 11)
108	—	Kuznetski forest	Kuznetski Leskhoz	Penza	40,000	A1, B2
109	—	Sengileyevskiye mountain	Sengileyevskiye Gory	Ul'yanovsk	22,400	A1
110	SU093	Watershed of Sura and Barysh rivers	Mezhdurech'ye Sury i Barysha	Ul'yanovsk	16,500	A1, B1i, B2
111	—	Privolzhskaya forest-steppe	Privolzhskaya Lesostep'	Ul'yanovsk	15,000	A1, B2
112	—	Cheremshanski Bay of Kuybyshev reservoir	Cheremshanski Zaliv Kuybyshevskogo vodokhranilischa	Ul'yanovsk	63,000	A1, A4i, A4iii, B1i, B2
113	SU099	Khoper Nature Reserve	Khoperski Zapovednik	Voronezh	16,178	A1
114	—	Flood-plain of Khoper river near Lake Ilmen'	Poima reki Khoper u ozera Ilmen'	Voronezh	4,000	A1
115	—	Khrenovskoy forest	Khrenovskoy Bor	Voronezh	35,000	A1, B2
116	—	Bereznyakovski forest	Bereznyakovski lesnoy massiv	Voronezh	13,200	A1
117	—	Voronezhski Nature Reserve	Voronezhski Zapovednik	Voronezh, Lipetsk	31,053	A1, B2
118	—	Vorono-Khoperski area	Vorono-Khopoerski	Voronezh, Tambov, Saratov	22,000	A1, A4i, B1i
119	—	Levo-Dobrinskaya valley	Levo-Dobrinskaya Dolina	Volgograd	3,000	A1, B2
120	—	Lake El'ton	Ozero El'ton	Volgograd	30,000	A1, A4i, B1i
121	—	Novokvasnikovski liman	Novokvasnikovski Liman	Volgograd	300	A1
122	—	Kalachinskaya loop of River Don	Kalachinskaya izluchina Dona	Volgograd	60,000	A1, B2
123	—	Danilovski forest	Danilovski Bor	Volgograd	10,000	A1, B2
124	—	Rubezhnoye forest	Urochishche Rubezhnoye	Volgograd	5,000	A1, B2
125	—	Akhtubinsk wetland	Akhtubinskoye Poozer'ye	Volgograd	138,000	A1, A4iii, B2
126	SU092	Vicinity of Borisoglebovka (Saratovski [Semenovski] Zakaznik)	Okrestnosti Borisoglebovki (Saratovski [Semenovski] Zakaznik)	Saratov	35,000	A1, A3, A4i, B1i, B2
127	—	Valley of Safarovka river	Dolina reki Safarovki	Saratov	2,500	A1
128	—	Siniye mountains	Siniye Gory	Saratov	15,000	A1, B2
129	—	Priyeruslanskiye sands	Priyeruslanskiye Peski	Saratov	20,000	A1, B2
130	—	Varfolomeyevskiye saltmarshes	Varfolomeyevskiye Limany	Saratov	2,800	A1, A4i, B1i
131	—	North part of Volgogradski reservoir	Severnaya zona Volgogradskogo vodokhranilis	Saratov	74,250	A1, A4i, B1i, B2
132	—	Vicinity of Voznesenka village	Okrestnosti sela Voznesenka	Saratov	1,200	A1
133	—	Sokino	Sokino	Saratov	30,330	A1
134	—	Almazovski area	Almazovski Zakaznik	Saratov	4,500	B2
135	—	Algaiski	Algaiski	Saratov	13,000	A1, A3, B2
136	—	Khvalynski National Park	Khvalynski Natsional'ny Park	Saratov	25,514	A1, B2
137	—	Rovno area	Rovenski	Saratov	8,220	A1
138	—	Stepan Rasin rock	Utes Stepana Rasina	Saratov	35,050	A1, B2
139	—	Rzhestyanka	Rzhestyanka	Saratov	8,000	A1, A3
140	SU059	Veselovskoye reservoir	Veselovskoye Vodokhranilishche	Rostov	230,000	A1, A4i, A4iii, B1i, B2
141	—	Delta of the River Don	Delta Dona	Rostov	53,800	A1, A4i, A4iii, B1i, B1iv, B2
142	—	Beglitskaya sand-spit	Beglitskaya Kosa	Rostov	1,414	A1, A4i, A4iii, B1i
143	—	Islands in the western part of Lake Manych-Gudilo	Ostrove v zapadnoy chasti ozera Manych-Gudilo	Rostov	19,200	A1, A4i, A4iii, B1i, B2, B3
144	—	Karaichevski forest	Karaichevskaya Lesnaya Dacha	Rostov	5,000	B2
145	—	Secretevskiye sands (Oblivski forest)	Urochishche Secretivskiye Peski (Oblivski Leskhoz)	Rostov	3,000	B2
146	—	Kalitvenski forest	Kalitvenskoye Lesnichestvo, Donetski Leskhoz	Rostov	1,200	B2
147	—	Gorodishchenski forest	Gorodishchenskaya Lesnaya Dacha	Rostov	3,000	B2
148	SU085	Chistaya Banka and Ivan-Karaul islands	Ostrova Chistaya Banka i Ivan-Karaul	Kalmykiya Republic	—	A4i, A4iii, B1i
149	—	Uttinskaya area	Uttinskaya	Kalmykiya Republic	98,000	A1, B2
150	SU057	Salt-lakes in the Primorsko-Akhtarsk area	Primorsko-Akhtarskaya sistema limanov	Krasnodarski kray	40,000	A1, A4i, B1i, B2, B3
151	—	Eastern coast of the Sea of Azov	Vostochnoe poberezh'ye Azovskogo morya	Krasnodarski kray	457,300	A1, A4i, B1i, B2, B3
152	—	Kiziltash limans	Kiziltashskiye Limany	Krasnodarski kray	28,000	A4i, B1i, B2, B3
153	—	Lower Urushtek river	Nizov'e reki Urushtek	Krasnodarski kray	1,764	B2, B3
154	—	Akhmet–Skala ridge	Khrebet Akhmet-Skala	Krasnodarski kray	2,300	B2
155	—	Kurdzhips river valley	Dolina reki Kurdzhips	Krasnodarski kray	10,230	B2
156	—	Lake Khanskoye	Ozero Khanskoye	Krasnodarski kray	8,000	A1, A4i, B1i, B2, B3
157	—	Yeyski salt-lakes	Yeyski Liman	Krasnodarski kray	24,000	A4i, B1i, B2, B3
158	—	Surroundings of Black Forest	Okrestnosti Chernogo Lesa	Krasnodarski kray	20	A4i, B1i, B2
159	—	Kalininski Plavny	Kalininskiye Plavny	Krasnodarski kray	3,000	A4i, B1i, B2
160	—	Mouth of Yeya river	Ust'ye reki Yeya	Krasnodarski kray	9,600	A1, A4i, B1i, B2
161	—	Imeretinskaya lowland	Imeretinskaya nizmennost'	Krasnodarski kray	1,500	A1
162	—	Valley of Urup river	Dolina reki Urup	Krasnodarski kray, Karachaevo-Cherkesskaya Republic	8,132	B2, B3
163	SU058	Caucasus Biosphere Reserve	Kavkazski Biospherny Zapovednik	Krasnodarski kray, Stavropolski kray, Adygeya Republic	280,338	A1, A2, A3, B1iv, B2
164	—	Dadynskiye lake	Dadynskiye ozero	Stavropolski kray	45,000	A1, A3, A4i, B1i, B2, B3

Table 1 ... continued. Summary of Important Bird Areas in European Russia.   218 IBAs covering 174,519 km²

IBA code	1989 code	International name	National name	Administrative region	Area (ha)	Criteria (see p. 11)
165	SU060	Lake Manych-Gudilo	Ozero Manych Gudilo	Stavropolski kray, Kalmykiya Republic	50,000	A1, A4i, B1i, B2, B3
166	SU061	Burukshunskiye limans	Burukshunskiye Limany	Stavropolski kray, Kalmykiya Republic	6,000	A1, A4i, B1i, B2
167	SU062	Teberdinski Nature Reserve	Teberdinski Zapovednik	Karachaevo-Cherkesskaya Republic	84,996	A1, A2, A3, B1iv, B2
168	SU063	Kabardino-Balkarski Nature Reserve	Kabardino-Balkarski Zapovednik	Kabardino-Balkarskaya Republic	74,099	B2
169	SU072	Severo-Osetinski (North Osetin) Nature Reserve	Severo-Osetinski Zapovednik	Severnaya Osetiya Republic	28,999	B2
170	SU083	Budary lakes	Budarskiye Ozera	Chechenskaya Republic	1,000	B1i
171	SU082	Agrakhanski Bay	Agrakhanski Zaliv	Dagestan Republic	39,000	A1, A4i, B1i, B2
172	SU084	Kizlyar Bay	Kizlyarski Zaliv	Dagestan Republic	19,061	A1, A4i, B1i
173	—	Mouth of Samur river	Ust'e reki Samur	Dagestan Republic	7,000	A1, A4i, B1i, B2, B3
174	—	Lake Adzhi	Ozero Adzhi	Dagestan Republic	2,000	A1, A4i, B1i, B2
175	—	Sources of Mazachai and Mullarchai rivers	Verkhov'ya rek Mazachai i Mullarchai	Dagestan Republic	10,000	A1, A3, B2
176	—	Karakol'skiye lakes	Karakol'skiye ozera	Dagestan Republic	10,000	A1, A4i, B1i, B2
177	—	Achikol'skiye lakes	Achikol'skiye Ozera	Dagestan Republic	20,000	A1, A4i, B1i, B2
178	SU087	Morskoy Biryuchek island	Ostrov Morskoy Biryuchek	Dagestan Republic, Kalmykiya Republic	30,000	A4i, B1i
179	SU086	Volga delta	Delta Volgi	Astrakhan	1,150,000	A1, A4i, A4iii, B1i, B2, B3
180	—	Western Ilmen area	Zapadnye podstepnye ilmeni	Astrakhan	590,000	A4i, A4iii, B1i, B2
181	—	Maly Zhemchuzhny island	Maly Zhemchuzhny Ostrov	Astrakhan	35	A4i, B1i, B2
182	—	Bogdinsko-Baskunchakski	Bogdinsko-Baskunchakski	Astrakhan	70,000	A1, A3, B2
183	SU116	Flood-plain of River Vetluga	Poima reki Vetlugi	Kostroma	—	B1i
184	—	Kamsko-Bakaldinskiye marshes	Kamsko-Bakaldinskiye Bolota	Nizhni Novgorod	120,000	B1i
185	—	Sitnikovski Nature Reserve	Sitnikovski Zakaznik	Nizhni Novgorod	2,117	A4i, B1i, B2
186	SU115	Gorki reservoir and the lower Unzha river	Gorkovskoye Vodokhranilishche i nizov'ya reki Unzha	Ivanovo, Nizhni Novgorod, Kostroma	72,100	B1i
187	SU094	Flood-plain of Algashka river	Poima reki Algashki	Chuvashskaya Republic	400	A1, A4iii, B1i
188	—	Sura environs	Prisur'ye	Chuvashskaya Republic	44,000	A1, B1i, B2
189	—	Arski fish-ponds	Arski rybkhoz	Tatarstan Republic	1,000	A1, B1i
190	—	Kamsko-Ikski area	Kamsko-Ikski	Tatarstan Republic	100,000	A1, A4i, B1i, B2, B3
191	—	Bulgarski	Bulgarski	Tatarstan Republic	25,000	A1, A4i, A4iii, B1i, B2
192	—	Cheremshanski forest	Cheremshanski Les	Tatarstan Republic, Ul'yanovsk	100,000	A1, B2
193	SU091	Zhigulevsk Nature Reserve	Zhigulevski Zapovednik	Samara	23,140	A1, B2, B3
194	—	Tashlinski forest	Tashlinski Les	Samara	1,000	A1, B2
195	—	Racheyski forest	Racheyski Bor	Samara	40,100	A1, B2, B3
196	—	Suskanski Nature Reserve	Suskanski Zakaznik	Samara	40,500	A1, A4i, B1i
197	—	Buzulukski forest	Buzulukski Bor	Samara, Orenburg	111,210	A1, B2, B3
198	—	Kamsko-Yayvenski wetland	Kamsko-Yayvenski vodno-bolotny complex	Perm	35,000	A1, B2
199	—	Verkhnevisherski mountain	Verkhnevisherski Gorny massiv	Perm	180,000	A3, B2, B3
200	—	Kumikushski wetland	Kumikushski vodno-bolotny complex	Perm	80,000	A1, A3, A4iii
201	—	Adovo-Chugrumski wetland	Adovo-Chugrumski vodno-bolotny complex	Perm	21,000	A1, A3, B2
202	—	Khvarkush and Zolotoy Kamen' ridges	Khrebet Kvarkush i Zolotoy Kamen'	Perm	130,000	A1, A4i, B1i, B2, B3
203	—	Nizhnekamskaya flood-plain	Nizhnekamskaya poima	Perm, Udmurtia Republic	8,000	A1, A4i, A4iii, B1i, B2
204	SU090	Bashkirski Nature Reserve	Bashkirski Zapovednik	Bashkortostan Republic	49,609	A1, B2
205	—	Octyabr'ski forest	Octyabr'ski Lesnoi massiv	Bashkortostan Republic	50,000	A1, B2
206	—	Mountain valley of Sakmara river	Gornaya Dolina reki Sakmary	Bashkortostan Republic	5,000	A1, B2
207	—	Nikiforovski forest	Nikiforovski Lesnoi massiv	Bashkortostan Republic	20,000	A1, B2
208	—	Watershed of Bel'skaya and Nugush rivers	Bel'sko-Nugushskoe Mezhdurech'ye	Bashkortostan Republic	150,000	A1, B2
209	—	Bel'skaya flood-plain	Bel'skaya poima	Bashkortostan Republic	42,800	A1, A4i, B1i, B2
210	—	Yamantau mountain	Gorny massiv Yamantau	Bashkortostan Republic	120,000	A1, A3, B2
211	—	Iremel'ski mountain	Iremel'ski gorny massiv	Bashkortostan Republic, Chelyabinsk	90,000	A1, A3, B2
212	—	Irendyk ridge	Khrebet Irendyk	Bashkortostan Republic	150,000	A1, A4i, A4iv, B1i, B1iv, B2
213	—	Maly Nakas ridge	Khrebet Maly Nakas	Bashkortostan Republic, Orenburg	50,000	A1, B2
214	—	Steppe valley of Sakmara river	Stepnaya Dolina reki Sakmary	Orenburg	75,000	A1, B2
215	—	Kupy area	Urochishche Kupy	Orenburg	2,000	A4iii, B1i
216	—	Kulaksay lowland	Nizina Kulaksay	Orenburg	5,000	A1, A3, A4i, B1i, B2
217	—	Shalkaro-Zhetykolski lake system	Shalkaro-Zhelkolski Ozerny Rayon	Orenburg	81,250	A1, A4i, A4iii, B1i, B2
218	—	Orenburgski Nature Reserve	Orenburgski Zapovednik	Orenburg	21,600	A1, A3, B2

Sites identified in the previous inventory of IBAs in Europe (Grimmett and Jones 1989) but no longer considered to be IBAs
SU098 Okskaya Dolina (Oka Valley), Ryazan Oblast; SU100 Les Na Vorskle, Belgorod Oblast; SU102 Prioksko – Terrasny, Serpukhov, Moskovskaya Oblast; SU106 Moskovskoye Morye, Konakovo, Kalinin Oblast; SU108 Prof. V.V. Alekhin Tsentralno-Chernozemny (Central Black Earth) Biosphere Reserve, Kursk and Belgorod Oblasts; SU109 Galichya Gora, Lipetsk Oblast; SU110* Osveyskoye Ozero (Lake Osveyskoye), Verkhnedvinsk, "Belorussia Oblast"; SU117 Votkinskoye Vodokhranilishche (Votkinskoye Reservoir), Perm Oblast; SU131 Watershed of the Rivers Lumbovka and Ponoy Reka, Lovozero, Murmansk Oblast; SU134 Chalmny-Varre, Lovozero, Murmansk Oblast; SU135 Watershed of the Rivers Iokanga and Ponoy Reka, Lovozero, Murmansk Oblast.
* Mistakenly treated as part of RSFSR in the previous inventory of IBAs in Europe (Grimmett and Jones 1989).

Table 2. Important Bird Areas in European Russia that are important for species of global conservation concern (meeting criterion A1).

Species	IBA code	Species	IBA code
Phalacrocorax pygmeus Pygmy Cormorant	171, 172, 173, 174, 176, 177, 179	*Falco naumanni* Lesser Kestrel	105, 141, 142, 164, 212, 216
Pelecanus crispus Dalmatian Pelican	143, 150, 151, 156, 164, 165, 166, 171, 172, 173, 174, 176, 177, 179, 217	*Tetrao mlokosiewiczi* Caucasian Black Grouse	163, 167, 175
Anser erythropus Lesser White-fronted Goose	019, 021, 027, 037, 040, 042, 045, 051, 055, 060, 067, 141, 164, 165, 173, 189, 190, 191, 216, 217	*Crex crex* Corncrake	002, 014, 016, 023, 024, 027, 040, 042, 043, 050, 051, 052, 053, 054, 055, 056, 060, 061, 063, 064, 069, 070, 074, 075, 076, 077, 079,
Branta ruficollis Red-breasted Goose	094, 100, 104, 118, 140, 141, 143, 164, 165, 216, 217		081, 083, 084, 085, 086, 087, 088, 090, 092, 093, 094, 095, 096, 097, 099, 100, 101, 104,
Aythya nyroca Ferruginous Duck	141, 164, 173, 174, 177, 179		105, 110, 113, 114, 115, 116, 117, 118, 131,
Polysticta stelleri Steller's Eider	010, 020, 025		141, 161, 163, 187, 188, 193, 195, 197, 198,
Oxyura leucocephala White-headed Duck	164		200, 203, 204, 208, 209, 210, 211, 212, 213
Haliaeetus albicilla White-tailed Eagle	007, 009, 020, 024, 028, 038, 039, 042, 045, 057, 058, 075, 106, 112, 113, 114, 122, 124, 125, 131, 136, 140, 141, 149, 163, 177, 179, 182, 191, 193, 196, 198, 200, 203	*Tetrax tetrax* Little Bustard	120, 127, 129, 135, 137, 139, 149, 164, 173, 174, 218
		Otis tarda Great Bustard	118, 126, 127, 128, 132, 137, 139, 164
Aegypius monachus Cinereous Vulture	149, 175	*Glareola nordmanni* Black-winged Pratincole	121, 126, 127, 130, 141, 142, 143, 150, 160, 164, 212, 217
Circus macrourus Pallid Harrier	128, 135, 173, 209, 212, 213, 216, 217	*Gallinago media* Great Snipe	039, 040, 042, 051, 052, 053, 063, 064, 070,
Aquila clanga Greater Spotted Eagle	050, 053, 054, 069, 071, 074, 075, 076, 077, 082, 084, 091, 093, 097, 099, 102, 107, 110, 115, 117, 133, 173, 179, 198, 202, 208, 209		074, 075, 076, 087, 088, 090, 093, 102, 131, 141, 191, 198, 200, 201, 202, 203, 209, 210, 211, 212
Aquila heliaca Imperial Eagle	093, 101, 105, 108, 109, 111, 113, 115, 117, 119, 122, 123, 128, 136, 138, 167, 182, 188, 192, 194, 197, 205, 206, 207, 208, 210, 211, 214, 218	*Acrocephalus paludicola* Aquatic Warbler	198, 203, 209

Table 3. Important Bird Areas in European Russia that support important numbers of one or more congregatory species (i.e. meeting criteria A4 and/or B1). IBAs meeting both criteria A4 and B1 for the species are shown in **bold**. IBAs meeting only criterion B1 for the species concerned, and not A4, are shown in normal type. For key to 'Season', see p. 7 .

Species	Season	IBA code	Species	Season	IBA code
Gavia arctica Black-throated Diver	B	**016, 024, 036**	*Anser fabalis* Bean Goose	B	**030, 036**
	P	044, 048		P	014, **016, 022, 023, 027, 035**, 042, 055, 068, **078**, 079, **094, 095, 112, 118**
Podiceps cristatus Great Crested Grebe	B	141		N	029
Podiceps grisegena Red-necked Grebe	B	141	*Anser albifrons* White-fronted Goose	B	**030**, 036
	P	044		P	014, **022, 023, 027, 035**, 046, 058, 062, 063,
Podiceps nigricollis Black-necked Grebe	B	141			064, 065, 066, **067**, 068, **070**, 074, **078, 079**,
Phalacrocorax carbo Cormorant	R	152			**081, 085, 086, 087, 088**, 089, 094, 095, 098,
	B	141, 156, **179**			100, **104, 112**, 118, 164, **165, 217**
	P	171, 172	*Anser erythropus* Lesser White-fronted Goose	P	**021, 027**, 040, 060, 164, **165**, 189, **191**, 216, **217**
	N	**164**, 181	*Anser anser* Greylag Goose	R	177
Phalacrocorax pygmeus Pygmy Cormorant	B	179		B	012, 140, 141, **166, 179**, 180, 190, 217
	P	174		W	**140**
Pelecanus onocrotalus White Pelican	N	**164**		P	064, 065, 066, 074, 075, 085, 086, 087, 088, 089, 094, 095, 096, 097, 098, 100, 104, 118,
Pelecanus crispus Dalmatian Pelican	R	177			**140, 141, 143, 152, 166**, 187, 188, 189, 191,
	B	**143, 150, 151, 156, 164, 165, 171, 176, 179, 217**			196
	P	**172, 173**, 174		N	**140**, 180, 217
	N	166	*Branta leucopsis* Barnacle Goose	B	**021, 030**
Nycticorax nycticorax Night Heron	B	159, **179**		P	014, **021, 022**, 034, **044**
Ardeola ralloides Squacco Heron	B	179	*Branta bernicla* Brent Goose	P	**021, 022, 044**
Egretta garzetta Little Egret	B	140, 143, 158, **159, 179**	*Branta ruficollis* Red-breasted Goose	P	**100, 104, 118, 140, 143, 164, 165, 216, 217**
	N	141	*Tadorna ferruginea* Ruddy Shelduck	R	**165**
Egretta alba Great White Egret	R	177		B	**180**
	B	**140, 150, 179, 180**		N	**164**
	P	**166, 172, 173**	*Tadorna tadorna* Shelduck	B	**180**
	N	**078, 141**		N	**165**
Ardea cinerea Grey Heron	B	179	*Anas penelope* Wigeon	B	045
	P	141		P	106, 187, **191**, 215
Plegadis falcinellus Glossy Ibis	B	**140, 151, 158, 159, 166, 179**	*Anas strepera* Gadwall	B	**190**
Platalea leucorodia Spoonbill	B	**140, 143, 150, 151, 164, 165, 166, 179, 180**		P	172, **190**
	P	173	*Anas crecca* Teal	B	045, **190**
Cygnus olor Mute Swan	R	164		P	**166, 190**, 191
	B	**179, 180**		N	**180**
	P	140, 178	*Anas platyrhynchos* Mallard	B	179, **190**
	N	141, 165		W	140
Cygnus columbianus Bewick's Swan	B	**030, 034, 036**		P	106, 141, 166, **190**
	P	**022, 044, 045, 048, 049**	*Anas acuta* Pintail	B	021, **036**, 045
Cygnus cygnus Whooper Swan	B	006, **012**		W	**178**
	W	179	*Anas querquedula* Garganey	P	**141, 190**
	P	**016, 023, 024**, 035, **042, 044, 045, 048, 049, 140, 141, 151**	*Anas clypeata* Shoveler	B	058, **190**
				P	**190**
	N	006, **007**		N	023

Table 3 ... continued. Important Bird Areas in European Russia that support important numbers of one or more congregatory species (i.e. meeting criteria A4 and/or B1). IBAs meeting both criteria A4 and B1 for the species are shown in **bold**. IBAs meeting only criterion B1 for the species concerned, and not A4, are shown in normal type. For key to 'Season', see p. 7.

Species	Season	IBA code
Netta rufina Red-crested Pochard	B	**160, 177, 179**
	P	141, 172
Aythya ferina Pochard	B	**190**
	P	141, 166, **190**
Aythya nyroca Ferruginous Duck	B	**179**
Aythya fuligula Tufted Duck	P	**044, 187**
Aythya marila Scaup	B	021, **036**
	P	044, 045, **190, 191**
Somateria mollissima Eider	R	010
	B	004, **009**
	W	005, 018
	P	035
	N	009
Somateria spectabilis King Eider	B	036
	W	005
	P	035
Polysticta stelleri Steller's Eider	W	010
	N	020, 025
Clangula hyemalis Long-tailed Duck	B	030
	P	044
Melanitta nigra Common Scoter	P	042, **044, 045**
Melanitta fusca Velvet Scoter	P	044
Bucephala clangula Goldeneye	B	036, **045**
	P	024, **044, 068**
	N	009, 050
Mergus serrator	B	**016**
Red-breasted Merganser	P	044, 048
Mergus merganser Goosander	B	030
	P	044, 048
Fulica atra Coot	R	177
	B	179, 180
	P	166, 174
	N	050
Grus grus Crane	B	016, 043, 056, 184
	P	016, **027**, 071, 072, 095, 110, **120, 209**
Himantopus himantopus	B	141, 143, **150, 151**, 152, 164
Black-winged Stilt	P	**141**
Recurvirostra avosetta Avocet	B	**150, 151, 152**
Glareola pratincola	B	150, 160, 165
Collared Pratincole	P	141
Glareola nordmanni	B	**126, 130, 164, 217**
Black-winged Pratincole	P	**141**
	N	**143**
Charadrius alexandrinus	P	120
Kentish Plover		
Pluvialis apricaria Golden Plover	P	016, 086
Vanellus vanellus Lapwing	P	016, 196
Calidris maritima Purple Sandpiper	P	003
Philomachus pugnax Ruff	P	166
Gallinago media Great Snipe	B	039, **051, 053, 087, 088, 202, 212**
	P	**131, 141**

Species	Season	IBA code
Numenius arquata Curlew	B	016, 056
	P	016
Tringa totanus Redshank	B	150
Tringa nebularia Greenshank	B	040
	P	024
Actitis hypoleucos	B	016
Common Sandpiper	P	016
Arenaria interpres Turnstone	B	018
Stercorarius parasiticus Arctic Skua	B	018
Larus ichthyaetus	B	**148, 151, 152, 164, 165, 181**
Great Black-headed Gull	P	**141, 142**
Larus minutus Little Gull	B	017, **023, 045, 203**
	P	**141, 142, 173**
Larus ridibundus Black-headed Gull	R	185
	P	044, **141, 142**
Larus genei Slender-billed Gull	B	**143, 165**
	P	**141, 142**
Larus canus Common Gull	R	185
	B	016, 018
	P	027, **044, 048**
Larus fuscus	B	018, 045
Lesser Black-backed Gull	P	**044, 048**
Larus argentatus Herring Gull	B	018
	P	**044, 048**
Larus cachinnans Yellow-legged Gull	B	152, 156, 157, **164, 165, 181**
	P	**141, 142**
Larus marinus	B	003
Great Black-backed Gull	P	048
Gelochelidon nilotica Gull-billed Tern	B	**143, 152, 164, 165**
	P	173
	N	141
Sterna caspia Caspian Tern	B	015, **152, 156, 181**
	N	141
Sterna sandvicensis Sandwich Tern	R	**152**
	B	157, 181
Sterna hirundo Common Tern	B	**016**, 152, 156, 157
	P	**141, 142, 190**
Sterna paradisaea Arctic Tern	B	020
Sterna albifrons Little Tern	B	045, 075, **150, 152, 203**
	P	**141, 142, 190, 191**
Chlidonias hybridus Whiskered Tern	B	**160, 165**
	P	**141**
Chlidonias niger Black Tern	B	075
	P	141
Chlidonias leucopterus	B	203
White-winged Black Tern	P	**141**, 173
Uria lomvia Brünnich's Guillemot	B	025, 026
Alca torda Razorbill	B	010
Cepphus grylle Black Guillemot	B	009, 010, 025
	R	020

surveys in 1998 (after the current IBA review was completed) have shown that at least 73 (48%) of these sites appear to meet IBA criteria. However, this shadow list is still bound to be incomplete since there are, even now, vast areas of European Russia that have never been ornithologically explored.

ORNITHOLOGICAL IMPORTANCE

There are 196 species of European conservation concern (SPECs) which breed regularly in European Russia (Tucker and Heath 1994). Twelve of them are globally threatened: *Pelecanus crispus, Anser erythropus, Aythya nyroca, Polysticta stelleri, Oxyura leucocephala, Aquila clanga, Aquila heliaca, Falco naumanni, Crex crex, Otis tarda, Chettusia gregaria* and *Acrocephalus paludicola*. The sites that hold significant numbers of these and eight other species of global conservation concern are listed in Table 2. Apart from these 20 species, a further 116 SPECs in Russia also have an unfavourable conservation status in Europe (Tucker and Heath 1994).

There are several endemic or restricted-range species in European Russia, most of which occur in the Caucasus Endemic Bird Area (EBA 122, one of only three EBAs in Europe: Stattersfield *et al.* 1998), for instance *Tetrao mlokosiewiczi, Tetraogallus caucasicus, Tetraogallus caspius, Prunella ocularis, Phylloscopus lorenzii* (formerly *P. sindianus*) and *Sitta krueperi*. Of the 47 species in Europe that are restricted to either the boreal biome or the Arctic/tundra biome, (when breeding) the majority of Arctic/tundra species and all of the boreal species breed regularly in European Russia. However, these species usually occur at relatively low densities, most being highly dispersed across these vast zones, and thus it is sometimes very difficult or impossible to identify particular IBAs for these biome-restricted species. It is easier to identify IBAs in highly developed regions, where suitable habitats are more scarce.

Table 1 lists the criteria under which IBAs in European Russia were identified, the main ones being importance for species of global conservation concern (meeting the A1 criterion; 152 sites), for species of European conservation concern (meeting B2/B3; 144 sites), and for large congregations of waterbirds or seabirds (A4, B1; 131 sites).

Most IBAs qualified under several criteria. Map 1 shows that the great majority of the IBAs (188 sites) qualify as being globally important (they meet 'A' criteria) and only 30 as regionally important (meeting 'B' criteria only). A total of 116 SPECs meet criteria in IBAs in Russia, and they are listed in Table 4. Many of these species breed at densities that are too low to meet the relevant numerical threshold, thus relatively few sites have qualified per species under the B2/B3 criteria.

A large proportion of the IBAs are important for migratory waterbirds of many different species, at some point in their annual life-cycle (i.e. when breeding, staging or wintering), and these 118 sites and 87 species are listed in Table 3. Most of these wetlands are located in the coastal zones of the Caspian, Black and Baltic Seas, the Arctic Ocean and along the flood-plains of large rivers, and some have been designated as Ramsar Sites (Table 5). A minority of sites are rich in species that meet IBA criteria, e.g. 29 sites have more than 10

Table 4. Species of European conservation concern with significant breeding populations at Important Bird Areas in European Russia (meeting any IBA criteria).

Species [1]	Minimum national breeding population (pairs) [2]	Proportion (%) of national population breeding at all IBAs in Russia	Species [1]	Minimum national breeding population (pairs) [2]	Proportion (%) of national population breeding at all IBAs in Russia
Gavia arctica Black-throated Diver	100,000	1	Larus minutus Little Gull	11,000	17
Phalacrocorax aristotelis Shag	1,000	20	Larus canus Common Gull	40,000	57
Phalacrocorax pygmeus Pygmy Cormorant	330	100[3]	Larus fuscus Lesser Black-backed Gull	2,100	100[3]
Pelecanus onocrotalus White Pelican	300	100[3]	Larus marinus Great Black-backed Gull	8,200	44
Pelecanus crispus Dalmatian Pelican	437	100[3]	Gelochelidon nilotica Gull-billed Tern	1,800	22
Nycticorax nycticorax Night Heron	9,000	61	Sterna caspia Caspian Tern	3,000	45
Ardeola ralloides Squacco Heron	5,500	24	Sterna sandvicensis Sandwich Tern	4,000	44
Ardea purpurea Purple Heron	40,000	9	Sterna albifrons Little Tern	5,000	27
Ciconia nigra Black Stork	400	13	Chlidonias hybridus Whiskered Tern	10,000	9
Ciconia ciconia White Stork	3,500	2	Chlidonias niger Black Tern	20,000	9
Plegadis falcinellus Glossy Ibis	10,300	100[3]	Alca torda Razorbill	2,000	33
Platalea leucorodia Spoonbill	2,300	69	Cepphus grylle Black Guillemot	23,500	7
Anser erythropus Lesser White-fronted Goose	500	6	Columba oenas Stock Dove	10,000	3
Branta leucopsis Barnacle Goose	4,000	63	Columba palumbus Woodpigeon	100,000	5
Tadorna ferruginea Ruddy Shelduck	6,000	100[3]	Otus scops Scops Owl	20,000	100[3]
Anas strepera Gadwall	55,000	2	Bubo bubo Eagle Owl	2,000	2
Anas acuta Pintail	150,000	3	Nyctea scandiaca Snowy Owl	—	National pop unknown
Netta rufina Red-crested Pochard	5,500	63	Strix aluco Tawny Owl	10,000	5
Aythya ferina Pochard	90,000	1	Alcedo atthis Kingfisher	10,000	5
Aythya nyroca Ferruginous Duck	500	99	Jynx torquilla Wryneck	50,000	4
Mergus albellus Smew	7,000	<1	Dendrocopos medius Middle Spotted Woodpecker	1,000	51
Oxyura leucocephala White-headed Duck	50	8	Picoides tridactylus Three-toed Woodpecker	10,000	35
Haliaeetus albicilla White-tailed Eagle	900	38	Melanocorypha yeltoniensis Black Lark	6,000	69
Gypaetus barbatus Lammergeier	40	30	Calandrella brachydactyla Short-toed Lark	100,000	2
Neophron percnopterus Egyptian Vulture	120	6	Lullula arborea Woodlark	10,000	11
Gyps fulvus Griffon Vulture	124	100[3]	Alauda arvensis Skylark	1,000,000	3
Aegypius monachus Cinereous Vulture	30	7	Riparia riparia Sand Martin	1,000,000	2
Circus macrourus Pallid Harrier	1,000	14	Anthus pratensis Meadow Pipit	1,000,000	1
Accipiter brevipes Levant Sparrowhawk	3,000	2	Prunella atrogularis Black-throated Accentor	1,000	10
Buteo rufinus Long-legged Buzzard	800	2	Luscinia luscinia Thrush Nightingale	100,000	5
Aquila pomarina Lesser Spotted Eagle	300	8	Phoenicurus phoenicurus Redstart	100,000	5
Aquila clanga Greater Spotted Eagle	800	10	Saxicola rubetra Whinchat	100,000	10
Aquila heliaca Imperial Eagle	600	12	Turdus merula Blackbird	10,000	29
Aquila chrysaetos Golden Eagle	500	7	Turdus philomelos Song Thrush	100,000	25
Hieraaetus pennatus Booted Eagle	500	8	Turdus viscivorus Mistle Thrush	10,000	41
Pandion haliaetus Osprey	2,500	5	Locustella fluviatilis River Warbler	100,000	2
Falco naumanni Lesser Kestrel	70	29	Acrocephalus paludicola Aquatic Warbler	250	14
Falco vespertinus Red-footed Falcon	15,000	1	Acrocephalus palustris Marsh Warbler	100,000	4
Falco cherrug Saker	120	1	Acrocephalus scirpaceus Reed Warbler	10,000	3
Falco rusticolus Gyrfalcon	50	24	Hippolais icterina Icterine Warbler	1,000,000	1
Falco peregrinus Peregrine	1,000	2	Sylvia borin Garden Warbler	500,000	7
Tetrao tetrix Black Grouse	100,000	7	Muscicapa striata Spotted Flycatcher	1,000,000	2
Tetrao mlokosiewiczi Caucasian Black Grouse	2,515	100[3]	Ficedula albicollis Collared Flycatcher	5,000	100[3]
Tetraogallus caucasicus Caucasian Snowcock	1,540	100[3]	Ficedula hypoleuca Pied Flycatcher	1,000,000	2
Coturnix coturnix Quail	100,000	2	Parus caeruleus Blue Tit	100,000	5
Porzana porzana Spotted Crake	10,000	3	Sitta krueperi Krüper's Nuthatch	—	National pop unknown
Crex crex Corncrake	1,000,000	1	Lanius collurio Red-backed Shrike	100,000	3
Grus grus Crane	30,000	3	Lanius minor Lesser Grey Shrike	10,000	1
Tetrax tetrax Little Bustard	18,000	2	Perisoreus infaustus Siberian Jay	10,000	11
Otis tarda Great Bustard	10,000	4	Fringilla coelebs Chaffinch	10,000	100[3]
Recurvirostra avosetta Avocet	1,730	100[3]	Carduelis chloris Greenfinch	100,000	6
Glareola pratincola Collared Pratincole	1,000	7	Loxia pytyopsittacus Parrot Crossbill	10,000	17
Glareola nordmanni Black-winged Pratincole	6,500	5	Carpodacus rubicilla Great Rosefinch	70	100[3]
Charadrius alexandrinus Kentish Plover	1,000	3	Emberiza hortulana Ortolan Bunting	10,000	8
Pluvialis apricaria Golden Plover	10,000	10			
Calidris maritima Purple Sandpiper	1,000	1			
Limicola falcinellus Broad-billed Sandpiper	100	6			
Gallinago media Great Snipe	150,000	1			
Limosa limosa Black-tailed Godwit	10,000	6			
Numenius phaeopus Whimbrel	10,000	6			
Tringa totanus Redshank	10,000	35			
Larus melanocephalus Mediterranean Gull	2,050	100[3]			

1. Only those species of European conservation concern (see Box 1, p. 12) that meet IBA criteria in Russia are listed.

2. Data are taken from the BirdLife/EBCC European Bird Database 1998 (Heath and Borggreve 2000).

3. The percentage of the national population in IBAs exceeds 100%. Usually this is because the national population estimate has not been updated recently whilst the IBA population estimate has been recently updated with new data as a result of comprehensive surveys of IBAs themselves. Also, the individual site count for a species may be the maximum or average over recent years, and summing these may record more birds than are present nationally in any single year.

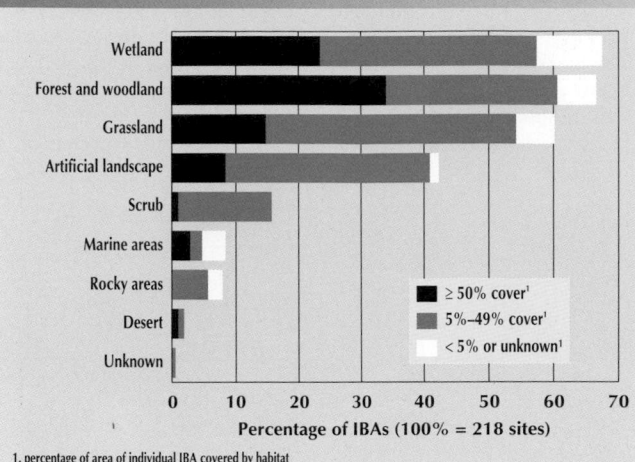

Figure 1. Habitats at Important Bird Areas in European Russia (see Appendix 3 for definitions of habitats).

1. percentage of area of individual IBA covered by habitat

qualifying species each, and six have more than 20 each, these being the Don delta (site 141; 36 species), Zaonezh'ye (site 016; 34 species), Lapland Biosphere Reserve (site 008; 30 species), Volga delta (site 179; 27 species), and Kenozer'ye and Dadynskiye lake (sites 024 and 164) both have 22 species.

It is difficult to assess how adequately breeding bird populations are covered by IBAs in European Russia (see Table 4), as national population data are still unsatisfactory for many bird species and not all IBAs have been identified yet. But there is no doubt that many species of European conservation concern are not adequately covered by the IBA network.

HABITATS

There is a mosaic of natural and semi-natural habitats in European Russia. Huge areas of the tundra and taiga are still very close to being 'natural'. At the same time, some parts of the country have been almost completely transformed by man's activities and infrastructure—mainly in the central and south-western administrative regions such as Moscow, Tula, Kaluga, Orel, Belgorod, Bryansk and Lipetsk, Kursk, Rostov, Krasnodar and Stavropol.

Eight main habitat-types are present in the 218 Russian IBAs, of which forests, wetlands and grasslands are the most frequent (Figure 1). Most of the Russian IBAs are located in real wilderness—in areas where there has been very little human impact. In contrast, some IBAs exist mainly due to man's non-intensive agricultural activities. For example, staging areas for migrating geese *Anser* and *Grus grus* often occur in agricultural landscapes, although never far from mires and forests, and some waders (Charadrii) prefer non-intensive pastures for breeding. Although more IBAs contain forest and woodland than any other main habitat-type (Figure 1), such habitat is present mostly as isolated tracts or small patches in the IBAs of central and southern European Russia, while the vast boreal forests in the north, especially in the north-east, are still hardly covered by the IBA network (see Map 1).

IMPACTS ON IBAs – LAND-USE AND THREATS

Russia covers a wide span of Europe from north to south, and can be divided into northern, central and southern zones in terms of the level of human development and of habitat destruction. The current socio-economic situation has affected land-use in European Russia. In general, the influence of man and his activities decreases from the south to the north of the country, as well as from the west to the east, and (within any particular administrative region) also from the centre to the boundaries. Most IBAs are currently state-owned. Figure 2 shows the most common forms of land-use on identified IBAs.

Agricultural activity occurs in 57% of IBAs, while forestry and hunting occur in more than 43% and 40% of IBAs respectively (Figure 2). The latter two land-uses are common within IBAs for two main reasons:

- The huge land-area of the former USSR was shared for management mainly between two sectors: the governmental forestry agencies (the major land-users) and the hunting societies (the secondary land-users).
- Most areas of relatively intact or little-modified habitat were used for hunting activities.

The current situation is much the same, except that private ownership of land is becoming more frequent and may in the future affect the overall balance of land-uses in the country, and possibly in IBAs.

Other types of land-use are not so widespread in IBAs. A very positive fact is that official nature-conservation activities take place in about 35% of IBAs, and at most such sites these activities cover more than half of the IBA.

The most frequent threats in Russian IBAs are the unsustainable exploitation of birds (51%) and the disturbance of birds (42%) (Figure 3). The former threat takes a variety of forms—excessive (legal) hunting of waterbirds, spring hunting (legal), poaching (illegal)—and is also a consequence of other threats, e.g. expansion of agriculture and forestry, water management, or the extraction industry, which 'invade' wild areas and not only destroy habitats, but also introduce more people into the landscape. The same can be said about disturbance of birds, as this is caused not only by direct and deliberate pursuit of birds, but also (and mainly) through other human activities (listed in Figure 3) which cause incidental, non-deliberate disturbance of sensitive species, for instance logging, drainage or recreation during the nesting season.

Overall, infrastructural development and urbanization are less frequent than the previously mentioned threats (Figure 3), at least for those IBAs already identified, although their severity for an individual IBA depends very much on its geographical location (the highly developed centre of European Russia versus the vast, little-populated north-east). This threat will certainly increase in importance in the future.

Recent drastic changes in the economy will certainly modify bird habitats and, eventually, bird populations. A large decrease in agricultural activity occurred during the last 10 years in Russia, and this reduction in land management poses a threat to certain bird species. Millions of hectares of agricultural land are currently being neglected, and haymaking and grazing have stopped on many meadows and pastures. Some industrial and intensive agricultural pressures on bird habitats have reduced, and some environmental pollution (e.g. from high use of artificial fertilizers) has sharply decreased. At the same time, clear-cutting of forests has become more widespread in recent years in the vast boreal zone, especially in concessions granted to foreign or joint Russian–foreign logging companies, where the resulting problems are most acute.

Further research is needed on the consequences for birds of these recent, large-scale changes in land-uses. In addition to the above-

Figure 2. Land-uses at Important Bird Areas in European Russia (see Appendix 3 for definitions of land-uses).

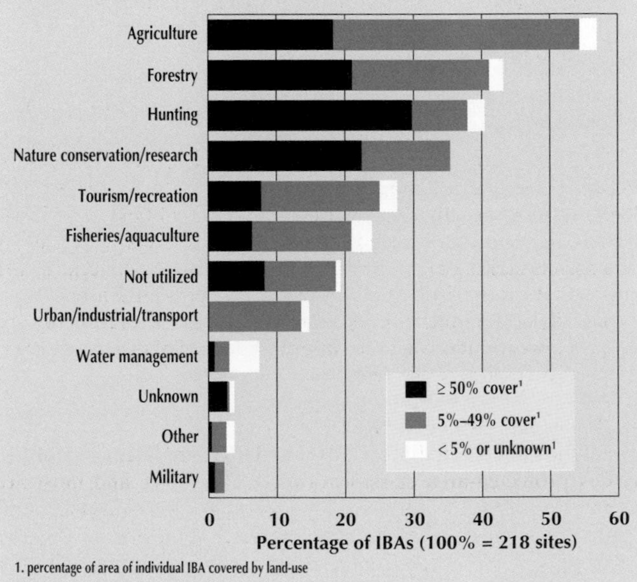

1. percentage of area of individual IBA covered by land-use

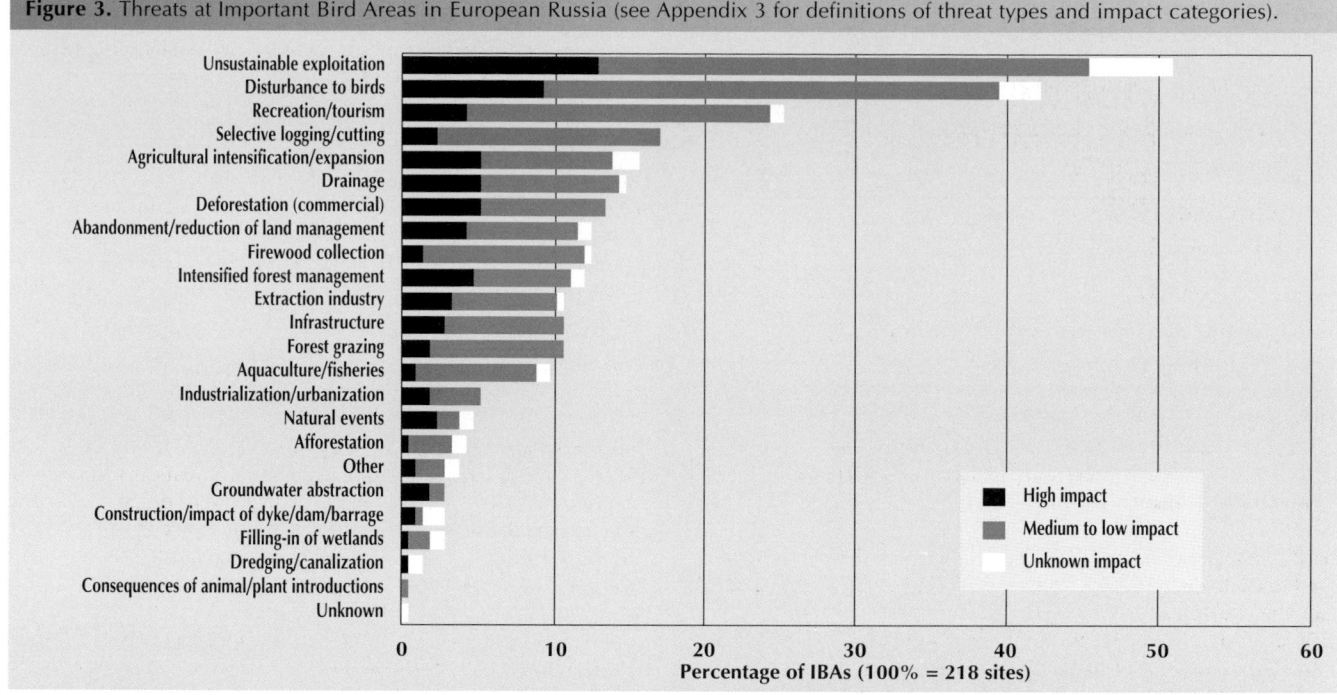

Figure 3. Threats at Important Bird Areas in European Russia (see Appendix 3 for definitions of threat types and impact categories).

mentioned threats, one of the most dangerous threats to IBAs is the ever greater decentralization of decision-making from the federal to the regional level, accompanied by increasingly complex and varied regional legislation, which sometimes makes it very difficult to monitor or affect the land-use and protected-area situation.

PROTECTION STATUS

Table 5 summarizes the available data on the national and international protection status of IBAs.

■ National protection

One of the most comprehensive attempts at biodiversity conservation in Russia has been the establishment of an extensive network of protected areas. The majority of protected areas in Russia are owned, administered and monitored by a number of state organizations, although many other organizations, including NGOs, are also involved in the process of creation or monitoring. There are also one or two privately owned protected areas in Russia, but this phenomenon is very new and still rare.

Three main federal laws regulate the management of all protected areas, together with many local laws. The federal laws are:
1. Federal law 'On Natural Environment Protection'.
2. Federal law 'On Specially Protected Areas'.
3. Federal law 'On Animal Protection'.

There are also other laws (for example, Forest law) which affect protected areas in certain ways.

There are four main levels of natural resource management in Russia: federal, regional (i.e. administrative regions, and republics), local authorities (districts within regions/republics), and landowners and land-users (including collective land-users). The process of decision-making at each level is preceded by the consent of the appropriate authorities at all lower levels and of land-users.

Details of the four main types of protected area nationally are given below—for more detailed information see Sobolev *et al.* (1995) and Blagovidov *et al.* (1995).

1. Zapovednik (Strict Nature Reserve)

This type of protected area falls mainly within category I of the IUCN protected-area classification (IUCN 1994), and most are administered by the Federal Committee for Environment and Nature Protection. There is a special Division of Nature Reserve Management within the Committee, and several Zapovedniks are also managed by universities or by the Academy of Science.

There are no analogues to the Zapovednik system elsewhere in the world. It was created in the former USSR and still exists in Russia as the main remnant of that former system of protected areas. There are currently Zapovedniks in all of the main physico-geographic zones of Russia. Establishment of a Zapovednik entails major restrictions on land-use. With the exception of scientific research, most forms of human activity are prohibited within its borders, including residence. Each Zapovednik is surrounded by a semi-protected buffer zone where a limited range of human development activities are allowed, provided that the reserve itself is unharmed. Allowed activities are agreed between the managers of the Zapovednik and the relevant local authorities. By the end of 1997 there were 99 Zapovedniks in the whole of Russia.

2. National Park

National Parks fall within category II of the IUCN protected-area classification (IUCN 1994). In Russia, National Parks have a short history as the first one was created in 1983. These areas are also federal institutions with special staff, being administered by the Federal Forest Service (mostly by regional units of that body) of the Ministry of Agriculture. In comparison with Zapovedniks, National Parks have a more flexible regime of economic development, and communities residing within the territory are typically incorporated into the park. Among the main themes of staff activity are not only environment protection, but also public education and awareness. There are 34 National Parks in Russia.

3. Natural Monument

Natural Monuments meet category III of the IUCN protected-area classification (IUCN 1994). Most often, Natural Monuments are designated to protect objects of special interest, such as a rock outcrop, or a rare bird's nest (e.g. stork *Ciconia* or raptor), or a water-source. Although the objectives of Natural Monuments are very similar to Zakazniks (see below), traditionally Natural Monuments have had a relatively small size (100–500 ha), but there are exceptions in some regions. The management of Natural Monuments is arranged in the same way as it is in Zakazniks (see below), and they have neither scientific nor law-enforcement staff.

4. Zakaznik (Special Purpose Reserve or Nature Refuge)

Zakazniks mostly meet category IV of the IUCN protected-area classification (IUCN 1994). Zakazniks are territories where either permanent or temporary limitations have been placed upon economic activities. There are several tens of federal Zakazniks in Russia, but more commonly they are established at the level of administrative regions or republics. There are more than 1,000 such regional Zakazniks, covering about 4% of the territory of Russia.

Table 5. Protection status of Important Bird Areas in European Russia. A tick (✔) indicates that an IBA overlaps with a protected area (to any extent).

IBA code	International name	Zapovednik	National Park	Natural Monument	Zakaznik	Ramsar Site	World Heritage Site	Biosphere Reserve
		National				International		
001	Nemanski forest							
002	Dal'ni forest				✔			
003	Ainov islands	✔						
004	Sem islands	✔						
005	Coastal belt of eastern Murmansk							
006	Watershed of the Rivers Strelna and Varzuga							
007	Middle reaches of the River Ponoy (Zakaznik Ponoyski)				✔			
008	Lapland Biosphere Reserve	✔						✔
009	Kandalaksha Bay	✔				✔		
010	Gavrilovski archipelago	✔						
011	Surroundings of Kiyesh'yaur lake							
012	Lakes of northern Karelia				✔			
013	Kivach Nature Reserve	✔						
014	Olonets plain				✔			
015	Palinsaari island							
016	Zaonezh'ye				✔			
017	South-eastern coast of Lake Ladoga				✔			
018	Onega Bay of White Sea				✔	✔		
019	Pinezhski Nature Reserve	✔						
020[1]	Solovetski archipelago						✔	
021	Torna–Shoina watershed							
022	Delta of River Severnaya Dvina				✔			
023	Lake Lacha				✔			
024	Kenozer'ye		✔					
025	Bezymyannaya and Gribovaya Bays and adjoining waters							
026	Arkhangelskaya Bay							
027	Kargopol' area				✔			
028	Vodlozero		✔					
029	Vashutkiny, Padimeyskiye and Khargeyskiye lakes							
030	Vaygach island				✔			
031	Varandeyskaya Lapta peninsula							
032	River Chernaya							
033	Southern coast of Cheshskaya Bay							
034	Kanin peninsula							
035	Khaypudyrskaya Bay (islands of B. Zelenets, Dolgi, Matveyev)							
036	Russki Zavorot peninsula				✔			
037	Middle reaches of Bolshaya Rogovaya river							
038	Pechoro-Ilychski Nature Reserve	✔					✔	✔
039	Yugyd Va		✔					
040	Valley of Sysola river			✔	✔			
041	Kilpola island and adjoining waters							
042	Mouth of Svir river	✔				✔		
043	Rakovye lakes				✔			
044	Berezovye islands of Vyborg Bay				✔	✔		
045	Koporski Bay							
046	Lake Vyalye and adjoining marshes				✔			
047	Narva reservoir							
048	Kurgalski peninsula					✔		
049	Swans area (southern shore of Finski Bay)				✔	✔		
050	Chudsko-Pskovski lake and adjacent areas				✔	✔		
051	Lake Ilmen' and adjoining marshy plain	✔			✔			
	Subtotal of IBAs	10	3	1	19	7	2	2

IBA code	International name	Zapovednik	National Park	Natural Monument	Zakaznik	Ramsar Site	World Heritage Site	Biosphere Reserve
		National				International		
052	Pereluchski Nature Reserve				✔			
053	Flood-plain of Volkhov river							
054	Redrovski Nature Reserve				✔			
055	Sources of the River Luga							
056	Polisto-Lovatskaya mire system	✔			✔			
057	Sizemski flood-plain of Sheksna reservoir		✔					
058	Rybinsk reservoir	✔						
059	Uglichskoy reservoir							
060	Central Forest Biosphere Reserve and adjacent areas	✔						✔
061	Sources of Osuga river							
062	Budnyanski mire				✔			
063	Stakhovski marshes							
064	Upper Mologa river (Verestovo lake)				✔			
065	Savtsinskoye marsh				✔			
066[1]	Orshinski marshes							
067	Flood-plain of Kotorosl' and Ust'e rivers							
068	Flood-plain of Kostroma river				✔			
069	Smolenskoye Pohozer'ye		✔					
070	Faustovo flood-plains of Moscow river				✔			
071	Homeland of the Crane (Dubna marshes and adjacent areas)							
072	Lotoshino crane gathering							
073	Danilovskoye marshes				✔			
074	Dedinivo flood-plain of Oka river				✔			
075	Zavidovo Nature Reserve, including Lotoshinski, Klinski and Diatlovo fish-ponds	✔						
076	Central Meshchera lake-system		✔		✔			
077	Nerussa–Desna woodland	✔						
078	Flood-plain of Iput' river in vicinity of Krutoayr				✔			
079	Flood-plain of Iput' river in vicinity of Kholevichami							
080	Kletnyanski forest				✔			
081	Desna flood-plain near Trubchevsk				✔			
082	Gavan'skiye oak-forest							
083	Kaluzhskiye Zaseki Nature Reserve	✔						
084	Oka River Valley Biosphere Reserve	✔						✔
085	Valley complex of Moksha and Oka rivers					✔		
086	Shilovo flood-plain of Oka river					✔		
087	Izhevsk flood-plain of Oka river				✔	✔		
088	Solotcha flood-plain of Oka river					✔		
089	Oka valley in vicinity of Murmino					✔		
090	Watershed of Tsna and Vysha rivers							
091	Terekhovski oak-forest							
092	Kulikovski forest				✔			
093	Upper Voronezh forest				✔			
094	Watershed of Bityug and Tsna rivers							
095	Zavoronezhski area							
096	Voroninski Nature Reserve	✔						
097	Tsninski forest							
098	Flood-plain of Sura river				✔			
099	Mordovian P. G. Smidovich Nature Reserve	✔						
100	Moksha valley in vicinity of Temnikov							
	Subtotal of IBAs	19	6	1	37	12	2	4

Table 5 ... continued. Protection status of Important Bird Areas in European Russia.
A tick (✔) indicates that an IBA overlaps with a protected area (to any extent).

IBA code	International name	Zapovednik	National Park	Natural Monument	Zakaznik	Ramsar Site	World Heritage Site	Biosphere Reserve
101	Ichalkovski		✔					
102	Flood-plain of Vad river				✔			
103	Insaro-Kovylkinski							
104	Moksha flood-plain in vicinity of Krasnoslobodsk				✔			
105	Flood-plain of Alatyr' river in vicinity of Ardatov				✔			
106	Surski reservoir							
107	Bekovskoye forest							
108	Kuznetski forest							
109¹	Sengileyevskiye mountain							
110	Watershed of Sura and Barysh rivers			✔	✔			
111	Privolzhskaya forest-steppe			✔				
112	Cheremshanski Bay of Kuybyshev reservoir				✔			
113	Khoper Nature Reserve	✔						
114	Flood-plain of Khoper river near Lake Ilmen'							
115	Khrenovskoy forest							
116	Bereznyakovski forest							
117	Voronezhski Nature Reserve	✔						✔
118	Vorono-Khoperski area							
119	Levo-Dobrinskaya valley							
120	Lake El'ton							
121	Novokvasnikovski liman							
122	Kalachinskaya loop of River Don							
123	Danilovski forest							
124	Rubezhnoye forest							
125	Akhtubinsk wetland				✔			
126	Vicinity of Borisoglebovka (Saratovski [Semenovski] Zakaznik)							
127	Valley of Safarovka river							
128	Siniye mountains							
129	Priyeruslanskiye sands				✔			
130	Varfolomeyevskiye saltmarshes							
131	North part of Volgogradski reservoir				✔			
132	Vicinity of Voznesenka village							
133	Sokino							
134	Almazovski area							
135	Algaiski							
136	Khvalynski National Park		✔					
137	Rovno area							
138	Stepan Rasin rock				✔			
139	Rzhestyanka							
140	Veselovskoye reservoir					✔		
141	Delta of the River Don	✔			✔			
142	Beglitskaya sand-spit			✔				
143	Islands in the western part of Lake Manych-Gudilo	✔				✔		
144	Karaichevski forest				✔			
145	Secretevskiye sands (Oblivski forest)							
146	Kalitvenski forest							
147	Gorodishchenski forest							
148	Chistaya Banka and Ivan-Karaul islands							
149	Uttinskaya area	✔						✔
150	Salt-lakes in the Primorsko-Akhtarsk area							
151	Eastern coast of the Sea of Azov				✔	✔		
152	Kiziltash limans							
153	Lower Urushtek river				✔			
154	Akhmet–Skala ridge							
155	Kurdzhips river valley				✔			
156	Lake Khanskoye							
157	Yeyski salt-lakes							
158	Surroundings of Black Forest							
159	Kalininski Plavny							
160	Mouth of Yeya river							
161	Imeretinskaya lowland							
162	Valley of Urup river				✔			
163	Caucasus Biosphere Reserve	✔						✔
164	Dadynskiye lake							
165	Lake Manych-Gudilo	✔					✔	✔
166	Burukshunskiye limans				✔			
167	Teberdinski Nature Reserve	✔						
168	Kabardino-Balkarski Nature Reserve	✔						
169	Severo-Osetinski (North Osetin) Nature Reserve	✔						
170	Budary lakes							
171	Agrakhanski Bay				✔			
172	Kizlyar Bay	✔						
173	Mouth of Samur river				✔			
174	Lake Adzhi							
175	Sources of Mazachai and Mullarchai rivers							
176	Karakol'skiye lakes							
177	Achikol'skiye lakes							
178	Morskoy Biryuchek island	✔			✔			
179	Volga delta	✔					✔	✔
180	Western Ilmen area				✔			
181	Maly Zhemchuzhny island			✔				
182	Bogdinsko-Baskunchakski				✔			
183	Flood-plain of River Vetluga							
184	Kamsko-Bakaldinskiye marshes	✔				✔		
185	Sitnikovski Nature Reserve				✔			
186	Gorki reservoir and the lower Unzha river							
187	Flood-plain of Algashka river							
188	Sura environs	✔						
189	Arski fish-ponds							
190	Kamsko-Ikski area				✔			
191	Bulgarski			✔				
192	Cheremshanski forest							
193	Zhigulevsk Nature Reserve	✔						
194	Tashlinski forest							
195	Racheyski forest				✔			
196	Suskanski Nature Reserve				✔			
197¹	Buzulukski forest							
198	Kamsko-Yayvenski wetland				✔			
199	Verkhnevisherski mountain	✔						
200	Kumikushski wetland				✔			
201	Adovo-Chugrumski wetland				✔			
202	Khvarkush and Zolotoy Kamen' ridges				✔			
203	Nizhnekamskaya flood-plain							
204	Bashkirski Nature Reserve	✔						
205	Octyabr'ski forest							
206	Mountain valley of Sakmara river							
207	Nikiforovski forest							
208	Watershed of Bel'skaya and Nugush rivers	✔	✔		✔			
209	Bel'skaya flood-plain							
Subtotal of IBAs (left)		24	8	4	50	15	2	6
Subtotal of IBAs (right)		38	9	6	67	18	2	9

Table 5 ... continued. Protection status of Important Bird Areas in European Russia. A tick (✔) indicates that an IBA overlaps with a protected area (to any extent).

IBA code	International name	National				International			IBA code	International name	National				International		
		Zapovednik	National Park	Natural Monument	Zakaznik	Ramsar Site	World Heritage Site	Biosphere Reserve			Zapovednik	National Park	Natural Monument	Zakaznik	Ramsar Site	World Heritage Site	Biosphere Reserve
210	Yamantau mountain	✔							215	Kupy area							
211	Iremel'ski mountain								216	Kulaksay lowland							
212	Irendyk ridge								217	Shalkaro-Zhetykolski lake system							
213	Maly Nakas ridge								218	Orenburgski Nature Reserve	✔						
214	Steppe valley of Sakmara river								**Total number of IBAs**		**40**	**9**	**6**	**67**	**18**	**2**	**9**
Subtotal of IBAs		39	9	6	67	18	2	9									

1. Protection status of IBAs 020, 066, 109 and 197 is unknown.

Box 1. International legislation and initiatives that are relevant to site conservation in Russia (see Appendix 1 for a general description of these agreements).

Global
Biodiversity Convention ✔
Ramsar Convention ✔
Bonn Convention
World Heritage Convention ✔
MAB Programme ✔

Pan-European
Bern Convention

Regional
Helsinki Convention

✔ Convention ratified/initiative supported
(✔) Convention signed

There are several common types of Zakaznik, such as zoological, ornithological, botanical, hydrobiological, and landscape. Hunting organizations are very active in the establishment of temporary Hunting Zakazniks, each lasting for 10–20 years. Zakazniks which are established by the federal government usually have a staff of rangers (game managers). In the case of other Zakazniks, the primary land-users are officially responsible for site protection and for management of suitable activities in the area, but there are no permanent staff in these areas.

Zakazniks and Natural Monuments play very significant roles, forming the 'backbone' of a regionally administered protected-area network.

In addition to the four major types of protected area, a variety of regulations allow for nature conservation in other ways. According to several federal laws, including the national law 'On Specially Protected Areas', any form of protected area can exist at the regional and local (district) levels (e.g. 'green belts' of towns, water-protection zones along rivers, privately owned protected areas). The types of restriction on economic activity, and their limits, depend on what is being protected at a particular area.

Fifty-two (24%) out of the total of 218 IBAs have a high level of overlap with the national protected-area system (mostly as Zapovedniks or National Parks), while 51 of the 218 IBAs have a moderate overlap

(Figure 4, Table 5). The remaining 115 IBAs (53%) have a low overlap (18 sites) or no protection at all (97 sites). Thus, only about half of the identified IBAs have a moderate or high overlap with the national protected-area system. In total, 39–40% of the total IBA area is covered by national types of protected area in Russia (Figure 4).

■ **International protection**
Russia is party to most of the relevant international legislation and initiatives concerning the conservation of sites in Europe (Box 1). There are only 18 IBAs in European Russia which overlap with officially designated Ramsar Sites (Table 5), but most of the other wetland IBAs feature in a shadow list of Ramsar Sites (Langeveld and Grimmett 1990). Nine IBAs are also protected at the international level as Biosphere Reserves (Table 5, Figure 5). In total, about 19% of the total IBA area in Russia is covered by international types of protected area (Figure 5).

■ **Future proposals**
Almost all protected areas in Russia conserve some bird habitat, hence proposals for their continued development remain a research priority for ornithologists (Galushin and Zubakin 1998). It should be noted that not all protected areas within IBAs were created for the purpose of bird conservation. So, a special attempt should be made as soon as possible to analyse the current protected-area regime, and to restrict human activity in some protected areas, to make sure that they really are conserving birds.

CONSERVATION

● A national Red Data Book for threatened and rare bird species was established in 1974—the second edition is under preparation at the moment—and this lists about 125 bird species or subspecies (in the whole of Russia) as nationally threatened. By a special decision of the government in 1996, all Red Data Book species and their subspecies are now strictly protected by federal laws (Galushin and Zubakin 1998). The compilation of regional Red Data Books is now underway in many regions of Russia.

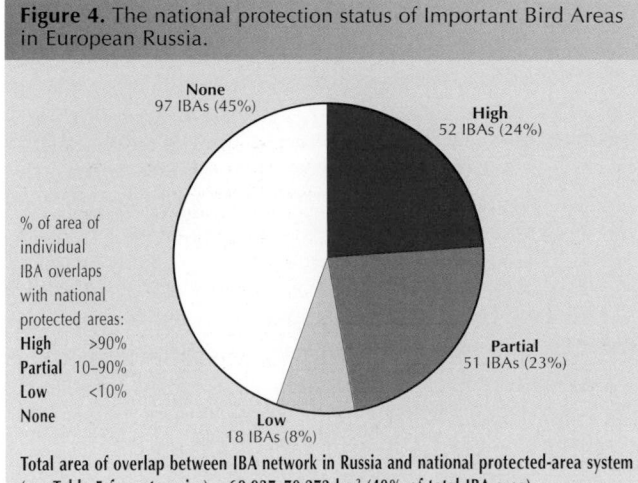

Figure 4. The national protection status of Important Bird Areas in European Russia.

None 97 IBAs (45%)
High 52 IBAs (24%)
Partial 51 IBAs (23%)
Low 18 IBAs (8%)

% of area of individual IBA overlaps with national protected areas:
High >90%
Partial 10–90%
Low <10%
None

Total area of overlap between IBA network in Russia and national protected-area system (see Table 5 for categories) = 68,937–70,272 km² (40% of total IBA area).

Figure 5. The international protection status of Important Bird Areas in European Russia.

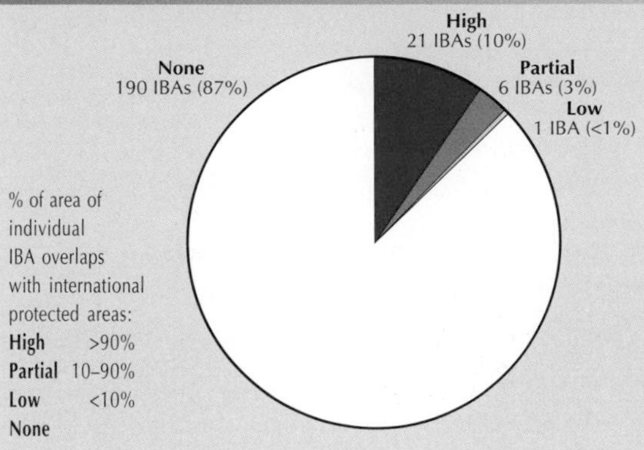

High 21 IBAs (10%)
Partial 6 IBAs (3%)
Low 1 IBA (<1%)
None 190 IBAs (87%)

% of area of individual IBA overlaps with international protected areas:
High >90%
Partial 10–90%
Low <10%
None

Total area of overlap between IBA network in Russia and international protected-area system (see Table 5 for categories) = 32,982 km² (19% of total IBA area).

Box 2. Shadow list of 151 sites in European Russia that are potentially IBAs. Those sites that were surveyed in 1998 (after the closing date for inclusion in this publication) and which were found to meet IBA criteria are marked with an asterisk (*). These latter sites (totalling 73) will certainly be included in the forthcoming national IBA inventory.

Arkhangelsk region
1. Delta reki Mezen' (Mezen' delta)
2. Kozhozerski Zakaznik Ostrov Dezhkin Kamen' (Dezhkin Kamen' island)
3. Southern tundra of Novaya Zemlya
4. Ust'ye reki Kara (Mouth of Kara river)
5. Lesnoi ostrov More-Yu (More Yu forest)
6. Bolvanskaya guba (Bolvanskaya Bay)
7. Pakhanicheskaya guba (Pakhanicheskaya Bay)
8. Kosminskaya systema ozer (Kosminskaya lake system)
9. Delta Pechory (Pechora delta)
10. Ostrov I proliv Sengeiski (Sengeiski Bay and island)
11. Ostrov Kolguev (Kolguev island)

Bashkortostan Republic
12. *Khrebet Shaitan-Tau (Shaitan-Tau ridge)
13. *Zilairskoye Prisakmar'ye
14. *Gorni massiv Kraka (Kraka mountain)
15. *Meneuzskiye Yary (Meneuzskiye bank)
16. *Usen'skiye Yary (Usen'skiye bank)
17. *Gornaya dolina reki Inzer (Mountain valley of Inzer river)
18. Zapovednik Basegi (Basegi Nature Reserve)
19. Nukaevskiye shishki (Nukaevskiye hills)
20. Andreevskiye shishki (Andreevskiye hills)
21. Muradymovskoye ushchel'ye ('Muradymovskoye Ushchel'ye' National Park)
22. Krasnokamski Les (Krasnokamski forest)
23. Kaltasinski Les (Kaltasinski forest)
24. *Uphimskoye Plato (Uphimskoye plateau)
25. *Pavlovskoye vodokhranilishche (Pavlovskoye reservoir)
26. *Aiskiye Yary (Aiskiye bank)
27. *Gornaya dolina reki Ai (Mountain valley of Ai river)
28. *Gornaya dolina reki Zilim (Mountain valley of Zilim river)
29. *Tazlarovskiye shishki (Tazlarovskiye hills)
30. *Uruyk (Uruyk area)
31. *Bakalinski Les (Bakalinski forest)
32. *Vedeneevskaya Dacha (Vedeneevskaya area)
33. *Prisuyn'skoye lesnichestvo (Prisuyn'skoye forest)
34. *Sharanskiye Bory (Sharanski forest)
35. *Buninski Les (Buninski forest)
36. *Usen'-Ivanovski Les (Usen'-Ivanovski forest)

Dagestan Republic
37. *Turalinskaya laguna (Turalinskaya lagoon)
38. *Sulakskaya laguna (Sulakskaya lagoon)
39. *Samurski Khrebet (Samurski ridge)
40. *Khrebet Kebyaktepe (Kebyaktepe ridge)
41. *Urochishche 'Laman-Kam' ('Laman-Kam' area)
42. *Temirgoiskiye Ozera (Temirgoiskiye lakes)
43. *Kayakentski Zakaznik (Kayakentski Reserve)
44. *Kasumkentski Zakaznik (Kasumkentski Reserve)
45. *Berkubinskaya Lesnaya Dacha (Berkubinski forest)

Ingushetiya Republic
46. Verkhov'ya reki Assy (Valley of Assa river)

Ivanovo region
47. Srednee techeniye reki Lukh (Middle stream of Lukh river)

Kalmykiya Republic
48. *Ozero Sostinskoye (Sostinskoye lake)

Kaluga region
49. *Bryansko-Zhizdryanskoye Poles'ye (Bryansko-Zhizdryanski forest, watershed of Reseta and Vytebet' rivers)

Karelia Republic
50. Shuiskiye polya (Shuiskiye fields)

Kaliningrad region
51. Vislinskaya kosa (Vislinskaya spit)
52. Yuzhnoye Poberezh'ye Kurshskogo Zaliva (Southern shore of Kurshski Bay)
53. Vostochnoye Poberezh'ye Kurshskogo Zaliva (Eastern shore of Kurshski Bay)
54. Dolina i ust'ye reki Deima (Valley and mouth of Deima river)
55. Ozero Vyshtenetskoye (Vyshtenetskoye lake)

Karachaevo-Cherkesskaya Republic
56. *Skalistyi Khrebet mezhdu rekami Urup i Malyi Zelenchuk (Skalinstyi ridge, watershed of Urup and Malyi Zelenchuk)
57. *Dolina reki Khasaut (Valley of Khasaut river)

Kirov region
58. *Kamsko-Poryshski taezhno-bolotni complex (Kamsko-Poryshski taiga–mire complex)
59. *Mezhdurech'ye Atsvezha I Yumy (Watershed of Atsvezha and Yuma rivers)

Komi Republic
60. Mezhdurech'ye Shchepkinoi I Ersy (Watershed of Shchepkina and Ersa rivers)
61. Bolotnaya sistema Usvanuyr (Usvanuyr mire system)

Krasnodarski kray and Adygeya Republic
62. Gora Autl' (Autl' mountain)
63. Sladko-Limanskoye okhotkhozyastvo (Sladko-Limanskoye hunting area)
64. Eiskiye plavni
65. Okretnosti gory Bolshoi Tkhach (Surroundings of Bolshoi Tkhach mountain)
66. *Verkhov'ya rek Kuna i Shisha (Sources of Kuna and Shisha rivers)
67. *Dolina reki Khodz' (Valley of Khodz' river)

Leningrad region
68. Severo-Zapadniye prigorody St
69. Yugo-Zapadniye prigorody St
70. Ivinski razliv (Ivinskoye lake and suroundings)
71. Shlisselburgskaya guba Ladozhskogo ozera (Shlisserburgskaya Bay of Lake Ladoga)
72. Rybkhoz Kovashi i Syur'evskoye boloto (Surroundings of Kovashi ponds)

Mordovia Republic
73. Purdoshanski (Purdoshanski area)
74. Sialeevskaya (Sialeevskaya area)
75. Ardatovski (Ardatovski area)
76. Umetski (Umetski area)
77. *Vyshinski (Vyshinski area)
78. *Rybkinski (Rybkinski area)
79. *Issinski (Issinski area)

Murmansk region
80. Ph'yarvann (Ph'yarvann)

Nizhni Novgorod region
81. Poima reki Oki v okrestnostyakh Pavlovo (Oka flood-plain in vicinity of Pavlovo)

Orenburg region
82. Donguzskaya step' (Donduzskaya steppe)
83. *Poima reki Ilek (Ilek flood-plain)
84. Chibendinskaya melovaya step' (Chibendinskaya steppe)
85. Okrestnosti Dombarovskogo (Vicinity of Dombarovskoye)
86. Iriklinskoye vodokhranilishche (Iriklinskoye reservoir)
87. Ozero Aike (Aike lake)

Orel region
88. Orlovskoye Poles'ye (Orlovskoye Poles'ye National Park)

Penza region
89. Zamechenski (Zamechenski area)

Perm' region
90. *Redrikovskiye bolota (Redrikovskiye mire)
91. *Krasnoye Plotbishche
92. *Bereznikovskiye bolota (Bereznikovskiye mire)

Pskov region
93. Sebezhskaya (Sebezhski National Park)

Rostov region
94. *Elanski (Elanski Areas)
95. *Ostrovnoi (Ostrovnoi area)
96. *Tsimlyanskiye peski (Tsimlyanskiye sands)
97. Liman Kholostonur (Kholostonur liman)
98. *Dudarevskya (Dudarevskaya area)
99. Reshetovskaya (Reshetovskaya area)
100. Chirski (Chirski area)
101. *Kundruychinskiye peski (Kundruychinskiye sands)
102. *Migulinskiye peski (Migulinskiye sands)

Ryazan' region
103. Dolinniy complex Mokshi i Oki (Valley complex of Oka and Moksha rivers)
104. Poima reki Proni (Flood-plain of Pronya river)
105. Rybkhoz 'Para' (Para fish-ponds)
106. Poima rek Mokhshi I Tsny (Flood-plain of Moksha and Tsna rivers)
107. Ozera Komgar' i Negar' (Komgar' and Negar' lakes)

Samara region
108. Baituganski Zakaznik (Baituganski reserve)
109. Pokhvistnevski lesnoi massiv (Pokhvistnevski forest)
110. Uzuykovski Bor (Uzuykovski forest)
111. Kondurchinskiye Bory (Kondurchinskiye forest)
112. *Chapaevskiye Limani(Chapaevskie liman)

Saratov region
113. Pamyatnik prirody Pady (Pady Natural Monument)
114. Dolina Khopra (Khoper valley)
115. *Krasnoyarskiye luga (Krasnoyarskiye meadows)
116. Kirovskaya step' (Kirovskaya steppe)
117. Pereluybski (Pereluybski area)
118. Okrestnosti gory Sinyaya (Surroundings of Sinyaya mountain)
119. *Agrotsenozy yuzhnoi i vostochnoi chasti Novouzenskogo raiona (Agricultural land of Novouzenski district)
120. *Cherkasski Zakaznik (Cherkasski Reserve)
121. *Okrestnosty Eruslana (Vicinity of Eruslan village)
122. *Okrestnosti Zelenogo Dola (Vicinity of Zeleni Dol village)
123. *Polynno-Zlakoviye stepi u sela Kanavka (Steppe in vicinity of Kanavka village)

Smolensk region
124. Rybkhoz Zherespeya (Zherespeya fish-ponds)
125. Lesniye massivy v poime Ugry (Forest in flood-plain of Ugra river)
126. *Sokolino-Kasplyanskaya (Sokolino-Kasplyanskaya area)

Stavropolski kray
127. *Solenoe ozero (Lake Solenoe)
128. *Irgaklinskaya lesnaya dacha (Irgaklinskaya area)
129. *Okrestnosti ozera Ptich'ye (Surroundings of Ptich'ye lake)
130. *Ostrov Pelikani (Pelikani island)
131. *Okrestnosti Kislovodska (Surroundings of Kislovodsk)

Tatarstan Republic
132. *Bugulminskiye Bory (Bugulminski forest)

Ul'yanovskaya region
133. *Starokulatkinskiye dubravy (Starokulatkinski forest)
134. *Zolotaya Gora i okrestnosti (Zolotaya mountain and surroundings)
135. *Karginskiye Kholmy (Karginskiye hills)

Vladimir region
136. Petushinskoye okhotkhozyastvo (Petushinski hunting area)

Volgograd region
137. *Cherebaevo (Cherebaevo area)
138. Teterevyatka (Teterevyatka area)
139. *Bulukhta (Gor'ko-Solenoe ozero) (Bulukhta, Gor'ko-Solenoe lake)
140. Zakaznik Drophini (Drophini reserve)
141. Pravoberezhe Volgogradskogo vodokhranilishcha (Right shore of Volgogradski reservoir)
142. Archadinskiye Peski (Archadinskiye sands)
143. Sarpinskiye Ozera (Sarpinskiye lakes)
144. Voiskovaya dubrava (Voiskovaya oak-forest)
145. Mezhdurech'ye Dona I Chira (Watershed of Don and Chir rivers)
146. Tsimlyanskoye vodokhranilishche (Tsimlyanski reservoir)
147. *Golubinskiye peski (Golubinskiye sands)
148. *Stepnovski Ugol (Stepnovski area)

Yaroslavl' region
149. *Dunilovskoye boloto (Dunilovskoye bog)
150. *Shalimovskoye boloto (Shalimovskoye bog)
151. *Poima reki Yukhot' (Yukhot' flood-plain)

- As mentioned previously, about half of the IBAs have (individually) a moderate to high overlap with nationally protected areas. This implies that the protected parts of the IBAs should have a specified land-use regime, formally agreed on paper with land-users, regional governmental organizations, etc. A network of regional governmental environment agencies was established in 1988 as the mechanism for controlling and managing protected areas and other conservation issues. These regional agencies (one per region for almost all administrative regions/republics) are supervised by the Government Committee for Nature Protection and Environment. But, because of a lack of staff and sometimes of funds, in reality at most sites there is no control of the land-use regime, and as a result there are many violations of the statutory protection. Only Zapovedniks and some federal Zakazniks and National Parks have something resembling a management plan. There has been no tradition in Russia to write management plans and then to really apply them in practice, so the majority of IBAs (even if protected) do have not them.

- Scientific research and monitoring of breeding, migrating and wintering birds are carried out at those IBAs which fully or partly overlap with federal nature reserves (Zapovedniks and National Parks). Some management work is done at IBAs in regions where there are active conservation NGOs, e.g. towards the creation of protected areas or towards the monitoring of rare species or of waterbird numbers. It is currently difficult to say exactly how many IBAs are under active management or research by RBCU members and projects, or by the Division for Nature Reserves or by other environmental NGOs, although RBCU has good working contacts with many of these other groups.

- In general, there are three top priorities for avian conservation research which will closely determine the future progress of IBA work in Russia (Galushin and Zubakin 1998):
  1. the assessment and prediction of the impact of present socio-economic conditions on bird diversity and populations;
  2. the survey, monitoring and comparison of bird fauna, populations and habitats in various regions;
  3. the implementation of conservation-biology practices, including the development of appropriate measures for the conservation of birds and their habitats.

ANALYTICAL METHODS

- IBA data-sheets were prepared in Russian, very similar to the data-sheets in English that had been prepared by the Secretariat of BirdLife International. A lack of recent ornithological information, and a scarcity of professional ornithologists and skilled amateur birdwatchers, are both real problems in Russia, therefore some additional boxes were added to the data-sheets, so that any available information from the last 10–15 years could also be included, in order to have as much data as possible about each IBA.

- As no strong and full scientific coordination was possible in Russia, each collaborator used their traditional methods of bird counting, such as absolute counts, transects, plots, etc. and then extrapolated data to cover the whole area suggested as an IBA, so as to produce estimates of minimum and maximum population size for bird species. Data were then checked at the RBCU office and defined more precisely, working together with collaborators if necessary and possible. Certain species (e.g. *Crex crex*, certain waders [Charadrii]) do not have a pair-breeding system, but counts are given as 'breeding pairs', unless otherwise stated, even though the actual unit of census may have been something else (e.g. the number of breeding individuals, or of calling or displaying males).

- Other sites in European Russia which have the potential to meet IBA criteria, following future investigations, but which are not covered by the current European IBA review, are listed in Box 2.

- Overall, this inventory of IBAs has improved knowledge of bird distributions in European Russia, and for several species has allowed a more accurate estimate of their total population size in European Russia.

GLOSSARY

kray administrative region.

liman a water-body in a shallow depression in the steppe zone, normally but not necessarily saline (can be brackish or fresh).
RBCU Russian Bird Conservation Union (Soyuz Okhrany Ptits Rossii).
taiga the coniferous forest of the boreal biome of northern Europe and Asia, lying between the temperate and the tundra biomes.

ACKNOWLEDGEMENTS

The current IBA review in European Russia is a result of huge amount of work carried out by a network of collaborators, who volunteered their energy and much free time in compiling data and surveying sites in the field. It was only through the enthusiasm of all these people that it was possible to organize this review within a very restricted time-schedule and with a rather small amount of funds.

We are indebted to the following authors of data-sheets (site-codes in brackets): V. A. Andreev (022), A. N. Antonchikov (118, 121, 126, 129, 130, 132), V. M. Anufriev (039, 040), V. V. Anufriev (035), N. V. Anzigitova (023, 027), A. V. Artem'ev (014, 017), O. V. Askeev and I. V. Askeev (189), V. O. Avdanin (021, 050), A. S. Ayupov (190, 191), Z. T. Bagautdinova (204), S. V. Bakka (184, 185), V. P. Belik (107, 108, 115, 119, 122, 123, 124, 144, 145, 146, 147, 192, 194, 197, 205, 206, 207, 214), A. V. Belyachenko (118, 121, 126, 129, 130, 131), V. V. Bianki (003), A. I. Bliznyuk (149, 165, 166, 178), V. S. Bogatov (171), N. S. Boiko (010), O. V. Borodin (109, 110, 111, 112), Yu. N. Bublichenko (048), O. M. Bukreeva (165), V. T. But'ev (027), V. A. Buzun (036), A. E. Cherenkov (018, 020), S. E. Cherenkov (165), V. F. Chernobay (125), E. V. Chernova (058), A. O. Choubine (120, 171), V. G. Chupachenko (077), A. V. Davygora (215, 216, 217), S. A. Dylyuk (011, 072), G. S. Dzhamirzoev (173, 174, 175, 176, 177), N. A. Egorova (083), M. Kh. Emtyl (150, 152, 156, 157, 158, 159, 160), G. S. Eremkin (064, 076), G. S. Fedchuk (058), Yu. P. Fedotov (077), V. V. Frolov (106), A. M. Gineev (151), O. V. Glushenkov (187), S. V. Golubev (058, 067, 068), Yu. A. Gorshkov (190, 191), E. A. Goryunov (084, 085, 086, 087, 088, 089, 090, 091), G. V. Grishanov (001, 002), G. F. Grishutkin (101, 099), E. B. Gruzdev (058), A. S. Gylyazov (007, 008), I. V. Il'inskiy (055), M. P. Il'yukh (164), N. P. Iovchenko (049), A. M. Ivanenko (152, 156, 157), M. N. Ivanova (060), I. V. Karyakin (198, 199, 200, 201, 202, 203, 208, 209, 210, 211, 212, 213), B. A. Kazakov (140), T. Yu. Khohlova (015, 016, 023, 024, 028), A. N. Khokhlov (164), S. K. Kochanov (037, 039), S. A. Korkina (106), S. M. Kosenko (077, 078, 079, 080, 081, 082), A. B. Kostin (083), V. A. Kovalev (042), V. G. Krivenko (021, 180), A. V. Kuznetsov (057), E. A. Kuznetsov (023, 025, 026, 027), A. S. Lapshin (100, 102, 103, 104, 105, 098), N. V. Lapshin (014, 017), E. A. Lebedeva (173), G. P. Lebedeva (193, 195, 196, 197), Yu. V. Lokhman (150, 152, 156, 157, 158, 159, 160), B. Yu. Losov (077), E. V. Lysenkov (100, 102, 103, 104, 105, 098), S. V. Mikhailov (043), V. A. Minoranskiy (141, 142, 143), A. L. Mischenko (051, 052, 053, 054, 056, 071, 074, 075), V. V. Morozov (127, 128), V. N. Moseikin (126, 133, 134, 135, 136, 137, 138, 139), N. N. Moshonkin (182), N. D. Neifeld (038), V. I. Nikolaev (061, 062, 063, 064, 065, 066, 075), G. A. Noskov (042, 043, 044, 048, 049), A. D. Numerov (114, 115, 116, 117), T. D. Paneva (010), I. V. Panteleev (193, 195, 196, 197), V. G. Pchelintsev (055), V. V. Piskunov (121, 126, 129, 130, 131), T. V. Pleshak (030), I. V. Pokrovskaya (025, 026), V. M. Polivanov (167), S. P. Rezviy (042, 045), S. V. Rudnitskiy (166), G. M. Rusanov (179, 180, 181), A. A. Rusinov (058, 067, 068), S. Yu. Rykova (019), V. S. Sarychev (115, 116, 092, 093), I. B. Savinich (045), V. Yu. Semashko (018, 020), A. I. Shepel (200, 201, 202), I. P. Shpilenok (077), S. L. Smirnova (109, 110, 111), E. N. Sokhina (125), A. Yu. Sokolov (114), O. V. Sukhanova (051, 053, 075), T. V. Sviridova (074), M. I. Tarantsev (140), G. M. Tertitskiy (018, 020), P. A. Tilba (152, 153, 154, 155, 161, 162, 163), V. G. Turchin (115, 116), P. D. Vengerov (114, 115, 116, 117), E. V. Vilkov (171, 172), G. V. Vinogradov (021), S. M. Volkov (069), G. P. Vorobiev (096, 097), I. I. Vorobiev (113), V. A. Yakovlev (188), M. V. Yakovleva (013), M. M. Zabelin (118, 094, 095), V. I. Zabelin (164), V. L. Zemlyanoy (133), V. B. Zimin (014, 017), A. A. Zolotarev (113), V. A. Zubakin (004, 070, 071, 073, 074).

We are also very grateful to other collaborators who contributed to the shadow list of potential IBAs (see Box 2) and to all of the participants in the IBA Programme in Russia, who continue to compile data in their own free time: L. N. Voronov, S. V. Bukharinov, A. Yu. Okolelov, K. V. Avilova, A. A. Mogilner, S. V. Kornev, L. D. Alba, S. V. Buslaev, Yu. D. Galchenkov, V. I. Garanin, Yu. A. Gorshkov, A. V. Zavyalov, B. Yu. Lozov, N. P. Malkov, V. G. Marrphin, E. Sisonenko, Yu. N. Tabanakov, V. V. Tolstyakov, O. V. Shvets, L. Ph. Skryleva, A. V. Dobrinov, A. Lastukhin, V. N. Melnikov, R. A. Khanov, Yu. V. Pishvanov, T. I. Chevanina, A. A. Chibilev, P. Pakhomov, V. D. Kokhanov, L. P. Uryadova, G. D. Rudnykh, V. S. Kuznetsov, B. A. Kozlov, V. I. Mironov, S. A. Fetisov, S. Nedosekin, M. A. Erashov, V. I. Pozdyshev, N. V. Markov, A. I. Dodonov, D. Yu. Suchkov, L. G. Onoprienko, S. V. Ruudnitski, V. N. Medvedev, R. A. Volkov, B. V. Khasminski, A. G. Fefilov, L. I. Nikolaev, D. I. Chukhlantsev, M. V. Gordin, Yu. G. Karpov, V. R. Roganov, O. V. Bakin, L. I. Kuts, A. I. Paliev, I. V.

Silchenko, D. G. Kosintsev, P. V. Kopylov, A. S. Galaktionov, V. A. Grudinin, A. S. Tolstykh, A. A. Medvedev, Yu. A. Bykov, L. D. Bekhtereva, E. P. Komlev, S. M. Volkov, V. I. Gorshkov, A. P. Bicherev, M. I. Demidova, E. V. Gavluyk, G. M. Salnikov, V. V. Bianki, V. D. Boyarshinov, V. I. Zabelin, R. Mnatsekanov, S. Vershinin, V. A. Telpov, V. P. Kazakov, V. A. Lapushkin, S. V. Fisher, A. V. Boikov, T. O. Barabashin, A. G. Varlamov, D. V. Bogomolov, M. Bubnov, O. N. Orlova, D. A. Solovkov, and O. A. Vitovich.

In addition, we thank the Russian office of Wetlands International for providing all available information on Ramsar Sites in European Russia.

Special thanks should be given to the Secretariat of BirdLife International, and especially to Melanie Heath, Tony Payne and Mike Evans, for their patience in answering all questions and in resolving problems that occurred during the work.

This review would have been almost impossible without substantial sponsorship from Vogelbescherming Nederland (BirdLife Partner in the Netherlands), the MATRA-Programme of the Netherlands Ministry of Foreign Affairs, the PIN-Programme of the Netherlands Ministry of Agriculture, Nature Conservation and Fisheries, the Netherlands Agricultural Council Moscow (Landbouwraad Moskou), the Royal Society for the Protection of Birds (BirdLife Partner in the UK), the Institute of Soviet–American Relations, and the Prins Bernhard Fonds, which all provided special grants for purching equipment, for coordination and for field projects within the framework variously of the IBA programme and of projects on globally threatened species in European Russia. We are especially grateful to Johanna Winkelman for all the practical help in the project and help in obtaining funds for the Russian IBA programme. Elena Lebedeva and Vladimir Galushin helped in the writing of the overview text. We are especially thankful also to Sergei Dyluyk and Sergei Bukreev who assisted the IBA Officer during the compilation and checking of the data and of this review, and to Yuri Chernikov, who helped with arrangements for field projects. Our greatest regards should be given to Victor Zubakin—the person who initiated the IBA programme in Russia, who supervised this work during the last four years, and who contributed a great deal to the current progress of the programme.

■ SITE ACCOUNTS

Nemanski forest B2 001
Admin region Kaliningrad
Coordinates 55°00′N 22°20′E
Altitude 0–50 m Area 17,000 ha

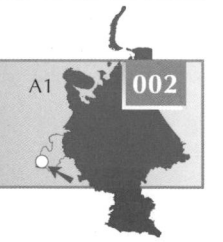

■ Site description
This forested area is located within one of the most developed regions in Russia.

Habitats Forest and woodland (87%; native coniferous forest; mixed forest), Grassland (12%), Wetland (1%)
Land-use Agriculture (12%), Forestry (30%), Hunting (100%), Tourism/recreation (10%)

■ Birds

Species		Season	Year	Pop min	Pop max	Acc	Criteria
[1] *Aquila pomarina* Lesser Spotted Eagle	B	1994	1		2	B	B2

1. Internationally important but not in 'Top 5' sites.

The best site for breeding raptors in the Kaliningrad region. Breeding species of global conservation concern that do not meet IBA criteria: *Aquila clanga* (1 pair), *Crex crex* (5–10 pairs). The only known breeding site for *Milvus milvus* in Russia.

■ Protection status
National None **International** None

■ Conservation issues

Threats Deforestation (commercial) (B)

Dal'ni forest A1 002
Admin region Kaliningrad
Coordinates 55°12′N 21°20′E
Altitude 0–10 m Area 4,000 ha

■ Site description
The area lies in one of the most developed regions of Russia, and includes many wet habitat-types, including some that are seasonally wet.

Habitats Forest and woodland (85%; mixed forest; alluvial/very wet forest), Grassland (10%; humid grassland)
Land-use Agriculture (4%), Forestry (40%), Hunting (100%), Nature conservation/research (100%), Not utilized (50%), Tourism/recreation (5%)

■ Birds

Species		Season	Year	Pop min	Pop max	Acc	Criteria
Crex crex Corncrake	B	1996	80	120	B	A1

Crex crex breeds in significant numbers, but another breeding species of global conservation concern does not meet IBA criteria: *Haliaeetus albicilla* (1–3 pairs).

■ Protection status
National High **International** None
4,000 ha of IBA covered by Zakaznik (Dyunniy, 8,000 ha).

■ Conservation issues

Threats Disturbance to birds (C), Forest grazing (C), Recreation/tourism (C), Selective logging/cutting (C), Unsustainable exploitation (C)

There are plans to create an international (Russian–Lithuanian) nature reserve here, covering the Neman delta.

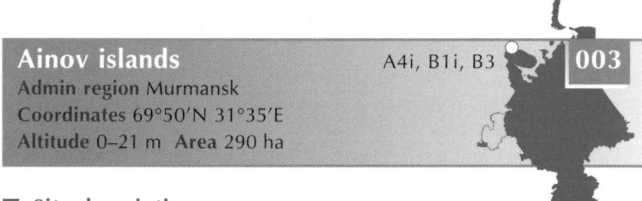

Ainov islands A4i, B1i, B3 003
Admin region Murmansk
Coordinates 69°50′N 31°35′E
Altitude 0–21 m Area 290 ha

■ Site description
Tundra islands in the Barents Sea.

Habitats Grassland (90%; humid grassland; tundra), Wetland (11%; tidal river/enclosed tidal water; coastal lagoon; fen/transition mire/spring)
Land-use Nature conservation/research (100%)

■ Birds

Species		Season	Year	Pop min	Pop max	Acc	Criteria
Calidris maritima Purple Sandpiper	P	1996	150	800	A	A4i, B1i
Larus marinus Great Black-backed Gull	B	1996	2,100	6,000	A	A4i, B1i, B3

The islands support important numbers of breeding *Larus marinus* and of migrating *Calidris maritima*.

■ Protection status
National High **International** None
290 ha of IBA covered by Zakaznik (Kandalakshskiy, 70,500 ha).

■ Conservation issues

Threats Other (U)

Pollution of seawater is a threat ('Other' threat, above).

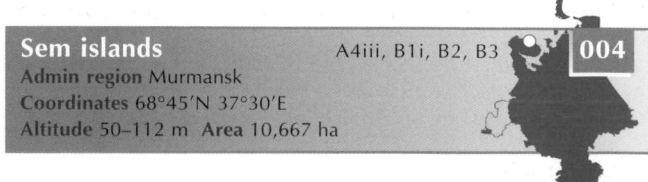

Sem islands A4iii, B1i, B2, B3 004
Admin region Murmansk
Coordinates 68°45′N 37°30′E
Altitude 50–112 m Area 10,667 ha

■ Site description

Habitats Marine areas (94%; sea inlet/coastal features), Rocky areas (6%; sea cliff/rocky shore)
Land-use Nature conservation/research (100%)

Cliffs and rocky shores of tundra islands in the Barents Sea. The IBA covers 667 ha of land and 10,000 ha of sea.

■ Birds

Species		Season	Year	Pop min	Pop max	Acc	Criteria
Somateria mollissima	Eider	B	1991	1,407	1,407	A	B1i
Larus marinus	Great Black-backed Gull	B	1991	550	550	A	B3

More than 25,000 pairs of seabirds breed here, comprising mainly *Rissa tridactyla*.

■ Protection status

National High **International** None
10,667 ha of IBA covered by Zapovednik (Kandalakshskiy, 70,500 ha).

Coastal belt of eastern Murmansk

A4i, B1i   005

Admin region Murmansk
Coordinates 68°00'N 39°00'E
Altitude 0–0 m **Area** 260 ha

■ Site description

Coastal shallows along the shore of the Barents Sea.

Habitats Marine areas (sea inlet/coastal features)

■ Birds

Species		Season	Year	Pop min	Pop max	Acc	Criteria
[1]*Somateria mollissima*	Eider	W	1988	—	—	—	A4i, B1i
[1]*Somateria spectabilis*	King Eider	W	1988	—	—	—	A4i, B1i

1. Up to 100,000 S. mollissima/S. spectabilis.

Two eider-duck *Somateria* species form congregations of up to 100,000 individuals in winter. Species of global conservation concern that do not meet IBA criteria: *Anser erythropus* (there is an old observation of one breeding pair, but no recent information is available).

■ Protection status

National None **International** None

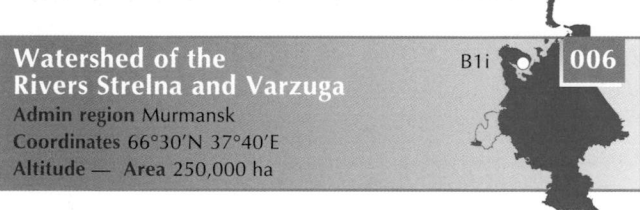

Watershed of the Rivers Strelna and Varzuga

B1i   006

Admin region Murmansk
Coordinates 66°30'N 37°40'E
Altitude — **Area** 250,000 ha

■ Site description

Extremely marshy northern taiga with a large number of lakes.

Habitats Forest and woodland, Wetland (standing fresh water; water-fringe vegetation)

■ Birds

Species		Season	Year	Pop min	Pop max	Acc	Criteria
Cygnus cygnus	Whooper Swan	B	1989	—	—	—	B1i
[1]*Cygnus cygnus*	Whooper Swan	N	1989	—	500	—	B1i

1. Pre-migration gathering.

Based on data in the previous European IBA inventory (Grimmett and Jones 1989), this is an important breeding and post-breeding site for *Cygnus cygnus*. Breeding species of global conservation concern that do not meet IBA criteria: *Haliaeetus albicilla* (1 pair). Other breeding species include *Anser fabalis* and *Pandion haliaetus* (1 pair).

■ Protection status

National None **International** None

■ Conservation issues

No recent information. A Zapovednik (Varzuga, 107,000 ha) was planned, but has not yet been created.

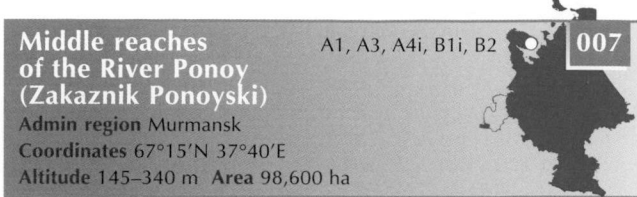

Middle reaches of the River Ponoy (Zakaznik Ponoyski)

A1, A3, A4i, B1i, B2   007

Admin region Murmansk
Coordinates 67°15'N 37°40'E
Altitude 145–340 m **Area** 98,600 ha

■ Site description

An area of very wet northern taiga with many lakes and rivers, in the central part of the Kola peninsula. Land-uses include reindeer-herding.

Habitats Forest and woodland (native coniferous forest), Wetland (standing fresh water; river/stream; raised bog; fen/transition mire/spring)
Land-use Agriculture (100%), Hunting, Tourism/recreation

■ Birds

Species		Season	Year	Pop min	Pop max	Acc	Criteria
[1]*Cygnus cygnus*	Whooper Swan	N	1989	500	—	—	A4i, B1i
Mergus albellus	Smew	B	1995	—	—	—	A3
Haliaeetus albicilla	White-tailed Eagle	B	1995	9	9	—	A1
Falco peregrinus	Peregrine	B	1995	1	10	—	B2
Tringa nebularia	Greenshank	B	1995	—	—	—	A3
Surnia ulula	Hawk Owl	R	1995	—	—	—	A3
Bombycilla garrulus	Waxwing	B	1995	—	—	—	A3
Parus cinctus	Siberian Tit	R	1995	—	—	—	A3
Perisoreus infaustus	Siberian Jay	B	1995	—	—	—	A3
Fringilla montifringilla	Brambling	B	1995	—	—	—	A3
Pinicola enucleator	Pine Grosbeak	B	1995	—	—	—	A3

1. Also breeds, but no accurate counts.

Breeding species include two raptors (in significant numbers) as well as eight of the 15 species in Europe that are restricted to the boreal biome when breeding (no specific counts have been made). Not less than 500 *Cygnus cygnus*, and possibly up to several thousand, congregate prior to migration.

■ Protection status

National High **International** None
98,600 ha of IBA covered by Zakaznik (Ponoysky, 98,600 ha).

■ Conservation issues

The extent of the site should possibly be increased so as to include some part of the surroundings of the Zakaznik, but insufficient ornithological data are available to justify this. To obtain further information, surveys are needed, but this is currently not feasible as the area is far from any roads and the only access is by helicopter, thus very expensive.

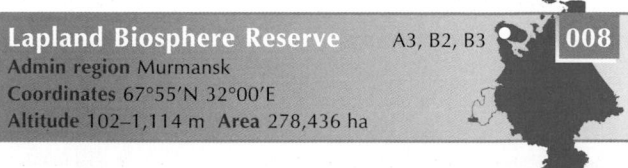

Lapland Biosphere Reserve

A3, B2, B3   008

Admin region Murmansk
Coordinates 67°55'N 32°00'E
Altitude 102–1,114 m **Area** 278,436 ha

■ Site description

An area of tundra (some wooded) near the town of Nikel.

Habitats Forest and woodland (63%; mixed forest; wooded tundra), Grassland (19%; tundra), Wetland (12%; standing fresh water; river/stream; raised bog), Rocky areas (6%; scree/boulders)
Land-use Nature conservation/research (100%)

■ Birds

Species		Season	Year	Pop min	Pop max	Acc	Criteria
[1]*Aythya marila*	Scaup	B	1995	20	20	C	A3
[1]*Clangula hyemalis*	Long-tailed Duck	B	1995	100	100	C	A3
[1]*Melanitta nigra*	Common Scoter	B	1995	50	80	C	A3
[2]*Mergus albellus*	Smew	B	1995	10	20	B	A3
[1]*Buteo lagopus*	Rough-legged Buzzard	B	1995	10	200	B	A3
Pluvialis apricaria	Golden Plover	B	1995	500	980	B	B3
[1,3]*Calidris minuta*	Little Stint	U	1995	2	7	C	A3
[1]*Calidris temminckii*	Temminck's Stint	B	1995	10	10	C	A3
Limicola falcinellus	Broad-billed Sandpiper	B	1995	5	—	B	B2

Species ... continued	Season	Year	Pop min	Pop max	Acc	Criteria
[2] *Lymnocryptes minimus* Jack Snipe	B	1995	10	10	C	A3
[1] *Tringa erythropus* Spotted Redshank	B	1995	200	200	B	A3
[2] *Tringa nebularia* Greenshank	B	1995	900	900	B	A3
[1] *Phalaropus lobatus* Red-necked Phalarope	B	1995	200	200	B	A3
[2] *Surnia ulula* Hawk Owl	R	1994	10	800	A	A3
[2] *Strix nebulosa* Great Grey Owl	R	1995	—	20	B	A3
Picoides tridactylus Three-toed Woodpecker	R	1995	2,500	3,500	B	B2
Anthus pratensis Meadow Pipit	B	1995	8,500	15,000	B	B3
[2] *Bombycilla garrulus* Waxwing	B	1995	100	5,000	B	A3
Phoenicurus phoenicurus Redstart	B	1995	3,900	7,500	B	B2
Turdus philomelos Song Thrush	B	1995	1,500	1,700	B	B3
[2] *Phylloscopus borealis* Arctic Warbler	B	1995	—	6,000	B	A3
[2] *Parus cinctus* Siberian Tit	R	1995	4,400	10,300	B	A3
[2] *Perisoreus infaustus* Siberian Jay	R	1995	880	2,000	B	A3, B2
[2] *Fringilla montifringilla* Brambling	B	1995	24,000	40,000	B	A3
[2] *Loxia leucoptera* Two-barred Crossbill	B	1995	2,000	31,000	B	A3
[2] *Loxia pytyopsittacus* Parrot Crossbill	B	1995	1,030	4,300	B	A3, B3
[2] *Pinicola enucleator* Pine Grosbeak	B	1995	900	5,000	B	A3
[1] *Calcarius lapponicus* Lapland Bunting	B	1995	100	100	C	A3
[1] *Plectrophenax nivalis* Snow Bunting	B	1995	130	700	B	A3
[2] *Emberiza rustica* Rustic Bunting	B	1995	2,900	5,500	B	A3

1. Arctic/tundra biome.
2. Boreal biome.
3. Breeding status uncertain (no. of possible pairs given).

The avifauna includes 24 of the 47 species in Europe that are restricted either to the Arctic/tundra biome or to the boreal biome when breeding. Significant proportion (≥1%) of national population breeding at site: *Aquila chrysaetos* (at least 2 pairs).

■ Protection status
National High **International** High
268,400 ha of IBA covered by Zapovednik (Laplandskiy, 268,400 ha). 268,400 ha of IBA covered by Biosphere Reserve (Laplandskiy, 268,400 ha).

■ Conservation issues

Threats Natural events (C), Extraction industry (C)

Forest fires can be a problem. The IBA lies close to the Monchegorsk industrial area, and parts of the site are affected by pollution from the ore industry.

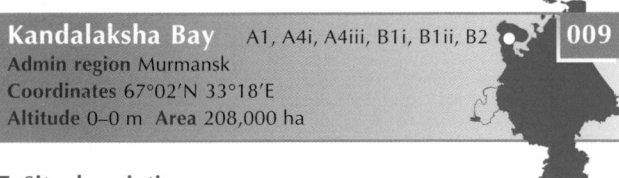

Kandalaksha Bay A1, A4i, A4iii, B1i, B1ii, B2 009
Admin region Murmansk
Coordinates 67°02'N 33°18'E
Altitude 0–0 m **Area** 208,000 ha

■ Site description
A large sea bay with a rocky coastline, and including many islands and alluvial sand deposits. The islands range from outcrops of rock and low-lying treeless islets to larger islands. There are some lakes on the larger islands, with coastal meadows and beds of reed *Phragmites* and sedge *Carex*.

Habitats Grassland (10%; humid grassland), Wetland (30%; tidal river/enclosed tidal water; coastal lagoon; standing fresh water; river/stream), Marine areas (80%; sea inlet/coastal features)
Land-use Fisheries/aquaculture, Hunting, Tourism/recreation

■ Birds

Species	Season	Year	Pop min	Pop max	Acc	Criteria
Somateria mollissima Eider	B	1988	—	9,500	—	A4i, B1i
[1] *Somateria mollissima* Eider	N	1988	10,000	12,000	—	B1i
[1] *Bucephala clangula* Goldeneye	N	1988	—	10,000	—	A4i, B1i
Haliaeetus albicilla White-tailed Eagle	B	1988	—	12	—	A1, B2
Cepphus grylle Black Guillemot	B	1988	300	500	—	B1ii, B2

1. Moulting.

Three species breed in important numbers along this coast, and more than 20,000 moulting individuals of *Somateria mollissima* and *Bucephala clangula* congregate offshore after the breeding season.

■ Protection status
National Partial **International** High
70,500 ha of IBA covered by Zapovednik (Kandalakshskiy, 70,500 ha). 208,000 ha of IBA covered by Ramsar Site (Kandalaksha Bay, 208,000 ha).

■ Conservation issues

Threats Aquaculture/fisheries (B), Disturbance to birds (B), Extraction industry (A), Recreation/tourism (B)

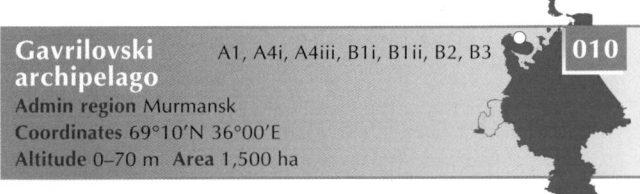

Gavrilovski archipelago A1, A4i, A4iii, B1i, B1ii, B2, B3 010
Admin region Murmansk
Coordinates 69°10'N 36°00'E
Altitude 0–70 m **Area** 1,500 ha

■ Site description
A group of rocky offshore islets, around which the sea does not freeze in winter, although situated in the tundra zone.

Habitats Grassland (tundra), Marine areas (sea inlet/coastal features), Rocky areas (sea cliff/rocky shore)
Land-use Nature conservation/research (100%)

■ Birds

Species	Season	Year	Pop min	Pop max	Acc	Criteria
Phalacrocorax aristotelis Shag	B	1995	200	200	A	B3
Somateria mollissima Eider	R	1995	2,500	2,500	A	B1i
Polysticta stelleri Steller's Eider	W	1995	2,000	2,000	A	A1, A4i, B1i
Larus marinus Great Black-backed Gull	B	1995	900	900	A	B3
Alca torda Razorbill	B	1995	500	500	A	B1ii
Cepphus grylle Black Guillemot	B	1995	800	800	A	B1ii, B2

Important numbers of the globally threatened *Polysticta stelleri* winter offshore, and there are more than 10,000 pairs of nesting waterbirds and seabirds during the breeding season.

■ Protection status
National High **International** None
1,500 ha of IBA covered by Zapovednik (Kandalakshskiy, 70,500 ha).

■ Conservation issues

Threats Aquaculture/fisheries (B)

Over-fishing is a problem, reducing the amount of food available for birds.

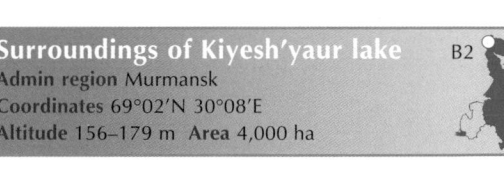

Surroundings of Kiyesh'yaur lake B2 011
Admin region Murmansk
Coordinates 69°02'N 30°08'E
Altitude 156–179 m **Area** 4,000 ha

■ Site description
A small area of marshy forest in the north-west of the Murmansk region. The site is a complex of fens, lakes and adjacent raised bogs and transition mires, which differs from the surrounding taiga (as observed in 1996) not only as a landscape, but also in terms of the birds it supports. The site is hardly used by local people, only by local hunters and berry-collectors in autumn (no more than 30–40 berry collectors at any one time).

Habitats Forest and woodland (32%; native coniferous forest; mixed forest), Wetland (73%; standing fresh water; raised bog; fen/transition mire/spring)
Land-use Not utilized (100%)

■ Birds

Species	Season	Year	Pop min	Pop max	Acc	Criteria
Limicola falcinellus Broad-billed Sandpiper	B	1996	—	—	C	B2

Limicola falcinellus is thought to breed at this site, although there have been no certain breeding records (nests discovered) in European Russia since 1964, due at least partly to the species's very cryptic behaviour and habit of breeding in colonies of up to 2–6 pairs only.

■ Protection status
National None **International** None

■ Conservation issues

> **Threats** Deforestation (commercial) (B), Extraction industry (B), Intensified forest management (B), Other (C)

'Other' threat refers to a variety of minor problems.

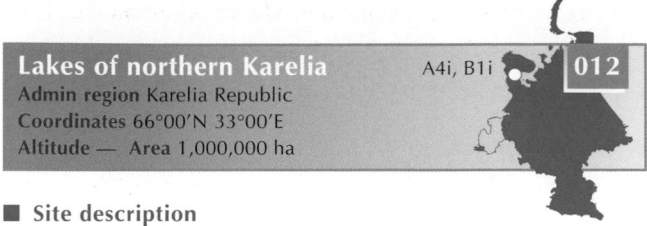

Lakes of northern Karelia A4i, B1i 012
Admin region Karelia Republic
Coordinates 66°00′N 33°00′E
Altitude — **Area** 1,000,000 ha

■ Site description
Northern taiga with a large number of lakes and marshes, including Lakes Keret, Eng, Nizhneye, Kum, and the south-eastern part of Lake Top. The boundaries of the most important wetlands need to be determined.

> **Habitats** Forest and woodland, Wetland (standing fresh water; water-fringe vegetation)

■ Birds

Species	Season	Year	Pop min	Pop max	Acc	Criteria
Cygnus cygnus Whooper Swan	B	1989	1,000	1,000	—	A4i, B1i
[1] *Anser anser* Greylag Goose	B	1989	—	—	—	B1i

> 1. The most northerly breeding site in Russia.

Based on data in the previous European IBA inventory (Grimmett and Jones 1989), this is an important breeding site for two wildfowl species, and an important staging site for migrating ducks.

■ Protection status
National Low **International** None
Part of IBA covered by Zakaznik (Ozero Keret).

■ Conservation issues
No recent information. The site was included in a plan for a Zapovednik in north Karelia.

Kivach Nature Reserve A3, B2, B3 013
Admin region Karelia Republic
Coordinates 62°13′N 34°00′E
Altitude 50–150 m **Area** 10,880 ha

■ Site description
Mainly coniferous forests (taiga) lying in the Suna river basin.

> **Habitats** Forest and woodland (89%; native coniferous forest; mixed forest), Wetland (11%; standing fresh water; river/stream; raised bog; fen/transition mire/spring)
> **Land-use** Nature conservation/research (100%), Water management (5%)

■ Birds

Species	Season	Year	Pop min	Pop max	Acc	Criteria
Podiceps auritus Slavonian Grebe	U	1996	—	—	B	A3
Lymnocryptes minimus Jack Snipe	U	1996	—	—	C	A3
Tringa nebularia Greenshank	B	1996	17	—	B	A3
Surnia ulula Hawk Owl	U	1996	0	1	—	A3
Strix nebulosa Great Grey Owl	R	1996	1	2	B	A3
Picoides tridactylus Three-toed Woodpecker	R	1996	44	200	B	B2
Bombycilla garrulus Waxwing	B	1996	6	12	B	A3
Turdus viscivorus Mistle Thrush	B	1996	52	175	B	B3
Phylloscopus borealis Arctic Warbler	B	1996	—	50	C	A3

Species ... continued	Season	Year	Pop min	Pop max	Acc	Criteria
Perisoreus infaustus Siberian Jay	R	1996	—	140	C	A3, B2
Fringilla montifringilla Brambling	B	1996	1,300	2,000	B	A3
Loxia leucoptera Two-barred Crossbill	B	1996	2	51	C	A3
Loxia pytyopsittacus Parrot Crossbill	B	1996	2	300	C	A3, B3
Emberiza rustica Rustic Bunting	B	1996	1,000	1,640	B	A3

The avifauna includes up to 12 of the 15 species in Europe that are restricted to the boreal biome when breeding.

■ Protection status
National High **International** None
10,880 ha of IBA covered by Zapovednik (Kivach, 10,880 ha).

■ Conservation issues
No major threats are known.

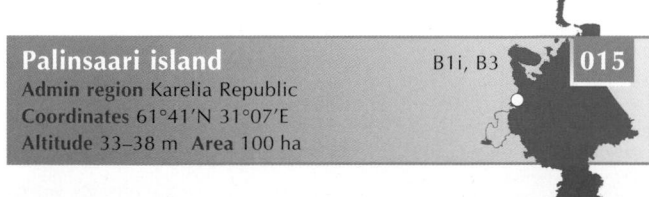

Olonets plain A1, A4i, A4iii, B1i, B2, B3 014
Admin region Karelia Republic
Coordinates 60°56′N 32°55′E
Altitude 9–59 m **Area** 18,000 ha

■ Site description
Wet agricultural land in the vicinity of the town of Olonets, near the shore of Lake Ladoga.

> **Habitats** Forest and woodland (70%; native coniferous forest; mixed forest), Wetland (raised bog), Artificial landscape (100%; highly improved reseeded grassland; arable land; perennial crops/orchards/groves)
> **Land-use** Agriculture (100%), Nature conservation/research (28%)

■ Birds

Species	Season	Year	Pop min	Pop max	Acc	Criteria
Anser fabalis Bean Goose	P	1997	200,000	300,000	A	A4i, B1i
Anser albifrons White-fronted Goose	P	1997	500,000	700,000	A	A4i, B1i
Branta leucopsis Barnacle Goose	P	1997	2,000	3,000	A	A4i, B1i
Crex crex Corncrake	B	1997	150	500	—	A1, B2
Numenius phaeopus Whimbrel	B	1997	100	200	—	B3

Hundreds of thousands of geese stage in the area during migration.

■ Protection status
National Partial **International** None
5,000 ha of IBA covered by Zakaznik (Olonetsky, 5,000 ha).

■ Conservation issues

> **Threats** Agricultural intensification/expansion (C), Extraction industry (A), Unsustainable exploitation (C)

Palinsaari island B1i, B3 015
Admin region Karelia Republic
Coordinates 61°41′N 31°07′E
Altitude 33–38 m **Area** 100 ha

■ Site description
A small island near the Valaam archipelago, in the northern part of Lake Ladoga. Human activities include the collection of birds' eggs ('Other' land-use, below).

> **Habitats** Scrub (50%; scrub), Wetland (10%; shingle/stony beach), Rocky areas (40%; rock stacks/islets)
> **Land-use** Other (100%), Tourism/recreation (100%)

■ Birds

Species	Season	Year	Pop min	Pop max	Acc	Criteria
Larus fuscus Lesser Black-backed Gull	B	1997	70	—	A	B3
Sterna caspia Caspian Tern	B	1993	24	24	A	B1i

Significant numbers of two colonial waterbirds breed here.

■ Protection status
National None **International** None

■ Conservation issues

Threats Afforestation (C), Aquaculture/fisheries (B), Disturbance to birds (A), Recreation/tourism (C), Unsustainable exploitation (A)

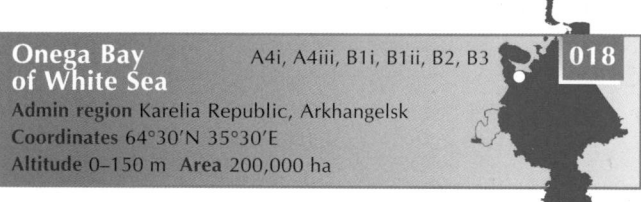

Zaonezh'ye A1, A3, A4i, A4iii, B1i, B2, B3 016
Admin region Karelia Republic
Coordinates 62°13'N 34°00'E
Altitude 33–202 m **Area** 330,000 ha

■ Site description
Numerous islands and peninsulas, separated by narrow channels, in Lake Onega, to the north of the town of Petrozavodsk.

Habitats Forest and woodland (25%; native coniferous forest; mixed forest), Scrub (5%; scrub), Wetland (60%; standing fresh water; river/stream; raised bog; water-fringe vegetation; fen/transition mire/spring), Artificial landscape (10%; highly improved reseeded grassland; arable land; other urban/industrial areas)

Land-use Agriculture (12%), Fisheries/aquaculture (50%), Forestry (20%), Hunting (20%), Nature conservation/research (35%), Not utilized (30%), Tourism/recreation (50%)

■ Birds

Species		Season	Year	Pop min	Pop max	Acc	Criteria
Gavia arctica	Black-throated Diver	B	1997	300	400	C	A4i, B1i
[1] *Cygnus cygnus*	Whooper Swan	P	1977	1,000	—	C	A4i, B1i
[1] *Anser fabalis*	Bean Goose	P	1977	5,000	—	C	A4i, B1i
Mergus serrator	Red-breasted Merganser	B	1997	1,000	1,800	B	A4i, B1i
Tetrao tetrix	Black Grouse	R	1997	5,000	6,000	B	B2
Crex crex	Corncrake	B	1997	120	1,000	C	A1, B2
Grus grus	Crane	B	1997	150	300	C	B1i
Grus grus	Crane	P	1997	600	800	C	B1i
[1] *Pluvialis apricaria*	Golden Plover	P	1976	20,000	—	B	A4i, B1i
[1] *Vanellus vanellus*	Lapwing	P	1976	10,000	70,000	C	A4i, B1i
Lymnocryptes minimus	Jack Snipe	B	1997	—	—	—	A3
Numenius arquata	Curlew	B	1997	—	1,500	C	A4i, B1i
[1] *Numenius arquata*	Curlew	P	1977	3,500	—	C	A4i, B1i
Tringa nebularia	Greenshank	B	1997	100	—	—	A3
Actitis hypoleucos	Common Sandpiper	B	1997	5,000	6,000	B	A4i, B1i
Actitis hypoleucos	Common Sandpiper	P	1997	—	30,000	C	A4i, B1i
Larus canus	Common Gull	B	1997	5,000	8,000	B	A4i, B1i, B2
Larus fuscus	Lesser Black-backed Gull	B	1997	200	300	B	B3
Sterna hirundo	Common Tern	B	1997	—	2,000	B	A4i, B1i
Columba palumbus	Woodpigeon	B	1997	3,000	4,000	C	B3
Strix nebulosa	Great Grey Owl	B	1997	1	—	—	A3
Jynx torquilla	Wryneck	B	1997	500	1,000	C	B2
Picoides tridactylus	Three-toed Woodpecker	R	1976	100	—	C	B2
Alauda arvensis	Skylark	B	1997	15,000	16,000	C	B2
Bombycilla garrulus	Waxwing	B	1976	50	100	—	A3
Saxicola rubetra	Whinchat	B	1997	2,000	2,500	C	B3
Turdus philomelos	Song Thrush	B	1997	15,000	20,000	B	B3
Acrocephalus palustris	Marsh Warbler	B	1997	1,000	2,000	C	B3
Sylvia borin	Garden Warbler	B	1997	10,000	20,000	B	B3
Phylloscopus borealis	Arctic Warbler	B	1997	100	150	C	A3
Lanius collurio	Red-backed Shrike	B	1997	300	1,000	C	B2
Perisoreus infaustus	Siberian Jay	B	1997	—	—	C	A3
Fringilla coelebs	Chaffinch	B	1997	100,000	120,000	B	B3
Fringilla montifringilla	Brambling	B	1997	5,000	10,000	B	A3
Loxia leucoptera	Two-barred Crossbill	B	1986	—	1,500	C	A3
Loxia pytyopsittacus	Parrot Crossbill	B	1986	200	1,500	C	A3, B3
Emberiza rustica	Rustic Bunting	B	1997	10,000	15,000	B	A3

1. No counts available for 1997 migration.

Many species of boreal forest, lake and mire breed, including important numbers of one species of global conservation concern, as well as 10 of the 15 species in Europe that are restricted to the boreal biome when breeding. Seven waterbirds stage in the area in significant numbers during migration, and the site holds 20,000 or more migrating waterbirds on a regular basis.

■ Protection status
National Partial **International** None
50,000 ha of IBA covered by Zakaznik (Kizhsky, 50,000 ha).

■ Conservation issues

Threats Abandonment/reduction of land management (U), Deforestation (commercial) (A), Intensified forest management (A)

South-eastern coast A4i, B1i, B2 017
of Lake Ladoga
Admin region Karelia Republic
Coordinates 60°50'N 32°40'E
Altitude 0–9 m **Area** 1,250 ha

■ Site description
Two groups of islands together with adjacent mainland shorelines, situated on the south-east coast of Lake Ladoga, south of the mouth of the Olonka river. Reedbeds (*Phragmites*) and exposed sediments fringe the flat, treeless shores. The shape of the coastline and the size of the reedbeds and exposed flats vary according to the changing level of Lake Ladoga.

Habitats Wetland (100%; mudflat/sandflat; sand-dunes/sand beach; shingle/stony beach; water-fringe vegetation)

Land-use Fisheries/aquaculture (100%), Hunting (60%), Nature conservation/research (80%), Not utilized (80%)

■ Birds

Species		Season	Year	Pop min	Pop max	Acc	Criteria
Larus minutus	Little Gull	B	1997	300	600	—	A4i, B1i, B2

Important numbers of *Larus minutus* breed.

■ Protection status
National Partial **International** None
100 ha of IBA covered by Zakaznik (Andrusovsky, area not known). Part of IBA (mainland shoreline) covered by Zakaznik (Olonetsky, 27,000 ha).

■ Conservation issues

Threats Unsustainable exploitation (B)

Onega Bay A4i, A4iii, B1i, B1ii, B2, B3 018
of White Sea
Admin region Karelia Republic, Arkhangelsk
Coordinates 64°30'N 35°30'E
Altitude 0–150 m **Area** 200,000 ha

■ Site description
Islands situated along the western shore of Onega Bay in the White Sea, with extensive foreshore and wet coastal meadow habitats. 'Other' land-use is seaweed harvesting.

Habitats Forest and woodland (20%; native coniferous forest; wooded tundra), Grassland (5%; tundra), Wetland (10%; tidal river/enclosed tidal water; shingle/stony beach; river/stream), Marine areas (50%; open sea; sea inlet/coastal features), Rocky areas (15%)

Land-use Fisheries/aquaculture (10%), Not utilized (90%), Other (30%), Tourism/recreation (10%)

■ Birds

Species		Season	Year	Pop min	Pop max	Acc	Criteria
Somateria mollissima	Eider	W	1988	20,000	—	C	B1i
Arenaria interpres	Turnstone	B	1995	320	350	A	A4i, B1i
Stercorarius parasiticus	Arctic Skua	B	1995	80	100	A	B1ii
Larus canus	Common Gull	B	1995	3,800	4,000	A	B1i, B2
Larus fuscus	Lesser Black-backed Gull	B	1995	1,000	1,000	A	B1i, B3
Larus argentatus	Herring Gull	B	1995	5,000	5,100	A	B1i
Larus marinus	Great Black-backed Gull	B	1995	90	100	A	B3

A number of coastal waterbirds breed in important numbers, notably gull species. The area is an important staging area for migrating *Cygnus cygnus*, *C. columbianus*, *Branta bernicla*, *B. leucopsis* and other geese and ducks, but no detailed information is available at present, although it is certain that more than 20,000 waterbirds are present regularly on migration. In winter, at least 20,000 *Somateria mollissima* congregate in the area.

■ **Protection status**
National Low **International** Low
Part of IBA covered by two Zakazniks (Kemskie Shkhery; Kuzova). 3,600 ha of IBA covered by Ramsar Site (Islands in Onega Bay (White Sea), 3,600 ha).

■ **Conservation issues**

Threats Aquaculture/fisheries (C), Disturbance to birds (C), Recreation/tourism (C), Unsustainable exploitation (C)

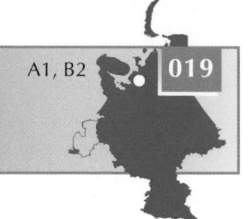

Pinezhski Nature Reserve
A1, B2 — 019
Admin region Arkhangelsk
Coordinates 64°40′N 43°20′E
Altitude — **Area** 41,244 ha

■ **Site description**
An area of coniferous forest near the town of Pinega, within the taiga zone. Pine *Pinus* and spruce *Picea* cover the majority of the area, with birch *Betula* on recently logged sites. Small raised bogs occur throughout the forest.

Habitats Forest and woodland (87%; native coniferous forest; mixed forest), Wetland (8%; river/stream; raised bog)
Land-use Nature conservation/research (100%)

■ **Birds**

Species	Season	Year	Pop min	Pop max	Acc	Criteria
Anser erythropus Lesser White-fronted Goose	P	1995	1	20	—	A1
Picoides tridactylus Three-toed Woodpecker	B	1995	415	—	—	B2

The globally threatened *Anser erythropus* occurs on passage.

■ **Protection status**
National High **International** None
41,244 ha of IBA covered by Zapovednik (Pinezhskiy, 41,244 ha).

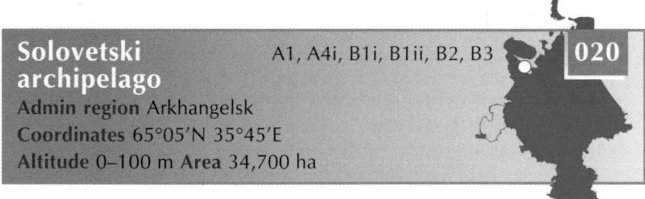

Solovetski archipelago
A1, A4i, B1i, B1ii, B2, B3 — 020
Admin region Arkhangelsk
Coordinates 65°05′N 35°45′E
Altitude 0–100 m **Area** 34,700 ha

■ **Site description**
The area is located on the northern edge of Onega Bay, and forms a complex with Onezhskaya Guba in the White Sea. The archipelago consists of several large islands surrounded by marine shallows, with extensive shorelines, beaches and coastal meadows.

Habitats Forest and woodland (50%; wooded tundra), Grassland (tundra), Wetland (38%; tidal river/enclosed tidal water; standing fresh water; river/stream; raised bog; fen/transition mire/spring), Marine areas (15%; open sea; sea inlet/coastal features), Rocky areas), Artificial landscape (5%; arable land; forestry plantation; other urban/industrial areas)
Land-use Forestry (80%), Nature conservation/research (90%), Tourism/recreation (30%)

■ **Birds**

Species	Season	Year	Pop min	Pop max	Acc	Criteria
Polysticta stelleri Steller's Eider	N	1996	5	1,000	B	A1, A4i, B1i
Haliaeetus albicilla White-tailed Eagle	B	1996	3	5	B	A1
Larus canus Common Gull	B	1994	650	900	B	B2
Larus fuscus Lesser Black-backed Gull	B	1996	340	650	A	B3
Sterna paradisaea Arctic Tern	B	1994	4,000	10,500	A	A4i, B1i
Cepphus grylle Black Guillemot	R	1996	388	390	A	B1ii, B2

A variety of coastal species breed in significant numbers, and non-breeding individuals of the globally threatened *Polysticta stelleri* congregate here.

■ **Protection status**
National High **International** High
34,700 ha of IBA covered by Historical Cultural and Natural Complex (Solovetsky, 34,700 ha). 34,700 ha of IBA covered by World Heritage Site (Solovetski, 34,700 ha).

■ **Conservation issues**
Solovetski archipelago is protected for its cultural value and is included on the UNESCO List of World Heritage Sites for this reason.

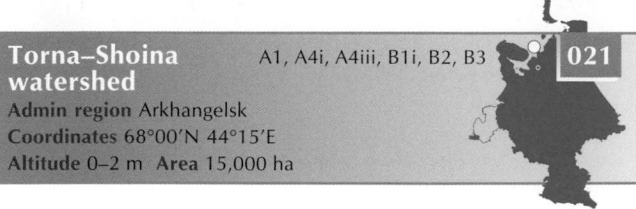

Torna–Shoina watershed
A1, A4i, A4iii, B1i, B2, B3 — 021
Admin region Arkhangelsk
Coordinates 68°00′N 44°15′E
Altitude 0–2 m **Area** 15,000 ha

■ **Site description**
The site is located about 420 km south-east of Arkhangelsk, on the eastern coast of the Kanin peninsula, and covers the watersheds of the Torna and Shoina rivers, with the latter forming the southern boundary of the site. Low-lying wetland habitats consist of mudflats, coastal marshes, dunes and estuaries. Adjacent to these lies a 2–5 m high terrace covered by tundra vegetation. The state reindeer farm legally owns the area, but no habitat-damage is apparent.

Habitats Grassland (tundra), Wetland (tidal river/enclosed tidal water; mudflat/sandflat; sand-dunes/sand beach; standing fresh water)
Land-use Agriculture, Fisheries/aquaculture, Hunting

■ **Birds**

Species	Season	Year	Pop min	Pop max	Acc	Criteria
Anser erythropus Lesser White-fronted Goose	P	1995	1,500	—	C	A1, A4i, B1i
Branta leucopsis Barnacle Goose	B	1994	—	2,000	B	A4i, B1i, B3
[1] *Branta leucopsis* Barnacle Goose	P	1995	—	—	B	A4i, B1i
[1] *Branta bernicla* Brent Goose	P	1995	—	—	B	A4i, B1i
Anas acuta Pintail	B	1995	—	3,000	B	B1i, B2
Aythya marila Scaup	B	1995	—	3,000	B	A4i, B1i

1. Up to 80,000 *B. leucopsis/B. bernicla*.

Breeding species in significant numbers include three wildfowl species. Tens of thousands of geese *Anser* stage in the area during migration, in particular the globally threatened *Anser erythropus* occurs in very significant numbers. A total of 30,000 small waders (*Calidris minuta, C. ferruginea, C. alpina*) congregate here during spring and autumn migration, and at least 1,000 moulting seaduck of four species also occur. Species of global conservation concern that do not meet IBA criteria: *Polysticta stelleri* (on migration; numbers almost certainly would meet criteria, but no systematic counts yet).

■ **Protection status**
National None **International** None

■ **Conservation issues**

Threats Unsustainable exploitation (U)

The area has been included on a 'shadow list' of potential Ramsar Sites.

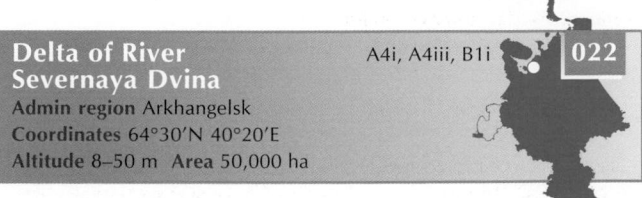

Delta of River Severnaya Dvina
A4i, A4iii, B1i — 022
Admin region Arkhangelsk
Coordinates 64°30′N 40°20′E
Altitude 8–50 m **Area** 50,000 ha

■ **Site description**
The delta of the River Severnaya Dvina at the White Sea, containing numerous meanders and islands.

Habitats Forest and woodland (alluvial/very wet forest), Grassland (humid grassland), Wetland (tidal river/enclosed tidal water; mudflat/sandflat; sand-dunes/sand beach; coastal lagoon; river/stream; raised bog), Artificial landscape (arable land)

Land-use Agriculture (15%), Fisheries/aquaculture (30%), Hunting (30%), Not utilized, Urban/industrial/transport

■ Birds

Species	Season	Year	Pop min	Pop max	Acc	Criteria
Cygnus columbianus Bewick's Swan	P	1997	1,000	9,000	—	A4i, B1i
¹ *Anser fabalis* Bean Goose	P	1997	—	—	—	A4i, B1i
¹ *Anser albifrons* White-fronted Goose	P	1997	—	—	—	A4i, B1i
Branta leucopsis Barnacle Goose	P	1997	5,000	8,000	—	A4i, B1i
Branta bernicla Brent Goose	P	1997	15,000	25,000	—	A4i, B1i

1. 52,000–80,000 *A. fabalis/A. albifrons*.

Very large numbers of wildfowl regularly occur on passage, especially *Cygnus columbianus* and geese *Anser*.

■ Protection status
National Partial **International** None
The IBA overlaps with Zakaznik (Dvinskoi, area not known).

■ Conservation issues

Threats Aquaculture/fisheries (C), Disturbance to birds (A), Infrastructure (B), Recreation/tourism (A), Unsustainable exploitation (A)

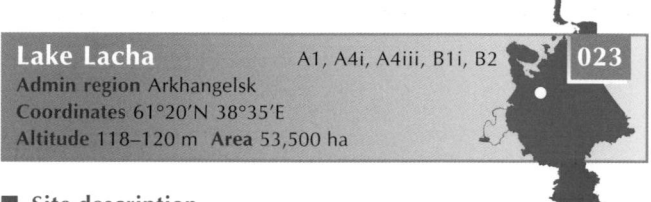

Lake Lacha   A1, A4i, A4iii, B1i, B2   023
Admin region Arkhangelsk
Coordinates 61°20′N 38°35′E
Altitude 118–120 m **Area** 53,500 ha

■ Site description
A large lake in the south of the Arkhangelsk region, surrounded by very wet forest and bogs.

Habitats Forest and woodland (10%; alluvial/very wet forest), Scrub (10%; scrub), Wetland (60%; standing fresh water; river/stream; raised bog), Artificial landscape (15%; arable land; urban parks/gardens)

Land-use Agriculture (10%), Fisheries/aquaculture (60%), Forestry (10%), Not utilized (20%), Tourism/recreation (20%), Urban/industrial/transport (5%)

■ Birds

Species	Season	Year	Pop min	Pop max	Acc	Criteria
Cygnus cygnus Whooper Swan	P	1997	300	2,000	B	A4i, B1i
¹ *Anser fabalis* Bean Goose	P	1996	—	—	B	A4i, B1i
¹ *Anser albifrons* White-fronted Goose	P	1996	—	—	B	A4i, B1i
Anas clypeata Shoveler	N	1997	600	1,000	B	B1i
Crex crex Corncrake	B	1997	10	30	C	A1
Larus minutus Little Gull	B	1997	500	800	B	A4i, B1i, B2
Larus canus Common Gull	B	1997	1,500	—	C	B2

1. Up to 30,000 *A. fabalis/A. albifrons*.

Huge numbers of wildfowl regularly stage at the site during migration (geese *Anser*) or gather on the lake after the breeding season (up to 40,000 duck, notably *Anas clypeata*). *Crex crex* breeds, as do important numbers of two gull *Larus* species. Species of global conservation concern that do not meet IBA criteria: *Haliaeetus albicilla* (more than 2 breeding pairs; 7–10 birds on passage).

■ Protection status
National Partial **International** None
20,000 ha of IBA covered by Zakaznik (Lachskiy Hunting Reserve, 20,000 ha).

■ Conservation issues

Threats Abandonment/reduction of land management (B), Afforestation (B), Deforestation (commercial) (C), Disturbance to birds (B), Firewood collection (B), Forest grazing (C), Industrialization/urbanization (C), Infrastructure (C), Intensified forest management (C), Natural events (A), Recreation/tourism (C), Selective logging/cutting (B), Unsustainable exploitation (B)

Irregular flooding is a threat ('Natural events', above).

Kenozer'ye   A1, A3, A4i, B1i, B2, B3   024
Admin region Arkhangelsk
Coordinates 61°55′N 38°07′E
Altitude 120–229 m **Area** 180,000 ha

■ Site description
Extensive tracts of coniferous forest, as well as six large lakes, in the middle zone of the taiga.

Habitats Forest and woodland (55%; native coniferous forest; mixed forest), Scrub (5%; scrub), Wetland (35%; standing fresh water; river/stream; raised bog), Artificial landscape (10%; highly improved reseeded grassland; arable land; other urban/industrial areas)

Land-use Agriculture (15%), Fisheries/aquaculture (20%), Forestry (40%), Hunting (20%), Nature conservation/research (20%), Not utilized (60%), Tourism/recreation (30%), Urban/industrial/transport (5%)

■ Birds

Species	Season	Year	Pop min	Pop max	Acc	Criteria
Gavia arctica Black-throated Diver	B	1997	300	400	B	A4i, B1i
Cygnus cygnus Whooper Swan	P	1997	100	800	C	A4i, B1i
Bucephala clangula Goldeneye	P	1997	2,000	3,500	C	B1i
Mergus albellus Smew	U	1997	10	50	C	A3
Haliaeetus albicilla White-tailed Eagle	B	1997	4	6	B	A1
Crex crex Corncrake	B	1997	50	100	B	A1
Lymnocryptes minimus Jack Snipe	U	1997	—	—	—	A3
Tringa nebularia Greenshank	B	1997	100	300	C	A3
Tringa nebularia Greenshank	P	1997	1,500	3,000	C	A4i, B1i
Larus minutus Little Gull	B	1997	150	200	B	B2
Larus canus Common Gull	B	1997	1,500	2,000	B	B2
Columba palumbus Woodpigeon	B	1997	1,500	3,000	B	B3
Strix nebulosa Great Grey Owl	R	1997	20	40	—	A3
Picoides tridactylus Three-toed Woodpecker	R	1997	200	400	C	B2
Bombycilla garrulus Waxwing	R	1997	50	300	B	A3
Saxicola rubetra Whinchat	B	1997	1,000	—	C	B3
Turdus viscivorus Mistle Thrush	B	1997	100	—	C	B3
Acrocephalus palustris Marsh Warbler	B	1997	1,500	2,000	B	B3
Fringilla coelebs Chaffinch	B	1997	100,000	120,000	B	B3
Fringilla montifringilla Brambling	B	1997	2,000	5,000	B	A3
Loxia leucoptera Two-barred Crossbill	R	1997	100	200	—	A3
Loxia pytyopsittacus Parrot Crossbill	R	1997	500	600	B	A3, B3
Emberiza rustica Rustic Bunting	B	1997	8,000	10,000	—	A3

Many species of boreal forest, lake and mire breed here, including two species of global conservation concern, as well as up to nine of the 15 species in Europe that are restricted to the boreal biome when breeding. Three waterbirds stage in the area in significant numbers during migration.

■ Protection status
National Partial **International** None
139,200 ha of IBA covered by National Park (Kenozyerskiy, 139,200 ha).

■ Conservation issues

Threats Abandonment/reduction of land management (B), Agricultural intensification/expansion (B), Deforestation (commercial) (A), Disturbance to birds (A), Firewood collection (B), Infrastructure (B), Intensified forest management (A), Recreation/tourism (C), Selective logging/cutting (A), Unsustainable exploitation (B)

Bezymyannaya and Gribovaya Bays and adjoining waters   A1, A4i, A4ii, B1i, B1ii, B3   025
Admin region Arkhangelsk
Coordinates 72°55′N 53°05′E
Altitude 0–816 m **Area** 140,000 ha

■ Site description
An area on the north-west shore of the southernmost island in the Novaya Zemlya archipelago.

Habitats Grassland (70%; tundra), Marine areas (30%; open sea; sea inlet/coastal features)
Land-use Military (100%), Nature conservation/research (100%)

■ Birds

Species		Season	Year	Pop min	Pop max	Acc	Criteria
[1] *Polysticta stelleri*	Steller's Eider	N	1994	300	—	B	A1, A4i, B1i
Calidris maritima	Purple Sandpiper	B	1994	10	—	C	B3
Uria lomvia	Brünnich's Guillemot	B	1995	140,000	315,000	A	A4ii, B1ii
Cepphus grylle	Black Guillemot	B	1995	118	118	A	B1ii

1. Single count.

The IBA is important for its non-breeding population of the globally threatened *Polysticta stelleri*, and for the large breeding colony of *Uria lomvia*. Current data for the site are incomplete, and further research is required. Ornithological data from the 1940s are available, for comparative purposes.

■ Protection status
National None **International** None

■ Conservation issues

> **Threats** Other (A), Unsustainable exploitation (B)

Radioactive contamination is a problem ('Other' threat). During recent years attempts have been made, with international support, to establish Novozemelskiy Strict Nature Reserve (Zapovednik). The area was designated as a Zapovednik up until the mid-1950s, when a lot of Zapovedniks lost their official status.

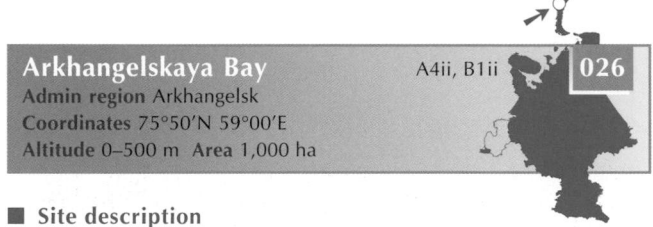

Arkhangelskaya Bay   A4ii, B1ii 026
Admin region Arkhangelsk
Coordinates 75°50′N 59°00′E
Altitude 0–500 m **Area** 1,000 ha

■ Site description
The area lies on the north-west shore of the northernmost island in the Novaya Zemlya archipelago.

> **Habitats** Grassland (90%; tundra), Rocky areas (10%; sea cliff/rocky shore)
> **Land-use** Military (100%)

■ Birds

Species		Season	Year	Pop min	Pop max	Acc	Criteria
Uria lomvia	Brünnich's Guillemot	B	1996	73,200	131,200	A	A4ii, B1ii

An important seabird breeding colony, which holds very large numbers of *Uria lomvia*. Other breeding seabirds include *Larus hyperboreus*, *Rissa tridactyla*, *Cepphus grylle*, *Alle alle* and *Fratercula arctica*.

■ Protection status
National None **International** None

■ Conservation issues

> **Threats** Other (A)

The IBA is threatened by radioactive pollution. Ornithological data are incomplete for the site, and further survey work is required. An international fauna monitoring project is being carried out by Russian and Norwegian biologists.

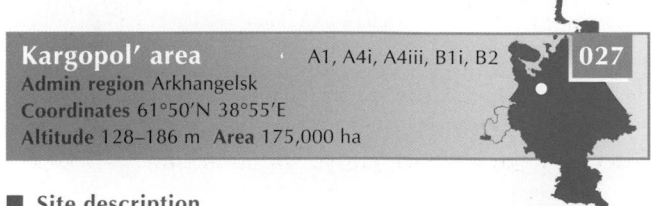

Kargopol' area   A1, A4i, A4iii, B1i, B2 027
Admin region Arkhangelsk
Coordinates 61°50′N 38°55′E
Altitude 128–186 m **Area** 175,000 ha

■ Site description

> **Habitats** Forest and woodland (70%; native coniferous forest; mixed forest; alluvial/very wet forest), Wetland (40%; raised bog; water-fringe vegetation; fen/transition mire/spring), Artificial landscape (8%; highly improved reseeded grassland; arable land; perennial crops/orchards/groves)
> **Land-use** Agriculture (8%), Forestry (70%), Hunting (99%), Nature conservation/research (15%)

Lying near to the town of Kargopol in the south of the Arkhangelsk region, habitats in the area include agricultural fields surrounded by fens and raised bogs.

■ Birds

Species		Season	Year	Pop min	Pop max	Acc	Criteria
Anser fabalis	Bean Goose	P	1996	30,000	—	B	A4i, B1i
Anser albifrons	White-fronted Goose	P	1996	70,000	—	B	A4i, B1i
Anser erythropus		P	1996	—	1,000	C	A1, A4i, B1i
Lesser White-fronted Goose							
Tetrao tetrix	Black Grouse	R	1991	500	1,000	C	B2
Crex crex	Corncrake	B	1996	200	200	A	A1
Grus grus	Crane	P	1996	4,000	10,000	A	A4i, B1i
Larus canus	Common Gull	P	1996	20,000	40,000	B	A4i, B1i
Bubo bubo	Eagle Owl	R	1991	10	20	C	B2

The site is a gathering point for more *Grus grus* than any other site in European Russia during the autumn migration, and also holds very important numbers of the globally threatened *Anser erythropus*. The globally threatened *Crex crex* breeds in good numbers, as does *Tetrao tetrix*.

■ Protection status
National Partial **International** None
23,600 ha of IBA covered by Zakaznik (Filatovskiy, 23,600 ha).

■ Conservation issues

> **Threats** Abandonment/reduction of land management (A), Disturbance to birds (C), Recreation/tourism (C)

A decline in arable cropping may have an negative effect on the numbers of *Grus grus* which gather here on passage, as cereal grain is their main food source.

Vodlozero   A1, B2 028
Admin region Arkhangelsk, Karelia Republic
Coordinates 62°35′N 36°55′E
Altitude 140–218 m **Area** 200,000 ha

■ Site description
A complex of habitats typical of the middle zone of the taiga.

> **Habitats** Forest and woodland (49%; native coniferous forest; mixed forest), Scrub (2%; scrub), Wetland (48%; standing fresh water; river/stream; raised bog; water-fringe vegetation; fen/transition mire/spring), Artificial landscape (4%; highly improved reseeded grassland; arable land; other urban/industrial areas)
> **Land-use** Fisheries/aquaculture (20%), Hunting (20%), Nature conservation/research (100%), Not utilized (50%), Tourism/recreation (10%)

■ Birds

Species		Season	Year	Pop min	Pop max	Acc	Criteria
Haliaeetus albicilla	White-tailed Eagle	B	1997	15	17	A	A1, B2
Aquila chrysaetos	Golden Eagle	B	1990	3	8	B	B2

Two eagle species breed in significant numbers. Species of global conservation concern that do not meet IBA criteria: *Aquila clanga* (status unknown).

■ Protection status
National Partial **International** None
180,000 ha of IBA covered by National Park (Vodlozerskiy, 468,340 ha).

■ Conservation issues

> **Threats** Abandonment/reduction of land management (C), Afforestation (C), Aquaculture/fisheries (A), Disturbance to birds (C), Firewood collection (C), Infrastructure (B), Recreation/tourism (B), Selective logging/cutting (B)

Vashutkiny, Padimeyskiye A4i, A4iii, B1i 029
and Khargeyskiye lakes
Admin region Arkhangelsk, Nenetski
Coordinates 68°00′N 62°00′E
Altitude — **Area** 25,000 ha

■ Site description
A lake system in the Bolshezemelskaya tundra.

Habitats Grassland (tundra), Wetland (standing fresh water)

■ Birds

Species	Season	Year	Pop min	Pop max	Acc	Criteria
[1] *Anser fabalis* Bean Goose	N	1989	50,000	50,000	—	A4i, B1i

1. Moulting.

An important breeding and moulting area for *Anser fabalis* and ducks (80,000–100,000), according to the previous pan-European IBA inventory (Grimmett and Jones 1989). No updated information.

■ Protection status
National None **International** None

■ Conservation issues
No recent information.

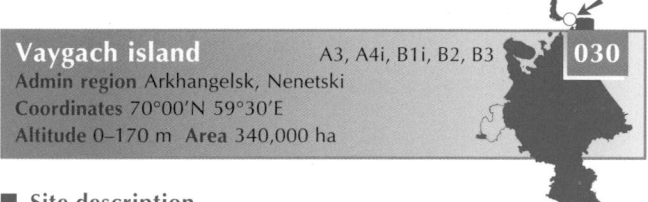

Vaygach island
A3, A4i, B1i, B2, B3   030
Admin region Arkhangelsk, Nenetski
Coordinates 70°00'N 59°30'E
Altitude 0–170 m **Area** 340,000 ha

■ Site description
A large tundra island located just off the mainland, north of the Ural mountains. Human activities include reindeer herding.

Habitats Grassland (100%; tundra)
Land-use Agriculture (30%), Hunting (100%), Nature conservation/research (90%)

■ Birds

Species	Season	Year	Pop min	Pop max	Acc	Criteria
Cygnus columbianus Bewick's Swan	B	—	—	75,000	—	A3, A4i, B1i
Anser fabalis Bean Goose	B	1987	—	33,000	—	A4i, B1i
Anser albifrons White-fronted Goose	B	1984	—	100,000	—	A3, A4i, B1i
Branta leucopsis Barnacle Goose	B	1987	2,500	3,000	—	A3, A4i, B1i, B3
Clangula hyemalis Long-tailed Duck	B	1987	20,000	—	—	A3, A4i, B1i
Mergus merganser Goosander	B	1987	2,500	3,000	—	A4i, B1i
Falco peregrinus Peregrine	B	1991	10	10	—	B2
Nyctea scandiaca Snowy Owl	B	1991	5	—	—	A3, B2

The breeding avifauna includes five of the 32 species in Europe that are restricted to the Arctic/tundra biome when breeding, and huge numbers of waterfowl overall. The northern third of the island is the most important for bird conservation. Breeding species of global conservation concern that do not meet IBA criteria: *Haliaeetus albicilla* (at least 4 pairs).

■ Protection status
National High **International** None
340,000 ha of IBA covered by Zakaznik (Vaigach, 340,000 ha).

■ Conservation issues

Threats Aquaculture/fisheries (C), Disturbance to birds (C), Unsustainable exploitation (B)

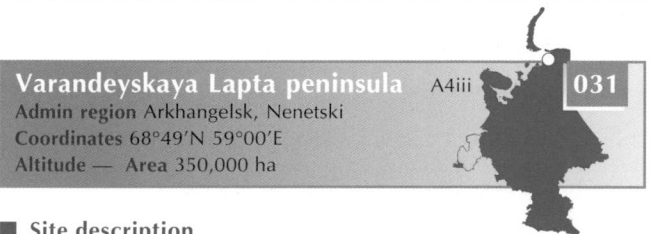

Varandeyskaya Lapta peninsula
A4iii   031
Admin region Arkhangelsk, Nenetski
Coordinates 68°49'N 59°00'E
Altitude — **Area** 350,000 ha

■ Site description
A low-lying peninsula with numerous lakes that are connected by channels with each other and to the Pechora Sea.

Habitats Wetland (standing fresh water)

■ Birds
One of the most important sites in north European Russia for breeding swans, geese, and ducks, and for moulting swans (2,000), geese (30,000–40,000), and ducks (100,000). Recent count data are not available for any bird species.

■ Protection status
National None **International** None

■ Conservation issues
Proposed as a Ramsar Site. No recent information.

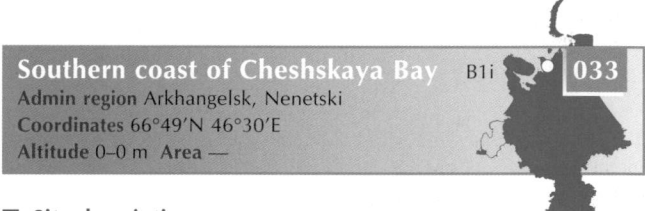

River Chernaya
A4iii   032
Admin region Arkhangelsk, Nenetski
Coordinates 68°07'N 57°00'E
Altitude — **Area** 200,000 ha

■ Site description
Low-lying marshy tundra with lakes.

Habitats Grassland (tundra), Wetland (standing fresh water; river/stream; water-fringe vegetation)

■ Birds
Important for breeding and moulting swans (500), geese (20,000–30,000), and diving ducks (20,000). Recent count data are not available for any bird species.

■ Protection status
National None **International** None

■ Conservation issues
No recent information.

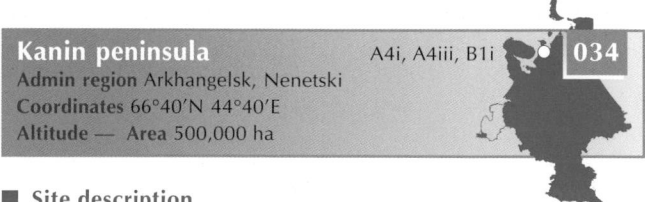

Southern coast of Cheshskaya Bay
B1i   033
Admin region Arkhangelsk, Nenetski
Coordinates 66°49'N 46°30'E
Altitude 0–0 m **Area** —

■ Site description
Low-lying coastal tundra in the vicinity of the Rivers Snopa, Oma, Vizha and Perepusk.

Habitats Grassland (tundra), Wetland (standing fresh water; river/stream)

■ Birds
Large numbers of geese and ducks occur on passage. The B1i criterion is applied at site-level rather than at species-level, as recent count data are not available for any bird species. The site may also prove to fulfil the A4i criterion once systematic counts have been made.

■ Protection status
National None **International** None

■ Conservation issues
No recent information.

Kanin peninsula
A4i, A4iii, B1i   034
Admin region Arkhangelsk, Nenetski
Coordinates 66°40'N 44°40'E
Altitude — **Area** 500,000 ha

■ Site description
Marshy, low-lying tundra with numerous rivers, lakes and channels between the Rivers Yazhma and Nyes.

Habitats Grassland (tundra), Wetland (standing fresh water; river/stream; water-fringe vegetation)

■ Birds
A breeding area for *Cygnus columbianus* and geese. Very large numbers of geese moult (50,000), and swans and geese (including *Branta leucopsis*) occur on passage. There are no recent counts for any species.

Species	Season	Year	Pop min	Pop max	Acc	Criteria
Cygnus columbianus Bewick's Swan	B	1989	—	—	—	A4i, B1i
Branta leucopsis Barnacle Goose	P	1989	—	—	—	B1i

■ **Protection status**
National None **International** None

■ **Conservation issues**
No recent information.

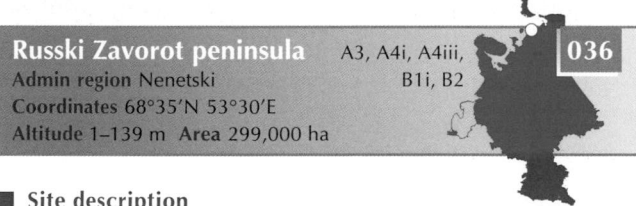

Khaypudyrskaya Bay (islands of B. Zelenets, Dolgi, Matveyev)
A4i, A4iii, B1i   035

Admin region Nenetski
Coordinates 68°55′N 59°50′E
Altitude 0–30 m **Area** 20,600 ha

■ **Site description**
A shallow bay with extensive mudflats, surrounded by marshy tundra and a number of lakes.

Habitats Grassland (10%; tundra), Wetland (70%; mudflat/sandflat; sand-dunes/sand beach; shingle/stony beach; coastal lagoon; river/stream), Marine areas (20%; open sea)
Land-use Fisheries/aquaculture (15%), Hunting (10%), Not utilized (75%)

■ **Birds**

Species	Season	Year	Pop min	Pop max	Acc	Criteria
Cygnus cygnus Whooper Swan	P	1992	300	—	—	B1i
[1] *Anser fabalis* Bean Goose	P	1992	—	—	—	A4i, B1i
[1] *Anser albifrons* White-fronted Goose	P	1992	—	—	—	A4i, B1i
[2] *Somateria mollissima* Eider	P	1992	—	—	—	A4i, B1i
[2] *Somateria spectabilis* King Eider	P	1992	—	—	—	A4i, B1i

1. Up to 20,000 *A. fabalis/A. albifrons*.
2. Up to 80,000 *S. mollissima/S. spectabilis*.

Migrating waterfowl occur in very large numbers, including up to 20,000 geese (*Anser fabalis* and *A. albifrons*), up to 80,000 eider duck (*Somateria mollissima* and *S. spectabilis*) and up to 40,000 other seaduck (*Aythya marila*, *Clangula hyemalis*, *Melanitta nigra* and *M. fusca*).

■ **Protection status**
National None **International** None

■ **Conservation issues**

Threats Disturbance to birds (B), Extraction industry (B), Unsustainable exploitation (C)

Russki Zavorot peninsula
A3, A4i, A4iii, B1i, B2   036

Admin region Nenetski
Coordinates 68°35′N 53°30′E
Altitude 1–139 m **Area** 299,000 ha

■ **Site description**
The area covers the northern part of the Russki Zavorot peninsula. Extensive marine shallows and low-lying tundra with numerous small lakes connected by channels.

Habitats Grassland (75%; tundra), Wetland (40%; tidal river/enclosed tidal water; standing fresh water; river/stream)
Land-use Agriculture (50%), Fisheries/aquaculture (20%), Hunting (100%)

■ **Birds**

Species	Season	Year	Pop min	Pop max	Acc	Criteria
Gavia arctica Black-throated Diver	B	1996	500	—	C	A4i, B1i
Cygnus columbianus Bewick's Swan	B	1996	60	—	C	A3, A4i, B1i
Anser fabalis Bean Goose	B	1996	—	1,700	C	A4i, B1i
Anser albifrons White-fronted Goose	B	1996	2,500	—	C	A3, B1i
Anas acuta Pintail	B	1996	—	6,500	C	A4i, B1i, B2
Aythya marila Scaup	B	1996	—	8,500	C	A3, A4i, B1i
Somateria spectabilis King Eider	B	1996	—	3,000	C	A3, A4i, B1i
Clangula hyemalis Long-tailed Duck	B	1996	8,000	—	C	A3
Bucephala clangula Goldeneye	B	1996	1,000	—	C	B1i

The breeding avifauna includes five species (all waterbirds) out of the 32 in Europe that are restricted to the Arctic/tundra biome when breeding. Very large numbers of waterbirds breed in the area (more than 20,000 individuals), based on extrapolations from count data

(individuals/km²), including geese, dabbling ducks, and seaduck such as *Clangula hyemalis*. These extrapolated totals are very approximate but allow preliminary identification of important species. After the breeding season, up to 10,000 moulting swans (*Cygnus columbianus* and *C. cygnus*) congregate in the area.

■ **Protection status**
National High **International** None
299,000 ha of IBA covered by Zakaznik (Nenetski, 440,000 ha).

■ **Conservation issues**

Threats Aquaculture/fisheries (B), Unsustainable exploitation (B)

A proposal has been put forward for the designation of a Zapovednik in the area (Nenetski). A scientific research programme is ongoing in conjunction with Groningen University (The Netherlands).

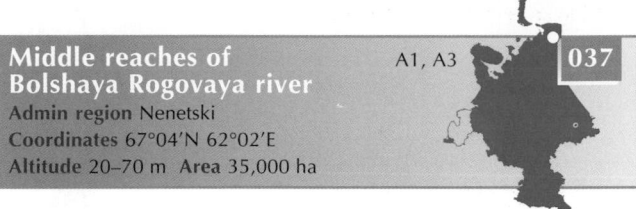

Middle reaches of Bolshaya Rogovaya river
A1, A3   037

Admin region Nenetski
Coordinates 67°04′N 62°02′E
Altitude 20–70 m **Area** 35,000 ha

■ **Site description**
Wet, wooded tundra and fens along a river valley in the southern tundra subzone.

Habitats Forest and woodland (13%; alluvial/very wet forest), Grassland (55%; tundra), Wetland (12%; fen/transition mire/spring)
Land-use Agriculture (5%), Unknown (95%)

■ **Birds**

Species	Season	Year	Pop min	Pop max	Acc	Criteria
Anser erythropus Lesser White-fronted Goose	B	1990	30	30	B	A1, A3
Aythya marila Scaup	B	1990	50	70	B	A3
Melanitta nigra Common Scoter	B	1990	100	120	B	A3
[1] *Calidris minuta* Little Stint	B	1990	—	—	—	A3
[1] *Calidris temminckii* Temminck's Stint	B	1990	—	—	—	A3
Phalaropus lobatus Red-necked Phalarope	B	1990	100	120	B	A3
Stercorarius longicaudus Long-tailed Skua	B	1990	10	15	B	A3
[1] *Anthus cervinus* Red-throated Pipit	B	1990	—	—	—	A3
Calcarius lapponicus Lapland Bunting	B	1990	300	400	B	A3

1. No special counts.

Nine of the 32 species in Europe that are restricted to the Arctic/tundra biome (when breeding) breed at the site in significant numbers, including the globally threatened *Anser erythropus*.

■ **Protection status**
National None **International** None

■ **Conservation issues**

Threats Firewood collection (C), Forest grazing (C)

Pechoro-Ilychski Nature Reserve
A1, B2   038

Admin region Komi Republic
Coordinates 62°30′N 59°00′E
Altitude 160–1,195 m **Area** 705,500 ha

■ **Site description**
Northern taiga forests in the upper reaches of the Pechora river.

Habitats Forest and woodland (85%; native coniferous forest), Grassland (2%; alpine/subalpine/boreal grassland), Wetland (5%; river/stream; raised bog), Rocky areas (8%; scree/boulders)
Land-use Nature conservation/research (100%)

■ **Birds**

Significant numbers of two raptors breed in the area.

Species		Season	Year	Pop min	Pop max	Acc	Criteria
Haliaeetus albicilla	White-tailed Eagle	B	1996	8	11	A	A1, B2
Aquila chrysaetos	Golden Eagle	R	1996	2	4	B	B2

■ Protection status
National High **International** High
705,500 ha of IBA covered by Zapovednik (Pechoro–Ilychskiy, 721,322 ha). 705,500 ha of IBA covered by Biosphere Reserve (Pechoro–Ilychskiy, 721,322 ha). 705,500 ha of IBA covered by World Heritage Site (Virgin Komi Forest, 3,280,000 ha).

■ Conservation issues

> **Threats** Disturbance to birds (C), Firewood collection (C), Recreation/tourism (C), Unsustainable exploitation (C)

Hunting, forestry and fishery activities take place in the buffer zone (650,000 ha) surrounding the site.

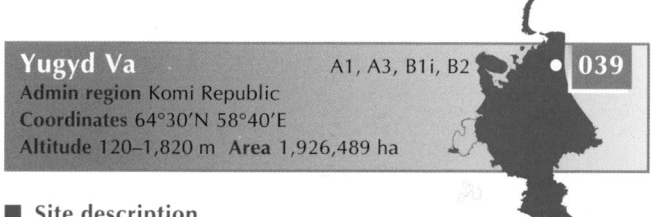

Yugyd Va
A1, A3, B1i, B2   039
Admin region Komi Republic
Coordinates 64°30′N 58°40′E
Altitude 120–1,820 m **Area** 1,926,489 ha

■ Site description
Habitats are characteristic of the subpolar region of the northern Ural mountains.

> **Habitats** Forest and woodland (50%; native coniferous forest; mixed forest), Grassland (20%; humid grassland; tundra), Wetland (30%; river/stream; raised bog; fen/transition mire/spring), Rocky areas (25%)
> **Land-use** Agriculture (10%), Fisheries/aquaculture (5%), Nature conservation/research (100%), Tourism/recreation (60%), Water management (20%)

■ Birds

Species		Season	Year	Pop min	Pop max	Acc	Criteria
Haliaeetus albicilla	White-tailed Eagle	B	1996	15	20	B	A1, B2
Gallinago media	Great Snipe	B	1996	100	200	B	A1, B1i
Surnia ulula	Hawk Owl	R	1996	—	—	—	A3
Strix nebulosa	Great Grey Owl	R	1996	—	—	—	A3
Bombycilla garrulus	Waxwing	B	—	—	—	—	A3
Phylloscopus borealis	Arctic Warbler	B	1996	Common		—	A3
Parus cinctus	Siberian Tit	B	1996	Common		—	A3
Perisoreus infaustus	Siberian Jay	B	1996	—	—	—	A3
Fringilla montifringilla	Brambling	B	1996	Common		—	A3
Loxia leucoptera	Two-barred Crossbill	B	1996	—	—	—	A3
Pinicola enucleator	Pine Grosbeak	B	1996	—	—	—	A3
Calcarius lapponicus	Lapland Bunting	B	1996	—	—	—	A3
Emberiza rustica	Rustic Bunting	B	1996	—	—	—	A3

Breeding species include 11 of the 15 species in Europe that are restricted to the boreal biome when breeding (no abundance counts have been made), as well as significant numbers of *Gallinago media* and of raptors.

■ Protection status
National High **International** None
1,926,489 ha of IBA covered by National Park (Yugyd Va, 1,926,489 ha).

■ Conservation issues

> **Threats** Disturbance to birds (C), Extraction industry (C), Unsustainable exploitation (C)

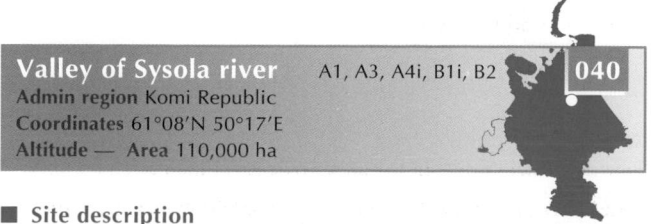

Valley of Sysola river
A1, A3, A4i, B1i, B2   040
Admin region Komi Republic
Coordinates 61°08′N 50°17′E
Altitude — **Area** 110,000 ha

■ Site description

> **Habitats** Forest and woodland (10%; native coniferous forest; mixed forest; alluvial/very wet forest), Scrub (10%; scrub), Grassland (30%; humid grassland), Wetland (4%; river/stream; fen/transition mire/spring), Artificial landscape (50%; highly improved reseeded grassland; arable land; urban parks/gardens)

Land-use Hunting (100%), Nature conservation/research (100%)

A valley to the south of the town of Syktyvkar. The area is highly developed.

■ Birds

Species		Season	Year	Pop min	Pop max	Acc	Criteria
Podiceps auritus	Slavonian Grebe	B	1996	15	30	—	A3
Anser erythropus Lesser White-fronted Goose		P	1996	50	150	—	A1, B1i
Crex crex	Corncrake	B	1996	200	350	B	A1
Gallinago media	Great Snipe	B	1996	20	30	B	A1
Tringa nebularia	Greenshank	B	1996	1,000	—	—	A3, A4i, B1i
Surnia ulula	Hawk Owl	R	1996	40	80	—	A3
Strix nebulosa	Great Grey Owl	R	1996	5	15	—	A3
Bombycilla garrulus	Waxwing	B	1996	200	600	—	A3
Phylloscopus borealis	Arctic Warbler	B	1996	2,200	—	—	A3
Parus cinctus	Siberian Tit	R	1996	100	200	—	A3
Perisoreus infaustus	Siberian Jay	R	1996	80	120	—	A3, B2
Fringilla montifringilla	Brambling	B	1996	2,000	2,100	—	A3
Loxia leucoptera	Two-barred Crossbill	B	1996	500	3,000	—	A3
[1] *Loxia pytyopsittacus*	Parrot Crossbill	U	1996	—	—	—	A3

1. No counts of abundance.

The globally threatened *Anser erythropus* stages in important numbers on passage. Two species of global conservation concern breed in the area, as do 11 of the 15 species in Europe that are restricted to the boreal biome (when breeding).

■ Protection status
National Low **International** None
500 ha of IBA covered by Zakaznik (Abkedzhskiy, 500 ha). 30 ha of IBA covered by Zakaznik (Bolotniy, Bortom Baza, 43 ha). 12 ha of IBA covered by Natural Monument (Gorsibskiy, 12 ha). 120 ha of IBA covered by Natural Monument (Kadzheromskiy, 120 ha).

■ Conservation issues

> **Threats** Agricultural intensification/expansion (C), Disturbance to birds (C), Drainage (C), Infrastructure (C), Unsustainable exploitation (B)

The site is also adjacent to Vizingskiy Zakaznik (9,400 ha).

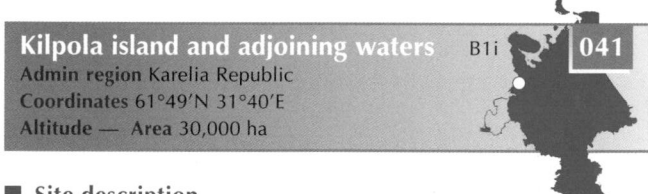

Kilpola island and adjoining waters
B1i   041
Admin region Karelia Republic
Coordinates 61°49′N 31°40′E
Altitude — **Area** 30,000 ha

■ Site description
Shallows with small islands in Lake Ladoga, east of the Gulf of Finland.

> **Habitats** Wetland (standing fresh water)

■ Birds
An important area for diving duck during migration. The B1i criterion is applied at site-level rather than at species-level, as recent count data are not available for any bird species. The site may also prove to fulfil the A4i criterion once systematic counts have been made.

■ Protection status
National None **International** None

■ Conservation issues
No recent information. A seasonal nature reserve (Zakaznik) has been proposed.

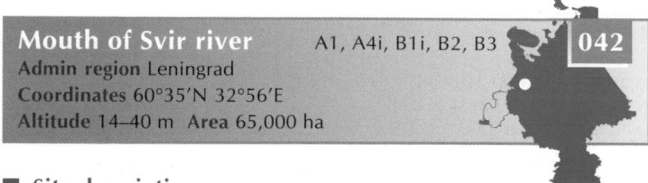

Mouth of Svir river
A1, A4i, B1i, B2, B3   042
Admin region Leningrad
Coordinates 60°35′N 32°56′E
Altitude 14–40 m **Area** 65,000 ha

■ Site description
Shallow waters around the mouth of the Svir river, where it enters Lake Ladoga.

Habitats Forest and woodland (52%; native coniferous forest; alluvial/very wet forest), Wetland (44%; sand-dunes/sand beach; standing fresh water; raised bog; fen/transition mire/spring), Artificial landscape (4%; highly improved reseeded grassland; arable land)

Land-use Agriculture (5%), Fisheries/aquaculture (15%), Forestry (10%), Hunting (20%), Nature conservation/research (65%)

■ Birds

Species	Season	Year	Pop min	Pop max	Acc	Criteria
Cygnus cygnus Whooper Swan	P	1995	500	1,100	C	A4i, B1i
Anser fabalis Bean Goose	P	1996	1,000	3,000	C	B1i
Anser erythropus Lesser White-fronted Goose	P	1996	8	30	C	A1
Melanitta nigra Common Scoter	P	1996	10,000	25,000	C	A4i, B1i
Haliaeetus albicilla White-tailed Eagle	B	1996	3	4	A	A1
Porzana porzana Spotted Crake	B	1996	10	140	C	B3
Crex crex Corncrake	B	1995	10	100	C	A1
Gallinago media Great Snipe	B	1995	10	60	C	A1
Numenius phaeopus Whimbrel	B	1995	400	500	C	B3
Larus minutus Little Gull	B	1995	20	130	C	B2
Acrocephalus scirpaceus Reed Warbler	B	1995	—	2,000	C	B3
Loxia pytyopsittacus Parrot Crossbill	B	1995	—	100	C	B3

Significant numbers of a variety of birds breed in the area, mainly waterbirds and including four species of global conservation concern. Large numbers of wildfowl stage in the area during migration.

■ Protection status

National Partial **International** High
41,436 ha of IBA covered by Zapovednik (Nizhne-Svirskiy, 41,436 ha). 60,500 ha of IBA covered by Ramsar Site (Svir Delta, 60,500 ha).

■ Conservation issues

Threats Abandonment/reduction of land management (A), Disturbance to birds (C), Industrialization/urbanization (C), Recreation/tourism (C), Selective logging/cutting (C)

The reduction in the area of agricultural land is negatively affecting geese and *Grus grus* which forage on this habitat during migration.

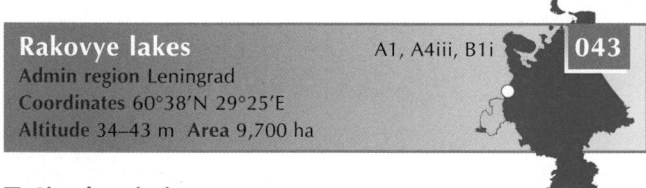

Rakovye lakes
A1, A4iii, B1i   043

Admin region Leningrad
Coordinates 60°38′N 29°25′E
Altitude 34–43 m **Area** 9,700 ha

■ Site description

A system of lakes formed from abandoned areas of peat-mining.

Habitats Forest and woodland (native coniferous forest), Wetland (70%; standing fresh water; fen/transition mire/spring)

■ Birds

Species	Season	Year	Pop min	Pop max	Acc	Criteria
Crex crex Corncrake	B	1996	20	—	—	A1
Grus grus Crane	B	1996	100	—	—	B1i

An important site for breeding *Crex crex* and *Grus grus*. There have been few counts of individual species, but in total up to 6,000 geese (mainly *Anser fabalis* and *A. albifrons*), 50,000 dabbling ducks (*Anas* spp.) and 150,000 diving ducks congregate in the area during autumn and spring migration.

■ Protection status

National Partial **International** None
6,142 ha of IBA covered by Zakaznik (Rakovie Ozera, 6,142 ha).

■ Conservation issues

Threats Aquaculture/fisheries (U), Construction/impact of dyke/dam/barrage (U), Disturbance to birds (U), Drainage (U), Intensified forest management (U), Unsustainable exploitation (U)

Berezovye islands of Vyborg Bay
A4i, A4iii, B1i   044

Admin region Leningrad
Coordinates 60°18′N 29°00′E
Altitude 0–43 m **Area** 12,000 ha

■ Site description

This area encompasses shallow waters, inlets, small bays and several small islands located near Vyborg Bay in the Gulf of Finland, southwest of the town of Primorsk.

Habitats Forest and woodland, Wetland (70%; tidal river/enclosed tidal water; shingle/stony beach; coastal lagoon; raised bog)

Land-use Fisheries/aquaculture, Tourism/recreation

■ Birds

Species	Season	Year	Pop min	Pop max	Acc	Criteria
Gavia arctica Black-throated Diver	P	1996	20,000	40,000	—	A4i, B1i
[1] *Podiceps grisegena* Red-necked Grebe	P	1996	—	—	—	B1i
Cygnus columbianus Bewick's Swan	P	1996	—	5,000	—	A4i, B1i
Cygnus cygnus Whooper Swan	P	1996	15,000	25,000	—	A4i, B1i
[2] *Branta leucopsis* Barnacle Goose	P	1996	—	—	—	A4i, B1i
[2] *Branta bernicla* Brent Goose	P	1996	—	—	—	A4i, B1i
Aythya fuligula Tufted Duck	P	1996	100,000	200,000	A	A4i, B1i
Aythya marila Scaup	P	1996	100,000	300,000	A	A4i, B1i
Clangula hyemalis Long-tailed Duck	P	1996	300,000	400,000	A	A4i, B1i
Melanitta nigra Common Scoter	P	1996	300,000	400,000	A	A4i, B1i
Melanitta fusca Velvet Scoter	P	1996	100,000	200,000	A	A4i, B1i
Bucephala clangula Goldeneye	P	1996	150,000	200,000	A	A4i, B1i
[3] *Mergus serrator* Red-breasted Merganser	P	1996	—	—	B	A4i, B1i
[3] *Mergus merganser* Goosander	P	1996	—	—	—	A4i, B1i
Larus ridibundus Black-headed Gull	P	1996	—	200,000	A	A4i, B1i
Larus canus Common Gull	P	1996	—	100,000	A	A4i, B1i
Larus fuscus Lesser Black-backed Gull	P	1996	—	50,000	A	A4i, B1i
Larus argentatus Herring Gull	P	1996	—	100,000	A	A4i, B1i

1. Up to 2,000 *P. cristatus/P. grisegena*.
2. Up to 70,000 *B. leucopsis/B. bernicla*.
3. Up to 15,000 *M. serrator/M. merganser*.

The area holds huge congregations of waterbirds during migration, including up to 500,000 wildfowl and up to 100,000 waders during migration, with *Anas penelope*, *A. acuta*, *A. querquedula*, *Charadrius hiaticula*, *Calidris minuta*, *Calidris temminckii*, *Calidris alpina*, *Gallinago gallinago*, *Numenius phaeopus* and *N. arquata* being among the most numerous species.

■ Protection status

National High **International** High
12,000 ha of IBA covered by Zakaznik (Berezovye Ostrova, 12,000 ha). 12,000 ha of IBA covered by Ramsar Site (Berezovye Islands, 12,000 ha).

■ Conservation issues

The building of a harbour with oil terminals poses a major threat to this IBA.

Threats Aquaculture/fisheries (A), Disturbance to birds (A), Dredging/canalization (U), Infrastructure (A), Intensified forest management (U)

Koporski Bay
A1, A4i, A4iii, B1i, B2, B3   045

Admin region Leningrad
Coordinates 59°47′N 28°45′E
Altitude 0–0 m **Area** 6,000 ha

■ Site description

The site comprises a number of sandy beaches partly covered by reedbeds, in the Gulf of Finland.

Habitats Forest and woodland (5%; mixed forest), Scrub (5%; scrub), Wetland (90%; tidal river/enclosed tidal water; mudflat/sandflat; sand-dunes/sand beach; coastal lagoon; fen/transition mire/spring)

Land-use Fisheries/aquaculture (80%), Hunting (90%), Military (10%), Tourism/recreation (50%), Urban/industrial/transport (5%)

■ Birds

Species	Season	Year	Pop min	Pop max	Acc	Criteria
Cygnus columbianus Bewick's Swan	P	1997	200	500	B	A4i, B1i
Cygnus cygnus Whooper Swan	P	1997	1,000	2,000	B	A4i, B1i
Anser erythropus Lesser White-fronted Goose	P	1997	15	30	B	A1
Anas penelope Wigeon	B	1997	2,000	5,000	B	B1i
Anas crecca Teal	B	1997	5,000	10,000	B	A4i, B1i
Anas acuta Pintail	B	1997	500	1,000	B	B1i
Aythya marila Scaup	P	1997	5,000	10,000	B	A4i, B1i
Melanitta nigra Common Scoter	P	1997	20,000	50,000	B	A4i, B1i
Bucephala clangula Goldeneye	B	1997	1,000	2,000	B	A4i, B1i
Haliaeetus albicilla White-tailed Eagle	P	1997	10	15	B	A1
Tringa totanus Redshank	B	1997	300	500	B	B2
Larus minutus Little Gull	B	1997	200	600	B	A4i, B1i, B2
Larus fuscus Lesser Black-backed Gull	B	1997	500	1,000	B	B1i, B3
Sterna albifrons Little Tern	B	1997	50	150	B	B1i, B2
Acrocephalus scirpaceus Reed Warbler	B	1997	200	500	B	B3

The site regularly holds more than 20,000 waterfowl during both the breeding and migration seasons, including important numbers of many individual species.

■ Protection status
National None **International** None

■ Conservation issues

Threats Aquaculture/fisheries (C), Recreation/tourism (C), Unsustainable exploitation (B)

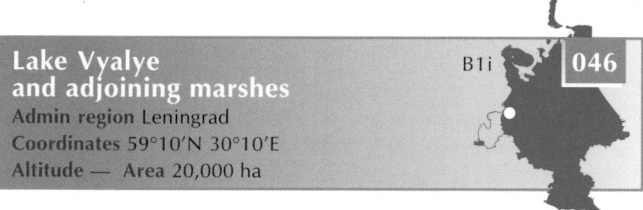

Lake Vyalye and adjoining marshes
B1i 046
Admin region Leningrad
Coordinates 59°10'N 30°10'E
Altitude — **Area** 20,000 ha

■ Site description
A freshwater lake and low-lying marshes.

Habitats Wetland (standing fresh water; water-fringe vegetation)

■ Birds

Species	Season	Year	Pop min	Pop max	Acc	Criteria
[1] *Anser albifrons* White-fronted Goose	P	1989	—	—	—	B1i

1. Large numbers.

Based on data in the previous pan-European IBA inventory (Grimmett and Jones 1989), this is an important staging site for *Anser albifrons*. Breeding species include *Grus grus*.

■ Protection status
National Partial **International** None
Part of IBA covered by Zakaznik (Ozero Vyalye).

■ Conservation issues
No recent information.

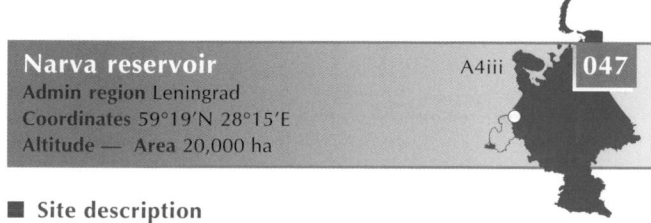

Narva reservoir
A4iii 047
Admin region Leningrad
Coordinates 59°19'N 28°15'E
Altitude — **Area** 20,000 ha

■ Site description
A reservoir with a hydroelectric power station.

Habitats Wetland (standing fresh water)
Land-use Water management

■ Birds
An important breeding site for ducks (25,000 pairs). Recent count data are not available for any species.

■ Protection status
National None **International** None

■ Conservation issues
No recent information.

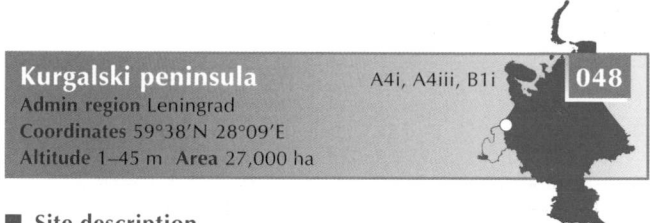

Kurgalski peninsula
A4i, A4iii, B1i 048
Admin region Leningrad
Coordinates 59°38'N 28°09'E
Altitude 1–45 m **Area** 27,000 ha

■ Site description
The area comprises the Kurgalski peninsula together with the surrounding shallow waters of the Baltic Sea.

Habitats Forest and woodland (native coniferous forest; mixed forest), Grassland (humid grassland), Wetland (mudflat/sandflat; coastal lagoon), Marine areas (sea inlet/coastal features)
Land-use Unknown

■ Birds

Species	Season	Year	Pop min	Pop max	Acc	Criteria
Gavia arctica Black-throated Diver	P	1993	10,000	20,000	—	A4i, B1i
Cygnus columbianus Bewick's Swan	P	1993	50,000	—	—	A4i, B1i
Cygnus cygnus Whooper Swan	P	1993	50,000	—	—	A4i, B1i
Mergus serrator Red-breasted Merganser	P	1993	—	20,000	—	A4i, B1i
Mergus merganser Goosander	P	1993	—	10,000	—	A4i, B1i
Larus canus Common Gull	P	1996	300,000	—	—	A4i, B1i
Larus fuscus Lesser Black-backed Gull	P	1996	150,000	—	—	A4i, B1i
Larus argentatus Herring Gull	P	1996	400,000	—	—	A4i, B1i
Larus marinus Great Black-backed Gull	P	1996	50,000	—	—	A4i, B1i

A very important staging area for waterbirds on passage, with up to 100,000 swans *Cygnus*, hundreds of thousands of geese, 1,200,000 ducks, 100,000 waders and 1,000,000 gulls regularly occurring here during spring and autumn migration.

■ Protection status
National None **International** High
27,000 ha of IBA covered by Ramsar Site (Kurgalsky peninsula, 65,000 ha).

■ Conservation issues

Threats Disturbance to birds (U)

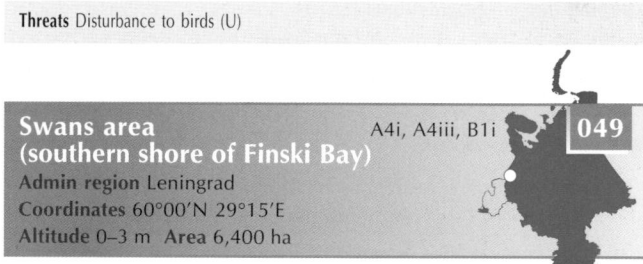

Swans area (southern shore of Finski Bay)
A4i, A4iii, B1i 049
Admin region Leningrad
Coordinates 60°00'N 29°15'E
Altitude 0–3 m **Area** 6,400 ha

■ Site description
Shallow waters along the southern shore of Finski Bay (Gulf of Finland) in the Baltic Sea.

Habitats Forest and woodland, Wetland, Marine areas (open sea; sea inlet/coastal features)

■ Birds

Species	Season	Year	Pop min	Pop max	Acc	Criteria
[1] *Cygnus columbianus* Bewick's Swan	P	1996	—	4,000	—	A4i, B1i
[1] *Cygnus cygnus* Whooper Swan	P	1996	5,000	—	—	A4i, B1i

1. Up to 25,000 *Cygnus* in total.

This is one of the most important sites on the White Sea–Baltic Sea flyway, with up to 25,000 swans (*Cygnus olor, C. columbianus, C. cygnus*), 100,000 ducks and 200,000 gulls staging here regularly on migration, mainly in spring.

■ Protection status
National High **International** High

6,400 ha of IBA covered by Zakaznik (Lebyazhiy Hunting Reserve, 6,400 ha). 6,400 ha of IBA covered by Ramsar Site ('Southern coast of the Gulf of Finland, Baltic Sea', 6,400 ha).

■ Conservation issues
Data are incomplete for individual bird species, and further survey work is required.

Chudsko-Pskovski lake and adjacent areas A1, A4i, A4iii, A4iv, B1i, B1iv **050**
Admin region Pskov
Coordinates 58°30′N 27°49′E
Altitude 30–70 m Area 251,400 ha

■ Site description
A large lake on the Russian–Estonian border, in a highly developed area.

Habitats Forest and woodland (10%), Grassland (5%), Wetland (80%), Artificial landscape (5%)
Land-use Fisheries/aquaculture, Tourism/recreation, Nature conservation/research (25%), Urban/industrial/transport

■ Birds

Species	Season	Year	Pop min	Pop max	Acc	Criteria
Bucephala clangula Goldeneye	N	—	—	5,600	—	A4i, B1i
Aquila clanga Greater Spotted Eagle	B	—	3	4	—	A1
Crex crex Corncrake	B	—	100	—	—	A1
Fulica atra Coot	N	—	—	34,500	—	B1i

Two species of global conservation concern breed in important numbers. At least 200,000–300,000 individuals of waterfowl stage here during spring migration, mainly *Anser fabalis*, *A. albifrons*, *Anas penelope*, *A. platyrhynchos*, *Aythya fuligula* and *Bucephala clangula*. The lake is also important for moulting waterfowl, notably *Anas platyrhynchos*, *Aythya ferina*, *Aythya fuligula* and *Bucephala clangula*. The narrow land-corridor between Chudskoe and Pskovskoe lakes acts as a major bottleneck for migrating birds: as many as 4 million (mainly passerines but also some raptors) have been estimated to pass in a single 5-hour period in early September.

■ Protection status
National Partial **International** Partial
64,900 ha of IBA covered by Zakaznik (Remdovsky, 64,900 ha). 93,600 ha of IBA covered by Ramsar Site (Pskovsko-Chudskaya Lowland, 93,600 ha).

■ Conservation issues

Threats Firewood collection (U), Recreation/tourism (U), Unsustainable exploitation (U)

It has not been decided whether this area should be treated as one IBA, or whether several IBAs should be identified along the Estonian and Russian shores. More field research is needed and has already been planned.

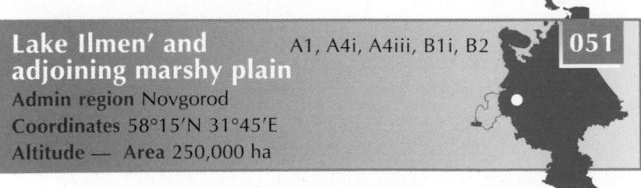

Lake Ilmen' and adjoining marshy plain A1, A4i, A4iii, B1i, B2 **051**
Admin region Novgorod
Coordinates 58°15′N 31°45′E
Altitude — Area 250,000 ha

■ Site description
One of the largest lakes in central European Russia, with surrounding fens and meadows.

Habitats Forest and woodland (5%), Grassland (22%; humid grassland), Wetland (65%; standing fresh water; fen/transition mire/spring), Artificial landscape (8%; highly improved reseeded grassland; arable land; other urban/industrial areas)
Land-use Agriculture (13%), Fisheries/aquaculture (59%), Forestry (5%), Hunting (40%), Tourism/recreation (15%)

■ Birds

Species	Season	Year	Pop min	Pop max	Acc	Criteria
Anser erythropus Lesser White-fronted Goose	P	1993	15	20	C	A1
Crex crex Corncrake	B	1995	1,500	2,500	B	A1, B2
Gallinago media Great Snipe	B	1995	200	300	C	A1, A4i, B1i

The area is important for three species of global conservation concern. It holds 20,000 or more migrating waterfowl on a regular basis, mainly *Anas penelope*, *A. crecca*, *A. platyrhynchos*, *A. querquedula*, *A. clypeata* and *Aythya fuligula*. Breeding species of global conservation concern that do not meet IBA criteria: *Haliaeetus albicilla* (1–2 pairs).

■ Protection status
National Low **International** None
8,600 ha of IBA covered by Zakaznik (Novgorodsky, 8,600 ha). 9,460 ha of IBA covered by Zakaznik (Vostochno–Ilmensky, 9,460 ha).

■ Conservation issues

Threats Abandonment/reduction of land management (C), Intensified forest management (C), Recreation/tourism (B)

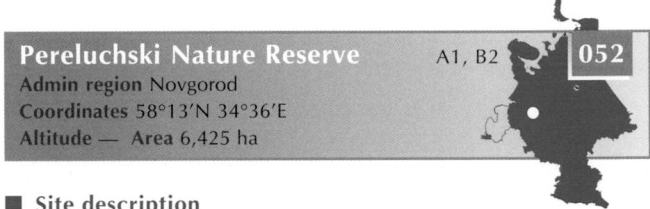

Pereluchski Nature Reserve A1, B2 **052**
Admin region Novgorod
Coordinates 58°13′N 34°36′E
Altitude — Area 6,425 ha

■ Site description
A large lake formed by the flooding of the Uver, S'ezha and Medvedka rivers.

Habitats Forest and woodland (50%), Grassland (15%; humid grassland), Wetland (15%; standing fresh water; fen/transition mire/spring), Artificial landscape (17%; arable land; urban parks/gardens)
Land-use Agriculture (5%), Forestry (40%), Hunting (70%), Tourism/recreation (5%)

■ Birds

Species	Season	Year	Pop min	Pop max	Acc	Criteria
Crex crex Corncrake	B	1991	15	50	C	A1
Gallinago media Great Snipe	B	1991	20	40	C	A1
Chlidonias niger Black Tern	B	1991	200	300	C	B2

Three flood-plain species breed in significant numbers, two of the three being species of global conservation concern.

■ Protection status
National High **International** None
6,425 ha of IBA covered by Zakaznik (Pereluchsky, 6,425 ha).

■ Conservation issues

Threats Agricultural intensification/expansion (A), Deforestation (commercial) (A), Unsustainable exploitation (C)

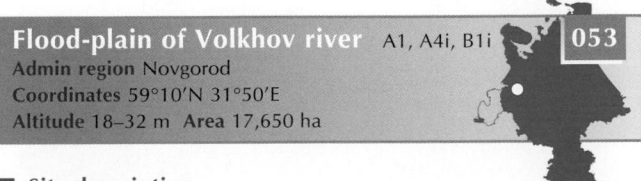

Flood-plain of Volkhov river A1, A4i, B1i **053**
Admin region Novgorod
Coordinates 59°10′N 31°50′E
Altitude 18–32 m Area 17,650 ha

■ Site description
A partly forested flood-plain containing a system of small lakes, with scrub present in very wet areas.

Habitats Forest and woodland (40%), Grassland (20%; humid grassland), Wetland (30%; standing fresh water; raised bog), Artificial landscape (10%)
Land-use Agriculture (30%), Forestry (40%), Hunting (95%), Not utilized (20%)

■ Birds
Three species of global conservation concern breed in significant numbers, including two globally threatened species.

Species	Season	Year	Pop min	Pop max	Acc	Criteria
Aquila clanga Greater Spotted Eagle	B	1993	2	2	C	A1
Crex crex Corncrake	B	1995	20	30	C	A1
Gallinago media Great Snipe	B	1995	50	150	C	A1, A4i, B1i

■ Protection status
National None **International** None

■ Conservation issues

Threats Abandonment/reduction of land management (B), Disturbance to birds (B), Drainage (B), Firewood collection (B), Industrialization/urbanization (A), Recreation/tourism (B), Unsustainable exploitation (C)

Plans for the establishment of a nature reserve (Zakaznik) have been proposed to the regional authority.

Redrovski Nature Reserve A1 054
Admin region Novgorod
Coordinates 58°32'N 35°00'E
Altitude 79–196 m **Area** 16,850 ha

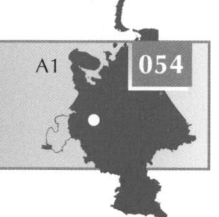

■ Site description
Three large lakes of glacial origin.

Habitats Forest and woodland (61%), Wetland (25%; standing fresh water; raised bog; fen/transition mire/spring), Artificial landscape (14%)
Land-use Agriculture (14%), Fisheries/aquaculture (16%), Forestry (70%), Not utilized (30%), Tourism/recreation (10%), Urban/industrial/transport (5%)

■ Birds

Species	Season	Year	Pop min	Pop max	Acc	Criteria
Aquila clanga Greater Spotted Eagle	B	1993	1	2	C	A1
Crex crex Corncrake	B	1995	20	50	A	A1

Two globally threatened species breed in significant numbers. Significant proportion (≥1%) of national population breeding at site: *Aquila pomarina* (1 pair).

■ Protection status
National High **International** None
16,850 ha of IBA covered by Zakaznik (Redrovsky, 16,850 ha).

■ Conservation issues

Threats Abandonment/reduction of land management (B), Afforestation (B), Intensified forest management (B), Unsustainable exploitation (C)

Sources of the River Luga A1, B1i 055
Admin region Novgorod, Leningrad
Coordinates 58°53'N 30°54'E
Altitude 53–77 m **Area** 49,600 ha

■ Site description
A large wetland complex.

Habitats Forest and woodland (29%; native coniferous forest; mixed forest; alluvial/very wet forest), Wetland (69%; standing fresh water; raised bog; water-fringe vegetation; fen/transition mire/spring)
Land-use Hunting (99%)

■ Birds

Species	Season	Year	Pop min	Pop max	Acc	Criteria
[1] *Anser fabalis* Bean Goose	P	1997	2,000	2,500	C	B1i
Anser erythropus Lesser White-fronted Goose	P	1997	14	—	B	A1
Crex crex Corncrake	B	1997	18	25	C	A1

1. Both subspecies present; number of *A. f. fabalis* probably exceeds threshold.

Significant numbers of two goose species occur, including the globally threatened *Anser erythropus*. Breeding species of global conservation concern that do not meet IBA criteria: *Haliaeetus albicilla* (1 pair), *Gallinago media* (at least 18 pairs).

■ Protection status
National None **International** None

■ Conservation issues

Threats Disturbance to birds (B), Drainage (C), Extraction industry (C), Unsustainable exploitation (B)

The area was partly destroyed by the peat-mining industry, which ceased activities in the early 1990s. The water-table at the site is now rising again, and the mire has started to regenerate naturally.

Polisto-Lovatskaya mire system A1, A4i, B1i, B2, B3 056
Admin region Novgorod, Pskov
Coordinates 57°15'N 30°40'E
Altitude 86–190 m **Area** 110,000 ha

■ Site description
One of the largest mire systems in Europe, located on the border between the Pskov and Novgorod regions.

Habitats Forest and woodland (10%), Wetland (80%; standing fresh water; raised bog; fen/transition mire/spring), Artificial landscape (10%)
Land-use Agriculture (6%), Forestry (30%), Hunting (10%), Other (20%)

■ Birds

Species	Season	Year	Pop min	Pop max	Acc	Criteria
Aquila chrysaetos Golden Eagle	R	1992	2	4	—	B2
Crex crex Corncrake	B	1992	80	100	—	A1
Grus grus Crane	B	1992	100	150	—	B1i
Pluvialis apricaria Golden Plover	B	1992	200	250	—	B3
Numenius phaeopus Whimbrel	B	1992	100	150	—	B3
Numenius arquata Curlew	B	1992	1,400	2,500	—	A4i, B1i

A variety of typically mire-breeding birds occur in important numbers, including the globally threatened *Crex crex*.

■ Protection status
National High **International** None
36,000 ha of IBA covered by Zapovednik (Polistovskiy, 36,000 ha). 36,900 ha of IBA covered by Zapovednik (Rdeiskiy, 36,900 ha). 27,200 ha of IBA covered by Zakaznik (Rdeysky gydrologichesky, 27,200 ha).

■ Conservation issues

Threats Deforestation (commercial) (C), Drainage (B), Extraction industry (C), Recreation/tourism (B), Unsustainable exploitation (C)

Sizemski flood-plain of Sheksna reservoir A1, B2 057
Admin region Vologda
Coordinates 59°20'N 38°30'E
Altitude 110–130 m **Area** 60,000 ha

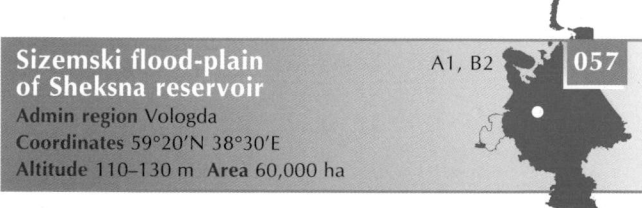

■ Site description
Reseeded grass meadows on the Sizemski flood-plain which are flooded in spring. The area has a small human population and is relatively undisturbed.

Habitats Forest and woodland (35%; native coniferous forest; mixed forest; alluvial/very wet forest), Wetland (60%; standing fresh water; river/stream; raised bog), Artificial landscape (5%; arable land)
Land-use Agriculture (10%), Fisheries/aquaculture (35%), Forestry (35%), Hunting (90%), Nature conservation/research (30%), Tourism/recreation (90%), Water management (35%)

■ Birds
Haliaeetus albicilla breeds in significant numbers. More than 20,000 geese stage at the site during migration according to local people, although further research will be required in order to confirm this.

Species		Season	Year	Pop min	Pop max	Acc	Criteria
Haliaeetus albicilla	White-tailed Eagle	B	1996	2	7	B	A1
Larus canus	Common Gull	B	1996	300	400	A	B2

■ Protection status
National Partial **International** None
16,000 ha of IBA covered by National Park (Russkiy Sever, 166,400 ha).

■ Conservation issues

> **Threats** Drainage (C), Firewood collection (C), Selective logging/cutting (C), Unsustainable exploitation (C)

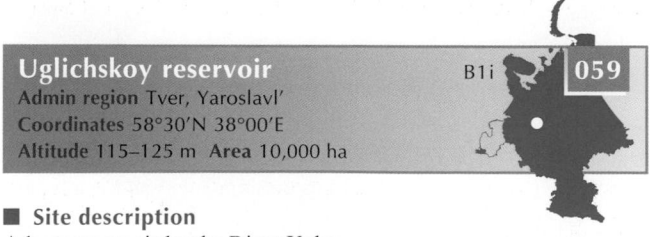

Rybinsk reservoir · A1, B1i, B2 · 058
Admin region Vologda, Yaroslavl'
Coordinates 58°35'N 38°00'E
Altitude 90–160 m **Area** 455,000 ha

■ Site description
One of the largest artificial reservoirs in European Russia, situated on the border between the Yaroslavl' and Vologda regions. Habitat features include shallows, pools, islands and surrounding forests.

> **Habitats** Forest and woodland (5%; native coniferous forest; mixed forest), Wetland (90%; standing fresh water; river/stream; raised bog; water-fringe vegetation; fen/transition mire/spring), Artificial landscape (3%; highly improved reseeded grassland; arable land; other urban/industrial areas)
> **Land-use** Agriculture (10%), Hunting (65%), Nature conservation/research (35%), Tourism/recreation (10%), Urban/industrial/transport (5%), Water management (40%)

■ Birds

Species		Season	Year	Pop min	Pop max	Acc	Criteria
Anser albifrons	White-fronted Goose	P	1996	7,500	7,500	A	B1i
Anas clypeata	Shoveler	B	1996	700	700	A	B1i
Haliaeetus albicilla	White-tailed Eagle	B	1996	22	28	B	A1, B2
Larus minutus	Little Gull	B	1996	150	150	B	B2
Larus canus	Common Gull	B	1996	1,750	1,750	B	B2
Sterna albifrons	Little Tern	B	1996	150	150	B	B2

Several waterbirds breed in significant numbers, and the forests support a notably large number of breeding *Haliaeetus albicilla*. Significant numbers of geese occur on passage; up to 10,000 (*Anser fabalis* and *A. albifrons*) were recorded in the mid-1980s.

■ Protection status
National Partial **International** None
112,673 ha of IBA covered by Zapovednik (Darvinskiy, 112,673 ha).

■ Conservation issues

> **Threats** Aquaculture/fisheries (B), Deforestation (commercial) (A), Disturbance to birds (B), Extraction industry (B), Firewood collection (B), Industrialization/urbanization (B), Infrastructure (B), Recreation/tourism (B), Unsustainable exploitation (A)

Uglichskoy reservoir · B1i · 059
Admin region Tver, Yaroslavl'
Coordinates 58°30'N 38°00'E
Altitude 115–125 m **Area** 10,000 ha

■ Site description
A large reservoir by the River Volga.

> **Habitats** Wetland (standing fresh water)
> **Land-use** Water management

■ Birds
An important area for passage and breeding geese and ducks. The B1i criterion is applied at site-level rather than at species-level, as recent count data are not available for any bird species. The site may also prove to fulfil the A4i criterion once systematic counts have been made.

■ Protection status
National None **International** None
No recent information.

■ Conservation issues
No recent information.

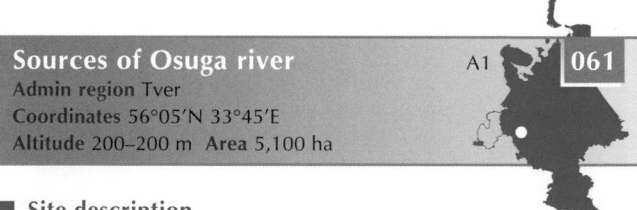

Central Forest Biosphere Reserve and adjacent areas · A1, B1i · 060
Admin region Tver
Coordinates 56°33'N 32°45'E
Altitude 230–270 m **Area** 63,680 ha

■ Site description
An area of marshes, raised bogs and wet forests on the watershed of the Rivers Volga and Zapadnaya Dvina, in the southern region of Tver.

> **Habitats** Forest and woodland (82%; native coniferous forest; mixed forest), Wetland (12%; standing fresh water; river/stream; raised bog), Artificial landscape (5%; highly improved reseeded grassland; arable land; other urban/industrial areas)
> **Land-use** Agriculture (5%), Forestry (13%), Hunting (61%), Nature conservation/research (100%), Not utilized (33%), Other (7%), Tourism/recreation (50%), Urban/industrial/transport (5%)

■ Birds

Species		Season	Year	Pop min	Pop max	Acc	Criteria
Anser erythropus Lesser White-fronted Goose		P	1994	20	200	B	A1, B1i
Crex crex	Corncrake	B	1995	40	70	A	A1

The globally threatened *Anser erythropus* and *Crex crex* occur in important numbers.

■ Protection status
National Partial **International** Partial
21,380 ha of IBA covered by Zapovednik (Tsentral'nolesnoy, 21,380 ha). 21,380 ha of IBA covered by Biosphere Reserve (Tsentral'nolesnoy, 21,380 ha).

■ Conservation issues

> **Threats** Afforestation (B), Other (C)

'Other' threat refers to a large variety of minor problems at the site, with little impact individually, such as firewood collection, drainage and recreation. The remainder of the site, outside the Zapovednik, is a buffer zone (42,300 ha).

Sources of Osuga river · A1 · 061
Admin region Tver
Coordinates 56°05'N 33°45'E
Altitude 200–200 m **Area** 5,100 ha

■ Site description
A mixture of forests and agricultural land situated along the watershed of the Osuga and Ramenka rivers.

> **Habitats** Forest and woodland (50%; mixed forest), Artificial landscape (50%; highly improved reseeded grassland; arable land)
> **Land-use** Agriculture (50%), Not utilized (50%)

■ Birds

Species		Season	Year	Pop min	Pop max	Acc	Criteria
Crex crex	Corncrake	B	1997	20	30	B	A1

The globally threatened *Crex crex* breeds in notable numbers.

■ Protection status
National None **International** None

■ Conservation issues

> **Threats** Other (C)

Hay-cutting activity can cause problems for *Crex crex*.

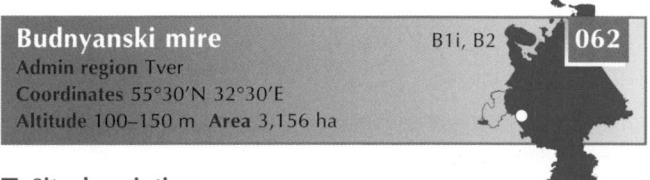

Budnyanski mire   B1i, B2   062
Admin region Tver
Coordinates 55°30'N 32°30'E
Altitude 100–150 m **Area** 3,156 ha

■ Site description
Raised bog and forest on the watershed between the Shesnitsa and Chichatka rivers, two tributaries of the Mezha river.

Habitats Forest and woodland (30%), Wetland (70%; standing fresh water; raised bog; fen/transition mire/spring)
Land-use Hunting (100%), Tourism/recreation (50%)

■ Birds

Species		Season	Year	Pop min	Pop max	Acc	Criteria
Anser albifrons	White-fronted Goose	P	1990	1,000	1,000	B	B1i
Aquila pomarina	Lesser Spotted Eagle	B	1990	3	4	A	B2

Breeding *Aquila pomarina* and staging *Anser albifrons* occur in significant numbers.

■ Protection status
National Partial **International** None
1,060 ha of IBA covered by Zakaznik (Boloto 'Budnyanskiy Mokh', 1,060 ha).

■ Conservation issues

Threats Unsustainable exploitation (U)

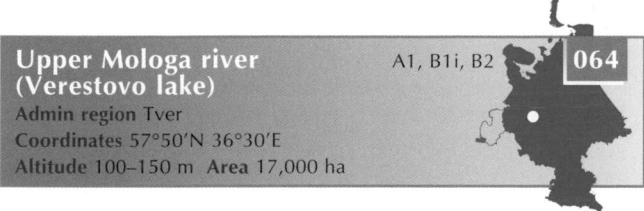

Stakhovski marshes   A1, B1i   063
Admin region Tver
Coordinates 56°02'N 32°40'E
Altitude 100–150 m **Area** 10,296 ha

■ Site description
An area of good quality marsh and bog in the southern part of the taiga zone, unique in central Russia. Most of the site has remained intact since the beginning of the 20th century, and is relatively unspoilt.

Habitats Forest and woodland (10%; native coniferous forest; mixed forest), Wetland (80%; fen/transition mire/spring), Artificial landscape (10%; highly improved reseeded grassland)
Land-use Hunting (100%), Tourism/recreation (50%)

■ Birds

Species		Season	Year	Pop min	Pop max	Acc	Criteria
Anser albifrons	White-fronted Goose	P	1990	1,000	1,000	C	B1i
Crex crex	Corncrake	B	1990	10	20	A	A1
Gallinago media	Great Snipe	B	1990	10	20	A	A1

Two species of global conservation concern breed in the IBA, although at low density (as is typical in these habitats). Significant proportion (≥1%) of national population breeding at site: *Aquila pomarina* (1–2 pairs).

■ Protection status
National High **International** None
10,296 ha of IBA covered by Zakaznik (Boloto 'Stakhovsky Mokh', 10,296 ha).

Upper Mologa river (Verestovo lake)   A1, B1i, B2   064
Admin region Tver
Coordinates 57°50'N 36°30'E
Altitude 100–150 m **Area** 17,000 ha

■ Site description
An area of fens and forested mires surrounding Verestovo lake, which is fed by the Mologa river.

Habitats Grassland (25%), Wetland (50%; standing fresh water; river/stream; fen/transition mire/spring), Artificial landscape (25%; highly improved reseeded grassland; arable land)
Land-use Agriculture (50%), Hunting (100%), Not utilized (50%), Tourism/recreation (50%), Urban/industrial/transport (10%)

■ Birds

Species		Season	Year	Pop min	Pop max	Acc	Criteria
Anser albifrons	White-fronted Goose	P	1990	6,000	8,000	B	B1i
Anser anser	Greylag Goose	P	1990	1,000	1,000	B	B1i
Crex crex	Corncrake	B	1990	50	100	C	A1
Gallinago media	Great Snipe	B	1990	20	50	C	A1
Limosa limosa	Black-tailed Godwit	B	1990	100	100	B	B2
Sterna albifrons	Little Tern	B	1990	100	200	C	B2
Chlidonias niger	Black Tern	B	1996	150	200	B	B2

The site is an important staging area for migrating geese *Anser*, and holds significant breeding numbers of several wetland birds, including two species of global conservation concern.

■ Protection status
National Partial **International** None
2,280 ha of IBA covered by Zakaznik (Ozero Verestovo, 2,280 ha).

■ Conservation issues

Threats Disturbance to birds (A), Other (U), Unsustainable exploitation (A)

Pollution of land and water is a problem ('Other' threat).

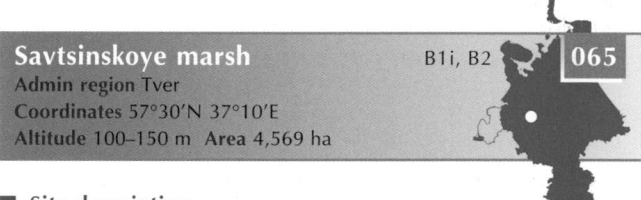

Savtsinskoye marsh   B1i, B2   065
Admin region Tver
Coordinates 57°30'N 37°10'E
Altitude 100–150 m **Area** 4,569 ha

■ Site description
An extensive area of fen and mire lying within the Lake Skorbezh depression, including the sources of the Yakhroma river.

Habitats Wetland (100%; standing fresh water; river/stream; fen/transition mire/spring)
Land-use Hunting (100%), Tourism/recreation (10%)

■ Birds

Species		Season	Year	Pop min	Pop max	Acc	Criteria
Anser albifrons	White-fronted Goose	P	1988	1,000	2,000	B	B1i
Anser anser	Greylag Goose	P	1988	500	1,000	B	B1i
Chlidonias niger	Black Tern	B	1988	100	200	B	B2

Important numbers of breeding *Chlidonias niger* and staging geese *Anser* occur here. Breeding species of global conservation concern that do not meet IBA criteria: *Crex crex* (10 pairs), *Gallinago media* (10 pairs).

■ Protection status
National High **International** None
4,569 ha of IBA covered by Zakaznik (Boloto Savtsinskoe, 4,569 ha).

■ Conservation issues

Threats Unsustainable exploitation (C)

Orshinski marshes   B1i   066
Admin region Tver
Coordinates 57°00'N 36°30'E
Altitude 100–100 m **Area** 43,200 ha

■ Site description
A large area of raised bog, part of which is still in pristine condition. Peat-mining is a land-use.

Habitats Forest and woodland (native coniferous forest; mixed forest), Wetland (100%; standing fresh water; raised bog)
Land-use Hunting (100%), Tourism/recreation (20%), Urban/industrial/transport (20%)

■ Birds

Species		Season	Year	Pop min	Pop max	Acc	Criteria
Anser albifrons	White-fronted Goose	P	1995	1,000	2,000	B	B1i
Anser anser	Greylag Goose	P	1995	500	1,000	B	B1i

Significant numbers of *Anser albifrons* and *A. anser* stage here on passage. Breeding species of global conservation concern that do not meet IBA criteria: *Gallinago media* (10 pairs).

■ Protection status
National Partial **International** None
30,000 ha of IBA covered by regionally protected mire (Orshinsky Okhranyaemoe Boloto, 30,000 ha).

■ Conservation issues

Threats Extraction industry (A), Unsustainable exploitation (A)

Part of the area has been destroyed by the peat-mining industry.

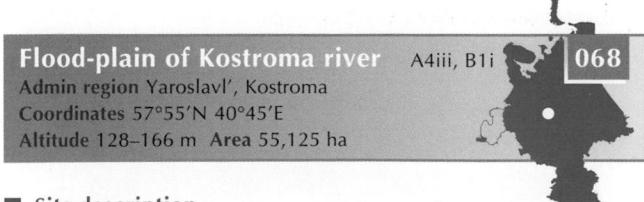

Flood-plain of Kotorosl' and Ust'e rivers
A1, A4i, B1i   067
Admin region Yaroslavl'
Coordinates 57°15′N 39°40′E
Altitude 165–174 m **Area** 4,200 ha

■ Site description
An area of wet forests and grasslands in the valley of the Kotorosl' river, to the south-west of the town of Gavrilov-Yam.

Habitats Forest and woodland (15%; alluvial/very wet forest), Scrub (30%; scrub), Grassland (15%; humid grassland), Wetland (30%; standing fresh water; river/stream), Artificial landscape (5%; arable land; other urban/industrial areas)
Land-use Hunting (100%), Nature conservation/research (100%), Tourism/recreation (20%), Urban/industrial/transport (5%)

■ Birds

Species		Season	Year	Pop min	Pop max	Acc	Criteria
[1] *Anser albifrons*	White-fronted Goose	P	1997	15,108	—	A	A4i, B1i
[1] *Anser erythropus*		P	1997	43	—	—	A1
	Lesser White-fronted Goose						

1. Only one count has been made.

Large and important numbers of geese *Anser* have been recorded in the area during migration, including the globally threatened *Anser erythropus*.

■ Protection status
National None **International** None

■ Conservation issues

Threats Construction/impact of dyke/dam/barrage (A), Disturbance to birds (B), Drainage (A), Recreation/tourism (B), Unsustainable exploitation (A)

Only one bird count has been made at the site.

Flood-plain of Kostroma river
A4iii, B1i   068
Admin region Yaroslavl', Kostroma
Coordinates 57°55′N 40°45′E
Altitude 128–166 m **Area** 55,125 ha

■ Site description
A large man-made reservoir on the border between Yaroslavl' and Kostroma regions. Meadows and forest surrounding the reservoir are subject to spring flooding.

Habitats Forest and woodland (65%; mixed forest; alluvial/very wet forest), Grassland (15%; humid grassland), Wetland (25%; standing brackish and salt water; river/stream; raised bog; fen/transition mire/spring)
Land-use Agriculture (12%), Fisheries/aquaculture (10%), Forestry (65%), Hunting (100%), Nature conservation/research (100%), Not utilized (50%), Tourism/recreation (10%), Water management

■ Birds

Species		Season	Year	Pop min	Pop max	Acc	Criteria
[1] *Anser fabalis*	Bean Goose	P	1997	1,019	—	B	B1i
Anser albifrons	White-fronted Goose	P	1997	9,834	—	B	B1i
Bucephala clangula	Goldeneye	P	1997	1,429	—	B	B1i

1. Likely to exceed threshold for *A. f. rossicus*.

A minimum total of 24,500 waterbirds of about 35 species pass through the area during spring migration, including significant numbers of three wildfowl.

■ Protection status
National Low **International** None
150 ha of IBA covered by Zakaznik (Sotinskiy, 500 ha). 2,000 ha of IBA covered by Zakaznik (Yaroslavskiy, 17,000 ha).

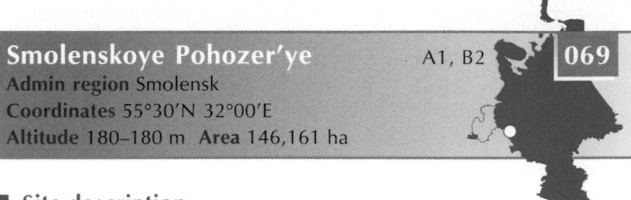

Smolenskoye Pohozer'ye
A1, B2   069
Admin region Smolensk
Coordinates 55°30′N 32°00′E
Altitude 180–180 m **Area** 146,161 ha

■ Site description
An area of forest, open bogs and lakes in the Smolensk region, surrounded by agricultural land.

Habitats Forest and woodland (90%; native coniferous forest; mixed forest), Wetland (6%; standing fresh water; river/stream; raised bog), Unknown (4%)
Land-use Nature conservation/research (100%)

■ Birds

Species		Season	Year	Pop min	Pop max	Acc	Criteria
Aquila pomarina	Lesser Spotted Eagle	B	1996	3	4	—	B2
Aquila clanga	Greater Spotted Eagle	B	1997	1	2	—	A1
Crex crex	Corncrake	B	1996	50	60	—	A1

An important site for forest-breeding raptors and *Crex crex*. Species of global conservation concern that do not meet IBA criteria: *Gallinago media* (no special counts, but a rather large number breed in the area).

■ Protection status
National High **International** None
146,161 ha of IBA covered by National Park (Smolenskoe Pohozerye, 146,161 ha).

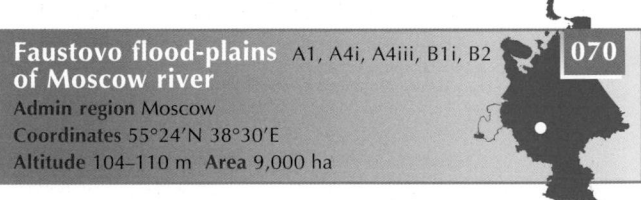

Faustovo flood-plains of Moscow river
A1, A4i, A4iii, B1i, B2   070
Admin region Moscow
Coordinates 55°24′N 38°30′E
Altitude 104–110 m **Area** 9,000 ha

■ Site description
The IBA encompasses the watershed of the Moskva and Nerskaya rivers. There is a network of lakes and channels, and the wet grasslands partly flood each spring.

Habitats Forest and woodland (1%; mixed forest), Scrub (2%; scrub), Grassland (50%; humid grassland), Wetland (14%; standing fresh water; river/stream), Artificial landscape (33%; highly improved reseeded grassland; arable land)
Land-use Agriculture (23%), Fisheries/aquaculture (10%), Hunting (100%), Nature conservation/research (24%), Water management (2%)

■ Birds

Species		Season	Year	Pop min	Pop max	Acc	Criteria
Anser albifrons	White-fronted Goose	P	1990	10,000	15,000	B	A4i, B1i
[1] *Crex crex*	Corncrake	B	1996	320	380	A	A1
Gallinago media	Great Snipe	B	1985	40	50	B	A1
[2] *Limosa limosa*	Black-tailed Godwit	B	1995	50	120	A	B2

1. Large increase.
2. Up to 120 pairs in 1985; 50 pairs in 1995.

Three species breed in important numbers in the wet grasslands. The site holds 20,000 or more migrating waterbirds on a regular basis, comprising mainly *Anser albifrons* with smaller numbers of *Anas penelope*, *Anas acuta* and *Anas querquedula*.

■ Protection status
National Partial **International** None
2,100 ha of IBA covered by Zakaznik (Moskvoretsky Poimenny, 2,100 ha).

■ Conservation issues

> **Threats** Agricultural intensification/expansion (B), Drainage (B), Groundwater abstraction (A), Unsustainable exploitation (B)

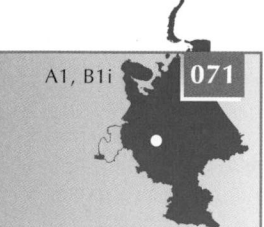

Homeland of the Crane (Dubna marshes and adjacent areas)
A1, B1i 071

Admin region Moscow
Coordinates 56°42′N 38°02′E
Altitude 125–167 m **Area** 38,500 ha

■ Site description
The site lies north of the Moscow region and comprises the flood-plain of the Dubna river. Habitats include bogs, wet forest, lakes, fens, arable land and reseeded grasslands.

> **Habitats** Forest and woodland (50%; native coniferous forest; mixed forest; alluvial/very wet forest), Grassland (12%; mesophile grassland; humid grassland), Wetland (49%; standing fresh water; river/stream; raised bog; fen/transition mire/spring), Artificial landscape (38%; highly improved reseeded grassland; arable land; other urban/industrial areas)
> **Land-use** Agriculture (48%), Forestry (50%), Hunting (100%), Nature conservation/research (63%), Urban/industrial/transport (2%)

■ Birds

Species	Season	Year	Pop min	Pop max	Acc	Criteria
Aquila clanga Greater Spotted Eagle	B	1996	1	3	B	A1
[1] *Grus grus* Crane	P	1996	960	1,200	A	B1i

1. Up to 3,400 in 1987; 20 pairs breed.

An important area for breeding *Aquila clanga*. *Grus grus* occurs in large numbers on passage.

■ Protection status
National Partial **International** None
23,000 ha of IBA covered by five nature reserves (Nature Monuments and Zakazniks), with the following names: Zhuravlinaya Rodina; Dubnensky Levoberezhny; Zabolotsky; Konstantinivsky Chrnoolshannik; Perekhodnoe Boloto V Torgashinskom Lesnichestve.

■ Conservation issues

> **Threats** Agricultural intensification/expansion (B), Disturbance to birds (B), Drainage (B), Firewood collection (B), Groundwater abstraction (A), Infrastructure (C), Unsustainable exploitation (A)

The area has been included on a 'shadow list' of potential Ramsar Sites.

Lotoshino crane gathering
B1i 072

Admin region Moscow, Tver
Coordinates 56°18′N 35°30′E
Altitude 150–182 m **Area** 28,200 ha

■ Site description
A complex of forests, bogs and fens.

> **Habitats** Forest and woodland (42%; native coniferous forest; mixed forest), Wetland (5%; raised bog; fen/transition mire/spring), Artificial landscape (54%; arable land; other urban/industrial areas)
> **Land-use** Agriculture (52%), Forestry (40%), Hunting (95%), Tourism/recreation (95%)

■ Birds
Important numbers of staging *Grus grus* occur, feeding in surrounding agricultural land. The total numbers are likely to be several times

Species	Season	Year	Pop min	Pop max	Acc	Criteria
Grus grus Crane	P	1995	1,100	—	B	B1i

greater than 1,100 since only part of the site has been surveyed. *Gallinago media* is said to breed here, and *Grus grus* certainly does, but no special surveys have been made.

■ Protection status
National None **International** None

■ Conservation issues

> **Threats** Deforestation (commercial) (B), Disturbance to birds (B), Drainage (B), Extraction industry (B), Industrialization/urbanization (C), Infrastructure (C), Intensified forest management (B), Unsustainable exploitation (C)

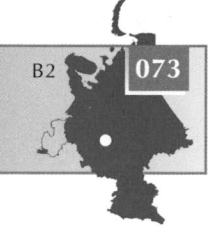

Danilovskoye marshes
B2 073

Admin region Moscow
Coordinates 55°42′N 38°47′E
Altitude 127–127 m **Area** 400 ha

■ Site description
A mire which has regenerated naturally on peat-mine workings following their abandonment.

> **Habitats** Forest and woodland (10%; mixed forest), Wetland (90%; standing fresh water; water-fringe vegetation; fen/transition mire/spring)
> **Land-use** Fisheries/aquaculture (30%), Hunting (100%), Nature conservation/research (100%)

■ Birds

Species	Season	Year	Pop min	Pop max	Acc	Criteria
Larus canus Common Gull	B	1994	600	650	B	B2

Significant numbers of *Larus canus* breed in the area. *Larus melanocephalus* is a new breeder for the Moscow region.

■ Protection status
National High **International** None
378 ha of IBA covered by Zakaznik (Danilovskoe boloto, 378 ha).

■ Conservation issues

> **Threats** Aquaculture/fisheries (C), Drainage (B), Infrastructure (C), Unsustainable exploitation (B)

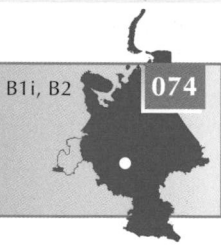

Dedinivo flood-plain of Oka river
A1, A4iii, B1i, B2 074

Admin region Moscow
Coordinates 55°10′N 39°18′E
Altitude 50–120 m **Area** 23,120 ha

■ Site description
An extensive area of forest and wet grassland, located on one of the widest parts of the Oka river flood-plain.

> **Habitats** Forest and woodland (55%; native coniferous forest; mixed forest; alluvial/very wet forest), Grassland (30%; humid grassland), Artificial landscape (15%; highly improved reseeded grassland; arable land)
> **Land-use** Agriculture (41%), Forestry (55%), Urban/industrial/transport (4%)

■ Birds

Species	Season	Year	Pop min	Pop max	Acc	Criteria
Anser albifrons White-fronted Goose	P	1988	5,000	10,000	—	B1i
Anser anser Greylag Goose	P	1988	1,000	—	—	B1i
Aquila clanga Greater Spotted Eagle	B	1996	2	3	B	A1
Crex crex Corncrake	B	1996	550	600	A	A1, B2
Gallinago media Great Snipe	B	1996	20	50	C	A1

The area holds one of the largest populations of breeding *Crex crex* at any site in Europe, as well as significant breeding numbers of two other species of global conservation concern. More than 20,000 wildfowl regularly occur on passage, the most numerous species being geese *Anser fabalis*, *A. albifrons* and *A. anser*.

■ Protection status
National Partial **International** None
3,600 ha of IBA covered by Zakaznik (Ozero Sosnovoe, 3,600 ha).

■ Conservation issues

Threats Abandonment/reduction of land management (B), Disturbance to birds (C), Extraction industry (C), Forest grazing (C), Infrastructure (C), Recreation/tourism (C), Selective logging/cutting (C)

Counts for individual species of wildfowl are incomplete, and further survey work is required.

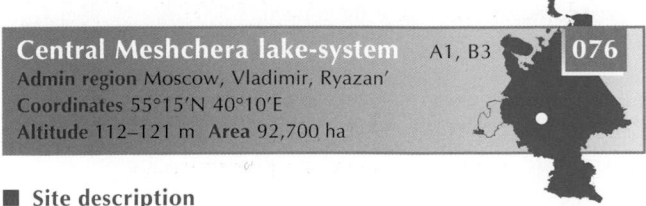

Zavidovo Nature Reserve, including Lotoshinski, Klinski and Diatlovo fish-ponds
A1, A4i, B1i, B2   075
Admin region Moscow, Tver
Coordinates 56°22′N 36°06′E
Altitude 100–150 m   Area 133,800 ha

■ Site description
A large expanse of native forest interspersed with small meadows. There are two large fish-ponds.

Habitats Forest and woodland (60%; native coniferous forest; mixed forest), Grassland (5%; humid grassland), Wetland (15%; standing fresh water; river/stream; fen/transition mire/spring), Artificial landscape (20%; highly improved reseeded grassland; arable land)
Land-use Agriculture (25%), Fisheries/aquaculture (15%), Forestry (70%), Hunting (95%), Nature conservation/research (100%), Not utilized (30%), Tourism/recreation (70%), Urban/industrial/transport (5%)

■ Birds

Species	Season	Year	Pop min	Pop max	Acc	Criteria
Anser anser Greylag Goose	P	1995	500	1,000	B	B1i
Haliaeetus albicilla White-tailed Eagle	N	1995	20	65	B	A1
Aquila clanga Greater Spotted Eagle	B	1995	4	5	A	A1
Crex crex Corncrake	B	1995	125	130	B	A1
Gallinago media Great Snipe	B	1995	20	30	B	A1
Sterna albifrons Little Tern	B	1995	50	200	B	B1i, B2
Chlidonias niger Black Tern	B	1995	600	700	A	A4i, B1i, B2

Three species of global conservation concern breed in important numbers. The fish-ponds attract raptors during their autumn migration, notably *Haliaeetus albicilla*. Significant proportion (≥1%) of national population breeding at site: *Aquila pomarina* (1–2 pairs).

■ Protection status
National High **International** None
125,442 ha of IBA covered by Zapovednik (Zavidovskiy, 125,442 ha).

■ Conservation issues

Threats Disturbance to birds (C), Recreation/tourism (B), Unsustainable exploitation (U)

Central Meshchera lake-system
A1, B3   076
Admin region Moscow, Vladimir, Ryazan'
Coordinates 55°15′N 40°10′E
Altitude 112–121 m   Area 92,700 ha

■ Site description
The area is located in central Russia at the meeting point of three regions: Moscow, Vladimir and Ryazan'. It comprises a large system of lakes along the valley of the Pra river, and is surrounded by wet forests and fens.

Habitats Forest and woodland (25%; alluvial/very wet forest), Wetland (64%; standing fresh water; river/stream; water-fringe vegetation), Artificial landscape (8%; highly improved reseeded grassland; arable land)
Land-use Agriculture (11%), Fisheries/aquaculture (40%), Forestry (25%), Hunting (100%), Not utilized (30%), Tourism/recreation (50%)

■ Birds

Species	Season	Year	Pop min	Pop max	Acc	Criteria
Aquila clanga Greater Spotted Eagle	B	1996	4	6	A	A1
Porzana porzana Spotted Crake	B	1995	100	150	—	B3
Crex crex Corncrake	B	1995	100	150	C	A1
[1] *Gallinago media* Great Snipe	B	1995	15	20	A	A1

1. Large increase.

Three species of global conservation concern breed within the IBA, two of which are globally threatened. Significant proportion (≥1%) of national population breeding at site: *Aquila pomarina* (1–2 pairs).

■ Protection status
National Partial **International** None
Part of IBA covered by two National Parks and one Zapovednik (names and areas not known).

■ Conservation issues
Information on the site is incomplete.

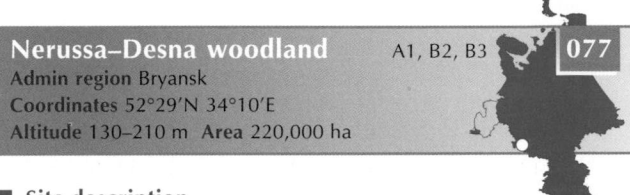

Nerussa–Desna woodland
A1, B2, B3   077
Admin region Bryansk
Coordinates 52°29′N 34°10′E
Altitude 130–210 m   Area 220,000 ha

■ Site description
This site is situated in an interesting area from the biogeographic point of view (Bryanskaya), where three very different habitat-types converge: deciduous broadleaved forest, southern taiga forest, and wooded steppe.

Habitats Forest and woodland (65%; native coniferous forest; mixed forest; alluvial/very wet forest), Grassland (8%; humid grassland), Wetland (15%; raised bog; fen/transition mire/spring), Artificial landscape (12%; arable land; other urban/industrial areas)
Land-use Agriculture (7%), Forestry (50%), Hunting (83%), Nature conservation/research (5%), Tourism/recreation (68%)

■ Birds

Species	Season	Year	Pop min	Pop max	Acc	Criteria
Ciconia nigra Black Stork	B	1995	30	50	B	B2
Ciconia ciconia White Stork	B	1995	38	38	A	B2
Aquila clanga Greater Spotted Eagle	B	1996	6	14	B	A1, B2
Tetrao tetrix Black Grouse	R	1994	1,000	1,500	B	B2
Crex crex Corncrake	B	1995	200	300	C	A1
Alcedo atthis Kingfisher	B	1996	100	150	B	B2
Dendrocopos medius Middle Spotted Woodpecker	R	1995	300	500	B	B3
Lullula arborea Woodlark	B	1995	100	200	B	B2
Ficedula albicollis Collared Flycatcher	B	1996	1,500	3,000	B	B3
Lanius collurio Red-backed Shrike	B	1996	2,000	—	—	B2

Breeding birds include two globally threatened species, with *Aquila clanga* occurring in particularly significant numbers, as well as important numbers of a notably wide variety of other species of forest and open country in good numbers. This area is one of only three places in Europe where as many as nine species of woodpecker are known to breed. Species of global conservation concern that do not meet IBA criteria: *Anser erythropus* (occurs on migration), *Haliaeetus albicilla* (5–10 birds on migration).

■ Protection status
National Partial **International** None
12,168 ha of IBA covered by Zapovednik (Bryanskiy Les, 12,168 ha). 24,712 ha of IBA covered by 12 regional protected areas (Zakazniks and Nature Monuments).

■ Conservation issues

Threats Deforestation (commercial) (B), Disturbance to birds (B), Extraction industry (C), Groundwater abstraction (C), Intensified forest management (B), Recreation/tourism (B)

The creation of a joint Russian–Ukrainian Biosphere Reserve is underway.

Flood-plain of Iput' river in vicinity of Krutoayr

A4i, A4iii, B1i | 078

Admin region Bryansk
Coordinates 53°10'N 32°38'E
Altitude 142–162 m **Area** 4,000 ha

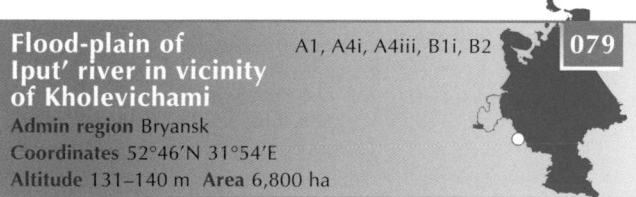

■ Site description
A tract of fens, forested mires and wet grasslands on the flood-plain of the Iput' river, between the villages of Krutoyar and Krasnoye. The area floods in spring.

Habitats Scrub (25%), Grassland (20%; humid grassland), Wetland (77%; river/stream; fen/transition mire/spring)
Land-use Agriculture (20%), Nature conservation/research (26%), Not utilized (74%)

■ Birds

Species		Season	Year	Pop min	Pop max	Acc	Criteria
Egretta alba	Great White Egret	N	1995	200	300	—	A4i, B1i
Anser fabalis	Bean Goose	P	1993	5,000	—	C	A4i, B1i
Anser albifrons	White-fronted Goose	P	1993	15,000	20,000	C	A4i, B1i

Up to 30,000 migrating *Anser fabalis* and *Anser albifrons* congregate in the area, and important numbers of non-breeding *Egretta alba* occur.

■ Protection status
National Partial **International** None
1,050 ha of IBA covered by Zakaznik (Kletnyansky, 39,100 ha).

■ Conservation issues

Threats Drainage (C), Unsustainable exploitation (B)

The area has only been surveyed during one field season so far, thus ornithological data are incomplete.

Flood-plain of Iput' river in vicinity of Kholevichami

A1, A4i, A4iii, B1i, B2 | 079

Admin region Bryansk
Coordinates 52°46'N 31°54'E
Altitude 131–140 m **Area** 6,800 ha

■ Site description
The flood-plain of the Iput' river between the villages of Unechi and Kholevichi. The area floods in spring and contains many oxbow lakes.

Habitats Forest and woodland (7%; alluvial/very wet forest), Scrub (50%; scrub), Grassland (60%; humid grassland), Wetland (30%; standing fresh water; river/stream; fen/transition mire/spring)
Land-use Agriculture (60%), Forestry (7%), Not utilized (30%)

■ Birds

Species		Season	Year	Pop min	Pop max	Acc	Criteria
Anser fabalis	Bean Goose	P	1996	3,000	—	C	B1i
Anser albifrons	White-fronted Goose	P	1996	5,000	15,000	C	A4i, B1i
Crex crex	Corncrake	B	1996	30	50	B	A1
Limosa limosa	Black-tailed Godwit	B	1996	50	100	B	B2
Tringa totanus	Redshank	B	1996	50	100	B	B2

The area holds 20,000 or more migrating waterbirds on a regular basis, in particular up to 17,000 *Anser fabalis* and *A. albifrons* congregate here during migration. Significant numbers of three species breed in the wet grasslands, including the globally threatened *Crex crex*, and the IBA is the main feeding area for 25 pairs of *Ciconia ciconia* which breed in surrounding villages.

■ Protection status
National None **International** None

■ Conservation issues

Threats Drainage (C), Unsustainable exploitation (B)

The area is situated in the zone affected by radioactive pollution from Chernobyl, and plans have been drawn up to relocate the local people.

Kletnyanski forest

B2 | 080

Admin region Bryansk
Coordinates 53°13'N 32°53'E
Altitude 142–192 m **Area** 38,100 ha

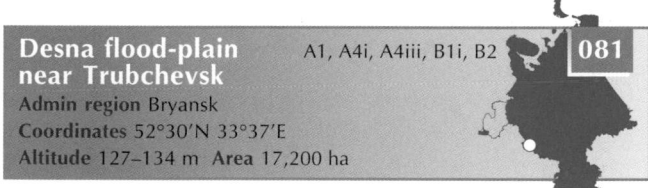

■ Site description
A large forest with numerous clearings, which are used for agriculture.

Habitats Forest and woodland (80%; broadleaved deciduous forest; native coniferous forest), Grassland (5%; dry siliceous grassland), Artificial landscape (13%; arable land)
Land-use Agriculture (18%), Forestry (80%), Nature conservation/research (100%)

■ Birds

Species		Season	Year	Pop min	Pop max	Acc	Criteria
Ciconia ciconia	White Stork	B	1996	15	33	B	B2

Significant numbers of *Ciconia ciconia* breed in the area.

■ Protection status
National High **International** None
38,100 ha of IBA covered by Zakaznik (Kletnyansky, 39,100 ha).

■ Conservation issues

Threats Unsustainable exploitation (B)

The nature reserve (Zakaznik) is no longer being managed, hence its legal protection status is not being enforced on the ground. There is pressure on the IBA from illegal hunting.

Desna flood-plain near Trubchevsk

A1, A4i, A4iii, B1i, B2 | 081

Admin region Bryansk
Coordinates 52°30'N 33°37'E
Altitude 127–134 m **Area** 17,200 ha

■ Site description
A system of oxbow lakes situated on the wet flood-plain of the Desna river. The flood-plain is becoming wetter.

Habitats Forest and woodland (6%; alluvial/very wet forest), Grassland (68%; humid grassland), Wetland (25%; standing fresh water; river/stream; fen/transition mire/spring)
Land-use Agriculture (34%), Hunting (96%), Not utilized (17%), Tourism/recreation (20%)

■ Birds

Species		Season	Year	Pop min	Pop max	Acc	Criteria
Anser albifrons	White-fronted Goose	P	1996	500	15,000	B	A4i, B1i
Crex crex	Corncrake	B	1996	200	—	C	A1
Limosa limosa	Black-tailed Godwit	B	1996	100	150	C	B2

Two species breed in the wet grasslands in significant numbers, including the globally threatened *Crex crex*. Up to 25,000 *Anser fabalis* and *A. albifrons* congregate at the site during migration.

■ Protection status
National Low **International** None
650 ha of IBA covered by Zakaznik (Desnyansko-Zherenskiy, 2,621 ha).

■ Conservation issues

Threats Disturbance to birds (B), Recreation/tourism (B), Unsustainable exploitation (B)

It is expected that goose congregations will be monitored over the 1997–1999 period.

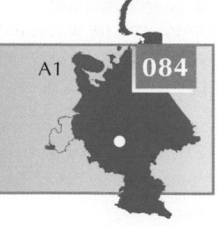

Gavan'skiye oak-forest

A1, B3 — **082**

Admin region Bryansk
Coordinates 52°54'N 34°03'E
Altitude 135–142 m **Area** 3,000 ha

■ Site description
The area contains one of the largest expanses of predominantly natural oak *Quercus* forest in Bryansk region.

Habitats Forest and woodland (70%; broadleaved deciduous forest; alluvial/very wet forest), Scrub (5%; scrub), Grassland (20%; humid grassland), Wetland (54%; fen/transition mire/spring)
Land-use Forestry (70%), Hunting (100%), Nature conservation/research (17%), Not utilized (10%), Tourism/recreation (10%)

■ Birds

Species	Season	Year	Pop min	Pop max	Acc	Criteria
Aquila clanga Greater Spotted Eagle	B	1996	2	—	C	A1
Dendrocopos medius Middle Spotted Woodpecker	R	1996	100	150	B	B3
Ficedula albicollis Collared Flycatcher	B	1996	500	700	B	B3

Significant numbers of three forest species breed, including the globally threatened *Aquila clanga*.

■ Protection status
National None **International** None

■ Conservation issues

Threats Deforestation (commercial) (B), Disturbance to birds (C), Firewood collection (C), Selective logging/cutting (B)

This area should be included in the proposed Pridnesnyansky National Park.

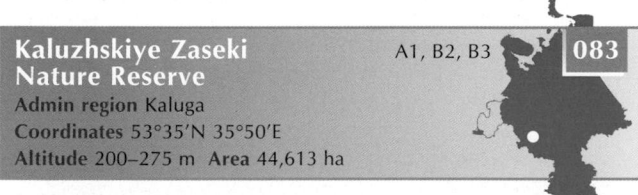

Kaluzhskiye Zaseki Nature Reserve

A1, B2, B3 — **083**

Admin region Kaluga
Coordinates 53°35'N 35°50'E
Altitude 200–275 m **Area** 44,613 ha

■ Site description
The IBA is located in the highly developed central part of Russia, on the boundary between the forest and forest-steppe habitat-zones. It includes mixed, wet and coniferous forests in the Zhizdra river valley, forming one of the largest unbroken tracts of forest in central Russia.

Habitats Forest and woodland (80%; broadleaved deciduous forest; native coniferous forest; mixed forest; alluvial/very wet forest), Scrub (15%; scrub), Grassland (15%; humid grassland; mesophile grassland), Wetland (4%; river/stream), Artificial landscape (31%; highly improved reseeded grassland; arable land; forestry plantation; urban parks/gardens; other urban/industrial areas)
Land-use Agriculture (25%), Forestry (40%), Hunting (50%), Nature conservation/research (50%)

■ Birds

Species	Season	Year	Pop min	Pop max	Acc	Criteria
Aquila pomarina Lesser Spotted Eagle	B	1996	4	4	A	B2
Crex crex Corncrake	B	1996	360	400	C	A1
Strix aluco Tawny Owl	R	1996	150	180	C	B3
Dendrocopos medius Middle Spotted Woodpecker	R	1996	15	20	B	B3
Saxicola rubetra Whinchat	B	1996	6,000	8,000	C	B3
Sylvia borin Garden Warbler	B	1996	5,000	5,200	C	B3
Parus caeruleus Blue Tit	B	1996	800	1,000	C	B3

The IBA holds important breeding numbers of a number of forest and grassland species, including *Crex crex* and *Aquila pomarina*.

■ Protection status
National Partial **International** None

18,533 ha of IBA covered by Zapovednik (Kaluzhskie Zaseki, 18,533 ha).

■ Conservation issues

Threats Deforestation (commercial) (B), Disturbance to birds (B), Firewood collection (B), Forest grazing (B), Intensified forest management (B)

Oka River Valley Biosphere Reserve

A1 — **084**

Admin region Ryazan'
Coordinates 54°45'N 40°45'E
Altitude 88–125 m **Area** 55,731 ha

■ Site description
The IBA is located in the south-eastern Meshchera lowlands, and is covered by wet mixed forests and dry pine *Pinus* forests, as well as bogs and small lakes.

Habitats Forest and woodland (80%; mixed forest; alluvial/very wet forest), Scrub (5%; scrub), Grassland (5%; humid grassland), Wetland (10%; river/stream; fen/transition mire/spring)
Land-use Nature conservation/research (95%)

■ Birds

Species	Season	Year	Pop min	Pop max	Acc	Criteria
Aquila clanga Greater Spotted Eagle	B	1987	5	7	A	A1
Crex crex Corncrake	B	1984	100	—	—	A1

Two globally threatened species breed in important numbers.

■ Protection status
National High **International** High
55,731 ha of IBA covered by Zapovednik (Oksky, 55,731 ha). 55,731 ha of IBA covered by Biosphere Reserve (Okski, 55,731 ha).

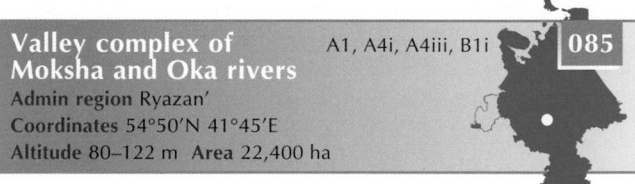

Valley complex of Moksha and Oka rivers

A1, A4i, A4iii, B1i — **085**

Admin region Ryazan'
Coordinates 54°50'N 41°45'E
Altitude 80–122 m **Area** 22,400 ha

■ Site description
The area is located between the Oka and Moksha rivers, far from any human settlements. There are many lakes.

Habitats Forest and woodland (10%; mixed forest), Scrub (15%; scrub), Grassland (80%; humid grassland), Wetland (15%; standing fresh water; river/stream)
Land-use Agriculture (20%), Forestry (10%), Tourism/recreation (30%)

■ Birds

Species	Season	Year	Pop min	Pop max	Acc	Criteria
Anser albifrons White-fronted Goose	P	1996	12	15,000	B	A4i, B1i
Anser anser Greylag Goose	P	1996	600	800	B	B1i
Crex crex Corncrake	B	1996	150	200	—	A1

The site holds up to 20,000 migrating waterbirds on a regular basis, with *Anser albifrons* being especially numerous. *Crex crex* breeds in significant numbers, but two other breeding species of global conservation concern do not meet IBA criteria: *Aquila clanga*, *Aquila heliaca*.

■ Protection status
National None **International** High
22,400 ha of IBA covered by Ramsar Site (Flood-plains of the Oka and Pra Rivers, 161,542 ha).

■ Conservation issues

Threats Disturbance to birds (B), Unsustainable exploitation (B)

Shilovo flood-plain of Oka river
A1, A4i, A4iii, B1i

086

Admin region Ryazan'
Coordinates 54°20'N 40°45'E
Altitude 90–115 m **Area** 22,000 ha

■ Site description
A large area of wet grassland used for agriculture (mainly for hay), located on one of the widest stretches of the Oka river flood-plain.

Habitats Grassland (54%; humid grassland), Wetland (8%; standing fresh water; river/stream; raised bog), Artificial landscape (25%; highly improved reseeded grassland; arable land)
Land-use Agriculture (30%), Hunting (80%)

■ Birds

Species	Season	Year	Pop min	Pop max	Acc	Criteria
Anser albifrons White-fronted Goose	P	1996	15,000	20,000	B	A4i, B1i
Anser anser Greylag Goose	P	1996	1,000	1,500	B	B1i
Crex crex Corncrake	B	1996	80	120	B	A1
Pluvialis apricaria Golden Plover	P	1996	8,000	10,000	B	B1i

Breeding species include the globally threatened *Crex crex*. The area holds 20,000 or more migrating waterbirds on a regular basis, mainly geese *Anser*, and is possibly the most important staging site for *Pluvialis apricaria* in central European Russia.

■ Protection status
National None **International** High
22,000 ha of IBA covered by Ramsar Site (Flood-plains of the Oka and Pra Rivers, 161,542 ha).

■ Conservation issues

Threats Disturbance to birds (B), Drainage (A), Unsustainable exploitation (A)

Izhevsk flood-plain of Oka river
A1, A4i, A4iii, B1i

087

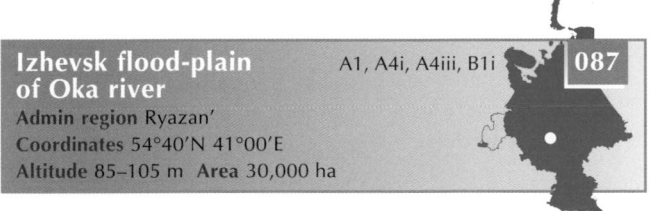

Admin region Ryazan'
Coordinates 54°40'N 41°00'E
Altitude 85–105 m **Area** 30,000 ha

■ Site description
Extensive wet grasslands on the flood-plain of the Oka river, used partly for agriculture.

Habitats Forest and woodland (5%; alluvial/very wet forest), Grassland (70%; humid grassland), Wetland (13%; standing fresh water; river/stream; fen/transition mire/spring), Artificial landscape (4%; arable land), Unknown (5%)
Land-use Agriculture (25%), Nature conservation/research (67%), Tourism/recreation (10%)

■ Birds

Species	Season	Year	Pop min	Pop max	Acc	Criteria
Anser albifrons White-fronted Goose	P	1996	15,000	20,000	B	A4i, B1i
Anser anser Greylag Goose	P	1996	1,000	1,500	—	B1i
Crex crex Corncrake	B	1996	200	300	B	A1
Gallinago media Great Snipe	B	1996	150	300	B	A1, A4i, B1i

Two species of global conservation concern breed in important numbers in the wet grasslands. The site holds 20,000 or more migrating waterbirds on a regular basis, mainly geese *Anser*.

■ Protection status
National Partial **International** High
20,000 ha of IBA covered by Zakaznik (Ryazansky, 36,500 ha). 30,000 ha of IBA covered by Ramsar Site (Flood-plains of the Oka and Pra Rivers, 161,542 ha).

■ Conservation issues

Threats Disturbance to birds (C), Recreation/tourism (C), Unsustainable exploitation (B)

Solotcha flood-plain of Oka river
A1, A4i, A4iii, B1i

088

Admin region Ryazan'
Coordinates 54°50'N 39°45'E
Altitude 98–106 m **Area** 12,000 ha

■ Site description
The site is located on one of the widest parts of the flood-plain of the Oka river, and comprises wet meadowland used for agriculture (mainly hay and pasture).

Habitats Forest and woodland (5%; mixed forest), Scrub (10%; scrub), Grassland (60%; humid grassland), Wetland (22%; standing fresh water; river/stream; fen/transition mire/spring), Artificial landscape (10%; arable land)
Land-use Agriculture (35%), Forestry (5%), Hunting (60%), Tourism/recreation (15%)

■ Birds

Species	Season	Year	Pop min	Pop max	Acc	Criteria
Anser albifrons White-fronted Goose	P	1996	10,000	15,000	B	A4i, B1i
Anser anser Greylag Goose	P	1996	500	800	B	B1i
Crex crex Corncrake	B	1996	40	60	B	A1
Gallinago media Great Snipe	B	1996	60	100	B	A1, A4i, B1i

Two species of global conservation concern breed in important numbers in the wet grasslands. The site holds up to 20,000 migrating waterbirds on a regular basis, mainly geese *Anser*.

■ Protection status
National None **International** High
12,000 ha of IBA covered by Ramsar Site (Flood-plains of the Oka and Pra Rivers, 161,542 ha).

■ Conservation issues

Threats Agricultural intensification/expansion (A), Disturbance to birds (B), Drainage (A), Unsustainable exploitation (A)

Oka valley in vicinity of Murmino
A4iii, B1i

089

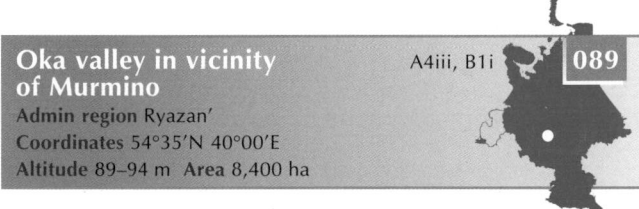

Admin region Ryazan'
Coordinates 54°35'N 40°00'E
Altitude 89–94 m **Area** 8,400 ha

■ Site description
A large area of wet grassland used partly for agriculture, located on one of the widest parts of the flood-plain of the Oka river.

Habitats Forest and woodland (5%; alluvial/very wet forest), Scrub (5%; scrub), Grassland (80%; humid grassland), Wetland (15%; standing fresh water; river/stream)
Land-use Agriculture (30%), Tourism/recreation (20%)

■ Birds

Species	Season	Year	Pop min	Pop max	Acc	Criteria
Anser albifrons White-fronted Goose	P	1996	10,000	12,000	B	B1i
Anser anser Greylag Goose	P	1996	500	800	B	B1i

The site holds more than 20,000 waterbirds on passage in years when the spring water-level is high, mainly comprising *Anser fabalis*, *A. albifrons*, *A. anser*, *Anas penelope*.

■ Protection status
National None **International** High
8,400 ha of IBA covered by Ramsar Site (Flood-plains of the Oka and Pra Rivers, 161,542 ha).

■ Conservation issues

Threats Disturbance to birds (A), Drainage (B), Recreation/tourism (A), Unsustainable exploitation (B)

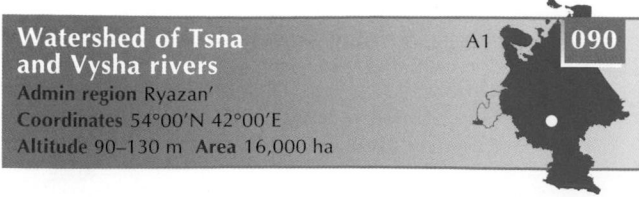

Watershed of Tsna and Vysha rivers

A1 | 090

Admin region Ryazan'
Coordinates 54°00'N 42°00'E
Altitude 90–130 m **Area** 16,000 ha

■ Site description

Habitats Forest and woodland (60%; mixed forest), Scrub (10%; scrub), Grassland (5%; humid grassland), Wetland (6%; standing fresh water; river/stream; fen/transition mire/spring), Artificial landscape (20%; arable land; other urban/industrial areas)
Land-use Agriculture (19%), Forestry (60%)

■ Birds

Species	Season	Year	Pop min	Pop max	Acc	Criteria
Crex crex Corncrake	B	1996	30	50	B	A1
Gallinago media Great Snipe	B	1996	10	20	B	A1

Two species of global conservation concern breed in significant numbers, but another such species does not meet IBA criteria: *Aquila clanga*.

■ Protection status
National None **International** None

■ Conservation issues

Threats Drainage (B), Forest grazing (B), Selective logging/cutting (B), Unsustainable exploitation (B)

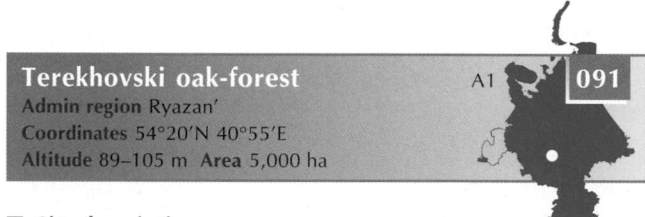

Terekhovski oak-forest

A1 | 091

Admin region Ryazan'
Coordinates 54°20'N 40°55'E
Altitude 89–105 m **Area** 5,000 ha

■ Site description
Oak *Quercus* forest on the banks of the Oka river.

Habitats Forest and woodland (85%; alluvial/very wet forest), Grassland (10%; humid grassland), Artificial landscape (5%; arable land)
Land-use Agriculture (15%), Forestry (85%)

■ Birds

Species	Season	Year	Pop min	Pop max	Acc	Criteria
Aquila clanga Greater Spotted Eagle	B	1996	2	—	A	A1

The globally threatened *Aquila clanga* breeds in the area.

■ Protection status
National None **International** None

■ Conservation issues

Threats Disturbance to birds (B), Forest grazing (C), Recreation/tourism (B), Selective logging/cutting (B), Unsustainable exploitation (U)

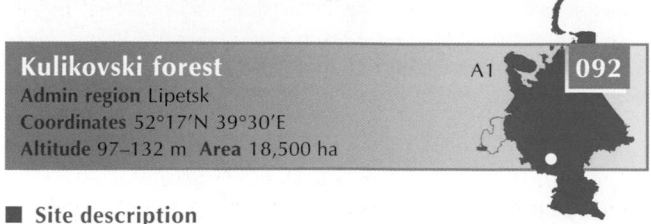

Kulikovski forest

A1 | 092

Admin region Lipetsk
Coordinates 52°17'N 39°30'E
Altitude 97–132 m **Area** 18,500 ha

■ Site description
The IBA includes the forested banks of the Voronezh river, which are traversed by many smaller streams and rivers.

Habitats Forest and woodland (85%; broadleaved deciduous forest; native coniferous forest; alluvial/very wet forest), Grassland (5%; humid grassland), Wetland (5%; standing fresh water; fen/transition mire/spring), Artificial landscape (5%; other urban/industrial areas)
Land-use Agriculture (5%), Forestry (93%), Tourism/recreation (20%)

■ Birds

Species	Season	Year	Pop min	Pop max	Acc	Criteria
Crex crex Corncrake	B	1996	30	60	C	A1

Crex crex breeds in significant numbers, although some other breeding species of global conservation concern do not meet IBA criteria: *Haliaeetus albicilla*, *Aquila clanga*, *Aquila heliaca*. Significant proportion (≥1%) of national population breeding at site: *Ficedula albicollis* (20–50 pairs).

■ Protection status
National High **International** None
10,000 ha of IBA covered by Zakaznik (Kolodetsky 'zoological' reserve, 10,000 ha). 8,500 ha of IBA covered by Zakaznik (Pervomayskiy 'zoological' reserve, 8,500 ha).

■ Conservation issues

Threats Deforestation (commercial) (C)

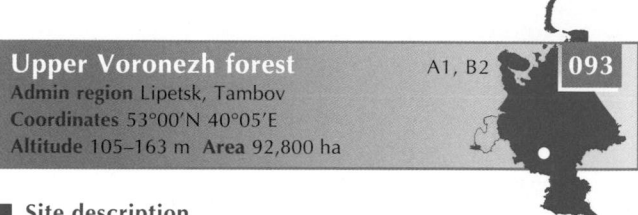

Upper Voronezh forest

A1, B2 | 093

Admin region Lipetsk, Tambov
Coordinates 53°00'N 40°05'E
Altitude 105–163 m **Area** 92,800 ha

■ Site description
One of the largest areas of forest in the forest-steppe zone of European Russia.

Habitats Forest and woodland (70%; broadleaved deciduous forest; native coniferous forest; alluvial/very wet forest), Grassland (20%; humid grassland), Wetland (5%; fen/transition mire/spring), Artificial landscape (20%; arable land; other urban/industrial areas)
Land-use Agriculture (20%), Fisheries/aquaculture (5%), Forestry (70%), Hunting (80%), Military (5%), Nature conservation/research (15%), Tourism/recreation (30%), Urban/industrial/transport (10%)

■ Birds

Species	Season	Year	Pop min	Pop max	Acc	Criteria
Aquila clanga Greater Spotted Eagle	B	1996	1	3	B	A1
Aquila heliaca Imperial Eagle	B	1996	1	2	C	A1, B2
Hieraaetus pennatus Booted Eagle	B	1996	3	6	B	B2
Crex crex Corncrake	B	1996	50	100	B	A1
Gallinago media Great Snipe	B	1996	10	20	C	A1
Lullula arborea Woodlark	B	1996	100	200	C	B2

Two globally threatened raptors breed, as do *Crex crex* and *Gallinago media*. However, one other species of global conservation concern does not meet IBA criteria: *Glareola nordmanni* (1–10 non-breeding birds).

■ Protection status
National Partial **International** None
12,300 ha of IBA covered by Zakaznik (Dobrovski 'Landscape' Reserve, 12,300 ha).

■ Conservation issues

Threats Disturbance to birds (B), Infrastructure (B), Intensified forest management (B), Unsustainable exploitation (B)

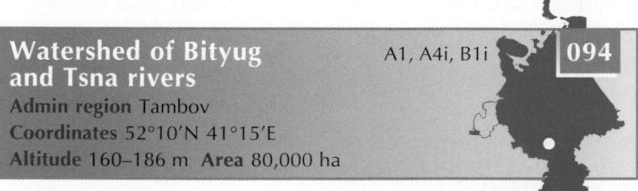

Watershed of Bityug and Tsna rivers

A1, A4i, B1i | 094

Admin region Tambov
Coordinates 52°10'N 41°15'E
Altitude 160–186 m **Area** 80,000 ha

■ Site description

Habitats Forest and woodland (20%; wooded steppe), Grassland (10%; steppe/dry calcareous grassland; humid grassland), Wetland (20%; standing fresh water; river/stream), Artificial landscape (60%; arable land; perennial crops/orchards/groves)
Land-use Agriculture (80%), Forestry (10%), Urban/industrial/transport (10%)

A varied landscape of mainly agricultural land, interspersed with rivers, streams, shallow lakes, and a number of small forest plantations.

■ Birds

Species	Season	Year	Pop min	Pop max	Acc	Criteria
Anser fabalis Bean Goose	P	1997	4,000	5,000	B	A4i, B1i
Anser albifrons White-fronted Goose	P	1997	3,000	4,000	B	B1i
Anser anser Greylag Goose	P	1997	1,000	1,500	B	B1i
Branta ruficollis Red-breasted Goose	P	1997	1	100	B	A1
Crex crex Corncrake	B	1997	150	200	A	A1

An important staging area for four species of goose during migration, including the globally threatened *Branta ruficollis*. *Crex crex* breeds in significant numbers, although some other breeding species of global conservation concern do not meet IBA criteria: *Circus macrourus* (5–7 pairs), *Tetrax tetrax* (5–7 pairs), *Acrocephalus paludicola* (3–5 pairs).

■ Protection status
National None **International** None

■ Conservation issues

Threats Agricultural intensification/expansion (C), Disturbance to birds (C), Firewood collection (C), Recreation/tourism (C), Unsustainable exploitation (C)

The creation of a federal nature reserve (Zakaznik) is planned

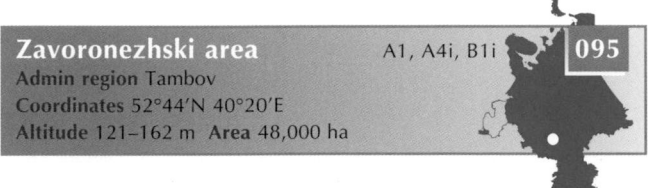

Zavoronezhski area
A1, A4i, B1i 095
Admin region Tambov
Coordinates 52°44'N 40°20'E
Altitude 121–162 m **Area** 48,000 ha

■ Site description
A large, flat depression surrounded by the Vorona, Palnoi Voronezh and Matyra rivers, with about 20 small fens and mires (totalling c.1,000 ha). The land is farmed non-intensively.

Habitats Forest and woodland (10%; alluvial/very wet forest; wooded steppe), Grassland (30%; steppe/dry calcareous grassland; humid grassland), Wetland (15%; standing fresh water; river/stream; fen/transition mire/spring), Artificial landscape (70%; highly improved reseeded grassland; arable land; perennial crops/orchards/groves; forestry plantation; urban parks/gardens)
Land-use Agriculture (80%), Forestry (10%), Hunting (90%), Tourism/recreation (10%)

■ Birds

Species	Season	Year	Pop min	Pop max	Acc	Criteria
Anser fabalis Bean Goose	P	1997	5,000	7,000	B	A4i, B1i
Anser albifrons White-fronted Goose	P	1997	4,000	5,000	B	B1i
Anser anser Greylag Goose	P	1997	1,500	2,000	B	B1i
Crex crex Corncrake	B	1997	250	300	A	A1
Grus grus Crane	P	1997	500	600	B	B1i

An important staging area for *Grus grus* and three species of geese *Anser* during migration; *Crex crex* breeds in large numbers. Species of global conservation concern that do not meet IBA criteria: *Circus macrourus* (on passage).

■ Protection status
National None **International** None

■ Conservation issues

Threats Agricultural intensification/expansion (C), Firewood collection (C), Selective logging/cutting (C), Unsustainable exploitation (C)

Plans have been drawn up for the creation of a Zapovednik.

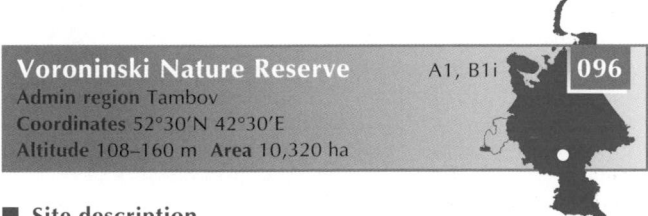

Voroninski Nature Reserve
A1, B1i 096
Admin region Tambov
Coordinates 52°30'N 42°30'E
Altitude 108–160 m **Area** 10,320 ha

■ Site description
The area comprises patches of forest along the banks of the Vorona river.

Habitats Forest and woodland (86%; mixed forest; alluvial/very wet forest), Grassland (11%; humid grassland), Wetland (14%; standing fresh water; river/stream; fen/transition mire/spring)
Land-use Nature conservation/research (100%)

■ Birds

Species	Season	Year	Pop min	Pop max	Acc	Criteria
Anser anser Greylag Goose	P	1996	—	2,000	B	B1i
Crex crex Corncrake	B	1996	110	150	A	A1

Crex crex breeds in significant numbers, although one other breeding species of global conservation concern does not meet IBA criteria: *Haliaeetus albicilla*. The area is also important for staging *Anser anser* during migration.

■ Protection status
National High **International** None
10,320 ha of IBA covered by Zapovednik (Voroninskiy, 10,320 ha).

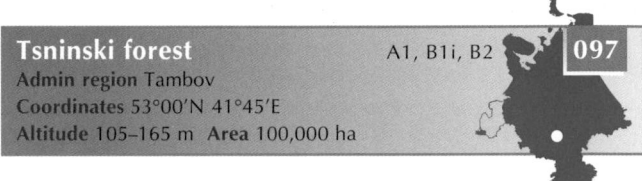

Tsninski forest
A1, B1i, B2 097
Admin region Tambov
Coordinates 53°00'N 41°45'E
Altitude 105–165 m **Area** 100,000 ha

■ Site description
The largest forest in the centre of the Tambov region.

Habitats Forest and woodland (90%; native coniferous forest; mixed forest; alluvial/very wet forest), Grassland (10%; humid grassland)
Land-use Forestry (100%), Hunting (100%)

■ Birds

Species	Season	Year	Pop min	Pop max	Acc	Criteria
Anser anser Greylag Goose	P	1996	1	3,000	C	B1i
Aquila clanga Greater Spotted Eagle	B	1996	3	—	C	A1
Hieraaetus pennatus Booted Eagle	B	1996	2	3	C	B2
Crex crex Corncrake	B	1996	400	500	C	A1, B2
Limosa limosa Black-tailed Godwit	B	1996	100	150	C	B2

The site supports important breeding numbers of several raptors and species of wet grasslands, including two globally threatened species. Two other species of global conservation concern do not meet IBA criteria: *Haliaeetus albicilla* (6–8 birds in winter), *Aquila heliaca* (breeding).

■ Protection status
National None **International** None

■ Conservation issues

Threats Deforestation (commercial) (C), Disturbance to birds (C), Intensified forest management (C)

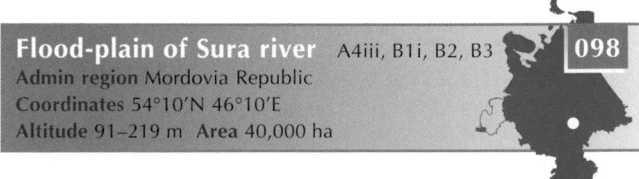

Flood-plain of Sura river
A4iii, B1i, B2, B3 098
Admin region Mordovia Republic
Coordinates 54°10'N 46°10'E
Altitude 91–219 m **Area** 40,000 ha

■ Site description
One half of the flood-plain of the Sura river is covered in wet forest and fen, and the other half is used for agriculture.

Habitats Forest and woodland (60%; broadleaved deciduous forest; native coniferous forest; alluvial/very wet forest), Scrub (5%), Grassland (30%; humid grassland), Wetland (15%; standing fresh water; river/stream; fen/transition mire/spring), Artificial landscape (8%; arable land)
Land-use Agriculture (34%), Forestry (60%), Hunting (28%), Nature conservation/research (25%), Not utilized (10%)

■ Birds

A variety of forest and riverine species breed in significant numbers. Thousands of geese *Anser* stage here on migration, and the site

Species		Season	Year	Pop min	Pop max	Acc	Criteria
Anser albifrons	White-fronted Goose	P	1996	2,000	3,000	B	B1i
Anser anser	Greylag Goose	P	1996	500	1,000	B	B1i
Porzana porzana	Spotted Crake	B	1996	150	200	B	B3
Strix aluco	Tawny Owl	B	1996	100	150	B	B3
Alcedo atthis	Kingfisher	B	1996	80	100	B	B2
Jynx torquilla	Wryneck	B	1996	400	600	B	B2
Lullula arborea	Woodlark	B	1996	200	300	B	B2
Luscinia luscinia	Thrush Nightingale	B	1996	1,500	2,000	B	B3
Ficedula albicollis	Collared Flycatcher	B	1996	150	200	B	B3

regularly holds up to 20,000 migrating waterbirds. Breeding species of global conservation concern that do not meet IBA criteria: *Aquila clanga* (at least 1 pair).

■ Protection status
National Partial **International** None
1,273 ha of IBA covered by Zakaznik (Kochkurovsky Hunting Reserve, 1,273 ha). 2,417 ha of IBA covered by Zakaznik (Bolsheberenznikovsky Hunting Reserve, 2,417 ha). 7,243 ha of IBA covered by Zakaznik (Dubensky Hunting Reserve, 7,243 ha).

■ Conservation issues

Threats Abandonment/reduction of land management (A), Deforestation (commercial) (A), Drainage (A), Forest grazing (A), Intensified forest management (A), Unsustainable exploitation (A)

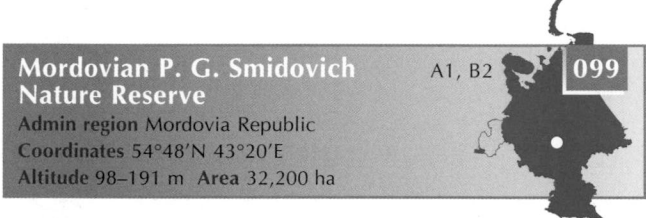

Mordovian P. G. Smidovich Nature Reserve A1, B2 **099**
Admin region Mordovia Republic
Coordinates 54°48'N 43°20'E
Altitude 98–191 m **Area** 32,200 ha

■ Site description
Broadleaved forests dissected by river valleys.

Habitats Forest and woodland (100%; native coniferous forest; mixed forest; alluvial/very wet forest)
Land-use Agriculture (6%), Nature conservation/research (100%)

■ Birds

Species		Season	Year	Pop min	Pop max	Acc	Criteria
Aquila clanga	Greater Spotted Eagle	B	1996	2	3	B	A1
Hieraaetus pennatus	Booted Eagle	B	1996	1	3	B	B2
Crex crex	Corncrake	B	1996	25	52	B	A1

An important site for two forest raptors and *Crex crex*. Two species of global conservation concern, *Aquila heliaca* and *Gallinago media*, have been recorded, but their status needs to be clarified.

■ Protection status
National High **International** None
32,200 ha of IBA covered by Zapovednik (Mordovskiy, 32,200 ha).

■ Conservation issues

Threats Abandonment/reduction of land management (C), Disturbance to birds (U), Drainage (B), Groundwater abstraction (A), Unsustainable exploitation (U)

All bird species are monitored in accordance with the Zapovednik laws.

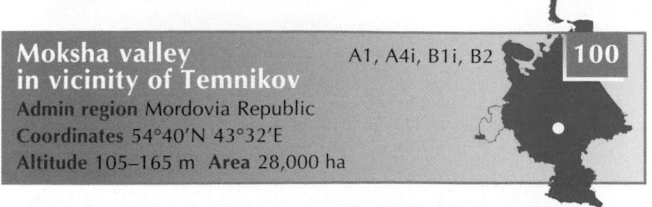

Moksha valley in vicinity of Temnikov A1, A4i, B1i, B2 **100**
Admin region Mordovia Republic
Coordinates 54°40'N 43°32'E
Altitude 105–165 m **Area** 28,000 ha

■ Site description

Habitats Forest and woodland (20%; broadleaved deciduous forest; native coniferous forest), Scrub (10%; scrub), Grassland (25%; humid grassland), Wetland (15%; standing fresh water; river/stream; fen/transition mire/spring), Artificial landscape (35%; arable land; other urban/industrial areas)

Land-use Agriculture (73%), Forestry (20%), Hunting (95%)

A flood-plain containing many old meanders and meadows, to the east of the town of Temnikov.

■ Birds

Species		Season	Year	Pop min	Pop max	Acc	Criteria
Anser albifrons	White-fronted Goose	P	1996	3,000	5,000	B	B1i
Anser anser	Greylag Goose	P	1996	200	300	B	B1i
Branta ruficollis	Red-breasted Goose	P	1996	500	1,000	C	A1, A4i, B1i
Crex crex	Corncrake	B	1996	150	200	B	A1
Alcedo atthis	Kingfisher	B	1996	120	130	B	B2

Thousands of geese stage here on passage, including the globally threatened *Branta ruficollis*, and important numbers of *Crex crex* breed.

■ Protection status
National None **International** None

■ Conservation issues

Threats Abandonment/reduction of land management (B), Drainage (B), Extraction industry (B), Selective logging/cutting (B), Unsustainable exploitation (A)

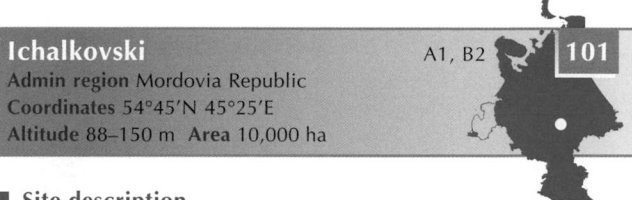

Ichalkovski A1, B2 **101**
Admin region Mordovia Republic
Coordinates 54°45'N 45°25'E
Altitude 88–150 m **Area** 10,000 ha

■ Site description
Extensive wet grasslands linked by alluvial forests.

Habitats Forest and woodland (20%; native coniferous forest; mixed forest; alluvial/very wet forest), Scrub (17%; scrub), Grassland (60%; humid grassland), Artificial landscape (3%; other urban/industrial areas)
Land-use Agriculture (30%), Nature conservation/research (80%)

■ Birds

Species		Season	Year	Pop min	Pop max	Acc	Criteria
Aquila heliaca	Imperial Eagle	B	1996	1	3	B	A1, B2
Crex crex	Corncrake	B	1996	500	1,000	C	A1, B2

Two globally threatened species breed in important numbers.

■ Protection status
National Low **International** None
800 ha of IBA covered by National Park (Smolniy, 36,482 ha).

■ Conservation issues

Threats Disturbance to birds (B), Selective logging/cutting (B), Unsustainable exploitation (C)

Ornithological data are incomplete for the site as survey work only began in 1996, and further research is required.

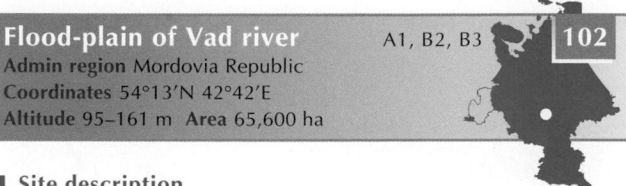

Flood-plain of Vad river A1, B2, B3 **102**
Admin region Mordovia Republic
Coordinates 54°13'N 42°42'E
Altitude 95–161 m **Area** 65,600 ha

■ Site description
The flood-plain of the Vad river is covered by forest in the south and by wet grasslands in the north.

Habitats Forest and woodland (70%; broadleaved deciduous forest; native coniferous forest; mixed forest; alluvial/very wet forest), Grassland (10%; humid grassland), Wetland (2%), Artificial landscape (23%; highly improved reseeded grassland; arable land; other urban/industrial areas)
Land-use Agriculture (17%), Forestry (70%), Hunting (80%), Nature conservation/research (20%), Not utilized (15%), Urban/industrial/transport (6%)

Birds

Species	Season	Year	Pop min	Pop max	Acc	Criteria
Aquila clanga Greater Spotted Eagle	B	1996	1	2	B	A1
Gallinago media Great Snipe	B	1996	20	40	B	A1
Columba oenas Stock Dove	B	1996	200	250	B	B3
Alcedo atthis Kingfisher	B	1996	80	100	B	B2
Picoides tridactylus Three-toed Woodpecker	R	1996	90	110	B	B2
Turdus viscivorus Mistle Thrush	R	1996	200	300	B	B3
Ficedula albicollis Collared Flycatcher	R	1996	400	500	B	B3

Aquila clanga and *Gallinago media* breed in significant numbers, although another breeding species of global conservation concern does not meet IBA criteria: *Aquila heliaca*. A number of forest species also breed in significant numbers.

Protection status
National Partial **International** None
8,000 ha of IBA covered by Zakaznik (Zubovo–Polyansky Hunting Reserve, 11,824 ha).

Conservation issues

Threats Deforestation (commercial) (B), Drainage (B), Firewood collection (B), Selective logging/cutting (B), Unsustainable exploitation (B)

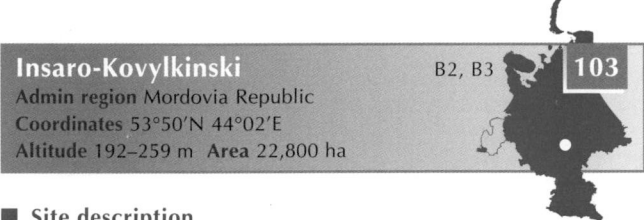

Insaro-Kovylkinski   B2, B3   **103**
Admin region Mordovia Republic
Coordinates 53°50'N 44°02'E
Altitude 192–259 m **Area** 22,800 ha

Site description
An area of hilly pasture, partly covered in scrub and small woods.

Habitats Forest and woodland (10%; broadleaved deciduous forest), Grassland (15%; humid grassland; mesophile grassland), Artificial landscape (75%; arable land; other urban/industrial areas)
Land-use Agriculture (80%), Forestry (10%), Hunting (95%), Urban/industrial/transport (8%)

Birds

Species	Season	Year	Pop min	Pop max	Acc	Criteria
Falco naumanni Lesser Kestrel	B	1996	1	3	—	B2
Coturnix coturnix Quail	B	1996	2,000	3,000	B	B2
Saxicola rubetra Whinchat	B	1996	1,000	1,500	B	B3
Emberiza hortulana Ortolan Bunting	B	1996	400	600	B	B2

Significant numbers of several species breed in the area, notably the globally threatened *Falco naumanni*. Breeding species of global conservation concern that do not meet IBA criteria: *Circus macrourus* (1–2 pairs).

Protection status
National None **International** None

Conservation issues

Threats Abandonment/reduction of land management (B), Agricultural intensification/expansion (A), Deforestation (commercial) (A), Firewood collection (B), Selective logging/cutting (B)

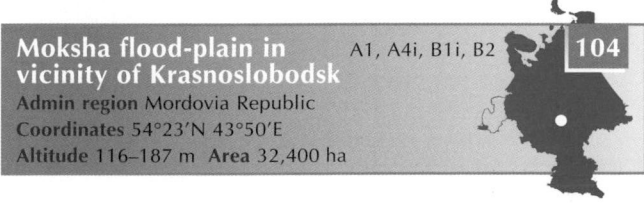

Moksha flood-plain in vicinity of Krasnoslobodsk   A1, A4i, B1i, B2   **104**
Admin region Mordovia Republic
Coordinates 54°23'N 43°50'E
Altitude 116–187 m **Area** 32,400 ha

Site description

Habitats Forest and woodland (17%; broadleaved deciduous forest; native coniferous forest; alluvial/very wet forest), Scrub (20%; scrub), Grassland (25%; steppe/dry calcareous grassland), Wetland (10%; standing fresh water; river/stream; fen/transition mire/spring), Artificial landscape (40%; highly improved reseeded grassland; arable land; other urban/industrial areas)

Land-use Agriculture (10%), Forestry (60%), Nature conservation/research (80%), Not utilized (20%)

An area of river flood-plain including both forest and agricultural land meadows, with many oxbow lakes.

Birds

Species	Season	Year	Pop min	Pop max	Acc	Criteria
Anser albifrons White-fronted Goose	P	1996	5,000	15,000	C	A4i, B1i
Anser anser Greylag Goose	P	1996	300	500	B	B1i
Branta ruficollis Red-breasted Goose	P	1996	500	1,000	B	A1, A4i, B1i
Crex crex Corncrake	B	1996	100	200	C	A1
Emberiza hortulana Ortolan Bunting	B	1996	100	150	B	B2

Two globally threatened species occur in significant numbers: *Crex crex* breeds and *Branta ruficollis* passes through on migration. Two other goose species also stage at the site in important numbers.

Protection status
National Partial **International** None
6,500 ha of IBA covered by Zakaznik (Krasnoslobodsky, 6,500 ha).

Conservation issues

Threats Agricultural intensification/expansion (A), Drainage (A), Recreation/tourism (B), Unsustainable exploitation (B)

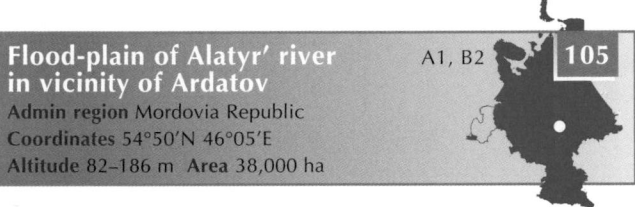

Flood-plain of Alatyr' river in vicinity of Ardatov   A1, B2   **105**
Admin region Mordovia Republic
Coordinates 54°50'N 46°05'E
Altitude 82–186 m **Area** 38,000 ha

Site description
An extensive area of the Alatyr' river flood-plain, with large areas of wet grassland which flood in spring. Higher, unflooded areas are forested.

Habitats Forest and woodland (20%; broadleaved deciduous forest; native coniferous forest; mixed forest), Scrub (5%; scrub), Grassland (37%; humid grassland), Wetland (10%; standing fresh water; river/stream; fen/transition mire/spring), Artificial landscape (30%; highly improved reseeded grassland; arable land; other urban/industrial areas)
Land-use Agriculture (28%), Forestry (25%), Hunting (50%), Nature conservation/research (50%), Urban/industrial/transport (5%)

Birds

Species	Season	Year	Pop min	Pop max	Acc	Criteria
Aquila heliaca Imperial Eagle	B	1996	3	4	A	A1, B2
Falco naumanni Lesser Kestrel	B	1996	5	10	B	A1, B2
Crex crex Corncrake	B	1996	20	40	B	A1
Emberiza hortulana Ortolan Bunting	B	1996	150	200	B	B2

Three globally threatened species breed in significant numbers, while two other breeding species of global conservation concern do not meet IBA criteria: *Circus macrourus* (3–5 pairs), *Aquila clanga* (at least 1 pair).

Protection status
National Low **International** None
500 ha of IBA covered by Zakaznik (Ardatovsky, 5,016 ha).

Conservation issues

Threats Afforestation (A), Agricultural intensification/expansion (A), Deforestation (commercial) (A), Disturbance to birds (B), Drainage (A), Unsustainable exploitation (A)

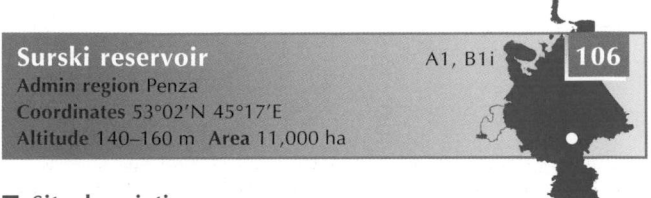

Surski reservoir   A1, B1i   **106**
Admin region Penza
Coordinates 53°02'N 45°17'E
Altitude 140–160 m **Area** 11,000 ha

Site description
One of the largest artificial reservoirs in central European Russia, located in the middle of the Penza region.

Habitats Wetland (100%; mudflat/sandflat; standing fresh water; river/stream; raised bog)
Land-use Fisheries/aquaculture (65%), Hunting (30%), Not utilized (40%), Tourism/recreation (100%), Water management

■ Birds

Species	Season	Year	Pop min	Pop max	Acc	Criteria
Anas penelope Wigeon	P	1995	5,000	6,000	A	B1i
Anas platyrhynchos Mallard	P	1995	15,000	25,000	A	B1i
Haliaeetus albicilla White-tailed Eagle	P	1995	5	14	A	A1

Significant numbers of three waterbirds stage at the site during migration, including one species of global conservation concern.

■ Protection status
National None **International** None

■ Conservation issues

Threats Disturbance to birds (A)

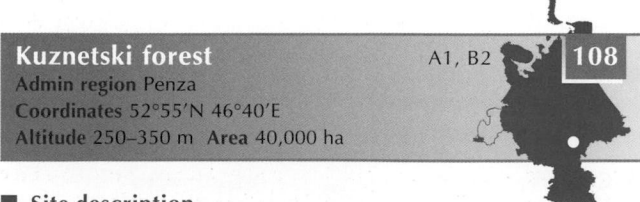

Bekovskoye forest   A1   107
Admin region Penza
Coordinates 52°25'N 43°45'E
Altitude 125–150 m **Area** 8,000 ha

■ Site description
One of the largest blocks of forest in the Penza region.

Habitats Forest and woodland (100%; broadleaved deciduous forest; native coniferous forest; alluvial/very wet forest)
Land-use Forestry (100%)

■ Birds

Species	Season	Year	Pop min	Pop max	Acc	Criteria
Aquila clanga Greater Spotted Eagle	B	1996	1	2	C	A1

A significant number of the globally threatened *Aquila clanga* breeds in the area, but another breeding species of global conservation concern does not meet IBA criteria: *Haliaeetus albicilla*. Information from local hunters and relevant literature shows that *Aquila clanga* has been present in the area for many years.

■ Protection status
National None **International** None

■ Conservation issues

Threats Intensified forest management (B)

Only a few days of ornithological survey were possible, thus bird data are incomplete.

Kuznetski forest   A1, B2   108
Admin region Penza
Coordinates 52°55'N 46°40'E
Altitude 250–350 m **Area** 40,000 ha

■ Site description
The largest tract of forest in the south-east of the Penza region.

Habitats Forest and woodland (70%; native coniferous forest; mixed forest; alluvial/very wet forest), Grassland (20%; steppe/dry calcareous grassland; humid grassland), Artificial landscape (10%; arable land)
Land-use Agriculture (30%), Forestry (70%)

■ Birds

Species	Season	Year	Pop min	Pop max	Acc	Criteria
Aquila heliaca Imperial Eagle	B	1996	3	10	C	A1, B2

Important numbers of the globally threatened *Aquila heliaca* breed in the area.

■ Protection status
National None **International** None
Not known.

■ Conservation issues

Threats Intensified forest management (C)

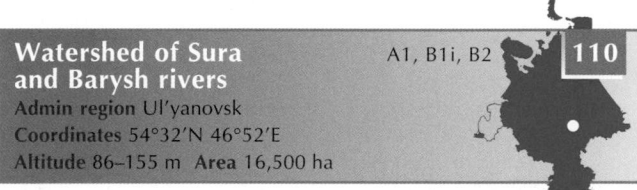

Sengileyevskiye mountain   A1   109
Admin region Ul'yanovsk
Coordinates 53°57'N 48°37'E
Altitude 53–330 m **Area** 22,400 ha

■ Site description
An area of forest on the shores of Kuybyshev reservoir.

Habitats Forest and woodland (84%; mixed forest), Grassland (9%; steppe/dry calcareous grassland), Artificial landscape (7%; arable land)
Land-use Agriculture (14%), Forestry (84%), Hunting (62%), Nature conservation/research (40%), Tourism/recreation (25%)

■ Birds

Species	Season	Year	Pop min	Pop max	Acc	Criteria
Aquila heliaca Imperial Eagle	B	1996	1	—	C	A1

Significant proportion (≥1%) of national population breeding at site: *Aquila chrysaetos* (1–2 pairs). *Hieraaetus pennatus* also breeds.

■ Protection status
National Partial **International** None
About 9,110 ha of IBA covered by eight regional protected areas (Zakazniks and Nature Monuments).

■ Conservation issues

Threats Abandonment/reduction of land management (A), Agricultural intensification/expansion (A), Disturbance to birds (B), Selective logging/cutting (A)

There are plans to establish a National Park here.

Watershed of Sura and Barysh rivers   A1, B1i, B2   110
Admin region Ul'yanovsk
Coordinates 54°32'N 46°52'E
Altitude 86–155 m **Area** 16,500 ha

■ Site description
Wet forest with open areas of mire and several lakes.

Habitats Forest and woodland (85%), Grassland (7%; humid grassland; mesophile grassland), Wetland (5%; standing fresh water; river/stream; raised bog), Artificial landscape (7%; arable land)
Land-use Agriculture (16%), Forestry (85%), Hunting (40%), Nature conservation/research (57%)

■ Birds

Species	Season	Year	Pop min	Pop max	Acc	Criteria
Aquila clanga Greater Spotted Eagle	B	1996	2	—	B	A1
Falco cherrug Saker	B	1985	1	1	A	B2
Crex crex Corncrake	B	1996	4	20	C	A1
Grus grus Crane	P	1996	200	600	A	B1i

An important area for species of open forest. Breeding species of global conservation concern that do not meet IBA criteria: *Aquila heliaca* (1 pair).

■ Protection status
National Partial **International** None
6 ha of IBA covered by Natural Monument (Boloto Konskoe, 6 ha). 17 ha of IBA covered by Natural Monument (Boloto Mokhovoe, 17 ha). 50 ha of IBA covered by Natural Monument (Boloto Mokhovoe Dolgoe, 50 ha). 43 ha of IBA covered by Natural

Monument (Boloto Mokhovoe-8, 43 ha). 234 ha of IBA covered by Natural Monument (Ozero Picherskoe, 234 ha). 9,200 ha of IBA covered by Zakaznik (Surskiy, 22,200 ha).

■ Conservation issues

Threats Firewood collection (C), Intensified forest management (A), Selective logging/cutting (A), Unsustainable exploitation (C)

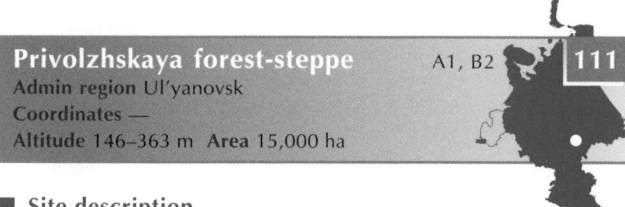

Privolzhskaya forest-steppe A1, B2 111
Admin region Ul'yanovsk
Coordinates —
Altitude 146–363 m **Area** 15,000 ha

■ Site description
An unbroken stretch of forest surrounded by steppe and pasture. Marmots *Marmota* and other rodents (the main prey of *Aquila heliaca*) are diverse and abundant on the steppe and agricultural land.

Habitats Forest and woodland (72%; mixed forest), Grassland (7%; steppe/dry calcareous grassland), Artificial landscape (21%; arable land)
Land-use Agriculture (27%), Forestry (72%), Nature conservation/research (2%), Tourism/recreation (7%)

■ Birds

Species	Season	Year	Pop min	Pop max	Acc	Criteria
Aquila heliaca Imperial Eagle	B	1996	3	7	A	A1, B2

The area holds one of the largest local populations of *Aquila heliaca* in Russia. Another globally threatened eagle species also breeds but does not meet IBA criteria: *Aquila clanga* (at least 1 pair).

■ Protection status
National Low **International** None
334 ha of IBA covered by Natural Monument (Zimina Gora, 334 ha).

■ Conservation issues

Threats Agricultural intensification/expansion (A), Deforestation (commercial) (C), Disturbance to birds (A), Forest grazing (B), Recreation/tourism (B), Selective logging/cutting (B)

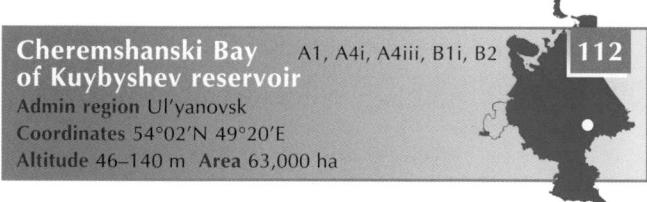

Cheremshanski Bay A1, A4i, A4iii, B1i, B2 112
of Kuybyshev reservoir
Admin region Ul'yanovsk
Coordinates 54°02'N 49°20'E
Altitude 46–140 m **Area** 63,000 ha

■ Site description
A shallow bay on the edge of Kuybyshev reservoir, which is situated in a highly developed part of the south-east Ul'yanovsk region. There are a number of fish-ponds.

Habitats Forest and woodland (9%; broadleaved deciduous forest; mixed forest), Wetland (73%; mudflat/sandflat; standing fresh water; river/stream), Artificial landscape (5%; arable land)
Land-use Agriculture (5%), Fisheries/aquaculture (68%), Forestry (8%), Hunting (10%), Tourism/recreation (90%), Water management

■ Birds

Species	Season	Year	Pop min	Pop max	Acc	Criteria
Anser fabalis Bean Goose	P	1993	100,000	—	B	A4i, B1i
Anser albifrons White-fronted Goose	P	1993	100,000	—	—	A4i, B1i
Haliaeetus albicilla White-tailed Eagle	R	1995	4	14	B	A1, B2

Important numbers of *Haliaeetus albicilla*, a raptor of global conservation concern, breed in the area. Huge numbers of waterbirds occur on passage, with *Anser fabalis* and *A. albifrons* the most numerous, together with thousands of ducks and up to 10,000 waders (*Calidris* and *Tringa*). The fish-ponds attract feeding *Haliaeetus albicilla* and other waterbirds.

■ Protection status
National Low **International** None
3,150 ha of IBA covered by Zakaznik (Cheremshansky 'fishery' reserve, 3,150 ha). 19 ha of IBA covered by Zakaznik (Ostrov Borok, 19 ha).

■ Conservation issues

Threats Agricultural intensification/expansion (C), Aquaculture/fisheries (B), Disturbance to birds (A), Forest grazing (C), Infrastructure (B), Intensified forest management (B), Recreation/tourism (A), Unsustainable exploitation (A)

The areas surrounding eagles' nest-sites are managed.

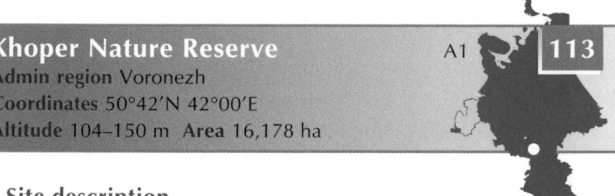

Khoper Nature Reserve A1 113
Admin region Voronezh
Coordinates 50°42'N 42°00'E
Altitude 104–150 m **Area** 16,178 ha

■ Site description
Alluvial forests and meadows situated along the most unspoilt stretch of the Khoper valley, where there is little disturbance from human activity.

Habitats Forest and woodland (84%; alluvial/very wet forest), Grassland (4%; humid grassland), Wetland (10%; standing fresh water; river/stream), Artificial landscape (5%; forestry plantation)
Land-use Nature conservation/research (100%)

■ Birds

Species	Season	Year	Pop min	Pop max	Acc	Criteria
Haliaeetus albicilla White-tailed Eagle	R	1996	3	5	A	A1
Aquila heliaca Imperial Eagle	W	1994	10	—	—	A1
Crex crex Corncrake	B	1996	30	—	B	A1

Three species of global conservation concern occur in significant numbers, while another one breeds within the Zapovednik but does not meet IBA criteria: *Aquila clanga* (1 pair; about 6 pairs breed around the IBA). In total about 100 species breed in the Zapovednik.

■ Protection status
National High **International** None
16,178 ha of IBA covered by Zapovednik (Khoperskiy, 16,178 ha).

■ Conservation issues

Threats Disturbance to birds (C), Forest grazing (C), Recreation/tourism (C), Unsustainable exploitation (C)

A complex ecological monitoring programme is underway within the Zapovednik.

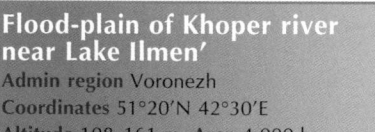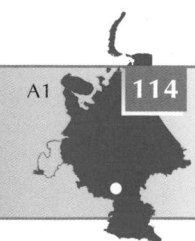

Flood-plain of Khoper river A1 114
near Lake Ilmen'
Admin region Voronezh
Coordinates 51°20'N 42°30'E
Altitude 108–161 m **Area** 4,000 ha

■ Site description
A small lake surrounded by meadows and wet forest, situated on the flood-plain of the Khoper river in the vicinity of Lake Ilmen'.

Habitats Forest and woodland (40%; native coniferous forest; mixed forest; alluvial/very wet forest), Grassland (39%; humid grassland), Wetland (15%; standing fresh water; river/stream; fen/transition mire/spring), Artificial landscape (6%; arable land; forestry plantation; other urban/industrial areas)
Land-use Agriculture (15%), Fisheries/aquaculture (10%), Forestry (40%), Not utilized (25%), Tourism/recreation (5%), Urban/industrial/transport (5%)

■ Birds

Species	Season	Year	Pop min	Pop max	Acc	Criteria
Haliaeetus albicilla White-tailed Eagle	P	1997	10	30	B	A1
Crex crex Corncrake	B	1997	50	100	B	A1

Two species of global conservation concern occur in significant numbers, while three others breed but do not meet IBA criteria: *Haliaeetus albicilla* (1–3 pairs), *Glareola nordmanni* (1–2 pairs), *Gallinago media* (1–2 pairs).

■ **Protection status**
National None **International** None

■ **Conservation issues**

> **Threats** Agricultural intensification/expansion (C), Aquaculture/fisheries (C), Disturbance to birds (C), Firewood collection (C), Forest grazing (C), Recreation/tourism (C), Selective logging/cutting (C), Unsustainable exploitation (B)

Before 1998 there was a temporary nature reserve (Zakaznik) in the area.

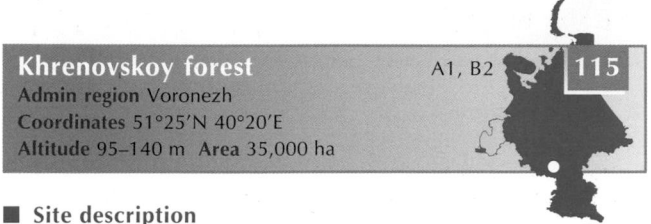

Khrenovskoy forest A1, B2 | 115
Admin region Voronezh
Coordinates 51°25'N 40°20'E
Altitude 95–140 m **Area** 35,000 ha

■ **Site description**
A large area of forest located in the central Voronezh region.

> **Habitats** Forest and woodland (80%; broadleaved deciduous forest; native coniferous forest; mixed forest), Grassland (10%; humid grassland), Wetland (10%)
> **Land-use** Agriculture (20%), Forestry (80%), Hunting (100%)

■ **Birds**

Species	Season	Year	Pop min	Pop max	Acc	Criteria
Aquila clanga Greater Spotted Eagle	B	1996	2	4	A	A1
Aquila heliaca Imperial Eagle	B	1996	2	—	C	A1, B2
Crex crex Corncrake	B	1996	100	200	C	A1

Three globally threatened species breed in significant numbers in the area, while another species of global conservation concern does not meet IBA criteria: *Haliaeetus albicilla* (1–5 birds in winter).

■ **Protection status**
National Low **International** None
Part of IBA covered by more than 20 small Nature Monuments (total area not known).

■ **Conservation issues**

> **Threats** Deforestation (commercial) (B), Disturbance to birds (C), Recreation/tourism (C), Unsustainable exploitation (C)

A proposal has been put forward to establish a nature reserve (Zapovednik) or nature park.

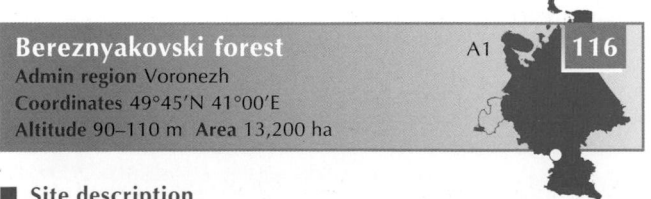

Bereznyakovski forest A1 | 116
Admin region Voronezh
Coordinates 49°45'N 41°00'E
Altitude 90–110 m **Area** 13,200 ha

■ **Site description**
A relatively large area of forest on the banks of the River Don, near to the village of Monastyrschina.

> **Habitats** Forest and woodland (80%; native coniferous forest; alluvial/very wet forest), Grassland (10%; steppe/dry calcareous grassland; humid grassland), Artificial landscape (10%; arable land)
> **Land-use** Agriculture (20%), Forestry (80%)

■ **Birds**

Species	Season	Year	Pop min	Pop max	Acc	Criteria
Crex crex Corncrake	B	1996	30	50	C	A1

Crex crex breeds in significant numbers, although other breeding species of global conservation concern do not meet IBA criteria: *Haliaeetus albicilla*, *Tetrax tetrax*, *Otis tarda* (at least 3 displaying males).

■ **Protection status**
National None **International** None

■ **Conservation issues**

> **Threats** Afforestation (B), Firewood collection (B), Selective logging/cutting (B), Unsustainable exploitation (C)

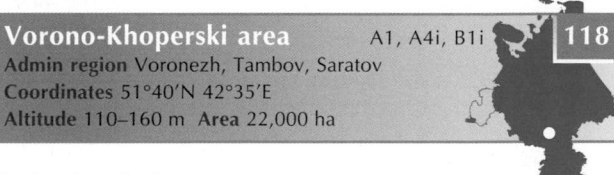

Voronezhski Nature Reserve A1, B2 | 117
Admin region Voronezh, Lipetsk
Coordinates 51°55'N 39°30'E
Altitude 90–169 m **Area** 31,053 ha

■ **Site description**
Large tracts of broadleaved and pine *Pinus* forest, located near to Usman on the border between the Lipetsk and Voronezh regions.

> **Habitats** Forest and woodland (94%; broadleaved deciduous forest; native coniferous forest; alluvial/very wet forest), Grassland (2%; humid grassland), Wetland (3%; river/stream; fen/transition mire/spring), Artificial landscape (2%)
> **Land-use** Nature conservation/research (100%)

■ **Birds**

Species	Season	Year	Pop min	Pop max	Acc	Criteria
Aquila clanga Greater Spotted Eagle	B	1996	1	2	A	A1
Aquila heliaca Imperial Eagle	B	1996	1	2	A	A1, B2
Hieraaetus pennatus Booted Eagle	B	1996	3	5	B	B2
Crex crex Corncrake	B	1996	100	130	C	A1

An important breeding area for three globally threatened species: *Crex crex* and two raptors. Species of global conservation concern that do not meet IBA criteria: *Haliaeetus albicilla* (3–5 birds in winter). In total about 125 species breed within the site.

■ **Protection status**
National High **International** High
31,053 ha of IBA covered by Zapovednik (Voronezhskiy, 31,053 ha). 31,053 ha of IBA covered by Biosphere Reserve (Voronezhskiy, 31,053 ha).

■ **Conservation issues**

> **Threats** Disturbance to birds (C), Recreation/tourism (C), Unsustainable exploitation (C)

Vorono-Khoperski area A1, A4i, B1i | 118
Admin region Voronezh, Tambov, Saratov
Coordinates 51°40'N 42°35'E
Altitude 110–160 m **Area** 22,000 ha

■ **Site description**
A low-lying area delimited by the Voronezh, Pal'noi Voronezh and Matyra rivers, and situated at the point where three regions of central European Russia meet. The area is relatively undeveloped, and access is difficult.

> **Habitats** Forest and woodland (10%; alluvial/very wet forest; wooded steppe), Grassland (10%; steppe/dry calcareous grassland; humid grassland), Wetland (10%; standing fresh water; river/stream), Artificial landscape (70%; arable land; perennial crops/orchards/groves)
> **Land-use** Agriculture (80%), Forestry (10%), Hunting (90%), Urban/industrial/transport (10%)

■ **Birds**

Species	Season	Year	Pop min	Pop max	Acc	Criteria
Anser fabalis Bean Goose	P	1997	5,000	6,000	A	A4i, B1i
Anser albifrons White-fronted Goose	P	1997	4,000	5,000	A	B1i
Anser anser Greylag Goose	P	1997	800	1,000	A	B1i
Branta ruficollis Red-breasted Goose	P	1997	800	1,000	A	A1, A4i, B1i
Crex crex Corncrake	B	1997	150	200	A	A1
[1] *Otis tarda* Great Bustard	B	1997	10	10	A	A1

1. Breeding individuals.

Two globally threatened species breed in significant numbers, in particular up to 32 individuals of *Otis tarda* were counted over only one-sixth of the area in spring 1997, suggesting that a comprehensive survey may reveal larger numbers. The area is also an important staging site for four species of geese during migration, especially for the globally threatened *Branta ruficollis*. Breeding species of global conservation concern that do not meet IBA criteria: *Aquila clanga*.

■ Protection status
National None **International** None

■ Conservation issues

Threats Afforestation (U), Agricultural intensification/expansion (B), Firewood collection (C), Forest grazing (C), Selective logging/cutting (C), Unsustainable exploitation (C)

The creation of a federal nature reserve is planned.

Levo-Dobrinskaya valley A1, B2 119
Admin region Volgograd
Coordinates 48°45′N 43°00′E
Altitude 100–120 m **Area** 3,000 ha

■ Site description
Extensive native grasslands (steppe and meadows) in a predominantly agricultural landscape to the west of the town of Volgograd.

Habitats Forest and woodland (2%; alluvial/very wet forest), Grassland (50%; steppe/dry calcareous grassland; mesophile grassland), Artificial landscape (45%; arable land; other urban/industrial areas)
Land-use Agriculture (95%), Urban/industrial/transport (5%)

■ Birds

Species		Season	Year	Pop min	Pop max	Acc	Criteria
Aquila heliaca	Imperial Eagle	R	1997	1	2	B	A1, B2

An important site for breeding *Aquila heliaca*. Breeding species of global conservation concern that do not meet IBA criteria: *Haliaeetus albicilla* (1 pair), *Tetrax tetrax* (5–15 pairs).

■ Protection status
National None **International** None

■ Conservation issues

Threats Abandonment/reduction of land management (A), Disturbance to birds (C)

Lake El'ton A1, A4i, B1i 120
Admin region Volgograd
Coordinates 49°10′N 46°50′E
Altitude 0–69 m **Area** 30,000 ha

■ Site description
A large salt-lake surrounded by steppe and dry grassland.

Habitats Grassland (steppe/dry calcareous grassland), Wetland (99%; mudflat/sandflat; standing brackish and salt water; river/stream)
Land-use Unknown (100%)

■ Birds

Species		Season	Year	Pop min	Pop max	Acc	Criteria
Grus grus	Crane	P	1997	15,000	20,000	A	A4i, B1i
[1] *Tetrax tetrax*	Little Bustard	B	1996	30	—	A	A1
Charadrius alexandrinus	Kentish Plover	P	1997	300	—	B	B1i

1. Breeding individuals.

Grus grus stages in the area in huge numbers during migration, and *Tetrax tetrax* (of global conservation concern) breeds in significant numbers.

■ Protection status
National None **International** None

Novokvasnikovski liman A1 121
Admin region Volgograd
Coordinates 50°32′N 46°30′E
Altitude 20–40 m **Area** 300 ha

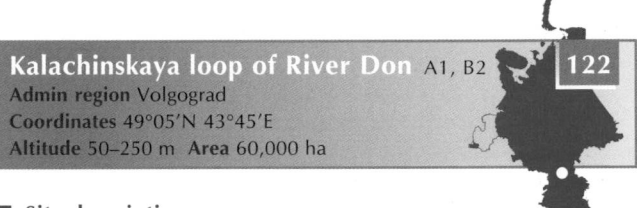

■ Site description
A small wetland surrounded by sandy steppes.

Habitats Grassland (60%; steppe/dry calcareous grassland), Wetland (40%; standing fresh water)
Land-use Agriculture (50%), Hunting (100%), Not utilized (50%)

■ Birds

Species		Season	Year	Pop min	Pop max	Acc	Criteria
Glareola nordmanni	Black-winged Pratincole	B	1997	5	20	A	A1

An important site for breeding *Glareola nordmanni*, which is thought to have undergone a large decrease over the last 10 years, although large natural fluctuations have not been ruled out. Other species of global conservation concern occur but do not meet IBA criteria: *Aythya nyroca* (at least 30 on passage), *Oxyura leucocephala* (1–2 on passage), *Haliaeetus albicilla* (at least 1 non-breeding bird).

■ Protection status
National None **International** None

■ Conservation issues

Threats Disturbance to birds (B), Drainage (C), Unsustainable exploitation (A)

Kalachinskaya loop of River Don A1, B2 122
Admin region Volgograd
Coordinates 49°05′N 43°45′E
Altitude 50–250 m **Area** 60,000 ha

■ Site description
Forest and steppic habitats bordering the River Don.

Habitats Forest and woodland (15%; broadleaved deciduous forest; alluvial/very wet forest), Grassland (70%; steppe/dry calcareous grassland), Artificial landscape (20%; arable land)
Land-use Agriculture (40%), Forestry (10%), Hunting (100%), Not utilized (50%)

■ Birds

Species		Season	Year	Pop min	Pop max	Acc	Criteria
Haliaeetus albicilla	White-tailed Eagle	B	1996	1	5	—	A1
Accipiter brevipes	Levant Sparrowhawk	B	1996	5	25	C	B2
Aquila heliaca	Imperial Eagle	B	1996	3	10	C	A1, B2
Hieraaetus pennatus	Booted Eagle	B	1996	1	10	—	B2

Significant numbers of four raptors breed in the area, including two of global conservation concern.

■ Protection status
National None **International** None

■ Conservation issues

Threats Abandonment/reduction of land management (B)

A short ornithological survey was carried out in 1996 but data remain incomplete.

Danilovski forest A1, B2 123
Admin region Volgograd
Coordinates 50°25′N 44°15′E
Altitude 25–125 m **Area** 10,000 ha

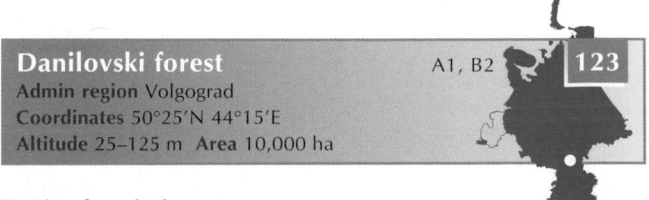

■ Site description
Forested river valleys, surrounded by an agricultural landscape.

Habitats Forest and woodland (95%; broadleaved deciduous forest; native coniferous forest), Wetland (5%; standing fresh water)

Land-use Forestry (100%)

■ Birds

Species		Season	Year	Pop min	Pop max	Acc	Criteria
Aquila heliaca	Imperial Eagle	B	1996	1	2	B	A1, B2

Significant numbers of the globally threatened *Aquila heliaca* breed in the area, but two other breeding eagles of global conservation concern do not meet IBA criteria: *Haliaeetus albicilla* (1 pair), *Aquila clanga* (1 pair).

■ Protection status

National None **International** None
Not known.

■ Conservation issues

Threats Selective logging/cutting (B)

One short ornithological survey was carried out in 1996, but available information on the site remains incomplete.

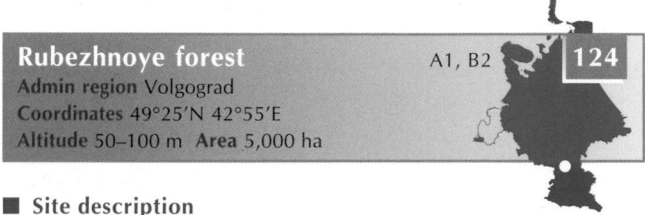

Rubezhnoye forest A1, B2 **124**
Admin region Volgograd
Coordinates 49°25'N 42°55'E
Altitude 50–100 m **Area** 5,000 ha

■ Site description
An area of forest surrounded by steppe.

Habitats Forest and woodland (40%; broadleaved deciduous forest; native coniferous forest), Grassland (60%; steppe/dry calcareous grassland; humid grassland)
Land-use Agriculture (45%), Forestry (40%), Hunting (100%), Not utilized (15%)

■ Birds

Species		Season	Year	Pop min	Pop max	Acc	Criteria
Haliaeetus albicilla	White-tailed Eagle	N	1996	30	50	B	A1
Accipiter brevipes	Levant Sparrowhawk	B	1996	6	15	B	B2
Hieraaetus pennatus	Booted Eagle	B	1996	3	5	B	B2

At least four raptors breed within the IBA, two of them in significant numbers. The other two, both species of global conservation concern, do not meet IBA criteria as breeders: *Haliaeetus albicilla* (2–4 pairs), *Aquila clanga* (at least 1 pair). However, important numbers of *H. albicilla* occur as non-breeders.

■ Protection status
National None **International** None

■ Conservation issues

Threats Selective logging/cutting (C)

A short ornithological survey was carried out in 1996, but information on the site remains incomplete.

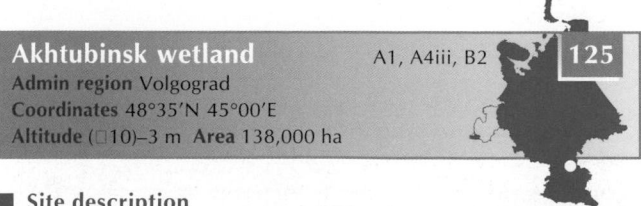

Akhtubinsk wetland A1, A4iii, B2 **125**
Admin region Volgograd
Coordinates 48°35'N 45°00'E
Altitude (□10)–3 m **Area** 138,000 ha

■ Site description
Located close to the centre of the Volgograd region, this site includes the northern part of the Volga–Akhtuba watershed, and extends from Volgograd to the Volga delta and Caspian Sea in the south. The area is surrounded by steppe and semi-desert.

Habitats Forest and woodland (14%; alluvial/very wet forest), Grassland (30%; humid grassland), Wetland (40%; standing fresh water; river/stream), Artificial landscape (16%)
Land-use Agriculture (13%), Fisheries/aquaculture (11%), Forestry (14%), Hunting (100%), Nature conservation/research (8%), Not utilized (40%), Tourism/recreation (30%), Water management (100%)

■ Birds

Species		Season	Year	Pop min	Pop max	Acc	Criteria
Haliaeetus albicilla	White-tailed Eagle	R	1998	24	30	A	A1, B2
Accipiter brevipes	Levant Sparrowhawk	B	1998	16	—	A	B2

Many pairs of *Haliaeetus albicilla*, a raptor of global conservation concern, breed in the area, as do at least 21,500 pairs of duck and at least 25,000 pairs of wader (Charadrii) and gull. In total, 82 species are known to breed in the area, most of which are included in various national or regional Red Data Books. The site is also an important staging post for migrating waders, wildfowl and raptors, with two bustards of global conservation concern, *Tetrax tetrax* and *Otis tarda*, also passing through. However, further survey work is needed in order to confirm numbers of migratory birds.

■ Protection status
National Low **International** None
12,000 ha of IBA covered by Zakaznik (Lescheevsky Hunting Reserve, 12,000 ha).

■ Conservation issues

Threats Construction/impact of dyke/dam/barrage (B), Disturbance to birds (A), Drainage (A), Extraction industry (U), Forest grazing (B), Industrialization/urbanization (A), Infrastructure (B), Intensified forest management (A), Recreation/tourism (A), Unsustainable exploitation (A)

As the Volga region potentially contains large oil reserves, oil exploration poses a very real threat to the area. There is an ongoing project aimed at establishing a Nature Park. As the area is located close to the large industrial centre of Volgograd, it could easily be used for educational purposes, and there are already plans in place for this.

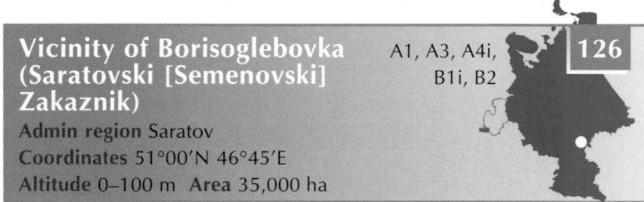

Vicinity of Borisoglebovka (Saratovski [Semenovski] Zakaznik) A1, A3, A4i, B1i, B2 **126**
Admin region Saratov
Coordinates 51°00'N 46°45'E
Altitude 0–100 m **Area** 35,000 ha

■ Site description
Former arable land that has reverted to steppe over the last 10–12 years, after the abandonment of cultivation. 'Forestry plantations' are narrow belts of trees.

Habitats Wetland, Artificial landscape (91%; arable land; forestry plantation)
Land-use Agriculture (86%), Forestry (5%)

■ Birds

Species		Season	Year	Pop min	Pop max	Acc	Criteria
Circus macrourus	Pallid Harrier	B	1996	1	3	A	A3
Accipiter brevipes	Levant Sparrowhawk	B	1996	10	20	B	A3, B2
Falco vespertinus	Red-footed Falcon	B	1996	100	200	B	B2
Anthropoides virgo	Demoiselle Crane	B	1996	3	5	B	A3
[1] *Otis tarda*	Great Bustard	B	1996	225	—	A	A1, B2
Glareola nordmanni	Black-winged Pratincole	B	1996	30	50	A	A1, A3, A4i, B1i

1. Breeding individuals.

A very important site for species restricted (when breeding) to the Eurasian steppe biome, including species of global conservation concern such as *Circus macrourus*, *Otis tarda* and *Glareola nordmanni*. Breeding species of global conservation concern that do not meet IBA criteria: *Tetrax tetrax* (at least 5 pairs).

■ Protection status
National None **International** None

■ Conservation issues

Threats Extraction industry (A)

The Saratov region is potentially one of the most important producers of oil in the lower Volga area of Russia, and exploratory drilling in the IBA has commenced. If large reserves are discovered, as seems likely, the IBA will be gravely threatened by the large-scale development of oil-extraction infrastructure and associated settlements, etc.

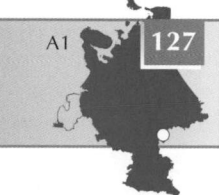

Valley of Safarovka river A1 127
Admin region Saratov
Coordinates 51°00'N 48°45'E
Altitude 50–79 m Area 2,500 ha

■ Site description
Meadows and steppe-grasslands on the flood-plain of the Safarovka river, used mainly as pasture land.

Habitats Forest and woodland (2%; alluvial/very wet forest), Grassland (50%; steppe/dry calcareous grassland; humid grassland), Wetland (7%; standing fresh water; river/stream), Artificial landscape (40%; highly improved reseeded grassland; arable land)
Land-use Agriculture (93%), Not utilized (7%), Tourism/recreation (10%)

■ Birds

Species	Season	Year	Pop min	Pop max	Acc	Criteria
[1] *Tetrax tetrax* Little Bustard	B	1997	40	60	—	A1
[1] *Otis tarda* Great Bustard	B	1997	50	70	—	A1
Glareola nordmanni Black-winged Pratincole	B	1997	30	40	—	A1

1. Breeding individuals.

Three species of global conservation concern breed in the steppic habitats in important numbers.

■ Protection status
National None **International** None

■ Conservation issues

Threats Agricultural intensification/expansion (C), Disturbance to birds (C), Firewood collection (C), Recreation/tourism (C), Unsustainable exploitation (C)

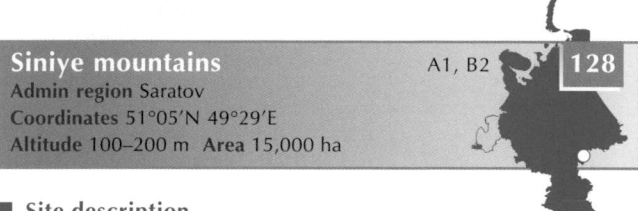

Siniye mountains A1, B2 128
Admin region Saratov
Coordinates 51°05'N 49°29'E
Altitude 100–200 m Area 15,000 ha

■ Site description
A range of hills covered by primary steppe, some parts of which have been turned over to arable farming.

Habitats Scrub (4%; scrub), Grassland (60%; steppe/dry calcareous grassland), Artificial landscape (30%; arable land)
Land-use Agriculture (30%), Unknown (70%)

■ Birds

Species	Season	Year	Pop min	Pop max	Acc	Criteria
Circus macrourus Pallid Harrier	B	1997	10	12	B	A1, B2
Aquila heliaca Imperial Eagle	B	1997	2	3	A	A1, B2
[1] *Otis tarda* Great Bustard	B	1997	50	1,000	B	A1, B2

1. Breeding individuals.

Three species of global conservation concern breed in important numbers.

■ Protection status
National None **International** None

■ Conservation issues

Threats Firewood collection (A)

Priyeruslanskiye sands A1, B2 129
Admin region Saratov
Coordinates 50°42'N 46°43'E
Altitude 50–70 m Area 20,000 ha

■ Site description
Primary steppe and agricultural land, adjacent to a forested area.

Habitats Forest and woodland (20%; mixed forest), Grassland (32%; steppe/dry calcareous grassland), Artificial landscape (48%; arable land; perennial crops/orchards/groves; forestry plantation)
Land-use Agriculture (48%), Forestry (52%), Nature conservation/research (50%)

■ Birds

Species	Season	Year	Pop min	Pop max	Acc	Criteria
Hieraaetus pennatus Booted Eagle	B	1996	2	2	A	B2
[1] *Tetrax tetrax* Little Bustard	B	1997	70	90	B	A1

1. Breeding individuals.

Breeding species of global conservation concern include *Tetrax tetrax*, while two others do not meet IBA criteria: *Haliaeetus albicilla* (at least 1 pair), *Otis tarda* (7–12 individuals).

■ Protection status
National Partial **International** None
10,400 ha of IBA covered by Zakaznik (D'yakovsky, 16,000 ha).

■ Conservation issues

Threats Agricultural intensification/expansion (B), Deforestation (commercial) (A), Disturbance to birds (B), Forest grazing (B), Selective logging/cutting (A), Unsustainable exploitation (A)

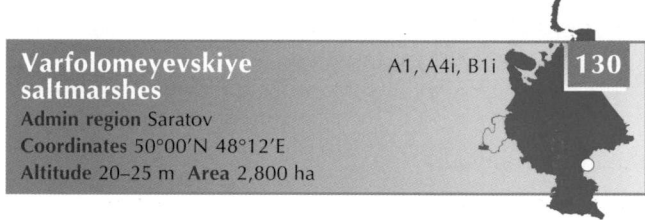

Varfolomeyevskiye saltmarshes A1, A4i, B1i 130
Admin region Saratov
Coordinates 50°00'N 48°12'E
Altitude 20–25 m Area 2,800 ha

■ Site description
Meadows, steppes and dry grasslands with a low level of agricultural activity (grazing).

Habitats Grassland (80%; steppe/dry calcareous grassland; humid grassland)
Land-use Hunting (100%)

■ Birds

Species	Season	Year	Pop min	Pop max	Acc	Criteria
Glareola nordmanni Black-winged Pratincole	B	1997	46	46	A	A1, A4i, B1i

Glareola nordmanni breeds here in important numbers. Some other species of global conservation concern pass through during migration but do not meet IBA criteria: *Anser erythropus* (7–10 birds), *Aythya nyroca* (10–30 birds), *Oxyura leucocephala* (1–2 birds), *Haliaeetus albicilla* (5–7 birds).

■ Protection status
National None **International** None

■ Conservation issues

Threats Agricultural intensification/expansion (A), Disturbance to birds (B), Drainage (C), Unsustainable exploitation (A)

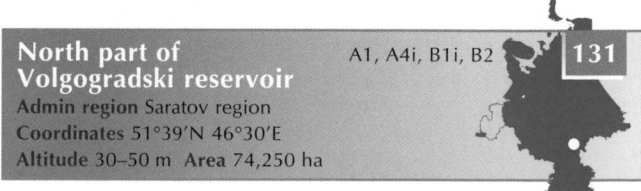

North part of Volgogradski reservoir A1, A4i, B1i, B2 131
Admin region Saratov region
Coordinates 51°39'N 46°30'E
Altitude 30–50 m Area 74,250 ha

■ Site description
The upper part of Volgogradski reservoir, with adjacent lakes and old river-meanders.

Habitats Forest and woodland (15%; alluvial/very wet forest), Grassland (35%; humid grassland), Wetland (50%; mudflat/sandflat; standing fresh water; river/stream)
Land-use Hunting (100%), Nature conservation/research (5%), Not utilized (75%), Tourism/recreation (20%), Water management

■ Birds

Species	Season	Year	Pop min	Pop max	Acc	Criteria
Haliaeetus albicilla White-tailed Eagle	B	1997	13	16	A	A1, B2
Haliaeetus albicilla White-tailed Eagle	P	1997	43	90	A	A1
Accipiter brevipes Levant Sparrowhawk	B	1997	15	—	B	B2
Hieraaetus pennatus Booted Eagle	B	1997	3	5	B	B2
Crex crex Corncrake	B	1997	250	700	B	A1, B2
Gallinago media Great Snipe	P	1997	500	1,000	B	A1, A4i, B1i

An important site for breeding raptors and for species of global conservation concern.

■ Protection status
National Low **International** None
3,600 ha of IBA covered by Zakaznik (Chernye vody, 3,600 ha).

■ Conservation issues

Threats Agricultural intensification/expansion (A), Aquaculture/fisheries (C), Disturbance to birds (A), Filling-in of wetlands (B), Firewood collection (B), Industrialization/urbanization (C), Recreation/tourism (A), Selective logging/cutting (C), Unsustainable exploitation (A)

Vicinity of Voznesenka village   A1   132
Admin region Saratov
Coordinates 51°31′N 47°25′E
Altitude 50–70 m **Area** 1,200 ha

■ Site description
Extensive arable land.

Habitats Artificial landscape (100%; arable land)
Land-use Agriculture (100%)

■ Birds

Species	Season	Year	Pop min	Pop max	Acc	Criteria
[1] *Otis tarda* Great Bustard	B	1997	36	36	A	A1

1. Breeding individuals.

Otis tarda breeds in important numbers.

■ Protection status
National None **International** None

■ Conservation issues

Threats Agricultural intensification/expansion (A), Disturbance to birds (A), Unsustainable exploitation (B)

Sokino   A1   133
Admin region Saratov
Coordinates 51°00′N 45°00′E
Altitude 100–250 m **Area** 30,330 ha

■ Site description
An area of mixed forest surrounded by agricultural land.

Habitats Forest and woodland (31%; broadleaved deciduous forest; mixed forest), Wetland (3%), Artificial landscape (66%; highly improved reseeded grassland; arable land; other urban/industrial areas)
Land-use Agriculture (62%), Forestry (31%)

■ Birds

Species	Season	Year	Pop min	Pop max	Acc	Criteria
Aquila clanga Greater Spotted Eagle	B	1996	3	—	A	A1

The globally threatened *Aquila clanga* breeds in important numbers.

■ Protection status
National None **International** None

■ Conservation issues
Bird data are incomplete as only a few days of surveying have been carried out.

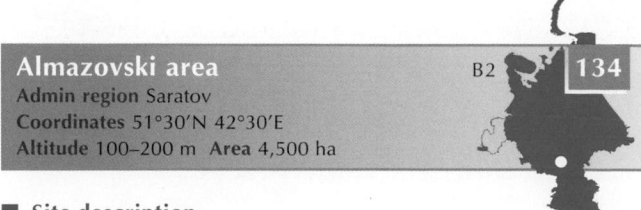

Almazovski area   B2   134
Admin region Saratov
Coordinates 51°30′N 42°30′E
Altitude 100–200 m **Area** 4,500 ha

■ Site description
The IBA is situated in the Khoper river valley, in the forest-steppe zone of the Saratov region.

Habitats Forest and woodland (50%), Grassland (40%; humid grassland), Wetland (2%), Artificial landscape (9%; arable land; other urban/industrial areas)
Land-use Agriculture (45%), Forestry (50%)

■ Birds

Species	Season	Year	Pop min	Pop max	Acc	Criteria
Aquila pomarina Lesser Spotted Eagle	B	1996	4	—	A	B2

One of the few areas in Russia in recent years where *Aquila pomarina* was found to breed.

■ Protection status
National None **International** None

■ Conservation issues
Bird data are incomplete.

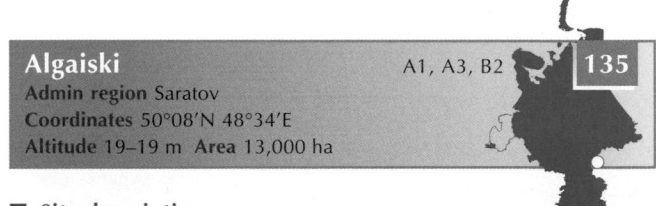

Algaiski   A1, A3, B2   135
Admin region Saratov
Coordinates 50°08′N 48°34′E
Altitude 19–19 m **Area** 13,000 ha

■ Site description
Flood-plain and steppe adjacent to a small river (Bol'shoi Uzen').

Habitats Grassland (54%; humid grassland), Artificial landscape (87%; highly improved reseeded grassland; arable land)
Land-use Agriculture (85%), Other (15%)

■ Birds

Species	Season	Year	Pop min	Pop max	Acc	Criteria
Circus macrourus Pallid Harrier	B	1996	10	15	B	A1, A3, B2
[1] *Tetrax tetrax* Little Bustard	B	1996	100	150	B	A1
Melanocorypha yeltoniensis Black Lark	B	1996	100	200	B	A3, B2

1. Breeding individuals.

Birds breeding in important numbers include two species of global conservation concern and two of the nine species in Europe that are restricted to the Eurasian steppe biome (when breeding).

■ Protection status
National None **International** None

■ Conservation issues
Data on bird species is incomplete and further survey work is required.

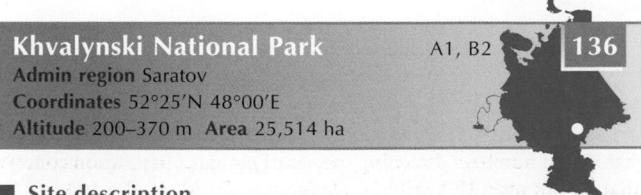

Khvalynski National Park   A1, B2   136
Admin region Saratov
Coordinates 52°25′N 48°00′E
Altitude 200–370 m **Area** 25,514 ha

■ Site description
A large area of forest in the north of the Saratov region.

Habitats Forest and woodland (77%; broadleaved deciduous forest; native coniferous forest), Artificial landscape (22%; arable land)

Land-use Agriculture (21%), Forestry (77%)

■ Birds

Species		Season	Year	Pop min	Pop max	Acc	Criteria
[1] *Haliaeetus albicilla*	White-tailed Eagle	W	1996	15	30	A	A1
Aquila heliaca	Imperial Eagle	B	1996	3	—	—	A1, B2

1. Min. 3 pairs also breed.

The area is important for two raptors of global conservation concern.

■ Protection status
National High **International** None
25,514 ha of IBA covered by National Park (Khvalynskiy, 25,514 ha).

■ Conservation issues

Threats Unknown

No special ornithological research has been carried out at the site, thus data are incomplete.

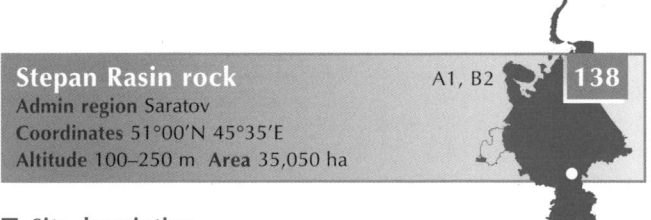

Rovno area
A1 137
Admin region Saratov
Coordinates 51°00′N 47°00′E
Altitude 50–100 m **Area** 8,220 ha

■ Site description
The site includes both grassland and cultivated land.

Habitats Forest and woodland (12%; wooded steppe), Artificial landscape (86%; highly improved reseeded grassland; arable land)
Land-use Agriculture (84%), Forestry (12%)

■ Birds

Species		Season	Year	Pop min	Pop max	Acc	Criteria
[1] *Tetrax tetrax*	Little Bustard	B	1996	25	50	B	A1
[1] *Otis tarda*	Great Bustard	B	1996	10	15	B	A1
Otis tarda	Great Bustard	P	1996	80	150	B	A1

1. Breeding individuals.

An important area for breeding *Tetrax tetrax* and *Otis tarda*, the latter also occurring in good numbers on passage. Breeding species of global conservation concern that do not meet IBA criteria: *Circus macrourus* (1–3 pairs).

■ Protection status
National None **International** None

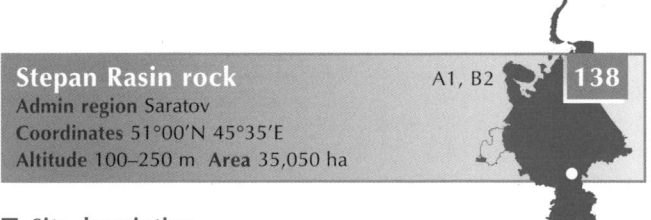

Stepan Rasin rock
A1, B2 138
Admin region Saratov
Coordinates 51°00′N 45°35′E
Altitude 100–250 m **Area** 35,050 ha

■ Site description
The IBA covers the high, forested valley-sides of the River Volga.

Habitats Forest and woodland (22%), Artificial landscape (68%)
Land-use Agriculture (68%), Forestry (22%), Urban/industrial/transport (5%)

■ Birds

Species		Season	Year	Pop min	Pop max	Acc	Criteria
Accipiter brevipes	Levant Sparrowhawk	B	1996	15	30	B	B2
Aquila heliaca	Imperial Eagle	B	1996	1	2	B	A1, B2

There is a high diversity of breeding raptors, including two species in significant numbers. Breeding species of global conservation concern that do not meet IBA criteria: *Haliaeetus albicilla* (1–2 pairs).

■ Protection status
National Partial **International** None
Part of IBA covered by regional Zakaznik (name and area not known).

■ Conservation issues
Bird data are incomplete.

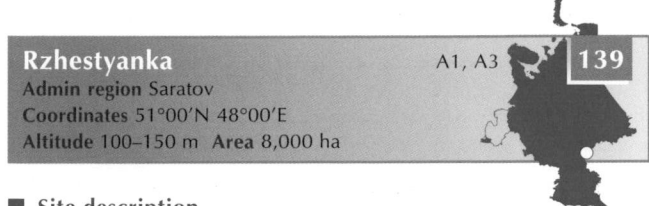

Rzhestyanka
A1, A3 139
Admin region Saratov
Coordinates 51°00′N 48°00′E
Altitude 100–150 m **Area** 8,000 ha

■ Site description
An area of agricultural land on the flood-plain of the Rzhestyanke river.

Habitats Artificial landscape (98%; highly improved reseeded grassland; arable land)
Land-use Agriculture (99%)

■ Birds

Species		Season	Year	Pop min	Pop max	Acc	Criteria
Circus macrourus	Pallid Harrier	B	1996	2	3	B	A3
[1] *Tetrax tetrax*	Little Bustard	B	1996	15	30	B	A1
[1] *Otis tarda*	Great Bustard	B	1996	40	60	B	A1
Melanocorypha yeltoniensis	Black Lark	B	1996	20	30	B	A3

1. Breeding individuals.

An important area for breeding *Tetrax tetrax* and *Otis tarda*, and for two of the nine species in Europe that are restricted to the Eurasian steppe biome (when breeding).

■ Protection status
National None **International** None

■ Conservation issues
Only a short ornithological survey of the area was carried out during a single field season, and further work is therefore needed.

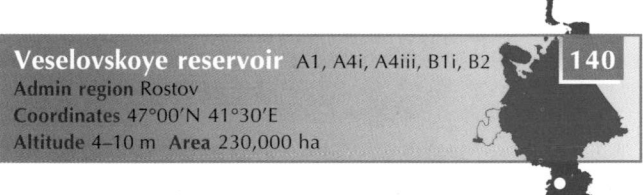

Veselovskoye reservoir
A1, A4i, A4iii, B1i, B2 140
Admin region Rostov
Coordinates 47°00′N 41°30′E
Altitude 4–10 m **Area** 230,000 ha

■ Site description
Salt-lakes partly covered by fringing vegetation.

Habitats Wetland (100%; standing fresh water; standing brackish and salt water; water-fringe vegetation)
Land-use Agriculture, Fisheries/aquaculture, Hunting (100%), Water management

■ Birds

Species		Season	Year	Pop min	Pop max	Acc	Criteria
Nycticorax nycticorax	Night Heron	B	1990	250	300	—	B2
Egretta garzetta	Little Egret	B	1990	500	600	—	A4i, B1i
Egretta alba	Great White Egret	B	1990	400	500	—	A4i, B1i
Plegadis falcinellus	Glossy Ibis	B	1990	300	300	—	A4i, B1i, B2
Platalea leucorodia	Spoonbill	B	1990	200	200	—	A4i, B1i, B2
Cygnus olor	Mute Swan	P	1990	1,500	1,500	—	B1i
Cygnus cygnus	Whooper Swan	P	1990	2,000	3,000	—	A4i, B1i
Anser anser	Greylag Goose	B	1995	800	900	—	B1i
Anser anser	Greylag Goose	W	1990	—	9,000	—	A4i, B1i
Anser anser	Greylag Goose	P	1995	1,000	100,000	—	A4i, B1i
[1] *Anser anser*	Greylag Goose	N	1995	7,000	10,000	—	A4i, B1i
Branta ruficollis	Red-breasted Goose	P	1990	100	25,000	A	A1, A4i, B1i
Branta ruficollis	Red-breasted Goose	W	1990	400	600	—	A1
Anas platyrhynchos	Mallard	W	1990	30,000	30,000	—	B1i
Haliaeetus albicilla	White-tailed Eagle	W	1990	30	40	—	A1

1. Feeding on rice-fields during May–June.

The wetland supports huge numbers of waterfowl at all times of the year. Up to 240,000 stage here during spring migration, with up to 1,500,000–3,000,000 during autumn migration, and up to 50,000 in winter. Up to 30,000 pairs of 50 species of waterbird breed in summer, including important numbers of colonial species.

■ Protection status
National None **International** High

230,000 ha of IBA covered by Ramsar Site (Veselovskoye reservoir, 309,000 ha).

■ **Conservation issues**

Threats Abandonment/reduction of land management (U)

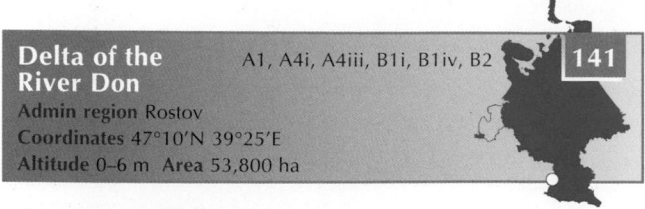

Delta of the River Don A1, A4i, A4iii, B1i, B1iv, B2 **141**
Admin region Rostov
Coordinates 47°10'N 39°25'E
Altitude 0–6 m **Area** 53,800 ha

■ **Site description**
The mouth and lower reaches of the River Don and surrounding wet grasslands, located to the west of the town of Rostov-on-Don and to the north of the town of Azov.

Habitats Grassland (30%; humid grassland), Wetland (40%; mudflat/sandflat; sand-dunes/sand beach; river/stream; water-fringe vegetation), Marine areas (9%; open sea), Artificial landscape (24%; perennial crops/orchards/groves; urban parks/gardens)
Land-use Agriculture (17%), Fisheries/aquaculture (14%), Hunting (20%), Nature conservation/research (49%), Not utilized (37%), Tourism/recreation (5%)

■ **Birds**

Species	Season	Year	Pop min	Pop max	Acc	Criteria
Podiceps cristatus Great Crested Grebe	B	1997	2,000	4,000	B	A4i, B1i
Podiceps grisegena Red-necked Grebe	B	1997	1,000	1,500	B	A4i, B1i
Podiceps nigricollis Black-necked Grebe	B	1997	500	800	B	A4i, B1i
Phalacrocorax carbo Cormorant	B	1997	1,000	1,200	A	B1i
Egretta garzetta Little Egret	N	1997	6,000	8,000	B	A4i, B1i
Egretta alba Great White Egret	N	1997	500	1,000	B	A4i, B1i
Ardea cinerea Grey Heron	P	1997	6,000	8,000	B	A4i, B1i
Cygnus olor Mute Swan	N	1997	4,000	6,000	B	A4i, B1i
Cygnus cygnus Whooper Swan	P	1997	500	1,500	B	A4i, B1i
Anser erythropus Lesser White-fronted Goose	P	1997	30	50	C	A1
Anser anser Greylag Goose	B	1997	80	100	B	B1i
Anser anser Greylag Goose	P	1997	10,000	20,000	B	A4i, B1i
Branta ruficollis Red-breasted Goose	P	1997	—	500	C	A1
Anas platyrhynchos Mallard	P	1997	30,000	40,000	B	B1i
Anas querquedula Garganey	P	1997	20,000	30,000	B	A4i, B1i
Netta rufina Red-crested Pochard	P	1997	6,000	8,000	B	A4i, B1i
Aythya ferina Pochard	P	1997	50,000	100,000	B	A4i, B1i
Aythya nyroca Ferruginous Duck	B	1997	25	30	C	A1, B2
Aythya nyroca Ferruginous Duck	P	1997	100	150	C	A1
[1] *Haliaeetus albicilla* White-tailed Eagle	R	1997	10	12	A	A1, B2
Falco naumanni Lesser Kestrel	P	1997	150	200	B	A1
Crex crex Corncrake	B	1997	700	800	B	A1, B2
Himantopus himantopus Black-winged Stilt	B	1997	100	120	B	B1i
Himantopus himantopus Black-winged Stilt	P	1997	1,500	3,000	B	A4i, B1i
Glareola pratincola Collared Pratincole	P	1997	80	100	B	B1i
Glareola nordmanni Black-winged Pratincole	P	1997	200	500	B	A1, A4i, B1i
Gallinago media Great Snipe	P	1997	1,000	2,000	C	A1, A4i, B1i
Larus ichthyaetus Great Black-headed Gull	P	1997	5,000	10,000	C	A4i, B1i
Larus minutus Little Gull	P	1997	1,200	1,600	C	A4i, B1i
Larus ridibundus Black-headed Gull	P	1997	250,000	500,000	C	A4i, B1i
Larus genei Slender-billed Gull	P	1997	3,500	4,000	C	A4i, B1i
Larus cachinnans Yellow-legged Gull	P	1997	150,000	250,000	C	A4i, B1i
Gelochelidon nilotica Gull-billed Tern	N	1997	100	200	C	B1i
Sterna caspia Caspian Tern	N	1997	50	100	C	B1i
Sterna hirundo Common Tern	P	1997	100,000	250,000	C	A4i, B1i
Sterna albifrons Little Tern	P	1997	10,000	20,000	C	A4i, B1i
Chlidonias hybridus Whiskered Tern	B	1997	100	120	C	B2
Chlidonias hybridus Whiskered Tern	P	1997	80,000	100,000	C	A4i, B1i
Chlidonias niger Black Tern	P	1997	60,000	90,000	C	A4i, B1i
Chlidonias leucopterus White-winged Black Tern	P	1997	100,000	150,000	C	A4i, B1i

1. Large increase.

Breeding species include three species of global conservation concern, including two globally threatened species in significant numbers, as well as important numbers of three grebes among other waterbirds. Other waterbirds congregate to feed in important numbers in

summer but do not breed. Hundreds of thousands of migrating waterbirds use the area as a staging post, with ducks, gulls and terns comprising most of the total. The site is a notable migratory bottleneck for raptors with more than 3,000 passing regularly in a season, including *Buteo buteo* (2,000–4,000 per season) and *Falco vespertinus* (1,000–1,600).

■ **Protection status**
National Partial **International** None
26,300 ha of IBA covered by Zapovednik (Donskoiy rybniy 'fishery reserve', 68,000 ha). IBA overlaps with Zakaznik (Azovski Uchastok Opytnogo Okhotkhozayistva, 6,000 ha). IBA overlaps with Zakaznik (Girlovskyiy, 5,000 ha).

■ **Conservation issues**

Threats Abandonment/reduction of land management (B), Disturbance to birds (B), Drainage (B), Industrialization/urbanization (B), Infrastructure (B), Recreation/tourism (B), Unsustainable exploitation (A)

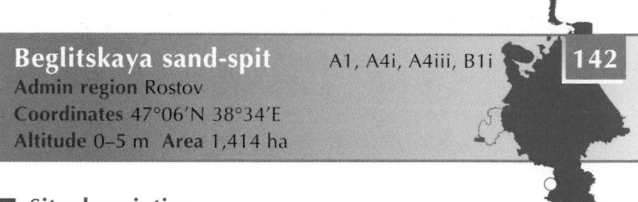

Beglitskaya sand-spit A1, A4i, A4iii, B1i **142**
Admin region Rostov
Coordinates 47°06'N 38°34'E
Altitude 0–5 m **Area** 1,414 ha

■ **Site description**
A narrow sand-spit on the north coast of the Sea of Azov, to the south-west of Taganrog.

Habitats Grassland (14%; humid grassland), Wetland (15%; mudflat/sandflat; sand-dunes/sand beach), Marine areas (71%; open sea; sea inlet/coastal features)
Land-use Nature conservation/research (72%), Not utilized (99%)

■ **Birds**

Species	Season	Year	Pop min	Pop max	Acc	Criteria
Falco naumanni Lesser Kestrel	P	1997	40	60	B	A1
Glareola nordmanni Black-winged Pratincole	P	1997	50	80	B	A1
Larus ichthyaetus Great Black-headed Gull	P	1997	5,000	7,000	B	A4i, B1i
Larus minutus Little Gull	P	1997	1,200	1,600	B	A4i, B1i
Larus ridibundus Black-headed Gull	P	1997	40,000	60,000	B	A4i, B1i
Larus genei Slender-billed Gull	P	1997	800	1,200	B	A4i, B1i
Larus cachinnans Yellow-legged Gull	P	1997	20,000	40,000	B	A4i, B1i
Sterna hirundo Common Tern	P	1997	15,000	20,000	C	A4i, B1i
Sterna albifrons Little Tern	P	1997	600	1,200	C	A4i, B1i

During migration, two species of global conservation concern pass through in significant numbers, and more than 80,000 gulls and terns stage in the area.

■ **Protection status**
National Partial **International** None
1,014 ha of IBA covered by Natural Monument (Beglitskaya Kosa, 1,014 ha).

■ **Conservation issues**

Threats Disturbance to birds (B), Extraction industry (C), Unsustainable exploitation (B)

Islands in the western part of Lake Manych-Gudilo A1, A4i, A4iii, B1i, B2, B3 **143**
Admin region Rostov
Coordinates 46°30'N 42°33'E
Altitude 13–49 m **Area** 19,200 ha

■ **Site description**
A complex of salt-lakes, river meanders and patches of primary steppe.

Habitats Grassland (44%; steppe/dry calcareous grassland; humid grassland), Wetland (54%; mudflat/sandflat; coastal lagoon; standing fresh water; standing brackish and salt water; water-fringe vegetation)

Land-use Agriculture (32%), Hunting (5%), Nature conservation/research (24%), Not utilized (64%)

■ Birds

Species	Season	Year	Pop min	Pop max	Acc	Criteria
Pelecanus onocrotalus White Pelican	B	1997	50	60	B	B2
Pelecanus crispus Dalmatian Pelican	B	1997	30	50	B	A1, A4i, B1i, B2
Egretta garzetta Little Egret	B	1997	80	90	A	B1i
Platalea leucorodia Spoonbill	B	1997	120	120	A	A4i, B1i, B2
Anser anser Greylag Goose	P	1997	6,000	10,000	C	A4i, B1i
Branta ruficollis Red-breasted Goose	P	1997	1,000	4,000	C	A1, A4i, B1i
Himantopus himantopus Black-winged Stilt	B	1997	100	140	B	B1i
Glareola nordmanni Black-winged Pratincole	N	1997	50	100	B	A1, A4i, B1i
Tringa totanus Redshank	B	1997	60	100	B	B2
Larus melanocephalus Mediterranean Gull	B	1997	300	500	B	B3
Larus genei Slender-billed Gull	B	1997	400	500	C	A4i, B1i
Gelochelidon nilotica Gull-billed Tern	B	1997	70	100	C	A4i, B1i, B2
Sterna albifrons Little Tern	B	1997	60	90	C	B2

A wide variety of waterbirds breed in important numbers, most notably *Pelecanus crispus*. Other species of global conservation concern which also occur in very significant numbers are *Branta ruficollis*, which stages in the area with other goose species during migration, and *Glareola nordmanni*, which feeds in the area during the breeding season.

■ Protection status
National Partial **International** High
4,591 ha of IBA covered by Zapovednik (Rostovskiy, 9,465 ha). 19,200 ha of IBA covered by Ramsar Site (Lake Manych-Gudilo, 112,600 ha).

■ Conservation issues

Threats Disturbance to birds (C), Unsustainable exploitation (B)

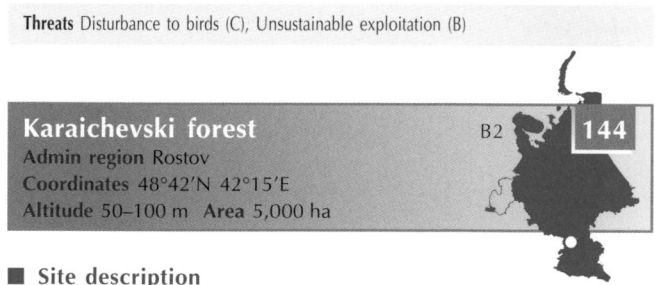

Karaichevski forest
B2 144
Admin region Rostov
Coordinates 48°42'N 42°15'E
Altitude 50–100 m **Area** 5,000 ha

■ Site description
Mainly pine *Pinus* forest, in the north-eastern part of the Rostov region.

Habitats Forest and woodland (70%; broadleaved deciduous forest; native coniferous forest; alluvial/very wet forest), Grassland (10%; steppe/dry calcareous grassland), Artificial landscape (18%; arable land; other urban/industrial areas)
Land-use Agriculture (25%), Forestry (70%), Urban/industrial/transport (3%)

■ Birds

Species	Season	Year	Pop min	Pop max	Acc	Criteria
Hieraaetus pennatus Booted Eagle	B	1997	5	10	A	B2

Significant numbers of *Hieraaetus pennatus* breed. Breeding species of global conservation concern that do not meet IBA criteria: *Tetrax tetrax* (1–10 pairs).

■ Protection status
National High **International** None
5,000 ha of IBA covered by Zakaznik (Ozero El'ton, 18,700 ha).

■ Conservation issues

Threats Consequences of animal/plant introductions (B), Selective logging/cutting (B)

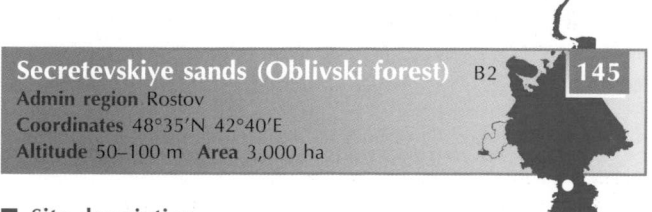

Secretevskiye sands (Oblivski forest)
B2 145
Admin region Rostov
Coordinates 48°35'N 42°40'E
Altitude 50–100 m **Area** 3,000 ha

■ Site description
An area of steppe interspersed with patches of forest.

Habitats Forest and woodland (50%; broadleaved deciduous forest; native coniferous forest; alluvial/very wet forest), Grassland (30%; steppe/dry calcareous grassland), Artificial landscape (10%; arable land)
Land-use Agriculture (40%), Forestry (60%), Hunting (100%)

■ Birds

Species	Season	Year	Pop min	Pop max	Acc	Criteria
[1] *Accipiter brevipes* Levant Sparrowhawk	B	1996	1	5	C	B2
[2] *Hieraaetus pennatus* Booted Eagle	B	1996	1	— —		B2

1. Below threshold but few sites identified nationally.
2. Near threshold.

The site supports a high density and species-richness of breeding raptors for its rather small area. Breeding species of global conservation concern that do not meet IBA criteria: *Aquila heliaca* (1 pair).

■ Protection status
National None **International** None

■ Conservation issues

Threats Disturbance to birds (C)

A short ornithological survey was carried out in 1996 over several days.

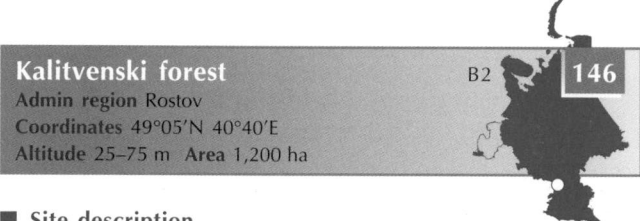

Kalitvenski forest
B2 146
Admin region Rostov
Coordinates 49°05'N 40°40'E
Altitude 25–75 m **Area** 1,200 ha

■ Site description
Forest surrounded by steppic habitats.

Habitats Forest and woodland (80%; broadleaved deciduous forest; native coniferous forest), Grassland (15%; steppe/dry calcareous grassland; humid grassland), Wetland (5%; standing fresh water)
Land-use Forestry (100%), Hunting (100%), Tourism/recreation (100%)

■ Birds

Species	Season	Year	Pop min	Pop max	Acc	Criteria
Hieraaetus pennatus Booted Eagle	B	1996	2	3	B	B2

An important site for breeding *Hieraaetus pennatus*. Breeding species of global conservation concern that do not meet IBA criteria: *Aquila heliaca*.

■ Protection status
National None **International** None

■ Conservation issues

Threats Recreation/tourism (B)

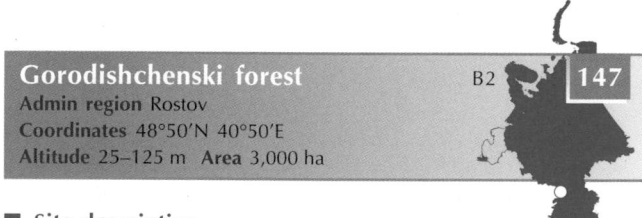

Gorodishchenski forest
B2 147
Admin region Rostov
Coordinates 48°50'N 40°50'E
Altitude 25–125 m **Area** 3,000 ha

■ Site description
An expanse of forest surrounded by steppe.

Habitats Forest and woodland (75%; native coniferous forest; mixed forest; alluvial/very wet forest), Scrub (5%; scrub), Grassland (20%; steppe/dry calcareous grassland)
Land-use Agriculture (20%), Forestry (80%), Hunting (100%)

■ Birds

Species	Season	Year	Pop min	Pop max	Acc	Criteria
Hieraaetus pennatus Booted Eagle	B	1996	2	3	A	B2

Important for breeding *Hieraaetus pennatus*. Breeding species of global conservation concern that do not meet IBA criteria: *Aquila heliaca*.

■ **Protection status**
National None **International** None

■ **Conservation issues**

Threats Recreation/tourism (C)

A short ornithological survey was carried out during the 1996 field season, although bird data remain incomplete.

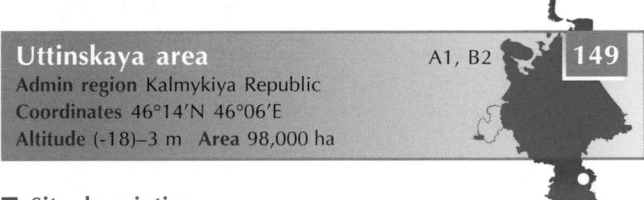

Chistaya Banka and Ivan-Karaul islands — A4i, A4iii, B1i — **148**
Admin region Kalmykiya Republic
Coordinates 45°10'N 48°00'E
Altitude — **Area** —

■ **Site description**
Bare islands, and shallows, in the northern Caspian Sea.

Habitats Marine areas (sea inlet/coastal features)

■ **Birds**

Species	Season	Year	Pop min	Pop max	Acc	Criteria
Larus ichthyaetus Great Black-headed Gull	B	1989	8,500	8,500	—	A4i, B1i

Based on data in the previous European IBA inventory (Grimmett and Jones 1989), the site is important for breeding Laridae, and for staging waterbirds (up to 750,000) including swans *Cygnus* (up to 14,000). The area is also important for wintering waterbirds, when conditions are favourable. No updated information.

■ **Protection status**
National None **International** None

■ **Conservation issues**
No recent information.

Uttinskaya area — A1, B2 — **149**
Admin region Kalmykiya Republic
Coordinates 46°14'N 46°06'E
Altitude (-18)–3 m **Area** 98,000 ha

■ **Site description**
The area is located inland in a semi-desert region of Kalmykiya Republic, and includes a few lakes and seasonally wet depressions.

Habitats Desert (100%; semi-desert)
Land-use Agriculture (100%)

■ **Birds**

Species	Season	Year	Pop min	Pop max	Acc	Criteria
Haliaeetus albicilla White-tailed Eagle	W	1996	9	250	A	A1
Aegypius monachus Cinereous Vulture	U	1996	—	16	—	A1
¹ *Buteo rufinus* Long-legged Buzzard	B	1996	12	45	B	B2
² *Tetrax tetrax* Little Bustard	P	1992	5,000	12,000	B	A1

1. Variation in numbers during 1970–1996.
2. Breeding individuals.

The site is important for its high numbers of wintering and breeding raptors, as well as being a key staging area for very large numbers of *Tetrax tetrax* on both spring and autumn passage. *Tetrax tetrax* also breeds (no data, further research required), as does *Anthropoides virgo* (255–270 pairs).

■ **Protection status**
National Partial **International** Partial
11,000 ha of IBA covered by Zapovednik (Chernyje Zemli, 125,000 ha). 11,000 ha of IBA covered by Biosphere Reserve (Chernyje Zemli, 125,000 ha).

■ **Conservation issues**

Threats Abandonment/reduction of land management (C), Unsustainable exploitation (C)

Salt-lakes in the Primorsko-Akhtarsk area — A1, A4i, B1i, B2, B3 — **150**
Admin region Krasnodarski kray
Coordinates 46°00'N 38°10'E
Altitude 0–100 m **Area** 40,000 ha

■ **Site description**
Shallow salt-lakes near the coast of the Sea of Azov, connected by a network of channels, with extensive beds of both emergent and submerged vegetation.

Habitats Grassland (40%; steppe/dry calcareous grassland), Wetland (50%; coastal lagoon; standing fresh water; standing brackish and salt water), Artificial landscape (10%)
Land-use Agriculture (40%), Fisheries/aquaculture (20%), Hunting (20%), Not utilized (10%), Tourism/recreation (5%)

■ **Birds**

Species	Season	Year	Pop min	Pop max	Acc	Criteria
Pelecanus crispus Dalmatian Pelican	B	1987	24	24	C	A1, A4i, B1i, B2
Egretta alba Great White Egret	B	1987	75	75	C	A4i, B1i
Platalea leucorodia Spoonbill	B	1987	75	75	C	A4i, B1i, B2
Himantopus himantopus Black-winged Stilt	B	1989	430	430	C	A4i, B1i
Recurvirostra avosetta Avocet	B	1989	550	550	C	A4i, B1i, B3
Glareola pratincola Collared Pratincole	B	1989	10	50	C	B1i, B2
Glareola nordmanni Black-winged Pratincole	B	1989	10	20	C	A1
Charadrius alexandrinus Kentish Plover	B	1994	30	30	C	B2
Tringa totanus Redshank	B	1989	3,000	3,000	C	A4i, B1i, B2
Sterna albifrons Little Tern	B	1994	200	300	C	A4i, B1i, B2

Important numbers of a wide variety of waterbirds breed, including two species of global conservation concern.

■ **Protection status**
National None **International** None

■ **Conservation issues**

Threats Agricultural intensification/expansion (U), Construction/impact of dyke/dam/barrage (U), Unsustainable exploitation (U)

The size of the overlap between the IBA and the Ramsar Site is not known.

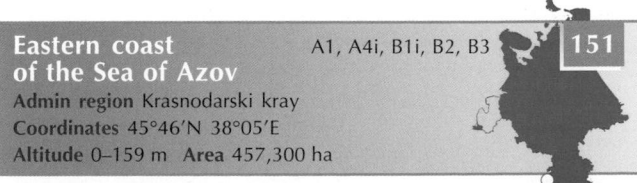

Eastern coast of the Sea of Azov — A1, A4i, B1i, B2, B3 — **151**
Admin region Krasnodarski kray
Coordinates 45°46'N 38°05'E
Altitude 0–159 m **Area** 457,300 ha

■ **Site description**
The IBA comprises the lower reaches and delta of the Kuban river, as well as adjacent coastal shallows of the Sea of Azov, including both open and closed bays and lagoons (salt-lakes).

Habitats Wetland (coastal lagoon; standing fresh water; standing brackish and salt water), Marine areas), Artificial landscape (arable land)
Land-use Agriculture, Forestry, Hunting, Tourism/recreation

■ **Birds**

Species	Season	Year	Pop min	Pop max	Acc	Criteria
Pelecanus crispus Dalmatian Pelican	B	1995	50	74	—	A1, A4i, B1i, B2
Plegadis falcinellus Glossy Ibis	B	1995	1,300	1,300	—	A4i, B1i, B2
Platalea leucorodia Spoonbill	B	1995	235	235	—	A4i, B1i, B2
Cygnus cygnus Whooper Swan	P	1995	1,000	3,000	—	A4i, B1i

Species ... continued	Season	Year	Pop min	Pop max	Acc	Criteria
Oxyura leucocephala White-headed Duck	B	—	1	—	—	B2
Himantopus himantopus Black-winged Stilt	B	1995	880	880	—	A4i, B1i
Recurvirostra avosetta Avocet	B	1995	670	670	—	A4i, B1i, B3
Larus ichthyaetus Great Black-headed Gull	B	1995	1,100	1,100	—	A4i, B1i

A good variety of waterbirds breed in important numbers, most notably the globally threatened *Pelecanus crispus*. Between 300,000 and 800,000 waterbirds winter in the area, while the total number of waterbirds which stage here during autumn migration is even larger, fluctuating between 2 million and 3 million. Breeding species of global conservation concern that do not meet IBA criteria: *Aythya nyroca* (no counts have been carried out).

■ Protection status
National Partial **International** Partial
45,000 ha of IBA covered by Zakaznik (Priazovskiy, 45,000 ha). 30,000 ha of IBA covered by Zakaznik (Tamano-Zaporozhskiy, 30,000 ha). 84,600 ha of IBA covered by Ramsar Site (Kuban Delta: Akhtaro-Grivenskaya Group of Limans, 84,600 ha). 88,400 ha of IBA covered by Ramsar Site (Kuban Delta: Group of Limans between Rivers Kuban and Protoka, 88,400 ha).

■ Conservation issues

Threats Natural events (U)

More regular monitoring is needed as the site is very important and lies in a highly developed area.

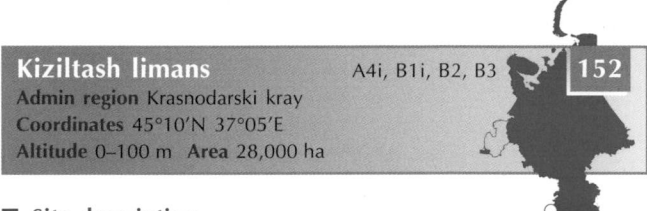

Kiziltash limans
A4i, B1i, B2, B3 152
Admin region Krasnodarski kray
Coordinates 45°10′N 37°05′E
Altitude 0–100 m **Area** 28,000 ha

■ Site description
A closed bay with shallow water, islands and coastal inlets.

Habitats Scrub (5%; scrub), Grassland (5%; steppe/dry calcareous grassland), Wetland (70%; mudflat/sandflat; sand-dunes/sand beach; shingle/stony beach; coastal lagoon), Artificial landscape (20%; arable land; perennial crops/orchards/groves; urban parks/gardens)
Land-use Fisheries/aquaculture (100%), Tourism/recreation (10%)

■ Birds

Species	Season	Year	Pop min	Pop max	Acc	Criteria
Phalacrocorax carbo Cormorant	R	1994	970	1,200	B	B1i
Anser anser Greylag Goose	P	1992	5,000	5,000	—	A4i, B1i
Himantopus himantopus Black-winged Stilt	B	1993	80	100	B	B1i
Recurvirostra avosetta Avocet	B	1993	400	400	A	A4i, B1i, B3
Larus ichthyaetus Great Black-headed Gull	B	1994	700	700	—	A4i, B1i
Larus melanocephalus Mediterranean Gull	B	1994	40	—	C	B3
Larus cachinnans Yellow-legged Gull	B	1994	6,000	7,000	B	A4i, B1i
Gelochelidon nilotica Gull-billed Tern	B	1994	50	—	A	B1i, B2
Sterna caspia Caspian Tern	B	1989	70	300	A	A4i, B1i, B2
Sterna sandvicensis Sandwich Tern	R	1990	200	1,200	A	A4i, B1i, B2
Sterna hirundo Common Tern	B	1994	2,400	2,400	B	B1i
Sterna albifrons Little Tern	B	1994	200	250	A	B1i, B2

A wide variety of gulls and terns breed in important numbers, as do three other waterbird species.

■ Protection status
National None **International** None

■ Conservation issues

Threats Disturbance to birds (C), Filling-in of wetlands (U), Infrastructure (B), Recreation/tourism (C), Unsustainable exploitation (U)

There is an ongoing initiative to establish a nature reserve (Zakaznik).

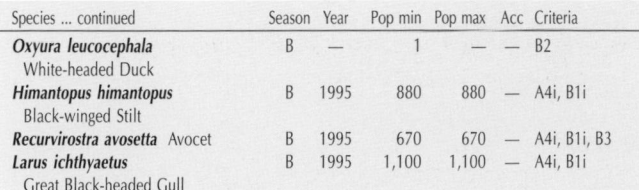

Lower Urushtek river
B2, B3 153
Admin region Krasnodarski kray
Coordinates 43°57′N 40°40′E
Altitude 800–1,900 m **Area** 1,764 ha

■ Site description
This site is located in the mountainous part of the Krasnodarski region.

Habitats Forest and woodland (20%; broadleaved deciduous forest; native coniferous forest), Scrub (10%; scrub), Grassland (35%; alpine/subalpine/boreal grassland), Rocky areas (35%; scree/boulders)
Land-use Agriculture (100%), Nature conservation/research (100%)

■ Birds

Species	Season	Year	Pop min	Pop max	Acc	Criteria
Gypaetus barbatus Lammergeier	R	1996	1	1	—	B2
Gyps fulvus Griffon Vulture	R	1996	21	24	A	B2
Strix aluco Tawny Owl	R	1996	100	100	A	B3
Dendrocopos medius Middle Spotted Woodpecker	R	1996	20	20	B	B3

Two vultures and two forest species breed in significant numbers. Species of global conservation concern that do not meet IBA criteria: *Aegypius monachus* (on passage), *Tetrao mlokosiewiczi* (up to 10 breeding pairs).

■ Protection status
National High **International** None
1,764 ha of IBA covered by Zakaznik (Pseboiskiy, 33,410 ha).

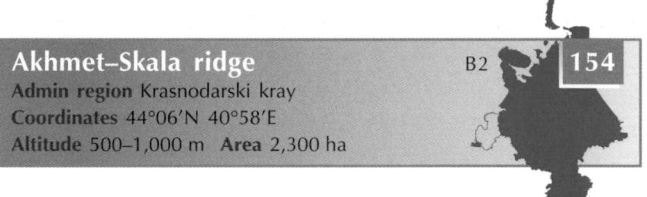

Akhmet–Skala ridge
B2 154
Admin region Krasnodarski kray
Coordinates 44°06′N 40°58′E
Altitude 500–1,000 m **Area** 2,300 ha

■ Site description
A narrow gorge with pastures in the mountainous part of the Krasnodarski region.

Habitats Forest and woodland (50%; broadleaved deciduous forest; wooded steppe), Scrub (8%; scrub), Grassland (30%; steppe/dry calcareous grassland), Rocky areas (10%; scree/boulders)
Land-use Agriculture (20%), Forestry (80%)

■ Birds

Species	Season	Year	Pop min	Pop max	Acc	Criteria
Neophron percnopterus Egyptian Vulture	B	1996	3	—	A	B2
Gyps fulvus Griffon Vulture	R	1996	20	40	A	B2

The area holds one of the largest breeding colonies of *Gyps fulvus* in the Caucasus mountains, as well as significant breeding numbers of another vulture, *Neophron percnopterus*. Species of global conservation concern that do not meet IBA criteria: *Aegypius monachus* (1–2 non-breeding birds).

■ Protection status
National None **International** None

■ Conservation issues

Threats Agricultural intensification/expansion (C), Deforestation (commercial) (C), Unsustainable exploitation (C)

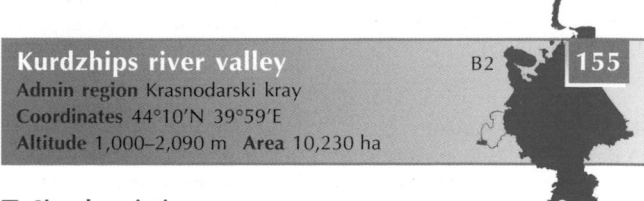

Kurdzhips river valley
B2 155
Admin region Krasnodarski kray
Coordinates 44°10′N 39°59′E
Altitude 1,000–2,090 m **Area** 10,230 ha

■ Site description
The area is located in the mountains of the Krasnodarski region.

Habitats Forest and woodland (83%; mixed forest; wooded steppe), Scrub (10%; scrub; sclerophyllous scrub/garrigue/maquis), Rocky areas (5%; scree/boulders)
Land-use Agriculture (10%), Forestry (70%), Hunting (80%), Nature conservation/research (1%), Urban/industrial/transport (5%)

■ Birds

Species	Season	Year	Pop min	Pop max	Acc	Criteria
Neophron percnopterus Egyptian Vulture	B	1996	1	2	A	B2
Gyps fulvus Griffon Vulture	R	1996	6	14	A	B2

Significant numbers of two vultures breed in the area. Species of global conservation concern that do not meet IBA criteria: *Haliaeetus albicilla* (wintering), *Falco naumanni* (passage).

■ Protection status
National High **International** High
25 ha of IBA covered by Zakaznik (Kamyshovaya Polyana, 25 ha).

■ Conservation issues

Threats Deforestation (commercial) (C), Disturbance to birds (C), Forest grazing (C), Intensified forest management (C), Recreation/tourism (C), Selective logging/cutting (C), Unsustainable exploitation (C)

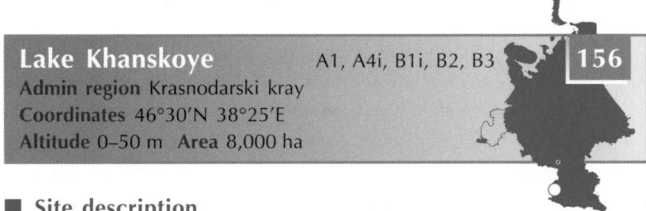

Lake Khanskoye
A1, A4i, B1i, B2, B3 — 156
Admin region Krasnodarski kray
Coordinates 46°30′N 38°25′E
Altitude 0–50 m **Area** 8,000 ha

■ Site description
A large, shallow lake with many islands, near the Black Sea coast and fringed with vegetation.

Habitats Wetland (100%; mudflat/sandflat; saltmarsh; shingle/stony beach; standing fresh water; standing brackish and salt water; water-fringe vegetation)
Land-use Forestry (10%), Military (10%), Not utilized (80%)

■ Birds

Species	Season	Year	Pop min	Pop max	Acc	Criteria
Phalacrocorax carbo Cormorant	B	1994	900	—	B	B1i
Pelecanus crispus Dalmatian Pelican	B	1994	56	—	B	A1, A4i, B1i, B2
Recurvirostra avosetta Avocet	B	1994	50	—	B	B3
Larus cachinnans Yellow-legged Gull	B	1994	2,500	—	C	A4i, B1i
Gelochelidon nilotica Gull-billed Tern	B	1994	20	25	B	B2
Sterna caspia Caspian Tern	B	1994	250	—	B	A4i, B1i, B2
Sterna sandvicensis Sandwich Tern	B	1994	410	—	B	B2
Sterna hirundo Common Tern	B	1994	2,500	—	B	B1i
Sterna albifrons Little Tern	B	1994	84	—	C	B2

Large and important numbers of waterbirds breed at the site, mainly gulls and terns, but including the globally threatened *Pelecanus crispus*.

■ Protection status
National None **International** None

■ Conservation issues

Threats Dredging/canalization (U), Unsustainable exploitation (U)

Yeyski salt-lakes
A4i, B1i, B2, B3 — 157
Admin region Krasnodarski kray
Coordinates 46°45′N 38°20′E
Altitude 0–100 m **Area** 24,000 ha

■ Site description
A system of salt-lakes with water-fringe vegetation, open to the Sea of Azov, in the western part of the Krasnodarski region, comprising one part of a much larger system of fresh- and saltwater bodies in this region.

Habitats Wetland (100%; saltmarsh; shingle/stony beach), Marine areas (sea inlet/coastal features)
Land-use Fisheries/aquaculture (5%), Tourism/recreation (20%), Unknown (75%)

■ Birds

Species	Season	Year	Pop min	Pop max	Acc	Criteria
Larus melanocephalus Mediterranean Gull	B	1994	—	1,000	—	B3
Larus cachinnans Yellow-legged Gull	B	1994	4,500	4,500	B	A4i, B1i
Sterna sandvicensis Sandwich Tern	B	1994	500	500	B	B1i, B2
Sterna hirundo Common Tern	B	1994	2,000	2,000	B	B1i
Sterna albifrons Little Tern	B	1994	150	150	B	B2

Important numbers of gulls and terns breed. One thousand pairs of *Larus melanocephalus* were recorded in 1989, but in 1994 none were found—although the situation is unclear, it seems likely that this is due to natural fluctuation rather than to extinction.

■ Protection status
National None **International** None

■ Conservation issues

Threats Agricultural intensification/expansion (U), Disturbance to birds (U), Filling-in of wetlands (U), Recreation/tourism (U)

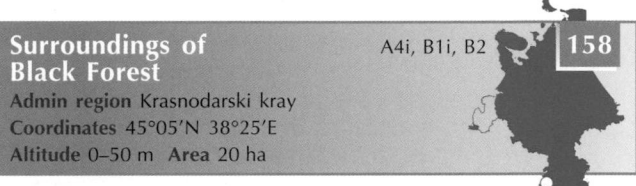

Surroundings of Black Forest
A4i, B1i, B2 — 158
Admin region Krasnodarski kray
Coordinates 45°05′N 38°25′E
Altitude 0–50 m **Area** 20 ha

■ Site description
A number of lakes to the north-east of the village of Ekaterininski.

Habitats Wetland (100%; standing fresh water)
Land-use Unknown (100%)

■ Birds

Species	Season	Year	Pop min	Pop max	Acc	Criteria
Nycticorax nycticorax Night Heron	B	1996	300	300	B	B2
Egretta garzetta Little Egret	B	1996	100	100	B	B1i
Plegadis falcinellus Glossy Ibis	B	1996	500	500	B	A4i, B1i, B2

Significant numbers of colonial waterbirds breed in the vicinity of the lakes.

■ Protection status
National None **International** None

■ Conservation issues

Threats Afforestation (U)

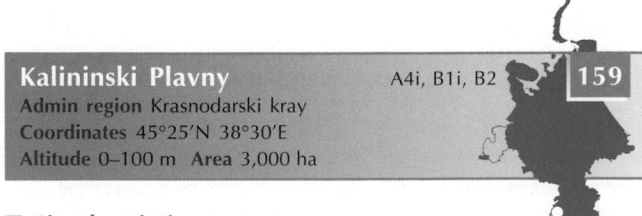

Kalininski Plavny
A4i, B1i, B2 — 159
Admin region Krasnodarski kray
Coordinates 45°25′N 38°30′E
Altitude 0–100 m **Area** 3,000 ha

■ Site description
The flood-plain of the Ponura river, partly covered by water-fringe vegetation.

Habitats Wetland (100%; standing fresh water; water-fringe vegetation)
Land-use Fisheries/aquaculture (5%), Hunting (90%)

■ Birds
Large and important numbers of several colonial waterbirds breed in the area. Available information suggests that breeding colonies move location from year to year.

Species	Season	Year	Pop min	Pop max	Acc	Criteria
Nycticorax nycticorax Night Heron	B	1992	2,500	3,000	B	A4i, B1i, B2
Egretta garzetta Little Egret	B	1992	2,000	2,000	B	A4i, B1i
Plegadis falcinellus Glossy Ibis	B	1992	4,000	4,000	B	A4i, B1i, B2
Chlidonias niger Black Tern	B	1992	250	250	B	B2

■ Protection status
National None **International** None

■ Conservation issues

Threats Disturbance to birds (U), Unsustainable exploitation (U)

Only part of the IBA was surveyed and additional surveys are needed, as bird data are incomplete.

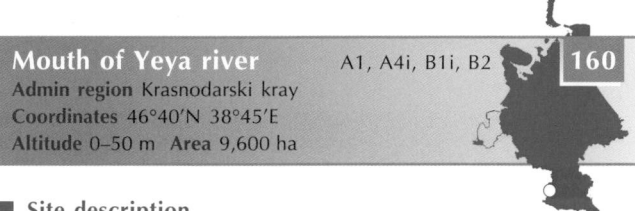

Mouth of Yeya river   A1, A4i, B1i, B2   160
Admin region Krasnodarski kray
Coordinates 46°40'N 38°45'E
Altitude 0–50 m **Area** 9,600 ha

■ Site description
The mouth of the Yeya river, including a number of lakes used in part as fish-ponds.

Habitats Wetland (100%; mudflat/sandflat; standing fresh water; river/stream; fen/transition mire/spring)
Land-use Fisheries/aquaculture (90%), Hunting (10%)

■ Birds

Species	Season	Year	Pop min	Pop max	Acc	Criteria
Plegadis falcinellus Glossy Ibis	B	1996	80	80	C	B2
Netta rufina Red-crested Pochard	B	1996	250	250	C	A4i, B1i, B2
Glareola pratincola Collared Pratincole	B	1996	50	50	C	B1i, B2
Glareola nordmanni Black-winged Pratincole	B	1996	11	11	C	A1
Chlidonias hybridus Whiskered Tern	B	1996	350	350	C	A4i, B1i, B2

Glareola nordmanni, of global conservation concern, breeds in the area, as do important numbers of four other waterbirds, notably *Netta rufina* and *Chlidonias hybridus*.

■ Protection status
National None **International** None

■ Conservation issues

Threats Agricultural intensification/expansion (U), Aquaculture/fisheries (U), Construction/impact of dyke/dam/barrage (U), Disturbance to birds (U)

Imeretinskaya lowland   A1   161
Admin region Krasnodarski kray
Coordinates 43°21'N 40°03'E
Altitude — **Area** 1,500 ha

■ Site description
An agricultural landscape surrounded by many towns and villages.

Habitats Scrub (10%; scrub), Wetland (10%), Artificial landscape (80%; highly improved reseeded grassland; arable land; perennial crops/orchards/groves; urban parks/gardens)
Land-use Agriculture (90%), Urban/industrial/transport (10%)

■ Birds

Species	Season	Year	Pop min	Pop max	Acc	Criteria
Crex crex Corncrake	P	1995	700	800	—	A1

An important staging area for *Crex crex* on migration, with up to 10,000 *Coturnix coturnix* as well.

■ Protection status
National None **International** None

■ Conservation issues

Threats Abandonment/reduction of land management (A), Disturbance to birds (A), Industrialization/urbanization (A), Infrastructure (A)

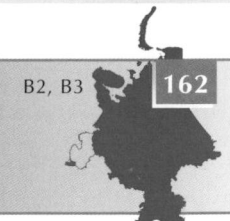

Valley of Urup river   B2, B3   162
Admin region Krasnodarski kray, Karachaevo-Cherkesskaya Republic
Coordinates 44°03'N 41°18'E
Altitude 500–1,000 m **Area** 8,132 ha

■ Site description
A narrow gorge on the border between the Krasnodarski region and the Karachaevo-Cherkesskaya Republic.

Habitats Forest and woodland (50%; broadleaved deciduous forest; wooded steppe), Scrub (5%; scrub), Grassland (15%; steppe/dry calcareous grassland), Wetland (5%; river/stream), Rocky areas (15%; scree/boulders), Artificial landscape (10%; highly improved reseeded grassland; arable land; other urban/industrial areas)
Land-use Agriculture (25%), Fisheries/aquaculture (5%), Nature conservation/research (35%), Not utilized (50%), Urban/industrial/transport (10%)

■ Birds

Species	Season	Year	Pop min	Pop max	Acc	Criteria
Gypaetus barbatus Lammergeier	R	1996	1	—	A	B2
Neophron percnopterus Egyptian Vulture	B	1996	3	—	A	B2
[1] *Gyps fulvus* Griffon Vulture	R	1996	22	55	A	B2
Aquila pomarina Lesser Spotted Eagle	B	1996	1	5	B	B2
Turdus merula Blackbird	B	1996	200	200	B	B3

1. Large decrease.

Four species of raptor, three of them vultures, breed in significant numbers. Species of global conservation concern that do not meet IBA criteria: *Aegypius monachus* (up to 3 non-breeding birds).

■ Protection status
National Partial **International** None
3,360 ha of IBA covered by Zakaznik (Belaya Skala 'Ornithological' Reserve, 3,360 ha).

■ Conservation issues

Threats Agricultural intensification/expansion (B), Deforestation (commercial) (C), Forest grazing (C)

It is necessary to increase the extent of Belaya Skala Zakaznik.

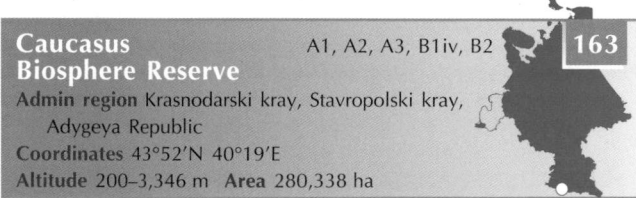

Caucasus Biosphere Reserve   A1, A2, A3, B1iv, B2   163
Admin region Krasnodarski kray, Stavropolski kray, Adygeya Republic
Coordinates 43°52'N 40°19'E
Altitude 200–3,346 m **Area** 280,338 ha

■ Site description
The reserve is located at the western end of the Greater Caucasus mountains.

Habitats Forest and woodland (62%; broadleaved deciduous forest; native coniferous forest), Grassland (21%; alpine/subalpine/boreal grassland), Wetland (1%; river/stream), Rocky areas (16%; scree/boulders)
Land-use Nature conservation/research (100%)

■ Birds

Species	Season	Year	Pop min	Pop max	Acc	Criteria
Haliaeetus albicilla White-tailed Eagle	W	1995	30	40	A	A1
Gypaetus barbatus Lammergeier	R	1995	8	8	A	B2
Gyps fulvus Griffon Vulture	R	1995	55	60	A	B2
Aegypius monachus Cinereous Vulture	R	1995	2	3	A	B2
Aquila chrysaetos Golden Eagle	R	1995	4	4	A	B2
[1] *Tetrao mlokosiewiczi* Caucasian Black Grouse	R	1995	1,500	1,500	A	A1, A2, A3, B2

Species ... continued	Season	Year	Pop min	Pop max	Acc	Criteria
[1] *Tetraogallus caucasicus* Caucasian Snowcock	R	1995	600	600	A	A2, A3
Crex crex Corncrake	B	1995	50	70	A	A1
[1] *Prunella collaris* Alpine Accentor	B	1995	800	800	A	A3
[2] *Sitta krueperi* Krüper's Nuthatch	R	1995	20,000	20,000	A	A3
[1] *Tichodroma muraria* Wallcreeper	R	1995	20	30	A	A3
[1] *Pyrrhocorax graculus* Alpine Chough	R	1995	1,000	1,000	A	A3
[1] *Carpodacus rubicilla* Great Rosefinch	R	1995	20	30	A	A3

1. Eurasian high-montane biome.
2. Mediterranean biome.

Breeding birds include several species of global conservation concern, and seven of the 31 species in Europe that are restricted (when breeding) either to the Eurasian high-montane biome or to the Mediterranean biome, as well as important numbers of several large raptors. The site is also a migratory bottleneck site, where (among other raptors) more than 10,000 *Buteo buteo* regularly pass in a season.

■ Protection status
National High **International** High
263,277 ha of IBA covered by Zapovednik (Kavkazskiy, 263,277 ha). 263,277 ha of IBA covered by Biosphere Reserve (Kavkazskiy, 263,277 ha).

■ Conservation issues

Threats Firewood collection (C), Forest grazing (C), Recreation/tourism (C)

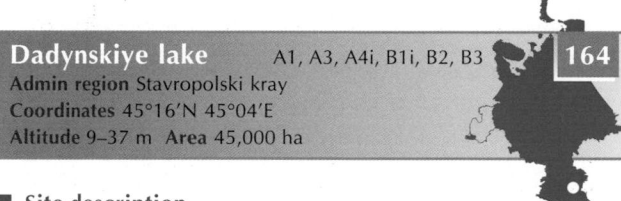

Dadynskiye lake   A1, A3, A4i, B1i, B2, B3   164
Admin region Stavropolski kray
Coordinates 45°16'N 45°04'E
Altitude 9–37 m **Area** 45,000 ha

■ Site description
A system of salt-lakes and adjoining steppe-grassland in the north of Stavropolski region, on the border with Kalmykiya Republic.

Habitats Grassland (48%; steppe/dry calcareous grassland), Wetland (52%; standing brackish and salt water; fen/transition mire/spring)
Land-use Agriculture (87%), Fisheries/aquaculture (11%), Other (2%)

■ Birds

Species	Season	Year	Pop min	Pop max	Acc	Criteria
Phalacrocorax carbo Cormorant	N	1996	5,000	—	B	A4i, B1i
Pelecanus onocrotalus White Pelican	N	1996	10,000	10,000	B	A4i, B1i
Pelecanus crispus Dalmatian Pelican	B	1996	10	12	A	A1, A4i, B1i, B2
Plegadis falcinellus Glossy Ibis	B	1996	80	90	A	B2
Platalea leucorodia Spoonbill	B	1996	45	100	A	A4i, B1i, B2
Cygnus olor Mute Swan	R	1996	50	500	B	B1i
Anser albifrons White-fronted Goose	P	1996	—	10,000	B	B1i
Anser erythropus Lesser White-fronted Goose	P	1996	10	300	B	A1, B1i
Branta ruficollis Red-breasted Goose	P	1996	500	4,000	B	A1, A4i, B1i
[1] *Tadorna ferruginea* Ruddy Shelduck	N	1996	30,000	30,000	—	A4i, B1i
[1,2] *Aythya nyroca* Ferruginous Duck	N	1996	70	—	—	A1
Oxyura leucocephala White-headed Duck	B	1996	3	5	B	A1, B2
Falco naumanni Lesser Kestrel	B	1996	12	20	A	A1, B2
[3] *Tetrax tetrax* Little Bustard	R	1996	50	—	B	A1
[3] *Otis tarda* Great Bustard	R	1996	—	200	B	A1, B2
Himantopus himantopus Black-winged Stilt	B	1996	180	200	A	B1i
Glareola nordmanni Black-winged Pratincole	B	1996	80	300	B	A1, A3, A4i, B1i, B2
Larus ichthyaetus Great Black-headed Gull	B	1996	1,000	1,500	A	A3, A4i, B1i
Larus melanocephalus Mediterranean Gull	B	1996	200	—	B	B3
Larus cachinnans Yellow-legged Gull	B	1996	2,000	—	B	A4i, B1i
Gelochelidon nilotica Gull-billed Tern	B	1996	50	60	A	B1i, B2
Sterna albifrons Little Tern	B	1996	50	60	B	B2

1. Moulting.
2. Also breeds but no counts have been made.
3. Breeding individuals.

A very important site for breeding species of the Eurasian steppe biome and for wetland birds, and for globally threatened species in particular. Among numerous species that breed in significant numbers are six species of global conservation concern. Three globally threatened wildfowl species occur in important numbers outside the breeding season. Significant proportion (≥1%) of national population breeding at site: *Recurvirostra avosetta* (at least 10 pairs).

■ Protection status
National None **International** None

■ Conservation issues

Threats Aquaculture/fisheries (C), Infrastructure (C), Unsustainable exploitation (A)

Research work is planned.

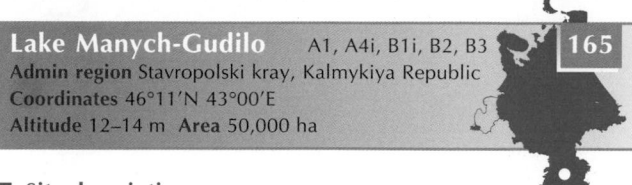

Lake Manych-Gudilo   A1, A4i, B1i, B2, B3   165
Admin region Stavropolski kray, Kalmykiya Republic
Coordinates 46°11'N 43°00'E
Altitude 12–14 m **Area** 50,000 ha

■ Site description
This large lake is situated in a deep depression on the border between the Stavropolski region and Kalmykiya Republic. There are extensive shallows and reedbeds (*Phragmites*).

Habitats Wetland (100%; standing brackish and salt water)
Land-use Hunting (40%), Nature conservation/research (60%)

■ Birds

Species	Season	Year	Pop min	Pop max	Acc	Criteria
Pelecanus onocrotalus White Pelican	B	1995	253	—	B	B2
Pelecanus crispus Dalmatian Pelican	B	1990	38	—	B	A1, A4i, B1i, B2
Platalea leucorodia Spoonbill	B	1995	524	649	A	A4i, B1i, B2
Cygnus olor Mute Swan	N	1995	2,600	—	B	A4i, B1i
Anser albifrons White-fronted Goose	P	1995	240,000	—	A	A4i, B1i
Anser erythropus Lesser White-fronted Goose	P	1995	13,800	—	B	A1, A4i, B1i
Branta ruficollis Red-breasted Goose	P	1995	42,000	80,000	A	A1, A4i, B1i
[1] *Tadorna ferruginea* Ruddy Shelduck	N	1995	30,000	—	A	A4i, B1i, B2
[2] *Tadorna tadorna* Shelduck	N	1989	22,000	22,000	—	A4i, B1i
Recurvirostra avosetta Avocet	B	1980	43	128	A	B3
Glareola pratincola Collared Pratincole	B	1980	4	38	—	B1i, B2
Larus ichthyaetus Great Black-headed Gull	B	1990	150	1,460	A	A4i, B1i
[3] *Larus melanocephalus* Mediterranean Gull	B	1995	1,500	—	A	B3
Larus genei Slender-billed Gull	B	1995	1,000	6,060	A	A4i, B1i
Larus cachinnans Yellow-legged Gull	B	1980	1,580	3,272	A	A4i, B1i
Gelochelidon nilotica Gull-billed Tern	B	1995	200	1,105	A	A4i, B1i, B2
Chlidonias hybridus Whiskered Tern	B	1980	—	425	A	A4i, B1i, B2

1. Between 1,300 and 25,000 pairs during 1973–1976.
2. Moulting.
3. Up to 13,625 pairs during 1970–1980.

All available data relates to the parts of the IBA falling within the Kalmykiya Republic and Stavropolski region. Hundreds of thousands of waterfowl, consisting mainly of geese and ducks, pass through the area at night during migration. In particular, most of the world population of the globally threatened *Branta ruficollis* migrates through the site. The lake also supports large and important numbers of many breeding or moulting waterbirds, notably the globally threatened *Pelecanus crispus*.

■ Protection status
National Partial **International** High
30,600 ha of IBA covered by Zapovednik (Chernye Zemli, 125,000 ha). 30,600 ha of IBA covered by Biosphere Reserve (Chernye Zemli, 125,000 ha). 50,000 ha of IBA covered by Ramsar Site (Lake Manych-Gudilo, 112,600 ha).

■ Conservation issues

Threats Filling-in of wetlands (C)

It is possible that another IBA will be identified in the future, covering the western part of the Manych lake system (Rostov region). Certain bird species are monitored as part of the work being carried out within the Zapovednik.

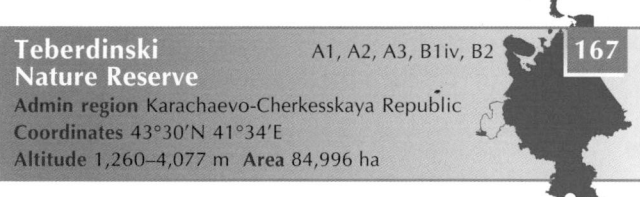

Burukshunskiye limans   A1, A4i, B1i, B2   166

Admin region Stavropolski kray, Kalmykiya Republic
Coordinates 45°59'N 42°25'E
Altitude 57–61 m **Area** 6,000 ha

■ Site description
A network of saline, brackish and freshwater bodies with fringing reedbeds (*Phragmites*), situated on the border between the Stavropolski region and the Kalmykiya Republic.

Habitats Grassland (50%; steppe/dry calcareous grassland), Wetland (50%; standing fresh water; standing brackish and salt water; river/stream)
Land-use Agriculture (50%), Hunting (50%)

■ Birds

Species	Season	Year	Pop min	Pop max	Acc	Criteria
Pelecanus crispus Dalmatian Pelican	N	1989	30	—	B	A1, A4i, B1i
Egretta alba Great White Egret	P	1973	350	400	B	A4i, B1i
Plegadis falcinellus Glossy Ibis	B	1995	150	—	—	A4i, B1i, B2
Platalea leucorodia Spoonbill	B	1988	50	—	A	B1i, B2
Anser anser Greylag Goose	B	1995	2,500	5,000	—	A4i, B1i
Anser anser Greylag Goose	P	1994	5,000	—	A	A4i, B1i
Anas crecca Teal	P	1973	45,000	50,000	B	A4i, B1i
Anas platyrhynchos Mallard	P	1994	10,000	65,000	A	B1i
Aythya ferina Pochard	P	1973	10,000	12,000	B	B1i
Fulica atra Coot	P	1973	35,000	40,000	B	A4i, B1i
Philomachus pugnax Ruff	P	1973	50,000	—	B	A4i, B1i

Large and important numbers of waterbirds stage at the area during migration (mainly waterfowl), and the globally threatened *Pelecanus crispus* is present but does not breed.

■ Protection status
National Partial **International** None
3,500 ha of IBA covered by Zakaznik (Burukshunsky, 3,500 ha).

■ Conservation issues

Threats Abandonment/reduction of land management (C), Agricultural intensification/expansion (C), Disturbance to birds (B)

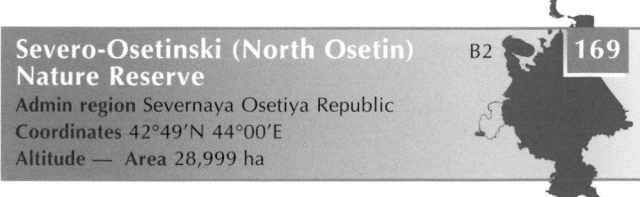

Teberdinski Nature Reserve   A1, A2, A3, B1iv, B2   167

Admin region Karachaevo-Cherkesskaya Republic
Coordinates 43°30'N 41°34'E
Altitude 1,260–4,077 m **Area** 84,996 ha

■ Site description
Large glaciers, alpine meadows and mountain forests, situated in the upper reaches of the Teberda river, on the northern slopes of the Greater Caucasus mountains.

Habitats Forest and woodland (34%), Grassland (65%; alpine/subalpine/boreal grassland)
Land-use Nature conservation/research (100%)

■ Birds
Breeding species include seven of the 31 species in Europe that are restricted (when breeding) either to the Eurasian high montane biome or to the Mediterranean biome. The area is a migratory bottleneck for many raptors, notably the globally threatened *Aquila heliaca*—certainly more than 3,000 raptors pass in total per season, but no special counts have been made.

Species	Season	Year	Pop min	Pop max	Acc	Criteria
Aquila heliaca Imperial Eagle	P	1996	40	60	B	A1
Aquila chrysaetos Golden Eagle	R	1996	5	—	A	B2
Falco peregrinus Peregrine	R	1996	5	7	A	B2
[1] *Tetrao mlokosiewiczi* Caucasian Black Grouse	R	1996	1,000	1,270	A	A1, A2, A3, B2

Species ... continued	Season	Year	Pop min	Pop max	Acc	Criteria
[1] *Tetraogallus caucasicus* Caucasian Snowcock	R	1996	900	1,200	A	A2, A3
[1] *Prunella collaris* Alpine Accentor	B	1996	500	1,000	A	A3
[2] *Sitta krueperi* Krüper's Nuthatch	B	1996	2,500	4,000	B	A3
[1] *Tichodroma muraria* Wallcreeper	B	1996	40	60	C	A3
[1] *Carpodacus rubicilla* Great Rosefinch	B	1996	50	100	C	A3
[2] *Emberiza melanocephala* Black-headed Bunting	U	1996	—	—	—	A3

1. Eurasian high-montane biome.
2. Mediterranean biome.

■ Protection status
National High **International** None
84,996 ha of IBA covered by Zapovednik (Teberdinskiy, 84,996 ha).

Kabardino-Balkarski Nature Reserve   B2   168

Admin region Kabardino-Balkarskaya Republic
Coordinates 43°39'N 42°30'E
Altitude — **Area** 74,099 ha

■ Site description
The upper reaches of the Rivers Cherek Balkarski, Cherek Bizengiyski, and Chegem, with forests and meadows (mainly high mountain zones; several 5,000 m peaks in the Bokovoy range) in a rugged landscape with deep ravines.

Habitats Forest and woodland, Grassland (alpine/subalpine/boreal grassland), Rocky areas (scree/boulders; inland cliff)

■ Birds

Species	Season	Year	Pop min	Pop max	Acc	Criteria
[1] *Tetrao mlokosiewiczi* Caucasian Black Grouse	R	1989	—	—	—	B2

1. No recent counts.

Based on data in the previous European IBA inventory (Grimmett and Jones 1989), the site is important for *Tetrao mlokosiewiczi*. Other breeding species include snowcock *Tetraogallus* and *Alectoris chukar*. No updated information.

■ Protection status
National High **International** None
74,099 ha of IBA covered by Zapovednik (Kabardino-Balkarsky, 74,099 ha).

■ Conservation issues
No recent information.

Severo-Osetinski (North Osetin) Nature Reserve   B2   169

Admin region Severnaya Osetiya Republic
Coordinates 42°49'N 44°00'E
Altitude — **Area** 28,999 ha

■ Site description
A mountainous area including forest, subalpine and alpine zones, glaciers, snow-fields, crags and screes on the northern slopes of the main ridge of the Caucasus range in the Ardon/Fiagdon basin (tributaries of the River Terek).

Habitats Forest and woodland, Grassland (alpine/subalpine/boreal grassland), Rocky areas (scree/boulders; inland cliff)

■ Birds

Species	Season	Year	Pop min	Pop max	Acc	Criteria
[1] *Tetrao mlokosiewiczi* Caucasian Black Grouse	R	1989	—	—	—	B2

1. No recent counts.

Based on data in the previous European IBA inventory (Grimmett and Jones 1989), the site is important for *Tetrao mlokosiewiczi*. A total of 157 species have been recorded, including *Gypaetus barbatus*, snowcock *Tetraogallus* and *Alectoris chukar*. No updated information.

■ **Protection status**
National High **International** None
28,999 ha of IBA covered by Zapovednik (Severo-Osetinsky, 28,999 ha).

■ **Conservation issues**
No recent information.

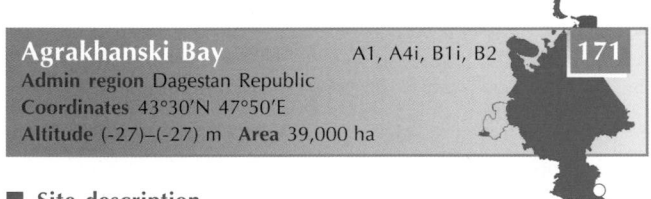

Budary lakes B1i **170**
Admin region Chechenskaya Republic
Coordinates 43°30′N 46°04′E
Altitude — **Area** 1,000 ha

■ **Site description**
Steppe lakes with *Phragmites* and *Typha* beds.

Habitats Wetland (standing fresh water; water-fringe vegetation)

■ **Birds**
A site for breeding grebes and ducks, and staging and wintering grebes, herons, swans and ducks. The B1i criterion is applied at site-level rather than at species-level, as recent count data are not available for any bird species. The site may also prove to fulfil the A4i criterion once systematic counts have been made.

■ **Protection status**
National None **International** None

■ **Conservation issues**
No recent information.

Agrakhanski Bay A1, A4i, B1i, B2 **171**
Admin region Dagestan Republic
Coordinates 43°30′N 47°50′E
Altitude (-27)–(-27) m **Area** 39,000 ha

■ **Site description**
The IBA includes Agrakhanski Bay, as well as coastal lakes on the western shore of the Caspian Sea, north of Makhachkala. A long peninsula, jutting into the Caspian Sea, borders the Bay. A channel was excavated in 1972, which resulted in the flooding and destruction of a main dyke, and a consequent drop in the water-level of Agrakhanski Bay (in previous years the bay was above sea-level). Today all that remains is a small expanse of open water in the southern part of the bay. Sand beaches and meadows provide good feeding habitat for migrating waders.

Habitats Scrub (20%; scrub; sclerophyllous scrub/garrigue/maquis), Wetland (80%; mudflat/sandflat; sand-dunes/sand beach; standing fresh water; standing brackish and salt water; river/stream)
Land-use Fisheries/aquaculture (50%), Hunting (50%), Tourism/recreation (10%), Urban/industrial/transport (5%)

■ **Birds**

Species	Season	Year	Pop min	Pop max	Acc	Criteria
[1] *Phalacrocorax carbo* Cormorant	P	1996	1,000	—	—	B1i
[1] *Phalacrocorax pygmeus* Pygmy Cormorant	B	1996	10	—	B	A1, B2
Pelecanus crispus Dalmatian Pelican	B	1996	119	—	B	A1, A4i, B1i, B2
Plegadis falcinellus Glossy Ibis	B	1988	20	65	—	B2

1. Data incomplete; census planned in 1997.

Breeding species include two species of global conservation concern. About 300,000 duck winter in the IBA and many other migrating waterbird species stage here. It is a particularly important site for waders, with tens of thousands stopping to feed on passage, especially

Calidris alpina, *C. alba* and *Tringa totanus*, but no detailed counts have been made.

■ **Protection status**
National Partial **International** None
Part of IBA covered by Zakaznik (Agrakhansky, 39,000 ha).

■ **Conservation issues**

Threats Aquaculture/fisheries (C), Disturbance to birds (C), Recreation/tourism (C), Unsustainable exploitation (B)

Rising water-levels in the Caspian Sea may improve the site further for waders.

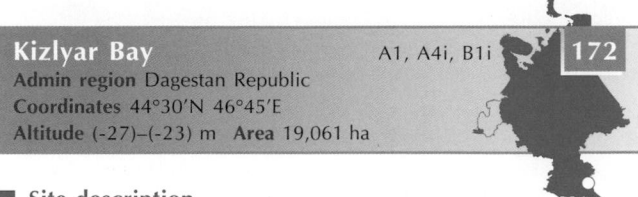

Kizlyar Bay A1, A4i, B1i **172**
Admin region Dagestan Republic
Coordinates 44°30′N 46°45′E
Altitude (-27)–(-23) m **Area** 19,061 ha

■ **Site description**
Extensive reedbeds (*Phragmites*) cover large expanses of shallow coastal waters of the Caspian Sea, at the border between the Dagestan and Kalmykiya Republics.

Habitats Grassland (20%; steppe/dry calcareous grassland; humid grassland), Desert (10%; semi-desert), Wetland (30%; mudflat/sandflat; shingle/stony beach; standing fresh water; standing brackish and salt water; water-fringe vegetation), Marine areas (50%; open sea)
Land-use Agriculture, Fisheries/aquaculture, Hunting

■ **Birds**

Species	Season	Year	Pop min	Pop max	Acc	Criteria
Phalacrocorax carbo Cormorant	P	1996	1,700	—	—	B1i
[1] *Phalacrocorax pygmeus* Pygmy Cormorant	P	1996	195	—	—	A1
[1] *Pelecanus crispus* Dalmatian Pelican	P	1996	45	—	—	A1, A4i, B1i
Egretta alba Great White Egret	P	1996	280	—	—	A4i, B1i
Anas strepera Gadwall	P	1996	1,105	—	—	B1i
Netta rufina Red-crested Pochard	P	1996	300	500	B	B1i

1. Data incomplete; census planned in 1997.

Important numbers of several waterbirds stage in the area during migration (notably the globally threatened *Pelecanus crispus*).

■ **Protection status**
National High **International** None
19,061 ha of IBA covered by Zapovednik (Dagestansky, 19,061 ha).

■ **Conservation issues**

Threats Disturbance to birds (C), Natural events (A), Recreation/tourism (C), Unsustainable exploitation (B)

The main threat is from the rising level of the Caspian Sea.

Mouth of Samur river A1, A4i, B1i, B2, B3 **173**
Admin region Dagestan Republic
Coordinates 41°52′N 48°30′E
Altitude (-27)–60 m **Area** 7,000 ha

■ **Site description**
The mouth of the Samur river, in the south of the Dagestan Republic near to the border with Azerbaijan. The site contains the largest expanse of dry subtropical forest remaining along the Caspian Sea coast. Reedbeds (*Phragmites*) are present in the river mouth and associated channels.

Habitats Forest and woodland (90%; broadleaved deciduous forest), Wetland (5%; mudflat/sandflat; sand-dunes/sand beach; standing fresh water; river/stream), Artificial landscape (5%; arable land; forestry plantation; urban parks/gardens; ruderal land)
Land-use Fisheries/aquaculture (2%), Forestry (95%), Nature conservation/research (100%)

◼ Birds

Species	Season	Year	Pop min	Pop max	Acc	Criteria
Phalacrocorax pygmeus Pygmy Cormorant	P	1997	17	40	A	A1
Pelecanus crispus Dalmatian Pelican	P	1996	100	150	A	A1, A4i, B1i
Egretta alba Great White Egret	P	1997	86	1,000	B	A4i, B1i
Platalea leucorodia Spoonbill	P	1996	12	300	B	A4i, B1i
[1] *Anser erythropus* Lesser White-fronted Goose	P	1996	30	40	B	A1
Aythya nyroca Ferruginous Duck	P	1989	10	100	B	A1
Circus macrourus Pallid Harrier	P	1989	1	50	C	A1
Aquila clanga Greater Spotted Eagle	P	1997	7	14	A	A1
[2] *Tetrax tetrax* Little Bustard	P	1985	1,500	2,000	A	A1
Larus minutus Little Gull	P	1989	10	1,000	C	A4i, B1i, B2
Gelochelidon nilotica Gull-billed Tern	P	1989	10	300	C	A4i, B1i
Chlidonias leucopterus White-winged Black Tern	P	1989	100	3,000	C	A4i, B1i
Dendrocopos medius Middle Spotted Woodpecker	R	1989	70	300	B	B3
Parus caeruleus Blue Tit	R	1989	400	1,000	B	B3

1. Most pass through without stopping.
2. Breeding individuals; do not occur every year.

Seven species of global conservation concern pass through the area on migration, including four globally threatened species, most notably *Pelecanus crispus*. Several other waterbirds also occur in important numbers on passage. Species of global conservation concern that do not meet IBA criteria: *Haliaeetus albicilla* (2–3 pairs are resident).

◼ Protection status

National High **International** None
7,000 ha of IBA covered by Zakaznik (Samursky, 11,200 ha).

◼ Conservation issues

Threats Deforestation (commercial) (B), Disturbance to birds (B), Firewood collection (A), Groundwater abstraction (C), Industrialization/urbanization (C), Infrastructure (C), Intensified forest management (B), Natural events (B), Recreation/tourism (B), Selective logging/cutting (A), Unsustainable exploitation (A)

The site is threatened by the sea-level rise that is occurring naturally in the Caspian Sea.

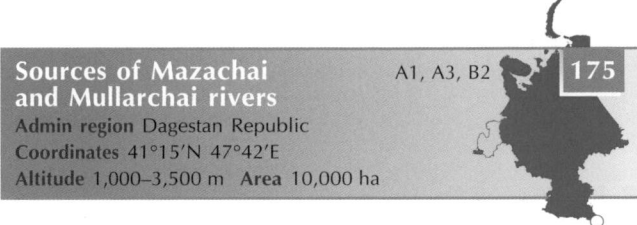

Lake Adzhi   A1, A4i, B1i, B2   174
Admin region Dagestan Republic
Coordinates 42°19'N 48°05'E
Altitude (-27)–(-8) m **Area** 2,000 ha

◼ Site description

A large salt-lake to the north-west of Derbent, not far from the coast of the Caspian Sea.

Habitats Desert (20%; semi-desert), Wetland (80%; sand-dunes/sand beach; standing brackish and salt water)
Land-use Agriculture (20%), Hunting (100%)

◼ Birds

Species	Season	Year	Pop min	Pop max	Acc	Criteria
Phalacrocorax pygmeus Pygmy Cormorant	P	1997	150	200	A	A1, A4i, B1i
Pelecanus crispus Dalmatian Pelican	P	1997	24	40	A	A1, A4i, B1i
Aythya nyroca Ferruginous Duck	B	1997	17	25	A	A1
Fulica atra Coot	P	1997	40,000	50,000	A	A4i, B1i
[1] *Tetrax tetrax* Little Bustard	P	1996	—	5,000	A	A1
Glareola pratincola Collared Pratincole	R	1997	10	15	A	B2

1. Breeding individuals.

Four species of global conservation occur in significant numbers, including two globally threatened species. Large numbers of *Fulica atra* stage in the area during migration.

◼ Protection status

National None **International** None

◼ Conservation issues

Threats Disturbance to birds (A), Extraction industry (C), Natural events (A), Recreation/tourism (C), Unsustainable exploitation (B)

Water-loss in summer due to evaporation poses a threat to nesting birds. A large conservation project was carried out in 1998, involving bird monitoring and educational activities for school children, with a grant from BP Amoco.

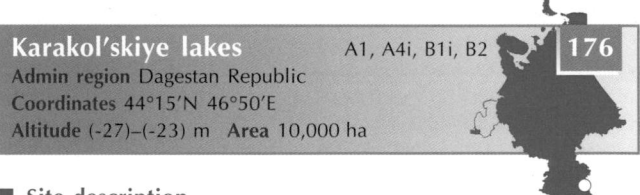

Sources of Mazachai and Mullarchai rivers   A1, A3, B2   175
Admin region Dagestan Republic
Coordinates 41°15'N 47°42'E
Altitude 1,000–3,500 m **Area** 10,000 ha

◼ Site description

A forested area in the Caucasus mountains, near to the border with Azerbaijan, along the middle reaches of the Samur river.

Habitats Forest and woodland (broadleaved deciduous forest), Grassland, Rocky areas
Land-use Agriculture (70%), Not utilized (30%)

◼ Birds

Species	Season	Year	Pop min	Pop max	Acc	Criteria
Gypaetus barbatus Lammergeier	R	1996	2	3	A	B2
[1] *Aegypius monachus* Cinereous Vulture	N	1997	—	20	—	A1
Tetrao mlokosiewiczi Caucasian Black Grouse	R	1997	15	20	A	A1
Tetraogallus caucasicus Caucasian Snowcock	R	1997	40	50	A	A3
[2] *Prunella collaris* Alpine Accentor	R	1996	8	10	B	A3
[2] *Pyrrhocorax graculus* Alpine Chough	R	1996	40	50	B	A3
[2] *Montifringilla nivalis* Snowfinch	R	1996	5	10	B	A3

1. Breeding occurs but number of pairs unknown.
2. Number of pairs may be higher.

Breeding birds that occur in significant numbers include two species of global conservation concern, as well as four of the 10 species in Europe that are restricted (when breeding) to the Eurasian high montane biome.

◼ Protection status

National None **International** None

◼ Conservation issues

Threats Disturbance to birds (B), Firewood collection (A), Forest grazing (A), Unsustainable exploitation (B)

Karakol'skiye lakes   A1, A4i, B1i, B2   176
Admin region Dagestan Republic
Coordinates 44°15'N 46°50'E
Altitude (-27)–(-23) m **Area** 10,000 ha

◼ Site description

A system of several freshwater lakes located near to the Caspian Sea coast, to the south of Kizlyarski Bay.

Habitats Wetland (95%; standing fresh water; water-fringe vegetation)
Land-use Fisheries/aquaculture (10%), Hunting (100%)

◼ Birds

Species	Season	Year	Pop min	Pop max	Acc	Criteria
[1] *Phalacrocorax pygmeus* Pygmy Cormorant	B	1997	20	25	B	A1, B2
Pelecanus crispus Dalmatian Pelican	B	1997	30	—	B	A1, A4i, B1i, B2

1. Up to 500 pairs in 1972.

Breeding species include two species of global conservation concern. A wide variety of other waterbirds breed, including *Platalea leucorodia*, *Plegadis falcinellus*, seven species of heron, *Anthropoides virgo*, and *Himantopus himantopus*, but their numbers have not yet been counted.

◼ Protection status

National None **International** None

■ Conservation issues

Threats Disturbance to birds (B), Unsustainable exploitation (A)

Achikol'skiye lakes   A1, A4i, B1i, B2   177
Admin region Dagestan Republic
Coordinates 43°47'N 47°10'E
Altitude (-20)–(-17) m   **Area** 20,000 ha

■ Site description
A system of freshwater lakes to the west and inland of Agrakhanski Bay of the Caspian Sea.

Habitats Wetland (100%; standing fresh water; water-fringe vegetation)
Land-use Fisheries/aquaculture (100%), Hunting (100%)

■ Birds

Species	Season	Year	Pop min	Pop max	Acc	Criteria
Phalacrocorax pygmeus Pygmy Cormorant	B	1988	—	20	C	A1, B2
Pelecanus crispus Dalmatian Pelican	R	1997	30	40	B	A1, A4i, B1i, B2
Egretta alba Great White Egret	R	1970	50	—	A	A4i, B1i
Anser anser Greylag Goose	R	1982	70	90	A	B1i
Netta rufina Red-crested Pochard	B	1982	1,200	1,300	A	A4i, B1i, B2
Aythya nyroca Ferruginous Duck	B	1982	250	300	A	A1, B2
Haliaeetus albicilla White-tailed Eagle	W	1997	10	15	A	A1
Fulica atra Coot	R	1982	9,000	10,000	A	B1i

A variety of waterbirds breed in important numbers, including three species of global conservation concern, notably *Pelecanus crispus* and *Aythya nyroca*.

■ Protection status
National None   **International** None

■ Conservation issues

Threats Aquaculture/fisheries (C), Disturbance to birds (B), Natural events (A), Unsustainable exploitation (B)

Overgrowth of the lakes by reed *Phragmites* is reducing the area of open water ('Natural events', above).

Morskoy Biryuchek island   A4i, B1i   178
Admin region Dagestan Republic, Kalmykiya Republic
Coordinates 44°44'N 47°03'E
Altitude (-26)–(-25) m   **Area** 30,000 ha

■ Site description
Morskoy Biryuchek island lies close to the western shoreline of the Caspian Sea. It has recently been submerged by the continuing rise in sea-level, and now forms an area of shallower water in the open sea.

Habitats Marine areas (100%; open sea)
Land-use Fisheries/aquaculture (69%), Nature conservation/research (31%)

■ Birds

Species	Season	Year	Pop min	Pop max	Acc	Criteria
[1] *Cygnus olor* Mute Swan	P	1975	3,000	4,000	B	A4i, B1i
Anas acuta Pintail	W	1975	32,600	—	B	A4i, B1i

1. Birds also overwinter.

Large numbers of waterfowl occur in winter and on migration.

■ Protection status
National Partial   **International** None
Part (not more than 5%) of IBA covered by Zapovednik (Dagestanski, 18,900 ha). 30,000 ha of IBA covered by Zakaznik (Ostrov Morskoy Biryuchek, 50,000 ha).

■ Conservation issues

Threats Filling-in of wetlands (C)

Occasional research work is carried out within Dagestanski Zapovednik.

Volga delta   A1, A4i, A4iii, B1i, B2, B3   179
Admin region Astrakhan
Coordinates 46°00'N 48°30'E
Altitude (-28)–(-25) m   **Area** 1,150,000 ha

■ Site description
The largest delta in Europe, on the north coast of the Caspian Sea, in the south of the Astrakhan region, comprising freshwater channels and lakes, extensive coastal shallows, alluvial islands and spits, with much water-fringe vegetation.

Habitats Forest and woodland (5%; alluvial/very wet forest), Grassland (20%; humid grassland), Wetland (75%; tidal river/enclosed tidal water; mudflat/sandflat; sand-dunes/ sand beach; coastal lagoon; standing fresh water; river/stream; water-fringe vegetation), Marine areas (sea inlet/coastal features), Artificial landscape (arable land)
Land-use Agriculture (10%), Fisheries/aquaculture (75%), Forestry (10%), Hunting (95%), Nature conservation/research (5%), Tourism/recreation (20%)

■ Birds

Species	Season	Year	Pop min	Pop max	Acc	Criteria
Phalacrocorax carbo Cormorant	B	1996	60,000	60,000	B	A4i, B1i
Phalacrocorax pygmeus Pygmy Cormorant	B	1995	300	—	A	A1, A4i, B1i, B2
Pelecanus crispus Dalmatian Pelican	B	1995	50	240	A	A1, A4i, B1i, B2
Nycticorax nycticorax Night Heron	B	1995	2,360	4,230	A	A4i, B1i, B2
[1] *Ardeola ralloides* Squacco Heron	B	1995	1,315	4,050	A	A4i, B1i, B2
Egretta garzetta Little Egret	B	1995	2,600	3,630	A	A4i, B1i
Egretta alba Great White Egret	B	1995	4,640	5,250	A	A4i, B1i
Ardea cinerea Grey Heron	B	1995	3,140	3,850	A	A4i, B1i
Ardea purpurea Purple Heron	B	1988	2,060	2,450	A	B2
Plegadis falcinellus Glossy Ibis	B	1995	3,685	4,530	A	A4i, B1i, B2
Platalea leucorodia Spoonbill	B	1995	250	350	A	A4i, B1i, B2
Cygnus olor Mute Swan	B	1995	5,000	6,000	A	A4i, B1i
Cygnus cygnus Whooper Swan	W	1995	30,000	30,000	B	A4i, B1i, B3
[1] *Anser anser* Greylag Goose	B	1995	5,000	13,000	A	A4i, B1i
Anas platyrhynchos Mallard	B	1995	7,000	12,000	A	B1i
Netta rufina Red-crested Pochard	B	1995	2,000	4,000	A	A4i, B1i, B2
Aythya nyroca Ferruginous Duck	B	1996	—	1,000	—	A1, A4i, B1i, B2
Haliaeetus albicilla White-tailed Eagle	B	1995	150	160	A	A1, B2
Aquila clanga Greater Spotted Eagle	B	1996	3	10	—	A1, B2
Pandion haliaetus Osprey	B	1995	20	25	A	B2
Fulica atra Coot	B	1995	130,000	170,000	A	A4i, B1i
Sterna sandvicensis Sandwich Tern	B	1995	40	40	B	B2
[2] *Chlidonias hybridus* Whiskered Tern	B	—	100	—	B	B2
Chlidonias niger Black Tern	B	1995	200	—	B	B2
Alcedo atthis Kingfisher	B	1995	100	—	B	B2
Parus caeruleus Blue Tit	R	1995	1,000	—	B	B3
Lanius minor Lesser Grey Shrike	B	1995	100	—	B	B2

1. Large decrease.
2. Numerous.

Immense numbers of waterbirds breed in the delta, including 56,800 pairs of herons, cormorants *Phalacrocorax*, *Plegadis falcinellus* and *Platalea leucorodia* alone, although this total has decreased in recent years. During migration, a total of 7 million waterbirds pass through the area in spring, and 5–10 million in the autumn. The number of waterfowl overwintering in the delta depends on the severity of the weather, but can include important numbers of *Cygnus cygnus*.

■ Protection status
National Low   **International** Partial
66,816 ha of IBA covered by Zapovednik (Astrakhanskiy, 66,816 ha). 66,816 ha of IBA covered by Biosphere Reserve (Astrakhanskiy, 66,816 ha). 800,000 ha of IBA covered by Ramsar Site (Volga delta, 800,000 ha).

■ Conservation issues

Threats Agricultural intensification/expansion (U), Natural events (U), Unsustainable exploitation (U)

The rising level of the Caspian Sea poses a threat to some habitats and bird species. There are many ongoing scientific monitoring projects.

Western Ilmen area — A4i, A4iii, B1i, B2 — 180
Admin region Astrakhan
Coordinates 46°00'N 47°30'E
Altitude (-24)–0 m Area 590,000 ha

■ Site description
A wetland on the border between Astrakhan region and Kalmykiya Republic, in the south-eastern part of the east European plain. The site extends west of the River Volga and stretches south to the coast of the Caspian Sea, following the natural boundary between the lake system and semi-desert areas.

Habitats Desert (57%; semi-desert), Wetland (13%; standing fresh water; standing brackish and salt water), Artificial landscape (30%; arable land)
Land-use Agriculture (85%), Fisheries/aquaculture (18%), Hunting (90%), Tourism/recreation (3%)

■ Birds

Species	Season	Year	Pop min	Pop max	Acc	Criteria
Nycticorax nycticorax Night Heron	B	1995	100	100	A	B2
Egretta alba Great White Egret	B	1995	1,260	1,260	A	A4i, B1i
Ardea purpurea Purple Heron	B	1995	1,500	1,500	A	B2
Platalea leucorodia Spoonbill	B	1995	70	70	A	A4i, B1i, B2
Cygnus olor Mute Swan	B	1995	1,000	1,500	A	A4i, B1i
Anser anser Greylag Goose	B	1995	1,000	1,000	A	B1i
[1] *Anser anser* Greylag Goose .	N	1995	9,000	9,000	B	A4i, B1i
Tadorna ferruginea Ruddy Shelduck	B	1995	1,500	1,500	C	A4i, B1i, B2
Tadorna tadorna Shelduck	B	1995	1,500	2,000	A	A4i, B1i
[1] *Anas crecca* Teal	N	1995	40,000	40,000	A	A4i, B1i
Fulica atra Coot	B	1995	25,000	25,000	A	A4i, B1i

1. Moulting.

Breeding species include a wide variety of colonial waterbirds and wildfowl in important numbers. The area supports a total of 1,000,000–1,500,000 waterbirds during migration, among which the most numerous species are wildfowl such as *Cygnus olor*, *C. columbianus*, *C. cygnus*, *Anser anser*, *Tadorna tadorna*, *Anas strepera*, *A. crecca*, *A. platyrhynchos*, *A. acuta*, *A. querquedula*, *Netta rufina* and *Aythya ferina*. Tens of thousands of wildfowl congregate to moult, notably *Anser anser* and *Anas crecca*. Breeding species of global conservation concern that do not meet IBA criteria (no counts): *Tetrax tetrax*, *Otis tarda*.

■ Protection status
National Low International None
6,700 ha of IBA is covered by Zakaznik (Ilmeno-Bugrobiy, 6,700 ha).

■ Conservation issues

Threats Abandonment/reduction of land management (B), Agricultural intensification/expansion (B), Disturbance to birds (B), Drainage (C), Natural events (B), Recreation/tourism (C), Unsustainable exploitation (C)

The area has been included on a 'shadow list' of potential Ramsar Sites.

Maly Zhemchuzhny island — A4i, B1i, B2 — 181
Admin region Astrakhan
Coordinates 45°00'N 48°18'E
Altitude (-27)–(-25) m Area 35 ha

■ Site description
A small island in the Caspian Sea, to the south of the Volga delta.

Habitats Wetland (100%; sand-dunes/sand beach; shingle/stony beach)
Land-use Nature conservation/research (30%), Unknown (70%)

■ Birds

Species	Season	Year	Pop min	Pop max	Acc	Criteria
Phalacrocorax carbo Cormorant	N	1996	6,000	10,000	B	A4i, B1i
[1] *Larus ichthyaetus* Great Black-headed Gull	B	1995	4,000	42,000	A	A4i, B1i
[1] *Larus cachinnans* Yellow-legged Gull	B	1995	1,000	1,500	A	A4i, B1i
[1] *Sterna caspia* Caspian Tern	B	1995	1,000	2,500	A	A4i, B1i, B2
[1] *Sterna sandvicensis* Sandwich Tern	B	1995	600	600	A	B1i, B2

1. Large decrease.

The island holds large and important breeding colonies of *Phalacrocorax carbo* and of four species of gull and tern; the latter have all undergone a large decrease during 1985–1995.

■ Protection status
National High International None
35 ha of IBA covered by Natural Monument (Maliy Zhemchuzhny Island, 35 ha).

■ Conservation issues

Threats Natural events (A)

Sea-level rise is causing flooding. Ornithologists from Astrakhan Zapovednik/Biosphere Reserve monitor the breeding colonies.

Bogdinsko-Baskunchakski — A1, A3, B2 — 182
Admin region Astrakhan
Coordinates 48°10'N 47°00'E
Altitude 10–10 m Area 70,000 ha

■ Site description
The area is located in the north-western part of the Astrakhan region, near the boundary with Kazakhstan.

Habitats Grassland (99%; steppe/dry calcareous grassland), Wetland (1%)
Land-use Agriculture (99%)

■ Birds

Species	Season	Year	Pop min	Pop max	Acc	Criteria
Haliaeetus albicilla White-tailed Eagle	R	1994	5	10	B	A1, B2
Buteo rufinus Long-legged Buzzard	R	1994	5	20	C	B2
Aquila heliaca Imperial Eagle	B	1994	5	30	C	A1, A3, B2
Anthropoides virgo Demoiselle Crane	B	1994	—	300	C	A3

An important breeding area for the globally threatened *Aquila heliaca*, and for two other raptors which breed in significant numbers, as well as *Anthropoides virgo* (restricted to the Eurasian steppe biome when breeding). Species of global conservation concern that do not meet IBA criteria: *Circus macrourus* (on passage), *Otis tarda* (on passage), *Tetrax tetrax* (breeding).

■ Protection status
National Partial International None
53,700 ha of IBA covered by Zakaznik (Bogdinsko-Baskunchaksky, 53,700 ha).

■ Conservation issues

Threats Extraction industry (C), Recreation/tourism (C), Unsustainable exploitation (B)

Flood-plain of River Vetluga — B1i — 183
Admin region Kostroma
Coordinates 57°30'N 45°10'E
Altitude — Area —

■ Site description
Flood-plain of the River Vetluga from Sharya to Krasnyye Baki.

Habitats Wetland (standing fresh water; river/stream)

■ Birds
A breeding and passage site for geese and ducks. The B1i criterion is applied at site-level rather than at species-level, as recent count data are not available for any bird species. The site may also prove to fulfil the A4i criterion once systematic counts have been made.

■ Protection status
National None International None

■ Conservation issues
No recent information.

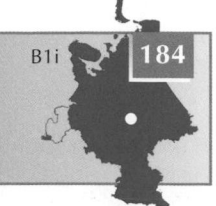

Kamsko-Bakaldinskiye marshes
B1i **184**

Admin region Nizhni Novgorod
Coordinates 56°15'N 45°05'E
Altitude 72–118 m Area 120,000 ha

■ Site description
One of the largest peatlands in European Russia, consisting of wet forest and open fen and mire.

Habitats Forest and woodland (65%; native coniferous forest; alluvial/very wet forest), Grassland (15%; humid grassland), Wetland (85%; standing fresh water; river/stream; raised bog; fen/transition mire/spring), Artificial landscape (5%)
Land-use Forestry (70%), Nature conservation/research (25%), Other

■ Birds

Species	Season	Year	Pop min	Pop max	Acc	Criteria
Grus grus Crane	B	1990	140	140	A	B1i

Even though available bird data are rather old and very incomplete, the area is one of the most important for birds in European Russia and still in a natural condition. Breeding species of global conservation concern that do not meet IBA criteria: *Aquila clanga* (1 pair), *Gallinago media* (at least 10 pairs). Significant proportion (≥1%) of national population breeding at site: *Aquila chrysaetos* (2 pairs).

■ Protection status
National Partial **International** High
46,940 ha of IBA covered by Zapovednik (Kerzhenskiy, 46,940 ha). There are also about 10 Nature Monuments which, together with the Zapovednik, cover 25% of the IBA. 120,000 ha of IBA covered by Ramsar Site (Kama-Bakaldino mires, 226,500 ha).

■ Conservation issues

Threats Deforestation (commercial) (A), Drainage (A), Extraction industry (B)

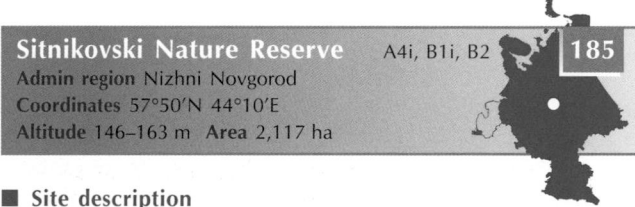

Sitnikovski Nature Reserve
A4i, B1i, B2 **185**

Admin region Nizhni Novgorod
Coordinates 57°50'N 44°10'E
Altitude 146–163 m Area 2,117 ha

■ Site description
An area of peat-bogs and disused, flooded peat-mine workings which are reverting naturally to bogs.

Habitats Wetland (85%; standing fresh water; raised bog; water-fringe vegetation)
Land-use Other, Tourism/recreation (5%)

■ Birds

Species	Season	Year	Pop min	Pop max	Acc	Criteria
Larus ridibundus Black-headed Gull	R	1990	20,700	—	A	A4i, B1i
Larus canus Common Gull	R	1990	7,200	—	A	A4i, B1i, B2

The largest inland breeding colony of gulls and terns in Europe, totalling a minimum of c.28,000 pairs.

■ Protection status
National High **International** None
2,117 ha of IBA covered by Zakaznik (Sitnikovsky, 2,117 ha).

Gorki reservoir and the lower Unzha river
B1i **186**

Admin region Ivanovo, Nizhni Novgorod, Kostroma
Coordinates 57°19'N 43°04'E
Altitude — Area 72,100 ha

■ Site description
A large reservoir.

Habitats Wetland (standing fresh water; river/stream)
Land-use Water management

■ Birds
An important area for staging and breeding ducks. The B1i criterion is applied at site-level rather than at species-level, as recent count data are not available for any bird species. The site may also prove to fulfil the A4i criterion once systematic counts have been made.

■ Protection status
National None **International** None

■ Conservation issues
No recent information.

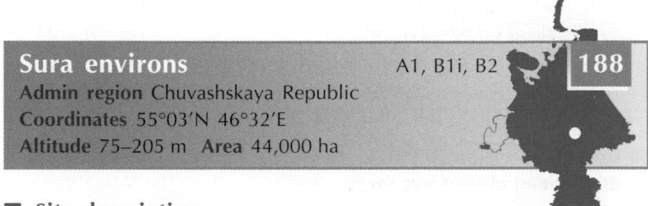

Flood-plain of Algashka river
A1, A4iii, B1i **187**

Admin region Chuvashskaya Republic
Coordinates 55°30'N 46°30'E
Altitude 78–79 m Area 400 ha

■ Site description
The flood-plain of the Algashka river lies in the south of the Chuvash Republic. There are extensive wet grasslands.

Habitats Forest and woodland (5%; alluvial/very wet forest), Scrub (5%; scrub), Grassland (80%; humid grassland), Wetland (5%; fen/transition mire/spring), Artificial landscape (10%; arable land)
Land-use Agriculture (90%), Forestry (5%), Hunting (100%), Not utilized (5%)

■ Birds

Species	Season	Year	Pop min	Pop max	Acc	Criteria
Anser anser Greylag Goose	P	1995	120	400	B	B1i
Anas penelope Wigeon	P	1995	1,000	13,000	B	B1i
Aythya fuligula Tufted Duck	P	1995	1,000	11,000	B	B1i
Crex crex Corncrake	R	1996	40	—	A	A1

Despite its rather small extent, the site is important for breeding *Crex crex* and as a staging area for migrating waterfowl, holding 20,000 or more on a regular basis. Apart from *Anas penelope* and *Aythya fuligula*, this total is otherwise comprised mainly of *Anas platyrhynchos*, *Anas acuta*, *Anas querquedula* and *Aythya ferina*.

■ Protection status
National None **International** None

■ Conservation issues

Threats Agricultural intensification/expansion (C), Disturbance to birds (C), Unsustainable exploitation (C)

Plans have been put forward for the establishment of a federal nature reserve (Zakaznik).

Sura environs
A1, B1i, B2 **188**

Admin region Chuvashskaya Republic
Coordinates 55°03'N 46°32'E
Altitude 75–205 m Area 44,000 ha

■ Site description
The flood-plain of the Sura river between the towns of Ardatov and Poretskoye. Habitats include a number of old meanders and lakes.

Habitats Forest and woodland (50%; broadleaved deciduous forest; native coniferous forest; mixed forest; alluvial/very wet forest), Grassland (20%; humid grassland), Wetland (8%; standing fresh water; river/stream; fen/transition mire/spring), Artificial landscape (20%; highly improved reseeded grassland; arable land; forestry plantation; other urban/industrial areas)
Land-use Agriculture (45%), Forestry (50%), Nature conservation/research (5%)

■ Birds
Breeding birds in significant numbers include two globally threatened species and *Riparia riparia*. Species of global conservation concern

that do not meet IBA criteria: *Circus macrourus* (at least 1 pair), *Aquila clanga* (at least 1 pair).

Species		Season	Year	Pop min	Pop max	Acc	Criteria
Anser anser	Greylag Goose	P	1997	300	1,000	B	B1i
Aquila heliaca	Imperial Eagle	B	1997	1	2	A	A1, B2
Crex crex	Corncrake	B	1997	100	300	C	A1
Riparia riparia	Sand Martin	B	1997	20,000	—	B	B2

■ Protection status
National Low **International** None
2,000 ha of IBA covered by Zapovednik (Prisurskiy, 19,000 ha).

■ Conservation issues

Threats Agricultural intensification/expansion (C), Deforestation (commercial) (C), Forest grazing (C), Recreation/tourism (B), Selective logging/cutting (C)

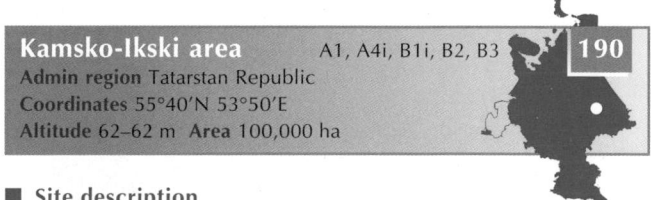

Arski fish-ponds   A1, B1i   189
Admin region Tatarstan Republic
Coordinates 56°05′N 49°50′E
Altitude 60–80 m **Area** 1,000 ha

■ Site description
A system of man-made fish-ponds located to the east of the town of Arsk.

Habitats Scrub (10%; scrub), Grassland (20%; humid grassland), Wetland (55%; standing fresh water), Artificial landscape (15%; highly improved reseeded grassland)
Land-use Agriculture (45%), Fisheries/aquaculture (55%)

■ Birds

Species		Season	Year	Pop min	Pop max	Acc	Criteria
Anser erythropus Lesser White-fronted Goose		P	1995	200	300	A	A1, B1i
Anser anser	Greylag Goose	P	1994	300	500	A	B1i

Although the site is of rather small extent, geese *Anser* stage in the area during migration in significant numbers, especially the globally threatened *Anser erythropus*, and 4,700–11,600 ducks also congregate here on spring migration.

■ Protection status
National None **International** None

■ Conservation issues

Threats Unsustainable exploitation (C)

Bird counts take place on a regular basis.

Kamsko-Ikski area   A1, A4i, B1i, B2, B3   190
Admin region Tatarstan Republic
Coordinates 55°40′N 53°50′E
Altitude 62–62 m **Area** 100,000 ha

■ Site description
Large areas of flood-plain with many lakes and meanders, covered by aquatic vegetation and wet forest.

Habitats Forest and woodland (native coniferous forest; alluvial/very wet forest), Scrub (20%; scrub), Grassland (41%; humid grassland), Wetland (39%; standing fresh water)
Land-use Agriculture (60%), Fisheries/aquaculture (39%), Nature conservation/research (5%)

■ Birds

Species		Season	Year	Pop min	Pop max	Acc	Criteria
Anser erythropus Lesser White-fronted Goose		P	1988	10	20	A	A1
Anser anser	Greylag Goose	B	1988	100	300	B	B1i
Anas strepera	Gadwall	B	1989	1,000	5,000	A	A4i, B1i, B2
Anas strepera	Gadwall	P	1989	1,000	10,000	A	A4i, B1i
Anas crecca	Teal	B	1989	2,000	10,000	A	A4i, B1i

Species ... continued		Season	Year	Pop min	Pop max	Acc	Criteria
Anas crecca	Teal	P	1989	5,500	27,000	A	A4i, B1i
Anas platyrhynchos	Mallard	B	1989	15,000	100,000	A	A4i, B1i
Anas platyrhynchos	Mallard	P	1989	30,000	200,000	A	A4i, B1i
Anas querquedula	Garganey	P	1989	500	50,000	A	A4i, B1i
Anas clypeata	Shoveler	B	1989	500	1,500	A	B1i
Anas clypeata	Shoveler	P	1989	1,400	31,000	A	A4i, B1i
Aythya ferina	Pochard	B	1989	150	5,000	A	A4i, B1i, B3
Aythya ferina	Pochard	P	1989	300	16,000	A	A4i, B1i
Aythya marila	Scaup	P	1989	—	8,000	B	A4i, B1i
Sterna hirundo	Common Tern	P	1995	500	10,000	A	A4i, B1i
Sterna albifrons	Little Tern	P	1988	20	1,000	B	A4i, B1i

Very large numbers of wildfowl breed and migrate through the area. Species of global conservation concern that do not meet IBA criteria: *Falco naumanni* (occurs, but status uncertain).

■ Protection status
National Partial **International** None
18,600 ha of IBA covered by Zakaznik (Kamsko-Iksky, 18,600 ha).

■ Conservation issues

Threats Construction/impact of dyke/dam/barrage (A), Unsustainable exploitation (B)

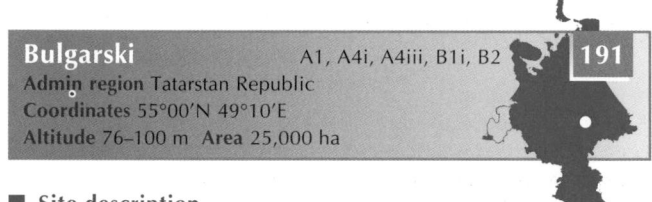

Bulgarski   A1, A4i, A4iii, B1i, B2   191
Admin region Tatarstan Republic
Coordinates 55°00′N 49°10′E
Altitude 76–100 m **Area** 25,000 ha

■ Site description
A shallow part of Kuybyshev reservoir and its islands, near the village of Bulgar.

Habitats Forest and woodland (20%; broadleaved deciduous forest; alluvial/very wet forest), Scrub (10%), Grassland (45%; humid grassland), Wetland (25%; standing fresh water)
Land-use Agriculture (60%), Forestry (20%), Military (3%), Tourism/recreation (17%), Water management

■ Birds

Species		Season	Year	Pop min	Pop max	Acc	Criteria
Anser erythropus Lesser White-fronted Goose		P	1990	10	20,000	B	A1, A4i, B1i
Anser anser	Greylag Goose	P	1995	500	3,000	A	B1i
Anas penelope	Wigeon	P	1989	10,000	70,000	A	A4i, B1i
Anas crecca	Teal	P	1989	4,000	10,000	A	B1i
Aythya marila	Scaup	P	1989	1,000	40,000	A	A4i, B1i
Haliaeetus albicilla	White-tailed Eagle	P	1991	10	15	A	A1
Gallinago media	Great Snipe	P	1994	100	150	B	A1
Sterna albifrons	Little Tern	B	1990	50	150	A	B2
Sterna albifrons	Little Tern	P	1990	500	1,000	A	A4i, B1i

An important stop-over site for migrating waterbirds, holding 20,000 or more on a regular basis, especially wildfowl.

■ Protection status
National Low **International** None
50 ha of IBA covered by Natural Monument (Ostrov Spassk, 50 ha).

■ Conservation issues

Threats Agricultural intensification/expansion (B), Disturbance to birds (C), Unsustainable exploitation (C)

The Bulgarsky Historical-Natural Complex lies adjacent to the site.

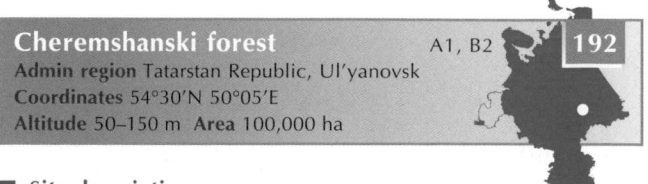

Cheremshanski forest   A1, B2   192
Admin region Tatarstan Republic, Ul'yanovsk
Coordinates 54°30′N 50°05′E
Altitude 50–150 m **Area** 100,000 ha

■ Site description
A large tract of forest surrounded by cultivated land and permanent pasture.

Habitats Forest and woodland (65%; broadleaved deciduous forest; native coniferous forest; mixed forest; alluvial/very wet forest), Grassland (20%; humid grassland; mesophile grassland), Artificial landscape (15%; arable land; other urban/industrial areas)
Land-use Agriculture (30%), Forestry (65%), Urban/industrial/transport (5%)

■ **Birds**

Species	Season	Year	Pop min	Pop max	Acc	Criteria
Aquila heliaca Imperial Eagle	B	1997	5	10	B	A1, B2

An important site for breeding *Aquila heliaca*.

■ **Protection status**
National None **International** None
There is no up-to-date information.

■ **Conservation issues**

Threats Disturbance to birds (C), Selective logging/cutting (B), Unsustainable exploitation (B)

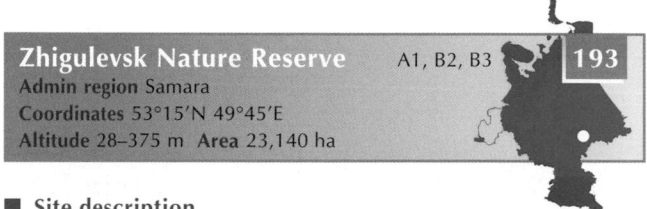

Zhigulevsk Nature Reserve A1, B2, B3 | 193
Admin region Samara
Coordinates 53°15'N 49°45'E
Altitude 28–375 m **Area** 23,140 ha

■ **Site description**
The site is located on the shore of the River Volga, and is dissected by gorges and ravines.

Habitats Forest and woodland (94%)
Land-use Nature conservation/research (100%)

■ **Birds**

Species	Season	Year	Pop min	Pop max	Acc	Criteria
Haliaeetus albicilla White-tailed Eagle	W	1996	10	15	A	A1
Crex crex Corncrake	B	1996	40	40	—	A1
Jynx torquilla Wryneck	B	1996	200	500	—	B2
Luscinia luscinia Thrush Nightingale	B	1996	1,600	1,600	A	B3
Phoenicurus phoenicurus Redstart	B	1996	700	1,600	—	B2
Turdus philomelos Song Thrush	B	1996	6,000	6,000	—	B3
Sylvia borin Garden Warbler	B	1996	2,500	5,000	—	B3
Ficedula albicollis Collared Flycatcher	B	1996	5,000	10,000	—	B3
Parus caeruleus Blue Tit	B	1996	3,000	3,000	—	B3
Carduelis chloris Greenfinch	B	1996	400	2,000	—	B3
Emberiza hortulana Ortolan Bunting	B	1996	100	100	—	B2

The area supports significant numbers of breeding birds of forest and forest-steppe habitats. *Haliaeetus albicilla* winters in important numbers, but also breeds in the area (3–4 pairs).

■ **Protection status**
National High **International** None
23,140 ha of IBA covered by Zapovednik (Zhigulevskiy, 23,140 ha).

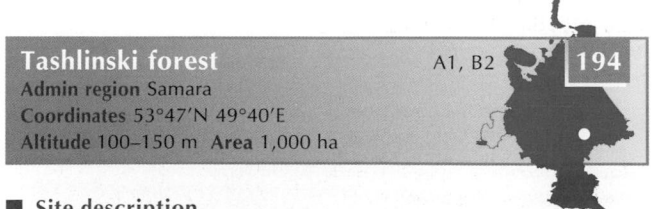

Tashlinski forest A1, B2 | 194
Admin region Samara
Coordinates 53°47'N 49°40'E
Altitude 100–150 m **Area** 1,000 ha

■ **Site description**
A small forest surrounded by primary steppe, in the north-west of the Samara region.

Habitats Forest and woodland (90%; broadleaved deciduous forest; native coniferous forest), Grassland (10%; steppe/dry calcareous grassland)
Land-use Agriculture (10%), Forestry (90%)

■ **Birds**

Species	Season	Year	Pop min	Pop max	Acc	Criteria
Aquila heliaca Imperial Eagle	B	1997	2	2	A	A1, B2

An important site for breeding *Aquila heliaca*.

■ **Protection status**
National None **International** None
There is no up-to-date information.

■ **Conservation issues**

Threats Selective logging/cutting (B), Unsustainable exploitation (C)

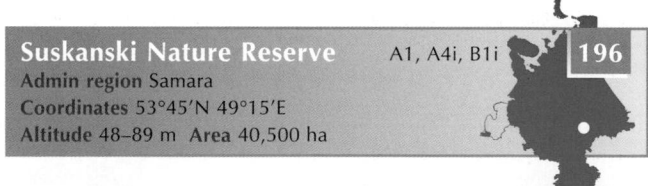

Racheyski forest A1, B2, B3 | 195
Admin region Samara
Coordinates 53°25'N 48°15'E
Altitude 200–315 m **Area** 40,100 ha

■ **Site description**
Forested hills surrounded by agricultural land, on the boundary between the Samara and Ul'yanovsk regions.

Habitats Forest and woodland (50%; broadleaved deciduous forest; native coniferous forest; mixed forest), Wetland (3%; river/stream; fen/transition mire/spring), Artificial landscape (47%; arable land; other urban/industrial areas)
Land-use Agriculture (40%), Forestry (50%), Urban/industrial/transport (10%)

■ **Birds**

Species	Season	Year	Pop min	Pop max	Acc	Criteria
Crex crex Corncrake	B	1997	400	600	B	A1, B2
Columba oenas Stock Dove	B	1997	40	100	B	B3
Jynx torquilla Wryneck	B	1997	800	1,000	B	B2
Lullula arborea Woodlark	B	1997	100	200	B	B2
Phoenicurus phoenicurus Redstart	B	1997	400	1,000	B	B2
Turdus viscivorus Mistle Thrush	B	1997	1,200	1,800	B	B3
Muscicapa striata Spotted Flycatcher	B	1997	3,000	10,000	B	B2
Carduelis chloris Greenfinch	B	1997	800	1,800	B	B3

Important numbers of *Crex crex* breed, and several species of forest/woodland are particularly common.

■ **Protection status**
National High **International** None
40,100 ha of IBA covered by Zakaznik (Staro-Racheiskiy, 40,100 ha).

■ **Conservation issues**

Threats Selective logging/cutting (B), Unsustainable exploitation (B), Other (B)

Damage is caused to tree-trunks by the collection of sap ('Other' threat).

Suskanski Nature Reserve A1, A4i, B1i | 196
Admin region Samara
Coordinates 53°45'N 49°15'E
Altitude 48–89 m **Area** 40,500 ha

■ **Site description**
The area includes stretches of shallow water along the shore of the Kuybyshev reservoir.

Habitats Forest and woodland (5%; broadleaved deciduous forest), Wetland (28%; mudflat/sandflat; standing fresh water), Artificial landscape (66%; arable land; perennial crops/orchards/groves)
Land-use Agriculture (65%), Fisheries/aquaculture (27%), Forestry (5%), Hunting (70%), Nature conservation/research (19%)

■ **Birds**

Species	Season	Year	Pop min	Pop max	Acc	Criteria
Anser anser Greylag Goose	P	1996	15	2,000	—	B1i
Haliaeetus albicilla White-tailed Eagle	W	1996	42	42	—	A1
Vanellus vanellus Lapwing	P	1996	180,000	—	—	A4i, B1i

Haliaeetus albicilla, of global conservation concern, winters in significant numbers, with 1–2 pairs also breeding. Several species occur in large numbers on passage, most importantly *Vanellus vanellus*.

■ Protection status
National High **International** None
40,500 ha of IBA covered by Zakaznik (Suskansky, 40,500 ha).

■ Conservation issues

Threats Dredging/canalization (A)

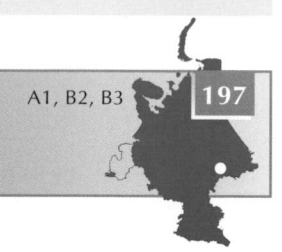

Buzulukski forest
Admin region Samara, Orenburg
Coordinates 53°00′N 52°00′E
Altitude 48–219 m **Area** 111,210 ha

A1, B2, B3 — 197

■ Site description
One of the largest tracts of pine *Pinus* forest in the steppe zone of southern European Russia, located on the border between the Samara and Orenburg regions.

Habitats Forest and woodland (80%; broadleaved deciduous forest; native coniferous forest; mixed forest; alluvial/very wet forest), Wetland (10%; river/stream; fen/transition mire/spring), Artificial landscape (10%; arable land; other urban/industrial areas)
Land-use Agriculture (4%), Forestry (90%), Not utilized (4%), Urban/industrial/transport (3%)

■ Birds

Species	Season	Year	Pop min	Pop max	Acc	Criteria
Aquila heliaca Imperial Eagle	B	1997	2	5	C	A1, B2
Crex crex Corncrake	B	1997	100	200	B	A1
Columba oenas Stock Dove	B	1997	100	200	B	B3
Columba palumbus Woodpigeon	B	1997	800	1,000	B	B3
Otus scops Scops Owl	B	1997	50	100	C	B2
Strix aluco Tawny Owl	R	1997	100	200	B	B3
Lullula arborea Woodlark	B	1997	450	500	B	B2
Luscinia luscinia Thrush Nightingale	B	1997	1,500	2,000	B	B3
Turdus philomelos Song Thrush	B	1997	2,500	3,000	B	B3
Turdus viscivorus Mistle Thrush	B	1997	2,500	2,700	B	B3
Locustella fluviatilis River Warbler	B	1997	1,500	1,700	B	B3
Acrocephalus palustris Marsh Warbler	B	1997	1,500	1,800	B	B3
Hippolais icterina Icterine Warbler	B	1997	9,000	10,000	B	B3
Sylvia borin Garden Warbler	B	1997	17,000	18,000	B	B3
Muscicapa striata Spotted Flycatcher	B	1997	20,000	21,000	B	B2
Ficedula hypoleuca Pied Flycatcher	B	1997	20,000	22,000	B	B3
Lanius collurio Red-backed Shrike	B	1997	300	1,000	C	B2
Carduelis chloris Greenfinch	B	1997	5,000	6,000	B	B3
Emberiza hortulana Ortolan Bunting	B	1997	50	100	C	B2

Breeding birds include two globally threatened species and many species of European conservation concern, in significant numbers.

■ Protection status
National High **International** None
111,210 ha of IBA covered by unknown type of protected area (Buzulukskiy Bor, 111,210 ha).

■ Conservation issues

Threats Groundwater abstraction (A), Selective logging/cutting (B), Unsustainable exploitation (C)

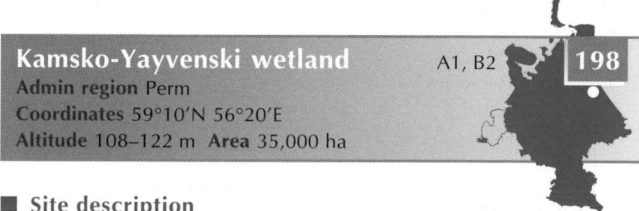

Kamsko-Yayvenski wetland
Admin region Perm
Coordinates 59°10′N 56°20′E
Altitude 108–122 m **Area** 35,000 ha

A1, B2 — 198

■ Site description
An area of bogs and very wet forest along the eastern shore of the Kamskoye reservoir.

Habitats Forest and woodland (40%; native coniferous forest; mixed forest), Grassland (2%; humid grassland), Wetland (58%; standing fresh water; raised bog)
Land-use Fisheries/aquaculture (10%), Hunting (10%), Nature conservation/research (30%), Water management (50%)

■ Birds

Species	Season	Year	Pop min	Pop max	Acc	Criteria
Haliaeetus albicilla White-tailed Eagle	B	1994	5	—	A	A1
Aquila clanga Greater Spotted Eagle	B	1994	1	3	A	A1
Crex crex Corncrake	B	1994	24	—	A	A1
Gallinago media Great Snipe	B	1994	30	—	A	A1
Acrocephalus paludicola Aquatic Warbler	B	1994	9	—	A	A1, B2

Five species of global conservation concern breed, including three globally threatened species.

■ Protection status
National Partial **International** None
10,000 ha of IBA covered by Zakaznik (Bereznikovskiy, 13,000 ha).

■ Conservation issues

Threats Disturbance to birds (A), Recreation/tourism (A), Unsustainable exploitation (A)

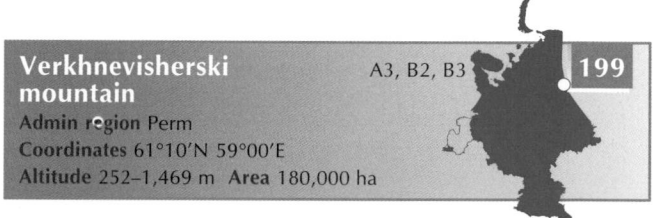

Verkhnevisherski mountain
Admin region Perm
Coordinates 61°10′N 59°00′E
Altitude 252–1,469 m **Area** 180,000 ha

A3, B2, B3 — 199

■ Site description
A forested mountain with alpine grassland and tundra-like habitat on the summit.

Habitats Forest and woodland (70%; native coniferous forest; mixed forest), Grassland (25%; alpine/subalpine/boreal grassland)
Land-use Nature conservation/research (100%)

■ Birds

Species	Season	Year	Pop min	Pop max	Acc	Criteria
Mergus albellus Smew	B	1990	10	—	A	A3
Pluvialis apricaria Golden Plover	B	1990	200	—	A	B3
Tringa nebularia Greenshank	B	1990	200	—	A	A3
Surnia ulula Hawk Owl	R	1990	20	—	A	A3
Strix nebulosa Great Grey Owl	R	1990	30	—	A	A3
Prunella atrogularis Black-throated Accentor	B	1990	50	—	A	B2
Phylloscopus borealis Arctic Warbler	B	1990	100	—	—	A3
Parus cinctus Siberian Tit	B	1990	Abundant	—		A3
Perisoreus infaustus Siberian Jay	B	1990	Abundant	—		A3
Fringilla montifringilla Brambling	B	1990	Abundant	—		A3
Loxia leucoptera Two-barred Crossbill	B	1990	Abundant	—		A3
Pinicola enucleator Pine Grosbeak	B	1990	100	—	A	A3

Breeding species include 10 of the 15 species in Europe that are restricted to the boreal biome (when breeding).

■ Protection status
National High **International** Partial
180,000 ha of IBA covered by Zapovednik (Visherskiy, 241,200 ha).

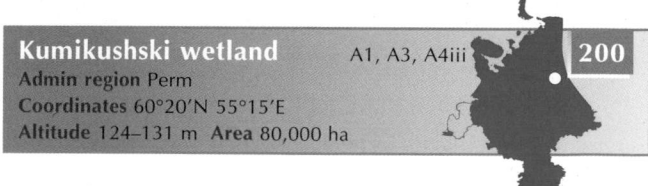

Kumikushski wetland
Admin region Perm
Coordinates 60°20′N 55°15′E
Altitude 124–131 m **Area** 80,000 ha

A1, A3, A4iii — 200

■ Site description
Open bogs and mires with a system of lakes.

Habitats Forest and woodland (15%; mixed forest), Wetland (83%; standing fresh water; river/stream; raised bog; water-fringe vegetation; fen/transition mire/spring)
Land-use Forestry

■ Birds
Breeding species include three species of global conservation concern, as well as 10 of the 15 species in Europe that are restricted to

the boreal biome when breeding (no counts of abundance have been made). Significant proportion (≥1%) of national population breeding at site: *Aquila chrysaetos* (2 pairs). A good variety of waterbirds either breed or occur on passage, with more than 20,000 staging in the area during migration.

Species		Season	Year	Pop min	Pop max	Acc	Criteria
Haliaeetus albicilla	White-tailed Eagle	B	1995	5	—	A	A1
Crex crex	Corncrake	B	1995	30	50	B	A1
Lymnocryptes minimus	Jack Snipe	B	1995	—	—	—	A3
Gallinago media	Great Snipe	B	1995	50	—	A	A1
Surnia ulula	Hawk Owl	R	1995	—	—	—	A3
Strix nebulosa	Great Grey Owl	R	1995	—	—	—	A3
Phylloscopus borealis	Arctic Warbler	B	1995	Common	—	—	A3
Parus cinctus	Siberian Tit	B	1995	Common	—	—	A3
Perisoreus infaustus	Siberian Jay	B	1995	Common	—	—	A3
Fringilla montifringilla	Brambling	B	1995	Common	—	—	A3
Loxia leucoptera	Two-barred Crossbill	B	1995	—	—	—	A3
Pinicola enucleator	Pine Grosbeak	B	1995	—	—	—	A3
Emberiza rustica	Rustic Bunting	B	1995	—	—	—	A3

■ **Protection status**

National High **International** None
78,400 ha of IBA covered by Zakaznik (Pernaty, 78,400 ha).

■ **Conservation issues**

Threats Drainage (A), Extraction industry (A), Filling-in of wetlands (A), Intensified forest management (A), Recreation/tourism (A), Unsustainable exploitation (A)

Data on individual bird species are incomplete, and further surveys are required.

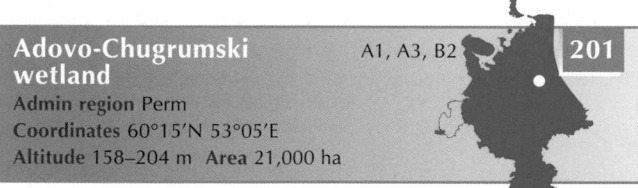

Adovo-Chugrumski wetland

A1, A3, B2 — 201

Admin region Perm
Coordinates 60°15′N 53°05′E
Altitude 158–204 m **Area** 21,000 ha

■ **Site description**

Two extensive raised bogs with a large lake, Adovo, in the southern part of the area.

Habitats Forest and woodland (10%; native coniferous forest), Wetland (90%; standing fresh water; raised bog)
Land-use Forestry (10%), Nature conservation/research (90%)

■ **Birds**

Species		Season	Year	Pop min	Pop max	Acc	Criteria
Podiceps auritus	Slavonian Grebe	B	1995	5	10	—	A3
Mergus albellus	Smew	B	1995	—	—	—	A3
Aquila chrysaetos	Golden Eagle	R	1993	4	6	A	B2
Lymnocryptes minimus	Jack Snipe	B	1995	100	200	—	A3
Gallinago media	Great Snipe	B	1995	40	60	—	A1
Tringa nebularia	Greenshank	B	1995	80	85	—	A3
Surnia ulula	Hawk Owl	R	1995	1	2	—	A3
Strix nebulosa	Great Grey Owl	R	1995	2	5	—	A3
Phylloscopus borealis	Arctic Warbler	B	1995	2,000	—	—	A3
Parus cinctus	Siberian Tit	R	1995	100	800	—	A3
Perisoreus infaustus	Siberian Jay	R	1995	10	20	—	A3
Fringilla montifringilla	Brambling	B	1995	400	500	—	A3
Loxia leucoptera	Two-barred Crossbill	R	1995	—	10	—	A3
Loxia pytyopsittacus	Parrot Crossbill	R	1995	—	—	—	A3
Pinicola enucleator	Pine Grosbeak	R	1995	—	—	—	A3
Emberiza rustica	Rustic Bunting	B	1995	1,500	1,500	—	A3

Breeding species include 14 of the 15 species in Europe that are restricted to the boreal biome (when breeding).

■ **Protection status**

National High **International** None
21,000 ha of IBA covered by Zakaznik (Ozero Adovo, 111,000 ha).

■ **Conservation issues**

Threats Intensified forest management (A), Unsustainable exploitation (A)

Khvarkush and Zolotoy Kamen' ridges

A1, A4i, B1i, B2, B3 — 202

Admin region Perm
Coordinates 60°15′N 58°35′E
Altitude 332–1,066 m **Area** 130,000 ha

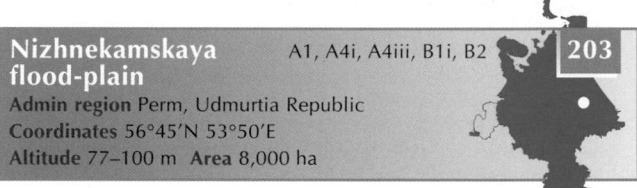

■ **Site description**

Two forested ridges in the mountainous part of the Perm region. Typical boreal montane habitats with spruce *Picea* forests at lower altitudes and treeline ecotone, alpine grassland and tundra-like habitat on the ridge-tops. Human activities include reindeer-herding.

Habitats Forest and woodland (40%; native coniferous forest; mixed forest; treeline ecotone), Grassland (60%; alpine/subalpine/boreal grassland)
Land-use Agriculture (60%), Forestry (40%)

■ **Birds**

Species		Season	Year	Pop min	Pop max	Acc	Criteria
Aquila clanga	Greater Spotted Eagle	B	1995	2	2	—	A1
Pluvialis apricaria	Golden Plover	B	1995	—	200	—	B3
Gallinago media	Great Snipe	B	1995	—	100	—	A1, A4i, B1i
Picoides tridactylus	Three-toed Woodpecker	R	1995	—	100	—	B2

Two species of global conservation concern breed here in important numbers, but data on species and numbers for the site as a whole are incomplete, and further surveys are needed.

■ **Protection status**

National Partial **International** None
23,000 ha of IBA covered by Zakaznik (Khrebet Kvarkush, 23,000 ha).

Nizhnekamskaya flood-plain

A1, A4i, A4iii, B1i, B2 — 203

Admin region Perm, Udmurtia Republic
Coordinates 56°45′N 53°50′E
Altitude 77–100 m **Area** 8,000 ha

■ **Site description**

A narrow strip of wet forest along the Kama river, situated on the border between the Udmurtia Republic and the Perm region.

Habitats Forest and woodland (60%; broadleaved deciduous forest; native coniferous forest; mixed forest; alluvial/very wet forest), Grassland (30%; humid grassland), Wetland (10%; fen/transition mire/spring)
Land-use Forestry

■ **Birds**

Species		Season	Year	Pop min	Pop max	Acc	Criteria
Haliaeetus albicilla	White-tailed Eagle	B	1991	5	—	—	A1
Crex crex	Corncrake	B	1996	95	—	—	A1
Gallinago media	Great Snipe	B	1996	75	—	—	A1
Larus minutus	Little Gull	B	1996	450	—	—	A4i, B1i, B2
Sterna albifrons	Little Tern	B	1991	200	—	—	A4i, B1i
Chlidonias leucopterus	White-winged Black Tern	B	1996	800	—	—	A4i, B1i
¹ *Acrocephalus paludicola*	Aquatic Warbler	B	1996	10	—	—	A1, B2

1. Singing males.

Four species of global conservation concern breed within the IBA, two of which are globally threatened, as well as three species of gull/tern in important numbers. The site holds 20,000 or more waterbirds during spring migration, on a regular basis.

■ **Protection status**

National None **International** None

■ **Conservation issues**

Threats Deforestation (commercial) (A), Disturbance to birds (A), Drainage (A), Extraction industry (A), Forest grazing (A), Intensified forest management (A), Recreation/tourism (A)

Bashkirski Nature Reserve
A1, B2 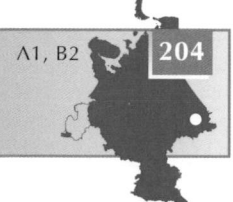 204

Admin region Bashkortostan Republic
Coordinates 53°22′N 57°52′E
Altitude — **Area** 49,609 ha

■ Site description
A forested massif in the southern Ural mountains. The forest is dominated by *Pinus*, *Larix* and *Betula*, and there are also some areas of forest-steppe.

Habitats Forest and woodland (76%; native coniferous forest; alluvial/very wet forest), Grassland (23%; steppe/dry calcareous grassland; humid grassland)
Land-use Nature conservation/research (100%)

■ Birds

Species	Season	Year	Pop min	Pop max	Acc	Criteria
Crex crex Corncrake	B	1995	100	150	—	A1
Picoides tridactylus Three-toed Woodpecker	B	1995	100	100	—	B2

Important numbers of *Crex crex* breed in the forest-steppe zone. Breeding species of global conservation concern that do not meet IBA criteria: *Aquila heliaca* (1 pair). Significant proportion (≥1%) of national population breeding at site: *Aquila chrysaetos* (2–3 pairs).

■ Protection status
National High **International** None
49,609 ha of IBA covered by Zapovednik (Bashkirsky, 49,609 ha).

Octyabr'ski forest
A1, B2 205

Admin region Bashkortostan Republic
Coordinates 54°23′N 53°40′E
Altitude 100–350 m **Area** 50,000 ha

■ Site description
A large forest in the forest-steppe zone, located in the extensive agricultural lands in the south-west of the Bashkortostan Republic.

Habitats Forest and woodland (65%; broadleaved deciduous forest; native coniferous forest; mixed forest), Grassland (20%; steppe/dry calcareous grassland; humid grassland; mesophile grassland), Artificial landscape (15%; arable land; urban parks/gardens)
Land-use Agriculture (30%), Forestry (65%), Urban/industrial/transport (5%)

■ Birds

Species	Season	Year	Pop min	Pop max	Acc	Criteria
Aquila heliaca Imperial Eagle	B	1997	2	5	C	A1, B2

An important area for breeding *Aquila heliaca*.

■ Protection status
National None **International** None

■ Conservation issues
Threats Selective logging/cutting (C), Unsustainable exploitation (B)

There is no precise information regarding the protection status of the area.

Mountain valley of Sakmara river
A1, B2 206

Admin region Bashkortostan Republic
Coordinates 51°55′N 57°37′E
Altitude 250–500 m **Area** 5,000 ha

■ Site description
Areas of broadleaved forest with patches of steppe and scrub, within the valley of the Sakmara river.

Habitats Forest and woodland (40%; broadleaved deciduous forest; mixed forest), Scrub (20%; scrub), Grassland (35%; steppe/dry calcareous grassland), Artificial landscape (5%; arable land)
Land-use Agriculture (40%), Forestry (60%)

■ Birds

Species	Season	Year	Pop min	Pop max	Acc	Criteria
Aquila heliaca Imperial Eagle	B	1997	4	5	B	A1, B2

An important area for breeding *Aquila heliaca*.

■ Protection status
National None **International** None
There is no up-to-date information.

■ Conservation issues
Threats Abandonment/reduction of land management (A), Disturbance to birds (C)

Nikiforovski forest
A1, B2 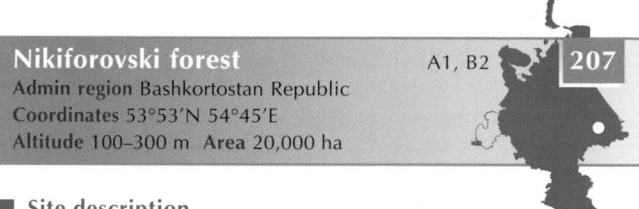 207

Admin region Bashkortostan Republic
Coordinates 53°53′N 54°45′E
Altitude 100–300 m **Area** 20,000 ha

■ Site description
An extensive area of unbroken forest, located north-west from the town of Sterlitamak in the forest-steppe zone.

Habitats Forest and woodland (50%; broadleaved deciduous forest; alluvial/very wet forest), Grassland (30%; steppe/dry calcareous grassland; humid grassland), Artificial landscape (20%; arable land; other urban/industrial areas)
Land-use Agriculture (45%), Forestry (50%), Urban/industrial/transport (5%)

■ Birds

Species	Season	Year	Pop min	Pop max	Acc	Criteria
Aquila heliaca Imperial Eagle	B	1997	2	3	B	A1, B2

An important area for breeding *Aquila heliaca*.

■ Protection status
National None **International** None

■ Conservation issues
Threats Disturbance to birds (B), Selective logging/cutting (B), Unsustainable exploitation (C)

Watershed of Bel'skaya and Nugush rivers
A1, B2 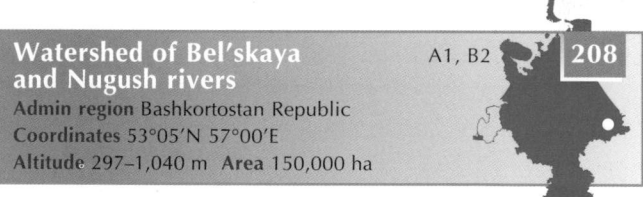 208

Admin region Bashkortostan Republic
Coordinates 53°05′N 57°00′E
Altitude 297–1,040 m **Area** 150,000 ha

■ Site description
The IBA covers the watershed between the Bel'skaya and Nugush rivers. Habitats include mountain ridges and rocky river-shores.

Habitats Forest and woodland (90%; broadleaved deciduous forest; native coniferous forest; mixed forest; alluvial/very wet forest; wooded steppe), Grassland (7%; humid grassland; mesophile grassland), Wetland (3%)
Land-use Nature conservation/research (100%)

■ Birds

Species	Season	Year	Pop min	Pop max	Acc	Criteria
Aquila clanga Greater Spotted Eagle	B	1996	3	—	A	A1
Aquila heliaca Imperial Eagle	B	1996	2	—	A	A1, B2
Crex crex Corncrake	B	1996	500	600	A	A1, B2
Otus scops Scops Owl	B	1996	10,000	—	A	B2

Two globally threatened eagles *Aquila* breed in important numbers, as does *Crex crex* locally in wet grassland along the two rivers.

■ Protection status
National High **International** None
Part of IBA covered by National Park (Bashkiriya, 98,000 ha). Part of IBA covered by Zapovednik (Shulgan Tash, 22,531 ha). Part of IBA covered by regional Zakaznik (Altyn-Solok).

Conservation issues

Threats Abandonment/reduction of land management (C), Deforestation (commercial) (A), Disturbance to birds (B), Forest grazing (B)

Bird data are incomplete, and further surveys are required.

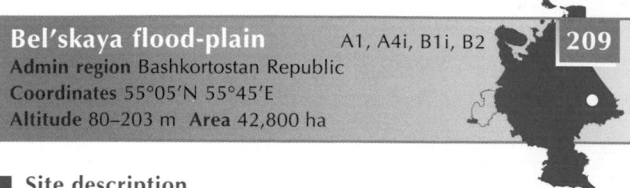

Bel'skaya flood-plain   A1, A4i, B1i, B2   **209**
Admin region Bashkortostan Republic
Coordinates 55°05′N 55°45′E
Altitude 80–203 m **Area** 42,800 ha

Site description
The valley flood-plain of the Bel'skaya river, to the north-west of the town of Ufa. Habitats consists primarily of wet grasslands, wet forest and numerous oxbow lakes.

Habitats Forest and woodland (50%; mixed forest; alluvial/very wet forest), Grassland (10%; humid grassland), Wetland (25%; standing fresh water; fen/transition mire/spring), Artificial landscape (15%; arable land; perennial crops/orchards/groves)
Land-use Agriculture, Forestry

Birds

Species	Season	Year	Pop min	Pop max	Acc	Criteria
Circus macrourus Pallid Harrier	B	1994	14	—	A	A1, B2
Aquila clanga Greater Spotted Eagle	B	1994	6	—	A	A1
Crex crex Corncrake	B	1994	100	—	A	A1
Grus grus Crane	P	1994	1,000	2,000	A	A4i, B1i
Gallinago media Great Snipe	B	1994	50	—	A	A1
Acrocephalus paludicola Aquatic Warbler	B	1994	12	—	A	A1, B2

Five species of global conservation concern breed, including three globally threatened species. The area attracts large numbers of *Grus grus* on passage.

Protection status
National None **International** None

Conservation issues

Threats Disturbance to birds (B), Drainage (A), Extraction industry (A), Industrialization/urbanization (A), Infrastructure (A), Recreation/tourism (B), Unsustainable exploitation (B)

Conservation measures should be taken to protect the site.

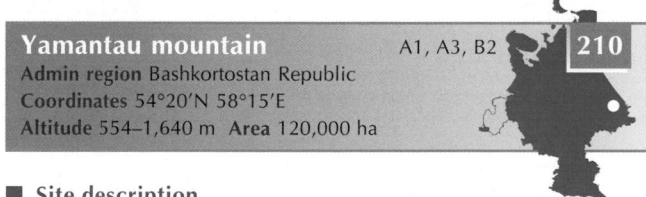

Yamantau mountain   A1, A3, B2   **210**
Admin region Bashkortostan Republic
Coordinates 54°20′N 58°15′E
Altitude 554–1,640 m **Area** 120,000 ha

Site description
A typical example of taiga forest, covering several high mountain-ridges dissected by the upper reaches of various rivers, located to the north-east of the town of Inzer.

Habitats Forest and woodland (90%; native coniferous forest; mixed forest), Grassland (10%; dry siliceous grassland)
Land-use Nature conservation/research (90%), Unknown (10%)

Birds

Species	Season	Year	Pop min	Pop max	Acc	Criteria
Mergus albellus Smew	B	1996	4	—	A	A3
Aquila heliaca Imperial Eagle	B	1996	2	—	A	A1, B2
Crex crex Corncrake	B	1996	20	—	A	A1
Gallinago media Great Snipe	B	1996	20	—	A	A1
Tringa nebularia Greenshank	B	1996	25	—	A	A3
Surnia ulula Hawk Owl	R	1996	5	—	A	A3
Strix nebulosa Great Grey Owl	R	1996	10	—	A	A3
Prunella atrogularis Black-throated Accentor	B	1996	30	—	A	B2
Phylloscopus borealis Arctic Warbler	B	1996	150	—	A	A3
Perisoreus infaustus Siberian Jay	B	1996	25	—	A	A3
Fringilla montifringilla Brambling	B	—	—	—	—	A3
Emberiza rustica Rustic Bunting	B	—	—	—	—	A3

Breeding species include three species of global conservation concern (two of which are globally threatened), as well as eight of the 15 species in Europe that are restricted to the boreal biome (when breeding). The avifauna contains west Siberian species, of biogeographical interest, e.g. *Prunella atrogularis*.

Protection status
National Partial **International** None
100,000 ha of IBA covered by Zapovednik (Yuzhno–Uralskiy, 254,914 ha).

Conservation issues

Threats Infrastructure (A)

Iremel'ski mountain   A1, A3, B2   **211**
Admin region Bashkortostan Republic, Chelyabinsk
Coordinates 54°30′N 59°00′E
Altitude 612–1,582 m **Area** 90,000 ha

Site description
The IBA is located in a mountainous part of the Bashkortostan Republic, to the south-east of the village of Meseda, near to the border with the Chelyabinsk region.

Habitats Forest and woodland (90%; native coniferous forest; mixed forest), Grassland (10%; alpine/subalpine/boreal grassland)
Land-use Forestry (20%), Tourism/recreation (80%)

Birds

Species	Season	Year	Pop min	Pop max	Acc	Criteria
Mergus albellus Smew	B	1996	5	—	—	A3
Aquila heliaca Imperial Eagle	B	1996	2	—	A	A1, B2
Crex crex Corncrake	B	1996	20	—	A	A1
Gallinago media Great Snipe	B	1996	20	—	A	A1
Tringa nebularia Greenshank	B	1996	18	—	—	A3
Surnia ulula Hawk Owl	R	1996	2	—	—	A3
Strix nebulosa Great Grey Owl	R	1996	5	—	—	A3
Prunella atrogularis Black-throated Accentor	B	1996	20	—	—	B2
Phylloscopus borealis Arctic Warbler	B	1996	Common	—	—	A3
Perisoreus infaustus Siberian Jay	B	1996	Common	—	—	A3
Fringilla montifringilla Brambling	B	1996	Common	—	—	A3
Loxia leucoptera Two-barred Crossbill	B	1996	Common	—	—	A3
Emberiza rustica Rustic Bunting	B	1996	Common	—	—	A3

Breeding species include three species of global conservation concern (two of which are globally threatened), and nine of the 15 species in Europe that are restricted to the boreal biome (when breeding).

Protection status
National None **International** None

Conservation issues

Threats Disturbance to birds (A), Infrastructure (A), Recreation/tourism (A)

A project is underway to establish a National Park here. Available bird data are incomplete and more survey work is required.

Irendyk ridge   A1, A4i, A4iv, B1i, B1iv, B2   **212**
Admin region Bashkortostan Republic
Coordinates 53°20′N 58°30′E
Altitude 416–1,118 m **Area** 150,000 ha

Site description
A narrow forested mountain ridge, 10–20 km in length and surrounded by steppe.

Habitats Forest and woodland (80%), Grassland (20%; steppe/dry calcareous grassland; humid grassland)
Land-use Agriculture (60%), Fisheries/aquaculture (5%), Forestry (40%), Urban/industrial/transport (5%)

■ **Birds**

Species		Season	Year	Pop min	Pop max	Acc	Criteria
Circus macrourus	Pallid Harrier	B	1996	50	100	A	A1, B2
Falco naumanni	Lesser Kestrel	B	1996	2	10	B	A1, B2
Crex crex	Corncrake	B	1996	300	—	A	A1
Glareola nordmanni	Black-winged Pratincole	B	1996	12	—	A	A1
Gallinago media	Great Snipe	B	1996	100	—	A	A1, A4i, B1i
Otus scops	Scops Owl	B	1996	7,000	7,000	A	B2

Five species of global conservation concern breed within the IBA. The ridge is a major migratory bottleneck site for more than 20,000 raptors, which breed mainly in western Siberia.

■ **Protection status**
National None **International** None

■ **Conservation issues**

Threats Agricultural intensification/expansion (A), Disturbance to birds (B), Intensified forest management (A)

A nature park is in the process of being established at the site.

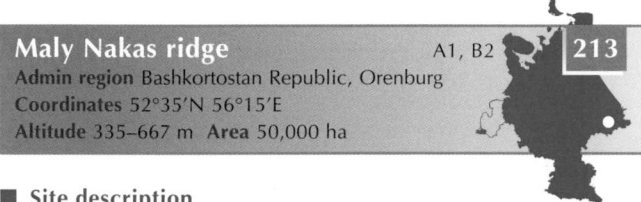

Maly Nakas ridge A1, B2 **213**
Admin region Bashkortostan Republic, Orenburg
Coordinates 52°35'N 56°15'E
Altitude 335–667 m **Area** 50,000 ha

■ **Site description**
The IBA is situated on the border between the Bashkortostan Republic and the Orenburg region, and contains oak-pine (*Quercus-Pinus*) forests.

Habitats Forest and woodland (80%; broadleaved deciduous forest), Grassland (20%; steppe/dry calcareous grassland; humid grassland)
Land-use Agriculture (35%), Forestry (60%), Urban/industrial/transport (5%)

■ **Birds**

Species		Season	Year	Pop min	Pop max	Acc	Criteria
Circus macrourus	Pallid Harrier	B	1996	15	—	A	A1, B2
Crex crex	Corncrake	B	1996	40	40	—	A1
Otus scops	Scops Owl	B	1996	3,000	—	A	B2

Significant numbers of two species of global conservation concern breed in the area.

■ **Protection status**
National None **International** None

■ **Conservation issues**

Threats Forest grazing (A), Infrastructure (A), Intensified forest management (A)

It has been suggested that a regional Zakaznik be created here.

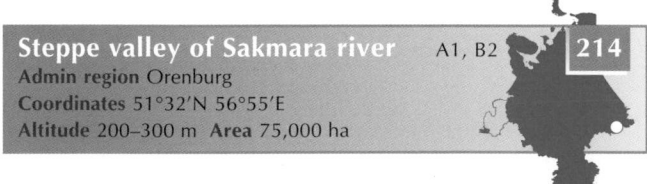

Steppe valley of Sakmara river A1, B2 **214**
Admin region Orenburg
Coordinates 51°32'N 56°55'E
Altitude 200–300 m **Area** 75,000 ha

■ **Site description**
A forest-steppe landscape, about half of which remains relatively natural, the other half having been converted to cultivated land.

Habitats Forest and woodland (15%; broadleaved deciduous forest; alluvial/very wet forest), Grassland (35%; steppe/dry calcareous grassland), Artificial landscape (50%; arable land; other urban/industrial areas)
Land-use Agriculture (80%), Forestry (15%), Urban/industrial/transport (5%)

■ **Birds**

Species		Season	Year	Pop min	Pop max	Acc	Criteria
Aquila heliaca	Imperial Eagle	B	1997	4	10	B	A1, B2

An important site for breeding *Aquila heliaca*.

■ **Protection status**
National None **International** None
There is no up-to-date information.

■ **Conservation issues**

Threats Abandonment/reduction of land management (A), Unsustainable exploitation (B)

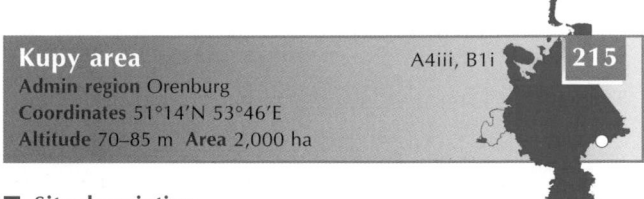

Kupy area A4iii, B1i **215**
Admin region Orenburg
Coordinates 51°14'N 53°46'E
Altitude 70–85 m **Area** 2,000 ha

■ **Site description**
Meadows on the flood-plain of the Ilek river, in the south-east of the Orenburg region near the border with Kazakhstan.

Habitats Forest and woodland (6%; alluvial/very wet forest), Grassland (79%; steppe/dry calcareous grassland; humid grassland), Wetland (15%; sand-dunes/sand beach; standing fresh water; river/stream; water-fringe vegetation)
Land-use Agriculture (80%), Fisheries/aquaculture (5%), Forestry (6%), Water management (8%)

■ **Birds**

Species		Season	Year	Pop min	Pop max	Acc	Criteria
Anas penelope	Wigeon	P	1997	8,000	10,000	B	B1i

The site supports 20,000 or more migrating waterbirds on a regular basis, involving more than 50 species, with *Anas penelope* occurring in important numbers. Breeding species of global conservation concern that do not meet IBA criteria: *Haliaeetus albicilla* (1–2 pairs), *Circus macrourus* (4–5 pairs).

■ **Protection status**
National None **International** None

■ **Conservation issues**

Threats Disturbance to birds (A), Firewood collection (B), Selective logging/cutting (B), Unsustainable exploitation (A)

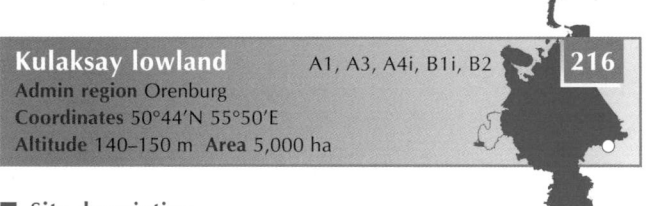

Kulaksay lowland A1, A3, A4i, B1i, B2 **216**
Admin region Orenburg
Coordinates 50°44'N 55°50'E
Altitude 140–150 m **Area** 5,000 ha

■ **Site description**
This area lies on a flyway used by geese *Anser/Branta* on spring migration, a route known about for more than 100 years, lying to the south-east of the town of Akbulak.

Habitats Forest and woodland (3%; broadleaved deciduous forest), Scrub (1%; scrub), Grassland (75%; steppe/dry calcareous grassland; humid grassland), Wetland (20%; sand-dunes/sand beach; standing fresh water; river/stream), Artificial landscape (1%)
Land-use Agriculture (75%), Fisheries/aquaculture (7%), Forestry (3%), Hunting (90%), Nature conservation/research (3%)

■ **Birds**

Species		Season	Year	Pop min	Pop max	Acc	Criteria
Anser erythropus	Lesser White-fronted Goose	P	1997	200	350	C	A1, B1i
Branta ruficollis	Red-breasted Goose	P	1997	2,430	—	B	A1, A4i, B1i
Circus macrourus	Pallid Harrier	B	1997	—	10	A	A1, A3, B2
Falco naumanni	Lesser Kestrel	P	1997	60	100	B	A1
Chettusia gregaria	Sociable Plover	B	1997	—	5	C	A3

Five species of global conservation concern occur in important numbers. Three of the four are globally threatened, staging in the area during migration, while *Chettusia gregaria* and *Circus macrourus* breed (both restricted to the Eurasian steppe biome when breeding). Breeding species of global conservation concern that do not meet IBA criteria:

Haliaeetus albicilla, Crex crex (10–15 pairs), *Tetrax tetrax* (8–10 pairs), and *Otis tarda* (no data).

■ **Protection status**
National Low **International** None
Some of the forest is protected, but no more information is available currently.

■ **Conservation issues**

Threats Disturbance to birds (A), Selective logging/cutting (B), Unsustainable exploitation (A)

There is a special limitation on spring hunting.

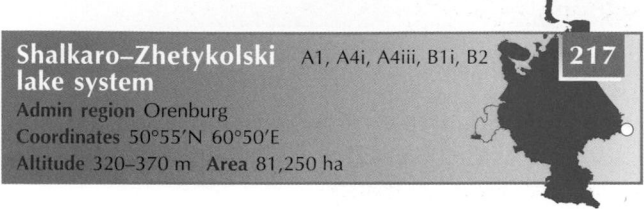

Shalkaro–Zhetykolski lake system A1, A4i, A4iii, B1i, B2 217
Admin region Orenburg
Coordinates 50°55′N 60°50′E
Altitude 320–370 m Area 81,250 ha

■ **Site description**
A large system of lakes in the steppe zone of the eastern Orenburg region, near to the border with Kazakhstan.

Habitats Grassland (80%; steppe/dry calcareous grassland; humid grassland), Wetland (20%; standing fresh water), Artificial landscape (30%; arable land)
Land-use Agriculture (65%), Not utilized (9%), Other (25%)

■ **Birds**

Species	Season	Year	Pop min	Pop max	Acc	Criteria
Pelecanus crispus Dalmatian Pelican	B	1996	—	13	—	A1, A4i, B1i, B2
Anser albifrons White-fronted Goose	P	1996	200,000	300,000	B	A4i, B1i
Anser erythropus Lesser White-fronted Goose	P	1996	500	1,500	B	A1, A4i, B1i
Anser anser Greylag Goose	B	1996	100	—	—	B1i
Anser anser Greylag Goose	N	1996	1,000	1,500	—	B1i
Branta ruficollis Red-breasted Goose	P	1996	10,000	15,000	A	A1, A4i, B1i
Circus macrourus Pallid Harrier	B	1996	10	100	B	A1, B2
Glareola nordmanni Black-winged Pratincole	B	1996	100	150	B	A1, A4i, B1i, B2

A very important area for species of global conservation concern. Three such species breed while two others stage here during migration,

all in highly significant numbers. Vast numbers of *Anser albifrons* (more than 200,000) also occur on passage. Further research on the spring and autumn migrations is required.

■ **Protection status**
National None **International** None

■ **Conservation issues**

Threats Abandonment/reduction of land management (A), Aquaculture/fisheries (B), Disturbance to birds (A), Unsustainable exploitation (A)

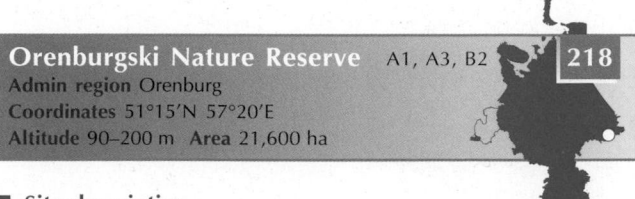

Orenburgski Nature Reserve A1, A3, B2 218
Admin region Orenburg
Coordinates 51°15′N 57°20′E
Altitude 90–200 m Area 21,600 ha

■ **Site description**
The area consists of several isolated expanses of undulating steppe, including four sections of the Orenburgski Nature Reserve which contain large patches of primary grassland steppe.

Habitats Grassland (90%; steppe/dry calcareous grassland)
Land-use Nature conservation/research (100%)

■ **Birds**

Species	Season	Year	Pop min	Pop max	Acc	Criteria
Aquila heliaca Imperial Eagle	B	1990	—	6	C	A1, A3, B2
[1] *Tetrax tetrax* Little Bustard	B	1990	—	43	C	A1
Melanocorypha yeltoniensis Black Lark	B	1990	4,000	12,000	C	A3, B2
Calandrella brachydactyla Short-toed Lark	B	1990	2,000	7,000	C	B2
Alauda arvensis Skylark	B	1990	11,000	30,000	C	B2

1. Breeding individuals.

An important breeding area for two globally threatened species, with significant numbers of three lark species also present (including one that is restricted to the Eurasian steppe biome when breeding).

■ **Protection status**
National High **International** None
21,600 ha of IBA covered by Zapovednik (Orenburgskiy, 21,653 ha).

REFERENCES

BLAGOVIDOV, A., CHEBAKOVA, I. AND WILLIAMS, M. (1995) *Immediate action plan for the protected-area system of Russia (priorities for investment)*. Washington, DC: World Bank/GEF.

GALUSHIN, V. M. AND ZUBAKIN, V. A. (1998) Research priorities for bird conservation in Russia. Pp. 355–366 in J. M. Marzluff and R. Sallabanks, eds. *Avian conservation. Research and management*. Washington, DC: Island Press.

GANUSEVYCH, S. A. (1983) [On the composition and distribution of raptors on the Kola Peninsula.] *Ecology of raptors*. Moscow. (In Russian.)

GANUSEVYCH, S. A. (1988) [Raptors of the Kola Peninsula.] *Ornithology Res.* 23: 73–80. (In Russian).

GRIMMETT, R. F. A. AND JONES, T. A., EDS. (1989) *Important bird areas in Europe*. Cambridge, UK: International Council for Bird Preservation (Techn. Publ. no. 3).

HEATH, M. F. AND BORGGREVE, C. (2000) *BirdLife International/EBCC European Bird Database 1998*. Cambridge, UK: BirdLife International.

IUCN (1994) *Guidelines for protected area management categories*. Gland, Switzerland, and Cambridge, UK: International Union for the Conservation of Nature and Natural Resources.

KALABIN, G. V., ED. (1992) [*Special protected areas in the Murmansk region*.] Apatity. (In Russian.)

KRIVENKO, V. G. (1995) Inventory of wetlands of international importance in the Russian Federation. Final report 1994–1995. Ministry of Protection of the Environment and Natural Resources of the Russian Federation. Centre for International Projects. (Unpublished.)

KRIVENKO, V. G., ED. (1998) [*Wetlands in Russia, Vol. 1 (Wetlands of international importance)*]. Moscow: Wetlands International (Publication No. 47). (In Russian.)

LANGEVELD, M. J. AND GRIMMETT, R. F. A. (1990) *Important Bird Areas in Europe: wetlands for the shadow list of Ramsar sites*. Cambridge, UK: International Council for Bird Preservation/Slimbridge, UK: International Wildfowl and Wetlands Research Bureau.

SKOKOVA, N. N. AND VINOGRADOV, V. G., EDS. (1988) [*Conservation of waterbird sites*.] Moscow. (In Russian.)

SOBOLEV, N. A., SHVARTS, E. A., KREINDLIN, M. L., MOKIEVSKI. V. O. AND ZUBAKIN, V. A. (1995) Russia's protected areas: a survey and identification of development problems. *Biodiversity and Conservation* 4: 964–983.

STATTERSFIELD, A. J., CROSBY, M. J., LONG, A. J. AND WEGE, D. C. (1998) *Endemic Bird Areas of the World: priorities for biodiversity conservation*. Cambridge, UK: BirdLife International (BirdLife Conservation Series no. 7).

TUCKER, G. M. AND HEATH, M. F. (1994) *Birds in Europe: their conservation status*. Cambridge, UK: BirdLife International (BirdLife Conservation Series no. 3).

VOLKOV, A. E., ED. (1996) *Strict Nature Reserves (Zapovedniki) of Russia. Collection of 'Chronicle of Nature' data for 1991–1992*. Moscow: Sabashnikov.

SLOVAKIA

PAVOL KAŇUCH

Imperial Eagle *Aquila heliaca*
on nest with young.
(PHOTO: Š. DANKO)

GENERAL INFORMATION

Slovakia is situated in central Europe and covers an area of 49,036 km². It is bordered by Ukraine to the east, Hungary to the south, Austria to the south-west, the Czech Republic to the west and Poland to the north (Map 1). The lowest point (92 m elevation) is in the south-east of the country and the highest point (2,265 m) is in the north. Slovakia is separated into eight administrative regions and 79 districts.

In geomorphological terms, Slovakia belongs to the Alp–Himalayan unit, with two sub-units represented, the Carpathians (c.65% of the land area) and the Pannonian plain (c.35%). Slovakia is a highly diverse country in terms of habitat types represented,

lying as it does on the boundary between important physical and biogeographical zones, including several major watersheds.

Slovakia has 32 Important Bird Areas (IBAs) covering 1,216,737 ha, or 25% of the land area (Table 1, Map 1). The IBAs are fairly evenly dispersed throughout the country, and have an average size of 38,021 ha. The previous international IBA inventory identified 16 IBAs (not including subsites) (Grimmett and Jones 1989), 15 of which were included in the total of 18 IBAs described by the 1992 national inventory (Hora and Kaňuch 1992), the exception being former site CZ016, Trnavské rybníky ponds. An additional two sites described in both the 1989 and 1992 inventories do not meet the current criteria (Table 1). Sixteen new IBAs have been identified since 1989 (Table 1), three of which were included

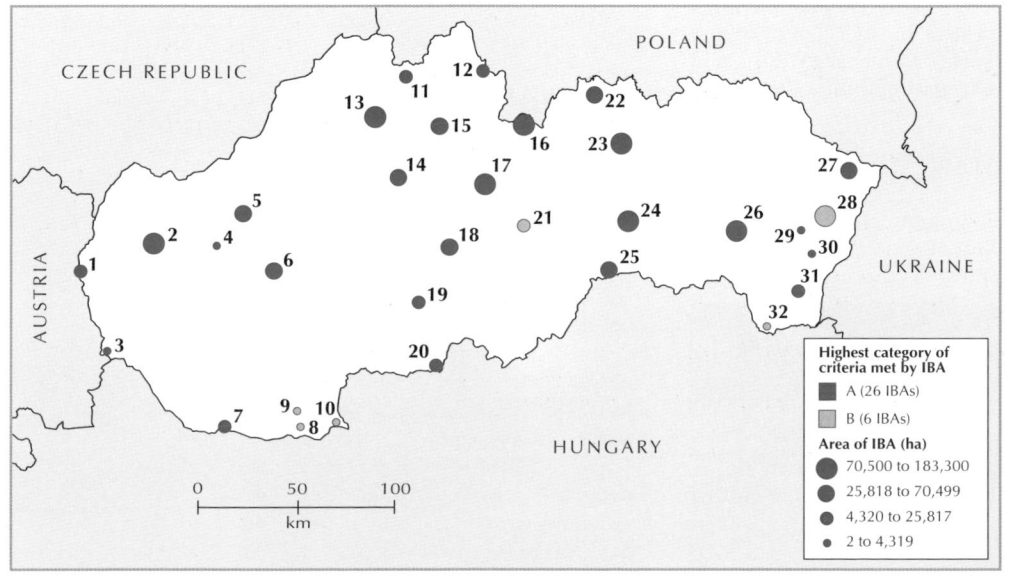

Map 1. Location, area and criteria category of Important Bird Areas in Slovakia.

653

Table 1. Summary of Important Bird Areas in Slovakia.   32 IBAs covering 12,167 km²

IBA code	National code	1989 code	International name	National name	Administrative region	Area (ha)	Criteria (see p. 11)
001	SR-01	CZ014	River Morava flood-plain	Niva Moravy	Bratislava, Trnava	18,935	A1, A4i, B1i, B2, B3
002	SR-05	—	Malé Karpaty	Malé Karpaty	Bratislava, Trenčín, Trnava	76,600	A1, B2, B3
003	—	—	Sysľovské fields	Sysľovské polia	Bratislava	3,860	A1, A4i, A4iii, B1i, B2, B3
004	SR-03	—	Sĺňava	Sĺnava	Trnava	690	A4iii, B1i
005	—	—	Považský Inovec	Považský Inovec	Trenčín, Trnava, Nitra	47,210	A1, B2
006	—	—	Tríbeč	Tríbeč	Trenčín, Nitra	27,590	A1, B2
007	SR-04, SR-04-1, SR-04-2, SR-04-3	CZ017, CZ017-1, CZ017-2, CZ017-3	River Danube flood-plain	Niva Dunaja	Bratislava, Trnava, Nitra	22,040	A1, A4i, A4iii, B1i, B2, B3
008	SR-04	CZ017	Jurský Chlm	Jurský Chlm	Nitra	53	B2
009	SR-04-5	CZ017-5	Parížske marshes	Parížske močiare	Nitra	184	B3
010	—	—	Burda	Burda	Nitra	2,700	B2
011	—	—	Riečnica	Riečnica	Žilina	4,320	A1
012	SR-06	CZ018	Oravská basin	Oravská kotlina	Žilina	16,745	A1, B2
013	SR-07	CZ019	Malá Fatra	Malá Fatra	Trenčín, Žilina	70,500	A1, B2, B3
014	SR-08	CZ020	Veľká Fatra	Veľká Fatra	Žilina, Banská Bystrica	60,610	A1, B2, B3
015	—	—	Chočské hills	Chočské vrchy	Žilina	25,818	A1, B2
016	SR-09	CZ021	Tatry	Tatry	Žilina, Prešov	98,420	A1, A3, B2, B3
017	SR-10	CZ022	Nízke Tatry	Nízke Tatry	Žilina, Banská Bystrica	183,000	A1, B2, B3
018	SR-11	—	Poľana	Poľana	Banská Bystrica	28,930	A1, B2, B3
019	—	—	Lešť	Lešť	Banská Bystrica	5,200	A1, B2, B3
020	—	—	River Ipeľ flood-plain	Niva Ipľa	Banská Bystrica, Nitra	7,715	A1, B2, B3
021	—	—	Muránska plateau	Muránska planina	Banská Bystrica	8,820	B2
022	—	—	Spišská Magura	Spišská Magura	Prešov	39,860	A1, B2
023	—	—	Levočské hills	Levočské vrchy	Prešov	71,400	A1, B2, B3
024	—	—	Volovské hills	Volovské vrchy	Košice	140,000	A1, B2, B3
025	SR-13	CZ024	Slovenský karst	Slovenský kras	Košice	50,230	A1, B2, B3
026	SR-14	CZ025	Slanské hills	Slanské vrchy	Prešov, Košice	70,500	A1, B2, B3
027	—	—	Bukovské hills	Bukovské vrchy	Prešov	40,100	A1, B2, B3
028	SR-15	CZ026	Vihorlatské hills	Vihorlatské vrchy	Prešov, Košice	74,630	B2, B3
029	SR-18	CZ029	Zemplínska Šírava	Zemplínska Šírava	Košice	3,015	A4i, A4iii, B1i
030	SR-17	CZ028	Senné	Senné	Košice	1,440	A4i, A4iii, B1i, B2, B3
031	SR-16	CZ027, CZ027-1	River Latorica flood-plain	Niva Latorice	Košice	15,620	A1, B2
032	SR-16	CZ027	Streda nad Bodrogom	Streda nad Bodrogom	Košice	2	B2

Sites and subsites identified in the previous inventory of IBAs in Europe (Grimmett and Jones 1989) but no longer considered to be IBAs
CZ014-1 Jakubovské rybníky ponds; CZ015 Súr peatbog; CZ016 Trnavské rybníky ponds; CZ017-4 Zlatná na Ostrove; CZ023 Pieniny mountains; CZ027-2 Tajba marshes.

in the 1992 national inventory (Hora and Kaňuch 1992). The borders of three IBAs (Záhorská lowland (former site CZ014), Podunajsko (former site CZ017) and East Slovakia marshes (former site CZ027)) have changed, with the most valuable areas incorporated into three current IBAs (River Morava flood-plain (001), River Danube flood-plain (007) and River Latorica flood-plain (031) respectively). As a result of these changes, three additional small IBAs have been created: Jurský Chlm (008) and Parížske marshes (009) used to be part of former site CZ017, and Streda nad Bodrogom (032) used to be part of former site CZ027.

ORNITHOLOGICAL IMPORTANCE

One hundred and fourteen species of European conservation concern (SPECs) breed regularly in Slovakia, of which five are globally

Table 2. Important Bird Areas in Slovakia that are important for species of global conservation concern (meeting criterion A1).

Species	IBA code
Haliaeetus albicilla White-tailed Eagle	007
Aquila heliaca Imperial Eagle	002, 005, 006, 024, 026
Crex crex Corncrake	001, 002, 011, 012, 013, 014, 015, 016, 017, 018, 019, 020, 022, 023, 024, 025, 026, 027, 031
Otis tarda Great Bustard	003

Table 3. Important Bird Areas in Slovakia that support important numbers of one or more congregatory species (i.e. meeting criteria A4 and/or B1). IBAs meeting both criteria A4 and B1 for the species are shown in **bold**. IBAs meeting only criterion B1 for the species concerned, and not A4, are shown in normal type. For key to 'Season', see p. 7.

Species	Season	IBA code
Tachybaptus ruficollis Little Grebe	P	**007**
Podiceps nigricollis Black-necked Grebe	P	**030**
Phalacrocorax carbo Cormorant	B	030
	P	001, **007**, 029
Egretta alba Great White Egret	B	**030**
	P	**003**, **007**
Platalea leucorodia Spoonbill	B	030
Anser fabalis Bean Goose	W	**003**
	P	001, **007**, **029**, 030
Anser albifrons White-fronted Goose	P	029
Anser anser Greylag Goose	W	003
	P	001, 004, **007**
Anas platyrhynchos Mallard	P	007, 029, 030
Aythya ferina Pochard	P	**007**
Aythya fuligula Tufted Duck	P	**007**
Bucephala clangula Goldeneye	P	**007**
Mergus albellus Smew	P	**007**
Larus minutus Little Gull	P	**029**
Larus ridibundus Black-headed Gull	P	**029**

threatened or near-threatened (*Aythya nyroca*, *Haliaeetus albicilla*, *Aquila heliaca*, *Crex crex* and *Otis tarda*) and another 60 have an unfavourable conservation status in Europe (Tucker and Heath 1994). Twenty-five SPECs regularly winter or occur whilst on migration. Significantly, Slovakia holds a large proportion (c.10% or more) of the European populations of four SPECs (*Aquila heliaca*, *A. pomarina*, *Falco cherrug* and *Ficedula albicollis*).

Nine IBAs (001, 007, 014, 016, 024, 025, 026, 027 and 030) have a minimum of ten bird species meeting IBA criteria. Three of these sites are wetlands important for breeding, wintering and passage species (River Morava flood-plain (001), River Danube flood-plain (007) and Senné (030)); the other six are mainly forested mountainous areas holding important breeding assemblages.

Twenty-three IBAs have been identified as being internationally important for globally threatened or near-threatened species (Table 2). One IBA (016) supports significant numbers of two species restricted to the Eurasian high-montane (alpine) biome (*Tichodroma muraria* and *Prunella collaris*), and therefore meets the A3 criterion. Five IBAs support at least 1% of the biogeographical population of at least one waterbird species, and therefore meet the A4i criterion (Table 3). Four of these sites hold more than 20,000 passage waterbirds on a regular basis, and thus qualify under the A4iii criterion (Table 1). Six IBAs meet the B1i criterion by supporting at least 1% of the regional flyway population of at least one species of waterbird (Table 3).

Twenty-eight IBAs are important breeding sites for 31 species that have an unfavourable conservation status in Europe (SPECs 2 and 3), and qualify under the B2 criterion (Tables 1 and 4). Nineteen IBAs support breeding species with a favourable conservation status but that are concentrated in Europe (SPEC 4), and therefore qualify under the B3 criterion (Tables 1 and 4).

Twenty-five SPECs with important European populations are not adequately covered by the Slovak IBA network due to the dispersed nature of their distributions (for example, *Falco tinnunculus*, *Columba palumbus*, *Streptopelia turtur*, *Strix aluco*, *Dendrocopos syriacus* and many passerines).

HABITATS

Forests cover 19,930 km² (41%) of the Slovakian land area, and are predominantly semi-natural in origin. Lowland floodplains support hardwood (*Quercus*, *Fraxinus*) and softwood (*Populus*, *Salix*) riverine forest. Broadleaved deciduous (*Quercus*, *Fagus*, *Carpinus*, *Acer*) and coniferous (*Pinus*) forests occur in the south of the country and up to medium altitudes in mountainous areas. The northern forested regions and high mountains hold coniferous (*Picea*, *Abies*) forest and subalpine scrub (*Pinus*). Twenty-six IBAs (81%) support forests, with cover exceeding 50% at 17 sites (Figure 1). This is a key habitat for *Ciconia nigra*, *Pernis apivorus*, *Aquila pomarina*, *A. heliaca*, *A. chrysaetos*, *Falco cherrug*, *Columba oenas*, *Picus canus*, *Picoides tridactylus*, *Phoenicurus phoenicurus*, *Turdus torquatus*, *Phylloscopus sibilatrix*, *Ficedula albicollis*, *Parus cristatus* and *Carduelis spinus*.

Artificial habitats are present at 29 IBAs (91%), and cover less than 50% of the IBA area with the exception of site 003, which comprises 95% arable land and is a key breeding site for *Falco vespertinus*, *Circus pygargus* and *Otis tarda* (50% of the Slovak breeding population), as well as an important wintering site for *Anser fabalis*, *A. anser* and *Otis tarda*. Ruderal and arable land provide important breeding habitat for *Crex crex* at several IBAs.

Grasslands occur at 27 IBAs (84%), with wet and/or mesophile meadows and boreal and alpine meadows of particular significance. Wet grasslands are the main breeding habitat of *Crex crex*. Scrub habitats are represented at 19 IBAs (59%), and are increasing in area following reductions in land-management practices over the last 10 years. Scrub provides nesting habitat for increasing populations of *Lanius collurio*, *Sylvia nisoria* and *Emberiza cia*.

Wetlands are found at 11 IBAs (34%), and comprise standing fresh water (lakes, reservoirs, fish-ponds), rivers and streams, and water-fringe vegetation. These are key breeding areas for colonial waterbirds including *Ardea purpurea*, *Nycticorax nycticorax*, *Platalea leucorodia* and *Chlidonias hybridus*, and for birds that nest in reedbeds (*Ixobrychus minutus*, *Botaurus stellaris* and *Locustella luscinioides*), marshes (*Porzana parva*) and along rivers, streams

Table 4. Species of European conservation concern with significant breeding populations at Important Bird Areas in Slovakia (meeting any IBA criteria).

Species [1]	Minimum national breeding population (pairs) [2]	Proportion (%) of national population breeding at all IBAs in Slovakia
Botaurus stellaris Bittern	50	30
Ixobrychus minutus Little Bittern	200	25
Nycticorax nycticorax Night Heron	100	100[3]
Ardea purpurea Purple Heron	40	45
Ciconia nigra Black Stork	300	64
Ciconia ciconia White Stork	1,025	18
Platalea leucorodia Spoonbill	10	100
Aythya ferina Pochard	2,300	2
Pernis apivorus Honey Buzzard	800	36
Milvus migrans Black Kite	50	56
Circaetus gallicus Short-toed Eagle	20	30
Circus pygargus Montagu's Harrier	30	13
Aquila pomarina Lesser Spotted Eagle	700	33
Aquila heliaca Imperial Eagle	30	60
Aquila chrysaetos Golden Eagle	60	93
Falco vespertinus Red-footed Falcon	30	27
Falco cherrug Saker	30	47
Tetrao tetrix Black Grouse	600 individuals	68
Porzana parva Little Crake	70	66
Crex crex Corncrake	600	100[3]
Otis tarda Great Bustard	10 individuals	50
Chlidonias hybridus Whiskered Tern	120	17
Columba oenas Stock Dove	3,500	51
Bubo bubo Eagle Owl	300	48
Caprimulgus europaeus Nightjar	900	36
Alcedo atthis Kingfisher	700	21
Merops apiaster Bee-eater	700	45
Jynx torquilla Wryneck	2,500	30
Picus canus Grey-headed Woodpecker	1,500	80
Dendrocopos medius Middle Spotted Woodpecker	2,500	11
Picoides tridactylus Three-toed Woodpecker	800	77
Riparia riparia Sand Martin	15,000	16
Monticola saxatilis Rock Thrush	30	47
Turdus torquatus Ring Ouzel	3,000	65
Locustella luscinioides Savi's Warbler	600	51
Sylvia nisoria Barred Warbler	6,000	16
Lanius minor Lesser Grey Shrike	220	53
Emberiza cia Rock Bunting	150	100[3]

Estimates of the total numbers of the following SPECs present in IBAs in Slovakia are not currently available: *Phoenicurus phoenicurus*, *Turdus viscivorus*, *Locustella fluviatilis*, *Phylloscopus sibilatrix*, *Ficedula albicollis*, *Parus cristatus*, *Lanius collurio* and *Carduelis spinus*.

1. Only those species of European conservation concern (see Box 1, p. 12) that meet IBA criteria in Slovakia are listed.
2. Data are taken from the BirdLife/EBCC European Bird Database 1998 (Heath and Borggreve 2000).
3. The percentage of the national population in IBAs exceeds 100%. Usually this is because the national population estimate has not been updated recently whilst the IBA population estimate has been recently updated with new data as a result of comprehensive surveys of IBAs themselves. Also, the individual site count for a species may be the maximum or average over recent years, and summing these may record more birds than are present nationally in any single year.

Figure 1. Habitats at Important Bird Areas in Slovakia (see Appendix 3 for definitions of habitats).

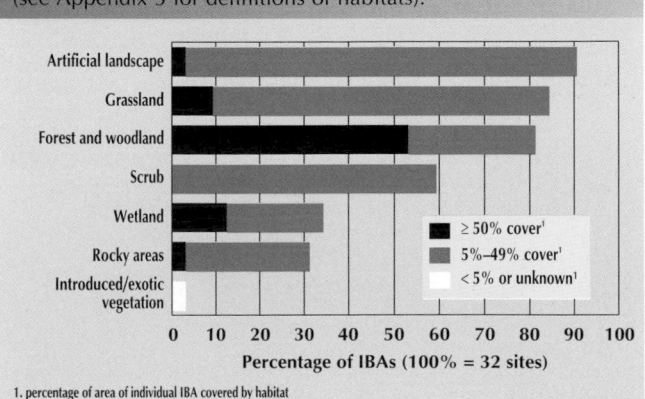

1. percentage of area of individual IBA covered by habitat

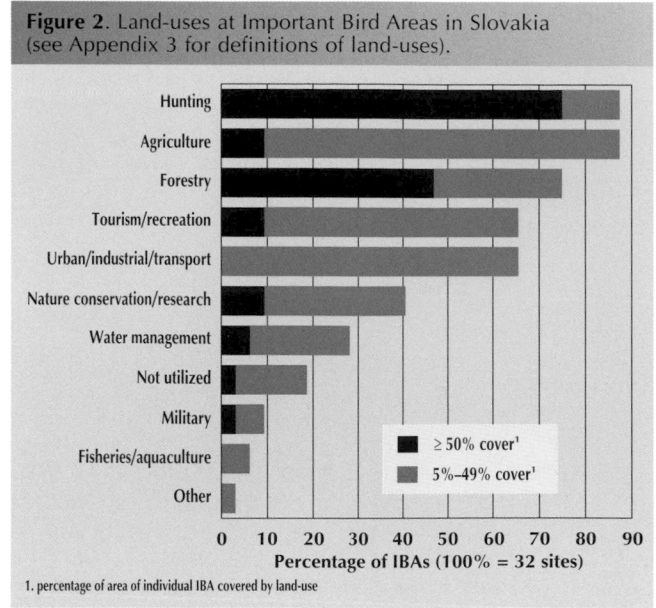

Figure 2. Land-uses at Important Bird Areas in Slovakia (see Appendix 3 for definitions of land-uses).

Forestry is present at 24 IBAs (75%), covering a minimum of 50% of the area of 15 of these. Forestry management tends to be very intensive, although conservation measures have been implemented in protected areas. Outside of these protected areas, measures are limited to seasonal adjustments of logging regimes and other forestry activities where these impact on the nesting sites of, for example, raptors.

Tourism/recreation is present at 21 IBAs (66%), mainly in mountainous regions and at wetland sites. Activity tends to be extensive (for example, trekking and biking), and only small areas are allocated exclusively for intensive recreational purposes (for example, ski-lifts).

The most important threats to Slovak IBAs are posed by intensive forestry practices (logging, construction of forest roads, use of heavy machinery, the introduction of non-native tree species), which affect 19 IBAs (59%), and commercial deforestation (large scale clear-cuts, soil erosion), which affects 18 IBAs (56%) and is of high importance at 12 of these (Figure 3). Together with natural events (tree-falls, forest fires) (14 IBAs, 44%), these threats have combined to cause a rapid decline in the quality of Slovak forests, with negative implications for breeding *Ciconia nigra*, raptors, woodpeckers and many passerines.

Human disturbance to birds at breeding and/or roosting sites poses a threat at 10 IBAs (31%). Together with unsustainable exploitation (nest robbery, photography, hunting) (17 IBAs, 53%) and recreation/tourism (trekking, paragliding, rock-climbing, watersports) (18 IBAs, 56%), disturbance adversely affects herons, *Ciconia nigra*, geese, raptors (eagles and falcons), *Otis tarda* and *Bubo bubo* (Figure 3).

The abandonment of agricultural land and changes in management practices (for example, reductions in grazing intensity) over the last decade have affected 21 IBAs (66%). Successional or intentional afforestation has taken place at 10 IBAs (31%), and burning has replaced grazing as a grassland management tool at 18 IBAs (56%). Both these threaten the breeding habitat of *Crex crex*. Agricultural intensification (conversion of meadows to arable land, scrub removal, pesticide and fertiliser use, growing unsuitable crops) is less of a problem, although at one site (003) it poses a significant threat to *Otis tarda* and *Circus pygargus*.

Infrastructure development (18 IBAs, 56%) and industrialization/urbanization (17 IBAs, 53%) cause general habitat degradation. Drainage, dredging/canalization, construction of dykes/dams and filling-in of wetlands affect lowland marshes, wet meadows and riverine flood-plains.

The most threatened IBAs are considered to be the River Danube flood-plain (007) (commercial deforestation, intensive forest

and canals (*Ixobrychus minutus*, *Alcedo atthis* and *Locustella fluviatilis*).

Rocky habitats are represented at 10 IBAs (31%) and are found in the high mountain ranges, as well as at inland cliffs, quarries, sand-dunes and sand banks. These provide breeding habitats for species including *Aquila chrysaetos*, *Falco cherrug*, *Bubo bubo*, *Merops apiaster* and *Riparia riparia*.

IMPACTS ON IBAs – LAND-USE AND THREATS

Agriculture, along with hunting, is the most commonly occurring land-use at Slovakian IBAs (28 IBAs, 88%), although it exceeds 50% of the IBA area at only three sites (Figure 2). Agricultural practices in IBAs are less intensive than in other parts of the country and are oriented towards cattle and sheep-grazing, haymaking or, in some places, the growing of wheat, potatoes, rape and other crops.

Hunting also takes place at 28 IBAs (88%), and exceeds 50% of the IBA area at 24 of these. Hunting is permitted across almost the entire country, with the exception of strict nature reserves, Ramsar Sites, and areas along state boundaries (Hunting Act No. 23/1962).

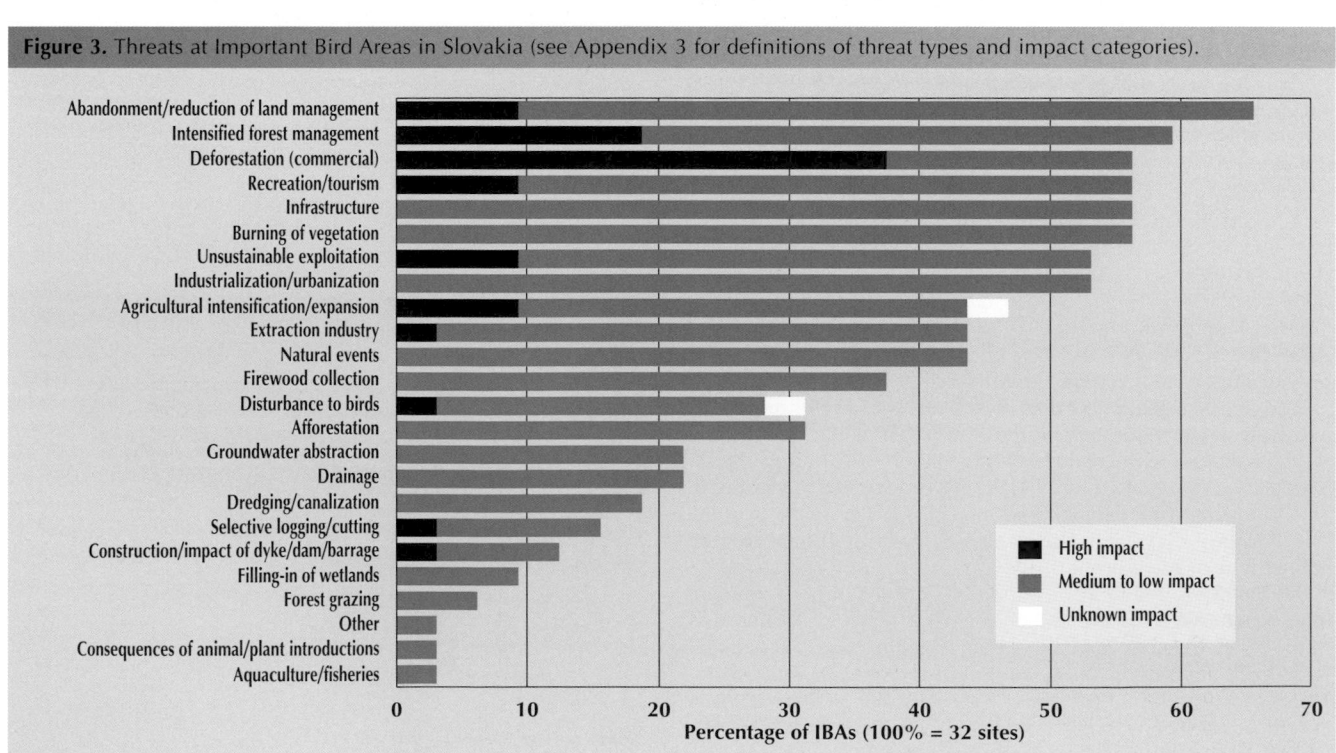

Figure 3. Threats at Important Bird Areas in Slovakia (see Appendix 3 for definitions of threat types and impact categories).

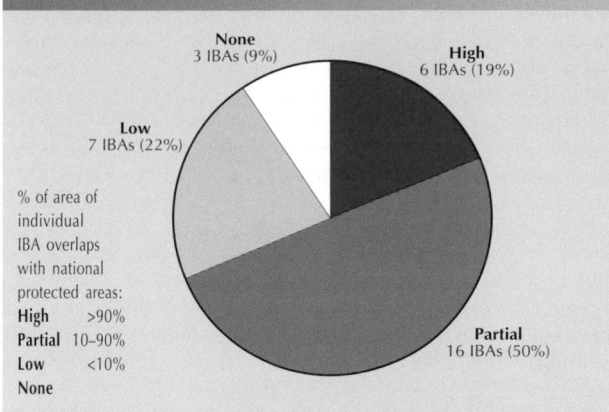

Figure 4. The national protection status of Important Bird Areas in Slovakia.

None 3 IBAs (9%)
High 6 IBAs (19%)
Low 7 IBAs (22%)
Partial 16 IBAs (50%)

% of area of individual IBA overlaps with national protected areas:
High >90%
Partial 10–90%
Low <10%
None

Total area of overlap between IBA network in Slovakia and national protected-area system (see Table 5 for categories) = 4,661–5,202 km² (38–43% of total IBA area).

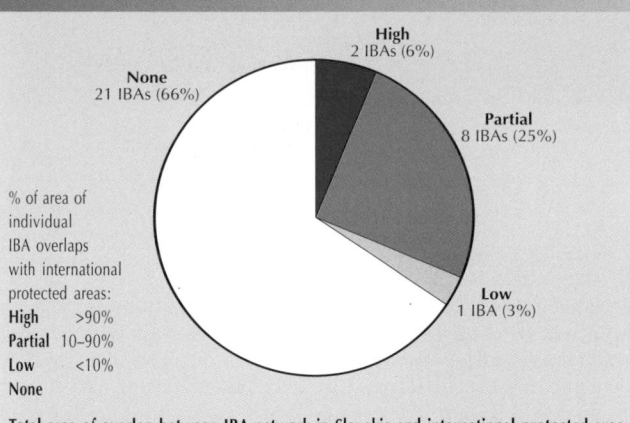

Figure 5. The international protection status of Important Bird Areas in Slovakia.

High 2 IBAs (6%)
None 21 IBAs (66%)
Partial 8 IBAs (25%)
Low 1 IBA (3%)

% of area of individual IBA overlaps with international protected areas:
High >90%
Partial 10–90%
Low <10%
None

Total area of overlap between IBA network in Slovakia and international protected-area system (see Table 5 for categories) = 2,046 km² (17% of total IBA area).

management, dam construction, recreation/tourism and unsustainable exploitation), Malé Karpaty (002) (situated near to an area of high population, commercial deforestation, disturbance and unsustainable exploitation) and Tatry (016) (recreation/tourism).

PROTECTION STATUS

Table 5 and Figures 4 and 5 summarize the national and international conservation status of all Slovak IBAs.

■ National protection
In 1994 the new Nature and Landscape Conservation Act No. 287 was passed, dividing Slovak protected areas into the following categories:

1. National Park (NP)
Large areas usually more than 1,000 ha in size. Predominantly unaffected by human activities, or with unique, natural landscape structures where nature protection commands a higher priority than other activities. NPs serve nature conservation, research, educational and recreational purposes; they are designated by the Slovak government and have special buffer zones.

2. Protected Landscape Area (PLA)
Large areas usually more than 1,000 ha in size, comprising fragmented ecosystems significant for the conservation of biological diversity and ecological stability, characteristic landscape features, or historical settlements. Forestry, agricultural and urban development activities are less strictly controlled than in NPs. PLAs are designated by the Ministry of the Environment and do not have buffer zones.

3. National Nature Reserve (NNR) and Nature Reserve (NR)
Smaller areas, usually up to 1,000 ha in size, that represent predominantly intact ecosystems or those generally unaffected by human activities, and areas of high biodiversity. NNRs are designated by the Ministry of the Environment and NRs by regional administrative authorities.

4. National Natural Monument (NNM) and Natural Monument (NM)
Point, linear or other smaller ecosystems that generally do not exceed 50 ha in area. They are of scientific, cultural, ecological, aesthetic or landscape significance, and include outcrops, rock formations, narrow valleys, dunes, sections of streams, springs, sinks and lakes. NNMs are designated by the Ministry of the Environment and NMs by regional administrative authorities.

5. Protected Range (PR)
Small areas usually up to 1,000 ha in size, that represent biocorridors, structural landscape elements, or areas important for biodiversity at the local or regional level. PRs are designated by regional administrative authorities.

In total, Slovakia has seven National Parks, 16 Protected Landscape Areas, 231 National Nature Reserves, 345 Nature Reserves, 45 National Nature Monuments, 217 Nature Monuments and 260 Protected Ranges, covering 19.5% of the land area (Vongrej *in litt.* —these totals are from a SAŽP database, and are correct as at 31 December 1998). Of 32 Slovak IBAs, six are fully protected (≥90% of area), and a further 23 are partly protected (Figure 4).

Table 5. Protection status of Important Bird Areas in Slovakia. A tick (✔) indicates that an IBA overlaps with a protected area (to any extent).

IBA code	International name	National							International		
		National Park	Protected Landscape Area	National Nature Reserve	Nature Reserve	National Natural Monument	Natural Monument	Protected Range	Ramsar Site	World Heritage Site	Biosphere Reserve
001	River Morava flood-plain		✔	✔	✔		✔	✔	✔		
002	Malé Karpaty		✔	✔	✔	✔					
003	Syslovské fields										
004	Sínava						✔				
005	Považský Inovec		✔	✔	✔		✔	✔			
006	Tríbeč		✔	✔	✔			✔			
007	River Danube flood-plain		✔	✔	✔		✔	✔	✔		
008	Jurský Chlm			✔							
009	Parížske marshes			✔					✔		
010	Burda				✔						
011	Riečnica		✔	✔	✔						
012	Oravská basin		✔	✔	✔		✔	✔	✔		
013	Malá Fatra	✔		✔	✔	✔	✔				
014	Veľká Fatra			✔	✔		✔	✔			
015	Chočské hills			✔	✔	✔	✔				
016	Tatry	✔		✔	✔	✔	✔				✔
017	Nízke Tatry	✔		✔	✔	✔	✔				
018	Poľana		✔	✔	✔	✔	✔	✔			✔
019	Lešť										
020	River Ipeľ flood-plain				✔		✔	✔	✔		
021	Muránska plateau	✔		✔	✔						
022	Spišská Magura				✔		✔				
023	Levočské hills				✔		✔	✔			
024	Volovské hills			✔	✔		✔	✔			
025	Slovenský karst		✔	✔	✔	✔				✔	✔
026	Slanské hills			✔	✔	✔	✔	✔			
027	Bukovské hills	✔		✔	✔		✔				✔
028	Vihorlatské hills		✔	✔	✔			✔			
029	Zemplínska Šírava							✔			
030	Senné				✔				✔		
031	River Latorica flood-plain		✔	✔	✔				✔		
032	Streda nad Bodrogom										
Total number of IBAs		5	11	22	24	8	17	15	7	1	4

Box 1. International legislation and initiatives that are relevant to site conservation in Slovakia (see Appendix 1 for a general description of these agreements).

Global
Biodiversity Convention ✔
Ramsar Convention ✔
Bonn Convention ✔
World Heritage Convention ✔
MAB Programme ✔

Pan-European
Bern Convention ✔

✔ Convention ratified/initiative supported
(✔) Convention signed

■ International protection

Slovakia has ratified several international conventions, treaties and initiatives (Box 1). Eleven Ramsar Sites have been designated of which seven overlap with seven IBAs (Table 5). A further two IBAs (004 and 029) meet Ramsar criteria but have not as yet been designated as Ramsar Sites. In addition Slovakia has four Biosphere Reserves, all of which overlap with IBAs, and two World Heritage Sites (one of which overlaps with IBA 025) (Table 5).

CONSERVATION

- Conservation initiatives are undertaken by statutory bodies (the Slovak government, Ministry of the Environment, regional and district authorities), state conservation organizations (SAŽP, National Park and Protected Landscape Area offices), national non-governmental organizations (Slovak Union of Protectors of Nature and Landscape, SOVS, Group for the Protection of Birds of Prey and Owls) and several regional or local bird/nature conservation societies and clubs.
- Statutory nature conservation activity is organized according to the Nature and Landscape Conservation Act (No. 287/1994) and subsequent legislation.
- In 1997 the Slovak government and parliament approved the National Biodiversity Strategy of Slovakia. It includes 23 strategic goals, many of which are relevant to the IBA concept.
- Eleven Slovak IBAs have full or partial management plans — mainly those designated as National Parks or Protected Landscape Areas.

ANALYTICAL METHODS

- For a number of SPECs, of which Slovakia holds less than 1% of the total European population (*Botaurus stellaris*, *Nycticorax nycticorax*, *Ardea purpurea*, *Platalea leucorodia*, *Milvus migrans*, *Circaetus gallicus*, *Circus pygargus*, *Falco vespertinus*, *Tetrao tetrix*, *Porzana parva*, *Otis tarda*, *Chlidonias hybridus*, *Caprimulgus europaeus*, *Monticola saxatilis*, *Locustella luscinioides*, *Lanius minor* and *Emberiza cia*), it has nevertheless been possible to assign B2/B3 criteria to sites that are known to hold internationally important numbers of these species, by

means of comparison with sites identified elsewhere in Europe under the B2/B3 criteria for these species.

- For the majority of the 32 IBAs, a sentence has been included in the site accounts detailing those SPECs that occur at the site but do not meet IBA criteria.
- Population figures for rare herons, raptors, crakes (except *Crex crex*), bee-eaters and some passerines (for example, *Prunella collaris*, *Lanius minor* and *Emberiza cia*) are based on good-quality data from research/monitoring programmes undertaken over the period 1994–1997.
- Population numbers for woodpeckers, *Crex crex* and most passerines tend to be estimates or are based on data from special sample plots.
- Passage figures are estimates of the total number of birds passing through in a season, and are based on maximum daily counts from the period 1994–1997.
- Land-use and threat data are from the period 1995–1998.
- Site boundaries were established and sizes of IBAs calculated from good-quality tourist maps derived from military maps (scale 1:50,000), and are available from SOVS.

GLOSSARY

karst a limestone region with underground drainage and many cavities and passages caused by the dissolution of the rock.
SAŽP Slovenská agentúra životného prostredia (Slovak Agency for the Environment, part of the Ministry of the Environment)—the state body responsible for nature conservation in Slovakia.
SOVS Spoločnosť pre ochranu vtáctva na Slovensku (Society for the Protection of Birds in Slovakia, BirdLife International Partner Designate in Slovakia).

ACKNOWLEDGEMENTS

Thanks go to the following volunteers, mainly professional ornithologists and/or conservationists working in the areas in question, for providing data for the site accounts: Miloš Balla, Tomáš Bělka, Mirko Bohuš, Marek Brinzík, Alžbeta Darolová, Štefan Danko, Miroslav Demko, Miroslav Dravecký, Joris Driessen, Miroslav Fulín, Ervín Hapl, Stanislav Harvančík, Jozef Chavko, Marián Janiga, Rudolf Jureček, Ján Kadlečík, Pavol Kaňuch, Dušan Karaska, Pavol Karč, Bohuslav Kloubec, Ján Korňan, Martin Korňan, Jaroslav Korvín, Anton Krištín, Rudolf Kropil, Viliam Kubán, Metod Macek, Pavol Majko, Štefan Matis, Michal Noga, Stanislav Ondruš, Samuel Pačenovský, Štefan Pčola, Peter Pjenčák, Radoslav Potočný, Leoš Prešinský, Milan Privrel, Peter Rác, Miroslav Saniga, Viera Stanová, Ján Svetlík, Ladislav Šimák, Ján Topercer jr., Alfréd Trnka, Róbert Trnka, Marcel Uhrín, Peter Urban, Slavomír Vongrej, Peter Vrlík, Axel Wieland and Július Žolner. Special thanks go to Michelle Machalka, US Peace Corps Volunteer, for calculating the sizes of IBAs and translating texts into English, and to Peter Urban, Ján Kadlečík and Slavomír Vongrej (SAŽP) for providing data on protected areas. The Swiss Association for the Protection of Birds (BirdLife International Partner in Switzerland) funded the Slovak IBA review.

■ SITE ACCOUNTS

River Morava flood-plain A1, A4i, B1i, B2, B3 **001**

Admin region Bratislava, Trnava
Coordinates 48°30′N 17°05′E
Altitude 141–167 m Area 18,935 ha

■ Site description

This 75-km-long and up to 5-km-wide flood-plain lies adjacent to the borders with Austria and the Czech Republic. Dykes and canals protect the surrounding landscape from seasonal high waters. The IBA comprises intact flood-plain forest (*Salix*, *Populus*, *Fraxinus* and *Ulmus*), water-fringe vegetation, extensive areas of wet meadow, marsh and peatbog and, in its eastern part, river terraces, sand-dunes and scattered human settlements. Drainage has allowed conversion to intensively managed arable land in places. Human activities include sport-fishing and cycling.

Habitats Forest and woodland (25%; broadleaved deciduous forest; alluvial/very wet forest), Grassland (35%; humid grassland; mesophile grassland), Wetland (10%; standing fresh water; river/stream; raised bog; water-fringe vegetation), Artificial landscape (30%; arable land; perennial crops/orchards/groves; other urban/industrial areas; ruderal land)
Land-use Agriculture (55%), Forestry (25%), Hunting (90%), Tourism/recreation (25%), Urban/industrial/transport (5%), Water management (5%)

■ Birds

Species	Season	Year	Pop min	Pop max	Acc	Criteria
[1] *Phalacrocorax carbo* Cormorant	P	1997	1,500	—	B	B1i
Ixobrychus minutus Little Bittern	B	1991	20	30	C	B2
Ciconia ciconia White Stork	B	1996	20	22	A	B2
Anser fabalis Bean Goose	P	1997	4,000	—	B	A4i, B1i
Anser anser Greylag Goose	P	1997	500	1,500	B	B1i
Milvus migrans Black Kite	B	1997	18	22	A	B2

Species ... continued		Season	Year	Pop min	Pop max	Acc	Criteria
Circus pygargus	Montagu's Harrier	B	1995	1	6	A	B3
Crex crex	Corncrake	B	1998	5	50	A	A1
Alcedo atthis	Kingfisher	R	1997	20	30	C	B2
Riparia riparia	Sand Martin	B	1991	500	1,000	C	B2
Locustella fluviatilis	River Warbler	B	1998	100	300	B	B3

1. Large increase over the last 3 years.

An important site for breeding species of flood-plain forest, wet grassland and other riverine habitats, and as a stop-over site for migrating geese. *Ciconia nigra*, *Pernis apivorus*, *Milvus milvus* and other raptors, *Porzana porzana*, *Asio flammeus*, *Sylvia nisoria* and *Lanius minor* also breed.

■ Protection status
National High **International** Partial
The IBA partially or wholly overlaps with the following national designated areas. *National Nature Reserves*: Horný les, Dolný les. *Nature Reserves*: Bogdalický vrch, Šmolzie. *Protected Landscape Area*: Záhorie. *Protected Ranges*: Kátovské jazero, Mŕtve rameno Lipa. *Natural Monuments*: Ivánek, Kátovské rameno. 4,971 ha of IBA covered by Ramsar Site (Alúvium Moravy (Morava river flood-plain), 4,971 ha).

■ Conservation issues

Threats Abandonment/reduction of land management (B), Agricultural intensification/expansion (A), Consequences of animal/plant introductions (C), Construction/impact of dyke/dam/barrage (B), Extraction industry (B), Industrialization/urbanization (B), Infrastructure (B), Recreation/tourism (B), Unsustainable exploitation (B)

Anglers and tourists cause disturbance to birds, and wildfowl are hunted whilst at roost. The plant *Aster novibelgii* has been introduced, and poses a low-impact threat to the meadow habitat of, amongst others, *Crex crex*. Conservation activities include protecting raptor nesting sites, stream and wet meadow restoration, and influencing agricultural and forestry activities. A management plan exists for part of the area.

Malé Karpaty
Admin region Bratislava, Trenčín, Trnava
Coordinates 48°32′N 17°23′E
Altitude 200–768 m **Area** 76,600 ha
A1, B2, B3 — 002

■ Site description
An extensive range of hills, 100 km long and up to 20 km wide, that forms the most westerly part of the Western Carpathians. The forests are mainly of *Fagus* with *Acer* and *Fraxinus* on higher ground and *Quercus*, *Ulmus* and *Pinus* at lower altitudes. In places they have been replaced by *Picea* plantations. Deforested zones near to villages have been converted into pasture, meadow, vineyards and arable land. Human activities include fish and duck-farming, intensive timber production and trekking.

Habitats Forest and woodland (70%; broadleaved deciduous forest; mixed forest), Scrub (5%; scrub), Grassland (5%; mesophile grassland), Artificial landscape (20%; perennial crops/orchards/groves; forestry plantation; urban parks/gardens; other urban/industrial areas)
Land-use Agriculture (15%), Forestry (70%), Hunting (90%), Tourism/recreation (20%), Urban/industrial/transport (5%)

■ Birds

Species		Season	Year	Pop min	Pop max	Acc	Criteria
Pernis apivorus	Honey Buzzard	B	1996	40	50	B	B3
Aquila heliaca	Imperial Eagle	R	1997	4	6	A	A1, B2
Crex crex	Corncrake	B	1996	10	20	—	A1
Columba oenas	Stock Dove	B	1996	200	300	C	B3
Dendrocopos medius	Middle Spotted Woodpecker	R	1996	40	50	B	B3

The IBA is a key area for several species of raptor, and is one of the two most important sites in Slovakia for *Aquila heliaca*. Also important for other forest species, including *Ciconia nigra*, *Circaetus gallicus*, *Falco peregrinus*, *Bubo bubo*, *Caprimulgus europaeus*, *Jynx torquilla* and *Picus canus*.

■ Protection status
National Partial **International** None
The IBA partially or wholly overlaps with the following national designated areas. *National Nature Reserves*: Dolina Hlbočе, Hajdúky, Kršlenica, Pohanská, Roštún, Záruby. *Nature Reserves*: Bolehlav, Buková, Čerenec, Chríb, Jurské jazero, Kamenec, Katarína, Lančársky Dubník, Lošonský háj, Nad Šenkárkou, Nové Pole, Orlie skaly, Pod Holým vrchom, Pod Pajštúnom, Skalné okno, Slopy, Strmina, Vysoká, Zlatá Studnička. *Protected Landscape Area*: Malé Karpaty. *National Natural Monument*: Driny. *Natural Monuments*: Bukovina, Čertov žľab, Limbašská vyvieračka, Tisové skaly, Vyvieračka pod Bachárkou, Zrubárka.

■ Conservation issues

Threats Agricultural intensification/expansion (U), Deforestation (commercial) (A), Disturbance to birds (A), Extraction industry (C), Groundwater abstraction (C), Industrialization/urbanization (B), Infrastructure (B), Intensified forest management (C), Natural events (C), Recreation/tourism (B), Unsustainable exploitation (A)

Threats include agricultural intensification, large-scale clear-cutting, disturbance caused by berry-collecting and hunting, construction of weekend cottages and fish-ponds, industrial pollution, limestone quarrying, road and powerline construction, selective logging, natural fires, ground erosion, cycling, paragliding, skiing and climbing, nest robbery and illegal hunting. Conservation activities include protecting raptor nesting sites, controlling tourism and influencing forestry practices. A management plan exists for part of the area.

Sysľovské fields
Admin region Bratislava
Coordinates 48°02′N 17°06′E
Altitude 130–137 m **Area** 3,860 ha
A1, A4i, A4iii, B1i, B2, B3 — 003

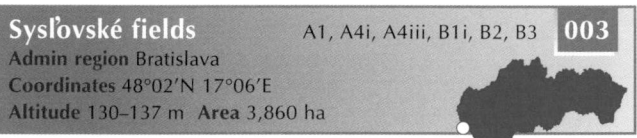

■ Site description
An open expanse of agricultural land located near to the borders with Austria and Hungary. What was originally steppe has recently been converted to intensively managed arable farmland. The IBA includes dried-up meanders of the River Danube and a network of shelterbelts.

Habitats Forest and woodland (5%; broadleaved deciduous forest), Artificial landscape (95%; arable land)
Land-use Agriculture (95%), Hunting (100%)

■ Birds

Species		Season	Year	Pop min	Pop max	Acc	Criteria
[1] *Egretta alba*	Great White Egret	P	1997	50	180	B	A4i, B1i
[1] *Anser fabalis*	Bean Goose	W	1997	8,000	20,000	C	A4i, B1i
Anser anser	Greylag Goose	W	1997	1,000	3,000	C	B1i
Circus pygargus	Montagu's Harrier	B	1997	3	5	A	B3
Falco vespertinus	Red-footed Falcon	B	1997	8	25	A	B2
[2] *Otis tarda*	Great Bustard	R	1997	5	15	A	A1, B2
[1] *Otis tarda*	Great Bustard	W	1997	30	90	A	A1, B2

1. Individuals.
2. Individuals. Large decrease over the last 10 years.

The IBA is important for steppic species and supports part of a transboundary population of *Otis tarda* (60–90 individuals) that moves between Slovakia, Austria and Hungary. The arable fields provide important winter roosting and feeding areas for geese, and hold 20,000 or more individuals of *Anser fabalis*, *A. albifrons* and *A. anser* on a regular basis. Breeding species of global conservation concern that do not meet IBA criteria: *Crex crex*.

■ Protection status
National None **International** None

■ Conservation issues

Threats Agricultural intensification/expansion (A), Disturbance to birds (B), Firewood collection (C), Infrastructure (B), Unsustainable exploitation (B)

Threats include large-scale fertilizer and pesticide use, disturbance caused by agricultural workers and hunters, road construction, the removal of trees for use as firewood, and the shooting of wintering geese. Monitoring of selected species takes place. Conservation projects include influencing agricultural management practices, eliminating predation by foxes *Vulpes vulpes*, guarding *Otis tarda* breeding sites, restoring shelterbelts, installing nest-boxes and artificial nests for *Falco tinnunculus* and *F. vespertinus*, and intervening in planning issues.

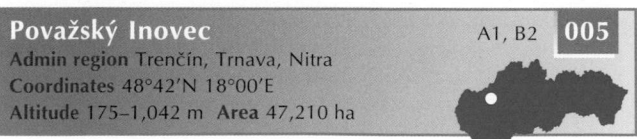

Síňava

Admin region Trnava
Coordinates 48°33'N 17°50'E
Altitude 154–158 m **Area** 690 ha

A4iii, B1i 004

Site description
The IBA comprises an artificial water reservoir and adjacent meadows situated on the River Váh. The gravel shores of the reservoir support scrub and trees. Water-fringe vegetation is present, and an artificial gravel islet 3 ha in extent has been built in the middle of the reservoir. The southern part of the IBA includes wet meadows and arable land, and is divided by man-made dykes and canals. These meadows were formerly extensively grazed by cattle, and are now abandoned and overgrown with *Salix* scrub.

Habitats Scrub (10%; scrub), Grassland (5%; humid grassland; mesophile grassland), Wetland (65%; shingle/stony beach; standing fresh water; river/stream; water-fringe vegetation), Artificial landscape (20%; arable land; other urban/industrial areas; ruderal land)
Land-use Agriculture (15%), Hunting (40%), Nature conservation/research (60%), Tourism/recreation (55%), Water management (55%)

Birds

Species	Season	Year	Pop min	Pop max	Acc	Criteria
Anser anser Greylag Goose	P	1997	50	400	A	B1i

The IBA is a very important roosting site for wintering and migrating wildfowl (Anatidae) and gulls (Laridae), and supports 20,000 or more passage waterbirds on a regular basis (including *Anas platyrhynchos*, *Aythya ferina*, *Aythya fuligula*, *Fulica atra*, *Larus argentatus*, *L. canus* and *L. ridibundus*).

Protection status
National Partial **International** None
The IBA partially or wholly overlaps with the following national designated areas. *Protected Range*: Síňava.

Conservation issues

Threats Abandonment/reduction of land management (B), Burning of vegetation (C), Industrialization/urbanization (B), Infrastructure (C), Recreation/tourism (A), Unsustainable exploitation (B)

A large summer/autumn outdoor recreational area has been established in the vicinity of the reservoir. Water-sports (for example, speedboats, water-skiing, wind-surfing and fishing) can pose a serious threat to migrating birds. Wildfowl hunting is an additional problem. Conservation activities include managing water-fringe vegetation and the artificial islet, thereby increasing its suitability for breeding gulls and terns.

Považský Inovec

Admin region Trenčín, Trnava, Nitra
Coordinates 48°42'N 18°00'E
Altitude 175–1,042 m **Area** 47,210 ha

A1, B2 005

Site description

Habitats Forest and woodland (60%; broadleaved deciduous forest; mixed forest; treeline ecotone), Scrub (5%; scrub), Grassland (10%; steppe/dry calcareous grassland; humid grassland; mesophile grassland), Artificial landscape (25%; arable land; perennial crops/orchards/groves; other urban/industrial areas; ruderal land)
Land-use Agriculture (25%), Forestry (60%), Hunting (90%), Tourism/recreation (15%), Urban/industrial/transport (10%)

The forests covering these hills and mountains of the Western Carpathians consist mainly of *Fagus*, *Acer*, *Fraxinus*, *Tilia* and, at lower altitudes, *Quercus*. Mesophile meadows occur within the forest

and on the edges of the IBA. The southern and western fringes are covered by arable land and densely populated urban areas. The IBA is popular for tourist activities such as trekking and cross-country skiing, although forestry and agriculture remain the main land-uses.

Birds

Species	Season	Year	Pop min	Pop max	Acc	Criteria
Aquila heliaca Imperial Eagle	B	1997	2	3	A	A1, B2

An important site for several species of raptor. Breeding species of global conservation concern that do not meet IBA criteria: *Crex crex*.

Protection status
National Low **International** None
The IBA partially or wholly overlaps with the following national designated areas. *National Nature Reserves*: Javorníček, Tematínske vrchy. *Nature Reserves*: Čepúšky, Dubový vŕšok, Holé brehy, Kňaží vrch, Kulháň, Považský Inovec, Prieľačina, Švibov. *Protected Ranges*: Hradisko, Okšovské duby. *Natural Monuments*: Malostankovské vresovisko, Mokvavý prameň, Obtočník Váhu, Pseudoterasa Váhu, Selecké kamenné more, Svinica, Veľký jarok, Visiace skaly.

Conservation issues

Threats Abandonment/reduction of land management (C), Agricultural intensification/expansion (C), Burning of vegetation (C), Deforestation (commercial) (A), Extraction industry (C), Firewood collection (C), Industrialization/urbanization (B), Infrastructure (C), Intensified forest management (A), Natural events (C), Recreation/tourism (B), Unsustainable exploitation (B)

The activities of foresters and egg thieves cause disturbance to birds. Eggs and juveniles are taken to supply the illegal trade in raptors. An additional low-impact threat is posed by tree falls. Conservation activities include protecting raptor nesting sites, reducing losses of raptors caused by collision with overhead powerlines, and influencing forestry practices.

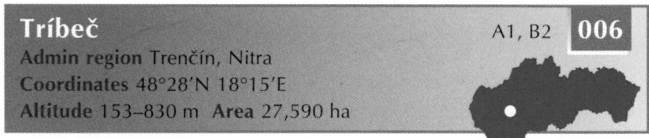

Tríbeč

Admin region Trenčín, Nitra
Coordinates 48°28'N 18°15'E
Altitude 153–830 m **Area** 27,590 ha

A1, B2 006

Site description
A range of hills, composed of limestone, dolomite and sandstone, that are part of the Western Carpathians. Forest covers the central part of the IBA, consisting of *Fagus* at higher altitudes, *Quercus* at lower altitudes and *Pinus* at the forest edge. Mesophile meadows, arable land, orchards and vineyards occur in the foothills. Due to substrate type, altitude and southerly aspect the IBA supports plant and animal communities typical of warmer areas.

Habitats Forest and woodland (70%; broadleaved deciduous forest; mixed forest), Scrub (5%; scrub), Grassland (5%; mesophile grassland), Artificial landscape (20%; arable land; perennial crops/orchards/groves; other urban/industrial areas; ruderal land)
Land-use Agriculture (20%), Forestry (70%), Hunting (95%), Tourism/recreation (10%), Urban/industrial/transport (5%)

Birds

Species	Season	Year	Pop min	Pop max	Acc	Criteria
Aquila heliaca Imperial Eagle	R	1997	3	4	A	A1, B2

Also important for forest- and scrub-nesting species including *Pernis apivorus*, *Jynx torquilla*, *Dendrocopos medius*, *Picus canus*, *Sylvia nisoria*, *Phoenicurus phoenicurus* and *Lanius collurio*. Breeding species of global conservation concern that do not meet IBA criteria: *Crex crex*.

Protection status
National Partial **International** None
The IBA partially or wholly overlaps with the following national designated areas. *National Nature Reserve*: Hrdovická. *Nature Reserves*: Kovarská hôrka, Solčiansky háj. *Protected Landscape Area*: Ponitrie. *Protected Ranges*: Park pri liečebnom ústave v Lefantovciach, Park v Horných Lefantovciach.

■ Conservation issues

Threats Abandonment/reduction of land management (C), Agricultural intensification/expansion (C), Disturbance to birds (C), Industrialization/urbanization (C), Natural events (B)

An *Aquila heliaca* conservation project has been undertaken, including the protection of nesting sites.

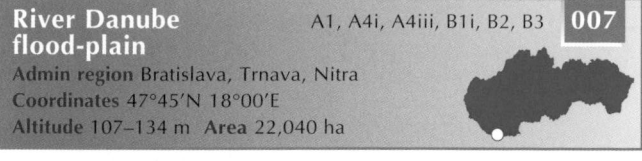

River Danube flood-plain A1, A4i, A4iii, B1i, B2, B3 **007**
Admin region Bratislava, Trnava, Nitra
Coordinates 47°45'N 18°00'E
Altitude 107–134 m **Area** 22,040 ha

■ Site description
The 150-km-long and up to 4-km-wide Danube flood-plain lies adjacent to the Hungarian border. The IBA covers the inundation zone of the river, numerous backwaters, oxbow lakes and islets, water-fringe vegetation, reedbed (*Phragmites*) and flood-plain forest (mainly *Populus*, *Fraxinus*, *Salix* and *Ulmus*). Forestry and water transport are the main land-uses, although tourism is likely to impact upon the area in the future.

Habitats Forest and woodland (30%; broadleaved deciduous forest; alluvial/very wet forest), Scrub (5%; scrub), Wetland (50%; shingle/stony beach; standing fresh water; river/stream; water-fringe vegetation), Artificial landscape (15%; highly improved reseeded grassland; arable land; forestry plantation; other urban/industrial areas; ruderal land)
Land-use Forestry (30%), Hunting (45%), Tourism/recreation (55%), Urban/industrial/transport (15%), Water management (40%)

■ Birds

Species	Season	Year	Pop min	Pop max	Acc	Criteria
Tachybaptus ruficollis Little Grebe	P	1997	700	1,400	B	A4i, B1i
Phalacrocorax carbo Cormorant	P	1997	2,500	5,000	B	A4i, B1i
Ixobrychus minutus Little Bittern	B	1997	15	30	C	B2
Egretta alba Great White Egret	P	1997	120	240	B	A4i, B1i
Anser fabalis Bean Goose	P	1997	15,000	30,000	B	A4i, B1i
Anser anser Greylag Goose	P	1997	3,000	6,000	B	A4i, B1i
Anas platyrhynchos Mallard	P	1997	40,000	80,000	B	B1i
Aythya ferina Pochard	P	1997	7,000	14,000	B	A4i, B1i
Aythya fuligula Tufted Duck	P	1997	8,000	16,000	B	A4i, B1i
Bucephala clangula Goldeneye	P	1997	8,000	16,000	B	A4i, B1i
Mergus albellus Smew	P	1997	700	1,400	B	A4i, B1i
Milvus migrans Black Kite	B	1997	7	10	B	B2
Haliaeetus albicilla White-tailed Eagle	W	1996	25	30	B	A1
Alcedo atthis Kingfisher	R	1997	30	50	B	B2
Riparia riparia Sand Martin	B	1997	900	1,300	B	B2
Locustella fluviatilis River Warbler	B	1997	100	200	C	B3

An important site for breeding species of flood-plain forests and other riverine habitats, and as a stop-over site for migrating waterbirds—holding more than 20,000 individuals on a regular basis. *Nycticorax nycticorax*, *Ciconia nigra*, *Pernis apivorus* and *Recurvirostra avosetta* also breed. Breeding species of global conservation concern that do not meet IBA criteria: *Aythya nyroca* (1–5 pairs), *Haliaeetus albicilla* and *Crex crex* (1–2 pairs).

■ Protection status
National Partial **International** Partial
The IBA partially or wholly overlaps with the following national designated areas. *National Nature Reserves*: Číčovské mŕtve rameno, Ostrov orliaka morského. *Nature Reserves*: Gajc, Opatovské jazero, Ostrov Kopáč, Ostrovné lúčky, Topoľové hony, Veľký Lél. *Protected Landscape Area*: Danube flood-plains. *Protected Ranges*: Bajdel, Poľovnícky les. *Natural Monuments*: Kráľovská lúka, Panský diel. 14,448 ha of IBA covered by Ramsar Site (Dunajské luhy (Danube flood-plains), 14,488 ha).

■ Conservation issues

Threats Afforestation (C), Construction/impact of dyke/dam/barrage (A), Deforestation (commercial) (A), Drainage (B), Dredging/canalization (B), Extraction industry (B), Filling-in of wetlands (B), Firewood collection (C), Groundwater abstraction (C), Industrialization/urbanization (B), Infrastructure (B), Intensified forest management (A), Recreation/tourism (A), Unsustainable exploitation (A)

The Danube Water Scheme, involving the building of a large water reservoir and a canal between Bratislava and Gabčíkovo, has destroyed or affected most of the valuable riparian habitats within the IBA, and will be a key factor determining future quality. Wildfowl shooting is a problem, and the activities of anglers, tourists, foresters and hunters cause disturbance to birds. Conservation activities include protecting raptor nesting sites, and influencing water management and forestry practices.

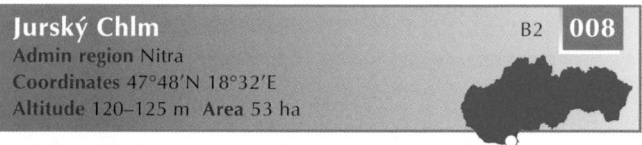

Jurský Chlm B2 **008**
Admin region Nitra
Coordinates 47°48'N 18°32'E
Altitude 120–125 m **Area** 53 ha

■ Site description
An area of sloping sandy ground 600 m in length, incorporating a vertical sand cliff. An abandoned apricot orchard lies to the north, with arable land to the south and east.

Habitats Scrub (40%; scrub), Grassland (15%; mesophile grassland), Rocky areas (30%; inland sand-dunes), Artificial landscape (15%; perennial crops/orchards/groves)
Land-use Agriculture (15%), Nature conservation/research (100%)

■ Birds

Species	Season	Year	Pop min	Pop max	Acc	Criteria
Merops apiaster Bee-eater	B	1997	17	22	A	B2
Riparia riparia Sand Martin	B	1997	200	1,000	B	B2

An important site for tunneling cliff-nesting species.

■ Protection status
National Partial **International** None
The IBA partially or wholly overlaps with the following national designated areas. *Nature Reserve*: Jurský Chlm.

■ Conservation issues

Threats Abandonment/reduction of land management (C), Extraction industry (C), Natural events (B)

Heavy rains pose a threat. Illegal sand extraction occurs on an infrequent basis.

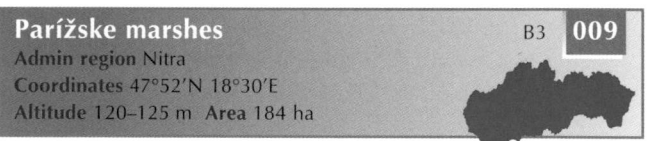

Parížske marshes B3 **009**
Admin region Nitra
Coordinates 47°52'N 18°30'E
Altitude 120–125 m **Area** 184 ha

■ Site description
This 4-km-long and up to 1-km-wide wetland is situated in an intensively farmed landscape lying upon alluvium from the Paríž stream. The IBA is almost entirely covered by extensive beds of *Phragmites*, *Typha* and *Carex* and there are only a few areas of open water. Nature conservation, research and, in the last few years, selective cutting and harvesting of reeds *Phragmites* ('Other' land-use) are the only land-uses.

Habitats Wetland (100%; standing fresh water; water-fringe vegetation)
Land-use Nature conservation/research (100%), Other (20%)

■ Birds

Species	Season	Year	Pop min	Pop max	Acc	Criteria
Porzana parva Little Crake	B	1998	15	25	A	B3
Locustella luscinioides Savi's Warbler	B	1998	200	200	B	B3

An important site for breeding wetland species; holds key Slovakian populations of *Porzana parva* and *Acrocephalus melanopogon*.

■ Protection status
National High **International** High
The IBA partially or wholly overlaps with the following national designated areas. *National Nature Reserve*: Parížske močiare. 184 ha

of IBA covered by Ramsar Site (Parížske močiare (Parížske marshes), 184 ha).

■ Conservation issues

Threats Abandonment/reduction of land management (B), Drainage (C), Other (C)

Conservation activities include increasing the area of open water by selective reed-cutting, and influencing water management practices. Research into the population dynamics of key bird species is undertaken. A management plan exists for the site.

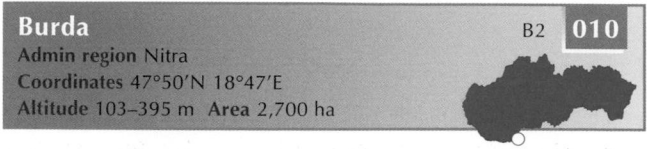

Burda
B2 **010**
Admin region Nitra
Coordinates 47°50′N 18°47′E
Altitude 103–395 m **Area** 2,700 ha

■ Site description
An area of hills situated close to the Hungarian border. Drought-tolerant plant and invertebrate communities occur, and the forests are mainly of *Quercus*. Scrub, urban areas and agricultural land comprise the outer reaches of the IBA, which is delimited in the south by the rocky gorge of the River Danube.

Habitats Forest and woodland (75%; broadleaved deciduous forest), Scrub (5%; scrub), Rocky areas (5%; inland cliff), Artificial landscape (15%; arable land; perennial crops/orchards/groves; other urban/industrial areas)
Land-use Agriculture (10%), Forestry (55%), Hunting (70%), Nature conservation/research (20%), Not utilized (5%), Tourism/recreation (25%), Urban/industrial/transport (5%)

■ Birds

Species	Season	Year	Pop min	Pop max	Acc	Criteria
Aquila heliaca Imperial Eagle	B	1997	—	1	A	B2
Merops apiaster Bee-eater	B	1997	10	15	A	B2

The IBA is important for breeding raptors, as well as for species of scrub and drought-tolerant habitats such as *Caprimulgus europaeus*, *Jynx torquilla* and *Emberiza cia*.

■ Protection status
National Partial **International** None
The IBA partially or wholly overlaps with the following national designated areas. *National Nature Reserves*: Kováčovské kopce-juh, Kováčovské kopce-sever.

■ Conservation issues

Threats Burning of vegetation (C), Deforestation (commercial) (A), Firewood collection (C), Industrialization/urbanization (B), Infrastructure (B), Intensified forest management (A), Recreation/tourism (B), Selective logging/cutting (B), Unsustainable exploitation (B)

Eggs and juveniles are taken to supply the illegal trade in raptors, and poaching is also a problem. The activities of tourists, zoologists and hunters cause disturbance to birds. Conservation activities include protecting raptor nesting sites.

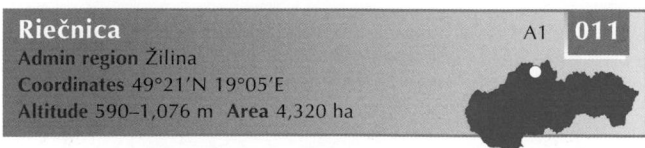

Riečnica
A1 **011**
Admin region Žilina
Coordinates 49°21′N 19°05′E
Altitude 590–1,076 m **Area** 4,320 ha

■ Site description
A relatively small area of hills that form part of the larger Kysucké range, situated in the buffer zone of the Nová Bystrica reservoir. The forests consist of *Picea*, *Fagus* and *Abies*, and are interspersed with mesophile and boreal meadows.

Habitats Forest and woodland (45%; native coniferous forest; mixed forest; treeline ecotone), Scrub (10%; scrub), Grassland (40%; alpine/subalpine/boreal grassland; mesophile grassland), Artificial landscape (5%; ruderal land)
Land-use Agriculture (15%), Forestry (45%), Hunting (95%), Water management (5%)

■ Birds

Species	Season	Year	Pop min	Pop max	Acc	Criteria
Crex crex Corncrake	B	1998	25	35	B	A1

The IBA holds one of the highest breeding densities of *Crex crex* in Slovakia.

■ Protection status
National High **International** None
The IBA partially or wholly overlaps with the following national designated areas. *Nature Reserves*: Javorinka, Zajačkova lúka. *Protected Landscape Area*: Kysuce.

■ Conservation issues

Threats Abandonment/reduction of land management (A), Afforestation (B), Intensified forest management (C)

The abandonment of meadow management leads to the succession of ruderal plants and scrub. Conservation research activities include studying the effects of machine- and hand-mowing regimes on *Crex crex* numbers.

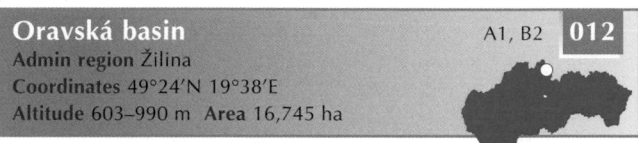

Oravská basin
A1, B2 **012**
Admin region Žilina
Coordinates 49°24′N 19°38′E
Altitude 603–990 m **Area** 16,745 ha

■ Site description
The IBA comprises a flat basin and surrounding hills located near to the Polish border. The forest consists mainly of *Picea*, with some *Abies* and *Pinus*, and low-lying wet forest also occurs (*Salix*, *Alnus* and *Populus*). Large parts of the IBA have been deforested and subsequently converted either to hay-meadow and pasture or to arable land. The Oravská reservoir lies in the centre of the IBA and supports dense water-fringe vegetation. The reservoir environs act as recreational and sport-fishing centres.

Habitats Forest and woodland (30%; broadleaved deciduous forest; native coniferous forest; mixed forest; alluvial/very wet forest; treeline ecotone), Scrub (10%; scrub; heathland), Grassland (5%; humid grassland), Wetland (30%; standing fresh water; river/stream; raised bog; water-fringe vegetation; fen/transition mire/spring), Artificial landscape (25%; arable land; forestry plantation; other urban/industrial areas)
Land-use Agriculture (25%), Forestry (25%), Hunting (75%), Tourism/recreation (15%), Urban/industrial/transport (5%), Water management (20%)

■ Birds

Species	Season	Year	Pop min	Pop max	Acc	Criteria
Ciconia nigra Black Stork	B	1996	14	19	A	B2
Aquila pomarina Lesser Spotted Eagle	B	1996	16	20	A	B2
[1] **Tetrao tetrix** Black Grouse	R	1996	60	70	A	B2
Crex crex Corncrake	B	1996	35	60	B	A1

1. Individuals.

An important site for breeding species of forest and wet grassland; Oravská reservoir is a stop-over site for migrating waterbirds. *Ciconia ciconia*, *Porzana porzana*, *Alcedo atthis*, *Riparia riparia* and *Lanius excubitor* also breed. Species of global conservation concern that do not meet IBA criteria: *Haliaeetus albicilla* (3–6 passage individuals).

■ Protection status
National Partial **International** Partial
The IBA partially or wholly overlaps with the following national designated areas. *National Nature Reserves*: Jelešňa, Sosnina. *Nature Reserve*: Rudné. *Protected Landscape Area*: Horná Orava. *Protected Range*: Vtáčí ostrov. *Natural Monument*: Slanický ostrov. 9,264 ha of IBA covered by Ramsar Site (Mokrade Oravskej kotliny (wetlands of the Oravská basin), 9,264 ha).

■ Conservation issues
Agricultural and forestry activities cause disturbance to birds. *Tetrao tetrix* is hunted illegally. Conservation activities include installing nest-boxes, providing supplementary feeding for *Haliaeetus albicilla*, managing an islet for breeding gulls and

terns, controlling tourism, angling and hunting activities, and influencing forestry practices. A management plan exists for part of the area.

Threats Abandonment/reduction of land management (C), Afforestation (C), Agricultural intensification/expansion (B), Burning of vegetation (B), Extraction industry (C), Filling-in of wetlands (C), Firewood collection (B), Industrialization/urbanization (B), Infrastructure (B), Intensified forest management (B), Recreation/tourism (C), Unsustainable exploitation (C)

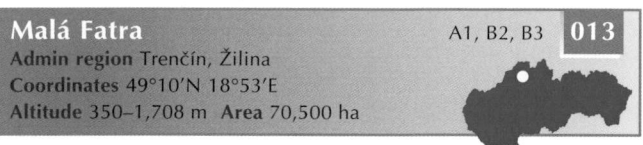

Malá Fatra — A1, B2, B3 — 013
Admin region Trenčín, Žilina
Coordinates 49°10'N 18°53'E
Altitude 350–1,708 m **Area** 70,500 ha

■ Site description
An extensive mountain range that forms part of the inner Western Carpathians. Karst features present include canyons, gorges, springs, waterfalls and caves. Forests consist mainly of *Fagus*, with *Quercus* at lower altitudes and *Pinus*, *Picea* and *Abies* on higher ground. Human activities include sheep- and cattle-grazing, military training, skiing and trekking, with the area receiving over one million visitors a year.

Habitats Forest and woodland (65%; broadleaved deciduous forest; native coniferous forest; mixed forest; treeline ecotone), Grassland (20%; steppe/dry calcareous grassland; alpine/subalpine/boreal grassland; humid grassland; mesophile grassland), Rocky areas (5%; scree/boulders; inland cliff; caves), Artificial landscape (10%; arable land; perennial crops/orchards/groves; forestry plantation; ruderal land)
Land-use Agriculture (20%), Forestry (65%), Hunting (85%), Military (5%), Nature conservation/research (5%), Tourism/recreation (35%), Urban/industrial/transport (5%)

■ Birds

Species	Season	Year	Pop min	Pop max	Acc	Criteria
Ciconia nigra Black Stork	B	1997	20	30	B	B2
Crex crex Corncrake	B	1997	70	140	B	A1, B2
Bubo bubo Eagle Owl	R	1997	15	20	A	B2
Picus canus Grey-headed Woodpecker	R	1997	150	200	C	B2
Picoides tridactylus Three-toed Woodpecker	R	1997	100	150	C	B2
Turdus torquatus Ring Ouzel	B	1997	200	350	C	B3
Phylloscopus sibilatrix Wood Warbler	B	1997	2,000	3,000	C	B3
Parus cristatus Crested Tit	R	1997	600	1,000	C	B3

An important site for breeding species of forest, rocky habitats and upland meadows. *Aquila chrysaetos*, *Tetrao tetrix*, *Prunella collaris*, *Monticola saxatilis* and *Tichodroma muraria* also breed.

■ Protection status
National Partial **International** None
IBA partially or wholly overlaps with the following national designated areas. *National Park*: Malá Fatra. *National Nature Reserves*: Chleb, Kľačianska Magura, Kľak, Kozol, Krivé, Prípor, Rozsutec, Šíp, Sokolec, Šrámková, Starý hrad, Suchý, Šútovská dolina, Veľká Bránica. *Nature Reserves*: Goľove mláky, Hajasová, Hrabinka, Hrádok, Močiar, Pod Rígľom, Veľká Lučivná. *National Natural Monument*: Kľacký vodopád. *Natural Monuments*: Domašínsky meander, Kraľoviansky meander, Šútovská epigenéza.

■ Conservation issues

Threats Abandonment/reduction of land management (C), Afforestation (C), Agricultural intensification/expansion (B), Construction/impact of dyke/dam/barrage (C), Deforestation (commercial) (A), Disturbance to birds (C), Drainage (C), Extraction industry (C), Groundwater abstraction (C), Infrastructure (C), Intensified forest management (B), Natural events (C), Recreation/tourism (B), Selective logging/cutting (B)

Threats include natural succession following land abandonment, conifer monocultures, fertilizer use, dam construction on the River Váh, clear-cuts, habitat destruction as a result of mining, abstracting groundwater to create artificial snow, road construction, the use of heavy forest machinery, wind damage, the construction of ski infrastructure and selective logging of trees. The drainage of wet meadows and marshes and the removal of boundary shrubs is followed by conversion to arable fields. Conservation activities include protecting raptor nesting sites, controlling tourism and influencing forestry practices. A management plan exists for part of the area.

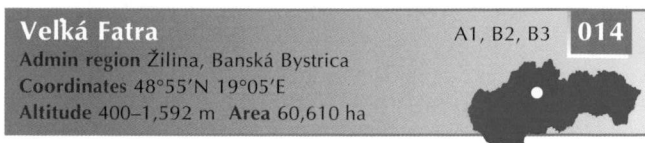

Veľká Fatra — A1, B2, B3 — 014
Admin region Žilina, Banská Bystrica
Coordinates 48°55'N 19°05'E
Altitude 400–1,592 m **Area** 60,610 ha

■ Site description
An extensive range of forested mountains situated in the inner Western Carpathians. Deep valleys and numerous limestone and dolomite karst formations (cliffs, canyons, stone towers and overhangs) characterize the IBA. The forest consists mainly of *Fagus*, *Abies*, *Acer*, *Picea*, *Pinus* and *Taxus*. Deforestation at higher altitudes has created mountain meadows and pasture. Human activities include cattle- and sheep-grazing, timber production and skiing, although the area is visited less frequently by tourists than mountains elsewhere in Slovakia.

Habitats Forest and woodland (80%; broadleaved deciduous forest; native coniferous forest; mixed forest; treeline ecotone), Grassland (10%; alpine/subalpine/boreal grassland; mesophile grassland), Rocky areas (5%; inland cliff; caves), Artificial landscape (5%; arable land; perennial crops/orchards/groves)
Land-use Agriculture (10%), Forestry (75%), Hunting (85%), Nature conservation/research (10%), Not utilized (5%), Tourism/recreation (25%)

■ Birds

Species	Season	Year	Pop min	Pop max	Acc	Criteria
Aquila chrysaetos Golden Eagle	R	1996	6	8	A	B2
¹ *Tetrao tetrix* Black Grouse	R	1997	50	80	B	B2
Crex crex Corncrake	B	1997	10	20	B	A1
Jynx torquilla Wryneck	B	1996	50	150	B	B2
Picus canus Grey-headed Woodpecker	R	1996	100	150	B	B2
Picoides tridactylus Three-toed Woodpecker	R	1996	100	150	B	B2
Phoenicurus phoenicurus Redstart	B	1996	50	150	B	B2
Turdus torquatus Ring Ouzel	B	1996	250	500	B	B3
Parus cristatus Crested Tit	R	1996	300	400	B	B3
Carduelis spinus Siskin	R	1997	100	1,000	C	B3

1. Individuals.

An important site for breeding species of forest and upland grassland. *Ciconia nigra*, *Aquila pomarina*, *Falco peregrinus*, *Bubo bubo*, *Caprimulgus europaeus*, *Monticola saxatilis* and *Ficedula albicollis* also breed.

■ Protection status
National High **International** None
The IBA partially or wholly overlaps with the following national designated areas. *National Nature Reserves*: Borišov, Čierny Kameň, Harmanecká tisina, Jánošíkova kolkáreň, Katova skala, Kornietová, Kundračka, Madačov, Rakšianske rašelinisko, Rojkovské rašelinisko, Rumbáre, Skalná Alpa, Suchý vrch, Tlstá, Veľká Skalná. *Nature Reserves*: Biela skala, Korbeľka. *Protected Landscape Area*: Veľká Fatra. *Protected range*: Háj pred Teplou dolinou. *Natural Monuments*: Žiar, Bukovinka, Dogerské skaly, Hradené jazero Blatné, Jazierske travertíny, Krkavá skala, Majerova skala, Matejkovský kamenný prúd, Prielom Teplého potoka, Rojkovská travertínová kopa, Vlčia skala.

■ Conservation issues

Threats Abandonment/reduction of land management (B), Afforestation (C), Agricultural intensification/expansion (B), Burning of vegetation (C), Deforestation (commercial) (B), Dredging/canalization (C), Extraction industry (C), Firewood collection (C), Forest grazing (C), Groundwater abstraction (C), Industrialization/urbanization (C), Infrastructure (C), Intensified forest management (B), Recreation/tourism (B), Selective logging/cutting (B)

Threats include a decrease in grazing intensity, soil erosion due to sheep-grazing, the burning of grassland, timber production, limestone quarrying, selective logging, the building of forest roads and the degradation of plant communities on ski slopes. Conservation research and nest-site protection is undertaken for *Aquila chrysaetos* and *Falco peregrinus*. Other conservation activities include controlling tourism and influencing forestry practices. A management plan exists for the area.

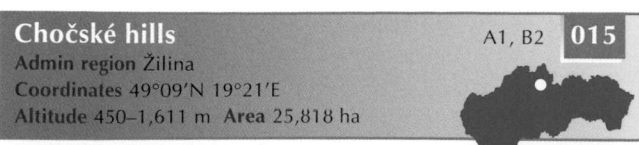

Chočské hills
A1, B2 **015**

Admin region Žilina
Coordinates 49°09'N 19°21'E
Altitude 450–1,611 m **Area** 25,818 ha

■ Site description
A mountainous area of dolomite and limestone situated in the Western Carpathians. Deep canyon valleys, cliffs, caves, underground rivers and other karst formations contribute to the IBA's sharp relief. The forests consist of *Picea*, *Fagus* and *Abies*, with extensive meadow and arable lands and urban areas covering the edges of the IBA. Human activities are generally extensive and include cattle and sheep-grazing, cereal-growing, haymaking and timber production.

Habitats Forest and woodland (50%; native coniferous forest; mixed forest), Scrub (5%; scrub), Grassland (25%; mesophile grassland), Rocky areas (5%; scree/boulders; inland cliff), Artificial landscape (15%; arable land; perennial crops/orchards/groves; other urban/industrial areas)
Land-use Agriculture (30%), Forestry (40%), Hunting (80%), Nature conservation/research (15%), Tourism/recreation (20%), Urban/industrial/transport (5%)

■ Birds

Species	Season	Year	Pop min	Pop max	Acc	Criteria
Crex crex Corncrake	B	1997	25	40	B	A1
Bubo bubo Eagle Owl	R	1997	15	25	B	B2

An important site for species of upland habitats and valley grasslands. *Aquila chrysaetos*, *Tetrao tetrix* and *Tichodroma muraria* also breed.

■ Protection status
National Partial **International** None
The IBA partially or wholly overlaps with the following national designated areas. *National Nature Reserves*: Choč, Kvačianska dolina, Prosiecka dolina, Šíp, Suchá dolina. *Nature Reserves*: Kunovo, Močiar, Mohylky, Turícke dubiny. *Protected range*: Borovicový háj v Liptovskej Sielnici. *National Natural Monuments*: Lúčanský vodopád, Liskovská jaskyňa. *Natural Monuments*: Bešeňovské travertíny, Lúčanské travertíny, Skalná päsť.

■ Conservation issues

Threats Agricultural intensification/expansion (B), Burning of vegetation (C), Deforestation (commercial) (C), Disturbance to birds (C), Industrialization/urbanization (C), Infrastructure (C), Intensified forest management (C), Recreation/tourism (C), Unsustainable exploitation (C)

Threats include agricultural chemical use, the removal of boundary shrubs between arable fields and meadows, spring burning of meadows, bushes and belts between arable fields, timber production, the enlargement of villages and recreational zones, road construction, the use of heavy forestry machinery, trekking and paragliding, and the direct effects of and disturbance caused by hunting. Conservation activities include protecting raptor nesting sites, reducing losses of raptors caused by collision with overhead powerlines, reducing illegal hunting of *Tetrao urogallus*, and influencing agricultural and forestry practices. The area has been proposed for designation as a National Park.

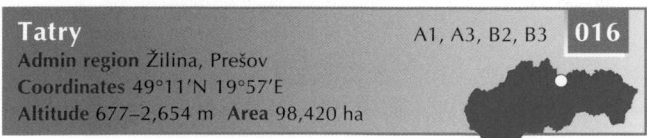

Tatry
A1, A3, B2, B3 **016**

Admin region Žilina, Prešov
Coordinates 49°11'N 19°57'E
Altitude 677–2,654 m **Area** 98,420 ha

■ Site description

Habitats Forest and woodland (45%; broadleaved deciduous forest; native coniferous forest; mixed forest; alluvial/very wet forest; treeline ecotone), Grassland (15%; steppe/dry calcareous grassland; dry siliceous grassland; alpine/subalpine/boreal grassland; humid grassland; mesophile grassland), Wetland (5%; standing fresh water; river/stream; raised bog; water-fringe vegetation; fen/transition mire/spring), Rocky areas (25%; scree/boulders; inland cliff; caves), Artificial landscape (10%; arable land; perennial crops/orchards/groves; forestry plantation; urban parks/gardens; other urban/industrial areas; ruderal land)
Land-use Agriculture (10%), Forestry (25%), Hunting (40%), Nature conservation/research (40%), Not utilized (15%), Tourism/recreation (40%), Urban/industrial/transport (5%)

An extensive range of mountains situated near to the Polish border. They form the northernmost and highest part of the Western Carpathians. The IBA includes the Eastern Tatras (High Tatras and Belanské Tatras), Western Tatras and part of the Podtatranská basin. The subalpine vegetation consists mainly of *Pinus* scrub, while the montane zone comprises *Picea* forest. Forests of *Betula*, *Abies* and *Acer* occur in the Belanské Tatras, and submontane areas consist of grassland, arable land and artificial habitats.

■ Birds

Species	Season	Year	Pop min	Pop max	Acc	Criteria
Ciconia nigra Black Stork	B	1997	20	40	B	B2
Aquila pomarina Lesser Spotted Eagle	B	1997	25	35	B	B2
Aquila chrysaetos Golden Eagle	R	1997	10	12	B	B2
[1] *Tetrao tetrix* Black Grouse	R	1997	60	100	B	B2
Crex crex Corncrake	B	1997	30	60	C	A1
Bubo bubo Eagle Owl	R	1997	30	50	B	B2
Picoides tridactylus Three-toed Woodpecker	R	1997	100	200	B	B2
Prunella collaris Alpine Accentor	R	1997	200	350	B	A3
Phoenicurus phoenicurus Redstart	B	1997	80	200	B	B2
Turdus torquatus Ring Ouzel	B	1997	500	1,000	B	B3
Parus cristatus Crested Tit	R	1997	1,500	2,500	C	B3
Tichodroma muraria Wallcreeper	B	1997	20	30	B	A3
Carduelis spinus Siskin	R	1997	1,500	2,500	C	B3

1. Individuals.

An important site for breeding species of forest and subalpine meadows; *Pernis apivorus* and *Lanius excubitor* also breed.

■ Protection status
National Partial **International** Partial
The IBA partially or wholly overlaps with the following national designated areas. *National Park*: Tatranský národný park. *National Nature Reserves*: Batizovská dolina, Belianske Tatry, Bielovodská dolina, Dolina Bielej vody, Furkotská dolina, Javorová dolina, Juráňova dolina, Kôprová dolina, Kotlový žľab, Mengusovská dolina, Mlynická dolina, Mních, Mokriny, Mraznica, Osobitá, Prameniště, Roháčske plesá, Sivý vrch, Skalnatá dolina, Slavkovská dolina, Štôlska dolina, Studené doliny, Suchá dolina, Tichá dolina, Uhlišťatká, Važecká dolina, Velická dolina. *Nature Reserves*: Blatá, Bor, Brezina, Čikovská, Fľak, Goliasová, Grapa, Hrádok nad Pavúčou dolinou, Jelšina, Kút, Machy, Mačie diery, Medzi Bormi, Pavlová, Pod Čerchľou, Poš, Rašelinisko, Slavkovský jarok, Surovec, Úplazíky. *National Natural Monuments*: Belianska jaskyňa, Brestovská jaskyňa. *Natural Monuments*: Alabastrová jaskyňa, Hybická tiesňava. 74,111 ha of IBA covered by Biosphere Reserve (Tatry, 74,111 ha).

■ Conservation issues

Threats Afforestation (C), Agricultural intensification/expansion (B), Burning of vegetation (C), Deforestation (commercial) (B), Dredging/canalization (B), Firewood collection (C), Groundwater abstraction (B), Industrialization/urbanization (B), Infrastructure (B), Intensified forest management (B), Recreation/tourism (A), Unsustainable exploitation (B)

Threats include timber production and associated intensive forestry practices and the construction of recreational centres and infrastructures. Tourists and egg thieves cause disturbance to birds. Eggs and juveniles are taken to supply the illegal trade in raptors, and illegal hunting of game bird species takes place. Pollution caused by lead emissions has led to a decline in numbers of *Prunella collaris*. Conservation activities include protecting raptor nesting sites, controlling tourism and influencing forestry practices. A management plan exists for part of the area.

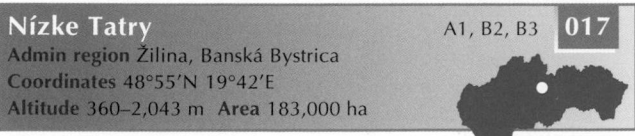

Nízke Tatry
A1, B2, B3 **017**

Admin region Žilina, Banská Bystrica
Coordinates 48°55'N 19°42'E
Altitude 360–2,043 m **Area** 183,000 ha

■ Site description
A mountain range over 80 km in length and up to 30 km wide that runs east–west through central Slovakia. The area is very diverse geomorphologically, with deep valleys separated by numerous ridges,

and limestone and dolomite karst formations. Forests are composed mainly of *Picea*, with *Fagus*, *Abies*, *Acer*, *Pinus* and occasionally *Taxus* at lower altitudes. Well known for its ski centres, trekking trails, public caves and recreational facilities.

Habitats Forest and woodland (75%; broadleaved deciduous forest; native coniferous forest; mixed forest; treeline ecotone), Grassland (10%; alpine/subalpine/boreal grassland; humid grassland; mesophile grassland), Rocky areas (5%; scree/boulders; inland cliff; caves), Artificial landscape (10%; arable land; perennial crops/orchards/groves; forestry plantation; urban parks/gardens; other urban/industrial areas; ruderal land)
Land-use Agriculture (10%), Forestry (75%), Hunting (90%), Not utilized (5%), Tourism/recreation (25%), Urban/industrial/transport (5%)

■ Birds

Species	Season	Year	Pop min	Pop max	Acc	Criteria
Aquila pomarina Lesser Spotted Eagle	B	1997	20	25	A	B2
Aquila chrysaetos Golden Eagle	R	1997	11	12	A	B2
[1] *Tetrao tetrix* Black Grouse	R	1997	150	200	B	B2
Crex crex Corncrake	B	1997	60	80	B	A1
Columba oenas Stock Dove	B	1997	100	150	B	B3
Bubo bubo Eagle Owl	R	1997	20	25	B	B2
Alcedo atthis Kingfisher	R	1997	20	40	C	B2
Picoides tridactylus Three-toed Woodpecker	R	1997	150	200	C	B2
Turdus torquatus Ring Ouzel	B	1997	300	500	C	B3
Lanius collurio Red-backed Shrike	B	1997	700	1,400	C	B2

1. Individuals.

An important site for breeding species of forest and both alpine and valley grasslands. *Ciconia nigra*, *C. ciconia*, *Pernis apivorus*, *Caprimulgus europaeus*, *Picus canus*, *Prunella collaris* and *Tichodroma muraria* also breed.

■ Protection status
National Partial **International** None
IBA partially or wholly overlaps with the following national designated areas. *National Parks*: Nizke Tatry, Slovenský raj. *National Nature Reserves*: Demänovská dolina, Hnilecká jelšina, Ďumbier, Jánska dolina, Meandre Hrona, Ohnište, Pod Latiborskou hoľou, Príboj, Salatín, Vernárska tiesňava. *Nature Reserves*: Baranovo, Barbolica, Breznianska skalka, Horné lazy, Jelšie, Kozí chrbát, Mackov bok, Mačková, Sliačske travertíny, Vrchovisko pri Pohorelskej Maši. *Protected Ranges*: Bodický rybník, Háj v Liptovskej Osade. *National Natural Monuments*: Stanišovská jaskyňa, Bystrianska jaskyňa, Brankovský vodopád, Vrbické pleso, Demänovské jaskyne. *Natural Monuments*: Žiar, Ľupčiansky skalný hríb, Hranovnické pleso, Meandre Lúžňanky, Mošnická jaskyňa, Moštenické travertíny.

■ Conservation issues

Threats Abandonment/reduction of land management (B), Afforestation (C), Deforestation (commercial) (A), Dredging/canalization (C), Extraction industry (C), Firewood collection (C), Industrialization/urbanization (C), Infrastructure (C), Intensified forest management (B), Natural events (B), Recreation/tourism (B), Unsustainable exploitation (C)

Tourists and egg thieves cause disturbance to birds. Eggs and juveniles are taken to supply the illegal trade in raptors, and illegal hunting of *Tetrao urogallus* takes place. Additional threats are posed by tree falls and flooding. Conservation activities include protecting raptor nesting sites, controlling tourism and influencing forestry practices. A management plan exists for part of the area.

Poľana   A1, B2, B3   018
Admin region Banská Bystrica
Coordinates 48°38′N 19°29′E
Altitude 385–1,458 m   **Area** 28,930 ha

■ Site description
The IBA comprises the Poľana mountains, the eastern part of the Zvolenská basin and the western edge of the Veporské hills. Forests consist of *Abies*, *Picea* and *Fagus* and are interspersed with numerous meadows and rocky areas. The rural landscape of the Zvolenská basin supports traditionally managed meadow, pasture and old orchards. Forestry and extensive agriculture (haymaking and sheep-grazing) are the main land-uses.

Habitats Forest and woodland (65%; broadleaved deciduous forest; native coniferous forest; mixed forest; treeline ecotone), Grassland (20%; mesophile grassland), Artificial landscape (15%; arable land; perennial crops/orchards/groves; other urban/industrial areas)
Land-use Agriculture (25%), Forestry (65%), Hunting (95%), Urban/industrial/transport (5%)

■ Birds

Species	Season	Year	Pop min	Pop max	Acc	Criteria
Pernis apivorus Honey Buzzard	B	1996	20	30	A	B3
Crex crex Corncrake	B	1996	30	50	B	A1
Phoenicurus phoenicurus Redstart	B	1996	60	100	B	B2
Lanius minor Lesser Grey Shrike	B	1996	90	120	A	B2

An important site for breeding species of forest and open cultivated country. *Ciconia nigra*, *Aquila pomarina*, *Alcedo atthis*, *Picus canus*, *Picoides tridactylus*, *Turdus torquatus*, *Sylvia nisoria*, *Ficedula albicollis* and *Lanius collurio* also breed.

■ Protection status
National Partial **International** Partial
The IBA partially or wholly overlaps with the following national designated areas. *National Nature Reserves*: Hrončecký grúň, Zadná Poľana, Ľubietovský Vepor. *Nature Reserves*: Mačinová, Pod Dudášom, Pri Bútľavke, Príslopy, Vrchslatina. *Protected Landscape Area*: Poľana. *Protected range*: Meandre Kamenistého potoka. *National Natural Monument*: Vodopád Bystré. *Natural Monuments*: Bátovský balvan, Havranka, Jánošíkova skala, Kalamárka, Melichova skala, Spády, Veporské skalky. 20,079 ha of IBA covered by Biosphere Reserve (Poľana, 20,079 ha).

■ Conservation issues

Threats Abandonment/reduction of land management (B), Agricultural intensification/expansion (B), Burning of vegetation (B), Deforestation (commercial) (A), Disturbance to birds (U), Dredging/canalization (B), Forest grazing (C), Intensified forest management (B), Selective logging/cutting (A)

The forests are relatively well conserved, although intensive forestry practices pose a threat. Additional threats include reduced management of meadows, intensive sheep- and cattle-grazing, and hunting. Conservation activities include influencing agricultural and forestry activities. A management plan exists for the area.

Lešť   A1, B2, B3   019
Admin region Banská Bystrica
Coordinates 48°23′N 19°18′E
Altitude 459–869 m   **Area** 5,200 ha

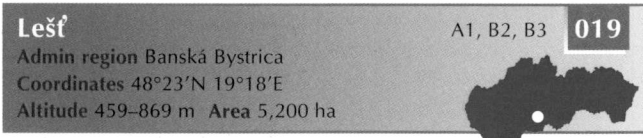

■ Site description
An area of hills in the northern part of the Krupinská plateau. The majority of the IBA is covered by extensively managed grassland, mixed forest and scrub. The IBA has been used for many years as a military training area, and contains few human settlements.

Habitats Forest and woodland (20%; mixed forest), Scrub (15%; scrub), Grassland (55%; mesophile grassland), Wetland (5%; standing fresh water; river/stream), Artificial landscape (5%; other urban/industrial areas; ruderal land)
Land-use Agriculture (20%), Forestry (15%), Hunting (25%), Military (70%), Urban/industrial/transport (5%)

■ Birds

Species	Season	Year	Pop min	Pop max	Acc	Criteria
Crex crex Corncrake	B	1994	30	60	B	A1
Sylvia nisoria Barred Warbler	B	1994	150	250	C	B3
Lanius collurio Red-backed Shrike	B	1994	1,000	2,000	C	B2

The IBA supports a variety of birds that breed in grassland, scrub and forest habitats. *Columba oenas*, *Caprimulgus europaeus*, *Jynx torquilla*, *Dendrocopos medius*, *Lullula arborea*, *Locustella fluviatilis*, *Ficedula albicollis* and *Phoenicurus phoenicurus* also breed.

■ Protection status
National None **International** None

■ Conservation issues

Threats Abandonment/reduction of land management (B)

Restricted access to the military training zones has meant that areas of grassland are not being managed and are reverting to scrub.

River Ipeľ flood-plain — A1, B2, B3 — 020
Admin region Banská Bystrica, Nitra
Coordinates 48°06′N 19°28′E
Altitude 124–196 m **Area** 7,715 ha

■ Site description
A 70-km-long and up to 3-km-wide stretch of the River Ipeľ flood-plain situated next to the Hungarian border. The river channel supports water-fringe vegetation and meanders through a flat landscape of extensively-managed wet meadows, arable land and scattered rural settlements.

Habitats Forest and woodland (5%; broadleaved deciduous forest; alluvial/very wet forest), Grassland (60%; humid grassland; mesophile grassland), Wetland (20%; standing fresh water; river/stream; water-fringe vegetation; fen/transition mire/spring), Artificial landscape (15%; arable land; perennial crops/orchards/groves; urban parks/gardens; other urban/industrial areas; ruderal land)
Land-use Agriculture (65%), Fisheries/aquaculture (5%), Hunting (85%), Urban/industrial/transport (10%), Water management (5%)

■ Birds

Species	Season	Year	Pop min	Pop max	Acc	Criteria
Ixobrychus minutus Little Bittern	B	1997	6	12	B	B2
Ciconia ciconia White Stork	B	1996	40	50	B	B2
Crex crex Corncrake	B	1997	20	40	C	A1
Alcedo atthis Kingfisher	R	1997	10	20	C	B2
Merops apiaster Bee-eater	B	1997	100	120	B	B2
Riparia riparia Sand Martin	B	1997	200	250	B	B2
Locustella luscinioides Savi's Warbler	B	1997	80	120	B	B3
Lanius minor Lesser Grey Shrike	B	1997	15	20	B	B2

An important site for breeding species of riverine habitats and wet grassland. *Porzana parva*, *Jynx torquilla* and *Locustella fluviatilis* also breed.

■ Protection status
National Low **International** Low
IBA partially or wholly overlaps with the following national designated areas. *Nature Reserve*: Kiarovský močiar. *Protected range*: Volavčia kolónia. Overlaps with international designated areas: 411 ha of IBA covered by Ramsar Site (Poiplie, 411 ha).

■ Conservation issues

Threats Agricultural intensification/expansion (A), Disturbance to birds (B), Drainage (B), Filling-in of wetlands (B), Industrialization/urbanization (C), Infrastructure (C)

The activities of photographers and anglers cause disturbance to birds.

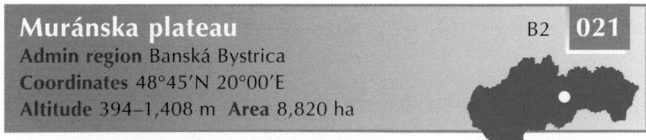

Muránska plateau — B2 — 021
Admin region Banská Bystrica
Coordinates 48°45′N 20°00′E
Altitude 394–1,408 m **Area** 8,820 ha

■ Site description
An area of hills belonging to the Spišsko-Gemerský karst. The forest consists mainly of *Fagus*, *Larix*, *Acer* and *Pinus*. Rocky slopes support dry meadows and scrub, and limestone cliffs, boulders, caves and other karst formations are also present. The IBA is important biogeographically as it lies on the northern boundary of the Pannonian zone.

Habitats Forest and woodland (80%; broadleaved deciduous forest; native coniferous forest; mixed forest; alluvial/very wet forest; treeline ecotone), Scrub (5%; scrub), Grassland (5%; steppe/dry calcareous grassland; humid grassland; mesophile grassland), Rocky areas (10%; scree/boulders; inland cliff; caves)
Land-use Agriculture (5%), Forestry (75%), Hunting (80%), Nature conservation/research (20%), Tourism/recreation (20%)

■ Birds
An important site for species of forest and rocky habitats. *Ciconia nigra*, *Aquila chrysaetos*, *Falco peregrinus* and other raptors, and *Emberiza cia* also breed. Breeding species of global conservation concern that do not meet IBA criteria: *Crex crex* (5–10 pairs).

■ Protection status
National High **International** None
The IBA partially or wholly overlaps with the following national designated areas. *National Park*: Muránska planina. *National Nature Reserves*: Cigánka, Hradová, Hrdzavá, Javorníková, Malá Stožka, Poludnica, Šarkanica, Veľká Stožka. *Nature Reserve*: Ľadová jama na Muráni.

■ Conservation issues

Threats Afforestation (C), Burning of vegetation (C), Deforestation (commercial) (B), Extraction industry (C), Infrastructure (C), Intensified forest management (B), Natural events (C), Recreation/tourism (C), Unsustainable exploitation (A)

The activities of tourists cause disturbance to birds. Eggs and juveniles are taken to supply the illegal trade in raptors. Additional low threats are posed by tree falls, forest fires and insect pests. Conservation activities include protecting raptor nesting sites and influencing forestry practices.

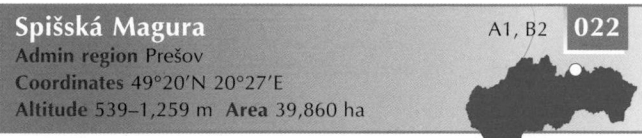

Spišská Magura — A1, B2 — 022
Admin region Prešov
Coordinates 49°20′N 20°27′E
Altitude 539–1,259 m **Area** 39,860 ha

■ Site description
An area of hills and mountains situated near to the Polish border. Coniferous forests of *Picea* and *Abies* are widespread, and extensive tracts of mesophile meadow and pasture occur on the edges of the IBA. The area is relatively uninhabited and on the whole remains unaffected by human activity, with tourism and recreation not as well developed as in other mountainous regions. Human activities include potato and cereal-growing, haymaking, sheep- and cattle-grazing and timber production.

Habitats Forest and woodland (50%; native coniferous forest; mixed forest; treeline ecotone), Scrub (10%; scrub), Grassland (30%; humid grassland; mesophile grassland), Artificial landscape (10%; arable land; perennial crops/orchards/groves; urban parks/gardens; other urban/industrial areas; ruderal land)
Land-use Agriculture (30%), Forestry (40%), Hunting (85%), Nature conservation/research (10%), Urban/industrial/transport (5%)

■ Birds

Species	Season	Year	Pop min	Pop max	Acc	Criteria
Aquila pomarina Lesser Spotted Eagle	B	1997	25	30	A	B2
Crex crex Corncrake	B	1997	70	100	B	A1, B2

An important site for species of forest and meadow grassland. *Ciconia nigra*, *C. ciconia*, *Pernis apivorus*, *Tetrao tetrix*, *Bubo bubo*, *Jynx torquilla*, *Picus canus*, *Picoides tridactylus*, *Turdus torquatus*, *Sylvia nisoria*, *Parus cristatus*, *Lanius excubitor* and *Carduelis spinus* also breed.

■ Protection status
National Low **International** None
The IBA partially or wholly overlaps with the following national designated areas. *Nature Reserves*: Jezerské jazero, Malé Jazerá, Pálenica, Skalka, Veľké Osturnianske jazero. *Natural Monument*: Jazero, Kráter.

■ Conservation issues

Threats Abandonment/reduction of land management (C), Deforestation (commercial) (B), Disturbance to birds (C), Industrialization/urbanization (C), Intensified forest management (B), Natural events (C)

Threats include commercial clear-cuts and the use of heavy machinery, disturbance to birds caused by forestry activities, the enlargement of villages and construction of new roads. An additional low threat is posed by tree falls.

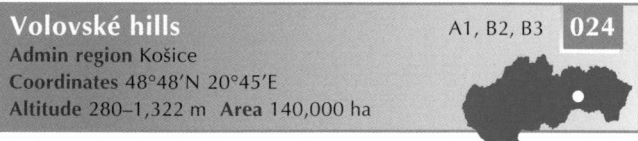

Levočské hills — A1, B2, B3 — 023

Admin region Prešov
Coordinates 49°08′N 20°40′E
Altitude 460–1,289 m Area 71,400 ha

■ Site description

The central part of these hills and mountains is covered by *Picea*, *Fagus* and *Abies* forest, with subalpine and mesophile meadows occurring on the ridges. Away from the centre the landscape is more open with arable land, pasture, small areas of mixed forest and a few villages. Almost half of the IBA area is used for military training and is closed to the public.

> **Habitats** Forest and woodland (60%; broadleaved deciduous forest; native coniferous forest; mixed forest; treeline ecotone), Scrub (5%; scrub), Grassland (10%; alpine/subalpine/boreal grassland; humid grassland; mesophile grassland), Artificial landscape (25%; arable land; perennial crops/orchards/groves; forestry plantation; urban parks/gardens; other urban/industrial areas; ruderal land)
>
> **Land-use** Agriculture (25%), Forestry (60%), Hunting (95%), Military (45%), Urban/industrial/transport (5%)

■ Birds

Species	Season	Year	Pop min	Pop max	Acc	Criteria
Aquila pomarina Lesser Spotted Eagle	B	1997	25	35	B	B2
Aquila chrysaetos Golden Eagle	R	1997	6	7	A	B2
Crex crex Corncrake	B	1997	60	100	C	A1, B2
Parus cristatus Crested Tit	R	1997	300	500	C	B3

An important site for forest and upland species. *Ciconia nigra*, *Tetrao tetrix*, *Picoides tridactylus* and *Turdus torquatus* also breed.

■ Protection status

National Low **International** None
The IBA partially or wholly overlaps with the following national designated areas. *Nature Reserves*: Bišár, Hájik, Valalská voda. *Protected range*: Uhliská. *Natural Monuments*: Jazerec, Podhorské.

■ Conservation issues

> **Threats** Abandonment/reduction of land management (B), Burning of vegetation (C), Construction/impact of dyke/dam/barrage (C), Deforestation (commercial) (A), Disturbance to birds (B), Firewood collection (C), Groundwater abstraction (C), Infrastructure (B), Intensified forest management (C), Natural events (C)

Forestry and military activities and paragliding cause disturbance to birds. Additional low threats are posed by tree falls, flooding and insect pests. Conservation activities include protecting raptor nesting sites.

Volovské hills — A1, B2, B3 — 024

Admin region Košice
Coordinates 48°48′N 20°45′E
Altitude 280–1,322 m Area 140,000 ha

■ Site description

This extensive range of hills and mountains is divided into several units by deep, broad river valleys. The relief is gentle in the south and sharper in the north, where gorges, canyons, cliffs and other scattered rock formations occur. The forests consist mainly of *Fagus*, *Picea*, *Abies* and *Acer*. Mesophile and boreal meadows exist at higher altitudes, whilst the edges of the IBA are covered by meadows, arable land and urban/industrial zones. The area as a whole is not densely populated.

> **Habitats** Forest and woodland (75%; broadleaved deciduous forest; native coniferous forest; mixed forest), Grassland (10%; steppe/dry calcareous grassland; alpine/subalpine/boreal grassland; humid grassland; mesophile grassland), Artificial landscape (15%; arable land; perennial crops/orchards/groves; forestry plantation; other urban/industrial areas; ruderal land)
>
> **Land-use** Agriculture (15%), Forestry (75%), Hunting (95%), Tourism/recreation (15%), Urban/industrial/transport (5%)

■ Birds

An important site for breeding species of forest and meadow grassland. *Ciconia ciconia*, *Pernis apivorus*, *Bubo bubo*, *Picus canus*, *Turdus*

torquatus, *Phylloscopus sibilatrix*, *Ficedula albicollis*, *Phoenicurus phoenicurus*, *Lanius collurio* and *Carduelis spinus* also breed.

Species	Season	Year	Pop min	Pop max	Acc	Criteria
Ciconia nigra Black Stork	B	1996	15	20	B	B2
Aquila pomarina Lesser Spotted Eagle	B	1996	15	20	A	B2
Aquila heliaca Imperial Eagle	R	1997	1	2	A	A1, B2
Aquila chrysaetos Golden Eagle	R	1997	6	8	A	B2
Crex crex Corncrake	B	1996	30	50	B	A1
Columba oenas Stock Dove	B	1997	130	150	B	B3
Jynx torquilla Wryneck	B	1997	50	80	B	B2
Dendrocopos medius Middle Spotted Woodpecker	R	1997	100	150	B	B3
Picoides tridactylus Three-toed Woodpecker	R	1996	50	70	B	B2
Locustella fluviatilis River Warbler	B	1997	150	200	B	B3
Sylvia nisoria Barred Warbler	B	1997	70	100	B	B3
Parus cristatus Crested Tit	R	1997	150	300	C	B3

■ Protection status

National Low **International** None
The IBA partially or wholly overlaps with the following national designated areas. *National Nature Reserves*: Červené skaly, Galmuská tisina. *Nature Reserve*: Kloptaň, Muráň, Rašelinisko Poľana. *Protected range*: Knola. *Natural Monuments*: Margecianska línia, Závadské skalky.

■ Conservation issues

> **Threats** Agricultural intensification/expansion (C), Burning of vegetation (C), Deforestation (commercial) (A), Extraction industry (C), Intensified forest management (A), Natural events (B), Recreation/tourism (C), Unsustainable exploitation (C)

Forestry activities cause disturbance to birds. Tree-falls and the legal and illegal hunting of birds pose additional threats. Conservation activities include protecting raptor nesting sites, and installing nest-boxes for owls.

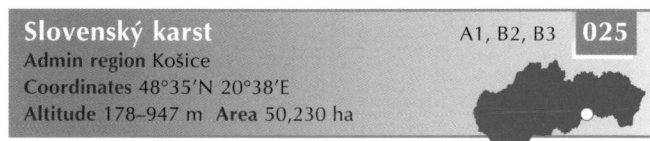

Slovenský karst — A1, B2, B3 — 025

Admin region Košice
Coordinates 48°35′N 20°38′E
Altitude 178–947 m Area 50,230 ha

■ Site description

An extensive area of hills and plateaus situated near to the Hungarian border. The IBA is part of the largest karst area in central Europe, and is characterized by karst holes, caverns, canyons, deep valleys and gorges. *Fagus* and *Quercus* forests predominate, and are interspersed with drought-tolerant and calcareous meadows at higher altitudes, and with arable land and wetlands on lower ground. Human activities include cattle- and sheep-grazing, cereal-growing, afforestation, timber production and quarrying.

> **Habitats** Forest and woodland (60%; broadleaved deciduous forest; native coniferous forest; mixed forest; wooded steppe; treeline ecotone), Scrub (10%; scrub), Grassland (5%; steppe/dry calcareous grassland; humid grassland; mesophile grassland), Rocky areas (5%; scree/boulders; inland cliff; caves), Artificial landscape (20%; arable land; perennial crops/orchards/groves; forestry plantation; urban parks/gardens; other urban/industrial areas; ruderal land), Introduced/exotic vegetation
>
> **Land-use** Agriculture (20%), Forestry (60%), Hunting (95%), Not utilized (5%), Tourism/recreation (35%), Urban/industrial/transport (5%)

■ Birds

Species	Season	Year	Pop min	Pop max	Acc	Criteria
Ixobrychus minutus Little Bittern	B	1996	3	5	B	B2
Ciconia ciconia White Stork	B	1996	18	22	A	B2
Aquila pomarina Lesser Spotted Eagle	B	1996	9	10	A	B2
Aquila heliaca Imperial Eagle	R	1996	0	1	A	B2
Crex crex Corncrake	B	1996	30	36	B	A1
Bubo bubo Eagle Owl	R	1996	15	18	B	B2
Jynx torquilla Wryneck	B	1996	80	150	C	B2
Dendrocopos medius Middle Spotted Woodpecker	R	1996	50	80	B	B3
Monticola saxatilis Rock Thrush	B	1996	10	15	B	B2
Locustella fluviatilis River Warbler	B	1996	150	250	C	B3
Sylvia nisoria Barred Warbler	B	1996	300	600	C	B3

Species ... continued		Season	Year	Pop min	Pop max	Acc	Criteria
Ficedula albicollis	Collared Flycatcher	B	1996	600	1,200	C	B3
Lanius collurio	Red-backed Shrike	B	1996	800	1,500	C	B2
Emberiza cia	Rock Bunting	B	1996	150	200	B	B2

An important site for breeding birds of forest, scrub and open heterogeneous landscapes. A migration route passes through the centre of the IBA along the Slaná river. *Ciconia nigra*, *Pernis apivorus*, *Circaetus gallicus* and other raptors, *Porzana parva*, *Caprimulgus europaeus*, *Alcedo atthis*, *Picus canus* and *Lullula arborea* also breed. Breeding species of global conservation concern that do not meet IBA criteria: *Aythya nyroca* (2–4 pairs).

■ Protection status
National Partial **International** Partial
The IBA partially or wholly overlaps with the following national designated areas. *National Nature Reserves*: Brzotínske skaly, Domické škrapy, Drieňovec, Havrania skala, Hrušovská lesostep, Jasovské dubiny, Kečovské škrapy, Palanta, Pod Strážnym hrebeňom, Turniansky hradný vrch, Zádielska tiesňava. *Nature Reserves*: Gerlachovské skaly, Kráľova studňa, Pod Fabiankou, Sokolia skala, Zemné hradisko. *Protected Landscape Area*: Slovenský kras. *National Natural Monuments*: Ardovská jaskyňa, Brázda, Diviačia priepasť, Domica, Drienovská jaskyňa, Gombasecká jaskyňa, Hrušovská jaskyňa, Jasovská jaskyňa, Krásnohorská jaskyňa, Kunia priepasť, Milada, Obrovská priepasť, Silická ľadnica, Skalistý potok, Snežná diera, Zvonivá jama. 36,166 ha of IBA covered by Biosphere Reserve (Slovenský kras, 36,166 ha).

■ Conservation issues

Threats Abandonment/reduction of land management (B), Afforestation (B), Burning of vegetation (B), Deforestation (commercial) (C), Drainage (C), Dredging/canalization (B), Extraction industry (B), Firewood collection (B), Groundwater abstraction (B), Industrialization/urbanization (B), Infrastructure (B), Natural events (C), Recreation/tourism (B), Unsustainable exploitation (B)

Threats include a reduction in grazing leading to natural succession, the planting of non-native *Pinus* and *Quercus*, large-scale timber production and small-scale clear-cuts, river regulation, habitat destruction caused by firewood-collection, drying-up of wetlands due to abstraction, the enlargement of villages and industrial zones, motorway construction and traffic disturbance, natural fires and wind storms, trekking and rock-climbing, nest robbery and spring burning of grasslands. Conservation activities include influencing agricultural, fisheries and forestry practices. Contains an underground World Heritage Site (The Caves of Slovak Karst).

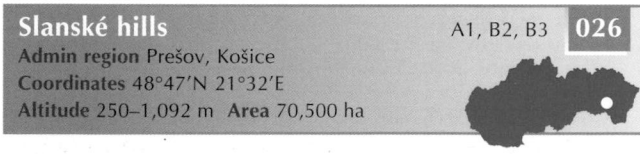

Slanské hills　　　　　　　　A1, B2, B3　026
Admin region Prešov, Košice
Coordinates 48°47′N 21°32′E
Altitude 250–1,092 m　**Area** 70,500 ha

■ Site description
The hills that form the IBA are 120 km long and up to 20 km wide, and are separated into five compartments by saddleback ridges. The forests consist mainly of *Fagus*, with *Acer* and *Abies* on higher ground and *Quercus* at lower altitudes. Mesophile meadows occur on the forest edge and within the forest at higher altitudes.

Habitats Forest and woodland (65%; broadleaved deciduous forest; mixed forest), Scrub (5%; scrub), Grassland (10%; humid grassland; mesophile grassland), Artificial landscape (20%; arable land; perennial crops/orchards/groves; forestry plantation; other urban/industrial areas; ruderal land)
Land-use Agriculture (20%), Forestry (65%), Hunting (95%), Tourism/recreation (5%), Urban/industrial/transport (5%)

■ Birds

Species		Season	Year	Pop min	Pop max	Acc	Criteria
Ciconia nigra	Black Stork	B	1997	20	25	B	B2
Pernis apivorus	Honey Buzzard	B	1997	45	55	B	B3
Circaetus gallicus	Short-toed Eagle	B	1998	2	3	B	B2
Aquila pomarina	Lesser Spotted Eagle	B	1997	35	40	A	B2

Species ... continued		Season	Year	Pop min	Pop max	Acc	Criteria
Aquila heliaca	Imperial Eagle	B	1997	5	7	A	A1, B2
Crex crex	Corncrake	B	1997	50	100	C	A1, B2
Columba oenas	Stock Dove	B	1997	250	400	C	B3
Jynx torquilla	Wryneck	B	1997	100	200	C	B2
Picus canus	Grey-headed Woodpecker	R	1997	100	150	C	B2
Dendrocopos medius Middle Spotted Woodpecker		R	1997	40	80	C	B3
Sylvia nisoria	Barred Warbler	B	1997	200	400	C	B3
Phylloscopus sibilatrix	Wood Warbler	B	1997	1,000	2,000	C	B3
Ficedula albicollis	Collared Flycatcher	B	1997	1,000	2,000	C	B3
Lanius collurio	Red-backed Shrike	B	1997	1,000	2,000	C	B2

The IBA is important for forest species, especially forest-nesting raptors. Shrubby grasslands in the foothills support nesting passerine species. Other species of note include *Ciconia ciconia* and *Bubo bubo*.

■ Protection status
National Low **International** None
The IBA partially or wholly overlaps with the following national designated areas. *National Nature Reserves*: Bačkovská dolina, Kokošovská dubina, Krčmárka, Malý Milič, Oblík, Šimonka. *Nature Reserves*: Dubová hora, Hermanovské skaly, Hlinianska jelšina, Malá Izra, Malé Brdo, Pusté pole, Rankovské skaly, Slanský hradný vrch, Veľký Milič, Zamutovská jelšina, Zamutovské skaly, Zbojnícky zámok. *Protected range*: Dubnícke bane. *National Natural Monument*: Herliansky gejzír. *Natural Monuments*: Miličská skala, Skaly pod Pariakovou, Trstinové jazero, Zapikan, Zárez Stravného potoka.

■ Conservation issues

Threats Abandonment/reduction of land management (B), Burning of vegetation (B), Deforestation (commercial) (A), Drainage (C), Infrastructure (B), Intensified forest management (A), Natural events (B), Unsustainable exploitation (C)

Threats include intensive deforestation, the construction of logging roads and wind-damage to trees. Forestry activities cause disturbance to birds. The legal and illegal hunting of birds also poses a threat. Conservation activities include protecting raptor nesting sites, installing nest-boxes for owls and influencing forestry practices.

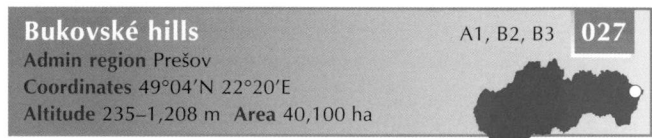

Bukovské hills　　　　　　　A1, B2, B3　027
Admin region Prešov
Coordinates 49°04′N 22°20′E
Altitude 235–1,208 m　**Area** 40,100 ha

■ Site description
A mountainous area situated near to the Ukrainian and Polish borders, forming a biogeographical frontier between the Eastern and Western Carpathians. Forest communities of *Fagus*, *Abies* and, at higher altitudes, *Acer* predominate, interspersed with pasture and meadow. Mountain grasslands (poloninas) occur above the treeline and *Alnus* covers river and stream banks. Human activities include cereal- and potato-growing, cattle-grazing and management of the Starina water reservoir.

Habitats Forest and woodland (80%; broadleaved deciduous forest; native coniferous forest; mixed forest; treeline ecotone), Grassland (15%; alpine/subalpine/boreal grassland; humid grassland; mesophile grassland), Artificial landscape (5%; arable land; perennial crops/orchards/groves; forestry plantation; other urban/industrial areas; ruderal land)
Land-use Agriculture (10%), Forestry (75%), Hunting (90%), Nature conservation/research (5%), Tourism/recreation (15%), Water management (5%)

■ Birds

Species		Season	Year	Pop min	Pop max	Acc	Criteria
Pernis apivorus	Honey Buzzard	B	1997	20	25	B	B3
Aquila pomarina	Lesser Spotted Eagle	B	1997	25	25	A	B2
Crex crex	Corncrake	B	1996	200	250	B	A1, B2
Columba oenas	Stock Dove	B	1997	1,000	1,200	B	B3
Caprimulgus europaeus	Nightjar	B	1997	150	200	C	B2
Jynx torquilla	Wryneck	B	1997	300	400	—	B2
Picus canus	Grey-headed Woodpecker	R	1997	500	600	B	B2

Species ... continued	Season	Year	Pop min	Pop max	Acc	Criteria
Phoenicurus phoenicurus Redstart	B	1997	300	400	B	B2
Turdus torquatus Ring Ouzel	B	1996	250	300	B	B3
Turdus viscivorus Mistle Thrush	B	1996	500	800	B	B3
Locustella fluviatilis River Warbler	B	1997	200	300	B	B3
Sylvia nisoria Barred Warbler	B	1997	150	300	B	B3
Phylloscopus sibilatrix Wood Warbler	B	1997	3,000	4,000	B	B3
Ficedula albicollis Collared Flycatcher	B	1997	3,000	3,500	B	B3
Lanius collurio Red-backed Shrike	B	1997	2,000	3,000	B	B2

An important site for breeding species of forest, meadow grassland and upland pasture. *Ciconia nigra*, *Alcedo atthis* and *Lanius excubitor* also breed.

■ Protection status
National Partial **International** High
The IBA partially or wholly overlaps with the following national designated areas. *National Park*: Poloniny. *National Nature Reserves*: Havešová, Pľaša, Riaba skala, Rožok, Stinská, Stužica. *Nature Reserves*: Bahno, Borsučiny, Bzana, Gazdoráň, Hlboké, Hrúnok, Ostrá, Pod Ruským, Ruské, Šípkova, Stinská slatina, Stružnická dolina, Udava. *Natural Monument*: Ulička. 40,100 ha of IBA covered by Biosphere Reserve (Východné Karpaty, 40,100 ha).

■ Conservation issues

Threats Abandonment/reduction of land management (C), Afforestation (C), Burning of vegetation (C), Deforestation (commercial) (A), Firewood collection (C), Intensified forest management (B), Recreation/tourism (C)

Threats include vegetation succession following land abandonment, tree-planting in the reservoir buffer zone, spring burning of village grassland, large-scale clear-cutting and logging of timber, the building of new forest roads and increasing transboundary tourism activities. Conservation activities include installing nest-boxes for owls and influencing forestry practices. A management plan exists for the area.

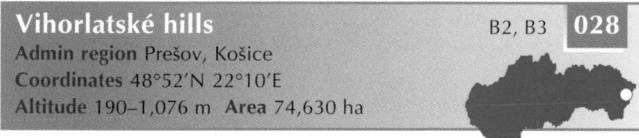

Vihorlatské hills
B2, B3 028
Admin region Prešov, Košice
Coordinates 48°52′N 22°10′E
Altitude 190–1,076 m **Area** 74,630 ha

■ Site description
An extensive range of hills and mountains situated near to the Ukrainian border. Deep valleys traverse the IBA, which includes numerous scattered rock features such as boulders, rock stacks and inland cliffs. *Fagus*, *Carpinus* and *Acer* forest cover the centre of the IBA, with *Picea* on higher ground and *Quercus* at lower altitudes. Mesophile meadows occur on north- and east-facing slopes, whereas warmer south- and west-facing slopes support bushes, vineyards and arable land. Part of the IBA (less than 5%) is a military training zone and is closed to the public.

Habitats Forest and woodland (55%; broadleaved deciduous forest; mixed forest), Scrub (5%; scrub), Grassland (15%; mesophile grassland), Artificial landscape (25%; arable land; perennial crops/orchards/groves; forestry plantation; other urban/industrial areas; ruderal land)
Land-use Agriculture (30%), Forestry (55%), Hunting (95%), Tourism/recreation (10%), Urban/industrial/transport (5%)

■ Birds

Species	Season	Year	Pop min	Pop max	Acc	Criteria
Ciconia ciconia White Stork	B	1997	15	20	A	B2
Pernis apivorus Honey Buzzard	B	1997	25	35	B	B3
Circaetus gallicus Short-toed Eagle	B	1997	3	4	A	B2
Aquila pomarina Lesser Spotted Eagle	B	1997	22	25	A	B2
Aquila heliaca Imperial Eagle	R	1997	1	1	A	B2
Picus canus Grey-headed Woodpecker	R	1997	100	150	B	B2
Dendrocopos medius Middle Spotted Woodpecker	R	1997	20	30	B	B3

An important site for forest species, especially forest-nesting raptors. *Ciconia nigra*, *Bubo bubo* and *Caprimulgus europaeus* also breed. Breeding species of global conservation concern that do not meet IBA criteria: *Crex crex*.

■ Protection status
National Low **International** None
The IBA partially or wholly overlaps with the following national designated areas. *National Nature Reserves*: Humenská, Humenský sokol, Jovsianska hrabina, Morské oko, Motrogon, Podstavka, Vihorlat, Vihorlatský prales. *Nature Reserves*: Chlmecká skalka, Drieň, Ďurova mláka, Jasenovská bučina, Jedlinka, Lysá, Lysák, Machnatý vrch, Pod Tŕstím, Roztoky, Vinianska stráň, Viniansky hradný vrch. *Protected Landscape Area*: Vihorlat. *Natural Monuments*: Beňatinský travertín, Čierny potok, Kamienka, Malé Morské oko, Podhorodský hradný vrch, Sninský kameň, Voniarsky jarok.

■ Conservation issues

Threats Abandonment/reduction of land management (C), Burning of vegetation (C), Deforestation (commercial) (A), Industrialization/urbanization (C), Intensified forest management (A), Natural events (B)

Tree-falls pose a threat. Conservation activities include protecting raptor nesting sites and influencing forestry practices.

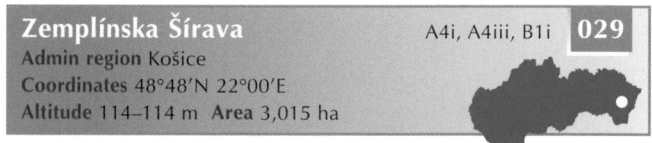

Zemplínska Šírava
A4i, A4iii, B1i 029
Admin region Košice
Coordinates 48°48′N 22°00′E
Altitude 114–114 m **Area** 3,015 ha

■ Site description
A water-supply reservoir built in the 1960s below the southern slopes of the Vihorlatské hills. The northern and western shores form an extensive recreational area and *Populus* stands grow on the southern shore. Muddy flats and *Salix* scrub cover the shallow eastern corner and shore. To the north-east are two small fish-ponds that are important for migrating birds.

Habitats Wetland (100%; mudflat/sandflat; standing fresh water; water-fringe vegetation)
Land-use Nature conservation/research (20%), Tourism/recreation (80%), Water management (100%)

■ Birds

Species	Season	Year	Pop min	Pop max	Acc	Criteria
Phalacrocorax carbo Cormorant	P	1995	1,200	—	B	B1i
Anser fabalis Bean Goose	P	1994	3,800	—	B	A4i, B1i
Anser albifrons White-fronted Goose	P	1994	6,000	—	B	B1i
Anas platyrhynchos Mallard	P	1997	22,500	—	B	B1i
Larus minutus Little Gull	P	1997	680	—	B	A4i, B1i
Larus ridibundus Black-headed Gull	P	1997	65,000	—	B	A4i, B1i

In spring and autumn the IBA acts as an important stop-over site for migrating waterbirds, holding over 20,000 individuals on a regular basis.

■ Protection status
National Partial **International** None
The IBA partially or wholly overlaps with the following national designated areas. *Protected Range*: Zemplínska Šírava.

■ Conservation issues

Threats Recreation/tourism (B), Unsustainable exploitation (B)

The activities of anglers and wind-surfers cause disturbance to birds, and wildfowl hunting is also a problem. Reedbeds (*Phragmites*) are not present due to rapid and frequent water-level fluctuations caused by water management practices. The IBA therefore does not support many breeding species.

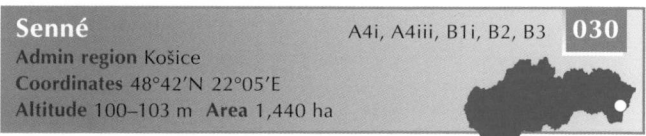

Senné
A4i, A4iii, B1i, B2, B3 030
Admin region Košice
Coordinates 48°42′N 22°05′E
Altitude 100–103 m **Area** 1,440 ha

■ Site description
An open, low-lying area that comprises 27 fish-ponds of varying size, wet meadows, pasture and arable fields interspersed with water canals,

bushes and solitary trees. The largest fish-pond contains three islets covered in dense *Salix* scrub and other ruderal vegetation.

> **Habitats** Scrub (5%; scrub), Grassland (50%; humid grassland; mesophile grassland), Wetland (40%; standing fresh water; river/stream; water-fringe vegetation), Artificial landscape (5%; arable land; other urban/industrial areas; ruderal land)
> **Land-use** Agriculture (40%), Fisheries/aquaculture (35%), Hunting (80%), Nature conservation/research (15%), Tourism/recreation (35%)

■ Birds

Species	Season	Year	Pop min	Pop max	Acc	Criteria
Podiceps nigricollis Black-necked Grebe	P	1997	1,000	—	C	A4i, B1i
Phalacrocorax carbo Cormorant	B	1997	70	120	A	B1i
Botaurus stellaris Bittern	B	1997	8	12	A	B2
Ixobrychus minutus Little Bittern	B	1996	3	5	—	B2
[1] *Nycticorax nycticorax* Night Heron	B	1995	100	140	B	B2
[2] *Egretta alba* Great White Egret	B	1997	35	65	A	A4i, B1i
Ardea purpurea Purple Heron	B	1997	15	25	A	B2
[3] *Platalea leucorodia* Spoonbill	B	1998	—	35	A	B1i, B2
Anser fabalis Bean Goose	P	1996	3,500	—	C	B1i
Anas platyrhynchos Mallard	P	1996	20,000	—	—	B1i
Aythya ferina Pochard	B	1997	35	40	B	B3
Chlidonias hybridus Whiskered Tern	B	1997	20	200	B	B2

1. The largest breeding colony in Slovakia.
2. Large increase over the last 5 years.
3. The only breeding location in Slovakia.

An important site for breeding and passage waterbirds, holding 20,000 or more individuals on a regular basis. During autumn and early spring this is the most important roosting site in Slovakia for *Circus cyaneus* (150–200 individuals). *Porzana parva*, *Recurvirostra avosetta*, *Limosa limosa*, *Chlidonias niger* and *Locustella luscinioides* also breed. Breeding species of global conservation concern that do not meet IBA criteria: *Aythya nyroca* (2–4 pairs), *Crex crex* (5 pairs).

■ Protection status
National Partial **International** Partial
The IBA partially or wholly overlaps with the following national designated areas. *National Nature Reserve*: Senné-rybníky. 425 ha of IBA covered by Ramsar Site (Senné-rybníky (Senné fish-ponds), 425 ha).

■ Conservation issues

> **Threats** Abandonment/reduction of land management (A), Aquaculture/fisheries (C), Burning of vegetation (C), Drainage (B), Recreation/tourism (B), Unsustainable exploitation (B)

The activities of anglers and photographers cause disturbance to birds, and wildfowl hunting is also a problem. A reduction in the intensity of fish production and a consequent decrease in the size of the benthic community have led to rapid declines in the number of breeding and passage waterbirds using the site. Conservation activities include protecting *Recurvirostra avosetta* nesting sites, managing meadows, dykes and islets through scrub and ruderal vegetation removal, and influencing agricultural and fisheries practices. A management plan exists for part of the National Nature Reserve.

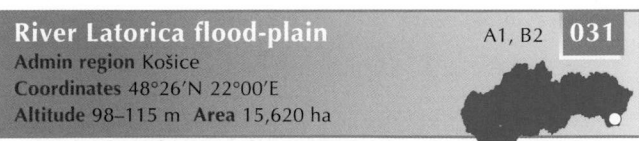

River Latorica flood-plain   A1, B2   031
Admin region Košice
Coordinates 48°26′N 22°00′E
Altitude 98–115 m **Area** 15,620 ha

■ Site description

> **Habitats** Forest and woodland (20%; broadleaved deciduous forest; alluvial/very wet forest), Scrub (15%; scrub), Grassland (10%; humid grassland; mesophile grassland), Wetland (10%; standing fresh water; river/stream; raised bog; water-fringe vegetation; fen/transition mire/spring), Artificial landscape (45%; arable land; perennial crops/orchards/groves; other urban/industrial areas; ruderal land)
> **Land-use** Agriculture (40%), Forestry (20%), Hunting (95%), Urban/industrial/transport (5%), Water management (10%)

The IBA comprises the Slovak part of the River Latorica and the lower sections of the Laborec and Ondava rivers. It covers an extensive complex of oxbow lakes, flood-plain forest, wet meadows, localized sand-dunes, artificial drainage canals and dykes. Hardwood forests

of *Quercus*, *Fraxinus*, *Ulmus* and *Carpinus* are present in addition to softwood communities of *Populus* and *Salix*. Reedbeds consist of *Phragmites*, *Typha* and *Carex*, while *Nymphaea*, *Nuphar*, *Trapa*, *Alisma* and *Stratiotes* form open water communities. Human activities include cattle-grazing.

■ Birds

Species	Season	Year	Pop min	Pop max	Acc	Criteria
Ixobrychus minutus Little Bittern	B	1997	3	5	A	B2
[1] *Ciconia ciconia* White Stork	B	1998	25	30	A	B2
Crex crex Corncrake	B	1997	20	30	C	A1
Alcedo atthis Kingfisher	R	1997	25	30	B	B2
Merops apiaster Bee-eater	B	1997	140	250	B	B2
Riparia riparia Sand Martin	B	1997	200	250	B	B2

1. An additional 25 pairs breed outside the IBA and come in to feed.

An important site for species of flood-plain forest and other riverine habitats. *Botaurus stellaris*, *Ardea purpurea*, *Ciconia nigra*, *Pernis apivorus*, *Milvus migrans* and other raptors, *Porzana porzana*, *Porzana parva*, *Dendrocopos medius* and *Lanius minor* also breed.

■ Protection status
National High **International** Partial
The IBA partially or wholly overlaps with the following national designated areas. *National Nature Reserves*: Latorický luh I., Latorický luh II. *Nature Reserves*: Dlhé Tice, Krátke Tice, Rašelinisko Boľ, Veľké Jazero, Zatínsky luh. *Protected Landscape Area*: Latorica. Overlaps with international designated areas: 4,358 ha of IBA covered by Ramsar Site (Latorica, 4,358 ha).

■ Conservation issues

> **Threats** Agricultural intensification/expansion (C), Burning of vegetation (C), Disturbance to birds (B), Extraction industry (B), Firewood collection (C), Selective logging/cutting (C)

Threats include the removal of boundary shrubs between arable fields and meadows, agricultural chemical use, spring burning of grass and reed *Phragmites*, disturbance caused by fish poachers, sand extraction and selective logging. The softwood forests have been drained in places and, along with mesophile meadows and pasture, have been converted to arable land.

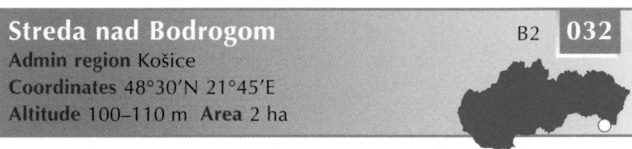

Streda nad Bodrogom   B2   032
Admin region Košice
Coordinates 48°30′N 21°45′E
Altitude 100–110 m **Area** 2 ha

■ Site description
The IBA comprises a group of 1.5–5 m high vertical sand walls surrounded by arable and ruderal land, vineyards and meadows. The walls were created by the extraction of sand from natural dunes covered by drought-tolerant vegetation.

> **Habitats** Grassland (20%; dry siliceous grassland), Rocky areas (60%; inland sand-dunes), Artificial landscape (20%; ruderal land)
> **Land-use** Not utilized (100%)

■ Birds

Species	Season	Year	Pop min	Pop max	Acc	Criteria
Merops apiaster Bee-eater	B	1997	45	60	A	B2

An important site for tunneling cliff-nesting species.

■ Protection status
National None **International** None

■ Conservation issues

> **Threats** Abandonment/reduction of land management (A), Agricultural intensification/expansion (B), Burning of vegetation (C), Extraction industry (A), Industrialization/urbanization (B), Natural events (C)

The site is potentially threatened by domestic waste deposition and by the illegal extraction of sand, which also causes disturbance to birds. Heavy rain poses a low-impact threat.

REFERENCES

BOHUŠ, M. (1993) [Comparison of two different forest stands bird communities in Danube river inundation] *Tichodroma* 5: 87–95. (In Slovak, with English summary.)

BOHUŠ, M. (1996) [White-tailed Eagle (*Haliaeetus albicilla*) in the Slovak Danubion region: the present status and its perspectives.] *Buteo* 8: 103–108. (In Slovak, with English summary.)

CHOBOT, J., ŠEVČÍK, B. AND STRAKOVÁ, J. (1991) [*Research into measures for conserving Great Bustard in Slovakia.*] Bratislava and Nitra, Slovakia: ÚV SPZ and VÚŽV. (In Slovak.)

CHYTIL, J. AND ČMELÍK, P. (1991) [Contribution to the knowledge of the avifauna in the lowland Záhorská nížina.] *Ochrana Prírody* 11: 102–130. (In Czech.)

DANKO, Š. (1984) [Report on the work of the zoological section of the VIIth East–Slovakian camp of nature conservationists in Remetské Hámre.] Pp. 81–87 in [*VIIth East–Slovakian camp of nature conservationists. Review of the scientific results.*] Michalovce, Czechoslovakia. (In Slovak.)

DANKO, Š. (1995) [Waterfowl and on water living birds of the Senné Natural Reserve and adjacent ponds area (Iňačovce, Eastern Slovakia) in 1975–1994.] *Tichodroma* 5: 22–47. (In Slovak, with English summary.)

DANKO, Š., DIVIŠ, T., DVORSKÁ, J., DVORSKÝ, M., CHAVKO, J., KARASKA, D., KLOUBEC, B., KURKA, P., MATUŠÍK, H., PEŠKE, L., SCHRÖPFER, L. AND VACÍK, R. (1994) The state of knowledge of breeding numbers of birds of prey (Falconiformes) and owls (Strigiformes) in the Czech and Slovak republics as of 1990 and their population trends in 1970–1990. *Buteo* 6: 1–89.

DAROLOVÁ, A. (1993) [Results of waterfowl census on the Danube and Morava rivers, Slovakia (1991–1992).] *Sylvia* 29: 36–40. (In Slovak, with English summary.)

FERIANC, O. (1955) [Inundation area at Senné (the district of Veľké Kapušany) as an important migration site for waterbirds in eastern Slovakia.] *Práce II. Sekcie SAV, Sér. Biol.* 1(4): 1–31. (In Slovak, with German and Russian summaries.)

FERIANC, O. (1967) [The influence of the new retention reservoir under Vihorlat on waterbirds migrating through eastern Slovakia.] *Biológia* 22(1): 45–57. (In Slovak, with German and Russian summaries.)

FERIANC, O. (1977) [Avian synusia in biotopes of the Zemplínska Šírava region.] *Acta Fac. Rer. Nat. Univ. Comen., Zool.* 22: 141–176. (In Slovak, with English and Russian summaries.)

FERIANC, O. AND FERIANCOVÁ, Z. (1956) [Birds of the High Tatras and notes to their hypsometric distribution and ecology.] *Acta Fac. Rer. Nat. Univ. Comen., Zool.* 2(7–9): 483–514. (In Slovak, with German and Russian summaries.)

FERIANCOVÁ-MASÁROVÁ, Z. (1963) [Birds of four habitats of surroundings of the Orava reservoir.] *Biológia* 18(1): 45–66. (In Slovak, with German summary.)

FERIANCOVÁ-MASÁROVÁ, Z. (1968) [Bird communities of western parts of Liptov (transect Háj-Chopok).] *Probl. Biol. Krajiny* 22: 7–58. (In Slovak, with English, German and Russian summaries.)

FERIANCOVÁ-MASÁROVÁ, Z. AND BRTEK, V. (1969) [Birds of the southern part of the Little Carpathians.] *Biol. Práce* 16(6): 7–76. (In Slovak.)

FIALA, J. (1997) [The influence of the structure of beech forest on the composition of ornithocoenoses in the Slanské hills.] Bratislava, Slovakia: Commenius University (Dipl. thesis). (In Slovak.)

FULÍN, M. (1996) [White Stork in Slovakia in the years 1994, 1995 and 1996.] *Chránené Územia Slovenska* 30: 31–33. (In Slovak.)

GRIMMETT, R. F. A. AND JONES T. A. (1989) *Important Bird Areas in Europe*. Cambridge, UK: International Council for Bird Preservation (Tech. Publ. 9).

GYIMESI, J. (1969) [Influence of climatic change on the avifauna of the Medzibodrožie.] *Zborn. Východoslov. Múz.* 10B: 53–57. (In Slovak, with German summary.)

HEATH, M. F. AND BORGGREVE, C. (2000) *BirdLife International/EBCC European Bird Database 1998*. Cambridge, UK: BirdLife International.

HELL, P. AND CHOBOT, J. (1993) [Will Great Bustard become extinct in our country?] *Tichodroma* 5: 125–135. (In Slovak, with German summary.)

HORA, J. AND KAŇUCH, P., EDS. (1992) [*Important Bird Areas in Czech and Slovak Republics.*] Proceedings of the seminar of the Czechoslovak section ICBP, Třeboň, 24–25 March 1992. Prague, Czecho-Slovakia: Czecho-Slovak section ICBP. (In Slovak, with English summaries.)

HORA, J. AND KAŇUCH, P., EDS. (1992) *Important Bird Areas in Europe: Czechoslovakia*. First edition. Praha, Czecho-Slovakia: Czechoslovak ICBP Section.

HRNČIAROVÁ, T., ED. (1989) [*Ecological assumptions for optimal use of the Zamagurie–Ždiar area (ecological study).*] Bratislava, Czechoslovakia: ÚEBE CBEV SAV. (In Slovak.)

HUBÁLEK, Z. (1984) [Nesting density of birds on the Silická planina plateau (Protected Landscape Area "The Slovak karst").] *Biológia* 39(6): 617–625. (In Czech, with English and Russian summaries.)

HUDEC, K., ED. (1983) [*Fauna of CSSR, Birds III.*] First edition. Praha, Czechoslovakia: Academia. (In Czech, with German summary.)

HUDEC, K., ED. (1994) [*Fauna of CR and SR, Birds I.*] Second edition. Praha, Czech Republic: Academia. (In Czech, with German (summary).)

HUDEC, K. AND ČERNÝ, W., EDS. (1977) [*Fauna of CSSR, Birds II.*] First edition. Praha, Czechoslovakia: Academia. (In Czech, with German summary.)

ILLAVSKÝ, J. (1997) [Breeding ornithocoenosis of a natural type growth of the innundation of river Danube and using its analysis for ecosozological purposes.] Bratislava, Slovakia: Commenius University (Dipl. thesis). (In Slovak.)

JANALÍK, F. (1960) [Birds of the Levočské Mountains] *Zprávy MOS* 2: 18–22. (In Czech.)

JANÍK, M. (1985) [Vertebrate fauna of the Suchý State Nature Reserve.] *Ochrana Prírody* 6: 189–211. (In Slovak, with English, German and Russian summaries.)

JANÍK, M. (1988) [Avifauna of the Kľačianska Magura State Nature Reserve in the Malá Fatra Protected Landscape Area.] *Ochrana Prírody* 9: 281–293. (In Slovak, with English, German and Russian summaries.)

JANÍK, M. (1988) [Avifauna of the Šrámková State Nature Reserve in the Malá Fatra Protected Landscape Area.] *Ochrana Prírody* 9: 295–310. (In Slovak, with English, German and Russian summaries.)

JANÍK, M. (1989) [Avifauna of the State Nature Reserve Pripor.] *Ochrana Prírody* 10: 369–383. (In Slovak, with English, German and Russian summaries.)

JANÍK, M. AND ŠTOLLMANN, A., EDS. (1981) [*Rozsutec.*] Martin, Slovakia. (In Slovak, with German summary.)

KADLEČÍK, J., ED. (1997) [*Wetlands management in Slovakia.*] Proceedings of the international seminar celebrating the 25th Anniversary of the Ramsar Convention, Zemplínska Šírava, 26–28 November 1996. Banská Bystrica, Slovakia: Slovenská agentúra životného prostredia. (In Slovak, with English summaries.)

KALIVODOVÁ, E. AND BRTEK, V. (1977) [Bird population in the northern part of the Little Carpathians.] *Biol. Práce* 23: 7–107. (In Slovak.)

KALIVODOVÁ, E. AND DAROLOVÁ, A. (1989) [*Birds of Slovak part of the Danube river and Žitný ostrov.*] Bratislava, Slovakia. (In Slovak.)

KALIVODOVÁ, E., DAROLOVÁ, A., FERIANCOVÁ-MASÁROVÁ, Z. AND KÜRTHY, A. (1994) [Birds of the lower flow of the floodplain of the river Morava.] *Tichodroma* 7: 67–72. (In Slovak, with English summary.)

KALIVODOVÁ, E., FERIANCOVÁ-MASÁROVÁ, Z., DAROLOVÁ, A. AND KÜRTHY, A. (1996) Ornithological evaluation of the lower stream part of the alluvium of the river Morava (Slovak–Austrian frontier). *Ekológia (Bratislava)* 15(2): 189–205.

KALIVODOVÁ, E., JANOTKOVÁ, D. AND KIS-CSÁJIOVÁ, K. (1987) [*Selective bibliography of zoological literature of Žitný ostrov and adjacent part of the Czechoslovak section of the river Danube.*] First edition. Bratislava, Czechoslovakia: ÚEBE SAV. (In Slovak.)

KARASKA, D. (1993) [Contribution to the distribution and biology of the Black Stork (*Ciconia nigra* L.) in the district Dolný Kubín.] *Tichodroma* 5: 61–67. (In Slovak.)

KLINDA, J. (1985) [*Protected Natural Areas in the Slovak Socialist Republic.*] Bratislava, Slovakia: Obzor. (In Slovak.)

KLINDA, J., ED. (1998) Environment of the Slovak republic. First edition. Bratislava, Slovakia: Ministry of the Environment of the Slovak Republic.

KLOUBEC, B. AND ČAPEK, M. (1993) [Hitherto research results of the avifauna in the 'Parížske močiare' swamp (SW Slovakia).] *Zprávy MOS* 51: 55–69. (In Slovak, with English summary.)

KOREŇ, M. AND ŠTEFFEK, J. (1996) [*Proposal of the national ecological network of Slovakia: NECONET.*] Bratislava, Slovakia: Nadácia IUCN, Svetová únia ochrany prírody. (In Slovak, with English summary.)

KORŇAN, M., ED. (1998) [*Research and conservation of the Krivánska Fatra.*] First edition. Varín, Slovakia: National Park Malá Fatra. (In Slovak.)

KOVAČOVSKÝ, P. AND RYCHLÍK, I. (1996) [The effect of environmental change in the area of the Gabčíkovo water dams on seasonal dynamics of water avifauna.] *Acta Environ. Univ. Com.* 6: 115–123. (In Slovak, with English summary.)

KRIŠTÍN, A. (1991) [Breeding status and breeding biology of Lesser Grey Shrike (*Lanius minor* L.) in the Central Slovakia (CSFR).] *Orn. Mitt.* 43: 131–133. (In German, with English summary.)

KRIŠTÍN, A. (1991) [On present status and ecology of Rock Bunting, *Emberiza cia*, in Czechoslovakia.] *Sylvia* 28: 115–120. (In Slovak, with English summary.)

KRIŠTÍN, A. (1991) [Ornithocoenoses of characteristic habitats of the Poľana Mountains] *Stredné Slovensko* 10: 165–182. (In Slovak, with English summary.)

KRIŠTÍN, A. (1995) [Birds and ornithocoenoses of sites Lešť and Gavúrky.] Pp. 100–104 in [*Biodiversity and nature conservation in areas used by previous Soviet army in the Slovak Republic.*] First edition. Bratislava, Slovakia: Nadácia IUCN, Svetová únia ochrany prírody. (In Slovak.)

KRIŠTÍN, A. (1995) Why the Lesser Grey Shrike (*Lanius minor*) survives in Slovakia: food and habitat preferences, breeding biology. *Folia zool.* 44 (4): 325–334.

KRIŠTÍN, A. AND ZACH, P. (1993) [Ornithocoenoses of southern Podpoľanie of the proposed important bird area of Europe.] Pp. 106–116 in P. Urban, ed. [*Fauna of the Poľana Mountains*] Zborník referátov zo seminára, Zvolen. (In Slovak, with English summary.)

KROPIL, R. (1991) [Avifauna of the Vrbické Pleso Protected Nature Formation in the Lower Tatras.] *Stredné Slovensko* 10: 295–304. (In Slovak, with English summary.)

KUBÁN, V. AND DUFFEK, K. (1987) [Birds hibernation at the Sĺňava water reservoir and within Piešťany town surroundings (west Slovakia). Part I.] *Tichodroma* 1: 12–81. (In Slovak.)

KUBÁN, V. AND MATOUŠEK, B. (1994) [Birds hibernation at the Sĺňava water reservoir and within Piešťany town surroundings (west Slovakia). Part II.] *Zbor. Slov. Nár. Múz., Prír. Vedy* 40: 95–132. (In Slovak.)

KUBÁN, V. AND MATOUŠEK, B. (1995) [Birds hibernation at the Sĺňava water reservoir and within Piešťany town surroundings (west Slovakia). Part III.] *Tichodroma* 8: 106–150. (In Slovak.)

KUBÁN, V., MATOUŠEK, B. AND MATOUŠKOVÁ, B. (1996) [Birds hibernation at the Sĺňava water reservoir and within Piešťany town surroundings (west Slovakia). Part IV.] *Tichodroma* 9: 134–174. (In Slovak.)

KUPCOVÁ, A. AND BOHAČÍK, L. (1980) [Avifauna of Gader's valley and Blatnica valley.] *Výsk. Práce z Ochrany Prírody* 3C: 277–300. (In Slovak.)

KUX, Z. AND RANDÍK, A. (1961) [Contribution to the knowledge of ornithofauna of the south Slovakian marshes at Gbelce, Čalovo and Gabčíkovo.] *Čas. Mor. Múz.* 46: 203–234. (In Czech.)

MICHALKO, J., ED. (1986) [*Geobotanical map of the CSSR.*] First edition. Bratislava, Czechoslovakia: Veda. (In Slovak.)

MIHÁL, I. (1976) [Avifaunistic intelligence from the Tatra National Park.] *Zborn. Prác o TANAP* 18: 80–118. (In Slovak, with English, German and Russian summaries.)

MOJŽIŠ, M. (1993) [Avifauna of the gravel-pit near Veľká nad Ipľom (district Lučenec).] *Tichodroma* 6: 197–200. (In Slovak, with English summary.)

MURIN, B., KRIŠTÍN, A., DAROLOVÁ, A., DANKO, Š. AND KROPIL, R. (1994) [Breeding bird population sizes in Slovakia.] *Sylvia* 30(2): 97–105. (In Slovak, with English summary.)

ORSZÁGHOVÁ, Z. AND TRNKA, A. (1990) Contribution to the knowledge of birds from the Orava region (Jelešňa brook). *Biológia* 45(6): 504–514.

PAGÁČ, J. AND VOLOŠČUK, I. (1983) [*Malá Fatra Protected Landscape Area.*] First edition. Bratislava, Czechoslovakia: Obzor. (In Slovak, with German and Russian summaries.)

PIKULA, J. (1961) [Birds of the alpine level of the Belaner Tatra.] *Biológia* 16(9): 668–677. (In Czech, with German and Russian summaries.)

ROZLOŽNÍK, M., KARASOVÁ, E. EDS. (1994) [*Slovak Karst Protected Landscape Area Biosphere Reserve.*] Martin, Slovakia: Osveta. (In Slovak, with German and Russian summaries.)

SANIGA, M. (1989) [Bird communities in the Suchý vrch protected area in the Veľká Fatra mountains.] *Tichodroma* 2: 31–42. (In Slovak, with English summary.)

SANIGA, M. (1990) [Livestock pasture influence on the changes of mountain ornithocoenoses in the Veľká Fatra mountains.] *Tichodroma* 3: 199–210. (In Slovak, with English summary.)

SANIGA, M. (1995) Breeding bird communities of the fir-beech to the dwarfed-pine vegetation tiers in the Veľká Fatra and Malá Fatra mountains. *Biológia* 50(2): 185–193.

SANIGA, M. (1995) Seasonal distribution, habitat and territory of the Wallcreeper (*Tichodroma muraria*) in the Veľká Fatra mountains. *Biológia* 50(2): 195–202.

SANIGA, M. (1996) [Bird communities of the subalpine meadows in the Veľká Fatra mountains] *Tichodroma* 9: 51–64. (In Slovak, with English summary.)

SLÁVIKOVÁ, D. AND KRAJČOVIČ, V., EDS. (1996) [*Conservation of biodiversity and management of permament meadows of the PLA BR Poľana.*] First edition. Bratislava, Slovakia: Nadácia IUCN, Svetová únia ochrany prírody. (In Slovak, with English summary.)

ŠTASTNÝ, K., RANDÍK, A. AND HUDEC, K. (1987) [*Atlas of the breeding distribution of birds in the CSSR 1973–1977.*] First edition. Praha, Czechoslovakia: Academia. (In Czech.)

STRAKA, P. AND GUZIOVÁ, Z. (1998) *National biodiversity strategy of Slovakia.* First edition. Bratislava, Slovakia: Ministry of the Environment of the Slovak Republic.

ŠTROFFEK, O. (1987) [*Low Tatras National Park.*] First edition. Bratislava, Czechoslovakia. (In Slovak, with German and Russian summaries.)

SVETLÍK, J. (1995) [Water component of the ornithocoenoses of Hrušovská reservoir.] Bratislava, Slovakia: Commenius University (Dipl. thesis). (In Slovak.)

TOPERCER, J. (1989) [Ornithocoenoses of the State Nature Reserve Skalná Alpa.] *Ochrana Prírody* 10: 271–287. (In Slovak.)

TRNKA, A., KRIŠTÍN, A., DANKO, Š., HARVANČÍK, S., KOCIAN, Ľ., KARASKA, D. AND MURIN, B. (1995) [Checklist of the birds of Slovakia.] *Tichodroma* 8: 7–21. (In Slovak, with English summary.)

TUCKER, G. M. AND HEATH, M. F. (1994) *Birds in Europe: their conservation status.* Cambridge, UK: BirdLife International (BirdLife Conservation Series no. 3).

URBAN, P. AND HRIVNÁK, R., EDS. (1997) [*Poiplie.*] Banská Bystrica, Slovakia. (In Slovak.)

VESTENICKÝ, K., ED. (1986) [*Veľká Fatra Protected Landscape Area.*] First edition. Bratislava, Czechoslovakia: Obzor. (In Slovak, with Russian and German summaries.)

VOLOŠČUK, I., ED. (1988) [*Východné Karpaty Protected Landscape Area.*] First edition. Bratislava, Czechoslovakia: Príroda. (In Slovak, with Russian, German and Hungarian summaries.)

VOLOŠČUK, I., ED. (1994) [*Tatra National Park Biosphere Reserve.*] First edition. Tatranská Lomnica, Slovakia: Gradus. (In Slovak, with German and Russian summary.)

VOLOŠČUK, I. AND PELIKÁN, V., EDS. (1991) [*Muránska Planina Protected Landscape Area.*] First edition. Bratislava, Slovakia: Obzor. (In Slovak, with English, German and Russian summaries.)

VOLOŠČUK, I. AND TERRAY, J., EDS. (1987) [*Vihorlat Protected Landscape Area.*] First edition. Bratislava, Czechoslovakia: Príroda. (In Slovak, with German, Russian and Hungarian summaries.)

VOSKÁR, J. (1978) [Avifauna of the protected study area Podvihorlatská nádrž: Zemplínska Šírava.] *Výsk. Práce z Ochrany Prírody* 1: 178–248. (In Slovak, with English, German and Russian summaries.)

VOSKÁR, J. (1978) [Effect of building fishponds region at Iňačovce on avifauna of the State natural reservation of Senné.] *Výsk. Práce z Ochrany Prírody* 1: 3–86. (In Slovak, with English, German and Russian summaries.)

ZACH, P. AND KRIŠTÍN, A. (1994) [Birds of the Kiarovský močiar State Nature Reserve.] *Tichodroma* 7: 95–101. (In Slovak, with English summary.)

ŽOLNER, J. (1983) [On the nesting of Red-backed Shrike (*Lanius collurio* L.) in the south-eastern part of the Slovak karst.] *Zborn. Východoslov. Múz.* 17AB: 43–53. (In Slovak, with German and Russian summaries.)

■ SWEDEN

LARS LINDELL, BJÖRN WELANDER AND STEVE DAHLFORS

Lake Ånnsjön (IBA 014). (PHOTO: ULLA FALKDALEN)

GENERAL INTRODUCTION

Sweden covers 450,000 km², making it the fourth largest country in Europe. The effect of the Atlantic Gulf Stream means that it has a milder climate than other areas at the same latitude. Sweden's flora and fauna are closely linked to the physical form of the landscape, which has been greatly affected by the cycle of glacial and interglacial periods.

Sweden has 63 Important Bird Areas (IBAs) covering 12,678 km² (Table 1, Map 1), equivalent to 3% of the land area. The number of IBAs has almost doubled since the previous international inventory, which identified 33 (Grimmett and Jones 1989).

Only nine of the 63 IBAs are located in the north of Sweden—sites are mainly concentrated in the densely populated and well-known regions to the south (Map 1). A lack of up-to-date information on some vast sites in the far north has meant that these have not been included in the current inventory.

ORNITHOLOGICAL IMPORTANCE

There are 54 species of European conservation concern (SPECs) breeding and/or regularly occurring in Swedish IBAs (Tucker and Heath 1994). Of these SPECs, four are of global conservation concern: *Anser erythropus*, *Haliaeetus albicilla*, *Crex crex* and *Gallinago media*. Nine sites were selected as IBAs on the basis of

internationally important numbers of one or more of these four species and therefore meet the A1 criterion (Table 2).

IBAs 001, 005, 009 and 014 hold significant numbers of up to eleven species whose distributions in Europe are largely or wholly confined (when breeding) to the Arctic/tundra biome, and therefore meet the A3 criterion. IBA 004 holds significant numbers of eight species whose distributions are similarly confined to the boreal biome, and therefore also meets the A3 criterion.

Sweden is particularly important for breeding waterbirds and seabirds, with the national populations of *Branta leucopsis*, *Recurvirostra avosetta*, *Sterna caspia* and *Cepphus grylle* found mainly within IBAs (Table 4). The island archipelagos of the Baltic in particular support large numbers of breeding ducks, waders, gulls, terns and auks (IBAs 020, 024, 027, 038 and 039). Vast areas of mountain and bog in the north, and wet coastal meadows in the south also hold a diversity of breeding ducks and waders (IBAs 001, 002, 004, 005, 009, 014, 037, 050, 051, 052, 054 and 055). A total of 29 sites qualify as IBAs under the A4i/A4ii criteria as they hold more than 1% of either the biogeographic or global population of at least one of the congregatory waterbirds and seabirds listed in Table 3.

Due to Sweden's northerly location in Europe, its IBAs tend to have been identified for breeding and passage species rather than for those that overwinter. Worth mentioning, however, are the assemblages of moulting geese in southern Sweden (for example, *Anser anser* which, post-moult, move to several IBAs—036, 037,

Table 1. Summary of Important Bird Areas in Sweden. 63 IBAs covering 12,678 km²

IBA code	1989 code	International name	National name	Administrative region	Area (ha)	Criteria (see p. 11)
001	SE033	Taavavuoma	Taavavuoma	Norrbotten	28,400	A3, B2, C6
002	SE032	Påkketan	Påkketan	Norrbotten	24,000	B2, C6
003	SE030	Lake Laidaure	Laidaure	Norrbotten	2,000	C2
004	SE031	Sjaunja	Sjaunja	Norrbotten	208,000	A1, A3, B2, C1, C6

673

Table 1 ... continued. Summary of Important Bird Areas in Sweden. 63 IBAs covering 12,678 km²

IBA code	1989 code	International name	National name	Administrative region	Area (ha)	Criteria (see p. 11)
005	SE027	Lake Tjålmejaure–Laisdalen valley	Tjålmejaure–Laisdalen	Norrbotten	22,200	A3, B2, C6
006	SE029	Lake Persöfjärden	Persöfjärden	Norrbotten	3,350	B1i, C2, C3, C6
007	SE028	Lake Gammelstadsviken	Gammelstadsviken	Norrbotten	440	B2, C2, C6
008	—	Skvolpen island	Skvolpen/Sandgrynnorna/Grillklippan	Norrbotten	2,500	B1i, B1ii, B2, C2, C6
009	SE026	Vindelfjällen mountains (including Lake Tärnasjön)	Vindelfjällen (med Tärnasjön)	Västerbotten	550,000	A3, B2, C6
010	SE025	River Umeälven delta	Umeälven delta	Västerbotten	1,500	A4i, B1i, C2, C3
011	—	Holmöarna archipelago	Holmöarna	Västerbotten	27,000	A4i, A4ii, B1i, B1ii, B2, C2, C3, C6
012	—	Bonden island	Bonden	Västerbotten	5	B1ii, B2, B3, C3
013	—	Gnäggen island	Gnäggen	Västerbotten	4	B1ii, B3, C3
014	SE024	Lake Ånnsjön–Storlien	Ånnsjön–Storlien	Jämtland	90,000	A1, A3, A4i, A4ii, B1i, B1iii, B2, B3, C1, C2, C6
015	SE023	River Dalälven–Hovran	Dalälven–Hovran	Dalarna	5,030	A4i, B1i, B3, C2, C6
016	SE021	River Svartån	Svartån	Västmanland	1,870	A4i, B1i, C2
017	SE022	River Dalälven–Färnebofjärden	Dalälven–Färnebofjärden	Uppsala	11,200	A4i, B1i, B2, C2, C6
018	—	Båtfors–Bredfors	Båtfors–Bredfors	Uppsala	2,700	C6
019	—	Ledskär–Karlholm Bay	Ledskär–Karlholm	Uppsala	3,500	A4i, B1i, C2, C3
020	—	Björn archipelago	Björns skärgård	Uppsala	3,000	A4i, B1i, B1ii, B2, B3, C2, C3, C6
021	—	Lake Tämnaren	Tämnaren	Uppsala	13,500	A4i, B1i, B2, C2, C3, C6
022	—	Florarna	Florarna	Uppsala	16,500	B3, C6
023	SE020	Lake Hjälstaviken	Hjälstaviken	Uppsala	820	A4i, B1i, C3
024	—	Gräsö archipelago	Gräsö skärgård	Stockholm	18,000	A1, A4i, B1i, B2, C1, C2, C3, C6
025	—	Dannemora	Dannemora	Uppsala	11,500	A1, B2, C1
026	—	Tarnan–Riala forest	Tarnan–Riala forest	Stockholm	7,500	B2, C6
027	SE019	Outer Stockholm archipelago	Stockholms yttre skärgård	Stockholm	9,100	A4i, A4ii, A4iii, B1i, B1ii, B2, B3, C2, C3, C4, C6
028	—	Lake Östra Styran	Östra Styran	Stockholm	117	C2
029	—	Hanveden–Hemfosa	Hanveden–Hemfosa	Stockholm	3,500	B2, C6
030	—	Sandemar	Sandemar	Stockholm	1,700	B1i, B3, C2, C3
031	—	Lake Tysslingen	Tysslingen	Örebro	600	A4i, B1i, C2, C3
032	—	Bay of Rynningeviken	Rynningeviken	Örebro	600	C6
033	SE018	Kvismaren	Kvismaren	Örebro	800	A4i, B1i, B3, C2, C3, C6
034	—	Lake Storhjälmaren	Storhjälmaren	Örebro	600	A4i, B1i, C2
035	SE017	Bay of Kilsviken	Kilsviken	Värmland	8,910	B2, C2, C6
036	SE013	Lake Tåkern	Tåkern	Östergötland	5,620	A4i, A4iii, B1i, B2, C2, C3, C4, C6
037	—	Bay of Svensksundsviken	Svensksundsviken	Östergötland	3,300	A1, A4i, B1i, C1, C3
038	—	Dannskär–Örskär islands	Dannskär–Örskär	Östergötland	95	A4i, B1i, B2, C2, C3, C6
039	SE012	St Anna archipelago	St Anna skärgård	Östergötland	5,690	B2, C6
040	SE015	Dättern–Södra Brandfjorden	Dättern–Södra Brandfjorden	Västra Götaland	3,320	B2, C6
041	SE016	Lake Östen	Östen	Västra Götaland	1,020	A4i, B1i, B3, C2, C3
042	SE014	Lake Hornborgasjön	Hornborgasjön	Västra Götaland	6,350	A4i, B1i, B1iv, B2, B3, C2, C3, C5, C6
043	SE011	Stigfjorden Fjord	Stigfjorden	Göteborg och Bohus	8,500	B1i, B2, B3, C2, C3, C6
044	—	Bay of Torslandaviken	Torslandaviken	Göteborg och Bohus	250	B1i, B2, B3, C2, C3
045	—	Bay of Kungsbackafjorden	Kungsbackafjorden	Göteborg och Bohus	4,000	A4i, B1i, C3
046	—	Lake Ralången	Ralången	Jönköping	54	C2
047	SE008	Lake Kävsjön and Store Mosse	Kävsjön and Store Mosse	Jönköping	7,450	B1i, C7
048	—	Lake Solgen	Solgen	Jönköping	4,000	A1, A4i, B1i, B3, C1, C2
049	SE010	Karlsö islands	Karlsöarna	Gotland	4,570	B1ii, B3, C3
050	SE009	Coastal areas around Gotland island	Gotlands strandängar	Gotland	4,100	A4i, B1i, B2, B3, C2, C3, C6
051	—	Båtafjorden Fjord	Båtafjorden	Halland	200	B3, C6
052	SE007	Getterön	Getteröns naturreservat	Halland	355	B1i, B3, C2, C3, C6
053	SE006	Lake Åsnen	Åsnen	Kronoberg	13,500	A1, A4i, B1i, B2, C1, C3, C6
054	SE005	Coastal areas around Öland island	Östra Ölands strandängar	Kalmar	10,190	A1, A4i, B1i, B2, B3, C1, C2, C3, C6
055	SE004	Ottenby	Ottenby	Kalmar	1,610	A4i, B1i, C2, C3
056	—	Kullaberg	Kullaberg	Skåne	7,500	B1ii, B3, C3, C6
057	—	Bay of Skälderviken	Skälderviken	Skåne	5,500	A4iii, B1i, B1ii, B1iv, B2, B3, C3, C4, C5, C6
058	—	North-east Scania coastline and archipelago	Skärgårdskusten i NÖ Skåne	Skåne	10,914	A1, A4i, B1i, B2, B3, C1, C2, C3, C6
059	—	Bay of Lundåkrabukten	Lundåkrabukten	Skåne	20,000	B1i, C2, C3
060	—	Bay of Lommabukten	Lommabukten	Skåne	30,000	B1i, B2, B3, C2, C3, C6
061	SE001	Falsterbo–Bay of Foteviken	Falsterbo–Foteviken	Skåne	20,000	A4i, A4iv, B1i, B1iv, B2, B3, C2, C3, C5, C6
062	SE002	River Klingavälsån–Lake Krankesjön	Klingavälsån–Krankesjön	Skåne	3,975	B1i, C2
063	SE003	River Helgeån	Helgeån	Skåne	5,300	A4i, B1i, B2, C2, C3, C6

050 and 055) and *Anser fabalis* overwintering at IBAs in the most southerly province, Skåne (IBAs 058, 060 and 062). In spring and autumn tens of thousands of *Branta leucopsis* and *B. bernicla* stop over on the Baltic islands (mainly Gotland and Öland) (IBAs 050, 054 and 055) (Table 3).

Due to the dispersed nature of their distribution, raptors are not adequately covered by the IBA network (Table 4). The incomplete nature of the Swedish IBA inventory has meant that a number of other breeding SPECs are not adequately covered either—for

Table 2. Important Bird Areas in Sweden that are important for species of global conservation concern (meeting criterion A1).

Species	IBA code
Anser erythropus Lesser White-fronted Goose	004
Haliaeetus albicilla White-tailed Eagle	004, 024, 037, 048, 053, 054, 058
Crex crex Corncrake	025
Gallinago media Great Snipe	014

675

Table 3. Important Bird Areas in Sweden that support important numbers of one or more congregatory species (i.e. meeting criteria A4 and/or B1). IBAs meeting both criteria A4 and B1 for the species are shown in **bold**. IBAs meeting only criterion B1 for the species concerned, and not A4, are shown in normal type. For key to 'Season', see p. 7.

Species	Season	IBA code
Podiceps grisegena Red-necked Grebe	B	036, 042
Phalacrocorax carbo Cormorant	B	038
	P	024, 057, 060
Cygnus olor Mute Swan	P	045
Cygnus columbianus Bewick's Swan	P	**050**
Cygnus cygnus Whooper Swan	W	043, **048**
	P	**015, 017, 031, 041, 042**, 062, **063**
	N	**016**
Anser fabalis Bean Goose	B	010
	W	**058**, 060, **063**
	P	006, 019, 021, **023**, 031, **033**, 036, 037, **041**, 042, **053**, 059, **063**
Anser anser Greylag Goose	B	061
	P	019, **021, 023, 037**, 042
	N	**036**
Branta leucopsis Barnacle Goose	B	**050, 055**
	P	**050, 054, 055**
Branta bernicla Brent Goose	W	**055**
	P	**055, 061**
Anas crecca Teal	B	010, 052
	P	019, 042
Anas acuta Pintail	P	042
Anas clypeata Shoveler	P	061
Aythya fuligula Tufted Duck	W	030
	P	030
Somateria mollissima Eider	B	**027, 050**
	N	**027**
Melanitta fusca Velvet Scoter	B	**027**
Bucephala clangula Goldeneye	P	**045**
	N	043, 044
Mergus albellus Smew	P	021
Mergus serrator Red-breasted Merganser	B	027
	P	**045**
Mergus merganser Goosander	B	**010, 027**
	P	019, **021, 053**
Lagopus mutus Ptarmigan	R	**014**
Grus grus Crane	P	**033, 042**, 061
Recurvirostra avosetta Avocet	B	**050, 054, 061**
Charadrius hiaticula Ringed Plover	B	**050**
Pluvialis apricaria Golden Plover	P	059, 060
Calidris alpina Dunlin	B	061
	P	019, 059, 061
Gallinago media Great Snipe	B	**014**
Tringa totanus Redshank	B	054
Arenaria interpres Turnstone	R	**011**
	B	**027, 050**
Stercorarius parasiticus Arctic Skua	B	027
Larus fuscus Lesser Black-backed Gull	B	027
Larus argentatus Herring Gull	B	058
	W	060
Sterna caspia Caspian Tern	B	008, **020, 024, 027, 038**, 050, 054, 058
	P	008, **019, 034**
	N	**021**
Sterna albifrons Little Tern	B	050
Uria aalge Guillemot	B	012, 027, 049
	W	056, 057
Alca torda Razorbill	B	012, 013, 020, 027, 049
	W	057
Cepphus grylle Black Guillemot	B	008, **011**, 012, 020, **027**

Table 4. Species of European conservation concern and species listed on Annex I of the EC Birds Directive with significant breeding populations at IBAs in Sweden (meeting any IBA criteria).

Species [1]	Minimum national breeding population (pairs) [2]	Proportion (%) of national population breeding at all IBAs in Sweden
Gavia stellata Red-throated Diver	1,000	6
Gavia arctica Black-throated Diver	5,000	2
Podiceps auritus Slavonian Grebe	1,200	3
Botaurus stellaris Bittern	200	33
Anser erythropus Lesser White-fronted Goose	5	100 [3]
Branta leucopsis Barnacle Goose	2,700	100 [3]
Mergus albellus Smew	75	16
Haliaeetus albicilla White-tailed Eagle	190	10
Circus aeruginosus Marsh Harrier	1,400	9
Circus cyaneus Hen Harrier	800	2
Aquila chrysaetos Golden Eagle	600	2
Pandion haliaetus Osprey	3,400	3
Falco rusticolus Gyrfalcon	100	10
Porzana porzana Spotted Crake	100	12
Crex crex Corncrake	250	5
Recurvirostra avosetta Avocet	1,000	90
Calidris maritima Purple Sandpiper	1,000	2
Limicola falcinellus Broad-billed Sandpiper	3,000	2
Gallinago media Great Snipe	700	6
Numenius phaeopus Whimbrel	7,500	2
Tringa totanus Redshank	10,000	13
Phalaropus lobatus Red-necked Phalarope	14,000	2
Larus canus Common Gull	100,000	6
Larus fuscus Lesser Black-backed Gull	15,000	8
Larus marinus Great Black-backed Gull	10,000	6
Sterna caspia Caspian Tern	425	96
Sterna hirundo Common Tern	20,000	4
Sterna paradisaea Arctic Tern	20,000	22
Sterna albifrons Little Tern	450	41
Chlidonias niger Black Tern	180	28
Alca torda Razorbill	9,000	42
Cepphus grylle Black Guillemot	7,000	100 [3]
Bubo bubo Eagle Owl	390	3
Nyctea scandiaca Snowy Owl	10	—[4]
Caprimulgus europaeus Nightjar	2,500	3
Lullula arborea Woodlark	2,000	5
Locustella naevia Grasshopper Warbler	3,000	3

1. Only those species of European conservation concern (see Box 1, p. 12) that meet IBA criteria in Sweden are listed, together with those species listed on Annex I of the EC Birds Directive that fulfil criterion C6 in IBAs in Sweden.
2. Data are taken from the BirdLife/EBCC European Bird Database 1998 (Heath and Borggreve 2000).
3. The percentage of the national population in IBAs exceeds 100%. Usually this is because the national population estimate has not been updated recently whilst the IBA population estimate has been recently updated with new data as a result of comprehensive surveys of IBAs themselves. Also, the individual site count for a species may be the maximum or average over recent years, and summing these may record more birds than are present nationally in any single year.
4. No population data available for Swedish IBAs.

example *Gavia stellata*, *G. arctica*, *Mergus albellus*, *Caprimulgus europaeus*, woodpeckers and other forest species (for example, *Perisoreus infaustus*).

HABITATS

Four principal vegetation zones run approximately south–north through Sweden: the Nemoral, Boreonemoral, Boreal and Alpine zones. The first is restricted to the south-west coastal fringe and contains vegetation strongly influenced by the oceanic climate, such as *Fagus* forest and *Calluna* heathland. The second zone is one of transition between the Nemoral and Boreal zones, and covers most of southern Sweden. It is typified by mixed forest comprising species that are rare or absent in the Boreal zone (for example, *Quercus* and *Corylus*). The majority of the Swedish land area falls within the Boreal zone—a western continuation of the Eurasian taiga or coniferous forest. Alpine habitats are restricted to the Caledonian mountains, a long chain of mountains in the north-west that rise to just over 2,000 m.

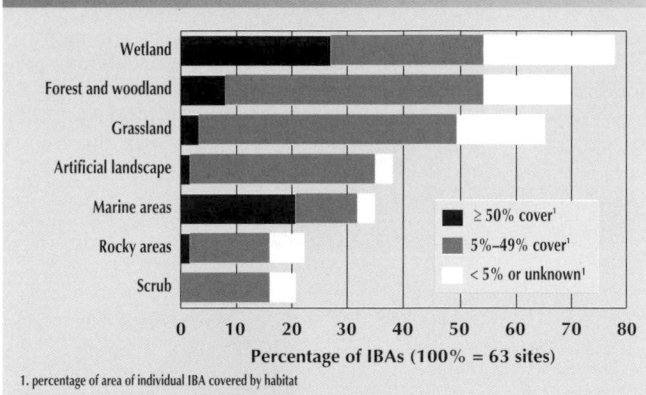

Figure 1. Habitats at Important Bird Areas in Sweden (see Appendix 3 for definitions of habitats).

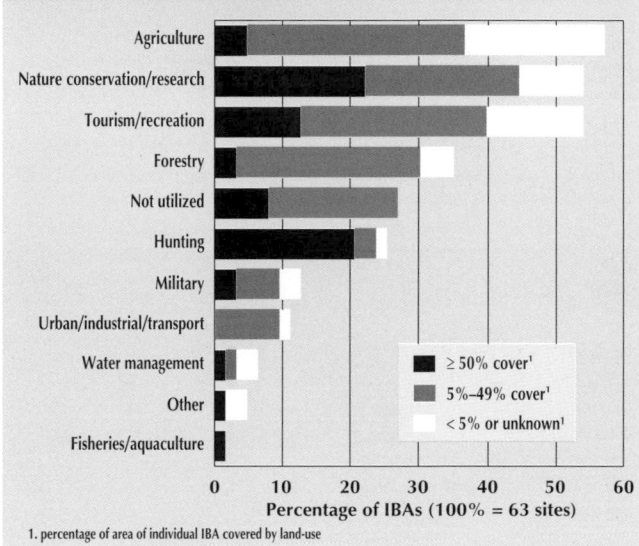

Figure 2. Land-uses at Important Bird Areas in Sweden (see Appendix 3 for definitions of land-uses).

Forests cover c.50% of the land area, with mountains, lakes and marshes comprising a further c.30%. Open water (including nearly 100,000 lakes) accounts for c.9% of the land area—if other wetland types are included this figure increases to c.25%. Agricultural land covers less than 10% of the country; major areas of urbanization and industry are restricted to the south, where 85% of the population lives.

The dominance of forest and wetland habitats at the national level is mirrored by the habitat composition of Swedish IBAs. Seventy-eight percent of IBAs contain some wetland habitat, with

forests and woodland occurring at 69% of sites (Figure 1). Key species include *Botaurus stellaris*, *Anas strepera*, *A. acuta*, *A. querquedula*, *Grus grus*, *Limosa limosa* and *Chlidonias niger* at wetland sites, and *Aquila chrysaetos*, *Pandion haliaetus*, *Caprimulgus europaeus*, *Jynx torquilla*, *Picus canus*, *P. viridis*, *Picoides tridactylus*, *Lullula arborea*, *Phoenicurus phoenicurus* and *Perisoreus infaustus* in forests.

Grassland habitats are also widespread and are found in 65% of IBAs, with humid grassland being the most common type. Key grassland species include *Crex crex*, *Calidris alpina*, *Numenius arquata* and *Alauda arvensis*. Thirty-five percent of IBAs include marine areas within their boundaries. Due to the importance of the Swedish coastline for migrating and moulting waterbirds, this figure ought to increase in the future. Key coastal species include *Haliaeetus albicilla*, *Tringa totanus*, *Sterna caspia* and *Cepphus grylle*.

The central and northern regions of Sweden tend to be dominated by forests and mountains, and do not hold many IBAs (Map 1). This anomaly is mainly due to a lack of data, but may also reflect the fact that large parts of these regions support a dispersed avifauna. Five IBAs have, however, been identified as being of importance for species whose distributions are largely or wholly confined to habitat-types present in northern Sweden, falling within the Arctic/tundra and boreal biomes. Marine areas are also under-represented due to a lack of data.

It is likely that additional IBAs will be identified in the near future, mainly in southern Sweden, covering coastal features, lakes and other wetland habitats.

IMPACTS ON IBAs – LAND-USE AND THREATS

Agriculture is the most commonly occurring land-use at Swedish IBAs (Figure 2), affecting 36 IBAs (57%). Nature conservation/research activities and tourism/recreation are also widespread, both being present at 34 sites (54%). Even though Sweden is a well-forested country, only 22 IBAs (35%) support forestry activities. Hunting takes place at the majority of IBAs, but has been under-recorded as a land-use and therefore appears further down Figure 2 than it should do.

Figure 3 summarizes the key threats and impacts to Swedish IBAs. Abandonment and reduction of land management is the single most important threat, affecting 31 sites (49%). Undergrazing is a particular problem at many of these (for example, IBAs 016, 023, 031, 036, 054, 058 and 059). American mink *Mustela vison* have been introduced to the Baltic Sea archipelagos, placing breeding ducks and colonies of terns and auks at risk. Breeding success in *Sterna caspia* has been severely reduced in recent years as a direct result of mink predation (for example, IBAs 027, 038 and 039). The negative effects of disturbance and recreation/tourism are also frequently encountered (17% and 14% of IBAs respectively).

Field surveys of potential IBAs indicate that such sites tend to be threatened by agricultural and forestry activities. These threats are not commonly encountered in the present list of IBAs (Figure 3),

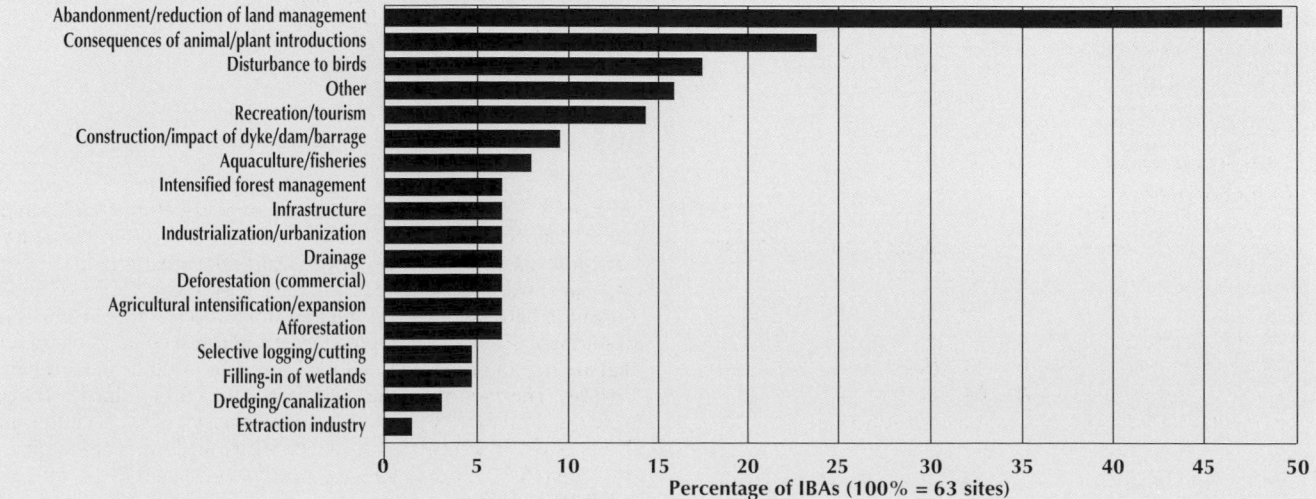

Figure 3. Occurrence of threats at Important Bird Areas in Sweden (see Appendix 3 for definitions of threat types and impact categories).

possibly reflecting the positive impacts of both legal protection and management-plan implementation.

PROTECTION STATUS

Table 5 and Figures 4 and 5 summarize the national and international protection status of all Swedish IBAs.

■ National protection

The most important national designations from the point of view of protecting birds are National Parks, Nature Reserves and Bird Sanctuaries. National Parks are state-owned, whereas the majority of Nature Reserves and Bird Sanctuaries are privately owned—some are owned by local municipalities. There are very few NGO-owned reserves in Sweden. The Swedish Environmental Protection Agency (EPA), working in close cooperation with the county

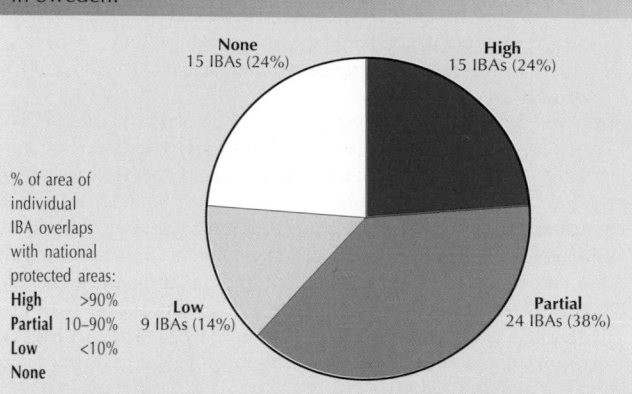

Figure 4. The national protection status of Important Bird Areas in Sweden.

% of area of individual IBA overlaps with national protected areas:
High >90%
Partial 10–90%
Low <10%
None

Total area of overlap between IBA network in Sweden and national protected-area system (see Table 5 for categories) = 5,848–5,877 km² (46% of total IBA area).

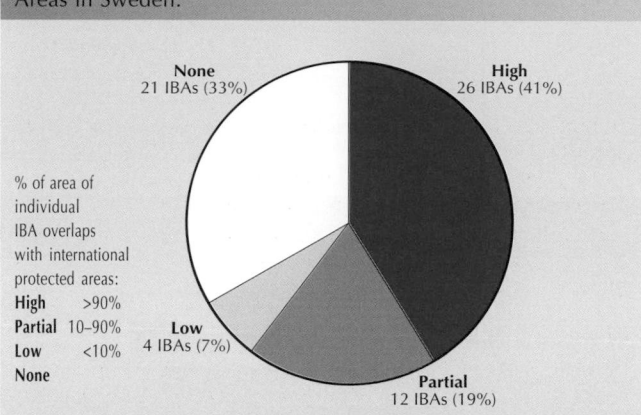

Figure 5. The international protection status of Important Bird Areas in Sweden.

% of area of individual IBA overlaps with international protected areas:
High >90%
Partial 10–90%
Low <10%
None

Total area of overlap between IBA network in Sweden and international protected-area system (see Table 5 for categories) = 9,527–9,861 km² (75–78% of total IBA area).

Table 5. Protection status of Important Bird Areas in Sweden.
A tick (✔) indicates that an IBA overlaps with a protected area (to any extent).

IBA code	International name	National Park	Nature Reserve	Bird Sanctuary	Private Reserve	Ramsar Site	World Heritage Site	Special Protection Area
001	Taavavuoma					✔		
002	Påkketan		✔					✔
003	Lake Laidaure	✔				✔	✔	
004	Sjaunja		✔			✔	✔	✔
005	Lake Tjålmejaure–Laisdalen valley		✔	✔		✔		
006	Lake Persöfjärden					✔		
007	Lake Gammelstadsviken		✔			✔		✔
008	Skvolpen island				✔			
009	Vindelfjällen mountains (including Lake Tärnasjön)		✔			✔		✔
010	River Umeälven delta		✔			✔		
011	Holmöarna archipelago		✔					✔
012	Bonden island		✔					✔
013	Gnäggen island							
014	Lake Ånnsjön–Storlien		✔	✔		✔		✔
015	River Dalälven–Hovran		✔			✔		
016	River Svartån		✔			✔		✔
017	River Dalälven–Färnebofjärden	✔	✔					
018	Båtfors–Bredfors		✔					
019	Ledskär–Karlholm Bay			✔				
020	Björn archipelago							
021	Lake Tämnaren							
022	Florarna		✔					✔
023	Lake Hjälstaviken		✔			✔		✔
024	Gräsö archipelago							
025	Dannemora							
026	Tarnan–Riala forest		✔					
027	Outer Stockholm archipelago		✔	✔		✔		✔
028	Lake Östra Styran							
029	Hanveden–Hemfosa							
030	Sandemar		✔					
031	Lake Tysslingen							
	Subtotal of IBAs	2	18	5	0	13	2	11
032	Bay of Rynningeviken		✔					✔
033	Kvismaren		✔			✔		✔
034	Lake Storhjälmaren							
035	Bay of Kilsviken		✔	✔		✔		✔
036	Lake Tåkern		✔			✔		✔
037	Bay of Svensksundsviken		✔					✔
038	Dannskär–Örskär islands			✔				
039	St Anna archipelago		✔	✔				✔
040	Dättern–Södra Brandfjorden		✔			✔		✔
041	Lake Östen		✔			✔		✔
042	Lake Hornborgasjön		✔	✔		✔		✔
043	Stigfjorden Fjord		✔			✔		✔
044	Bay of Torslandaviken							
045	Bay of Kungsbackafjorden		✔					✔
046	Lake Ralången							
047	Lake Kävsjön and Store Mosse	✔				✔		✔
048	Lake Solgen							
049	Karlsö islands		✔					✔
050	Coastal areas around Gotland island		✔	✔		✔		✔
051	Båtafjorden Fjord							
052	Getterön		✔			✔		✔
053	Lake Åsnen		✔			✔		✔
054	Coastal areas around Öland island			✔		✔		✔
055	Ottenby		✔			✔		✔
056	Kullaberg		✔					✔
057	Bay of Skälderviken		✔	✔				✔
058	North-east Scania coastline and archipelago		✔	✔				✔
059	Bay of Lundåkrabukten		✔					
060	Bay of Lommabukten		✔					✔
061	Falsterbo–Bay of Foteviken		✔			✔		✔
062	River Klingavälsån–Lake Krankesjön		✔			✔		✔
063	River Helgeån		✔		✔	✔		✔
	Total number of IBAs	**3**	**42**	**13**	**1**	**29**	**2**	**36**

Box 1. International legislation and initiatives that are relevant to site conservation in Sweden (see Appendix 1 for a general description of these agreements).

Global	
Biodiversity Convention	✔
Ramsar Convention	✔
Bonn Convention	✔
World Heritage Convention	✔
MAB Programme	✔
Pan-European	
Bern Convention	✔
Regional	
EC Birds Directive	✔
EC Habitats Directive	✔
Helsinki Convention	✔

✔ Convention ratified/initiative supported
(✔) Convention signed

administrations, has plans for the protection of additional areas of importance.

In 1999 there were 26 National Parks, almost 2,500 Nature Reserves and 1,260 Bird Sanctuaries. Forty-eight IBAs (76%) are either wholly or partly protected nationally (Figure 4), compared to c.8% of the Swedish land area as a whole (mainly in mountainous regions) (data from Swedish EPA).

■ International protection
Sweden has a number of international obligations, both within the legislative framework of the European Union and under various international conventions (Box 1).

CONSERVATION

- The Swedish bird reporting system is well developed, with a large number of birdwatchers contributing to annual reports. Field surveys of breeding and passage species for monitoring purposes are commonplace. Twenty bird observatories also provide data.
- On a larger scale the EPA and county administrations are responsible for basic environmental data collection.
- NGOs run projects to gather data on particular species, for example, divers (Gaviidae), *Phalacrocorax carbo sinensis*, *Haliaeetus albicilla*, *Falco rusticolus*, *F. peregrinus* and *Sterna caspia*.

ANALYTICAL METHODS

- The current review of Swedish IBAs was, for various reasons, undertaken without an IBA officer in place. Information on candidate IBAs was collected with the assistance of the 25 regional branches of SOF. Reporting was uneven due to differences in local knowledge and levels of activity, and the quality of the material received varied. As a result data are incomplete for many IBAs, and there are undoubtedly many sites that would qualify as IBAs if more were known about them. For the same reasons several important species were not covered by the review, including woodpeckers and other forest species.
- Most bird data are from the late 1990s.
- Wintering and passage figures mainly equate to total number of birds in a season.
- The following sites were proposed as IBAs, but did not meet IBA criteria based upon current available data: Lake Angarn, Lake Bodasjön, Dumme mosse, Lake Fysingen, Erstad marshland and Lake Landsjon.
- Threats and land-use data are based on estimates made by the regional informants during the mid- to late-1990s. Hunting has been under-recorded as a land-use, and takes place in many more IBAs than is suggested by Figure 2. Threat importance data are incomplete and have not been used in the generation of Figure 3.

GLOSSARY

EPA Environmental Protection Agency.
NGO non-governmental organisation.
skerry a small islet or rocky reef in the sea, exposed at low tide.
SOF Sveriges Ornitologiska Förening (Swedish Ornithological Society, BirdLife International Partner in Sweden).
SPA Special Protection Area (designated under Article 4 of the EC Birds Directive).

ACKNOWLEDGEMENTS

Steve Dahlfors co-ordinated the early stages of the current review. Site information was provided mainly by SOF's regional branches. Torsten Larsson at the Swedish EPA gave advice and provided conservation data.

■ SITE ACCOUNTS

Taavavuoma   A3, B2, C6   001
Admin region Norrbotten
Coordinates 68°30′N 20°42′E
Altitude 900–1,000 m **Area** 28,400 ha

■ Site description
A mosaic of marshes, watercourses, lakes and pools lying in a depression on one of the most northerly Lapland plateaus. The IBA forms part of the River Lainio's catchment, and the only land-use is reindeer *Rangifer tarandus* herding ('Other' land-use).

Habitats Wetland (standing fresh water; river/stream; water-fringe vegetation)
Land-use Other

■ Birds

Species	Season	Year	Pop min	Pop max	Acc	Criteria
Gavia stellata Red-throated Diver	B	—	5	20	—	B2, C6
Anser erythropus Lesser White-fronted Goose	B	—	0	1	—	A3
Clangula hyemalis Long-tailed Duck	B	—	—	—	—	A3
Mergus albellus Smew	B	—	—	—	—	B2
Falco rusticolus Gyrfalcon	B	—	1	3	—	A3, B2
Calidris maritima Purple Sandpiper	B	—	1	3	—	A3
Gallinago media Great Snipe	B	—	3	10	—	B2, C6
Limosa lapponica Bar-tailed Godwit	B	—	5	10	—	A3
Tringa erythropus Spotted Redshank	B	—	40	70	—	A3
Tringa glareola Wood Sandpiper	B	—	90	150	—	C6
Phalaropus lobatus Red-necked Phalarope	B	—	150	200	—	A3

Species ... continued	Season	Year	Pop min	Pop max	Acc	Criteria
Stercorarius longicaudus Long-tailed Skua	B	—	5	35	—	A3
Anthus cervinus Red-throated Pipit	B	—	—	—	—	A3
Carduelis hornemanni Arctic Redpoll	B	—	—	—	—	A3
Calcarius lapponicus Lapland Bunting	B	—	—	—	—	A3

Important for breeding waterbirds, raptors and waders. Breeding birds include 11 out of the 32 species in Europe that are restricted (when breeding) to the Arctic/tundra biome. Breeding species of global conservation concern that do not meet IBA criteria: *Haliaeetus albicilla*.

■ Protection status
National None **International** High
28,400 ha of IBA covered by Ramsar Site (Taavavuoma, 28,700 ha).

■ Conservation issues
No serious threats are known at the site.

Påkketan   B2, C6   002
Admin region Norrbotten
Coordinates 68°05′N 20°22′E
Altitude 340–788 m **Area** 24,000 ha

■ Site description
Situated in the mountainous north of Sweden, the site covers a valley containing lakes and marshes. The extensive tracts of coniferous forest are mainly old, with regeneration occurring following forest fires.

Habitats Forest and woodland (60%; native coniferous forest), Wetland (40%; standing fresh water; water-fringe vegetation)
Land-use Not utilized (100%)

■ Birds

Species	Season	Year	Pop min	Pop max	Acc	Criteria
Gavia stellata Red-throated Diver	B	—	5	10	—	B2, C6
Falco rusticolus Gyrfalcon	B	—	1	2	—	B2
Tringa glareola Wood Sandpiper	B	—	30	40	—	C6

The site is important for breeding waterbirds, raptors and waders. Breeding species of global conservation concern that do not meet IBA criteria: *Anser erythropus*, *Haliaeetus albicilla* and *Gallinago media*.

■ Protection status
National High **International** High
IBA overlaps with Nature Reserve (21,000 ha). IBA overlaps with Special Protection Area (21,600 ha).

■ Conservation issues
No serious threats are known at the site.

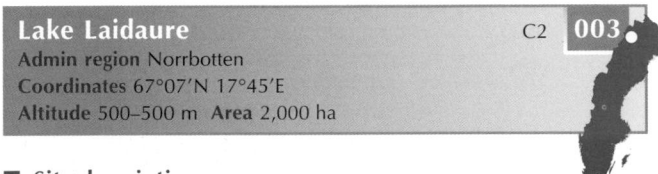

Lake Laidaure C2 003
Admin region Norrbotten
Coordinates 67°07′N 17°45′E
Altitude 500–500 m **Area** 2,000 ha

■ Site description
This site comprises the delta of the Rapaälvens river and Lake Laidaure, into which the delta is gradually expanding from the west. To the south is Sarek National Park, and to the north a zone of coniferous forest.

Habitats Forest and woodland (20%; broadleaved deciduous forest; mixed forest), Wetland (80%; tidal river/enclosed tidal water)
Land-use Nature conservation/research (100%), Tourism/recreation (100%)

■ Birds

Species	Season	Year	Pop min	Pop max	Acc	Criteria
[1] *Cygnus cygnus* Whooper Swan	P	1997	50	200	A	C2

1. Occurs on spring passage.

The delta becomes ice-free early in the spring and is consequently an important staging area for migrants.

■ Protection status
National Partial **International** High
IBA overlaps with National Park (300 ha). 2,000 ha of IBA covered by Ramsar Site (Laidaure, 4,150 ha). IBA overlaps with World Heritage Site.

■ Conservation issues

Threats Abandonment/reduction of land management (U), Disturbance to birds (U)

Sjaunja A1, A3, B2, C1, C6 004
Admin region Norrbotten
Coordinates 67°17′N 19°49′E
Altitude 368–1703 m **Area** 208,000 ha

■ Site description
An extensive, largely untouched wilderness area with a wide range of habitats dominated by wetlands, with forest to the east and mountainous territory to the west. The main wetlands comprise open marshes, shallow lakes and wet *Betula* forest. There are 44,000 ha of virgin *Picea* and *Pinus* forest in the drier areas.

Habitats Forest and woodland (30%; native coniferous forest; mixed forest; alluvial/very wet forest; wooded tundra; treeline ecotone), Scrub (10%; heathland), Grassland (10%; alpine/subalpine/boreal grassland; tundra), Wetland (60%; standing fresh water; river/stream; water-fringe vegetation), Rocky areas (5%; inland cliff)

Land-use Forestry (5%), Hunting (100%), Military (100%), Nature conservation/research (100%), Urban/industrial/transport (5%)

■ Birds

Species	Season	Year	Pop min	Pop max	Acc	Criteria
Podiceps auritus Slavonian Grebe	B	1996	—	4	B	A3
[1] *Anser erythropus* Lesser White-fronted Goose	B	1996	—	5	A	A1, C1
[2] *Mergus albellus* Smew	B	1996	—	5	A	A3, B2
Haliaeetus albicilla White-tailed Eagle	B	1996	3	5	A	A1, B2, C1, C6
Circus cyaneus Hen Harrier	B	1996	5	15	A	B2, C6
Aquila chrysaetos Golden Eagle	B	1996	2	6	A	B2, C6
Falco columbarius Merlin	B	1996	5	20	A	C6
Falco rusticolus Gyrfalcon	B	1996	1	2	A	B2
Lymnocryptes minimus Jack Snipe	B	1996	—	—	—	A3
[1] *Surnia ulula* Hawk Owl	B	1996	—	15	B	A3
[1] *Strix nebulosa* Great Grey Owl	B	1996	0	1	B	A3
[1] *Asio flammeus* Short-eared Owl	B	1996	—	30	B	B2, C6
Aegolius funereus Tengmalm's Owl	B	1996	5	15	B	C6
[1] *Phylloscopus borealis* Arctic Warbler	B	1996	—	2	A	A3
Pinicola enucleator Pine Grosbeak	B	1996	2	12	B	A3
Emberiza rustica Rustic Bunting	B	—	—	—	—	A3

1. Large decrease.
2. Large increase.

The IBA is important for breeding wetland and forest species, including a diversity of raptors. Breeding birds include eight out of the 15 species in Europe that are restricted (when breeding) to the boreal biome. Species of global conservation concern that do not meet IBA criteria: *Gallinago media* (three breeding pairs). Numbers of birds given as breeding in the IBA are probably underestimates due to the size of the survey area.

■ Protection status
National High **International** High
IBA overlaps with Nature Reserve (285,000 ha). 188,600 ha of IBA covered by Ramsar Site (Sjaunja, 188,600 ha). 208,000 ha of IBA covered by World Heritage Site (Lapponia, 940,000 ha). IBA overlaps with Special Protection Area (281,000 ha).

■ Conservation issues

Threats Construction/impact of dyke/dam/barrage (B), Extraction industry (U)

Attempts have been made to start mineral exploration in the IBA— these are currently on hold for economic reasons. Proposals have been put forward by the Swedish EPA to designate the area as a National Park.

Lake Tjålmejaure– Laisdalen valley A3, B2, C6 005
Admin region Norrbotten
Coordinates 66°18′N 16°15′E
Altitude 750–750 m **Area** 22,200 ha

■ Site description
Two converging valleys in the mountains of northern Sweden, containing small rivers and their deltas. The southern valley holds a large lake system with flat shores, which form an important nesting habitat for waterbirds. The narrower northern valley contains the River Laisälven, which is bordered by a strip of marshland and surrounded by *Betula* forest, with some *Pinus*.

Habitats Forest and woodland (broadleaved deciduous forest; native coniferous forest), Wetland (standing fresh water; river/stream; water-fringe vegetation)
Land-use Tourism/recreation (60%)

■ Birds

Species	Season	Year	Pop min	Pop max	Acc	Criteria
Gavia stellata Red-throated Diver	B	—	5	10	—	B2, C6
Anser erythropus Lesser White-fronted Goose	B	—	0	1	—	A3
Buteo lagopus Rough-legged Buzzard	B	—	—	—	—	A3
Falco rusticolus Gyrfalcon	B	—	2	3	—	A3, B2
Calidris maritima Purple Sandpiper	B	—	—	—	—	A3

Species ... continued	Season	Year	Pop min	Pop max	Acc	Criteria
Tringa erythropus Spotted Redshank	B	—	40	70	—	A3
Tringa glareola Wood Sandpiper	B	—	30	40	—	C6
Phalaropus lobatus Red-necked Phalarope	B	—	10	30	—	A3
Stercorarius longicaudus Long-tailed Skua	B	—	5	20	—	A3
Nyctea scandiaca Snowy Owl	B	—	—	—	—	A3
Anthus cervinus Red-throated Pipit	B	—	—	—	—	A3

Important for breeding waterbirds, raptors and waders, and one of the final staging areas for northward-moving spring migrants. Breeding birds include nine out of the 32 species in Europe that are restricted (when breeding) to the Arctic/tundra biome. Breeding species of global conservation concern that do not meet IBA criteria: *Gallinago media*.

■ Protection status
National Partial **International** High
IBA overlaps with extensive Bird Sanctuary. IBA overlaps with Nature Reserve (500 ha). 21,400 ha of IBA covered by Ramsar Site (Tjålmejaure–Laisdalen, 21,400 ha).

■ Conservation issues
No serious threats are known at the site.

Lake Persöfjärden   B1i, C2, C3, C6   006
Admin region Norrbotten
Coordinates 65°46′N 22°07′E
Altitude 0–10 m   **Area** 3,350 ha

■ Site description
A lake, c.15 km long, which was isolated from the Gulf of Bothnia by land elevation. The shallow waters have favoured the spread of *Scirpus* and *Phragmites*, which almost divide the lake in two at one point. Floating vegetation is also extensive and parts of the south-western end of the lake have been invaded by *Salix* scrub.

Habitats Forest and woodland (20%; mixed forest), Wetland (50%; mudflat/sandflat; standing fresh water; water-fringe vegetation; fen/transition mire/spring), Artificial landscape (30%; highly improved reseeded grassland; arable land; ruderal land)
Land-use Agriculture (20%), Forestry (10%)

■ Birds

Species	Season	Year	Pop min	Pop max	Acc	Criteria
[1] *Cygnus cygnus* Whooper Swan	P	1996	100	200	B	C2
Anser fabalis Bean Goose	P	1996	300	800	A	B1i, C3
Pandion haliaetus Osprey	B	1996	3	10	B	C6
Bonasa bonasia Hazel Grouse	R	1996	10	30	C	C6

1. Large increase.

The area is important as a resting area for migrating geese, ducks, raptors and waders. 210 species of bird have been recorded.

■ Protection status
National None **International** High
3,320 ha of IBA covered by Ramsar Site (Persöfjärden, 3,320 ha).

■ Conservation issues

Threats Abandonment/reduction of land management (B), Construction/impact of dyke/dam/barrage (B), Dredging/canalization (B)

Dredging undertaken by land-owners poses a threat.

Lake Gammelstadsviken   B2, C2, C6   007
Admin region Norrbotten
Coordinates 65°37′N 22°00′E
Altitude 2–5 m   **Area** 440 ha

■ Site description
A shallow (1–4 m in depth) nutrient-rich lake at the head of the Gulf of Bothnia, formed when rising land isolated a bay from the sea. Fine marine sediments with overlying mud deposits cover the lake floor.

Water exchange is minimal due to the low rate of inflow to the lake. Large sections of the shoreline are marshy, with *Phragmites*, *Typha* and *Equisetum* present; the lake itself supports floating vegetation. Mixed forests surround the lake.

Habitats Forest and woodland (10%; mixed forest; alluvial/very wet forest), Wetland (100%; standing fresh water; water-fringe vegetation; fen/transition mire/spring)
Land-use Nature conservation/research (100%)

■ Birds

Species	Season	Year	Pop min	Pop max	Acc	Criteria
Mergus albellus Smew	B	1996	10	30	B	B2, C2
Tringa glareola Wood Sandpiper	B	1996	20	40	C	C6

The IBA is important for breeding waterbirds, waders and gulls.

■ Protection status
National High **International** High
IBA overlaps with Nature Reserve (450 ha). 430 ha of IBA covered by Ramsar Site (Gammelstadsviken, 430 ha). IBA overlaps with Special Protection Area.

■ Conservation issues

Threats Industrialization/urbanization (U), Infrastructure (U)

The main threat comes from the expansion of the nearby town of Luleå.

Skvolpen island   B1i, B1ii, B2, C2, C6   008
Admin region Norrbotten
Coordinates 65°20′N 22°30′E
Altitude 0–8 m   **Area** 2,500 ha

■ Site description
An island at the northern end of the Gulf of Bothnia.

Habitats Marine areas (100%; sea inlet/coastal features)
Land-use Nature conservation/research (100%)

■ Birds

Species	Season	Year	Pop min	Pop max	Acc	Criteria
Sterna caspia Caspian Tern	B	1998	25	25	—	B1i, B2, C2, C6
Sterna caspia Caspian Tern	P	1996	20	50	A	B1i, C2
Cepphus grylle Black Guillemot	B	1996	50	100	B	B1ii, B2

This is an important site for breeding seabirds.

■ Protection status
National High **International** None
2,500 ha of IBA covered by Bird Sanctuary (Skvolpen, 2,500 ha).

■ Conservation issues

Threats Disturbance to birds (A)

Surveys undertaken in 1999 show increases in numbers of *Phalacrocorax carbo*, *Somateria mollissima* and several species of seabird (for example, *Cepphus grylle*). This is thought to be as a result of nutrient enrichment in the Gulf of Bothnia leading to increases in fish stocks.

Vindelfjällen mountains (including Lake Tärnasjön)   A3, B2, C6   009
Admin region Västerbotten
Coordinates 65°54′N 15°58′E
Altitude 400–1,609 m   **Area** 550,000 ha

■ Site description
An extensive mountainous area supporting a mosaic of mires, virgin *Picea* forest and mountain *Betula* forest, with valleys containing rivers and lake systems. The northern end of Lake Tärnasjön adjoins a delta formed by the River Tärna. The lake is surrounded by seasonally

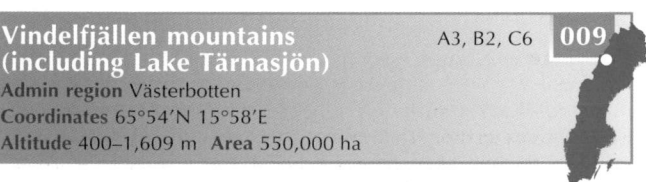

flooded marshland, and the whole area is used for reindeer *Rangifer tarandus* grazing ('Other' land-use), fishing and hiking.

Habitats Forest and woodland (broadleaved deciduous forest; native coniferous forest), Wetland (standing fresh water; river/stream; water-fringe vegetation; fen/transition mire/spring)
Land-use Hunting, Other, Tourism/recreation

■ Birds

Species	Season	Year	Pop min	Pop max	Acc	Criteria
Gavia stellata Red-throated Diver	B	—	5	20	—	B2, C6
Anser erythropus Lesser White-fronted Goose	B	—	0	1	—	A3
Aythya marila Scaup	B	—	—	—	—	A3
Aquila chrysaetos Golden Eagle	B	—	4	8	—	B2, C6
Falco rusticolus Gyrfalcon	B	—	5	14	—	A3, B2
Calidris maritima Purple Sandpiper	B	—	1	3	—	A3
Gallinago media Great Snipe	B	—	5	10	—	B2, C6
Tringa erythropus Spotted Redshank	B	—	40	70	—	A3
Tringa glareola Wood Sandpiper	B	—	100	200	—	C6
Phalaropus lobatus Red-necked Phalarope	B	—	50	150	—	A3
Stercorarius longicaudus Long-tailed Skua	B	—	10	60	—	A3

Important for breeding waterbirds, raptors and waders. Breeding birds include seven out of the 32 species in Europe that are restricted (when breeding) to the Arctic/tundra biome. Breeding species of global conservation concern that do not meet IBA criteria: *Haliaeetus albicilla*.

■ Protection status
National High **International** High
550,000 ha of IBA covered by Nature Reserve (550,000 ha). 11,800 ha of IBA covered by Ramsar Site (Tärnasjön, 11,800 ha). 550,000 ha of IBA covered by Special Protection Area (550,000 ha).

■ Conservation issues
No serious threats are known at the site. The site is very rich botanically, and there is also considerable geological interest.

River Umeälven delta   A4i, B1i, C2, C3   010
Admin region Västerbotten
Coordinates 63°45'N 20°19'E
Altitude 0–5 m **Area** 1,500 ha

■ Site description
The delta of a river system that flows into the Gulf of Bothnia in north-east Sweden. Temporal habitats range from mudflats to areas of primary vegetation. Much of the delta shoreline is surrounded by water-meadows, although there is also deciduous forest with a few conifers. *Phragmites* is scarce. The area is used for commercial shipping, leisure boating, and general recreation.

Habitats Forest and woodland (20%; broadleaved deciduous forest), Grassland (5%; humid grassland), Wetland (65%; tidal river/enclosed tidal water; mudflat/sandflat), Artificial landscape (10%; ruderal land)
Land-use Forestry, Nature conservation/research (10%), Tourism/recreation (10%), Urban/industrial/transport

■ Birds

Species	Season	Year	Pop min	Pop max	Acc	Criteria
Cygnus cygnus Whooper Swan	P	1996	200	300	B	C2
Anser fabalis Bean Goose	B	1996	900	1,200	B	B1i, C3
Anas crecca Teal	B	1996	2,000	2,500	B	B1i, C3
Mergus merganser Goosander	B	1996	1,400	1,800	B	A4i, B1i, C3

The western parts of the IBA (Vasterfjarden) are also important for breeding gulls. Up to 10,000 ducks and 7,000–8,000 waders stop over whilst on passage in late April–May. Passage species of global conservation concern that do not meet IBA criteria: *Haliaeetus albicilla*.

■ Protection status
National Low **International** Partial
IBA overlaps with Nature Reserve (Tuvan, 70 ha). 1,040 ha of IBA covered by Ramsar Site (Umeälv delta, 1,040 ha).

■ Conservation issues

Threats Infrastructure (U)

The construction of new roads and a railway (Bottniabanan) threaten the IBA.

Holmöarna archipelago   A4i, A4ii, B1i, B1ii, B2, C2, C3, C6   011
Admin region Västerbotten
Coordinates 63°45'N 21°00'E
Altitude 0–26 m **Area** 27,000 ha

■ Site description
An archipelago located 10 km from the Swedish mainland and 15 km from the outer Finnish skerries. The larger islands support *Picea*, *Alnus* and *Betula* forests and areas of bog. Of the four largest islands only the most northerly is inhabited. Access to the southern island is restricted due to military activity.

Habitats Forest and woodland (10%; native coniferous forest; mixed forest), Wetland (10%; standing fresh water; blanket bog), Marine areas (85%; open sea; sea inlet/coastal features)

■ Birds

Species	Season	Year	Pop min	Pop max	Acc	Criteria
Gavia stellata Red-throated Diver	B	1996	25	—	B	B2, C6
Gavia arctica Black-throated Diver	B	1996	25	—	B	C6
Haliaeetus albicilla White-tailed Eagle	B	1996	4	—	C	B2
Pandion haliaetus Osprey	B	1996	10	—	C	C6
Arenaria interpres Turnstone	B	1996	250	—	A	A4i, B1i, C3
[1] *Sterna caspia* Caspian Tern	B	1996	5	—	A	B2, C6
[1] *Sterna hirundo* Common Tern	B	1996	325	—	A	C6
[1] *Sterna paradisaea* Arctic Tern	B	1996	1,400	—	A	C2
[1] *Cepphus grylle* Black Guillemot	B	1996	2,700	—	A	A4ii, B1ii, B2
1. Large increase.						

The IBA holds a rich breeding bird fauna, including marine species (for example, *Melanitta fusca*, *Stercorarius parasiticus* and *Cepphus grylle*) as well as those of taiga forest (for example, *Tetrao urogallus*, *Grus grus* and *Strix uralensis*). The spring and autumn migration periods see large numbers of seabirds and passerines pass through.

■ Protection status
National High **International** High
25,000 ha of IBA covered by Nature Reserve (Holmöarna, 25,000 ha). 25,000 ha of IBA covered by Special Protection Area (25,000 ha).

■ Conservation issues

Land-use Military (20%), Nature conservation/research (90%)

No serious threats are known at the site. The island of Stora Fjaderagg, north-east of Holmön, holds a bird ringing station. The sea areas east of Holmöarna are known to be of great importance for marine life.

Bonden island   B1ii, B2, B3, C3   012
Admin region Västerbotten
Coordinates 63°26'N 20°03'E
Altitude 0–25 m **Area** 5 ha

■ Site description
A rocky island located 20 km off the Swedish coast. There is no vegetation, and numerous blocks of stone of varying size form breeding sites for auks.

Habitats Marine areas (open sea; sea inlet/coastal features), Rocky areas (100%; scree/boulders)
Land-use Nature conservation/research (100%)

■ Birds

Species	Season	Year	Pop min	Pop max	Acc	Criteria
[1] *Uria aalge* Guillemot	B	1996	200	1,000	B	B1ii, C3
Alca torda Razorbill	B	1996	2,000	4,000	B	B1ii, B3, C3

Species ... continued	Season	Year	Pop min	Pop max	Acc	Criteria
Cepphus grylle Black Guillemot	B	1996	350	500	B	B1ii, B2

1. Large increase.

This is an important site for breeding seabirds.

■ Protection status
National High **International** High
5 ha of IBA covered by Nature Reserve (Bonden, 400 ha). 5 ha of IBA covered by Special Protection Area (400 ha).

■ Conservation issues

Threats Disturbance to birds (U)

Unknown numbers of unauthorized visitors land on the island during the protected period (1 April to 1 July). Regular auk counts are undertaken.

Gnäggen island
B1ii, B3, C3 **013**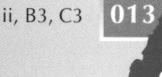
Admin region Västerbotten
Coordinates 62°57'N 18°37'E
Altitude 0–8 m **Area** 4 ha

■ Site description
A small island situated in the Gulf of Bothnia.

Habitats Marine areas (100%; open sea; sea inlet/coastal features)
Land-use Nature conservation/research (60%), Not utilized (40%)

■ Birds

Species	Season	Year	Pop min	Pop max	Acc	Criteria
[1] *Alca torda* Razorbill	B	1996	200	650	A	B1ii, B3, C3

1. Large increase.

This is an important for breeding seabirds.

■ Protection status
National None **International** None

■ Conservation issues
No serious threats are known at the site.

Lake Ånnsjön–Storlien
A1, A3, A4i, A4ii, B1i, B1iii, **014**
B2, B3, C1, C2, C6
Admin region Jämtland
Coordinates 63°16'N 12°33'E
Altitude 499–1,493 m **Area** 90,000 ha

■ Site description
A very shallow, nutrient-poor lake in the upper part of the River Indal system, partly surrounded by marshy areas and with a sandy ridge along one 2 km stretch of shoreline. The confluence of two rivers at the western end of the site has formed the Handol delta and there are other deltas to the north-west and south-east. The lower River Handolan contains rapids, waterfalls, and gorges; there is extensive forest nearby. 'Other' land-use (below) is grazing land for reindeer *Rangifer tarandus*.

Habitats Forest and woodland (50%; broadleaved deciduous forest; native coniferous forest; mixed forest; wooded tundra; treeline ecotone), Grassland (30%; tundra), Wetland (20%; river/stream; fen/transition mire/spring)
Land-use Forestry (20%), Hunting (80%), Nature conservation/research (10%), Other (50%), Tourism/recreation (25%), Water management (10%)

■ Birds

Species	Season	Year	Pop min	Pop max	Acc	Criteria
Gavia stellata Red-throated Diver	B	1996	15	30	B	B2, C6
Gavia arctica Black-throated Diver	B	1996	12	25	B	C6
Aythya marila Scaup	B	1996	25	50	C	A3
Clangula hyemalis Long-tailed Duck	B	1996	10	30	C	A3
Melanitta nigra Common Scoter	B	1996	100	200	B	A3
Circus cyaneus Hen Harrier	B	1996	—	20	C	B2, C6
Buteo lagopus Rough-legged Buzzard	B	1996	5	50	C	A3

Species ... continued	Season	Year	Pop min	Pop max	Acc	Criteria
Falco tinnunculus Kestrel	B	1996	10	40	C	B2
Falco columbarius Merlin	B	1996	10	40	C	C6
Lagopus mutus Ptarmigan	R	1996	400	1,000	C	A4ii, B1iii, C2
Tetrao tetrix Black Grouse	R	1996	100	200	C	C6
Tetrao urogallus Capercaillie	R	1996	200	400	C	C6
Grus grus Crane	B	1996	15	50	C	C6
Charadrius morinellus Dotterel	B	1996	25	75	C	C6
Pluvialis apricaria Golden Plover	B	1996	100	200	C	C6
Calidris temminckii Temminck's Stint	B	1996	1	20	C	A3
Calidris maritima Purple Sandpiper	B	1996	20	50	C	A3, B3
Limicola falcinellus Broad-billed Sandpiper	B	1996	25	75	B	B2
Philomachus pugnax Ruff	B	1996	150	300	B	B3, C6
Gallinago media Great Snipe	B	1996	25	150	B	A1, A4i, B1i, B2, C1, C2, C6
Numenius phaeopus Whimbrel	B	1996	100	200	C	B3
Tringa erythropus Spotted Redshank	B	1996	1	5	A	A3
Tringa totanus Redshank	B	1996	150	250	B	B2
[1] *Tringa glareola* Wood Sandpiper	B	1996	150	300	B	B2, C6
Phalaropus lobatus Red-necked Phalarope	B	1996	50	150	B	A3
Stercorarius longicaudus Long-tailed Skua	B	1996	10	50	C	A3

1. Significant numbers; B2 assigned even though threshold not met.

The IBA is very important for a variety of breeding waterbirds, raptors, grouse and waders. Breeding birds include nine out of the 32 species in Europe that are restricted (when breeding) to the Arctic/tundra biome.

■ Protection status
National Partial **International** Partial
400 ha of IBA covered by Bird Sanctuary (Enadeltat, 400 ha). 400 ha of IBA covered by Bird Sanctuary (Hallsnaset, 400 ha). 100 ha of IBA covered by Bird Sanctuary (Topptjarn (Storlien), 100 ha). IBA overlaps with Nature Reserve (Valadalens, 117,500 ha). 11,000 ha of IBA covered by Ramsar Site (Ånnsjön, 11,000 ha). IBA overlaps with Special Protection Area (117,500 ha).

■ Conservation issues
No serious threats are known at the site.

River Dalälven–Hovran
A4i, B1i, B3, C2, C6 **015**
Admin region Dalarna
Coordinates 60°18'N 16°03'E
Altitude 80–80 m **Area** 5,030 ha

■ Site description
This site includes some broader stretches of the River Dalälven, notably Lake Hovran (in fact part of the river) and several smaller lagoons. Open areas around the lakes support *Salix*/*Phragmites* vegetation. Arable land and coniferous and deciduous forests surround the IBA.

Habitats Forest and woodland (broadleaved deciduous forest; native coniferous forest), Wetland (standing fresh water; water-fringe vegetation), Artificial landscape (arable land)
Land-use Agriculture

■ Birds

Species	Season	Year	Pop min	Pop max	Acc	Criteria
[1] *Cygnus cygnus* Whooper Swan	P	1997	1,500	2,000	—	A4i, B1i, C2
Pandion haliaetus Osprey	B	1997	—	10	—	C6
Locustella naevia Grasshopper Warbler	B	1997	—	40	—	B3

1. Also breeds (1–2 pairs).

The IBA supports breeding wetland species, and is an important stop-over site for migrating waterbirds and waders. Breeding species of global conservation concern that do not meet IBA criteria: *Crex crex*.

■ Protection status
National Low **International** High
IBA overlaps with two Nature Reserves (Kloster and Stackaren, totalling 215 ha). 5,030 ha of IBA covered by Ramsar Site (Hovran area, 5,130 ha).

■ Conservation issues

Threats Other (U)

The only known problem is that of dramatic water-level fluctuations, which can result in the destruction of nests ('Other' threat).

River Svartån — A4i, B1i, C2 — 016
Admin region Västmanland
Coordinates 59°53'N 16°21'E
Altitude 60–60 m **Area** 1,870 ha

■ Site description
This area contains three nutrient-rich lakes: Fläcksjön, Gussjön and Gorgen, all connected by the River Svartån and surrounded by low-lying water-meadows prone to spring flooding. Associated vegetation includes areas of *Phragmites*, *Scirpus* and wet *Betula* forest. The land is used for cattle-grazing and is one of the largest areas remaining in Sweden where mowing still takes place.

Habitats Forest and woodland (alluvial/very wet forest), Grassland, Wetland (standing fresh water; water-fringe vegetation)
Land-use Agriculture, Nature conservation/research

■ Birds

Species	Season	Year	Pop min	Pop max	Acc	Criteria
Cygnus cygnus Whooper Swan	N	1994	—	2,300	—	A4i, B1i, C2

The lake margins and adjacent meadows also provide breeding habitat for a number of wetland species. Breeding species of global conservation concern that do not meet IBA criteria: *Crex crex*.

■ Protection status
National Low **International** Partial
78 ha of IBA covered by Nature Reserve (Flackebo, 78 ha). 1,870 ha of IBA covered by Ramsar Site (Svartån, 1,990 ha). IBA overlaps with four Special Protection Areas (totalling 1,321 ha).

■ Conservation issues

Threats Abandonment/reduction of land management (U)

Succession takes place if land is abandoned or left unmanaged. Large areas are now managed through governmental conservation action and funding, with the aim of maintaining and improving conditions for breeding and passage birds. Counts are undertaken regularly. Plans exist to designate five 'consultation areas' (totalling 1,535 ha) as Nature Reserves.

River Dalälven–Färnebofjärden — A4i, B1i, B2, C2, C6 — 017
Admin region Uppsala
Coordinates 60°13'N 16°46'E
Altitude 50–75 m **Area** 11,200 ha

■ Site description
An extensive lake and wetland complex situated along the River Dalälven. Much of the area floods regularly and comprises freshwater marsh and peatbogs. The surrounding forests of both coniferous and deciduous species are largely old and undisturbed. Commercial forestry is, however, carried out in some areas.

Habitats Forest and woodland (30%; mixed forest), Wetland (70%; tidal river/enclosed tidal water; mudflat/sandflat; shingle/stony beach; river/stream; blanket bog; water-fringe vegetation)
Land-use Forestry, Nature conservation/research (95%), Tourism/recreation (5%)

■ Birds

Species	Season	Year	Pop min	Pop max	Acc	Criteria
Cygnus cygnus Whooper Swan	P	1996	1,000	1,200	A	A4i, B1i, C2
Haliaeetus albicilla White-tailed Eagle	R	1996	2	3	A	B2
Pandion haliaetus Osprey	B	1996	25	30	A	B2, C6
[1] *Bonasa bonasia* Hazel Grouse	R	1996	40	50	B	C6
[1] *Tetrao tetrix* Black Grouse	R	1996	90	100	B	C6

Species ... continued	Season	Year	Pop min	Pop max	Acc	Criteria
[1] *Tetrao urogallus* Capercaillie	R	1996	25	50	B	C6
[2] *Grus grus* Crane	B	1996	15	20	A	C6
Tringa glareola Wood Sandpiper	B	1996	10	15	B	C6
Glaucidium passerinum Pygmy Owl	R	1996	45	55	B	C6
Strix uralensis Ural Owl	R	1996	20	30	A	C6
Aegolius funereus Tengmalm's Owl	B	1996	1	25	B	C6
Dryocopus martius Black Woodpecker	R	1996	35	45	A	C6

1. Large decrease.
2. Large increase.

The IBA supports a diversity of breeding species of wetland and forest habitats.

■ Protection status
National High **International** None
IBA overlaps with National Park. IBA overlaps with Nature Reserve (4,640 ha).

■ Conservation issues

Threats Construction/impact of dyke/dam/barrage (U), Deforestation (commercial) (U), Intensified forest management (C), Recreation/tourism (C)

A Ramsar Site (20,100 ha) is likely to be designated in the near future.

Båtfors–Bredfors — C6 — 018
Admin region Uppsala
Coordinates 60°21'N 17°10'E
Altitude 35–65 m **Area** 2,700 ha

■ Site description
A lake situated in the lower reaches of the Dalälvens river, which is subject to spring flooding. Rich shoreline vegetation is present.

Habitats Forest and woodland (40%; broadleaved deciduous forest; native coniferous forest; mixed forest; alluvial/very wet forest), Wetland (60%; mudflat/sandflat; shingle/stony beach; standing fresh water; river/stream; water-fringe vegetation; fen/transition mire/spring)
Land-use Military (100%)

■ Birds

Species	Season	Year	Pop min	Pop max	Acc	Criteria
Pandion haliaetus Osprey	B	1996	6	10	B	C6
Glaucidium passerinum Pygmy Owl	R	1996	5	10	B	C6
Dryocopus martius Black Woodpecker	R	1996	10	20	B	C6

This site is important for breeding species of forest and wetland habitats. Species of global conservation concern that do not meet IBA criteria: *Haliaeetus albicilla* (resident).

■ Protection status
National Partial **International** None
IBA overlaps with two Nature Reserves (totalling 1,732 ha).

■ Conservation issues

Threats Construction/impact of dyke/dam/barrage (C), Disturbance to birds (B), Intensified forest management (C), Selective logging/cutting (C)

Ledskär–Karlholm Bay — A4i, B1i, C2, C3 — 019
Admin region Uppsala
Coordinates 60°30'N 17°43'E
Altitude 0–15 m **Area** 3,500 ha

■ Site description
The IBA comprises two shallow bays in the Gulf of Bothnia and an archipelago of several hundreds of islets and skerries.

Habitats Forest and woodland (20%; broadleaved deciduous forest; native coniferous forest; alluvial/very wet forest), Scrub (5%; scrub), Grassland (5%; humid grassland), Wetland (5%; mudflat/sandflat), Marine areas (45%; open sea; sea inlet/coastal features), Rocky areas (10%; sea cliff/rocky shore; scree/boulders), Artificial landscape (15%; arable land)

Land-use Agriculture (15%), Forestry (10%), Hunting (95%), Tourism/recreation (10%)

■ Birds

Species	Season	Year	Pop min	Pop max	Acc	Criteria
Cygnus cygnus Whooper Swan	P	1996	50	150	A	C2
Anser fabalis Bean Goose	P	1996	500	2,500	A	B1i, C3
Anser anser Greylag Goose	P	1996	1,000	2,500	A	B1i, C3
Anas crecca Teal	P	1996	1,000	4,000	A	B1i, C3
Mergus merganser Goosander	P	1996	100	2,000	A	B1i, C3
Calidris alpina Dunlin	P	1996	100	800	A	B1i, C3
Sterna caspia Caspian Tern	P	1996	50	150	A	A4i, B1i, C2

The site is important for passage wildfowl and waders. Species of global conservation concern that do not meet IBA criteria: *Anser erythropus* (2 passage birds), *Haliaeetus albicilla* (breeding), *Crex crex* (1–3 breeding pairs), *Gallinago media* (1–5 passage birds). More than 150 species of bird breed in the IBA, with c.250 species having been recorded in total.

■ Protection status
National Partial **International** None
IBA overlaps with Bird Sanctuary (part of Ledskär bay).

■ Conservation issues

Threats Abandonment/reduction of land management (B), Afforestation (C), Consequences of animal/plant introductions (B)

American mink *Mustela vison* pose a threat to breeding birds. Areas of wet meadow are being restored.

Björn archipelago A4i, B1i, B1ii, B2, B3, C2, C3, C6 020
Admin region Uppsala
Coordinates 60°38′N 17°59′E
Altitude 0–10 m **Area** 3,000 ha

■ Site description
A small archipelago located in the southern part of the Gulf of Bothnia, comprising numerous small skerries and a few islands.

Habitats Forest and woodland (5%; mixed forest), Grassland (5%; dry siliceous grassland), Marine areas (90%; open sea; sea inlet/coastal features)
Land-use Forestry (5%), Military (5%), Nature conservation/research (20%), Tourism/recreation (5%)

■ Birds

Species	Season	Year	Pop min	Pop max	Acc	Criteria
Haliaeetus albicilla White-tailed Eagle	B	1996	2	4	B	B2, C6
Larus fuscus Lesser Black-backed Gull	B	1996	150	200	B	B3
[1] *Sterna caspia* Caspian Tern	B	1996	40	50	B	A4i, B1i, B2, C2, C6
Alca torda Razorbill	B	1996	40	50	B	B1ii, C3
[1] *Cepphus grylle* Black Guillemot	B	1996	80	100	B	B1ii, B2

1. Large decrease.

An important site for breeding gulls and seabirds.

■ Protection status
National None **International** None

■ Conservation issues

Threats Consequences of animal/plant introductions (A)

The expanding American mink *Mustela vison* population in the archipelago poses a major threat to breeding birds.

Lake Tämnaren A4i, B1i, B2, C2, C3, C6 021
Admin region Uppsala
Coordinates 60°10′N 17°20′E
Altitude 35–50 m **Area** 13,500 ha

■ Site description
A large, nutrient-rich freshwater lake with extensive reedbeds (*Phragmites*) and adjoining areas of wetland.

Habitats Forest and woodland (45%; broadleaved deciduous forest; native coniferous forest; mixed forest; alluvial/very wet forest), Grassland (5%; humid grassland), Wetland (35%; mudflat/sandflat; standing fresh water; water-fringe vegetation), Artificial landscape (30%; arable land)
Land-use Agriculture (30%), Forestry (45%), Not utilized (5%), Tourism/recreation (20%)

■ Birds

Species	Season	Year	Pop min	Pop max	Acc	Criteria
Botaurus stellaris Bittern	B	1996	3	9	B	C6
Cygnus cygnus Whooper Swan	P	1996	50	150	B	C2
Anser fabalis Bean Goose	P	1996	200	1,200	A	B1i, C3
Anser anser Greylag Goose	P	1996	2,500	4,500	A	A4i, B1i, C3
Mergus albellus Smew	P	1996	30	370	A	B1i, C2
Mergus merganser Goosander	P	1996	2,000	10,000	A	A4i, B1i, C3
Circus aeruginosus Marsh Harrier	B	1996	10	15	A	C6
Crex crex Corncrake	B	1996	5	10	B	B2
Sterna caspia Caspian Tern	N	1996	50	150	A	A4i, B1i, C2
Sterna hirundo Common Tern	P	1996	500	1,500	C	C6

An important area for breeding wetland species and as a stop-over site for passage wildfowl. Breeding species of global conservation concern that do not meet IBA criteria: *Haliaeetus albicilla*.

■ Protection status
National None **International** None

■ Conservation issues

Threats Abandonment/reduction of land management (B), Aquaculture/fisheries (B), Consequences of animal/plant introductions (B), Filling-in of wetlands (A), Other (B)

American mink *Mustela vison* pose a threat to breeding birds. Lake water is supplied to Uppsala—the resulting water regime is unfavorable to birds ('Other' threat).

Florarna B3, C6 022
Admin region Uppsala
Coordinates 60°18′N 17°50′E
Altitude 28–45 m **Area** 16,500 ha

■ Site description
A reasonably undisturbed mosaic of mire and wet forest.

Habitats Forest and woodland (45%; broadleaved deciduous forest; native coniferous forest; mixed forest; alluvial/very wet forest), Wetland (45%; shingle/stony beach; standing fresh water; blanket bog; fen/transition mire/spring), Rocky areas (10%; scree/boulders)
Land-use Hunting (100%), Nature conservation/research (30%), Tourism/recreation (40%)

■ Birds

Species	Season	Year	Pop min	Pop max	Acc	Criteria
Pandion haliaetus Osprey	B	1996	10	15	C	C6
Bonasa bonasia Hazel Grouse	R	1996	100	200	C	C6
Tetrao tetrix Black Grouse	R	1996	50	100	C	C6
Tetrao urogallus Capercaillie	R	1996	40	100	C	C6
Grus grus Crane	B	1996	15	30	B	C6
Tringa glareola Wood Sandpiper	B	1996	8	15	A	C6
Glaucidium passerinum Pygmy Owl	R	1996	30	50	C	C6
Strix uralensis Ural Owl	R	1996	15	25	B	C6
Aegolius funereus Tengmalm's Owl	R	1996	1	25	C	C6
Dryocopus martius Black Woodpecker	R	1996	20	40	C	C6
Loxia pytyopsittacus Parrot Crossbill	R	1996	20	100	C	B3

This is an important site for breeding species of forest and mire. Species of global conservation concern that do not meet IBA criteria: *Haliaeetus albicilla* (2–10 non-breeding birds).

■ Protection status
National Partial **International** Partial
IBA overlaps with Nature Reserve (5,100 ha). IBA overlaps with Special Protection Area.

■ Conservation issues

Threats Abandonment/reduction of land management (C), Selective logging/cutting (C)

Lake Hjälstaviken
A4i, B1i, C3 **023**

Admin region Uppsala
Coordinates 59°40′N 17°22′E
Altitude 3–35 m **Area** 820 ha

■ Site description
Shallow (average depth 1 m), almost enclosed bay of Lake Mälaren, surrounded by wet, tussocky meadows which merge into drier pasture and fields. Deciduous copses overlook the bay and there is a conifer-covered hill with bare rock outcrops along the eastern edge. Only 30 ha of open water remain, the rest being choked by invasive *Phragmites*, *Scirpus* and *Typha*.

Habitats Forest and woodland (10%; broadleaved deciduous forest; native coniferous forest), Scrub (5%; scrub), Grassland (20%; humid grassland; mesophile grassland), Wetland (40%; mudflat/sandflat; standing fresh water; water-fringe vegetation), Rocky areas (5%; inland cliff), Artificial landscape (20%; arable land)
Land-use Agriculture (35%), Forestry (15%), Nature conservation/research (100%), Tourism/recreation (80%)

■ Birds

Species	Season	Year	Pop min	Pop max	Acc	Criteria
Anser fabalis Bean Goose	P	1996	3,000	5,000	A	A4i, B1i, C3
Anser anser Greylag Goose	P	1996	4,000	5,000	A	A4i, B1i, C3

The IBA supports important numbers of passage wildfowl, and the surrounding arable land is an important feeding area. Species of global conservation concern that do not meet IBA criteria: *Anser erythropus* (up to 5 passage birds), *Crex crex* (1–3 breeding pairs) and *Gallinago media* (5–10 passage birds).

■ Protection status
National High **International** High
820 ha of IBA covered by Nature Reserve (Hjalstaviken, 821 ha). 770 ha of IBA covered by Ramsar Site (Hjälstaviken, 770 ha). IBA overlaps with Special Protection Area.

■ Conservation issues

Threats Abandonment/reduction of land management (U), Consequences of animal/plant introductions (U), Disturbance to birds (U), Other (U)

Threats include overgrowth of grassland vegetation due to undergrazing and the effects of introduced American mink *Mustela vison*. Submerged aquatic vegetation has been greatly impoverished in recent years and this, together with the decreasing area of open water, has resulted in the decline of some bird species, notably ducks ('Other' threat). The water-level is artificially managed—a more beneficial management regime was decided upon in 1996.

Gräsö archipelago
A1, A4i, B1i, B2, C1, C2, C3, C6 **024**

Admin region Stockholm
Coordinates 60°20′N 18°30′E
Altitude 0–10 m **Area** 18,000 ha

■ Site description
An archipelago extending along the eastern side of the island of Gräsö, comprising small islands and skerries, some of which have only sparse vegetation cover.

Habitats Forest and woodland (5%; native coniferous forest), Grassland (5%; steppe/dry calcareous grassland), Marine areas (90%; open sea; sea inlet/coastal features)
Land-use Hunting (80%), Nature conservation/research (25%), Tourism/recreation (5%)

■ Birds

Species	Season	Year	Pop min	Pop max	Acc	Criteria
[1] *Phalacrocorax carbo* Cormorant	P	1996	2,000	3,000	A	B1i, C3
[2] *Haliaeetus albicilla* White-tailed Eagle	P	1996	20	28	A	A1, C1
Sterna caspia Caspian Tern	B	1996	75	85	A	A4i, B1i, B2, C2, C6
Sterna hirundo Common Tern	B	1996	90	100	A	C6

1. Large increase.
2. Also breeds (1–2 pairs).

An important site for breeding terns and passage waterbirds and raptors.

■ Protection status
National None **International** None

■ Conservation issues

Threats Consequences of animal/plant introductions (A), Disturbance to birds (B), Recreation/tourism (B)

American mink *Mustela vison* pose a threat to breeding birds.

Dannemora
A1, B2, C1 **025**

Admin region Uppsala
Coordinates 60°12′N 17°53′E
Altitude 24–55 m **Area** 11,500 ha

■ Site description
A mosaic of forest and lakes with open agricultural areas in the valleys.

Habitats Forest and woodland (55%; broadleaved deciduous forest; native coniferous forest; mixed forest; alluvial/very wet forest), Scrub (5%; scrub), Grassland (5%; humid grassland), Wetland (20%; mudflat/sandflat; sand-dunes/sand beach; standing fresh water; fen/transition mire/spring), Rocky areas (5%; scree/boulders), Artificial landscape (10%; arable land; ruderal land)
Land-use Agriculture (10%), Forestry (45%), Hunting (80%), Tourism/recreation (20%)

■ Birds

Species	Season	Year	Pop min	Pop max	Acc	Criteria
Crex crex Corncrake	B	1996	5	25	C	A1, B2, C1

Important for breeding species of wetland and grassland habitats. Breeding species of global conservation concern that do not meet IBA criteria: *Haliaeetus albicilla*.

■ Protection status
National None **International** None

■ Conservation issues

Threats Abandonment/reduction of land management (U), Afforestation (U), Consequences of animal/plant introductions (A), Selective logging/cutting (U)

American mink *Mustela vison* pose a threat. Restoration of some of the lakes has begun, resulting in an increase in numbers of waterbirds.

Tarnan–Riala forest
B2, C6 **026**

Admin region Stockholm
Coordinates 59°35′N 18°25′E
Altitude — **Area** 7,500 ha

■ Site description

Habitats Forest and woodland (70%; native coniferous forest; mixed forest), Wetland (25%; standing fresh water; raised bog), Artificial landscape (5%; arable land)
Land-use Agriculture (5%), Forestry (70%), Not utilized (10%), Tourism/recreation (15%)

■ Birds

Species	Season	Year	Pop min	Pop max	Acc	Criteria
Gavia arctica Black-throated Diver	B	—	44	52	—	B2, C6
Bubo bubo Eagle Owl	B	—	1	3	—	B2, C6
Caprimulgus europaeus Nightjar	B	—	40	70	—	B2, C6

This site is important for forest species, including raptors and owls, and some waterbirds. Species of global conservation concern that do not meet IBA criteria: *Haliaeetus albicilla* (breeding and wintering).

■ Protection status
National Low **International** None
16 ha of IBA covered by Nature Reserve (Bromseby, 16 ha). 216 ha of IBA covered by Nature Reserve (Trehörningen, 216 ha).

■ Conservation issues

Threats Deforestation (commercial) (U)

Plans exist for the designation of c.30 smaller protected areas (less than 10 ha each) by the Swedish Forestry Commission, involving the setting up of management agreements with land-owners.

Outer Stockholm archipelago	A4i, A4ii, A4iii, B1i, B1ii, B2, B3, C2, C3, C4, C6	027

Admin region Stockholm
Coordinates 59°25′N 19°20′E
Altitude 0–10 m **Area** 9,100 ha

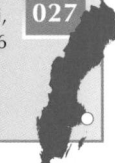

■ Site description

The main area of interest can be divided into four island groups: Stora Nassa—c.400 closely spaced rocky islets with little or no vegetation. The largest island has maritime *Betula* forest whilst others support *Juniperus*. Wet grasslands are also present. Lilla Nassa—smaller area than Stora Nassa but with islands more spread out and with very little vegetation. Gillöga—flat islands in shallow waters with abundant cover and submerged offshore reefs. Svenska Högarna—a flat island with *Juniperus*, and heather *Calluna*. The archipelago is largely uninhabited but during the summer is a popular leisure (boating) area.

Habitats Forest and woodland (5%; broadleaved deciduous forest), Grassland (5%; dry siliceous grassland), Marine areas (90%; open sea; sea inlet/coastal features), Rocky areas (rock stacks/islets)
Land-use Hunting (50%), Military (5%), Nature conservation/research (10%), Tourism/recreation (50%)

■ Birds

Species	Season	Year	Pop min	Pop max	Acc	Criteria
Somateria mollissima Eider	B	1996	36,500	36,700	B	A4i, B1i, C3
Somateria mollissima Eider	N	1996	20,000	40,000	C	A4i, B1i, C3
Melanitta fusca Velvet Scoter	B	1996	3,850	4,190	B	A4i, B1i, C3
Mergus serrator Red-breasted Merganser	B	1996	590	615	B	B1i, C3
Mergus merganser Goosander	B	1996	640	660	B	A4i, B1i, C3
Tringa totanus Redshank	B	1996	355	370	B	B2
Arenaria interpres Turnstone	B	1996	790	840	B	A4i, B1i, C3
Stercorarius parasiticus Arctic Skua	B	1996	175	200	B	B1ii, C3
Larus canus Common Gull	B	1996	4,500	5,000	B	B2
¹ *Larus fuscus* Lesser Black-backed Gull	B	1996	950	1,300	B	B1i, B3, C3
Larus marinus Great Black-backed Gull	B	1996	460	480	B	B3
¹ *Sterna caspia* Caspian Tern	B	1996	100	250	B	A4i, B1i, B2, C2, C6
Sterna paradisaea Arctic Tern	B	1996	2,490	—	C	C2
² *Uria aalge* Guillemot	B	1996	200	400	B	B1ii, C3
² *Alca torda* Razorbill	B	1996	1,400	2,000	B	B1ii, B3, C3
Cepphus grylle Black Guillemot	B	1996	4,000	4,400	B	A4ii, B1ii, B2, C3

1. Large decrease.
2. Large increase.

This is a very important breeding area for seaducks, waders, gulls and seabirds.

■ Protection status

National Partial **International** High
IBA overlaps with Nature Reserve (3,400 ha); large areas are also designated as Bird Sanctuaries. 9,100 ha of IBA covered by Ramsar Site (Stockholm, outer archipelago, 15,000 ha). IBA overlaps with Special Protection Area.

■ Conservation issues

Threats Consequences of animal/plant introductions (A), Recreation/tourism (B)

American mink *Mustela vison* are a threat to breeding birds. Recreational activities may disturb breeding birds.

Lake Östra Styran	C2	028

Admin region Stockholm
Coordinates 59°00′N 17°50′E
Altitude 20–30 m **Area** 117 ha

■ Site description

A shallow wetland with extensive reedbeds (*Phragmites*).

Habitats Forest and woodland (10%; broadleaved deciduous forest; alluvial/very wet forest), Grassland (5%; humid grassland), Wetland (85%; standing fresh water; water-fringe vegetation), Artificial landscape (10%; arable land)

■ Birds

Species	Season	Year	Pop min	Pop max	Acc	Criteria
Cygnus cygnus Whooper Swan	P	1997	200	250	B	C2

This is an important site for breeding and passage wetland species.

■ Protection status
National None **International** None

■ Conservation issues

Land-use Agriculture (10%), Forestry (5%), Hunting (90%), Tourism/recreation (100%)

No serious threats are known at the site. Recent restoration work has led to an increase in spring and summer water-levels, benefiting many species of waterbird.

Hanveden–Hemfosa	B2, C6	029

Admin region Stockholm
Coordinates 59°05′N 18°00′E
Altitude 50–80 m **Area** 3,500 ha

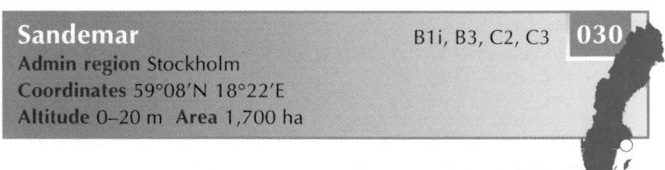

■ Site description
An area of forest interspersed with a few lakes, situated to the south of Stockholm.

Habitats Forest and woodland (100%; native coniferous forest; mixed forest; alluvial/very wet forest)
Land-use Forestry (90%), Hunting (100%)

■ Birds

Species	Season	Year	Pop min	Pop max	Acc	Criteria
Bonasa bonasia Hazel Grouse	R	1996	25	40	B	C6
Tetrao tetrix Black Grouse	R	1996	25	35	B	C6
Tetrao urogallus Capercaillie	R	1996	50	75	B	C6
Grus grus Crane	B	1996	12	18	B	C6
Bubo bubo Eagle Owl	R	1996	7	10	B	B2, C6
Glaucidium passerinum Pygmy Owl	R	1996	20	30	B	C6
Aegolius funereus Tengmalm's Owl	R	1996	2	10	B	C6
Caprimulgus europaeus Nightjar	B	1996	30	40	B	B2, C6
Lullula arborea Woodlark	B	1996	50	60	B	C6

Important site for breeding forest species, including raptors and owls.

■ Protection status
National None **International** None

■ Conservation issues

Threats Deforestation (commercial) (A)

Sandemar	B1i, B3, C2, C3	030

Admin region Stockholm
Coordinates 59°08′N 18°22′E
Altitude 0–20 m **Area** 1,700 ha

■ Site description
A shallow bay of the Baltic Sea situated near to Stockholm.

Habitats Forest and woodland (10%; native coniferous forest; alluvial/very wet forest), Grassland (5%; humid grassland), Marine areas (85%; open sea), Artificial landscape (10%; highly improved reseeded grassland)
Land-use Agriculture (25%), Forestry (5%), Tourism/recreation (100%)

■ Birds
Sandemar is important as a stop-over site for passage wildfowl. Species of global conservation concern that do not meet IBA criteria: *Haliaeetus albicilla* (resident).

Species	Season	Year	Pop min	Pop max	Acc	Criteria
Cygnus cygnus Whooper Swan	W	1996	20	30	A	B3, C2
Aythya fuligula Tufted Duck	W	—	10,000	—	—	B1i, C3
Aythya fuligula Tufted Duck	P	1996	8,000	12,000	B	B1i, C3

■ Protection status
National Partial **International** None
IBA overlaps with Nature Reserve (Sandemar, 387 ha).

■ Conservation issues

Threats Abandonment/reduction of land management (U)

The shoreline was recently restored and a large proportion is now grazed, benefiting birds that feed at the site.

Lake Tysslingen
A4i, B1i, C2, C3 **031**
Admin region Örebro
Coordinates 59°18'N 15°02'E
Altitude 30–40 m Area 600 ha

■ Site description

Habitats Forest and woodland (5%; alluvial/very wet forest), Grassland (10%; humid grassland), Wetland (90%; standing fresh water; water-fringe vegetation), Artificial landscape (5%; arable land)
Land-use Agriculture (20%), Not utilized (80%)

■ Birds

Species	Season	Year	Pop min	Pop max	Acc	Criteria
[1] *Cygnus cygnus* Whooper Swan	P	1998	20,000	—	A	A4i, B1i, C2
Anser fabalis Bean Goose	P	1996	2,000	2,500	A	B1i, C3

1. Max. 3,000 in one day on spring passage.

An important site for passage wildfowl—the most important stop-over site in northern Europe for *Cygnus cygnus*. A total of c.230 species have been recorded, 90 of which regularly breed.

■ Protection status
National None **International** None

■ Conservation issues

Threats Abandonment/reduction of land management (U), Disturbance to birds (U)

Overgrowth of grassland vegetation has occurred due to undergrazing.

Bay of Rynningeviken
C6 **032**
Admin region Örebro
Coordinates 59°17'N 15°16'E
Altitude 22–24 m Area 600 ha

■ Site description
A nutrient-rich, shallow bay of Lake Hjälmaren, surrounded by cattle-grazed wet meadows. The bay was, until recently, a landfill site—restoration was undertaken during 1992–1996 by the city of Örebro authorities.

Habitats Forest and woodland (15%; broadleaved deciduous forest; alluvial/very wet forest), Scrub (10%; scrub), Grassland (40%; humid grassland), Wetland (30%; standing fresh water; water-fringe vegetation), Artificial landscape (5%; ruderal land)
Land-use Nature conservation/research (100%), Tourism/recreation (60%)

■ Birds

Species	Season	Year	Pop min	Pop max	Acc	Criteria
Botaurus stellaris Bittern	B	1996	3	6	A	C6

This is an important site for breeding wetland passerines and passage wildfowl and waders.

■ Protection status
National Partial **International** Partial

IBA overlaps with 2 Nature Reserves (totalling 560 ha). IBA overlaps with Special Protection Area (560 ha).

■ Conservation issues

Threats Abandonment/reduction of land management (B), Industrialization/urbanization (B)

Kvismaren
A4i, B1i, B3, C2, C3, C6 **033**
Admin region Örebro
Coordinates 59°10'N 15°22'E
Altitude 22–30 m Area 800 ha

■ Site description
Kvismaren is a flat fertile agricultural valley. Extensive marshy areas originally surrounded two lakes, but following drainage in the 1880s the lakes disappeared. They have now been replaced by extensive reedbeds (*Phragmites*) and *Salix* thickets surrounded by marshy meadows, low-lying pasture and arable land, and densely wooded areas. The main wetland is enclosed by embankments and canals to protect nearby arable land from flooding. Three areas of open water, covering c.230 ha, have recently been restored as shallow lakes or water-meadows. The IBA contains an important ornithological station.

Habitats Forest and woodland (10%; alluvial/very wet forest), Scrub (10%; scrub), Grassland (20%; humid grassland), Wetland (70%; mudflat/sandflat; standing fresh water; water-fringe vegetation)
Land-use Agriculture, Hunting (5%), Nature conservation/research (85%), Not utilized (10%)

■ Birds

Species	Season	Year	Pop min	Pop max	Acc	Criteria
Anser fabalis Bean Goose	P	1996	5,000	25,000	A	A4i, B1i, C3
Circus aeruginosus Marsh Harrier	B	1996	15	18	A	C6
Grus grus Crane	P	1996	200	2,500	A	A4i, B1i, C2
Locustella naevia Grasshopper Warbler	B	1996	25	50	A	B3

The site is important for breeding species of wetland and wet grassland habitats, as well as for passage wildfowl and waders. Breeding species of global conservation concern that do not meet IBA criteria: *Crex crex*.

■ Protection status
National High **International** High
IBA overlaps with Nature Reserve (732 ha). 780 ha of IBA covered by Ramsar Site (Kvismaren, 780 ha). IBA overlaps with Special Protection Area (732 ha).

■ Conservation issues

Threats Abandonment/reduction of land management (A), Other (U)

Increasing numbers of *Anser fabalis* and *Grus grus* have led to conflict with farmers ('Other' threat). A programme has been undertaken both to alleviate this problem and to compensate farmers for crop losses. Continued restoration of the western part of the IBA is expected to begin soon.

Lake Storhjälmaren
A4i, B1i, C2 **034**
Admin region Örebro
Coordinates 59°18'N 15°50'E
Altitude 22–35 m Area 600 ha

■ Site description
An area of shoals in the central part of Lake Hjälmaren.

Habitats Wetland (100%; shingle/stony beach; standing fresh water)
Land-use Tourism/recreation (100%)

■ Birds

Species	Season	Year	Pop min	Pop max	Acc	Criteria
Sterna caspia Caspian Tern	P	1996	50	300	A	A4i, B1i, C2

The site is also important as a stop-over site for *Larus minutus* and *Chlidonias niger*, especially during late summer.

■ **Protection status**
National None **International** None

■ **Conservation issues**

Threats Other (U)

High levels of water quality are crucial to maintaining suitable conditions for breeding insects, upon which the gulls and terns feed. Large algal blooms may have a negative effect ('Other' threat).

Bay of Kilsviken — B2, C2, C6 — 035
Admin region Värmland
Coordinates 59°03'N 14°04'E
Altitude 45–55 m Area 8,910 ha

■ **Site description**
Kilsviken is a nutrient-rich bay off Lake Vänern and is surrounded by agricultural land. The shoreline is largely made up of reedbeds (*Phragmites*) and water-meadows and there is rich aquatic vegetation. Associated with Kilsviken is Kolstrandsviken Bay, which is moderately-rich in nutrients and contains mudflats, and Åråsviken Bay. The northern part of Åråsviken supports extensive areas of *Phragmites*, and grazing-meadows and damp forests occur on the many islands.

Habitats Forest and woodland (15%; broadleaved deciduous forest; native coniferous forest; mixed forest), Grassland (10%; humid grassland; mesophile grassland), Wetland (70%; mudflat/sandflat; sand-dunes/sand beach; shingle/stony beach; standing fresh water; river/stream; water-fringe vegetation), Rocky areas (5%; scree/boulders), Artificial landscape (5%; highly improved reseeded grassland; arable land)
Land-use Agriculture (5%), Forestry (5%), Nature conservation/research (25%), Not utilized (25%), Tourism/recreation (10%)

■ **Birds**

Species		Season	Year	Pop min	Pop max	Acc	Criteria
Botaurus stellaris	Bittern	B	1997	5	10	A	B2, C6
¹ *Cygnus cygnus*	Whooper Swan	P	1997	50	100	A	C2
Circus aeruginosus	Marsh Harrier	B	1997	7	10	A	C6
Sterna hirundo	Common Tern	B	1997	50	100	A	C6

1. Also overwinters.

The IBA is important for breeding waterbirds and raptors, and as a stop-over site for migrating waders. Wintering species of global conservation concern that do not meet IBA criteria: *Haliaeetus albicilla* (4–8 birds).

■ **Protection status**
National Partial **International** High
IBA overlaps with Bird Sanctuary (Dyro-Mallskars Skar). IBA overlaps with Nature Reserve (Inner Kilsviken, 132 ha). IBA overlaps with Nature Reserve (Noton-Arasviken). IBA overlaps with Nature Reserve (Vallholmen, 107 ha). 8,910 ha of IBA covered by Ramsar Site (Kilsviken, 8,910 ha). IBA overlaps with three Special Protection Areas (totalling 2,554 ha).

■ **Conservation issues**

Threats Abandonment/reduction of land management (U), Consequences of animal/plant introductions (U), Disturbance to birds (U), Intensified forest management (U), Other (U), Recreation/tourism (U)

American mink *Mustela vison* are a threat to breeding birds. Canoeing and other recreational activities may endanger important breeding areas. The bays' sediments still contain mercury (Hg) from a former paper factory ('Other' threat).

Lake Tåkern — A4i, A4iii, B1i, B2, C2, C3, C4, C6 — 036
Admin region Östergötland
Coordinates 58°21'N 14°49'E
Altitude 94–100 m Area 5,620 ha

■ **Site description**
A shallow, nutrient-rich lake that was partly drained in the 19th century, allowing extensive reedbeds to colonize about one third of the total area. The shallow waters (average depth 0.8 m) are rich in aquatic flora. The surrounding grassland is mainly grazed, and there are some areas of arable land.

Habitats Forest and woodland (10%; broadleaved deciduous forest; native coniferous forest), Grassland (5%; steppe/dry calcareous grassland), Wetland (80%; standing fresh water; water-fringe vegetation)
Land-use Agriculture (10%), Forestry (10%), Hunting (95%), Nature conservation/research (100%)

■ **Birds**

Species		Season	Year	Pop min	Pop max	Acc	Criteria
Podiceps grisegena	Red-necked Grebe	B	1995	35	50	A	B1i, C3
Botaurus stellaris	Bittern	B	1997	24	38	A	B2, C2, C6
Cygnus cygnus	Whooper Swan	P	—	200	300	—	C2
¹ *Anser fabalis*	Bean Goose	P	1997	13,000	25,000	A	A4i, B1i, C3
² *Anser anser*	Greylag Goose	N	1997	5,000	6,600	A	A4i, B1i, C3
Circus aeruginosus	Marsh Harrier	B	1997	40	50	A	C6
Chlidonias niger	Black Tern	B	1997	25	40	A	C2, C6

1. Large decrease.
2. Large increase.

The IBA is important for breeding waterbirds and other species of wetland habitats. It also holds over 20,000 passage waterbirds on a regular basis. Breeding species of global conservation concern that do not meet IBA criteria: *Crex crex*.

■ **Protection status**
National High **International** High
IBA overlaps with Nature Reserve (5,420 ha). 5,620 ha of IBA covered by Ramsar Site (Tåkern, 5,650 ha). 5,620 ha of IBA covered by Special Protection Area (5,620 ha).

■ **Conservation issues**

Threats Abandonment/reduction of land management (U), Other (U)

Some meadows have become overgrown as a result of undergrazing, with a consequent adverse effect on waders. Mechanical methods (for example, mowing) are being used to simulate the effects of grazing. The turbidity of the lake has increased, leading to a decrease in the number of birds using the site ('Other' threat).

Bay of Svensksundsviken — A1, A4i, B1i, C1, C3 — 037
Admin region Östergötland
Coordinates 58°35'N 15°25'E
Altitude 0–2 m Area 3,300 ha

■ **Site description**
A shallow bay containing some 20 islands, surrounded by extensive grazed meadows and reedbeds *Phragmites*. Dryer areas support *Juniperus*.

Habitats Forest and woodland (5%; mixed forest), Scrub (5%; scrub), Grassland (5%; humid grassland), Wetland (20%; water-fringe vegetation), Marine areas (70%; sea inlet/coastal features)
Land-use Nature conservation/research (60%)

■ **Birds**

Species		Season	Year	Pop min	Pop max	Acc	Criteria
Anser fabalis	Bean Goose	P	1996	4,000	6,000	A	A4i, B1i, C3
Anser anser	Greylag Goose	P	1996	4,000	5,000	A	A4i, B1i, C3
Haliaeetus albicilla	White-tailed Eagle	N	1996	10	16	A	A1, C1

The IBA is important for breeding waterbirds and as a stop-over site for passage wildfowl and waders.

■ **Protection status**
National Partial **International** Partial
2,026 ha of IBA covered by Nature Reserve (Svensksundsvikens, 2,026 ha). 2,026 ha of IBA covered by Special Protection Area (2,026 ha).

■ **Conservation issues**

Threats Abandonment/reduction of land management (C)

A Ramsar Site (3,680 ha) is likely to be designated in the near future.

Dannskär–Örskär islands
A4i, B1i, B2, C2, C3, C6　038

Admin region Östergötland
Coordinates 58°25′N 16°54′E
Altitude 0–5 m　**Area** 95 ha

■ Site description
An archipelago comprising islands and skerries, some devoid of vegetation.

Habitats Marine areas (100%; sea inlet/coastal features)
Land-use Nature conservation/research (100%)

■ Birds

Species	Season	Year	Pop min	Pop max	Acc	Criteria
Phalacrocorax carbo Cormorant	B	1997	100	500	A	B1i, C3
Sterna caspia Caspian Tern	B	1997	100	150	A	A4i, B1i, B2, C2, C6

An important site for breeding waterbirds, raptors and terns. Species of global conservation concern that do not meet IBA criteria: *Haliaeetus albicilla* (resident).

■ Protection status
National Partial　**International** None
IBA overlaps with Bird Sanctuary (40 ha).

■ Conservation issues

Threats Consequences of animal/plant introductions (U)

American mink *Mustela vison* pose a threat to breeding birds.

St Anna archipelago
B2, C6　039

Admin region Östergötland
Coordinates 58°22′N 17°00′E
Altitude 0–20 m　**Area** 5,690 ha

■ Site description
An archipelago comprising hundreds of islands and skerries. The larger islands close to the mainland support trees and tall vegetation, whilst those further out support little or no tall vegetation. The area can only be reached by boat and is frequented by tourists during the summer, although no significant disturbance is caused to birds.

Habitats Forest and woodland (broadleaved deciduous forest), Marine areas (open sea; sea inlet/coastal features)
Land-use Tourism/recreation

■ Birds

Species	Season	Year	Pop min	Pop max	Acc	Criteria
Sterna caspia Caspian Tern	B	—	10	—	—	B2, C6

The islands furthest from the mainland support the richest birdlife. *Somateria mollissima* breed in large numbers; other breeders include *Anser anser*, *Tringa totanus*, *Actitis hypoleucos*, gulls and auks. Breeding species of global conservation concern that do not meet IBA criteria: *Haliaeetus albicilla*.

■ Protection status
National Partial　**International** Low
IBA overlaps with several Bird Sanctuaries. IBA overlaps with Nature Reserve (Väggö, 162 ha). IBA overlaps with Special Protection Area (162 ha).

■ Conservation issues

Threats Consequences of animal/plant introductions (U)

Decreases in the numbers of some waders (*Tringa totanus*, *Arenaria interpres* and *Charadrius hiaticula*) have been noted, but the causes are unknown. American mink *Mustela vison* have a very negative effect on some breeding species (for example, terns and auks).

Dättern–Södra Brandfjorden
B2, C6　040

Admin region Västra Götaland
Coordinates 58°23′N 12°35′E
Altitude 44–44 m　**Area** 3,320 ha

■ Site description
Dättern is an almost enclosed bay of Lake Vänern with a *Phragmites*-dominated shoreline. Large areas of sand and clay are exposed when the water-level is low. The sound connecting Dättern with the main lake becomes ice-free early in the spring. The bay is surrounded by grazed meadows, and there is an ancient *Alnus* wood, 73 ha in size.

Habitats Grassland (humid grassland), Wetland (standing fresh water; water-fringe vegetation)
Land-use Agriculture

■ Birds

Species	Season	Year	Pop min	Pop max	Acc	Criteria
Botaurus stellaris Bittern	B	1996	10	12	—	B2, C6
Circus aeruginosus Marsh Harrier	B	1996	—	17	—	C6

The expanses of sand and clay form important resting areas for waders such as *Calidris ferruginea*. Species of global conservation concern that do not meet IBA criteria: *Haliaeetus albicilla* (non-breeding) and *Gallinago media* (passage).

■ Protection status
National Partial　**International** High
IBA overlaps with Nature Reserve (1,482 ha). 3,320 ha of IBA covered by Ramsar Site (Dättern, 3,920 ha). IBA overlaps with Special Protection Area (1,482 ha).

■ Conservation issues

Threats Abandonment/reduction of land management (U)

Overgrown lakeside meadows are being invaded by scrub.

Lake Östen
A4i, B1i, B3, C2, C3　041

Admin region Västra Götaland
Coordinates 58°34′N 13°54′E
Altitude 80–80 m　**Area** 1,020 ha

■ Site description
A shallow, nutrient-rich lake situated in a generally flat landscape, except for a few higher areas that are covered by coniferous forest. The lake was lowered three times by drainage projects in the nineteenth century and the reclaimed land, now grazed water-meadows, forms an important wader habitat. The rapid water exchange in the lake means that the period of ice-cover is quite short. Livestock-grazing is the main land-use.

Habitats Forest and woodland (native coniferous forest), Grassland (humid grassland), Wetland (standing fresh water)
Land-use Agriculture

■ Birds

Species	Season	Year	Pop min	Pop max	Acc	Criteria
[1] *Cygnus cygnus* Whooper Swan	P	—	—	1,000	—	A4i, B1i, C2
[2] *Anser fabalis* Bean Goose	P	—	—	10,500	—	A4i, B1i, C3
Locustella naevia Grasshopper Warbler	B	—	—	60	—	B3

1. Decreasing.
2. Spring passage; 8,000 on autumn passage.

The site is important as a stop-over site for passage waterbirds and waders. Passage species of global conservation concern that do not meet IBA criteria: *Anser erythropus*, *Crex crex* and *Gallinago media*.

■ Protection status
National High　**International** High
IBA overlaps with Nature Reserve (Östen, 1,420 ha). 1,010 ha of IBA covered by Ramsar Site (Östen, 1,010 ha). IBA overlaps with Special Protection Area.

Conservation issues

Threats Abandonment/reduction of land management (U), Drainage (U), Dredging/canalization (U)

Habitat deterioration has occurred, and the site is slowly reverting to marsh. An unfavourable water regime is assisting the successional process, and drainage, dredging and reclamation projects are ongoing. Breeding wetland birds have almost disappeared. Management agreements exist between the National Environmental Board and land-owners.

Lake Hornborgasjön
A4i, B1i, B1iv, B2, B3, C2, C3, C5, C6   **042**

Admin region Västra Götaland
Coordinates 58°19′N 13°33′E
Altitude 119–128 m **Area** 6,350 ha

Site description
A shallow calcareous lake that has undergone extensive restoration work over the last five years, involving water-level management. The lake's surroundings are mainly cultivated or cattle-grazed, although there are some forested areas. More than 100,000 people visit the lake each year.

Habitats Forest and woodland (15%; native coniferous forest; mixed forest), Grassland (20%; dry siliceous grassland; humid grassland), Wetland (50%; standing fresh water; raised bog; water-fringe vegetation), Artificial landscape (20%; arable land)
Land-use Agriculture (30%), Forestry (5%), Nature conservation/research (40%), Not utilized (25%), Tourism/recreation

Birds

Species	Season	Year	Pop min	Pop max	Acc	Criteria
[1] *Podiceps grisegena* Red-necked Grebe	B	1996	40	60	A	B1i, C3
[1] *Botaurus stellaris* Bittern	B	1996	10	14	A	B2, C6
[1] *Cygnus cygnus* Whooper Swan	P	1996	700	900	A	A4i, B1i, C2
[1] *Anser fabalis* Bean Goose	P	1996	1,500	2,000	A	B1i, C3
[1] *Anser anser* Greylag Goose	P	1996	1,800	2,000	A	B1i, C3
Anas crecca Teal	P	1996	6,000	7,000	A	B1i, C3
[1] *Anas acuta* Pintail	P	1996	400	500	A	B1i, C3
[1] *Circus aeruginosus* Marsh Harrier	B	1996	20	35	A	C6
Porzana porzana Spotted Crake	B	1996	5	25	A	C6
[2] *Grus grus* Crane	P	1996	6,000	10,000	A	A4i, B1i, C2
[1] *Chlidonias niger* Black Tern	B	1996	25	45	A	C2, C6
[3] *Locustella naevia* Grasshopper Warbler	B	1996	30	50	A	B3

1. Large increase.
2. Daily maxima: 6,000–7,000 on spring passage; 3,500–4,000 on autumn passage.
3. Large decrease.

The IBA is important for breeding wetland birds, and is a migratory bottleneck site, where up to 10,000 *Grus grus* regularly pass in spring. Species of global conservation concern that do not meet IBA criteria: *Haliaeetus albicilla* (3–5 passage birds), *Crex crex* (1–2 breeding pairs), *Gallinago media* (5–20 passage birds).

Protection status
National Partial **International** High
15 ha of IBA covered by Nature Reserve (Fageluddens, 15 ha). IBA overlaps with another Nature Reserve (4,124 ha). 110 ha of IBA covered by Bird Sanctuary (Bjurum-Dagsnäs, 110 ha). 6,350 ha of IBA covered by Ramsar Site (Hornborgasjön, 6,370 ha). IBA overlaps with Special Protection Area.

Conservation issues

Threats Abandonment/reduction of land management (U), Aquaculture/fisheries (U)

Stigfjorden Fjord
B1i, B2, B3, C2, C3, C6   **043**

Admin region Göteborg Och Bohus
Coordinates 58°04′N 11°37′E
Altitude 0–60 m **Area** 8,500 ha

Site description
A fjord between two large islands situated off the west Swedish coast, with extensive shallow waters and a *Zostera*-covered clay sea-floor.

The islands have well-managed coastal meadows with a saltmarsh character and some forest, mostly deciduous and dominated by *Quercus*. Human activities include boating, swimming, fishing, and grazing for conservation purposes.

Habitats Grassland (10%; mesophile grassland), Marine areas (90%; sea inlet/coastal features)
Land-use Agriculture (10%), Nature conservation/research, Not utilized (15%), Tourism/recreation, Water management (75%)

Birds

Species	Season	Year	Pop min	Pop max	Acc	Criteria
Cygnus cygnus Whooper Swan	W	1997	400	500	B	B1i, B3, C2
Bucephala clangula Goldeneye	N	1997	2,000	4,000	B	B1i, C3
[1] *Bubo bubo* Eagle Owl	R	1997	2	4	A	B2, C6

1. Increasing.

The IBA is also important for passage waterbirds and waders. Species of global conservation concern that do not meet IBA criteria: *Haliaeetus albicilla* (4–10 wintering birds).

Protection status
National Partial **International** Partial
IBA overlaps with five Nature Reserves (totalling 8,539 ha). 5,180 ha of IBA covered by Ramsar Site (Stigfjorden, 5,180 ha). IBA overlaps with Special Protection Area (1,470 ha).

Conservation issues

Threats Abandonment/reduction of land management (U), Aquaculture/fisheries (U), Consequences of animal/plant introductions (U)

American mink *Mustela vison* pose a threat to breeding birds.

Bay of Torslandaviken
B1i, B2, B3, C2, C3   **044**

Admin region Göteborg och Bohus
Coordinates 57°40′N 11°50′E
Altitude 0–10 m **Area** 250 ha

Site description
The Bay of Torslandaviken forms one of two branches of the mouth of one of Sweden's largest rivers.

Habitats Scrub (1%; scrub), Grassland (13%; mesophile grassland), Wetland (69%; mudflat/sandflat; standing brackish and salt water; water-fringe vegetation), Marine areas (15%; sea inlet/coastal features), Rocky areas (3%; sea cliff/rocky shore), Artificial landscape (other urban/industrial areas; ruderal land)
Land-use Agriculture (5%), Not utilized (75%), Urban/industrial/transport (20%)

Birds

Species	Season	Year	Pop min	Pop max	Acc	Criteria
Cygnus cygnus Whooper Swan	W	1997	150	200	C	B3, C2
Aythya marila Scaup	W	1997	20	30	C	B2
Bucephala clangula Goldeneye	N	1997	2,000	3,000	C	B1i, C3

This is one of the most important sites on the west coast for wintering and passage waterbirds and shorebirds, due to an abundance of food caused by nutrient input from a water-purification plant at the river mouth. A total of 203 species of bird have been recorded in the Bay.

Protection status
National None **International** None

Conservation issues

Threats Construction/impact of dyke/dam/barrage (A), Drainage (A), Filling-in of wetlands (A), Industrialization/urbanization (A), Infrastructure (A)

Part of the site is embanked and is being filled with mud from the adjacent harbour. The continuation of this work will probably eliminate most of the remaining valuable wetland habitats. Additional threats include drainage of adjacent wetlands, the construction of wind-power plants, controlled tipping, and pollution by industrial surface water. Concerned locals have established the Society of Torsviken Nature Reserve with the aim of protecting valuable wetland habitats.

Bay of Kungsbackafjorden A4i, B1i, C3 045
Admin region Göteborg och Bohus
Coordinates 57°24′N 12°06′E
Altitude 0–2 m Area 4,000 ha

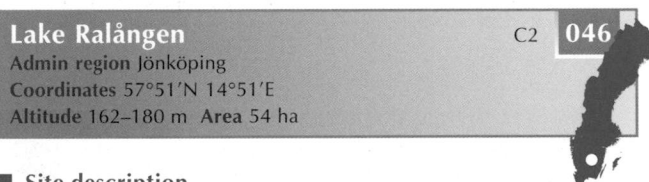

■ Site description

Habitats Grassland (5%; humid grassland), Marine areas (80%; sea inlet/coastal features), Rocky areas (5%; sea cliff/rocky shore), Artificial landscape (10%; highly improved reseeded grassland; arable land)
Land-use Hunting (100%), Nature conservation/research (40%), Tourism/recreation, Water management

■ Birds

Species	Season	Year	Pop min	Pop max	Acc	Criteria
Cygnus olor Mute Swan	P	1997	1,000	2,000	B	B1i, C3
Bucephala clangula Goldeneye	P	1997	4,000	5,000	B	A4i, B1i, C3
Mergus serrator Red-breasted Merganser	P	1997	4,000	5,000	B	A4i, B1i, C3

The IBA is important as a stop-over site for passage waterbirds.

■ Protection status
National Low **International** Low
IBA overlaps with two Nature Reserves (totalling 139 ha). IBA overlaps with two Special Protection Areas (totalling 138 ha).

■ Conservation issues

Threats Disturbance to birds (U), Recreation/tourism (U)

Lake Ralången C2 046
Admin region Jönköping
Coordinates 57°51′N 14°51′E
Altitude 162–180 m Area 54 ha

■ Site description
A shallow, nutrient-rich lake situated in an intensively managed agricultural landscape.

Habitats Forest and woodland (20%; mixed forest; alluvial/very wet forest), Grassland (20%; humid grassland), Wetland (50%; standing fresh water; river/stream; water-fringe vegetation), Artificial landscape (10%; highly improved reseeded grassland; arable land)
Land-use Agriculture (10%), Forestry (20%), Hunting (60%), Nature conservation/research (20%), Not utilized (30%), Tourism/recreation (5%)

■ Birds

Species	Season	Year	Pop min	Pop max	Acc	Criteria
Cygnus cygnus Whooper Swan	P	1996	60	220	A	C2

This is an important site for passage waterbirds. Species of global conservation concern that do not meet IBA criteria: *Haliaeetus albicilla* (1–2 wintering birds) and *Crex crex* (4 non-breeding birds).

■ Protection status
National None **International** None

■ Conservation issues

Threats Afforestation (C), Agricultural intensification/expansion (C), Aquaculture/fisheries (C), Construction/impact of dyke/dam/barrage (B)

Lake Kävsjön and Store Mosse B1i, C7 047
Admin region Jönköping
Coordinates 57°18′N 13°57′E
Altitude 170–170 m Area 7,450 ha

■ Site description
A freshwater lake and the largest bog in Sweden south of Lapland.

Kävsjön was formerly much larger but drainage in the 19th century reduced its size considerably. This led, however, to the creation of important damp grasslands on the reclaimed land and these areas are now being managed for birds, after a period of neglect. Store Mosse comprises fen and raised bog habitats with scattered sandy ridges (covered by *Pinus*) and sand/gravel/rock moraines. The only land-uses are grazing and conservation activities.

Habitats Grassland (humid grassland), Wetland (standing fresh water; raised bog)
Land-use Agriculture, Nature conservation/research

■ Birds
An important site for large spring passage numbers of *Cygnus cygnus*, *Anser fabalis* and *Grus grus*. Three species listed on Annex I of the EC Birds Directive also breed: *Porzana porzana*, *Grus grus* and *Asio flammeus*. Species of global conservation concern that do not meet IBA criteria: *Haliaeetus albicilla* (non-breeding).

■ Protection status
National High **International** High
IBA overlaps with National Park (7,850 ha). 7,450 ha of IBA covered by Ramsar Site (Store Mosse and Kävsjön, 7,580 ha). IBA overlaps with Special Protection Area.

■ Conservation issues

Threats Abandonment/reduction of land management (U)

The only reported problem is that of scrub invasion in some areas.

Lake Solgen A1, A4i, B1i, B3, C1, C2 048
Admin region Jönköping
Coordinates 57°34′N 15°05′E
Altitude 193–240 m Area 4,000 ha

■ Site description

Habitats Forest and woodland (25%; broadleaved deciduous forest; native coniferous forest; mixed forest), Scrub (5%; scrub), Grassland (5%; dry siliceous grassland), Wetland (65%; mudflat/sandflat; standing fresh water; water-fringe vegetation), Rocky areas (5%; sea cliff/rocky shore), Artificial landscape (5%; highly improved reseeded grassland; arable land)
Land-use Agriculture (10%), Forestry (40%), Hunting (100%), Tourism/recreation (25%)

■ Birds

Species	Season	Year	Pop min	Pop max	Acc	Criteria
Cygnus cygnus Whooper Swan	W	1996	500	1,200	B	A4i, B1i, B3, C2
[1] **Haliaeetus albicilla** White-tailed Eagle	P	1996	6	20	A	A1, C1

1. Large increase.

This is an important site for wetland species, including several raptors.

■ Protection status
National None **International** None

■ Conservation issues

Threats Abandonment/reduction of land management (U), Afforestation (U), Deforestation (commercial) (U), Disturbance to birds (A), Recreation/tourism (A)

Karlsö islands B1ii, B3, C3 049
Admin region Gotland
Coordinates 57°17′N 18°01′E
Altitude 0–40 m Area 4,570 ha

■ Site description
Two islands with cliffs situated off south-west Gotland. The tops of the islands are flat and support *Juniperus* and a few copses. Sheep-grazing is the only land-use.

Habitats Scrub, Rocky areas (sea cliff/rocky shore)

Land-use Agriculture, Tourism/recreation

■ Birds

Species		Season	Year	Pop min	Pop max	Acc	Criteria
Uria aalge	Guillemot	B	1980	8,000	9,000	—	B1ii, C3
Alca torda	Razorbill	B	1997	—	4,000	—	B1ii, B3, C3

The IBA supports large numbers of breeding seabirds, including c.75% of the Baltic breeding population of *Uria aalge*. Numbers of *Alca torda* have increased by 50% over the last decade.

■ Protection status
National Partial **International** Partial
IBA overlaps with Nature Reserve (Lille Karlsö, 926 ha). IBA overlaps with Nature Reserve (Stora Karlsö, 1,426 ha). IBA overlaps with Special Protection Area (2,100 ha).

■ Conservation issues
No serious threats are known at the site. Auks are counted regularly. Guided tours/information are provided for visitors.

Coastal areas around Gotland island
A4i, B1i, B2, B3, C2, C3, C6 **050**
Admin region Gotland
Coordinates 57°24′N 18°42′E
Altitude 0–20 m **Area** 4,100 ha

■ Site description
The site comprises four main areas: Faludden (57°00′N 18°22′E—1,810 ha), Grötlingboholme (57°07′N 18°30′E—1,050 ha), Lausholmar (57°18′N 18°45′E—540 ha) and Skenholmen (57°48′N 19°03′E—700 ha). All four are situated on the eastern coast of Gotland and consist of very low-lying peninsulas and/or islands with a gravel-covered limestone foundation. Essentially treeless and covered mainly by short grassy vegetation used for grazing livestock. Lausholmar is used for military target practice outside of the breeding season.

Habitats Grassland, Wetland (shingle/stony beach)
Land-use Agriculture, Military

■ Birds

Species		Season	Year	Pop min	Pop max	Acc	Criteria
Cygnus columbianus	Bewick's Swan	P	—	—	1,000	—	A4i, B1i, C2
Branta leucopsis	Barnacle Goose	B	—	2,600	—	—	A4i, B1i, C2
Branta leucopsis	Barnacle Goose	P	—	60,000	—	—	A4i, B1i, C2
Somateria mollissima	Eider	B	—	—	10,000	—	A4i, B1i, C3
Recurvirostra avosetta	Avocet	B	—	—	450	—	A4i, B1i, B3, C2, C6
Charadrius hiaticula	Ringed Plover	B	—	—	1,000	—	A4i, B1i, C3
Arenaria interpres	Turnstone	B	—	—	500	—	A4i, B1i, C3
Sterna caspia	Caspian Tern	B	—	20	—	—	B1i, B2, C2, C6
Sterna albifrons	Little Tern	B	—	—	250	—	B1i, B2, C6

Parts of the IBA are rich in breeding species; other areas are important as wintering grounds for *Clangula hyemalis*. The IBA as a whole supports large numbers of migrating swans and geese, and Grötlingboholme is the most important Baltic moulting ground for *Anser anser*.

■ Protection status
National Partial **International** High
IBA overlaps with Bird Sanctuary (Furilden, 280 ha). IBA overlaps with Bird Sanctuary (Norsholmen, 115 ha). IBA overlaps with Bird Sanctuary (Ugnen, 280 ha). IBA overlaps with Bird Sanctuary (Vastergarus utholme, 52 ha). IBA overlaps with Nature Reserve (Grotlingboholme, 285 ha). IBA overlaps with Nature Reserve (Lans holmar, 580 ha). IBA overlaps with Nature Reserve (Rone Ytterholme, 228 ha). 4,100 ha of IBA covered by Ramsar Site (Gotland, east coast, 4,220 ha). IBA overlaps with Special Protection Area.

■ Conservation issues

Threats Other (U)

Oil pollution ('Other' threat) is a regular occurrence (c.500 incidents in the Baltic Sea annually). The entire coastal area was surveyed during 1996 for its breeding birds.

Båtafjorden Fjord
B3, C6 **051**
Admin region Halland
Coordinates 57°15′N 12°10′E
Altitude 0–1 m **Area** 200 ha

■ Site description
A small bay in Kattegatt with adjoining wet meadows. Human activities include livestock-grazing.

Habitats Grassland (75%; mesophile grassland), Marine areas (25%; sea inlet/coastal features)
Land-use Agriculture (75%)

■ Birds

Species		Season	Year	Pop min	Pop max	Acc	Criteria
Recurvirostra avosetta	Avocet	B	1997	10	15	A	B3, C6

The site is important for both breeding and passage waders. Passage species of global conservation concern that do not meet IBA criteria: *Gallinago media* (2–5 birds).

■ Protection status
National None **International** None

■ Conservation issues

Threats Consequences of animal/plant introductions (C)

American mink *Mustela vison* pose a threat to breeding birds.

Getterön
B1i, B3, C2, C3, C6 **052**
Admin region Halland
Coordinates 57°07′N 12°13′E
Altitude 0–10 m **Area** 355 ha

■ Site description
Originally an island, the site has been joined to the mainland by an artificial embankment and roadway, a process that resulted in the partial enclosure and desalinization of Farehammarsviken Bay (the main part of the reserve). The bay is shallow and brackish with a freshwater inflow. It contains areas of marshy vegetation and is surrounded by grazed coastal meadows. In addition to agricultural activities, the IBA supports a bird observatory.

Habitats Grassland (52%; humid grassland), Wetland (40%; standing fresh water; water-fringe vegetation), Artificial landscape (8%; arable land)
Land-use Agriculture (55%), Nature conservation/research, Not utilized (45%), Tourism/recreation

■ Birds

Species		Season	Year	Pop min	Pop max	Acc	Criteria
Cygnus cygnus	Whooper Swan	P	—	150	200	—	C2
Anas crecca	Teal	B	1996	2,600	—	A	B1i, C3
¹ *Recurvirostra avosetta*	Avocet	B	1996	58	—	A	B3, C6

1. Large increase.

Goose grazing is important in maintaining the open landscape. Species of global conservation concern that do not meet IBA criteria: *Haliaeetus albicilla* (wintering) and *Crex crex* (passage). Three hundred and twenty species have been recorded at the site.

■ Protection status
National High **International** High
IBA overlaps with Nature Reserve (Getteron, 360 ha). 340 ha of IBA covered by Ramsar Site (Getterön, 340 ha). IBA overlaps with Special Protection Area (344 ha).

■ Conservation issues

Threats Recreation/tourism (B)

Lake Åsnen — A1, A4i, B1i, B2, C1, C3, C6 — 053

Admin region Kronoberg
Coordinates 56°40'N 14°42'E
Altitude 160–160 m **Area** 13,500 ha

■ Site description

A large, nutrient-poor lake with many small bays, peninsulas and islands, surrounded by mainly coniferous forest (especially *Picea*). There is some deciduous woodland, particularly on the islands, which is important due to its great age. Wetland habitats are found all around the lake and include grazed wet meadows. Human activities include grazing, regulation of the lake water-level and boating.

Habitats Forest and woodland (broadleaved deciduous forest; native coniferous forest), Grassland (mesophile grassland), Wetland (standing fresh water)

Land-use Agriculture, Forestry, Tourism/recreation, Water management

■ Birds

Species	Season	Year	Pop min	Pop max	Acc	Criteria
[1] *Anser fabalis* Bean Goose	P	—	—	8,000	—	A4i, B1i, C3
Mergus merganser Goosander	P	—	—	10,000	—	A4i, B1i, C3
[2] *Haliaeetus albicilla* White-tailed Eagle	P	—	20	—	—	A1, C1
Pandion haliaetus Osprey	B	1993	—	50	—	B2, C6

1. Spring passage.
2. Autumn passage; also winters.

The IBA supports a rich and diverse breeding bird fauna (waterbirds, raptors, waders and forest species), and is a stop-over site during both spring and autumn migration for wildfowl and raptors. Species of global conservation concern that do not meet IBA criteria: *Crex crex* (breeding).

■ Protection status

National Partial **International** High
260 ha of IBA covered by Nature Reserve (Agnas, 260 ha). 149 ha of IBA covered by Nature Reserve (Bjurkarr, 149 ha). 368 ha of IBA covered by Nature Reserve (Gryto, 368 ha). 60 ha of IBA covered by Nature Reserve (Lango, 60 ha). 157 ha of IBA covered by Nature Reserve (Toftasa Myr, 157 ha). 1,500 ha of IBA covered by Nature Reserve (Utnasuddens Ovarld, 1,500 ha). 1,224 ha of IBA covered by Nature Reserve (Vastra Asnens Ovarld, 1,224 ha). 13,500 ha of IBA covered by Ramsar Site (Åsnen, 16,800 ha). IBA overlaps with Special Protection Area.

■ Conservation issues

Threats Abandonment/reduction of land management (U), Consequences of animal/plant introductions (U)

Meadows have become overgrown, although some of the older examples have now been restored. American mink *Mustela vison* cause problems for breeding birds and canoeists create disturbance. Twenty Bird Sanctuaries have been designated as part of an ongoing initiative, ranging from 2.1–97 ha in size (621 ha in total)—most are situated within Nature Reserves.

Coastal areas around Öland island — A1, A4i, B1i, B2, B3, C1, C2, C3, C6 — 054

Admin region Kalmar
Coordinates 56°40'N 16°45'E
Altitude 0–5 m **Area** 10,190 ha

■ Site description

Öland is a long, narrow island close to the south-east coast of mainland Sweden. These three distinct sites are located on the low-lying east coast of Öland along a major migration route for birds moving to/from north-east Scandinavia and north-west Russia. The main habitat consists of grazed coastal meadows with marshy areas and scrub. The shores comprise sand beaches or low chalk cliffs and the shallow offshore waters contain many sandbanks. Apart from grazing, arable farming is the only significant land-use.

Habitats Scrub, Grassland, Wetland (sand-dunes/sand beach), Rocky areas (sea cliff/rocky shore)
Land-use Agriculture

■ Birds

Species	Season	Year	Pop min	Pop max	Acc	Criteria
[1] *Branta leucopsis* Barnacle Goose	B	1997	400	500	—	C2
Branta leucopsis Barnacle Goose	P	1997	4,000	6,000	—	A4i, B1i, C2
[2] *Haliaeetus albicilla* White-tailed Eagle	B	1997	4	5	—	A1, B2, C1, C6
Recurvirostra avosetta Avocet	B	1988	250	300	—	A4i, B1i, B3, C2, C6
Tringa totanus Redshank	B	1988	—	800	—	B1i, B2, C3
[1] *Sterna caspia* Caspian Tern	B	1996	20	—	—	B1i, B2, C2, C6
Sterna albifrons Little Tern	B	1988	—	50	—	B2, C6

1. Increasing.
2. Increasing. Also winters.

The coastal meadows support a rich breeding bird fauna, and are used by thousands of wildfowl and waders as a stop-over site whilst on passage. The passerine migration is also of great importance.

■ Protection status

National Low **International** Partial
310 ha of IBA covered by Bird Sanctuary (Sodviken, 310 ha). 130 ha of IBA covered by Bird Santuary (Stora Oren, 130 ha). 8,460 ha of IBA covered by Ramsar Site (Öland, eastern coastal areas, 8,460 ha). IBA overlaps with Special Protection Area.

■ Conservation issues

Threats Abandonment/reduction of land management (U)

The number of grazing animals (mainly cows) is decreasing, and as a result vegetation succession is causing the grasslands to become less important for birds. The local government supports grazing in selected areas of high importance. All coastal meadows were mapped during the 1988 and 1998 breeding seasons, with preliminary results showing decreases in numbers of *Limosa limosa*, *Tringa totanus* and other breeding waders. Migrating birds are counted during the autumn.

Ottenby — A4i, B1i, C2, C3 — 055

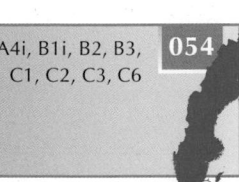

Admin region Kalmar
Coordinates 56°12'N 16°24'E
Altitude 0–2 m **Area** 1,610 ha

■ Site description

This site forms the southernmost tip of the island of Öland and consists of deciduous woodland with *Betula*, *Quercus*, and *Populus tremula*, open grazing-land, scrub, sand/pebble beaches, sandbanks and small bays. There are also extensive shallows and seaweed-covered beaches. The dominant human activity is cattle-raising.

Habitats Forest and woodland (broadleaved deciduous forest), Scrub, Grassland, Wetland (sand-dunes/sand beach; shingle/stony beach; coastal lagoon)
Land-use Agriculture, Nature conservation/research

■ Birds

Species	Season	Year	Pop min	Pop max	Acc	Criteria
[1] *Branta leucopsis* Barnacle Goose	P	—	20,000	60,000	—	A4i, B1i, C2
[2] *Branta bernicla* Brent Goose	P	—	50,000	65,000	—	A4i, B1i, C3

1. Larger numbers occur on autumn passage.
2. Totals vary from year to year. Larger numbers occur on spring passage.

The IBA supports a rich breeding bird fauna, and attracts large numbers of migrating waterbirds, cranes, raptors and passerines.

■ Protection status

National High **International** High
1,610 ha of IBA covered by Nature Reserve (Ottenby, 1,610 ha). 1,610 ha of IBA covered by Ramsar Site (Ottenby, 1,610 ha). IBA overlaps with Special Protection Area.

■ Conservation issues

No serious threats are known at the site. Ottenby Bird Observatory manages the Nature Reserve with the help of EU funding—wet meadows are managed for waders. The observatory (owned by SOF) also monitors breeding birds (e.g. *Crex crex*) and carries out research into bird migration. Some 200,000 people visit every year; a new visitor's centre opened in 1997.

Kullaberg   B1ii, B3, C3, C6   056

Admin region Skåne
Coordinates 56°18'N 12°28'E
Altitude 0–188 m   **Area** 7,500 ha

■ Site description

A high rocky outcrop that points in the direction of the Kattegatt.

Habitats Forest and woodland (15%; broadleaved deciduous forest; native coniferous forest), Wetland (5%; standing fresh water), Marine areas (60%; open sea), Artificial landscape (30%; highly improved reseeded grassland; arable land; forestry plantation)
Land-use Agriculture (25%), Fisheries/aquaculture (50%), Forestry (10%), Nature conservation/research (20%)

■ Birds

Species	Season	Year	Pop min	Pop max	Acc	Criteria
[1] *Milvus milvus* Red Kite	B	1996	1	2	A	B3, C6
Uria aalge Guillemot	W	1996	50	500	C	B1ii, C3
Lanius collurio Red-backed Shrike	B	1996	20	30	B	C6

1. Large increase.

This is an important site for wintering and passage seabirds and seaduck, including *Somateria mollissima*, *Melanitta nigra*, *Melanitta fusca*, *Bucephala clangula* and *Cepphus grylle*.

■ Protection status

National Partial **International** Partial
IBA overlaps with two Nature Reserves (totalling 1,276 ha). IBA overlaps with Special Protection Area (1,276 ha).

■ Conservation issues

Threats Abandonment/reduction of land management (U), Consequences of animal/plant introductions (U), Intensified forest management (U)

American mink *Mustela vison* pose a threat to breeding birds.

Bay of Skälderviken   A4iii, B1i, B1ii, B1iv, B2, B3, C3, C4, C5, C6   057

Admin region Skåne
Coordinates 56°13'N 12°45'E
Altitude 0–5 m   **Area** 5,500 ha

■ Site description

A bay of the Kattegatt with a varied shoreline, comprising cliffs, sand beaches and wet meadows. Several shallow water areas in the bay itself provide feeding opportunities for wintering and passage seabirds.

Habitats Grassland (30%; humid grassland), Wetland (sand-dunes/sand beach), Marine areas (10%; open sea), Rocky areas (sea cliff/rocky shore), Artificial landscape (60%; highly improved reseeded grassland; arable land; urban parks/gardens)
Land-use Agriculture (85%), Not utilized (10%), Urban/industrial/transport (5%)

■ Birds

Species	Season	Year	Pop min	Pop max	Acc	Criteria
Phalacrocorax carbo Cormorant	P	1996	500	2,000	B	B1i, C3
[1] *Milvus milvus* Red Kite	B	1996	1	3	A	B3, C6
Recurvirostra avosetta Avocet	B	1996	15	35	A	B3, C6
Sterna albifrons Little Tern	B	1996	10	25	B	B2, C6
Uria aalge Guillemot	W	1996	100	1,000	C	B1ii, C3
Alca torda Razorbill	W	1996	50	500	C	B1ii, C3

1. Large increase.

Important for wintering seaducks and seabirds, the site is also a major migratory bottleneck site, where more than 5,000 raptors regularly pass in autumn (mainly *Pernis apivorus* and *Buteo buteo*). Wintering species of global conservation concern that do not meet IBA criteria: *Haliaeetus albicilla* (1–3 birds). More than 140 breeding species have been recorded.

■ Protection status

National Partial **International** Partial
IBA overlaps with Bird Sanctuary and Nature Reserve. IBA overlaps with Special Protection Area (280 ha).

■ Conservation issues

Threats Abandonment/reduction of land management (U), Agricultural intensification/expansion (U), Aquaculture/fisheries (U), Consequences of animal/plant introductions (U)

Nutrient-rich run-off enters the bay via streams that drain one of Sweden's most intensively farmed agricultural areas. American mink *Mustela vison* pose a threat to breeding birds. Development of the shoreline may become a problem in the future. A Ramsar Site (1,320 ha) is likely to be designated in the near future.

North-east Scania coastline and archipelago   A1, A4i, B1i, B2, B3, C1, C2, C3, C6   058

Admin region Skåne
Coordinates 56°04'N 14°38'E
Altitude 0–15 m   **Area** 10,914 ha

■ Site description

Habitats Forest and woodland (15%; native coniferous forest; mixed forest), Scrub (10%; scrub; heathland), Grassland (10%; humid grassland; mesophile grassland), Wetland (25%; fen/transition mire/spring), Marine areas (20%; sea inlet/coastal features), Rocky areas (5%; scree/boulders), Artificial landscape (20%; highly improved reseeded grassland; arable land; forestry plantation)
Land-use Agriculture (40%), Forestry (10%), Hunting (5%), Military (15%), Not utilized (30%), Tourism/recreation (5%)

■ Birds

Species	Season	Year	Pop min	Pop max	Acc	Criteria
Anser fabalis Bean Goose	W	1996	3,000	8,000	A	A4i, B1i, C3
Milvus milvus Red Kite	R	1996	5	6	B	B3, C6
Haliaeetus albicilla White-tailed Eagle	W	1996	10	20	A	A1, C1
[1] *Recurvirostra avosetta* Avocet	B	1996	12	15	A	B3, C6
Larus argentatus Herring Gull	B	1996	4,000	4,800	A	B1i
Larus marinus Great Black-backed Gull	B	1996	90	100	A	B3
Sterna caspia Caspian Tern	B	1996	15	17	A	B1i, B2, C2, C6
[1] *Sterna albifrons* Little Tern	B	1996	30	33	A	B2, C6
Lullula arborea Woodlark	B	1996	25	40	B	C6

1. Large increase.

This is an important site for breeding gulls, wintering raptors and passage wildfowl.

■ Protection status

National Low **International** Low
IBA overlaps with Bird Sanctuary (80 ha). IBA overlaps with Nature Reserve (50 ha). IBA overlaps with Special Protection Area (1,011 ha).

■ Conservation issues

Threats Abandonment/reduction of land management (U), Agricultural intensification/expansion (U), Other (U)

Undergrazing is a problem, and the shoreline is subject to frequent oil spills from ships ('Other' threat).

Bay of Lundåkrabukten   B1i, C2, C3   059

Admin region Skåne
Coordinates 55°52'N 12°50'E
Altitude 0–10 m   **Area** 20,000 ha

■ Site description

A shallow bay in the straits of Öresund, situated 20–30 km to the north of a new bridge linking Sweden and Denmark. The beaches are of sand and clay; grazed meadows are also present.

Habitats Grassland (10%; steppe/dry calcareous grassland; dry siliceous grassland), Wetland (25%; mudflat/sandflat; sand-dunes/sand beach; water-fringe vegetation), Marine areas (70%; open sea)
Land-use Nature conservation/research (5%), Not utilized (85%), Tourism/recreation (5%), Urban/industrial/transport (5%)

■ Birds

Species	Season	Year	Pop min	Pop max	Acc	Criteria
Anser fabalis Bean Goose	P	1996	800	1,200	C	B1i, C3
Pluvialis apricaria Golden Plover	P	1996	8,000	10,000	A	B1i, C2
Calidris alpina Dunlin	P	1996	800	1,000	B	B1i, C3

This is important as a stop-over site for passage wildfowl and waders, as well as for wintering wildfowl (for example, *Anas penelope*, *Aythya fuligula* and *Bucephala clangula*).

■ Protection status
National Low **International** None
IBA overlaps with Nature Reserve (218 ha).

■ Conservation issues

Threats Abandonment/reduction of land management (U), Disturbance to birds (A), Recreation/tourism (A)

Undergrazing is a problem. A Ramsar Site (1,960 ha) is likely to be designated in the near future.

Bay of Lommabukten B1i, B2, B3, C2, C3, C6 060
Admin region Skåne
Coordinates 55°44′N 12°59′E
Altitude 0–5 m **Area** 30,000 ha

■ Site description
A shallow bay in the straits of Öresund, situated to the north of a new bridge linking Sweden and Denmark. The beaches are of sand and clay.

Habitats Grassland (15%; steppe/dry calcareous grassland; humid grassland), Wetland (40%; mudflat/sandflat; sand-dunes/sand beach; water-fringe vegetation), Marine areas (35%; open sea), Artificial landscape (20%; highly improved reseeded grassland; arable land; urban parks/gardens)
Land-use Agriculture (5%), Nature conservation/research (5%), Not utilized (70%), Tourism/recreation (10%), Urban/industrial/transport (20%)

■ Birds

Species	Season	Year	Pop min	Pop max	Acc	Criteria
Phalacrocorax carbo Cormorant	P	1996	1,000	2,000	B	B1i, C3
Cygnus cygnus Whooper Swan	W	1996	—	224	B	B3, C2
Anser fabalis Bean Goose	W	1996	—	1,642	B	B1i, C3
Recurvirostra avosetta Avocet	B	1996	20	40	A	B3, C6
Pluvialis apricaria Golden Plover	P	1996	5,000	10,000	B	B1i, C2
Larus argentatus Herring Gull	W	1996	10,000	15,000	A	B1i
Sterna albifrons Little Tern	B	1996	—	5	A	B2, C6

This is an important site for wintering wildfowl, breeding and passage waders, and both wintering and passage gulls.

■ Protection status
National Partial **International** Partial
IBA overlaps with Nature Reserve. IBA overlaps with Special Protection Area.

■ Conservation issues

Threats Abandonment/reduction of land management (U), Industrialization/urbanization (U), Infrastructure (U), Other (U), Recreation/tourism (B)

Polluting discharges from shipping lanes ('Other' threat) and development of the shoreline pose the greatest threats to the site. The region as a whole is currently undergoing economic expansion.

Falsterbo–Bay of Foteviken A4i, A4iv, B1i, B1iv, 061
Admin region Skåne B2, B3, C2, C3, C5, C6
Coordinates 55°25′N 12°55′E
Altitude 0–6 m **Area** 20,000 ha

■ Site description
An area of shallow coastal waters comprising lagoons, sandbanks and beaches. Also included are coastal grasslands, marshland, heather *Calluna* moorland, wet heaths and some cultivated land. Ten percent of the area at the lower end of Falsterbo is a golf course.

Habitats Forest and woodland (5%; mixed forest), Scrub (5%; heathland), Grassland (10%; mesophile grassland), Wetland (20%; sand-dunes/sand beach; coastal lagoon; water-fringe vegetation), Marine areas (25%; open sea), Artificial landscape (35%; arable land; urban parks/gardens; ruderal land)
Land-use Agriculture (5%), Nature conservation/research (30%), Not utilized (25%), Tourism/recreation (25%), Urban/industrial/transport (10%)

■ Birds

Species	Season	Year	Pop min	Pop max	Acc	Criteria
Anser anser Greylag Goose	B	1996	100	900	A	B1i, C3
Branta bernicla Brent Goose	P	1996	1,500	42,000	A	A4i, B1i, C3
Anas clypeata Shoveler	P	1996	100	800	A	B1i, C3
Grus grus Crane	P	1996	—	760	A	B1i, C2
Recurvirostra avosetta Avocet	B	1996	170	300	A	A4i, B1i, B3, C2, C6
[1] *Calidris alpina* Dunlin	B	1996	60	122	A	B1i, C3
Calidris alpina Dunlin	P	1996	100	6,000	A	B1i, C3
Sterna albifrons Little Tern	B	1996	25	44	A	B2, C6

1. *C. alpina schinzii.*

The IBA is a major migratory bottleneck site, where more than 20,000 raptors regularly pass in spring and autumn (mainly *Pernis apivorus*, *Accipiter nisus* and *Buteo buteo*). Large numbers of passerines also pass through, with 1,100,000 *Fringilla coelebs* and *Fringilla montifringilla* having been recorded on a single October morning. The area is also important for wintering wildfowl. A total of 340 species have been recorded, with yearly totals exceeding 200 species.

■ Protection status
National Partial **International** Partial
IBA overlaps with seven Nature Reserves (totalling c.42,600 ha). 7,450 ha of IBA covered by Ramsar Site (Falsterbo–Foteviken, 7,450 ha). IBA overlaps with Special Protection Area (13,640 ha).

■ Conservation issues

Threats Abandonment/reduction of land management (U)

River Klingavälsån– Lake Krankesjön B1i, C2 062
Admin region Skåne
Coordinates 55°37′N 13°37′E
Altitude 20–20 m **Area** 3,975 ha

■ Site description
The area contains shallow eutrophic lakes, meandering streams, reedbeds (*Phragmites*), riverside meadows (flooded annually), marshland, *Alnus* forest and *Salix* thickets. Large parts of the site are used to graze cattle and for haymaking. Human activities also include fishing, bathing and military exercises.

Habitats Forest and woodland, Grassland (mesophile grassland), Wetland (standing fresh water; river/stream; water-fringe vegetation)
Land-use Agriculture, Military, Tourism/recreation

■ Birds

Species	Season	Year	Pop min	Pop max	Acc	Criteria
Cygnus cygnus Whooper Swan	P	—	150	400	—	B1i, C2

The site is important as a stop-over site for passage swans, geese and ducks, and also supports a diversity of breeding waterbirds, as well as wintering *Anser fabalis* and five species of raptor. Species of global conservation concern that do not meet IBA criteria: *Haliaeetus albicilla* (wintering) and *Crex crex* (breeding and passage).

■ Protection status
National Partial **International** High
IBA covered by two Nature Reserves (totalling 2,321 ha). 3,975 ha of IBA covered by Ramsar Site (Klingavälsån–Krankesjön, 3,975 ha). IBA overlaps with Special Protection Area (2,900 ha).

■ Conservation issues

Threats Abandonment/reduction of land management (U), Drainage (U)

Drainage has impoverished the fauna and flora of some of the meadowland. A reduction in grazing intensity has had an adverse effect on wader numbers.

River Helgeån A4i, B1i, B2, C2, C3, C6 063

Admin region Skåne
Coordinates 56°01′N 14°09′E
Altitude 0–10 m **Area** 5,300 ha

■ Site description

The IBA covers the plains situated along the final 35 km of the River Helgeån before it enters the Baltic Sea, and incorporates two lakes (Araslövsjön and Hammarsjön). The river meadows are interspersed with grazed areas, bushes, reedbeds (*Phragmites*) and wet woodlands. Intensively managed agricultural land surrounds the IBA.

Habitats Forest and woodland (mixed forest; alluvial/very wet forest), Grassland (humid grassland), Wetland (standing fresh water; river/stream; water-fringe vegetation)
Land-use Agriculture, Nature conservation/research

■ Birds

Species	Season	Year	Pop min	Pop max	Acc	Criteria
Botaurus stellaris Bittern	B	1996	—	10	—	B2, C6
[1] *Cygnus cygnus* Whooper Swan	P	—	—	800	—	A4i, B1i, C2
Anser fabalis Bean Goose	W	1996	—	5,000	—	A4i, B1i, C3
Anser fabalis Bean Goose	P	—	—	15,000	—	A4i, B1i, C3

Species … continued	Season	Year	Pop min	Pop max	Acc	Criteria
Circus aeruginosus Marsh Harrier	B	1996	—	20	—	C6

1. Spring passage; also overwinters.

The site is important for breeding species of wet grassland and other riverine habitats. Species of global conservation concern that do not meet IBA criteria: *Haliaeetus albicilla* (wintering) and *Crex crex* (breeding).

■ Protection status

National Low **International** High
IBA overlaps with two Nature Reserves (totalling 283 ha). IBA overlaps with Private Reserve (80 ha). 5,300 ha of IBA covered by Ramsar Site (Helgeån, 5,500 ha). IBA overlaps with eight Special Protection Areas (totalling 2,062 ha).

■ Conservation issues

Threats Abandonment/reduction of land management (U), Agricultural intensification/expansion (U), Drainage (U), Filling-in of wetlands (U)

Threats include the effects of reductions in grazing intensity and nutrient-rich agricultural run-off. Reedbeds and sedge-beds are expanding rapidly, encroaching into areas of open water. Drainage and the filling-in of wet areas are additional threats. Government, local authorities and NGOs are working together to secure the site's future, and nature tourism is being promoted. The maintenance of grazing and mowing is a conservation priority. Only 5% of the Ramsar Site was protected by 1997. Census work and ringing are undertaken at the Nedre Helgeåns field station.

REFERENCES

AHLÉN, I. AND TJERNBERG, M., EDS. (1996) *Rödlistade ryggradsdjur i Sverige—Artfakta* [*Swedish Red Data Book of vertebrates 1996*]. Uppsala, Sweden: ArtDatabanken, SLU. (In Swedish.)

ANON. (1989) *Nationalparksplan för Sverige*. Solna, Sweden: Naturvårdsverket. (In Swedish with English summary.)

ANON. (1997) *Skyddad natur*. Stockholm: Naturvårdsverket (Rapport 4738). (In Swedish with English summary.)

GRIMMETT, R. F. A. AND JONES, T. A. (1989) *Important Bird Areas in Europe*. Cambridge, UK: International Council for Bird Preservation (Techn. Publ. 9).

HEATH, M. F. AND BORGGREVE, C. (2000) *BirdLife International/EBCC European Bird Database 1998*. Cambridge, UK: BirdLife International.

OTTOSSON, U., JOHANSSON, K. AND PETTERSSON, J. (1989) Hackfagel-bestanden av and-och masfaglar samt vadare pa Olands strandangar [Breeding ducks, geese, gulls, terns and waders on coastal meadows on Oland]. *Calidris* 18: 47–87. (In Swedish.)

TUCKER, G. M. AND HEATH, M. F. (1994) *Birds in Europe: their conservation status*. Cambridge, UK: BirdLife International (BirdLife Conservation Series no. 3).

SWITZERLAND

Lorenz Heer, Verena Keller, Werner Müller and Hans Schmid

Augstmatthorn (IBA 018). (photo: Lorenz Heer/[SVS/BirdLife Switzerland])

GENERAL INTRODUCTION

Switzerland is a small land-locked country in central Europe surrounded by Germany in the north, Austria and Liechtenstein in the east, Italy in the south and France in the west. Thirty-one sites are identified as Important Bird Areas (IBAs), covering 13% or 5,474 km² of the total surface area of 41,293 km². The previous pan-European inventory identified 13 IBAs (Grimmett and Jones 1989). Twenty new sites have been added, mainly in montane areas (Table 1). Part of one site, former site CH006, has been dropped, whilst the Pointes de Marin area of this site has been incorporated into current site 011.

Topographically, the country can be separated into three main regions. The Jura mountains form the north-western border of Switzerland and occupy approximately 10% of the country's land area. The region is characterized by limestone mountains reaching a maximum altitude of 1,677 m. It contains three IBAs (001, 002, 003). The Alps (up to 4,634 m) cross southern Switzerland from west to east, and occupy about 60% of the country's area. There are five IBAs in the northern Alps (016, 017, 018, 019, 020), five in the central Alps (021, 022, 023, 024, 025) and six in the southern Alps (026, 027, 028, 029, 030, 031). These two mountain chains enclose the Central Plateau, which is typified by glacial sediments, large lakes, river systems, several parts of which are IBAs (006,

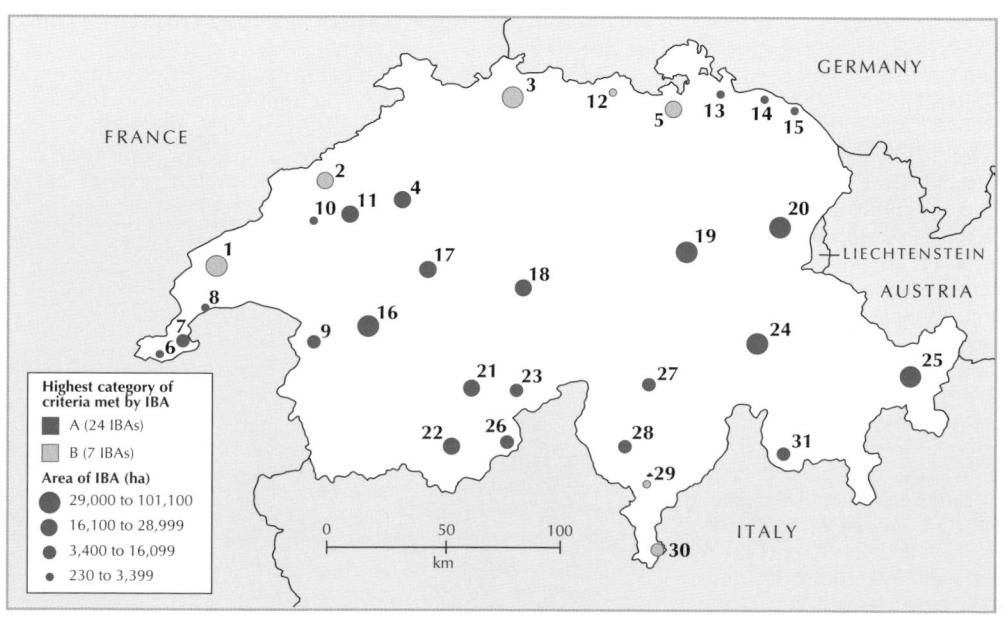

Map 1. Location, area and criteria category of Important Bird Areas in Switzerland.

Highest category of criteria met by IBA
■ A (24 IBAs)
■ B (7 IBAs)

Area of IBA (ha)
● 29,000 to 101,100
● 16,100 to 28,999
● 3,400 to 16,099
● 230 to 3,399

699

Table 1. Summary of Important Bird Areas in Switzerland.   31 IBAs covering 5,474 km²

IBA code	1989 code	International name	National name	Administrative region	Area (ha)	Criteria (see p. 11)
001	—	Mont Tendre	Mont Tendre	Vaud	31,000	B2, B3
002	—	La Brévine and Les Ponts-de-Martel	La Brévine et Les Ponts-de-Martel	Neuchâtel	23,200	B2, B3
003	—	Jura mountains of Baselland/Solothurn	Tafeljura-Landschaft Baselland/Solothurn	Aargau, Basel-Stadt, Basel-Landschaft, Solothurn	35,000	B2, B3
004	—	'Grosses Moos' plain and Niederried reservoir	Grosses Moos und Stausee Niederried	Bern, Fribourg	16,100	A4i, B1i, B2, B3
005	—	Lowlands of Zurich and lower valley of the River Thur	Zürcher Unterland und unteres Thurtal	Schaffhausen, Thurgau, Zürich	22,700	B2, B3
006	CH012	River Rhône: Geneva–Verbois reservoir	Rhône: Genève–Barrage de Verbois	Genève	1,100	A4i, B1i
007	CH011	Lake Geneva: Versoix and Hermance–Geneva	Lac Léman: Versoix–Hermance–Genève	Genève	3,400	A4i, B1i
008	CH010	Lake Geneva: Rolle–Céligny	Lac Léman: Rolle–Céligny	Genève, Vaud	1,500	A4i, B1i
009	CH009	Lake Geneva: Grangettes	Lac Léman: Les Grangettes	Valais, Vaud	6,600	A4i, B1i
010	CH005	Lake Neuchâtel: Corcelettes–Vaumarcus	Lac de Neuchâtel: Corcelettes–Vaumarcus	Vaud	690	A4i, B1i
011	CH006ᵖ, CH007, CH008	Lake Neuchâtel: southern shore	Rive sud du lac de Neuchâtel	Bern, Fribourg, Neuchâtel, Vaud	17,000	A4i, A4iii, B1i, B2
012	CH004	Klingnau reservoir	Klingnauer Stausee	Aargau	410	B1i
013	CH003	End of Lake Constance and River Rhine until Bibermühle	Untersee-Ende und Rhein bis Bibermühle	Schaffhausen, Thurgau	480	A4i, A4iii, B1i
014	CH002	Lake Constance: Bay of Ermatingen	Untersee: Ermatinger Becken	Thurgau	530	A4i, A4iii, B1i
015	CH001	Lake Constance: Bay of Constance	Bodensee: Konstanzer Bucht	Thurgau	230	A4iii, B1i
016	—	Pre-alpine region of Pays d'Enhaut	Pays d'Enhaut	Bern, Fribourg, Vaud	37,100	A3, B2, B3
017	—	Pre-alpine region of Gurnigel	Gurnigel	Bern, Fribourg	16,800	A3, B1iv, B2, B3
018	—	Augstmatthorn	Augstmatthorn	Bern	17,200	A3, B2, B3
019	—	Pre-alpine region of Schwyz	Schwyzer Randalpen	Zug, Schwyz	35,600	A3, B2, B3
020	—	Upper Toggenburg and Säntis	Oberes Toggenburg/Säntis	St. Gallen, Appenzell-I.RH., Appenzell-A.RH.	38,600	A3, B2, B3
021	—	Central Valais between Sierre and Visp	Zentralwallis von Siders bis Visp	Valais	27,800	A3, B2, B3
022	—	Valley of Zermatt	Mattertal	Valais	22,100	A3, B2, B3
023	—	Aletsch region	Aletschregion	Valais	4,750	A3, B2
024	—	Heinzenberg mountain and surrounding valleys	Heinzenberg–Domleschg–Safiental	Graubünden	29,000	A3, B2, B3
025	—	Lower Engadine and Swiss National Park	Unterengadin–Nationalpark	Graubünden	101,100	A3, B2, B3
026	—	Simplon region	Simplon	Valais	14,700	A3, B2, B3
027	—	Piora–Dötra	Piora–Dötra	Ticino	9,700	A3, B2
028	—	Maggia valley	Valle Maggia	Ticino	14,700	A3, B2
029	CH013	Bolle di Magadino	Bolle di Magadino	Ticino	1,400	B1i
030	—	Generoso mountain	Monte Generoso	Ticino	6,100	B2
031	—	Bregaglia valley	Val Bregaglia	Graubünden	10,800	A3, B2

Site identified in the previous inventory of IBAs in Europe (Grimmett and Jones 1989) but no longer considered to be an IBA
CH006ᵖ Lac de Neuchâtel: Colombier – Canal de la Thielle

p = part of IBA

007, 008, 009, 010, 011, 012, 013, 014, 015), and agricultural landscapes (IBAs 004, 005).

ORNITHOLOGICAL IMPORTANCE

Ninety-eight species of European conservation concern (SPECs) breed regularly in Switzerland (Tucker and Heath 1994). Ten species are listed as SPEC 2, 36 as SPEC 3 and 51 as SPEC 4. *Crex crex*, the only SPEC 1 species, occurs in Switzerland in small numbers, but no longer breeds regularly. *Crex crex* does not meet criteria at any site but is recorded in three IBAs fulfilling criteria for other species.

About 500,000 waterbirds regularly winter in Switzerland. Eleven IBAs are important as wintering and stop-over sites (004, 006, 007, 008, 009, 010, 011, 012, 013, 014, 015). They are selected as IBAs under criteria A4i and B1i, as they hold more than 1% of the biogeographic or flyway populations for species listed in Table 2. Together, they hold approximately 20–30% of all waterbirds wintering in Switzerland. The IBAs on Lac de Neuchâtel (010, 011) are particularly important for *Netta rufina* and since the beginning of the 1990s they have regularly held 15–25% of the south-west/central European population. Several IBAs are important for resident *Mergus merganser*, part of a discrete central European breeding population (Table 2). In winter these birds mix with

migrating individuals from northern European populations. Additionally, 20–30 individuals of *Aythya nyroca* (SPEC 1) winter on Swiss waters.

For breeding species the selection of IBAs centres on areas with the highest densities of birds. This approach is adopted primarily because many of these species are dispersed breeders. IBAs hold a considerable proportion of the Swiss breeding population of a number of SPECs (meeting criteria B2 or B3), such as *Milvus*

Table 2. Important Bird Areas in Switzerland that support important numbers of one or more congregatory species (i.e. meeting criteria A4 and/or B1). IBAs meeting both criteria A4 and B1 for the species are shown in **bold**. IBAs meeting only criterion B1 for the species concerned, and not A4, are shown in normal type. For key to 'Season', see p. 7.

Species	Season	IBA code
Podiceps cristatus Great Crested Grebe	W	**007, 008, 009, 011**
Phalacrocorax carbo Cormorant	W	**009**
Anas strepera Gadwall	W	**004**, 012, **014**
Netta rufina Red-crested Pochard	W	**010, 011**
Aythya ferina Pochard	W	**011, 013**, 014, 015
Aythya fuligula Tufted Duck	W	**006**, 010, **011, 013**, 014
Mergus merganser Goosander	R	006, 007, 008, 011

Table 3. Species of European conservation concern with significant breeding populations at Important Bird Areas in Switzerland (meeting any IBA criteria).

Species [1]	Minimum national breeding population (pairs) [3]	Proportion (%) of national population breeding at all IBAs in Switzerland [4]
Milvus migrans Black Kite	1,200	>25
Milvus milvus Red Kite	800	>20
Aquila chrysaetos [2] Golden Eagle	300	>10
Falco tinnunculus Kestrel	3,000	>15
Falco peregrinus [2] Peregrine	200	>10
Tetrao tetrix Black Grouse	7,500	>15
Alectoris graeca Rock Partridge	3,000	>15
Tyto alba [2] Barn Owl	1,000	>10
Jynx torquilla Wryneck	2,000	>20
Picus canus Grey-headed Woodpecker	1,000	>15
Picus viridis Green Woodpecker	5,000	>20
Picoides tridactylus Three-toed Woodpecker	1,000	>10
Phoenicurus phoenicurus Redstart	10,000	>15
Monticola saxatilis Rock Thrush	800	>30
Turdus torquatus Ring Ouzel	40,000	>20
Serinus citrinella Citril Finch	10,000	>25

1. Only those species of European conservation concern (see Box 1, p. 12) that meet IBA criteria in Switzerland are listed.
2. Sites not selected based on B2/B3 criteria for those species alone (see overview text).
3. Data are taken from the BirdLife/EBCC European Bird Database 1998 (Heath and Borggreve 2000).
4. Approximate minimum proportion based on knowledge of the populations present in Switzerland.

migrans, *M. milvus*, *Picus viridis*, *Monticola saxatilis*, *Turdus torquatus* and *Serinus citrinella* (Table 3). Of the IBAs in the Jura, three in the northern Alps (016, 019, 020), four in the central Alps (021, 022, 024, 025) and one in the southern Alps (026) hold 5–10 species meeting the B2 or B3 criteria.

For three highly dispersed breeding species, *Aquila chrysaetos*, *Falco peregrinus* and *Tyto alba*, application of the IBA criteria would have resulted in the selection of extremely large IBAs. Therefore, these three species were not considered during the initial selection of IBAs but are used as supporting arguments for prioritizing candidate sites.

Switzerland is particularly important for alpine species which are characteristic of the Eurasian high-montane biome, in particular *Prunella collaris*, *Tichodroma muraria*, *Pyrrhocorax graculus*, *Montifringilla nivalis* and *Serinus citrinella*. Fourteen sites meet the A3 criterion. However, no sites are selected on the basis of meeting the A3 criterion alone, but biome-restricted species are used to support the final selection of IBAs based on criteria B2 and B3. Other important species of the Eurasian high-montane biome, though not restricted to it, are *Tetrao tetrix*, *Alectoris graeca*, *Monticola saxatilis* and *Turdus torquatus*.

HABITATS

Switzerland's varied topography results in a high diversity of habitats, dependent upon factors such as altitude, aspect, slope and substrate. There are often steep altitudinal gradients in small areas. Five altitudinal zones (colline, montane, subalpine, alpine, nival) can be distinguished with characteristic vegetation-types providing habitats for different bird communities. Agricultural land (15,800 km², 38% of surface area) and forests (30%) occupy the largest part of the country, followed by unproductive land (21%), urban areas (6%) and lakes and rivers (4%) (Aepli Elsenbeer *et al.* 1997). Land cover varies between regions, agricultural land dominating on the Central Plateau and forests and unproductive land in the Alps.

Twenty-eight IBAs (90%) support forest (Figure 1). In the colline and montane zones these tend to be *Quercus* forests at lower altitudes and *Fagus* forests in higher areas. However, these have largely been altered by man and are often mixed with planted *Picea abies*. In the Jura mountains, these forests are mixed with *Abies alba* and planted *Picea abies*. Typical breeding species of the colline and montane zones include *Milvus milvus*, *M. migrans*, *Jynx torquilla*, *Picus canus*,

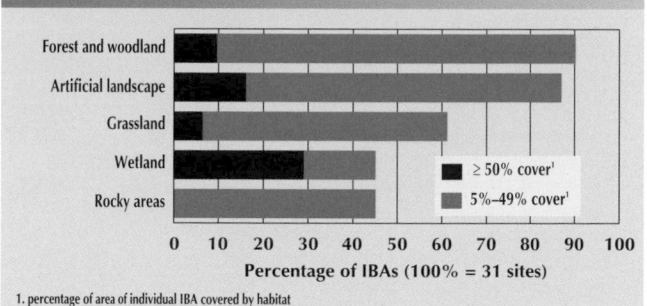

Figure 1. Habitats at Important Bird Areas in Switzerland (see Appendix 3 for definitions of habitats).

P. viridis, *Dendrocopos medius* and *Phoenicurus phoenicurus*. The subalpine zone has extensive conifer forests that extend up to the treeline. *Picea abies* dominates in the northern Alps, whilst in the central Alps *Pinus cembra* and *Larix decidua* are widespread. *Tetrao tetrix*, *Picoides tridactylus*, *Turdus torquatus* and *Serinus citrinella* reach their highest densities in these forests and in the transition zone at their upper limits.

Artificial landscapes, which occur in all IBAs and in 87% occupy more than 5% of the total area (Figure 1), are primarily arable land, highly improved reseeded grassland and human settlements on the Central Plateau and in the valleys of the mountainous regions. The arable landscape is dominated by cereal crops, potatoes, oil-seed rape and maize, interspersed at lower elevations by vineyards and orchards.

Grasslands are found in 19 IBAs (60%) (Figure 1). They include pasture and alpine meadows above 1,000 m. In many areas the treeline has been lowered by deforestation to create pastures. In the nival zone, the alpine grasslands give way to extensive rocky areas (found in 45% of IBAs) and permanent lying snow (Figure 1). These zones are important for species such as *Alectoris graeca*, *Prunella collaris*, *Monticola saxatilis*, *Tichodroma muraria*, *Pyrrhocorax graculus* and *Montifringilla nivalis*.

The other major habitat in the IBAs is wetland, which occurs in 14 sites, in nine of which it occupies more than 50% of the area of the IBA. These large wetlands are generally parts of the big freshwater lakes found on the Central Plateau and include open water, water-fringe vegetation, fens and alluvial forests. They are of great importance to moulting, passage and wintering waterbirds and breeding species associated with reedbeds (*Phragmites*).

IMPACTS ON IBAs – LAND-USE AND THREATS

The landscape has been greatly altered by man for urban, agricultural and industrial development. Remaining natural and semi-natural habitats are under high pressure from recreation and tourism, including lakes on the Central Plateau as well as forests and increasingly remote alpine regions. Recreation and tourism is

Figure 2. Land-uses at Important Bird Areas in Switzerland (see Appendix 3 for definitions of land-uses).

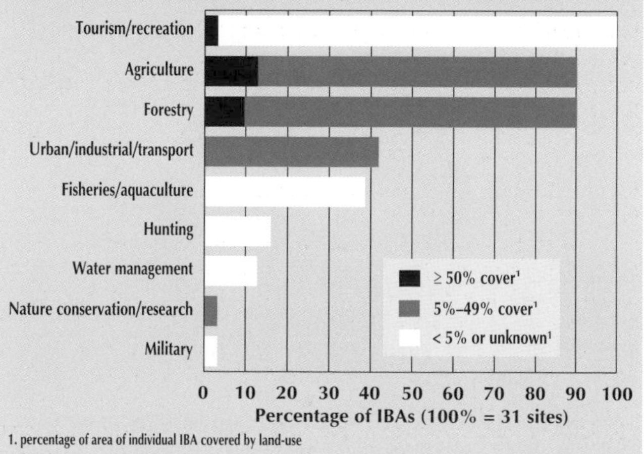

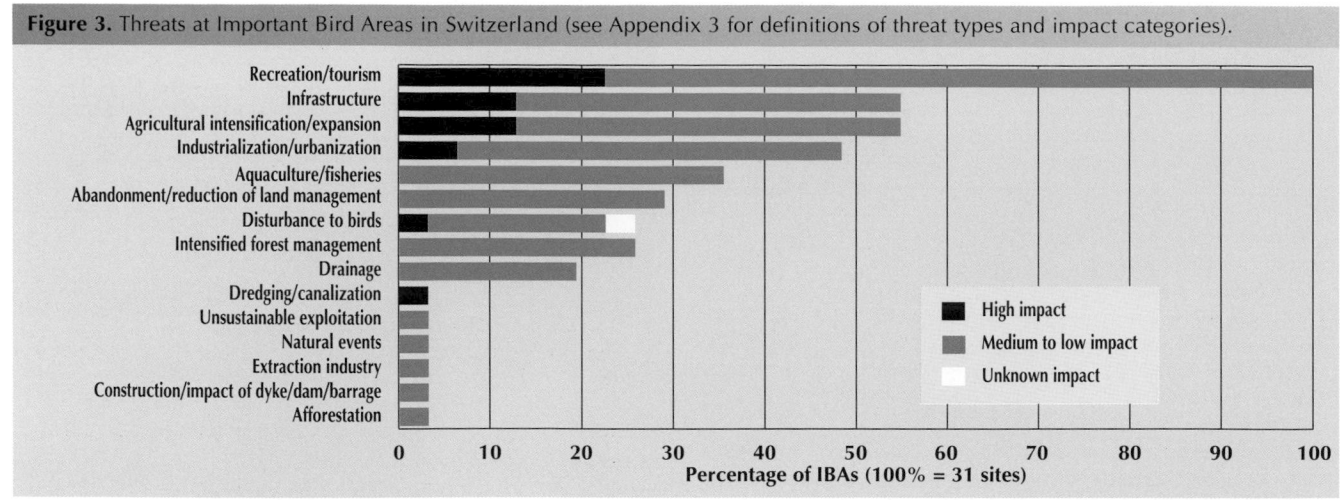

Figure 3. Threats at Important Bird Areas in Switzerland (see Appendix 3 for definitions of threat types and impact categories).

the most widespread land-use and threat to IBAs, although its extent and importance can be difficult to quantify (Figures 2 and 3). Whilst the hunting of waterbirds has been reduced since the previous pan-European inventory (Grimmett and Jones 1989), disturbance from water sports, fishing, boats and walkers is continuing to increase. Control of water-levels, canalization of rivers and embankment of shorelines has further reduced the quality and availability of habitat for many wetland birds, although these are largely historical problems rather than current threats. Efforts to lower nutrient input to wetlands have been successful, reducing eutrophication problems, which has benefited *Netta rufina*, but may reduce food availability for wintering waterbirds.

In mountainous regions, natural habitats occur mainly on steep inaccessible slopes and above the treeline. Despite increasing exploitation for tourism, habitats and their associated bird communities in the Alps have been less affected than those in the lowlands. However, infrastructure development, particularly increasing road density and other transport networks, are a major threat (Figure 3), especially as they facilitate access to remote areas resulting in more intense disturbance of birds such as *Tetrao tetrix*.

Twenty-eight IBAs have some sort of agricultural land-use (Figure 2). On the Central Plateau, natural habitats have become very rare. In most areas, agriculture is very intensive and features such as fallow strips, hedges and trees are scarce. Meadows are heavily fertilized and are cut frequently, offering few suitable habitat for species such as *Crex crex* and *Coturnix coturnix*. However, changes in agricultural policy are favouring more environment-friendly land-use practises. Whilst this is likely to stop further degradation of agricultural areas, to date it has not improved the habitat for birds. In contrast, marginal agricultural areas in the mountains are being abandoned. Whilst this leads to increased forest cover, many open areas in the Alps are being lost as habitats

for species of open and semi-open landscapes. This applies in particular to the south of Switzerland where species like *Tetrao tetrix* and *Alectoris graeca* are affected.

Forestry remains an important land-use (Figure 2). Despite major clearance during the last century, forests still occupy 30% of the country's land area and are expanding again. The majority are managed, which has led to changes in the composition and age structure of tree communities. Woodpeckers and other hole-nesting birds suffer from a shortage of dead wood and breeding sites, but the situation is gradually improving.

PROTECTION STATUS

■ National protection

Legislation in Switzerland is organized on federal, cantonal (regional) and communal levels. Habitat inventories, which identify the majority of protected areas, are part of federal legislation, although implementation is usually a cantonal matter. Most IBAs overlap with some protected areas included in the federal inventories. Only three contain no nationally protected areas at all (Figure 4). However, protection offered by some federal legislation is not particularly strong. Parts of many IBAs are also protected by cantonal or communal legislation which often offers stronger protection. However, details of these reserves are not included in this inventory.

National protected areas fall into the following categories:

1. National Park

The only Swiss National Park (established 1914) lies within site 025. It provides complete protection and human intervention in the successional processes is prohibited. Public access is restricted to marked paths.

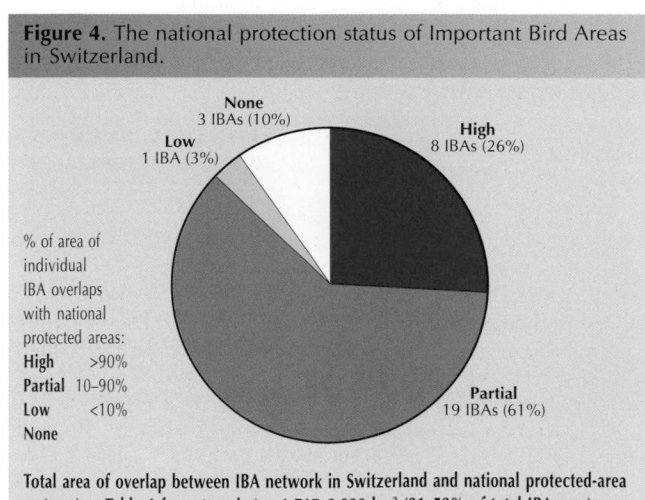

Figure 4. The national protection status of Important Bird Areas in Switzerland.

% of area of individual IBA overlaps with national protected areas:

High >90%
Partial 10–90%
Low <10%
None

Total area of overlap between IBA network in Switzerland and national protected-area system (see Table 4 for categories) = 1,717–2,920 km² (31–53% of total IBA area).

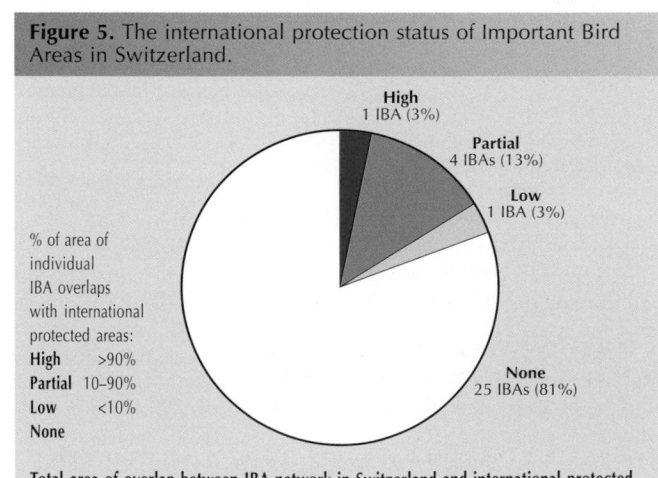

Figure 5. The international protection status of Important Bird Areas in Switzerland.

% of area of individual IBA overlaps with international protected areas:

High >90%
Partial 10–90%
Low <10%
None

Total area of overlap between IBA network in Switzerland and international protected-area system (see Table 4 for categories) = 69–81 km² (1% of total IBA area).

Table 4. Protection status of Important Bird Areas in Switzerland. A tick (✔) indicates that an IBA overlaps with a protected area (to any extent).

IBA code	International name	National Park	Reserves for Waterbirds and Migrants of International Importance	Mire Landscapes of Particular Beauty and of National Importance	Fenlands of National Importance	Raised and Transitional Bogs of National Importance	Floodplains of National Importance	Inventory of Landscapes and Natural Monuments of National Importance	Federal Hunting Reserves	Ramsar Site
					National				International
001	Mont Tendre			✔	✔	✔	✔	✔	✔	
002	La Brévine and Les Ponts-de-Martel			✔	✔	✔		✔		
003	Jura mountains of Baselland/Solothurn							✔		
004	'Grosses Moos' plain and Niederried reservoir		✔		✔		✔	✔		✔
005	Lowlands of Zurich and lower valley of the River Thur			✔	✔	✔	✔	✔		
006	River Rhône: Geneva–Verbois reservoir		✔				✔	✔		✔
007	Lake Geneva: Versoix and Hermance–Geneva									
008	Lake Geneva: Rolle–Céligny									
009	Lake Geneva: Grangettes		✔	✔	✔		✔	✔		✔
010	Lake Neuchâtel: Corcelettes–Vaumarcus						✔	✔		
011	Lake Neuchâtel: southern shore		✔	✔	✔		✔	✔		✔
012	Klingnau reservoir		✔				✔	✔		✔
013	End of Lake Constance and River Rhine until Bibermühle			✔	✔			✔		
014	Lake Constance: Bay of Ermatingen			✔	✔			✔		
015	Lake Constance: Bay of Constance									
016	Pre-alpine region of Pays d'Enhaut			✔	✔	✔	✔	✔	✔	
017	Pre-alpine region of Gurnigel			✔	✔	✔				
018	Augstmatthorn			✔	✔	✔		✔	✔	
019	Pre-alpine region of Schwyz			✔	✔	✔	✔	✔	✔	
020	Upper Toggenburg and Säntis			✔	✔	✔		✔	✔	
021	Central Valais between Sierre and Visp				✔		✔	✔	✔	
022	Valley of Zermatt				✔	✔		✔		
023	Aletsch region					✔		✔	✔	
024	Heinzenberg mountain and surrounding valleys				✔		✔	✔		
025	Lower Engadine and Swiss National Park	✔		✔	✔	✔	✔	✔		
026	Simplon region					✔		✔		
027	Piora–Dötra			✔	✔	✔	✔	✔		
028	Maggia valley					✔	✔	✔		
029	Bolle di Magadino		✔		✔		✔	✔		✔
030	Generoso mountain							✔		
031	Bregaglia valley				✔	✔		✔		
Total number of IBAs		1	6	14	20	15	15	27	7	6

Box 1. International legislation and initiatives that are relevant to site conservation in Switzerland (see Appendix 1 for a general description of these agreements).

Global	
Biodiversity Convention	✔
Ramsar Convention	✔
Bonn Convention	✔
World Heritage Convention	✔
MAB Programme	✔

Pan-European	
Bern Convention	✔

✔ Convention ratified/initiative supported
(✔) Convention signed

2. Reserves for Waterbirds and Migrants of International and National Importance

These reserves cover parts of lakes and rivers and provide protection for passage and breeding waterbirds. Hunting is prohibited and other human activities are restricted.

3. Mire Landscapes of Particular Beauty and of National Importance (1996)

This inventory protects mire areas with buffer zones with the aim of preserving the landscape with its characteristic elements/structures.

4. Fenlands of National Importance (1994)

Sites are fully protected. Building, soil modification, peat-cutting and drainage are forbidden.

5. Raised and Transitional Bogs of National Importance (1991)

Sites are fully protected. Building, soil modification, peat cutting and drainage are forbidden.

6. Floodplains of National Importance (1992)

Designed to protect sites and their fauna and flora. The natural water dynamics must be maintained or if possible restored.

7. Inventory of Landscapes and Natural Monuments of National Importance (1977)

Extensive areas with the aim of protecting the landscape as a whole. Interventions are possible as long as they do not impair the site as a whole.

8. Federal Hunting Reserves (1991)

Hunting is prohibited at these sites.

■ International protection

Switzerland is party to several international initiatives and conventions (Box 1). Switzerland has additionally signed and ratified other conventions and programmes, for example the Alpine Convention and the African-Eurasian Waterbird Agreement. International protection of IBAs is generally absent with the exception of six IBAs which overlap with six Ramsar Sites (Figure 5).

CONSERVATION

- NGOs play an important role in the management of protected areas. In accordance with the political structure of the country, conservation work by NGOs is carried out at national, cantonal and communal levels. On a national level, Schweizer Vogelschutz SVS – BirdLife Switzerland, Pro Natura Schweiz and other NGOs carry out national conservation projects for sites, species and habitats and are involved in lobbying and public awareness work. Regionally, local conservation associations, for example, the approximately 500 local societies that are members of BirdLife Switzerland, conduct conservation projects or manage local nature reserves.
- National species-protection plans focus on *Crex crex, Tetrao urogallus* and *Alauda arvensis*. Species action plans have also been prepared at regional levels, for example for *Lanius senator* and *Athene noctua*.
- Monitoring programmes exist for most IBAs that are important for waterbirds. They are coordinated by the Swiss Ornithological Institute in Sempach, under the mandate of the Swiss Agency for the Environment, Forests and Landscape.

ANALYTICAL METHODS

- IBAs were identified mainly on the basis of data held by the Swiss Ornithological Institute, in particular the database on the waterbird census and data for the distribution atlas of breeding birds 1993–1996 (Schmid *et al.* 1998). Local experts were consulted for all IBAs to obtain additional information and to draw site boundaries.
- The atlas of breeding birds 1993–1996 includes interpolated abundance maps which are based on a simplified territory mapping of 7.1% of all 1 km squares in the country. These abundance maps were used to select sites based on high densities for species meeting IBA criteria. The number of breeding pairs was estimated on the basis of the abundance maps. Regional inventories provided additional information.

   This density-based approach was adopted primarily because many species are dispersed breeders. Therefore, it is difficult to apply criteria based on absolute numbers as any area large enough would potentially meet criteria. In order to prioritize between sites, IBAs were only selected where several breeding species met criteria. This allowed the selection of the most important sites as IBAs.

- Numbers of waterbirds are based on counts in mid-November and mid-January. Mean and maximum numbers are presented for the period 1993/94–1997/98 (Swiss Ornithological Institute Sempach, unpublished).
- Site 029 does not strictly meet any IBA species criteria. However, it is the main wetland site in Switzerland south of the Alps. It has been identified as a biogeographically unique wetland under the Ramsar Convention. It has high ornithological importance as a stop-over site for migratory birds, particularly waterbirds, and as a breeding site for wetland birds. For these reasons the site has been included in the IBA inventory with criterion B1i being applied at a site level.
- The main habitats were determined from data on land-use provided by the Federal Department of Statistics. Additional information is based mainly on the breeding bird distribution atlas (Schmid *et al.* 1998), the inventory for waterbird reserves (Marti and Schifferli 1987), and on information from the current monitoring programme on waterbird reserves of international importance. .Additional information was provided by local experts.

GLOSSARY

Alpine zone above the treeline, dominated by alpine meadows, scree and rocky areas.
Colline zone 200–600 m above sea-level, the lowest areas of Switzerland.
Montane zone 400–1,800 m above sea-level, most areas of the Central Plateau and the valley bottoms of the Jura and Alps, characterized by agricultural landscapes and *Fagus* and *Quercus* forests.
Nival the highest zone in the Alps where there is permanent lying snow.
Subalpine zone 1,600–2,300 m above sea-level, zone in the Jura and Alps up to the treeline, mostly traditional agriculture and conifer forests.

ACKNOWLEDGEMENTS

The IBA project group consisted of Lorenz Heer and Werner Müller from Schweizer Vogelschutz SVS – BirdLife Switzerland and Verena Keller, Hans Schmid and Olivier Biber (until May 1998) from the Swiss Ornithological Institute Sempach. Niklaus Zbinden and Beat Naef-Daenzer (Swiss Ornithological Institute) were also involved in the analysis of data. Fifty-one local experts supplied additional data and comments on the draft list of IBAs. Jürg Schenker (Swiss Agency for the Environment, Forests and Landscape) contributed maps of the federal inventories for each IBA. The project was financially supported by the Swiss Agency for the Environment, Forests and Landscape.

■ SITE ACCOUNTS

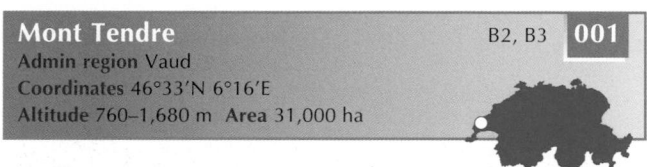

Mont Tendre
B2, B3 | 001
Admin region Vaud
Coordinates 46°33'N 6°16'E
Altitude 760–1,680 m **Area** 31,000 ha

■ Site description
Two mountain chains in the Jura range, separated by an open valley which contains wet meadows, bogs and a small lake.

Habitats Forest and woodland (66%; native coniferous forest; mixed forest; treeline ecotone), Grassland (23%; alpine/subalpine/boreal grassland), Artificial landscape (8%; highly improved reseeded grassland; arable land)
Land-use Agriculture (29%), Forestry (66%), Tourism/recreation

■ Birds

Species	Season	Year	Pop min	Pop max	Acc	Criteria
Milvus migrans Black Kite	B	1996	20	—	A	B2
Jynx torquilla Wryneck	B	1996	10	40	A	B2
Turdus torquatus Ring Ouzel	B	1996	1,500	2,500	A	B3
Serinus citrinella Citril Finch	B	1996	500	—	A	B3

An important site for breeding subalpine species, particularly *Turdus torquatus* and *Serinus citrinella*. Species of global conservation concern that do not meet IBA criteria: *Crex crex*.

■ Protection status
National High **International** None
3,430 ha of IBA covered by Federal Hunting Reserve (Le Noirmont, 3,430 ha). 25,600 ha of IBA covered by Inventory of Landscapes and Natural Monuments of National Importance (Vallée de Joux et Haut Jura Vaudois, 26,843 ha). 954 ha of IBA covered by Mire Landscapes of Particular Beauty and of National Importance (Creux du Croue; Vallée de Joux; total area 954 ha). 88 ha of IBA covered by Flood-plains of National Importance (Sagnes de la Burtignière, 88 ha). 313 ha of IBA covered by 13 Fenlands of National Importance (total area 313 ha). 110 ha of IBA covered by 18 Raised and Transitional Bogs of National Importance (total area 110 ha).

■ Conservation issues

Threats Agricultural intensification/expansion (B), Intensified forest management (C), Recreation/tourism (A)

The forest tree community is changing as a result of the decline of forest grazing. This has resulted in increased grazing pressure on meadows.

The site is part of a national project on *Crex crex* and mowing dates are now delayed in some meadows.

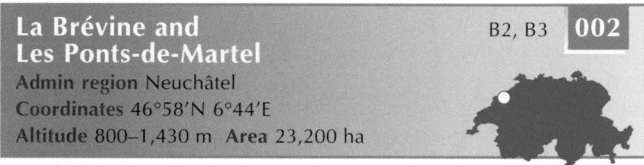

La Brévine and Les Ponts-de-Martel
B2, B3 | 002
Admin region Neuchâtel
Coordinates 46°58'N 6°44'E
Altitude 800–1,430 m **Area** 23,200 ha

■ Site description
An area of the Jura mountains with open valleys, containing extensive raised bogs and wet meadows, and extensive subalpine forest on the slopes.

Habitats Forest and woodland (39%; native coniferous forest; mixed forest), Grassland (22%; alpine/subalpine/boreal grassland), Wetland (6%; raised bog; blanket bog), Artificial landscape (33%; highly improved reseeded grassland; arable land; other urban/industrial areas)
Land-use Agriculture (56%), Forestry (39%), Tourism/recreation, Urban/industrial/transport (6%)

■ Birds

Species	Season	Year	Pop min	Pop max	Acc	Criteria
Milvus migrans Black Kite	B	1996	20	—	A	B2
Milvus milvus Red Kite	B	1996	30	—	A	B3
Phoenicurus phoenicurus Redstart	B	1996	40	100	A	B2
Turdus torquatus Ring Ouzel	B	1996	250	400	A	B3

An important site for breeding raptors, particularly *Milvus migrans*, *M. milvus* and *Falco tinnunculus*, and species associated with subalpine conifer forest. Species of global conservation concern that do not meet IBA criteria: *Crex crex*.

■ Protection status
National Partial **International** None
3,200 ha of IBA covered by 3 Inventory of Landscapes and Natural Monuments of National Importance (Creux du Van et Gorges de l'Areuse; Tourbière des Ponts-de-Martel; Vallée de la Brévine; total area 3,220 ha). 277 ha of IBA covered by 13 Raised and Transitional Bogs of National Importance (total area 277 ha). 19 ha of IBA covered by 4 Fenlands of National Importance (total area 19 ha). 2,624 ha of IBA covered by 2 Mire Landscapes of Particular Beauty and of National Importance (La Brévine; Les Ponts-de-Martel; total area 2,624 ha).

■ Conservation issues

Threats Agricultural intensification/expansion (B), Drainage (B), Infrastructure (B), Intensified forest management (C), Recreation/tourism (B)

One of the main threats is agricultural intensification in bog areas. The site is included in a *Crex crex* conservation project and mowing has been delayed in some sites.

Jura mountains of Baselland/Solothurn
B2, B3 | 003

Admin region Aargau, Basel-Stadt, Basel-Landschaft, Solothurn
Coordinates 47°26'N 7°39'E
Altitude 270–1,205 m **Area** 35,000 ha

■ Site description

Hills in the Jura mountains dominated by deciduous woodland and a diverse mosaic of meadows and orchards.

Habitats Forest and woodland (46%; broadleaved deciduous forest; mixed forest), Artificial landscape (52%; highly improved reseeded grassland; arable land; perennial crops/orchards/groves; other urban/industrial areas)
Land-use Agriculture (42%), Forestry (46%), Tourism/recreation, Urban/industrial/transport (15%)

■ Birds

Species		Season	Year	Pop min	Pop max	Acc	Criteria
Milvus migrans	Black Kite	B	1996	75	—	A	B2
Milvus milvus	Red Kite	R	1996	80	—	A	B3
Falco tinnunculus	Kestrel	R	1996	60	—	A	B2
Falco peregrinus	Peregrine	R	1996	3	—	A	B2
Jynx torquilla	Wryneck	B	1996	25	50	A	B2
Picus canus	Grey-headed Woodpecker	R	1996	100	300	A	B2
Picus viridis	Green Woodpecker	R	1996	300	500	A	B2
Phoenicurus phoenicurus	Redstart	B	1996	300	600	A	B2

The site is important for species breeding in lowland forests, such as *Picus canus*, *Dendrocopos medius* and *Phoenicurus phoenicurus*.

■ Protection status

National Partial **International** None
6,660 ha of IBA covered by 2 Inventory of Landscapes and Natural Monuments of National Importance (Belchen–Passwang–Gebiet; Gempenplateau; total area 11,015 ha).

■ Conservation issues

Threats Agricultural intensification/expansion (A), Industrialization/urbanization (A), Infrastructure (A), Intensified forest management (C), Recreation/tourism (B)

The main threats are from the proximity of urban areas which results in habitat destruction within the IBA from building and disturbance from recreation. Species conservation programmes have started for *Athene noctua* and *Lanius senator*.

'Grosses Moos' plain and Niederried reservoir
A4i, B1i, B2, B3 | 004

Admin region Bern, Fribourg
Coordinates 46°58'N 7°11'E
Altitude 430–610 m **Area** 16,100 ha

■ Site description

A richly-structured agricultural landscape with small villages in the western part of the Central Plateau. The Niederried reservoir and the Petersinsel have water-fringe vegetation, marshy areas and alluvial forest.

Habitats Forest and woodland (17%; broadleaved deciduous forest; mixed forest; alluvial/very wet forest), Wetland (11%; standing fresh water; river/stream; water-fringe vegetation), Artificial landscape (70%; arable land; perennial crops/orchards/groves; other urban/industrial areas)
Land-use Agriculture (62%), Fisheries/aquaculture, Forestry (17%), Tourism/recreation, Urban/industrial/transport (8%), Water management

■ Birds

Species		Season	Year	Pop min	Pop max	Acc	Criteria
[1] *Anas strepera*	Gadwall	W	1998	260	470	A	A4i, B1i
Milvus migrans	Black Kite	B	1996	80	—	A	B2
Milvus milvus	Red Kite	R	1996	10	—	A	B3
Picus canus	Grey-headed Woodpecker	R	1996	40	80	A	B2

1. Mean and maximum numbers.

An important area for birds of open and semi-open landscapes, and for wintering ducks on the reservoir.

■ Protection status

National Partial **International** Low
303 ha of IBA covered by Inventory of Landscapes and Natural Monuments of National Importance (Stausee Niederried, 303 ha). 648 ha of IBA covered by Mire Landscapes of Particular Beauty and of National Importance (Petersinsel, 648 ha). 135 ha of IBA covered by 6 Fenlands of National Importance (Grosses Moos and Niederried, 135 ha). 293 ha of IBA covered by 3 Flood-plains of National Importance (Hagneckdelta; Heidenweg/St. Petersinsel; Niederried–Oltigenmatt; total area 293 ha). 303 ha of IBA covered by Ramsar Site (Aarestau Niederried, 303 ha).

■ Conservation issues

Threats Agricultural intensification/expansion (A), Drainage (C), Industrialization/urbanization (C), Infrastructure (B), Recreation/tourism (C)

The main threat is from agricultural intensification and fragmentation of the landscape as a result of road-building.

Lowlands of Zurich and lower valley of the River Thur
B2, B3 | 005

Admin region Schaffhausen, Thurgau, Zürich
Coordinates 47°32'N 8°34'E
Altitude 340–470 m **Area** 22,700 ha

■ Site description

A lowland area of open river valleys with a mosaic of *Quercus* woodlands, marshland, agricultural land and small villages.

Habitats Forest and woodland (36%; broadleaved deciduous forest), Artificial landscape (60%; highly improved reseeded grassland; arable land; forestry plantation; perennial crops/orchards/groves; other urban/industrial areas)
Land-use Agriculture (52%), Forestry (36%), Tourism/recreation, Urban/industrial/transport (10%), Water management

■ Birds

Species		Season	Year	Pop min	Pop max	Acc	Criteria
Milvus migrans	Black Kite	B	1996	50	—	A	B2
Milvus milvus	Red Kite	R	1996	50	—	A	B3
Tyto alba	Barn Owl	R	1996	3	—	A	B2
Picus canus	Grey-headed Woodpecker	R	1996	20	40	A	B2
Picus viridis	Green Woodpecker	R	1996	100	200	A	B2

An important site for breeding woodpeckers and raptors, and for wintering *Milvus milvus*.

■ Protection status

National Partial **International** None
12,299 ha of IBA covered by 5 Inventory of Landscapes and Natural Monuments of National Importance (Untersee-Hochrhein; Glaziallandschaft Neerach–Stadel; Glaziallandschaft zwischen Thur und Rhein; Irchel; Lagerengebiet; total area 31,154 ha). 1 ha of IBA covered by Raised and Transitional Bogs of National Importance (Räubrichseen, 1 ha). 154 ha of IBA covered by 9 Fenlands of National Importance (total area 154 ha). 584 ha of IBA covered by Mire Landscapes of Particular Beauty and of National Importance (Neeracher Ried, 584 ha). 432 ha of IBA covered by Flood-plains of National Importance (Eggrank–Thurspitz, 432 ha).

■ Conservation issues

Threats Agricultural intensification/expansion (A), Aquaculture/fisheries (C), Industrialization/urbanization (B), Infrastructure (B), Intensified forest management (C), Recreation/tourism (C)

The main threats are from agricultural intensification and habitat destruction as a result of urban development.

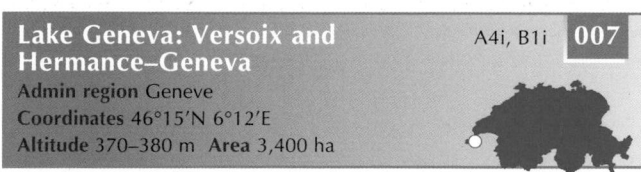

| River Rhône: Geneva–Verbois reservoir | A4i, B1i | 006 |

Admin region Geneve
Coordinates 46°11'N 6°06'E
Altitude 360–420 m **Area** 1,100 ha

■ Site description
The site covers the outflow from Lake Geneva and part of the River Rhône, which is partly dammed. The river runs through part of the city of Geneva and a steep, forested valley. In the bay of Geneva, water-fringe vegetation has been removed but some reedbeds (*Phragmites*) remain along the river.

Habitats Forest and woodland (30%; broadleaved deciduous forest; alluvial/very wet forest), Grassland (5%; mesophile grassland), Wetland (12%; river/stream; standing fresh water; water-fringe vegetation), Artificial landscape (53%; highly improved reseeded grassland; arable land; perennial crops/orchards/groves; urban parks/gardens; other urban/industrial areas)
Land-use Agriculture (39%), Fisheries/aquaculture, Forestry (30%), Tourism/recreation, Urban/industrial/transport (27%), Water management

■ Birds

Species	Season	Year	Pop min	Pop max	Acc	Criteria
[1] *Aythya fuligula* Tufted Duck	W	1998	9,000	13,000	A	A4i, B1i
Mergus merganser Goosander	R	1996	15	25	A	B1i

1. Mean and maximum numbers.

An important wintering site for waterbirds.

■ Protection status
National High **International** High
1,100 ha of IBA covered by Inventory of Landscapes and Natural Monuments of National Importance (Le Rhône genevois–Vallons de l'Allondon et de La Laire, 1,929 ha). 1,032 ha of IBA covered by Water and Migratory Bird Reserve (Rhône–Verbois, 1,032 ha). 1,032 ha of IBA covered by Ramsar Site (Rade de Genève et Rhône en aval de Genève, 1,032 ha).

■ Conservation issues

Threats Aquaculture/fisheries (C), Construction/impact of dyke/dam/barrage (C), Industrialization/urbanization (C), Recreation/tourism (B)

The main threat was from disturbance from boats, which has now been greatly restricted.

| Lake Geneva: Versoix and Hermance–Geneva | A4i, B1i | 007 |

Admin region Geneve
Coordinates 46°15'N 6°12'E
Altitude 370–380 m **Area** 3,400 ha

■ Site description
The site covers a large bay with a predominantly developed shoreline. Water-fringe vegetation has largely been destroyed.

Habitats Wetland (94%; standing fresh water), Artificial landscape (5%; other urban/industrial areas)
Land-use Fisheries/aquaculture, Tourism/recreation (100%)

■ Birds

Species	Season	Year	Pop min	Pop max	Acc	Criteria
[1] *Podiceps cristatus* Great Crested Grebe	W	1998	2,000	7,000	A	A4i, B1i
Mergus merganser Goosander	R	1996	65	75	A	B1i

1. Mean and maximum numbers.

An important wintering site for waterbirds, particularly *Podiceps cristatus* and ducks. Breeding *Mergus merganser* are part of a geographically separate alpine population.

■ Protection status
National None **International** None

■ Conservation issues

Threats Aquaculture/fisheries (C), Disturbance to birds (B), Industrialization/urbanization (C), Recreation/tourism (A)

The main threat is disturbance from boats. The site is protected from hunting by cantonal legislation.

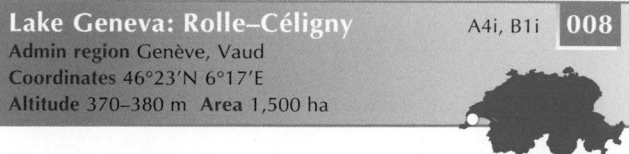

| Lake Geneva: Rolle–Céligny | A4i, B1i | 008 |

Admin region Genève, Vaud
Coordinates 46°23'N 6°17'E
Altitude 370–380 m **Area** 1,500 ha

■ Site description
Part of Lake Geneva with both natural and artificial, developed shorelines.

Habitats Forest and woodland (9%; broadleaved deciduous forest; alluvial/very wet forest), Wetland (62%; standing fresh water), Artificial landscape (29%; highly improved reseeded grassland; arable land; urban parks/gardens; other urban/industrial areas)
Land-use Agriculture (18%), Fisheries/aquaculture, Forestry (8%), Hunting, Tourism/recreation, Urban/industrial/transport (10%)

■ Birds

Species	Season	Year	Pop min	Pop max	Acc	Criteria
[1] *Podiceps cristatus* Great Crested Grebe	W	1998	1,200	3,700	A	A4i, B1i
Mergus merganser Goosander	R	1996	40	50	A	B1i

1. Mean and maximum numbers.

An important site for wintering *Podiceps cristatus* and ducks.

■ Protection status
National None **International** None

■ Conservation issues

Threats Aquaculture/fisheries (C), Disturbance to birds (B), Industrialization/urbanization (C), Recreation/tourism (A)

One of the main threats is disturbance from boats.

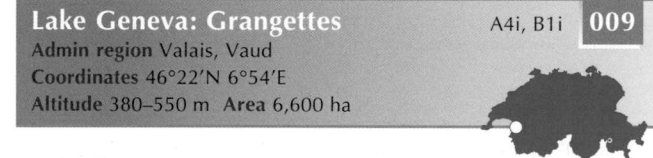

| Lake Geneva: Grangettes | A4i, B1i | 009 |

Admin region Valais, Vaud
Coordinates 46°22'N 6°54'E
Altitude 380–550 m **Area** 6,600 ha

■ Site description
This site includes the upper part of Lake Geneva, with areas of both artificial and natural shoreline, and the degraded delta of the River Rhône, with reedbeds (*Phragmites*), alluvial forests and fens.

Habitats Forest and woodland (8%; broadleaved deciduous forest; alluvial/very wet forest), Wetland (76%; river/stream; standing fresh water; water-fringe vegetation; fen/transition mire/spring), Artificial landscape (15%; highly improved reseeded grassland; arable land; forestry plantation; urban parks/gardens; other urban/industrial areas; ruderal land)
Land-use Agriculture (8%), Fisheries/aquaculture, Forestry (8%), Tourism/recreation, Urban/industrial/transport (8%)

■ Birds

Species	Season	Year	Pop min	Pop max	Acc	Criteria
[1] *Podiceps cristatus* Great Crested Grebe	W	1998	3,000	4,000	A	A4i, B1i
[1] *Phalacrocorax carbo* Cormorant	W	1998	1,600	3,900	A	A4i, B1i

1. Mean and maximum numbers.

An important site for wintering waterbirds, moulting ducks and migrating waders.

■ Protection status

National High **International** Partial

1,011 ha of IBA covered by Inventory of Landscapes and Natural Monuments of National Importance (Les Grangettes, 1,011 ha). 100 ha of IBA covered by Inventory of Landscapes and Natural Monuments of National Importance (Tour d'Aï–Dent de Corjon, 12,505 ha). 6,010 ha of IBA covered by Water and Migratory Bird Reserve (Les Grangettes, 6,010 ha). 1,011 ha of IBA covered by Mire Landscapes of Particular Beauty and of National Importance (Les Grangettes, 1,011 ha). 361 ha of IBA covered by Flood-plains of National Importance (Les Grangettes, 361 ha). 72 ha of IBA covered by 5 Fenlands of National Importance (total area 72 ha). 330 ha of IBA covered by Ramsar Site (Les Grangettes, 330 ha).

■ Conservation issues

Threats Afforestation (B), Agricultural intensification/expansion (B), Aquaculture/fisheries (C), Drainage (B), Extraction industry (C), Industrialization/urbanization (C), Infrastructure (C), Recreation/tourism (A)

One of the main threats is erosion of the shoreline in the delta. Agricultural intensification and drainage, recreational activities, and afforestation with *Populus* and *Picea* plantations are also major threats. There are proposals to restrict boat access to some additional areas. Restoration projects for the delta exist.

Lake Neuchâtel: Corcelettes–Vaumarcus   A4i, B1i   010

Admin region Vaud
Coordinates 46°49′N 6°44′E
Altitude 425–435 m **Area** 690 ha

■ Site description

The site is part of a large lake and includes shoreline and open water. The shore has some areas of reedbed (*Phragmites*) and alluvial forest.

Habitats Forest and woodland (10%; broadleaved deciduous forest; alluvial/very wet forest), Wetland (85%; standing fresh water; water-fringe vegetation), Artificial landscape (5%; other urban/industrial areas)
Land-use Fisheries/aquaculture, Forestry (10%), Hunting, Tourism/recreation

■ Birds

Species	Season	Year	Pop min	Pop max	Acc	Criteria
[1] *Netta rufina* Red-crested Pochard	W	1998	870	2,200	A	A4i, B1i
[1] *Aythya fuligula* Tufted Duck	W	1998	4,600	9,600	A	B1i

1. Mean and maximum numbers.

An important site for wintering waterbirds, especially ducks.

■ Protection status

National Partial **International** None

162 ha of IBA covered by Inventory of Landscapes and Natural Monuments of National Importance (Grèves vaudoises de la rive gauche du lac, 162 ha). 91 ha of IBA covered by 3 Flood-plains of National Importance (Les Grèves de Concise; Les Grèves de Corcelles; Les Grèves de Grandson–Bonvillars–Onnens; total area 91 ha).

■ Conservation issues

Threats Aquaculture/fisheries (C), Disturbance to birds (B), Industrialization/urbanization (C), Recreation/tourism (B)

Main threats are from disturbance caused by hunting and recreation.

Lake Neuchâtel: southern shore   A4i, A4iii, B1i, B2   011

Admin region Bern, Fribourg, Neuchâtel, Vaud
Coordinates 46°52′N 6°55′E
Altitude 430–460 m **Area** 17,000 ha

■ Site description

An area including the southern shore and shallow areas of Lake Neuchâtel, together with open water. The shoreline is fringed by reedbeds (*Phragmites*), sedge-beds (*Carex*), marshland and alluvial forest.

Habitats Forest and woodland (14%; broadleaved deciduous forest; mixed forest; alluvial/very wet forest), Wetland (57%; standing fresh water; water-fringe vegetation; fen/transition mire/spring), Artificial landscape (29%; highly improved reseeded grassland; arable land; other urban/industrial areas)
Land-use Agriculture (16%), Fisheries/aquaculture, Forestry (14%), Hunting, Tourism/recreation, Urban/industrial/transport (7%)

■ Birds

Species	Season	Year	Pop min	Pop max	Acc	Criteria
[1] *Podiceps cristatus* Great Crested Grebe	W	1998	1,500	2,400	A	A4i, B1i
[1] *Netta rufina* Red-crested Pochard	W	1998	5,900	8,700	A	A4i, B1i
[1] *Aythya ferina* Pochard	W	1998	24,000	28,000	A	A4i, B1i
[1] *Aythya fuligula* Tufted Duck	W	1998	25,000	54,000	A	A4i, B1i
Mergus merganser Goosander	R	1996	15	25	A	B1i
Milvus migrans Black Kite	B	1996	40	—	A	B2
Picus canus Grey-headed Woodpecker	R	1996	20	—	A	B2

1. Mean and maximum numbers.

An important area for wintering waterbirds, migrating waders and breeding species associated with reedbeds. The site holds 20,000 or more waterbirds in winter, on a regular basis.

■ Protection status

National Partial **International** Partial

2,545 ha of IBA covered by 4 Water and Migratory Bird Reserves (Chevroux–Portalban; Fanel–Chablais de Cudrefin; Yvonand–Cheyres; Grandson–Champ Pittet; total area 2,545 ha). 4,218 ha of IBA covered by Inventory of Landscapes and Natural Monuments of National Importance (Rive sud du lac de Neuchâtel, 4,218 ha). 5,405 ha of IBA covered by Mire Landscapes of Particular Beauty and of National Importance (Grande Cariçaie, 5,405 ha). 733 ha of IBA covered by Fenlands of National Importance (total area 733 ha). 1,505 ha of IBA covered by 8 Flood-plains of National Importance (Les Grèves d'Yverdon–Les Tuileries; Les Grèves d'Yverdon–Yvonand; Les Grèves d'Yvonand–Cheyres; Les Grèves de Chevroux–Portalban; Les Grèves de Cheyres–Font; Les Grèves de Portalban–Cudrefin; Les Grèves du Chablais de Cudrefin; Seewald–Fanel; total area 1,505 ha). 3,063 ha of IBA covered by Ramsar Site (Rive sud du lac de Neuchâtel, 3,063 ha). 1,155 ha of IBA covered by Ramsar Site (Baie du Fanel et Le Chablais, 1,155 ha).

■ Conservation issues

Threats Agricultural intensification/expansion (C), Aquaculture/fisheries (C), Disturbance to birds, Infrastructure (B), Intensified forest management (C), Natural events (C), Recreation/tourism (A)

There is high tourist pressure, particularly in summer. Water-levels are artificially regulated so many marshland areas dry out.

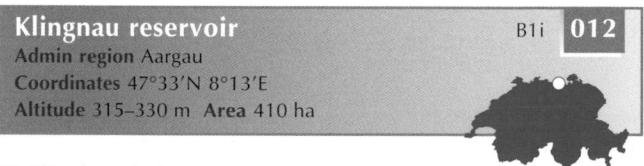

Klingnau reservoir   B1i   012

Admin region Aargau
Coordinates 47°33′N 8°13′E
Altitude 315–330 m **Area** 410 ha

■ Site description

A shallow, artificial reservoir on the River Aare. It has mudflats, reedbeds (*Phragmites*) and alluvial forests.

Habitats Forest and woodland (5%; broadleaved deciduous forest; alluvial/very wet forest), Wetland (88%; standing fresh water; river/stream; water-fringe vegetation), Artificial landscape (5%; highly improved reseeded grassland; arable land)
Land-use Agriculture (5%), Fisheries/aquaculture, Forestry (5%), Tourism/recreation

■ Birds

Species	Season	Year	Pop min	Pop max	Acc	Criteria
[1] *Anas strepera* Gadwall	W	1998	300	700	A	B1i

1. Mean and maximum numbers.

An important wintering site for waterbirds, with a large number of species. A passage site for waders and ducks.

■ Protection status

National High **International** Partial
355 ha of IBA covered by Inventory of Landscapes and Natural Monuments of National Importance (Aarelandschaft bei Klingnau, 364 ha). 355 ha of IBA covered by Water and Migratory Bird Reserve (Klingnauer Stausee, 355 ha). 112 ha of IBA covered by Flood-plains of National Importance (Auenreste Klingnauer Stausee, 112 ha). 355 ha of IBA covered by Ramsar Site (Lac artificiel de Klingnau, 355 ha).

■ Conservation issues

Threats Agricultural intensification/expansion (C), Industrialization/urbanization (C), Intensified forest management (C), Recreation/tourism (C)

No serious threats are known at this site.

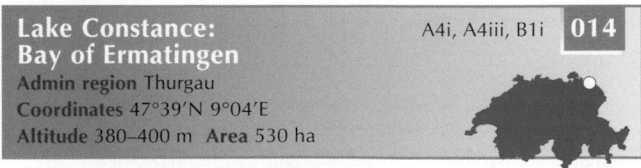

End of Lake Constance and River Rhine until Bibermühle
A4i, A4iii, B1i **013**
Admin region Schaffhausen, Thurgau
Coordinates 47°38′N 8°49′E
Altitude 400–400 m **Area** 480 ha

■ Site description

This area includes the end of Lake Untersee (part of Lake Constance) and a predominantly natural section of the River Rhine. The shoreline has small bays with areas of reedbed (*Phragmites*) and mudflats.

Habitats Forest and woodland (5%; broadleaved deciduous forest; alluvial/very wet forest), Wetland (88%; standing fresh water; river/stream), Artificial landscape (6%; highly improved reseeded grassland; arable land)
Land-use Agriculture (5%), Fisheries/aquaculture, Forestry (5%), Hunting, Tourism/recreation

■ Birds

Species		Season	Year	Pop min	Pop max	Acc	Criteria
[1] *Aythya ferina*	Pochard	W	1998	9,000	14,000	A	A4i, B1i
[1] *Aythya fuligula*	Tufted Duck	W	1998	17,000	25,000	A	A4i, B1i

1. Mean and maximum numbers.

The site regularly holds 20,000 or more waterbirds in winter, on a regular basis (including *Bucephala clangula*, 1,700 individuals).

■ Protection status

National High **International** None
480 ha of IBA covered by Water and Migratory Bird Reserve (Stein am Rhein, 480 ha). 6 ha of IBA covered by Fenlands of National Importance (Untersee and River Rhine, 6 ha). 480 ha of IBA covered by Inventory of Landscapes and Natural Monuments of National Importance (Untersee–Hochrhein, 12,827 ha).

■ Conservation issues

Threats Aquaculture/fisheries (B), Disturbance to birds (B), Recreation/tourism (B)

The main threat is disturbance from boats, divers and hunters.

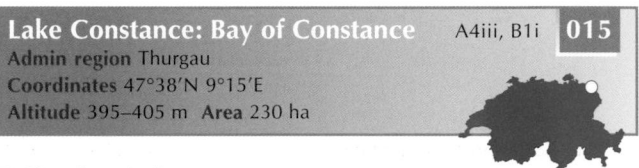

Lake Constance: Bay of Ermatingen
A4i, A4iii, B1i **014**
Admin region Thurgau
Coordinates 47°39′N 9°04′E
Altitude 380–400 m **Area** 530 ha

■ Site description

The IBA includes a large shallow bay with a natural shoreline, including mudbanks, reedbeds (*Phragmites*) and marshy areas. It also covers part of the River Rhine between Lakes Constance and Untersee. The Swiss part of a transboundary IBA together with the German IBA 'Untersee of Lake Constance' (site 231).

Habitats Wetland (70%; standing fresh water; water-fringe vegetation), Artificial landscape (30%; highly improved reseeded grassland; arable land; other urban/industrial areas)
Land-use Agriculture (19%), Fisheries/aquaculture, Hunting, Tourism/recreation, Urban/industrial/transport (11%)

■ Birds

Species		Season	Year	Pop min	Pop max	Acc	Criteria
[1,2] *Anas strepera*	Gadwall	W	1998	1,700	3,100	A	A4i, B1i
[1,2] *Aythya ferina*	Pochard	W	1998	6,000	9,900	A	B1i
[1,2] *Aythya fuligula*	Tufted Duck	W	1998	7,000	9,700	A	B1i

1. Data for Swiss IBA 014 and German IBA 231 combined.
2. Mean and maximum numbers.

The site holds 20,000 or more waterbirds in winter, on a regular basis. Waterbird numbers are given for the whole bay of Ermatingen including both the Swiss and German IBAs.

■ Protection status

National High **International** None
530 ha of IBA covered by Water and Migratory Bird Reserve (Ermatinger Becken, 570 ha). 60 ha of IBA covered by Fenlands of National Importance (Espen Riet, 60 ha). 500 ha of IBA covered by Inventory of Landscapes and Natural Monuments of National Importance (Untersee–Hochrhein, 12,827 ha).

■ Conservation issues

Threats Aquaculture/fisheries (B), Disturbance to birds (A), Industrialization/urbanization (C), Recreation/tourism (A)

One of the main threats is disturbance from recreational activities, particularly boating and walking. Hunting is allowed in some places.

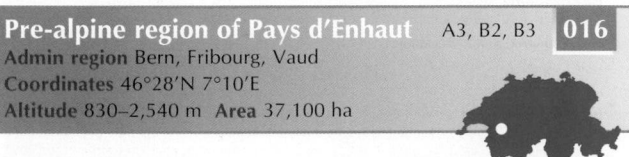

Lake Constance: Bay of Constance
A4iii, B1i **015**
Admin region Thurgau
Coordinates 47°38′N 9°15′E
Altitude 395–405 m **Area** 230 ha

■ Site description

A shallow bay on Lake Constance with a mainly artificial shoreline. The Swiss part of a transboundary IBA together with the German IBA 'Lake Constance–Obersee, and the adjacent Seerhein' (site 227).

Habitats Wetland (94%; standing fresh water), Artificial landscape (5%; urban parks/gardens)
Land-use Fisheries/aquaculture, Tourism/recreation, Urban/industrial/transport (5%)

■ Birds

Species		Season	Year	Pop min	Pop max	Acc	Criteria
[1,2] *Aythya ferina*	Pochard	W	1998	1,400	9,000	A	B1i

1. Mean and maximum numbers.
2. Data for Swiss IBA 015 and German IBA 227 combined.

The site holds 20,000 or more waterbirds in winter, on a regular basis (includes *Aythya fuligula* 2,500–5,600 individuals). The site only fulfils criteria if the Swiss and German IBAs are considered together.

■ Protection status

National None **International** None

■ Conservation issues

Threats Aquaculture/fisheries (C), Infrastructure (B), Recreation/tourism (B)

The main threat is disturbance from boats. Most of the area is protected from hunting by cantonal legislation.

Pre-alpine region of Pays d'Enhaut
A3, B2, B3 **016**
Admin region Bern, Fribourg, Vaud
Coordinates 46°28′N 7°10′E
Altitude 830–2,540 m **Area** 37,100 ha

■ Site description

An area of subalpine forests and alpine meadows with rocky areas at higher elevations and small villages in the valley bottoms.

Habitats Forest and woodland (36%; native coniferous forest; mixed forest), Grassland (45%; alpine/subalpine/boreal grassland), Rocky areas (7%; inland cliff), Artificial landscape (12%; highly improved reseeded grassland; arable land; other urban/industrial areas)
Land-use Agriculture (46%), Forestry (32%), Tourism/recreation

■ Birds

Species	Season	Year	Pop min	Pop max	Acc	Criteria
Falco tinnunculus Kestrel	B	1996	40	70	A	B2
Falco peregrinus Peregrine	R	1996	3	5	A	B2
Tetrao tetrix Black Grouse	R	1996	200	500	A	B2
Alectoris graeca Rock Partridge	R	1996	70	110	A	B2
Picoides tridactylus Three-toed Woodpecker	R	1996	20	50	A	B2
¹ *Prunella collaris* Alpine Accentor	R	1996	60	150	A	A3
Phoenicurus phoenicurus Redstart	B	1996	40	90	A	B2
Monticola saxatilis Rock Thrush	B	1996	25	60	A	B2
Turdus torquatus Ring Ouzel	B	1996	1,500	2,500	A	B3
¹ *Tichodroma muraria* Wallcreeper	R	1996	20	—	A	A3
¹ *Pyrrhocorax graculus* Alpine Chough	R	1996	50	200	A	A3
¹ *Montifringilla nivalis* Snowfinch	R	1996	10	25	A	A3
¹ *Serinus citrinella* Citril Finch	B	1996	500	—	A	A3, B3

1. Eurasian high-montane biome.

An important site for species breeding in conifer forests. *Tetrao tetrix, Picoides tridactylus, Turdus torquatus* and *Serinus citrinella* reach high densities.

■ Protection status

National Partial **International** None
2,298 ha of IBA covered by 2 Federal Hunting Reserves (Les Bimis–Ciernes Picat; Pierreuse–Gummfluh, total area 2,298 ha). 20,582 ha of IBA covered by 3 Inventory of Landscapes and Natural Monuments of National Importance (La Pierreuse–Gummfluh–Vallée de l'Etivaz; Tour d'Aï–Dent de Corjon; Vanil Noir; total area 25,106 ha). 2,835 ha of IBA covered by 2 Mire Landscapes of Particular Beauty and of National Importance (Col des Mosses/La Lécherette; Lauenensee; total area 2,835 ha). 68 ha of IBA covered by 2 Flood-plains of National Importance (La Sarine près Château–d'Oex; Louibach (Rohr–Oey); total area 68 ha. 781 ha of IBA covered by 34 Fenlands of National Importance (total area 781 ha). 70 ha of IBA covered by 8 Raised and Transitional Bogs of National Importance (total area 70 ha).

■ Conservation issues

Threats Agricultural intensification/expansion (B), Drainage (C), Infrastructure (B), Recreation/tourism (B)

No serious threats are known at this site.

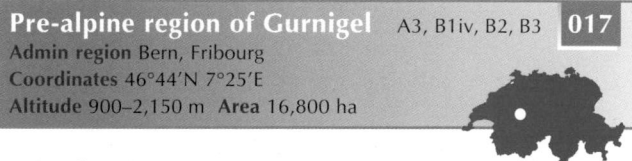

Pre-alpine region of Gurnigel   A3, B1iv, B2, B3   017
Admin region Bern, Fribourg
Coordinates 46°44′N 7°25′E
Altitude 900–2,150 m Area 16,800 ha

■ Site description
A subalpine landscape with mixed and natural conifer forests at lower elevations. Above the treeline, there are extensive alpine meadows and rocky areas.

Habitats Forest and woodland (40%; native coniferous forest; mixed forest), Grassland (50%; alpine/subalpine/boreal grassland), Rocky areas (5%; inland cliff)
Land-use Agriculture (40%), Forestry (38%), Military, Tourism/recreation

■ Birds

Species	Season	Year	Pop min	Pop max	Acc	Criteria
Falco tinnunculus Kestrel	B	1996	30	60	A	B2
Tetrao tetrix Black Grouse	R	1996	100	200	A	B2
¹ *Prunella collaris* Alpine Accentor	R	1996	20	60	A	A3
Turdus torquatus Ring Ouzel	B	1996	900	1,500	A	B3
¹ *Tichodroma muraria* Wallcreeper	R	1996	Uncommon		—	A3
¹ *Pyrrhocorax graculus* Alpine Chough	R	1996	60	100	A	A3
¹ *Serinus citrinella* Citril Finch	B	1996	300	—	A	A3, B3

1. Eurasian high-montane biome.

An important site for species associated with subalpine forest, particularly *Picus viridis, Turdus torquatus* and *Serinus citrinella*. The site is a migratory bottleneck, where more than 3,000 raptors regularly pass in autumn.

■ Protection status
National Partial **International** None

4,507 ha of IBA covered by Mire Landscapes of Particular Beauty and of National Importance (Gurnigel/Gantrisch, 4,507 ha). 39 ha of IBA covered by 11 Raised and Transitional Bogs of National Importance (total area 39 ha). 684 ha of IBA covered by 18 Fenlands of National Importance (total area 684 ha).

■ Conservation issues

Threats Infrastructure (C), Intensified forest management (C), Recreation/tourism (B)

The main threat is from recreational activities.

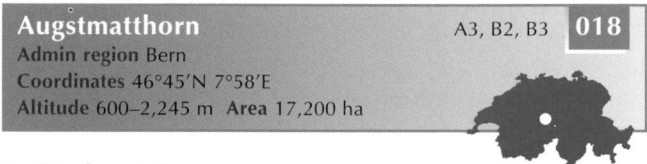

Augstmatthorn   A3, B2, B3   018
Admin region Bern
Coordinates 46°45′N 7°58′E
Altitude 600–2,245 m Area 17,200 ha

■ Site description
A mountainous area with alpine meadows dominant at higher elevations and natural conifer forest, interspersed with bogs and pastures at lower altitudes.

Habitats Forest and woodland (39%; native coniferous forest; mixed forest; treeline ecotone), Grassland (32%; alpine/subalpine/boreal grassland), Wetland (13%; raised bog; fen/transition mire/spring), Rocky areas (11%; inland cliff), Artificial landscape (5%; other urban/industrial areas)
Land-use Agriculture (41%), Forestry (37%), Tourism/recreation

■ Birds

Species	Season	Year	Pop min	Pop max	Acc	Criteria
Falco tinnunculus Kestrel	B	1996	25	50	A	B2
¹ *Prunella collaris* Alpine Accentor	R	1996	20	50	A	A3
Turdus torquatus Ring Ouzel	B	1996	800	1,300	A	B3
¹ *Tichodroma muraria* Wallcreeper	R	1996	—	—	—	A3
¹ *Pyrrhocorax graculus* Alpine Chough	R	1996	60	100	A	A3
¹ *Montifringilla nivalis* Snowfinch	R	1996	20	40	A	A3
¹ *Serinus citrinella* Citril Finch	B	1996	300	—	A	A3, B3

1. Eurasian high-montane biome.

An important site for species associated with subalpine forest.

■ Protection status
National Partial **International** None
2,010 ha of IBA covered by Federal Hunting Reserve (Augstmatthorn, 2,010 ha). 2,275 ha of IBA covered by Inventory of Landscapes and Natural Monuments of National Importance (Hohgant, 2,275 ha). 1,868 ha of IBA covered by 38 Fenlands of National Importance (total area 1,910 ha). 417 ha of IBA covered by 40 Raised and Transitional Bogs of National Importance (total area 417 ha). 8,300 ha of IBA covered by Mire Landscapes of Particular Beauty and of National Importance (Habkern/Sörenberg; Rotmoos/Eriz; 12,229 ha).

■ Conservation issues

Threats Agricultural intensification/expansion (C), Drainage (C), Infrastructure (C), Recreation/tourism (B)

The main threat is from recreational activities.

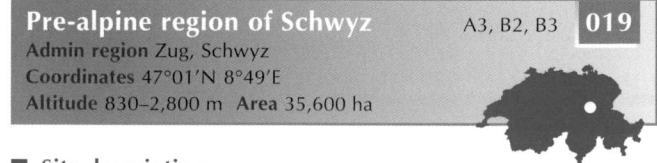

Pre-alpine region of Schwyz   A3, B2, B3   019
Admin region Zug, Schwyz
Coordinates 47°01′N 8°49′E
Altitude 830–2,800 m Area 35,600 ha

■ Site description
A hilly area in the northern foothills of the Alps with lakes, bogs, villages, extensive woodlands, alpine meadows and karst mountains.

Habitats Forest and woodland (31%; native coniferous forest; mixed forest; treeline ecotone), Grassland (35%; alpine/subalpine/boreal grassland; mesophile grassland), Rocky areas (16%; inland cliff), Artificial landscape (15%; highly improved reseeded grassland; other urban/industrial areas)
Land-use Agriculture (41%), Forestry (28%), Tourism/recreation, Urban/industrial/transport (2%)

■ Birds

Species	Season	Year	Pop min	Pop max	Acc	Criteria
Falco tinnunculus Kestrel	B	1996	50	—	A	B2
Tetrao tetrix Black Grouse	R	1996	100	200	A	B2
Alectoris graeca Rock Partridge	R	1996	—	—	—	B2
Picus viridis Green Woodpecker	R	1996	80	150	A	B2
Picoides tridactylus Three-toed Woodpecker	R	1996	30	60	A	B2
¹ *Prunella collaris* Alpine Accentor	R	1996	250	450	A	A3
Monticola saxatilis Rock Thrush	B	1996	10	20	A	B2
Turdus torquatus Ring Ouzel	B	1996	800	1,400	A	B3
¹ *Tichodroma muraria* Wallcreeper	R	1996	—	—	—	A3
¹ *Pyrrhocorax graculus* Alpine Chough	R	1996	250	500	A	A3
¹ *Montifringilla nivalis* Snowfinch	R	1996	100	200	A	A3
¹ *Serinus citrinella* Citril Finch	B	1996	200	400	A	A3, B3

1. Eurasian high-montane biome.

An important site for species associated with subalpine forests.

■ Protection status

National Partial **International** None

8,150 ha of IBA covered by 2 Federal Hunting Reserves (Mythen; Silbern–Jagern–Bodmerenwald; total area 8,500 ha). 8,774 ha of IBA covered by 2 Inventory of Landscapes and Natural Monuments of National Importance (Silberen; Moorlandschaft Rothenthurm–Altmatt–Biberbrugg; 9,043 ha). 32 ha of IBA covered by Flood-plains of National Importance (Biber im Aegeried, 32 ha). 4,440 ha of IBA covered by 4 Mire Landscapes of Particular Beauty and of National Importance (Rothenthurm; Schwantenau; Breitried/Unteriberg; Ibergeregg; total area 4,440 ha). 523 ha of IBA covered by 14 Raised and Transitional Bogs of National Importance (total area 523 ha). 1,776 ha of IBA covered by 56 Fenlands of National Importance (total area 1,776 ha).

■ Conservation issues

Threats Infrastructure (C), Recreation/tourism (B)

The main threat is from recreational activities.

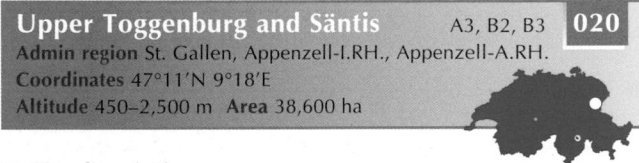

Upper Toggenburg and Säntis A3, B2, B3 020
Admin region St. Gallen, Appenzell-I.RH., Appenzell-A.RH.
Coordinates 47°11′N 9°18′E
Altitude 450–2,500 m Area 38,600 ha

■ Site description
A mountainous area with mixed and conifer forest, alpine meadows and rocky areas.

Habitats Forest and woodland (38%; native coniferous forest; mixed forest; treeline ecotone), Grassland (43%; alpine/subalpine/boreal grassland), Rocky areas (7%; inland cliff), Artificial landscape (11%; arable land; other urban/industrial areas)
Land-use Agriculture (40%), Forestry (30%), Tourism/recreation

■ Birds

Species	Season	Year	Pop min	Pop max	Acc	Criteria
Aquila chrysaetos Golden Eagle	R	1996	7	8	A	B2
Falco tinnunculus Kestrel	B	1996	70	200	A	B2
Falco peregrinus Peregrine	R	1996	2	5	A	B2
Tetrao tetrix Black Grouse	R	1996	250	450	A	B2
Picus canus Grey-headed Woodpecker	R	1996	5	20	A	B2
Picus viridis Green Woodpecker	R	1996	200	400	A	B2
Picoides tridactylus Three-toed Woodpecker	R	1996	30	110	A	B2
¹ *Prunella collaris* Alpine Accentor	R	1996	100	—	A	A3
Monticola saxatilis Rock Thrush	B	1996	5	15	A	B2
Turdus torquatus Ring Ouzel	B	1996	1,500	2,500	A	B3
¹ *Tichodroma muraria* Wallcreeper	R	1996	—	—	—	A3
¹ *Pyrrhocorax graculus* Alpine Chough	R	1996	300	500	A	A3
¹ *Montifringilla nivalis* Snowfinch	R	1996	40	150	A	A3
¹ *Serinus citrinella* Citril Finch	B	1996	400	—	A	A3, B3

1. Eurasian high-montane biome.

An important site for alpine species and species associated with subalpine forest.

■ Protection status
National High **International** None

2,590 ha of IBA covered by Federal Hunting Reserve (Säntis; Säntisgebiet; Speer–Churfirsten–Alvier; total area 48,233 ha). 4,026 ha of IBA covered by 3 Mire Landscapes of Particular Beauty and of National Importance (Schwägalp; Gräppelen; Vorder Höhi; total area 4,026 ha). 142 ha of IBA covered by Raised and 23 Transitional Bogs of National Importance (total area 142 ha). 760 ha of IBA covered by 30 Fenlands of National Importance (total area 760 ha).

■ Conservation issues

Threats Agricultural intensification/expansion (C), Recreation/tourism (B)

The main threats are from recreational activities.

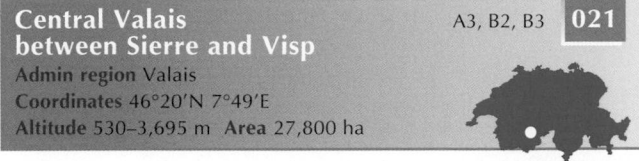

Central Valais between Sierre and Visp A3, B2, B3 021
Admin region Valais
Coordinates 46°20′N 7°49′E
Altitude 530–3,695 m Area 27,800 ha

■ Site description
A broad river valley in the central Alps. The valley is dominated by agricultural land, characterized by small plots, and some alluvial forests. The IBA includes a south-facing hillside with some traditional agriculture and xerophytic vegetation.

Habitats Forest and woodland (31%; broadleaved deciduous forest; native coniferous forest; mixed forest; alluvial/very wet forest; treeline ecotone), Grassland (24%; steppe/dry calcareous grassland; alpine/subalpine/boreal grassland), Rocky areas (26%; inland cliff), Artificial landscape (18%; highly improved reseeded grassland; arable land; perennial crops/orchards/groves; other urban/industrial areas)
Land-use Agriculture (28%), Forestry (26%), Tourism/recreation, Urban/industrial/transport (5%), Water management

■ Birds

Species	Season	Year	Pop min	Pop max	Acc	Criteria
Aquila chrysaetos Golden Eagle	R	1996	5	—	A	B2
Falco peregrinus Peregrine	R	1996	2	5	A	B2
Alectoris graeca Rock Partridge	R	1996	60	110	A	B2
Jynx torquilla Wryneck	B	1996	50	—	A	B2
¹ *Prunella collaris* Alpine Accentor	R	1996	150	—	A	A3
Phoenicurus phoenicurus Redstart	B	1996	100	—	A	B2
Monticola saxatilis Rock Thrush	B	1996	40	100	A	B2
Turdus torquatus Ring Ouzel	B	1996	300	600	A	B3
¹ *Tichodroma muraria* Wallcreeper	R	1996	—	—	—	A3
¹ *Pyrrhocorax graculus* Alpine Chough	R	1996	250	450	A	A3
¹ *Montifringilla nivalis* Snowfinch	R	1996	100	200	A	A3
¹ *Serinus citrinella* Citril Finch	B	1996	150	300	A	A3

1. Eurasian high-montane biome.

An important site for species found in semi-open landscapes, including *Alectoris graeca*, *Jynx torquilla*, *Phoenicurus phoenicurus* and *Monticola saxatilis*.

■ Protection status
National Partial **International** None

6,300 ha of IBA covered by 3 Federal Hunting Reserves (Alpjuhorn; Leukerbad; Wilerhorn; total area 12,980 ha). 8,666 ha of IBA covered by 4 Inventory of Landscapes and Natural Monuments of National Importance (Bergji–Platten; Berner Hochalpen and Aletsch–Bietschhorn–Gebiet; Pfynwald–Illgraben; Raron–Heidnischbiel; total area 48,506 ha). 5 ha of IBA covered by Fenlands of National Importance (Mutt, 5 ha). 348 ha of IBA covered by Flood-plains of National Importance (Pfynwald, 348 ha).

■ Conservation issues

Threats Abandonment/reduction of land management (C), Agricultural intensification/expansion (B), Industrialization/urbanization (A), Infrastructure (A), Recreation/tourism (B), Unsustainable exploitation (C)

The main threats in the valley are from infrastructural developments, particularly road and railway, the building of a golf course, and industrial development. There are projects to remove dams along some sections of the River Rhône.

Valley of Zermatt — A3, B2, B3 — 022

Admin region Valais
Coordinates 46°06'N 7°47'E
Altitude 695–3,380 m **Area** 22,100 ha

■ Site description
The site consists of a long valley running from south to north in the central Alps. Habitats include natural conifer forests, alpine meadows, rocky areas, traditional agricultural landscapes and urban areas.

Habitats Forest and woodland (26%; native coniferous forest; mixed forest; treeline ecotone), Grassland (33%; alpine/subalpine/boreal grassland), Rocky areas (33%; inland cliff), Artificial landscape (7%; arable land; perennial crops/orchards/groves; urban parks/gardens; other urban/industrial areas)
Land-use Agriculture (24%), Forestry (24%), Tourism/recreation

■ Birds

Species		Season	Year	Pop min	Pop max	Acc	Criteria
Aquila chrysaetos	Golden Eagle	R	1996	5	5	A	B2
Tetrao tetrix	Black Grouse	R	1996	150	250	A	B2
Alectoris graeca	Rock Partridge	R	1996	80	130	A	B2
Jynx torquilla	Wryneck	B	1996	20	—	A	B2
[1] Prunella collaris	Alpine Accentor	R	1996	200	400	A	A3
Monticola saxatilis	Rock Thrush	B	1996	25	60	A	B2
Turdus torquatus	Ring Ouzel	B	1996	350	600	A	B3
[1] Tichodroma muraria	Wallcreeper	R	1996	Rare	—		A3
[1] Pyrrhocorax graculus	Alpine Chough	R	1996	300	550	A	A3
[1] Montifringilla nivalis	Snowfinch	R	1996	200	400	A	A3
[1] Serinus citrinella	Citril Finch	B	1996	100	250	A	A3

1. Eurasian high-montane biome.

An important site for species breeding in subalpine and alpine habitats.

■ Protection status
National Low **International** None
2,100 ha of IBA covered by Inventory of Landscapes and Natural Monuments of National Importance (Dent Blanche–Matterhorn–Monte Rosa, 30,271 ha). 5 ha of IBA covered by Raised and Transitional Bogs of National Importance (Boniger See, 5 ha). 3 ha of IBA covered by 2 Fenlands of National Importance (total area 3 ha).

■ Conservation issues

Threats Abandonment/reduction of land management (B), Industrialization/urbanization (B), Infrastructure (A), Recreation/tourism (A)

Mountain railways provide tourist access to remote areas. Therefore, the main threats are from tourism and related infrastructure developments, in both summer and winter.

Aletsch region — A3, B2 — 023

Admin region Valais
Coordinates 46°22'N 8°04'E
Altitude 900–2,930 m **Area** 4,750 ha

■ Site description
A mountain ridge in the central Alps, bordering the Aletsch glacier. The south-facing slope has conifer forests, alpine meadows, pastures and villages. The north-facing hillside has native *Larix–Pinus* forest and scree.

Habitats Forest and woodland (32%; native coniferous forest; treeline ecotone), Grassland (41%; alpine/subalpine/boreal grassland), Rocky areas (18%; inland cliff), Artificial landscape (8%; other urban/industrial areas; perennial crops/orchards/groves; urban parks/gardens)
Land-use Agriculture (41%), Forestry (31%), Tourism/recreation

■ Birds

Species		Season	Year	Pop min	Pop max	Acc	Criteria
Alectoris graeca	Rock Partridge	R	1996	25	40	A	B2
[1] Prunella collaris	Alpine Accentor	R	1996	30	—	A	A3
Monticola saxatilis	Rock Thrush	B	1996	5	30	A	B2
[1] Tichodroma muraria	Wallcreeper	R	1996	—	—	—	A3

Species ... continued		Season	Year	Pop min	Pop max	Acc	Criteria
[1] Pyrrhocorax graculus	Alpine Chough	R	1996	100	200	A	A3
[1] Montifringilla nivalis	Snowfinch	R	1996	20	30	A	A3
[1] Serinus citrinella	Citril Finch	B	1996	40	100	A	A3

1. Eurasian high-montane biome.

An important site for species breeding in subalpine and alpine habitats.

■ Protection status
National Partial **International** None
1,510 ha of IBA covered by Federal Hunting Reserve (Aletschwald, 1,510 ha). 1,100 ha of IBA covered by Inventory of Landscapes and Natural Monuments of National Importance (Berner Hochalpen and Aletsch–Bietschhorn–Gebiet, 42,866 ha). 7 ha of IBA covered by 2 Raised and Transitional Bogs of National Importance (total area 7 ha).

■ Conservation issues

Threats Agricultural intensification/expansion (C), Industrialization/urbanization (B), Infrastructure (B), Recreation/tourism (B)

A regional ski-centre, within the IBA, has been extended and plans for further developments exist.

Heinzenberg mountain and surrounding valleys — A3, B2, B3 — 024

Admin region Graubünden
Coordinates 46°44'N 9°19'E
Altitude 600–2,880 m **Area** 29,000 ha

■ Site description
The IBA consists of central alpine valleys, with forests and traditional agricultural landscapes, and mountainous regions.

Habitats Forest and woodland (45%; native coniferous forest; mixed forest; alluvial/very wet forest; treeline ecotone), Grassland (42%; alpine/subalpine/boreal grassland), Rocky areas (7%; inland cliff), Artificial landscape (5%; arable land; perennial crops/orchards/groves; urban parks/gardens; other urban/industrial areas)
Land-use Agriculture (39%), Forestry (39%), Tourism/recreation

■ Birds

Species		Season	Year	Pop min	Pop max	Acc	Criteria
Aquila chrysaetos	Golden Eagle	R	1996	9	9	A	B2
Tetrao tetrix	Black Grouse	R	1996	100	200	A	B2
Alectoris graeca	Rock Partridge	R	1996	40	70	A	B2
Jynx torquilla	Wryneck	B	1996	25	60	A	B2
Picus viridis	Green Woodpecker	R	1996	150	—	A	B2
Picoides tridactylus	Three-toed Woodpecker	R	1996	15	40	A	B2
[1] Prunella collaris	Alpine Accentor	R	1996	75	150	A	A3
Monticola saxatilis	Rock Thrush	B	1996	5	25	A	B2
Turdus torquatus	Ring Ouzel	B	1996	500	1,000	A	B3
[1] Tichodroma muraria	Wallcreeper	R	1996	—	—	—	A3
[1] Pyrrhocorax graculus	Alpine Chough	R	1996	100	200	A	A3
[1] Montifringilla nivalis	Snowfinch	R	1996	40	60	A	A3
[1] Serinus citrinella	Citril Finch	B	1996	150	—	A	A3

1. Eurasian high-montane biome.

An important site for species associated with subalpine habitats, including *Tetrao tetrix*, *Picus viridis* and *Turdus torquatus*.

■ Protection status
National Partial **International** None
2,697 ha of IBA covered by 3 Inventory of Landscapes and Natural Monuments of National Importance (Ruinaulta; Trockengebiet im unteren Domleschg; Auenlandschaft am Unterlauf des Hinterrheins; total area 2,697 ha). 236 ha of IBA covered by 3 Flood-plains of National Importance (Rhäzünser Rheinauen Cauma; Cumparduns; total area 236 ha). 57 ha of IBA covered by 5 Fenlands of National Importance (total area 57 ha).

■ Conservation issues

Threats Abandonment/reduction of land management (C), Agricultural intensification/expansion (C), Industrialization/urbanization (C), Infrastructure (C), Recreation/tourism (C)

No serious threats are known at this site.

Lower Engadine and Swiss National Park

A3, B2, B3 **025**

Admin region Graubünden
Coordinates 46°44′N 10°13′E
Altitude 1030–3,160 m **Area** 101,100 ha

■ Site description

This site encompasses the lower part of the central alpine Engadine valley, the Swiss National Park and the Val Müstair in the south. The site includes natural forests, traditional agriculture and alpine regions.

Habitats Forest and woodland (28%; native coniferous forest; mixed forest; treeline ecotone), Grassland (33%; steppe/dry calcareous grassland; alpine/subalpine/boreal grassland), Rocky areas (32%; inland cliff), Artificial landscape (6%; arable land; perennial crops/orchards/groves; urban parks/gardens; other urban/industrial areas)
Land-use Agriculture (27%), Forestry (22%), Nature conservation/research (32%), Tourism/recreation

■ Birds

Species	Season	Year	Pop min	Pop max	Acc	Criteria
Aquila chrysaetos Golden Eagle	R	1996	17	18	A	B2
Tetrao tetrix Black Grouse	R	1996	100	300	A	B2
Alectoris graeca Rock Partridge	R	1996	60	—	A	B2
Jynx torquilla Wryneck	B	1996	20	40	A	B2
Picoides tridactylus Three-toed Woodpecker	R	1996	50	100	A	B2
[1] **Prunella collaris** Alpine Accentor	R	1996	500	—	A	A3
Monticola saxatilis Rock Thrush	B	1996	20	—	A	B2
Turdus torquatus Ring Ouzel	B	1996	1,500	3,000	A	B3
[1] **Tichodroma muraria** Wallcreeper	R	1996	10	—	A	A3
[1] **Pyrrhocorax graculus** Alpine Chough	R	1996	500	—	A	A3
[1] **Montifringilla nivalis** Snowfinch	R	1996	500	1,500	A	A3
[1] **Serinus citrinella** Citril Finch	B	1996	1,000	—	A	A3, B3

1. Eurasian high-montane biome.

An important area for species associated with subalpine and alpine habitats and areas used for traditional agriculture. Species of global conservation concern that do not meet criteria: *Crex crex*.

■ Protection status

National Partial **International** None
16,887 ha of IBA covered by National Park (Swiss, 16,887 ha). 30,649 ha of IBA covered by 2 Inventory of Landscapes and Natural Monuments of National Importance (Piz Arina; Schweizerischer Nationalpark und Randgebiete; 34,240 ha). 1,096 ha of IBA covered by 2 Mire Landscapes of Particular Beauty and of National Importance (Buffalora; Tamangur; total area 1,096 ha). 187 ha of IBA covered by 7 Flood-plains of National Importance (Strada; Plan–Sot; San Batrumieu; Panas–ch–Resgia; Craviz; Il Rom Valchava–Graveras (Müstair); Lischana–Suronnas; total area 187 ha). 0.1 ha of IBA covered by Raised and Transitional Bogs of National Importance (Lai Nair, 0.1 ha). 105 ha of IBA covered by 8 Fenlands of National Importance (total area 105 ha).

■ Conservation issues

Threats Abandonment/reduction of land management (C), Agricultural intensification/expansion (C), Infrastructure (B), Intensified forest management (C), Recreation/tourism (B)

There are plans to double the size of the National Park by creating buffer zones. A reintroduction programme of *Gypaetus barbatus* is underway. Some parts of the site are included in an action plan for *Crex crex*.

Simplon region

A3, B2, B3 **026**

Admin region Valais
Coordinates 46°10′N 8°05′E
Altitude 850–4,020 m **Area** 14,700 ha

■ Site description

A high mountain region, in the southern Alps, with extensive forests, scrub, alpine meadows and rocky areas.

Habitats Forest and woodland (18%; native coniferous forest; mixed forest; treeline ecotone), Grassland (37%; alpine/subalpine/boreal grassland), Rocky areas (42%; inland cliff)
Land-use Agriculture (21%), Forestry (12%), Tourism/recreation

■ Birds

Species	Season	Year	Pop min	Pop max	Acc	Criteria
Tetrao tetrix Black Grouse	R	1996	120	200	A	B2
Alectoris graeca Rock Partridge	R	1996	70	110	A	B2
Jynx torquilla Wryneck	B	1996	20	30	A	B2
Picus viridis Green Woodpecker	R	1996	50	150	A	B2
[1] **Prunella collaris** Alpine Accentor	R	1996	150	250	A	A3
Monticola saxatilis Rock Thrush	B	1996	20	—	A	B2
Turdus torquatus Ring Ouzel	B	1996	200	400	A	B3
[1] **Tichodroma muraria** Wallcreeper	R	1996	—	—	—	A3
[1] **Pyrrhocorax graculus** Alpine Chough	R	1996	200	300	A	A3
[1] **Montifringilla nivalis** Snowfinch	R	1996	100	250	A	A3
[1] **Serinus citrinella** Citril Finch	B	1996	100	200	A	A3

1. Eurasian high-montane biome.

An important area for species of subalpine and alpine habitats.

■ Protection status

National Partial **International** None
11,498 ha of IBA covered by Inventory of Landscapes and Natural Monuments of National Importance (Laggintal–Zwischbergental, 11,498 ha). 67 ha of IBA covered by Raised and Transitional Bogs of National Importance (Simplonpass/Hopschusee, 67 ha).

■ Conservation issues

Threats Abandonment/reduction of land management (C), Recreation/tourism (C)

No serious threats are known at this site.

Piora–Dötra

A3, B2 **027**

Admin region Ticino
Coordinates 46°30′N 8°47′E
Altitude 950–3,190 m **Area** 9,700 ha

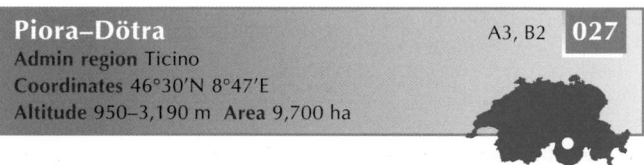

■ Site description

High-lying open valleys in the southern Alps. Most areas are above the treeline and scrub, alpine meadows and rocky areas dominate.

Habitats Forest and woodland (21%; native coniferous forest; treeline ecotone), Grassland (55%; alpine/subalpine/boreal grassland), Rocky areas (19%; inland cliff)
Land-use Agriculture (36%), Forestry (16%), Tourism/recreation

■ Birds

Species	Season	Year	Pop min	Pop max	Acc	Criteria
Alectoris graeca Rock Partridge	R	1996	25	50	A	B2
[1] **Prunella collaris** Alpine Accentor	R	1996	100	—	A	A3
Monticola saxatilis Rock Thrush	B	1996	10	20	A	B2
[1] **Tichodroma muraria** Wallcreeper	R	1996	—	—	—	A3
[1] **Pyrrhocorax graculus** Alpine Chough	R	1996	40	80	A	A3
[1] **Montifringilla nivalis** Snowfinch	R	1996	50	100	A	A3
[1] **Serinus citrinella** Citril Finch	B	1996	20	60	A	A3

1. Eurasian high-montane biome.

An important area for species breeding above the treeline.

■ Protection status

National Partial **International** None
5,600 ha of IBA covered by Inventory of Landscapes and Natural Monuments of National Importance (Piora–Lucomagno–Dötra, 9,690 ha). 43 ha of IBA covered by Flood-plains of National Importance (Campall, 43 ha). 2,745 ha of IBA covered by Mire Landscapes of Particular Beauty and of National Importance (Lucomagno/Dötra, 2,745 ha). 57 ha of IBA covered by 11 Fenlands of National Importance (total area 57 ha). 61 ha of IBA covered by 5 Raised and Transitional Bogs of National Importance (total area 61 ha).

■ Conservation issues

Threats Abandonment/reduction of land management (C), Disturbance to birds (C), Recreation/tourism (B)

No serious threats are known at this site.

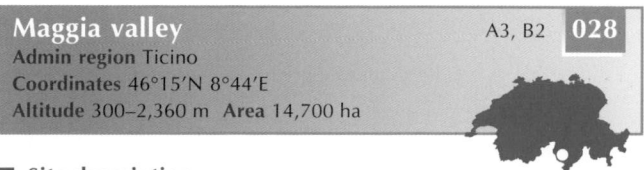

Maggia valley — A3, B2 — 028

Admin region Ticino
Coordinates 46°15'N 8°44'E
Altitude 300–2,360 m **Area** 14,700 ha

■ Site description

This site contains a low-altitude valley with extensive alluvial areas and a mountainous region in the southern Alps. The steep slopes are forested and, at higher elevations, alpine meadows and rocky areas dominate.

Habitats Forest and woodland (61%; broadleaved deciduous forest; native coniferous forest; alluvial/very wet forest; treeline ecotone), Grassland (24%; alpine/subalpine/boreal grassland), Rocky areas (7%; inland cliff)
Land-use Agriculture (9%), Forestry (52%), Tourism/recreation

■ Birds

Species		Season	Year	Pop min	Pop max	Acc	Criteria
Alectoris graeca	Rock Partridge	R	1996	40	60	A	B2
Jynx torquilla	Wryneck	B	1996	20	40	A	B2
¹ *Prunella collaris*	Alpine Accentor	R	1996	30	50	A	A3
Phoenicurus phoenicurus	Redstart	B	1996	100	—	A	B2
Monticola saxatilis	Rock Thrush	B	1996	10	25	A	B2
¹ *Tichodroma muraria*	Wallcreeper	R	1996	—	—	—	A3
¹ *Pyrrhocorax graculus*	Alpine Chough	R	1996	25	—	A	A3
¹ *Montifringilla nivalis*	Snowfinch	R	1996	—	—	—	A3
¹ *Serinus citrinella*	Citril Finch	B	1996	—	—	—	A3

1. Eurasian high-montane biome.

An important site for breeding species found in the treeline ecotone and in semi-open landscapes. *Tetrao tetrix, Jynx torquilla, Phoenicurus phoenicurus* and *Monticola saxatilis* occur in high densities.

■ Protection status

National Partial **International** None
3,800 ha of IBA covered by Inventory of Landscapes and Natural Monuments of National Importance (Val Verzasca, 19,932 ha). 439 ha of IBA covered by 2 Flood-plains of National Importance (Maggia; Saleggio; total area 439 ha). 3 ha of IBA covered by Raised and Transitional Bogs of National Importance (Piano sopra Visletto, 3 ha).

■ Conservation issues

Threats Abandonment/reduction of land management (B), Industrialization/urbanization (C), Recreation/tourism (B)

There is substantial recreational pressure along the Maggia river, but higher areas are largely undisturbed.

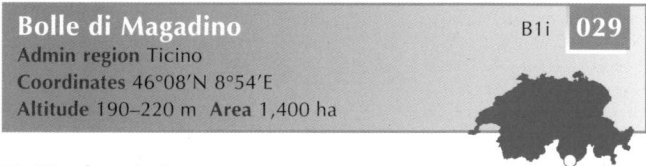

Bolle di Magadino — B1i — 029

Admin region Ticino
Coordinates 46°08'N 8°54'E
Altitude 190–220 m **Area** 1,400 ha

■ Site description

The site includes a delta formed by the Ticino and Verzasca rivers in a wide valley surrounded by high mountains. There are extensive alluvial forests and reedbeds (*Phragmites*), marshland and agricultural areas.

Habitats Forest and woodland (16%; broadleaved deciduous forest; alluvial/very wet forest), Grassland (14%), Wetland (18%; standing fresh water; river/stream; water-fringe vegetation; fen/transition mire/spring), Artificial landscape (52%; highly improved reseeded grassland; arable land; urban parks/gardens; other urban/industrial areas)
Land-use Agriculture (56%), Fisheries/aquaculture, Forestry (16%), Tourism/recreation, Urban/industrial/transport (17%)

■ Birds

The site is very important for migratory birds crossing the Alps, and for waterbirds and breeding species associated with reedbeds. It is the only Swiss wetland south of the Alps. It is regarded as a biogeographically unique wetland under Ramsar Convention criteria. As a result it is included in the IBA inventory (criterion B1i having been applied at a site level) despite not fulfilling species criteria.

■ Protection status

National Partial **International** Partial
661 ha of IBA covered by Inventory of Landscapes and Natural Monuments of National Importance (Delta del Ticino e della Verzasca, 661 ha). 353 ha of IBA covered by 3 Flood-plains of National Importance (total area 353 ha). 82 ha of IBA covered by 9 Fenlands of National Importance (total area 82 ha). 1,066 ha of IBA covered by Mire Landscapes of Particular Beauty and of National Importance (Piano di Magadino, 1,066 ha). 661 ha of IBA covered by Ramsar Site (Bolle di Magadino, 661 ha).

■ Conservation issues

Threats Agricultural intensification/expansion (A), Aquaculture/fisheries (B), Disturbance to birds (C), Drainage (C), Dredging/canalization (A), Infrastructure (A), Recreation/tourism (B)

The main threats are disturbance from recreational activities.

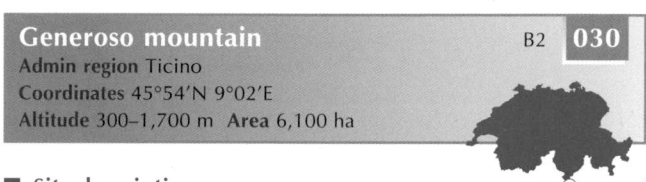

Generoso mountain — B2 — 030

Admin region Ticino
Coordinates 45°54'N 9°02'E
Altitude 300–1,700 m **Area** 6,100 ha

■ Site description

A mountainous area in the southern foothills of the Alps. The site is dominated by deciduous forests. There are also small villages with areas of traditional agriculture.

Habitats Forest and woodland (76%; broadleaved deciduous forest), Grassland (9%; mesophile grassland), Artificial landscape (15%; perennial crops/orchards/groves; urban parks/gardens; other urban/industrial areas)
Land-use Agriculture (9%), Forestry (76%), Tourism/recreation, Urban/industrial/transport (7%)

■ Birds

Species		Season	Year	Pop min	Pop max	Acc	Criteria
Jynx torquilla	Wryneck	B	1996	20	30	A	B2
Phoenicurus phoenicurus	Redstart	B	1996	150	250	A	B2

An important site for species associated with agriculture and forest in the foothills and montane zone.

■ Protection status

National High **International** None
6,100 ha of IBA covered by Inventory of Landscapes and Natural Monuments of National Importance (Monte Generoso, 6,203 ha).

■ Conservation issues

Threats Abandonment/reduction of land management (B), Recreation/tourism (C)

The main threat is the abandonment of traditional agriculture, which results in the loss of hay-meadows as they succeed to scrub and forest.

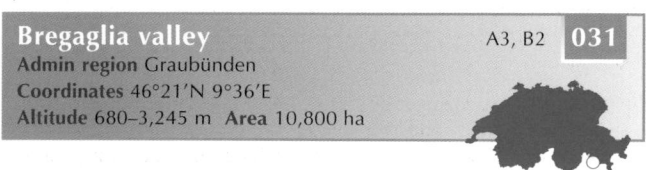

Bregaglia valley — A3, B2 — 031

Admin region Graubünden
Coordinates 46°21'N 9°36'E
Altitude 680–3,245 m **Area** 10,800 ha

■ Site description

This site encompasses an alpine valley and its surrounding slopes in the southern Alps. The valley bottom contains settlements and pastures. At low elevations, the slopes are covered by forests, changing with increasing altitude to scrub and then alpine meadows and rocky areas.

Habitats Forest and woodland (40%; broadleaved deciduous forest; native coniferous forest; mixed forest; treeline ecotone), Grassland (30%; alpine/subalpine/boreal grassland), Rocky areas (22%; inland cliff), Artificial landscape (6%; arable land; perennial crops/orchards/groves; urban parks/gardens)
Land-use Agriculture (20%), Forestry (32%), Tourism/recreation

■ Birds

Species	Season	Year	Pop min	Pop max	Acc	Criteria
Alectoris graeca Rock Partridge	R	1996	40	70	A	B2
Jynx torquilla Wryneck	B	1996	20	—	A	B2
[1] *Prunella collaris* Alpine Accentor	R	1996	80	—	A	A3
Monticola saxatilis Rock Thrush	B	1996	5	25	A	B2
[1] *Tichodroma muraria* Wallcreeper	R	1996	—	—	—	A3
[1] *Pyrrhocorax graculus* Alpine Chough	R	1996	30	50	A	A3
[1] *Montifringilla nivalis* Snowfinch	R	1996	30	60	A	A3
[1] *Serinus citrinella* Citril Finch	B	1996	20	50	A	A3

1. Eurasian high-montane biome.

An important site for different species of a wide range of altitudes and habitats, from 700 m to alpine.

■ Protection status

National Partial **International** None

1,900 ha of IBA covered by 2 Inventory of Landscapes and Natural Monuments of National Importance (Oberengadiner Seenlandschaft und Berninagruppe; Val Bondasca–Val da'l Albigna; total area 41,818 ha). 49 ha of IBA covered by 3 Raised and Transitional Bogs of National Importance (total area, 49 ha). 7 ha of IBA covered by Fenlands of National Importance (Passo del Maloja, 7 ha).

■ Conservation issues

Threats Abandonment/reduction of land management (B), Agricultural intensification/expansion (C), Recreation/tourism (B)

The abandonment of traditional agriculture is one of the main threats.

REFERENCES

AEPLI ELSENBEER, M.-F., HALTMEYER, C., KÄSTLI, E., KYBURZ, G., TSCHUDIN, A. AND WIENER, D. (1997) *Umwelt in der Schweiz 1997*. Bern, Switzerland: Bundesamt für Statistik und Bundesamt für Umwelt, Wald und Landschaft.

GRIMMETT, R. F. A. AND JONES, T. A. (1989) *Important Bird Areas in Europe*. Cambridge, UK: International Council for Bird Preservation (Techn. Publ. 9).

HEATH, M. F. AND BORGGREVE, C. (2000) *BirdLife International/EBCC European Bird Database 1998*. Cambridge, UK: BirdLife International.

MARTI, C. AND SCHIFFERLI, L. (1987) Inventar der Schweizer Wasservogelgebiete von internationaler Bedeutung–Erste Revision 1986. *Ornithol. Beob.* 84: 1–47. (In German.)

SCHIFFERLI, L. AND KESTENHOLZ, M. (1995) Inventar der Schweizer Wasservogelgebiete von nationaler Bedeutung als Brut-, Rast- und Überwinterungsgebiete–Revision 1995. *Ornithol. Beob.* 92: 413–433.

SCHMID, H., LUDER, R., NAEF-DAENZER, B., GRAF, R. AND ZBINDEN, N. (1998) *Schweizer Brutvogelatlas. Verbreitung der Brutvögel in der Schweiz und im Fürstentum Liechtenstein 1993–1996./Atlas des oiseaux nicheurs de Suisse. Distribution des oiseaux nicheurs en Suisse et au Liechtenstein de 1993 à 1996*. Sempach, Switzerland: Schweizerische Vogelwarte/Station ornithologique suisse.

TUCKER, G. M. AND HEATH, M. F. (1994) *Birds in Europe: their conservation status*. Cambridge, UK: BirdLife International (BirdLife Conservation Series no. 3).

UNITED KINGDOM,
THE CHANNEL ISLANDS AND THE ISLE OF MAN

Ian Fisher, David Gibbons, Guy Thompson and Dave Pritchard

Breeding colony of Guillemot *Uria aalge* and Kittiwake *Rissa tridactyla* on the Farne Islands (IBA 023). (PHOTO: PAUL GORIUP)

THE UNITED KINGDOM

GENERAL INTRODUCTION

The United Kingdom comprises Great Britain (England, Scotland and Wales) and Northern Ireland, covering over 244,000 km². It is a densely populated and industrialized country, with diverse landscapes, over 85% of which are used for agriculture or forestry. Maritime influences are important, and the climate is warmer and wetter than at the same latitudes in central or eastern Europe.

The United Kingdom has 287 Important Bird Areas (IBAs) which cover more than 31,000 km², representing over 12% of its surface area (Table 1, Map 1). Of these, 80 are in England (covering over 9,000 km²), 17 are in Northern Ireland (over 1,900 km²), 173 are in Scotland (over 18,000 km²) and 17 are in Wales (over 2,000 km²).

The 1989 inventory of IBAs in Europe (Grimmett and Jones 1989) identified 261 IBAs in the United Kingdom. Of these, 239 are represented here, some with boundary amendments and many as combined sites (for details see Table 1). Seventy-six IBAs have been newly identified since the 1989 inventory.

In 1992, an IBA inventory covering the UK, Channel Islands and Isle of Man was published (Pritchard *et al.* 1992), a joint publication between the RSPB, the Joint Nature Conservation Committee and the Statutory Conservation Agencies: the Countryside Council for Wales, English Nature and Scottish Natural Heritage. The IBAs corresponded with the list of designated and proposed Special Protection Areas and Ramsar Sites as published in *Hansard* (17 July 1991 columns 203–208 and 219–224 and 18 July 1991 columns 256–257). This latest review is based on the 1992 inventory (itself based on that of 1989), with 232 of the 239 UK sites in the 1992 inventory represented here in some way, either as identical, merged, amended or split sites. Despite this, the IBAs documented here differ somewhat from the 1992 inventory, with IBAs defined on their ornithological interest, irrespective of (proposed) designation status (Table 1). This divergence is inevitable given the differences in selection criteria. Though IBA boundaries are often the same as SPA or Ramsar Site boundaries (where relevant), this is not always the case. Many of the 61 sites added since the 1992 inventory qualify because they hold important populations of species of European conservation concern. Since some of these species are not yet identified in legislation for special protection, the corresponding sites may have no designation status at all.

Separate overviews are presented for the Channel Islands (p. 815) and for the Isle of Man (p. 817); data for these sites are not included within this UK overview text or the accompanying tables and figures.

ORNITHOLOGICAL IMPORTANCE

One hundred and two species of European conservation concern (SPECs) regularly breed in the UK (Tucker and Heath 1994). Among these, *Crex crex* is globally threatened, *Haliaeetus albicilla* is near-threatened and *Loxia scotica* is endemic. Fifty of these SPECs have an unfavourable conservation status in Europe. Seven species classed as SPECs on the basis of their winter populations occur during winter or on passage in the UK, and four of these have an unfavourable conservation status in Europe.

Table 1 and Map 1 present the criteria by which each IBA qualifies. A total of 147 IBAs in the UK qualify under one or more 'A' criteria; a further 82 qualify under B (but not A) criteria. Twenty-one sites qualify because they contain important populations of a species of global conservation concern (Table 2).

A high proportion of UK IBAs are important for wintering and passage waterbirds (Table 3). One hundred and forty-nine sites regularly support over 20,000 wintering or passage waterbirds or more than 1% of the biogeographic or flyway population of a waterbird species (i.e. meeting criteria A4i, A4iii or B1i). The five most important sites are The Wash (077), Ribble and Alt estuaries

Map 1. Location, area and criteria category of Important Bird Areas in the United Kingdom.

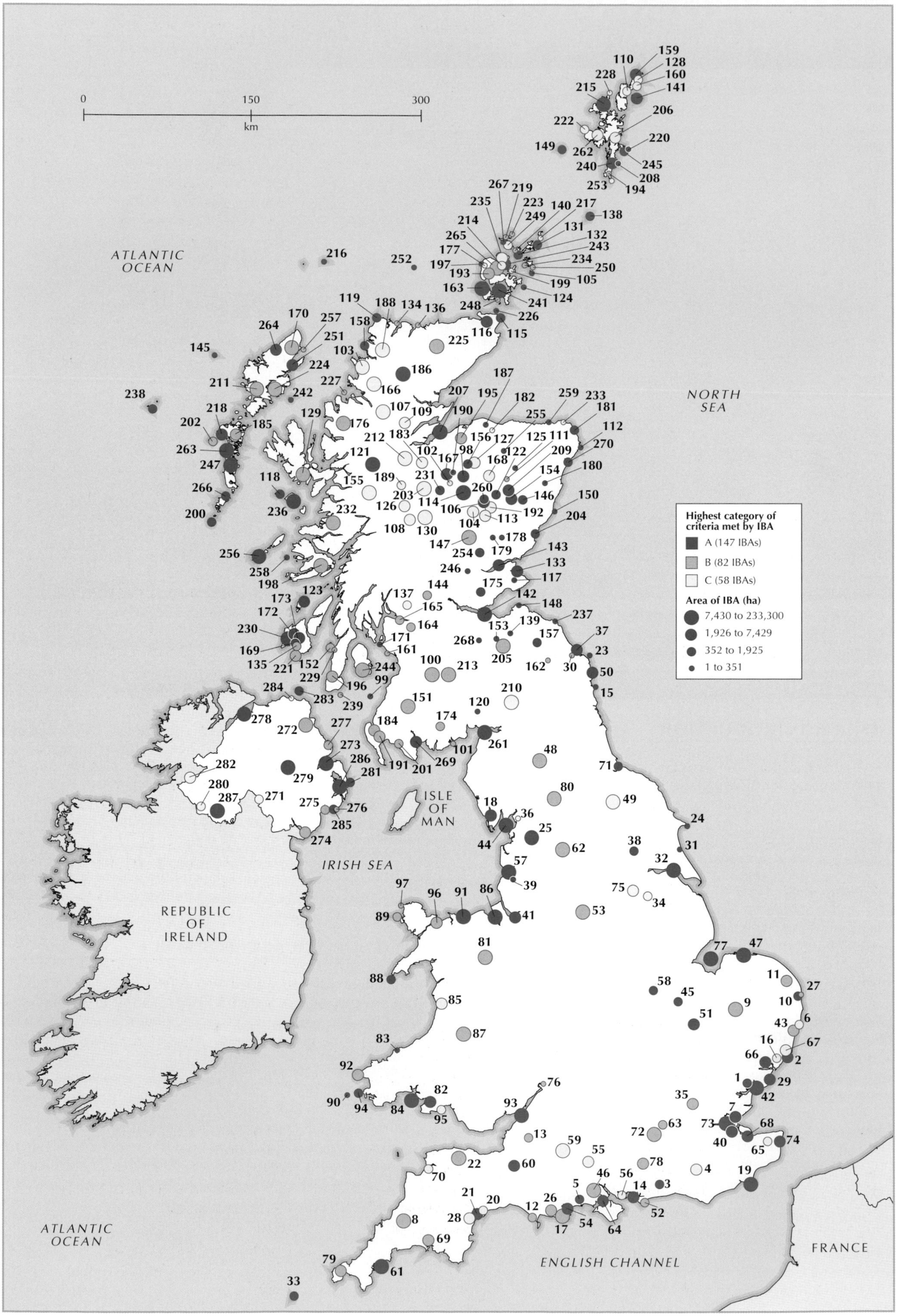
0
150
300
km
ATLANTIC OCEAN
NORTH SEA
ISLE OF MAN
IRISH SEA
REPUBLIC OF IRELAND
ATLANTIC OCEAN
ENGLISH CHANNEL
FRANCE
Highest category of criteria met by IBA
A (147 IBAs)
B (82 IBAs)
C (58 IBAs)
Area of IBA (ha)
7,430 to 233,300
1,926 to 7,429
352 to 1,925
1 to 351

Table 1. Summary of Important Bird Areas in the United Kingdom. 287 IBAs covering 31,241 km²

IBA code	National code	1989 code	International/National name	Administrative region	Area (ha)	Criteria (see p. 11)
001	914A	GB175	Abberton reservoir	South East	726	A4iii, B1i, C3, C4, C6
002	911A	GB172	Alde/Ore estuary	East Anglia	2,416	A4i, A4iii, B1i, B2, B3, C2, C3, C4, C6
003	1216A	GB201	Arun valley	South East	1,373	A4iii, C4, C6
004	—	—	Ashdown forest	South East	3,207	C6
005	1109A	GB192	Avon valley	South East, South West	1,385	A4i, B1i, B2, C2, C3, C6
006	—	—	Benacre to Easton Bavents	East Anglia	516	C6
007	917A	GB179	Benfleet and Southend marshes	South East	2,750	A4i, A4iii, B1i, B2, C3, C4
008	1014B	GB182	Bodmin Moor	South West	7,996	B1i, B2, C2, C6
009ᵉ	920A	GB170	Breckland heaths and Thetford forest	East Anglia	26,419	B2, C6
010ᵖ	925A	—	Breydon Water	East Anglia	515	A4i, A4iii, B1i, B2, C2, C4, C6
011ᵖ	925A	GB166–169	Broadland	East Anglia	5,485	B1i, B2, C3, C6
012	1009A	GB187	Chesil Beach and The Fleet	South West	1,000	B1i, B2, C3, C6
013	1004A	GB186	Chew valley lake	South West	570	B1i, C3
014	1101A	GB196	Chichester and Langstone Harbours	South East	5,970	A4i, A4iii, B1i, B2, C2, C3, C4, C6
015	603A	GB145	Coquet Island	North	22	A4i, A4iii, B1i, B1ii, B2, C2, C3, C4, C6
016	926A	—	Deben estuary	East Anglia	981	C6
017ᵖ	1010A	GB188, GB189	Dorset heaths and forests	South West	10,288	B2, C6
018	503A	GB134	Duddon estuary	North	5,120	A4iii, B1i, B2, C3, C4, C6
019	1209A	GB204	Dungeness to Pett Levels	South East	9,080	A4i, A4iii, B1i, B2, C2, C3, C4, C6
020	1012A	—	East Devon heaths	South West	1,370	C6
021	1008A	GB183	Exe estuary	South West	2,180	A4iii, B2, C4, C6
022	—	—	Exmoor coast and heaths	South West	24,300	B2, B3, C6
023	602A	GB143	Farne Islands	North	101	A4i, A4iii, B1i, B1ii, B2, B3, C2, C3, C4, C6
024	610A	GB155	Flamborough Head and Bempton cliffs	Yorkshire and Humberside	315	A4i, A4ii, A4iii, B1i, B1ii, B2, B3, C3, C4
025	515A	GB138	Forest of Bowland	North West	80,300	A4i, A4iii, B1i, B2, B3, C3, C4, C6
026	—	—	Frome flood-plain	South West	2,700	B2, C6
027	927A	—	Great Yarmouth North Denes	East Anglia	146	B1i, B2, C2, C6
028	—	—	Haldon	South West	2,910	C6
029	913A	GB174	Hamford Water	South East	2,143	A4i, A4iii, B1i, B2, C3, C4, C6
030	604A	GB146	Holburn Lake and Moss	North	28	B1i, C3
031	617A	GB156	Hornsea Mere	Yorkshire and Humberside	230	A4i, B1i, C3, C6
032	611A	GB157, G237	Humber flats, marshes and coast	Yorkshire and Humberside, East Midlands	16,490	A4i, A4iii, B1i, B2, C2, C3, C4, C6
033	1006A	GB180	Isles of Scilly coastal habitats	South West	926	A4i, B1i, B2, B3, C2, C3, C6
034	—	—	Laughton forest	East Midlands	1,170	C6
035	1211A	GB197	Lea valley	South East	2,550	B1i, C3, C6
036	509A	GB137	Leighton Moss	North West	128	C6
037	601A	GB142	Lindisfarne	North	3,679	A4i, A4iii, B1i, B2, C2, C3, C4, C6
038	609A	GB154	Lower Derwent valley	Yorkshire and Humberside	915	A4iii, B1i, B2, C3, C4, C6
039	511A	GB140	Martin Mere	North West	120	A4i, A4iii, B1i, B2, B3, C2, C3, C4, C6
040	1203A	GB207	Medway estuary and marshes	South East	6,840	A4i, A4iii, B1i, B2, C3, C4, C6
041	513A	GB158	Mersey estuary	North West	7,274	A4i, A4iii, B1i, B2, C3, C4, C6
042	924A	GB176–178	Mid-Essex coast	South East	22,817	A4i, A4iii, B1i, B2, C2, C3, C4, C6
043	910A	GB171	Minsmere–Walberswick	East Anglia	2,190	B3, C6
044	508A	GB135	Morecambe Bay	North, North West	41,970	A4i, A4iii, B1i, B2, B3, C2, C3, C4, C6
045	803A	GB162	Nene Washes	East Anglia	1,310	A4i, A4iii, B1i, B2, C2, C3, C4, C6
046	1103A	GB193	The New Forest	South East	41,410	B2, C6
047	903A	GB165	North Norfolk coast	East Anglia	7,700	A4i, A4iii, B1i, B2, B3, C2, C3, C4, C6
048	627A	GB147–150	North Pennine moors	North	136,547	B1i, B2, B3, C2, C3, C6
049	616A	GB152	North Yorkshire moors	North, Yorkshire and Humberside	142,250	C6
050	613A	GB144	Northumberland coast	North	1,926	A4i, B1i, B2, C3, C6
051	804A	GB163	Ouse Washes	East Anglia	2,403	A4i, A4iii, B1i, B2, B3, C2, C3, C4, C6
052	1204A	GB202	Pagham Harbour	South East	636	B1i, C3
053	702A	GB159	Peak District moors	Yorkshire and Humberside, East Midlands, West Midlands, North West	37,092	B1i, B3, C3, C6
054ᵖ	1011A	GB188	Poole Harbour	South West	5,130	A4iii, B1i, B2, C3, C4, C6
055	1110A	GB190	Porton Down	South East, South West	2,160	C6
056	1105A	—	Portsmouth Harbour	South East	1,249	C7
057	510A	GB139	Ribble and Alt estuaries	North West	15,934	A4i, A4iii, B1i, B2, B3, C2, C3, C4, C6
058	805A	GB161	Rutland Water	East Midlands	1,556	A4iii, B1i, C3, C4
059	—	—	Salisbury Plain	South East, South West	19,690	C6
060	1003A	GB185	Somerset Levels and Moors	South West	6,390	A4iii, B1i, B2, C3, C4, C6
061	—	—	South Cornwall coast	South West	11,170	A4i, B1i, C2, C6
062	—	—	South Pennine moors	Yorkshire and Humberside, North West	21,000	B3, C6

Table 1 ... continued. Summary of Important Bird Areas in the United Kingdom. 287 IBAs covering 31,241 km²

IBA code	National code	1989 code	International/National name	Administrative region	Area (ha)	Criteria (see p. 11)
063	1217A	GB198	South-west London water-bodies	South East	1,830	B1i, C3, C6
064	1106A	GB194	Southampton Water and Solent marshes	South East	6,000	A4i, A4iii, B1i, B2, C3, C4, C6
065	1212A	GB205	Stodmarsh	South East	481	C6
066	912A	GB173	Stour and Orwell estuary	East Anglia, South East	3,379	A4i, A4iii, B1i, B2, C3, C4
067	—	—	Suffolk Sandlings and coastal forest	East Anglia	3,890	C6
068	1201A	GB208	The Swale	South East	6,514	A4i, A4iii, B1i, B2, B3, C3, C4, C6
069	1014A	GB181	Tamar complex	South West	2,380	B2, C6
070	1005A	GB184	Taw and Torridge estuary	South West	1,750	C7
071	606A	GB151	Teesmouth and Cleveland coast	North	1,300	A4i, A4iii, B1i, B2, C3, C4, C6
072ᵉ	1214A	GB199	Thames basin heathlands	South East	9,150	B2, C6
073ᵉ	1202A	GB206	Thames estuary and marshes	South East	12,030	A4iii, B1i, B2, C3, C4, C6
074ᵉ	1207A	GB209	Thanet coast and Sandwich Bay	South East	2,560	A4i, B1i, C3
075	517A	GB141	Thorne and Hatfield Moors	Yorkshire and Humberside	3,320	C6
076	705A	GB160	Walmore Common	South West	90	B2, C6
077	802A	GB164	The Wash	East Midlands, East Anglia	67,000	A4i, A4iii, B1i, B2, B3, C2, C3, C4, C6
078	1213A	GB195, GB200	Wealden heaths	South East	5,062	B2, C6
079	—	—	West Penwith coast and moors	South West	3,390	B2, C6
080	621A	GB153	Yorkshire Dale moorlands	North, Yorkshire and Humberside	16,430	B1i, B2, B3, C2, C3, C6
081	1311A	GB211	Berwyn	Wales	24,187	B2, C6
082	1501A	GB222	Burry Inlet	Wales	6,600	A4i, A4iii, B1i, B2, C3, C4
083	—	—	Cardigan Island	Wales	15	A4i, B1i, B3, C3
084	1409A	GB221, GB240	Carmarthen Bay	Wales	44,582	A4iii, B2, C4, C6
085	1401A	GB216	Cors Fochno and Dyfi	Wales	3,792	C6
086	1301A	GB210	Dee estuary	North West, Wales	16,688	A4i, A4iii, B1i, B2, C3, C4, C6
087	1411A	GB217	Elenydd–Mallaen	Wales	30,022	B3, C6
088	1312A	GB215	Glannau Aberdaron and Ynys Enlli	Wales	505	A4ii, B1ii, B2, C3, C6
089	1310A	GB214	Glannau Ynys Gybi	Wales	352	B2, C6
090	1404A	GB220	Grassholm	Wales	10	A4ii, A4iii, B1ii, B2, C3, C4
091	—	—	North Wales coast	Wales	13,660	A4i, A4iii, B1i, C3, C4
092	1406A	GB218	Pembrokeshire cliffs	Wales	2,360	B2, B3, C6
093	1502A	GB224	Severn estuary	South West, Wales	59,950	A4i, A4iii, B1i, B2, B3, C2, C3, C4, C6
094	1405A	GB219	Skokholm and Skomer	Wales	422	A4i, A4ii, A4iii, B1i, B1ii, B2, B3, C2, C3, C4, C6
095	1503A	GB223	Swansea Bay–Blackpill	Wales	490	C7
096	1303A	GB212, GB239	Traeth Lafan, Conwy Bay	Wales	2,700	B1i, C3
097	1306A	GB213	Ynys Feurig, Cemlyn Bay and The Skerries	Wales	85	B1i, B2, C2, C6
098	256A	GB081	Abernethy forest	Scotland	5,800	A1, B1i, B2, C1, C3, C6
099	309A	GB103	Ailsa Craig	Scotland	100	A4ii, A4iii, B1i, B1ii, B2, B3, C3, C4
100	—	—	Airds Moss and Muirkirk uplands	Scotland	19,800	B2, C6
101	—	—	Almorness Point and Hestan Island	Scotland	73	B3
102	254A	GB084	Alvie	Scotland	340	C7
103ᵖ	159A	GB024	Assynt lochs	Scotland	10,700	C6
104	285A	—	Atholl/Glen Tilt	Scotland	6,166	C6
105	—	—	Auskerry	Scotland	90	A4ii, B1ii, B2, C2, C6
106	—	—	Ballochbuie forest	Scotland	2,031	A1, B2, C1, C6
107	163A	—	Beinn Dearg	Scotland	13,715	C7
108	255A	—	Ben Alder	Scotland	6,548	C6
109	164A	—	Ben Wyvis	Scotland	5,500	C6
110	272A	GB038	Blackpark and Gutcher, Yell	Scotland	1,050	C7
111	—	—	Bluemill	Scotland	260	B2
112ᵉ	249B	GB072	Buchan Ness to Collieston coast	Scotland	208	A4iii, B3, C4
113	401A	GB110	Caenlochan	Scotland	6,600	C6
114	224A	GB080	Cairngorms	Scotland	49,113	A1, B2, C1, C2, C6
115	118A	GB019	Caithness cliffs	Scotland	1,053	A4i, A4ii, A4iii, B1i, B1ii, B2, B3, C2, C3, C4
116	117A	GB020	Caithness lochs	Scotland	3,016	A4i, B1i, B3, C2, C3, C6
117	413A	GB123	Cameron reservoir	Scotland	68	A4i, B1i, C3
118	—	—	Canna and Sanday	Scotland	1,356	A4i, B1i, B3, C2, C3
119	123A	GB022	Cape Wrath	Scotland	1,010	A4iii, B3, C4
120	319A	GB107	Castle Loch, Lochmaben	Scotland	107	A4i, B1i, C3
121	156A	GB031	Central Highland hills and glens	Scotland	230,248	A1, B2, C1, C6
122	—	—	Coilacriech	Scotland	390	A1, B2, C1
123ᵉ	317A	GB089	Colonsay and Oronsay	Scotland	5,086	A4iii, B1i, B2, C2, C4, C6
124	215A	GB065	Copinsay	Scotland	152	A4iii, B3, C4
125	—	—	Correen Hills	Scotland	266	A4i, B1i, B2, C3
126	261A	—	Creag Meagaidh	Scotland	6,986	C6
127	—	—	Cromdale Hills	Scotland	7,060	C6

Table 1 ... continued. Summary of Important Bird Areas in the United Kingdom. 287 IBAs covering 31,241 km²

IBA code	National code	1989 code	International/National name	Administrative region	Area (ha)	Criteria (see p. 11)
128	235A	GB036	Crussa Field and the Heogs	Scotland	470	C7
129	—	—	Cuillin Hills, Skye	Scotland	29,300	B2, C6
130	230A	GB118	Drumochter Hills	Scotland	9,445	C6
131	233A	GB049	East Sanday	Scotland	1,515	A4i, B1i, B2, C3, C6
132	243A	GB054	Eday	Scotland	930	A4iii, B3, C4
133	414A	GB122	Eden estuary, Tentsmuir Point and Abertay sands	Scotland	3,000	A4i, A4iii, B1i, B2, C2, C4, C6
134	—	—	Eilean Hoan	Scotland	30	B1i, B2, C2, C6
135	305D	GB096	Eilean na Muice Duibh, Islay	Scotland	574	B1i, B2, C2, C3, C6
136	—	—	Eilean nan Ron	Scotland	180	B1i, C2
137[e]	302A	GB104	Endrick Mouth and Loch Lomond Islands	Scotland	820	C6
138	209A	GB046	Fair Isle	Scotland	561	A4i, A4iii, B1i, B1ii, B2, B3, C2, C3, C4, C6
139	424A	GB127	Fala Flow	Scotland	318	A4i, B1i, C3
140	—	—	Faray and Holm of Faray	Scotland	80	B2, B3
141	203A	GB037	Fetlar	Scotland	2,450	A4iii, C4, C6
142	441A	GB124	Firth of Forth	Scotland	43,301	A4i, A4iii, B1i, B2, B3, C2, C3, C4, C6
143	412A	GB121	Firth of Tay	Scotland	6,100	A4i, B1i, B2, C2, C6
144	419A	GB120	Flanders Moss and Lake of Menteith	Scotland	1,170	B1i, C3
145	102A	GB002	Flannan Isles	Scotland	59	A4ii, A4iii, B1ii, B2, B3, C2, C4, C6
146	—	—	Forest of Birse	Scotland	850	A1, B2, C1
147	—	—	Forest of Clunie	Scotland	12,050	B2, C6
148	417A	GB125	Forth Islands	Scotland	132	A4i, A4ii, A4iii, B1i, B1ii, B2, B3, C2, C3, C4, C6
149	206A	GB042	Foula	Scotland	1,323	A4i, A4ii, A4iii, B1i, B1ii, B2, B3, C2, C3, C4, C6
150	227A	GB075	Fowlsheugh	Scotland	10	A4i, A4ii, A4iii, B1i, B1ii, B3, C3, C4
151	—	—	Galloway Forest Park	Scotland	76,000	B2, C6
152	—	—	Gigha Island and islets	Scotland	442	B1ii, B2
153	423A	GB126	Gladhouse reservoir	Scotland	187	A4i, B1i, C3
154	277A	GB078	Glen Tanar	Scotland	4,180	A1, B2, C1, C6
155	165A	—	Glengarry lochs	Scotland	53,500	C6
156	—	—	Grantown-on-Spey	Scotland	520	A1, B2, C1, C2
157	428A	GB131	Greenlaw Moor and Hule Moss	Scotland	1,200	A4i, B1i, C3
158	124A	GB023	Handa	Scotland	363	A4ii, A4iii, B1ii, B3, C3, C4
159	201A	GB035	Hermaness and Saxa Vord, Unst	Scotland	2,654	A4ii, A4iii, B1ii, B2, B3, C3, C4
160	284A	—	Hill of Colvadale and Sobul	Scotland	1,600	C7
161	—	—	Horse Island	Scotland	20	B3
162	429A	GB130	Hoselaw Loch	Scotland	50	B1i, C3
163	214A	GB062	Hoy	Scotland	11,170	A4ii, A4iii, B1ii, B2, B3, C2, C3, C4, C6
164	—	—	Inchinnan, Renfrew	Scotland	1,030	B1i, B3, C2, C6
165	306A	GB105	Inner Clyde estuary	Scotland	1,670	B1i, C3
166[p]	151A	GB024	Inverpolly, Loch Urigill and nearby lochs	Scotland	27,880	C6
167	258A	GB082	Kinveachy	Scotland	5,250	A1, B2, C1, C6
168	—	—	Ladder hills	Scotland	4,420	C6
169	305C	GB095	Laggan, Islay	Scotland	1,230	A4i, B1i, B2, C2, C3, C6
170	157A	GB016	Lewis peatlands	Scotland	64,000	B1i, B2, B3, C3, C6
171	—	—	Little Cumbrae Island	Scotland	300	A4i, B1i, B3, C3
172	305A	GB093	Loch Gruinart, Islay	Scotland	3,261	A4i, A4iii, B1i, B2, B3, C2, C3, C4, C6
173	305B	GB094	Loch Indaal and Bridgend flats, Islay	Scotland	3,750	A4i, B1i, B2, C2, C6
174	311A	GB109	Loch Ken and Dee marshes	Scotland	1,090	B1i, C2, C3
175	411A	GB117	Loch Leven	Scotland	1,870	A4i, A4iii, B1i, B2, B3, C3, C4
176[e]	153A	GB027	Loch Maree and nearby lochs and mountains	Scotland	68,611	B2, C6
177[e]	271A	GB244	Loch of Isbister	Scotland	140	C7
178	405A	GB233	Loch of Kinnordy	Scotland	85	A4i, B1i, C3
179	406A	GB112	Loch of Lintrathen	Scotland	189	A4i, B1i, C3
180	226A	GB074	Loch of Skene	Scotland	124	A4i, B1i, B3, C2, C3, C6
181	221A	GB071	Loch of Strathbeg	Scotland	913	A4i, A4iii, B1i, B2, B3, C2, C3, C4, C6
182	274A	GB068	Loch Oire	Scotland	8	C6
183	155A	GB032	Loch Ruthven and nearby lochs	Scotland	5,490	C6
184	—	—	Loch Ryan	Scotland	4,240	B2
185[e]	150A	GB018	Loch Scadavay	Scotland	5,564	B2, C2, C6
186	161A	—	Loch Shin and nearby lochs	Scotland	48,500	A1, B1i, B2, C1, C3, C6
187	220A	GB067	Loch Spynie	Scotland	93	A4i, B1i, C3
188	160A	—	Loch Stack, Loch nam Brac and nearby lochs	Scotland	10,410	C6
189	166A	—	Loch Tarff and nearby lochs	Scotland	1,330	C6
190	275A	GB083	Loch Vaa	Scotland	45	A1, B2, C1, C6
191	312A	GB106	Lochinch and Torrs Warren	Scotland	4,710	B1i, C2, C3
192	228A	GB079	Lochnagar	Scotland	4,427	C6

Table 1 ... continued. Summary of Important Bird Areas in the United Kingdom. 287 IBAs covering 31,241 km²

IBA code	National code	1989 code	International/National name	Administrative region	Area (ha)	Criteria (see p. 11)
193	213A	GB060	Lochs of Harray and Stenness	Scotland	1,930	B1i, B2, B3, C2, C3, C6
194ᵉ	265A	GB045	Lochs of Spiggie and Brow	Scotland	145	B3, C7
195	—	—	Lower Findhorn valley	Scotland	4,280	B2, C6
196ᵖ	308A	GB099	Machrihanish	Scotland	2,520	B1i, C2, C3, C6
197	212A	GB057	Marwick Head	Scotland	9	A4iii, B1ii, C3, C4
198	—	—	Mid-Mull hills and glens	Scotland	44,800	B2, C6
199	267A	GB056	Mill Dam, Shapinsay	Scotland	16	C7
200	112A	GB015	Mingulay and Berneray	Scotland	911	A4ii, A4iii, B1ii, B3, C3, C4
201	—	—	Mochrum and Castle Lochs	Scotland	460	B1i, C3
202	107A	GB007	Monach Islands	Scotland	595	B1i, B1ii, B2, C2, C3
203	253A	GB231	Monadhliath	Scotland	10,696	C6
204	403A	GB111	Montrose basin	Scotland	984	A4i, A4iii, B1i, B2, B3, C3, C4
205	—	—	Moorfoot Hills	Scotland	9,220	B3
206	280A	—	Moorland areas, Central Shetland	Scotland	2,790	C7
207	162A	GB028–030, GB033, GB034, GB066	Moray basin, firths and bays	Scotland	134,660	A4i, A4iii, B1i, B2, B3, C2, C3, C4, C6
208	236A	GB044	Mousa	Scotland	200	A4ii, B1ii, B2, C2, C6
209	279A	GB076	Muir of Dinnet	Scotland	2,280	A1, A4i, A4iii, B1i, B2, C1, C3, C4, C6
210	—	—	Newcastleton Hills	Scotland	7,679	C6
211	157B	GB017	North Harris mountains	Scotland	18,570	B2, C6
212	167A	—	North Inverness lochs	Scotland	11,270	C6
213	—	—	North Lowther Hills	Scotland	25,880	B2, C6
214	231B	GB058	North Mainland coast	Scotland	420	C7
215	204A	GB040	North Roe and Tingon, Mainland Shetland	Scotland	7,560	A4ii, B1ii, B2, B3, C2, C3, C6
216	101A	GB001	North Rona and Sula Sgeir	Scotland	130	A4ii, A4iii, B1ii, B2, B3, C3, C4, C6
217	241A	GB048	North Ronaldsay coast	Scotland	220	C7
218ᵖ	—	GB005, GB008, GB009, GB241	North Uist machair and islands	Scotland	6,900	A1, B1i, B2, C1, C2, C3, C6
219	—	—	North Westray coast	Scotland	140	B1ii, B2, C2, C6
220	208A	GB043	Noss	Scotland	343	A4ii, A4iii, B1ii, B2, B3, C3, C4
221	305H	GB097	The Oa: Islay	Scotland	4,380	B1i, C2, C3, C6
222	205A	GB041	Papa Stour	Scotland	590	C6
223	211A	GB051	Papa Westray (North Hill and Holm)	Scotland	245	B1ii, B2, C2, C6
224	—	—	Park, Lewis	Scotland	16,220	B2, C6
225	115	GB021	Peatlands	Scotland	140,570	B1i, B2, B3, C2, C3, C6
226	113A	GB064	Pentland Firth Islands	Scotland	270	A4iii, B3, C2, C4, C6
227	126A	GB026	Priest Island	Scotland	138	B2, C2
228	202A	GB039	Ramna Stacks and Gruney	Scotland	11	C6
229	307A	GB098	Rhunahaorine Point	Scotland	326	B1i, C2, C3
230	305G	GB090–092	Rinns, Islay	Scotland	12,084	A4i, B1i, B2, C2, C3, C6
231	223A	GB085	River Spey – Insh marshes	Scotland	1,540	A1, B1i, B2, B3, C1, C3
232ᵖ	—	GB086	Rois-Bheinn	Scotland	20,600	B2, C6
233ᵉ	268A	GB070	Rosehearty to Fraserburgh coast	Scotland	130	C7
234	—	—	Rothiesholm peninsula, Stronsay	Scotland	310	B3
235	237A	GB055	Rousay (Part)	Scotland	2,310	C6
236	134A	GB025	Rum	Scotland	10,794	A4ii, A4iii, B1ii, B2, C3, C4
237	427A	GB132	St Abbs Head to Fast Castle	Scotland	247	A4iii, B1ii, B3, C3, C4
238	103A	GB003	St Kilda	Scotland	865	A4ii, A4iii, B1ii, B2, B3, C2, C3, C4, C6
239	318A	GB100	Sanda Island	Scotland	210	B3
240	—	—	Sandwick and Clift Hills	Scotland	2,100	A4ii, B1ii, B3, C3
241	—	—	Scapa Flow	Scotland	26,140	A4i, B1i, B1ii, B2, C2, C3, C6
242	104A	GB004	Shiant Isles	Scotland	212	A4i, A4ii, A4iii, B1i, B1ii, B2, B3, C2, C3, C4
243	—	—	Sounds around Wyre	Scotland	4,800	A4i, B1i, C2, C6
244	—	—	South Arran	Scotland	19,000	B2, C6
245	—	—	South Bressay	Scotland	1,600	A4ii, B1ii, B3, C3
246	440A	GB114–116	South Tayside goose roosts	Scotland	331	A4i, A4iii, B1i, C3, C4
247	108A	GB010–013	South Uist machair and lochs	Scotland	8,900	A1, A4i, B1i, B2, B3, C1, C2, C3, C6
248	—	—	South Walls and Switha	Scotland	260	B1i, B2, C2
249	232A	GB053	South Westray coast	Scotland	530	C7
250	242A	GB050	South-eastern Stronsay	Scotland	110	B2
251	—	—	Stornoway to Back, Lewis	Scotland	2,130	A1, B2, C1
252	218A	GB063	Sule Skerry and Sule Stack	Scotland	19	A4ii, A4iii, B1ii, B2, B3, C2, C3, C4, C6
253	251A	GB047	Sumburgh Head	Scotland	39	C7
254	407A	GB113	Tay–Isla valley	Scotland	760	A4i, B1i, B2, C3, C6

Table 1 ... continued. Summary of Important Bird Areas in the United Kingdom. 287 IBAs covering 31,241 km²

IBA code	National code	1989 code	International/National name	Administrative region	Area (ha)	Criteria (see p. 11)
255	—	—	Tips of Corsemaul and Mortlach	Scotland	310	A4i, A4iii, B1i, B2, C3, C4
256	303A	GB087	Tiree and Coll	Scotland	16,510	A1, A4i, B1i, B2, B3, C1, C2, C3, C6
257	—	—	Tolsta Head, Lewis	Scotland	150	B3
258	304A	GB088	Treshnish Isles	Scotland	240	A4ii, A4iii, B1i, B1ii, B2, B3, C2, C4, C6
259	247A	GB069	Troup, Pennan and Lion Heads	Scotland	320	A4i, A4iii, B1i, B1ii, B3, C3, C4
260	—	—	Upper Deeside plantations	Scotland	1,010	A1, B2, C1
261	501A	GB133	Upper Solway flats and marshes	North, Scotland	45,240	A4i, A4iii, B1i, B2, B3, C2, C3, C4, C6
262	283A	—	West Burrafirth	Scotland	3,910	C6
263	—	—	West Coast of Benbecula	Scotland	233,300	A1, B2, C1, C2, C6
264	—	—	West Coast, Lewis	Scotland	2,230	A1, B2, C1, C6
265	231A, 270A	GB059, GB061	West Mainland moors	Scotland	7,430	B2, C6
266	111A	GB014	West Sound of Barra	Scotland	1,310	A1, B1i, B2, C1, C2
267	210A	GB052	West Westray	Scotland	350	A4i, A4iii, B1i, B1ii, C3, C4, C6
268	425A	GB128	Westwater	Scotland	50	A4i, A4iii, B1i, C3, C4
269	316A	GB108	Wigtown Bay	Scotland	3,470	A4i, B1i, B2, C3
270	222A	GB073	Ythan estuary, Sands of Forvie and Meikle Loch	Scotland	1,040	A4i, A4iii, B1i, B2, C2, C3, C4, C6
271	2012A	GB256	Annaghroe, River Blackwater	Northern Ireland	440	C6
272	—	—	Antrim plateau	Northern Ireland	71,100	B2, C6
273	2010A	GB249	Belfast Lough	Northern Ireland	11,700	A4i, A4iii, B1i, C3, C4
274	2016A	GB254	Carlingford Lough including Green Island	Northern Ireland	4,660	B1i, B2, C3, C6
275	2014A	GB253	Dundrum Inner Bay	Northern Ireland	500	B1i, C3
276	2015A	GB251	Killough Harbour and Coney Island Bay	Northern Ireland	240	B1i, C3
277	2004A	GB248	Larne Lough and Swan/Blue Circle Islands	Northern Ireland	1,160	B1i, B2, C3, C6
278ᵉ	2003A	GB245	Lough Foyle and River Foyle	Northern Ireland	21,803	A4i, A4iii, B1i, B2, B3, C2, C3, C4, C6
279	2009A	GB257	Lough Neagh and Lough Beg	Northern Ireland	50,165	A4i, A4iii, B1i, B2, B3, C2, C3, C4, C6
280	2008A	GB260	Lower Lough Macnean	Northern Ireland	510	C6
281	2017A	GB250	Outer Ards peninsula	Northern Ireland	1,016	A4i, B1i, C3, C6
282	2005A	GB261	Pettigoe plateau	Northern Ireland	2,700	C6
283	2001A	GB247	Rathlin Island	Northern Ireland	1,500	A4ii, A4iii, B1ii, B3, C3, C4
284	2002A	GB246	Sheep Island	Northern Ireland	4	C7
285	—	—	South Down coast	Northern Ireland	437	A4i, B1i, C3
286	2011A	GB252	Strangford Lough and islands	Northern Ireland	15,580	A4i, A4iii, B1i, B2, C2, C3, C4, C6
287	2007A	GB259	Upper Lough Erne	Northern Ireland	9,110	A4i, B1i, B3, C2, C6

ᵉ Area of IBA has been considerably extended since 1989/1992 IBA inventory (Grimmett and Jones 1989; Pritchard *et al.* 1992).
ᵖ Area of IBA has been considerably reduced since 1989/1992 IBA inventory (Grimmett and Jones 1989; Pritchard *et al.* 1992).

Sites identified in the first inventory of IBAs in Europe (Grimmett and Jones 1989) but no longer considered to be IBAs
GB006 Loch an Duin; GB077 St Cyrus; GB101 North end of Bute; GB102 North Arran Mountains; GB119 Ben Dubhchraig; GB136 Shap Fells; GB191 Windsor Forest and Great Park; GB203 Pevensey levels; GB225 Clett Stacks; GB227 Inchnadamph; GB228 Isay; GB229 North Sutor of Cromarty; GB230 Black Isle sites; GB232 Forfar, Rescobie and Balgavies Lochs; GB234 Loch Mahaick; GB235 Haughs of Clyde; GB236 Loch Lyoch and Cleuch reservoirs; GB238 Great and Little Orme; GB242 Slapton Ley; GB243 Christchurch Harbour; GB255 Sandy Island including Gun's Island; GB258 Lower Lough Erne.

Site identified in the inventory of IBAs in the UK (Pritchard *et al.* 1992) but no longer considered to be an IBA
523A North of England montane sites.

(057), Mid-Essex coast (042), Morecambe Bay (044), and Humber flats, marshes and coast (032).

Because of its extensive Atlantic coastline, the UK has many large breeding seabird colonies. Forty-six sites regularly hold over 10,000 pairs of breeding seabirds or more than 1% of the global or distinct population of a seabird species (i.e. meeting criteria A4ii, A4iii, or B1ii). The five most important such sites are St Kilda (238), Skokholm and Skomer (094), Caithness cliffs (115), Foula (149) and Shiant Isles (242).

Twenty sites regularly hold over 10,000 pairs of breeding waterbirds (including gulls and terns), the five most important being Flamborough Head and Bempton cliffs (024), Fowlsheugh (150), Caithness cliffs (115), Troup, Pennan and Lion Heads (259) and Forth Islands (148).

Two sites qualify under A4i for non-breeding assemblages of gulls: Loch of Skene (180) for *Larus canus* and Hornsea Mere (031) for *Larus minutus*.

Table 2. Important Bird Areas in the United Kingdom that are important for species of global conservation concern (meeting criterion A1).

Species	IBA code
Crex crex Corncrake	218, 247, 251, 256, 263, 264, 266
Loxia scotica Scottish Crossbill	098, 106, 114, 121, 122, 146, 154, 156, 167, 186, 190, 209, 231, 260

One hundred and eighty-seven IBAs qualify on the basis of supporting an important population of one or more SPECs (criteria B2 and B3). Many of these sites also qualify under other criteria. Species for which B2/B3 are the only qualifying criteria at the A/B-level include breeding *Gavia stellata, Milvus milvus, Circus cyaneus, Aquila chrysaetos, Pandion haliaetus, Falco peregrinus, Tetrao tetrix, Larus marinus, Asio flammeus, Caprimulgus europaeus, Picus viridis, Saxicola rubetra, Saxicola torquata, Turdus torquatus* and *Pyrrhocorax pyrrhocorax*, and wintering *Melanitta fusca*. Table 4 shows SPECs and those species listed on Annex I of the EC Birds Directive with significant breeding populations at IBAs in the UK, i.e. those species meeting criteria B2/B3 or C6, and the proportion of the national population breeding at IBAs.

The United Kingdom is a member state of the European Union, so sites can additionally qualify under C criteria. Nearly all 287 sites in the UK qualify under one or more C criteria, though only 58 under C criteria alone (41 mainly under C6, 17 under C7). Species which qualify at one or more sites under the C criteria (again mainly C6) alone are: *Gavia arctica, Botaurus stellaris, Mergus albellus* (winter only), *Pernis apivorus, Circus aeruginosus, Circus pygargus, Falco columbarius, Tetrao urogallus, Porzana porzana, Grus grus, Burhinus oedicnemus, Charadrius morinellus, Philomachus pugnax* (mainly in winter), *Tringa glareola, Phalaropus lobatus, Larus melanocephalus, Sterna hirundo, Sterna paradisaea, Lullula arborea* and *Sylvia undata*.

Table 3. Important Bird Areas in the United Kingdom that support important numbers of one or more congregatory species (i.e. meeting criteria A4 and/or B1). IBAs meeting both criteria A4 and B1 for the species are shown in **bold**. IBAs meeting only criterion B1 for the species concerned, and not A4, are shown in normal type. For key to 'Season', see p. 7).

Species	Season	IBA code
Gavia immer Great Northern Diver	W	**061, 241, 243**
Podiceps auritus Slavonian Grebe	W	061, 207, 241
Fulmarus glacialis Fulmar	B	**149, 238**
Puffinus puffinus Manx Shearwater	B	**088, 094, 236**
Hydrobates pelagicus Storm Petrel	B	**094, 105, 145, 208, 252, 258**
Oceanodroma leucorhoa Leach's Petrel	B	145, 238
Sula bassana Gannet	B	**090, 099, 148, 159, 216, 220, 238, 252**
Phalacrocorax carbo Cormorant	R	001, 201
	B	096, 148
Phalacrocorax aristotelis Shag	B	**023, 033, 115, 118, 138,** 148, **149, 242**
	W	**241**
Cygnus columbianus Bewick's Swan	W	**005, 010, 019, 039, 045, 051, 057, 093, 279**
Cygnus cygnus Whooper Swan	W	039, **051,** 164, 180, 193, 207, **247, 278, 279, 287**
Anser brachyrhynchus Pink-footed Goose	W	**039, 047, 057, 077, 117, 120, 139, 142,** 144, **153, 157, 175, 178, 181, 204, 246, 261, 268, 269, 270**
Anser albifrons White-fronted Goose	W	116, 135, 169, 172, 174, 191, 196, 221, 229, 230, 256
Anser anser Greylag Goose	R	186, 225, 247, 256
	W	011, 030, 037, 098, **116,** 162, **179, 180,** 181, 187, 191, 193, **207, 209,** 218, 231, **246, 254,** 256
Branta leucopsis Barnacle Goose	W	123, 134, 135, 136, **169, 172, 173,** 181, 202, 218, **230,** 242, 248, 256, 258, **261,** 266
Branta bernicla Brent Goose	W	**007,** 012, **014, 029,** 037, **040, 042, 047,** 052, **064, 077,** 274, 275, 276, 277, **278,** 281, **286**
Tadorna tadorna Shelduck	W	**032, 040, 041, 042, 044,** 057, 066, **077, 086,** 093, 142
Anas penelope Wigeon	W	047, **051, 057, 207**
Anas strepera Gadwall	R	051
	W	001, 005, 031, 035, 051, 058, 063
Anas crecca Teal	W	001, 029, 038, 041, 042, 057, 060, 086, 207
Anas acuta Pintail	W	018, 039, 040, 041, 044, 045, 047, 051, 057, 066, 068, 077, 082, 086, 093, 261
Anas clypeata Shoveler	W	001, 013, 019, 051, 058, 063, 068, 175
Aythya ferina Pochard	W	**279**
Aythya fuligula Tufted Duck	W	**279**
Aythya marila Scaup	W	279
Melanitta nigra Common Scoter	W	**091**
Bucephala clangula Goldeneye	W	**279**
Mergus serrator Red-breasted Merganser	W	207
Haematopus ostralegus Oystercatcher	R	218, 247
	W	**042, 044, 057, 077, 082, 086, 207, 261**
	P	**042, 044, 057, 077, 082, 086,** 207, **261**
Recurvirostra avosetta Avocet	W	002
	P	002
Charadrius hiaticula Ringed Plover	R	047, 218, 247
	W	014, 029, 040, 042, 064, 066, 131, 207, 218, 247, 256, 281, 285
	P	007, 014, 018, 029, 032, 040, 042, 044, 047, 057, 064, 066, 068, 073, 074, 077, 086, 093, 207, 261

Species	Season	IBA code
Pluvialis apricaria Golden Plover	W	008, **032,** 042
	P	**032**
Pluvialis squatarola Grey Plover	W	**007, 014, 029, 040, 042, 044, 057, 066, 068, 077, 086**
	P	**014, 029,** 032, **040, 042, 044, 057, 068, 077**
Calidris canutus Knot	W	**007,** 018, **032, 042, 044,** 047, **057,** 068, 071, **077, 086,** 142, 207, **261,** 286
	P	018, 032, 042, **044, 057, 077,** 086, 261
Calidris alba Sanderling	W	**057**
	P	**032, 044, 057, 077**
Calidris maritima Purple Sandpiper	W	**050, 131**
	P	**131**
Calidris alpina Dunlin	R	048, 218, 247
	B	053, 080, 170, 225
	W	**014, 032, 040, 041, 042, 044, 057, 066, 077, 086, 093,** 261
	P	**014,** 032, 040, **042, 044, 057,** 077
Limosa limosa Black-tailed Godwit	W	014, 029, 042, 051, 054, 057, 064, 066, 068, 086
	P	014, 029, 040, 042, 051, 054, 057, 066, 068, 077, 086
Limosa lapponica Bar-tailed Godwit	W	**014, 032, 037, 042, 044, 047, 057, 077, 133, 142, 143, 207, 261, 278**
	P	**014, 037, 042, 057, 077, 142, 207, 261**
Numenius arquata Curlew	W	042, 044, 077, 086, 093, 207, 261
	P	042, 044, 077, 086, 207, 261
Tringa totanus Redshank	R	025, 042, 077, 247
	W	002, 014, 018, **032, 040, 041, 042, 044, 057,** 066, 068, 073, **077, 086,** 093, **142,** 165, 204, **207, 261,** 273, 286
	P	014, 018, **032, 040, 041, 042, 044, 057,** 066, 073, **077, 086,** 093, **142,** 204, 207, **261,** 273, 286
Arenaria interpres Turnstone	W	**033, 042, 044, 050, 057, 066, 074, 077, 131, 142, 247, 256, 273, 281, 285**
	P	**040, 042, 044, 050, 066, 071, 074, 077, 131, 273**
Stercorarius skua Great Skua	B	**149, 159, 163, 215, 220, 238, 240, 245**
Larus minutus Little Gull	N	**031**
Larus canus Common Gull	B	**125, 255**
	N	**180**
Larus fuscus Lesser Black-backed Gull	B	**002,** 023, **025, 033, 044,** 057, **083, 093, 094,** 099, **148, 171, 261**
Larus argentatus Herring Gull	B	**044, 115, 148,** 150
Rissa tridactyla Kittiwake	B	**024, 115, 150, 259, 267**
Sterna sandvicensis Sandwich Tern	B	**015, 023, 047,** 097, **270,** 286
Sterna dougallii Roseate Tern	B	**015, 148**
Sterna albifrons Little Tern	B	027, **047**
Uria aalge Guillemot	B	024, **115,** 138, 148, 149, **150,** 158, 197, 200, 216, 220, 237, 259, 267, 283
Alca torda Razorbill	B	**024, 115, 150, 158, 200, 242, 283**
Cepphus grylle Black Guillemot	B	115, 152, 159, 202, 219, 223, 241
Fratercula arctica Puffin	B	015, 023, 138, 148, 149, 159, **238, 242,** 252

No sites in the UK qualified under the A2, A3, A4iv, B1iii, B1iv or C5 criteria. One site which might have qualified under B1iii (a large *Riparia riparia* colony) was recently destroyed. It was not considered appropriate for A2 to be applied to *Loxia scotica*.

HABITATS

The UK's unusual variations in geology and climate have produced a wide diversity of habitats in a restricted area, with natural and semi-natural biological features of outstanding interest. At a broad scale, 80% of IBAs contain some wetland habitat, many of these being estuarine and coastal. Almost half contain heathland or moorland habitats, while over 65% have grassland habitats, 19%

with humid grasslands. Over 40% have some rocky areas, a significant number of these being coastal cliffs (Figure 1).

Estuaries provide some of the most important habitats at IBAs, such as mud- and sandflats, saltmarshes, grazing marshes and dune systems. Almost two million waders and wildfowl winter on UK estuaries or use them as stop-over sites on migration. In total, 59 IBAs are estuarine or non-estuarine coastal areas (such as rocky shores). Three of these sites are more than 50,000 ha in extent (Moray basin, firths and bays 207; The Wash 077; and Severn estuary 093), while 13 more are over 10,000 ha.

In addition to estuarine wetlands, 63 sites encompass important inland wetlands. These include open water, river and stream systems, and flood-plains. Their ornithological importance includes breeding divers and grebes, and wintering and breeding waterfowl.

Table 4. Species of European conservation concern and species listed on Annex I of the EC Birds Directive with significant breeding populations at IBAs in the United Kingdom (meeting any IBA criteria).

Species [1]	Minimum national breeding population (pairs) [2]	Proportion (%) of national population breeding at all IBAs in the United Kingdom
Gavia stellata Red-throated Diver	935	53
Gavia arctica Black-throated Diver	155	70
Podiceps auritus Slavonian Grebe	70	41
Puffinus puffinus Manx Shearwater	220,000	33
Hydrobates pelagicus Storm Petrel	20,000	100 [3]
Oceanodroma leucorhoa Leach's Petrel	10,000	33
Sula bassana Gannet	201,000	87
Phalacrocorax aristotelis Shag	37,500	49
Botaurus stellaris Bittern	12	100 [3]
Anas strepera Gadwall	790	43
Anas acuta Pintail	8	100 [3]
Pernis apivorus Honey Buzzard	4	50
Milvus milvus Red Kite	160	13
Circus aeruginosus Marsh Harrier	157	52
Circus cyaneus Hen Harrier	670	29
Circus pygargus Montagu's Harrier	7	43
Aquila chrysaetos Golden Eagle	422	31
Pandion haliaetus Osprey	99	12
Falco columbarius Merlin	1,330	39
Falco peregrinus Peregrine	1,285	20
Tetrao tetrix Black Grouse	6,510	13
Tetrao urogallus Capercaillie	1,100	22
Porzana porzana Spotted Crake	1	100 [3]
Crex crex Corncrake	640	71
Grus grus Crane	3	100
Recurvirostra avosetta Avocet	450	100 [3]
Burhinus oedicnemus Stone Curlew	210	39
Charadrius morinellus Dotterel	840	49
Pluvialis apricaria Golden Plover	22,600	44
Philomachus pugnax Ruff	2	100 [3]
Numenius phaeopus Whimbrel	530	66
Tringa totanus Redshank	32,000	17
Tringa glareola Wood Sandpiper	1	100 [3]
Phalaropus lobatus Red-necked Phalarope	36	81
Stercorarius skua Great Skua	8,500	85
Larus melanocephalus Mediterranean Gull	13	100 [3]
Larus canus Common Gull	68,500	25
Larus fuscus Lesser Black-backed Gull	85,000	100 [3]
Larus marinus Great Black-backed Gull	20,000	43
Sterna sandvicensis Sandwich Tern	17,000	70
Sterna dougallii Roseate Tern	72	100 [3]
Sterna hirundo Common Tern	14,000	51
Sterna paradisaea Arctic Tern	44,000	53
Sterna albifrons Little Tern	2,400	71
Alca torda Razorbill	107,000	94
Cepphus grylle Black Guillemot	18,500	24
Fratercula arctica Puffin	451,500	95
Asio flammeus Short-eared Owl	1,000	14
Caprimulgus europaeus Nightjar	3,400	66
Picus viridis Green Woodpecker	15,000	1
Lullula arborea Woodlark	600	74
Saxicola rubetra Whinchat	14,000	3
Saxicola torquata Stonechat	9,000	20
Turdus torquatus Ring Ouzel	5,500	3
Sylvia undata Dartford Warbler	1,600	100 [3]
Pyrrhocorax pyrrhocorax Chough	342	32
Loxia scotica Scottish Crossbill	300	23 [4]

1. Only those species of European conservation concern (see Box 1, p. 12) that meet IBA criteria in the United Kingdom are listed, together with those species listed on Annex I of the EC Birds Directive that fulfil criterion C6 in IBAs in the United Kingdom.
2. Data are taken from the BirdLife/EBCC European Bird Database 1998 (Heath and Borggreve 2000).
3. The percentage of the national population in IBAs exceeds 100%. Usually this is because the national population estimate has not been updated recently whilst the IBA population estimate has been recently updated with new data as a result of comprehensive surveys of IBAs themselves. Also, the individual site count for a species may be the maximum or average over recent years, and summing these may record more birds than are present nationally in any single year.
4. This is an absolute minimum as most of the population size is unknown.

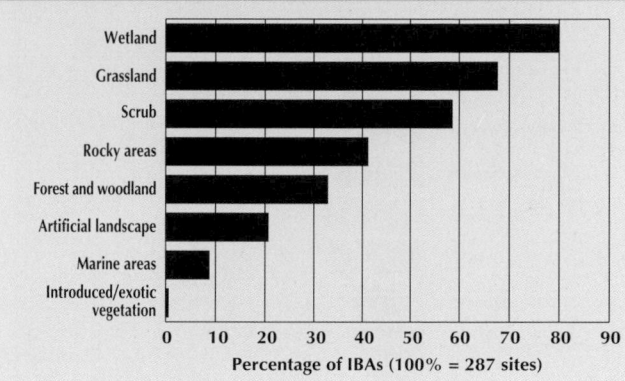

Figure 1. Occurrence of habitats at Important Bird Areas in the United Kingdom (see Appendix 3 for definitions of habitats).

These sites include several extensive upland loch systems and their catchments. The largest freshwater body in the UK, Lough Neagh (279), is in Northern Ireland.

Forty-eight UK IBAs contain extensive components of upland moorland or grassland, important for upland breeding birds. The largest of these is Central Highland hills and glens (121), a massive area of over 230,000 ha, particularly important for breeding birds of prey and waders.

Seventy sites support important rock and cliff habitats for breeding seabirds, gulls and terns. Many of these are islands, the largest being Tiree and Coll (256); Hoy (163); and Rum (236). Long stretches of coastal cliff include Pembrokeshire cliffs (092); Caithness cliffs (115); and Flamborough Head and Bempton cliffs (024).

Peatland habitat is of exceptional importance in the UK, with The Peatlands (225) in Caithness and Sutherland being one of the world's most outstanding examples of this ecosystem.

A further 33 sites encompass important areas of lowland heathland, the largest of these being The New Forest (046); Breckland heaths and Thetford forest (009); Exmoor coast and heaths (022); and Salisbury Plain (059).

Two further habitats are of particular importance and are very characteristic of the UK. The machairs of the Hebrides support most of the UK's remnant breeding population of *Crex crex* and are very important for breeding waders. Remnant Caledonian pine forests, such as those found at Abernethy forest (098), are important for *Tetrao tetrix*, *Tetrao urogallus* and the endemic *Loxia scotica*.

IMPACTS ON IBAs – LAND-USE AND THREATS

Figure 2 shows the most common forms of land-use on IBAs in the UK. Although the degree of intensity of use is difficult to determine on many sites, agricultural operations are undertaken on 58% of them. Tourism and recreation directly affect 34% of IBAs. The next most frequent forms of land-use are forestry, hunting and fisheries/aquaculture, each of which occur on 16–18% of IBAs, with many IBAs being used for more than one activity. A third of UK IBAs have some part of their area devoted to nature conservation and research.

Figure 3 shows the key threats to and impacts on IBAs. Forty-six percent of sites are affected by recreation and tourism, mostly at moderate levels, while 38% are threatened by industrial, urban or infrastructure developments (7% highly threatened). Thirty-one percent are under threat from agricultural intensification, mostly at moderate levels. Other common threats are those posed through water management (drainage, filling of wetlands, groundwater abstraction, dredging and canalization, and construction of dykes and dams), affecting 32% of sites (5% high), aquaculture and fisheries (25% of sites), and the minerals extraction industry (26% of sites).

Seventeen percent of sites are under threat from 'natural' events, most of these related to sea-level rise around coastal areas. This major threat to a large number of estuarine and low-lying coastal areas has two detrimental effects: flooding and erosion of areas, and the destruction of habitats and disturbance to wildlife caused by developments to ameliorate the effects of sea-level rise, such as sea defences.

One hundred and nine IBAs (38%) have at least one high-impact threat, a further 119 (41%) at least one medium-impact threat, and

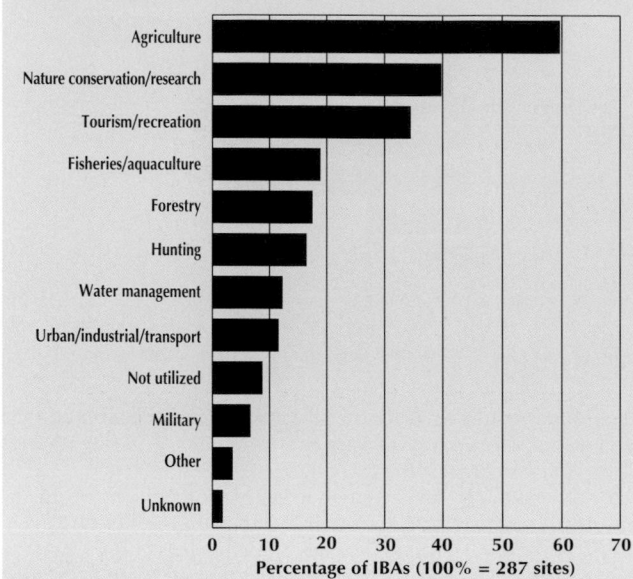

Figure 2. Occurrence of land-uses at Important Bird Areas in the United Kingdom (see Appendix 3 for definitions of land-uses).

an additional 21 sites (7%) at least one low-impact threat. Of the 17 sites under the most high-level threats, three are in the Thames estuary (Medway estuary and marshes; Thames estuary and marshes; and The Swale), where the main threats come from general disturbance to birds, recreation and tourism, urban, industrial and infrastructure developments, dredging and groundwater abstraction.

PROTECTION STATUS

Table 5 and Figures 4 and 5 summarize the national and international protection status of IBAs in the UK.

■ National protection
The main categories of protected area in the UK are:

1. Site of Special Scientific Interest (SSSI)
SSSIs are the backbone of statutory site protection in the UK, forming a network of nationally important sites. They are mostly in private ownership and are selected and notified by one of the three Statutory Agencies: Countryside Council for Wales (CCW), English Nature (EN) or Scottish Natural Heritage (SNH). They

are notified on the basis of biological, geological or physiographical interest, under section 28 of the Wildlife and Countryside Act 1981. Special consultation arrangements apply to land-use operations on these sites and, generally speaking, adequate protection depends on voluntary cooperation by owners and occupiers.

2. Area of Special Scientific Interest (ASSI)
ASSIs are the equivalent of SSSIs in Northern Ireland, and are declared by the Department of the Environment (Northern Ireland) under the Nature Conservation and Amenity Land Order 1985.

3. National Nature Reserve (NNR)
NNRs are usually managed by the Statutory Agencies or by agreement with the Department of the Environment (Northern Ireland), for the conservation of biological, geological or physiographical features. They are notified under section 19 of the National Parks and Access to the Countryside Act 1949, or section 35 of the Wildlife and Countryside Act 1981. There is a little-used Marine Nature Reserve (MNR) equivalent for marine sites.

4. National Park (NP)
Generally in upland areas, National Parks were designated in the 1950s for landscape and amenity purposes, under the National Parks and Access to the Countryside Act 1949. They are inhabited, and entail no special state ownership. There are some special planning constraints and consultative arrangements, administered by a National Park Authority for each Park. One or two additional areas, although not formally designated in the same way, function in a similar manner under other arrangements.

Other designations include Area of Outstanding Natural Beauty (AONB); Heritage Coast; Local Nature Reserve (LNR); National Scenic Area; Country Park; and non-statutory nature reserve owned or managed by a non-governmental organization (NGO) or private body. Within the site accounts, protected area information is given only for international designations, SSSIs, ASSIs, NNRs, MNRs, NPs and NGO reserves, although IBAs also overlap with the other-mentioned designations. Information on the NGO reserves is restricted mainly to the holdings of the Royal Society for the Protection of Birds (RSPB, the BirdLife Partner in the UK).

Over 85% of the UK IBAs are covered in some part by SSSI/ASSI status, with almost 1,300 SSSIs/ASSIs partially or wholly overlapping with IBAs (Table 5). Twenty percent of IBAs are also partly NNRs, 4% partly LNRs, and nearly 35% are partly reserves run by a wide variety of non-governmental conservation bodies such as the RSPB. Eighty NNRs, 15 LNRs and 148 other reserves partially or wholly overlap with the IBAs. The number and area of IBAs covered by nationally protected areas is shown in Figure 4.

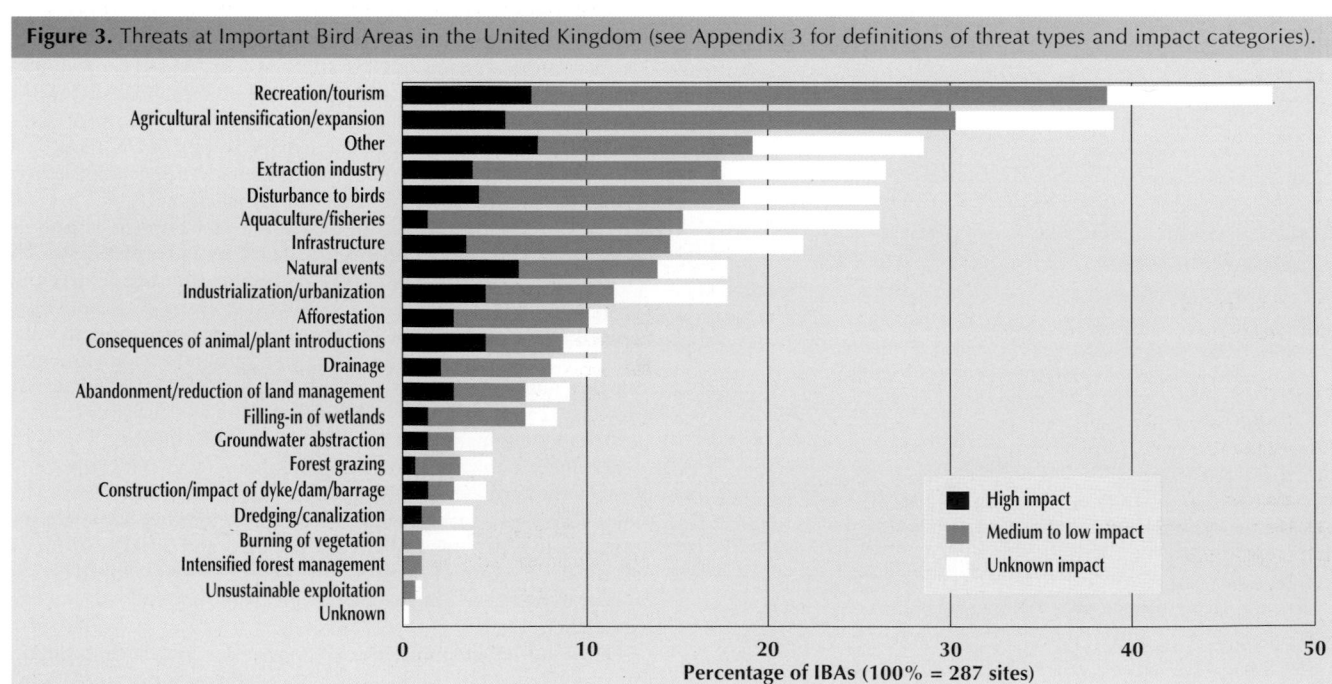

Figure 3. Threats at Important Bird Areas in the United Kingdom (see Appendix 3 for definitions of threat types and impact categories).

Figure 4. The national protection status of Important Bird Areas in the United Kingdom.

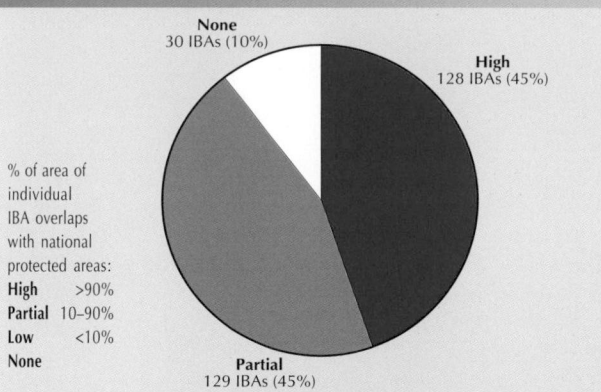

% of area of individual IBA overlaps with national protected areas:
High   >90%
Partial   10–90%
Low   <10%
None

Total area of overlap between IBA network in the United Kingdom and national protected-area system (see Table 5 for categories) = 8,666–9,785 km² (28–31% of total IBA area).

Figure 5. The international protection status of Important Bird Areas in the United Kingdom.

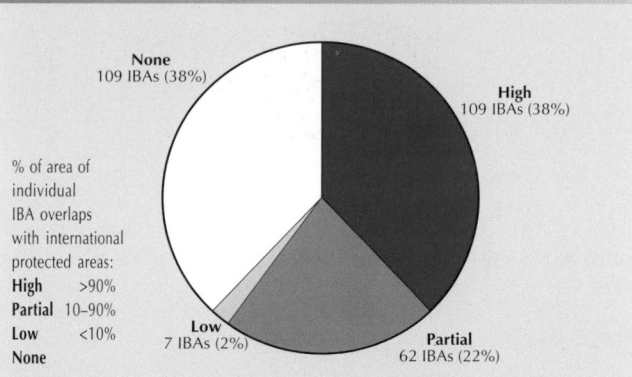

% of area of individual IBA overlaps with international protected areas:
High   >90%
Partial   10–90%
Low   <10%
None

Total area of overlap between IBA network in the United Kingdom and international protected-area system (see Table 5 for categories) = 7,832–7,882 km² (25% of total IBA area).

Table 5. Protection status of Important Bird Areas in the United Kingdom. A tick (✔) indicates that an IBA overlaps with a protected area (to any extent).

IBA code	International name	National Nature Reserve	Marine Nature Reserve	National Park	Reserve	Site of Special Scientific Interest	Area of Special Scientific Interest	Ramsar Site	World Heritage Site	Biosphere Reserve	Special Protection Area
001	Abberton reservoir					✔		✔			✔
002	Alde/Ore estuary	✔		✔	✔			✔			✔
003	Arun valley				✔	✔					
004	Ashdown forest				✔	✔					✔
005	Avon valley					✔		✔			✔
006	Benacre to Easton Bavents	✔				✔					✔
007	Benfleet and Southend marshes	✔				✔					✔
008	Bodmin Moor					✔					
009	Breckland heaths and Thetford forest	✔			✔	✔					
010	Breydon Water			✔	✔	✔		✔			✔
011	Broadland	✔		✔	✔	✔		✔			✔
012	Chesil Beach and The Fleet					✔		✔			✔
013	Chew valley lake					✔					✔
014	Chichester and Langstone Harbours				✔	✔		✔			✔
015	Coquet Island				✔	✔					✔
016	Deben estuary					✔		✔			✔
017	Dorset heaths and forests				✔	✔					✔
018	Duddon estuary			✔	✔	✔		✔			✔
019	Dungeness to Pett Levels				✔	✔					
020	East Devon heaths				✔	✔					✔
021	Exe estuary				✔	✔		✔			✔
022	Exmoor coast and heaths			✔		✔					
023	Farne Islands					✔					✔
024	Flamborough Head and Bempton cliffs				✔	✔					✔
025	Forest of Bowland					✔					
026	Frome flood-plain					✔					
027	Great Yarmouth North Denes	✔				✔					✔
028	Haldon					✔					
029	Hamford Water	✔			✔	✔		✔			✔
030	Holburn Lake and Moss					✔		✔			✔
031	Hornsea Mere				✔	✔					✔
032	Humber flats, marshes and coast				✔	✔		✔			✔
033	Isles of Scilly coastal habitats					✔					
034	Laughton forest					✔					
035	Lea valley				✔	✔					
036	Leighton Moss				✔	✔		✔			✔
037	Lindisfarne	✔				✔		✔			✔
Subtotal of IBAs		**8**	**0**	**4**	**19**	**37**	**0**	**16**	**0**	**0**	**27**
038	Lower Derwent valley	✔			✔	✔		✔			✔
039	Martin Mere				✔	✔		✔			✔
040	Medway estuary and marshes	✔			✔	✔		✔			✔
041	Mersey estuary					✔		✔			✔
042	Mid-Essex coast	✔				✔		✔			✔
043	Minsmere–Walberswick	✔				✔		✔			✔
044	Morecambe Bay				✔	✔		✔			✔
045	Nene Washes				✔	✔		✔			✔
046	The New Forest					✔		✔			✔
047	North Norfolk coast	✔			✔	✔		✔			✔
048	North Pennine moors	✔			✔	✔					✔
049	North Yorkshire moors			✔		✔					✔
050	Northumberland coast					✔					
051	Ouse Washes				✔	✔		✔			✔
052	Pagham Harbour					✔		✔			✔
053	Peak District moors			✔		✔					✔
054	Poole Harbour				✔	✔					
055	Porton Down					✔					✔
056	Portsmouth Harbour					✔		✔			✔
057	Ribble and Alt estuaries	✔			✔	✔		✔			✔
058	Rutland Water					✔		✔			✔
059	Salisbury Plain					✔					✔
060	Somerset Levels and Moors				✔	✔		✔			✔
061	South Cornwall coast					✔					
062	South Pennine moors					✔					✔
063	South-west London water-bodies					✔					
064	Southampton Water and Solent marshes					✔		✔			✔
065	Stodmarsh					✔		✔			✔
066	Stour and Orwell estuary				✔	✔		✔			✔
067	Suffolk Sandlings and coastal forest				✔	✔					
068	The Swale	✔			✔	✔		✔			✔
069	Tamar complex					✔					✔
070	Taw and Torridge estuary				✔	✔					
071	Teesmouth and Cleveland coast					✔		✔			✔
072	Thames basin heathlands	✔				✔					
073	Thames estuary and marshes	✔			✔	✔					
074	Thanet coast and Sandwich Bay					✔		✔			✔
Subtotal of IBAs		**18**	**0**	**6**	**38**	**74**	**0**	**38**	**0**	**0**	**56**

Table 5 ... continued. Protection status of Important Bird Areas in the United Kingdom.
A tick (✔) indicates that an IBA overlaps with a protected area (to any extent).

IBA code	International name	National Nature Reserve	Marine Nature Reserve	National Park	Reserve	Site of Special Scientific Interest	Area of Special Scientific Interest	Ramsar Site	World Heritage Site	Biosphere Reserve	Special Protection Area
075	Thorne and Hatfield Moors					✔					
076	Walmore Common					✔		✔			✔
077	The Wash	✔			✔	✔		✔			✔
078	Wealden heaths					✔		✔			✔
079	West Penwith coast and moors					✔					
080	Yorkshire Dale moorlands			✔		✔					
081	Berwyn	✔		✔	✔	✔					✔
082	Burry Inlet					✔		✔			✔
083	Cardigan Island										
084	Carmarthen Bay					✔					
085	Cors Fochno and Dyfi			✔	✔	✔		✔			
086	Dee estuary				✔	✔		✔			✔
087	Elenydd–Mallaen	✔			✔	✔					✔
088	Glannau Aberdaron and Ynys Enlli					✔					✔
089	Glannau Ynys Gybi				✔	✔					✔
090	Grassholm			✔	✔	✔					✔
091	North Wales coast					✔					
092	Pembrokeshire cliffs			✔	✔	✔					✔
093	Severn estuary	✔				✔		✔			✔
094	Skokholm and Skomer		✔	✔		✔					✔
095	Swansea Bay–Blackpill					✔					
096	Traeth Lafan, Conwy Bay			✔							✔
097	Ynys Feurig, Cemlyn Bay and The Skerries				✔	✔					✔
098	Abernethy forest	✔			✔	✔					✔
099	Ailsa Craig					✔					✔
100	Airds Moss and Muirkirk uplands					✔					✔
101	Almorness Point and Hestan Island										
102	Alvie	✔				✔					
103	Assynt lochs					✔					
104	Atholl/Glen Tilt					✔					
105	Auskerry					✔					✔
106	Ballochbuie forest										✔
107	Beinn Dearg					✔					✔
108	Ben Alder					✔					
109	Ben Wyvis					✔					✔
110	Blackpark and Gutcher, Yell				✔	✔					
111	Bluemill										
112	Buchan Ness to Collieston coast					✔					✔
113	Caenlochan					✔					✔
114	Cairngorms	✔				✔		✔			✔
115	Caithness cliffs					✔					✔
116	Caithness lochs					✔		✔			✔
117	Cameron reservoir					✔		✔			✔
118	Canna and Sanday					✔					✔
119	Cape Wrath					✔					✔
120	Castle Loch, Lochmaben					✔		✔			✔
121	Central Highland hills and glens	✔				✔					
122	Coilacriech					✔					
123	Colonsay and Oronsay				✔	✔					✔
124	Copinsay				✔	✔					✔
125	Correen Hills					✔					
126	Creag Meagaidh	✔				✔					✔
127	Cromdale Hills										
128	Crussa Field and the Heogs					✔					
Subtotal of IBAs		**27**	**1**	**13**	**52**	**122**	**0**	**49**	**0**	**0**	**90**

IBA code	International name	National Nature Reserve	Marine Nature Reserve	National Park	Reserve	Site of Special Scientific Interest	Area of Special Scientific Interest	Ramsar Site	World Heritage Site	Biosphere Reserve	Special Protection Area
129	Cuillin Hills, Skye					✔					
130	Drumochter Hills					✔					✔
131	East Sanday					✔		✔			✔
132	Eday					✔					✔
133	Eden estuary, Tentsmuir Point and Abertay sands					✔					✔
134	Eilean Hoan				✔						✔
135	Eilean na Muice Duibh, Islay	✔				✔		✔			✔
136	Eilean nan Ron					✔					✔
137	Endrick Mouth and Loch Lomond Islands	✔				✔		✔			✔
138	Fair Isle					✔					✔
139	Fala Flow					✔		✔			✔
140	Faray and Holm of Faray										
141	Fetlar				✔	✔					✔
142	Firth of Forth				✔	✔					
143	Firth of Tay					✔					✔
144	Flanders Moss and Lake of Menteith	✔				✔					✔
145	Flannan Isles					✔					✔
146	Forest of Birse										
147	Forest of Clunie					✔					
148	Forth Islands	✔			✔	✔					✔
149	Foula					✔					✔
150	Fowlsheugh				✔	✔					✔
151	Galloway Forest Park	✔				✔		✔		✔	
152	Gigha Island and islets										
153	Gladhouse reservoir					✔		✔			✔
154	Glen Tanar	✔				✔					✔
155	Glengarry lochs					✔					
156	Grantown-on-Spey										
157	Greenlaw Moor and Hule Moss					✔		✔			✔
158	Handa	✔			✔	✔					✔
159	Hermaness and Saxa Vord, Unst	✔				✔					✔
160	Hill of Colvadale and Sobul					✔					
161	Horse Island				✔						
162	Hoselaw Loch				✔	✔		✔			✔
163	Hoy				✔	✔					
164	Inchinnan, Renfrew										
165	Inner Clyde estuary				✔	✔					
166	Inverpolly, Loch Urigill and nearby lochs				✔	✔					
167	Kinveachy	✔				✔					
168	Ladder Hills					✔					
169	Laggan, Islay					✔					✔
170	Lewis peatlands					✔					
171	Little Cumbrae Island										
172	Loch Gruinart, Islay				✔	✔		✔			✔
173	Loch Indaal and Bridgend flats, Islay					✔		✔			✔
174	Loch Ken and Dee marshes				✔	✔		✔			✔
175	Loch Leven	✔			✔	✔		✔			
176	Loch Maree and nearby lochs and mountains	✔				✔		✔			✔
177	Loch of Isbister				✔	✔					
178	Loch of Kinnordy				✔	✔		✔			✔
179	Loch of Lintrathen				✔	✔		✔			✔
180	Loch of Skene					✔		✔			✔
Subtotal of IBAs		**38**	**1**	**13**	**69**	**166**	**0**	**65**	**0**	**1**	**121**

Table 5 ... continued. Protection status of Important Bird Areas in the United Kingdom.
A tick (✔) indicates that an IBA overlaps with a protected area (to any extent).

IBA code	International name	National Nature Reserve	Marine Nature Reserve	National Park	Reserve	Site of Special Scientific Interest	Area of Special Scientific Interest	Ramsar Site	World Heritage Site	Biosphere Reserve	Special Protection Area
181	Loch of Strathbeg				✔	✔		✔			✔
182	Loch Oire					✔					
183	Loch Ruthven and nearby lochs				✔	✔					✔
184	Loch Ryan										
185	Loch Scadavay					✔					✔
186	Loch Shin and nearby lochs					✔					✔
187	Loch Spynie					✔		✔			✔
188	Loch Stack, Loch nam Brac and nearby lochs					✔					
189	Loch Tarff and nearby lochs					✔					
190	Loch Vaa					✔					✔
191	Lochinch and Torrs Warren					✔					✔
192	Lochnagar										✔
193	Lochs of Harray and Stenness					✔					
194	Lochs of Spiggie and Brow				✔	✔					✔
195	Lower Findhorn valley					✔					
196	Machrihanish					✔					✔
197	Marwick Head				✔	✔					✔
198	Mid-Mull hills and glens					✔					
199	Mill Dam, Shapinsay				✔						
200	Mingulay and Berneray					✔					✔
201	Mochrum and Castle Lochs					✔					
202	Monach Islands	✔				✔					✔
203	Monadhliath					✔					
204	Montrose basin					✔		✔			✔
205	Moorfoot Hills					✔					
206	Moorland areas, Central Shetland					✔					
207	Moray basin, firths and bays	✔			✔	✔		✔			✔
208	Mousa					✔					✔
209	Muir of Dinnet	✔				✔					
210	Newcastleton Hills					✔					
211	North Harris mountains					✔					✔
212	North Inverness lochs					✔					✔
213	North Lowther Hills					✔					✔
214	North Mainland coast										
215	North Roe and Tingon, Mainland Shetland					✔		✔			✔
216	North Rona and Sula Sgeir	✔				✔					
217	North Ronaldsay coast										
218	North Uist machair and islands				✔	✔					
219	North Westray coast										
220	Noss	✔				✔					✔
221	The Oa: Islay										
222	Papa Stour					✔					
223	Papa Westray (North Hill and Holm)				✔	✔					✔
224	Park, Lewis										
225	Peatlands	✔			✔	✔					✔
226	Pentland Firth Islands					✔					✔
227	Priest Island				✔	✔					✔
228	Ramna Stacks and Gruney				✔	✔					✔
229	Rhunahaorine Point					✔					✔
230	Rinns, Islay				✔	✔		✔			✔
231	River Spey – Insh marshes				✔	✔		✔			✔
232	Rois-Bheinn	✔				✔		✔			
233	Rosehearty to Fraserburgh coast					✔					
234	Rothiesholm peninsula, Stronsay										
	Subtotal of IBAs	**45**	**1**	**13**	**82**	**211**	**0**	**73**	**0**	**1**	**150**

IBA code	International name	National Nature Reserve	Marine Nature Reserve	National Park	Reserve	Site of Special Scientific Interest	Area of Special Scientific Interest	Ramsar Site	World Heritage Site	Biosphere Reserve	Special Protection Area
235	Rousay (Part)				✔	✔					
236	Rum	✔				✔					✔
237	St Abbs Head to Fast Castle	✔				✔					✔
238	St Kilda	✔				✔			✔	✔	✔
239	Sanda Island					✔					
240	Sandwick and Clift Hills										
241	Scapa Flow				✔	✔					
242	Shiant Isles					✔					✔
243	Sounds around Wyre					✔					
244	South Arran					✔					
245	South Bressay										
246	South Tayside goose roosts					✔		✔			✔
247	South Uist machair and lochs	✔				✔		✔		✔	✔
248	South Walls and Switha										
249	South Westray coast										
250	South-eastern Stronsay										
251	Stornoway to Back, Lewis					✔					
252	Sule Skerry and Sule Stack					✔					✔
253	Sumburgh Head				✔	✔					✔
254	Tay–Isla valley					✔					
255	Tips of Corsemaul and Mortlach										
256	Tiree and Coll				✔	✔		✔			✔
257	Tolsta Head, Lewis										
258	Treshnish Isles					✔					✔
259	Troup, Pennan and Lion Heads					✔					✔
260	Upper Deeside plantations					✔					
261	Upper Solway flats and marshes	✔			✔	✔		✔			✔
262	West Burrafirth										
263	West coast of Benbecula					✔					
264	West coast, Lewis					✔					
265	West Mainland moors				✔	✔					
266	West Sound of Barra					✔					
267	West Westray				✔	✔					✔
268	Westwater					✔		✔			✔
269	Wigtown Bay					✔					
270	Ythan estuary, Sands of Forvie and Meikle Loch					✔		✔			
271	Annaghroe, River Blackwater										
272	Antrim plateau	✔					✔				
273	Belfast Lough						✔	✔			✔
274	Carlingford Lough including Green Island	✔			✔		✔	✔			✔
275	Dundrum Inner Bay	✔					✔				
276	Killough Harbour and Coney Island Bay										
277	Larne Lough and Swan/Blue Circle Islands	✔			✔		✔	✔			✔
278	Lough Foyle and River Foyle	✔			✔	✔					✔
279	Lough Neagh and Lough Beg	✔			✔		✔	✔			✔
280	Lower Lough Macnean	✔									
281	Outer Ards peninsula						✔				
282	Pettigoe plateau						✔	✔			✔
283	Rathlin Island	✔			✔		✔				✔
284	Sheep Island						✔				✔
285	South Down coast						✔				
286	Strangford Lough and islands	✔	✔		✔		✔	✔			✔
287	Upper Lough Erne	✔					✔	✔			✔
	Total number of IBAs	**60**	**2**	**13**	**95**	**239**	**13**	**86**	**1**	**3**	**173**

◼ International protection

The UK is bound by several international directives for the conservation of sites (Box 1). The main categories of international protection in the UK are Special Protection Area (SPA), Special Area for Conservation (SAC), Ramsar Site, Biogenetic Reserve, Biosphere Reserve and World Heritage Site. UK policy is for all SPAs, SACs and Ramsar Sites also to be notified as SSSI/ASSI. Over 60% of UK's IBAs are protected in some part by SPA status, and nearly 30% by Ramsar Site designation (Table 5). In total, 173 SPAs and 86 Ramsar Sites partially or wholly overlap with the inventory sites. Because of slow progress in implementing the EC Birds Directive, the UK has assumed a policy of protecting identified candidate SPAs as though they were already designated, so the actual number of IBAs potentially protected by SPA status is much higher, about 220 IBAs (76%). A small number of IBAs overlap with proposed SACs, three with Biosphere Reserves and one with a World Heritage Site (Table 5). The number and area of IBAs covered by internationally protected areas is shown in Figure 5.

ANALYTICAL METHODS

- Many species of conservation concern in the UK, the Channel Islands and the Isle of Man are dispersed species (non-congregatory when breeding), such as *Alauda arvensis* and *Turdus philomelos*, which have declined dramatically on a national scale over the past 25 years. A site-based approach will not guarantee the conservation of these species; 'wider countryside' measures are therefore required.

- Information on habitats, land-uses, threats to sites and the overlap between IBAs and protected areas proved difficult to collect, and for many sites is minimal.

- Bird data have been collated from a wide variety of sources. These include the major national generic monitoring schemes, particularly the Wetland Birds Survey (WeBS) for waterfowl and the Seabird Colony Register (SCR) for breeding seabirds and some waterbirds, but also numerous national single-species and site-specific surveys. The most up-to-date counts have been used; however, because some areas have not been surveyed for many years, the data used range from the 1980s to 1997. Where surveys from different years have been combined to provide a figure for a site, this has been done using common sense and local knowledge of the sites.

- Almost 8,000 bird records are included in the BirdLife IBA Database for the UK, Channel Islands and Isle of Man. Over 1,000 of these pass one or more site-specific criteria; over 800 of the remainder occur in numbers equal to or greater than 1% of UK populations, but do not qualify under any of the IBA criteria. These latter records are listed in the main text of the 'Birds' section; unless otherwise stated, the counts quoted are five-year means for the period 1990–1995, and quoted percentage figures refer to the proportion of the national UK population of that species present at the IBA in question.

- All non-breeding-season counts refer to numbers of individuals, all breeding-season counts to pairs. This is the case even if breeding season records were collected in other ways (e.g. singing male

Crex crex). Numbers of territories, singing males, nests and apparently occupied nests/territories were considered to be equivalent to numbers of pairs. Breeding-season counts were sometimes of individual birds—particularly for gulls, terns and auks. All counts of individuals were divided by two to convert to pairs, except for *Sterna* spp., *Uria aalge* and *Alca torda* which were divided by 1.5 (as recommended by Lloyd *et al.* 1991).

- All counts have been rounded as follows: 1–100, not rounded; 101–1,000 to nearest 5; 1,001–5,000 to nearest 10; 5,001–10,000 to nearest 50; 10,001–50,000 to nearest 100; 50,001–100,000 to nearest 500 and 100,001+ to nearest 1,000. Population data are often extrapolated or calculated from accurate counts, and are therefore estimates based on scientific knowledge. An accuracy code of A has been applied in such cases.

- For 20 sites, three species (*Oceanodroma leucorhoa*, *Tetrao urogallus* and *Loxia scotica*) were allowed to qualify under one or more criteria in the absence of quantitative data. For all other cases, quantitative data were used.

- Counts of wintering and passage wildfowl and waders are largely derived from the Wetland Bird Survey (WeBS). The majority of these counts are 'five-year peak means' (the peak count of each season averaged over the five years).

- Non-breeding waders were split into passage (P) and wintering (W) on the basis of the months in which they were recorded. Counts of waders during the months of April to October were taken to be passage birds, those during November to March wintering birds. For wildfowl, counts during the months of September to March were taken to be wintering birds. Five-year peak means were calculated for each species of waterbird for passage and wintering periods separately. This is a very simplistic approach to a complex problem. There will have been great overlap between passage and wintering birds for a given species; different species have different dates of passage/wintering; passage counts are unreliable because of a continual throughput of birds.

- Breeding visitors (B) were distinguished from breeding residents (R) as follows: first, all migrants were classified as B, as were all breeding seabirds (*Rissa tridactyla*, *Uria aalge*, *Alca torda*, *Cepphus grylle*, *Fratercula arctica*), gulls (*Larus* spp.), terns (*Sterna* spp.), *Phalacrocorax carbo* and *P. aristotelis*, even though some seabirds do remain at their breeding colony during the winter. Second, a species was classified as resident if there were breeding and wintering records at the same site. Finally, if the season remained unclear, an atlas of wintering bird distributions (Lack 1986) was examined to see whether the species remained in the general area over winter; if it did it was classified as R. This was a very grey area. For example, some *Falco columbarius* may leave their breeding grounds in the winter in north-west Scotland but not in southern Scotland.

- In order to determine which sites qualified as A4iii, the following were calculated: the number of pairs of breeding seabirds, the number of wintering waterbirds and the number of passage waterbirds. If the total was greater than 10,000 (for the first measure) or 20,000 (last two) for one or more of these measures then the site qualified as A4iii. The definition of A4iii does not really consider breeding waterbirds, but as the definition of waterbirds in this review incorporates gulls, terns and cormorants, etc. there could be several sites with more than 20,000 birds in the breeding season. To see whether or not this was the case, the number of breeding pairs of waterbirds at each site was also calculated. If this value was greater than 10,000, then the site qualified as A4iii. The results of these calculations are given in the site-account texts.

- The species-specific values of 'n' in the application of the B2/B3 criterion have been adhered to, with only two exceptions (*Crex crex* and *Asio flammeus*, where two and one additional sites were nominated respectively). Similarly, species-specific numerical thresholds have been adhered to, the only exceptions being two sites for *Cepphus grylle* which fell just below the threshold. In no case was a species at a site allowed to qualify if there were fewer than two breeding pairs or four non-breeding individuals.

- The UK is split into 11 Level 1 NUTS regions (the 'administrative regions' which feature in Table 1 and the site accounts). These regions are based on human population sizes and as a consequence Scotland is a single, large Level 1 NUTS region. This presents a problem for criterion C6 (the best 5 sites for an Annex I species in a NUTS region) as many of the best sites for Annex I species are in Scotland. The criterion allows the 'n=5' ruling to be broken in exceptional cases. This has been invoked for the following breeding species in Scotland (number of sites in parentheses): *Gavia stellata* (7), *G. arctica* (8), *Oceanodroma leucorhoa* (6), *Circus cyaneus* (10), *Aquila chrysaetos* (9), *Falco columbarius* (8), *Charadrius morinellus* (9) and *Sterna paradisaea* (8), and for *Circus aeruginosus* (6) in one English region. SPA criteria in the UK allow a site to qualify if it holds ≥1% of the UK population of an Annex I species; if the 'n=5' ruling had not been broken, many potential SPA sites would have been omitted from the inventory.

- Even if a site was one of the best five in a NUTS region for an Annex I species, it has not qualified as C6 if it held less than 1% (rarely <0.5%) of the UK population for the relevant season, nor if there were fewer than two breeding pairs of the species in question or 20 non-breeding waterbirds.

- In the UK, criterion C2 is equivalent to a subset of B1 but for Annex I species only and with slightly lower thresholds for *Hydrobates pelagicus* and *Sterna paradisaea*; criterion C3 is equivalent to B1 for non-Annex I species; C4 is identical to A4iii.

- Criterion C7 has been applied to 17 sites. A number of C7 sites in Shetland have very high densities of breeding *Numenius phaeopus* (Blackpark and Gutcher, Yell; Crussa Field and the Heogs; Hill of Colvadale and Sobul; Moorland areas, Central Shetland). Although *Numenius phaeopus* is a SPEC, the UK population is too small to allow these sites to qualify as B3. Nevertheless, densities at these sites are probably substantially higher than elsewhere in the species' range.

- Allocation of criteria B2/B3 in the Channel Islands and Isle of Man was complex. These islands are tiny and for no species do they contain populations which approach 1% of the European. Strictly, they should not be allowed to qualify under B2/B3 at all. This approach would seem anomalous as, for example, the Isle of Man Hills, which has many more breeding *Circus cyaneus* than some nearby sites in the UK, would not qualify while the nearby sites could. For this reason the UK B2/B3 thresholds have been applied to the Channel Islands and Isle of Man – though any sites which qualified were not included in the 'n' sites for the UK.

- A small number of bird records were considered too sensitive to publish. At these sites, relevant criteria have not been allocated to the species, only to the site itself.

- Species for which ≥1% of their UK population (breeding or non-breeding, separately) occurs at the site, but which do not meet any criteria, are listed in the site-account text.

- Readers requiring a comprehensive list of the species-specific thresholds for all criteria and values of 'n' for B2/B3 should contact the RSPB's Conservation Science Department.

- Site accounts within the review are numbered alphabetically within country to ensure that they are easy to find. Site numbers do not relate back to either of the previous reviews because of the significant changes in site boundaries, mainly splitting and lumping of sites.

GLOSSARY

ASSI Area of Special Scientific Interest.
BAP Biodiversity Action Plan.
dubh lochan a small peaty pool found within mires.
drumlin a long oval mound of boulder clay moulded by glacial action.
ESA Environmentally Sensitive Area.
GCT Game Conservancy Trust.
IDB Internal Drainage Board.
in-bye land semi-improved rough grazing land lying between lowland arable land and unenclosed upland moorland. Normally enclosed and may include hay-meadows or crops such as turnips.
ITE Institute for Terrestrial Ecology.
JNCC Joint Nature Conservation Committee, the UK government's wildlife adviser.
LNR Local Nature Reserve.
MoD Ministry of Defence.
NGO non-governmental organisation.
NNR National Nature Reserve.
NUTS Nomenclature des Unités Territoriales Statistiques—the administrative regions of the European Union are called NUTS regions, and are designated by the EC Statistical Office.
RSPB Royal Society for the Protection of Birds (BirdLife International Partner in the UK).
SAC Special Area for Conservation.
skerry a reef or rocky island.
SNH Scottish Natural Heritage.
SPA Special Protection Area (designated under Article 4 of the EC Birds Directive).
SSSI Site of Special Scientific Interest.
voe a small bay or creek in Orkney or Shetland.
WeBS the national Wetland Bird Survey, co-organized by the British Trust for Ornithology, the Wildfowl and Wetlands Trust, JNCC and RSPB.

ACKNOWLEDGEMENTS

Many people helped directly and indirectly with the collation of data. Members of RSPB staff across the United Kingdom were involved, and it is not possible to mention them all. Particular thanks are due to all of the RSPB's Conservation Officers who spent considerable time helping define IBAs and collating data, and to Ellen Kelly and James Phillips, and to a team of data-entry staff and volunteers: Paul Britten, Barbara Clitherow, Peter Levitt, Helen Morrow, and Lisa Murfitt. The work would not have been possible without the large volumes of data that were provided by staff from other organisations, namely Kate Thompson at the JNCC Seabirds and Cetaceans Branch, Ray Waters and Julianne Evans at the British Trust for Ornithology and Peter Cranswick and Mark Pollitt at the Wildfowl and Wetlands Trust. Allen Moore and Aron Sapsford kindly provided data for the Isle of Man sites. Particular thanks go to Melanie Heath and Tony Payne at the BirdLife Secretariat for their help and support. Finally, we must also thank all of the volunteer workers who have participated in the surveys (such as WeBS) which provided an invaluable source of data.

■ SITE ACCOUNTS

Abberton reservoir	A4iii, B1i, C3, C4, C6	**001**
Admin region South East		
Coordinates 51°49'N 0°51'E		
Altitude 10–20 m Area 726 ha		

■ Site description

This reservoir was created following the flooding of a long shallow valley, and supports fringing reed *Phragmites* and *Salix* swamp. Water is pumped mainly from the River Stour, 14 km to the north.

Habitats Grassland, Wetland (standing fresh water; water-fringe vegetation), Artificial landscape (arable land)

Land-use Nature conservation/research, Water management (100%)

■ Birds

The reservoir and adjacent grassland are important for moulting and wintering wildfowl. The site holds 36,500 wintering waterbirds on a regular basis, and it is nationally important for wintering

Phalacrocorax carbo (360 birds, 2%), *Cygnus olor* (440 birds, 1%), *Anas penelope* (3,170 birds, 1%), *Anas acuta* (390 birds, 1%), *Aythya ferina* (1,510 birds, 2%), *Aythya fuligula* (1,860 birds, 2%), *Bucephala clangula* (550 birds, 2%), *Fulica atra* (12,200 birds, 10%), *Philomachus pugnax* (28 birds, 4%) and *Limosa limosa* (79 birds, 1%). The IBA is also nationally important for summer moulting assemblages of *Cygnus olor* (590 birds, 2%) and *Aythya ferina* (3,120 birds, 4%).

Species	Season	Year	Pop min	Pop max	Acc	Criteria
Phalacrocorax carbo Cormorant	R	1995	505	505	A	B1i, C3
Anas strepera Gadwall	W	1995	430	430	A	B1i, C3
Anas crecca Teal	W	1995	4,550	4,550	A	B1i, C3
Anas clypeata Shoveler	W	1995	685	685	A	B1i, C3
Pluvialis apricaria Golden Plover	W	1995	3,300	3,300	A	C6

■ Protection status

National High **International** High
IBA partly or wholly overlaps with the following national designated areas. *Site of Special Scientific Interest:* Abberton Reservoir. Overlaps with international designated areas: 726 ha of IBA covered by Special

Protection Area (Abberton Reservoir, 726 ha). 726 ha of IBA covered by Ramsar Site (Abberton Reservoir, 726 ha).

■ Conservation issues

Threats Agricultural intensification/expansion (B), Disturbance to birds (B), Infrastructure (U), Recreation/tourism (C)

A 1996 proposal to increase the size of the reservoir is being examined, with studies and consultation focusing on the impact on the reservoir's bird populations. Research into the tree-nesting *Phalacrocorax carbo* colony is ongoing, and there is a management plan for the site.

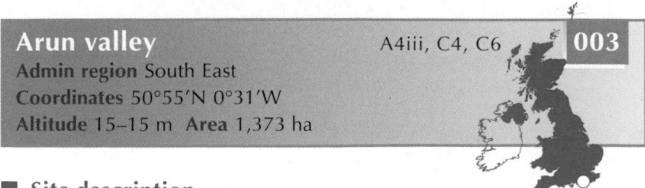

Alde/Ore estuary
A4i, A4iii, B1i, B2, B3, C2, C3, C4, C6 | 002
Admin region East Anglia
Coordinates 52°04'N 1°30'E
Altitude 0–5 m **Area** 2,416 ha

■ Site description
This estuary complex includes the Rivers Alde, Butley and Ore, with Havergate Island, and is of considerable geomorphological interest.

Habitats Grassland, Wetland (tidal river/enclosed tidal water; mudflat/sandflat; saltmarsh; shingle/stony beach; coastal lagoon; river/stream; water-fringe vegetation), Artificial landscape (arable land)
Land-use Agriculture, Nature conservation/research

■ Birds

Species		Season	Year	Pop min	Pop max	Acc	Criteria
Recurvirostra avosetta	Avocet	R	1994	105	—	A	B3, C6
Recurvirostra avosetta	Avocet	W	1995	735	735	A	B1i, B2, C2, C6
Recurvirostra avosetta	Avocet	P	1995	760	760	A	B1i, C2, C6
Tringa totanus	Redshank	W	1995	1,830	1,830	A	B1i, C3
Larus fuscus	Lesser Black-backed Gull	B	1991	8,200	—	A	A4i, B1i, B3, C3
Sterna sandvicensis	Sandwich Tern	B	1994	300	—	A	B2, C6
Sterna hirundo	Common Tern	B	1993	95	95	A	C6
Sterna albifrons	Little Tern	B	1995	25	25	A	C6

Orfordness and Havergate Island are important for breeding gulls and terns. The IBA holds 12,200 pairs of breeding waterbirds and 23,100 wintering waterbirds on a regular basis, and is nationally important for breeding *Larus argentatus* (2,520 pairs, 1991, 1%). The site is also nationally important for wintering *Tadorna tadorna* (1,220 birds, 2%), *Anas penelope* (3,970 birds, 1%), *Anas crecca* (1,900 birds, 1%) and *Limosa limosa* (320 birds, 4%); and for passage *Limosa limosa* (295 birds, 4%).

■ Protection status
National High **International** High
IBA partly or wholly overlaps with the following national designated areas. *National Nature Reserve:* Orfordness–Havergate. *Reserves:* Boyton Marshes, Havergate Island, Hazelwood Marshes, Orfordness. *Site of Special Scientific Interest:* Alde–Ore Estuary. Overlaps with international designated areas: 2,416 ha of IBA covered by Special Protection Area (Alde/Ore Estuary, 2,416 ha). 2,416 ha of IBA covered by Ramsar Site (Alde/Ore Estuary, 2,416 ha).

■ Conservation issues

Threats Natural events (B), Recreation/tourism (B)

Threats include sea-level rise that may result in erosion and flooding, habitat loss caused by coastal defence works and increased recreational disturbance. Management plans exist for the Suffolk Coast Project and the Suffolk Coast Area of Outstanding Natural Beauty.

Arun valley
A4iii, C4, C6 | 003
Admin region South East
Coordinates 50°55'N 0°31'W
Altitude 15–15 m **Area** 1,373 ha

■ Site description
The Arun valley exhibits an unusual range of physical and chemical conditions and a correspondingly high diversity of flora and fauna.

Alluvial grazing-marsh, pasture and cultivated land are all present, forming a mixed wet and dry field and ditch network that supports a rich floral community.

Habitats Forest and woodland (broadleaved deciduous forest; mixed forest), Scrub (scrub), Grassland (humid grassland), Wetland (river/stream; fen/transition mire/spring), Artificial landscape (arable land)
Land-use Agriculture, Forestry, Nature conservation/research, Tourism/recreation

■ Birds

Species		Season	Year	Pop min	Pop max	Acc	Criteria
Cygnus columbianus	Bewick's Swan	W	1995	71	71	A	C6
Philomachus pugnax	Ruff	W	1995	99	99	A	C6

The IBA is important for wintering wildfowl and holds 37,800 wintering waterbirds on a regular basis. It is nationally important for breeding *Anas acuta* (2 pairs, 1991, 5%) and *Anas querquedula* (2 pairs, 1991, 2%). The site is also nationally important for wintering *Anas crecca* (2,130 birds, 2%), *Anas clypeata* (160 birds, 2%), *Vanellus vanellus* (28,500 birds, 2%) and *Gallinago gallinago* (1,410 birds, 1%).

■ Protection status
National Partial **International** None
IBA partly or wholly overlaps with the following national designated areas. *Reserves:* Amberley Wildbrooks, Pulborough Brooks, Waltham Brooks. *Sites of Special Scientific Interest:* Amberley Wild Brooks, Arun Banks, Arundel Park, Hurston Warren, Pulborough Brooks, Waltham Brooks.

■ Conservation issues

Threats Disturbance to birds (B), Groundwater abstraction (A), Infrastructure (B), Recreation/tourism (B)

Management plans exist for Pulborough Brooks, Waltham Brooks and Amberley Wildbrooks, in addition to Environment Agency Water Level Management Plans and the Arun Valley Management Plan of the Countryside Management Project. A breeding wader survey was undertaken in 1996, and lobbying for SPA designation continues.

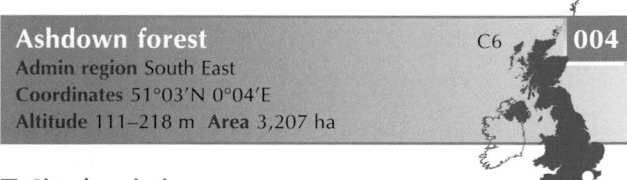

Ashdown forest
C6 | 004
Admin region South East
Coordinates 51°03'N 0°04'E
Altitude 111–218 m **Area** 3,207 ha

■ Site description
A large expanse of woodland and heathland cut by streams, with scattered boggy areas.

Habitats Forest and woodland (broadleaved deciduous forest), Scrub (heathland), Wetland (standing fresh water; river/stream; fen/transition mire/spring)
Land-use Agriculture, Forestry, Nature conservation/research, Tourism/recreation

■ Birds

Species		Season	Year	Pop min	Pop max	Acc	Criteria
Caprimulgus europaeus	Nightjar	B	1992	36	36	A	C6
Sylvia undata	Dartford Warbler	R	1994	29	29	A	C6

The heathland and woodland support a typical range of species.

■ Protection status
National High **International** High
IBA partly or wholly overlaps with the following national designated areas. *Reserve:* Old Lodge. *Sites of Special Scientific Interest:* Ashdown Forest, Rock Wood, Scords Wood and Brockhoult Mount, Weir Wood Reservoir. Overlaps with international designated areas: 3,207 ha of IBA covered by Special Protection Area (Ashdown Forest, 3,207 ha).

■ Conservation issues

Threats Abandonment/reduction of land management (C), Industrialization/urbanization (U), Infrastructure (B), Other (C), Recreation/tourism (A)

Permission has been granted for inert waste deposition at the site. Additional threats include acid deposition over 62% of the site ('Other' threat, above), a lack of management, recreational pressure and road development. The area is managed by the Ashdown forest conservators, whose recent management initiatives have included fencing for grazing and some bird monitoring. A management plan exists for the site.

Avon valley
A4i, B1i, B2, C2, C3, C6   **005**

Admin region South East, South West
Coordinates 50°47'N 1°48'W
Altitude 3–25 m **Area** 1,385 ha

■ Site description
The IBA comprises about 20 km of the Avon valley, the flood-plain of which contains a variety of habitats. The river itself is probably the most diverse chalk river system in the UK, with an aquatic flora that includes important *Ranunculus* beds, reflecting its chalk and acid qualities. Adjacent hay-meadows also support a rich flora.

Habitats Forest and woodland (broadleaved deciduous forest; mixed forest), Grassland (humid grassland), Wetland (standing fresh water; river/stream; water-fringe vegetation; fen/transition mire/spring), Artificial landscape (highly improved reseeded grassland; arable land)
Land-use Agriculture

■ Birds

Species		Season	Year	Pop min	Pop max	Acc	Criteria
Cygnus columbianus	Bewick's Swan	W	1995	170	170	A	A4i, B1i, B2, C2, C6
Anas strepera	Gadwall	W	1995	665	665	A	B1i, C3
Lullula arborea	Woodlark	R	1994	4	4	A	C6
Sylvia undata	Dartford Warbler	R	1994	19	19	A	C6

Meadows, fen and carr attract a wide range of wintering and breeding wetland birds, with heathland species breeding in adjacent areas. The site is also nationally important for breeding *Cettia cetti* (40 pairs, 1990, 14%); and for wintering *Cygnus olor* (315 birds, 1%), *Anser albifrons albifrons* (96 birds, 2%), *Anas penelope* (3,030 birds, 1%), *Anas clypeata* (155 birds, 2%) and *Fulica atra* (2,170 birds, 2%).

■ Protection status
National High **International** High
IBA partly or wholly overlaps with the following national designated areas. *Sites of Special Scientific Interest:* Avon Valley (Bickton to Christchurch), Hurn Common, Kitten's Farm Meadows, The New Forest River Avon System, Town Common. Overlaps with international designated areas: 1,385 ha of IBA covered by Special Protection Area (Avon Valley, 1,385 ha). 1,385 ha of IBA covered by Ramsar Site (Avon Valley, 1,385 ha).

■ Conservation issues

Threats Agricultural intensification/expansion (A), Disturbance to birds (B), Drainage (A), Extraction industry (B), Infrastructure (B), Recreation/tourism (B)

The main threat is agricultural intensification, which has led to a decline in numbers of breeding waders. A revised ESA programme, in conjunction with the Environment Agency Water Level Management Plan initiative, will be key mechanisms in improving management. Additional threats include recreational disturbance and the development of the Christchurch and Salisbury bypasses.

Benacre to Easton Bavents
C6   **006**

Admin region East Anglia
Coordinates 52°21'N 1°42'E
Altitude 0–10 m **Area** 516 ha

■ Site description
Reedbeds and other wetland habitats situated along the Suffolk coast just north of Southwold. The IBA includes ancient woodland, saltmarsh, shingle and sand-dune communities, and brackish and freshwater communities that inhabit coastal lagoons, reedbeds and the river valley. The cliffs and beach have geological and physiographical importance.

Habitats Forest and woodland (broadleaved deciduous forest), Grassland, Wetland (shingle/stony beach; coastal lagoon; standing brackish and salt water; water-fringe vegetation; fen/transition mire/spring)
Land-use Agriculture, Nature conservation/research

■ Birds

Species		Season	Year	Pop min	Pop max	Acc	Criteria
Circus aeruginosus	Marsh Harrier	R	1990	4	4	A	C6

The IBA holds a diverse assemblage of breeding and wintering species, and is also nationally important for breeding *Panurus biarmicus* (16 pairs, 1992, 4%).

■ Protection status
National High **International** High
IBA partly or wholly overlaps with the following national designated areas. *National Nature Reserve:* Benacre to Easton Bavents. *Site of Special Scientific Interest:* Benacre to Easton Bavents. Overlaps with international designated areas: 516 ha of IBA covered by Special Protection Area (Benacre to Easton Bavents, 516 ha).

■ Conservation issues

Threats Natural events (A)

Sea-level rise is a threat. Benacre NNR is under a nature reserve agreement, and there is ongoing *Botaurus stellaris* monitoring. A management plan exists for the site.

Benfleet and Southend marshes
A4i, A4iii, B1i, B2, C3, C4   **007**

Admin region South East
Coordinates 51°31'N 0°40'E
Altitude 0–46 m **Area** 2,750 ha

■ Site description
The IBA extends eastwards from Canvey Island along the foreshore to Southend, covering extensive areas of mudflats and saltmarsh. It supports distinct sea-wall and saltmarsh plant communities, in addition to a diverse ditch and grassland flora.

Habitats Scrub (scrub), Grassland, Wetland (tidal river/enclosed tidal water; mudflat/sandflat; saltmarsh; standing fresh water; river/stream)
Land-use Agriculture, Fisheries/aquaculture, Nature conservation/research, Tourism/recreation

■ Birds

Species		Season	Year	Pop min	Pop max	Acc	Criteria
Branta bernicla	Brent Goose	W	1995	5,050	5,050	A	A4i, B1i, C3
Charadrius hiaticula	Ringed Plover	P	1995	745	745	A	B1i, C3
Pluvialis squatarola	Grey Plover	W	1995	4,400	4,400	A	A4i, B1i, C3
Calidris canutus	Knot	W	1995	8,550	8,550	A	A4i, B1i, B2, C3
Calidris alpina	Dunlin	W	1995	10,400	10,400	A	B2

The IBA is important for wintering geese and waders, and holds 34,700 wintering waterbirds on a regular basis. It is also nationally important for breeding *Panurus biarmicus* (20 pairs, 1992, 5%), for wintering *Charadrius hiaticula* (370 birds, 1%), and for passage *Pluvialis squatarola* (1,420 birds, 3%). *Branta bernicla* are the *bernicla* subspecies.

■ Protection status
National Partial **International** Partial
IBA partly or wholly overlaps with the following national designated areas. *National Nature Reserve:* Leigh. *Site of Special Scientific Interest:* Benfleet and Southend Marshes. Overlaps with international designated areas: 2,251 ha of IBA covered by Special Protection Area (Benfleet and Southend Marshes, 2,251 ha). 2,251 ha of IBA covered by Ramsar Site (Benfleet and Southend Marshes, 2,251 ha).

■ Conservation issues

Threats Agricultural intensification/expansion (C), Aquaculture/fisheries (B), Industrialization/urbanization (C), Natural events (A), Recreation/tourism (C)

Intensive recreational activity, an important shellfish industry, past housing and marina proposals, and sea-level rise all pose threats to the IBA. Southend Borough Council is coordinating the management and promoting public awareness of Southend flats. A management plan exists for the site.

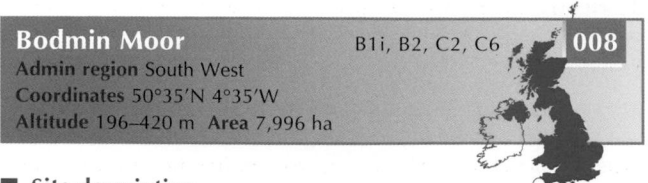

Bodmin Moor
B1i, B2, C2, C6 · 008

Admin region South West
Coordinates 50°35'N 4°35'W
Altitude 196–420 m **Area** 7,996 ha

■ Site description
Bodmin Moor occupies much of the central part of east Cornwall, and is notable as a low-altitude moorland with Atlantic elements in its flora and fauna. Acid grassland, heathland, and bog and mire wetland plant communities are widespread.

Habitats Forest and woodland (mixed forest), Scrub (scrub; heathland), Grassland, Wetland (standing fresh water; river/stream; fen/transition mire/spring), Rocky areas (scree/boulders), Artificial landscape (forestry plantation)
Land-use Agriculture

■ Birds

Species		Season	Year	Pop min	Pop max	Acc	Criteria
Pluvialis apricaria	Golden Plover	W	1995	10,000	10,000	A	B1i, C2, C6
Saxicola torquata	Stonechat	B	1984	200	200	A	B2

The IBA is important for breeding waders and other moorland species, and wintering raptors.

■ Protection status
National Partial **International** None
IBA partly or wholly overlaps with the following national designated areas. *Sites of Special Scientific Interest:* Bodmin Moor – North, Cabilla Manor Wood, Dozmary Pool, Upper Fowey Valley.

■ Conservation issues

Threats Abandonment/reduction of land management (U), Agricultural intensification/expansion (A), Extraction industry (U), Infrastructure (C), Other (U), Recreation/tourism (C)

Threats include recreational disturbance and the use of microlight aircraft, acidification in afforested areas ('Other' threat, above), overgrazing and neglect, and inappropriate land management.

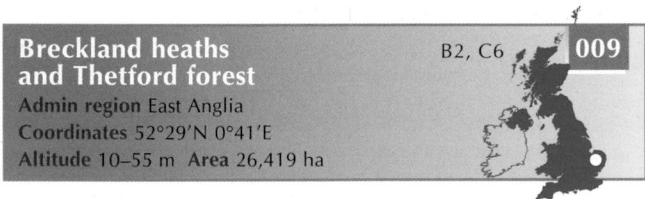

Breckland heaths and Thetford forest
B2, C6 · 009

Admin region East Anglia
Coordinates 52°29'N 0°41'E
Altitude 10–55 m **Area** 26,419 ha

■ Site description
A large, fragmented area of heathland, forest and arable farmland, containing a wide variety of habitats. The IBA supports a flora, characterized by continental species, that is unique in Britain.

Habitats Forest and woodland (broadleaved deciduous forest; mixed forest), Scrub (heathland), Grassland, Wetland (standing fresh water; water-fringe vegetation; fen/transition mire/spring), Artificial landscape (arable land; forestry plantation)
Land-use Agriculture, Forestry, Military, Nature conservation/research, Tourism/recreation

■ Birds

Species		Season	Year	Pop min	Pop max	Acc	Criteria
Burhinus oedicnemus	Stone Curlew	B	1995	43	43	A	C6
Caprimulgus europaeus	Nightjar	B	1992	315	315	A	B2, C6
Lullula arborea	Woodlark	B	1994	150	150	A	C6

The IBA is important for a range of breeding heathland species. It is also nationally important for wintering *Anas strepera* (195 birds, 2%).

■ Protection status
National Partial **International** None

IBA partly or wholly overlaps with the following national designated areas. *National Nature Reserves:* Cavenham Heath, Thetford Heath, Weeting Heath. *Sites of Special Scientific Interest (several of which are also Nature Reserves):* Barnham Heath, Barnham Cross Common, Beeches Pit, West Stow, Berner's Heath – Icklingham, Bridgham and Brettenham Heaths, Cavenham/Icklingham Heaths, Cranberry Rough, Hockham, Cranwich Camp, Deadman's Grave – Icklingham, Didlington Park Lakes, East Wretham Heath, Eriswell Low Warren, Foxhole Heath, Gooderstone Warren, Grimes Graves, Lakenheath Warren, Little Heath – Barnham, London Road Industrial Estate – Brandon, Middle Harling Fen, Old Bodney Camp, RAF Lakenheath, Rex Graham Reserve, Stanford Training Area, Thetford Golf Course and Marsh, Thetford Heath, Thompson Water Carr and Common, Wangford Warren and Carr, Weather and Horn Heaths, Weeting Heath, West Stow Heath, Wretham Park Meres.

■ Conservation issues

Threats Abandonment/reduction of land management (A), Afforestation (C), Agricultural intensification/expansion (A), Extraction industry (C), Infrastructure (B), Other (U), Recreation/tourism (B)

Threats include recreational disturbance, infrastructure developments, including roads, and overhead powerlines, and acidification ('Other' threat, above). The majority of the populations of three key breeding species exist outside nationally protected areas. *Burhinus oedicnemus* occurs on arable land, and *Caprimulgus europaeus* and *Lullula arborea* occur in clear-felled or recently restocked areas of forest. All three are therefore vulnerable to changes in farming or forestry practices. A forest design plan exists, which has a nature conservation component. Most heaths are in ESA agreements, and the RSPB operates a protection scheme for *Burhinus oedicnemus*.

Breydon Water
A4i, A4iii, B1i, B2, C2, C4, C6 · 010

Admin region East Anglia
Coordinates 52°36'N 1°40'E
Altitude 0–10 m **Area** 515 ha

■ Site description
A tidal estuary containing the only intertidal flats on the east coast of Norfolk, which is complemented by adjacent wet grassland in the Broadland IBA (011).

Habitats Wetland (100%; tidal river/enclosed tidal water; mudflat/sandflat; saltmarsh; water-fringe vegetation)
Land-use Hunting, Nature conservation/research, Tourism/recreation

■ Birds

Species		Season	Year	Pop min	Pop max	Acc	Criteria
Cygnus columbianus	Bewick's Swan	W	1995	375	375	A	A4i, B1i, B2, C2, C6
Pluvialis apricaria	Golden Plover	W	1995	4,350	4,350	A	C6
Pluvialis apricaria	Golden Plover	P	1995	1,670	1,670	A	C6

The IBA is important for wintering and passage wildfowl and waders, and holds 41,000 wintering waterbirds on a regular basis. It is nationally important for wintering *Anser albifrons albifrons* (165 birds, 3%), *Anas penelope* (4,540 birds, 2%), *Anas clypeata* (195 birds, 2%), *Vanellus vanellus* (23,600 birds, 1%), *Limosa limosa* (215 birds, 3%). The site is also nationally important for passage *Charadrius hiaticula* (350 birds, 1%) and *Limosa limosa* (130 birds, 2%).

■ Protection status
National High **International** High
IBA partly or wholly overlaps with the following national designated areas. *Reserve:* Breydon Water. *National Park:* The Broads. *Site of Special Scientific Interest:* Breydon Water. Overlaps with international designated areas: 515 ha of IBA covered by Special Protection Area (Breydon Water, 515 ha). 515 ha of IBA covered by Ramsar Site (Breydon Water, 515 ha).

■ Conservation issues

Threats Natural events (A), Recreation/tourism (B)

Recreational disturbance can be a problem. The site is regularly monitored as part of the WeBS scheme.

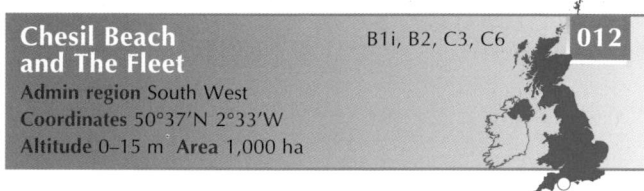

Broadland
B1i, B2, C3, C6   011

Admin region East Anglia
Coordinates 52°44′N 1°29′E
Altitude 0–10 m   **Area** 5,485 ha

■ Site description

A series of flooded medieval peat-diggings situated within the flood-plains of five principal river valley systems. The IBA comprises a mosaic of reed *Phragmites*-fringed shallow lakes, open water, fen habitats, carr woodland and grazing-marshes. This area includes four sites that were treated as separate IBAs in the previous international IBA inventory (Grimmett and Jones 1989): 'Upper Thurne Broads and Marshes' (former site GB166), 'Ant Broads and Marshes' (former site GB167), 'Bure Broads and Marshes' (former site GB168) and 'Yare Broads and Marshes' (former site GB169).

Habitats Forest and woodland (broadleaved deciduous forest; alluvial/very wet forest), Scrub (scrub), Grassland, Wetland (tidal river/enclosed tidal water; standing fresh water; river/stream; water-fringe vegetation; fen/transition mire/spring)
Land-use Agriculture, Nature conservation/research, Tourism/recreation

■ Birds

Species	Season	Year	Pop min	Pop max	Acc	Criteria
Botaurus stellaris Bittern	R	1995	2	2	A	C6
Cygnus columbianus Bewick's Swan	W	1995	67	67	A	C6
Anser anser Greylag Goose	W	1995	1,050	1,050	A	B1i, C3
Anas strepera Gadwall	R	1992	–	60	A	B2
Circus aeruginosus Marsh Harrier	R	1992	19	19	A	C6
[1] *Circus cyaneus* Hen Harrier	W	1989	20	20	A	C6
[2] *Grus grus* Crane	R	1993	–	–	A	C6
Sterna hirundo Common Tern	B	1993	155	155	A	C6

1. Mean annual peak 1984–1989.
2. No counts available.

The IBA is important for a wide variety of breeding and wintering birds. It is nationally important for breeding *Anas querquedula* (3 pairs, 1992, 2%), *Anas clypeata* (60 pairs, 1992, 6%), *Aythya ferina* (40 pairs, 1992, 10%), *Cettia cetti* (30 pairs, 1992, 11%), *Locustella luscinioides* (6 pairs, 1992, 40%), *Panurus biarmicus* (74 pairs, 1992, 18%) and feral *Anser anser*. The site is also important for wintering *Phalacrocorax carbo* (360 birds, 2%), *Anser fabalis* (175 birds, 39%), *Anser albifrons* (205 birds, 3%), *Anas penelope* (4,280 birds, 1%), *Anas strepera* (295 birds, 4%), *Anas crecca* (1,710 birds, 1%), *Anas clypeata* (255 birds, 2%), *Philomachus pugnax* (10 birds, 1%) and *Calcarius lapponicus* (140 birds, 70%).

■ Protection status

National High   **International** High
IBA partly or wholly overlaps with the following national designated areas. *National Nature Reserves:* Bure Marshes, Hickling Broad, Ludham Marshes, Mid-Yare. *Reserves:* Alderfen Broad, Barton Broad, Berney Marshes, Buckenham and Cantley Marshes, Burgh Common, Carlton Marshes, Hardley Flood, Heigham Holmes, Hickling Broad, Horsey Mere, How Hill, Martham Broad, Mid-Yare, Oulton Marshes, Ranworth and Cockshoot Broads, Strumpshaw/Surlingham Marshes, Upton Fen. *National Park:* The Broads. *Sites of Special Scientific Interest:* Alderfen Broad, Ant Broads and Marshes, Barnby Broad and Marshes, Broad Fen (Dilham), Bure Broads and Marshes, Burgh Common and Muck Fleet Marshes, Calthorpe Broad, Crostwick Marsh, Damgate Marshes, Decoy Carr, Acle, Duncan's Marsh, Claxton, Geldeston Meadows, Hall Farm Fen (Hemsby), Hardley Flood, Havergate Marshes, Limpenhoe Meadows, Ludham – Potter Heigham Marshes, Poplar Farm Meadows (Langley), Priory Meadows (Hickling), Shallam Dyke Marshes (Thurne), Smallburgh Fen, Sprat's Water and Marshes, Carlton Colville, Stanley and Alder Carrs, Upper Thurne Broads and Marshes, Upton Broad and Marshes, Yare Broads and Marshes. Overlaps with international designated areas: 5,485 ha of IBA covered by Special Protection Area (Broadland, 5,485 ha). 5,485 ha of IBA covered by Ramsar Site (Broadland, 5,485 ha).

■ Conservation issues

Threats Abandonment/reduction of land management (B), Agricultural intensification/expansion (B), Disturbance to birds (C), Drainage (B), Groundwater abstraction (B), Industrialization/urbanization (C), Infrastructure (U), Natural events (B), Other (U), Recreation/tourism (A)

Threats include poor water quality, erosion and disturbance caused by boat traffic, disturbance caused by shooting and water-sports, waste disposal, and residential, industrial and wind-power developments. The whole area is vulnerable to acid deposition ('Other' threat, above) and sea-level rise. Various reserve and water management plans exist for the area, and a range of research initiatives are undertaken, including monitoring of *Botaurus stellaris*, breeding waders and the ESA. A fen management strategy is in place, and part of the area has been put forward as a candidate SAC.

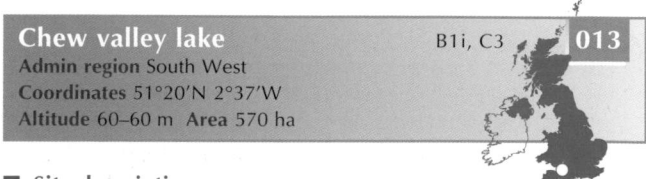

Chesil Beach and The Fleet
B1i, B2, C3, C6   012

Admin region South West
Coordinates 50°37′N 2°33′W
Altitude 0–15 m   **Area** 1,000 ha

■ Site description

Chesil Beach is one of the largest shingle structures in Britain, measuring 150–200 m in width, and running for 28 km from Burton Bradstock in the west to the Isle of Portland in the east. The beach encloses The Fleet, the largest tidal lagoon in Britain.

Habitats Scrub (scrub), Grassland (steppe/dry calcareous grassland), Wetland (mudflat/sandflat; saltmarsh; shingle/stony beach; coastal lagoon; water-fringe vegetation)
Land-use Tourism/recreation

■ Birds

Species	Season	Year	Pop min	Pop max	Acc	Criteria
Branta bernicla Brent Goose	W	1995	3,220	3,220	A	B1i, C3
Sterna albifrons Little Tern	B	1995	90	90	A	B2, C6

The IBA supports large numbers of wildfowl in winter, and is also nationally important for wintering *Cygnus olor* (1,110 birds, 4%), *Anas penelope* (5,850 birds, 2%), *Anas strepera* (110 birds, 1%), *Anas clypeata* (155 birds, 2%), *Mergus serrator* (225 birds, 2%) and *Fulica atra* (2,630 birds, 2%). *Branta bernicla* are the *bernicla* subspecies.

■ Protection status

National Partial   **International** Partial
IBA partly or wholly overlaps with the following national designated areas. *Sites of Special Scientific Interest:* Chesil Beach and The Fleet, Cogden Farm and Beach, Crookhill Brick Pit, Isle of Portland, Portland Harbour Shore, West Dorset Coast. Overlaps with international designated areas: 750 ha of IBA covered by Special Protection Area (Chesil Beach and The Fleet, 750 ha). 750 ha of IBA covered by Ramsar Site (Chesil Beach and The Fleet, 750 ha).

■ Conservation issues

Threats Agricultural intensification/expansion (B), Other (B), Recreation/tourism (B)

Threats include disturbance to *Sterna albifrons* in areas with public access, caravan and hotel developments, nutrient enrichment of saline lagoons, and a conflict of interest that has arisen in areas of farmland where *Branta bernicla* cause crop damage ('Other' threat, above). A lottery-funded management plan for the SAC is in preparation.

Chew valley lake
B1i, C3   013

Admin region South West
Coordinates 51°20′N 2°37′W
Altitude 60–60 m   **Area** 570 ha

■ Site description

One of the largest freshwater bodies in south-west England, supporting a sparse open-water plant community. The IBA also includes areas of managed pasture.

Habitats Forest and woodland (mixed forest), Grassland (steppe/dry calcareous grassland; mesophile grassland), Wetland (standing fresh water; water-fringe vegetation)
Land-use Tourism/recreation

■ Birds

Species	Season	Year	Pop min	Pop max	Acc	Criteria
Anas clypeata Shoveler	W	1995	420	420	A	B1i, C3

This large artificial reservoir supports breeding wetland species and attracts wintering and passage wildfowl. It is also nationally important for breeding *Podiceps cristatus* (50 pairs, 1992, 1%), and for wintering *Tachybaptus ruficollis* (79 birds, 2%), *Podiceps cristatus* (530 birds, 4%), *Phalacrocorax carbo* (175 birds, 1%), *Anas strepera* (185 birds, 2%), *Anas crecca* (2,060 birds, 1%) and *Mergus merganser* (120 birds, 1%).

■ Protection status
National High **International** High
IBA partly or wholly overlaps with the following national designated areas. *Site of Special Scientific Interest:* Chew Valley Lake. Overlaps with international designated areas: 565 ha of IBA covered by Special Protection Area (Chew Valley Lake, 565 ha).

■ Conservation issues

Threats Recreation/tourism (C)

Disturbance from recreational activities including fishing, birdwatching and sailing pose a threat to the IBA.

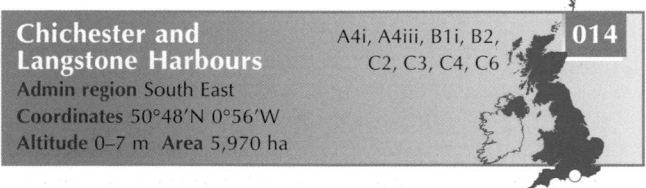

Chichester and Langstone Harbours   A4i, A4iii, B1i, B2, C2, C3, C4, C6   014
Admin region South East
Coordinates 50°48'N 0°56'W
Altitude 0–7 m **Area** 5,970 ha

■ Site description
This site covers two harbours joined by a stretch of water that separates Hayling Island from the mainland. Tidal channels drain the river basins and penetrate far inland. Habitats include extensive mudflats and associated saltmarshes, sand-dunes, islands, and areas of *Juncus* marsh and reedbed (*Phragmites*).

Habitats Forest and woodland (broadleaved deciduous forest), Scrub (scrub), Grassland, Wetland (tidal river/enclosed tidal water; mudflat/sandflat; saltmarsh; sand-dunes/sand beach; shingle/stony beach; coastal lagoon; standing fresh water; water-fringe vegetation)
Land-use Agriculture, Fisheries/aquaculture, Forestry, Nature conservation/research, Tourism/recreation

■ Birds

Species	Season	Year	Pop min	Pop max	Acc	Criteria
Branta bernicla Brent Goose	W	1995	16,600	16,600	A	A4i, B1i, C3
Charadrius hiaticula Ringed Plover	W	1995	875	875	A	B1i, C3
Charadrius hiaticula Ringed Plover	P	1995	1,810	1,810	A	B1i, C3
Pluvialis squatarola Grey Plover	W	1995	3,770	3,770	A	A4i, B1i, C3
Pluvialis squatarola Grey Plover	P	1995	3,350	3,350	A	A4i, B1i, C3
Calidris alpina Dunlin	W	1995	47,400	47,400	A	A4i, B1i, B2, C3
Calidris alpina Dunlin	P	1995	22,700	22,700	A	A4i, B1i, C3
Limosa limosa Black-tailed Godwit	W	1995	1,090	1,090	A	B1i, C3
Limosa limosa Black-tailed Godwit	P	1995	1,110	1,110	A	B1i, C3
Limosa lapponica Bar-tailed Godwit	W	1995	1,760	1,760	A	A4i, B1i, B2, C2, C6
Limosa lapponica Bar-tailed Godwit	P	1995	1,180	1,180	A	A4i, B1i, C2, C6
Numenius arquata Curlew	W	1995	1,820	1,820	A	B2
Tringa totanus Redshank	W	1995	1,860	1,860	A	B1i, C3
Tringa totanus Redshank	P	1995	1,980	1,980	A	B1i, C3
Sterna albifrons Little Tern	B	1995	95	95	A	B2, C6

The IBA is important for breeding terns and wintering and passage wildfowl and waders. It holds 95,100 wintering and 40,200 passage waterbirds on a regular basis. The site is nationally important

for wintering *Tachybaptus ruficollis* (54 birds, 1%), *Phalacrocorax carbo* (185 birds, 1%), *Tadorna tadorna* (2,360 birds, 3%), *Anas crecca* (1,640 birds, 1%), *Anas acuta* (310 birds, 1%), *Mergus serrator* (265 birds, 3%), *Philomachus pugnax* (18 birds, 3%) and *Tringa nebularia* (12 birds, 2%). The IBA is also important for passage *Calidris alba* (350 birds, 1%), *Numenius phaeopus* (125 birds, 3%) and *Tringa nebularia* (155 birds, 28%). *Branta bernicla* are the *bernicla* subspecies.

■ Protection status
National High **International** High
IBA partly or wholly overlaps with the following national designated areas. *Reserves:* Farlington Marshes, Langstone Harbour, Nutbourne Marshes, Pilsey Island. *Sites of Special Scientific Interest:* Bracklesham Bay, Chichester Harbour, Langstone Harbour, Warblington Meadow. Overlaps with international designated areas: 5,810 ha of IBA covered by Special Protection Area (Chichester and Langstone Harbours, 5,810 ha). 5,810 ha of IBA covered by Ramsar Site (Chichester and Langstone Harbours, 5,810 ha).

■ Conservation issues

Threats Aquaculture/fisheries (U), Filling-in of wetlands (C), Industrialization/urbanization (B), Infrastructure (B), Natural events (A), Recreation/tourism (B)

Threats include sea-level rise that may result in erosion and habitat loss due to coastal defence improvements, disturbance from leisure activities, and housing, infrastructure and leisure developments. Management plans exist for both Chichester Harbour and Langstone Harbour. The IBA is monitored as part of the WeBS.

Coquet Island   A4i, A4iii, B1i, B1ii, B2, C2, C3, C4, C6   015
Admin region North
Coordinates 55°20'N 1°32'W
Altitude 0–15 m **Area** 22 ha

■ Site description
A small flat-topped island located about 1 km off the Northumberland coast at Amble.

Habitats Grassland, Rocky areas (sea cliff/rocky shore; rock stacks/islets)
Land-use Nature conservation/research (100%)

■ Birds

Species	Season	Year	Pop min	Pop max	Acc	Criteria
Sterna sandvicensis Sandwich Tern	B	1995	1,540	1,540	A	A4i, B1i, B2, C2, C6
Sterna dougallii Roseate Tern	B	1994	36	36	A	A4i, B1i, B2, C2, C6
Sterna hirundo Common Tern	B	1993	765	765	A	C2, C6
Sterna paradisaea Arctic Tern	B	1994	710	710	A	C6
Fratercula arctica Puffin	B	1994	12,700	12,700	A	B1ii, B2, C3

The IBA supports large colonies of breeding seabirds, notably terns, and holds 12,800 pairs on a regular basis. It is also nationally important for breeding *Somateria mollissima* (395 pairs, 1990, 1%) and *Larus ridibundus* (3,080 pairs, 1994, 2%).

■ Protection status
National High **International** High
IBA partly or wholly overlaps with the following national designated areas. *Reserve:* Coquet Island. *Site of Special Scientific Interest:* Coquet Island. Overlaps with international designated areas: 22 ha of IBA covered by Special Protection Area (Coquet Island, 22 ha).

■ Conservation issues

Threats Aquaculture/fisheries (U), Natural events (B), Recreation/tourism (C)

Threats include recreational disturbance, over-fishing, and habitat degradation caused by high numbers of rabbits *Oryctolagus cuniculus* and *Fratercula arctica*. This has led to a decrease in ground cover and increased predation of terns. The RSPB undertakes research and seabird monitoring, while Durham University carries out research on terns. There is a management plan for the site.

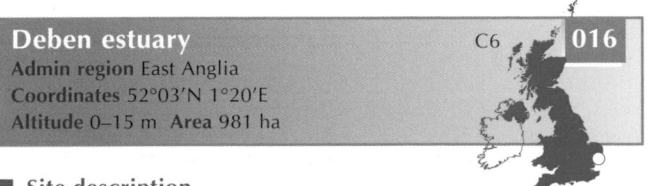

Deben estuary C6 016
Admin region East Anglia
Coordinates 52°03′N 1°20′E
Altitude 0–15 m Area 981 ha

■ Site description

A narrow estuary extending south-eastwards from the town of Woodbridge for a distance of over 12 km, reaching the sea just to the north of the town of Felixstowe. Extensive intertidal mudflats support an important invertebrate community.

Habitats Scrub (scrub), Wetland (tidal river/enclosed tidal water; mudflat/sandflat; saltmarsh; sand-dunes/sand beach; water-fringe vegetation)
Land-use Agriculture, Nature conservation/research, Tourism/recreation

■ Birds

Species	Season	Year	Pop min	Pop max	Acc	Criteria
Circus aeruginosus Marsh Harrier	R	1990	4	4	A	C6
Recurvirostra avosetta Avocet	W	1995	83	83	A	C6

The IBA is important for wintering wildfowl and waders, and is also nationally important for wintering *Tachybaptus ruficollis* (61 birds, 1%), *Branta bernicla bernicla* (2,440 birds, 2%), *Tadorna tadorna* (905 birds, 1%), *Limosa limosa* (96 birds, 1%), and *Tringa totanus* (1,380 birds, 1%). The site is also nationally important for passage *Limosa limosa* (210 birds, 3%) and *Tringa totanus* (1,240 birds, 1%).

■ Protection status

National High **International** High
IBA partly or wholly overlaps with the following national designated areas. *Sites of Special Scientific Interest:* Bawdsey Cliff, Deben Estuary, Ferry Cliff, Ramsholt Cliff. Overlaps with international designated areas: 981 ha of IBA covered by Special Protection Area (Deben Estuary, 981 ha). 981 ha of IBA covered by Ramsar Site (Deben Estuary, 981 ha).

■ Conservation issues

Threats Infrastructure (U), Natural events (A), Recreation/tourism (B)

Threats include sea-level change that may result in flooding and erosion, coastal defence improvements that may cause habitat loss, and disturbance from sailing and other leisure pursuits and developments. There is no site-specific management plan, but the IBA is covered by the Suffolk Coast and Heaths Project and Management Plan.

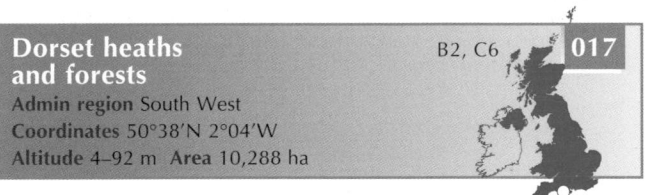

Dorset heaths and forests B2, C6 017
Admin region South West
Coordinates 50°38′N 2°04′W
Altitude 4–92 m Area 10,288 ha

■ Site description

A large, fragmented area situated around Poole Harbour and to the west of Wareham, overlying the infertile and acidic Bagshot Beds. The area comprises mainly lowland heathland and mires, with associated woodland and grassland. This area includes two sites that were treated as separate IBAs in the previous international IBA inventory (Grimmett and Jones 1989): part of 'Poole Basin' (former site GB188) and 'Horton Common and Holt Heath' (former site GB189).

Habitats Forest and woodland (broadleaved deciduous forest; native coniferous forest; mixed forest), Scrub (scrub; heathland), Grassland, Wetland (saltmarsh; water-fringe vegetation; fen/transition mire/spring)
Land-use Unknown

■ Birds

The IBA holds important populations of specialist heathland birds. It is also nationally important for breeding *Falco subbuteo* (17 pairs, 1992, 3%).

Species	Season	Year	Pop min	Pop max	Acc	Criteria
Circus cyaneus Hen Harrier	W	1992	12	12	A	C6
Caprimulgus europaeus Nightjar	B	1992	545	545	A	B2, C6
Picus viridis Green Woodpecker	R	1993	155	155	A	B2
Lullula arborea Woodlark	B	1994	65	65	A	C6
Saxicola torquata Stonechat	B	1993	750	750	A	B2
Sylvia undata Dartford Warbler	B	1994	610	610	A	C6

■ Protection status

National Partial **International** Partial
IBA partly or wholly overlaps with the following national designated areas. *Reserves:* Arne, Grange Heath, Heathlands Project – Trigon, Heathlands Project – Black Hill, Stoborough Heath. *Sites of Special Scientific Interest:* Arne, Avon Valley (Bickton to Christchurch), Bere Stream, Black Hill Heath, Blue Pool and Norden Heaths, Bourne Valley, Brenscombe Heath, Bugdens Copse and Meadows, Canford Heath, Christchurch Harbour, Corfe Meadows, Corfe and Barrow Hills, Cranborne Common, Cull-Peppers Dish, East Holme Meadows, Ebblake Bog, Ferndown Common, Gore Heath, Hartland Moor, Holt and West Moors Heaths, Holtheath and Forest, Holton Heath, Horton Common, Hurn Common, Hyde Heath, Kitten's Farm Meadows, Lions Hill, Matchams, Moors River, Morden Bog, Norden, Oakers Bog, Oakers Wood, Parley Common, Poole Harbour, Povington and Grange Heaths, Purbeck Ridge (East), Purbeck Ridge (West), Rempstone Heaths, Sandford Heath, Slop Bog and Uddens Heath, Stoborough and Creech Heaths, Studland Cliffs, Studland and Godlingston Heaths, Talbot Pit, The Moors, Thrasher's Heath, Town Common, Turbary and Kinson Commons, Turners Puddle Heath, Upton Heath, Verwood Heaths, Warmwell Heath, Winfrith Heath. Overlaps with international designated areas: 8,169 ha of IBA covered by Special Protection Area (Dorset Heaths, 8,169 ha).

■ Conservation issues

Threats Abandonment/reduction of land management (A), Burning of vegetation (B), Extraction industry (A), Industrialization/urbanization (A), Infrastructure (B), Natural events (B), Other (U), Recreation/tourism (C)

Threats include pressure from road construction, housing developments and mineral extraction, pollution from waste-disposal sites, natural and accidental fire hazards, recreational activities, and inappropriate land management ('Other' threat, above). Funding from English Nature's Wildlife and Reserve Enhancement Scheme has been targeted for habitat restoration and management, with work also underway through the RSPB Dorset Heathland Project. A revised Dorset Heathlands Strategy was adopted in 1997.

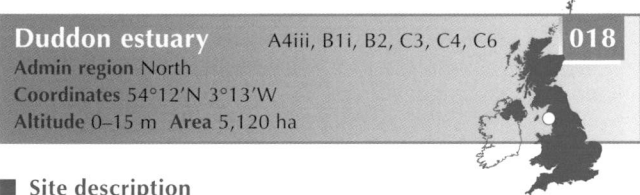

Duddon estuary A4iii, B1i, B2, C3, C4, C6 018
Admin region North
Coordinates 54°12′N 3°13′W
Altitude 0–15 m Area 5,120 ha

■ Site description

The IBA is situated to the north-west of Morecambe Bay, and covers a complex of habitats including intertidal mudflats, saltmarshes, sand-dunes and lagoons. The former iron-ore workings at Hodbarrow now comprise a lagoon of considerable wildlife interest.

Habitats Forest and woodland (1%; broadleaved deciduous forest), Scrub (1%; scrub), Grassland (2%), Wetland (96%; mudflat/sandflat; saltmarsh; sand-dunes/sand beach; shingle/stony beach; standing fresh water; river/stream)
Land-use Tourism/recreation

■ Birds

Species	Season	Year	Pop min	Pop max	Acc	Criteria
Anas acuta Pintail	W	1995	1,550	1,550	A	B1i, C3
Charadrius hiaticula Ringed Plover	P	1995	585	585	A	B1i, C3
Calidris canutus Knot	W	1995	5,300	5,300	A	B1i, B2, C3
Calidris canutus Knot	P	1995	3,580	3,580	A	B1i, C3
Calidris alpina Dunlin	W	1995	10,600	10,600	A	B2
Limosa lapponica Bar-tailed Godwit	W	1995	315	315	A	C6
Numenius arquata Curlew	W	1995	2,190	2,190	A	B2
Tringa totanus Redshank	W	1995	1,720	1,720	A	B1i, C3
Tringa totanus Redshank	P	1995	1,630	1,630	A	B1i, C3

Species ... continued	Season	Year	Pop min	Pop max	Acc	Criteria
Sterna sandvicensis Sandwich Tern	B	1993	100	100	A	C6
Sterna albifrons Little Tern	B	1995	14	14	A	C6

The estuary is important for breeding terns and wintering wildfowl and waders, and supports 36,100 wintering and 21,900 passage waterbirds on a regular basis. It is also nationally important for wintering *Tadorna tadorna* (1,100 birds, 1%), *Mergus serrator* (155 birds, 1%), *Haematopus ostralegus* (6,450 birds, 2%) and *Calidris alba* (605 birds, 3%), and for passage *Haematopus ostralegus* (6,800 birds, 2%) and *Calidris alba* (880 birds, 4%).

■ Protection status
National Partial **International** High
IBA partly or wholly overlaps with the following national designated areas. *Reserve:* Hodbarrow Lagoon. *Sites of Special Scientific Interest:* Duddon Estuary, Duddon Mosses, Haverigg Haws, Hodbarrow Lagoon, North Walney, Sandscale Haws. Overlaps with international designated areas: 5,120 ha of IBA covered by Special Protection Area (Duddon Estuary, 6,806 ha). 5,120 ha of IBA covered by Ramsar Site (Duddon Estuary, 6,806 ha).

■ Conservation issues

Threats Consequences of animal/plant introductions (B), Construction/impact of dyke/dam/barrage (A), Industrialization/urbanization (A), Infrastructure (B), Natural events (U), Recreation/tourism (B)

Threats include increased recreational disturbance, proposed road, barrage and industrial developments, cord-grass *Spartina* encroachment, and sea-level change which may lead to flooding, erosion and consequent improvements to existing sea defences. Part of the site will be incorporated into the Morecambe Bay SAC management scheme.

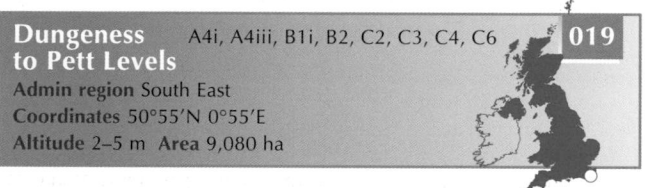

Dungeness to Pett Levels
A4i, A4iii, B1i, B2, C2, C3, C4, C6   019
Admin region South East
Coordinates 50°55′N 0°55′E
Altitude 2–5 m **Area** 9,080 ha

■ Site description
The IBA includes inland wetlands, grazing-marsh and arable land, and two shingle-beaches at Dungeness and Rye Harbour. The shingle-beach systems support very unusual vegetation-types.

Habitats Grassland (humid grassland), Wetland (mudflat/sandflat; saltmarsh; shingle/stony beach; standing fresh water; river/stream; water-fringe vegetation; fen/transition mire/spring), Artificial landscape (highly improved reseeded grassland; arable land)
Land-use Agriculture, Military, Nature conservation/research, Tourism/recreation

■ Birds

Species	Season	Year	Pop min	Pop max	Acc	Criteria
[1] *Cygnus columbianus* Bewick's Swan	W	1996	325	325	A	A4i, B1i, B2, C2, C6
[1] *Anas clypeata* Shoveler	W	1996	515	515	A	B1i, C3
[1] *Mergus albellus* Smew	W	1996	38	38	A	C6
[1] *Pluvialis apricaria* Golden Plover	W	1996	2,850	2,850	A	C6
[1] *Philomachus pugnax* Ruff	W	1996	47	47	A	C6
Sterna sandvicensis Sandwich Tern	B	1995	100	100	A	C6
Sterna hirundo Common Tern	B	1995	280	280	A	C6
Sterna albifrons Little Tern	B	1995	41	41	A	C6

1. Mean count.

The IBA is important for breeding terns and wintering wildfowl, and holds 33,200 wintering waterbirds on a regular basis. It is also nationally important for breeding *Anas strepera* (8 pairs, 1995, 1%) and *Panurus biarmicus* (4 pairs, 1992, 1%), for wintering *Podiceps cristatus* (320 birds, 1993–1996, 3%), *Phalacrocorax carbo* (315 birds, 1993–1996, 2%), *Anser albifrons albifrons* (185 birds, 1993–1996, 3%), *Anas penelope* (5,750 birds, 1993–1996, 2%), *Anas strepera* (250 birds, 1993–1996, 3%), *Anas crecca* (1,760 birds, 1993–1996, 1%), *Melanitta nigra* (885 birds, 1993–1996, 2%), *Fulica atra* (1,480 birds, 1993–1996, 1%) and *Calidris alba* (410 birds, 1993–1996, 2%), and for passage *Numenius phaeopus* (440 birds, 1993–1996, 12%).

■ Protection status
National Partial **International** None
IBA partly or wholly overlaps with the following national designated areas. *Reserves:* Dungeness, Rye Harbour. *Sites of Special Scientific Interest:* Camber Sands and Rye Saltings, Dungeness, Hastings Cliffs and Pett Beach, Houghton Green Cliff, North Lade, Pett Level, Romney Warren, Rye Harbour, Walland Marsh, Winchelsea Cutting.

■ Conservation issues

Threats Agricultural intensification/expansion (B), Extraction industry (A), Groundwater abstraction (A), Industrialization/urbanization (B), Infrastructure (A), Natural events (U), Recreation/tourism (B)

Threats include the development of Rye Harbour, sea-level change, disturbance from leisure activities and developments, airport expansion, and water abstraction. Formal confirmation of SPA and Ramsar designations from the Department of the Environment, Transport and the Regions are anticipated. Two major wetland creation initiatives have been undertaken by private land-owners in the IBA, and there is a management plan for the site.

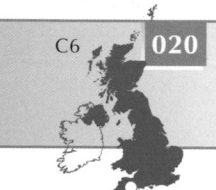

East Devon heaths
C6   020
Admin region South West
Coordinates 50°41′N 3°20′W
Altitude 61–176 m **Area** 1,370 ha

■ Site description
These areas form the largest blocks of lowland heath in Devon.

Habitats Forest and woodland (mixed forest), Scrub (scrub; heathland), Wetland (fen/transition mire/spring)
Land-use Unknown

■ Birds

Species	Season	Year	Pop min	Pop max	Acc	Criteria
Caprimulgus europaeus Nightjar	B	1992	79	79	A	C6
Sylvia undata Dartford Warbler	R	1994	130	130	A	C6

The site supports a range of breeding heathland birds.

■ Protection status
National Partial **International** Partial
IBA partly or wholly overlaps with the following national designated areas. *Reserve:* Aylesbeare and Harpford Commons. *Site of Special Scientific Interest:* East Devon Pebblebed Heaths. Overlaps with international designated areas: 1,119 ha of IBA covered by Special Protection Area (East Devon Heaths, 1,119 ha).

■ Conservation issues

Threats Abandonment/reduction of land management (C), Extraction industry (A), Other (C), Recreation/tourism (C)

Mineral extraction poses a significant threat, and inappropriate land management is also a problem ('Other' threat, above). The 1996 East Devon Heathland Strategy is in place. These heaths are reported to be the best lowland heaths for butterflies in England.

Exe estuary
A4iii, B2, C4, C6   021
Admin region South West
Coordinates 50°39′N 3°26′W
Altitude 0–2 m **Area** 2,180 ha

■ Site description
A complex of habitats, extending over 10 km south from Exeter to the open sea at Dawlish Warren. Broad intertidal flats and grazing-marshes are the dominant habitats. Extensive mussel, eel-grass *Zostera* and algal beds and a sand-spit further increase the habitat diversity.

Habitats Grassland (7%; humid grassland), Wetland (93%; tidal river/enclosed tidal water; mudflat/sandflat; saltmarsh; sand-dunes/sand beach; river/stream; water-fringe vegetation)
Land-use Fisheries/aquaculture, Tourism/recreation

■ Birds

Species		Season	Year	Pop min	Pop max	Acc	Criteria
Podiceps auritus	Slavonian Grebe	W	1990	20	20	A	C6
Recurvirostra avosetta	Avocet	W	1995	360	360	A	B2, C6
Calidris alpina	Dunlin	W	1995	6,150	6,150	A	B2
Limosa lapponica	Bar-tailed Godwit	W	1995	430	430	A	C6

The site is important for wintering and passage wildfowl and waders, and regularly holds 23,200 wintering waterbirds. It is nationally important for breeding *Cettia cetti* (5 pairs, 1995, 2%), for wintering *Branta bernicla bernicla* (2,120 birds, 2%), *Mergus serrator* (125 birds, 1%), *Haematopus ostralegus* (4,690 birds, 1%), *Pluvialis squatarola* (440 birds, 1%), *Limosa limosa* (585 birds, 8%) and *Tringa nebularia* (10 birds, 2%). The area is also nationally significant for passage *Haematopus ostralegus* (4,020 birds, 1%) and *Limosa limosa* (395 birds, 5%).

■ Protection status

National High **International** High
IBA partly or wholly overlaps with the following national designated areas. *Reserve:* Exe Estuary. *Sites of Special Scientific Interest:* Dawlish Cliffs, Dawlish Warren, Exe Estuary. Overlaps with international designated areas: 2,182 ha of IBA covered by Special Protection Area (Exe Estuary, 2,182 ha). 2,182 ha of IBA covered by Ramsar Site (Exe Estuary, 2,182 ha).

■ Conservation issues

Threats Aquaculture/fisheries (C), Disturbance to birds (C), Dredging/canalization (C), Industrialization/urbanization (U), Natural events (U), Other (U), Recreation/tourism (C)

Threats include sea-level changes that may lead to flooding, erosion and coastal defence improvements, disturbance from leisure activities and developments, the extension of workshops and cesspit construction, wildfowling and inappropriate land management ('Other' threat, above). Estuary and water-level management plans are in preparation.

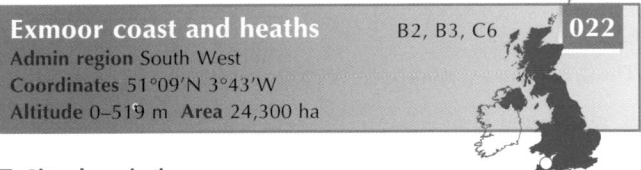

Exmoor coast and heaths   B2, B3, C6   **022**
Admin region South West
Coordinates 51°09'N 3°43'W
Altitude 0–519 m **Area** 24,300 ha

■ Site description

Upland moorland and grassland, including all of the heathland on Exmoor and the Quantocks, and rocky coastal habitats.

Habitats Forest and woodland (broadleaved deciduous forest; mixed forest), Scrub (scrub; heathland), Grassland, Wetland (river/stream), Rocky areas (sea cliff/rocky shore)
Land-use Agriculture, Nature conservation/research, Tourism/recreation

■ Birds

Species		Season	Year	Pop min	Pop max	Acc	Criteria
Falco peregrinus	Peregrine	R	1995	20	—	A	B2, C6
Caprimulgus europaeus	Nightjar	B	1994	56	56	A	C6
Saxicola rubetra	Whinchat	B	1993	450	450	A	B3
Saxicola torquata	Stonechat	R	1993	300	300	A	B2

This highly fragmented site supports a number of moorland species, including *Falco columbarius*.

■ Protection status

National Partial **International** None
IBA partly or wholly overlaps with the following national designated areas. *National Park:* Exmoor. *Sites of Special Scientific Interest:* Barle Valley, Barricane Beach, Braunton Burrows, Glenthorne, Mill Rock, Morte Point, Napp's Cave, Nettlecombe Park, North Exmoor, Porlock Marsh, Saunton to Baggy Point Coast, South Exmoor, The Quantocks, Watersmeet, West Exmoor Coast and Woods.

■ Conservation issues

Threats Abandonment/reduction of land management (B), Agricultural intensification/expansion (B)

Much of the heathland and moorland has been neglected, or is threatened by the intensification of farming. The Exmoor National Park BAP is in preparation and an ESA-designation is in place.

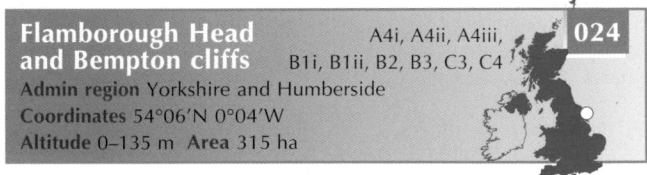

Farne Islands   A4i, A4iii, B1i, B1ii, B2, B3,   **023**
Admin region North   C2, C3, C4, C6
Coordinates 55°37'N 1°38'W
Altitude 0–19 m **Area** 101 ha

■ Site description

A group of islands and rock stacks lying between 2 km and 6 km off the Northumberland coast at Bamburgh. Vegetation is limited to pioneer species due to the maritime conditions and the impact of large numbers of seabirds.

Habitats Grassland (mesophile grassland), Rocky areas (sea cliff/rocky shore; rock stacks/islets)
Land-use Nature conservation/research (100%)

■ Birds

Species		Season	Year	Pop min	Pop max	Acc	Criteria
Phalacrocorax aristotelis	Shag	B	1995	1,020	1,020	A	A4i, B1i, B3, C2, C3
Larus fuscus	Lesser Black-backed Gull	B	1995	1,380	1,380	A	B1i, B3, C3
Sterna sandvicensis	Sandwich Tern	B	1995	1,840	1,840	A	A4i, B1i, B2, C2, C6
Sterna dougallii	Roseate Tern	B	1995	2	2	A	C6
Sterna hirundo	Common Tern	B	1995	250	250	A	C6
Sterna paradisaea	Arctic Tern	B	1995	3,070	3,070	A	C2, C6
Fratercula arctica	Puffin	B	1993	34,700	34,700	A	B1ii, B2, C3

The IBA supports large numbers of breeding seabirds, especially terns and auks. It holds 54,200 breeding seabirds and 14,200 breeding waterbirds on a regular basis, and is nationally important for breeding *Phalacrocorax carbo* (225 pairs, 1995, 3%), *Somateria mollissima* (1,450 pairs, 1989, 5%), *Rissa tridactyla* (6,300 pairs, 1995, 1%) and *Uria aalge* (19,000 pairs, 1995, 3%).

■ Protection status

National High **International** High
IBA partly or wholly overlaps with the following national designated areas. *Site of Special Scientific Interest:* The Farne Islands. Overlaps with international designated areas: 101 ha of IBA covered by Special Protection Area (Farne Islands, 101 ha).

■ Conservation issues

Threats Aquaculture/fisheries (U), Natural events (B), Recreation/tourism (B)

Threats include soil erosion caused by visitors and the *Fratercula arctica* and seal colonies, disturbance caused by intense visitor pressure and over-fishing. The National Trust manages the islands, and the surrounding waters are of great value in terms of marine conservation. A management plan exists for the site.

Flamborough Head   A4i, A4ii, A4iii,   **024**
and Bempton cliffs   B1i, B1ii, B2, B3, C3, C4
Admin region Yorkshire and Humberside
Coordinates 54°06'N 0°04'W
Altitude 0–135 m **Area** 315 ha

■ Site description

Chalk cliffs that project into the North Sea from the Yorkshire coast.

Habitats Grassland, Marine areas (open sea), Rocky areas (sea cliff/rocky shore)
Land-use Agriculture, Fisheries/aquaculture, Nature conservation/research, Tourism/recreation, Urban/industrial/transport

■ Birds

The site is important for its large breeding colonies, which hold 46,100 pairs of breeding seabirds and 76,000 pairs of breeding waterbirds on a regular basis.

Species		Season	Year	Pop min	Pop max	Acc	Criteria
Rissa tridactyla	Kittiwake	B	1994	75,000	—	A	A4i, B1i, C3
Uria aalge	Guillemot	B	1994	30,000	—	A	B1ii, C3
Alca torda	Razorbill	B	1994	7,500	—	A	A4ii, B1ii, B3, C3
Fratercula arctica	Puffin	B	1994	6,000	—	A	B2

■ Protection status

National High **International** High

IBA partly or wholly overlaps with the following national designated areas. *Reserve:* Bempton Cliffs. *Site of Special Scientific Interest:* Flamborough Head. Overlaps with international designated areas: 315 ha of IBA covered by Special Protection Area (Flamborough Head and Bempton Cliffs, 315 ha).

■ Conservation issues

Threats Extraction industry (A), Infrastructure (B), Recreation/tourism (A)

Threats include disturbance from oil and gas exploration and associated shipping and air traffic, disturbance from rock-climbing, hand-gliding and helicopter pleasure rides, line and hooks discarded by sea-anglers, and coastal defence maintenance works. A Flamborough Headland Heritage Coast Management Strategy and shoreline management plan exists, and the candidate SAC will eventually have a scheme of management.

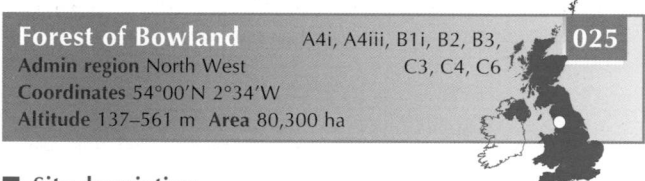

Forest of Bowland
A4i, A4iii, B1i, B2, B3, C3, C4, C6
Admin region North West
Coordinates 54°00'N 2°34'W
Altitude 137–561 m **Area** 80,300 ha

025

■ Site description

The Forest of Bowland forms a western outlier to the Pennines, with gentle slopes and level ground on ridges. Fast-flowing streams drain an extensive area of upland moorland and blanket mire, and bracken *Pteridium* may dominate on lower ground.

Habitats Forest and woodland (5%; broadleaved deciduous forest), Scrub (75%; heathland), Grassland (5%; humid grassland), Wetland (15%; river/stream; blanket bog)
Land-use Agriculture (90%), Fisheries/aquaculture (5%), Forestry (5%), Hunting (90%), Water management (40%)

■ Birds

Species		Season	Year	Pop min	Pop max	Acc	Criteria
Circus cyaneus	Hen Harrier	R	1994	14	—	A	C6
Falco columbarius	Merlin	R	1994	17	—	A	C6
Falco peregrinus	Peregrine	R	1994	10	—	A	C6
Tringa totanus	Redshank	R	1993	520	520	A	B1i, B2, C3
Larus fuscus	Lesser Black-backed Gull	B	1992	11,500	11,500	A	A4i, B1i, B3, C3
Asio flammeus	Short-eared Owl	R	1994	9	—	A	C6

The IBA supports a typical range of breeding upland birds, and is a breeding stronghold of *Circus cyaneus*. The site holds 12,000 pairs of breeding waterbirds on a regular basis, and is nationally important for breeding *Vanellus vanellus* (3,570 pairs, 1993, 2%) and *Numenius arquata* (895 pairs, 1993, 2%).

■ Protection status

National Partial **International** Partial

IBA partly or wholly overlaps with the following national designated areas. *Sites of Special Scientific Interest:* Bowland Fells, Tarnbrook Meadows. Overlaps with international designated areas: 16,002 ha of IBA covered by Special Protection Area (Bowland Fells, 16,002 ha).

■ Conservation issues

Threats Afforestation (C), Agricultural intensification/expansion (A), Other (A)

The impact of farming is the most important threat to birds. 'Other' threats are posed by human persecution of raptors, and acidification, which affects 51% of the site. The RSPB has an annual wardening agreement on North-West Water's estate. The heather moorland on the steeper slopes is managed for *Lagopus lagopus*.

Frome flood-plain
B2, C6

026

Admin region South West
Coordinates 50°41'N 2°15'W
Altitude 5–49 m **Area** 2,700 ha

■ Site description

This site includes all of the flood-plain between Dorchester and Poole Harbour, with lowland wet grassland the dominant habitat.

Habitats Grassland (80%; humid grassland), Wetland (20%; river/stream; water-fringe vegetation; fen/transition mire/spring)
Land-use Agriculture

■ Birds

Species		Season	Year	Pop min	Pop max	Acc	Criteria
Cygnus columbianus	Bewick's Swan	W	1995	0	110	A	B2, C6

The IBA is important for wintering wildfowl.

■ Protection status

National Partial **International** None

IBA partly or wholly overlaps with the following national designated areas. *Sites of Special Scientific Interest:* East Holme Meadows, East Stoke Fen, Povington and Grange Heaths, Turners Puddle Heath, Winfrith Heath, Worgret Heath.

■ Conservation issues

Threats Agricultural intensification/expansion (U)

The Purbeck BAP has been prepared, and advisory work is underway.

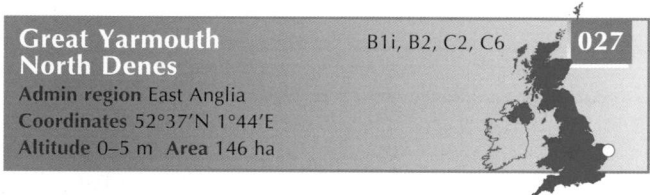

Great Yarmouth North Denes
B1i, B2, C2, C6

027

Admin region East Anglia
Coordinates 52°37'N 1°44'E
Altitude 0–5 m **Area** 146 ha

■ Site description

The IBA comprises two component parts: an actively accreting low sand-dune system and a wide shingle-beach at Great Yarmouth, and the beach and fore-dune ridge at Winterton-Horsey dunes four miles to the north. Marram-grass *Ammophila* stabilizes the dune system, while grey hair-grass *Corynephorus* also covers large areas.

Habitats Wetland (100%; sand-dunes/sand beach; shingle/stony beach)
Land-use Nature conservation/research, Tourism/recreation

■ Birds

Species		Season	Year	Pop min	Pop max	Acc	Criteria
Sterna albifrons	Little Tern	B	1995	250	250	A	B1i, B2, C2, C6

The IBA holds important numbers of *Sterna albifrons*.

■ Protection status

National High **International** High

IBA partly or wholly overlaps with the following national designated areas. *National Nature Reserve:* Winterton Dunes. *Sites of Special Scientific Interest:* Great Yarmouth North Denes, Winterton–Horsey Dunes. Overlaps with international designated areas: 146 ha of IBA covered by Special Protection Area (Great Yarmouth North Denes, 146 ha).

■ Conservation issues

Threats Natural events (A), Recreation/tourism (A)

Threats include disturbance of the *Sterna albifrons* colony by dogs and people, predation of the terns, tourism development, and beach erosion. There is no management plan for the Great Yarmouth North Denes part of the IBA, except for the RSPB *S. albifrons* protection scheme, in existence since 1986.

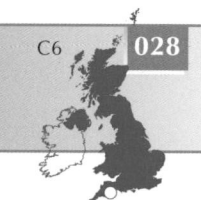

Haldon
C6 **028**

Admin region South West
Coordinates 50°37'N 3°33'W
Altitude 113–247 m **Area** 2,910 ha

■ Site description
Forested heathland to the west of the Exe estuary.

Habitats Scrub (20%; heathland), Artificial landscape (80%; forestry plantation)
Land-use Agriculture, Forestry

■ Birds

Species	Season	Year	Pop min	Pop max	Acc	Criteria
Caprimulgus europaeus Nightjar	B	1992	100	100	A	C6
Lullula arborea Woodlark	R	1995	6	10	A	C6
Sylvia undata Dartford Warbler	R	1995	12	12	A	C6

The IBA supports a range of breeding heathland species.

■ Protection status
National Partial **International** None
IBA partly or wholly overlaps with the following national designated areas. *Sites of Special Scientific Interest:* Buller's Hill Quarry, Great Haldon Heaths, Haldon Forest, Little Haldon Heaths, Tower Wood Quarry.

■ Conservation issues

Threats Abandonment/reduction of land management (B), Afforestation (A)

The site requires measures for heathland management including the clearance of existing areas of forest and encroaching trees. Forest Enterprise is preparing an integrated SSSI and forest design plan, and the Devon County Heathland Strategy is also in preparation.

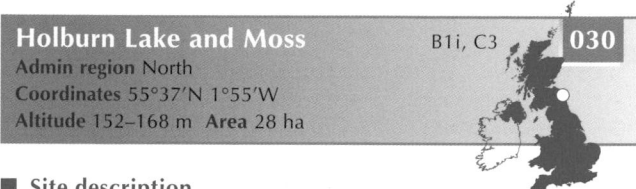

Hamford Water
A4i, A4iii, B1i, B2, C3, C4, C6 **029**

Admin region South East
Coordinates 51°52'N 1°14'E
Altitude 0–4 m **Area** 2,143 ha

■ Site description
A large, shallow estuarine basin comprising tidal creeks and islands, sand-dunes and extensive areas of saltmarsh.

Habitats Scrub (scrub), Grassland, Wetland (tidal river/enclosed tidal water; mudflat/sandflat; saltmarsh; sand-dunes/sand beach; shingle/stony beach)
Land-use Agriculture, Hunting, Nature conservation/research, Tourism/recreation

■ Birds

Species	Season	Year	Pop min	Pop max	Acc	Criteria
Branta bernicla Brent Goose	W	1995	5,400	5,400	A	A4i, B1i, C3
Anas crecca Teal	W	1995	4,020	4,020	A	B1i, C3
Recurvirostra avosetta Avocet	W	1995	290	290	A	B2, C6
Recurvirostra avosetta Avocet	P	1995	210	210	A	C6
Charadrius hiaticula Ringed Plover	W	1995	640	640	A	B1i, C3
Charadrius hiaticula Ringed Plover	P	1995	1,180	1,180	A	B1i, C3
Pluvialis apricaria Golden Plover	W	1995	3,270	3,270	A	C6
Pluvialis squatarola Grey Plover	W	1995	1,970	1,970	A	A4i, B1i, C3
Pluvialis squatarola Grey Plover	P	1995	2,490	2,490	A	A4i, B1i, C3
Calidris alpina Dunlin	W	1995	6,000	6,000	A	B2
Philomachus pugnax Ruff	W	1995	44	44	A	C6
Limosa limosa Black-tailed Godwit	W	1995	1,520	1,520	A	B1i, C3
Limosa limosa Black-tailed Godwit	P	1995	1,620	1,620	A	B1i, C3
Limosa lapponica Bar-tailed Godwit	W	1995	380	380	A	C6
Sterna albifrons Little Tern	B	1995	43	—	A	C6

The IBA is important for wintering waders and wildfowl and breeding terns. It regularly holds 38,500 wintering waterbirds, and is nationally important for breeding *Larus ridibundus* (3,910 pairs, 1989, 2%) and for wintering *Tadorna tadorna* (1,400 birds, 2%) and *Tringa totanus* (1,430 birds, 1%). *Branta bernicla* are the *bernicla* subspecies.

■ Protection status
National High **International** High

IBA partly or wholly overlaps with the following national designated areas. *National Nature Reserve:* Hamford Water. *Reserves:* John Weston Reserve, Skipper's Island. *Sites of Special Scientific Interest:* Hamford Water, The Naze. Overlaps with international designated areas: 2,143 ha of IBA covered by Special Protection Area (Hamford Water, 2,143 ha). 2,143 ha of IBA covered by Ramsar Site (Hamford Water, 2,143 ha).

■ Conservation issues

Threats Natural events (A), Recreation/tourism (B)

Threats include disturbance from caravan sites, past proposals for marina expansion, saltmarsh erosion caused by rising sea-level, and the flooding of nests of terns and *Tringa totanus* by high tides.

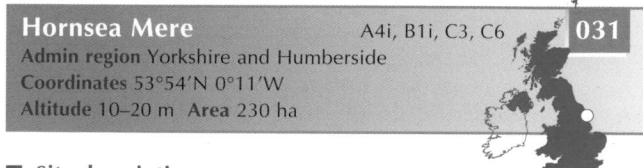

Holburn Lake and Moss
B1i, C3 **030**

Admin region North
Coordinates 55°37'N 1°55'W
Altitude 152–168 m **Area** 28 ha

■ Site description
This site comprises a lake and surrounding mire and swamp, and is situated about 5 km inland from the Northumberland coast. The lake supports *Typha* and a floating mat of vegetation, with bracken *Pteridium* and gorse *Ulex* occurring in drier parts of the site. Human activities include peat extraction ('Other' land-use, below).

Habitats Scrub (heathland), Wetland (standing fresh water; blanket bog; water-fringe vegetation; fen/transition mire/spring)
Land-use Agriculture, Other

■ Birds

Species	Season	Year	Pop min	Pop max	Acc	Criteria
Anser anser Greylag Goose	W	1995	1,600	1,600	A	B1i, C3

The site is important for wintering wildfowl and waders. *Anser anser* are from the Icelandic breeding population.

■ Protection status
National High **International** High
IBA partly or wholly overlaps with the following national designated areas. *Site of Special Scientific Interest:* Holburn Lake and Moss. Overlaps with international designated areas: 28 ha of IBA covered by Special Protection Area (Holburn Moss, 28 ha). 28 ha of IBA covered by Ramsar Site (Holburn Moss, 28 ha).

■ Conservation issues

Threats Afforestation (B), Burning of vegetation (B), Disturbance to birds (B), Drainage (B), Extraction industry (A), Recreation/tourism (C)

Threats include unpermitted recreational disturbance by bird-watchers, uncontrolled heather-burning, and the effects of nearby shooting. Peat extraction may alter the underlying hydrology of the site.

Hornsea Mere
A4i, B1i, C3, C6 **031**

Admin region Yorkshire and Humberside
Coordinates 53°54'N 0°11'W
Altitude 10–20 m **Area** 230 ha

■ Site description
Hornsea Mere lies immediately inland of Hornsea on the Humberside coast. The lake is only 1–2 m deep and is the only remaining glacial lake in east Yorkshire. It provides a classic example of wetland succession from open water to reedbed (*Phragmites*) to species-rich fen and *Alnus* carr.

Habitats Forest and woodland (broadleaved deciduous forest; alluvial/very wet forest), Wetland (standing fresh water; water-fringe vegetation; fen/transition mire/spring)
Land-use Agriculture, Fisheries/aquaculture, Nature conservation/research, Tourism/recreation, Water management

■ Birds

Species	Season	Year	Pop min	Pop max	Acc	Criteria
Branta leucopsis Barnacle Goose	W	1995	185	185	A	C6
Anas strepera Gadwall	W	1995	300	300	A	B1i, C3
Larus minutus Little Gull	N	1995	2,000	2,000	A	A4i, B1i, C3

The IBA supports a wide range of breeding and wintering wetland birds. It is also nationally important for wintering *Bucephala clangula* (385 birds, 1%) and *Fulica atra* (1,650 birds, 1%).

■ Protection status
National High **International** High
IBA partly or wholly overlaps with the following national designated areas. *Reserve:* Hornsea Mere. *Site of Special Scientific Interest:* Hornsea Mere. Overlaps with international designated areas: 230 ha of IBA covered by Special Protection Area (Hornsea Mere, 230 ha).

■ Conservation issues

Threats Abandonment/reduction of land management (U), Agricultural intensification/ expansion (B), Recreation/tourism (A)

Threats include disturbance from motorcycle and trail bike activities, agricultural pollution, and a lack of management.

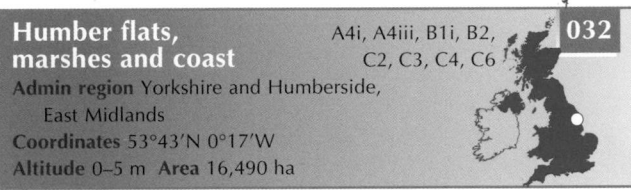

Humber flats, marshes and coast   A4i, A4iii, B1i, B2, C2, C3, C4, C6   **032**
Admin region Yorkshire and Humberside, East Midlands
Coordinates 53°43′N 0°17′W
Altitude 0–5 m **Area** 16,490 ha

■ Site description
The IBA covers the Humber estuary, and coastline to the north and south of the Humber mouth. It includes an elongated shingle-spit capped by sand-dunes (Spurn Point), extensive intertidal habitats (especially mudflats), saline lagoons and reedbeds (*Phragmites*). This area includes two sites that were treated as separate IBAs in the previous international IBA inventory (Grimmett and Jones 1989): 'Humber Flats, Marshes, and Coast' (former site GB157) and 'Tetney Marshes' (former site GB237).

Habitats Scrub (scrub), Wetland (tidal river/enclosed tidal water; mudflat/sandflat; saltmarsh; sand-dunes/sand beach; shingle/stony beach; coastal lagoon; standing fresh water; river/ stream; water-fringe vegetation; fen/transition mire/spring), Artificial landscape (arable land)
Land-use Agriculture, Fisheries/aquaculture, Hunting, Nature conservation/research, Tourism/recreation, Urban/industrial/transport

■ Birds

Species	Season	Year	Pop min	Pop max	Acc	Criteria
Tadorna tadorna Shelduck	W	1995	3,850	3,850	A	A4i, B1i, C3
Circus aeruginosus Marsh Harrier	R	1995	11	11	A	C6
Recurvirostra avosetta Avocet	R	1995	4	4	A	C6
Charadrius hiaticula Ringed Plover	P	1995	860	860	A	B1i, C3
Pluvialis apricaria Golden Plover	W	1995	30,600	30,600	A	A4i, B1i, C2, C6
Pluvialis apricaria Golden Plover	P	1995	18,200	18,200	A	A4i, B1i, C2, C6
Pluvialis squatarola Grey Plover	P	1995	1,770	1,770	A	A4i, B1i, C3
Calidris canutus Knot	W	1995	35,400	35,400	A	A4i, B1i, B2, C3
Calidris canutus Knot	P	1995	6,000	6,000	A	B1i, C3
Calidris alba Sanderling	P	1995	1,510	1,510	A	A4i, B1i, C3
Calidris alpina Dunlin	W	1995	24,400	24,400	A	A4i, B1i, B2, C3
Calidris alpina Dunlin	P	1995	21,700	21,700	A	B1i, C3
Philomachus pugnax Ruff	W	1995	20	20	A	C6
Philomachus pugnax Ruff	P	1995	130	130	A	C6
Limosa lapponica Bar-tailed Godwit	W	1995	1,560	1,560	A	A4i, B1i, B2, C2, C6
Limosa lapponica Bar-tailed Godwit	P	1995	610	610	A	C6
Numenius arquata Curlew	W	1995	2,730	2,730	A	B2
Tringa totanus Redshank	W	1995	4,820	4,820	A	A4i, B1i, C3
Tringa totanus Redshank	P	1995	5,200	5,200	A	A4i, B1i, C3
Sterna albifrons Little Tern	B	1995	92	92	A	B2, C6
Asio flammeus Short-eared Owl	R	1995	5	—	A	C6

The IBA is important for breeding raptors and waders and wintering wildfowl and waders. It regularly holds 160,700 wintering and 69,100 passage waterbirds. It is nationally important for breeding *Tadorna tadorna* (150 pairs, 1995, 1%), *Aythya ferina* (25 pairs, 1995, 6%), *Charadrius hiaticula* (100 pairs, 1995, 1%) and *Panurus biarmicus* (60

pairs, 1995, 15%). The site is nationally significant for wintering *Branta bernicla bernicla* (2,780 birds, 3%), *Anas penelope* (4,590 birds, 2%), *Anas crecca* (1,480 birds, 1%), *Anas acuta* (290 birds, 1%), *Aythya ferina* (950 birds, 1%), *Haematopus ostralegus* (5,350 birds, 1%), *Charadrius hiaticula* (325 birds, 1%), *Pluvialis squatarola* (1,570 birds, 4%), *Vanellus vanellus* (33,700 birds, 2%) and *Calidris alba* (595 birds, 3%). The site is also important for passage *Haematopus ostralegus* (4,000 birds, 1%).

■ Protection status
National High **International** High
IBA partly or wholly overlaps with the following national designated areas. *Reserves:* Blacktoft Sands, Tetney Marshes. *Sites of Special Scientific Interest:* Humber Flats and Marshes – Barton Barrow Clay Pits, Humber Flats and Marshes, Pyewipe and Cleethorpes, Humber Flats and Marshes – Spurnhead to Saltflat, Humber Flats and Marshes – Upper Humber, Humber Flats and Marshes – the Grues, North Lincolnshire Coast, Saltfleetby Theddlethorpe Dunes, South Ferriby Cliffs, The Lagoons. Overlaps with international designated areas: 15,230 ha of IBA covered by Special Protection Area (Humber Flats, Marshes and Coast, 15,230 ha). 15,230 ha of IBA covered by Ramsar Site (Humber Flats, Marshes and Coast, 15,230 ha).

■ Conservation issues

Threats Aquaculture/fisheries (C), Disturbance to birds (B), Dredging/canalization (U), Extraction industry (U), Filling-in of wetlands (C), Industrialization/urbanization (A), Infrastructure (B), Other (B), Recreation/tourism (C)

Threats include intense industrial development, disturbance from leisure activities and development, especially motorcycling and water-sports, discharged oil and industrial effluents from shipping activities ('Other' threat, above), rubbish-tipping, wildfowling, and coastal defence improvements. The Humber Estuary Management Strategy (HEMS) complements various shoreline, Heritage Coast, Wildlife Trust, and RSPB Reserve management plans.

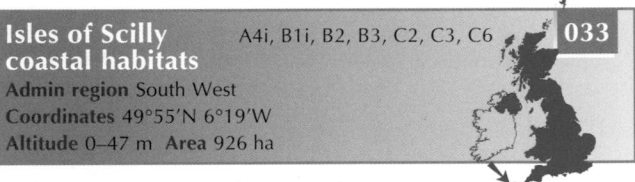

Isles of Scilly coastal habitats   A4i, B1i, B2, B3, C2, C3, C6   **033**
Admin region South West
Coordinates 49°55′N 6°19′W
Altitude 0–47 m **Area** 926 ha

■ Site description
The Isles of Scilly comprise over 200 low-lying granitic islands and rocks, situated 28 miles to the south-west of Land's End. The habitats here are subject to extreme maritime influences. The flora includes a number of Mediterranean and West European species not found elsewhere in Britain.

Habitats Scrub (heathland), Grassland (mesophile grassland), Wetland (mudflat/sandflat; sand-dunes/sand beach; shingle/stony beach; coastal lagoon; standing fresh water), Marine areas (80%; open sea), Rocky areas (sea cliff/rocky shore; rock stacks/islets)
Land-use Tourism/recreation

■ Birds

Species	Season	Year	Pop min	Pop max	Acc	Criteria
Hydrobates pelagicus Storm Petrel	B	1992	2,130	2,130	A	B2, C2, C6
Phalacrocorax aristotelis Shag	B	1987	1,200	1,200	A	A4i, B1i, B3, C2, C3
Arenaria interpres Turnstone	W	1985	940	940	A	A4i, B1i, C3
Larus fuscus Lesser Black-backed Gull	B	1987	3,760	3,760	A	A4i, B1i, B3, C3
Larus marinus Great Black-backed Gull	B	1987	1,000	1,000	A	B3
Sterna dougallii Roseate Tern	B	1994	5	5	A	C6
Sterna hirundo Common Tern	B	1994	105	105	A	C6

These islands are of prime importance for breeding seabirds and some wintering wader species. They are also nationally important for wintering *Egretta garzetta* (13 birds, 1995–1998, 3%), *Charadrius hiaticula* (310 birds, 1984–1985, 1%), *Calidris alba* (330 birds, 1984–1985, 1%) and *Tringa nebularia* (13 birds, 1998, 3%).

■ Protection status
National Partial **International** None
IBA partly or wholly overlaps with the following national designated areas. *Sites of Special-Scientific Interest:* Annet, Big Pool and Browarth

Point (St Agnes), Castle Down (Tresco), Chapel Down (St Martins), Eastern Isles, Great Pool (Tresco), Gugh, Higher Moors and Porth Hellick Pool (St Mary's), Lower Moors (St Mary's), Norrard Rocks, Peninnis Head (St Mary's), Pentle Bay (Tresco), Plains and Great Bay (St Martin's), Pool of Bryher and Popplestone Bank (Bryher), Porth Seal (St Martin's), Rushy Bay and Heathy Hill (Bryher), Samson (with Green, White, Puffin and Stoney Islands), Shipman Head and Shipman Down (Bryher), St Helens (with Northwethel and Men-a-Vaur), Tean, Western Rocks, White Island (off St Martin's), Wingletang Down (St Agnes).

■ Conservation issues

Threats Other (U), Recreation/tourism (B)

Threats include disturbance from visitors and inappropriate land management ('Other' treat, above). Monitoring of breeding seabirds and wintering shorebirds has clarified the importance of the site, and it is awaiting SPA designation.

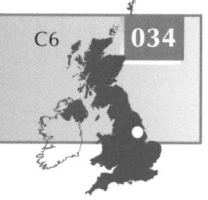

Laughton forest   C6   034
Admin region East Midlands
Coordinates 53°29'N 0°42'W
Altitude 3–30 m **Area** 1,170 ha

■ Site description
A small mixed forest, mainly pine *Pinus*, situated in the north-western corner of Lincolnshire. Areas of unimproved acid grassland and heathland command SSSI status, and contain characteristic communities. Scotton and Laughton forest ponds support plant species of acid fen/mire.

Habitats Forest and woodland (broadleaved deciduous forest), Scrub (heathland), Artificial landscape (forestry plantation)
Land-use Forestry (93%), Nature conservation/research (7%)

■ Birds

Species	Season	Year	Pop min	Pop max	Acc	Criteria
Caprimulgus europaeus Nightjar	B	1991	41	41	A	C6
Lullula arborea Woodlark	B	1989	8	—	A	C6

The site is important for breeding *Caprimulgus europaeus* and *Lullula arborea*.

■ Protection status
National Partial **International** None
IBA partly or wholly overlaps with the following national designated areas. *Sites of Special Scientific Interest:* Scotton Beck Fields, Scotton Common, Scotton and Laughton Forest Ponds.

■ Conservation issues

Threats Abandonment/reduction of land management (B)

The two key breeding birds, *Caprimulgus europaeus* and *Lullula arborea*, occur mainly outside nationally protected areas in clear-felled or recently restocked areas of forest. Both species are therefore vulnerable to changes in forestry practices. The area is managed on behalf of a private owner by Forest Enterprise, to include *Lullula arborea* monitoring. A management plan exists for the site.

Lea valley   B1i, C3, C6   035
Admin region South East
Coordinates 51°38'N 0°00'W
Altitude 16–29 m **Area** 2,550 ha

■ Site description

Habitats Grassland (humid grassland), Wetland (standing fresh water; river/stream; fen/transition mire/spring)
Land-use Fisheries/aquaculture, Military, Nature conservation/research, Tourism/recreation, Urban/industrial/transport, Water management

A series of wetlands and reservoirs situated along the River Lea, to

the north-east of London. A rich aquatic and marginal flora is present in the reservoirs and streams.

■ Birds

Species	Season	Year	Pop min	Pop max	Acc	Criteria
[1] *Botaurus stellaris* Bittern	W	1998	7	7	A	C6
Anas strepera Gadwall	W	1995	300	300	A	B1i, C3

1. Mean for winters 1993/94–1997/98.

The IBA is important for several breeding wetland bird species, including a large heronry, wintering wildfowl and late summer moults of *Aythya fuligula*. It is also nationally important for breeding *Ardea cinerea* (160 pairs, 1992, 1%) and *Anas strepera* (10 pairs, 1995, 1%); and for wintering *Podiceps cristatus* (190 birds, 2%), *Phalacrocorax carbo* (345 birds, 2%), *Anas clypeata* (325 birds, 3%), *A. fuligula* (2,170 birds, 2%) and *Fulica atra* (2,020 birds, 2%).

■ Protection status
National Partial **International** None
IBA partly or wholly overlaps with the following national designated areas. *Reserve:* Rye House Marsh. *Sites of Special Scientific Interest:* Chingford Reservoirs, Cornmill Stream and Old River Lea, Rye Meads, Turnford and Cheshunt Pits, Waltham Abbey, Walthamstow Marshes, Walthamstow Reservoirs.

■ Conservation issues

Threats Recreation/tourism (B)

Recreational disturbance, particularly from water-sports, is a problem. A *Botaurus stellaris* viewing scheme is in operation, and some reedbed (*Phragmites*) creation has taken place. The local BAP is in preparation, and part of the IBA and an adjacent site have been put forward as a candidate SPA on the basis of wintering *Anas strepera*, *A. clypeata* and *Botaurus stellaris*. The site is monitored as part of the WeBS.

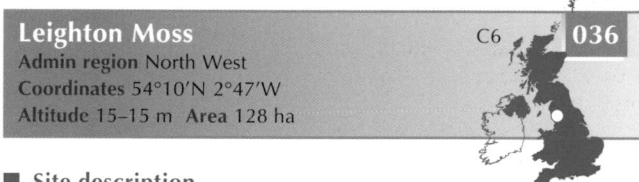

Leighton Moss   C6   036
Admin region North West
Coordinates 54°10'N 2°47'W
Altitude 15–15 m **Area** 128 ha

■ Site description
The IBA is situated between Silverdale and Warton on the edge of Morecambe Bay, and contains the largest reedbed (*Phragmites*) in north-west England.

Habitats Forest and woodland (broadleaved deciduous forest), Wetland (standing fresh water; water-fringe vegetation; fen/transition mire/spring)
Land-use Nature conservation/research (100%)

■ Birds

Species	Season	Year	Pop min	Pop max	Acc	Criteria
Botaurus stellaris Bittern	R	1995	4	4	A	C6

The IBA is important for breeding reedbed species and wintering wildfowl. It is also nationally important for breeding *Anas clypeata* (12 pairs, 1994, 1%), *Aythya ferina* (14 pairs, 1994, 3%), *Rallus aquaticus* (40 pairs, 1994, 6%) and *Panurus biarmicus* (40 pairs, 1994, 10%); and for wintering *Anas clypeata* (140 birds, 1%).

■ Protection status
National High **International** High
IBA partly or wholly overlaps with the following national designated areas. *Reserve:* Leighton Moss and Morecambe Bay. *Sites of Special Scientific Interest:* Cringlebarrow and Deepdale, Hawes Water, Leighton Moss, Morecambe Bay, Thrang End and Yealand Hall Allotment, Trowbarrow Quarry, Warton Crag. Overlaps with international designated areas: 128 ha of IBA covered by Special Protection Area (Leighton Moss, 128 ha). 128 ha of IBA covered by Ramsar Site (Leighton Moss, 128 ha).

■ Conservation issues

Threats Agricultural intensification/expansion (A)

Nutrient enrichment from agricultural run-off is a major threat, and may influence water quality at the RSPB-owned reserve. A management plan exists for the site.

Lindisfarne   A4i, A4iii, B1i, B2, C2, C3, C4, C6   037
Admin region North
Coordinates 55°40'N 1°50'W
Altitude 0–20 m   **Area** 3,679 ha

■ Site description
A stretch of coastline running from near Berwick-upon-Tweed south to Budle Bay, including Holy Island and the extensive intertidal flats of Holy Island Sands and Budle Bay. The rocky shores support a rich algal flora, and areas of saltmarsh and sand-dune are also present.

Habitats Wetland (mudflat/sandflat; saltmarsh; sand-dunes/sand beach; shingle/stony beach), Rocky areas (sea cliff/rocky shore)
Land-use Fisheries/aquaculture, Nature conservation/research (80%), Tourism/recreation

■ Birds

Species	Season	Year	Pop min	Pop max	Acc	Criteria
Cygnus cygnus Whooper Swan	W	1995	67	67	A	C6
Anser anser Greylag Goose	W	1995	1,700	1,700	A	B1i, C3
Branta bernicla Brent Goose	W	1995	2,115	2,115	A	B1i, C3
Pluvialis apricaria Golden Plover	W	1995	3,180	3,180	A	C6
Calidris alpina Dunlin	W	1995	6,950	6,950	A	B2
Limosa lapponica Bar-tailed Godwit	W	1995	3,710	3,710	A	A4i, B1i, B2, C2, C6
Limosa lapponica Bar-tailed Godwit	P	1995	2,900	2,900	A	A4i, B1i, C2, C6
Sterna albifrons Little Tern	B	1995	38	38	A	C6

This area supports breeding terns and attracts large numbers of wintering wildfowl, including the majority of the Spitzbergen breeding population of *Branta bernicla hrota*. The site regularly holds 41,500 wintering waterbirds, and is nationally important for wintering *Phalacrocorax carbo* (315 birds, 2%), *Tadorna tadorna* (1,010 birds, 1%), *Anas penelope* (8,150 birds, 3%), *Somateria mollissima* (2,130 birds, 3%), *Melanitta nigra* (710 birds, 2%) and *Pluvialis squatarola* (1,450 birds, 3%). The area is also important for passage *Charadrius hiaticula* (400 birds, 1%), *Pluvialis squatarola* (1,510 birds, 3%), *Calidris alba* (365 birds, 2%) and *Tringa totanus* (1,320 birds, 1%); and for summer moulting assemblages of *Somateria mollissima* (1,130 birds, 1%). *Anser anser* are from the Icelandic breeding population.

■ Protection status
National High   **International** High
IBA partly or wholly overlaps with the following national designated areas. *National Nature Reserve:* Lindisfarne. *Sites of Special Scientific Interest:* Bamburgh Coast and Hills, Lindisfarne, Spindlestone Heughs. Overlaps with international designated areas: 3,679 ha of IBA covered by Special Protection Area (Lindisfarne, 3,679 ha). 3,679 ha of IBA covered by Ramsar Site (Lindisfarne, 3,679 ha).

■ Conservation issues

Threats Aquaculture/fisheries (B), Consequences of animal/plant introductions (B), Disturbance to birds (A), Industrialization/urbanization (U), Natural events (B), Recreation/tourism (A)

Threats include cord-grass *Spartina* encroachment and eel-grass *Zostera* decline, housing and leisure developments, intense visitor pressure, and disturbance from shooting, wind-surfing and microlights. Changes in sea-level may lead to erosion and flooding, requiring coastal defence improvements. A management plan for Holy Island and a Recreation Strategy are being drafted. English Nature has undertaken research on wildfowling, and put forward a proposal for trial sanctuary areas.

Lower Derwent valley   A4iii, B1i, B2,   038
Admin region Yorkshire and Humberside   C3, C4, C6
Coordinates 53°53'N 0°55'W
Altitude 6–8 m   **Area** 915 ha

■ Site description
A mosaic of neutral alluvial flood-meadows, fens, swamps, *Alnus* carr and freshwater habitats lying adjacent to the River Derwent,

Pocklington Canal and Thornton Beck. The unimproved flood-meadows are amongst the most important in Europe.

Habitats Forest and woodland (broadleaved deciduous forest; alluvial/very wet forest), Grassland, Wetland (standing fresh water; river/stream; blanket bog; water-fringe vegetation; fen/transition mire/spring)
Land-use Agriculture, Nature conservation/research, Water management

■ Birds

Species	Season	Year	Pop min	Pop max	Acc	Criteria
Cygnus columbianus Bewick's Swan	W	1995	45	45	A	C6
Cygnus cygnus Whooper Swan	W	1995	52	52	A	C6
[1] *Anas strepera* Gadwall	R	1995	33	33	A	B2
Anas crecca Teal	W	1995	5,800	5,800	A	B1i, C3
Porzana porzana Spotted Crake	B	1995	6	6	A	C6
Pluvialis apricaria Golden Plover	W	1995	5,050	5,050	A	C6
Philomachus pugnax Ruff	R	1995	6	6	A	C6
Philomachus pugnax Ruff	W	1995	115	115	A	C6

1. Mean count.

This site supports a variety of breeding wetland birds and attracts large numbers of wildfowl in winter. It regularly holds 38,100 wintering waterbirds, and is nationally important for breeding *Podiceps nigricollis* (6 pairs, 13%), *Anas penelope* (9 pairs, 3%), *Anas crecca* (40 pairs, 3%), *Anas acuta* (4 pairs, 10%), *Anas querquedula* (7 pairs, 6%), *Anas clypeata* (90 pairs, 9%), *Aythya ferina* (13 pairs, 3%), *Rallus aquaticus* (12 pairs, 2%) and *Larus ridibundus* (1,940 pairs, 1%). The site is also nationally important for wintering *Anas penelope* (9,750 birds, 3%), *Anas clypeata* (105 birds, 1%) and *Aythya ferina* (1,660 birds, 2%). Breeding species of global conservation concern that do not meet IBA criteria: *Crex crex*.

■ Protection status
National High   **International** High
IBA partly or wholly overlaps with the following national designated areas. *National Nature Reserve:* Derwent Ings. *Reserve:* Wheldrake Ings. *Sites of Special Scientific Interest:* Breighton Meadows, Derwent Ings, Melbourne and Thornton Ings, Newton Mask, Pocklington Canal, River Derwent, Wheldrake Ings. Overlaps with international designated areas: 915 ha of IBA covered by Special Protection Area (Lower Derwent Valley, 915 ha). 915 ha of IBA covered by Ramsar Site (Lower Derwent Valley, 915 ha).

■ Conservation issues

Threats Agricultural intensification/expansion (U), Drainage (C), Extraction industry (B), Groundwater abstraction (A)

Coal extraction may result in surface subsidence, with hydrological implications for the site. An English Nature management plan exists for the National Nature Reserve.

Martin°Mere   A4i, A4iii, B1i, B2, B3,   039
Admin region North West   C2, C3, C4, C6
Coordinates 53°37'N 2°52'W
Altitude 3–3 m   **Area** 120 ha

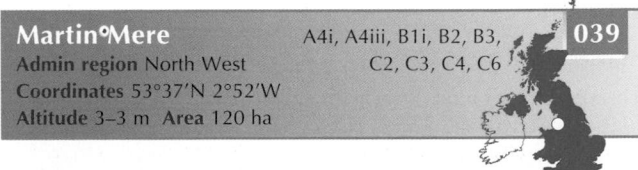

■ Site description
The IBA comprises a low-lying wetland complex.

Habitats Grassland (humid grassland), Wetland (standing fresh water)
Land-use Nature conservation/research (100%)

■ Birds

Species	Season	Year	Pop min	Pop max	Acc	Criteria
Cygnus columbianus Bewick's Swan	W	1995	600	600	A	A4i, B1i, B2, C2, C6
Cygnus cygnus Whooper Swan	W	1995	595	595	A	B1i, B3, C2, C6
Anser brachyrhynchus Pink-footed Goose	W	1995	5,600	5,600	A	A4i, B1i, C3
Anas acuta Pintail	W	1995	1,010	1,010	A	B1i, C3
Philomachus pugnax Ruff	W	1995	34	34	A	C6

The IBA holds internationally important numbers of wintering wildfowl, supporting 24,300 wintering waterbirds on a regular basis. It is also nationally important for wintering *Anas penelope* (7,650 birds, 3%) and *Anas crecca* (2,860 birds, 2%).

■ **Protection status**

National High **International** High

IBA partly or wholly overlaps with the following national designated areas. *Reserve:* Martin Mere Wildfowl Trust. *Sites of Special Scientific Interest:* Martin Mere, Burscough. Overlaps with international designated areas: 119 ha of IBA covered by Special Protection Area (Martin Mere, 119 ha). 119 ha of IBA covered by Ramsar Site (Martin Mere, 119 ha).

■ **Conservation issues**

Threats Disturbance to birds (C), Other (U)

The IBA is threatened by intensive shooting close to the reserve, and is at particular risk from acid deposition ('Other' threat, above). There is a management plan for the site.

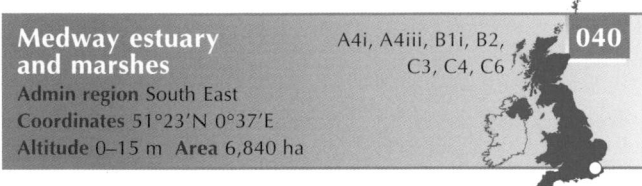

Medway estuary and marshes   A4i, A4iii, B1i, B2, C3, C4, C6   **040**
Admin region South East
Coordinates 51°23′N 0°37′E
Altitude 0–15 m **Area** 6,840 ha

■ **Site description**

The Medway estuary forms a single tidal system with the Swale and joins the Thames estuary between the Isle of Grain and Sheerness. It has a complex arrangement of tidal channels, which drain around large islands of saltmarsh and grazing-marsh. The mudflats support extensive beds of algae and eel-grass *Zostera*.

Habitats Grassland (humid grassland), Wetland (tidal river/enclosed tidal water; mudflat/sandflat; saltmarsh; shingle/stony beach; river/stream; water-fringe vegetation), Artificial landscape (arable land)
Land-use Agriculture, Fisheries/aquaculture, Tourism/recreation, Urban/industrial/transport

■ **Birds**

Species		Season	Year	Pop min	Pop max	Acc	Criteria
Branta bernicla	Brent Goose	W	1995	4,420	4,420	A	A4i, B1i, C3
Tadorna tadorna	Shelduck	W	1995	5,900	5,900	A	A4i, B1i, C3
Anas acuta	Pintail	W	1995	695	695	A	B1i, C3
Recurvirostra avosetta	Avocet	R	1992	34	34	A	C6
Recurvirostra avosetta	Avocet	W	1995	170	170	A	C6
Recurvirostra avosetta	Avocet	P	1995	310	310	A	C6
Charadrius hiaticula	Ringed Plover	W	1995	730	730	A	B1i, C3
Charadrius hiaticula	Ringed Plover	P	1995	1,160	1,160	A	B1i, C3
Pluvialis squatarola	Grey Plover	W	1995	3,690	3,690	A	A4i, B1i, C3
Pluvialis squatarola	Grey Plover	P	1995	3,430	3,430	A	A4i, B1i, C3
Calidris alpina	Dunlin	W	1995	27,700	27,700	A	A4i, B1i, B2, C3
Calidris alpina	Dunlin	P	1995	16,600	16,600	A	B1i, C3
Limosa limosa	Black-tailed Godwit	P	1995	1,310	1,310	A	B1i, C3
Numenius arquata	Curlew	W	1995	1,960	1,960	A	B2
Tringa totanus	Redshank	W	1995	3,630	3,630	A	A4i, B1i, C3
Tringa totanus	Redshank	P	1995	5,800	5,800	A	A4i, B1i, C3
Arenaria interpres	Turnstone	P	1995	1,140	1,140	A	A4i, B1i, C3

The IBA is important for wintering and passage wildfowl, holding 69,200 wintering and 35,200 passage waterbirds on a regular basis. Terns and gulls breed on saltmarsh islands, and wildfowl breed on the grazing-marshes. The site is also nationally important for wintering *Tachybaptus ruficollis* (52 birds, 1%), *Podiceps cristatus* (120 birds, 1%), *Phalacrocorax carbo* (420 birds, 3%), *Anas penelope* (4,920 birds, 2%), *Anas crecca* (2,020 birds, 1%), *Anas clypeata* (115 birds, 1%), *Limosa limosa* (695 birds, 9%), *Tringa erythropus* (18 birds, 4%) and *Tringa nebularia* (9 birds, 2%). *Branta bernicla* are the *bernicla* subspecies.

■ **Protection status**

National Partial **International** Partial

IBA partly or wholly overlaps with the following national designated areas. *National Nature Reserve:* Chetney. *Reserve:* Nor Marsh and Motney Hill. *Sites of Special Scientific Interest:* Medway Estuary and Marshes, South Thames Estuary and Marshes. Overlaps with international designated areas: 4,683 ha of IBA covered by Special Protection Area (Medway Estuary and Marshes, 4,683 ha). 4,683 ha of IBA covered by Ramsar Site (Medway Estuary and Marshes, 4,683 ha).

■ **Conservation issues**

Threats Agricultural intensification/expansion (B), Aquaculture/fisheries (U), Dredging/canalization (A), Extraction industry (C), Filling-in of wetlands (C), Groundwater abstraction (U), Industrialization/urbanization (A), Infrastructure (A), Natural events (U), Recreation/tourism (A)

Threats include road, powerline, industrial, wharf, marina and recreational developments, sea-level rise and associated coastal defence work, erosion of saltmarsh, and land-based dredging disposal. An estuary management plan is in preparation for the Medway and Swale. English Nature, the Ministry of Agriculture, Fisheries and Food, and the Medway Ports Authority are carrying out trials designed to retain dredging material within the estuary.

Mersey estuary   A4i, A4iii, B1i, B2, C3, C4, C6   **041**
Admin region North West
Coordinates 53°18′N 2°50′W
Altitude 0–12 m **Area** 7,274 ha

■ **Site description**

Extensive intertidal areas in the Mersey estuary, including large areas of mudflats and saltmarshes.

Habitats Wetland (tidal river/enclosed tidal water; mudflat/sandflat; saltmarsh; standing fresh water; river/stream; water-fringe vegetation), Rocky areas (sea cliff/rocky shore)
Land-use Nature conservation/research, Urban/industrial/transport

■ **Birds**

Species		Season	Year	Pop min	Pop max	Acc	Criteria
Tadorna tadorna	Shelduck	W	1995	5,300	5,300	A	A4i, B1i, C3
Anas crecca	Teal	W	1995	12,400	12,400	A	B1i, C3
Anas acuta	Pintail	W	1995	3,210	3,210	A	B1i, C3
Pluvialis apricaria	Golden Plover	W	1995	2,650	2,650	A	C6
Calidris alpina	Dunlin	W	1995	46,600	46,600	A	A4i, B1i, B2, C3
Numenius arquata	Curlew	W	1995	1,230	1,230	A	B2
Tringa totanus	Redshank	W	1995	4,610	4,610	A	A4i, B1i, C3
Tringa totanus	Redshank	P	1995	4,350	4,350	A	A4i, B1i, C3

The estuary is of international importance for wintering wildfowl and waders. It regularly holds 102,900 wintering waterbirds, and is also nationally important for wintering *Podiceps cristatus* (130 birds, 1%), *Phalacrocorax carbo* (360 birds, 2%), *Anas penelope* (10,800 birds, 4%), *Pluvialis squatarola* (1,450 birds, 3%) and *Limosa limosa* (250 birds, 3%).

■ **Protection status**

National Partial **International** Partial

IBA partly or wholly overlaps with the following national designated areas. *Reserve:* Seaforth NR. *Sites of Special Scientific Interest:* Altcar Sand-dunes and Foreshore, Mersey Estuary, North Wirral Foreshore. Overlaps with international designated areas: 5,033 ha covered by Special Protection Area (Mersey Estuary, 5,033 ha). 5,033 ha covered by Ramsar Site (Mersey Estuary, 5,033 ha).

■ **Conservation issues**

Threats Construction/impact of dyke/dam/barrage (U), Extraction industry (B), Filling-in of wetlands (B), Industrialization/urbanization (B), Infrastructure (B), Natural events (B), Recreation/tourism (C)

Threats include the development of an airport, hotels, a river crossing, pipelines, a power station and the proposed Mersey barrage, and sea-level rise that may result in flooding, erosion and improvements to coastal defences. The RSPB leases parts of the estuary for management as reserves. A management plan exists for the area.

Mid-Essex coast   A4i, A4iii, B1i, B2, C2, C3, C4, C6   **042**
Admin region South East
Coordinates 51°47′N 1°00′E
Altitude 0–6 m **Area** 22,817 ha

■ **Site description**

A large complex of estuaries and sand-silt flats, including the

Blackwater, Crouch, Colne and Dengie Estuaries. Foulness and Maplin Sands is one of the three largest continuous sand-silt flats in Britain. This area includes three sites that were treated as separate IBAs in the previous international IBA inventory (Grimmett and Jones 1989): 'Blackwater, Colne and Dengie' (former site GB176), 'River Crouch marshes' (former site GB177) and 'Foulness and Maplin Sands' (former site GB178).

> **Habitats** Grassland, Wetland (tidal river/enclosed tidal water; mudflat/sandflat; saltmarsh; sand-dunes/sand beach; shingle/stony beach; river/stream; water-fringe vegetation)
> **Land-use** Agriculture, Fisheries/aquaculture, Military, Nature conservation/research

■ Birds

Species	Season	Year	Pop min	Pop max	Acc	Criteria
Branta bernicla Brent Goose	W	1995	29,600	29,600	A	A4i, B1i, C3
Tadorna tadorna Shelduck	W	1995	5,700	5,700	A	A4i, B1i, C3
Anas crecca Teal	W	1995	4,150	4,150	A	B1i, C3
Haematopus ostralegus Oystercatcher	W	1995	15,800	15,800	A	A4i, B1i, C3
Haematopus ostralegus Oystercatcher	P	1995	11,100	11,100	A	A4i, B1i, C3
Recurvirostra avosetta Avocet	W	1995	120	120	A	C6
Charadrius hiaticula Ringed Plover	W	1995	835	835	A	B1i, C3
Charadrius hiaticula Ringed Plover	P	1995	1,700	1,700	A	B1i, C3
Pluvialis apricaria Golden Plover	W	1995	12,500	12,500	A	B1i, C2, C6
Pluvialis squatarola Grey Plover	W	1995	8,700	8,700	A	A4i, B1i, C3
Pluvialis squatarola Grey Plover	P	1995	6,500	6,500	A	A4i, B1i, C3
Calidris canutus Knot	W	1995	37,600	37,600	A	A4i, B1i, B2, C3
Calidris canutus Knot	P	1995	7,450	7,450	A	B1i, C3
Calidris alpina Dunlin	W	1995	48,300	48,300	A	A4i, B1i, B2, C3
Calidris alpina Dunlin	P	1995	30,800	30,800	A	A4i, B1i, C3
Philomachus pugnax Ruff	W	1995	50	50	A	C6
Limosa limosa Black-tailed Godwit	W	1995	1,130	1,130	A	B1i, C3
Limosa limosa Black-tailed Godwit	P	1995	1,090	1,090	A	B1i, C3
Limosa lapponica Bar-tailed Godwit	W	1995	7,550	7,550	A	A4i, B1i, B2, C2, C6
Limosa lapponica Bar-tailed Godwit	P	1995	3,380	3,380	A	A4i, B1i, C2, C6
Numenius arquata Curlew	W	1995	5,500	5,500	A	A4i, B1i, B2, C3
Numenius arquata Curlew	P	1995	6,550	6,550	A	A4i, B1i, C3
Tringa totanus Redshank	R	1993	895	895	A	B1i, B2, C3
Tringa totanus Redshank	W	1995	5,650	5,650	A	A4i, B1i, C3
Tringa totanus Redshank	P	1995	5,450	5,450	A	A4i, B1i, C3
Arenaria interpres Turnstone	W	1995	1,030	1,030	A	A4i, B1i, C3
Arenaria interpres Turnstone	P	1995	900	900	A	A4i, B1i, C3
Sterna sandvicensis Sandwich Tern	B	1995	330	330	A	B2, C6
Sterna hirundo Common Tern	B	1995	125	—	A	C6
Sterna albifrons Little Tern	B	1995	58	58	A	B2, C6

The IBA is important for wintering and passage waders and wildfowl and for breeding terns. It regularly holds 230,400 wintering and 81,300 passage waterbirds, and is also nationally important for breeding *Panurus biarmicus* (19 pairs, 1992, 5%), for wintering *Tachybaptus ruficollis* (80 birds, 2%), *Podiceps cristatus* (370 birds, 3%), *Phalacrocorax carbo* (725 birds, 5%), *Anas penelope* (5,350 birds, 2%), *Anas strepera* (120 birds, 1%), *Anas acuta* (365 birds, 1%), *Anas clypeata* (205 birds, 2%), *Bucephala clangula* (545 birds, 2%), *Mergus serrator* (145 birds, 1%), *Vanellus vanellus* (34,200 birds, 2%), *Calidris alba* (315 birds, 1%), *Tringa erythropus* (4 birds, 1%), *Tringa nebularia* (8 birds, 1%) and *Tringa ochropus* (10 birds, 1%); and for passage *Calidris alba* (555 birds, 2%) and *Tringa nebularia* (205 birds, 37%). *Branta bernicla* are the *bernicla* subspecies.

■ Protection status
National High **International** High
IBA partly or wholly overlaps with the following national designated areas. *National Nature Reserves:* Blackwater Estuary, Colne Estuary, Dengie, Old Hall Marshes. *Reserves:* Blue House Farm, Bradwell Shell Bank, Colne Point, Fingringhoe Wick, Lion Creek, Northey Island, Old Hall Marshes, Ray Island, Tollesbury Wick Marshes. *Sites of Special Scientific Interest:* Blackwater Estuary, Burnham-on-Crouch, Colne Estuary, Crouch and Roach Estuaries, Dengie, Foulness, The Cliff. Overlaps with international designated areas: 22,817 ha of IBA covered by Special Protection Area (Mid-Essex Coast, 22,817 ha). 22,817 ha of IBA covered by Ramsar Site (Mid-Essex Coast, 22,817 ha).

■ Conservation issues

> **Threats** Agricultural intensification/expansion (B), Aquaculture/fisheries (C), Disturbance to birds (B), Industrialization/urbanization (B), Infrastructure (C), Natural events (A), Recreation/tourism (B)

Threats include disturbance caused by recreational and air activities, the development of a wharf, sea defences, homes and shops, carparks, marinas, holiday parks and an airport, and saltmarsh loss caused by sea-level rise. A management plan exists for the Blackwater estuary (Maldon and Colchester Districts), where experiments on managed retreat are being carried out. A harbour management plan also exists for the Crouch estuary (Crouch Harbour Authority). Part of the area has been put forward as a candidate SAC.

Minsmere–Walberswick
B3, C6 **043**
Admin region East Anglia
Coordinates 52°18′N 1°36′E
Altitude 0–21 m **Area** 2,190 ha

■ Site description
The IBA covers a complex of habitats, including one of the largest intact reedbeds (*Phragmites*) in the UK. The site also includes the tidal Blyth estuary, and areas of brackish lagoon, lowland heathland and woodland.

> **Habitats** Forest and woodland (native coniferous forest; mixed forest), Scrub (scrub; heathland), Grassland, Wetland (tidal river/enclosed tidal water; saltmarsh; sand-dunes/sand beach; shingle/stony beach; standing fresh water; standing brackish and salt water; water-fringe vegetation)
> **Land-use** Nature conservation/research, Tourism/recreation

■ Birds

Species	Season	Year	Pop min	Pop max	Acc	Criteria
Botaurus stellaris Bittern	R	1995	8	8	A	C6
Circus aeruginosus Marsh Harrier	R	1994	7	—	A	C6
Recurvirostra avosetta Avocet	R	1994	105	—	A	B3, C6
Recurvirostra avosetta Avocet	W	1995	195	195	A	C6
Sterna albifrons Little Tern	B	1994	28	—	A	C6
Caprimulgus europaeus Nightjar	B	1994	24	—	A	C6
Lullula arborea Woodlark	B	1994	19	—	A	C6

The IBA supports a rich diversity of breeding, wintering and passage species, and is noted for breeding *Recurvirostra avosetta*. It is also nationally important for breeding *Anas strepera* (14 pairs, 1994, 2%), *Aythya ferina* (5 pairs, 1994, 1%), *Rallus aquaticus* (20 pairs, 1994, 3%) and *Panurus biarmicus* (35 pairs, 1992, 9%), for wintering *Anas strepera* (90 birds, 1%) and *Limosa limosa* (335 birds, 4%), and for passage *Limosa limosa* (285 birds, 4%).

■ Protection status
National High **International** High
IBA partly or wholly overlaps with the following national designated areas. *National Nature Reserves:* Walberswick, Westleton Heath. *Reserve:* Minsmere. *Sites of Special Scientific Interest:* Minsmere–Walberswick Heaths and Marshes. Overlaps with international designated areas: 2,004 ha of IBA covered by Special Protection Area (Minsmere–Walberswick, 2,004 ha). 2,004 ha of IBA covered by Ramsar Site (Minsmere–Walberswick, 2,004 ha).

■ Conservation issues

> **Threats** Industrialization/urbanization (C), Infrastructure (B), Natural events (A), Recreation/tourism (C)

Threats include sea-level rise that may result in erosion and flooding, saline intrusion, coastal erosion caused by the construction of the Sizewell C nuclear power-station, habitat loss caused by coastal defence development, and disturbance to tern colonies. Management plans exist for Walberswick National Nature Reserve and Minsmere RSPB Reserve. Intensive *Botaurus stellaris* monitoring is carried out, and heathland re-creation is underway at Minsmere in an area adjacent to the IBA.

Morecambe Bay
A4i, A4iii, B1i, B2, B3, **044**
Admin region North, North West   C2, C3, C4, C6
Coordinates 54°07′N 2°58′W
Altitude 0–30 m **Area** 41,970 ha

■ Site description
The IBA covers Morecambe Bay and the Lune estuary, with the Leven,

Kent, Keer, Lune and Wyre river channels draining through intertidal flats of sand and silt. The whole system is dynamic, with shifting channels formed by the cycle of erosion and accretion. The site also includes important saltmarshes.

Habitats Wetland (100%; tidal river/enclosed tidal water; mudflat/sandflat; saltmarsh; sand-dunes/sand beach; shingle/stony beach; standing fresh water; standing brackish and salt water; water-fringe vegetation)

Land-use Agriculture, Fisheries/aquaculture, Hunting, Nature conservation/research, Tourism/recreation

■ Birds

Species	Season	Year	Pop min	Pop max	Acc	Criteria
Tadorna tadorna Shelduck	W	1995	5,800	5,800	A	A4i, B1i, C3
Anas acuta Pintail	W	1995	2,930	2,930	A	B1i, C3
Haematopus ostralegus Oystercatcher	W	1995	52,000	52,000	A	A4i, B1i, C3
Haematopus ostralegus Oystercatcher	P	1995	61,000	61,000	A	A4i, B1i, C3
Charadrius hiaticula Ringed Plover	P	1995	1,720	1,720	A	B1i, C3
Pluvialis apricaria Golden Plover	W	1995	3,700	3,700	A	C6
Pluvialis squatarola Grey Plover	W	1995	1,820	1,820	A	A4i, B1i, C3
Pluvialis squatarola Grey Plover	P	1995	1,780	1,780	A	A4i, B1i, C3
Calidris canutus Knot	W	1995	29,600	29,600	A	A4i, B1i, B2, C3
Calidris canutus Knot	P	1995	12,400	12,400	A	A4i, B1i, C3
Calidris alba Sanderling	P	1995	1,970	1,970	A	A4i, B1i, C3
Calidris alpina Dunlin	W	1995	60,500	60,500	A	A4i, B1i, B2, C3
Calidris alpina Dunlin	P	1995	26,800	26,800	A	A4i, B1i, C3
Limosa lapponica Bar-tailed Godwit	W	1995	2,490	2,490	A	A4i, B1i, B2, C2, C6
Limosa lapponica Bar-tailed Godwit	P	1995	840	840	A	C6
Numenius arquata Curlew	W	1995	13,500	13,500	A	A4i, B1i, B2, C3
Numenius arquata Curlew	P	1995	17,400	17,400	A	A4i, B1i, C3
Tringa totanus Redshank	W	1995	6,600	6,600	A	A4i, B1i, C3
Tringa totanus Redshank	P	1995	8,300	8,300	A	A4i, B1i, C3
Arenaria interpres Turnstone	W	1995	1,750	1,750	A	A4i, B1i, C3
Arenaria interpres Turnstone	P	1995	1,950	1,950	A	A4i, B1i, C3
Larus fuscus Lesser Black-backed Gull	B	1991	17,000	—	A	A4i, B1i, B3, C3
Larus argentatus Herring Gull	B	1990	11,000	—	A	A4i, B1i
Sterna sandvicensis Sandwich Tern	B	1994	380	380	A	B2, C6

This area is of outstanding importance for wintering and passage wildfowl and waders, and for breeding wildfowl, gulls and terns. It holds 28,600 pairs of breeding waterbirds, and 222,800 wintering and 149,100 passage waterbirds on a regular basis. The site is also nationally important for breeding *Somateria mollissima* (950 pairs, 1992, 3%), for wintering *Podiceps cristatus* (265 birds, 2%), *Phalacrocorax carbo* (905 birds, 6%), *Anser brachyrhynchus* (2,040 birds, 1%), *Anas penelope* (6,150 birds, 2%), *Anas crecca* (2,020 birds, 1%), *Somateria mollissima* (7,450 birds, 10%), *Bucephala clangula* (355 birds, 1%), *Mergus serrator* (285 birds, 3%), *Charadrius hiaticula* (470 birds, 2%), *Vanellus vanellus* (16,600 birds, 1%), *Calidris alba* (270 birds, 1%), *Limosa limosa* (120 birds, 2%) and *Tringa nebularia* (8 birds, 1%), for passage *Limosa limosa* (305 birds, 4%), and for summer moulting assemblages of *Somateria mollissima* (5,250 birds, 7%).

■ Protection status
National Partial **International** Partial
IBA partly or wholly overlaps with the following national designated areas. *Reserves:* Foulney Island, Leighton Moss and Morecambe Bay. *Sites of Special Scientific Interest:* Arnside Knott, Barker Scar, Barnaby Sands Marsh, Burrows Marsh, Cockerham Marsh, Far Arnside, Humphrey Head, Iron Pit Spring Quarry, Jack Scout, Leighton Moss, Lune Estuary, Meathop Woods and Quarry, Morecambe Bay, Roudsea Wood and Mosses, Sea Wood, Skelwith Hill, South Walney and Piel Channel Flats, Wyre Estuary. Overlaps with international designated areas: 35,863 ha of IBA covered by Special Protection Area (Morecambe Bay, 35,863 ha). 35,863 ha of IBA covered by Ramsar Site (Morecambe Bay, 35,863 ha).

■ Conservation issues

Threats Construction/impact of dyke/dam/barrage (U), Extraction industry (U), Industrialization/urbanization (B), Infrastructure (B), Natural events (B), Recreation/tourism (B)

Threats include the proposed Morecambe Bay Barrage, the Lancaster Western bypass, mobile home developments, recreational pressure, and sea-level rise, which may result in erosion and flooding. The Morecambe Bay Strategy is in place, and the Wyre estuary is a candidate SPA. The RSPB manages 2,587 ha of Morecambe Bay, and owns about 1,514 ha.

Nene Washes   A4i, A4iii, B1i, B2, C2, C3, C4, C6   045
Admin region East Anglia
Coordinates 52°33′N 0°13′W
Altitude 2–3 m **Area** 1,310 ha

■ Site description
The cycle of winter storage of flood-waters and traditional summer cattle-grazing at this site has given rise to a mosaic of rough grassland and wet pasture, with a diverse ditch flora.

Habitats Grassland (humid grassland), Wetland (tidal river/enclosed tidal water; standing fresh water; water-fringe vegetation)

Land-use Agriculture, Hunting, Nature conservation/research

■ Birds

Species	Season	Year	Pop min	Pop max	Acc	Criteria
Cygnus columbianus Bewick's Swan	W	1995	1,640	1,640	A	A4i, B1i, B2, C2, C6
Anas acuta Pintail	W	1995	1,210	1,210	A	B1i, C3
Porzana porzana Spotted Crake	B	1995	2	2	A	C6
Philomachus pugnax Ruff	W	1995	95	95	A	C6

The IBA supports a variety of breeding ducks and waders, and is important for wintering wildfowl. It holds 22,600 wintering waterbirds on a regular basis, and is also nationally important for breeding *Anas penelope* (3 pairs, 1995, 1%), *Anas strepera* (24 pairs, 1995, 3%), *Anas querquedula* (2 pairs, 1995, 2%), *Anas clypeata* (41 pairs, 1995, 4%) and *Limosa limosa* (14 pairs, 1995, 26%), and for wintering *Anas penelope* (6,400 birds, 2%), *Anas strepera* (175 birds, 2%), *Anas crecca* (1,930 birds, 1%), *Anas clypeata* (270 birds, 3%), *Aythya ferina* (1,040 birds, 1%) and *Limosa limosa* (290 birds, 4%).

■ Protection status
National High **International** High
IBA partly or wholly overlaps with the following national designated areas. *Reserve:* Nene Washes. *Sites of Special Scientific Interest:* Adventurers' Land, Nene Washes (Whittlesey). Overlaps with international designated areas: 1,310 ha of IBA covered by Special Protection Area (Nene Washes, 1,310 ha). 1,310 ha of IBA covered by Ramsar Site (Nene Washes, 1,310 ha).

■ Conservation issues

Threats Agricultural intensification/expansion (A), Disturbance to birds (A), Infrastructure (C), Industrialization/urbanization (C), Natural events (B), Recreation/tourism (C)

Threats include a proposed relief road within 500 m of the north-east end of the site, residential development, spring flooding, and wildfowling, which causes disturbance to feeding and roosting birds. A RSPB management plan exists for part of the site.

The New Forest   B2, C6   046
Admin region South East
Coordinates 50°52′N 1°34′W
Altitude 2–127 m **Area** 41,410 ha

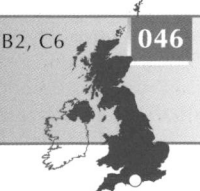

■ Site description
A large expanse of enclosed woodland, both ancient and more recent, with open areas of heathland, and broken by numerous valleys and mires. The forest supports a rich lichen, fern, moss and liverwort flora.

Habitats Forest and woodland (broadleaved deciduous forest; mixed forest), Scrub (scrub; heathland), Grassland (humid grassland), Wetland (river/stream; fen/transition mire/spring), Artificial landscape (forestry plantation)

Land-use Agriculture, Forestry, Tourism/recreation

■ Birds

Species	Season	Year	Pop min	Pop max	Acc	Criteria
Pernis apivorus Honey Buzzard	B	1996	2	2	A	C6
Circus cyaneus Hen Harrier	W	1992	15	15	A	C6
Caprimulgus europaeus Nightjar	B	1992	325	325	A	B2, C6
Lullula arborea Woodlark	R	1994	58	58	A	C6
Saxicola torquata Stonechat	R	1992	430	—	A	B2
Sylvia undata Dartford Warbler	R	1994	540	540	A	C6

The IBA is also nationally important for breeding *Falco subbuteo* (25 pairs, 1992, 5%) and *Phylloscopus sibilatrix* (350 pairs, 1992, 2%).

■ Protection status
National Partial **International** Partial
IBA partly or wholly overlaps with the following national designated areas. *Sites of Special Scientific Interest:* Fletchwood Meadows, Landford Bog, Landford Heath, Langley Wood and Homan's Copse, Loosehanger Copse and Meadows, Norley Copse and Meadow, North Solent, Poors Common, Roydon Woods, Sowley Pond, The New Forest, Whiteparish Common. Overlaps with international designated areas: 28,002 ha of IBA covered by Special Protection Area (New Forest, 28,002 ha). 28,002 ha of IBA covered by Ramsar Site (New Forest, 28,002 ha).

■ Conservation issues

Threats Infrastructure (U), Other (U), Recreation/Tourism (U)

'Other' threats are posed by acid deposition and commercial mushroom picking. Road development (associated with port expansion, for example) and considerable recreational disturbance are additional threats. Areas of privately-owned land surround a large central core of Crown Land. NGOs are pressing for improved management of the forest, with clear objectives and a proper management plan. The New Forest Committee coordinates the work of the statutory bodies. Research on birds and other taxa has been undertaken, and the area is a candidate SAC.

North Norfolk coast — 047
A4i, A4iii, B1i, B2, B3, C2, C3, C4, C6
Admin region East Anglia
Coordinates 52°58'N 0°49'E
Altitude 0–5 m **Area** 7,700 ha

■ Site description
This site extends for over 40 km from Hunstanton in the west to Salthouse in the east, and includes extensive intertidal sand and mudflats, and some of Europe's best saltmarshes. A diverse saltmarsh flora, extensive reedbeds (*Phragmites*) and dune systems are present alongside grazing-marshes that hold a rich diversity of aquatic plant species. The site is also of great geomorphological interest.

Habitats Forest and woodland (mixed forest), Scrub (scrub), Wetland (mudflat/sandflat; saltmarsh; sand-dunes/sand beach; shingle/stony beach; coastal lagoon; standing fresh water; standing brackish and salt water; water-fringe vegetation)
Land-use Agriculture, Fisheries/aquaculture, Nature conservation/research, Tourism/recreation

■ Birds

Species		Season	Year	Pop min	Pop max	Acc	Criteria
Botaurus stellaris	Bittern	R	1995	5	5	A	C6
Anser brachyrhynchus Pink-footed Goose		W	1995	15,800	15,800	A	A4i, B1i, C3
Branta bernicla	Brent Goose	W	1995	12,100	12,100	A	A4i, B1i, C3
Anas penelope	Wigeon	W	1995	13,800	13,800	A	B1i, C3
Anas acuta	Pintail	W	1995	1,280	1,280	A	B1i, C3
Circus aeruginosus	Marsh Harrier	R	1990	8	8	A	C6
Recurvirostra avosetta	Avocet	R	1989	110	110	A	B3, C6
Recurvirostra avosetta	Avocet	W	1995	120	120	A	C6
Charadrius hiaticula	Ringed Plover	R	1993	280	280	A	B1i, C3
Charadrius hiaticula	Ringed Plover	P	1995	885	885	A	B1i, C3
Pluvialis apricaria	Golden Plover	W	1995	2,640	2,640	A	C6
Calidris canutus	Knot	W	1995	7,600	7,600	A	B1i, B2, C3
Philomachus pugnax	Ruff	W	1995	39	39	A	C6
Limosa lapponica	Bar-tailed Godwit	W	1995	1,280	1,280	A	A4i, B1i, B2, C2, C6
Limosa lapponica	Bar-tailed Godwit	P	1995	740	740	A	C6
Sterna sandvicensis	Sandwich Tern	B	1995	3,040	3,040	A	A4i, B1i, B2, C2, C6
Sterna hirundo	Common Tern	B	1993	155	155	A	C6
Sterna albifrons	Little Tern	B	1995	370	370	A	A4i, B1i, B2, C2, C6

The IBA is important for a variety of breeding species, wintering wildfowl and migrating waders. It regularly holds 79,500 wintering waterbirds, and is also nationally important for breeding *Haematopus ostralegus* (410 pairs, 1993, 1%), *Larus ridibundus* (4,100 pairs, 1992, 2%) and *Panurus biarmicus* (41 pairs, 1992, 10%), for wintering *Anser albifrons albifrons* (300 birds, 5%), *Tadorna tadorna* (960 birds, 1%),

Anas strepera (165 birds, 2%), *Anas crecca* (3,150 birds, 2%), *Anas clypeata* (170 birds, 2%), *Melanitta nigra* (1,900 birds, 5%), *Charadrius hiaticula* (360 birds, 1%), *Pluvialis squatarola* (1,200 birds, 3%) and *Calidris alba* (395 birds, 2%), and for passage *Pluvialis squatarola* (945 birds, 2%) and *Calidris alba* (535 birds, 2%). *Branta bernicla* are the *bernicla* subspecies.

■ Protection status
National High **International** High
IBA partly or wholly overlaps with the following national designated areas. *National Nature Reserves:* Blakeney Point, Holkham, Scolt Head. *Reserves:* Blakeney Point, Cley/Salthouse, Holme, Titchwell Marsh. *Sites of Special Scientific Interest:* Morston Cliff, North Norfolk Coast. Overlaps with international designated areas: 7,700 ha of IBA covered by Special Protection Area (North Norfolk Coast, 7,700 ha). 7,700 ha of IBA covered by Ramsar Site (North Norfolk Coast, 7,700 ha).

■ Conservation issues

Threats Extraction industry (C), Filling-in of wetlands (C), Natural events (A), Recreation/tourism (B)

Threats include proposals for marinas and golf courses, sea-level rise that may lead to erosion, flooding and habitat loss through sea defence development, and disturbance and trampling damage caused by visitors. English Nature, the RSPB, National Trust, Norfolk Wildlife Trust and Norfolk Ornithologists' Association manage much of the coast as a nature reserve. The Norfolk Coast Project visitor management strategy exists alongside a shoreline management plan and various nature reserve management plans. *Botaurus stellaris* monitoring is undertaken, and part of the area is a candidate SAC.

North Pennine moors — 048
B1i, B2, B3, C2, C3, C6
Admin region North
Coordinates 54°41'N 2°26'W
Altitude 170–893 m **Area** 136,547 ha

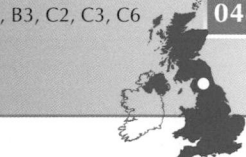

■ Site description
A series of upland moorland sites, straddling the Cumbrian, Durham, North Yorkshire and Northumberland borders. The heather *Calluna* and grass moorlands are predominantly managed for game interests. This area includes four sites that were treated as separate IBAs in the previous international IBA inventory (Grimmett and Jones 1989): 'Muggleswick, Stanhope and Wolsingham Commons' (former site GB147), 'Bollihope and Middleton Commons' (former site GB148), 'Upper Teesdale and Moor House' (former site GB149) and 'Bowes Moor' (former site GB150).

Habitats Forest and woodland (broadleaved deciduous forest; mixed forest), Scrub (scrub; heathland), Grassland, Wetland (standing fresh water; river/stream; blanket bog; fen/transition mire/spring)
Land-use Agriculture (90%), Forestry (3%), Military (5%), Nature conservation/research (2%)

■ Birds

Species		Season	Year	Pop min	Pop max	Acc	Criteria
Circus cyaneus	Hen Harrier	R	1994	5	—	A	C6
Falco columbarius	Merlin	R	1996	88	88	A	C6
Tetrao tetrix	Black Grouse	R	1994	115	115	A	B2
Pluvialis apricaria	Golden Plover	R	1992	2,250	2,250	A	B3, C2, C6
Calidris alpina	Dunlin	R	1992	80	—	A	B1i, C3

The IBA is important for breeding raptors, waders and other upland birds. It is also nationally important for breeding *Numenius arquata* (1,000 pairs, 1992, 3%).

■ Protection status
National Partial **International** Low
IBA partly or wholly overlaps with the following national designated areas. *National Nature Reserve:* Upper Teesdale. *Reserve:* Geltsdale. *Sites of Special Scientific Interest:* Appleby Fells, Bollihope, Pikestone, Eggleston and Woodland Fells, Bowlees and Friar House Meadows, Geltsdale and Glendue Fells, Helbeck Wood, Middle Crossthwaite, Middleton Quarry, Moor House and Cross Fell, Park End Wood,

Pus Gill, Swindale Wood, Teesdale Allotments, Upper Teesdale. Overlaps with international designated areas: 3,894 ha of IBA covered by Special Protection Area (Moor House, 3,894 ha).

■ **Conservation issues**

Threats Abandonment/reduction of land management (B), Agricultural intensification/ expansion (A), Extraction industry (U), Infrastructure (B), Other (A)

'Other' threats to the IBA are posed by raptor persecution and acid deposition, with wind-farm developments an additional threat. A management plan exists for the North Pennines Area of Outstanding Natural Beauty, and English Nature are designating an SPA in phases. Research is being carried out into *Tetrao tetrix* and waders.

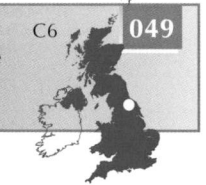

North Yorkshire moors   C6   **049**
Admin region North, Yorkshire and Humberside
Coordinates 54°19'N 1°15'W
Altitude 30–394 m **Area** 142,250 ha

■ **Site description**
The largest continuous tract of open heather *Calluna* moorland in England and Wales, with long fingers of moor and heath extending down to farmland or abutting woodland edges. Boggy flushes and valley mires are dominated by *Juncus*. The area is managed for game interests.

Habitats Forest and woodland (broadleaved deciduous forest; mixed forest), Scrub (scrub; heathland), Grassland (steppe/dry calcareous grassland; humid grassland; mesophile grassland), Wetland (river/stream; blanket bog; fen/transition mire/spring), Rocky areas (sea cliff/rocky shore), Artificial landscape (arable land; forestry plantation)
Land-use Agriculture (30%), Forestry (15%), Hunting (30%), Military (10%), Nature conservation/research (10%), Urban/industrial/transport (5%), Water management (5%)

■ **Birds**

Species	Season	Year	Pop min	Pop max	Acc	Criteria
Falco columbarius Merlin	R	1996	40	40	A	C6
Pluvialis apricaria Golden Plover	R	1996	615	615	A	C6
Caprimulgus europaeus Nightjar	B	1992	89	89	A	C6

The IBA supports a variety of breeding upland species, and is also nationally important for breeding *Numenius arquata* (950 pairs, 1996, 3%).

■ **Protection status**
National High **International** Partial
IBA partly or wholly overlaps with the following national designated areas. *National Park:* North Yorkshire Moors. *Sites of Special Scientific Interest:* Ashberry and Reins Wood, Barn Hill Meadows, Beast Cliff – Miller's Nab, Beck Hole, Biller Howe Dale, Blaiskey Bank Springs, Botton Head, Boulby Quarries, Bride Stones, Broughton Bank, Bull Ings, Castle Hill Wood, Castlebeck and Scar Woods, Cawthorn Moor, Cliff Ridge, Cockrah Wood, Cropton Banks and Howlgate Head Woods, Duncombe Park, Ellerburn Bank, Ellers Wood and Sand Dale, Fairy Call Beck, Farndale, Fylingdales Moor, Gowerdale Windy Pits/ Peak Scar, Hackness Head Quarry, Hackness Rock Pit, Haugh and Gundale Slacks, Hawsker Bottoms, Hayburn Wyke, Hill House Nab, Hole of Horcum, Iron Scar and Hundale Point to Scalby Ness, Kildale Hall, Langbaurgh Ridge, Littlebeck Wood, Low Pasture, Hawnby, Maw Wyke to Miller's Nab, May Moss, Nabgate, Newtondale, Noddle End, Pinkney and Gerrick Woods, Raincliffe and Forge Valley Woods, Rievaulx Woods, Roseberry Topping, Runswick Bay, Ruston Cottage Pasture, Ryedale Windy Pits, Scar End Wood, Seive Dale Fen, Shaws Gate Quarry, Sleightholme Dale, Snaper Farm Meadows, Spikers Hill Quarry, Spring Wood, Hawnby, Staithes – Port Mulgrave, Tranmire, Tripsdale Troutsdale and Rosekirk Dale Fens, Whitby Saltwick. Overlaps with international designated areas: IBA overlaps with Special Protection Area (North York Moors).

■ **Conservation issues**

Threats Abandonment/reduction of land management (U), Burning of vegetation (U), Other (B)

Deliberate and accidental fires threaten ground-nesting species, and bracken *Pteridium* invasion of open moorland is a problem

where heather management is poor. 'Other' threats are posed by acid deposition and raptor persecution. A North York Moors National Park management plan is currently being developed (but not specifically to address nature conservation). An Objective 5b moorland regeneration programme will run until 2000, except in the Cleveland part of the IBA and a few other small areas run by the National Park.

Northumberland coast   A4i, B1i, B2, C3, C6   **050**
Admin region North
Coordinates 55°28'N 1°35'W
Altitude 0–15 m **Area** 1,926 ha

■ **Site description**
The IBA covers much of the coastline between the Scottish border and the Tyne estuary, which consists of sandy bays separated by rocky headlands and backed by sand-dunes and both soft and hard cliffs.

Habitats Grassland, Wetland (tidal river/enclosed tidal water; mudflat/sandflat; sand-dunes/sand beach; shingle/stony beach; standing fresh water), Marine areas (sea inlet/coastal features), Rocky areas (sea cliff/rocky shore)
Land-use Fisheries/aquaculture, Nature conservation/research, Tourism/recreation

■ **Birds**

Species	Season	Year	Pop min	Pop max	Acc	Criteria
Cygnus cygnus Whooper Swan	W	1995	68	68	A	C6
Calidris maritima Purple Sandpiper	W	1995	535	535	A	A4i, B1i, C3
Philomachus pugnax Ruff	P	1995	38	38	A	C6
Arenaria interpres Turnstone	W	1995	1,130	1,130	A	A4i, B1i, C3
Arenaria interpres Turnstone	P	1995	970	970	A	A4i, B1i, C3
Sterna paradisaea Arctic Tern	B	1993	—	245	A	C6
Sterna albifrons Little Tern	B	1993	49	49	A	B2, C6

The IBA is important for breeding terns and wintering waders. It is also nationally important for wintering *Phalacrocorax carbo* (165 birds, 1%), *Cygnus olor* (370 birds, 1%), *Somateria mollissima* (2,100 birds, 3%), *Bucephala clangula* (590 birds, 2%) and *Charadrius hiaticula* (320 birds, 1%), for passage *Calidris maritima* (290 birds, 1%), and for summer moulting assemblages of *Cygnus olor* (460 birds, 2%) and *Somateria mollissima* (860 birds, 1%).

■ **Protection status**
National High **International** None
IBA partly or wholly overlaps with the following national designated areas. *Sites of Special Scientific Interest:* Alnmouth Saltmarsh and Dunes, Bamburgh Coast and Hills, Bamburgh Dunes, Burnmouth Coast, Castle Point to Cullernose Point, Cresswell Ponds, Cresswell and Newbiggin Shores, Hadston Links, Howick to Seaton Point, Low Hauxley Shore, Newton Links, Northumberland Shore, River Coquet and Coquet Valley Woodlands, River Tweed, Sandy Bay, Tweed Estuary, Tynemouth to Seaton Sluice, Warkworth Dunes and Saltmarsh.

■ **Conservation issues**

Threats Extraction industry (B), Infrastructure (U), Natural events (B), Recreation/tourism (B)

Threats include erosion and flooding caused by sea-level rise, and associated improvements to sea defences, disturbance from recreational activities, and the development of caravan sites, holiday homes, car parks and marinas. The site is a candidate SPA. A management plan was drawn up in 1993, and a Recreational Strategy in 1998. Estuary Management Plans have been prepared for the Tweed, Aln, Coquet, Blyth and Wansbeck rivers. Tern research is undertaken by Northumbria Water plc.

Ouse Washes   A4i, A4iii, B1i, B2, B3,   **051**
Admin region East Anglia   C2, C3, C4, C6
Coordinates 52°21'N 0°02'E
Altitude 1–2 m **Area** 2,403 ha

■ **Site description**
The Ouse Washes lie between the Old and New Bedford Rivers and act as a flood-water storage system during the winter months, subjecting the unimproved neutral grassland to regular winter flooding. The flood

meadow sward is characterized by many reed, grass and herb species. A diverse aquatic flora also exists at the site.

Habitats Grassland, Wetland (standing fresh water; river/stream; water-fringe vegetation)
Land-use Agriculture, Nature conservation/research, Water management

■ Birds

Species	Season	Year	Pop min	Pop max	Acc	Criteria
Cygnus columbianus Bewick's Swan	W	1995	4,690	4,690	A	A4i, B1i, B2, C2, C6
Cygnus cygnus Whooper Swan	W	1995	820	820	A	A4i, B1i, B3, C2, C6
Anas penelope Wigeon	W	1995	28,500	28,500	A	A4i, B1i, C3
Anas strepera Gadwall	R	1995	155	155	A	B1i, B2, C3
Anas strepera Gadwall	W	1995	370	370	A	B1i, C3
Anas acuta Pintail	W	1995	1,550	1,550	A	B1i, C3
Anas clypeata Shoveler	W	1995	765	765	A	B1i, C3
Philomachus pugnax Ruff	W	1995	135	135	A	C6
Philomachus pugnax Ruff	P	1995	135	135	A	C6
Limosa limosa Black-tailed Godwit	W	1995	1,540	1,540	A	B1i, C3
Limosa limosa Black-tailed Godwit	P	1995	705	705	A	B1i, C3

The IBA is important for breeding ducks and wintering wildfowl. It holds 62,900 wintering waterbirds on a regular basis, and is also nationally important for breeding *Anas penelope* (14 pairs, 1995, 5%), *Anas acuta* (3 pairs, 1995, 7%), *Anas querquedula* (2 pairs, 1995, 2%), *Anas clypeata* (67 pairs, 1995, 7%), *Aythya ferina* (5 pairs, 1995, 1%) and *Limosa limosa* (5 pairs, 1995, 9%), and for wintering *Phalacrocorax carbo* (235 birds, 2%), *Cygnus olor* (610 birds, 2%), *Anser fabalis* (6 birds, 1%), *Anas crecca* (3,690 birds, 3%), *Aythya ferina* (2,580 birds, 3%) and *Fulica atra* (1,850 birds, 1%).

■ Protection status
National High **International** High
IBA partly or wholly overlaps with the following national designated areas. *Reserves:* Ouse Washes, Welney. *Site of Special Scientific Interest:* Ouse Washes. Overlaps with international designated areas: 2,403 ha of IBA covered by Special Protection Area (Ouse Washes, 2,403 ha). 2,403 ha of IBA covered by Ramsar Site (Ouse Washes, 2,403 ha).

■ Conservation issues

Threats Agricultural intensification/expansion (B), Disturbance to birds (C), Drainage (C), Extraction industry (C), Infrastructure (C), Natural events (A), Recreation/tourism (C)

Threats include disturbance caused by wildfowling and footpath use, and flooding, which can result in a major loss of habitat and breeding species during spring and summer. There is a management plan for the site, part of which is a candidate SAC.

Pagham Harbour   B1i, C3   052
Admin region South East
Coordinates 50°45′N 0°45′W
Altitude 0–1 m **Area** 636 ha

■ Site description
A central area of mudflats and saltmarsh, and surrounding brackish marsh and pasture. The harbour itself has a narrow opening to the sea, flanked by shingle-beaches.

Habitats Forest and woodland (broadleaved deciduous forest), Scrub (scrub), Grassland, Wetland (tidal river/enclosed tidal water; mudflat/sandflat; saltmarsh; shingle/stony beach; coastal lagoon; water-fringe vegetation)
Land-use Nature conservation/research, Tourism/recreation

■ Birds

Species	Season	Year	Pop min	Pop max	Acc	Criteria
Branta bernicla Brent Goose	W	1995	3,010	3,010	A	B1i, C3

The IBA supports large numbers of wintering wildfowl, and is also nationally important for wintering *Phalacrocorax carbo* (150 birds, 1%), *Anas acuta* (600 birds, 2%), *Pluvialis squatarola* (1,100 birds, 3%), *Limosa limosa* (165 birds, 2%), and for passage *Pluvialis squatarola* (555 birds, 1%). *Branta bernicla* are the *bernicla* subspecies.

■ Protection status
National High **International** High

IBA partly or wholly overlaps with the following national designated areas. *Sites of Special Scientific Interest:* Bognor Reef, Pagham Harbour. Overlaps with international designated areas: 636 ha of IBA covered by Special Protection Area (Pagham Harbour, 636 ha). 636 ha of IBA covered by Ramsar Site (Pagham Harbour, 636 ha).

■ Conservation issues

Threats Natural events (A), Recreation/tourism (C)

Threats to the IBA are posed by sea-level rise, which may result in erosion, flooding and habitat loss associated with coastal defence development, and leisure developments. The site is monitored as part of the WeBS, and there is a management plan.

Peak District moors   B1i, B3, C3, C6   053
Admin region Yorkshire and Humberside, East Midlands, West Midlands, North West
Coordinates 53°21′N 1°44′W
Altitude 98–636 m **Area** 37,092 ha

■ Site description
This IBA marks the southernmost extent of a habitat typical of northern British uplands. It is cut by fast-flowing rivers and streams, and contains areas of wet in-bye land and reservoirs. Dwarf shrubs dominate the open moorland and mire habitats, with adjacent unenclosed pasture and grassland. The Eastern Moors block is included in the site.

Habitats Scrub (35%; heathland), Grassland (40%), Wetland (25%; standing fresh water; river/stream; blanket bog; fen/transition mire/spring), Artificial landscape (5%; forestry plantation)
Land-use Agriculture (90%), Forestry (5%), Hunting (50%), Military (5%), Water management (50%)

■ Birds

Species	Season	Year	Pop min	Pop max	Acc	Criteria
Falco columbarius Merlin	R	1991	25	25	A	C6
Pluvialis apricaria Golden Plover	R	1991	500	500	A	C6
Calidris alpina Dunlin	B	1991	70	70	A	B1i, C3
Turdus torquatus Ring Ouzel	B	1991	80	80	A	B3

The IBA is important for breeding waders, raptors and other upland species. It is also nationally important for breeding *Numenius arquata* (450 pairs, 1991, 1%) and for summer breeding and non-breeding assemblages of *Larus fuscus* (2,760 birds, 1994, 6%).

■ Protection status
National High **International** High
IBA partly or wholly overlaps with the following national designated areas. *National Park:* Peak District. *Sites of Special Scientific Interest:* Dark Peak, Eastern Moors, Leek Moors. Overlaps with international designated areas: 37,092 ha of IBA is covered by Special Protection Area (South Pennine Moors (Phase 1), 37,092 ha).

■ Conservation issues

Threats Agricultural intensification/expansion (A), Infrastructure (U), Other (U), Recreation/tourism (C)

Threats include overgrazing of many moorland areas, which has led to a loss of heather *Calluna*, the drainage and improvement of farmland that fringes areas of moorland, which has led to a decline in wader populations and other moorland-edge species, and acid deposition ('Other' threat, above). The Peak District BAP is being prepared, and the RSPB undertook surveys of the North Staffordshire moors in 1985, 1992 and 1997. There is a management plan for the area.

Poole Harbour   A4iii, B1i, B2, C3, C4, C6   054
Admin region South West
Coordinates 50°42′N 2°00′W
Altitude 0–21 m **Area** 5,130 ha

■ Site description
A drowned valley that forms one of the largest natural harbours in

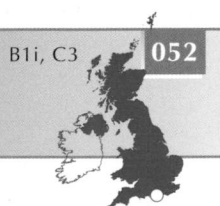

the world, with the five islands representing high ground between the former river valleys. Habitat-types include mudflats, saltmarsh, reed *Phragmites*-swamp and heathland.

Habitats Forest and woodland (broadleaved deciduous forest; mixed forest), Scrub (heathland), Grassland, Wetland (tidal river/enclosed tidal water; mudflat/sandflat; saltmarsh; river/stream; water-fringe vegetation; fen/transition mire/spring), Rocky areas (sea cliff/rocky shore)
Land-use Tourism/recreation, Urban/industrial/transport

■ Birds

Species	Season	Year	Pop min	Pop max	Acc	Criteria
Recurvirostra avosetta Avocet	W	1995	315	315	A	B2, C6
Recurvirostra avosetta Avocet	P	1995	125	125	A	C6
Calidris alpina Dunlin	W	1995	5,500	5,500	A	B2
Limosa limosa Black-tailed Godwit	W	1995	1,490	1,490	A	B1i, C3
Limosa limosa Black-tailed Godwit	P	1995	810	810	A	B1i, C3
Numenius arquata Curlew	W	1995	1,790	1,790	A	B2
Larus melanocephalus Mediterranean Gull	B	1996	6	6	A	C6
Sterna sandvicensis Sandwich Tern	B	1995	105	105	A	C6
Sterna hirundo Common Tern	B	1995	150	150	A	C6
Caprimulgus europaeus Nightjar	B	1992	43	43	A	C6
Sylvia undata Dartford Warbler	R	1994	71	71	A	C6

The IBA is important for wintering wildfowl, and regularly holds 27,000 wintering waterbirds. It is also nationally important for breeding *Larus ridibundus* (3,000 pairs, 1992, 2%), and for wintering *Phalacrocorax carbo* (360 birds, 2%), *Egretta garzetta* (100 birds, 1997, 17%), *Branta bernicla bernicla* (1,480 birds, 1%), *Tadorna tadorna* (2,790 birds, 4%), *Anas clypeata* (135 birds, 1%), *Mergus serrator* (360 birds, 3%), *Tringa erythropus* (5 birds, 1%), *Tringa totanus* (1,400 birds, 1%) and *Tringa nebularia* (7 birds, 1%).

■ Protection status
National Partial **International** None
IBA partly or wholly overlaps with the following national designated areas. *Reserve:* Arne. *Sites of Special Scientific Interest:* Arne, Ham Common, Hartland Moor, Holton Heath, Morden Bog, Poole Harbour, Rempstone Heaths, Sandford Heath, Stoborough and Creech Heaths, Studland and Godlingston Heaths, The Moors, Wareham Meadows.

■ Conservation issues

Threats Extraction industry (U), Industrialization/urbanization (U), Infrastructure (U), Natural events (B), Recreation/tourism (U)

Threats include infrastructure and urban development, disturbance from marinas and hotel/leisure facilities, oil pollution caused by exploration in the harbour, and sea-level rise that may result in erosion, flooding and associated sea defence development. An aquatic management plan is complete and being implemented. The Poole Harbour steering group is reviewing the terrestrial management plan, and there is an advisory effort following completion of the Purbeck BAP. The area is a candidate SPA and Ramsar Site.

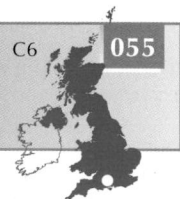

Porton Down	C6	055

Admin region South East, South West
Coordinates 51°07′N 1°39′W
Altitude 100–171 m **Area** 2,160 ha

■ Site description
Porton Down, to the north-east of Salisbury, is one of the largest uninterrupted tracts of semi-natural chalk grassland in Britain.

Habitats Forest and woodland (broadleaved deciduous forest; mixed forest), Scrub (scrub; heathland), Grassland (steppe/dry calcareous grassland), Artificial landscape (forestry plantation)
Land-use Military

■ Birds

Species	Season	Year	Pop min	Pop max	Acc	Criteria
Burhinus oedicnemus Stone Curlew	B	1996	20	20	A	C6

The IBA supports breeding downland bird species.

■ Protection status
National Partial **International** Partial
IBA partly or wholly overlaps with the following national designated areas. *Site of Special Scientific Interest:* Porton Down. Overlaps with international designated areas: 1,227 ha of IBA covered by Special Protection Area (Porton Down, 1,227 ha).

■ Conservation issues

Threats Disturbance to birds (B), Other (U)

Threats include conflicts with military use of the site and inappropriate land management ('Other' threat, above). The MoD and English Nature are producing a management plan, and the RSPB undertake monitoring of *Burhinus oedicnemus*.

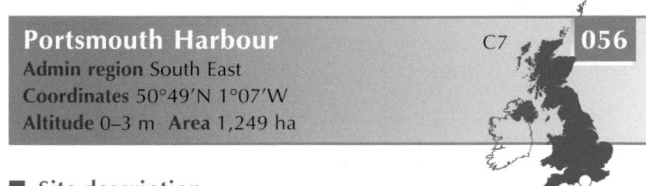

Portsmouth Harbour	C7	056

Admin region South East
Coordinates 50°49′N 1°07′W
Altitude 0–3 m **Area** 1,249 ha

■ Site description
A large industrialized estuary that includes one of the four largest expanses of mudflats and tidal creeks on the south coast of Britain.

Habitats Wetland (100%; tidal river/enclosed tidal water; mudflat/sandflat; saltmarsh; river/stream)
Land-use Tourism/recreation

■ Birds

Species	Season	Year	Pop min	Pop max	Acc	Criteria
Branta bernicla Brent Goose	W	1995	2,820	2,820	A	C7
Pluvialis squatarola Grey Plover	W	1995	52	52	A	C7
Calidris alpina Dunlin	W	1995	4,650	4,650	A	C7
Limosa limosa Black-tailed Godwit	W	1995	21	21	A	C7

The IBA holds important numbers of wintering wildfowl and waders. *Branta bernicla* are the *bernicla* subspecies.

■ Protection status
National High **International** High
IBA partly or wholly overlaps with the following national designated areas. *Site of Special Scientific Interest:* Portsmouth Harbour. Overlaps with international designated areas: 1,249 ha of IBA covered by Special Protection Area (Portsmouth Harbour, 1,249 ha). 1,249 ha of IBA covered by Ramsar Site (Portsmouth Harbour, 1,249 ha).

■ Conservation issues

Threats Industrialization/urbanization (B), Infrastructure (C), Natural events (A), Recreation/tourism (B)

Threats include residential development, the effects of erosion and flooding following possible sea-level rise, habitat loss from coastal defence development, disturbance caused by marina development and the possibility of water pollution as a result of ongoing tipping adjacent to the site. A management plan is in preparation.

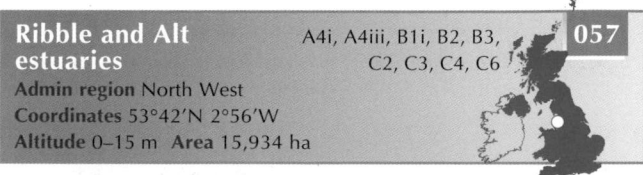

Ribble and Alt estuaries	A4i, A4iii, B1i, B2, B3, C2, C3, C4, C6	057

Admin region North West
Coordinates 53°42′N 2°56′W
Altitude 0–15 m **Area** 15,934 ha

■ Site description
Intertidal mudflats and saltmarsh extending from the Ribble estuary in the north to Crosby in the south, and includes the mouth of the River Alt.

Habitats Grassland, Wetland (tidal river/enclosed tidal water; mudflat/sandflat; saltmarsh; sand-dunes/sand beach; standing fresh water; river/stream)
Land-use Agriculture, Nature conservation/research, Tourism/recreation, Urban/industrial/transport

■ Birds

Species	Season	Year	Pop min	Pop max	Acc	Criteria
Cygnus columbianus Bewick's Swan	W	1995	180	180	A	A4i, B1i, B2, C2, C6
Cygnus cygnus Whooper Swan	W	1995	94	94	A	B3, C6
Anser brachyrhynchus Pink-footed Goose	W	1995	17,900	17,900	A	A4i, B1i, C3
Tadorna tadorna Shelduck	W	1995	3,530	3,530	A	B1i, C3
Anas penelope Wigeon	W	1995	78,000	78,000	A	A4i, B1i, C3
Anas crecca Teal	W	1995	7,050	7,050	A	B1i, C3
Anas acuta Pintail	W	1995	1,880	1,880	A	B1i, C3
Haematopus ostralegus Oystercatcher	W	1995	16,700	16,700	A	A4i, B1i, C3
Haematopus ostralegus Oystercatcher	P	1995	13,000	13,000	A	A4i, B1i, C3
Charadrius hiaticula Ringed Plover	P	1995	1,230	1,230	A	B1i, C3
Pluvialis apricaria Golden Plover	W	1995	4,470	4,470	A	C6
Pluvialis apricaria Golden Plover	P	1995	2,340	2,340	A	C6
Pluvialis squatarola Grey Plover	W	1995	5,400	5,400	A	A4i, B1i, C3
Pluvialis squatarola Grey Plover	P	1995	7,550	7,550	A	A4i, B1i, C3
Calidris canutus Knot	W	1995	56,000	56,000	A	A4i, B1i, B2, C3
Calidris canutus Knot	P	1995	64,000	64,000	A	A4i, B1i, C3
Calidris alba Sanderling	W	1995	3,150	3,150	A	A4i, B1i, C3
Calidris alba Sanderling	P	1995	6,800	6,800	A	A4i, B1i, C3
Calidris alpina Dunlin	W	1995	37,000	37,000	A	A4i, B1i, B2, C3
Calidris alpina Dunlin	P	1995	33,400	33,400	A	A4i, B1i, C3
Limosa limosa Black-tailed Godwit	W	1995	820	820	A	B1i, C3
Limosa limosa Black-tailed Godwit	P	1995	2,600	2,600	A	B1i, C3
Limosa lapponica Bar-tailed Godwit	W	1995	15,500	15,500	A	A4i, B1i, B2, C2, C6
Limosa lapponica Bar-tailed Godwit	P	1995	13,500	13,500	A	A4i, B1i, C2, C6
Numenius arquata Curlew	W	1995	1,840	1,840	A	B2
Tringa totanus Redshank	W	1995	3,040	3,040	A	A4i, B1i, C3
Tringa totanus Redshank	P	1995	3,480	3,480	A	A4i, B1i, C3
Arenaria interpres Turnstone	W	1995	830	830	A	A4i, B1i, C3
Larus fuscus Lesser Black-backed Gull	B	1993	1,780	1,780	A	B1i, B3, C3
Sterna hirundo Common Tern	B	1994	230	230	A	C6

These estuaries are of international importance for wintering and passage wildfowl and waders. The IBA regularly holds 11,300 pairs of breeding waterbirds, 281,200 wintering waterbirds and 159,400 passage waterbirds. It is also nationally important for breeding *Larus ridibundus* (9,000 pairs, 1993, 5%), and for wintering *Phalacrocorax carbo* (220 birds, 1%), *Melanitta nigra* (415 birds, 1%) and *Vanellus vanellus* (25,000 birds, 2%).

■ Protection status

National Partial **International** High

IBA partly or wholly overlaps with the following national designated areas. *National Nature Reserves:* Ainsdale Sand-dunes, Ribble Marshes. *Reserves:* Marshside, Southport Sanctuary. *Sites of Special Scientific Interest:* Ainsdale Sand-dunes, Altcar Sand-dunes and Forshore, Formby Sand-dunes and Foreshore, Freshfield Dune Heath, Helsketh Golf Links, Lytham St Annes Dunes, Newton Marsh, Ribble Estuary, Southport Sand-dunes and Foreshore. Overlaps with international designated areas: 15,934 ha of IBA covered by Special Protection Area (Ribble and Alt Estuaries, 15,934 ha). 15,934 ha of IBA covered by Ramsar Site (Ribble and Alt Estuaries, 15,934 ha).

■ Conservation issues

Threats Extraction industry (B), Filling-in of wetlands (U), Industrialization/urbanization (U), Infrastructure (B), Natural events (B), Recreation/tourism (B)

Threats include wind-power development, a hovercraft service, development proposals for an airport, pipeline, trunk road, leisure centre and marina, recreational disturbance, and sea-level rise that could result in erosion, flooding and habitat loss through associated coastal defence improvements. A Ribble Estuary Strategy and Sefton Coast management plan both exist.

Rutland Water

A4iii, B1i, C3, C4 — **058**

Admin region East Midlands
Coordinates 52°39′N 0°37′W
Altitude 90–110 m **Area** 1,556 ha

■ Site description

The largest man-made reservoir in Britain and a mosaic of associated wetland and lakeside habitats.

Habitats Forest and woodland (mixed forest), Scrub (scrub), Grassland, Wetland (standing fresh water; water-fringe vegetation)

Land-use Agriculture, Fisheries/aquaculture, Forestry, Nature conservation/research, Tourism/recreation, Water management

■ Birds

Species	Season	Year	Pop min	Pop max	Acc	Criteria
Anas strepera Gadwall	W	1995	1,160	1,160	A	B1i, C3
Anas clypeata Shoveler	W	1995	550	550	A	B1i, C3

This site is internationally important for wintering wildfowl, holding 21,900 wintering waterbirds on a regular basis. It is also nationally important for wintering *Podiceps cristatus* (855 birds, 7%), *Phalacrocorax carbo* (555 birds, 4%), *Anas penelope* (4,110 birds, 1%), *Aythya ferina* (1,000 birds, 1%), *Aythya fuligula* (2,110 birds, 2%), *Bucephala clangula* (425 birds, 1%) and *Fulica atra* (3,470 birds, 3%), and for summer moulting assemblages of *Cygnus olor* (300 birds, 1%).

■ Protection status

National High **International** High

IBA partly or wholly overlaps with the following national designated areas. *Sites of Special Scientific Interest:* Burley and Rushpit Woods, Rutland Water. Overlaps with international designated areas: 1,556 ha of IBA covered by Special Protection Area (Rutland Water, 1,556 ha). 1,360 ha of IBA covered by Ramsar Site (Rutland Water, 1,360 ha).

■ Conservation issues

Threats Agricultural intensification/expansion (C), Groundwater abstraction (U), Recreation/tourism (C)

Threats include disturbance caused by increased recreational use, damage to sensitive areas of the site caused by the cycle track, increased water abstraction, and nutrient enrichment of the reservoir. *Pandion haliaetus* has been reintroduced to the site in recent years. Constant ringing of *Phalacrocorax carbo* is undertaken by the Ministry of Agriculture, Fisheries and Food, and a management plan exists for the site.

Salisbury Plain

C6 — **059**

Admin region South East, South West
Coordinates 51°13′N 2°04′W
Altitude 94–212 m **Area** 19,690 ha

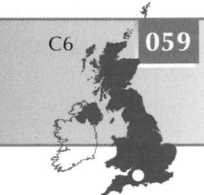

■ Site description

Three large expanses of heathland and grassland with scattered woods, supporting an exceptional chalk grassland flora and fauna. Much of the site is a military training area.

Habitats Forest and woodland (broadleaved deciduous forest), Scrub (heathland), Grassland (steppe/dry calcareous grassland; humid grassland), Wetland (river/stream)
Land-use Military

■ Birds

Species	Season	Year	Pop min	Pop max	Acc	Criteria
Circus cyaneus Hen Harrier	W	1996	10	10	A	C6
Burhinus oedicnemus Stone Curlew	B	1996	18	18	A	C6

The site also supports large numbers of farmland and grassland passerines.

■ Protection status

National High **International** High

IBA partly or wholly overlaps with the following national designated areas. *Sites of Special Scientific Interest:* Bratton Downs, Salisbury Plain. Overlaps with international designated areas: 19,690 ha of IBA covered by Special Protection Area (Salisbury Plain, 19,690 ha).

■ Conservation issues

Threats Abandonment/reduction of land management (B), Disturbance to birds (B), Infrastructure (B)

Conflicts arise due to the extensive use of the site for military purposes. English Nature and the MoD are preparing a management plan, and monitoring and research on *Burhinus oedicnemus* is carried out by the RSPB.

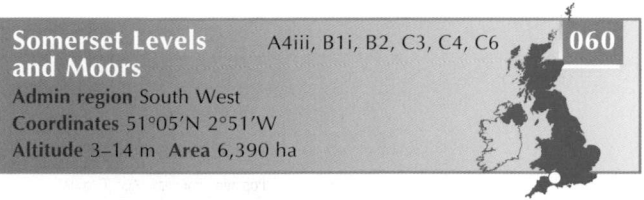

Somerset Levels and Moors

A4iii, B1i, B2, C3, C4, C6 — 060

Admin region South West
Coordinates 51°05'N 2°51'W
Altitude 3–14 m **Area** 6,390 ha

■ Site description
The Levels and Moors have formed in the valleys of five rivers, which drain a large part of north Somerset. The whole area is low-lying, and the naturally poor drainage has encouraged peat build-up. Habitat-types include wet grassland, fen and raised bog.

Habitats Forest and woodland (broadleaved deciduous forest; mixed forest), Scrub (scrub; heathland), Grassland, Wetland (river/stream; raised bog; water-fringe vegetation; fen/transition mire/spring), Artificial landscape (arable land)
Land-use Agriculture, Water management

■ Birds

Species	Season	Year	Pop min	Pop max	Acc	Criteria
Cygnus columbianus Bewick's Swan	W	1995	160	160	A	B2, C6
Anas strepera Gadwall	R	1996	60	60	A	B2
Anas crecca Teal	W	1995	8,900	8,900	A	B1i, C3
Pluvialis apricaria Golden Plover	W	1995	1,720	1,720	A	C6

The IBA is important for breeding and wintering wildfowl and other wetland birds. It holds 49,700 wintering waterbirds on a regular basis. The area is also nationally important for wintering *Cygnus olor* (385 birds, 1%), *Anas penelope* (8,850 birds, 3%), *Anas strepera* (97 birds, 1%), *Anas clypeata* (350 birds, 3%), *Vanellus vanellus* (25,900 birds, 2%) and *Gallinago gallinago* (1,010 birds, 1%), and for passage *Numenius phaeopus* (1,100 birds, 1992, 31%).

■ Protection status
National Partial **International** High
IBA partly or wholly overlaps with the following national designated areas. *Reserve:* West Sedgemoor. *Sites of Special Scientific Interest:* Aller and Beer Woods, Catcott, Edington and Chilton Moors, Curry and Hay Moors, Fivehead Woods and Meadow, Greylake, Kings Sedgemoor, Meare Heath, Moorlinch, North Curry Meadow, North Moor, Shapwick Heath, Southlake Moor, Tealham and Tadham Moors, West Moor, West Sedgemoor, Westhay Moor, Westhoy Heath, Wet Moor. Overlaps with international designated areas: 6,390 ha of IBA covered by Special Protection Area (Somerset Levels and Moors, 6,390 ha). 6,390 ha of IBA covered by Ramsar Site (Somerset Levels and Moors, 6,390 ha).

■ Conservation issues

Threats Drainage (A), Extraction industry (C), Groundwater abstraction (B), Other (U)

Threats to the IBA are posed by land drainage and raising, and inappropriate land and water management ('Other' threat, above). Wetland habitat creation is being carried out at Avalon marshes, and water-level management plans are in preparation.

South Cornwall coast

A4i, B1i, C2, C6 — 061

Admin region South West
Coordinates 50°11'N 4°56'W
Altitude 0–76 m **Area** 11,170 ha

■ Site description
A long stretch of coastline running from the Helford River to St Austell, incorporating the estuary complexes of the Fal and Helford, and extending 6 km out to sea.

Habitats Wetland (tidal river/enclosed tidal water; sand-dunes/sand beach; shingle/stony beach), Marine areas (open sea; sea inlet/coastal features), Rocky areas (sea cliff/rocky shore)
Land-use Fisheries/aquaculture, Military

■ Birds

Species	Season	Year	Pop min	Pop max	Acc	Criteria
Gavia arctica Black-throated Diver	W	1995	135	135	A	C6

Species ... continued	Season	Year	Pop min	Pop max	Acc	Criteria
Gavia immer Great Northern Diver	W	1995	84	84	A	A4i, B1i, C2, C6
Podiceps auritus Slavonian Grebe	W	1995	50	50	A	B1i, C2, C6

The nearshore area supports important numbers of divers and grebes . The site is also nationally important for wintering *Podiceps grisegena* (26 birds, 1995, 17%) and *Podiceps nigricollis* (26 birds, 1995, 22%).

■ Protection status
National Partial **International** None
IBA partly or wholly overlaps with the following national designated areas. *Sites of Special Scientific Interest:* Fal complex, Merthen Wood, Rosemullion.

■ Conservation issues

Threats Disturbance to birds (B)

Naval training off Dodman Point causes problems of disturbance. The Fal estuary and SAC management plans are being developed.

South Pennine moors

B3, C6 — 062

Admin region Yorkshire and Humberside, North West
Coordinates 53°54'N 2°04'W
Altitude 0–317 m **Area** 21,000 ha

■ Site description
Several huge upland blocks comprising heather moorland and blanket peatland habitats, which fall within the broader South Pennine Moors Natural Area.

Habitats Forest and woodland (broadleaved deciduous forest; mixed forest), Scrub (heathland), Wetland (blanket bog)
Land-use Agriculture, Tourism/recreation

■ Birds

Species	Season	Year	Pop min	Pop max	Acc	Criteria
Falco columbarius Merlin	R	1995	51	51	A	C6
Falco peregrinus Peregrine	R	1995	—	10	A	C6
Pluvialis apricaria Golden Plover	R	1995	705	705	A	B3, C6

The IBA holds important numbers of upland species, and is also nationally important for breeding *Numenius arquata* (695 pairs, 1995, 2%).

■ Protection status
National Partial **International** High
IBA partly or wholly overlaps with the following national designated areas. *Sites of Special Scientific Interest:* Broadhead Clough, Crimsworth Dean, Derby Delph Quarry, Haworth Moor, Ladcastle and Den Quarries, Park Clough, Pule Hill, Standedge Road Cutting, Withens Clough. Overlaps with international designated areas: 21,000 ha of IBA covered by Special Protection Area (South Pennine Moors (Phase II), 21,000 ha).

■ Conservation issues

Threats Agricultural intensification/expansion (U), Infrastructure (U), Recreation/tourism (U)

The main threats arise from a lack of coordinated strategic conservation management, increased recreational disturbance and development, wind-power development and inappropriate grazing management.

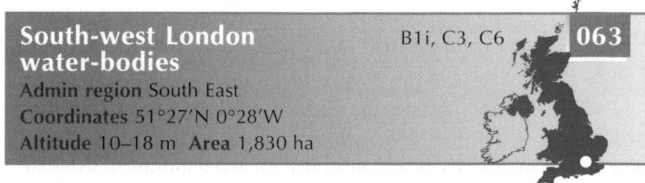

South-west London water-bodies

B1i, C3, C6 — 063

Admin region South East
Coordinates 51°27'N 0°28'W
Altitude 10–18 m **Area** 1,830 ha

■ Site description
These widely scattered water-bodies on the south-west margins of London are used primarily as water-supply reservoirs. Some are now

disused and include flooded gravel-pits and alluvial grassland. The shorelines are fringed with dense *Salix* scrub, and the river and ditch networks support a diverse aquatic flora.

Habitats Forest and woodland (mixed forest), Scrub (scrub), Grassland, Wetland (standing fresh water; river/stream)

Land-use Nature conservation/research, Tourism/recreation, Water management

■ Birds

Species	Season	Year	Pop min	Pop max	Acc	Criteria
Anas strepera Gadwall	W	1995	580	580	A	B1i, C3
Anas clypeata Shoveler	W	1995	645	645	A	B1i, C3
Mergus albellus Smew	W	1995	28	28	A	C6

The IBA supports large numbers of wintering wildfowl, and is also nationally important for wintering *Podiceps cristatus* (715 birds, 6%), *Phalacrocorax carbo* (700 birds, 5%), *Aythya fuligula* (2,080 birds, 2%) and *Fulica atra* (2,220 birds, 2%).

■ Protection status
National Partial **International** None
IBA partly or wholly overlaps with the following national designated areas. *Sites of Special Scientific Interest:* Dumsey Meadow, Staines Moor, Wraysbury and Hythe End Gravel Pits.

■ Conservation issues

Threats Disturbance to birds (U), Extraction industry (U), Filling-in of wetlands (C), Industrialization/urbanization (B), Infrastructure (B), Recreation/tourism (B)

Threats to these sites include disturbance from maintenance works and unpermitted access, aggregate extraction, and pressures for further industrial, recreational, infrastructure and urban development. Major opportunities exist for enhancement. The sites have been put forward for designation as an SPA and Ramsar Site, and are monitored as part of the WeBS.

Southampton Water and Solent marshes	A4i, A4iii, B1i, B2, C3, C4, C6	**064**

Admin region South East
Coordinates 50°46′N 1°25′W
Altitude 0–15 m **Area** 6,000 ha

■ Site description
The estuaries, saltmarshes and mudflats around Southampton Water and the western Solent, including habitats on both the mainland and the Isle of Wight. The mudflats support beds of algae and eel-grass *Zostera*. Shingle and both neutral and calcareous grassland vegetation communities exist within the IBA.

Habitats Forest and woodland (broadleaved deciduous forest; mixed forest), Grassland, Wetland (tidal river/enclosed tidal water; mudflat/sandflat; saltmarsh; shingle/stony beach; coastal lagoon; river/stream; water-fringe vegetation)

Land-use Nature conservation/research, Tourism/recreation, Urban/industrial/transport

■ Birds

Species	Season	Year	Pop min	Pop max	Acc	Criteria
Branta bernicla Brent Goose	W	1995	7,700	7,700	A	A4i, B1i, C3
Charadrius hiaticula Ringed Plover	W	1995	575	575	A	B1i, C3
Charadrius hiaticula Ringed Plover	P	1995	615	615	A	B1i, C3
Calidris alpina Dunlin	W	1995	12,300	12,300	A	B2
Limosa limosa Black-tailed Godwit	W	1995	985	985	A	B1i, C3
Numenius arquata Curlew	W	1995	1,750	1,750	A	B2
Sterna sandvicensis Sandwich Tern	B	1994	300	300	A	C6
Sterna hirundo Common Tern	B	1994	450	450	A	C6
Sterna albifrons Little Tern	B	1994	41	41	A	C6

The IBA is important for breeding terns and wintering wildfowl, and holds 15,000 pairs of breeding waterbirds and 49,000 wintering waterbirds on a regular basis. It is also nationally important for breeding *Larus ridibundus* (14,200 pairs, 1994, 7%), for wintering *Tachybaptus ruficollis* (77 birds, 2%), *Phalacrocorax carbo* (225 birds, 2%), *Tadorna tadorna* (1,360 birds, 2%), *Anas penelope* (4,160 birds, 1%), *Anas strepera* (100 birds, 1%), *Anas crecca* (3,750 birds, 3%), *Anas*

clypeata (175 birds, 2%), *Mergus serrator* (115 birds, 1%), *Pluvialis squatarola* (1,320 birds, 3%), *Philomachus pugnax* (10 birds, 1%), *Tringa erythropus* (13 birds, 3%), *Tringa totanus* (1,230 birds, 1%) and *Tringa nebularia* (17 birds, 3%), and for passage *Pluvialis squatarola* (835 birds, 2%) and *Limosa limosa* (480 birds, 6%). *Branta bernicla* are the *bernicla* subspecies.

■ Protection status
National Partial **International** Partial
IBA partly or wholly overlaps with the following national designated areas. *Sites of Special Scientific Interest:* Bouldnor and Hamstead Cliffs, Brading Marshes, Eling and Bury Marshes, Freshwater Marshes, Gurnard Ledge to Saltmead Ledge, Hart's Farm Meadows, Hurst Castle and Lymington River Estuary, Hythe–Calshot Marshes, Kings Quay Shore, Lee on the Solent to Itchen Estuary, Lincegrove and Hackett's Marshes, Locks Farm Meadow, Lower Test Valley, Lymington River Reedbeds, Medina Estuary, Newton Harbour, North Solent, Ryde Sands, Sowley Pond, St Helen's Duver, St Helen's Ledges, Titchfield Haven, Upper Hamble Estuary and Woods, Whitecliff Bay and Bembridge Ledges, Yar Estuary. Overlaps with international designated areas: 5,508 ha of IBA covered by Special Protection Area (Southampton Water and Solent Marshes, 5,508 ha). 5,508 ha of IBA covered by Ramsar Site (Southampton Water and Solent Marshes, 5,508 ha).

■ Conservation issues

Threats Aquaculture/fisheries (U), Dredging/canalization (A), Extraction industry (C), Filling-in of wetlands (C), Industrialization/urbanization (A), Infrastructure (A), Natural events (U), Recreation/tourism (B)

Threats include extensive recreational disturbance to wildfowl rafts and wader roosts, marina, carpark and port developments, and sea-level rise. A management plan is being written for the Solent SAC (much of the remainder of the site is a candidate SAC), and shoreline management plans already exist. The IBA is monitored as part of the WeBS.

Stodmarsh	C6	**065**

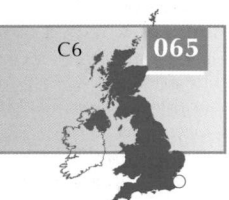

Admin region South East
Coordinates 51°18′N 1°11′E
Altitude 2–15 m **Area** 481 ha

■ Site description
The IBA covers about 6 km of the Stour flood-plain downstream of Canterbury. The site includes flooded gravel-pits, reedbeds (*Phragmites*) and lagoons, in an area that has undergone colliery subsidence. Margins are well-vegetated with scrub and *Alnus* carr, which supports a diverse ground flora. Fen communities exist in areas of cut reedbed, with a rich aquatic flora present in some of the dykes.

Habitats Forest and woodland (alluvial/very wet forest), Scrub (scrub), Grassland, Wetland (standing fresh water; river/stream; water-fringe vegetation; fen/transition mire/spring)

Land-use Nature conservation/research

■ Birds

Species	Season	Year	Pop min	Pop max	Acc	Criteria
Botaurus stellaris Bittern	W	1996	—	5	A	C6
Circus cyaneus Hen Harrier	W	1987	—	9	A	C6

The site supports a wide range of wetland birds including notable populations of breeding and wintering reedbed species. It is also nationally important for breeding *Panurus biarmicus* (40 pairs, 1992, 10%), and for wintering *Anas strepera* (130 birds, 2%) and *Anas clypeata* (160 birds, 2%).

■ Protection status
National High **International** High
IBA partly or wholly overlaps with the following national designated areas. *Site of Special Scientific Interest:* Stodmarsh. Overlaps with international designated areas: 481 ha of IBA covered by Special Protection Area (Stodmarsh, 481 ha). 481 ha of IBA covered by Ramsar Site (Stodmarsh, 481 ha).

■ Conservation issues

Threats Extraction industry (C), Groundwater abstraction (B), Industrialization/ urbanization (C), Infrastructure (U), Recreation/tourism (C)

Threats include residential development adjacent to the site, recreational disturbance, problems of water quantity and quality, and reservoir development. An English Nature management plan exists for the National Nature Reserve.

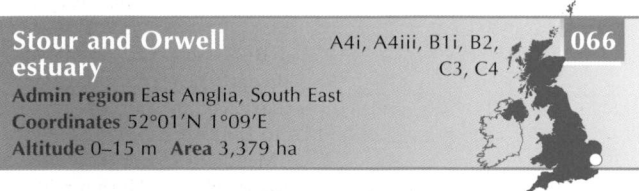

Stour and Orwell estuary
A4i, A4iii, B1i, B2, C3, C4
066
Admin region East Anglia, South East
Coordinates 52°01′N 1°09′E
Altitude 0–15 m **Area** 3,379 ha

■ Site description
The Stour estuary straddles the eastern part of the Essex/Suffolk border and comprises five main bays, whilst the Orwell is a relatively long and narrow estuary. Both estuaries support extensive mudflats and saltmarshes.

Habitats Forest and woodland (broadleaved deciduous forest), Grassland (humid grassland), Wetland (tidal river/enclosed tidal water; mudflat/sandflat; saltmarsh), Marine areas (sea inlet/coastal features), Rocky areas (sea cliff/rocky shore)
Land-use Agriculture, Fisheries/aquaculture, Nature conservation/research, Urban/ industrial/transport

■ Birds

Species	Season	Year	Pop min	Pop max	Acc	Criteria
Tadorna tadorna Shelduck	W	1995	3,140	3,140	A	B1i, C3
Anas acuta Pintail	W	1995	700	700	A	B1i, C3
Charadrius hiaticula Ringed Plover	W	1995	665	665	A	B1i, C3
Charadrius hiaticula Ringed Plover	P	1995	925	925	A	B1i, C3
Pluvialis squatarola Grey Plover	W	1995	3,460	3,460	A	A4i, B1i, C3
Calidris canutus Knot	W	1995	3,330	3,330	A	B2
Calidris alpina Dunlin	W	1995	24,700	24,700	A	A4i, B1i, B2, C3
Limosa limosa Black-tailed Godwit	W	1995	2,110	2,110	A	B1i, C3
Limosa limosa Black-tailed Godwit	P	1995	1,710	1,710	A	B1i, C3
Numenius arquata Curlew	W	1995	2,140	2,140	A	B2
Tringa totanus Redshank	W	1995	3,320	3,320	A	A4i, B1i, C3
Tringa totanus Redshank	P	1995	2,210	2,210	A	B1i, C3
Arenaria interpres Turnstone	W	1995	850	850	A	A4i, B1i, C3
Arenaria interpres Turnstone	P	1995	750	750	A	A4i, B1i, C3

The IBA supports important numbers of wintering waders and wildfowl. It regularly holds 63,000 wintering and 21,600 passage waterbirds, and is also nationally important for wintering *Podiceps cristatus* (230 birds, 2%), *Phalacrocorax carbo* (190 birds, 1%), *Branta bernicla bernicla* (2,420 birds, 2%) and *Anas penelope* (4,110 birds, 1%), and for passage *Pluvialis squatarola* (1,610 birds, 1%).

■ Protection status
National High **International** High
IBA partly or wholly overlaps with the following national designated areas. *Reserves:* Hogmarsh, Stour, Wrabners Marsh. *Sites of Special Scientific Interest:* Orwell Estuary, Stour Estuary. Overlaps with international designated areas: 3,379 ha of IBA covered by Special Protection Area (Stour and Orwell Estuary, 3,379 ha). 3,379 ha of IBA covered by Ramsar Site (Stour and Orwell Estuary, 3,379 ha).

■ Conservation issues

Threats Aquaculture/fisheries (C), Dredging/canalization (A), Filling-in of wetlands (A), Industrialization/urbanization (B), Natural events (A), Recreation/tourism (B)

Threats include oil, industrial and sewage pollution, sea-level rise that may lead to flooding, erosion and habitat loss through harbour dredging, and industrial and recreational developments and disturbance. Major losses of intertidal land to port/commercial development have taken place at Fagbury flats (Orwell) and Bathside Bay (Stour), the latter being outside nationally protected areas. The Stour/Orwell management plan has been produced through the Suffolk Coast and Heaths Project. A major research and monitoring programme is underway with the aim of understanding and addressing the problem of saltmarsh erosion.

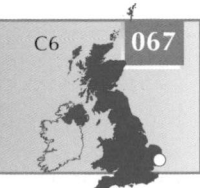

Suffolk Sandlings and coastal forest
C6
067
Admin region East Anglia
Coordinates 52°07′N 1°29′E
Altitude 2–31 m **Area** 3,890 ha

■ Site description
A fragmented site, comprising forested areas and heathland, running from Dunwich in the north to Rendlesham forest in the south.

Habitats Forest and woodland (broadleaved deciduous forest), Scrub (heathland), Grassland, Artificial landscape (forestry plantation)
Land-use Agriculture, Forestry, Nature conservation/research

■ Birds

Species	Season	Year	Pop min	Pop max	Acc	Criteria
Caprimulgus europaeus Nightjar	B	1992	135	135	A	C6
Lullula arborea Woodlark	B	1986	25	25	A	C6

The IBA is also nationally important for wintering *Anas strepera* (93 birds, 1%) and *Anas clypeata* (175 birds, 2%).

■ Protection status
National Partial **International** None
IBA partly or wholly overlaps with the following national designated areas. *Reserves:* Hollesley Heath, North Warren. *Sites of Special Scientific Interest:* Blaxhall Heath, North Warren and Thorpeness Mere, Snape Warren, Sutton and Hollesley Heaths, Tunstall Common.

■ Conservation issues

Threats Abandonment/reduction of land management (A)

The two key breeding birds, *Caprimulgus europaeus* and *Lullula arborea*, occur mainly outside nationally protected areas in clear-felled or recently restocked areas of forest. Both species are therefore vulnerable to changes in forestry practices. The Suffolk Coast and Heaths Project is developing a management plan for the whole area, which includes large areas managed by Forest Enterprise. Many of the heaths are managed through the Sandlings Group, with several subject to Countryside Stewardship agreements. *Lullula arborea* monitoring is carried out.

The Swale
A4i, A4iii, B1i, B2, B3, C3, C4, C6
068
Admin region South East
Coordinates 51°21′N 0°52′E
Altitude 0–27 m **Area** 6,514 ha

■ Site description
Mudflats and saltmarshes bordering the Swale, which separates the Isle of Sheppey from the Kent mainland, in addition to extensive brackish and freshwater grazing-marshes on both sides of the channel.

Habitats Scrub (scrub), Grassland (humid grassland), Wetland (tidal river/enclosed tidal water; mudflat/sandflat; saltmarsh; shingle/stony beach; standing fresh water; water-fringe vegetation), Artificial landscape (arable land)
Land-use Agriculture, Fisheries/aquaculture, Hunting, Tourism/recreation, Urban/ industrial/transport

■ Birds

Species	Season	Year	Pop min	Pop max	Acc	Criteria
Anas acuta Pintail	W	1995	830	830	A	B1i, C3
Anas clypeata Shoveler	W	1995	460	460	A	B1i, C3
Recurvirostra avosetta Avocet	R	1995	75	—	A	B3, C6
Recurvirostra avosetta Avocet	W	1995	170	170	A	C6
Recurvirostra avosetta Avocet	P	1995	130	130	A	C6
Charadrius hiaticula Ringed Plover	P	1995	605	605	A	B1i, C3
Pluvialis apricaria Golden Plover	W	1995	2,640	2,640	A	C6
Pluvialis squatarola Grey Plover	W	1995	2,020	2,020	A	A4i, B1i, C3
Pluvialis squatarola Grey Plover	P	1995	1,890	1,890	A	A4i, B1i, C3
Calidris canutus Knot	W	1995	4,760	4,760	A	B1i, B2, C3
Calidris alpina Dunlin	W	1995	11,500	11,500	A	B2
Philomachus pugnax Ruff	W	1995	73	73	A	C6

Species ... continued	Season	Year	Pop min	Pop max	Acc	Criteria
Limosa limosa Black-tailed Godwit	W	1995	1,520	1,520	A	B1i, C3
Limosa limosa Black-tailed Godwit	P	1995	760	760	A	B1i, C3
Limosa lapponica Bar-tailed Godwit	W	1995	460	460	A	C6
Limosa lapponica Bar-tailed Godwit	P	1995	410	410	A	C6
Numenius arquata Curlew	W	1995	1,550	1,550	A	B2
Tringa totanus Redshank	W	1995	1,540	1,540	A	B1i, C3
Larus melanocephalus Mediterranean Gull	B	1995	5	5	A	C6

The IBA is important for wintering wildfowl, regularly holding 67,400 wintering waterbirds. It is also nationally important for breeding *Anas clypeata* (25 pairs, 1995, 3%), *Aythya ferina* (33 pairs, 1995, 8%), *Larus ridibundus* (2,000 pairs, 1995, 1%) and *Panurus biarmicus* (6 pairs, 1992, 1%), for wintering *Tachybaptus ruficollis* (110 birds, 3%), *Phalacrocorax carbo* (205 birds, 1%), *Anser albifrons albifrons* (1,450 birds, 24%), *Branta bernicla bernicla* (2,710 birds, 3%), *Tadorna tadorna* (2,650 birds, 3%), *Anas penelope* (11,600 birds, 4%), *Anas strepera* (87 birds, 1%), *Anas crecca* (2,960 birds, 2%) and *Tringa erythropus* (5 birds, 1%), and for passage *Tringa totanus* (1,250 birds, 1%).

■ Protection status
National High **International** High
IBA partly or wholly overlaps with the following national designated areas. *National Nature Reserves:* South Swale, Swale. *Reserves:* Elmley Marshes, Oare Marshes. *Sites of Special Scientific Interest:* The Swale, Warden Point. Overlaps with international designated areas: 6,514 ha of IBA covered by Special Protection Area (The Swale, 6,514 ha). 6,514 ha of IBA covered by Ramsar Site (The Swale, 6,514 ha).

■ Conservation issues

Threats Agricultural intensification/expansion (B), Aquaculture/fisheries (U), Drainage (U), Extraction industry (C), Filling-in of wetlands (C), Groundwater abstraction (U), Industrialization/urbanization (A), Infrastructure (A), Natural events (U), Recreation/tourism (A)

Threats include development (for example, the second Swale crossing), sea-level rise that may result in erosion, flooding and habitat loss through coastal defence development, and disturbance from recreational activities. An estuary management plan is in preparation for the Medway and Swale, and water-level management plans are being drawn up by the IDB.

Tamar complex — B2, C6 — 069
Admin region South West
Coordinates 50°25′N 4°12′W
Altitude 0–15 m **Area** 2,380 ha

■ Site description
The Tamar estuary system is a large marine inlet on the English Channel coast, and includes the estuaries of the Rivers Tamar, Lynher and Tavy, which collectively drain an extensive part of Devon and Cornwall. The site comprises extensive mudflats and areas of saltmarsh, freshwater reedmarsh *Phragmites*, and fen.

Habitats Forest and woodland (broadleaved deciduous forest; mixed forest), Grassland, Wetland (tidal river/enclosed tidal water; mudflat/sandflat; saltmarsh; river/stream; fen/transition mire/spring), Rocky areas (sea cliff/rocky shore)
Land-use Tourism/recreation

■ Birds

Species	Season	Year	Pop min	Pop max	Acc	Criteria
Recurvirostra avosetta Avocet	W	1995	195	195	A	C6
Calidris alpina Dunlin	W	1995	5,700	5,700	A	B2

The IBA is important for wintering waders, and is also nationally important for wintering *Egretta garzetta* (100 birds, 1997, 17%), *Tadorna tadorna* (830 birds, 1%), *Limosa limosa* (95 birds, 1%), *Tringa erythropus* (17 birds, 4%) and *Tringa nebularia* (26 birds, 5%).

◙ Protection status
National High **International** Partial
IBA partly or wholly overlaps with the following national designated areas. *Sites of Special Scientific Interest:* Lynher Estuary, St John's

Lake, Tamar–Tavy Estuary, Warleigh Point. Overlaps with international designated areas: 1,955 ha of IBA covered by Special Protection Area (Tamar Estuaries Complex, 1,955 ha).

■ Conservation issues

Threats Industrialization/urbanization (U), Recreation/tourism (C)

Threats include plans for the development of a power station, the construction of homes and marinas and associated reductions in water quality, and recreational disturbance. The Tamar/Tavy estuary and Tamar SAC management plans are in preparation.

Taw and Torridge estuary — C7 — 070
Admin region South West
Coordinates 51°03′N 4°11′W
Altitude 0–10 m **Area** 1,750 ha

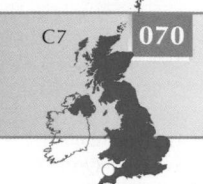

■ Site description
The two major arms of this estuarine complex, the Rivers Taw and Torridge, enter the sea between the dune systems of Northam and Braunton Burrows, and extend inland as far as Barnstable and Bideford respectively.

Habitats Wetland (100%; tidal river/enclosed tidal water; mudflat/sandflat; saltmarsh; sand-dunes/sand beach; river/stream)
Land-use Tourism/recreation

■ Birds

Species	Season	Year	Pop min	Pop max	Acc	Criteria
Numenius arquata Curlew	W	1995	1,000	1,000	A	C7

The IBA supports a diverse assemblage of wintering wildfowl and waders. It is also nationally important for wintering *Tringa nebularia* (14 birds, 3%).

■ Protection status
National Partial **International** None
IBA partly or wholly overlaps with the following national designated areas. *Reserve:* Isley Marsh. *Sites of Special Scientific Interest:* Braunton Burrows, Fremington Quay Cliffs, Northam Burrows, Taw–Torridge Estuary.

■ Conservation issues

Threats Disturbance to birds (C), Extraction industry (C), Infrastructure (U), Other (B), Recreation/tourism (B)

Threats include development proposals for marinas and a holiday village that threaten intertidal areas, recreational demands and disturbance, a proposed tidal defence scheme, inappropriate land and water management ('Other' threat, above) and wildfowling. An estuary management plan was adopted in 1995.

Teesmouth and Cleveland coast — A4i, A4iii, B1i, B2, C3, C4, C6 — 071
Admin region North
Coordinates 54°38′N 1°10′W
Altitude 0–85 m **Area** 1,300 ha

■ Site description
The IBA comprises the Tees estuary, nearby marshes, rocky and sandy beaches on either side of the mouth of the estuary, and surrounding damp grassland.

Habitats Grassland (humid grassland), Wetland (tidal river/enclosed tidal water; mudflat/sandflat; saltmarsh; sand-dunes/sand beach; coastal lagoon), Marine areas (sea inlet/coastal features)
Land-use Fisheries/aquaculture, Nature conservation/research, Urban/industrial/transport

■ Birds
The IBA is important for breeding terns and wintering wildfowl. It regularly holds 20,500 wintering waterbirds, and is also nationally

important for wintering *Phalacrocorax carbo* (310 birds, 2%), *Tadorna tadorna* (1,040 birds, 1%), *Calidris alba* (360 birds, 2%) and *Calidris maritima* (300 birds, 1%), and for passage *Charadrius hiaticula* (390 birds, 1%), *Calidris alba* (590 birds, 3%), *Calidris ferruginea* (12 birds, 2%), *Calidris maritima* (230 birds, 1%), *Tringa totanus* (1,360 birds, 1%) and *Tringa nebularia* (10 birds, 2%).

Species	Season	Year	Pop min	Pop max	Acc	Criteria
Calidris canutus Knot	W	1995	3,780	3,780	A	B1i, B2, C3
Philomachus pugnax Ruff	P	1995	45	45	A	C6
Arenaria interpres Turnstone	P	1995	765	765	A	A4i, B1i, C3
Sterna albifrons Little Tern	B	1995	80	80	A	B2, C6

■ Protection status
National Partial **International** Partial
IBA partly or wholly overlaps with the following national designated areas. *Sites of Special Scientific Interest:* Castle Eden Dene, Cowpen Marsh, Durham Coast, Hart Warren Dunes, Hawthorn Dene, Hawthorn Quarry, Redcar Rocks, Seal Sands, Seaton Dunes and Common, South Gare and Coatham Sands. Overlaps with international designated areas: 942 ha of IBA covered by Special Protection Area (Teesmouth/Cleveland Coast (Phase 1), 942 ha). 942 ha of IBA covered by Ramsar Site (Teesmouth/Cleveland Coast (Phase 1), 942 ha).

■ Conservation issues
> **Threats** Aquaculture/fisheries (B), Filling-in of wetlands (A), Industrialization/urbanization (A), Infrastructure (A), Recreation/tourism (C)

Threats include bait-gathering, recreational disturbance, coastal defence improvements, and oil refinery, pipeline and industrial developments. The Tees Estuary Management Plan is complete, and Durham University has undertaken considerable research, including post-barrage monitoring.

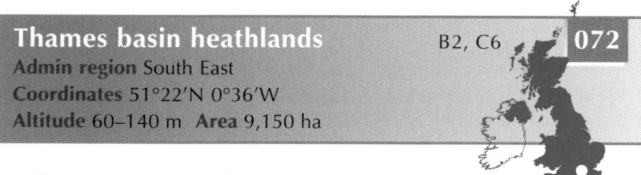

Thames basin heathlands   B2, C6   072
Admin region South East
Coordinates 51°22'N 0°36'W
Altitude 60–140 m **Area** 9,150 ha

■ Site description
The IBA contains several widely separated fragments of what was once an almost continuous block of heathland in the Thames basin. It includes much of the remaining heathland and mire in Surrey, north-east Hampshire and south Berkshire. The habitat mosaics comprise acidic grassland and heathland, and areas of invasive *Ulex*, *Betula*, *Quercus* and *Pinus sylvestris*.

> **Habitats** Forest and woodland (broadleaved deciduous forest; mixed forest), Scrub (heathland), Grassland, Wetland (standing fresh water; fen/transition mire/spring), Artificial landscape (forestry plantation)
> **Land-use** Forestry, Military, Nature conservation/research, Tourism/recreation, Urban/industrial/transport

■ Birds

Species	Season	Year	Pop min	Pop max	Acc	Criteria
Caprimulgus europaeus Nightjar	B	1992	155	155	A	B2, C6
Lullula arborea Woodlark	R	1994	67	67	A	C6
Sylvia undata Dartford Warbler	R	1994	115	115	A	C6

The IBA holds important breeding populations of specialist heathland birds.

■ Protection status
National Partial **International** None
IBA partly or wholly overlaps with the following national designated areas. *National Nature Reserves:* Castle Bolton, Chobham Common. *Sites of Special Scientific Interest:* Ash to Brookwood Heaths, Bourley and Long Valley, Bramshill, Broadmore to Bagshot Woods and Heaths, Castle Bottom to Yateley Common, Chobham Common, Colony Bog and Bagshot Heath, Eelmoor Marsh, Foxlease and Ancells Meadow, Greenham Common, Greenham and Crookham Commons, Hazeley Heath, Horsell Common, Ockham and Wisley Common, Pamber Forest and Silchester Common, Rapley Lakes,

Sandhurst to Owlsmoor Bogs and Heaths, Smarts and Prey Heaths, Snelsmore Common, Warren Heath Ponds, Wasing Wood Ponds, Wellington College Bog, Whitmoor Common.

■ Conservation issues
> **Threats** Abandonment/reduction of land management (A), Afforestation (A), Burning of vegetation (U), Disturbance to birds (U), Industrialization/urbanization (C), Infrastructure (C), Natural events (A), Other (B), Recreation/tourism (B)

The main threat is lack of appropriate management. Additional threats include increased noise and emissions pollution, military training and recreational disturbance, residential developments, acid deposition ('Other' threat, above), and summer heathland and scrub fires. Parts of the site have been put forward for SPA-designation. Monitoring of *Caprimulgus europaeus*, *Lullula arborea* and *Sylvia undata* is carried out in most years. Heathland Management Projects exist in Hampshire and Surrey. Countryside Stewardship and the Wildlife Enhancement Scheme are in operation.

Thames estuary and marshes   A4iii, B1i, B2, C3, C4, C6   073
Admin region South East
Coordinates 51°28'N 0°32'E
Altitude 0–15 m **Area** 12,030 ha

■ Site description
These marshes extend for about 15 km along the coast on the south side of the Thames, and include areas of the inner Thames up to the Thames barrier. Habitat-types include extensive grazing-marshes, saltmarshes, mudflats and pits. Reed *Phragmites* and duckweed *Lemna* dominate the freshwater dykes, with *Ceratophyllum* in the more brackish dykes.

> **Habitats** Forest and woodland (broadleaved deciduous forest; mixed forest), Scrub (scrub), Grassland (humid grassland), Wetland (tidal river/enclosed tidal water; mudflat/sandflat; saltmarsh; coastal lagoon; standing fresh water; river/stream; water-fringe vegetation), Artificial landscape (arable land)
> **Land-use** Agriculture, Nature conservation/research, Urban/industrial/transport

■ Birds

Species	Season	Year	Pop min	Pop max	Acc	Criteria
Recurvirostra avosetta Avocet	R	1995	33	—	A	C6
Recurvirostra avosetta Avocet	W	1995	205	205	A	B2, C6
Charadrius hiaticula Ringed Plover	P	1995	585	585	A	B1i, C3
Calidris alpina Dunlin	W	1995	12,900	12,900	A	B2
Tringa totanus Redshank	W	1995	1,890	1,890	A	B1i, C3
Tringa totanus Redshank	P	1995	1,680	1,680	A	B1i, C3

Waders and wildfowl breed on the grazing-marshes, which also attract wintering raptors. The IBA attracts a wide range of wintering estuarine and wetland birds, and regularly holds 36,000 wintering waterbirds. It is also nationally important for breeding *Ardea cinerea* (225 pairs, 1995, 2%) and *Panurus biarmicus* (12 pairs, 1992, 3%), for wintering *Tachybaptus ruficollis* (145 birds, 3%), *Phalacrocorax carbo* (165 birds, 1%), *Anser albifrons albifrons* (79 birds, 1%), *Branta bernicla bernicla* (1,240 birds, 1%), *Tadorna tadorna* (1,830 birds, 2%), *Anas strepera* (130 birds, 2%), *Anas crecca* (1,570 birds, 1%), *Anas acuta* (295 birds, 1%), *Anas clypeata* (155 birds, 2%), *Charadrius hiaticula* (405 birds, 1%), *Pluvialis squatarola* (965 birds, 2%), *Philomachus pugnax* (12 birds, 2%) and *Limosa limosa* (255 birds, 3%), and for passage *Pluvialis squatarola* (580 birds, 1%) and *Limosa limosa* (515 birds, 7%).

■ Protection status
National Partial **International** None
IBA partly or wholly overlaps with the following national designated areas. *National Nature Reserves:* High Halstour, Northward Hill. *Reserves:* Higham Bight, Northward Hill. *Sites of Special Scientific Interest:* Inner Thames Marshes, Lion Pit, Mucking Flats and Marshes, Northward Hill, Purfleet Chalk Pits, South Thames Estuary and Marshes, West Thurrock Lagoons and Marshes.

■ Conservation issues
Threats include sea-level rise that may result in erosion and flooding, considerable infrastructure development, including the Channel Tunnel Rail Link and road development, dredging proposals, a lack

of management, and water shortages for wetland enhancements. An estuary management plan initiative is in place. The RSPB is pressing for the mudflats and grazing-marshes of the inner Thames to be included in the existing SSSI and candidate SPA and Ramsar Site.

Threats Abandonment/reduction of land management (A), Agricultural intensification/ expansion (B), Aquaculture/fisheries (U), Drainage (U), Dredging/canalization (U), Extraction industry (C), Groundwater abstraction (A), Industrialization/urbanization (A), Infrastructure (A), Natural events (A), Recreation/tourism (B)

Thanet coast and Sandwich Bay

A4i, B1i, C3   074

Admin region South East
Coordinates 51°18′N 1°23′E
Altitude 0–15 m **Area** 2,560 ha

■ Site description
The IBA covers Sandwich Bay and the estuary of the River Stour at Pegwell Bay, incorporating a wide range of habitats including rocky coastline, mudflats and shingle-beaches.

Habitats Scrub (scrub), Wetland (tidal river/enclosed tidal water; mudflat/sandflat; saltmarsh; sand-dunes/sand beach; shingle/stony beach; coastal lagoon; river/stream; fen/transition mire/spring), Marine areas (sea inlet/coastal features), Rocky areas (sea cliff/rocky shore), Artificial landscape (arable land)
Land-use Nature conservation/research, Tourism/recreation

■ Birds

Species		Season	Year	Pop min	Pop max	Acc	Criteria
Charadrius hiaticula	Ringed Plover	P	1995	500	500	A	B1i, C3
Arenaria interpres	Turnstone	W	1995	1,100	1,100	A	A4i, B1i, C3
Arenaria interpres	Turnstone	P	1995	940	940	A	A4i, B1i, C3

The IBA is important for wintering and passage waders. It is also nationally important for wintering *Podiceps cristatus* (390 birds, 3%), *Pluvialis squatarola* (530 birds, 1%), *Calidris alba* (610 birds, 3%), and for passage *Calidris alba* (325 birds, 1%).

■ Protection status
National High **International** Partial
IBA partly or wholly overlaps with the following national designated areas. *Sites of Special Scientific Interest:* Sandwich Bay and Hacklinge Marshes, Thanet Coast. Overlaps with international designated areas: 1,870 ha of IBA covered by Special Protection Area (Thanet Coast and Sandwich Bay, 1,870 ha). 2,169 ha of IBA covered by Ramsar Site (Thanet Coast and Sandwich Bay, 2,169 ha).

■ Conservation issues

Threats Groundwater abstraction (U), Infrastructure (B), Natural events (U), Recreation/ tourism (B)

Recreational disturbance, road and hoverport development, sea-level rise that may result in erosion, flooding and habitat loss through coastal defence development all pose threats to the IBA. A management plan exists for Sandwich and Pegwell Bay Local Nature Reserve. The area is a candidate SAC for its shingle-beach flora and fauna.

Thorne and Hatfield moors

C6   075

Admin region Yorkshire and Humberside
Coordinates 53°32′N 0°56′W
Altitude 2–6 m **Area** 3,320 ha

■ Site description
These two moors, lying to the east and north-east of Doncaster, are the largest remaining areas of lowland peatbog in England. Much peat extraction has already taken place ('Other' land-use, below).

Habitats Scrub (scrub; heathland), Wetland (standing fresh water; raised bog; fen/ transition mire/spring)
Land-use Agriculture (10%), Nature conservation/research (30%), Other (60%)

■ Birds

Species		Season	Year	Pop min	Pop max	Acc	Criteria
Caprimulgus europaeus	Nightjar	B	1992	82	82	A	C6

The IBA is also important for a range of breeding waders and wintering raptors, and is a northern outpost for *Luscinia megarhynchos*. It is also nationally important for breeding *Anas crecca* (18 pairs, 1993, 1%).

■ Protection status
National High **International** None
IBA partly or wholly overlaps with the following national designated areas. *Sites of Special Scientific Interest:* Hatfield Moors, Thorne Crowle and Goole Moors.

■ Conservation issues

Threats Drainage (B), Extraction industry (A), Groundwater abstraction (B), Industrialization/urbanization (C)

There are both short- and long-term implications of continued peat extraction for both sites, and a further threat is posed to the mire hydrology by continuing over-extraction of water from the underlying aquifer. A management plan has been drafted, and the site put forward for SAC, SPA and Ramsar designation. A mineral review is also underway, and the Thorne and Hatfield Moors Conservation Forum has been set up.

Walmore Common

B2, C6   076

Admin region South West
Coordinates 51°49′N 2°22′W
Altitude 5–15 m **Area** 90 ha

■ Site description
This IBA lies in the Severn Vale, about 10 km south-west of Gloucester, in an area subject to winter flooding. A network of ditches that support aquatic and marginal plants separates grass fields, which hold small numbers of breeding waders. Part of the site is common land.

Habitats Grassland (humid grassland), Wetland (standing fresh water; water-fringe vegetation)
Land-use Agriculture (100%)

■ Birds

Species		Season	Year	Pop min	Pop max	Acc	Criteria
Cygnus columbianus	Bewick's Swan	W	1995	120	120	A	B2, C6

The site is important for wintering wildfowl and waders.

■ Protection status
National Partial **International** Partial
IBA partly or wholly overlaps with the following national designated areas. *Site of Special Scientific Interest:* Walmore Common. Overlaps with international designated areas: 53 ha of IBA covered by Special Protection Area (Walmore Common, 53 ha). 53 ha of IBA covered by Ramsar Site (Walmore Common, 53 ha).

■ Conservation issues

Threats Agricultural intensification/expansion (B), Drainage (B)

Surface water drainage poses a threat. The production of a water-level management plan by the West Gloucestershire IDB is therefore a high priority. English Nature/RSPB/Walmore Common Trustees operate an ongoing hydrological monitoring programme that will inform such a plan. The common land is subject to a management plan drawn up by English Nature and the Trustees.

The Wash

A4i, A4iii, B1i, B2, B3, C2, C3, C4, C6   077

Admin region East Midlands, East Anglia
Coordinates 52°56′N 0°18′E
Altitude 0–6 m **Area** 67,000 ha

■ Site description
The IBA comprises one of the most important areas of estuarine

mudflats, sandbanks and saltmarsh in the UK. Included at the eastern end of the site are the low chalk cliffs at Hunstanton. Dune and saltmarsh communities show a typical flora and fauna, although much of the upper saltmarsh zone has been reclaimed. The Wash supports an important shellfishery.

Habitats Wetland (tidal river/enclosed tidal water; mudflat/sandflat; saltmarsh; sand-dunes/sand beach; standing brackish and salt water; water-fringe vegetation), Rocky areas (sea cliff/rocky shore)
Land-use Fisheries/aquaculture, Military, Nature conservation/research, Urban/industrial/transport

■ Birds

Species	Season	Year	Pop min	Pop max	Acc	Criteria
Cygnus columbianus Bewick's Swan	W	1995	76	76	A	B2, C6
Cygnus cygnus Whooper Swan	W	1995	68	68	A	C6
Anser brachyrhynchus Pink-footed Goose	W	1995	23,900	23,900	A	A4i, B1i, C3
Branta bernicla Brent Goose	W	1995	22,200	22,200	A	A4i, B1i, C3
Tadorna tadorna Shelduck	W	1995	16,300	16,300	A	A4i, B1i, C3
Anas acuta Pintail	W	1995	1,230	1,230	A	B1i, C3
Circus aeruginosus Marsh Harrier	R	1995	23	—	A	C6
Circus pygargus Montagu's Harrier	B	1995	2	2	A	C6
Haematopus ostralegus Oystercatcher	W	1995	27,300	27,300	A	A4i, B1i, C3
Haematopus ostralegus Oystercatcher	P	1995	26,500	26,500	A	A4i, B1i, C3
Recurvirostra avosetta Avocet	R	1995	45	45	A	B3, C6
Recurvirostra avosetta Avocet	W	1995	95	95	A	C6
Recurvirostra avosetta Avocet	P	1995	200	200	A	C6
Charadrius hiaticula Ringed Plover	P	1995	1,720	1,720	A	B1i, C3
Pluvialis apricaria Golden Plover	W	1995	6,100	6,100	A	C6
Pluvialis apricaria Golden Plover	P	1995	4,650	4,650	A	C6
Pluvialis squatarola Grey Plover	W	1995	9,700	9,700	A	A4i, B1i, C3
Pluvialis squatarola Grey Plover	P	1995	13,300	13,300	A	A4i, B1i, C3
Calidris canutus Knot	W	1995	139,000	139,000	A	A4i, B1i, B2, C3
Calidris canutus Knot	P	1995	133,000	133,000	A	A4i, B1i, C3
Calidris alba Sanderling	P	1995	1,530	1,530	A	A4i, B1i, C3
Calidris alpina Dunlin	W	1995	36,000	36,000	A	A4i, B1i, B2, C3
Calidris alpina Dunlin	P	1995	46,700	46,700	A	A4i, B1i, C3
Limosa limosa Black-tailed Godwit	P	1995	1,450	1,450	A	B1i, C3
Limosa lapponica Bar-tailed Godwit	W	1995	11,200	11,200	A	A4i, B1i, B2, C2, C6
Limosa lapponica Bar-tailed Godwit	P	1995	13,300	13,300	A	A4i, B1i, C2, C6
Numenius arquata Curlew	W	1995	3,740	3,740	A	A4i, B1i, B2, C3
Numenius arquata Curlew	P	1995	8,800	8,800	A	A4i, B1i, C3
Tringa totanus Redshank	R	1994	580	580	A	B1i, B2, C3
Tringa totanus Redshank	W	1995	3,180	3,180	A	A4i, B1i, C3
Tringa totanus Redshank	P	1995	7,000	7,000	A	A4i, B1i, C3
Arenaria interpres Turnstone	W	1995	800	800	A	A4i, B1i, C3
Arenaria interpres Turnstone	P	1995	1,150	1,150	A	A4i, B1i, C3
Sterna hirundo Common Tern	B	1989	230	230	A	C6
Sterna albifrons Little Tern	B	1993	38	38	A	C6

This extensive site is an important breeding area for several species of wildfowl, and supports large concentrations of passage and wintering waders and wildfowl. The IBA holds 336,700 wintering and 264,400 passage waterbirds on a regular basis, and is also nationally important for breeding *Larus ridibundus* (2,870 pairs, 1989, 2%), for wintering *Tachybaptus ruficollis* (87 birds, 2%), *Phalacrocorax carbo* (250 birds, 2%), *Anser fabalis* (7 birds, 2%), *Anser albifrons albifrons* (99 birds, 2%), *Anas penelope* (3,530 birds, 1%), *Calidris alba* (305 birds, 1%), *Limosa limosa* (585 birds, 8%), *Tringa erythropus* (6 birds, 1%) and *Carduelis flavirostris* (17,000 birds, 1986, 9%), and for passage *Numenius phaeopus* (270 birds, 8%), *Tringa erythropus* (140 birds, 33%) and *Tringa nebularia* (225 birds, 40%). *Branta bernicla* are the *bernicla* subspecies.

■ Protection status
National High **International** High
IBA partly or wholly overlaps with the following national designated areas. *National Nature Reserves:* Gibraltar Point, The Wash. *Reserves:* Frampton Marshes, Gibraltar Point, Snettisham. *Sites of Special Scientific Interest:* Gibraltar Point, Hunstanton Cliffs, The Wash. Overlaps with international designated areas: 62,211 ha of IBA covered by Special Protection Area (The Wash, 62,211 ha). 414 ha of IBA covered by Special Protection Area (Gibraltar Point, 414 ha). 62,211 ha of IBA covered by Ramsar Site (The Wash, 62,211 ha). 414 ha of IBA covered by Ramsar Site (Gibraltar Point, 414 ha).

■ Conservation issues

Threats Aquaculture/fisheries (B), Disturbance to birds (B), Dredging/canalization (B), Filling-in of wetlands (C), Industrialization/urbanization (C), Natural events (B)

Threats include proposals for the expansion of steelworks, power stations and chemical works, sea-level rise that may lead to erosion and changes in fishery/shellfishery management, sewage and other effluent, and disturbance from a military firing range. A management plan exists for the area, and part of the site is a candidate SAC.

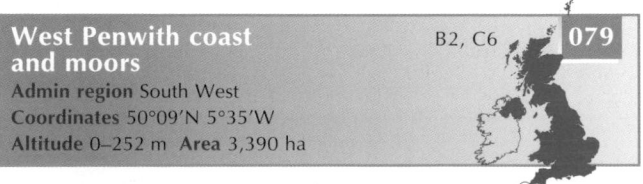

Wealden heaths	B2, C6	078
Admin region South East		
Coordinates 51°06'N 0°47'W		
Altitude 37–260 m **Area** 5,062 ha		

■ Site description
Extensive heathland fragments located in north-east Hampshire, south-west Surrey and West Sussex, overlying the acidic soils of the Folkstone and Sandgate Beds. The IBA comprises areas of heath, mire and woodland. This area includes two sites that were treated as separate IBAs in the previous international IBA Inventory (Grimmett and Jones 1989): 'Woolmer Forest' (former site GB195) and 'Thursley, Hankley and Frensham Commons' (former site GB200).

Habitats Forest and woodland (broadleaved deciduous forest; mixed forest), Scrub (scrub; heathland), Grassland, Wetland (standing fresh water; fen/transition mire/spring)
Land-use Agriculture, Forestry, Military, Nature conservation/research, Tourism/recreation

■ Birds

Species	Season	Year	Pop min	Pop max	Acc	Criteria
Caprimulgus europaeus Nightjar	B	1992	140	140	A	B2, C6
Lullula arborea Woodlark	R	1994	44	—	A	C6
Sylvia undata Dartford Warbler	R	1994	160	160	A	C6

The IBA supports breeding populations of specialist heathland birds.

■ Protection status
National Partial **International** Partial
IBA partly or wholly overlaps with the following national designated areas. *Sites of Special Scientific Interest:* Blackmoor, Bramshott and Ludshott Commons, Broxhead and Kingsley Common, Charleshill, Coates Castle, Conford Moor, Devil's Punchbowl, Forest Mere, Hankley Farm, Iping Common, Lavington Common, Northpark Copse to Snapelands Copse, Shortheath Common, Thursley, Hankley, Frensham Commons, Woolmer Forest. Overlaps with international designated areas: 3,923 ha of IBA covered by Special Protection Area (Wealden Heaths (Phase 1 & 2), 3,923 ha). 625 ha of IBA covered by Ramsar Site (Thursley and Ockley Bog, 625 ha).

■ Conservation issues

Threats Abandonment/reduction of land management (A), Burning of vegetation (U), Infrastructure (B), Other (U), Recreation/tourism (C)

Threats include disturbance from recreational activities, acid deposition ('Other' threat, above), the accidental and deliberate lighting of fires, motorway and trunk road development, and a lack of management leading to vegetation succession. Heathland Projects exist in Hampshire, Surrey and West Sussex, and *Lullula arborea* and *Sylvia undata* monitoring is undertaken almost annually. MoD management plans exist for some sites, and both Countryside Stewardship and the Wildlife Enhancement Scheme are in operation.

West Penwith coast and moors	B2, C6	079
Admin region South West		
Coordinates 50°09'N 5°35'W		
Altitude 0–252 m **Area** 3,390 ha		

■ Site description
A stretch of rocky coastline and a large number of moorland areas, situated mainly to the north and west of Land's End.

Habitats Scrub (heathland), Grassland, Rocky areas (sea cliff/rocky shore)
Land-use Agriculture

■ Birds

Species	Season	Year	Pop min	Pop max	Acc	Criteria
Falco peregrinus Peregrine	R	1995	12	—	A	C6
Saxicola torquata Stonechat	R	1993	100	160	A	B2

The IBA is important for cliff-nesting and heathland species.

■ Protection status

National Partial **International** None

IBA partly or wholly overlaps with the following national designated areas. *Sites of Special Scientific Interest:* Aire Point to Carrick Du, Chyenhal Moor, Porthgwarra to Pordenack Point, Treen Cliff.

■ Conservation issues

Threats Abandonment/reduction of land management (A)

The areas of heathland are largely neglected, although an ESA has now been designated with 2,775 ha of heathland covered under the agreement.

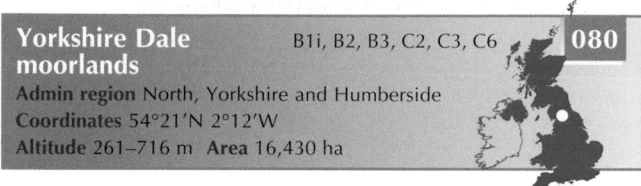

Yorkshire Dale moorlands B1i, B2, B3, C2, C3, C6 **080**
Admin region North, Yorkshire and Humberside
Coordinates 54°21'N 2°12'W
Altitude 261–716 m **Area** 16,430 ha

■ Site description

An upland area rich in habitat-types, including extensive areas of moorland, associated grassland and blanket bog. Areas of limestone plateau support herb-rich calcareous grassland. The heather *Calluna*-dominated heath is managed for game interests.

Habitats Scrub (heathland), Grassland, Wetland (blanket bog; fen/transition mire/spring), Artificial landscape (highly improved reseeded grassland)
Land-use Agriculture, Tourism/recreation

■ Birds

Species	Season	Year	Pop min	Pop max	Acc	Criteria
Falco columbarius Merlin	B	1996	80	80	A	C6
Falco peregrinus Peregrine	R	1996	20	20	A	B2, C6
Pluvialis apricaria Golden Plover	R	1992	2,000	—	A	B3, C2, C6
Calidris alpina Dunlin	B	1992	100	—	A	B1i, C3

The IBA is important for a range of breeding upland species.

■ Protection status

National Partial **International** None

IBA partly or wholly overlaps with the following national designated areas. *National Park:* Yorkshire Dales. *Sites of Special Scientific Interest:* Abbotside/Askrigg Commons, Cliff Beck Meadow, Buttertubs, Feetham Holme, Harkers House Meadows, Len Pastures, Crackpot, Lovely Seat – Stainton Moor, Mallerstang to Swaledale Head, Muker Meadows, New Close, Calvert Houses, Ox Close, Stephen Ings, Crackpot.

■ Conservation issues

Threats Agricultural intensification/expansion (A), Extraction industry (U), Other (C), Recreation/tourism (B)

'Other' threats are posed by the continued persecution of raptors and acid deposition. Disturbance and erosion caused by recreation and tourism are additional problems.

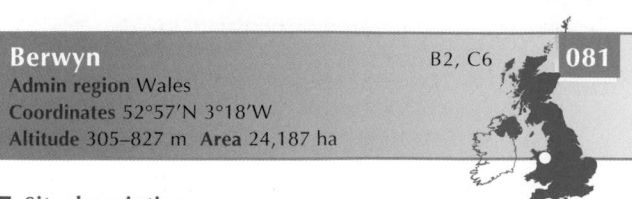

Berwyn B2, C6 **081**
Admin region Wales
Coordinates 52°57'N 3°18'W
Altitude 305–827 m **Area** 24,187 ha

■ Site description

One of the largest areas of *Calluna*-dominated heath and blanket mire remaining in Wales, running south-west from near Llangollen.

Habitats Scrub (heathland), Grassland, Wetland (blanket bog; water-fringe vegetation)
Land-use Agriculture, Forestry, Tourism/recreation

■ Birds

Species	Season	Year	Pop min	Pop max	Acc	Criteria
Circus cyaneus Hen Harrier	R	1990	14	14	A	C6
Falco columbarius Merlin	R	1991	15	15	A	C6
Falco peregrinus Peregrine	R	1990	18	18	A	B2, C6
Asio flammeus Short-eared Owl	B	1988	5	—	A	C6

This area supports a wide range of upland birds, including several species of breeding raptor.

■ Protection status

National High **International** High

IBA partly or wholly overlaps with the following national designated areas. *National Nature Reserve:* Berwyn. *Reserve:* Lake Vyrnwy. *National Park:* Snowdonia. *Sites of Special Scientific Interest:* Afron Dyfrdwy, Berwyn, Cynwyd Forest Quarry. Overlaps with international designated areas: 24,187 ha of IBA covered by Special Protection Area (Berwyn, 24,187 ha).

■ Conservation issues

Threats Abandonment/reduction of land management (A), Afforestation (A), Agricultural intensification/expansion (A), Other (A)

'Other' threats are posed by acidification and human persecution of raptors. The area is a candidate SAC.

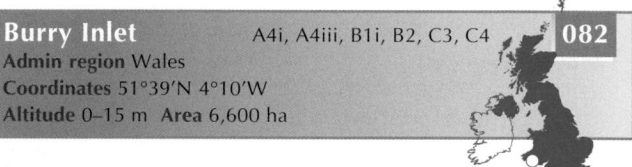

Burry Inlet A4i, A4iii, B1i, B2, C3, C4 **082**
Admin region Wales
Coordinates 51°39'N 4°10'W
Altitude 0–15 m **Area** 6,600 ha

■ Site description

The Burry inlet forms a large intertidal area between the Gower peninsula and Llanelli. Large sand-dune systems and the most extensive area of saltmarsh in Wales occur within the IBA.

Habitats Grassland, Wetland (tidal river/enclosed tidal water; mudflat/sandflat; saltmarsh; sand-dunes/sand beach)
Land-use Unknown

■ Birds

Species	Season	Year	Pop min	Pop max	Acc	Criteria
Anas acuta Pintail	W	1995	1,420	1,420	A	B1i, C3
Haematopus ostralegus Oystercatcher	W	1995	12,600	12,600	A	A4i, B1i, C3
Haematopus ostralegus Oystercatcher	P	1995	11,000	11,000	A	A4i, B1i, C3
Calidris alpina Dunlin	W	1995	7,050	7,050	A	B2
Numenius arquata Curlew	W	1995	1,390	1,390	A	B2

The IBA attracts internationally important numbers of wintering wildfowl and waders. It holds 33,900 wintering waterbirds on a regular basis, and is also nationally important for wintering *Tadorna tadorna* (1,110 birds, 1%), *Anas clypeata* (240 birds, 2%), *Pluvialis squatarola* (445 birds, 1%), and for passage *Numenius phaeopus* (150 birds, 4%).

■ Protection status

National High **International** High

IBA partly or wholly overlaps with the following national designated areas. *Sites of Special Scientific Interest:* Broughton Bay, Burry Inlet and Loughor Estuary, Cwm Ivy Marsh Dunes and Tor, Pembrey Coast, Pyllau Machynys (Machynys Ponds), Whiteford Burrows – Landimore Marsh. Overlaps with international designated areas: 6,600 ha of IBA covered by Special Protection Area (Burry Inlet and Loughor Estuary, 6,660 ha). 6,600 ha of IBA covered by Ramsar Site (Burry Inlet and Loughor Estuary, 6,660 ha).

■ Conservation issues

Threats Aquaculture/fisheries (U), Disturbance to birds (U), Extraction industry (B), Filling-in of wetlands (A), Industrialization/urbanization (U), Natural events (B), Recreation/tourism (U)

Threats include sea-level change that may result in erosion and flooding, proposed marina developments, and disturbance from recreation and unregulated shooting. The area is a candidate SAC.

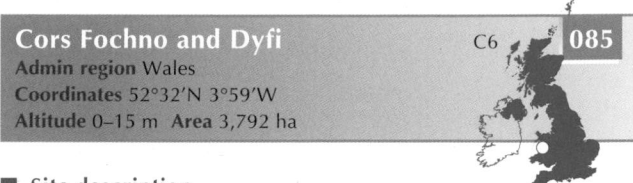

Cardigan Island
A4i, B1i, B3, C3 — 083

Admin region Wales
Coordinates 52°07′N 4°41′W
Altitude 0–52 m **Area** 15 ha

■ Site description
A small rocky island just to the north of the Cardigan estuary.

Habitats Grassland, Rocky areas (sea cliff/rocky shore)
Land-use Not utilized

■ Birds

Species		Season	Year	Pop min	Pop max	Acc	Criteria
Larus fuscus	Lesser Black-backed Gull	B	1993	3,540	3,540	A	A4i, B1i, B3, C3

The IBA is important for breeding seabirds.

■ Protection status
National None **International** None

■ Conservation issues
No serious threats are known at the site.

Carmarthen Bay
A4iii, B2, C4, C6 — 084

Admin region Wales
Coordinates 51°40′N 4°27′W
Altitude 0–56 m **Area** 44,582 ha

■ Site description
The site comprises three broad estuaries that drain into the Bay (the Taf, Tywi and Gwendraeth) in addition to the Bay itself, Laugharne Burrows, St Margaret's Island and part of the Pembrey coast. A wide range of coastal habitats are represented. This area includes two sites that were treated as separate IBAs in the previous international IBA inventory (Grimmett and Jones 1989): 'Carmarthen Bay' (former site GB221) and 'St Margaret's Island' (former site GB240).

Habitats Grassland, Wetland (tidal river/enclosed tidal water; mudflat/sandflat; saltmarsh; standing fresh water; water-fringe vegetation; fen/transition mire/spring), Marine areas (open sea), Rocky areas (sea cliff/rocky shore), Artificial landscape
Land-use Fisheries/aquaculture, Tourism/recreation

■ Birds

Species		Season	Year	Pop min	Pop max	Acc	Criteria
Pluvialis apricaria	Golden Plover	W	1995	4,520	4,520	A	C6
Numenius arquata	Curlew	W	1995	1,250	1,250	A	B2

The IBA is important for wintering wildfowl, and holds 33,000 wintering waterbirds on a regular basis. It is also nationally important for breeding *Phalacrocorax carbo* (270 pairs, 1989, 4%), for wintering *Phalacrocorax carbo* (215 birds, 1%), *Melanitta nigra* (11,000 birds, 1990, 29%), *Haematopus ostralegus* (4,910 birds, 1%) and *Calidris alba* (425 birds, 2%), and for passage *Haematopus ostralegus* (4,760 birds, 1%) and *Calidris alba* (430 birds, 2%).

■ Protection status
National Partial **International** None
IBA partly or wholly overlaps with the following national designated areas. *Sites of Special Scientific Interest:* Amroth to Wiseman's Bridge Cliffs, Broughton Bay, Cors Penally (Penally Marsh), Craig Ddu – Wharley Point Cliffs, Creigiau Llansteffan (Llansteffan Cliffs), Cwm Ivy Marsh Dunes and Tor, Gower Coast – Rhossili to Port Eynon, Hean Castle Cliffs, Laugharne and Pendine Burrows, Marros–Pendine Coast, Pembrey Coast, Rhossili Down, Saint Margaret's Island, Saundersfoot Cliffs, Taf/Ely Estuary, Tenby Cliffs, Whiteford Burrows – Landimore Marsh, Whitehill Down.

■ Conservation issues

Threats Aquaculture/fisheries (B), Disturbance to birds (C), Natural events (C), Other (B), Recreation/tourism (C)

Threats include bivalve harvesting, disturbance from motorbike scrambling and uncontrolled shooting, dune erosion and invasion by *Hippophae rhamnoides*, and the possibility of oil spills ('Other' threat, above). Part of the site is a candidate SAC.

Cors Fochno and Dyfi
C6 — 085

Admin region Wales
Coordinates 52°32′N 3°59′W
Altitude 0–15 m **Area** 3,792 ha

■ Site description
This west coast estuary is of outstanding physiographic interest for its sand-dune complex, extensive tract of actively-growing raised mire and diverse flood-plain habitats. The sand-dune system comprises all stages of dune formation and associated flora.

Habitats Grassland (humid grassland), Wetland (tidal river/enclosed tidal water; mudflat/sandflat; saltmarsh; sand-dunes/sand beach; river/stream; raised bog; fen/transition mire/spring)
Land-use Fisheries/aquaculture

■ Birds

Species		Season	Year	Pop min	Pop max	Acc	Criteria
Anser albifrons	White-fronted Goose	W	1995	140	140	A	C6

The IBA is important for wintering wildfowl, and is also nationally important for wintering *Anas penelope* (3,900 birds, 1%). *Anser albifrons* are the *flavirostris* subspecies.

■ Protection status
National High **International** Partial
IBA partly or wholly overlaps with the following national designated areas. *Reserve:* Ynys-Hir. *Sites of Special Scientific Interest:* Craig y Don, Dyfi, Pencarreg-Gopa a Moel Hyrddod. Overlaps with international designated areas: 2,492 ha of IBA covered by Ramsar Site (Cors Fochno and Dyfi, 2,492 ha).

■ Conservation issues

Threats Aquaculture/fisheries (U), Extraction industry (U), Infrastructure (C), Natural events (U), Other (B)

Threats include sea-level change that may result in erosion, flooding and habitat loss through coastal defence development, oil and gas exploration, acid deposition ('Other' threat, above) and infrastructure developments. The area is a candidate SAC.

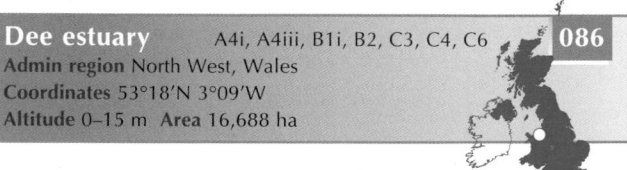

Dee estuary
A4i, A4iii, B1i, B2, C3, C4, C6 — 086

Admin region North West, Wales
Coordinates 53°18′N 3°09′W
Altitude 0–15 m **Area** 16,688 ha

■ Site description
The Dee estuary lies between the Wirral peninsula and the north Wales coast and consists of a very large intertidal area, some 20 km long and up to 9 km wide. The site comprises extensive mudflats and saltmarshes, with sand-dune and maritime cliff-top communities also represented.

Habitats Wetland (100%; tidal river/enclosed tidal water; mudflat/sandflat; saltmarsh; sand-dunes/sand beach; shingle/stony beach; water-fringe vegetation)
Land-use Agriculture, Fisheries/aquaculture, Hunting, Nature conservation/research

■ Birds

Species		Season	Year	Pop min	Pop max	Acc	Criteria
Cygnus columbianus	Bewick's Swan	W	1995	54	54	A	C6
Tadorna tadorna	Shelduck	W	1995	7,000	7,000	A	A4i, B1i, C3

Species ... continued		Season	Year	Pop min	Pop max	Acc	Criteria
Anas crecca	Teal	W	1995	5,950	5,950	A	B1i, C3
Anas acuta	Pintail	W	1995	7,200	7,200	A	B1i, C3
Haematopus ostralegus	Oystercatcher	W	1995	30,200	30,200	A	A4i, B1i, C3
Haematopus ostralegus	Oystercatcher	P	1995	28,200	28,200	A	A4i, B1i, C3
Charadrius hiaticula	Ringed Plover	P	1995	535	535	A	B1i, C3
Pluvialis squatarola	Grey Plover	W	1995	1,940	1,940	A	A4i, B1i, C3
Calidris canutus	Knot	W	1995	19,300	19,300	A	A4i, B1i, B2, C3
Calidris canutus	Knot	P	1995	5,900	5,900	A	B1i, C3
Calidris alpina	Dunlin	W	1995	23,800	23,800	A	A4i, B1i, B2, C3
Limosa limosa	Black-tailed Godwit	W	1995	1,610	1,610	A	B1i, C3
Limosa limosa	Black-tailed Godwit	P	1995	1,620	1,620	A	B1i, C3
Limosa lapponica	Bar-tailed Godwit	W	1995	935	935	A	B2, C6
Numenius arquata	Curlew	W	1995	3,860	3,860	A	A4i, B1i, B2, C3
Numenius arquata	Curlew	P	1995	4,740	4,740	A	A4i, B1i, C3
Tringa totanus	Redshank	W	1995	7,250	7,250	A	A4i, B1i, C3
Tringa totanus	Redshank	P	1995	8,350	8,350	A	A4i, B1i, C3
Sterna albifrons	Little Tern	B	1995	65	65	A	B2, C6

The IBA is important for wintering and passage wildfowl and waders, and holds 126,200 wintering and 64,500 passage waterbirds on a regular basis. It is also nationally important for wintering *Phalacrocorax carbo* (340 birds, 2%), *Anas penelope* (4,500 birds, 2%), *Calidris alba* (965 birds, 4%), *Tringa erythropus* (10 birds, 2%) and *Tringa nebularia* (7 birds, 1%), and for passage *Pluvialis squatarola* (1,090 birds, 3%) and *Calidris alba* (300 birds, 1%).

■ Protection status

National Partial **International** Partial
IBA partly or wholly overlaps with the following national designated areas. *Reserves:* Dee Estuary, Dee Estuary – Tayton Sands, Dee Estuary – Oakenholt Marsh, Dee Estuary – Point of Air and NRA. *Sites of Special Scientific Interest:* Dee Cliffs, Dee Estuary, Gronant Dunes and Talacre Warren, Heswall Dales, North Wirral Foreshore, Red Rocks. Overlaps with international designated areas: 13,055 ha of IBA covered by Special Protection Area (Dee Estuary, 13,055 ha). 13,055 ha of IBA covered by Ramsar Site (Dee Estuary, 13,055 ha).

■ Conservation issues

Threats Aquaculture/fisheries (C), Consequences of animal/plant introductions (B), Disturbance to birds (B), Extraction industry (U), Filling-in of wetlands (C), Industrialization/urbanization (U), Infrastructure (U), Natural events (B), Recreation/tourism (B)

Threats include sea-level change and associated coastal defence measures, disturbance from shooting and increased public access, pollution from industrial sources, sewage and tipping, infrastructure and industrial developments, and accretion of cord-grass *Spartina*. The RSPB owns, leases or has management agreements for a total of 4,715 ha, and a Dee Estuary Strategy is in place.

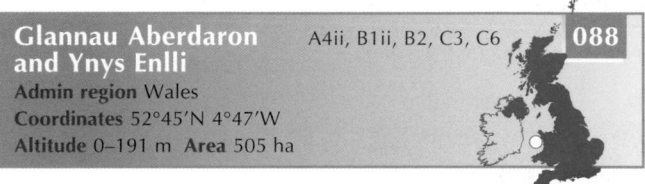

Elenydd–Mallaen
B3, C6   087
Admin region Wales
Coordinates 52°16'N 3°39'W
Altitude 141–641 m   **Area** 30,022 ha

■ Site description

One of the most important areas of hill country in Wales, this area is dominated by blocks of upland rising to 460 m, separated by steep-sided valleys. The uplands are covered by *Calluna* heath and mire, with woodland and grassland in the valleys. The cliff crags hold an interesting flora, whilst the *Quercus* woodland supports many mosses, liverworts and lichens.

Habitats Forest and woodland (broadleaved deciduous forest), Scrub (heathland), Grassland, Wetland (river/stream; raised bog; fen/transition mire/spring), Rocky areas (inland cliff)
Land-use Agriculture, Forestry, Tourism/recreation

■ Birds

Species		Season	Year	Pop min	Pop max	Acc	Criteria
Milvus milvus	Red Kite	R	1997	20	20	A	B3, C6
Milvus milvus	Red Kite	W	1996	50	—	A	C6
Falco peregrinus	Peregrine	R	1996	11	11	A	C6

The IBA supports a wide range of breeding birds, including five species of raptor. *Corvus corax* occur in nationally important numbers.

■ Protection status

National Partial **International** High
IBA partly or wholly overlaps with the following national designated areas. *National Nature Reserves:* Alt Rhyd y Groes, Claerwen. *Reserves:* Gwenffrwd/Dinas, Wye/Elan. *Sites of Special Scientific Interest:* Cabon Lakeside Woodlands, Cae'r Meirch, Caeau Cnwch – Ty'n-y-Graig a Llanfadog, Caeau Penglaneinon, Caeau Troed-Rhiw-Drain, Caen Cnwch a Ty'n-y-Graig, Carn Gafallt, Carn Gafallt, Coed y Cefn, Coedydd Glannau a Cwm Coel, Cwm Doethie – Mynydd Mallaen, Cwm Gwynllyn, Elenydd, Gweunydd Ty'n-y-Llidiart, Rhos Yr Hafod, Rhosydd Llanwrthwl, Vicarage Meadows. Overlaps with international designated areas: 30,022 ha of IBA covered by Special Protection Area (Elenydd–Mallaen, 30,022 ha).

■ Conservation issues

Threats Afforestation (B), Agricultural intensification/expansion (B), Burning of vegetation (U), Drainage (B), Extraction industry (B), Forest grazing (B), Other (C), Recreation/tourism (B)

Threats include overgrazing, the illegal burning of moorland, acid deposition ('Other' threat, above), and disturbance in some areas from four-wheel-drive vehicles and motorcycles. The area is a candidate SAC.

Glannau Aberdaron and Ynys Enlli
A4ii, B1ii, B2, C3, C6   088
Admin region Wales
Coordinates 52°45'N 4°47'W
Altitude 0–191 m   **Area** 505 ha

■ Site description

A section of coast at the tip of the Llyn peninsula together with the island of Bardsey and the smaller Gwylan islands. The coastline is rocky with many crags, screes and low cliffs. Maritime heathland dominated by *Calluna* and *Ulex* is diversified by flushes and adjoining grassland. A rich fern and bryophyte flora occurs on Bardsey, whilst sea spray and guano influence the Gwylan flora.

Habitats Scrub (heathland), Grassland, Wetland (fen/transition mire/spring), Rocky areas (sea cliff/rocky shore; rock stacks/islets; scree/boulders)
Land-use Agriculture, Nature conservation/research, Tourism/recreation

■ Birds

Species		Season	Year	Pop min	Pop max	Acc	Criteria
Puffinus puffinus	Manx Shearwater	B	1992	4,300	4,300	A	A4ii, B1ii, B2, C3
Falco peregrinus	Peregrine	R	1995	12	—	A	C6
Pyrrhocorax pyrrhocorax	Chough	R	1992	19	19	A	B2, C6

The site is important for breeding seabirds and other cliff-nesting species.

■ Protection status

National High **International** High
IBA partly or wholly overlaps with the following national designated areas. *Sites of Special Scientific Interest:* Glannau Aberdaron, Ynys Enlli – Bardsey Island, Ynysoedd y Gwylanod – Gwylan Islands. Overlaps with international designated areas: 505 ha of IBA covered by Special Protection Area (Glannau Aberdaron, 505 ha).

■ Conservation issues

Threats Agricultural intensification/expansion (U), Recreation/tourism (U)

The maintenance of appropriate grazing regimes is important for *Pyrrhocorax pyrrhocorax*. The site is a candidate SAC.

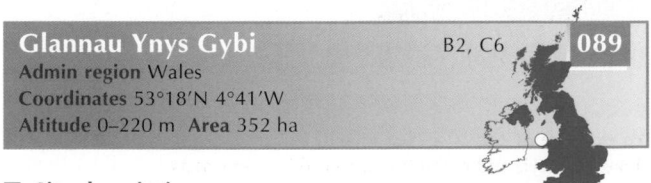

Glannau Ynys Gybi
B2, C6   089
Admin region Wales
Coordinates 53°18'N 4°41'W
Altitude 0–220 m   **Area** 352 ha

■ Site description

The site comprises the cliffs on the western side of Holy Island, which are formed from geologically complex and impressively folded strata rising to 120 m. There are also many small offshore stacks and islets.

Habitats Scrub (heathland), Rocky areas (sea cliff/rocky shore; rock stacks/islets; scree/boulders)
Land-use Nature conservation/research, Tourism/recreation

■ Birds

Species		Season	Year	Pop min	Pop max	Acc	Criteria
Pyrrhocorax pyrrhocorax	Chough	R	1992	9	9	A	B2, C6

The site is important for seabirds and other cliff-breeders.

■ Protection status

National High **International** High
IBA partly or wholly overlaps with the following national designated areas. *Reserve:* South Stack Cliffs. *Sites of Special Scientific Interest:* Glannau Ynys Gybi – Holy Island Coast, Pant Yr Hyman, Rhoscolyn Coast, Rhoscolyn Reedbed, Tre Wilmot. Overlaps with international designated areas: 352 ha of IBA covered by Special Protection Area (Glannau Ynys Gybi/Holy Island Coast, 352 ha).

■ Conservation issues

Threats Industrialization/urbanization (C), Other (U), Recreation/tourism (B)

The proposed development of housing, and a hotel, golf course and equestrian centre threatens maritime heathland, whilst acid deposition is also a problem ('Other' threat, above).

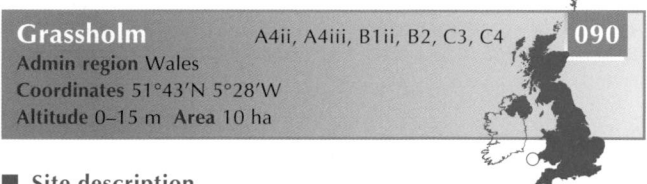

Grassholm — A4ii, A4iii, B1ii, B2, C3, C4 — 090
Admin region Wales
Coordinates 51°43'N 5°28'W
Altitude 0–15 m **Area** 10 ha

■ Site description

A low-lying, flat-topped basalt island situated about 18 km west of the mainland Dyfed coast. Vegetation is limited by exposure to wind, salt spray and the large numbers of seabirds.

Habitats Grassland, Rocky areas (sea cliff/rocky shore; rock stacks/islets)
Land-use Nature conservation/research, Tourism/recreation

■ Birds

Species		Season	Year	Pop min	Pop max	Acc	Criteria
Sula bassana	Gannet	B	1996	—	33,000	A	A4ii, B1ii, B2, C3

The site is important for its seabird colonies, including a very large gannetry. The site regularly holds 33,500 pairs of breeding seabirds.

■ Protection status

National High **International** High
IBA partly or wholly overlaps with the following national designated areas. *Reserve:* Grassholm. *Site of Special Scientific Interest:* Grassholm. Overlaps with international designated areas: 10 ha of IBA covered by Special Protection Area (Grassholm, 10 ha).

■ Conservation issues

Threats Other (B), Recreation/tourism (B)

Threats include pollution from oil spills, discarded netting and waste ('Other' threat, above), and disturbance from visitors.

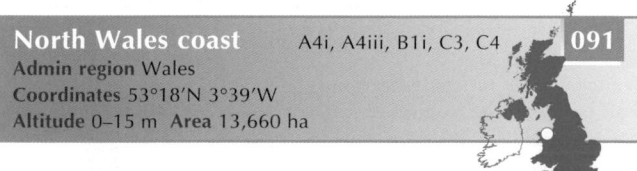

North Wales coast — A4i, A4iii, B1i, C3, C4 — 091
Admin region Wales
Coordinates 53°18'N 3°39'W
Altitude 0–15 m **Area** 13,660 ha

■ Site description

An expanse of the Irish Sea coastline stretching from Little Orme's Head to Rhyl, and extending about 6 km seawards.

Habitats Wetland (sand-dunes/sand beach; shingle/stony beach), Marine areas (open sea; sea inlet/coastal features)
Land-use Tourism/recreation, Urban/industrial/transport

■ Birds

Species		Season	Year	Pop min	Pop max	Acc	Criteria
Melanitta nigra	Common Scoter	W	1995	—	50,000	A	A4i, B1i, C3

The site holds 52,200 wintering waterbirds on a regular basis, and *Tadorna tadorna* and *Charadrius hiaticula* breed along the shoreline.

■ Protection status

National Partial **International** None
IBA partly or wholly overlaps with the following national designated areas. *Sites of Special Scientific Interest:* Little Orme's Head, Llanddules Beach, Rhyd y Foel Limestone.

■ Conservation issues

Threats Extraction industry (U), Infrastructure (U)

Threats include offshore exploration for gas and oil and the potential for oil spills, as well as possible wind-turbine developments.

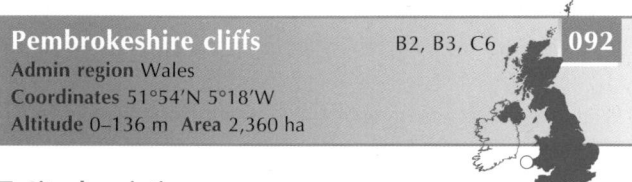

Pembrokeshire cliffs — B2, B3, C6 — 092
Admin region Wales
Coordinates 51°54'N 5°18'W
Altitude 0–136 m **Area** 2,360 ha

■ Site description

The coastline around St David's and Strumble Heads is varied and highly indented with many offshore islands and stacks. The cliffs vary in aspect and exposure to prevailing winds, with some near-vertical faces up to 140 m in height.

Habitats Scrub (scrub; heathland), Grassland, Wetland (sand-dunes/sand beach; shingle/stony beach; river/stream; water-fringe vegetation), Rocky areas (sea cliff/rocky shore; rock stacks/islets; scree/boulders; caves)
Land-use Nature conservation/research, Tourism/recreation

■ Birds

Species		Season	Year	Pop min	Pop max	Acc	Criteria
Falco peregrinus	Peregrine	R	1995	12	—	A	C6
Alca torda	Razorbill	B	1994	1,480	—	A	B3
Pyrrhocorax pyrrhocorax	Chough	R	1992	30	30	A	B2, C6

The IBA is important for breeding seabirds and other cliff-nesting species.

■ Protection status

National Partial **International** Partial
IBA partly or wholly overlaps with the following national designated areas. *Reserve:* Ramsey Island. *National Park:* Pembrokeshire. *Sites of Special Scientific Interest:* Castlemartin Cliffs and Dunes, Castlemartin Corse, Dwrhyd Pit, Ramsey, St David's Peninsula Coast, Stackpole Courtyard Flats and Walled Garden, Stackpole Quay – Trewent Point, Stackpole to Castlemartin Cliffs and Bosherston, Strumble Head to Llechdafad Cliffs. Overlaps with international designated areas: 845 ha of IBA covered by Special Protection Area (Ramsey and St David's Peninsula Coast, 845 ha). 1,122 ha of IBA covered by Special Protection Area (Castlemartin Coast, 1,122 ha).

■ Conservation issues

Threats Industrialization/urbanization (A)

Being so close to the Milford Haven oil refinery makes the site very vulnerable to oil pollution.

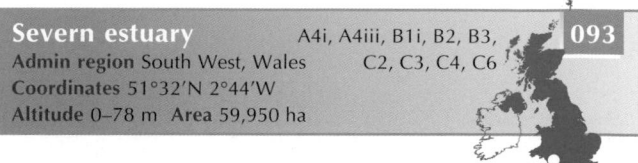

Severn estuary — A4i, A4iii, B1i, B2, B3, C2, C3, C4, C6 — 093
Admin region South West, Wales
Coordinates 51°32'N 2°44'W
Altitude 0–78 m **Area** 59,950 ha

■ Site description

The estuary is fed by five major rivers (the Severn, Wye, Usk, Parrett and Avon) in addition to other lesser rivers. Classically funnel-shaped, the estuary has the second widest tidal range in the world and is characterized by strong currents, mobile sediments and high turbidity. Large expanses of cord-grass *Spartina* occur.

> **Habitats** Forest and woodland (mixed forest), Scrub (scrub; heathland), Grassland (steppe/dry calcareous grassland; humid grassland), Wetland (tidal river/enclosed tidal water; mudflat/sandflat; saltmarsh; shingle/stony beach; standing brackish and salt water; river/stream; water-fringe vegetation), Rocky areas (sea cliff/rocky shore), Introduced/exotic vegetation
> **Land-use** Unknown

■ Birds

Species	Season	Year	Pop min	Pop max	Acc	Criteria
Cygnus columbianus Bewick's Swan	W	1995	285	285	A	A4i, B1i, B2, C2, C6
Tadorna tadorna Shelduck	W	1995	3,420	3,420	A	B1i, C3
Anas acuta Pintail	W	1995	610	610	A	B1i, C3
Charadrius hiaticula Ringed Plover	P	1995	985	985	A	B1i, C3
Calidris alpina Dunlin	W	1995	46,500	46,500	A	A4i, B1i, B2, C3
Numenius arquata Curlew	W	1995	3,890	3,890	A	A4i, B1i, B2, C3
Tringa totanus Redshank	W	1995	2,330	2,330	A	B1i, C3
Tringa totanus Redshank	P	1995	1,800	1,800	A	B1i, C3
Larus fuscus Lesser Black-backed Gull	B	1987	2,050	2,050	A	A4i, B1i, B3, C3

The site supports internationally important numbers of wintering and passage wildfowl and waders, in addition to important breeding bird populations. It holds 84,900 wintering waterbirds on a regular basis, and is also nationally important for wintering *Anser albifrons albifrons* (2,750 birds, 45%), *Anas penelope* (4,200 birds, 1%), *Anas strepera* (300 birds, 4%), *Anas crecca* (2,890 birds, 2%), *Anas clypeata* (110 birds, 1%), *Aythya ferina* (1,610 birds, 2%) and *Pluvialis squatarola* (830 birds, 2%), and for passage *Numenius phaeopus* (2,000 birds, 1992, 56%).

■ Protection status
National Partial **International** Partial
IBA partly or wholly overlaps with the following national designated areas. *National Nature Reserve:* Bridgewater Bay. *Sites of Special Scientific Interest:* Aust Cliff, Berrow Dunes, Brean Down, Bridgewater Bay, Bushey Close, Court Farm, Sydling, Ellenborough Park West, Flat Holm, Frampton Pools, Gwent Levels – Magor and Undy, Gwent Levels – Nash and Goldcliff, Gwent Levels – Redwick and Llandevenny, Gwent Levels – Rumney and Peterstone, Gwent Levels – St Brides, Gwent Levels – Whitson, Lydney Cliff, Middle Hope, Penarth Coast, Portishead Pier to Black Nore, Purton Passage, Severn Estuary, Spring Cove Cliffs, Steep Holm, Sully Island, Sydling Valley Downs, Taf/Ely Estuary, Uphill Cliff, Upper Severn Estuary. Overlaps with international designated areas: 2,703 ha of IBA covered by Ramsar Site (Bridgewater Bay, 2,703 ha). 16,940 ha of IBA covered by Special Protection Area (Severn Estuary, 16,940 ha). 16,940 ha of IBA covered by Ramsar Site (Severn Estuary, 16,940 ha). 1,357 ha of IBA covered by Special Protection Area (Upper Severn Estuary, 1,357 ha). 1,357 ha of IBA covered by Ramsar Site (Upper Severn Estuary, 1,357 ha).

■ Conservation issues

> **Threats** Construction/impact of dyke/dam/barrage (U), Dredging/canalization (U), Extraction industry (U), Filling-in of wetlands (U), Industrialization/urbanization (A), Infrastructure (A), Natural events (A), Recreation/tourism (U)

Threats include sea-level rise that may result in erosion, flooding and habitat loss from coastal defence measures, development for industry, housing, infrastructure and recreation, and recreational disturbance. The area is a candidate SAC.

> ## Skokholm and Skomer
> A4i, A4ii, A4iii, B1i, B1ii, B2, B3, C2, C3, C4, C6 **094**
> **Admin region** Wales
> **Coordinates** 51°44'N 5°17'W
> **Altitude** 0–79 m **Area** 422 ha

■ Site description
These two islands have a plateau-like form, and are bounded by cliffs reaching 70 m in height on Skomer. Salt spray and nutrient enrichment

from seabirds affect the vegetation, which includes maritime grassland and *Juncus* flushes.

> **Habitats** Scrub (heathland), Grassland, Wetland (standing fresh water; water-fringe vegetation; fen/transition mire/spring), Rocky areas (sea cliff/rocky shore; scree/boulders)
> **Land-use** Unknown

■ Birds

Species	Season	Year	Pop min	Pop max	Acc	Criteria
Puffinus puffinus Manx Shearwater	B	1996	—	157,000	A	A4ii, B1ii, B2, C3
Hydrobates pelagicus Storm Petrel	B	1995	4,400	4,400	A	A4ii, B1ii, B2, C2, C6
Larus fuscus Lesser Black-backed Gull	B	1995	18,500	18,500	A	A4i, B1i, B3, C3
Alca torda Razorbill	B	1995	2,870	2,870	A	B3
Asio flammeus Short-eared Owl	R	1996	0	15	A	B2, C6
Pyrrhocorax pyrrhocorax Chough	R	1992	5	5	A	C6

The IBA is important for its breeding colonies, which hold 176,000 pairs of breeding seabirds and 21,800 pairs of breeding waterbirds on a regular basis. The site is also nationally important for breeding *Anas acuta* (2 pairs, 1996, 5%) and *Fratercula arctica* (4,580 pairs, 1995, 1%).

■ Protection status
National High **International** High
IBA partly or wholly overlaps with the following national designated areas. *Marine Nature Reserve:* Skomer. *Sites of Special Scientific Interest:* Skokholm, Skomer Island. Overlaps with international designated areas: 422 ha of IBA covered by Special Protection Area (Skokholm and Skomer, 422 ha).

■ Conservation issues

> **Threats** Consequences of animal/plant introductions (C), Industrialization/urbanization (B), Recreation/tourism (C)

Threats include overgrazing by rabbits *Oryctolagus cuniculus*, some disturbance of breeding birds by visitors, and the possibility of oil pollution from the nearby Milford Haven oil terminal. The site is a candidate SAC.

> ## Swansea Bay–Blackpill
> C7 **095**
> **Admin region** Wales
> **Coordinates** 51°35'N 3°59'W
> **Altitude** 0–10 m **Area** 490 ha

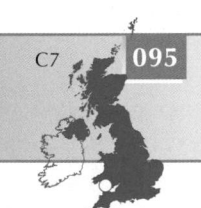

■ Site description
The site covers parts of Swansea Bay, including mudflats at the eastern and western ends that extend for over 1 km at low water. A small area of sand-dunes are also present, although these have been partly converted to a golf course.

> **Habitats** Wetland (100%; mudflat/sandflat; sand-dunes/sand beach)
> **Land-use** Fisheries/aquaculture, Tourism/recreation

■ Birds

Species	Season	Year	Pop min	Pop max	Acc	Criteria
Charadrius hiaticula Ringed Plover	W	1995	175	175	A	C7
Calidris alba Sanderling	W	1995	180	180	A	C7

The site is important for wintering waders.

■ Protection status
National High **International** None
IBA partly or wholly overlaps with the following national designated areas. *Sites of Special Scientific Interest:* Blackpill–Swansea, Oystermouth Old Quarry.

■ Conservation issues

> **Threats** Aquaculture/fisheries (B), Consequences of animal/plant introductions (C), Filling-in of wetlands (C), Recreation/tourism (B)

Threats include invasion of the saltmarsh by cord-grass *Spartina*, and recreational disturbance from dogs and bait-diggers.

Traeth Lafan, Conwy Bay   B1i, C3   096

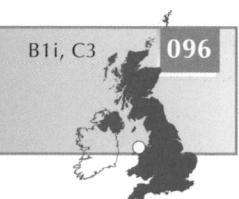

Admin region Wales
Coordinates 53°15'N 4°03'W
Altitude 0–50 m **Area** 2,700 ha

■ Site description

This large intertidal area, at the eastern end of the Menai Straits, contains a range of habitats including exposed and sheltered sands and mudflats diversified by freshwater streams. The site includes 'Traeth Lafan (Lavan Sands), Conway Bay' (former site GB212) and 'Puffin Island' (former site GB239) that were treated separately in the previous European IBA inventory (Grimmett and Jones 1989).

Habitats Wetland (tidal river/enclosed tidal water; mudflat/sandflat; river/stream), Rocky areas (rock stacks/islets)
Land-use Fisheries/aquaculture, Tourism/recreation

■ Birds

Species	Season	Year	Pop min	Pop max	Acc	Criteria
Phalacrocorax carbo Cormorant	B	1995	705	705	A	B1i, C3

The IBA is important for breeding *Phalacrocorax carbo* on Puffin Island, and wintering and passage wildfowl. It is also nationally important for wintering *Haematopus ostralegus* (4,060 birds, 1%), *Tringa nebularia* (14 birds, 3%), and for summer moulting assemblages of *Podiceps cristatus* (500 birds, 1992, 4%).

■ Protection status

National High **International** High
IBA partly or wholly overlaps with the following national designated areas. *Sites of Special Scientific Interest:* Coedydd Afon Menai, Friars Road Shore, Lleiniog, Puffin Island – Ynys Seiriol, Traeth Lafan. Overlaps with international designated areas: 2,642 ha of IBA covered by Special Protection Area (Traeth Lavan, 2,642 ha).

■ Conservation issues

Threats Aquaculture/fisheries (U), Consequences of animal/plant introductions (U), Extraction industry (U), Other (C)

Threats include oil pollution ('Other' threat, above) and the establishment of cord-grass *Spartina* in a small area of the site.

Ynys Feurig, Cemlyn Bay and The Skerries   B1i, B2, C2, C6   097

Admin region Wales
Coordinates 53°24'N 4°37'W
Altitude 0–15 m **Area** 85 ha

■ Site description

Ynys Feurig is a group of small, low-lying islands situated up to 1 km offshore, whilst the very exposed Skerries lie 3 km out to sea. The vegetation on most of the islands is sparse. At Cemlyn Bay, a shingle storm-beach forms a bar between a tidal lagoon surrounded by saltmarsh and the open shore.

Habitats Wetland (mudflat/sandflat; saltmarsh; shingle/stony beach; coastal lagoon; standing brackish and salt water), Rocky areas (rock stacks/islets)
Land-use Not utilized

■ Birds

Species	Season	Year	Pop min	Pop max	Acc	Criteria
Sterna sandvicensis Sandwich Tern	B	1995	650	650	A	B1i, B2, C2, C6
Sterna dougallii Roseate Tern	B	1995	10	10	A	B2, C6
Sterna hirundo Common Tern	B	1995	125	125	A	C6
Sterna paradisaea Arctic Tern	B	1995	1,280	1,280	A	C2, C6

The IBA supports large tern colonies.

■ Protection status

National High **International** High
The IBA partly or wholly overlaps with the following national designated areas. *Reserve:* Skerries. *Sites of Special Scientific Interest:*

Cemlyn Bay, Rhosneigr, Rhosneigr Reefs, The Skerries, Ynys Feurig. Overlaps with international designated areas: 85 ha of IBA covered by Special Protection Area (Ynys Feurig, Cemlyn Bay and The Skerries, 85 ha).

■ Conservation issues

Threats Disturbance to birds (B), Natural events (B)

Nesting terns are vulnerable to human disturbance and predation by red fox *Vulpes vulpes*.

Abernethy forest   A1, B1i, B2, C1, C3, C6   098

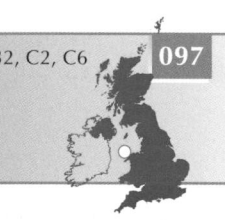

Admin region Scotland
Coordinates 57°13'N 3°38'W
Altitude 200–505 m **Area** 5,800 ha

■ Site description

The largest tract of native pinewood *Pinus sylvestris* in Britain, representing part of a once continuous area of woodland that covered the lower slopes of the Cairngorms. The site includes some completely undisturbed high forest, with a *Juniperus* scrub layer.

Habitats Forest and woodland (broadleaved deciduous forest; native coniferous forest), Scrub (heathland), Wetland (standing fresh water; river/stream; fen/transition mire/spring)
Land-use Forestry (90%), Hunting (10%), Nature conservation/research

■ Birds

Species	Season	Year	Pop min	Pop max	Acc	Criteria
Anser anser Greylag Goose	W	1995	1,300	1,300	A	B1i, C3
Pandion haliaetus Osprey	B	1994	2	2	A	B2, C6
Tetrao tetrix Black Grouse	R	1996	140	140	A	B2
Tetrao urogallus Capercaillie	R	1996	45	45	A	C6
Tringa glareola Wood Sandpiper	B	1994	3	—	A	C6
Loxia scotica Scottish Crossbill	R	1994	Abundant	—		A1, B2, C1, C6

The IBA is important for various pinewood bird specialists. The site is nationally important for breeding *Bucephala clangula* (27 pairs, 1994, 25%). It is also nationally important for wintering *Mergus merganser* (215 birds, 2%). *Anser anser* are from the Icelandic breeding population.

■ Protection status

National High **International** High
IBA partly or wholly overlaps with the following national designated areas. *National Nature Reserve:* Abernethy Forest. *Reserve:* Loch Garten. *Site of Special Scientific Interest:* Abernethy. Overlaps with international designated areas: 5,800 ha of IBA covered by Special Protection Area (Abernethy Forest, 5,800 ha).

■ Conservation issues

Threats Burning of vegetation (B), Forest grazing (B)

Grazing pressure from red deer *Cervus elaphus* poses a threat, although this has reduced in importance over recent years, and forest fires remain a hazard. Research projects are undertaken on the RSPB Reserve, and there is a management plan for the site.

Ailsa Craig   A4ii, A4iii, B1i, B1ii, B2, B3, C3, C4   099

Admin region Scotland
Coordinates 55°15'N 5°06'W
Altitude 0–338 m **Area** 100 ha

■ Site description

A cone-shaped granitic island in the outer part of the Firth of Clyde.

Habitats Rocky areas (100%; sea cliff/rocky shore)
Land-use Not utilized (100%)

■ Birds

The high cliffs support important seabird colonies, which hold 36,700 breeding pairs on a regular basis. The IBA is also nationally important for breeding *Larus argentatus* (2,350 pairs, 1987, 1%).

Species		Season	Year	Pop min	Pop max	Acc	Criteria
Sula bassana	Gannet	B	1995	32,500	32,500	A	A4ii, B1ii, B2, C3
Larus fuscus	Lesser Black-backed Gull	B	1987	1,800	1,800	A	B1i, B3, C3

■ Protection status
National High **International** High

IBA partly or wholly overlaps with the following national designated areas. *Site of Special Scientific Interest:* Ailsa Graig. Overlaps with international designated areas: 100 ha of IBA covered by Special Protection Area (Ailsa Craig, 100 ha).

■ Conservation issues

Threats	Consequences of animal/plant introductions (C)

Predation by rats *Rattus norvegicus* was a problem, but eradication has now been achieved following a Glasgow University monitoring and eradication programme.

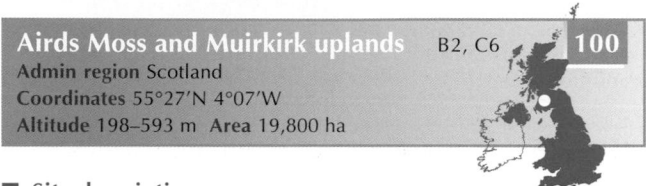

Airds Moss and Muirkirk uplands B2, C6 100
Admin region Scotland
Coordinates 55°27′N 4°07′W
Altitude 198–593 m **Area** 19,800 ha

■ Site description
Includes the largest remaining continuous block of unforested moorland in south-west Scotland. The main habitats include heather and grass moorland and blanket bog.

Habitats	Scrub (heathland), Grassland, Wetland (river/stream; blanket bog), Artificial landscape (forestry plantation)
Land-use	Agriculture, Forestry, Urban/industrial/transport

■ Birds

Species		Season	Year	Pop min	Pop max	Acc	Criteria
[1] *Circus cyaneus*	Hen Harrier	R	1995	16	16	A	C6
[1] *Falco columbarius*	Merlin	R	1995	10	10	A	C6
Pluvialis apricaria	Golden Plover	R	1989	180	180	A	C6
Asio flammeus	Short-eared Owl	R	1995	10	10	A	B2, C6

1. Mean count.

The site is also nationally important for breeding *Numenius arquata* (510 pairs, 1989, 1%).

■ Protection status
National Partial **International** Partial

IBA partly or wholly overlaps with the following national designated areas. *Sites of Special Scientific Interest:* Birk Knowes, Blood Moss and Slot Burn, Dunside, Garpel Water, Greenock Mains, Ree Burn and Glenbuck Loch. Overlaps with international designated areas: IBA overlaps with Special Protection Area (Muirkirk Uplands and North Lowther Hills).

■ Conservation issues

Threats	Afforestation (B), Extraction industry (A), Infrastructure (U), Other (A)

Under serious threat from open-cast mining. Additional threats include windfarms and persecution of raptors ('Other' threat, above). SNH are undertaking research to fill in gaps in knowledge of the site.

Almorness Point and Hestan Island B3 101
Admin region Scotland
Coordinates 54°50′N 3°48′W
Altitude 0–62 m **Area** 73 ha

■ Site description
A small island and rocky headland at the mouth of Auchencairn Bay.

Habitats	Grassland (80%), Rocky areas (20%; sea cliff/rocky shore; rock stacks/islets)
Land-use	Agriculture (100%)

■ Birds

Species		Season	Year	Pop min	Pop max	Acc	Criteria
Larus fuscus	Lesser Black-backed Gull	B	1995	1,300	1,300	A	B3

An important area for breeding seabirds, it holds nationally important numbers of breeding *Larus argentatus* (2,000 pairs, 1995, 1%).

■ Protection status
National None **International** None

■ Conservation issues

Threats	Natural events (U), Other (U)

The main threats to seabirds are from ground predators (red foxes *Vulpes vulpes*) and outbreaks of botulism ('Other' threat, above). An ESA (Stewartry) plan has been drawn up for the Almorness peninsula.

Alvie C7 102
Admin region Scotland
Coordinates 57°09′N 3°51′W
Altitude 210–358 m **Area** 340 ha

■ Site description
A complex area consisting of the wooded Torr Alvie, which slopes down to the north to a series of lochs and marshes. The mainly *Betula* woodland also includes *Populus*, *Sorbus*, *Pinus sylvestris* and *Juniperus*, and one of the few pure *Quercus* stands in the middle Spey valley.

Habitats	Forest and woodland (broadleaved deciduous forest; mixed forest), Wetland (standing fresh water; fen/transition mire/spring)
Land-use	Forestry (70%), Water management (30%)

■ Birds
The lochs and marshes are important for both breeding and wintering waterbirds. The site is also nationally important for breeding *Turdus iliacus* (2 pairs, 1989, 3%).

■ Protection status
National High **International** None

IBA partly or wholly overlaps with the following national designated areas. *National Nature Reserve:* Craigiellachie. *Sites of Special Scientific Interest:* Alvie, Craigiellachie.

■ Conservation issues

Threats	Unknown

Ongoing *Bucephala clangula* monitoring takes place. The site is a candidate SPA.

Assynt lochs C6 103
Admin region Scotland
Coordinates 58°11′N 5°13′W
Altitude 0–764 m **Area** 10,700 ha

■ Site description
Loch Assynt is the largest of these nutrient-poor lochs in the north-west Highlands. Broadleaved *Betula* and *Sorbus* forest survives on higher ground with blanket and valley mires, wet heath and acid fen vegetation lower down.

Habitats	Forest and woodland (broadleaved deciduous forest), Scrub (heathland), Wetland (standing fresh water; river/stream; fen/transition mire/spring)
Land-use	Hunting (100%)

■ Birds

Species		Season	Year	Pop min	Pop max	Acc	Criteria
[1] *Gavia arctica*	Black-throated Diver	B	1995	6	6	A	C6

1. Mean count.

The site is also nationally important for breeding *Gavia stellata* (10 pairs, 1994, 1%) and *Turdus iliacus* (6 pairs, 1996, 8%).

■ Protection status
National Partial **International** None
IBA partly or wholly overlaps with the following national designated areas. *Sites of Special Scientific Interest:* Ardvar Woodlands, Ben More Assynt, Inchnadamph, Loch Beannach Islands.

■ Conservation issues

Threats Afforestation (C), Agricultural intensification/expansion (B), Aquaculture/fisheries (B), Construction/impact of dyke/dam/barrage (A), Disturbance to birds (C), Extraction industry (B), Forest grazing (B)

Disturbance from mining activity, grazing pressure from red deer *Cervus elaphus*, hydroelectric schemes and fish-farming all threaten the IBA. Breeding *Gavia arctica* are monitored by the RSPB annually. The area is a candidate SPA and Ramsar Site.

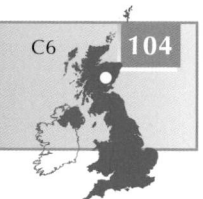

Atholl/Glen Tilt   C6   104
Admin region Scotland
Coordinates 56°54′N 3°29′W
Altitude 800–1,120 m   **Area** 6,166 ha

■ Site description
A series of 11 montane plateaux ranging from Beinn Dearg in the west to Carn a Gheoidh in the east, most of which are above 800 m. Various uncommon plant communities are present, including sugar limestone grassland and heath vegetation, and both montane and summit communities.

Habitats Scrub (40%; heathland), Grassland (59%; steppe/dry calcareous grassland), Rocky areas (1%; inland cliff)
Land-use Agriculture, Hunting

■ Birds

Species	Season	Year	Pop min	Pop max	Acc	Criteria
Charadrius morinellus Dotterel	B	1987	—	27	A	C6

The IBA is important for breeding upland birds.

■ Protection status
National Partial **International** None
IBA partly or wholly overlaps with the following national designated areas. *Sites of Special Scientific Interest:* Beinn a Ghlo, Glas Tulaichean.

■ Conservation issues

Threats Disturbance to birds (B), Other (B), Recreation/tourism (B)

Threats include disturbance from tourism, recreation and increased public access, and the effects of atmospheric pollution ('Other' threat, above). The only known survey of the site was a joint Nature Conservancy Council/SNH Montane Plateaux Ecology Project undertaken during the late 1980s and early 1990s.

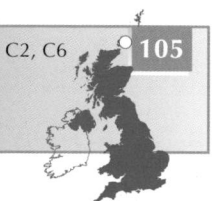

Auskerry   A4ii, B1ii, B2, C2, C6   105
Admin region Scotland
Coordinates 59°01′N 2°33′W
Altitude 0–10 m   **Area** 90 ha

■ Site description
A small island to the south of Stronsay in the Orkney archipelago.

Habitats Scrub (heathland), Grassland, Marine areas (open sea), Rocky areas (sea cliff/rocky shore)
Land-use Agriculture (100%)

■ Birds

Species	Season	Year	Pop min	Pop max	Acc	Criteria
Hydrobates pelagicus Storm Petrel	B	1995	3,610	3,610	A	A4ii, B1ii, B2, C2, C6

The IBA supports large numbers of breeding seabirds, and is also nationally important for breeding *Sterna paradisaea* (670 pairs, 1993, 2%).

■ Protection status
National High **International** High
IBA partly or wholly overlaps with the following national designated areas. *Site of Special Scientific Interest:* Auskerry. Overlaps with international designated areas: 90 ha of IBA covered by Special Protection Area (Auskerry, 90 ha).

■ Conservation issues

Threats Extraction industry (U)

There is an ongoing threat of oil pollution.

Ballochbuie forest   A1, B2, C1, C6   106
Admin region Scotland
Coordinates 56°59′N 3°19′W
Altitude 290–770 m   **Area** 2,031 ha

■ Site description
A large area of native pinewood and associated old *Pinus* plantations.

Habitats Forest and woodland (40%; broadleaved deciduous forest; native coniferous forest), Scrub (10%; heathland), Grassland (10%), Rocky areas (1%; inland cliff), Artificial landscape (39%; forestry plantation)
Land-use Forestry (40%), Hunting (70%), Nature conservation/research (10%)

■ Birds

Species	Season	Year	Pop min	Pop max	Acc	Criteria
Loxia scotica Scottish Crossbill	R	1995	Common		—	A1, B2, C1, C6

The IBA also supports breeding *Tetrao tetrix* and *Tetrao urogallus*.

■ Protection status
National None **International** Partial
Overlaps with international designated areas: 1,629 ha of IBA covered by Special Protection Area (Ballochbuie, 1,629 ha).

■ Conservation issues

Threats Forest grazing (A), Other (A), Recreation/tourism (C)

Threats to the IBA are deer overgrazing, inappropriate forestry practices ('Other' threat, above) and recreational disturbance. SNH has a 'memorandum of understanding' with Balmoral Estate over the management of the site.

Beinn Dearg   C7   107
Admin region Scotland
Coordinates 57°47′N 4°54′W
Altitude 30–1,084 m   **Area** 13,715 ha

■ Site description
A large and diverse massif that has been deeply dissected by glacial action, but exhibits rounded summits. Landform and geological diversity has resulted in a wide range of upland vegetation communities including summit communities of cushion herbs, lichens and mosses.

Habitats Forest and woodland (native coniferous forest), Scrub (heathland), Grassland (steppe/dry calcareous grassland), Wetland (standing fresh water; blanket bog; fen/transition mire/spring), Rocky areas (scree/boulders; inland cliff)
Land-use Hunting

■ Birds

Species	Season	Year	Pop min	Pop max	Acc	Criteria
Charadrius morinellus Dotterel	B	1993	6	—	A	C7

The site holds an assemblage of breeding upland birds.

■ Protection status
National Partial **International** Partial
IBA partly or wholly overlaps with the following national designated areas. *Site of Special Scientific Interest:* Beinn Dearg. Overlaps with

international designated areas: 5,568 ha of IBA covered by Special Protection Area (Beinn Dearg, 5,568 ha).

■ Conservation issues

Threats Agricultural intensification/expansion (U), Disturbance to birds (B), Forest grazing (B), Recreation/tourism (B)

Problems are posed by disturbance from increased public access and recreation, and habitat degradation due to high densities of grazing animals (mainly red deer *Cervus elaphus*, but also sheep). This is the third most botanically diverse mountain in Britain.

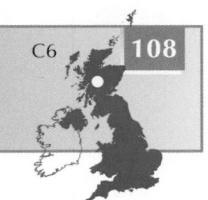

Ben Alder
Admin region Scotland
Coordinates 56°50'N 4°28'W
Altitude 367–1,148 m **Area** 6,548 ha

C6 108

■ Site description
Remote summit plateaus with high altitude limestone outcrops, situated between Lochs Ericht and Laggan. The site is geographically and ecologically intermediate between the mountains of the western and eastern Highlands. Highly diverse plant communities are present, including those associated with lengthy snow cover and limestone outcrops.

Habitats Scrub (heathland), Grassland (steppe/dry calcareous grassland), Wetland (blanket bog), Rocky areas (scree/boulders; inland cliff)
Land-use Hunting

■ Birds

Species	Season	Year	Pop min	Pop max	Acc	Criteria
Charadrius morinellus Dotterel	B	1993	11	—	A	C6

The IBA supports an assemblage of breeding upland species.

■ Protection status
National High **International** None
IBA partly or wholly overlaps with the following national designated areas. *Site of Special Scientific Interest:* Ben Alder and Aonach Beag.

■ Conservation issues

Threats Agricultural intensification/expansion (B), Other (B), Recreation/tourism (B)

Habitat disturbance occurs as a result of high livestock levels, and overgrazing by deer ('Other' threat, above). The area is a candidate SPA, with a smaller area a candidate SAC. There is an ongoing survey of divers (Gaviidae).

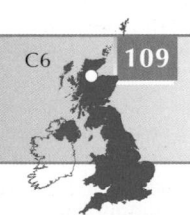

Ben Wyvis
Admin region Scotland
Coordinates 57°41'N 4°33'W
Altitude 220–1,046 m **Area** 5,500 ha

C6 109

■ Site description
The only major mountain massif in the eastern Highlands north of the Great Glen. Its size, altitude and location give it a unique character midway between the continental Cairngorm massif and the oceanic mountains of the western Highlands. Summit heath and bryophyte-rich snowbed areas complement montane and submontane dwarf shrub heath, upland *Betula* forests and blanket bog.

Habitats Forest and woodland (broadleaved deciduous forest), Scrub (heathland), Grassland (steppe/dry calcareous grassland), Wetland (standing fresh water; blanket bog; fen/transition mire/spring)
Land-use Agriculture, Hunting

■ Birds

Species	Season	Year	Pop min	Pop max	Acc	Criteria
Charadrius morinellus Dotterel	B	1993	9	—	A	C6

The site holds an assemblage of breeding upland birds.

■ Protection status
National High **International** High
IBA partly or wholly overlaps with the following national designated areas. *Sites of Special Scientific Interest:* Allt nan Caorach, Ben Wyvis, Carn Gorm. Overlaps with international designated areas: 5,500 ha of IBA covered by Special Protection Area (Ben Wyvis, 5,500 ha).

■ Conservation issues

Threats Agricultural intensification/expansion (B), Disturbance to birds (A), Recreation/tourism (A)

The IBA is affected by disturbance from increased public access and recreation, and habitat degradation due to high densities of grazing animals. There is also a possibility of development for skiing, including a funicular railway.

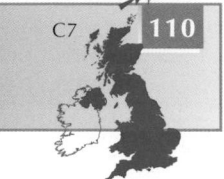

Blackpark and Gutcher, Yell
Admin region Scotland
Coordinates 60°40'N 1°01'W
Altitude 0–110 m **Area** 1,050 ha

C7 110

■ Site description
A mosaic of moorland and blanket bog, which overlies deep peat. *Calluna*, *Eriophorum* and *Scirpus* dominate the blanket bog plant community, which is interspersed with areas of acid grassland and *Sphagnum*-rich mire.

Habitats Grassland, Wetland (standing fresh water; blanket bog; fen/transition mire/spring)
Land-use Agriculture (100%), Nature conservation/research

■ Birds

Species	Season	Year	Pop min	Pop max	Acc	Criteria
Gavia stellata Red-throated Diver	B	1994	6	6	A	C7
Numenius phaeopus Whimbrel	B	1992	23	23	A	C7
Stercorarius parasiticus Arctic Skua	B	1992	27	27	A	C7

The IBA supports an assemblage of breeding moorland birds.

■ Protection status
National Partial **International** None
IBA partly or wholly overlaps with the following national designated areas. *Reserve:* Black Park. *Sites of Special Scientific Interest:* Gutcher, North Sandwick.

■ Conservation issues

Threats Agricultural intensification/expansion (B)

A management plan exists for the RSPB reserve.

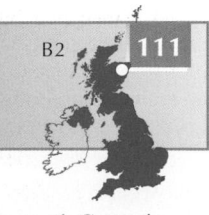

Bluemill
Admin region Scotland
Coordinates 57°11'N 2°57'W
Altitude 290–411 m **Area** 260 ha

B2 111

■ Site description
A small area of moorland and acid grassland in south Grampian.

Habitats Forest and woodland (5%; mixed forest), Scrub (55%; heathland), Grassland (40%)
Land-use Agriculture (100%)

■ Birds

Species	Season	Year	Pop min	Pop max	Acc	Criteria
Larus canus Common Gull	B	1995	3,250	—	A	B2

The IBA supports a number of breeding moorland and grassland species.

■ Protection status
National None **International** None

■ Conservation issues

Threats Agricultural intensification/expansion (B)

Regular ringing of gull chicks takes place.

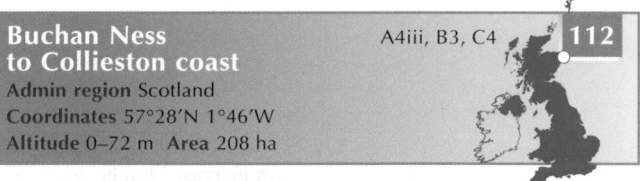

Buchan Ness to Collieston coast   A4iii, B3, C4   **112**
Admin region Scotland
Coordinates 57°28'N 1°46'W
Altitude 0–72 m **Area** 208 ha

■ Site description
The IBA comprises south-east facing granitic cliffs, interrupted by the sandy beach at Cruden Bay, and offshore stacks.

Habitats Scrub (2%; heathland), Grassland (5%), Wetland (2%; sand-dunes/sand beach; standing brackish and salt water), Rocky areas (91%; sea cliff/rocky shore; rock stacks/islets)
Land-use Not utilized

■ Birds

Species	Season	Year	Pop min	Pop max	Acc	Criteria
Alca torda Razorbill	B	1995	1,940	1,940	A	B3

The site holds 23,800 pairs of breeding seabirds and 28,100 pairs of breeding waterbirds on a regular basis. The IBA is nationally important for breeding *Larus argentatus* (2,960 pairs, 1995, 2%), *Rissa tridactyla* (25,000 pairs, 1995, 5%) and *Uria aalge* (18,700 pairs, 1995, 3%).

■ Protection status
National High **International** High
IBA partly or wholly overlaps with the following national designated areas. *Sites of Special Scientific Interest:* Bullers of Buchan Coast, Collieston to Whinnyfold Coast. Overlaps with international designated areas: 208 ha of IBA covered by Special Protection Area (Buchan Ness to Collieston Coast, 208 ha).

■ Conservation issues

Threats Aquaculture/fisheries (A)

Auks are accidentally caught in fixed offshore salmon nets. Monitoring for the Joint Nature Conservation Committee Seabird Colony Register is carried out here.

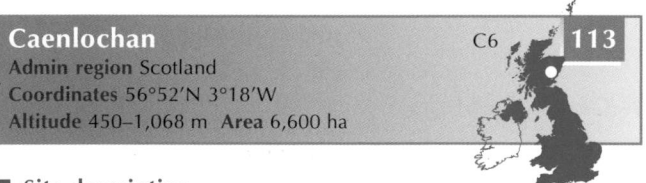

Caenlochan   C6   **113**
Admin region Scotland
Coordinates 56°52'N 3°18'W
Altitude 450–1,068 m **Area** 6,600 ha

■ Site description
A wide variety of habitats are supported by these hills, with their many crags and steep rocky slopes. Dwarf shrub communities predominate, although small areas of herb-rich communities do occur. The IBA is also notable for its high-altitude bog and lichen-rich communities, and snow-bed vegetation. Base-rich flushes increase the plant diversity despite grazing by deer and sheep.

Habitats Scrub (heathland), Grassland (steppe/dry calcareous grassland), Wetland (fen/transition mire/spring)
Land-use Agriculture (50%), Hunting (100%), Tourism/recreation (10%)

■ Birds

Species	Season	Year	Pop min	Pop max	Acc	Criteria
Charadrius morinellus Dotterel	B	1992	—	47	A	C6

The IBA also holds important populations of raptors and other upland breeding birds.

■ Protection status
National Partial **International** High
IBA partly or wholly overlaps with the following national designated areas. *Sites of Special Scientific Interest:* Caenlochan, Glen Callater,

Red Craig. Overlaps with international designated areas: 5,975 ha of IBA covered by Special Protection Area (Caenlochan, 5,975 ha).

■ Conservation issues

Threats Disturbance to birds (A), Infrastructure (A)

The IBA is threatened by the development of skiing infrastructure, and increased public access. Part of the site is located within the scope of the East Grampian Deer Management Plan being developed by the Deer Commission for Scotland.

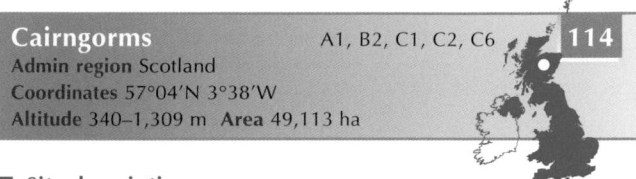

Cairngorms   A1, B2, C1, C2, C6   **114**
Admin region Scotland
Coordinates 57°04'N 3°38'W
Altitude 340–1,309 m **Area** 49,113 ha

■ Site description
An area of massive summits, cut into separate areas by steep-sided glacial troughs.

Habitats Forest and woodland (broadleaved deciduous forest; native coniferous forest), Scrub (scrub; heathland), Grassland (steppe/dry calcareous grassland), Wetland (blanket bog)
Land-use Forestry (10%), Hunting (50%), Nature conservation/research (50%), Tourism/recreation

■ Birds

Species	Season	Year	Pop min	Pop max	Acc	Criteria
Circus cyaneus Hen Harrier	R	1990	—	15	A	C6
Aquila chrysaetos Golden Eagle	R	1992	8	8	A	B2, C6
Pandion haliaetus Osprey	B	1991	2	2	A	B2, C6
Falco columbarius Merlin	B	1992	25	25	A	C6
Falco peregrinus Peregrine	R	1990	10	10	A	C6
Tetrao urogallus Capercaillie	R	1990	125	125	A	C6
Charadrius morinellus Dotterel	B	1990	240	240	A	C2, C6
Loxia scotica Scottish Crossbill	R	1996	Abundant	—	A1, B2, C1, C6

This site is very important for a range of breeding birds associated with montane plateaus and pinewoods *Pinus sylvestris*. The site is also nationally important for breeding *Bucephala clangula* (5 pairs, 1989, 5%), *Lagopus mutus* (1,500 pairs, 1990, 15%) and *Plectrophenax nivalis* (40 pairs, 1990, 40%).

■ Protection status
National High **International** High
IBA partly or wholly overlaps with the following national designated areas. *National Nature Reserve:* Cairngorms. *Sites of Special Scientific Interest:* Allt Mor, Cairngorms, Dollar Glen, Eastern Cairngorms, Inchrory, Morrone Birkwood, North Rothiemurchus Pinewood, Northern Corries, River Feshie. Overlaps with international designated areas: 49,113 ha of IBA covered by Special Protection Area (Cairngorms, 49,113 ha). 173 ha of IBA covered by Ramsar Site (Cairngorm Lochs, 173 ha).

■ Conservation issues

Threats Afforestation (A), Forest grazing (U), Infrastructure (A), Other (A), Recreation/tourism (A)

Threats include disturbance and habitat degradation associated with increased public access and the proposed railway development to replace the existing chairlift, overgrazing by deer, problems with birds striking deer fences and inappropriate forestry management ('Other' threat, above). A partnership management strategy is being developed, with most NGOs campaigning for better management of this proposed National Park, SPA, SAC and World Heritage Site. Research is ongoing, and a management strategy is being developed.

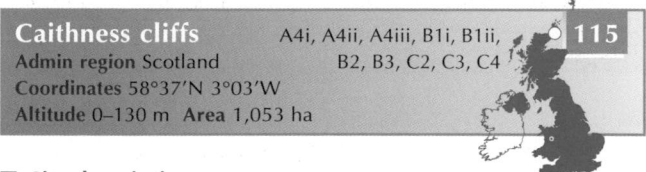

Caithness cliffs   A4i, A4ii, A4iii, B1i, B1ii,   **115**
Admin region Scotland   B2, B3, C2, C3, C4
Coordinates 58°37'N 3°03'W
Altitude 0–130 m **Area** 1,053 ha

■ Site description
The IBA comprises sections of cliff-lined coast at Dunnet Head, Duncansby Head to Skirza Head, and Wick to Helmsdale. Patches of

species-rich maritime heath occur, giving way to acidic heath further inland.

Habitats Scrub (heathland), Grassland, Rocky areas (sea cliff/rocky shore)
Land-use Agriculture

■ Birds

Species	Season	Year	Pop min	Pop max	Acc	Criteria
Phalacrocorax aristotelis Shag	B	1987	2,540	2,540	A	A4i, B1i, B3, C2, C3
Larus argentatus Herring Gull	B	1987	9,550	9,550	A	A4i, B1i
Larus marinus Great Black-backed Gull	B	1987	875	875	A	B3
Rissa tridactyla Kittiwake	B	1987	40,800	40,800	A	A4i, B1i, C3
Uria aalge Guillemot	B	1987	87,000	87,000	A	A4ii, B1ii, C3
Alca torda Razorbill	B	1987	11,100	11,100	A	A4ii, B1ii, B3, C3
Cepphus grylle Black Guillemot	B	1987	725	725	A	B1ii, B2

These cliffs support 127,000 pairs of breeding seabirds, and 54,000 pairs of breeding waterbirds on a regular basis. The site is also nationally important for breeding *Fulmarus glacialis* (27,100 pairs, 1986–1987, 5%) and *Phalacrocorax carbo* (250 pairs, 1985–1986, 3%).

■ Protection status

National High **International** High
IBA partly or wholly overlaps with the following national designated areas. *Sites of Special Scientific Interest:* Berriedale Cliffs, Berriedale Water, Burn of Latheronwheel, Castle of Old Wick to Craig Hammel, Craig Hammel to Sgaps Geo, Dunbeath to Sgaps Geo, Duncansby Head, Dunnet Head, Helmsdale Coast, Hill of Warehouse, Knockinnon Heath, Langwell Water, Ousdale Burn. Overlaps with international designated areas: 443 ha of IBA covered by Special Protection Area (East Caithness Cliffs, 443 ha). 610 ha of IBA covered by Special Protection Area (North Caithness Cliffs, 610 ha).

■ Conservation issues

Threats Aquaculture/fisheries (B), Extraction industry (B), Other (B), Recreation/tourism (U)

Threats to the coastline include oil pollution from passing tankers ('Other' threat, above), development of oil-extraction facilities and inshore oil fields, and disturbance from recreational activities.

Caithness lochs   A4i, B1i, B3, C2, C3, C6   116

Admin region Scotland
Coordinates 58°35'N 3°16'W
Altitude 20–100 m **Area** 3,016 ha

■ Site description

A series of lochs spread over a wide area in north-east Caithness, and situated roughly in the triangle formed by Wick, Duncansby Head and Thurso. The lochs are rich to moderately rich in nutrients, and support a diverse aquatic flora. A mire system has developed along the old course of the River Forss.

Habitats Grassland (humid grassland), Wetland (standing fresh water; blanket bog; fen/transition mire/spring)
Land-use Agriculture, Forestry, Tourism/recreation

■ Birds

Species	Season	Year	Pop min	Pop max	Acc	Criteria
Cygnus cygnus Whooper Swan	W	1996	—	185	A	B3
[1] *Anser albifrons* White-fronted Goose	W	1994	410	410	A	B1i, C2, C3
[1] *Anser anser* Greylag Goose	W	1994	4,490	4,490	A	A4i, B1i, C3
Porzana porzana Spotted Crake	B	1992	2	2	A	C6

1. Mean annual peak 1989–1994.

The IBA is important for both breeding and wintering waterbirds, and is also nationally important for breeding *Anas penelope* (9 pairs, 1993–1994, 3%). *Anser albifrons* are the *flavirostris* subspecies, and *Anser anser* are from the Icelandic breeding population.

■ Protection status

National Partial **International** Low

IBA partly or wholly overlaps with the following national designated areas. *Sites of Special Scientific Interest:* Broubster Leans, Loch Heilen, Loch Lieurary, Loch of May, Loch Scarmclate, Loch Watten. Overlaps with international designated areas: 240 ha of IBA covered by Special Protection Area (Caithness Lochs, 240 ha). 240 ha of IBA covered by Ramsar Site (Caithness Lochs, 240 ha).

■ Conservation issues

Threats Afforestation (A), Agricultural intensification/expansion (A), Aquaculture/fisheries (B), Drainage (A), Infrastructure (C), Recreation/tourism (U)

Threats include disturbance from recreational activities and loss of semi-natural habitat, whilst proposed wind-farm developments may increase the risk of bird strikes. Wintering *Anser albifrons flavirostris* are monitored by a study group.

Cameron reservoir   A4i, B1i, C3   117

Admin region Scotland
Coordinates 56°17'N 2°50'W
Altitude 152–152 m **Area** 68 ha

■ Site description

Situated about 5 km west of St Andrews, this reservoir was formed following the impoundment of the Cameron Burn. The reservoir is moderately nutrient-rich and supports fringing aquatic and marginal vegetation, which is succeeded by *Salix* carr.

Habitats Scrub (scrub), Grassland, Wetland (standing fresh water; water-fringe vegetation)
Land-use Not utilized (90%), Tourism/recreation (10%)

■ Birds

Species	Season	Year	Pop min	Pop max	Acc	Criteria
[1] *Anser brachyrhynchus* Pink-footed Goose	W	1994	13,700	13,700	A	A4i, B1i, C3

1. Mean annual peak 1989–1994.

The IBA is important for wintering waterbirds, and as an autumn and winter roost for geese.

■ Protection status

National High **International** High
IBA partly or wholly overlaps with the following national designated areas. *Site of Special Scientific Interest:* Cameron Reservoir. Overlaps with international designated areas: 68 ha of IBA covered by Special Protection Area (Cameron Reservoir, 68 ha). 68 ha of IBA covered by Ramsar Site (Cameron Reservoir, 68 ha).

■ Conservation issues

Threats Disturbance to birds (A), Other (A), Recreation/tourism (A)

The decommissioning of the reservoir as a public water supply may affect the future presence of areas of open water ('Other' threat, above). Disturbance to roosting wildfowl caused by increased shooting activity is an additional problem. The Local Authority have proposed that the site be designated as a Local Nature Reserve, enabling a management plan to be drawn up.

Canna and Sanday   A4i, B1i, B3, C2, C3   118

Admin region Scotland
Coordinates 57°03'N 6°32'W
Altitude 0–210 m **Area** 1,356 ha

■ Site description

Two islands and associated islets and stacks, to the north-west of the much larger island of Rum. They support a variety of grassland habitats along with species-rich maritime heathland and machair-type calcareous grassland.

Habitats Forest and woodland (mixed forest), Scrub (heathland), Grassland (steppe/dry calcareous grassland; mesophile grassland; machair), Wetland (blanket bog), Rocky areas (sea cliff/rocky shore; rock stacks/islets)

Land-use Agriculture

■ Birds

Species		Season	Year	Pop min	Pop max	Acc	Criteria
Phalacrocorax aristotelis	Shag	B	1995	980	980	A	A4i, B1i, B3, C2, C3

The IBA holds important seabird colonies. Breeding species of global conservation concern that do not meet IBA criteria: *Crex crex* (2 pairs).

■ Protection status

National Partial **International** High

IBA partly or wholly overlaps with the following national designated areas. *Site of Special Scientific Interest:* Canna and Sanday. Overlaps with international designated areas: 1,341 ha of IBA covered by Special Protection Area (Canna and Sanday, 1,341 ha).

■ Conservation issues

Threats Agricultural intensification/expansion (C)

There is a management plan for the site, which includes management for *Crex crex*.

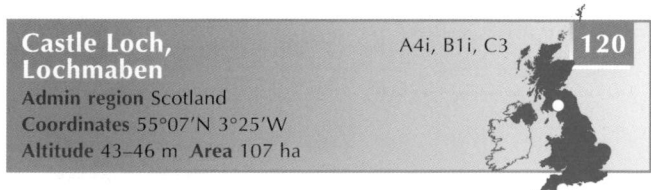

Cape Wrath
A4iii, B3, C4   119

Admin region Scotland
Coordinates 58°37'N 4°59'W
Altitude 0–371 m **Area** 1,010 ha

■ Site description

Two stretches of sandstone cliff on the Cape Wrath headland. The lower slopes are vegetated by *Calluna* and *Juniperus* heath. Sheep graze the area, and some deer-stalking takes place.

Habitats Scrub (heathland), Rocky areas (sea cliff/rocky shore)
Land-use Agriculture, Hunting, Military

■ Birds

Species		Season	Year	Pop min	Pop max	Acc	Criteria
Alca torda	Razorbill	B	1988	1,330	1,330	A	B3

The IBA holds 17,100 pairs of breeding seabirds and 10,800 pairs of breeding waterbirds on a regular basis. The site is also nationally important for breeding *Rissa tridactyla* (10,300 pairs, 1987–1988, 2%) and *Uria aalge* (9,800 pairs, 1987–1988, 1%).

■ Protection status

National High **International** High

IBA partly or wholly overlaps with the following national designated areas. *Sites of Special Scientific Interest:* Cape Wrath–Durness, Durness. Overlaps with international designated areas: 1,010 ha of IBA covered by Special Protection Area (Cape Wrath, 1,010 ha).

■ Conservation issues

Threats Disturbance to birds (U)

Disturbance results from a MoD bombing and live firing range.

Castle Loch, Lochmaben
A4i, B1i, C3   120

Admin region Scotland
Coordinates 55°07'N 3°25'W
Altitude 43–46 m **Area** 107 ha

■ Site description

A shallow loch with large stands of emergent *Phragmites* and *Glyceria*, surrounded by swamps, *Salix* scrub, mature woodland and an area of grazed wet grassland at the southern end. The IBA also includes the nearby Hightae Mill Loch.

Habitats Forest and woodland (5%), Grassland (5%), Wetland (90%; standing fresh water; water-fringe vegetation)

Land-use Agriculture (5%), Nature conservation/research (90%), Tourism/recreation (95%)

■ Birds

Species		Season	Year	Pop min	Pop max	Acc	Criteria
[1] *Anser brachyrhynchus* Pink-footed Goose		W	1994	13,300	13,300	A	A4i, B1i, C3

1. Mean annual peak 1989–1994.

The IBA is important for wintering geese and other wildfowl.

■ Protection status

National Partial **International** High

IBA partly or wholly overlaps with the following national designated areas. *Site of Special Scientific Interest:* Castle Loch. Overlaps with international designated areas: 107 ha of IBA covered by Special Protection Area (Castle Loch, 107 ha). 107 ha of IBA covered by Ramsar Site (Castle Loch, 107 ha).

■ Conservation issues

Threats Agricultural intensification/expansion (U), Consequences of animal/plant introductions (U), Disturbance to birds (U), Recreation/tourism (B)

Threats include human disturbance, e.g. controlled shooting activity, and nutrient pollution through agricultural run-off. An additional threat is posed by the introduction of *Nymphoides peltata* to neighbouring lochs. The RSPB have recently been appointed to the LNR advisory/management committee. Inland WeBS counts are carried out by the warden and a management plan exists for the site.

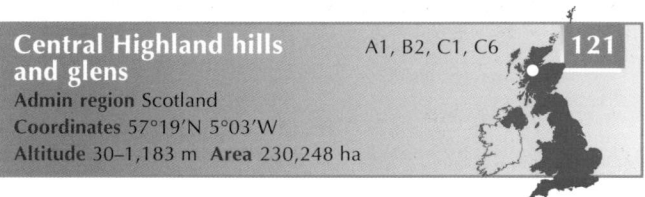

Central Highland hills and glens
A1, B2, C1, C6   121

Admin region Scotland
Coordinates 57°19'N 5°03'W
Altitude 30–1,183 m **Area** 230,248 ha

■ Site description

A massive area that extends from Ross and Cromarty in the north to the Affric–Cannich mountains in the south. Extensive stands of native pinewood *Pinus sylvestris* support rich lichen communities, and are interspersed with glens.

Habitats Forest and woodland (broadleaved deciduous forest; native coniferous forest), Scrub (heathland), Grassland (steppe/dry calcareous grassland), Wetland (standing fresh water; river/stream; fen/transition mire/spring)
Land-use Forestry (10%), Hunting (80%), Water management (10%)

■ Birds

Species		Season	Year	Pop min	Pop max	Acc	Criteria
Aquila chrysaetos	Golden Eagle	R	1992	—	31	A	B2, C6
Loxia scotica	Scottish Crossbill	R	1996	Common	—	A1, B2, C1, C6

This is an important area for raptors and other specialist montane and forest birds. The IBA is also nationally important for breeding *Gavia arctica* (4 pairs, 1991–1995, 3%).

■ Protection status

National Partial **International** None

IBA partly or wholly overlaps with the following national designated areas. *National Nature Reserve:* Strath Farrar. *Sites of Special Scientific Interest:* Achanalt Marshes, Achnasheen Terraces, Affric–Cannich Hill/Glen, Allt Tigh Cumhaig, Attadale, Glen Affric, Glen Strathfarrar, Hangman's Bridge, Levishie Wood, Liatrie Burn, Monar Forest, Urquhart Bay Woods.

■ Conservation issues

Threats Afforestation (C), Burning of vegetation (U), Forest grazing (B), Other (A)

Threats include over-grazing by red deer *Cervus elaphus*, forest fires, and bird strikes caused by deer fences ('Other' threat, above). Parts of the site are managed as National Nature Reserves through a management scheme, with conservation a prime objective at Glen Affric. Part of the area is a candidate SAC, and the Affric–Cannich Hills and Glens are a candidate SPA.

Coilacriech A1, B2, C1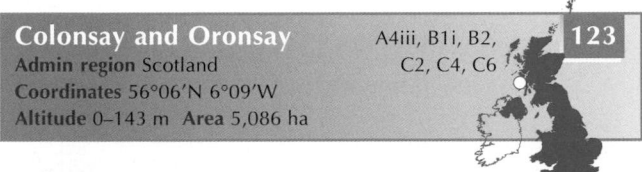

Admin region Scotland
Coordinates 57°03'N 3°07'W
Altitude 233–580 m **Area** 390 ha

■ Site description

A wooded valley side along the River Dee, located to the west of Ballater. Comprises mainly self-sown coniferous forest of native stock, with small open areas and scree.

Habitats Forest and woodland (90%; native coniferous forest; mixed forest), Scrub (5%; heathland), Rocky areas (5%; scree/boulders)
Land-use Hunting

■ Birds

Species	Season	Year	Pop min	Pop max	Acc	Criteria
Loxia scotica Scottish Crossbill	R	1996	Frequent	—		A1, B2, C1
Loxia scotica Scottish Crossbill	W	1995	Frequent	—		A1, B2, C1

This site also supports *Tetrao tetrix* and *Lagopus lagopus*, and wintering *Tetrao urogallus*.

■ Protection status

National None **International** None

■ Conservation issues

No serious threats are known at the site.

Colonsay and Oronsay A4iii, B1i, B2, C2, C4, C6 123

Admin region Scotland
Coordinates 56°06'N 6°09'W
Altitude 0–143 m **Area** 5,086 ha

■ Site description

Inner Hebridean island group with high craggy cliffs, machair, sand-dunes, heathland and farmed areas. A herb-rich sward occurs under the influence of sea spray, whilst the mainly acidic underlying rock supports wet, dry and maritime heaths.

Habitats Forest and woodland (broadleaved deciduous forest), Scrub (heathland), Grassland (mesophile grassland), Wetland (sand-dunes/sand beach; shingle/stony beach; standing fresh water; blanket bog), Rocky areas (sea cliff/rocky shore; inland cliff), Artificial landscape (highly improved reseeded grassland; arable land)
Land-use Nature conservation/research, Tourism/recreation

■ Birds

Species	Season	Year	Pop min	Pop max	Acc	Criteria
[1] *Branta leucopsis* Barnacle Goose	W	1994	500	500	A	B1i, B2, C2
Pyrrhocorax pyrrhocorax Chough	R	1996	10	—	A	B2, C6

1. Mean annual peak 1989–1994.

The IBA holds 11,000 pairs of breeding seabirds on a regular basis, and is also nationally important for breeding *Crex crex* (globally threatened: 8 calling males, 1996, 2%), *Rissa tridactyla* (5,650 pairs, 1986, 1%) and *Uria aalge* (9,050 pairs, 1986, 1%), and for wintering *Anser albifrons flavirostris* (200 birds, 1%). *Branta leucopsis* are from the Greenland breeding population.

■ Protection status

National Partial **International** Partial
IBA partly or wholly overlaps with the following national designated areas. *Reserve:* Oronsay. *Sites of Special Scientific Interest:* Loch Fada, North Colonsay, Oronsay, West Colonsay Seabird Cliffs. Overlaps with international designated areas: 973 ha of IBA covered by Special Protection Area (North Colonsay and Western Cliffs, 973 ha).

■ Conservation issues

Threats Recreation/tourism (C)

Tern colonies are under increasing pressure from disturbance by tourists. The RSPB lease and manage Oronsay.

Copinsay A4iii, B3, C4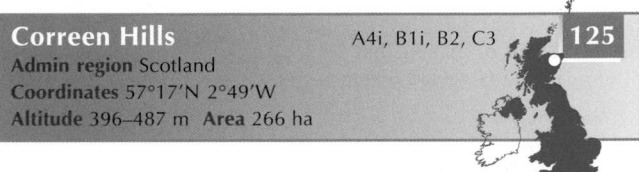

Admin region Scotland
Coordinates 58°53'N 2°41'W
Altitude 0–48 m **Area** 152 ha

■ Site description

The island of Copinsay, three islets and a rock stack. The south-east face of Copinsay consists of sheer cliffs. The three islets to the west are linked to Copinsay by a storm beach exposed at low water. Splash zone communities occur, with grassland covering the majority of the island.

Habitats Grassland, Rocky areas (sea cliff/rocky shore; rock stacks/islets)
Land-use Agriculture (50%)

■ Birds

Species	Season	Year	Pop min	Pop max	Acc	Criteria
Larus marinus Great Black-backed Gull	B	1994	—	695	A	B3

The site is important for breeding seabirds, holding 16,500 pairs on a regular basis. It is also nationally important for breeding *Uria aalge* (20,440 birds, 1994, 2%).

■ Protection status

National High **International** High
IBA partly or wholly overlaps with the following national designated areas. *Reserve:* Copinsay. *Site of Special Scientific Interest:* Copinsay. Overlaps with international designated areas: 152 ha of IBA covered by Special Protection Area (Copinsay, 152 ha).

■ Conservation issues

Threats Extraction industry (U)

A management plan exists for the RSPB Reserve. Attempts are being made to encourage *Crex crex* recolonization.

Correen Hills A4i, B1i, B2, C3 125

Admin region Scotland
Coordinates 57°17'N 2°49'W
Altitude 396–487 m **Area** 266 ha

■ Site description

The western hilltops of the Correen Hills, situated in Grampian region.

Habitats Scrub (40%; heathland), Grassland (60%)
Land-use Agriculture (100%)

■ Birds

Species	Season	Year	Pop min	Pop max	Acc	Criteria
Larus canus Common Gull	B	1995	—	6,600	A	A4i, B1i, B2, C3

The IBA supports several species of breeding gulls.

■ Protection status

National High **International** None
IBA partly or wholly overlaps with the following national designated areas. *Site of Special Scientific Interest:* Correen Hills.

■ Conservation issues

Threats Agricultural intensification/expansion (B)

The gull colony is rapidly decreasing in size. There is periodic Joint Nature Conservation Committee gull monitoring.

Creag Meagaidh C6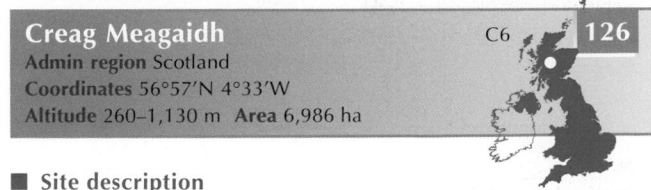

Admin region Scotland
Coordinates 56°57'N 4°33'W
Altitude 260–1,130 m **Area** 6,986 ha

■ Site description

An outstanding upland site, with uninterrupted vegetation transition from the shores of Loch Laggan to the summit of Creag Meagaidh at over 1,100 m. The site encompasses some massive cliffs, the highest measuring 400 m on Coire Ardair. Grass, heath and flush vegetation occur alongside extensive *Betula* forest, with typical summit plateau communities at higher elevations.

Habitats Forest and woodland (broadleaved deciduous forest), Scrub (heathland), Grassland (steppe/dry calcareous grassland), Wetland (standing fresh water; fen/transition mire/spring), Rocky areas (inland cliff)
Land-use Nature conservation/research (100%)

■ Birds

Species	Season	Year	Pop min	Pop max	Acc	Criteria
Charadrius morinellus Dotterel	B	1993	21	21	A	C6

This montane area supports a suite of breeding upland birds.

■ Protection status
National Partial **International** Partial
IBA partly or wholly overlaps with the following national designated areas. *National Nature Reserve:* Creag Meagaidh. *Site of Special Scientific Interest:* Creag Meagaidh. Overlaps with international designated areas: 2,873 ha of IBA covered by Special Protection Area (Creag Meagaidh, 2,873 ha).

■ Conservation issues

Threats Recreation/tourism (C)

SNH manage a reserve here, and there is an ongoing management plan.

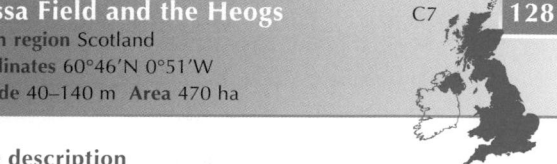

Cromdale Hills
C6   127
Admin region Scotland
Coordinates 57°20′N 3°28′W
Altitude 280–722 m **Area** 7,060 ha

■ Site description
A large block of upland that straddles the boundary between the Grampian and Highland regions.

Habitats Forest and woodland (1%; broadleaved deciduous forest), Scrub (89%; heathland), Grassland (10%)
Land-use Agriculture (100%)

■ Birds
The IBA supports breeding waders and other upland birds.

■ Protection status
National None **International** None

■ Conservation issues

Threats Agricultural intensification/expansion (C), Burning of vegetation (U), Disturbance to birds (B), Intensified forest management (B)

Crussa Field and the Heogs
C7   128
Admin region Scotland
Coordinates 60°46′N 0°51′W
Altitude 40–140 m **Area** 470 ha

■ Site description
The site comprises herb-rich maritime heathland, the Heogs rocks and a number of disused chromite quarries.

Habitats Scrub (90%; heathland), Rocky areas (10%)
Land-use Agriculture (100%)

■ Birds
The site is important for breeding moorland birds.

Species	Season	Year	Pop min	Pop max	Acc	Criteria
Numenius phaeopus Whimbrel	B	1994	23	23	A	C7

Species ... continued	Season	Year	Pop min	Pop max	Acc	Criteria
Stercorarius parasiticus Arctic Skua	B	1992	42	42	A	C7

■ Protection status
National High **International** None
IBA partly or wholly overlaps with the following national designated areas. *Sites of Special Scientific Interest:* Crussa Field and the Heogs, Keen of Hamar.

■ Conservation issues

Threats Agricultural intensification/expansion (B)

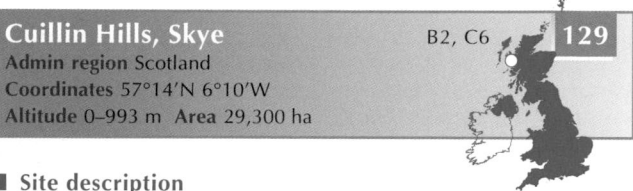

Cuillin Hills, Skye
B2, C6   129
Admin region Scotland
Coordinates 57°14′N 6°10′W
Altitude 0–993 m **Area** 29,300 ha

■ Site description
A series of mountain peaks and associated river valleys in the southern half of the Isle of Skye.

Habitats Forest and woodland (mixed forest), Scrub (scrub; heathland), Grassland (steppe/dry calcareous grassland), Wetland (river/stream; blanket bog), Rocky areas (scree/boulders, inland cliff)
Land-use Agriculture, Forestry, Tourism/recreation

■ Birds

Species	Season	Year	Pop min	Pop max	Acc	Criteria
Aquila chrysaetos Golden Eagle	R	1992	9	9	A	B2, C6

The site is important for breeding upland bird species.

■ Protection status
National Partial **International** None
IBA partly or wholly overlaps with the following national designated areas. *Sites of Special Scientific Interest:* Allt Geodh a'Ghamna, Allt Grillan Gorge, Cuillins, Elgol Coast, Lochs at Sligachan, Meall a'Mhaoil, Talisker.

■ Conservation issues

Threats Recreation/tourism (B)

Some restoration of native forest has taken place.

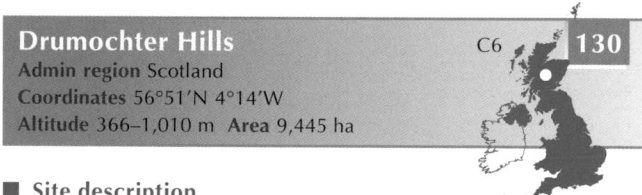

Drumochter Hills
C6   130
Admin region Scotland
Coordinates 56°51′N 4°14′W
Altitude 366–1,010 m **Area** 9,445 ha

■ Site description
The site includes the rounded summits on either side of the Drumochter pass, and several plateaus, which are divided by steep-sided stream gullies. Montane communities present include grassland, high altitude blanket mires and lichen-rich heaths.

Habitats Forest and woodland (broadleaved deciduous forest), Scrub (heathland), Grassland (steppe/dry calcareous grassland), Wetland (standing fresh water; river/stream; blanket bog; fen/transition mire/spring), Rocky areas (scree/boulders)
Land-use Agriculture (50%), Hunting (100%)

■ Birds

Species	Season	Year	Pop min	Pop max	Acc	Criteria
Charadrius morinellus Dotterel	B	1992	70	—	A	C6

This area supports a range of birds associated with montane plateaus and open moorland.

■ Protection status
National High **International** High

IBA partly or wholly overlaps with the following national designated areas. *Site of Special Scientific Interest:* Drumochter Hills. Overlaps with international designated areas: 9,445 ha of IBA covered by Special Protection Area (Drumochter Hills, 9,445 ha).

■ Conservation issues

Threats	Disturbance to birds (U), Forest grazing (U), Other (A), Recreation/tourism (A)

Trampling from red deer *Cervus elaphus* is problematic for some ground-nesting species ('Other' threat, above), with additional threats posed by *C. elaphus* overgrazing, and disturbance and erosion caused by increased public access and recreation (to potentially include skiing). SNH research on *Charadrius morinellus* is ongoing. The site is currently undergoing designation as a SAC.

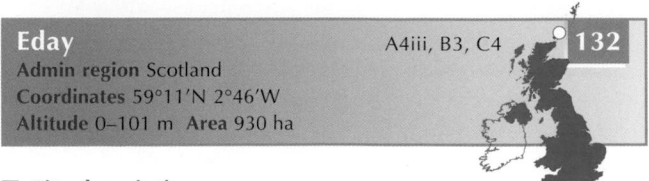

East Sanday
A4i, B1i, B2, C3, C6 | **131**
Admin region Scotland
Coordinates 59°16'N 2°28'W
Altitude 0–10 m Area 1,515 ha

■ Site description
A low-lying rocky coastline interspersed with sandy bays. Sand-dune and machair habitats support species-rich plant communities.

Habitats Grassland (machair), Wetland (mudflat/sandflat; saltmarsh; sand-dunes/sand beach; shingle/stony beach), Rocky areas (sea cliff/rocky shore)
Land-use Fisheries/aquaculture (5%), Not utilized (95%)

■ Birds

Species	Season	Year	Pop min	Pop max	Acc	Criteria
Charadrius hiaticula Ringed Plover	W	1994	—	710	A	B1i, C3
Calidris maritima Purple Sandpiper	W	1994	—	780	A	A4i, B1i, C3
Calidris maritima Purple Sandpiper	P	1987	1,060	1,060	A	A4i, B1i, C3
Limosa lapponica Bar-tailed Godwit	W	1994	—	870	A	B2
Arenaria interpres Turnstone	W	1994	—	1,270	A	A4i, B1i, C3
Arenaria interpres Turnstone	P	1987	1,800	1,800	A	A4i, B1i, C3
Sterna sandvicensis Sandwich Tern	B	1994	135	135	A	C6

The IBA is important for both wintering and breeding waders, and is also nationally important for breeding *Sterna paradisaea* (450 pairs, 1994, 1%) and for wintering *Calidris alba* (300 birds, 1993–1994, 1%) and *Plectrophenax nivalis* (340 birds, 1993–1994, 4%).

■ Protection status
National High **International** High
IBA partly or wholly overlaps with the following national designated areas. *Sites of Special Scientific Interest:* Central Sanday, East Sanday Coast, Northwall. Overlaps with international designated areas: 1,515 ha of IBA covered by Special Protection Area (East Sanday Coast, 1,515 ha). 1,515 ha of IBA covered by Ramsar Site (East Sanday Coast, 1,515 ha).

■ Conservation issues

Threats	Aquaculture/fisheries (B), Extraction industry (B)

The cockle *Cardium* fishery in Otterswick is currently unregulated. Regulating orders are under discussion.

Eday
A4iii, B3, C4 | **132**
Admin region Scotland
Coordinates 59°11'N 2°46'W
Altitude 0–101 m Area 930 ha

■ Site description
The IBA covers three separate parts of the island of Eday, in addition to the island of the Calf of Eday, which is located to the north. Maritime grassland and moorland, sometimes submontane in character, occur with nutrient-poor freshwater lochs.

Habitats Scrub (heathland), Grassland (humid grassland), Wetland (standing fresh water), Rocky areas (sea cliff/rocky shore)
Land-use Agriculture

■ Birds

Species	Season	Year	Pop min	Pop max	Acc	Criteria
Larus marinus Great Black-backed Gull	B	1996	940	940	A	B3

The IBA supports notable breeding populations of seabirds (10,700 pairs on a regular basis) and upland species. The site is also nationally important for breeding *Gavia stellata* (10 pairs, 1991–1996, 1%), *Phalacrocorax carbo* (225 pairs, 1995, 3%), *Numenius phaeopus* (8 pairs, 1995, 2%), *Stercorarius parasiticus* (110 pairs, 1992, 3%) and *Uria aalge* (8,450 pairs, 1986, 1%), and for wintering *Calidris maritima* (250 birds, 1992, 1%).

■ Protection status
National Partial **International** Partial
IBA partly or wholly overlaps with the following national designated areas. *Sites of Special Scientific Interest:* Calf of Eday, Doomy and Whitemaw Hill, Mill Loch – Eday. Overlaps with international designated areas: 238 ha of IBA covered by Special Protection Area (Calf of Eday, 238 ha).

■ Conservation issues

Threats	Agricultural intensification/expansion (B), Aquaculture/fisheries (B), Drainage (B), Extraction industry (B)

The expansion of aquaculture into offshore feeding areas poses a threat.

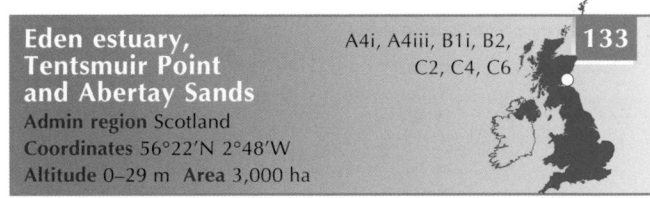

Eden estuary, Tentsmuir Point and Abertay Sands
A4i, A4iii, B1i, B2, C2, C4, C6 | **133**
Admin region Scotland
Coordinates 56°22'N 2°48'W
Altitude 0–29 m Area 3,000 ha

■ Site description
A fairly small estuary situated just north of St Andrews that supports a wide diversity of habitats. The site includes extensive sandflats at the mouth of the estuary, and mudflats that support eel-grass *Zostera*. Saltmarsh, wetland and sand-dune habitats also occur.

Habitats Forest and woodland, Scrub (scrub), Wetland (tidal river/enclosed tidal water; mudflat/sandflat; saltmarsh; standing fresh water; standing brackish and salt water)
Land-use Fisheries/aquaculture, Tourism/recreation

■ Birds

Species	Season	Year	Pop min	Pop max	Acc	Criteria
Limosa lapponica Bar-tailed Godwit	W	1995	1,650	1,650	A	A4i, B1i, B2, C2, C6
Sterna albifrons Little Tern	B	1994	40	40	A	C6

The IBA supports large numbers of wintering waders and wildfowl, holding 35,100 wintering waterbirds on a regular basis. The site is also nationally important for wintering *Tadorna tadorna* (1,190 birds, 2%), *Somateria mollissima* (15,000 birds, 1992, 19%), *Melanitta nigra* (1,630 birds, 4%), *Mergus serrator* (115 birds, 1%), *Haematopus ostralegus* (4,210 birds, 1%), *Pluvialis squatarola* (940 birds, 2%), *Limosa limosa* (155 birds, 2%) and *Tringa totanus* (1,370 birds, 1%), and for passage *Pluvialis squatarola* (735 birds, 2%), *Limosa limosa* (130 birds, 2%) and *Tringa totanus* (1,320 birds, 1%). Breeding species of global conservation concern that do not meet IBA criteria: *Crex crex*.

■ Protection status
National Partial **International** Partial
IBA partly or wholly overlaps with the following national designated areas. *Sites of Special Scientific Interest:* Barry Links, Earlshall Muir, Eden Estuary, Morton Lochs, Tayport – Tentsmuir Coast. Overlaps with international designated areas: IBA overlaps with Special Protection Area (Firth of Tay and Eden Estuary).

■ Conservation issues

Threats	Disturbance to birds (B), Infrastructure (C), Natural events (B), Recreation/tourism (B)

Threats include coastal erosion, and disturbance from the adjacent airport and from wildfowling. SNH has a management plan for

Tentsmuir Point, and a management plan exists for the Eden estuary Local Nature Reserve.

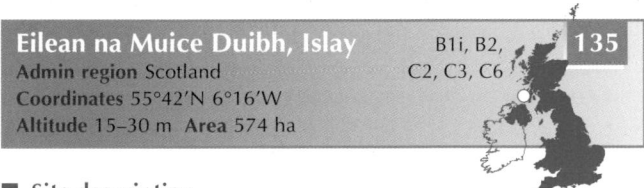

Eilean Hoan
B1i, B2, C2, C6 — 134
Admin region Scotland
Coordinates 58°34′N 4°40′W
Altitude 0–24 m **Area** 30 ha

■ Site description
A small rocky island off the north coast of Sutherland. Human activities include sheep-grazing.

Habitats Grassland (100%), Rocky areas (sea cliff/rocky shore)
Land-use Agriculture (100%), Nature conservation/research (100%)

■ Birds

Species	Season	Year	Pop min	Pop max	Acc	Criteria
[1] *Oceanodroma leucorhoa* Leach's Petrel	B	1994	—	—	A	C6
Branta leucopsis Barnacle Goose	W	1994	495	495	A	B1i, B2, C2

1. No counts available.

Notable breeding birds include a few pairs of *Sterna paradisaea* and *Hydrobates pelagicus*. *Branta leucopsis* are from the Greenland breeding population.

■ Protection status
National High **International** High
IBA partly or wholly overlaps with the following national designated areas. *Reserve:* Eilean Hoan. Overlaps with international designated areas: 30 ha of IBA covered by Special Protection Area (North Sutherland Coastal Islands).

■ Conservation issues
No serious threats are known at the site. There is no visitor access to this leased RSPB Reserve, and a management plan is available.

Eilean na Muice Duibh, Islay
B1i, B2, C2, C3, C6 — 135
Admin region Scotland
Coordinates 55°42′N 6°16′W
Altitude 15–30 m **Area** 574 ha

■ Site description
The site is bounded by the Rivers Duich and Laggan and two roads, and comprises a relatively undisturbed expanse of patterned mire with scattered peaty pools and lochs. These include deep watershed pools, a feature normally associated with more northerly blanket mires. In some areas the vegetation is modified by the trampling and nutrient input of gulls.

Habitats Scrub (heathland), Grassland (humid grassland), Wetland (standing fresh water; fen/transition mire/spring)
Land-use Nature conservation/research

■ Birds

Species	Season	Year	Pop min	Pop max	Acc	Criteria
[1] *Anser albifrons* White-fronted Goose	W	1996	1,210	1,210	A	B1i, C2, C3, C6
Branta leucopsis Barnacle Goose	W	1990	—	1,530	A	B1i, B2, C2

1. Seasonal mean 1995–1996.

The IBA is important as a roost especially in winter, and as a night feeding area for *Anser albifrons flavirostris*. *Branta leucopsis* are from the Greenland breeding population.

■ Protection status
National High **International** High
IBA partly or wholly overlaps with the following national designated areas. *National Nature Reserve:* Duich Moss. *Site of Special Scientific Interest:* Islay – Eilean na Muice Duibh (Duich Moss). Overlaps with international designated areas: 574 ha of IBA covered by Ramsar Site (Eilean na Muice Dubh, Islay, 574 ha). 574 ha of IBA covered by Special Protection Area (Eilean na Muice Duibh, Islay, 574 ha).

■ Conservation issues
The spread of *Rhododendron ponticum* poses a threat to the site, as does the possibility of bird strikes caused by a proposed wind power development on adjacent ground. SNH lease part of the IBA and hold management agreements over other areas, enabling them to operate a management plan for the whole site. They have also undertaken positive remedial management, including the damming of drains and restoration of high water-tables.

Threats Abandonment/reduction of land management (B), Consequences of animal/plant introductions (U), Disturbance to birds (U), Drainage (A), Extraction industry (A), Infrastructure (B)

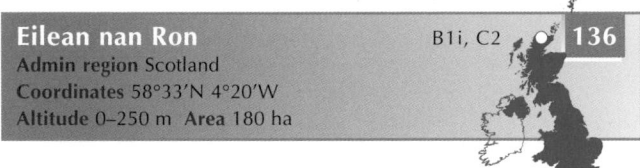

Eilean nan Ron
B1i, C2 — 136
Admin region Scotland
Coordinates 58°33′N 4°20′W
Altitude 0–250 m **Area** 180 ha

■ Site description
A small rocky island off the north coast of Sutherland.

Habitats Scrub (heathland), Grassland, Rocky areas (sea cliff/rocky shore)
Land-use Agriculture

■ Birds

Species	Season	Year	Pop min	Pop max	Acc	Criteria
Branta leucopsis Barnacle Goose	W	1994	—	350	A	B1i, C2

This is also an important site for breeding seabirds. *Branta leucopsis* are from the Greenland breeding population.

■ Protection status
National High **International** High
IBA partly or wholly overlaps with the following national designated areas. *Site of Special Scientific Interest:* Eilean nan Ron. Overlaps with international designated areas: 180 ha of IBA covered by Special Protection Area (North Sutherland Coastal Islands).

■ Conservation issues
No serious threats are known at the site.

Endrick Mouth and Loch Lomond Islands
C6 — 137
Admin region Scotland
Coordinates 56°04′N 4°31′W
Altitude 14–85 m **Area** 820 ha

■ Site description
The site includes a series of large, wooded islands in the southern part of Loch Lomond, and an area of marshland in the south-east corner of the loch.

Habitats Forest and woodland (mixed forest), Grassland, Wetland (standing fresh water; fen/transition mire/spring)
Land-use Agriculture (20%), Forestry, Nature conservation/research (80%)

■ Birds

Species	Season	Year	Pop min	Pop max	Acc	Criteria
Tetrao urogallus Capercaillie	R	1998	35	35	A	C6

The site is also nationally important for wintering *Anser albifrons flavirostris* (265 birds, 2%).

■ Protection status
National Partial **International** Partial
IBA partly or wholly overlaps with the following national designated areas. *National Nature Reserve:* Loch Lomond. *Sites of Special Scientific Interest:* Aber Bog, Gartocharn Bog and Bell Moss, Endrick Mouth and Islands, Inchlonaig, Inchmoan, Inchmurrin, Inchtavannach and Inchconnachan, Portnellan–Ross Priory–Claddochside, Ross Park. Overlaps with international designated

areas: 486 ha of IBA covered by Special Protection Area (Loch Lomond, 486 ha). 236 ha of IBA covered by Ramsar Site (Loch Lomond, 236 ha).

■ Conservation issues

Threats Agricultural intensification/expansion (B), Groundwater abstraction (U), Industrialization/urbanization (U), Recreation/tourism (A), Unsustainable exploitation (U)

Threats include disturbance from intensive watersports and other recreational activities, and sewage pollution. Joint SNH/RSPB/Scottish Ornithological Club counts of *Tetrao urogallus* are undertaken annually on the Loch Lomond Islands.

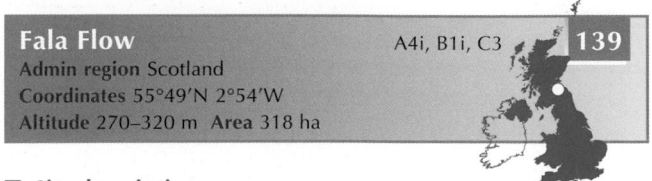

Fair Isle A4i, A4iii, B1i, B1ii, B2, B3, C2, C3, C4, C6 **138**
Admin region Scotland
Coordinates 59°32'N 1°37'W
Altitude 0–217 m **Area** 561 ha

■ Site description
An island of Old Red Sandstone situated halfway between the Shetland mainland and Orkney, which has been home to a bird observatory since 1947. Maritime grassland occurs around the coasts.

Habitats Scrub (heathland), Grassland, Rocky areas (sea cliff/rocky shore)
Land-use Agriculture (90%)

■ Birds

Species	Season	Year	Pop min	Pop max	Acc	Criteria
Phalacrocorax aristotelis Shag	B	1990	1,070	1,070	A	A4i, B1i, B3, C2, C3
Stercorarius skua Great Skua	B	1995	130	130	A	B3
Sterna paradisaea Arctic Tern	B	1995	1,200	1,200	A	C2, C6
Uria aalge Guillemot	B	1994	25,200	25,200	A	B1ii, C3
Alca torda Razorbill	B	1988	2,050	2,050	A	B3
Fratercula arctica Puffin	B	1995	8,700	8,700	A	B1ii, B2, C3

The island supports large colonies of breeding seabirds, and is also important as a stop-over site for migrating birds. It holds 72,400 breeding seabirds and 21,900 breeding waterbirds on a regular basis, and is nationally important for breeding *Fulmarus glacialis* (35,200 pairs, 1991, 6%), *Stercorarius parasiticus* (87 pairs, 1995, 3%) and *Rissa tridactyla* (19,300 pairs, 1988, 4%). Fair Isle also has an endemic subspecies of *Troglodytes troglodytes*.

■ Protection status
National High **International** High
IBA partly or wholly overlaps with the following national designated areas. *Site of Special Scientific Interest:* Fair Isle. Overlaps with international designated areas: 561 ha of IBA covered by Special Protection Area (Fair Isle, 561 ha).

■ Conservation issues

Threats Agricultural intensification/expansion (B), Aquaculture/fisheries (B), Disturbance to birds (C)

Unsustainable fishing of sandeels *Ammodytes* poses a potential threat to seabirds. There is a management plan for the site.

Fala Flow A4i, B1i, C3 **139**
Admin region Scotland
Coordinates 55°49'N 2°54'W
Altitude 270–320 m **Area** 318 ha

■ Site description
The IBA comprises an area of blanket mire and pools, situated in the Lammermuir Hills to the south-east of Edinburgh. Such mires are scarce and declining in Midlothian, and this example is relatively undisturbed.

Habitats Scrub (20%; heathland), Grassland (20%), Wetland (60%; standing fresh water; blanket bog; fen/transition mire/spring)
Land-use Agriculture (98%), Tourism/recreation (80%), Water management (2%)

■ Birds

Species	Season	Year	Pop min	Pop max	Acc	Criteria
[1] *Anser brachyrhynchus* Pink-footed Goose	W	1996	9,400	9,400	A	A4i, B1i, C3

1. Mean annual peak 1991–1996.

The site is a major wintering roost site for *Anser brachyrhynchus*, and supports a suite of breeding moorland birds including *Lagopus lagopus*, *Tetrao tetrix*, *Numenius arquata*, *Gallinago gallinago*, *Vanellus vanellus*, *Tringa totanus* and *Pluvialis apricaria*.

■ Protection status
National High **International** High
IBA partly or wholly overlaps with the following national designated areas. *Site of Special Scientific Interest:* Fala Flow. Overlaps with international designated areas: 318 ha of IBA covered by Special Protection Area (Fala Flow, 318 ha). 318 ha of IBA covered by Ramsar Site (Fala Flow, 318 ha).

■ Conservation issues

Threats Agricultural intensification/expansion (C)

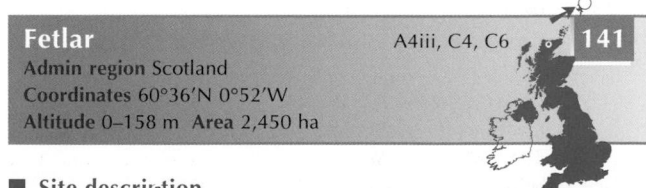

Faray and Holm of Faray B2, B3 **140**
Admin region Scotland
Coordinates 59°13'N 2°49'W
Altitude 0–32 m **Area** 80 ha

■ Site description
The site comprises the small island of Holm of Faray and the majority of the coastline of the larger island of Faray, with the exception of the south-east section between The Nev and the Point of Scaraber.

Habitats Scrub (heathland), Grassland, Rocky areas (sea cliff/rocky shore)
Land-use Agriculture

■ Birds

Species	Season	Year	Pop min	Pop max	Acc	Criteria
Larus marinus Great Black-backed Gull	B	1987	270	270	A	B3
Cepphus grylle Black Guillemot	B	1984	165	165	A	B2

These small islands are important for breeding seabirds.

■ Protection status
National None **International** None

■ Conservation issues
No serious threats are known at the site, which is a candidate SAC.

Fetlar A4iii, C4, C6 **141**
Admin region Scotland
Coordinates 60°36'N 0°52'W
Altitude 0–158 m **Area** 2,450 ha

■ Site description
The site covers a large expanse of the island of Fetlar, comprising mainly species-rich heathland and grasslands, marshes, cliffs and rocky shore.

Habitats Scrub (heathland), Wetland (blanket bog), Rocky areas (sea cliff/rocky shore)
Land-use Agriculture (100%), Nature conservation/research

■ Birds

Species	Season	Year	Pop min	Pop max	Acc	Criteria
Phalaropus lobatus Red-necked Phalarope	B	1995	27	—	A	C6

The IBA holds 13,100 breeding seabirds on a regular basis, and is the best site in the UK for breeding *Phalaropus lobatus*. It is also nationally important for breeding *Fulmarus glacialis* (12,600 pairs, 1986, 2%) and *Numenius phaeopus* (70 pairs, 1989, 13%).

■ Protection status

National High **International** High

IBA partly or wholly overlaps with the following national designated areas. *Reserve:* Fetlar. *Sites of Special Scientific Interest:* Fetlar, Funzie, Lamb Hoga, North Fetlar, Tressa Ness to Colbinstoft, Trona Mires, Virva. Overlaps with international designated areas: 2,450 ha of IBA covered by Special Protection Area (Fetlar, 2,639 ha).

■ Conservation issues

Threats Agricultural intensification/expansion (B), Aquaculture/fisheries (B)

Unsustainable fishing of sandeels *Ammodytes* poses a potential threat to seabirds. A management plan exists for the RSPB reserve.

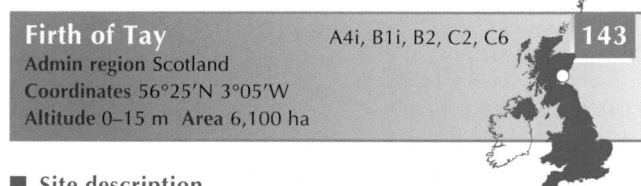

Firth of Forth
Admin region Scotland
Coordinates 55°59′N 3°18′W
Altitude 0–30 m **Area** 43,301 ha
A4i, A4iii, B1i, B2, B3, C2, C3, C4, C6
142

■ Site description

A complex site that stretches for over 100 km from the River Forth at Stirling eastwards past Edinburgh, and along the coasts of Fife and East Lothian before culminating in a wide mouth. The IBA covers large areas of intertidal flats and inshore waters, in addition to saltmarsh and sand-dune systems, maritime grassland, heath and fen.

Habitats Scrub (heathland), Grassland, Wetland (tidal river/enclosed tidal water; mudflat/sandflat; saltmarsh; sand-dunes/sand beach; shingle/stony beach; coastal lagoon; standing brackish and salt water; water-fringe vegetation; fen/transition mire/spring), Marine areas (open sea; sea inlet/coastal features), Rocky areas (sea cliff/rocky shore)
Land-use Nature conservation/research (5%), Tourism/recreation, Urban/industrial/transport (5%)

■ Birds

Species	Season	Year	Pop min	Pop max	Acc	Criteria
Anser brachyrhynchus Pink-footed Goose	W	1995	12,800	12,800	A	A4i, B1i, C3
Tadorna tadorna Shelduck	W	1995	3,560	3,560	A	B1i, C3
Aythya marila Scaup	W	1995	195	195	A	B2
Pluvialis apricaria Golden Plover	W	1995	3,130	3,130	A	C6
Pluvialis apricaria Golden Plover	P	1995	3,340	3,340	A	C6
Calidris canutus Knot	W	1995	7,550	7,550	A	B1i, B2, C3
Calidris alpina Dunlin	W	1995	8,650	8,650	A	B2
Limosa lapponica Bar-tailed Godwit	W	1995	2,380	2,380	A	A4i, B1i, B2, C2, C6
Limosa lapponica Bar-tailed Godwit	P	1995	1,530	1,530	A	A4i, B1i, C2, C6
Numenius arquata Curlew	W	1995	2,220	2,220	A	B2
Tringa totanus Redshank	W	1995	4,190	4,190	A	A4i, B1i, C3
Tringa totanus Redshank	P	1995	4,150	4,150	A	A4i, B1i, C3
Arenaria interpres Turnstone	W	1995	1,080	1,080	A	A4i, B1i, C3
[1] *Larus fuscus* Lesser Black-backed Gull	B	1990	865	865	A	B3
Sterna hirundo Common Tern	B	1996	690	690	A	C2, C6

1. Rosyth Dockyard only.

The site holds 82,100 wintering and 28,600 passage waterbirds on a regular basis. It is also nationally important for wintering *Podiceps cristatus* (655 birds, 6%), *Phalacrocorax carbo* (710 birds, 5%), *Anas crecca* (1,570 birds, 1%), *Somateria mollissima* (7,550 birds, 10%), *Clangula hyemalis* (710 birds, 3%), *Melanitta nigra* (2,650 birds, 7%), *Bucephala clangula* (2,300 birds, 7%), *Mergus serrator* (610 birds, 6%), *Haematopus ostralegus* (8,650 birds, 2%), *Charadrius hiaticula* (355 birds, 1%) and *Pluvialis squatarola* (665 birds, 2%), for passage *Haematopus ostralegus* (8,200 birds, 2%), *Charadrius hiaticula* (470 birds, 2%) and *Pluvialis squatarola* (565 birds, 1%), and for summer moulting assemblages of *Somateria mollissima* (5,950 birds, 8%).

■ Protection status

National Partial **International** None

IBA partly or wholly overlaps with the following national designated areas. *Reserves:* Aberlady Bay, Cambus Pool, Skinflats, Torry Bay. *Sites of Special Scientific Interest:* Abbey Craig, Aberlady Bay, Alloa Inches, Barnsmuir Coast, Blackness Bay, Burntisland – Kirkcaldy Coast, Carlingnose, Dumbarnie Links, Dunbar coast, East Wemyss – Anstruther Coast, Fife Ness Coast, Forth Bridge – Granton Shore, Gosford Bay to Port Seton, Gullane to Broad Sands, Kinneil Kerse, Leith to Prestonpans, North Berwick Coast, Ruddons Point, Skinflats, Torry Bay, Tyninghame Shore, Wardie Shore.

■ Conservation issues

Threats Construction/impact of dyke/dam/barrage (U), Extraction industry (U), Filling-in of wetlands (B), Industrialization/urbanization (B), Infrastructure (C), Natural events (U), Other (U), Recreation/tourism (B)

Threats include pollution from refuse disposal, disturbance from increased recreational activity, nutrient enrichment of the estuary ('Other' threat, above) and sea-level rise. Infrastructure development and industrial expansion pose additional problems, with housing, marina and oil terminal developments planned, and a proposal put forward for a barrage. Proposals also exist for marine aggregate extraction and deep mining, which may lead to subsidence and habitat change. A Forth Estuary Forum has been established. The area is a candidate SPA, to include the existing Firth of Forth Islands SPA.

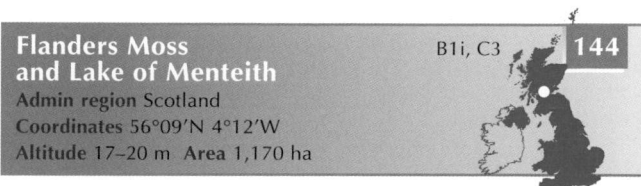

Firth of Tay
Admin region Scotland
Coordinates 56°25′N 3°05′W
Altitude 0–15 m **Area** 6,100 ha
A4i, B1i, B2, C2, C6
143

■ Site description

This site includes the Inner Tay, with some of the largest reedbeds (*Phragmites*) in Britain, and the extensive intertidal mudflats on one side of the mouth of the river.

Habitats Wetland (tidal river/enclosed tidal water; mudflat/sandflat; saltmarsh; shingle/stony beach; water-fringe vegetation)
Land-use Agriculture (5%), Nature conservation/research (20%), Urban/industrial/transport (5%)

■ Birds

Species	Season	Year	Pop min	Pop max	Acc	Criteria
Limosa lapponica Bar-tailed Godwit	W	1996	1,500	—	A	A4i, B1i, B2, C2, C6

The IBA is important for wintering and passage wildfowl and waders, and supports several breeding reedbed species. It is also nationally important for breeding *Rallus aquaticus* (125 pairs, 1992, 18%) and *Panurus biarmicus* (18 pairs, 1994–1995, 4%), and for wintering *Somateria mollissima* (1,730 birds, 2%).

■ Protection status

National Partial **International** Partial

IBA partly or wholly overlaps with the following national designated areas. *Sites of Special Scientific Interest:* Balmerino – Wormit Shore, Barry Links, Flisk Wood, Inner Tay Estuary, Monifeith Bay. Overlaps with international designated areas: IBA overlaps with Special Protection Area (Firth of Tay and Eden Estuary).

■ Conservation issues

Threats Burning of vegetation (U), Filling-in of wetlands (A), Recreation/tourism (B)

Threats include disturbance from recreational activities, landfill on the intertidal area, dumping of rubbish in the reedbeds, and reedbed fires during the *Panurus biarmicus* breeding season. The landfill can support large rat *Rattus* populations in the estuary reedbeds, which in turn threaten breeding birds.

Flanders Moss and Lake of Menteith
Admin region Scotland
Coordinates 56°09′N 4°12′W
Altitude 17–20 m **Area** 1,170 ha
B1i, C3
144

■ Site description

The Lake of Menteith is a shallow water-body, with fringing reedbeds (*Phragmites*) in some bays. The nearby Flanders Moss is the largest remaining intact lowland raised mire in the UK, whose plant communities are relatively undisturbed. Human activities include peat extraction ('Other' land-use, below).

Habitats Scrub (heathland), Grassland, Wetland (standing fresh water; fen/transition mire/spring)
Land-use Nature conservation/research (50%), Other (17%), Water management (33%)

■ Birds

Species	Season	Year	Pop min	Pop max	Acc	Criteria
[1] *Anser brachyrhynchus* Pink-footed Goose	W	1994	2,550	2,550	A	B1i, C3
1. Mean annual peak 1989–1994.						

The IBA is important for wintering waterbirds.

■ Protection status
National Partial **International** Partial
IBA partly or wholly overlaps with the following national designated areas. *National Nature Reserve:* Flanders Moss. *Sites of Special Scientific Interest:* Flanders Moss, Killlorn Moss, Lake of Menteith, Loch Macanrie Fens. Overlaps with international designated areas: IBA overlaps with Special Protection Area (Lake of Menteith).

■ Conservation issues

Threats Afforestation (B), Agricultural intensification/expansion (B), Disturbance to birds (A), Drainage (B), Extraction industry (B), Recreation/tourism (A)

Disturbance and recreation are interlinked through fishing, shooting and other activities. Peat extraction was formerly the main threat to the site, but planning permission was bought-out by SNH. SNH and the Scottish Wildlife Trusts are involved in the removal of *Betula* scrub which has invaded some sites, whilst drainage ditches require blocking. The site has also been damaged by forestry, and commercial plantations owned by Forest Enterprise and SNH are to be removed.

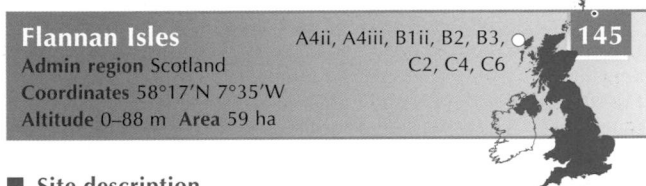

Flannan Isles
A4ii, A4iii, B1ii, B2, B3, C2, C4, C6
Admin region Scotland
Coordinates 58°17′N 7°35′W
Altitude 0–88 m **Area** 59 ha

■ Site description
Six rocky islands and outlying skerries located about 30 km west of Lewis, and supporting predominantly maritime grassland vegetation. A lighthouse is situated within the IBA ('Other' land-use, below).

Habitats Grassland (90%; humid grassland), Rocky areas (10%; rock stacks/islets)
Land-use Not utilized (98%), Other (2%)

■ Birds

Species	Season	Year	Pop min	Pop max	Acc	Criteria
Hydrobates pelagicus Storm Petrel	B	1991	100	10,000	A	A4ii,B1ii,B2,C2,C6
Oceanodroma leucorhoa Leach's Petrel	B	1991	100	10,000	A	B1ii, B2, C2, C6
Alca torda Razorbill	B	1988	1,770	1,770	A	B3

These islands are of major importance for their breeding seabird colonies, which support 30,000 pairs on a regular basis. They are also nationally important for breeding *Uria aalge* (9,050 pairs, 1988, 1%).

■ Protection status
National High **International** High
IBA partly or wholly overlaps with the following national designated areas. *Site of Special Scientific Interest:* Flannan Islands. Overlaps with international designated areas: 59 ha of IBA covered by Special Protection Area (Flannan Islands, 59 ha).

■ Conservation issues

Threats Aquaculture/fisheries (U), Consequences of animal/plant introductions (A), Extraction industry (B), Other (B)

Threats include the effects of introduced rats *Rattus* and the possibility of oil spills ('Other' threat, above).

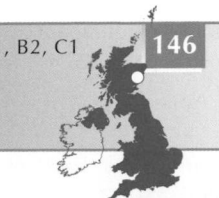

Forest of Birse
A1, B2, C1 · 146
Admin region Scotland
Coordinates 57°00′N 2°42′W
Altitude 160–380 m **Area** 850 ha

■ Site description
This site covers the section of the Forest of Birse situated between Burnfoot and Turfgate, and contains mainly coniferous woodland.

Habitats Forest and woodland (30%; broadleaved deciduous forest; native coniferous forest), Scrub (30%; heathland), Artificial landscape (40%; forestry plantation)
Land-use Forestry (40%), Hunting (60%)

■ Birds

Species	Season	Year	Pop min	Pop max	Acc	Criteria
Loxia scotica Scottish Crossbill	R	1995	Frequent	—		A1, B2, C1

Important for breeding raptors and other upland and forest species.

■ Protection status
National None **International** None

■ Conservation issues

Threats Forest grazing (C), Intensified forest management (C)

Threatened by intensive forestry practices and deer-grazing.

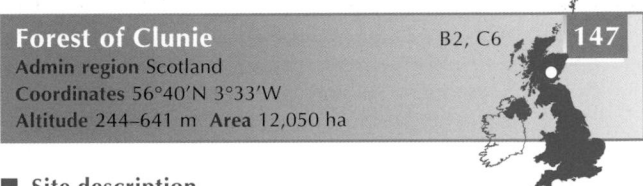

Forest of Clunie
B2, C6 · 147
Admin region Scotland
Coordinates 56°40′N 3°33′W
Altitude 244–641 m **Area** 12,050 ha

■ Site description
An area of heather moorland to the north-west of Blairgowrie.

Habitats Forest and woodland (broadleaved deciduous forest; native coniferous forest), Scrub (heathland), Artificial landscape (forestry plantation)
Land-use Agriculture (80%), Forestry (20%), Hunting (80%), Tourism/recreation (5%)

■ Birds

Species	Season	Year	Pop min	Pop max	Acc	Criteria
Circus cyaneus Hen Harrier	R	1996	—	20	A	B2, C6
Pandion haliaetus Osprey	B	1995	8	8	A	B2, C6
Tetrao tetrix Black Grouse	R	1996	400	—	A	B2
Asio flammeus Short-eared Owl	R	1994	—	15	A	B2, C6

This upland area is important for raptors, and also supports a large number of breeding waders.

■ Protection status
National Partial **International** None
IBA partly or wholly overlaps with the following national designated areas. *Sites of Special Scientific Interest:* Balyoukan Juniper Wood, Brerachan Meadows, Den of Riechip, Pitarrig Meadow, Straloch Moraines.

■ Conservation issues

Threats Afforestation (U), Agricultural intensification/expansion (U), Other (U)

Overgrazing occurs on the margins, whilst raptor persecution remains a problem ('Other' threat). Long-term monitoring of *Circus cyaneus* and *Tetrao tetrix* is undertaken here.

Forth Islands
A4i, A4ii, A4iii, B1i, B1ii, B2, B3, C2, C3, C4, C6 · 148
Admin region Scotland
Coordinates 56°04′N 2°46′W
Altitude 0–76 m **Area** 132 ha

■ Site description
A large group of islands situated in the Firth of Forth. The inner islands are generally low-lying, whilst those in the Outer Firth are

higher, steeper and rockier. The islands support extensive maritime cliff-top grasslands.

Habitats Grassland, Rocky areas (rock stacks/islets)
Land-use Nature conservation/research (100%), Tourism/recreation (80%)

■ **Birds**

Species	Season	Year	Pop min	Pop max	Acc	Criteria
Sula bassana Gannet	B	1994	39,800	39,800	A	A4ii, B1ii, B2, C3
Phalacrocorax carbo Cormorant	B	1995	470	470	A	B1i, C3
Phalacrocorax aristotelis Shag	B	1995	885	885	A	B1i, B3, C2, C3
Larus fuscus Lesser Black-backed Gull	B	1995	7,200	7,200	A	A4i, B1i, B3, C3
Larus argentatus Herring Gull	B	1995	13,000	13,000	A	A4i, B1i
Sterna sandvicensis Sandwich Tern	B	1994	130	—	A	C6
Sterna dougallii Roseate Tern	B	1995	17	—	A	A4i, B1i, B2, C2, C6
Sterna hirundo Common Tern	B	1994	305	—	A	C6
Uria aalge Guillemot	B	1995	20,700	—	A	B1ii, C3
Alca torda Razorbill	B	1994	2,480	—	A	B3
Fratercula arctica Puffin	B	1995	20,000	—	A	B1ii, B2, C3

The IBA holds 84,700 pairs of breeding seabirds and 32,500 pairs of breeding waterbirds on a regular basis. It is also nationally important for breeding *Somateria mollissima* (1,660 pairs, 1995, 5%), *Rissa tridactyla* (9,900 pairs, 1995, 2%) and *Sterna paradisaea* (540 pairs, 1994, 1%).

■ **Protection status**
National Partial **International** Partial
IBA partly or wholly overlaps with the following national designated areas. *National Nature Reserve:* Isle of May. *Reserves:* Fidra Islands, Inchmickery, Long Craig. *Sites of Special Scientific Interest:* Bass Rock, Forth Islands, Gullane to Broad Sands, Inchmickery, Isle of May, Long Craig. Overlaps with international designated areas: 105 ha of IBA covered by Special Protection Area (Firth of Forth Islands, 105 ha).

■ **Conservation issues**

Threats Natural events (B)

Threats include gull predation, which may lower the breeding success of terns. A management plan is in preparation.

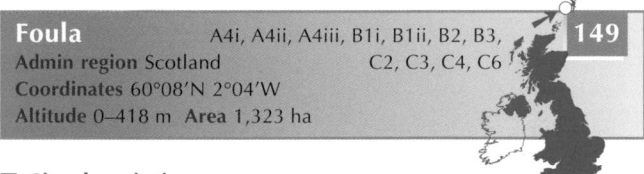

Foula   A4i, A4ii, A4iii, B1i, B1ii, B2, B3, **149**
Admin region Scotland   C2, C3, C4, C6
Coordinates 60°08′N 2°04′W
Altitude 0–418 m **Area** 1,323 ha

■ **Site description**
An island characterized by steep slopes and a cool oceanic climate. Vegetation types include mire and cliff-top communities, with submaritime and montane communities on higher ground.

Habitats Grassland, Wetland (fen/transition mire/spring), Rocky areas (sea cliff/rocky shore)
Land-use Agriculture (90%)

■ **Birds**

Species	Season	Year	Pop min	Pop max	Acc	Criteria
Fulmarus glacialis Fulmar	B	1987	46,800	46,800	A	A4ii, B1ii, C3
[1] *Oceanodroma leucorhoa* Leach's Petrel	B	1987	—	—	A	C6
Phalacrocorax aristotelis Shag	B	1987	2,400	2,400	A	A4i, B1i, B3, C2, C3
Stercorarius skua Great Skua	B	1992	2,170	2,170	A	A4ii, B1ii, B3, C3
Sterna paradisaea Arctic Tern	B	1995	1,000	1,000	A	C6
Uria aalge Guillemot	B	1987	25,100	25,100	A	B1ii, C3
Alca torda Razorbill	B	1987	4,150	4,150	A	B3
Fratercula arctica Puffin	B	1987	48,000	48,000	A	B1ii, B2, C3

1. No counts available.

The site holds very large populations of cliff and moorland nesting seabirds, totalling 127,000 pairs on a regular basis. The IBA is also nationally important for breeding *Gavia stellata* (11 pairs, 1994, 1%) and *Stercorarius parasiticus* (125 pairs, 1995, 4%).

■ **Protection status**
National High **International** High
IBA partly or wholly overlaps with the following national designated areas. *Sites of Special Scientific Interest:* Foula, Foula Coast. Overlaps

with international designated areas: 1,323 ha of IBA covered by Special Protection Area (Foula, 1,323 ha).

■ **Conservation issues**

Threats Agricultural intensification/expansion (B), Aquaculture/fisheries (B), Consequences of animal/plant introductions (B)

Unsustainable fishing of sandeels *Ammodytes* poses a potential threat to seabirds. The predation of breeding birds by introduced species, particularly feral cats *Felis catus*, rats *Rattus norvegicus* and hedgehogs *Erinaceus europaeus*, is also a problem.

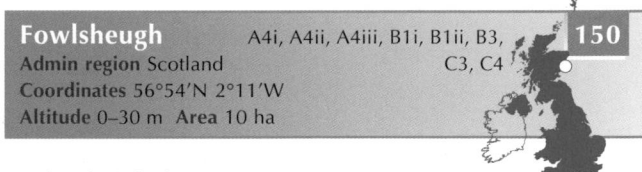

Fowlsheugh   A4i, A4ii, A4iii, B1i, B1ii, B3, **150**
Admin region Scotland   C3, C4
Coordinates 56°54′N 2°11′W
Altitude 0–30 m **Area** 10 ha

■ **Site description**
The IBA covers sheer cliffs on the east coast of Grampian region, and associated species-poor cliff-top grassland.

Habitats Grassland (10%), Rocky areas (90%; sea cliff/rocky shore)
Land-use Nature conservation/research (100%)

■ **Birds**

Species	Season	Year	Pop min	Pop max	Acc	Criteria
Larus argentatus Herring Gull	B	1992	6,250	6,250	A	B1i
Rissa tridactyla Kittiwake	B	1992	61,500	61,500	A	A4i, B1i, C3
Uria aalge Guillemot	B	1992	44,400	44,400	A	B1ii, C3
Alca torda Razorbill	B	1992	5,650	5,650	A	A4ii, B1ii, B3, C3

The site holds 52,900 pairs of breeding seabirds and 67,900 pairs of breeding waterbirds on a regular basis.

■ **Protection status**
National High **International** High
IBA partly or wholly overlaps with the following national designated areas. *Site of Special Scientific Interest:* Fowlsheugh. *Reserve:* Fowlsheugh. Overlaps with international designated areas: 10 ha of IBA covered by Special Protection Area (Fowlsheugh, 10 ha).

■ **Conservation issues**

Threats Aquaculture/fisheries (U), Disturbance to birds (U), Other (C)

Threats to the IBA are posed by offshore oil spills ('Other' threat), an inshore fishery, and disturbance. The RSPB own the reserve and there is ongoing annual monitoring of seabird plots and productivity. A management plan exists for part of the site.

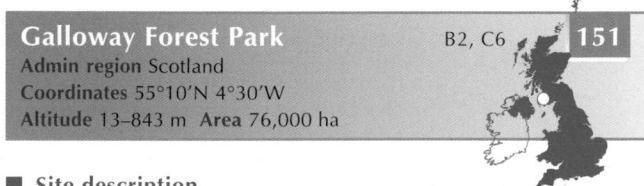

Galloway Forest Park   B2, C6 **151**
Admin region Scotland
Coordinates 55°10′N 4°30′W
Altitude 13–843 m **Area** 76,000 ha

■ **Site description**
A very large area of forest, including lochs, rivers and moorland, that stretches from Newton Stewart in Dumfries and Galloway into the Strathclyde region.

Habitats Forest and woodland (2%; broadleaved deciduous forest), Grassland (humid grassland; mesophile grassland), Wetland (standing fresh water; river/stream; blanket bog), Artificial landscape (60%; forestry plantation)
Land-use Agriculture (8%), Forestry (60%), Nature conservation/research (65%), Water management (7%)

■ **Birds**

Species	Season	Year	Pop min	Pop max	Acc	Criteria
Falco peregrinus Peregrine	R	1995	19	19	A	B2, C6
Tetrao tetrix Black Grouse	R	1995	120	—	A	B2
Asio flammeus Short-eared Owl	R	1995	10	—	A	B2, C6

The IBA supports a range of breeding waders and waterbirds, in addition to species of forest and moorland.

■ Protection status

National Partial **International** Partial

IBA partly or wholly overlaps with the following national designated areas. *National Nature Reserve:* Silver Flowe. *Sites of Special Scientific Interest:* Cairnbaber, Cairnsmore of Fleet, Clatteringshaws Dam Quarry, Cleugh, Ellergower Moss, Glentrool Oakwoods, Kenmure Holms, Laughenghie and Airie Hills, Loch Doon, Merrick-Kells, Talnotry Mine. Overlaps with international designated areas: 8,924 ha of IBA covered by Biosphere Reserve (Silver Flowe–Merrick-Kells, 8,924 ha). 619 ha of IBA covered by Ramsar Site (Silver Flowe, 619 ha).

■ Conservation issues

Threats	Agricultural intensification/expansion (A), Other (U)

Threats include overgrazing by sheep, deer and feral goats, and acidification ('Other' threat, above). The Galloway Forest Bird Project is Forest Enterprise-led and encompasses a range of ongoing survey and monitoring work on, amongst others, *Aquila chrysaetos*, *Falco peregrinus*, *F. columbarius*, *Tetrao tetrix*, *Circus cyaneus*, *Tyto alba*, *F. tinnunculus*, *Corvus corax* and *Cinclus cinclus*. There is a management plan for the site, part of which is a candidate SAC.

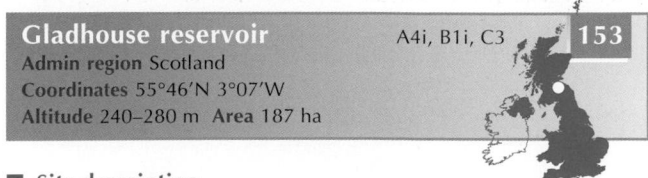

Gigha Island and islets   B1ii, B2   152

Admin region Scotland
Coordinates 55°41′N 5°44′W
Altitude 0–56 m   **Area** 442 ha

■ Site description

A large island and series of smaller islets, stacks and rocks, located to the west of Rhunahaorine Point.

Habitats Scrub (heathland), Grassland, Marine areas (open sea), Rocky areas (sea cliff/rocky shore; rock stacks/islets)
Land-use Agriculture, Not utilized

■ Birds

Species	Season	Year	Pop min	Pop max	Acc	Criteria
Cepphus grylle Black Guillemot	B	1991	290	290	A	B1ii, B2

The IBA is important for breeding seabirds. Breeding species of global conservation concern that do not meet IBA criteria: *Crex crex* (1 pair in 1995, although none present 1997–1998).

■ Protection status

National None **International** None

■ Conservation issues

Threats	Consequences of animal/plant introductions (A)

A potential threat exists from American mink *Mustela vison* predation if they move from the mainland. There is therefore an urgent need to establish the breeding location of the large numbers of *Cepphus grylle*.

Gladhouse reservoir   A4i, B1i, C3   153

Admin region Scotland
Coordinates 55°46′N 3°07′W
Altitude 240–280 m   **Area** 187 ha

■ Site description

Lying at the foot of the Moorfoot Hills, about 29 km south of Edinburgh, Gladhouse reservoir is a large, moderately nutrient-rich loch containing several small islands. It supports some aquatic and marginal vegetation.

Habitats Forest and woodland (1%; mixed forest), Scrub (1%; scrub), Wetland (97%; standing fresh water; water-fringe vegetation; fen/transition mire/spring), Artificial landscape (1%; forestry plantation)
Land-use Tourism/recreation (97%), Water management (100%)

■ Birds

Species	Season	Year	Pop min	Pop max	Acc	Criteria
[1] *Anser brachyrhynchus* Pink-footed Goose	W	1996	2,940	2,940	A	A4i, B1i, C3

1. Mean annual peak 1991–1996.

The IBA is important for wintering waterbirds.

■ Protection status

National High **International** High

IBA partly or wholly overlaps with the following national designated areas. *Reserve:* Gladhouse Reservoir. *Site of Special Scientific Interest:* Gladhouse Reservoir. Overlaps with international designated areas: 187 ha of IBA covered by Special Protection Area (Gladhouse Reservoir, 187 ha). 187 ha of IBA covered by Ramsar Site (Gladhouse Reservoir, 187 ha).

■ Conservation issues

Threats	Disturbance to birds (B), Other (C), Recreation/tourism (B)

Threats include the disturbance caused by shooting to roost and foraging areas, nutrient enrichment of the reservoir and changes in water-level ('Other' threat, above). There is a management plan for the site.

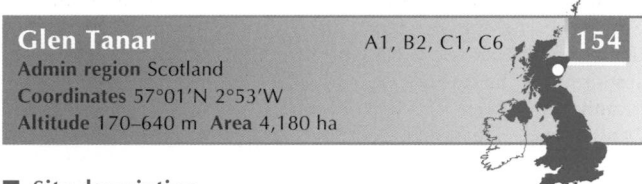

Glen Tanar   A1, B2, C1, C6   154

Admin region Scotland
Coordinates 57°01′N 2°53′W
Altitude 170–640 m   **Area** 4,180 ha

■ Site description

The Forest of Glen Tanar covers the slopes of Glen Tanar and tributary valleys. It is the third largest expanse of native pinewood *Pinus sylvestris* in Britain, with heather moorland above the treeline.

Habitats Forest and woodland (30%; native coniferous forest), Scrub (60%; heathland), Wetland (1%; fen/transition mire/spring), Artificial landscape (9%; forestry plantation)
Land-use Forestry (20%), Hunting, Tourism/recreation

■ Birds

Species	Season	Year	Pop min	Pop max	Acc	Criteria
Tetrao urogallus Capercaillie	R	1990	—	45	A	C6
Loxia scotica Scottish Crossbill	R	1990	Frequent	—		A1, B2, C1

The IBA is important for several characteristic pinewood species, including *Tetrao tetrix* which occurs at nationally important levels.

■ Protection status

National High **International** High

IBA partly or wholly overlaps with the following national designated areas. *National Nature Reserve:* Glen Tanar. *Site of Special Scientific Interest:* Glen Tanar. Overlaps with international designated areas: 4,180 ha of IBA covered by Special Protection Area (Glen Tanar, 4,180 ha).

■ Conservation issues

Threats	Forest grazing (U), Other (U)

Inappropriate forestry practices ('Other' threat, above) and deer-grazing threaten the IBA. A considerable number of research projects are ongoing, including monitoring of *Tetrao urogallus* by the Institute of Terrestrial Ecology.

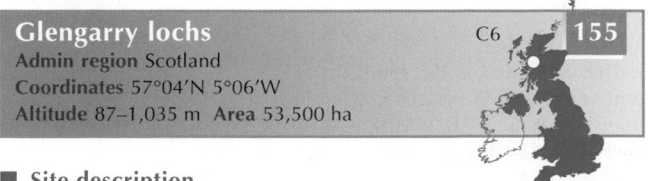

Glengarry lochs   C6   155

Admin region Scotland
Coordinates 57°04′N 5°06′W
Altitude 87–1,035 m   **Area** 53,500 ha

■ Site description

Nutrient-poor lochs and lochans with fringing aquatic vegetation. The surrounding catchment area incorporates upland heath and mire, upland broadleaved woodland, commercial forestry plantations and remnants of Caledonian pine forest.

Habitats Forest and woodland (broadleaved deciduous forest; native coniferous forest), Scrub (heathland), Grassland (steppe/dry calcareous grassland), Wetland (standing fresh water; river/stream; water-fringe vegetation; fen/transition mire/spring), Artificial landscape (forestry plantation)
Land-use Fisheries/aquaculture, Forestry, Hunting, Water management

■ Birds

Species	Season	Year	Pop min	Pop max	Acc	Criteria
Falco columbarius Merlin	B	1995	10	10	A	C6

The site is also nationally important for breeding *Gavia arctica* (4 pairs, 1991–1995, 3%), *Melanitta nigra* (16 pairs, 1995, 21%) and *Aquila chrysaetos* (4 pairs, 1992, 1%).

■ Protection status
National Partial **International** None
IBA partly or wholly overlaps with the following national designated areas. *Sites of Special Scientific Interest:* Garry Falls, Quoich Spillway.

■ Conservation issues

Threats Afforestation (B), Aquaculture/fisheries (B), Construction/impact of dyke/dam/barrage (B), Recreation/tourism (B), Unsustainable exploitation (B)

All of the main lochs are already dammed, and flooding has negative consequences for the breeding success of divers (Gaviidae) and *Melanitta nigra*. There is a continued threat from egg-collecting. Forest Enterprise runs the Caledonian Pinewood Regeneration Scheme on the south side of Loch Garry, while other native forest regeneration schemes exist elsewhere within the IBA.

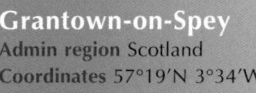

Grantown-on-Spey
A1, B2, C1, C2 **156**
Admin region Scotland
Coordinates 57°19′N 3°34′W
Altitude 200–210 m **Area** 520 ha

■ Site description
An area of coniferous woodland immediately adjacent to the town of Grantown-on-Spey.

Habitats Forest and woodland (broadleaved deciduous forest; native coniferous forest)
Land-use Forestry (100%)

■ Birds

Species	Season	Year	Pop min	Pop max	Acc	Criteria
Loxia scotica Scottish Crossbill	R	1994	15	15	A	A1, B2, C1, C2

The site also supports breeding *Parus cristatus* and *Tetrao urogallus*.

■ Protection status
National None **International** None

■ Conservation issues

Threats Other (U)

Inappropriate forest management is a problem ('Other' threat, above).

Greenlaw Moor and Hule Moss
A4i, B1i, C3 **157**
Admin region Scotland
Coordinates 55°44′N 2°28′W
Altitude 183–285 m **Area** 1,200 ha

■ Site description
The IBA is located in the south Lammermuir Hills, and comprises heather moorland in the east and raised mire in the west, in addition to the two pools of Hule Moss. The heath is the largest remaining example of mid-altitude moorland in the Borders.

Habitats Forest and woodland (2%), Scrub (30%; heathland), Wetland (68%; standing fresh water; river/stream; blanket bog; fen/transition mire/spring)

Land-use Agriculture (98%), Tourism/recreation (90%), Water management (3%)

■ Birds

Species	Season	Year	Pop min	Pop max	Acc	Criteria
[1] *Anser brachyrhynchus* Pink-footed Goose	W	1996	15,400	15,400	A	A4i, B1i, C3

1. Mean annual peak 1991–1996.

The site also supports a suite of breeding and wintering moorland birds including waders, *Tetrao tetrix*, *Falco columbarius*, *Circus cyaneus* and *Falco peregrinus*.

■ Protection status
National High **International** Partial
IBA partly or wholly overlaps with the following national designated areas. *Site of Special Scientific Interest:* Greenlaw Moor. Overlaps with international designated areas: 248 ha of IBA covered by Special Protection Area (Greenlaw Moor, 248 ha). 248 ha of IBA covered by Ramsar Site (Greenlaw Moor, 248 ha).

■ Conservation issues

Threats Agricultural intensification/expansion (U)

Agricultural change in surrounding farmland may affect use of the site by *Anser brachyrhynchus*.

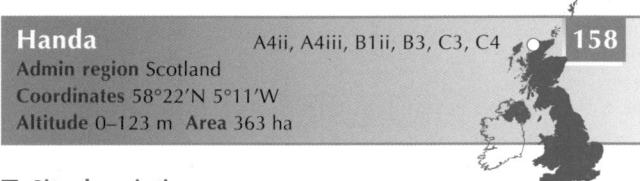

Handa
A4ii, A4iii, B1ii, B3, C3, C4 **158**
Admin region Scotland
Coordinates 58°22′N 5°11′W
Altitude 0–123 m **Area** 363 ha

■ Site description
A sandstone island with precipitous cliffs located a short way off the west coast of Sutherland. The vegetation comprises submaritime grass and heathland, with more species-rich maritime heathland on the clifftops. Herb-rich grassland occurs in more sheltered areas.

Habitats Scrub (heathland), Grassland, Wetland (standing fresh water), Rocky areas (sea cliff/rocky shore)
Land-use Nature conservation/research

■ Birds

Species	Season	Year	Pop min	Pop max	Acc	Criteria
Stercorarius skua Great Skua	B	1995	115	115	A	B3
Uria aalge Guillemot	B	1994	76,000	76,000	A	B1ii, C3
Alca torda Razorbill	B	1987	11,000	11,000	A	A4ii, B1ii, B3, C3

The island is of major importance for breeding seabirds, holding 91,100 pairs on a regular basis. It is also nationally important for breeding *Rissa tridactyla* (7,400 pairs, 1995, 1%).

■ Protection status
National High **International** High
IBA partly or wholly overlaps with the following national designated areas. *National Nature Reserve:* Handa. *Reserve:* Handa. *Site of Special Scientific Interest:* Handa Island. Overlaps with international designated areas: 363 ha of IBA covered by Special Protection Area (Handa, 363 ha).

■ Conservation issues
No serious threats are known. The island is leased by the Scottish Wildlife Trust, and monitoring of the seabird colonies takes place.

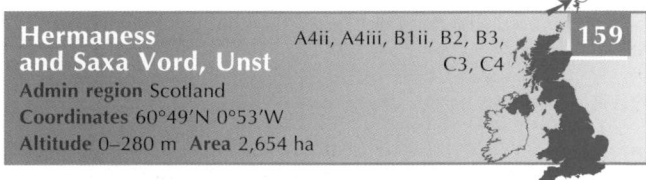

Hermaness and Saxa Vord, Unst
A4ii, A4iii, B1ii, B2, B3, C3, C4 **159**
Admin region Scotland
Coordinates 60°49′N 0°53′W
Altitude 0–280 m **Area** 2,654 ha

■ Site description
The IBA is situated at the most northern tip of Britain, and comprises

heathland, small nutrient-poor lochans and burns, and sea cliffs. Closely grazed species-rich maritime grassland occurs on the cliff-tops, with blanket bog and acid grassland vegetation communities also present.

Habitats Scrub (heathland), Grassland (humid grassland), Wetland (blanket bog), Rocky areas (sea cliff/rocky shore)
Land-use Agriculture (100%)

■ Birds

Species	Season	Year	Pop min	Pop max	Acc	Criteria
Sula bassana Gannet	B	1994	12,000	12,000	A	A4ii, B1ii, B2, C3
Stercorarius skua Great Skua	B	1992	1,220	1,220	A	A4ii, B1ii, B3, C3
Cepphus grylle Black Guillemot	B	1982	190	190	A	B1ii, B2
Fratercula arctica Puffin	B	1995	19,100	—	A	B1ii, B2, C3

The site holds 70,600 pairs of breeding seabirds on a regular basis, and is also nationally important for breeding *Gavia stellata* (9 pairs, 1994, 1%), *Fulmarus glacialis* (26,200 pairs, 1986–1987, 5%), *Numenius phaeopus* (14 pairs, 1994, 3%), *Stercorarius parasiticus* (115 pairs, 1992, 4%) and *Uria aalge* (11,400 pairs, 1991, 2%).

■ Protection status
National Partial **International** Partial
IBA partly or wholly overlaps with the following national designated areas. *National Nature Reserve:* Hermaness. *Sites of Special Scientific Interest:* Hermaness, Norwick, Norwick Meadows, Saxa Vord, Tonga Greff. Overlaps with international designated areas: 980 ha of IBA covered by Special Protection Area (Hermaness and Saxa Vord, Unst, 980 ha).

■ Conservation issues

Threats Agricultural intensification/expansion (B), Aquaculture/fisheries (B), Extraction industry (U)

A proposal exists to extract peat commercially from a small part of the IBA. Unsustainable fishing of sandeels *Ammodytes* poses a potential threat to seabirds. There is a management plan for the site.

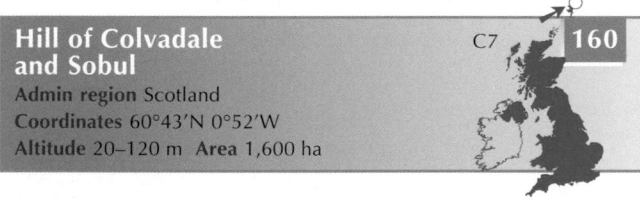

Hill of Colvadale and Sobul
C7 160
Admin region Scotland
Coordinates 60°43′N 0°52′W
Altitude 20–120 m **Area** 1,600 ha

■ Site description
Heathland overlying magnesium silicate rocks, with areas of deep peat, wet flush and mire. Plant communities present include herb-rich sedge grass heath and also species-poor wet and dry heaths.

Habitats Scrub (heathland), Grassland, Wetland (fen/transition mire/spring)
Land-use Agriculture (100%)

■ Birds

Species	Season	Year	Pop min	Pop max	Acc	Criteria
Numenius phaeopus Whimbrel	B	1994	23	23	A	C7
Stercorarius parasiticus Arctic Skua	B	1992	77	77	A	C7

The IBA holds a rich assemblage of breeding birds.

■ Protection status
National Partial **International** None
IBA partly or wholly overlaps with the following national designated areas. *Sites of Special Scientific Interest:* Hill of Colvadale and Sobul, Qui Ness to Pund Stacks, Skeo Taing to Clugan.

■ Conservation issues

Threats Agricultural intensification/expansion (B), Aquaculture/fisheries (U), Extraction industry (U)

Unsustainable fishing of sandeels *Ammodytes* poses a potential threat to seabirds.

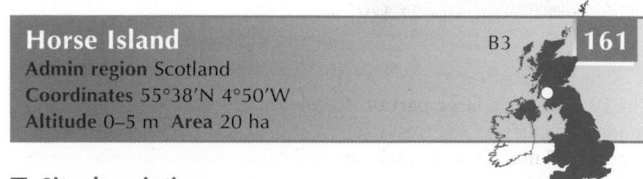

Horse Island
B3 161
Admin region Scotland
Coordinates 55°38′N 4°50′W
Altitude 0–5 m **Area** 20 ha

■ Site description
A small rocky island close to the coastline north of Ardrossan.

Habitats Grassland, Rocky areas (sea cliff/rocky shore)
Land-use Nature conservation/research (100%)

■ Birds

Species	Season	Year	Pop min	Pop max	Acc	Criteria
Larus fuscus Lesser Black-backed Gull	B	1994	1,150	1,150	A	B3

The site is also nationally important for breeding *Somateria mollissima* (365 pairs, 1994, 1%).

■ Protection status
National High **International** None
IBA partly or wholly overlaps with the following national designated areas. *Reserve:* Horse Island.

■ Conservation issues

Threats Disturbance to birds (U)

Human access to the island is the main cause of disturbance. An RSPB management agreement exists for the site.

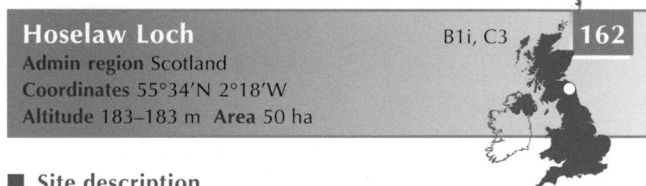

Hoselaw Loch
B1i, C3 162
Admin region Scotland
Coordinates 55°34′N 2°18′W
Altitude 183–183 m **Area** 50 ha

■ Site description
A small loch located on the northern slopes of the Cheviot Hills, supporting little emergent vegetation. The IBA also includes surrounding fen and well-developed raised mire.

Habitats Forest and woodland (2%; mixed forest), Scrub (5%; scrub), Wetland (83%; standing fresh water; raised bog; fen/transition mire/spring), Artificial landscape (10%; highly improved reseeded grassland)
Land-use Agriculture (10%), Forestry (3%), Nature conservation/research (100%), Water management (40%)

■ Birds

Species	Season	Year	Pop min	Pop max	Acc	Criteria
Anser anser Greylag Goose	W	1995	1,430	1,430	A	B1i, C3

The IBA is important for wintering waterbirds. *Anser anser* are from the Icelandic breeding population.

■ Protection status
National High **International** High
IBA partly or wholly overlaps with the following national designated areas. *Reserve:* Din Moss and Hoselaw Loch. *Site of Special Scientific Interest:* Din Moss and Hoselaw Loch. Overlaps with international designated areas: 50 ha of IBA covered by Special Protection Area (Din Moss and Hoselaw Loch, 50 ha). 50 ha of IBA covered by Ramsar Site (Din Moss and Hoselaw Loch, 50 ha).

■ Conservation issues

Threats Disturbance to birds (A), Other (B), Recreation/tourism (A)

Disturbance to wildfowl from shooting on adjacent land and nutrient pollution of the loch ('Other' threat, above) pose threats to the IBA.

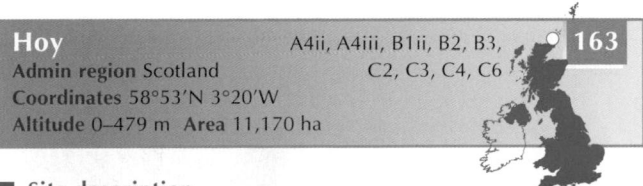

Hoy	A4ii, A4iii, B1ii, B2, B3,	**163**
Admin region Scotland	C2, C3, C4, C6	
Coordinates 58°53'N 3°20'W		
Altitude 0–479 m **Area** 11,170 ha		

■ Site description

The IBA covers a large part of the high island of Hoy, with Old Red Sandstone cliffs on the west coast reaching 338 m. These include the famous 137 m high rock stack, the Old Man of Hoy. The site includes Orkney's only remaining piece of relict deciduous woodland, and lichen and bryophyte-rich heaths.

Habitats Forest and woodland (mixed forest), Scrub (scrub; heathland), Grassland (alpine/subalpine/boreal grassland), Wetland (standing fresh water; river/stream), Rocky areas (sea cliff/rocky shore; rock stacks/islets)
Land-use Agriculture (65%), Nature conservation/research (35%)

■ Birds

Species	Season	Year	Pop min	Pop max	Acc	Criteria
Gavia stellata Red-throated Diver	B	1994	58	58	A	B2, C2, C6
Stercorarius skua Great Skua	B	1996	2,120	2,120	A	A4ii, B1ii, B3, C3
Larus marinus Great Black-backed Gull	B	1996	645	645	A	B3

The IBA is important for breeding seabirds (56,000 pairs on a regular basis), raptors and waders. It is also nationally important for breeding *Fulmarus glacialis* (37,000 pairs, 1986, 7%), *Stercorarius parasiticus* (96 pairs, 1996, 3%), *Sterna paradisaea* (525 pairs, 1987–1995, 1%) and *Uria aalge* (13,900 pairs, 1986, 2%).

■ Protection status
National Partial **International** None
IBA partly or wholly overlaps with the following national designated areas. *Reserve:* Hoy. *Site of Special Scientific Interest:* Hoy.

■ Conservation issues

Threats Afforestation (C), Agricultural intensification/expansion (B)

Native woodland regeneration is being encouraged through planting and protection measures, with progress being monitored. Monitoring of heathland regeneration and of geomorphological features is also undertaken. The area is a candidate SPA, and a management plan exists for the RSPB Reserve.

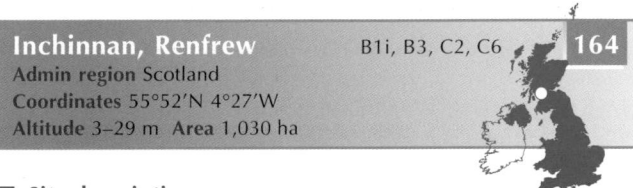

Inchinnan, Renfrew	B1i, B3, C2, C6	**164**
Admin region Scotland		
Coordinates 55°52'N 4°27'W		
Altitude 3–29 m **Area** 1,030 ha		

■ Site description
A small site situated along the Black Cart River in Renfrewshire.

Habitats Grassland (humid grassland), Wetland (river/stream)
Land-use Agriculture (95%), Water management (5%)

■ Birds

Species	Season	Year	Pop min	Pop max	Acc	Criteria
Cygnus cygnus Whooper Swan	W	1994	260	260	A	B1i, B3, C2, C6

The IBA is important for wintering *Cygnus cygnus*.

■ Protection status
National None **International** None

■ Conservation issues

Threats Agricultural intensification/expansion (U), Disturbance to birds (U), Industrialization/urbanization (U)

SNH has undertaken a swan survey during the winters of 1994/95–1998/99 as part of development studies. The main swan roosting area is at the consultation stage for SSSI designation, but feeding areas remain unprotected.

Inner Clyde estuary	B1i, C3	**165**
Admin region Scotland		
Coordinates 55°56'N 4°38'W		
Altitude 0–5 m **Area** 1,670 ha		

■ Site description
Extensive areas of intertidal habitats bounded by areas of heavy industry. Habitats present include saltmarsh, mudflats and eel-grass *Zostera* and mussel *Mytilus* beds.

Habitats Wetland (100%; tidal river/enclosed tidal water; mudflat/sandflat; saltmarsh)
Land-use Nature conservation/research

■ Birds

Species	Season	Year	Pop min	Pop max	Acc	Criteria
Tringa totanus Redshank	W	1995	2,180	2,180	A	B1i, C3

The IBA is important for wintering waders and wildfowl, and is also nationally important for wintering *Phalacrocorax carbo* (280 birds, 2%), *Bucephala clangula* (370 birds, 1%), *Haematopus ostralegus* (5,250 birds, 1%) and *Tringa nebularia* (11 birds, 2%), and for passage *Tringa totanus* (1,340 birds, 1%).

■ Protection status
National High **International** None
IBA partly or wholly overlaps with the following national designated areas. *Reserves:* Dumbuck, Finlaystone, Inner Clyde, Langbank. *Sites of Special Scientific Interest:* Ardmore Point, Dumbarton Rock, Dumbuck Foreshore – Pillar Bank, Erskine to Langbank, Geilston Burn.

■ Conservation issues

Threats Aquaculture/fisheries (B), Disturbance to birds (B), Filling-in of wetlands (B), Industrialization/urbanization (A), Recreation/tourism (B)

Threats to the estuary include disturbance from recreational activities including wildfowling and motorcycling, and leisure, industrial, housing and retail developments. Three RSPB reserves are included: Dumbuck at Dumbarton, Finlaystone at Port Glasgow, and Langbank. The Clyde Forum has been established and is in the process of drawing up management guidelines. The area is a candidate SPA.

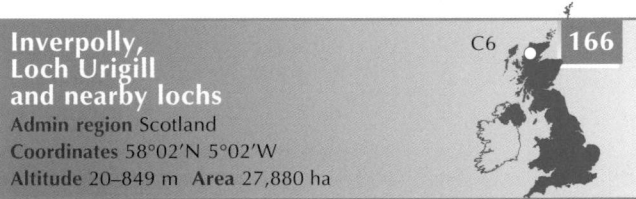

Inverpolly, Loch Urigill and nearby lochs	C6	**166**
Admin region Scotland		
Coordinates 58°02'N 5°02'W		
Altitude 20–849 m **Area** 27,880 ha		

■ Site description
The site comprises several large nutrient-poor lochs and many lochans along with their catchments.

Habitats Forest and woodland (broadleaved deciduous forest), Scrub (heathland), Wetland (standing fresh water; river/stream; blanket bog; fen/transition mire/spring)
Land-use Agriculture, Hunting, Tourism/recreation

■ Birds

Species	Season	Year	Pop min	Pop max	Acc	Criteria
[1] *Gavia arctica* Black-throated Diver	B	1995	9	9	A	C6
1. Mean count.						

The IBA is also nationally important for breeding *Anas penelope* (12 pairs, 1994, 4%) and *Tringa nebularia* (15 pairs, 1995, 1%).

■ Protection status
National Partial **International** None
IBA partly or wholly overlaps with the following national designated areas. *Reserve:* Ben More Coigach. *Sites of Special Scientific Interest:* Ben More Assynt, Cam Loch Islands, Inchnadamph, Inverpolly, Knockan Cliff (including Port Inverpolly).

Conservation issues

Threats Afforestation (C), Agricultural intensification/expansion (B), Aquaculture/fisheries (B), Extraction industry (B)

Part of the area carries a NNR designation (leased), for which SNH has a management plan. The site is a candidate SPA.

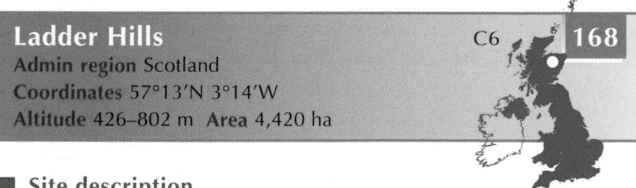

Kinveachy   A1, B2, C1, C6   167
Admin region Scotland
Coordinates 57°14′N 3°53′W
Altitude 290–741 m **Area** 5,250 ha

Site description
The principal stands of this remnant Caledonian pine *Pinus sylvestris* forest lie south-west of Carrbridge on either side of the River Dulnain. The stocking is irregular, with dense stands of mature woodland separated by open moorland with scattered trees. Broadleaved woodland, *Juniperus* scrub, moorland, wet heathland and fen areas occur within the forest.

Habitats Forest and woodland (broadleaved deciduous forest; native coniferous forest), Scrub (heathland), Wetland (river/stream; fen/transition mire/spring)
Land-use Forestry (25%), Hunting (75%)

Birds

Species	Season	Year	Pop min	Pop max	Acc	Criteria
Tetrao urogallus Capercaillie	R	1996	30	30	A	C6
Loxia scotica Scottish Crossbill	R	1996	Abundant	—		A1, B2, C1, C6

The site is notable for breeding pinewood species, and nationally important numbers of breeding *Parus cristatus*.

Protection status
National High **International** None
IBA partly or wholly overlaps with the following national designated areas. *National Nature Reserve:* Craigiellachie. *Sites of Special Scientific Interest:* Craigiellachie, Kinveachy Forest.

Conservation issues

Threats Agricultural intensification/expansion (B), Forest grazing (A), Other (A), Recreation/tourism (B)

Threats include overgrazing by red deer *Cervus elaphus* and birds striking deer fences ('Other' threat, above). Some research has been carried out into pinewood birds and also into bird strikes. The site is a candidate SPA.

Ladder Hills   C6   168
Admin region Scotland
Coordinates 57°13′N 3°14′W
Altitude 426–802 m **Area** 4,420 ha

Site description
An upland block to the north-east of the Cairngorms.

Habitats Scrub (69%; heathland), Grassland (10%), Wetland (21%; river/stream; blanket bog)
Land-use Hunting (95%)

Birds
The IBA supports a wide range of breeding moorland species.

Protection status
National High **International** None
IBA partly or wholly overlaps with the following national designated areas. *Site of Special Scientific Interest:* Ladder Hills.

Conservation issues

Threats Agricultural intensification/expansion (U), Recreation/tourism (U)

The area is threatened by agricultural practices (grazing), and by a potential expansion of skiing facilities.

Laggan, Islay   A4i, B1i, B2, C2, C3, C6   169
Admin region Scotland
Coordinates 55°43′N 6°18′W
Altitude 0–39 m **Area** 1,230 ha

Site description
The IBA includes the rocky headland of Laggan Point, the broad, sandy sweep of Laggan Bay and adjacent *Juncus*-rich grassland.

Habitats Grassland (dry siliceous grassland; humid grassland), Wetland (sand-dunes/sand beach; blanket bog)
Land-use Agriculture (95%), Forestry (5%)

Birds

Species	Season	Year	Pop min	Pop max	Acc	Criteria
[1] *Anser albifrons* White-fronted Goose	W	1997	330	330	A	B1i, C2, C3
[1] *Branta leucopsis* Barnacle Goose	W	1997	2,760	2,760	A	A4i, B1i, B2, C2, C6
Pyrrhocorax pyrrhocorax Chough	R	1988	3	—	A	C6

1. Mean seasonal peak 1994–1997.

The IBA is important for wintering geese, which come from Eilean na Muice Duibh (135) to feed. *Anser albifrons* are the *flavirostris* subspecies, and *Branta leucopsis* are from the Greenland breeding population. Breeding species of global conservation concern that do not meet IBA criteria: *Crex crex* (2 pairs, 1995, although none present in 1997/98).

Protection status
National High **International** High
IBA partly or wholly overlaps with the following national designated areas. *Site of Special Scientific Interest:* Laggan Peninsula and Bay. Overlaps with international designated areas: 1,230 ha of IBA covered by Special Protection Area (Laggan Peninsula and Bay, 1,230 ha).

Conservation issues

Threats Agricultural intensification/expansion (B), Recreation/tourism (B)

Disturbance caused to waders and terns by human visitors is a problem.

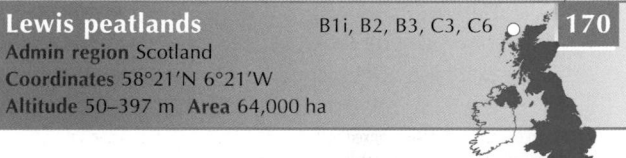

Lewis peatlands   B1i, B2, B3, C3, C6   170
Admin region Scotland
Coordinates 58°21′N 6°21′W
Altitude 50–397 m **Area** 64,000 ha

Site description
These peatlands cover the greater part of the island, and are interspersed with freshwater lochs and complexes of bog pools.

Habitats Scrub (10%; heathland), Grassland (5%), Wetland (85%; standing fresh water; blanket bog), Rocky areas (scree/boulders)
Land-use Agriculture (95%), Fisheries/aquaculture (3%), Forestry (2%)

Birds

Species	Season	Year	Pop min	Pop max	Acc	Criteria
Gavia stellata Red-throated Diver	B	1992	23	23	A	B2, C6
Gavia arctica Black-throated Diver	B	1992	10	10	A	C6
Aquila chrysaetos Golden Eagle	R	1992	9	—	A	B2, C6
Falco columbarius Merlin	R	1995	9	9	A	C6
Pluvialis apricaria Golden Plover	R	1995	710	710	A	B3, C6
Calidris alpina Dunlin	B	1995	850	850	A	B1i, C3

The area is important for breeding waders, divers and raptors. It is also nationally important for breeding *Tringa nebularia* (63 pairs, 1995, 6%). Breeding species of global conservation concern that do not meet IBA criteria: *Crex crex* (4 pairs).

Protection status
National Partial **International** None
IBA partly or wholly overlaps with the following national designated areas. *Sites of Special Scientific Interest:* Achmore Bog, Little Loch Roag Valley Bog, Loch Laxavat Ard and Loch Laxavat Iorach, Loch

na Cartach, Loch nan Eilean Valley Bog, Loch Scarrasdale Bog, North Harris.

■ Conservation issues

Threats Afforestation (A), Agricultural intensification/expansion (B), Aquaculture/fisheries (B), Extraction industry (B)

Crofter forestry constitutes a threat.

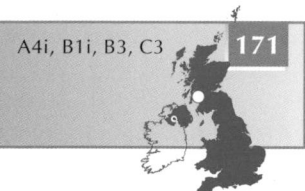

Little Cumbrae Island   A4i, B1i, B3, C3   171
Admin region Scotland
Coordinates 55°43′N 4°57′W
Altitude 0–107 m **Area** 300 ha

■ Site description
A small island in the Outer Clyde estuary, just south of Great Cumbrae and the town of Millport.

Habitats Scrub, Grassland, Rocky areas (sea cliff/rocky shore)
Land-use Agriculture (100%)

■ Birds

Species	Season	Year	Pop min	Pop max	Acc	Criteria
Larus fuscus Lesser Black-backed Gull	B	1986	3,000	3,000	A	A4i, B1i, B3, C3

The site is important for breeding seabirds, and is also nationally important for breeding *Larus argentatus* (3,500 pairs, 1986, 2%).

■ Protection status
National None **International** None

■ Conservation issues
No serious threats are known at the site, which is private land.

Loch Gruinart, Islay   A4i, A4iii, B1i, B2, B3,   172
Admin region Scotland   C2, C3, C4, C6
Coordinates 55°48′N 6°20′W
Altitude 0–60 m **Area** 3,261 ha

■ Site description
The IBA comprises a north-facing sea loch over 5 km in length, and adjacent grassland, heathland, saltmarsh, mudflat and sand-dune habitats.

Habitats Forest and woodland (mixed forest), Scrub (heathland), Grassland (humid grassland; mesophile grassland), Wetland (mudflat/sandflat; saltmarsh; sand-dunes/sand beach; standing fresh water; river/stream; blanket bog), Marine areas (sea inlet/coastal features), Artificial landscape (arable land)
Land-use Agriculture (30%), Nature conservation/research (30%)

■ Birds

Species	Season	Year	Pop min	Pop max	Acc	Criteria
[1] *Cygnus cygnus* Whooper Swan	W	1995	135	135	A	B3
[2] *Anser albifrons* White-fronted Goose	W	1997	940	940	A	B1i, C2, C3
[2] *Branta leucopsis* Barnacle Goose	W	1997	11,800	11,800	A	A4i, B1i, B2, C2, C6

1. Mean annual peak 1991–1995.
2. Mean seasonal peak 1994–1997.

The site holds 23,200 wintering waterbirds on a regular basis, and is also nationally important for breeding *Crex crex* (globally threatened: 10 pairs, 1995, 2%). *Anser albifrons* are the *flavirostris* subspecies, while *Branta leucopsis* are from the Greenland breeding population.

■ Protection status
National High **International** High
IBA partly or wholly overlaps with the following national designated areas. *Reserve:* Loch Gruinart – Islay. *Site of Special Scientific Interest:* Gruinart Flats. Overlaps with international designated areas: 3,261 ha of IBA covered by Special Protection Area (Gruinart Flats, Islay, 3,261 ha). 3,261 ha of IBA covered by Ramsar Site (Gruinart Flats, Islay, 3,261 ha).

■ Conservation issues

Threats Agricultural intensification/expansion (B), Aquaculture/fisheries (U), Disturbance to birds (B)

A management plan exists for the RSPB Reserve, with SNH management agreements at Ardnave and Craigens.

Loch Indaal   A4i, B1i, B2, C2, C6   173
and Bridgend Flats, Islay
Admin region Scotland
Coordinates 55°46′N 6°15′W
Altitude 0–15 m **Area** 3,750 ha

■ Site description
The site includes large sea loch of Indaal and the sheltered Bridgend Flats. Saltmarsh and mudflat communities occur that are scarce within the Inner Hebrides.

Habitats Wetland (13%; mudflat/sandflat; saltmarsh), Marine areas (87%; sea inlet/coastal features)
Land-use Agriculture (5%)

■ Birds

Species	Season	Year	Pop min	Pop max	Acc	Criteria
[1] *Branta leucopsis* Barnacle Goose	W	1997	10,000	10,000	A	A4i, B1i, B2, C2, C6
Aythya marila Scaup	W	1995	975	975	A	B2

1. Estimate of numbers of birds regularly using site as a night roost 1994–1997.

The IBA is important for wintering geese and other wildfowl, and is also nationally important for wintering *Mergus serrator* (160 birds, 2%). *Branta leucopsis* are from the Greenland breeding population.

■ Protection status
National Partial **International** Low
IBA partly or wholly overlaps with the following national designated areas. *Sites of Special Scientific Interest:* Islay – Bridgend Flats, Laggan Peninsular and Bay. Overlaps with international designated areas: 331 ha of IBA covered by Special Protection Area (Bridgend Flats, Islay, 331 ha). 331 ha of IBA covered by Ramsar Site (Bridgend Flats, Islay, 331 ha).

■ Conservation issues

Threats Aquaculture/fisheries (U), Infrastructure (A), Other (A)

An oil spill in 1996 caused little long-term damage but reoccurrences pose a threat ('Other' threat, above).

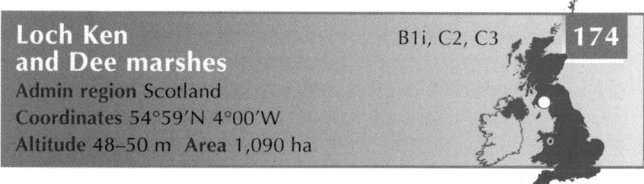

Loch Ken   B1i, C2, C3   174
and Dee marshes
Admin region Scotland
Coordinates 54°59′N 4°00′W
Altitude 48–50 m **Area** 1,090 ha

■ Site description
A highly complex system of lochs, swamps, fens, grassland and *Salix* carr, stretching for about 20 km along the courses of the Rivers Ken and Dee.

Habitats Scrub (scrub), Grassland (2%), Wetland (90%; standing fresh water; fen/transition mire/spring), Artificial landscape (8%; highly improved reseeded grassland)
Land-use Agriculture (10%), Nature conservation/research (5%), Tourism/recreation (90%), Urban/industrial/transport (10%), Water management (80%)

■ Birds

Species	Season	Year	Pop min	Pop max	Acc	Criteria
Anser albifrons White-fronted Goose	W	1995	265	265	A	B1i, C2, C3

The IBA is also nationally important for wintering *Anser fabalis* (5 birds, 1%). *Anser albifrons* are the *flavirostris* subspecies.

■ Protection status

National High **International** Partial
IBA partly or wholly overlaps with the following national designated areas. *Reserves:* Loch Ken and Dee Marshes, Threave. *Sites of Special Scientific Interest:* Airds of Kells Wood, Kenmure Holms, River Dee (Parton to Crossmichael), Threave and Carlingwark Loch, Water of Ken Woods. Overlaps with international designated areas: 769 ha of IBA covered by Special Protection Area (Loch Ken and River Dee Marshes, 769 ha). 769 ha of IBA covered by Ramsar Site (Loch Ken and Dee Marshes, 769 ha).

■ Conservation issues

Threats Agricultural intensification/expansion (B), Construction/impact of dyke/dam/barrage (B), Recreation/tourism (B)

Threats include disturbance of goose roosting and feeding areas, mainly as a result of water-sports and other recreational activities, and water-level fluctuations caused by hydroelectric operations. An advisory/management committee operates, and the site is counted as part of the inland WeBS and by the RSPB, who lease part of the site as a reserve. There is a management plan for the site.

Loch Leven   A4i, A4iii, B1i, B2, B3, C3, C4   175

Admin region Scotland
Coordinates 56°11′N 3°22′W
Altitude 113–335 m **Area** 1,870 ha

■ Site description

Loch Leven lies midway between the estuaries of the Forth and Tay rivers, and is the largest nutrient-rich loch in Britain, supporting a range of aquatic plants. The IBA also covers adjacent damp, unimproved pasture.

Habitats Grassland (humid grassland), Wetland (standing fresh water), Artificial landscape (arable land)
Land-use Agriculture (5%), Fisheries/aquaculture (100%)

■ Birds

Species		Season	Year	Pop min	Pop max	Acc	Criteria
Cygnus cygnus	Whooper Swan	W	1995	120	120	A	B3
Anser brachyrhynchus Pink-footed Goose		W	1995	19,200	19,200	A	A4i, B1i, C3
Anas strepera	Gadwall	R	1992	—	70	A	B2
Anas clypeata	Shoveler	W	1995	520	520	A	B1i, C3

This site is of major importance for both breeding and wintering wildfowl, and holds 31,900 wintering waterbirds on a regular basis. It is also nationally important for breeding *Anas penelope* (6 pairs, 1992, 2%), *Anas clypeata* (20 pairs, 1992, 2%), *Aythya fuligula* (500 pairs, 1992, 6%) and *Larus ridibundus* (8,000 pairs, 1992, 4%); for wintering *Phalacrocorax carbo* (450 birds, 3%), *Anas strepera* (220 birds, 3%), *Anas crecca* (2,150 birds, 2%), *Aythya ferina* (830 birds, 1%), *Aythya fuligula* (3,280 birds, 4%) and *Bucephala clangula* (335 birds, 1%); and for summer moulting assemblages of *Cygnus olor* (300 birds, 1%).

■ Protection status

National Partial **International** Partial
IBA partly or wholly overlaps with the following national designated areas. *National Nature Reserve:* Loch Leven. *Reserve:* Vane Farm. *Site of Special Scientific Interest:* Loch Leven. Overlaps with international designated areas: 1,612 ha of IBA covered by Ramsar Site (Loch Leven, 1,612 ha).

■ Conservation issues

Threats Agricultural intensification/expansion (B), Industrialization/urbanization (A), Natural events (B)

Threats include shoreline erosion, and the release of industrial and domestic effluent, including sewage, which has led to increased algal blooms and a reduction in aquatic vegetation. The Loch Leven Catchment Management Group has produced a catchment plan with the aim of reducing phosphate input.

Loch Maree and nearby lochs and mountains   B2, C6   176

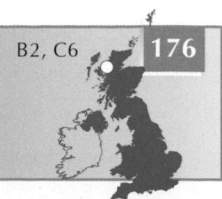

Admin region Scotland
Coordinates 57°41′N 5°31′W
Altitude 10–1,010 m **Area** 68,611 ha

■ Site description

A large loch containing many wooded islands. The adjacent catchment covers freshwater lochs and a variety of habitat-types, including important stands of native pinewood.

Habitats Forest and woodland (broadleaved deciduous forest; native coniferous forest), Scrub (heathland), Grassland (steppe/dry calcareous grassland), Wetland (standing fresh water; blanket bog)
Land-use Hunting (100%)

■ Birds

Species		Season	Year	Pop min	Pop max	Acc	Criteria
Gavia arctica	Black-throated Diver	B	1991	17	—	A	C6
Aquila chrysaetos	Golden Eagle	R	1992	13	—	A	B2, C6

Nationally important numbers of breeding *Tringa nebularia* are also present.

■ Protection status

National Partial **International** Low
IBA partly or wholly overlaps with the following national designated areas. *National Nature Reserve:* Loch Maree Islands. *Sites of Special Scientific Interest:* An Teallach, Ardlair–Letterewe, Baosbheinn, Beinn Eighe, Coille Dubh, Coulin Pinewood, Fionn Loch Islands, Loch Maree, Loch Maree Islands, Meall-an t-Sithe–Creag Rainich, Talladale Gorge, Torridon Forest. Overlaps with international designated areas: 3,174 ha of IBA covered by Special Protection Area (Loch Maree, 3,174 ha). 3,174 ha of IBA covered by Ramsar Site (Loch Maree, 3,174 ha).

■ Conservation issues

Threats Afforestation (C), Agricultural intensification/expansion (B), Aquaculture/fisheries (B), Forest grazing (U), Construction/impact of dyke/dam/barrage (A), Recreation/tourism (U)

Threats include overgrazing by red deer *Cervus elaphus* and, to a lesser extent, by sheep, and recreational disturbance.

Loch of Isbister   C7   177

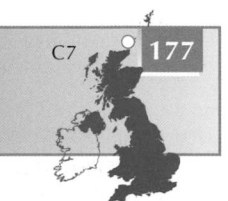

Admin region Scotland
Coordinates 59°05′N 3°18′W
Altitude 15–20 m **Area** 140 ha

■ Site description

This site includes both the nutrient-enriched Loch of Isbister and basin mire separated from the loch by low ridges of glacial till. Open water transitional plant communities and bog habitats support a very rich assemblage of wetland plants. A reedbed (*Phragmites*) is also present.

Habitats Wetland (100%; standing fresh water; water-fringe vegetation; fen/transition mire/spring)
Land-use Agriculture (5%), Nature conservation/research (95%)

■ Birds

Species		Season	Year	Pop min	Pop max	Acc	Criteria
[1] *Anas acuta*	Pintail	R	1994	7	7	A	C7

1. Mean annual peak 1989–1994.

The IBA is important for both breeding and wintering wildfowl. The site is also nationally important for breeding *Anas penelope* (5 pairs, 1989–1994, 2%) and for wintering *Anser albifrons flavirostris* (150 birds, 1991–1996, 1%).

■ Protection status

National High **International** None
IBA partly or wholly overlaps with the following national designated areas. *Reserve:* Loons and Loch of Banks. *Sites of Special Scientific Interest:* Loch of Banks, Loch of Isbister and the Loons.

■ Conservation issues

Threats Aquaculture/fisheries (C), Disturbance to birds (C), Drainage (B), Recreation/tourism (C)

The creation of a no-shooting buffer zone by the RSPB and local land-owners has reduced disturbance to birds. A management plan exists for the RSPB Reserve.

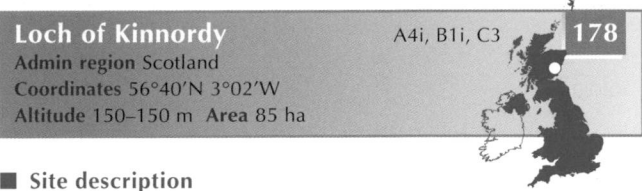

Loch of Kinnordy — A4i, B1i, C3 — 178
Admin region Scotland
Coordinates 56°40′N 3°02′W
Altitude 150–150 m Area 85 ha

■ Site description

A nutrient-rich loch that was formerly much larger in extent, and surrounding wetland communities.

Habitats Forest and woodland (broadleaved deciduous forest), Grassland (humid grassland), Wetland (standing fresh water; fen/transition mire/spring)
Land-use Agriculture, Fisheries/aquaculture, Tourism/recreation

■ Birds

Species	Season	Year	Pop min	Pop max	Acc	Criteria
[1] *Anser brachyrhynchus* Pink-footed Goose	W	1994	7,050	7,050	A	A4i, B1i, C3

1. Mean annual peak 1989–1994.

The site is also nationally important for breeding *Podiceps nigricollis* (11 pairs, 1994, 23%), *Anas strepera* (9 pairs, 1994, 1%), *Anas clypeata* (18 pairs, 1994, 2%), *Aythya ferina* (7 pairs, 1994, 2%) and *Larus ridibundus* (7,000 pairs, 1992, 4%).

■ Protection status
National High **International** High
IBA partly or wholly overlaps with the following national designated areas. *Reserve:* Loch of Kinnordy. *Site of Special Scientific Interest:* Loch of Kinnordy. Overlaps with international designated areas: 85 ha of IBA covered by Special Protection Area (Loch of Kinnordy, 85 ha). 85 ha of IBA covered by Ramsar Site (Loch of Kinnordy, 85 ha).

■ Conservation issues

Threats Abandonment/reduction of land management (B), Agricultural intensification/expansion (B), Aquaculture/fisheries (B), Natural events (A), Other (B), Recreation/tourism (B)

Threats include disturbance to wintering wildfowl from fishermen, fluctuations in water-level that may affect the breeding success of wildfowl ('Other' threat, above), and nutrient-enrichment from large gull and wildfowl colonies. A management plan exists for the RSPB reserve.

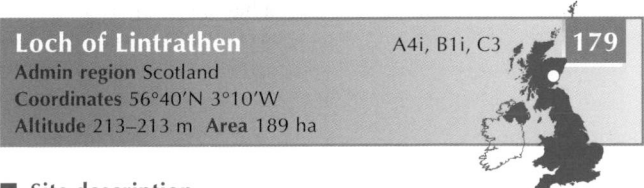

Loch of Lintrathen — A4i, B1i, C3 — 179
Admin region Scotland
Coordinates 56°40′N 3°10′W
Altitude 213–213 m Area 189 ha

■ Site description
The Loch of Lintrathen is situated in the foothills above Strathmore, and occupies a glacial basin. It contains no emergent vegetation, and is now used as a reservoir.

Habitats Grassland (humid grassland), Wetland (standing fresh water)
Land-use Water management (100%)

■ Birds

Species	Season	Year	Pop min	Pop max	Acc	Criteria
[1] *Anser anser* Greylag Goose	W	1994	3,610	3,610	A	A4i, B1i, C3

1. Mean annual peak 1989–1994.

The IBA is important for wintering waterbirds. *Anser anser* are from the Icelandic breeding population.

■ Protection status
National High **International** High
IBA partly or wholly overlaps with the following national designated areas. *Reserve:* Loch of Lintrathen. *Site of Special Scientific Interest:* Loch of Lintrathen. Overlaps with international designated areas: 189 ha of IBA covered by Special Protection Area (Loch of Lintrathen, 189 ha). 189 ha of IBA covered by Ramsar Site (Loch of Lintrathen, 189 ha).

■ Conservation issues
No serious threats are known at the site.

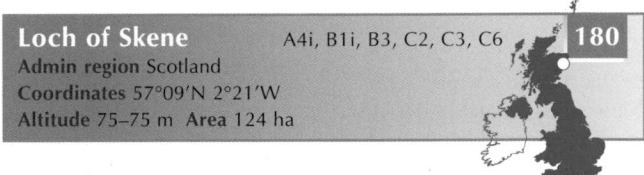

Loch of Skene — A4i, B1i, B3, C2, C3, C6 — 180
Admin region Scotland
Coordinates 57°09′N 2°21′W
Altitude 75–75 m Area 124 ha

■ Site description
Situated about 15 km west of Aberdeen, the Loch of Skene is less than 2 m in depth and is fringed by reedbed and *Betula–Salix* carr.

Habitats Scrub (scrub), Grassland (5%; humid grassland), Wetland (95%; standing fresh water; water-fringe vegetation)
Land-use Hunting (100%), Tourism/recreation (100%)

■ Birds

Species	Season	Year	Pop min	Pop max	Acc	Criteria
Cygnus cygnus Whooper Swan	W	1995	265	265	A	B1i, B3, C2, C6
Anser anser Greylag Goose	W	1995	12,200	12,200	A	A4i, B1i, C3
[1] *Larus canus* Common Gull	N	1992	—	45,000	A	A4i, B1i, C3

1. Roosting birds.

The site is important for large numbers of wintering wildfowl, and is also nationally important for breeding *Aythya fuligula* (100 pairs, 1992, 1%) and for wintering *Cygnus olor* (310 birds, 1%). *Anser anser* are from the Icelandic breeding population.

■ Protection status
National High **International** High
IBA partly or wholly overlaps with the following national designated areas. *Site of Special Scientific Interest:* Loch of Skene. Overlaps with international designated areas: 124 ha of IBA covered by Special Protection Area (Loch of Skene, 124 ha). 124 ha of IBA covered by Ramsar Site (Loch of Skene, 124 ha).

■ Conservation issues

Threats Agricultural intensification/expansion (B), Consequences of animal/plant introductions (B), Disturbance to birds (A), Recreation/tourism (A)

Threats include disturbance to wildfowl particularly from shooting and sailing, deterioration in water quality due to nutrient enrichment from agricultural run-off, and some American mink *Mustela vison* predation.

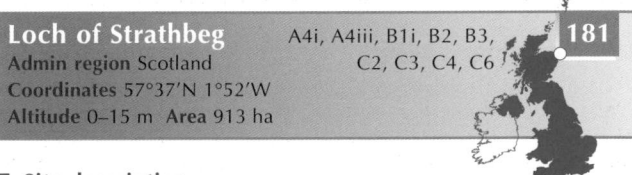

Loch of Strathbeg — A4i, A4iii, B1i, B2, B3, C2, C3, C4, C6 — 181
Admin region Scotland
Coordinates 57°37′N 1°52′W
Altitude 0–15 m Area 913 ha

■ Site description
The Loch of Strathbeg is the largest dune-lake in Britain (an area of 200 ha), and is situated inland from Rattray Head, the north-eastern point of the Buchan coast. The IBA also covers surrounding calcareous dunes and dune-slacks.

Habitats Wetland (80%; sand-dunes/sand beach; standing fresh water; water-fringe vegetation; fen/transition mire/spring), Artificial landscape (20%; highly improved reseeded grassland)
Land-use Agriculture (15%), Nature conservation/research (95%)

■ Birds
The IBA is important for wintering wildfowl and breeding terns, and holds 42,800 wintering waterbirds on a regular basis. The

site is also nationally important for wintering *Anas crecca* (1,860 birds, 1%). *Anser anser* are from the Icelandic breeding population, while *Branta leucopsis* are from the Svalbard breeding population.

Species	Season	Year	Pop min	Pop max	Acc	Criteria
Cygnus cygnus Whooper Swan	W	1995	155	155	A	B3
Anser brachyrhynchus Pink-footed Goose	W	1995	32,500	32,500	A	A4i, B1i, C3
[1] *Anser anser* Greylag Goose	W	1994	2,270	2,270	A	B1i, C3
Branta leucopsis Barnacle Goose	W	1995	130	130	A	B1i, C2
Sterna sandvicensis Sandwich Tern	B	1995	480	480	A	B2, C6

1. Mean annual peak 1989–1994.

■ **Protection status**

National High **International** Partial
IBA partly or wholly overlaps with the following national designated areas. *Reserve:* Loch of Strathbeg. *Site of Special Scientific Interest:* Loch of Strathbeg. Overlaps with international designated areas: 615 ha of IBA covered by Special Protection Area (Loch of Strathbeg, 615 ha). 615 ha of IBA covered by Ramsar Site (Loch of Strathbeg, 615 ha).

■ **Conservation issues**

Threats Agricultural intensification/expansion (A), Disturbance to birds (C), Other (B), Recreation/tourism (C)

Threats include pressure from shooting, and a decrease in water quality that is thought to have resulted in a decline in the numbers of diving duck ('Other' threat, above). There is a management plan for the RSPB Reserve, with research and monitoring ongoing.

Loch Oire C6 182
Admin region Scotland
Coordinates 57°37′N 3°11′W
Altitude 30–30 m Area 8 ha

■ **Site description**
Located about 7 km east of Elgin, Loch Oire is one of the few lochans remaining in the hummocky glacial deposits of lowland Moray. An undisturbed aquatic plant community is present, including a variety of emergent and submerged vegetation-types, and sedge-fen.

Habitats Wetland (100%; standing fresh water; water-fringe vegetation; fen/transition mire/spring)
Land-use Fisheries/aquaculture (100%)

■ **Birds**
The IBA is important for both breeding and wintering waterbirds.

■ **Protection status**
National Partial **International** None
IBA partly or wholly overlaps with the following national designated area. *Site of Special Scientific Interest:* Loch Oire.

■ **Conservation issues**

Threats Agricultural intensification/expansion (U), Consequences of animal/plant introductions (A), Disturbance to birds (B)

Threats to the site include human disturbance from adjacent roads and lay-bys, and high levels of American mink *Mustela vison* predation.

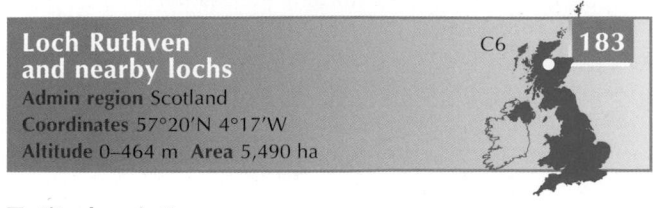

Loch Ruthven and nearby lochs C6 183
Admin region Scotland
Coordinates 57°20′N 4°17′W
Altitude 0–464 m Area 5,490 ha

■ **Site description**
Loch Ashie and Loch Ruthven are of a medium size and are

moderately rich in nutrients, with rocky margins. The catchment includes additional smaller lochs. Stands of *Carex rostrata* border the lochs, with extensive marshy zones and transitional plant communities also present.

Habitats Scrub (heathland), Grassland, Wetland (standing fresh water; river/stream; fen/transition mire/spring), Artificial landscape (forestry plantation)
Land-use Agriculture (60%), Forestry (20%), Water management (20%)

■ **Birds**

Species	Season	Year	Pop min	Pop max	Acc	Criteria
Podiceps auritus Slavonian Grebe	B	1996	15	15	A	C6

The IBA is important for breeding waterbirds, waders and raptors.

■ **Protection status**
National Partial **International** Partial
IBA partly or wholly overlaps with the following national designated areas. *Reserve:* Loch Ruthven. *Sites of Special Scientific Interest:* Creag nan Clag, Loch Ruthven. Overlaps with international designated areas: IBA covered by Special Protection Area (Great Glen Lochs).

■ **Conservation issues**

Threats Afforestation (B), Consequences of animal/plant introductions (B), Natural events (B), Other (A), Recreation/tourism (A)

Threats include competition for food from introduced rainbow trout *Salmo gairdneri*, predation by American mink *Mustela vison*, recreational disturbance, changing water-levels ('Other' threat, above), and natural predation by red fox *Vulpes vulpes*, Eurasian otter *Lutra lutra* and pike *Esox lucius*. Ruthven is managed as an RSPB reserve with monitoring an ongoing activity. A management plan exists for the site.

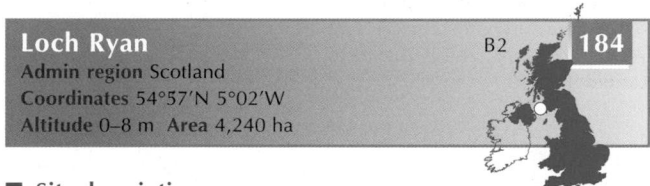

Loch Ryan B2 184
Admin region Scotland
Coordinates 54°57′N 5°02′W
Altitude 0–8 m Area 4,240 ha

■ **Site description**
A large, shallow sea loch at the western end of Dumfries and Galloway, which supports the only commercial native oysterbeds in Scotland. Stranraer is located at the base of the loch, with its ferry port.

Habitats Wetland (98%; mudflat/sandflat; shingle/stony beach; standing brackish and salt water), Marine areas (2%; sea inlet/coastal features)
Land-use Fisheries/aquaculture, Tourism/recreation (1%), Urban/industrial/transport (2%)

■ **Birds**

Species	Season	Year	Pop min	Pop max	Acc	Criteria
[1] *Aythya marila* Scaup	W	1995	780	780	A	B2

1. Mean annual peak 1991–1995.

The IBA supports important numbers of wintering waterbirds. It is also nationally important for wintering *Podiceps cristatus* (210 birds, 1991–1995, 2%), *Podiceps nigricollis* (7 birds, 1991–1995, 6%), *Somateria mollissima* (985 birds, 1991–1995, 1%) and *Mergus serrator* (110 birds, 1991–1995, 1%).

■ **Protection status**
National None **International** None

■ **Conservation issues**

Threats Disturbance to birds (A), Dredging/canalization (B), Infrastructure (B)

The main threats are from dredging, port development and disturbance caused by ferry bow-waves. In 1986 the site was designated a Marine Consultation Area, and is now being pushed as a SAC by Scottish Wildlife Link. Monitoring is undertaken by WeBS and RSPB.

Loch Scadavay

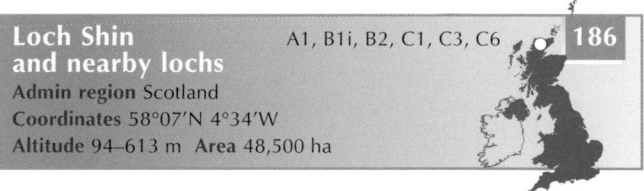

B2, C2, C6 · **185**

Admin region Scotland
Coordinates 57°35'N 7°15'W
Altitude 10–160 m **Area** 5,564 ha

■ Site description

The largest freshwater body in North Uist, defined by an intricate shoreline and containing many islands. The water is nutrient-poor.

Habitats Scrub (35%; scrub; heathland), Wetland (65%; standing fresh water; blanket bog)
Land-use Agriculture, Hunting

■ Birds

Species		Season	Year	Pop min	Pop max	Acc	Criteria
Gavia stellata	Red-throated Diver	B	1994	51	51	A	B2, C2, C6
Gavia arctica	Black-throated Diver	B	1993	5	—	A	C6

The site holds important numbers of breeding divers, and is nationally important for breeding Hebridean *Anser anser* (8 pairs, 1993, 1%).

■ Protection status

National Partial **International** Partial
IBA partly or wholly overlaps with the following national designated areas. *Site of Special Scientific Interest:* Loch Scadavay. Overlaps with international designated areas: IBA overlaps with Special Protection Area (Mointeach Scadabhaigh).

■ Conservation issues

Threats Afforestation (U), Aquaculture/fisheries (U), Consequences of animal/plant introductions (A), Extraction industry (C), Other (U)

Threats include changes in water quality due to nutrient-enrichment ('Other' threat, above), peat extraction, and the adverse effects of introduced American mink *Mustela vison*, polecat *M. putorius*, ferret *M. putorius furo* and hedgehog *Erinaceus europaeus*. The site is a candidate SAC.

Loch Shin and nearby lochs

A1, B1i, B2, C1, C3, C6 · **186**

Admin region Scotland
Coordinates 58°07'N 4°34'W
Altitude 94–613 m **Area** 48,500 ha

■ Site description

One very large, and several smaller, nutrient-poor lochs and surrounding catchments. The IBA supports a flora and fauna characteristic of upland heaths, mires and lochs.

Habitats Forest and woodland (broadleaved deciduous forest), Scrub (heathland), Wetland (standing fresh water; blanket bog), Artificial landscape (forestry plantation)
Land-use Agriculture, Forestry, Hunting, Water management

■ Birds

Species		Season	Year	Pop min	Pop max	Acc	Criteria
Gavia arctica	Black-throated Diver	B	1995	7	—	A	C6
Anser anser	Greylag Goose	R	1994	—	100	A	B1i, C3
Falco columbarius	Merlin	R	1995	9	9	A	C6
[1] *Loxia scotica*	Scottish Crossbill	R	1995	—	—	A	A1, B2, C1
1. No counts available.							

The IBA is also nationally important for breeding *Gavia stellata* (9 pairs, 1995, 1%), *Anas penelope* (8 pairs, 1995, 3%), *Aquila chrysaetos* (4 pairs, 1992, 1%), *Tringa nebularia* (17 pairs, 1988–1991, 2%) and *Turdus iliacus* (7 pairs, 1988–1991, 9%). *Anser anser* are from the Hebridean population.

■ Protection status

National Partial **International** Partial
IBA partly or wholly overlaps with the following national designated areas. *Sites of Special Scientific Interest:* Ben Klibreck, Cnoc an

Alaskie, Druim nam Bad, Grudie Peatlands, Strath Duchally. Overlaps with international designated areas: IBA overlaps with Special Protection Area (Lairg/Strathbrora Lochs).

■ Conservation issues

Threats Afforestation (B), Agricultural intensification/expansion (C), Aquaculture/fisheries (A), Construction/impact of dyke/dam/barrage (C), Forest grazing (B)

The Loch Shin Dam is a source of hydroelectric power. Additional threats include overgrazing by red deer *Cervus elaphus* and sheep, coniferous afforestation, and phosphate run-off from the catchment area. There are also ongoing concerns regarding the expansion of salmon smolt farms on Loch Shin and the implications for *Gavia arctica*. Breeding *G. arctica* are monitored annually by the RSPB.

Loch Spynie

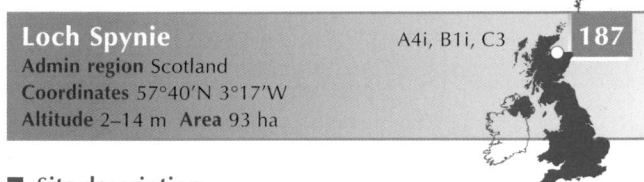

A4i, B1i, C3 · **187**

Admin region Scotland
Coordinates 57°40'N 3°17'W
Altitude 2–14 m **Area** 93 ha

■ Site description

Loch Spynie developed during the 16th century following the closure of a tidal inlet by a shingle-spit. This gave rise to a shallow, fertile lagoon, surrounded by marshes.

Habitats Wetland (100%; standing fresh water; water-fringe vegetation; fen/transition mire/spring)
Land-use Nature conservation/research (40%), Tourism/recreation

■ Birds

Species		Season	Year	Pop min	Pop max	Acc	Criteria
[1] *Anser anser*	Greylag Goose	W	1994	5,650	5,650	A	A4i, B1i, C3
1. Mean annual peak 1989–1994.							

The site is important for wintering wildfowl. *Anser anser* are from the Icelandic breeding population.

■ Protection status

National High **International** High
IBA partly or wholly overlaps with the following national designated areas. *Site of Special Scientific Interest:* Loch Spynie. Overlaps with international designated areas: 93 ha of IBA covered by Special Protection Area (Loch Spynie, 93 ha). 93 ha of IBA covered by Ramsar Site (Loch Spynie, 93 ha).

■ Conservation issues

Threats Agricultural intensification/expansion (B), Drainage (B), Other (U), Recreation/tourism (B)

Threats include recreational disturbance and the effects of lead poisoning (from shot) on wildfowl ('Other' threat, above).

Loch Stack, Loch nam Brac and nearby lochs

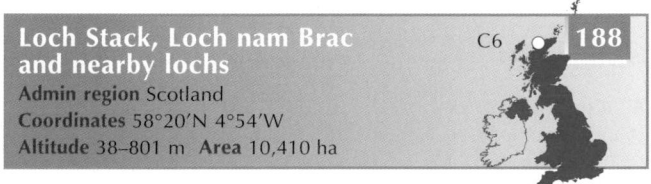

C6 · **188**

Admin region Scotland
Coordinates 58°20'N 4°54'W
Altitude 38–801 m **Area** 10,410 ha

■ Site description

Numerous open water-bodies ranging from dubh lochans to quite large, shallow nutrient-poor lochs, of which Loch Stack is the largest.

Habitats Scrub (heathland), Grassland (steppe/dry calcareous grassland), Wetland (standing fresh water; blanket bog)
Land-use Fisheries/aquaculture, Forestry, Hunting

■ Birds

Species		Season	Year	Pop min	Pop max	Acc	Criteria
[1] *Gavia arctica*	Black-throated Diver	B	1995	5	5	A	C6
1. Mean annual peak 1991–1995.							

The IBA is important for breeding upland species.

■ Protection status
National Partial **International** None
IBA partly or wholly overlaps with the following national designated areas. *Sites of Special Scientific Interest:* Foinaven, Loch Stack, Stack Woods.

■ Conservation issues
Threats Afforestation (C), Agricultural intensification/expansion (C), Aquaculture/ fisheries (C)

There is potential for aquaculture in the lochs. Breeding *Gavia arctica* are monitored annually by RSPB. The area is a candidate SPA.

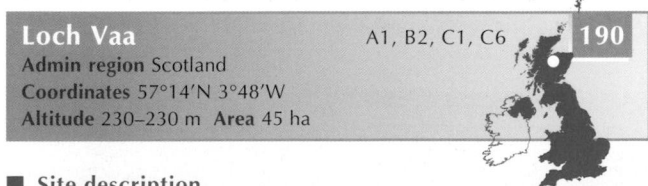

Loch Tarff and nearby lochs — C6 — 189
Admin region Scotland
Coordinates 57°08′N 4°36′W
Altitude 200–786 m **Area** 1,330 ha

■ Site description
Lochs and lochans with wooded islands and locally extensive sedge-beds, and the surrounding catchment area.

Habitats Forest and woodland (broadleaved deciduous forest), Scrub (heathland), Grassland, Wetland (standing fresh water; river/stream; fen/transition mire/spring)
Land-use Agriculture (40%), Forestry (40%), Water management (20%)

■ Birds
Species		Season	Year	Pop min	Pop max	Acc	Criteria
Podiceps auritus	Slavonian Grebe	B	1996	5	5	A	C6

The site is also nationally important for breeding *Gavia arctica* (2 pairs, 1991–1996, 1%), *Melanitta nigra* (4 pairs, 1995, 5%) and *Turdus iliacus* (2 pairs, 1995, 3%).

■ Protection status
National Partial **International** None
IBA partly or wholly overlaps with the following national designated area. *Site of Special Scientific Interest:* Easter Ness Forest.

■ Conservation issues
Threats Afforestation (B), Consequences of animal/plant introductions (A), Industrialization/urbanization (A), Recreation/tourism (B)

American mink *Mustela vison* predation and the potential development of small-scale hydro-power schemes pose threats to the IBA. There is ongoing monitoring of divers and grebes, and part of the IBA is undergoing designation as a SPA.

Loch Vaa — A1, B2, C1, C6 — 190
Admin region Scotland
Coordinates 57°14′N 3°48′W
Altitude 230–230 m **Area** 45 ha

■ Site description
A small spring-fed loch, moderately rich in nutrients, about 500 m in diameter and surrounded by deciduous woodland and *Pinus sylvestris* plantations.

Habitats Forest and woodland (broadleaved deciduous forest), Wetland (standing fresh water; water-fringe vegetation), Artificial landscape (forestry plantation)
Land-use Forestry (15%), Tourism/recreation, Water management (85%)

■ Birds
Species		Season	Year	Pop min	Pop max	Acc	Criteria
Loxia scotica	Scottish Crossbill	R	1996		Abundant	—	A1, B2, C1, C6

The site is also important for breeding waterbirds, and is nationally important for breeding *Parus cristatus*.

■ Protection status
National High **International** High

IBA partly or wholly overlaps with the following national designated areas. *Site of Special Scientific Interest:* Loch Vaa. Overlaps with international designated areas: 45 ha of IBA covered by Special Protection Area (Loch Vaa, 45 ha).

■ Conservation issues
Threats Other (A), Recreation/tourism (B)

The IBA is vulnerable to recreational disturbance, particularly from anglers and birdwatchers, and fluctuations in water level ('Other' threat, above). There is ongoing monitoring of grebes.

Lochinch and Torrs Warren — B1i, C2, C3 — 191
Admin region Scotland
Coordinates 54°54′N 4°57′W
Altitude 0–29 m **Area** 4,710 ha

■ Site description
Lochinch (also known as White Loch) is shallow and rich in nutrients. Torrs Warren lies to the south, at the head of Luce Bay, and is the largest acidic dune system in western Scotland, with a very varied dune morphology.

Habitats Scrub (15%; heathland), Wetland (35%; sand-dunes/sand beach; standing fresh water), Artificial landscape (50%; highly improved reseeded grassland; arable land; forestry plantation)
Land-use Agriculture (45%), Forestry (5%), Military (45%), Tourism/recreation (10%)

■ Birds
Species		Season	Year	Pop min	Pop max	Acc	Criteria
[1] *Anser albifrons*	White-fronted Goose	W	1994	630	630	A	B1i, C2, C3
[1] *Anser anser*	Greylag Goose	W	1994	2,790	2,790	A	B1i, C3
1. Mean annual peak 1989–1994.							

The IBA is important for wintering geese. *Anser albifrons* are the *flavirostris* subspecies, while *Anser anser* are from the Icelandic breeding population.

■ Protection status
National Partial **International** High
IBA partly or wholly overlaps with the following national designated areas. *Sites of Special Scientific Interest:* Torrs Warren – Luce Sands, White Loch – Lochinch. Overlaps with international designated areas: 4,710 ha of IBA covered by Special Protection Area (Loch of Inch and Torrs Warren, 4,710 ha).

■ Conservation issues
Threats Agricultural intensification/expansion (B), Disturbance to birds (U), Drainage (A)

Disturbance is caused to birds by illegal shooting. The MoD operates a conservation group at Torrs Warren, and there is a management plan for the site.

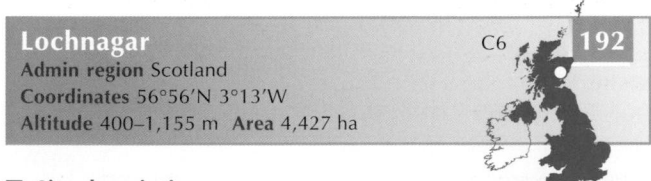

Lochnagar — C6 — 192
Admin region Scotland
Coordinates 56°56′N 3°13′W
Altitude 400–1,155 m **Area** 4,427 ha

■ Site description
Lochnagar is the highest of the hills to the south of Deeside. It is drained by fast-flowing streams, and there are scattered lochs. An extensive area of *Betula nana* scrub is present.

Habitats Scrub (50%; scrub; heathland), Grassland (45%; steppe/dry calcareous grassland), Rocky areas (5%; inland cliff)
Land-use Hunting (100%)

■ Birds
Species		Season	Year	Pop min	Pop max	Acc	Criteria
Charadrius morinellus	Dotterel	B	1996	27	27	A	C6

The IBA supports an assemblage of upland breeding birds.

Protection status

National None **International** Partial

IBA partly or wholly overlaps with international designated area: 1,178 ha of IBA covered by Special Protection Area (Lochnagar, 1,178 ha).

Conservation issues

Threats Other (A), Recreation/tourism (A)

Disturbance from increased public access and overgrazing by deer ('Other' threat, above) pose threats to the IBA. The site does not have SSSI status as it is owned by the Queen, and is managed through a Memorandum of Understanding.

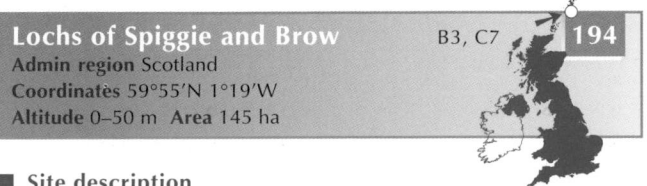

Lochs of Harray and Stenness B1i, B2, B3, C2, C3, C6 **193**
Admin region Scotland
Coordinates 59°01'N 3°14'W
Altitude 0–10 m **Area** 1,930 ha

Site description

Run-off from a large part of Orkney's West Mainland enters the sea via these two lochs. The shallow freshwater Loch of Harray becomes brackish at the junction with the Loch of Stenness, which is entirely brackish and classed as a lagoon. The flora and fauna therefore consists of brackish, marine and freshwater species.

Habitats Wetland (standing fresh water; standing brackish and salt water; water-fringe vegetation)
Land-use Fisheries/aquaculture (100%), Water management (100%)

Birds

Species	Season	Year	Pop min	Pop max	Acc	Criteria
Cygnus cygnus Whooper Swan	W	1995	215	215	A	B1i, B3, C2, C6
Anser anser Greylag Goose	W	1995	2,050	2,050	A	B1i, C3
Aythya marila Scaup	W	1995	315	315	A	B2

The lochs support large numbers of wintering wildfowl. The site is also nationally important for wintering *Cygnus olor* (560 birds, 2%), *Anas penelope* (4,630 birds, 2%), *Aythya ferina* (985 birds, 1%), *Aythya fuligula* (1,570 birds, 2%) and *Bucephala clangula* (370 birds, 1%). *Anser anser* are from the Icelandic breeding population.

Protection status

National High **International** None

IBA partly or wholly overlaps with the following national designated area. *Site of Special Scientific Interest:* Lochs of Harray and Stenness.

Conservation issues

Threats Agricultural intensification/expansion (A), Consequences of animal/plant introductions (U)

The spread of Canadian pondweed *Elodea canadensis* has threatened the long-term ecological balance of the Loch of Harray, although it has recently begun to die back. Nutrient pollution as a result of agricultural run-off is a problem that has been investigated by the Scottish Agricultural College. The Loch of Stenness is a candidate SAC.

Lochs of Spiggie and Brow B3, C7 **194**
Admin region Scotland
Coordinates 59°55'N 1°19'W
Altitude 0–50 m **Area** 145 ha

Site description

The Loch of Spiggie was formed by a sand-bar cutting off a shallow voe from the sea. Both lochs have slightly brackish waters. The IBA also includes the smaller Loch of Hinwell.

Habitats Wetland (standing fresh water; standing brackish and salt water; water-fringe vegetation)
Land-use Fisheries/aquaculture, Hunting, Nature conservation/research

Birds

Species	Season	Year	Pop min	Pop max	Acc	Criteria
Cygnus cygnus Whooper Swan	W	1995	135	135	A	B3

The IBA is important for wintering wildfowl.

Protection status

National High **International** High

IBA partly or wholly overlaps with the following national designated areas. *Reserve:* Loch of Spiggie. *Sites of Special Scientific Interest:* Lochs of Spiggie and Brow, Quendale. Overlaps with international designated areas: 145 ha of IBA covered by Special Protection Area (Lochs of Spiggie and Brow, 145 ha).

Conservation issues

Threats Agricultural intensification/expansion (B), Disturbance to birds (U), Drainage (B), Other (U), Recreation/tourism (B)

Threats to the site include disturbance to birds from wildfowlers and fishermen, and pollution ('Other' threat, above). A management plan exists for the RSPB Reserve.

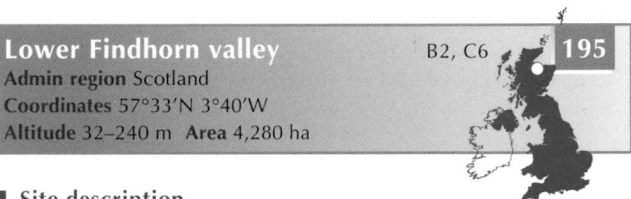

Lower Findhorn valley B2, C6 **195**
Admin region Scotland
Coordinates 57°33'N 3°40'W
Altitude 32–240 m **Area** 4,280 ha

Site description

A large wooded area along the River Findhorn, including Darnaway forest and Altyre woods.

Habitats Forest and woodland (5%; broadleaved deciduous forest), Grassland (1%; humid grassland), Wetland (2%; river/stream; water-fringe vegetation), Artificial landscape (92%; arable land; forestry plantation)
Land-use Agriculture (10%), Forestry (90%)

Birds

The IBA is important for breeding raptors and *Tetrao urogallus*.

Protection status

National Partial **International** None

IBA partly or wholly overlaps with the following national designated areas. *Sites of Special Scientific Interest:* Boghole – Muckle Burn, Lower Findhorn Woods, Randolph's Leap.

Conservation issues

Threats Disturbance to birds (B), Other (C)

The only real threats are inappropriate forestry practices ('Other' threat, above), and disturbance.

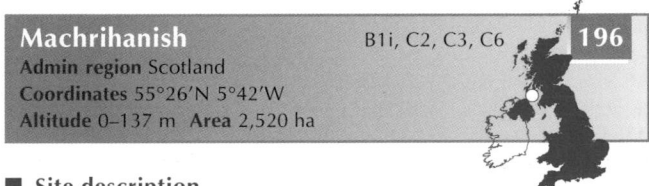

Machrihanish B1i, C2, C3, C6 **196**
Admin region Scotland
Coordinates 55°26'N 5°42'W
Altitude 0–137 m **Area** 2,520 ha

Site description

The IBA comprises pasture and arable farmland, and a loch situated about 4 km to the north-east.

Habitats Grassland, Wetland (sand-dunes/sand beach; standing fresh water; water-fringe vegetation), Artificial landscape (arable land)
Land-use Agriculture (83%), Tourism/recreation (4%), Urban/industrial/transport (10%), Water management (3%)

Birds

Species	Season	Year	Pop min	Pop max	Acc	Criteria
Anser albifrons White-fronted Goose	W	1994	—	1,100	A	B1i, C2, C3, C6

The site is also nationally important for wintering *Mergus serrator* (200 birds, 1992, 2%). *Anser albifrons* are the *flavirostris* subspecies.

■ Protection status

National Partial **International** Partial

IBA partly or wholly overlaps with the following national designated areas. *Sites of Special Scientific Interest:* Machrihanish Dunes, Tangy Loch. Overlaps with international designated areas: IBA overlaps with Special Protection Area (Kintyre Goose Roosts).

■ Conservation issues

> **Threats** Agricultural intensification/expansion (B), Aquaculture/fisheries (U)

Westport Marsh (an *Anas querquedula* breeding site) has recently been drained.

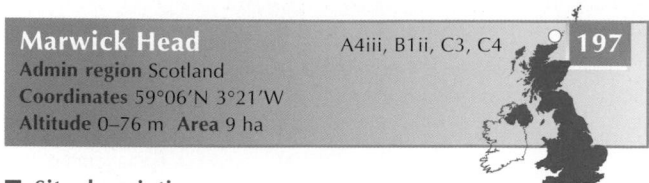

Marwick Head
A4iii, B1ii, C3, C4　197
Admin region Scotland
Coordinates 59°06′N 3°21′W
Altitude 0–76 m **Area** 9 ha

■ Site description

A short section of eroded sandstone cliffs and associated maritime grassland on the west coast of Orkney Mainland.

> **Habitats** Grassland, Rocky areas (sea cliff/rocky shore)
> **Land-use** Nature conservation/research (100%)

■ Birds

Species	Season	Year	Pop min	Pop max	Acc	Criteria
Uria aalge Guillemot	B	1991	24,400	24,400	A	B1ii, C3

The site holds 26,000 pairs of breeding seabirds on a regular basis, and is also nationally important for breeding *Rissa tridactyla* (6,850 pairs, 1994, 1%).

■ Protection status

National High **International** High

IBA partly or wholly overlaps with the following national designated areas. *Reserve:* Marwick Head. *Site of Special Scientific Interest:* Marwick Head. Overlaps with international designated areas: 9 ha of IBA covered by Special Protection Area (Marwick Head, 9 ha).

■ Conservation issues

> **Threats** Extraction industry (U)

Oil pollution poses an ongoing threat. Monitoring of seabird breeding success is carried out by the Joint Nature Conservation Committee. A management plan exists for the RSPB Reserve.

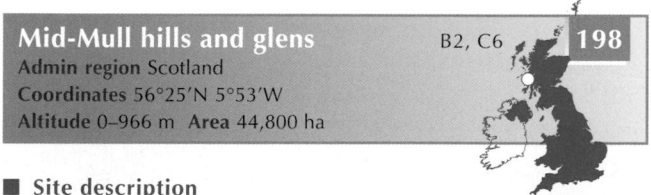

Mid-Mull hills and glens
B2, C6　198
Admin region Scotland
Coordinates 56°25′N 5°53′W
Altitude 0–966 m **Area** 44,800 ha

■ Site description

A very large upland block that covers the main part of the island of Mull.

> **Habitats** Forest and woodland (broadleaved deciduous forest), Scrub (heathland), Grassland, Wetland (blanket bog), Rocky areas (sea cliff/rocky shore; scree/boulders; inland cliff), Artificial landscape (forestry plantation)
> **Land-use** Agriculture (85%), Forestry (15%)

■ Birds

Species	Season	Year	Pop min	Pop max	Acc	Criteria
Aquila chrysaetos Golden Eagle	R	1992	16	16	A	B2, C6

The IBA is important for breeding upland species.

■ Protection status

National Partial **International** None

IBA partly or wholly overlaps with the following national designated areas. *Sites of Special Scientific Interest:* Allt Molach, Ardmeanach,

Ardura–Auchnacraig, Ben More – Scarisdale, Coladoir Bog, Cruach Choireadail, Gribun Shore and Crags, Loch Ba Woodland, Loch Squabain, South Mull Coast.

■ Conservation issues

> **Threats** Afforestation (A), Disturbance to birds (B)

The main threat is posed by afforestation.

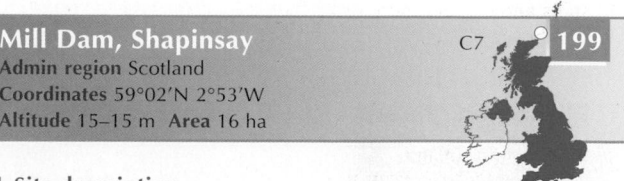

Mill Dam, Shapinsay
C7　199
Admin region Scotland
Coordinates 59°02′N 2°53′W
Altitude 15–15 m **Area** 16 ha

■ Site description

An artificial water-body now largely choked by encroaching vegetation, with open water appearing mainly after heavy rains.

> **Habitats** Wetland (standing fresh water; water-fringe vegetation)
> **Land-use** Nature conservation/research (100%)

■ Birds

Species	Season	Year	Pop min	Pop max	Acc	Criteria
Cygnus cygnus Whooper Swan	W	1995	60	60	A	C7
Anas acuta Pintail	R	1994	4	4	A	C7

The site is also nationally important for breeding *Anas clypeata* (15 pairs, 1994, 2%).

■ Protection status

National High **International** None

IBA partly or wholly overlaps with the following national designated area. *Reserve:* Mill Dam – Shapinsay.

■ Conservation issues

> **Threats** Agricultural intensification/expansion (B)

Vegetation succession is occurring as a result of fertilizer run-off. The RSPB warden now closely controls water-levels, and a management plan exists for the site.

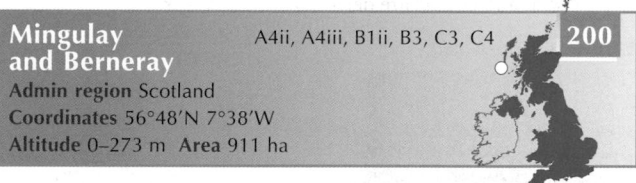

Mingulay and Berneray
A4ii, A4iii, B1ii, B3, C3, C4　200
Admin region Scotland
Coordinates 56°48′N 7°38′W
Altitude 0–273 m **Area** 911 ha

■ Site description

Two islands at the southern end of the Outer Hebridean chain, both with sheer cliffs. The vegetation present comprises maritime grassland, machair and heath. Four to five crofters farm the land.

> **Habitats** Scrub (heathland), Grassland (humid grassland; machair), Rocky areas (sea cliff/rocky shore; rock stacks/islets)
> **Land-use** Agriculture (100%)

■ Birds

Species	Season	Year	Pop min	Pop max	Acc	Criteria
Phalacrocorax aristotelis Shag	B	1985	720	720	A	B3
Uria aalge Guillemot	B	1985	21,400	21,400	A	B1ii, C3
Alca torda Razorbill	B	1985	11,300	11,300	A	A4ii, B1ii, B3, C3

These islands are of major importance, holding 45,800 pairs of breeding seabirds and 10,000 pairs of breeding waterbirds on a regular basis. The IBA is also nationally important for breeding *Fulmarus glacialis* (10,500 pairs, 1985, 2%) and *Rissa tridactyla* (8,600 pairs, 1985, 2%).

■ Protection status

National High **International** High

IBA partly or wholly overlaps with the following national designated areas. *Site of Special Scientific Interest:* Mingulay and Berneray.

Overlaps with international designated areas: 911 ha of IBA covered by Special Protection Area (Mingulay and Berneray, 911 ha).

■ **Conservation issues**

Threats Aquaculture/fisheries (B), Consequences of animal/plant introductions (A), Extraction industry (B), Other (A)

Threats include fish-stock depletion and the predatory effects of introduced American mink *Mustela vison* and rats *Rattus norvegicus*. Oil spills and oil pollution also pose a threat to the islands ('Other' threat, above).

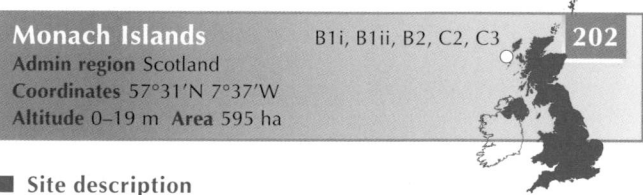

Mochrum and Castle Lochs B1i, C3 201

Admin region Scotland
Coordinates 54°50'N 4°39'W
Altitude 74–77 m **Area** 460 ha

■ **Site description**
Two lochs, with associated wetlands and numerous islands, situated about 3 km from the coast of outer Wigtown Bay.

Habitats Wetland (100%; standing fresh water; blanket bog; water-fringe vegetation)
Land-use Agriculture (30%), Water management (70%)

■ **Birds**

Species	Season	Year	Pop min	Pop max	Acc	Criteria
Phalacrocorax carbo Cormorant	R	1991	520	520	A	B1i, C3

These lochs hold the largest inland *Phalacrocorax carbo* colony in Great Britain. Sixty different bird species breed within the SSSI.

■ **Protection status**
National High **International** None
IBA partly or wholly overlaps with the following national designated area. *Site of Special Scientific Interest:* Mochrum Lochs.

■ **Conservation issues**
No serious threats are known at the site. The active blanket mire is a listed candidate SAC, and the freshwater lochs are intermittently covered by an inland WeBS count, though not currently. The North Solway Ringing Group visits the *Phalacrocorax carbo* colonies every year or two, and counts are derived from these trips.

Monach Islands B1i, B1ii, B2, C2, C3 202

Admin region Scotland
Coordinates 57°31'N 7°37'W
Altitude 0–19 m **Area** 595 ha

■ **Site description**
A chain of five uninhabited islands, located about 10 km off the west coast of North Uist, which support the best uncultivated machair in the UK.

Habitats Grassland (humid grassland; machair), Wetland (fen/transition mire/spring), Rocky areas (sea cliff/rocky shore; inland sand-dunes)
Land-use Agriculture (100%)

■ **Birds**

Species	Season	Year	Pop min	Pop max	Acc	Criteria
[1] *Branta leucopsis* Barnacle Goose	W	1988	760	760	A	B1i, B2, C2
Cepphus grylle Black Guillemot	B	1987	425	425	A	B1ii, B2, C3

1. Mean annual peak 1984–1988.

The machair and coastline attracts wintering geese and breeding seabirds. *Branta leucopsis* are from the Greenland breeding population.

■ **Protection status**
National High **International** High
IBA partly or wholly overlaps with the following national designated areas. *National Nature Reserve:* Monach Islands. *Site of Special Scientific Interest:* Monach Islands. Overlaps with international

designated areas: 595 ha of IBA covered by Special Protection Area (Monach Isles, 595 ha).

■ **Conservation issues**

Threats Consequences of animal/plant introductions (A), Extraction industry (A), Other (A)

Threats include the predatory effects of introduced American mink *Mustela vison*, polecat *Mustela putorius*, rats *Rattus norvegicus* and hedgehog *Erinaceus europaeus*, and oil spills and associated pollution ('Other' threat, above).

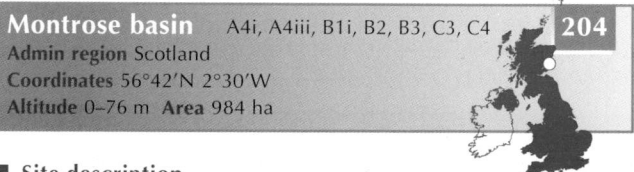

Monadhliath C6 203

Admin region Scotland
Coordinates 57°06'N 4°15'W
Altitude 350–945 m **Area** 10,696 ha

■ **Site description**
A large area of high-altitude plateau, with steep-sided gullies and large cliff-fringed corries. Species-poor lochs punctuate the plateau, which supports continental and oceanic heaths rich in lichens and a wide range of late snow-bed communities.

Habitats Scrub (heathland), Grassland (steppe/dry calcareous grassland), Wetland (standing fresh water; blanket bog; fen/transition mire/spring), Rocky areas (inland cliff)
Land-use Agriculture (20%), Hunting (80%)

■ **Birds**

Species	Season	Year	Pop min	Pop max	Acc	Criteria
Charadrius morinellus Dotterel	B	1993	8	—	A	C6

The IBA supports a suite of breeding upland birds, including a number of species of raptor.

■ **Protection status**
National Partial **International** None
IBA partly or wholly overlaps with the following national designated area. *Site of Special Scientific Interest:* Monadhliath.

■ **Conservation issues**

Threats Agricultural intensification/expansion (U), Disturbance to birds (B), Other (U), Recreation/tourism (U)

Threats include raptor persecution, habitat degradation as a result of high livestock levels and deer grazing ('Other' threat, above), and the possibility of development for skiing. Part of the IBA is a candidate SPA.

Montrose basin A4i, A4iii, B1i, B2, B3, C3, C4 204

Admin region Scotland
Coordinates 56°42'N 2°30'W
Altitude 0–76 m **Area** 984 ha

■ **Site description**
The Montrose basin is about 3 km across, almost circular in shape, and forms the estuary of the South Esk River. Duns Dish, a lowland loch about 4 km north-west of Montrose basin, is also included within the IBA.

Habitats Wetland (tidal river/enclosed tidal water; mudflat/sandflat; fen/transition mire/spring)
Land-use Agriculture, Hunting, Nature conservation/research

■ **Birds**

Species	Season	Year	Pop min	Pop max	Acc	Criteria
Cygnus cygnus Whooper Swan	W	1995	105	105	A	B3
Anser brachyrhynchus Pink-footed Goose	W	1995	26,000	26,000	A	A4i, B1i, C3
Calidris canutus Knot	W	1995	3,120	3,120	A	B2
Tringa totanus Redshank	W	1995	2,450	2,450	A	B1i, C3
Tringa totanus Redshank	P	1995	2,320	2,320	A	B1i, C3

The IBA supports large numbers of wintering wildfowl and waders, holding 49,400 wintering waterbirds on a regular basis. The site is also nationally important for breeding *Somateria mollissima* (400 pairs, 1992, 1%), for wintering *Anas penelope* (4,440 birds, 2%) and *Somateria mollissima* (1,790 birds, 2%), and for summer moulting assemblages of *Somateria mollissima* (880 birds, 1%).

■ **Protection status**
National High **International** High
IBA partly or wholly overlaps with the following national designated areas. *Sites of Special Scientific Interest:* Dun's Dish, Montrose Basin. Overlaps with international designated areas: 984 ha of IBA covered by Special Protection Area (Montrose Basin, 984 ha). 984 ha of IBA covered by Ramsar Site (Montrose Basin, 984 ha).

■ **Conservation issues**

Threats Disturbance to birds (C), Recreation/tourism (C)

Shooting is restricted in the Basin since the creation of an Local Nature Reserve (LNR) in 1981. The Scottish Wildlife Trusts manage the LNR on behalf of Angus Council.

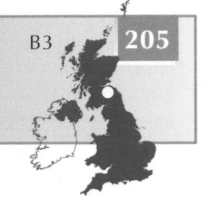

Moorfoot Hills   B3   205
Admin region Scotland
Coordinates 55°42′N 3°01′W
Altitude 170–659 m **Area** 9,220 ha

■ **Site description**
One large and several smaller blocks of upland moorland to the north-east of Peebles.

Habitats Scrub (40%; heathland), Grassland (40%), Wetland (20%; river/stream; blanket bog)
Land-use Agriculture (100%), Tourism/recreation (50%)

■ **Birds**

Species	Season	Year	Pop min	Pop max	Acc	Criteria
Turdus torquatus Ring Ouzel	B	1986	—	66	A	B3

The IBA holds an assemblage of breeding upland species.

■ **Protection status**
National High **International** None
IBA partly or wholly overlaps with the following national designated areas. *Sites of Special Scientific Interest:* Dundreich Plateau, Moorfoot Hills.

■ **Conservation issues**

Threats Agricultural intensification/expansion (U)

The area is overgrazed by sheep in parts.

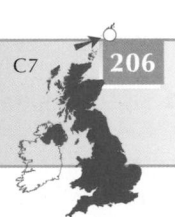

Moorland areas, central Shetland   C7   206
Admin region Scotland
Coordinates 60°15′N 1°13′W
Altitude 10–200 m **Area** 2,790 ha

■ **Site description**
The IBA comprises stretches of blanket bog, with lochans, in addition to a variety of other habitats including wet and dry heaths and mires, acid grassland and areas of marsh.

Habitats Scrub (heathland), Grassland, Wetland (standing fresh water; blanket bog; water-fringe vegetation; fen/transition mire/spring)
Land-use Agriculture (100%)

■ **Birds**

Species	Season	Year	Pop min	Pop max	Acc	Criteria
Numenius phaeopus Whimbrel	B	1992	93	93	A	C7
Stercorarius parasiticus Arctic Skua	B	1992	43	43	A	C7

The IBA supports a suite of breeding moorland birds. The site is also nationally important for breeding *Gavia stellata* (10 pairs, 1994, 1%).

■ **Protection status**
National Partial **International** None
IBA partly or wholly overlaps with the following national designated areas. *Sites of Special Scientific Interest:* Catfirth, Loch of Girlsta, Sandwater, South Whiteness.

■ **Conservation issues**

Threats Agricultural intensification/expansion (B)

Part of the site is a candidate SPA.

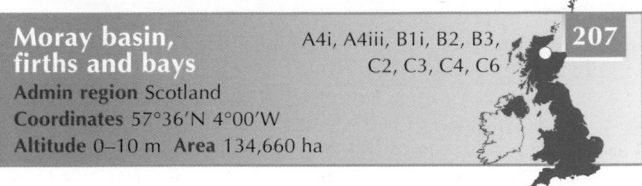

Moray basin, firths and bays   A4i, A4iii, B1i, B2, B3, C2, C3, C4, C6   207
Admin region Scotland
Coordinates 57°36′N 4°00′W
Altitude 0–10 m **Area** 134,660 ha

■ **Site description**
A complex area of coastline and estuary, including Loch Fleet, Dornoch Firth, Loch Eye, Cromarty Firth, Beauly Firth, and Moray Firth (south shore including Burghead and Spey Bay), stretching from Helmsdale south to Spey Bay. This area includes six sites that were treated as separate IBAs in the previous international IBA inventory (Grimmett and Jones 1989): 'Lower Dornoch Firth (including Morrich More)' (former site GB028), 'Loch Eye' (former site GB029), 'Cromarty Firth' (former site GB030), 'Beauly Firth' (former site GB033), 'Moray Firth: Munlochy Bay to Findhorn Bay' (former site GB034) and 'Moray Firth: Burghead and Spey Bays' (former site GB066).

Habitats Scrub (scrub; heathland), Grassland, Wetland (tidal river/enclosed tidal water; mudflat/sandflat; saltmarsh; sand-dunes/sand beach; shingle/stony beach; standing fresh water), Marine areas (open sea), Rocky areas (sea cliff/rocky shore)
Land-use Fisheries/aquaculture, Tourism/recreation

■ **Birds**

Species	Season	Year	Pop min	Pop max	Acc	Criteria
Podiceps auritus Slavonian Grebe	W	1995	—	66	A	B1i, C2
Cygnus cygnus Whooper Swan	W	1995	295	295	A	B1i, B3, C2, C6
[1] *Anser anser* Greylag Goose	W	1994	23,200	23,200	A	A4i, B1i, C3
Anas penelope Wigeon	W	1995	31,400	31,400	A	A4i, B1i, C3
Anas crecca Teal	W	1995	4,760	4,760	A	B1i, C3
Aythya marila Scaup	W	1995	—	455	A	B2
Melanitta fusca Velvet Scoter	W	1995	—	540	A	B2
Mergus serrator Red-breasted Merganser	W	1995	—	1,790	A	B1i, C3
Haematopus ostralegus Oystercatcher	W	1995	11,100	11,100	A	A4i, B1i, C3
Haematopus ostralegus Oystercatcher	P	1995	10,600	10,600	A	B1i, C3
Charadrius hiaticula Ringed Plover	W	1995	500	500	A	B1i, C3
Charadrius hiaticula Ringed Plover	P	1995	670	670	A	B1i, C3
Calidris canutus Knot	W	1995	5,400	5,400	A	B1i, B2, C3
Calidris alpina Dunlin	W	1995	13,500	13,500	A	B2
Limosa lapponica Bar-tailed Godwit	W	1995	3,970	3,970	A	A4i, B1i, B2, C2, C6
Limosa lapponica Bar-tailed Godwit	P	1995	2,020	2,020	A	A4i, B1i, C2, C6
Numenius arquata Curlew	W	1995	5,300	5,300	A	A4i, B1i, B2, C3
Numenius arquata Curlew	P	1995	3,720	3,720	A	A4i, B1i, C3
Tringa totanus Redshank	W	1995	5,150	5,150	A	A4i, B1i, C3
Tringa totanus Redshank	P	1995	5,600	5,600	A	A4i, B1i, C3
Sterna hirundo Common Tern	B	1995	310	310	A	C6

1. Mean annual peak 1989–1994.

These coastal areas form an integral unit that is internationally important for populations of wintering and passage wildfowl. The IBA holds 130,000 wintering and 31,000 passage waterbirds on a regular basis, and is also nationally important for breeding *Phalacrocorax carbo* (280 pairs, 1990, 4%), and for wintering *Phalacrocorax carbo* (775 birds, 5%), *Cygnus olor* (380 birds, 1%), *Anser brachyrhynchus* (2,140 birds, 1989–1994, 1%), *Tadorna tadorna* (1,060 birds, 1%), *Somateria mollissima* (1,710 birds, 1994–1995, 2%), *Clangula hyemalis* (3,740 birds, 1994–1995, 16%), *Melanitta nigra* (2,760 birds, 1994–1995, 7%), *Bucephala clangula* (975 birds, 1994–

1995, 3%), *Mergus merganser* (605 birds, 1994–1995, 7%), *Calidris maritima* (260 birds, 1%) and *Tringa nebularia* (8 birds, 1%). *Anser anser* are from the Icelandic breeding population.

■ **Protection status**

National Partial **International** Low

IBA partly or wholly overlaps with the following national designated areas. *National Nature Reserve:* Mound Alderwoods. *Reserves:* Cromarty Firth, Edderton Sands, Fairy Glen, Loch Fleet, Udale Bay. *Sites of Special Scientific Interest:* Ardersier Glacial Deposits, Ballinreach Coastal Gorges, Beauly Firth, Clashach–Covesea, Conon Islands, Cromarty Firth, Culbin Sands, Forest and Findhorn Bay, Dornoch Firth, Dunrobin Coast, Easter Fearn, Garbh Allt, Helmsdale Coast Inverbrora, Ledmore Wood, Loch Fleet, Lossiemouth East Quarry, Lossiemouth Shore, Masonshaugh, Morrich More, Mound Alderwoods, Munlochy Bay, Nigg Bay, Rosemarkie to Cromarty/ Shandwick Coast, Spey Bay, Tarbat Ness, The Dens, Whiteness Head. Overlaps with international designated areas: 7,836 ha of IBA covered by Special Protection Area (Dornoch Firth and Loch Fleet, 7,836 ha). 7,836 ha of IBA covered by Ramsar Site (Dornoch Firth and Loch Fleet, 7,836 ha). 205 ha of IBA covered by Special Protection Area (Loch Eye, 205 ha). 205 ha of IBA covered by Ramsar Site (Loch Eye, 205 ha). 2,410 ha of IBA covered by Special Protection Area (Moray and Nairn Coast, 2,410 ha). 2,410 ha of IBA covered by Ramsar Site (Moray and Nairn Coast, 2,410 ha).

■ **Conservation issues**

Threats Aquaculture/fisheries (A), Disturbance to birds (A), Extraction industry (B), Industrialization/urbanization (U), Infrastructure (U), Other (B), Recreation/tourism (A)

Threats include development for homes, oil-rig construction and decommissioning, sewage disposal, uncontrolled wildfowling in sensitive areas, recreational disturbance, commercial shellfisheries, oil pollution ('Other' threat, above), land claim and land-fill. The area is monitored four times a year by means of a coordinated WeBS count. Cromarty Firth and the Inner Moray Firth are both candidate SPAs.

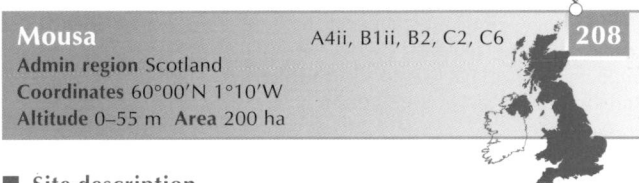

Mousa   A4ii, B1ii, B2, C2, C6   **208**
Admin region Scotland
Coordinates 60°00'N 1°10'W
Altitude 0–55 m **Area** 200 ha

■ **Site description**

A low-lying island with a few freshwater lochs and tidal pools in the south-east corner. Habitat-types present include acidic and maritime grassland and heathland, and areas of marsh that are moderately rich in nutrients.

Habitats Scrub (heathland), Grassland, Wetland (tidal river/enclosed tidal water; standing fresh water), Rocky areas (sea cliff/rocky shore)
Land-use Agriculture (100%)

■ **Birds**

Species		Season	Year	Pop min	Pop max	Acc	Criteria
Hydrobates pelagicus	Storm Petrel	B	1996	6,800	6,800	A	A4ii,B1ii,B2,C2,C6

The island is also nationally important for breeding *Sterna paradisaea* (765 pairs, 1994, 2%).

■ **Protection status**

National High **International** High

IBA partly or wholly overlaps with the following national designated areas. *Site of Special Scientific Interest:* Mousa. Overlaps with international designated areas: 200 ha of IBA covered by Special Protection Area (Mousa, 200 ha).

■ **Conservation issues**

Threats Aquaculture/fisheries, Recreation/tourism

Unsustainable fishing of sandeels *Ammodytes* poses a potential threat to seabirds, and terns are susceptible to disturbance from tourists.

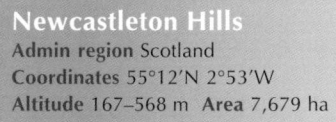

Muir of Dinnet   A1, A4i, A4iii, B1i, B2,   **209**
Admin region Scotland   C1, C3, C4, C6
Coordinates 57°05'N 2°56'W
Altitude 161–498 m **Area** 2,280 ha

■ **Site description**

Two large lochs and associated heath, woodland and mire habitats that exhibit a classic vegetational succession from open water to fen.

Habitats Forest and woodland (58%; broadleaved deciduous forest; native coniferous forest), Scrub (15%; heathland), Wetland (20%; standing fresh water; water-fringe vegetation; fen/transition mire/spring), Artificial landscape (7%; highly improved reseeded grassland; arable land)
Land-use Nature conservation/research (100%)

■ **Birds**

Species		Season	Year	Pop min	Pop max	Acc	Criteria
Anser anser	Greylag Goose	W	1995	19,800	19,800	A	A4i, B1i, C3
[1] *Loxia scotica*	Scottish Crossbill	N	1995	—	—	A	A1, B2, C1

1. Occurs at low densities in non-breeding season.

The site holds 21,700 wintering waterbirds on a regular basis. *Anser anser* are from the Icelandic breeding population.

■ **Protection status**

National High **International** None

IBA partly or wholly overlaps with the following national designated areas. *National Nature Reserve:* Muir of Dinnet. *Site of Special Scientific Interest:* Muir of Dinnet.

■ **Conservation issues**

Threats Other (U)

Few obvious threats are apparent. The ITE have undertaken several projects on the lochs, including studies of Eurasian otter *Lutra lutra* and nutrient enrichment on Loch Davan ('Other' threat, above). There is a management plan for the site, which is also a candidate SPA.

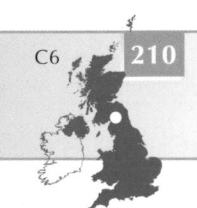

Newcastleton Hills   C6   **210**
Admin region Scotland
Coordinates 55°12'N 2°53'W
Altitude 167–568 m **Area** 7,679 ha

■ **Site description**

An outstanding area of moorland that straddles the boundary between the Dumfries and Galloway region the and Borders region.

Habitats Scrub (heathland), Grassland (humid grassland), Wetland (blanket bog)
Land-use Agriculture, Tourism/recreation

■ **Birds**

Species		Season	Year	Pop min	Pop max	Acc	Criteria
Circus cyaneus	Hen Harrier	R	1994	12	12	A	C6

This is an important site for a number of breeding upland species.

■ **Protection status**

National High **International** None

IBA partly or wholly overlaps with the following national designated areas. *Site of Special Scientific Interest:* Langholm – Newcastleton Hills.

■ **Conservation issues**

Threats Abandonment/reduction of land management (U), Agricultural intensification/ expansion (U)

Threats include inappropriate burning of heather and overgrazing by sheep. Since 1991 the site has been the subject of an intensive study by ITE/GCT (part funded by RSPB) into the relationship between *Lagopus lagopus* and predators.

North Harris mountains

B2, C6   **211**

Admin region Scotland
Coordinates 57°59'N 6°54'W
Altitude 0–679 m   **Area** 18,570 ha

■ Site description
Rocky hills with steep slopes, covered by montane grassland and moorland. The hills are drained by fast-flowing streams, and there are numerous nutrient-poor lochs (some of which are reverting to bog). Species-poor wet heath also occurs due to the oceanic character of the site.

Habitats Scrub (heathland), Grassland (steppe/dry calcareous grassland), Wetland (standing brackish and salt water; river/stream; blanket bog)
Land-use Agriculture (95%), Fisheries/aquaculture (5%)

■ Birds

Species	Season	Year	Pop min	Pop max	Acc	Criteria
Aquila chrysaetos Golden Eagle	R	1994	9	9	A	B2, C6

These mountains are important for breeding raptors, waders and other upland species.

■ Protection status
National Partial   **International** Partial
IBA partly or wholly overlaps with the following national designated areas. *Site of Special Scientific Interest:* North Harris. Overlaps with international designated area: 13,134 ha of IBA covered by Special Protection Area (North Harris Mountains, 13,134 ha).

■ Conservation issues
No serious threats are known at the site. Bryophytes typical of Atlantic coasts are well represented, including a moss whose world distribution is limited to western Scotland, Ireland and the Isle of Man.

North Inverness lochs

C6   **212**

Admin region Scotland
Coordinates 57°22'N 4°33'W
Altitude 50–525 m   **Area** 11,270 ha

■ Site description
A group of freshwater lochs and lochans characterized by moderate nutrient levels, and surrounding catchment areas. Sedge-beds are locally extensive.

Habitats Forest and woodland (broadleaved deciduous forest), Scrub (heathland), Grassland (humid grassland), Wetland (standing fresh water; river/stream; fen/transition mire/spring)
Land-use Agriculture (70%), Forestry (30%)

■ Birds

Species	Season	Year	Pop min	Pop max	Acc	Criteria
[1] *Podiceps auritus* Slavonian Grebe	B	1995	9	9	A	C6

1. Mean annual peak 1991–1995.

The site is also nationally important for breeding *Turdus iliacus* (6 pairs, 1995, 8%).

■ Protection status
National Partial   **International** Partial
IBA partly or wholly overlaps with the following national designated areas. *Sites of Special Scientific Interest:* Balnagrantach, Gartally Limestone Quarries. Overlaps with international designated areas: IBA overlaps with Special Protection Area (Great Glen Lochs).

■ Conservation issues

Threats Afforestation (B), Consequences of animal/plant introductions (B), Disturbance to birds (U)

American mink *Mustela vison* predation and competition with rainbow trout *Salmo gairdneri* are likely to affect breeding waterbirds, whilst *Podiceps auritus* are vulnerable to inadvertent and deliberate disturbance. Regular monitoring of *P. auritus* takes place.

North Lowther Hills

B2, C6   **213**

Admin region Scotland
Coordinates 55°27'N 3°53'W
Altitude 171–587 m   **Area** 25,880 ha

■ Site description
An upland block to the east of Airds Moss, comprising moorland and areas of active blanket bog.

Habitats Scrub (heathland), Grassland, Wetland (river/stream; blanket bog)
Land-use Agriculture, Hunting, Tourism/recreation

■ Birds

Species	Season	Year	Pop min	Pop max	Acc	Criteria
Circus cyaneus Hen Harrier	R	1995	—	19	A	B2, C6
Falco peregrinus Peregrine	R	1989	8	—	A	C6

The IBA supports a range of breeding upland species.

■ Protection status
National Partial   **International** Partial
IBA partly or wholly overlaps with the following national designated areas. *Sites of Special Scientific Interest:* Back Wood, Leadhills–Wanlockhead, Ravengill, Ree Burn, Rough Flow Moss. Overlaps with international designated areas: IBA overlaps with Special Protection Area (Muirkirk Uplands and North Lowther Hills).

■ Conservation issues

Threats Agricultural intensification/expansion (U), Disturbance to birds (U), Recreation/tourism (U)

The northern part of the site is a study area for the ITE/GCT Langholm Project on relationships between raptors and *Lagopus lagopus*. A management agreement exists for Rough Flow Moss, and there is ongoing monitoring of raptors by the South Strathclyde and Dumfries and Galloway Raptor Study Group.

North Mainland coast

C7   **214**

Admin region Scotland
Coordinates 59°05'N 3°02'W
Altitude 0–15 m   **Area** 420 ha

■ Site description
A low-lying rocky coastline interspersed with sandy bays.

Habitats Wetland (sand-dunes/sand beach), Rocky areas (sea cliff/rocky shore)
Land-use Not utilized

■ Birds

Species	Season	Year	Pop min	Pop max	Acc	Criteria
Calidris maritima Purple Sandpiper	W	1994	—	89	A	C7
Numenius arquata Curlew	W	1994	—	575	A	C7
Tringa totanus Redshank	W	1994	—	405	A	C7
Arenaria interpres Turnstone	W	1994	—	655	A	C7

The IBA is important for wintering waders, and is also nationally important for wintering *Clangula hyemalis* (265 birds, 1993–1994, 1%) and *Plectrophenax nivalis* (110 birds, 1993–1994, 1%).

■ Protection status
National None   **International** None

■ Conservation issues

Threats Aquaculture/fisheries (U)

The expansion of aquaculture poses a threat.

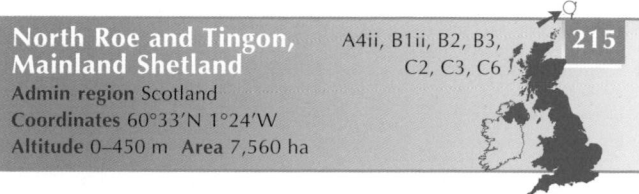

North Roe and Tingon, Mainland Shetland

A4ii, B1ii, B2, B3, C2, C3, C6 — **215**

Admin region Scotland
Coordinates 60°33′N 1°24′W
Altitude 0–450 m **Area** 7,560 ha

■ Site description

This site contains some of the highest quality blanket bog in Shetland, in addition to many pools and acid lochans, some with small islands. The important tree and scrub cover comprises *Betula*, *Sorbus*, *Salix* and *Juniperus*, and numerous Arctic-alpine species characterize the flora and invertebrate fauna.

Habitats Scrub (scrub; heathland), Wetland (standing fresh water; blanket bog)
Land-use Agriculture (100%)

■ Birds

Species		Season	Year	Pop min	Pop max	Acc	Criteria
Gavia stellata	Red-throated Diver	B	1994	66	66	A	B2, C2, C6
Falco columbarius	Merlin	R	1994	—	9	A	C6
Stercorarius skua	Great Skua	B	1992	165	165	A	A4ii, B1ii, B3, C3

The IBA holds an important assemblage of breeding moorland birds, and is nationally important for breeding *Numenius phaeopus* (31 pairs, 1994, 6%) and *Stercorarius parasiticus* (140 pairs, 1992, 4%).

■ Protection status

National Partial **International** Partial
IBA partly or wholly overlaps with the following national designated areas. *Sites of Special Scientific Interest:* Ronas Hill – North Roe, Tingon, Uyea – North Roe Coast, Villians of Hamnavoe. Overlaps with international designated areas: IBA overlaps with Special Protection Area and Ramsar Site (Ronas Hill, North Roe and Tingon, 5,470 ha).

■ Conservation issues

Threats Agricultural intensification/expansion (B), Aquaculture/fisheries (B)

Unsustainable fishing of sandeels *Ammodytes* poses a potential threat to seabirds.

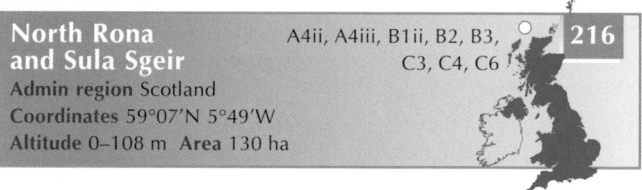

North Rona and Sula Sgeir

A4ii, A4iii, B1ii, B2, B3, C3, C4, C6 — **216**

Admin region Scotland
Coordinates 59°07′N 5°49′W
Altitude 0–108 m **Area** 130 ha

■ Site description

Two islands, with a number of outlying rocky islets, lying about 65 km north of the island of Lewis. Sula Sgeir is located about 15 km to the west of the far larger North Rona. The islands support submaritime grassland modified locally by sea spray.

Habitats Grassland (85%), Rocky areas (15%; sea cliff/rocky shore; rock stacks/islets)
Land-use Agriculture (90%), Not utilized (10%)

■ Birds

Species		Season	Year	Pop min	Pop max	Acc	Criteria
[1] *Oceanodroma leucorhoa*	Leach's Petrel	B	1986	—	—	A	C6
Sula bassana	Gannet	B	1994	10,400	10,400	A	A4ii, B1ii, B2, C3
Larus marinus	Great Black-backed Gull	B	1986	735	735	A	B3
Uria aalge	Guillemot	B	1986	28,900	28,900	A	B1ii, C3
Alca torda	Razorbill	B	1986	1,550	1,550	A	B3

1. No counts available.

These islands are of major importance for breeding seabirds, holding 55,200 pairs on a regular basis. The site is also nationally important for breeding *Fulmarus glacialis* (9,000 pairs, 1985–1986, 2%), *Rissa tridactyla* (5,050 pairs, 1986, 1%) and *Fratercula arctica* (5,250 pairs, 1986, 1%).

■ Protection status

National Partial **International** None

IBA partly or wholly overlaps with the following national designated areas. *National Nature Reserve:* North Rona and Sula Sgeir. *Site of Special Scientific Interest:* North Rona and Sula Sgeir.

■ Conservation issues

Threats Aquaculture/fisheries (U), Consequences of animal/plant introductions (A), Extraction industry (C), Recreation/tourism (U)

Exploration licences exist for the seas to the north-west and oil pollution is therefore a threat. The islands are also vulnerable to pressure from increased numbers of visitors. The site is a candidate SPA.

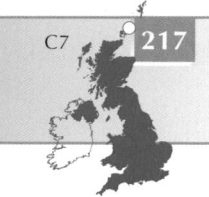

North Ronaldsay coast

C7 — **217**

Admin region Scotland
Coordinates 59°20′N 2°25′W
Altitude 0–5 m **Area** 220 ha

■ Site description

A low-lying rocky shoreline interspersed with sandy bays, where the seaweeds are grazed by North Ronaldsay sheep.

Habitats Wetland (sand-dunes/sand beach), Rocky areas (sea cliff/rocky shore)
Land-use Agriculture (100%)

■ Birds

Species		Season	Year	Pop min	Pop max	Acc	Criteria
[1] *Calidris maritima*	Purple Sandpiper	W	1984	275	275	A	C7
Cepphus grylle	Black Guillemot	B	1990	125	125	A	C7

1. Mean count.

The IBA is also nationally important for wintering *Plectrophenax nivalis* (115 birds, 1993–1994, 1%).

■ Protection status

National None **International** None

■ Conservation issues

Threats Extraction industry (B)

The channel between North Ronaldsay and Fair Isle is a tanker route, and oil pollution is therefore an ongoing threat.

North Uist machair and islands

A1, B1i, B2, C1, C2, C3, C6 — **218**

Admin region Scotland
Coordinates 57°35′N 7°28′W
Altitude 0–196 m **Area** 6,900 ha

■ Site description

A complex of islands and coastal machair, on the west coast of North Uist. This area includes four sites that were treated as separate IBAs in the previous international IBA inventory (Grimmett and Jones 1989): 'West Sound of Harris' (former site GB005), 'Balranald' (former site GB008), 'Baleshare and Kirkibost' (former site GB009) and part of 'Kilpheder to Smerclate' (former site GB241).

Habitats Scrub (1%; heathland), Grassland (75%; humid grassland; machair), Wetland (7%; saltmarsh; sand-dunes/sand beach; standing fresh water; fen/transition mire/spring), Rocky areas (2%; sea cliff/rocky shore; scree/boulders; inland sand-dunes), Artificial landscape (15%; highly improved reseeded grassland; arable land)
Land-use Agriculture (100%), Hunting (100%)

■ Birds

Species		Season	Year	Pop min	Pop max	Acc	Criteria
[1] *Hydrobates pelagicus*	Storm Petrel	B	1990	225	—	A	B2
Anser anser	Greylag Goose	W	1992	—	300	A	B1i, C3
[2] *Branta leucopsis*	Barnacle Goose	W	1998	1,552	1,552	A	B1i, B2, C2
Crex crex	Corncrake	B	1995	51	51	A	A1, B2, C1, C2, C6
Haematopus ostralegus	Oystercatcher	R	1995	875	—	A	B1i, C3

Species ... continued	Season	Year	Pop min	Pop max	Acc	Criteria
Charadrius hiaticula Ringed Plover	R	1995	335	335	A	B1i, C3
Charadrius hiaticula Ringed Plover	W	1995	585	—	A	B1i, C3
Calidris alpina Dunlin	R	1995	305	305	A	B1i, C3
Tringa totanus Redshank	R	1995	485	485	A	B2
Sterna albifrons Little Tern	B	1991	27	27	A	C6

1. Shillay and Little Shillay only.
2. Mean annual peak 1994–1998.

The IBA is important for both breeding waders and wintering geese and waders. It is also nationally important for breeding *Anas clypeata* (13 pairs, 1991–1993, 1%), and for wintering *Calidris alba* (415 birds, 1993, 2%) and *Calidris maritima* (365 birds, 1993, 2%). *Anser anser* are from the Hebridean population, while *Branta leucopsis* are from the Greenland breeding population.

■ Protection status
National Partial **International** None
IBA partly or wholly overlaps with the following national designated areas. *Reserve:* Balranald. *Sites of Special Scientific Interest:* Baleshare and Kirkibost, Balranald Bog and Loch nam Feithean, Machairs Robach and Newton, Vallay.

■ Conservation issues

Threats Agricultural intensification/expansion (B), Consequences of animal/plant introductions (A), Drainage (B), Extraction industry (C), Other (A)

The main threats are posed by introduced American mink *Mustela vison*, polecats *M. putorius*, ferrets *M. putorius furo*, hedgehogs *Erinaceus europaeus* and rats *Rattus* on coastal islands, and oil spills ('Other' threat, above). There is ongoing monitoring of *Crex crex*. Part of the area is a candidate SPA and SAC.

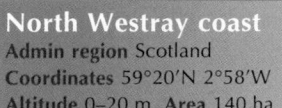

North Westray coast
B1ii, B2, C2, C6 **219**
Admin region Scotland
Coordinates 59°20′N 2°58′W
Altitude 0–20 m **Area** 140 ha

■ Site description
Two sections of coastline on North Westray.

Habitats Wetland (sand-dunes/sand beach; shingle/stony beach), Rocky areas (sea cliff/rocky shore)
Land-use Agriculture, Not utilized

■ Birds

Species	Season	Year	Pop min	Pop max	Acc	Criteria
Sterna paradisaea Arctic Tern	B	1994	—	1,300	A	C2, C6
Cepphus grylle Black Guillemot	B	1984	205	205	A	B1ii, B2

The IBA is important for breeding seabirds.

■ Protection status
National None **International** None

■ Conservation issues

Threats Extraction industry (U)

Stone-quarrying has taken place in the past.

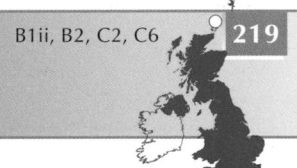

Noss
A4ii, A4iii, B1ii, B2, B3, C3, C4 **220**
Admin region Scotland
Coordinates 60°08′N 1°01′W
Altitude 0–181 m **Area** 343 ha

■ Site description
An island located off the east coast of Bressay, which in turn lies off the east coast of mainland Shetland. The eastern part of the island slopes steeply.

Habitats Scrub (heathland), Grassland, Rocky areas (sea cliff/rocky shore)
Land-use Agriculture (100%)

■ Birds

Species	Season	Year	Pop min	Pop max	Acc	Criteria
Sula bassana Gannet	B	1994	7,300	7,300	A	A4ii, B1ii, B2, C3
Stercorarius skua Great Skua	B	1992	425	425	A	A4ii, B1ii, B3, C3
Uria aalge Guillemot	B	1991	26,100	26,100	A	B1ii, C3

One of the largest seabird colonies in Britain, holding 41,800 breeding pairs on a regular basis. The IBA is also nationally important for breeding *Fulmarus glacialis* (5,850 pairs, 1993, 1%).

■ Protection status
National High **International** High
IBA partly or wholly overlaps with the following national designated areas. *National Nature Reserve:* Noss. *Site of Special Scientific Interest:* Noss. Overlaps with international designated areas: 343 ha of IBA covered by Special Protection Area (Noss, 343 ha).

■ Conservation issues

Threats Aquaculture/fisheries (B), Consequences of animal/plant introductions (U)

Unsustainable fishing of sandeels *Ammodytes* poses a potential threat to seabirds. Introduced rabbits *Oryctolagus cuniculus* and cats *Felis catus* are subject to control measures. There is a management plan for the site.

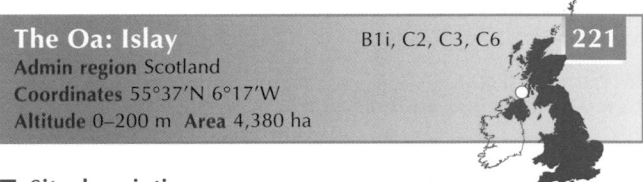

The Oa: Islay
B1i, C2, C3, C6 **221**
Admin region Scotland
Coordinates 55°37′N 6°17′W
Altitude 0–200 m **Area** 4,380 ha

■ Site description
A peninsula in the south-west of Islay, exposed to the prevailing south-westerly weather. This results in a highly oceanic climate with closer ecological affinities to western Ireland than to the rest of Britain. The IBA includes rocky shore, blanket mire, heathland and farmland habitats.

Habitats Scrub (heathland), Wetland (blanket bog), Rocky areas (sea cliff/rocky shore), Artificial landscape (arable land)
Land-use Agriculture (95%), Forestry (5%)

■ Birds

Species	Season	Year	Pop min	Pop max	Acc	Criteria
Anser albifrons White-fronted Goose	W	1989	1,490	1,490	A	B1i, C2, C3, C6
Pyrrhocorax pyrrhocorax Chough	R	1996	7	7	A	C6

The site is also important for breeding raptors and other upland species. *Anser albifrons* are the *flavirostris* subspecies.

■ Protection status
National None **International** None

■ Conservation issues

Threats Abandonment/reduction of land management (U), Disturbance to birds (U)

Pyrrhocorax pyrrhocorax is vulnerable to disturbance at its nesting and roosting sites, and has been adversely affected by a decline in cattle-grazing levels. The area is a candidate SPA.

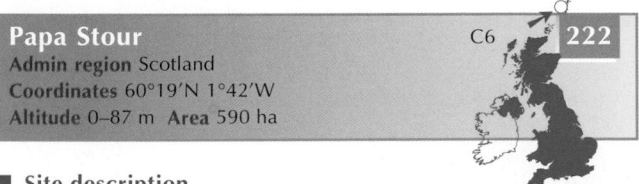

Papa Stour
C6 **222**
Admin region Scotland
Coordinates 60°19′N 1°42′W
Altitude 0–87 m **Area** 590 ha

■ Site description
This site covers the northern and western parts of Papa Stour, and contains a number of lochs and offshore skerries. Lichen-rich heath is the dominant habitat-type.

Habitats Scrub (70%; heathland), Wetland (standing fresh water), Rocky areas (sea cliff/rocky shore; rock stacks/islets)
Land-use Agriculture (100%)

■ Birds

Species	Season	Year	Pop min	Pop max	Acc	Criteria
Sterna paradisaea Arctic Tern	B	1994	1,060	1,060	A	C6

The site supports an important assemblage of breeding seabirds and waders, and is also nationally important for breeding *Charadrius hiaticula* (100 pairs, 1992, 1%).

■ Protection status

National High **International** None

IBA partly or wholly overlaps with the following national designated areas. *Sites of Special Scientific Interest:* Papa Stour, Papa Stour Coast, Papa Stour Fishbed.

■ Conservation issues

Threats Agricultural intensification/expansion (B), Aquaculture/fisheries (B), Other (C), Recreation/tourism (U)

Oil pollution ('Other' threat, above) and unsustainable fishing of sandeels *Ammodytes* pose potential threats to seabirds. Disturbance from visitors to the visitor centre is also a problem. The site is a candidate SPA.

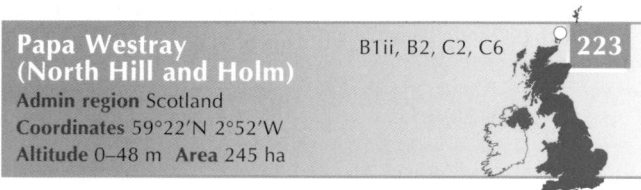

Papa Westray (North Hill and Holm)
B1ii, B2, C2, C6   223
Admin region Scotland
Coordinates 59°22'N 2°52'W
Altitude 0–48 m **Area** 245 ha

■ Site description

North Hill is the northern part of Papa Westray, and consists of a rocky coastline and maritime heath and grassland. The Holm is an island of 48 ha situated off the east coast of Papa Westray.

Habitats Scrub (heathland), Grassland, Wetland (standing fresh water), Rocky areas (sea cliff/rocky shore)
Land-use Agriculture, Nature conservation/research

■ Birds

Species	Season	Year	Pop min	Pop max	Acc	Criteria
Sterna paradisaea Arctic Tern	B	1995	1,690	1,690	A	C2, C6
Cepphus grylle Black Guillemot	B	1995	190	190	A	B1ii, B2

The site is important for breeding seabirds, and is also nationally important for breeding *Stercorarius parasiticus* (150 pairs, 1994, 5%).

■ Protection status

National High **International** High

IBA partly or wholly overlaps with the following national designated areas. *Reserve:* North Hill – Papa Westray. *Sites of Special Scientific Interest:* Holm of Papa Westray, North Hill – Papa Westray. Overlaps with international designated areas: 245 ha of IBA covered by Special Protection Area (North Hill, Papa Westray, 245 ha).

■ Conservation issues

Threats Agricultural intensification/expansion (C)

Ongoing monitoring of breeding seabirds is undertaken on North Hill, whilst Glasgow University conduct studies of *Cepphus grylle* on Holm. North Hill is subject to communal grazing under an RSPB Reserve Agreement. There is a management plan for the site.

Park, Lewis
B2, C6   224
Admin region Scotland
Coordinates 57°59'N 6°37'W
Altitude 0–572 m **Area** 16,220 ha

■ Site description

A large upland block to the east of the North Harris mountains.

Habitats Forest and woodland, Scrub (95%; heathland), Grassland, Wetland (5%; blanket bog)
Land-use Agriculture

■ Birds

Species	Season	Year	Pop min	Pop max	Acc	Criteria
Aquila chrysaetos Golden Eagle	R	1992	8	8	A	B2, C6

The IBA holds a typical assemblage of upland birds, and is also nationally important for breeding *Tringa nebularia* (11 pairs, 1994, 1%).

■ Protection status

National None **International** None

■ Conservation issues

No serious threats are known at the site.

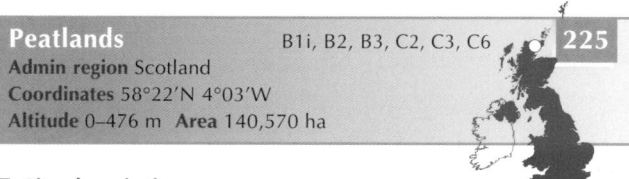

Peatlands
B1i, B2, B3, C2, C3, C6   225
Admin region Scotland
Coordinates 58°22'N 4°03'W
Altitude 0–476 m **Area** 140,570 ha

■ Site description

The largest and most intact area of blanket bog in Scotland, lying across Caithness and Sutherland. Human activities include commercial peat extraction ('Other' land-use, below).

Habitats Scrub (heathland), Grassland, Wetland (blanket bog; water-fringe vegetation; fen/transition mire/spring)
Land-use Hunting, Other

■ Birds

Species	Season	Year	Pop min	Pop max	Acc	Criteria
Gavia stellata Red-throated Diver	B	1995	155	155	A	B2, C2, C6
Gavia arctica Black-throated Diver	B	1995	31	31	A	C6
Anser anser Greylag Goose	R	1995	200	200	A	B1i, C3
Circus cyaneus Hen Harrier	R	1995	54	54	A	B2, C6
Aquila chrysaetos Golden Eagle	R	1992	5	5	A	B2
Falco columbarius Merlin	B	1995	49	49	A	C6
Falco peregrinus Peregrine	R	1995	9	9	A	C6
Pluvialis apricaria Golden Plover	B	1995	2,410	2,410	A	B3, C2, C6
Calidris alpina Dunlin	B	1995	1,970	1,970	A	B1i, C3
Tringa glareola Wood Sandpiper	B	1995	6	6	A	C6
Asio flammeus Short-eared Owl	B	1995	35	—	A	B2, C6

The IBA is of outstanding international importance for breeding divers, waders and raptors. It is also nationally important for breeding *Anas penelope* (99 pairs, 1995, 33%), *Anas crecca* (335 pairs, 1995, 21%), *Melanitta nigra* (29 pairs, 1995, 38%), *Tringa nebularia* (395 pairs, 1995, 36%) and *Stercorarius parasiticus* (140 pairs, 1995, 4%). *Anser anser* are from the Hebridean population.

■ Protection status

National Partial **International** Partial

IBA partly or wholly overlaps with the following national designated areas. *National Nature Reserves:* Blar nam Faoileag, Strathy Bogs. *Reserves:* Carn nam Muc, Forsinard. *Sites of Special Scientific Interest:* Armadale Gorge, Bad na Gallaig, Bad nam Bo, Badanloch Bogs, Ben Griams, Ben Hope, Ben Hutig, Ben Klibreck, Ben Loyal, Blar nam Faoileag, Burn of Latheronwheel, Cnoc an Alaskie, Coire na Beinne Mires, Dirlot Gorge, Druim nam Bad, Dunbeath Water, Dunnet Head, Forsinard Bogs, Grudie Peatlands, Knockfin Heights, Lambsdale Leans, Leavad, Loch Caluim Flows, Loch Meadie Peatlands, Loch More Wetlands, Lochan Buidhe Mires, Lon a'Chuil, Mallart, Morven and Scaraben, Rumsdale Peatlands, Shielton Peatlands, Skelpick Peatlands, Skinsdale Peatlands, Slethill Peatlands, Strathmore Peatlands, Strathy Bogs, Stroupster Peatlands, Syre Peatlands, Truderscaig, West Borgie, West Halladale, West Strathnaver. Overlaps with international designated areas: IBA overlaps with Special Protection Area (The Peatlands of Caithness and Sutherland).

■ Conservation issues

Threats Afforestation (B), Agricultural intensification/expansion (C), Drainage (U), Extraction industry (C), Other (C)

Existing forestry and grazing damage by red deer *Cervus elaphus* are a problem ('Other' threat, above).

Pentland Firth Islands A4iii, B3, C2, C4, C6 226

Admin region Scotland
Coordinates 58°41′N 3°07′W
Altitude 0–30 m **Area** 270 ha

■ Site description

The IBA comprises two islands and a group of rocky islets located in the Pentland Firth. These support a variety of habitats including maritime heath, rocky shores, marsh, moorland and open fresh water.

Habitats Scrub (heathland), Grassland, Wetland (standing fresh water), Rocky areas (sea cliff/rocky shore; rock stacks/islets)
Land-use Agriculture, Not utilized

■ Birds

Species	Season	Year	Pop min	Pop max	Acc	Criteria
Larus marinus Great Black-backed Gull	B	1986	285	—	A	B3
Sterna paradisaea Arctic Tern	B	1994	1,750	1,750	A	C2, C6

These islands are important for large numbers of breeding seabirds, holding 11,600 pairs on a regular basis. They are also nationally important for breeding *Uria aalge* (9,200 pairs, 1986, 1%).

■ Protection status

National Partial **International** Partial
IBA partly or wholly overlaps with the following national designated areas. *Site of Special Scientific Interest:* Stroma. Overlaps with international designated areas: 165 ha of IBA covered by Special Protection Area (Pentland Firth Islands, 165 ha).

■ Conservation issues

Threats Agricultural intensification/expansion (B), Aquaculture/fisheries (C), Extraction industry (B)

A tanker route passes through the Pentland Firth, and oil pollution is therefore a threat.

Priest Island B2, C2 227

Admin region Scotland
Coordinates 57°57′N 5°30′W
Altitude 0–78 m **Area** 138 ha

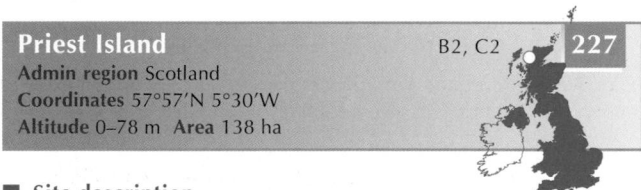

■ Site description

The outermost and most exposed of the Summer Isles, lying about 6 km to the west of Ullapool. Heath communities are interspersed with species-rich maritime heath and other cliff communities that exist where sea spray and guano supply nutrients.

Habitats Forest and woodland (broadleaved deciduous forest), Scrub (heathland), Wetland (standing fresh water)
Land-use Nature conservation/research (100%)

■ Birds

Species	Season	Year	Pop min	Pop max	Acc	Criteria
Hydrobates pelagicus Storm Petrel	B	1995	2,210	2,210	A	B2, C2

The island is important for breeding seabirds.

■ Protection status

National High **International** High
IBA partly or wholly overlaps with the following national designated areas. *Reserve:* Priest Island. *Site of Special Scientific Interest:* Priest Island. Overlaps with international designated areas: 138 ha of IBA covered by Special Protection Area (Priest Island, 138 ha).

■ Conservation issues

No serious threats are known at the site. The island is a RSPB Reserve, with *Hydrobates pelagicus* the subject of sporadic monitoring and research. There is a management plan for the site.

Ramna Stacks and Gruney C6 228

Admin region Scotland
Coordinates 60°39′N 1°18′W
Altitude 0–30 m **Area** 11 ha

■ Site description

With the exception of Gruney, where guano-enriched maritime grassland occurs, these rocky islands support little or no vegetation.

Habitats Grassland (humid grassland), Rocky areas (sea cliff/rocky shore; rock stacks/islets)
Land-use Agriculture (70%)

■ Birds

Species	Season	Year	Pop min	Pop max	Acc	Criteria
Oceanodroma leucorhoa Leach's Petrel	B	1994	22	22	A	C6

The site is important for breeding seabirds.

■ Protection status

National High **International** High
IBA partly or wholly overlaps with the following national designated areas. *Reserve:* Ramna Stacks and Gruney. *Site of Special Scientific Interest:* Ramna Stacks and Gruney. Overlaps with international designated areas: 11 ha of IBA covered by Special Protection Area (Ramna Stacks and Gruney, 11 ha).

■ Conservation issues

Threats Aquaculture/fisheries (B), Extraction industry (A)

The close proximity of the site to the Sullom Voe oil terminal makes the risk of oil pollution very high. Unsustainable fishing of sandeels *Ammodytes* poses a potential threat to seabirds. Part of the site is a RSPB reserve with a management plan.

Rhunahaorine Point B1i, C2, C3 229

Admin region Scotland
Coordinates 55°40′N 5°40′W
Altitude 0–10 m **Area** 326 ha

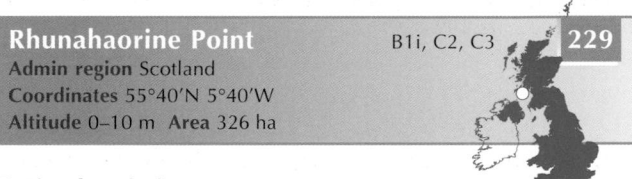

■ Site description

Rhunahaorine is one of the largest vegetated shingle forelands in Britain, with older ridges running south-west to north-east, and younger ridges running north-west to south-east. The site includes adjacent grasslands and associated coastal heath.

Habitats Scrub (heathland), Grassland, Wetland (shingle/stony beach), Artificial landscape (arable land)
Land-use Agriculture (95%)

■ Birds

Species	Season	Year	Pop min	Pop max	Acc	Criteria
[1] *Anser albifrons* White-fronted Goose	W	1994	995	995	A	B1i, C2, C3

1. Mean annual peak 1989–1994.

The site is also nationally important for summer moulting assemblages of *Mergus serrator* (400 birds, 1992, 4%). *Anser albifrons* are the *flavirostris* subspecies.

■ Protection status

National High **International** Partial
IBA partly or wholly overlaps with the following national designated areas. *Site of Special Scientific Interest:* Rhunahaorine Point. Overlaps with international designated areas: IBA overlaps with Special Protection Area (Kintyre Goose Roosts).

■ Conservation issues

Threats Afforestation (B), Agricultural intensification/expansion (B), Disturbance to birds (A), Infrastructure (B), Recreation/tourism (C)

Wintering wildfowl are vulnerable to disturbance, and nesting terns are disturbed by visitors to the nearby caravan park. The outcome of a proposal to build wind turbines at Largie Estate will be decided by a public inquiry.

Rinns, Islay

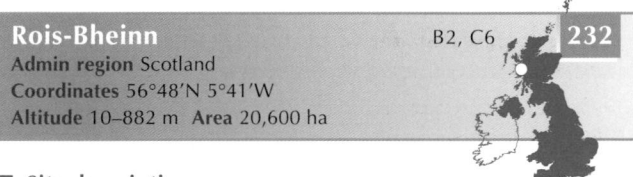

A4i, B1i, B2, C2, C3, C6   230

Admin region Scotland
Coordinates 55°46'N 6°24'W
Altitude 0–232 m   **Area** 12,084 ha

Site description

A mosaic of natural and semi-natural habitats, exposed to the prevailing south-westerly weather and experiencing an oceanic climate. The site consists of low hills running down to a rocky coastline. This area includes three sites that were treated as separate IBAs in the previous international IBA inventory (Grimmett and Jones 1989): 'Islay: Rinns' (former site GB090), 'Islay: Glac na Criche' (former site GB091) and 'Islay: Feur Lochain' (former site GB092).

Habitats Forest and woodland (mixed forest), Scrub (heathland), Grassland (humid grassland; machair), Wetland (standing fresh water; blanket bog), Rocky areas (sea cliff/rocky shore), Artificial landscape (arable land)
Land-use Agriculture (90%), Urban/industrial/transport (5%), Water management (5%)

Birds

Species	Season	Year	Pop min	Pop max	Acc	Criteria
¹ *Anser albifrons* White-fronted Goose	W	1997	2,590	2,590	A	B1i, C2, C3, C6
¹ *Branta leucopsis* Barnacle Goose	W	1997	3,640	3,640	A	A4i, B1i, B2, C2, C6
Pyrrhocorax pyrrhocorax Chough	R	1994	21	21	A	B2, C6

1. Mean seasonal peak 1994–1997.

The IBA supports breeding raptors and waders, and wintering geese which come from roosts in other Islay IBAs to feed in this area. *Anser albifrons* are the *flavirostris* subspecies, and *Branta leucopsis* are from the Greenland breeding population. The site is also nationally important for breeding *Anas crecca* (16 pairs, 1994, 1%), *Melanitta nigra* (20 pairs, 1995, 26%) and *Crex crex* (globally threatened: 6 pairs, 1995, 1%).

Protection status

National Partial   **International** Partial
IBA partly or wholly overlaps with the following national designated areas. *Reserves:* Loch Gruinart, Islay. *Sites of Special Scientific Interest:* Islay – Feur Lochain, Islay – Glac na Criche, Islay – Rinns of Islay. Overlaps with international designated areas: 9,407 ha of IBA covered by Special Protection Area (Rinns of Islay, 9,407 ha). 3,586 ha of IBA covered by Ramsar Site (Rinns of Islay, 3,586 ha).

Conservation issues

Threats Abandonment/reduction of land management (B), Afforestation (B), Agricultural intensification/expansion (B), Drainage (B), Recreation/tourism (B)

High-intensity agricultural management and recreational disturbance pose threats to the IBA.

River Spey – Insh marshes

A1, B1i, B2, B3, C1, C3   231

Admin region Scotland
Coordinates 57°05'N 4°00'W
Altitude 220–290 m   **Area** 1,540 ha

Site description

The Insh marshes form the largest single-unit flood-plain mire of the poor-fen type in Britain. They are also the most northerly, the site lying within the flat valley floor of the River Spey between Kincraig and Kingussie.

Habitats Grassland (humid grassland), Wetland (standing fresh water; river/stream; fen/transition mire/spring)

Land-use Agriculture (50%), Fisheries/aquaculture, Nature conservation/research (80%), Tourism/recreation

Birds

Species	Season	Year	Pop min	Pop max	Acc	Criteria
Cygnus cygnus Whooper Swan	W	1995	135	135	A	B3
Anser anser Greylag Goose	W	1995	1,120	1,120	A	B1i, C3
Loxia scotica Scottish Crossbill	W	1995	Uncommon		—	A1, B2, C1

The IBA supports diverse breeding and wintering bird communities, and is also nationally important for breeding *Anas penelope* (29 pairs, 1994, 10%), *Anas crecca* (84 pairs, 1994, 5%), *Anas acuta* (2 pairs, 1994, 5%) and *Bucephala clangula* (46 pairs, 1994, 42%). *Anser anser* are from the Icelandic breeding population.

Protection status

National Partial   **International** Partial
IBA partly or wholly overlaps with the following national designated areas. *Reserve:* Insh Marshes. *Sites of Special Scientific Interest:* Creag Dubh, River Spey – Insh Marshes. Overlaps with international designated areas: 1,159 ha of IBA covered by Special Protection Area (River Spey – Insh Marshes, 1,159 ha). 1,159 ha of IBA covered by Ramsar Site (River Spey – Insh Marshes, 1,159 ha).

Conservation issues

Threats Aquaculture/fisheries (U), Other (A), Recreation/tourism (U)

Loch Insh is vulnerable to disturbance from canoeists, water skiers and a commercial fishery, and bad water management elsewhere in the system ('Other' threat, above). Management plans exist for the RSPB Reserve and ongoing monitoring takes place.

Rois-Bheinn

B2, C6   232

Admin region Scotland
Coordinates 56°48'N 5°41'W
Altitude 10–882 m   **Area** 20,600 ha

Site description

This site comprises Loch Shiel, Claish Moss and a large upland block to the north-west. Habitats present include nutrient-poor lochs, raised mires, upland moorland, and small remnants of ancient semi-natural acidic oak *Quercus* forest along some of the loch sides and lower glens.

Habitats Forest and woodland (broadleaved deciduous forest), Scrub (heathland), Grassland, Wetland (standing fresh water; raised bog)
Land-use Agriculture, Fisheries/aquaculture, Forestry, Hunting

Birds

Species	Season	Year	Pop min	Pop max	Acc	Criteria
Aquila chrysaetos Golden Eagle	R	1992	8	8	A	B2, C6

The wet areas and lochs support breeding waterbirds and wintering wildfowl, whilst the upland blocks are important for breeding raptors and other species. The site is also nationally important for breeding *Gavia arctica* (3 pairs, 1996, 2%).

Protection status

National Partial   **International** Low
IBA partly or wholly overlaps with the following national designated areas. *National Nature Reserve:* Claish Moss. *Sites of Special Scientific Interest:* Claish Moss, Loch Moidart, Loch Shiel, Lochailort. Overlaps with international designated areas: 563 ha of IBA covered by Ramsar Site (Claish Moss, 563 ha).

Conservation issues

Threats Recreation/tourism (B)

Pleasure boats and angling cause disturbance to birds on Loch Shiel. Claish Moss National Nature Reserve and Loch Shiel are partly covered by management plans, and research is progressing into the fisheries present on the loch.

Rosehearty to Fraserburgh coast

C7 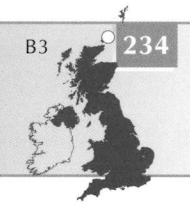 **233**

Admin region Scotland
Coordinates 57°41'N 2°03'W
Altitude 0–15 m **Area** 130 ha

■ Site description
An exposed north-facing rocky and sandy shoreline running west from the town of Fraserburgh. The IBA includes a narrow fringe of sand-dunes and saltmarsh.

Habitats Wetland (70%; mudflat/sandflat; saltmarsh; sand-dunes/sand beach; shingle/stony beach; coastal lagoon), Rocky areas (30%; sea cliff/rocky shore)
Land-use Not utilized (100%)

■ Birds

Species		Season	Year	Pop min	Pop max	Acc	Criteria
Calidris maritima	Purple Sandpiper	W	1995	120	120	A	C7
Arenaria interpres	Turnstone	W	1995	570	570	A	C7

The IBA is important for wintering waders.

■ Protection status
National Partial **International** None
IBA partly or wholly overlaps with the following national designated areas. *Site of Special Scientific Interest:* Rosehearty to Fraserburgh Coast.

■ Conservation issues

Threats Disturbance to birds (U), Filling-in of wetlands (U), Other (U)

Oil pollution and illegal dumping ('Other' threat, above) pose a threat to the IBA.

Rothiesholm peninsula, Stronsay

B3 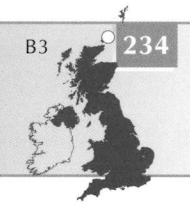 **234**

Admin region Scotland
Coordinates 59°05'N 2°40'W
Altitude 0–41 m **Area** 310 ha

■ Site description
A peninsula situated at the south-western end of the island of Stronsay, forming the western arm of the Bay of Holland.

Habitats Scrub (heathland), Grassland, Wetland (shingle/stony beach), Rocky areas (sea cliff/rocky shore)
Land-use Agriculture (100%)

■ Birds

Species		Season	Year	Pop min	Pop max	Acc	Criteria
Larus marinus	Great Black-backed Gull	B	1995	400	400	A	B3

The IBA holds important seabird colonies.

■ Protection status
National None **International** None

■ Conservation issues

Threats Agricultural intensification/expansion (B)

Rousay (Part)

C6  **235**

Admin region Scotland
Coordinates 59°09'N 3°02'W
Altitude 0–250 m **Area** 2,310 ha

■ Site description
This site comprises moorland and hilltop montane communities, and a number of lochs, including the moderately nutrient-rich Muckle Water.

Habitats Scrub (heathland), Grassland (alpine/subalpine/boreal grassland), Wetland (standing fresh water; blanket bog; fen/transition mire/spring)
Land-use Agriculture (50%), Not utilized (50%), Nature conservation/research

■ Birds

Species		Season	Year	Pop min	Pop max	Acc	Criteria
Sterna paradisaea	Arctic Tern	B	1995	925	925	A	C6

The IBA supports an important assemblage of breeding moorland birds, including *Stercorarius parasiticus* (142 birds, 1992, 4%).

■ Protection status
National High **International** None
IBA partly or wholly overlaps with the following national designated areas. *Reserve:* Trumland–Rousay. *Site of Special Scientific Interest:* Rousay.

■ Conservation issues

Threats Agricultural intensification/expansion (B), Extraction industry (B)

Monitoring of *Sterna paradisaea*, *Stercorarius parasiticus*, *Rissa tridactyla* and raptor breeding success is undertaken. Part of the IBA is a RSPB Reserve, for which a management plan exists. The site is a candidate SPA.

Rum

A4ii, A4iii, B1ii, B2, C3, C4 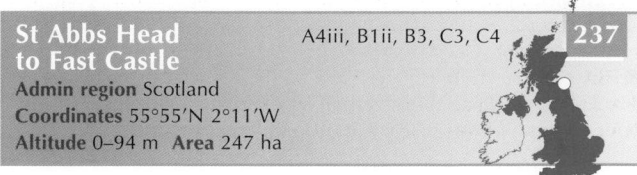 **236**

Admin region Scotland
Coordinates 56°59'N 6°19'W
Altitude 0–812 m **Area** 10,794 ha

■ Site description
An island consisting of mountainous terrain and contrasting rock types, which supports a variety of habitat-types.

Habitats Forest and woodland (broadleaved deciduous forest), Scrub (heathland), Grassland (steppe/dry calcareous grassland), Wetland (mudflat/sandflat; sand-dunes/sand beach), Rocky areas (sea cliff/rocky shore; rock stacks/islets)
Land-use Nature conservation/research (100%)

■ Birds

Species		Season	Year	Pop min	Pop max	Acc	Criteria
Puffinus puffinus	Manx Shearwater	B	1990	63,000	63,000	A	A4ii, B1ii, B2, C3

The IBA holds 66,200 pairs of breeding seabirds on a regular basis, and is also nationally important for breeding *Aquila chrysaetos* (4 pairs, 1992, 1%).

■ Protection status
National High **International** High
IBA partly or wholly overlaps with the following national designated areas. *National Nature Reserve:* Rum. *Site of Special Scientific Interest:* Rum. Overlaps with international designated areas: 10,794 ha of IBA covered by Special Protection Area (Rum, 10,794 ha).

■ Conservation issues

Threats Aquaculture/fisheries (C)

Fisheries in the waters around Rum pose some threat to seabirds. Various research and monitoring projects have been undertaken, including a long-term study of red deer *Cervus elaphus*. A management plan exists for the island.

St Abbs Head to Fast Castle

A4iii, B1ii, B3, C3, C4 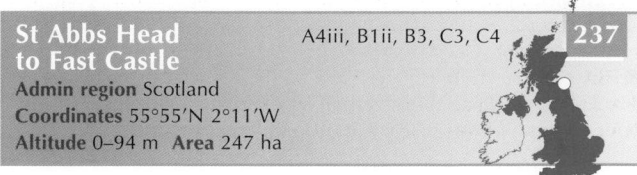 **237**

Admin region Scotland
Coordinates 55°55'N 2°11'W
Altitude 0–94 m **Area** 247 ha

■ Site description
Exposed cliffs and cliff-ledges, which extend for over 10 km along the Berwickshire coast.

Habitats Forest and woodland (1%; broadleaved deciduous forest), Scrub (5%; scrub), Wetland (5%; standing fresh water), Rocky areas (89%; sea cliff/rocky shore)
Land-use Agriculture (10%), Nature conservation/research (20%)

■ Birds

Species	Season	Year	Pop min	Pop max	Acc	Criteria
Phalacrocorax aristotelis Shag	B	1995	430	430	A	B3
Uria aalge Guillemot	B	1993	20,800	20,800	A	B1ii, C3
Alca torda Razorbill	B	1993	1,470	1,470	A	B3

The site holds 23,200 pairs of breeding seabirds and 21,600 pairs of breeding waterbirds on a regular basis. It is also nationally important for breeding *Phalacrocorax carbo* (305 pairs, 1989, 4%) and *Rissa tridactyla* (19,800 pairs, 1987–1995, 4%), and for wintering *Somateria mollissima* (1,210 birds, 1995–1996, 2%).

■ Protection status
National Partial **International** High
IBA partly or wholly overlaps with the following national designated areas. *National Nature Reserve:* St Abbs Head. *Sites of Special Scientific Interest:* Berwickshire Coast Intertidal, Coldingham Loch, St Abbs Head–Fast Castle. Overlaps with international designated areas: 247 ha of IBA covered by Special Protection Area (St Abbs Head to Fast Castle, 247 ha).

■ Conservation issues

Threats Aquaculture/fisheries (U)

Unsustainable fishing poses a potential threat to seabirds. Annual seabird monitoring is undertaken at the site.

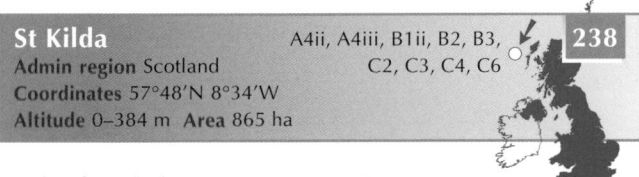

St Kilda A4ii, A4iii, B1ii, B2, B3, C2, C3, C4, C6 **238**
Admin region Scotland
Coordinates 57°48′N 8°34′W
Altitude 0–384 m **Area** 865 ha

■ Site description
A group of islands and smaller rocky islets with precipitous cliffs, situated about 70 km west of North Uist. The vegetation, influenced by sea spray, seabirds and livestock, consists of acidic grassland and submaritime heath.

Habitats Scrub (83%; heathland), Grassland (5%; humid grassland), Rocky areas (10%; rock stacks/islets), Artificial landscape (2%; other urban/industrial areas)
Land-use Military (2%), Nature conservation/research (98%)

■ Birds

Species	Season	Year	Pop min	Pop max	Acc	Criteria
Fulmarus glacialis Fulmar	B	1987	63,000	63,000	A	A4ii, B1ii, C3
Oceanodroma leucorhoa Leach's Petrel	B	1987	3,200	6,400	A	B1ii, B2, C2, C6
Sula bassana Gannet	B	1994	60,500	60,500	A	A4ii, B1ii, B2, C3
Stercorarius skua Great Skua	B	1994	145	—	A	A4ii, B1ii, B3, C3
Alca torda Razorbill	B	1987	2,560	2,560	A	B3
Fratercula arctica Puffin	B	1987	130,000	130,000	A	A4ii, B1ii, B2, C3

These islands are of outstanding importance for their breeding seabirds, holding 275,700 pairs on a regular basis. The IBA is also nationally important for breeding *Rissa tridactyla* (7,850 pairs, 1987, 2%) and *Uria aalge* (15,200 pairs, 1987, 2%). An endemic subspecies of *Troglodytes troglodytes* occurs on the islands.

■ Protection status
National High **International** High
IBA partly or wholly overlaps with the following national designated areas. *National Nature Reserve:* St Kilda. *Site of Special Scientific Interest:* St Kilda. Overlaps with international designated areas: 865 ha of IBA covered by Biosphere Reserve (St Kilda, 865 ha). 865 ha of IBA covered by Special Protection Area (St Kilda, 865 ha). 865 ha of IBA covered by World Heritage Site (St Kilda, 865 ha).

■ Conservation issues

Threats Aquaculture/fisheries (U), Consequences of animal/plant introductions (A), Disturbance to birds (U), Extraction industry (B), Other (B), Recreation/tourism (B)

Introduced rats *Rattus norvegicus* pose a threat. The islands are also vulnerable to disturbance from military activities and visitors, and to oil spills ('Other' threat, above). A management plan is in progress, and seabird research is carried out.

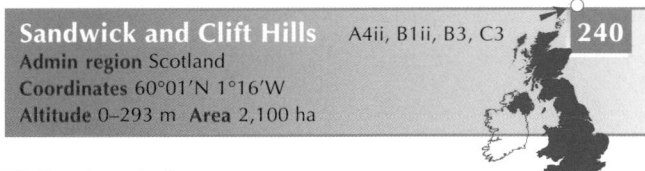

Sanda Island B3 **239**
Admin region Scotland
Coordinates 55°16′N 5°34′W
Altitude 0–123 m **Area** 210 ha

■ Site description
A grassy island with cliffs and associated islets.

Habitats Grassland, Rocky areas (sea cliff/rocky shore; rock stacks/islets)
Land-use Agriculture, Not utilized

■ Birds

Species	Season	Year	Pop min	Pop max	Acc	Criteria
Phalacrocorax aristotelis Shag	B	1995	690	690	A	B3
Alca torda Razorbill	B	1995	2,170	2,170	A	B3

The island is important for breeding seabirds.

■ Protection status
National Partial **International** None
IBA partly or wholly overlaps with the following national designated areas. *Sites of Special Scientific Interest:* Sanda Islands.

■ Conservation issues

Threats Consequences of animal/plant introductions (A)

Predation by American mink *Mustela vison* is a threat.

Sandwick and Clift Hills A4ii, B1ii, B3, C3 **240**
Admin region Scotland
Coordinates 60°01′N 1°16′W
Altitude 0–293 m **Area** 2,100 ha

■ Site description
A large block of moorland located to the south-west of Cunningsburgh.

Habitats Scrub (heathland), Grassland, Wetland (river/stream)
Land-use Agriculture (100%)

■ Birds

Species	Season	Year	Pop min	Pop max	Acc	Criteria
Stercorarius skua Great Skua	B	1992	155	155	A	A4ii, B1ii, B3, C3

The site is also nationally important for breeding *Numenius phaeopus* (6 pairs, 1992, 1%) and *Stercorarius parasiticus* (42 pairs, 1992, 1%).

■ Protection status
National None **International** None

■ Conservation issues

Threats Agricultural intensification/expansion (C), Aquaculture/fisheries (B)

Unsustainable fishing of sandeels *Ammodytes* poses a potential threat to seabirds.

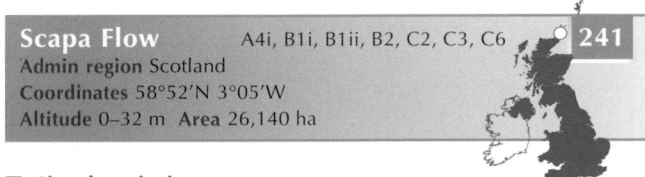

Scapa Flow A4i, B1i, B1ii, B2, C2, C3, C6 **241**
Admin region Scotland
Coordinates 58°52′N 3°05′W
Altitude 0–32 m **Area** 26,140 ha

■ Site description
A large sea area that separates the islands of Orkney Mainland, Hoy and South Ronaldsay. An oil terminal occupies part of the IBA ('Other' land-use, below).

Habitats Wetland (sand-dunes/sand beach; shingle/stony beach), Marine areas (open sea; sea inlet/coastal features), Rocky areas (sea cliff/rocky shore; rock stacks/islets)

Land-use Fisheries/aquaculture, Other

■ Birds

Species	Season	Year	Pop min	Pop max	Acc	Criteria
Gavia immer Great Northern Diver	W	1989	—	170	A	A4i, B1i, C2, C6
Podiceps auritus Slavonian Grebe	W	1995	50	50	A	B1i, C2
Phalacrocorax aristotelis Shag	W	1989	—	2,800	A	A4i, B1i, C2, C3
Melanitta fusca Velvet Scoter	W	1989	—	41	A	B2
Cepphus grylle Black Guillemot	B	1983	415	415	A	B1ii, B2

The IBA is important for wintering waterbirds, and is also nationally important for wintering *Podiceps grisegena* (5 birds, 1988–1989, 3%), *Somateria mollissima* (895 birds, 1988–1989, 1%), *Clangula hyemalis* (1,010 birds, 1988–1989, 4%) and *Mergus serrator* (425 birds, 1988–1989, 4%).

■ Protection status

National Partial **International** None

IBA partly or wholly overlaps with the following national designated areas. *Reserves:* Hobbister, North Hoy. *Sites of Special Scientific Interest:* Hoy, Lochs of Harray and Stenness, Muckle Head and Selwick, Stromness Heaths and Coast, Waulkmill.

■ Conservation issues

Threats Aquaculture/fisheries (U), Extraction industry (U)

Threats include fish-farming, the destruction of the seabed through shellfish dredging, and oil pollution. A repeat waterbird survey is scheduled for 1998/1999.

Shiant Isles   A4i, A4ii, A4iii, B1i, B1ii, B2, B3, C2, C3, C4   **242**
Admin region Scotland
Coordinates 57°53'N 6°21'W
Altitude 0–125 m **Area** 212 ha

■ Site description

Two large and two small islands with associated skerries, lying about 6 km west of Lewis in the Minch. The vegetation consists primarily of maritime heath and grassland.

Habitats Scrub (80%; heathland), Grassland (10%; humid grassland), Rocky areas (10%; sea cliff/rocky shore; rock stacks/islets)

Land-use Agriculture (90%), Not utilized (10%)

■ Birds

Species	Season	Year	Pop min	Pop max	Acc	Criteria
Phalacrocorax aristotelis Shag	B	1986	1,780	1,780	A	A4i, B1i, B3, C2, C3
[1] *Branta leucopsis* Barnacle Goose	W	1988	490	490	A	B1i, B2, C2
Alca torda Razorbill	B	1986	7,350	7,350	A	A4ii, B1ii, B3, C3
[2] *Fratercula arctica* Puffin	B	1970	76,000	76,000	A	A4ii, B1ii, B2, C3

1. Mean annual peak 1984–1988.
2. No recent counts.

The islands support 102,600 pairs of breeding seabirds on a regular basis, and are used by wintering and passage Greenland *Branta leucopsis*. They are also nationally important for breeding *Fulmarus glacialis* (6,800 pairs, 1986, 1%) and *Uria aalge* (12,300 pairs, 1986, 2%).

■ Protection status

National High **International** High

IBA partly or wholly overlaps with the following national designated areas. *Site of Special Scientific Interest:* Shiant Isles. Overlaps with international designated areas: 212 ha of IBA covered by Special Protection Area (Shiant Isles, 212 ha).

■ Conservation issues

Threats Aquaculture/fisheries (U), Consequences of animal/plant introductions (U), Extraction industry (A), Other (A)

The introduced population of black rats *Rattus rattus* may predate ground-nesting seabirds, and there are threats from oil spills ('Other' threat, above) and shipping.

Sounds around Wyre   A4i, B1i, C2, C6   **243**
Admin region Scotland
Coordinates 59°06'N 2°59'W
Altitude 0–18 m **Area** 4,800 ha

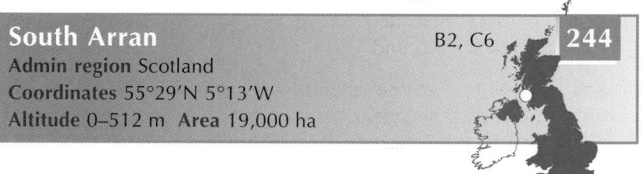

■ Site description

A large sea area comprising the sounds of Eynhallow, Gairsay, Rousay and Wyre. Human activities include marl extraction ('Other' land-use, below).

Habitats Wetland (sand-dunes/sand beach; shingle/stony beach), Marine areas (open sea; sea inlet/coastal features), Rocky areas (sea cliff/rocky shore; rock stacks/islets)

Land-use Fisheries/aquaculture, Other

■ Birds

Species	Season	Year	Pop min	Pop max	Acc	Criteria
Gavia immer Great Northern Diver	W	1990	—	100	A	A4i, B1i, C2, C6

The IBA is important for wintering divers, and is also nationally important for wintering *Somateria mollissima* (2,590 birds, 1989–1990, 3%) and *Clangula hyemalis* (2,160 birds, 1989–1990, 9%).

■ Protection status

National Partial **International** None

IBA partly or wholly overlaps with the following national designated areas. *Sites of Special Scientific Interest:* Eynhallow, Rousay.

■ Conservation issues

Threats Aquaculture/fisheries (U), Extraction industry (U)

Marl extraction poses a threat. A five-year licence has been granted to ascertain whether the process is sustainable.

South Arran   B2, C6   **244**
Admin region Scotland
Coordinates 55°29'N 5°13'W
Altitude 0–512 m **Area** 19,000 ha

■ Site description

A large upland area at the southern end of the Isle of Arran, located in the Outer Clyde estuary.

Habitats Scrub (heathland), Grassland, Rocky areas (sea cliff/rocky shore)

Land-use Agriculture (100%)

■ Birds

Species	Season	Year	Pop min	Pop max	Acc	Criteria
Circus cyaneus Hen Harrier	R	1995	—	19	A	B2, C6

The IBA is important for breeding raptors and other upland species.

■ Protection status

National Partial **International** None

IBA partly or wholly overlaps with the following national designated areas. *Sites of Special Scientific Interest:* Ard Bheinn, Benlister Glen, Gleann Dubh.

■ Conservation issues

Threats Afforestation (B), Agricultural intensification/expansion (U), Recreation/tourism (U)

There are proposals for further afforestation of this area, which is affected by overgrazing and disturbance from tourism and recreation. Raptor Study Group monitoring is carried out here.

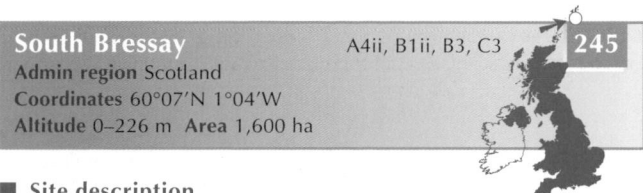

South Bressay   A4ii, B1ii, B3, C3   **245**
Admin region Scotland
Coordinates 60°07'N 1°04'W
Altitude 0–226 m Area 1,600 ha

■ Site description
The southern half of the island of Bressay, situated off the eastern coast of the Shetland Mainland.

Habitats Scrub (heathland), Grassland
Land-use Agriculture (100%)

■ Birds

Species	Season	Year	Pop min	Pop max	Acc	Criteria
Stercorarius skua Great Skua	B	1992	230	230	A	A4ii, B1ii, B3, C3

The site is also nationally important for breeding *Stercorarius parasiticus* (69 pairs, 1992, 2%).

■ Protection status
National None **International** None

■ Conservation issues

Threats Agricultural intensification/expansion (C), Aquaculture/fisheries (B)

Unsustainable fishing of sandeels *Ammodytes* poses a potential threat to seabirds.

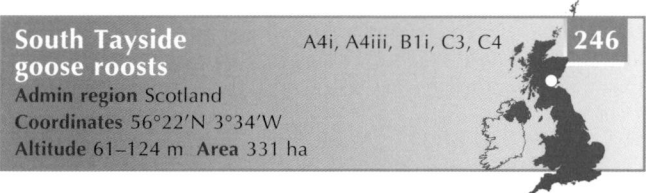

South Tayside goose roosts   A4i, A4iii, B1i, C3, C4   **246**
Admin region Scotland
Coordinates 56°22'N 3°34'W
Altitude 61–124 m Area 331 ha

■ Site description
A series of freshwater lochs and smaller water bodies with associated wetland habitats, including raised mire, base-rich flushes and fen. Ancient woodland notable for its lichen flora also occurs within the IBA. This area includes three sites that were treated as separate IBAs in the previous international IBA inventory (Grimmett and Jones 1989): 'Dupplin Lochs' (former site GB114), 'Drummond Lochs' (former site GB115) and 'Carsebreck and Rhynd Lochs' (former site GB116).

Habitats Forest and woodland (broadleaved deciduous forest), Wetland (standing fresh water; raised bog; water-fringe vegetation; fen/transition mire/spring)
Land-use Agriculture, Fisheries/aquaculture, Tourism/recreation, Water management

■ Birds

Species	Season	Year	Pop min	Pop max	Acc	Criteria
[1] *Anser brachyrhynchus* Pink-footed Goose	W	1994	47,000	47,000	A	A4i, B1i, C3
[1] *Anser anser* Greylag Goose	W	1994	4,340	4,340	A	A4i, B1i, C3

1. Mean annual peak 1989–1994.

The IBA is important as a roost for wintering geese, and holds 56,700 wintering waterbirds on a regular basis. *Anser anser* are from the Icelandic breeding population.

■ Protection status
National High **International** High
IBA partly or wholly overlaps with the following national designated areas. *Sites of Special Scientific Interest:* Carsebreck and Rhynd Lochs, Drummond Lochs, Dupplin Lakes. Overlaps with international designated areas: 331 ha of IBA covered by Special Protection Area (South Tayside Goose Roosts, 331 ha). 331 ha of IBA covered by Ramsar Site (South Tayside Goose Roosts, 331 ha).

■ Conservation issues

Threats Construction/impact of dyke/dam/barrage (U), Disturbance to birds (U)

Repairs to the dam at Carsebreck Loch have caused problems of water-level fluctuation and disturbance.

South Uist machair and lochs   A1, A4i, B1i, B2, B3, C1, C2, C3, C6   **247**
Admin region Scotland
Coordinates 57°19'N 7°20'W
Altitude 0–80 m Area 8,900 ha

■ Site description
A coastal strip of typical wet and dry machair, containing both large and small shallow lochs. This area includes four sites that were treated as separate IBAs in the previous international IBA inventory (Grimmett and Jones 1989): 'Bagh nam Foailean to Ardivachar' (former site GB010), 'Iochdair and Geirinish Machair and Loch Bee' (former site GB011), 'Na Meadhoinean Iar (including Loch Druidibeg)' (former site GB012) and 'Machair Lochs (including Lochs Hallan and Kilpheder), South Uist' (former site GB013).

Habitats Forest and woodland (1%; mixed forest), Scrub (10%; heathland), Grassland (50%; machair), Wetland (18%; tidal river/enclosed tidal water; standing fresh water; river/stream; water-fringe vegetation), Rocky areas (1%; inland sand-dunes), Artificial landscape (20%; highly improved reseeded grassland; arable land)
Land-use Agriculture (100%), Hunting (100%)

■ Birds

Species	Season	Year	Pop min	Pop max	Acc	Criteria
Cygnus cygnus Whooper Swan	W	1989	—	1,010	A	A4i, B1i, B3, C2, C6
Anser anser Greylag Goose	R	1995	30	30	A	B1i, C3
Porzana porzana Spotted Crake	B	1990	2	2	A	C6
Crex crex Corncrake	B	1995	52	52	A	A1, B2, C1, C2, C6
Haematopus ostralegus Oystercatcher	R	1995	615	615	A	B1i, C3
Charadrius hiaticula Ringed Plover	R	1995	465	465	A	B1i, C3
[1] *Charadrius hiaticula* Ringed Plover	W	1995	785	785	A	B1i, C3
Calidris alpina Dunlin	R	1995	405	405	A	B1i, C3
Tringa totanus Redshank	R	1995	545	545	A	B1i, B2, C3
[1] *Arenaria interpres* Turnstone	W	1995	850	850	A	A4i, B1i, C3
Sterna albifrons Little Tern	B	1991	32	32	A	C6

1. Mean count.

The IBA holds a rich assemblage of breeding and wintering birds. It is also nationally important for wintering *Calidris alba* (1,060 birds, 1993–1995, 5%) and *Calidris maritima* (310 birds, 1993–1995, 1%). *Anser anser* are from the Hebridean population.

■ Protection status
National Partial **International** Partial
IBA partly or wholly overlaps with the following national designated areas. *National Nature Reserve:* Loch Druidibeg. *Sites of Special Scientific Interest:* Bornish and Ormiclate Machairs, Howmore Estuary, Lochs Roag and Fada, Loch Bee, Loch Bee Machair, Loch Druidibeg, Loch Hallan. Overlaps with international designated areas: 1,677 ha of IBA covered by Biosphere Reserve (Loch Druidibeg, 1,677 ha). 3,352 ha of IBA covered by Special Protection Area (South Uist Machair and Lochs, 3,352 ha). 3,352 ha of IBA covered by Ramsar Site (South Uist Machair and Lochs, 3,352 ha).

■ Conservation issues

Threats Agricultural intensification/expansion (B), Consequences of animal/plant introductions (A), Drainage (B), Extraction industry (C), Other (A)

Main threats are introduced American mink *Mustela vison*, polecats *M. putorius*, ferrets *M. putorius furo* and hedgehogs *Erinaceus europaeus*, and oil spills ('Other' threat, above). *Crex crex* monitoring and research into the causes of declines in wader numbers are taking place. A rabbit *Oryctolagus cuniculus* exclusion zone of c.700 ha has been set up with a view to controlling their numbers. Most of the site is a candidate SAC, while much of the area outside the existing SPA is a candidate SPA.

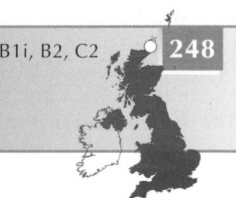

South Walls and Switha   B1i, B2, C2   **248**
Admin region Scotland
Coordinates 58°47'N 3°06'W
Altitude 0–57 m Area 260 ha

■ Site description
This site comprises three separate areas on the island of South Walls, in addition to the much smaller island of Switha.

Habitats Scrub (heathland), Grassland, Rocky areas (sea cliff/rocky shore)
Land-use Agriculture (100%)

■ Birds

Species	Season	Year	Pop min	Pop max	Acc	Criteria
Branta leucopsis Barnacle Goose	W	1995	1,100	1,100	A	B1i, B2, C2

The area is important for breeding seabirds and waders, and wintering geese. Breeding species of global conservation concern that do not meet IBA criteria: *Crex crex*. *Branta leucopsis* are from the Greenland breeding population.

■ Protection status
National None **International** None

■ Conservation issues

Threats Agricultural intensification/expansion (U)

SNH run a refuge scheme for the geese, and contract a researcher to monitor *Branta leucopsis* utilization of the site.

South Westray coast
C7 **249**
Admin region Scotland
Coordinates 59°16′N 2°56′W
Altitude 0–10 m **Area** 530 ha

■ Site description
A low-lying rocky coastline interspersed with sandy bays.

Habitats Wetland (sand-dunes/sand beach; shingle/stony beach), Rocky areas (sea cliff/rocky shore)
Land-use Not utilized (100%)

■ Birds

Species	Season	Year	Pop min	Pop max	Acc	Criteria
Calidris alba Sanderling	W	1994	—	27	A	C7
Calidris maritima Purple Sandpiper	W	1994	—	415	A	C7

The IBA is important for wintering waders.

■ Protection status
National None **International** None

■ Conservation issues

Threats Disturbance to birds (C), Extraction industry (U), Infrastructure (U)

Sand extraction at the site has recently been proposed.

South-eastern Stronsay
B2 **250**
Admin region Scotland
Coordinates 59°04′N 2°32′W
Altitude 0–23 m **Area** 110 ha

■ Site description
The IBA comprises a low-lying rocky shoreline, interspersed with sandy bays.

Habitats Wetland (sand-dunes/sand beach), Rocky areas (sea cliff/rocky shore)
Land-use Not utilized (100%)

■ Birds

Species	Season	Year	Pop min	Pop max	Acc	Criteria
Cepphus grylle Black Guillemot	B	1983	165	165	A	B2

The IBA is important for breeding seabirds and wintering waders and wildfowl. Breeding species of global conservation concern that do not meet IBA criteria: *Crex crex*.

■ Protection status
National None **International** None

■ Conservation issues

Threats Disturbance to birds (C), Other (C)

The coastline is vulnerable to disturbance and oil pollution ('Other' threat, above).

Stornoway to Back, Lewis
A1, B2, C1 **251**
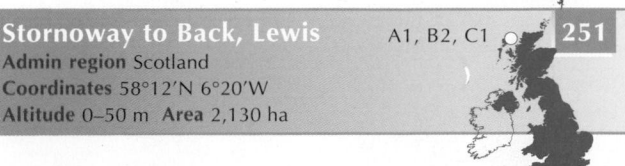
Admin region Scotland
Coordinates 58°12′N 6°20′W
Altitude 0–50 m **Area** 2,130 ha

■ Site description
An area of agricultural land situated to the east and north of Stornoway.

Habitats Forest and woodland, Scrub (5%; heathland), Grassland (80%), Artificial landscape (3%; arable land)
Land-use Agriculture (80%), Military (5%), Urban/industrial/transport (15%)

■ Birds

Species	Season	Year	Pop min	Pop max	Acc	Criteria
Crex crex Corncrake	B	1995	27	27	A	A1, B2, C1

The site is also nationally important for breeding *Sterna paradisaea* (570 pairs, 1990, 1%).

■ Protection status
National Partial **International** None
IBA partly or wholly overlaps with the following national designated areas. *Sites of Special Scientific Interest:* Gress Saltings, Stornoway Castle Woodlands, Tong Saltings.

■ Conservation issues

Threats Agricultural intensification/expansion (U)

Sule Skerry and Sule Stack
A4ii, A4iii, B1ii, B2, B3, C2, C3, C4, C6 **252**
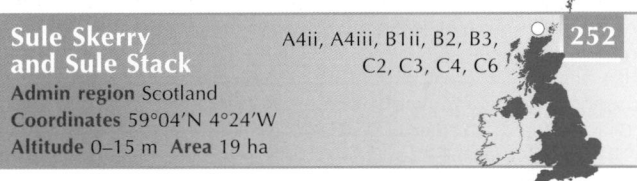
Admin region Scotland
Coordinates 59°04′N 4°24′W
Altitude 0–15 m **Area** 19 ha

■ Site description
Sule Skerry lies about 60 km west of Orkney Mainland, with Sule Stack a further 8 km to the south-west. The vegetation on Sule Skerry is limited by sea spray and bird activity, and is dominated by *Tripleurospermum inodorum* during the summer. A lighthouse is present ('Other' land-use, below). Sule Stack is a high, bare rock stack, with no vascular plants.

Habitats Rocky areas (100%; rock stacks/islets)
Land-use Not utilized (95%), Other (5%)

■ Birds

Species	Season	Year	Pop min	Pop max	Acc	Criteria
Hydrobates pelagicus Storm Petrel	B	1986	1,000	10,000	A	A4ii, B1ii, B2, C2, C6
Sula bassana Gannet	B	1994	4,890	4,890	A	A4ii, B1ii, B2, C3
Phalacrocorax aristotelis Shag	B	1993	700	700	A	B3
Fratercula arctica Puffin	B	1993	43,400	43,400	A	B1ii, B2, C3

The site holds 63,800 pairs of breeding seabirds on a regular basis, and is also nationally important for breeding *Uria aalge* (9,600 pairs, 1993, 1%).

■ Protection status
National High **International** High
IBA partly or wholly overlaps with the following national designated areas. *Sites of Special Scientific Interest:* Sule Skerry, Sule Stack. Overlaps with international designated areas: 19 ha of IBA covered by Special Protection Area (Sule Skerry and Sule Stack, 19 ha).

■ Conservation issues

Threats Extraction industry (U)

Oil pollution is a threat. Attempts are being made to make the surrounding sea area a Marine Environment High Risk Area (MEHRA). A ringing group regularly visit Sule Skerry to ring seabirds, especially *Fratercula arctica*, and to census breeding species.

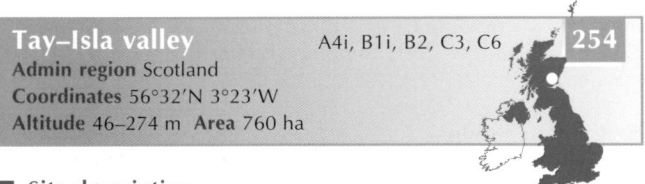

Sumburgh Head 253
Admin region Scotland
Coordinates 59°51′N 1°16′W
Altitude 0–80 m **Area** 39 ha
C7

■ Site description
The IBA comprises boulder-strewn beaches and cliffs along the east side of Sumburgh Head, the most southerly tip of the Shetland mainland.

Habitats Grassland (80%), Wetland (shingle/stony beach), Rocky areas (sea cliff/rocky shore)
Land-use Agriculture (80%), Nature conservation/research, Tourism/recreation

■ Birds
The IBA is important for its colonies of breeding seabirds.

■ Protection status
National High **International** High
IBA partly or wholly overlaps with the following national designated areas. *Reserve:* Sumburgh Head. *Site of Special Scientific Interest:* Sumburgh Head. Overlaps with international designated areas: 39 ha of IBA covered by Special Protection Area (Sumburgh Head, 39 ha).

■ Conservation issues

Threats Aquaculture/fisheries (B)

Unsustainable fishing of sandeels *Ammodytes* poses a potential threat to seabirds. The site is a RSPB reserve, and has a management plan.

Tay–Isla valley 254
Admin region Scotland
Coordinates 56°32′N 3°23′W
Altitude 46–274 m **Area** 760 ha
A4i, B1i, B2, C3, C6

■ Site description
The IBA covers the confluence of the Tay and Isla rivers, about 15 km north of Perth. The valley floors in this area support a complex of wetland habitats, including shallow lochs, rivers, pastures and some especially diverse marginal fens. Unusual vegetation-types found along the River Tay include unimproved pasture and riverine shingle-beds.

Habitats Grassland (humid grassland; mesophile grassland), Wetland (standing fresh water; river/stream; fen/transition mire/spring)
Land-use Agriculture, Fisheries/aquaculture (100%), Nature conservation/research (10%)

■ Birds

Species	Season	Year	Pop min	Pop max	Acc	Criteria
¹ *Anser anser* Greylag Goose	W	1994	5,100	5,100	A	A4i, B1i, C3

1. Mean annual peak 1989–1994.

The site is important for breeding raptors and wintering waterbirds. *Anser anser* are from the Icelandic breeding population.

■ Protection status
National High **International** None
IBA partly or wholly overlaps with the following national designated areas. *Sites of Special Scientific Interest:* Cardney Wood, Den of Riechip, Fungarth Juniper Wood, Hare Myre, Monk Myre and Stormont Loch, Lochs Clunie and Marlee, Lochs of Butterstone, Craiglush and Lowes, Meikleour Area.

■ Conservation issues

Threats Agricultural intensification/expansion (U)

The site is a candidate SPA.

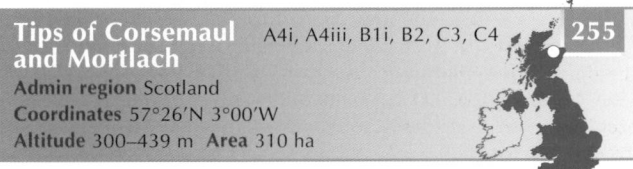

Tips of Corsemaul and Mortlach 255
Admin region Scotland
Coordinates 57°26′N 3°00′W
Altitude 300–439 m **Area** 310 ha
A4i, A4iii, B1i, B2, C3, C4

■ Site description
Three upland areas to the east and south-east of Dufftown.

Habitats Scrub (60%; heathland), Grassland (40%)
Land-use Agriculture (30%)

■ Birds

Species	Season	Year	Pop min	Pop max	Acc	Criteria
Larus canus Common Gull	B	1995	—	22,300	A	A4i, B1i, B2, C3

The site holds 22,500 pairs of breeding waterbirds on a regular basis.

■ Protection status
National None **International** None

■ Conservation issues

Threats Agricultural intensification/expansion (U), Burning of vegetation (U)

Possible threats are posed by sheep-grazing and moor-burning. Joint Nature Conservation Committee Seabird Colony Register monitoring is carried out here.

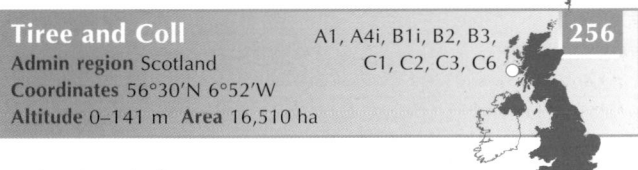

Tiree and Coll 256
Admin region Scotland
Coordinates 56°30′N 6°52′W
Altitude 0–141 m **Area** 16,510 ha
A1, A4i, B1i, B2, B3, C1, C2, C3, C6

■ Site description
Two large Inner Hebridean islands and associated islets. Coll is a whale-backed island, with many lochs, while Tiree is a low, flat island overlooked by three hills. Unlike Coll, most of the peat deposits on Tiree have been cut away in the past. Extensive sand-dune, machair, moorland and grassland complexes are present.

Habitats Scrub (heathland), Grassland (humid grassland; mesophile grassland; machair), Wetland (sand-dunes/sand beach; shingle/stony beach; standing fresh water; river/stream; blanket bog; fen/transition mire/spring), Rocky areas (sea cliff/rocky shore; scree/boulders; inland cliff), Artificial landscape (highly improved reseeded grassland; arable land)
Land-use Agriculture, Nature conservation/research, Tourism/recreation

■ Birds

Species	Season	Year	Pop min	Pop max	Acc	Criteria
¹ *Cygnus cygnus* Whooper Swan	W	1989	145	145	A	B3
Anser albifrons White-fronted Goose	W	1996	2,110	2,110	A	B1i, C2, C3, C6
Anser anser Greylag Goose	R	1996	90	—	A	B1i, C3
¹ *Anser anser* Greylag Goose	W	1989	380	380	A	B1i, C3
Branta leucopsis Barnacle Goose	W	1996	2,010	2,010	A	B1i, B2, C2
Crex crex Corncrake	B	1996	155	155	A	A1, B2, C1, C2, C6
¹ *Charadrius hiaticula* Ringed Plover	W	1989	1,030	1,030	A	B1i, C3
¹ *Arenaria interpres* Turnstone	W	1989	1,040	1,040	A	A4i, B1i, C3
Sterna albifrons Little Tern	B	1995	—	70	A	B2, C6

1. Mean count.

This IBA is of major international importance for a range of birds of wetland and low intensity agricultural land. It is also nationally important for breeding *Gavia stellata* (10 pairs, 1993–1996, 1%), *Anas acuta* (2 pairs, 1994, 5%), *Charadrius hiaticula* (100 pairs, 1994, 1%), *Stercorarius parasiticus* (49 pairs, 1987, 2%), *Sterna hirundo* (185 pairs, 1995, 1%) and *Sterna paradisaea* (465 pairs, 1995, 1%), as well as for wintering *Calidris alba* (380 birds, 1989, 2%). *Anser albifrons* are the *flavirostris* subspecies, *A. anser* are from the Hebridean population, and *Branta leucopsis* are from the Greenland breeding population.

■ Protection status

National Partial **International** Partial

IBA partly or wholly overlaps with the following national designated areas. *Reserves:* Coll, The Reef. *Sites of Special Scientific Interest:* An Fhaodhail and the Reef, Ceann a'Mhara, Crossapol and Gunna, Hough Bay and Balevullin Machair, North East Coll Lochs and Moors, North-east Coll Lochs and Moors, Totamore Dunes. Overlaps with international designated areas: 2,321 ha of IBA covered by Special Protection Area (Coll, 2,321 ha). 2,208 ha of IBA covered by Ramsar Site (Coll, 2,208 ha).

■ Conservation issues

Threats Agricultural intensification/expansion (B), Extraction industry (U), Infrastructure (U), Recreation/tourism (B)

Threats include recreational and tourism disturbance, and wind-power development. Crofting rights apply to most of Tiree, and a RSPB management plan exists for Coll Reserve and for The Reef, Tiree. Tiree wetlands are a candidate SPA.

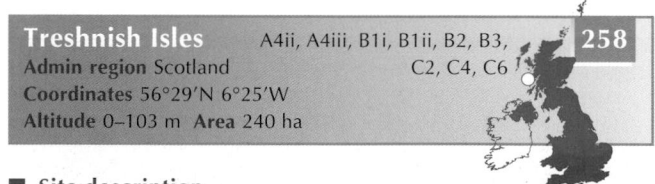

Tolsta Head, Lewis
B3   257

Admin region Scotland
Coordinates 58°20'N 6°09'W
Altitude 0–73 m **Area** 150 ha

■ Site description

A headland and associated stacks forming the easternmost point of the Isle of Lewis.

Habitats Scrub (90%; heathland), Grassland, Rocky areas (10%; sea cliff/rocky shore)
Land-use Agriculture (90%), Not utilized (10%)

■ Birds

Species	Season	Year	Pop min	Pop max	Acc	Criteria
Larus marinus Great Black-backed Gull	B	1988	260	260	A	B3

The IBA is important for breeding seabirds and gulls.

■ Protection status

National None **International** None

■ Conservation issues

No serious threats are known at the site.

Treshnish Isles
A4ii, A4iii, B1i, B1ii, B2, B3,
C2, C4, C6   258

Admin region Scotland
Coordinates 56°29'N 6°25'W
Altitude 0–103 m **Area** 240 ha

■ Site description

A string of rocky islands and skerries with cliffs and screes, but each with its own character. There is a strong maritime influence on the grassland and heathland vegetation communities.

Habitats Scrub (heathland), Grassland, Rocky areas (sea cliff/rocky shore; scree/boulders)
Land-use Not utilized (100%)

■ Birds

Species	Season	Year	Pop min	Pop max	Acc	Criteria
Hydrobates pelagicus Storm Petrel	B	1996	5,050	5,050	A	A4ii,B1ii,B2,C2,C6
[1] *Branta leucopsis* Barnacle Goose	W	1988	565	565	A	B1i, B2, C2
Larus marinus Great Black-backed Gull	B	1993	265	—	A	B3

1. Mean annual peak 1984–1988.

The islands are important for breeding seabirds, supporting 16,900 pairs on a regular basis. The IBA is also nationally important for breeding *Uria aalge* (8,650 pairs, 1993, 1%). Breeding species of global conservation concern that do not meet IBA criteria: *Crex crex* (at

least 2 pairs). *Branta leucopsis* are from the Greenland breeding population.

■ Protection status

National High **International** High

IBA partly or wholly overlaps with the following national designated areas. *Site of Special Scientific Interest:* Treshnish Isles. Overlaps with international designated areas: 240 ha of IBA covered by Special Protection Area (Treshnish Isles, 240 ha).

■ Conservation issues

Threats Recreation/tourism (B)

The site is vulnerable to disturbance from the increasing numbers of uncontrolled visitors landed on Lunga by commercial operators during the summer.

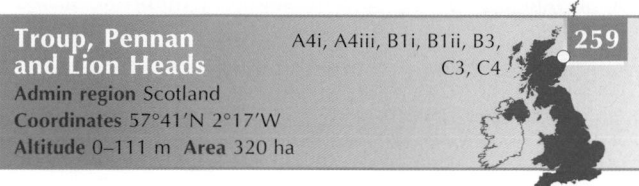

Troup, Pennan and Lion Heads
A4i, A4iii, B1i, B1ii, B3, C3, C4   259

Admin region Scotland
Coordinates 57°41'N 2°17'W
Altitude 0–111 m **Area** 320 ha

■ Site description

A stretch of low cliffs and small areas of maritime grassland, heathland and herb-rich grasslands and flushes situated along the north Buchan coast.

Habitats Scrub (2%; scrub; heathland), Grassland (6%), Wetland (2%; shingle/stony beach), Rocky areas (90%; sea cliff/rocky shore)
Land-use Not utilized (100%)

■ Birds

Species	Season	Year	Pop min	Pop max	Acc	Criteria
Rissa tridactyla Kittiwake	B	1995	31,700	31,700	A	A4i, B1i, C3
Uria aalge Guillemot	B	1995	29,900	29,900	A	B1ii, C3
Alca torda Razorbill	B	1995	3,220	3,220	A	B3

The site holds 38,400 pairs of breeding seabirds and 36,100 pairs of breeding waterbirds on a regular basis. It is also nationally important for breeding *Larus argentatus* (4,200 pairs, 1995, 2%), and for one of only two *Sula bassana* breeding colonies on the UK mainland.

■ Protection status

National Partial **International** Partial

IBA partly or wholly overlaps with the following national designated areas. *Site of Special Scientific Interest:* Gamrie and Pennan Coast. Overlaps with international designated areas: 174 ha of IBA covered by Special Protection Area (Troup, Pennan and Lion Heads, 174 ha).

■ Conservation issues

Threats Disturbance to birds (C), Other (B)

Oil pollution is a potential threat ('Other' threat, above). Monitoring for the Joint Nature Conservation Committee Seabird Colony Register is carried out here.

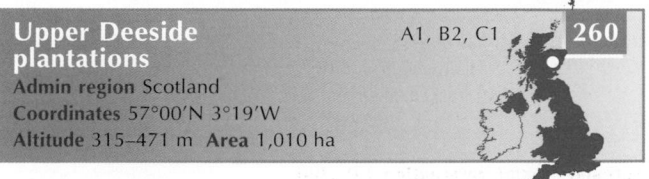

Upper Deeside plantations
A1, B2, C1   260

Admin region Scotland
Coordinates 57°00'N 3°19'W
Altitude 315–471 m **Area** 1,010 ha

■ Site description

Valley side, covered with coniferous forest, situated to the north of the River Dee at Braemar opposite the Ballochbuie forest.

Habitats Forest and woodland (5%; broadleaved deciduous forest), Artificial landscape (95%; forestry plantation)
Land-use Forestry (80%)

■ Birds

Species	Season	Year	Pop min	Pop max	Acc	Criteria
Loxia scotica Scottish Crossbill	R	1996	Frequent		—	A1, B2, C1

Tetrao urogallus and *T. tetrix* are present in low numbers, and *Falco peregrinus* and waders also breed.

■ Protection status
National Partial **International** None
IBA partly or wholly overlaps with the following national designated areas. *Site of Special Scientific Interest:* Craig Leek.

■ Conservation issues

Threats Forest grazing (U), Intensified forest management (C)

Threats include inappropriate forestry practices and deer grazing.

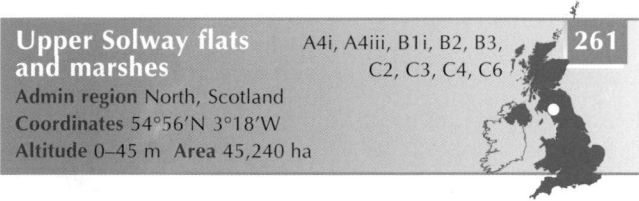

Upper Solway flats and marshes   A4i, A4iii, B1i, B2, B3, C2, C3, C4, C6   **261**
Admin region North, Scotland
Coordinates 54°56′N 3°18′W
Altitude 0–45 m **Area** 45,240 ha

■ Site description
One of the largest and most important areas of continuous intertidal habitat in Britain. The system is a dynamic one, with shifting channels undergoing phases of erosion and accretion.

Habitats Grassland (5%; humid grassland), Wetland (85%; tidal river/enclosed tidal water; mudflat/sandflat; saltmarsh), Artificial landscape (10%; highly improved reseeded grassland; arable land)
Land-use Agriculture (10%), Fisheries/aquaculture (80%), Nature conservation/research

■ Birds

Species	Season	Year	Pop min	Pop max	Acc	Criteria
Cygnus cygnus Whooper Swan	W	1995	115	115	A	B3
Anser brachyrhynchus Pink-footed Goose	W	1995	10,800	10,800	A	A4i, B1i, C3
Branta leucopsis Barnacle Goose	W	1995	12,700	12,700	A	A4i, B1i, B2, C2, C6
Anas acuta Pintail	W	1995	1,890	1,890	A	B1i, C3
Aythya marila Scaup	W	1995	2,210	2,210	A	B2
Haematopus ostralegus Oystercatcher	W	1995	36,800	36,800	A	A4i, B1i, C3
Haematopus ostralegus Oystercatcher	P	1995	35,200	35,200	A	A4i, B1i, C3
Charadrius hiaticula Ringed Plover	P	1995	1,080	1,080	A	B1i, C3
Pluvialis apricaria Golden Plover	W	1995	5,550	5,550	A	C6
Pluvialis apricaria Golden Plover	P	1995	4,190	4,190	A	C6
Calidris canutus Knot	W	1995	13,200	13,200	A	A4i, B1i, B2, C3
Calidris canutus Knot	P	1995	4,350	4,350	A	B1i, C3
Calidris alpina Dunlin	W	1995	14,800	14,800	A	B1i, B2, C3
Limosa lapponica Bar-tailed Godwit	W	1995	2,550	2,550	A	A4i, B1i, B2, C2, C6
Limosa lapponica Bar-tailed Godwit	P	1995	1,690	1,690	A	A4i, B1i, C2, C6
Numenius arquata Curlew	W	1995	6,250	6,250	A	A4i, B1i, B2, C3
Numenius arquata Curlew	P	1995	5,250	5,250	A	A4i, B1i, C3
Tringa totanus Redshank	W	1995	2,790	2,790	A	B1i, C3
Tringa totanus Redshank	P	1995	3,250	3,250	A	A4i, B1i, C3
[1] *Larus fuscus* Lesser Black-backed Gull	B	1991	2,000	—	A	A4i, B1i, B3, C3

1. On Rockcliffe marsh.

The IBA is important for wintering wildfowl and waders, supporting 127,800 wintering and 70,900 passage waterbirds on a regular basis. It is also nationally important for wintering *Phalacrocorax carbo* (465 birds, 3%), *Tadorna tadorna* (1,850 birds, 2%), *Charadrius hiaticula* (385 birds, 1%), *Pluvialis squatarola* (940 birds, 2%) and *Calidris alba* (255 birds, 1%), and for passage *Pluvialis squatarola* (740 birds, 2%), *Calidris alba* (590 birds, 3%) and *Limosa limosa* (190 birds, 2%). *Branta leucopsis* are from the Svalbard breeding population.

■ Protection status
National Partial **International** Partial
IBA partly or wholly overlaps with the following national designated areas. *National Nature Reserve:* Caerlaverock. *Reserves:* Campfield Marsh, Drum Burn, Mersehead, Rockcliffe Marsh Reserve, Southwick. *Sites of Special Scientific Interest:* Bowness Common, Finglandrigg Woods, Glasson Moss, Kirkconnell Flow, Longbridge Muir, Rockcliffe Marsh, Royal Ordnance, Powfoot, Southerness Coast, Upper Solway Flats and Marshes. Overlaps with international

designated areas: 29,951 ha of IBA covered by Special Protection Area (Upper Solway Flats and Marshes, 29,951 ha). 29,951 ha of IBA covered by Ramsar Site (Upper Solway Flats and Marshes, 29,951 ha).

■ Conservation issues

Threats Aquaculture/fisheries (A), Construction/impact of dyke/dam/barrage (A), Disturbance to birds (C), Extraction industry (U), Industrialization/urbanization (U), Infrastructure (U), Natural events (U), Other (B), Recreation/tourism (C)

The main threat is posed by shell-fisheries. Additional threats include an upgraded nuclear power station, a proposed tidal barrage, the M6 motorway extension, sea-level rise leading to erosion, flooding and habitat loss, military activity ('Other' threat), sewage/toxic waste pollution, oil and gas exploration, and illegal wildfowling. The Solway Partnership is part of SNH's Firths initiative, and is enabling moves towards a sustainable management strategy for the area. Habitat management initiatives exist on many sites, including schemes for *Branta leucopsis*, and there are many reserve holdings.

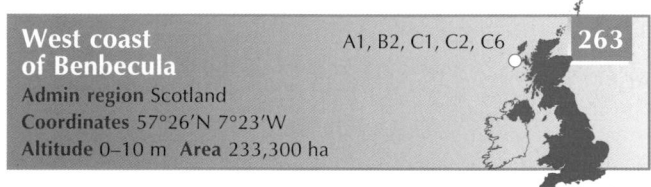

West Burrafirth   C6   **262**
Admin region Scotland
Coordinates 60°16′N 1°30′W
Altitude 0–106 m **Area** 3,910 ha

■ Site description
Blanket bog and heather moorland, with many lochs and several small areas of upland mire.

Habitats Scrub (heathland), Grassland, Wetland (standing fresh water; blanket bog; fen/transition mire/spring)
Land-use Agriculture (100%)

■ Birds

Species	Season	Year	Pop min	Pop max	Acc	Criteria
Gavia stellata Red-throated Diver	B	1994	17	17	A	C6

The site supports an assemblage of breeding moorland birds, and is also nationally important for breeding *Numenius phaeopus* (42 pairs, 1992, 8%).

■ Protection status
National None **International** None

■ Conservation issues

Threats Agricultural intensification/expansion (B)

The site would be vulnerable to any agricultural intensification.

West coast of Benbecula   A1, B2, C1, C2, C6   **263**
Admin region Scotland
Coordinates 57°26′N 7°23′W
Altitude 0–10 m **Area** 233,300 ha

■ Site description
The IBA includes machair, lochs and shoreline habitats on the island of Benbecula.

Habitats Scrub (heathland), Grassland (humid grassland; machair), Wetland (mudflat/sandflat; sand-dunes/sand beach; shingle/stony beach; standing fresh water), Rocky areas (sea cliff/rocky shore)
Land-use Agriculture (100%), Hunting (100%)

■ Birds

Species	Season	Year	Pop min	Pop max	Acc	Criteria
[1] *Crex crex* Corncrake	B	1997	45	45	A	A1, B2, C1, C2, C6
Limosa lapponica Bar-tailed Godwit	W	1991	675	675	A	B2
Phalaropus lobatus Red-necked Phalarope	B	1995	2	2	A	C6

1. Calling males.

Both *Charadrius hiaticula* (390 birds, 1991–1996, >1%) and *Podiceps auritus* (4 birds, 1%) winter in nationally important numbers, whilst *Calidris alba* (350 birds, 1991–1996, >1%) stop over on passage.

■ Protection status
National Partial **International** None
IBA partly or wholly overlaps with the following national designated areas. *Site of Special Scientific Interest:* West Benbecula Lochs.

■ Conservation issues

> **Threats** Consequences of animal/plant introductions (A), Drainage (C), Extraction industry (B)

Threats include predation by introduced American mink *Mustela vison*, polecats *M. putorius*, ferrets *M. putorius furo* and hedgehogs *Erinaceus europaeus*, and oil spills and pollution. Ongoing monitoring of *Crex crex*. The site is a candidate SPA.

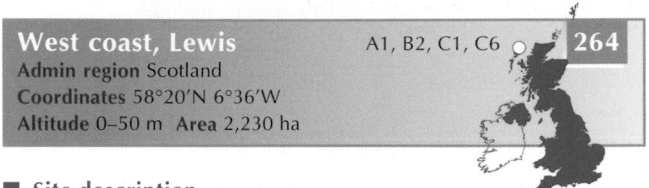

West coast, Lewis A1, B2, C1, C6 264
Admin region Scotland
Coordinates 58°20′N 6°36′W
Altitude 0–50 m **Area** 2,230 ha

■ Site description
Area of agricultural land on the north-west coast of the Isle of Lewis.

> **Habitats** Forest and woodland, Scrub (10%; heathland), Grassland (80%), Wetland (river/stream), Artificial landscape (5%; arable land)
> **Land-use** Agriculture (100%)

■ Birds

Species	Season	Year	Pop min	Pop max	Acc	Criteria
Crex crex Corncrake	B	1995	43	43	A	A1, B2, C1, C6

The IBA is also important for breeding waders and other upland species.

■ Protection status
National Partial **International** None
IBA partly or wholly overlaps with the following national designated areas. *Sites of Special Scientific Interest:* Loch Stiapavat, Port of Ness.

■ Conservation issues

> **Threats** Agricultural intensification/expansion (U)

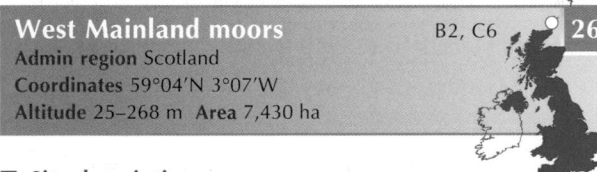

West Mainland moors B2, C6 265
Admin region Scotland
Coordinates 59°04′N 3°07′W
Altitude 25–268 m **Area** 7,430 ha

■ Site description
Three blocks of moorland situated on the Orkney Mainland, cut by numerous dales containing small burns. Human activities include domestic peat extraction ('Other' land-use, below). This area includes two sites that were treated as separate IBAs in the previous international IBA inventory (Grimmett and Jones 1989): 'West Mainland Moors' (former site GB059) and 'Orphir and Stenness Hills' (former site GB061), and one site that was treated as a separate IBA in the UK national IBA inventory (Pritchard *et al.* 1992): 'Keelylang' (former site 270A).

> **Habitats** Scrub (scrub; heathland), Grassland (humid grassland), Wetland (standing fresh water; river/stream; blanket bog)
> **Land-use** Agriculture (60%), Nature conservation/research, Not utilized (35%), Other (5%)

■ Birds

Species	Season	Year	Pop min	Pop max	Acc	Criteria
Gavia stellata Red-throated Diver	B	1994	16	16	A	C6
Circus cyaneus Hen Harrier	R	1996	23	23	A	B2, C6
Falco columbarius Merlin	R	1996	10	10	A	C6
Asio flammeus Short-eared Owl	R	1995	22	22	A	B2, C6

The site is important for breeding raptors and other moorland birds. It is also nationally important for breeding *Numenius phaeopus* (9 pairs,

1993, 2%) and *Stercorarius parasiticus* (45 pairs, 1992, 1%). Breeding species of global conservation concern that do not meet IBA criteria: *Crex crex*.

■ Protection status
National Partial **International** None
IBA partly or wholly overlaps with the following national designated areas. *Reserves:* Birsay Moors and Cottasgarth, Hobbister. *Sites of Special Scientific Interest:* Glims Moss and Durkadale, Keelylang Hill and Swartaback Burn, Lochs of Harray and Stenness, Orphir and Stenness Hills, West Mainland Moors.

■ Conservation issues

> **Threats** Agricultural intensification/expansion (B), Extraction industry (B)

A management plan exists for Birsay Moors and Cottasgarth RSPB Reserve. Ongoing monitoring of raptor breeding success is undertaken. The site is a candidate SPA.

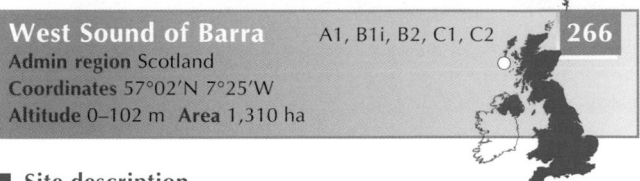

West Sound of Barra A1, B1i, B2, C1, C2 266
Admin region Scotland
Coordinates 57°02′N 7°25′W
Altitude 0–102 m **Area** 1,310 ha

■ Site description
The site comprises the machair-covered isthmus of Eoligarry and low-lying islands. Intertidal cockleshell banks are abundant.

> **Habitats** Scrub (2%; heathland), Grassland (50%; humid grassland; mesophile grassland; machair), Wetland (33%; mudflat/sandflat; sand-dunes/sand beach; shingle/stony beach), Rocky areas (5%; sea cliff/rocky shore)
> **Land-use** Agriculture (100%)

■ Birds

Species	Season	Year	Pop min	Pop max	Acc	Criteria
Branta leucopsis Barnacle Goose	W	1988	370	370	A	B1i, C2
Crex crex Corncrake	B	1996	40	40	A	A1, B2, C1

The IBA is also nationally important for wintering *Calidris maritima* (330 birds, 1992, 2%). *Branta leucopsis* are from the Greenland breeding population.

■ Protection status
National Partial **International** None
IBA partly or wholly overlaps with the following national designated areas. *Site of Special Scientific Interest:* Eoligarry.

■ Conservation issues

> **Threats** Abandonment/reduction of land management (U), Consequences of animal/plant introductions (B), Drainage (U), Extraction industry (B), Infrastructure (B), Other (B)

A new airplane landing strip has been built on the Eoligarry machair. Additional threats are posed by introduced American mink *Mustela vison*, polecats *M. putorius*, ferrets *M. putorius furo*, hedgehogs *Erinaceus europaeus* and rats *Rattus* (on small islands), changes in agricultural use, including undergrazing, and oil spills ('Other' threat, above). Ongoing monitoring of *Crex crex*. Parts of the area are a candidate SPA and Ramsar Site.

West Westray A4i, A4iii, B1i, B1ii, C3, C4, C6 267
Admin region Scotland
Coordinates 59°18′N 3°00′W
Altitude 0–169 m **Area** 350 ha

■ Site description
The site comprises Old Red Sandstone cliffs along the western coast of Westray, together with adjoining areas of grassland and maritime sedge-heath. The site is very exposed.

> **Habitats** Scrub (heathland), Grassland, Rocky areas (sea cliff/rocky shore)
> **Land-use** Agriculture (100%), Nature conservation/research

■ Birds

Species	Season	Year	Pop min	Pop max	Acc	Criteria
Rissa tridactyla Kittiwake	B	1987	31,000	31,000	A	A4i, B1i, C3
Sterna paradisaea Arctic Tern	B	1994	1,140	1,140	A	C6
Uria aalge Guillemot	B	1987	40,600	40,600	A	B1ii, C3

The IBA holds 45,000 pairs of breeding seabirds and 32,200 pairs of breeding waterbirds on a regular basis. It is also nationally important for breeding *Stercorarius parasiticus* (95 pairs, 1992, 3%) and *Alca torda* (1,180 pairs, 1987, 1%).

■ Protection status
National High **International** High
IBA partly or wholly overlaps with the following national designated areas. *Reserve:* Noup Cliffs. *Site of Special Scientific Interest:* West Westray. Overlaps with international designated areas: 350 ha of IBA covered by Special Protection Area (West Westray, 350 ha).

■ Conservation issues

Threats Agricultural intensification/expansion (C)

There is ongoing monitoring of *Sterna paradisaea* breeding success. Part of the IBA is covered by the Noup Cliffs RSPB Reserve, for which a management plan exists.

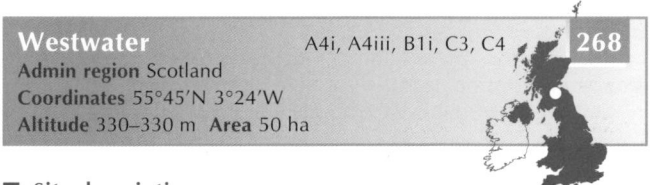

Westwater　　　　　A4i, A4iii, B1i, C3, C4　　**268**
Admin region Scotland
Coordinates 55°45'N 3°24'W
Altitude 330–330 m **Area** 50 ha

■ Site description
An artificial water body situated in the Pentland Hills. No emergent vegetation is present.

Habitats Scrub (heathland), Wetland (standing fresh water; water-fringe vegetation)
Land-use Water management (80%)

■ Birds

Species	Season	Year	Pop min	Pop max	Acc	Criteria
[1] *Anser brachyrhynchus* Pink-footed Goose	W	1996	38,900	38,900	A	A4i, B1i, C3

1. Mean annual peak 1991–1996.

This reservoir is of outstanding importance as a winter roost for *Anser brachyrhynchus*, and holds 39,300 wintering waterbirds on a regular basis.

■ Protection status
National High **International** High
IBA partly or wholly overlaps with the following national designated areas. *Site of Special Scientific Interest:* Westwater Reservoir. Overlaps with international designated areas: 50 ha of IBA covered by Special Protection Area (Westwater Reservoir, 50 ha). 50 ha of IBA covered by Ramsar Site (Westwater Reservoir, 50 ha).

■ Conservation issues

Threats Agricultural intensification/expansion (U), Other (U)

The main threats are posed by changes in agricultural practices in the surrounding area, and the problems caused by goose faeces in relation to water quality for human consumption ('Other' threat, above).

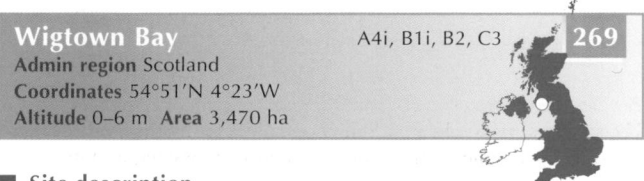

Wigtown Bay　　　　　A4i, B1i, B2, C3　　**269**
Admin region Scotland
Coordinates 54°51'N 4°23'W
Altitude 0–6 m **Area** 3,470 ha

■ Site description
A large estuary draining the Rivers Cree and Bladnoch and several burns. The site includes extensive areas of intertidal mudflats and adjacent grazed saltmarshes.

Habitats Wetland (95%; tidal river/enclosed tidal water; mudflat/sandflat; saltmarsh; river/stream), Marine areas (5%; sea inlet/coastal features)
Land-use Agriculture (10%)

■ Birds

Species	Season	Year	Pop min	Pop max	Acc	Criteria
[1] *Anser brachyrhynchus* Pink-footed Goose	W	1994	4,630	4,630	A	A4i, B1i, C3
Numenius arquata Curlew	W	1995	1,660	1,660	A	B2

1. Mean annual peak 1989–1994.

The IBA supports large numbers of wintering wildfowl and waders. It is also nationally important for wintering *Cygnus cygnus* (92 birds, 1%).

■ Protection status
National Partial **International** None
IBA partly or wholly overlaps with the following national designated areas. *Site of Special Scientific Interest:* Cree Estuary.

■ Conservation issues

Threats Aquaculture/fisheries (U), Disturbance to birds (B)

Threats include disturbance caused by illegal shooting. The advisory/management committee includes conservation bodies and land-owners, and WeBS monitoring is undertaken. The site is listed as a candidate SPA, although it may not qualify under new thresholds. A management plan exists for the site.

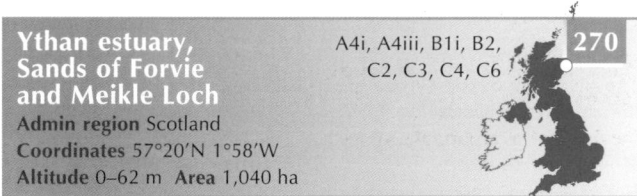

Ythan estuary,　　A4i, A4iii, B1i, B2,　　**270**
Sands of Forvie　　C2, C3, C4, C6
and Meikle Loch
Admin region Scotland
Coordinates 57°20'N 1°58'W
Altitude 0–62 m **Area** 1,040 ha

■ Site description
The long, narrow estuary of the River Ythan runs in a north-south direction, entering the sea 18 km north of Aberdeen. Large tracts of sand-dunes exist either side of the river mouth, which comprises extensive mud and gravel flats. The Sands of Forvie sand-dune system contains a complete range of dune types and supports lichen-rich heath.

Habitats Scrub (58%; heathland), Wetland (42%; tidal river/enclosed tidal water; mudflat/sandflat; saltmarsh; sand-dunes/sand beach; standing fresh water; river/stream; water-fringe vegetation)
Land-use Fisheries/aquaculture (15%), Nature conservation/research (100%)

■ Birds

Species	Season	Year	Pop min	Pop max	Acc	Criteria
[1] *Anser brachyrhynchus* Pink-footed Goose	W	1994	17,900	17,900	A	A4i, B1i, C3
[2] *Sterna sandvicensis* Sandwich Tern	B	1991	1,120	1,120	A	A4i, B1i, B2, C2, C6
Sterna albifrons Little Tern	B	1991	22	22	A	C6

1. Mean annual peak 1989–1994.
2. Have not bred successfully for the last three years.

The IBA is important for breeding seabirds and holds 26,700 wintering waterbirds on a regular basis, including an important goose roost at Meikle Loch. It is also nationally important for breeding *Somateria mollissima* (370 pairs, 1995, 1%) and *Sterna hirundo* (175 pairs, 1991, 1%), for wintering *Somateria mollissima* (1,930 birds, 2%) and *Plectrophenax nivalis* (190 birds, 1994, 2%), and for summer moulting assemblages of *Somateria mollissima* (1,210 birds, 2%).

■ Protection status
National Partial **International** Partial
IBA partly or wholly overlaps with the following national designated areas. *Sites of Special Scientific Interest:* Foveran Links, Meikle Loch and Kippet Hills, Sands of Forvie and Ythan Estuary Lochs. Overlaps with international designated areas: 467 ha of IBA covered by Ramsar Site (Ythan Estuary and Meikle Loch, 467 ha).

■ Conservation issues

> Threats Other (A), Recreation/tourism (U)

Threats include recreational disturbance from walkers, anglers, wind-surfers and a local holiday park. Investigations into the causes of nutrient enrichment of the estuary ('Other' threat, above), algal weed mats and depressed invertebrate populations are currently under way. The site is a candidate Nitrate Vulnerable Zone. The University of Aberdeen, Scottish Environmental Protection Agency and Macaulay Land-Use Research Institute are carrying out additional research projects. A reserve management plan exists.

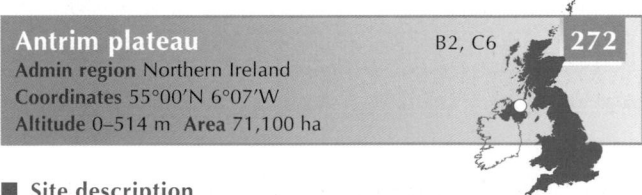

Annaghroe, River Blackwater   C6   271
Admin region Northern Ireland
Coordinates 54°20'N 6°52'W
Altitude 20–70 m Area 440 ha

■ Site description
The IBA covers grazed, periodically flooded meadows situated along the River Blackwater.

> Habitats Grassland (100%; humid grassland)
> Land-use Agriculture (100%)

■ Birds

Species		Season	Year	Pop min	Pop max	Acc	Criteria
Cygnus cygnus	Whooper Swan	W	1992	50	50	A	C6
¹*Anser albifrons*	White-fronted Goose	W	1992	90	90	A	C6

1. Mean count.

The site is important for wintering wildfowl. *Anser albifrons* are the *flavirostris* subspecies.

■ Protection status
National None **International** None

■ Conservation issues

> Threats Drainage (A)

The site is managed to provide flooded meadows for breeding waders and wintering wildfowl. Detailed annual monitoring of wildfowl was initiated by the RSPB in 1994, and breeding waders are now also monitored.

Antrim plateau   B2, C6   272
Admin region Northern Ireland
Coordinates 55°00'N 6°07'W
Altitude 0–514 m Area 71,100 ha

■ Site description
An extensive upland plateau that is the dominant geographical feature of County Antrim. It supports fine remnant semi-natural *Quercus* woodlands and is drained by fast-flowing streams, including the rivers of the famous nine glens of Antrim. Human activities include commercial peat extraction ('Other' land-use, below).

> Habitats Forest and woodland (broadleaved deciduous forest), Scrub (heathland), Grassland, Wetland (river/stream; blanket bog), Rocky areas (sea cliff/rocky shore), Artificial landscape (forestry plantation)
> Land-use Agriculture, Forestry, Nature conservation/research, Other, Tourism/recreation, Urban/industrial/transport

■ Birds

Species		Season	Year	Pop min	Pop max	Acc	Criteria
Circus cyaneus	Hen Harrier	R	1995	—	13	A	C6
Falco peregrinus	Peregrine	R	1995	25	25	A	B2, C6
Pyrrhocorax pyrrhocorax	Chough	R	1995	3	3	A	C6

The area supports a typical assemblage of upland species and is also important for *Phylloscopus sibilatrix*.

■ Protection status
National Partial **International** None
IBA partly or wholly overlaps with the following national designated areas. *National Nature Reserves:* Breen Forest, Glenariff North, Glenariff Waterfalls Forest, Slieveanorra Forest, Straidkilly. *Areas of Special Scientific Interest:* Cleggan Valley, Garron Plateau, Glen Burn, Glenariff, Gortnagory, Scawt Hill, Tievebulliagh.

■ Conservation issues

> Threats Afforestation (A), Agricultural intensification/expansion (A), Other (C), Unsustainable exploitation (B)

Main threats are posed by sheep overgrazing, afforestation of blanket bog, reclamation of moorland and mechanical peat extraction. Some raptor persecution takes place ('Other' threat, above). Part of the site, the Garron plateau, is a candidate SAC and candidate Ramsar Site, and a conservation plan is being drafted for this area (4,650 ha). A number of National Nature Reserves, National Trust and Ulster Wildlife Trust reserves contained within the IBA have management plans, and there has been a recent RSPB *Numenius arquata* project.

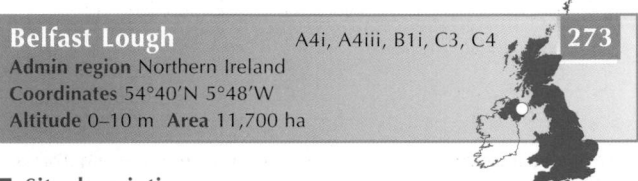

Belfast Lough   A4i, A4iii, B1i, C3, C4   273
Admin region Northern Ireland
Coordinates 54°40'N 5°48'W
Altitude 0–10 m Area 11,700 ha

■ Site description
A sea lough with an area of tidal mudflats reduced in size by development. The outer shores are mainly rocky with a few sandy bays.

> Habitats Wetland (mudflat/sandflat; sand-dunes/sand beach; coastal lagoon), Marine areas (sea inlet/coastal features), Rocky areas (sea cliff/rocky shore)
> Land-use Nature conservation/research, Tourism/recreation, Urban/industrial/transport, Water management

■ Birds

Species		Season	Year	Pop min	Pop max	Acc	Criteria
Tringa totanus	Redshank	W	1995	2,020	2,020	A	B1i, C3
Tringa totanus	Redshank	P	1995	2,030	2,030	A	B1i, C3
Arenaria interpres	Turnstone	W	1995	850	850	A	A4i, B1i, C3
Arenaria interpres	Turnstone	P	1995	715	715	A	A4i, B1i, C3

The IBA is important for wintering waders and wildfowl, with man-made lagoons in the Inner Harbour holding the main wader roost. The site holds 20,800 wintering waterbirds on a regular basis, and is also nationally important for wintering *Podiceps cristatus* (1,410 birds, 12%), *Phalacrocorax carbo* (380 birds, 3%), *Somateria mollissima* (925 birds, 1%), *Bucephala clangula* (560 birds, 2%), *Mergus serrator* (185 birds, 2%), *Haematopus ostralegus* (6,200 birds, 2%) and *Limosa limosa* (295 birds, 4%), and for passage *Haematopus ostralegus* (6,250 birds, 2%) and *Limosa limosa* (285 birds, 4%).

■ Protection status
National Partial **International** Low
IBA partly or wholly overlaps with the following national designated areas. *Reserve:* Belfast Lough. *Areas of Special Scientific Interest:* Ballymacormick Point, Inner Belfast Lough, Outer Belfast Lough. Overlaps with international designated areas: 432 ha of IBA covered by Special Protection Area (Belfast Lough, 432 ha). 432 ha of IBA covered by Ramsar Site (Belfast Lough, 432 ha).

■ Conservation issues

> Threats Filling-in of wetlands (U), Industrialization/urbanization (U), Infrastructure (U), Recreation/tourism (U)

Threats include car-park development, industrial and port development, disturbance from recreational activity, pollution from domestic refuse disposal and hard-core tipping, and pollution from a landfill site and the port. A conservation plan is being developed for the Belfast Lough SPA. An agreement reached by the Belfast Harbour Commissioners and conservation bodies has secured the future of the remaining mudflats, lagoon and associated wetland area as an RSPB reserve, for which a management plan exists.

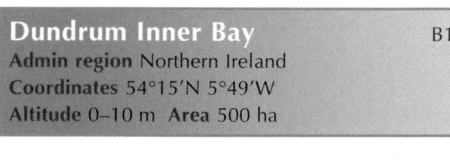

Carlingford Lough including Green Island
B1i, B2, C3, C6 — **274**

Admin region Northern Ireland
Coordinates 54°03'N 6°08'W
Altitude 0–10 m **Area** 4,660 ha

■ Site description

A narrow sea lough with significant expanses of mudflat and saltmarsh, and several small rock and shingle islands. Mountains surround the lough. This is a cross-border site, the southern shore lying in County Louth in the Republic of Ireland (IBA 122). The stated area of 4,660 ha covers the entire site on both sides of the border, but other data given here (habitats, land-use, threats and birds) are specific to the UK side.

Habitats Wetland (mudflat/sandflat; saltmarsh), Marine areas (sea inlet/coastal features), Rocky areas (rock stacks/islets)

Land-use Fisheries/aquaculture, Nature conservation/research, Tourism/recreation, Urban/industrial/transport, Water management

■ Birds

Species	Season	Year	Pop min	Pop max	Acc	Criteria
Branta bernicla Brent Goose	W	1995	320	320	A	B1i, C3
Aythya marila Scaup	W	1995	555	555	A	B2
Sterna sandvicensis Sandwich Tern	B	1995	270	270	A	C6
Sterna hirundo Common Tern	B	1995	250	250	A	C6

The IBA is important for breeding terns and wintering waterbirds. It is also nationally important for wintering *Podiceps cristatus* (215 birds, 2%). *Branta bernicla* are from the Canadian/Greenland breeding population of the *hrota* subspecies.

■ Protection status

National Partial **International** Partial
IBA partly or wholly overlaps with the following national designated areas. *National Nature Reserve:* Rostrevor Forest. *Reserve:* Carlingford Lough Islands. Areas of Special Scientific Interest: Carlingford Lough. Overlaps with international designated areas: 827 ha of IBA covered by Special Protection Area (Carlingford Lough, 827 ha). 827 ha of IBA covered by Ramsar Site (Carlingford Lough, 827 ha).

■ Conservation issues

Threats Aquaculture/fisheries (U), Industrialization/urbanization (U), Natural events (B), Recreation/tourism (U)

Threats include leisure and warehouse developments, sewage pollution, and natural erosion. A management plan exists for Carlingford Lough Islands RSPB Reserve.

Dundrum Inner Bay
B1i, C3 — **275**

Admin region Northern Ireland
Coordinates 54°15'N 5°49'W
Altitude 0–10 m **Area** 500 ha

■ Site description

An enclosed sandy bay with extensive mudflats, which is fed by four small rivers.

Habitats Wetland (mudflat/sandflat; river/stream), Marine areas (sea inlet/coastal features)
Land-use Agriculture, Fisheries/aquaculture, Military, Nature conservation/research, Tourism/recreation

■ Birds

Species	Season	Year	Pop min	Pop max	Acc	Criteria
Branta bernicla Brent Goose	W	1995	210	210	A	B1i, C3

The site is also nationally important for wintering *Melanitta nigra* (1,200 birds, 3%) and *Tringa nebularia* (12 birds, 2%). Wintering *Branta bernicla* are from the Canadian/Greenland breeding population of the *hrota* subspecies.

■ Protection status
National High **International** None

IBA partly or wholly overlaps with the following national designated areas. *National Nature Reserve:* Murlough. *Area of Special Scientific Interest:* Murlough.

■ Conservation issues

Threats Aquaculture/fisheries (U), Industrialization/urbanization (U), Recreation/tourism (U)

Fly-tipping, sewage pollution and disturbance from recreational activity pose threats to the IBA. The site is a candidate SPA and candidate SAC, and a conservation plan will be prepared.

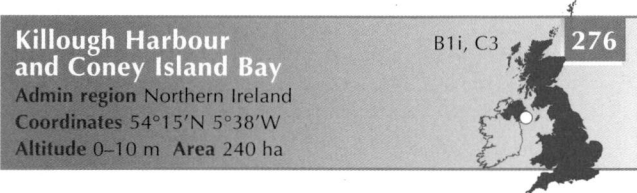

Killough Harbour and Coney Island Bay
B1i, C3 — **276**

Admin region Northern Ireland
Coordinates 54°15'N 5°38'W
Altitude 0–10 m **Area** 240 ha

■ Site description
The IBA comprises a small estuary with tidal mudflats and shingle banks.

Habitats Wetland (100%; tidal river/enclosed tidal water; mudflat/sandflat; shingle/stony beach)
Land-use Fisheries/aquaculture, Tourism/recreation

■ Birds

Species	Season	Year	Pop min	Pop max	Acc	Criteria
Branta bernicla Brent Goose	W	1994	—	330	A	B1i, C3

The site is important for wintering waterbirds. Wintering *Branta bernicla* are from the Canadian/Greenland breeding population of the *hrota* subspecies.

■ Protection status
National None **International** None

■ Conservation issues

Threats Filling-in of wetlands (U), Recreation/tourism (U)

The RSPB are campaigning for the site to be put forward for designation as a SPA.

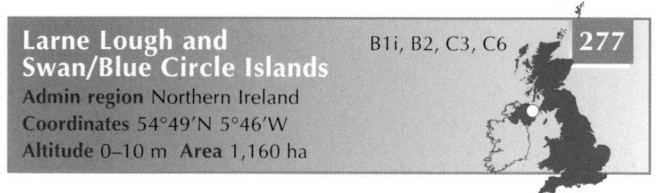

Larne Lough and Swan/Blue Circle Islands
B1i, B2, C3, C6 — **277**

Admin region Northern Ireland
Coordinates 54°49'N 5°46'W
Altitude 0–10 m **Area** 1,160 ha

■ Site description

A sea lough containing mudflats, mussel-beds and a small area of saltings. The IBA includes the small, vegetated Swan Island, and the man-made 'Blue Circle' Island.

Habitats Wetland (mudflat/sandflat; saltmarsh), Marine areas (sea inlet/coastal features), Rocky areas (rock stacks/islets)
Land-use Agriculture, Fisheries/aquaculture, Nature conservation/research, Tourism/recreation, Urban/industrial/transport

■ Birds

Species	Season	Year	Pop min	Pop max	Acc	Criteria
Branta bernicla Brent Goose	W	1995	220	220	A	B1i, C3
Sterna sandvicensis Sandwich Tern	B	1995	235	235	A	C6
Sterna dougallii Roseate Tern	B	1995	7	7	A	B2, C6
Sterna hirundo Common Tern	B	1995	220	220	A	C6

The mudflats are important for wintering *Branta bernicla hrota* from the Canadian/Greenland breeding population, whilst Swan/Blue Circle Islands support an important mixed tern colony. The IBA is also nationally important for wintering *Mergus serrator* (195 birds, 2%) and *Tringa nebularia* (12 birds, 2%).

■ Protection status

National Partial **International** Partial
IBA partly or wholly overlaps with the following national designated areas. *National Nature Reserve:* Swan Island. *Reserve:* Swan/Blue Circle Islands. Overlaps with international designated areas: 1 ha of IBA covered by Special Protection Area (Swan Island, 1 ha). Overlaps with international designated areas: 396 ha of IBA covered by Special Protection Area (Larne Lough, 396 ha). 396 ha of IBA covered by Ramsar Site (Larne Lough, 396 ha).

■ Conservation issues

> **Threats** Aquaculture/fisheries (U), Disturbance to birds (B), Filling-in of wetlands (B), Industrialization/urbanization (B)

Threats include pollution from a land-fill site and the port, and disturbance of breeding terns. A conservation plan is in preparation, and a RSPB management plan exists for Swan/Blue Circle Islands.

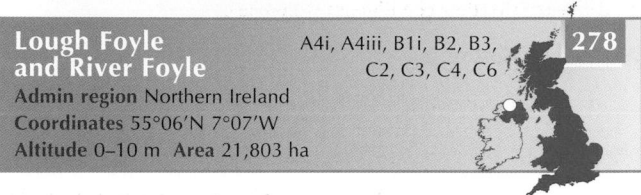

Lough Foyle and River Foyle — A4i, A4iii, B1i, B2, B3, C2, C3, C4, C6 — **278**
Admin region Northern Ireland
Coordinates 55°06′N 7°07′W
Altitude 0–10 m **Area** 21,803 ha

■ Site description

A large shallow estuary comprising extensive mudflats, shell ridges, mussel-beds, low-lying reclaimed farmland and limited areas of saltwater marsh. This is a cross-border IBA, with a minority of the site falling within the Republic of Ireland (IBA 004)—the stated area of 21,803 ha refers to the whole site (on both sides of the border) but other data given here (habitats, land-uses, threats and birds) are specific to the UK side.

> **Habitats** Wetland (tidal river/enclosed tidal water; mudflat/sandflat; saltmarsh; shingle/stony beach; river/stream; water-fringe vegetation), Artificial landscape (highly improved reseeded grassland; arable land)
> **Land-use** Agriculture, Fisheries/aquaculture, Military, Nature conservation/research, Tourism/recreation, Urban/industrial/transport

■ Birds

Species		Season	Year	Pop min	Pop max	Acc	Criteria
Cygnus columbianus	Bewick's Swan	W	1995	97	97	A	B2, C6
Cygnus cygnus	Whooper Swan	W	1995	785	785	A	A4i, B1i, B3, C2, C6
Branta bernicla	Brent Goose	W	1995	3,820	3,820	A	A4i, B1i, C3
Pluvialis apricaria	Golden Plover	W	1995	5,050	5,050	A	C6
Pluvialis apricaria	Golden Plover	P	1995	2,100	2,100	A	C6
Limosa lapponica	Bar-tailed Godwit	W	1995	2,150	2,150	A	A4i, B1i, B2, C2, C6
Limosa lapponica	Bar-tailed Godwit	P	1995	495	495	A	C6
Numenius arquata	Curlew	W	1995	1,980	1,980	A	B2

The IBA is internationally important for wintering wildfowl and waders. It holds 35,900 wintering waterbirds on a regular basis, and is also nationally important for wintering *Podiceps cristatus* (135 birds, 1%), *Anas penelope* (9,550 birds, 3%) and *Tringa nebularia* (22 birds, 4%). *Branta bernicla* are from the Canadian/Greenland breeding population of the *hrota* subspecies.

■ Protection status

National Partial **International** None
IBA partly or wholly overlaps with the following national designated areas. *National Nature Reserves:* Magilligan Point, Roe Estuary. *Reserve:* Lough Foyle. *Areas of Special Scientific Interest:* Lough Foyle, Magilligan.

■ Conservation issues

> **Threats** Agricultural intensification/expansion (B), Aquaculture/fisheries (B), Disturbance to birds (B), Drainage (B), Dredging/canalization (U), Filling-in of wetlands (B), Industrialization/urbanization (U), Infrastructure (U), Other (B), Recreation/tourism (B)

Threats include industrial, port and coastal sea defence developments, disturbance from unregulated shooting, and waste disposal. The estuary is exposed to large quantities of raw and partially treated sewage, oil and chemical pollution ('Other' threat, above), and this is likely to become more of a problem. The site is a candidate SPA and Ramsar Site, and a conservation plan will be prepared. Management plans exist for the RSPB reserve and the National Nature Reserves.

Lough Neagh and Lough Beg — A4i, A4iii, B1i, B2, B3, C2, C3, C4, C6 — **279**
Admin region Northern Ireland
Coordinates 54°37′N 6°24′W
Altitude 0–20 m **Area** 50,165 ha

■ Site description

Shallow water-bodies with associated damp grassland, reedbed (*Phragmites*), islands, fen and pasture. Lough Neagh is the largest UK freshwater lake, with water-levels subject to erratic, artificial change.

> **Habitats** Scrub (scrub), Grassland (humid grassland; mesophile grassland), Wetland (standing fresh water; water-fringe vegetation; fen/transition mire/spring)
> **Land-use** Agriculture, Fisheries/aquaculture, Hunting, Nature conservation/research, Tourism/recreation, Urban/industrial/transport

■ Birds

Species		Season	Year	Pop min	Pop max	Acc	Criteria
Cygnus columbianus	Bewick's Swan	W	1995	225	225	A	A4i, B1i, B2, C2, C6
Cygnus cygnus	Whooper Swan	W	1995	1,070	1,070	A	A4i, B1i, B3, C2, C6
Aythya ferina	Pochard	W	1995	28,900	28,900	A	A4i, B1i, C3
Aythya fuligula	Tufted Duck	W	1995	21,800	21,800	A	A4i, B1i, C3
Aythya marila	Scaup	W	1995	3,300	3,300	A	B1i, B2, C3
Bucephala clangula	Goldeneye	W	1995	11,500	11,500	A	A4i, B1i, C3
Pluvialis apricaria	Golden Plover	W	1995	5,550	5,550	A	C6
Sterna hirundo	Common Tern	B	1995	115	115	A	C6

The IBA is important for wintering wildfowl. It regularly holds 100,900 wintering waterbirds, and is nationally important for breeding *Podiceps cristatus* (750 pairs, 1992, 16%); for wintering *Tachybaptus ruficollis* (405 birds, 9%), *Podiceps cristatus* (1,010 birds, 9%), *Phalacrocorax carbo* (720 birds, 5%), *Cygnus olor* (1,430 birds, 5%), *Anas penelope* (3,660 birds, 1%), *Anas strepera* (160 birds, 2%), *Anas crecca* (1,930 birds, 1%), *Anas clypeata* (155 birds, 2%) and *Fulica atra* (6,600 birds, 5%); and for summer moulting assemblages of *Cygnus olor* (1,750 birds, 6%).

■ Protection status

National High **International** High
IBA partly or wholly overlaps with the following national designated areas. *National Nature Reserves:* Farr's Bay, Lough Beg, Lough Neagh, Randalstown Forest, Rea's Wood Forest. *Reserve:* Portmore Lough. *Areas of Special Scientific Interest:* Culnafay, Lough Beg, Lough Neagh, Lough Neagh – Oxford Island, Portmore Lough. Overlaps with international designated areas: 40,835 ha of IBA covered by Special Protection Area (Lough Neagh and Lough Beg, 40,835 ha). 50,165 ha of IBA covered by Ramsar Site (Lough Neagh and Lough Beg, 50,165 ha).

■ Conservation issues

> **Threats** Agricultural intensification/expansion (A), Aquaculture/fisheries (U), Disturbance to birds (A), Drainage (U), Groundwater abstraction (U), Infrastructure (U), Industrialization/urbanization (U), Other (U), Recreation/tourism (A)

Threats include marina, caravan site and sewage works developments, poorly regulated wildfowling and too few wildlife refuges, coastal defence improvements, and pollution ('Other' threat, above). A conservation plan is in preparation, and a RSPB management plan exists for Portmore Lough. Powerline collisions involving swans are being monitored in conjunction with Northern Ireland Electricity.

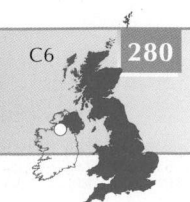

Lower Lough Macnean — C6 — **280**
Admin region Northern Ireland
Coordinates 54°17′N 7°48′W
Altitude 40–50 m **Area** 510 ha

■ Site description

The IBA comprises a freshwater lake and islands.

> **Habitats** Grassland (humid grassland), Wetland (standing fresh water; water-fringe vegetation)
> **Land-use** Agriculture, Tourism/recreation

■ Birds

Species		Season	Year	Pop min	Pop max	Acc	Criteria
Anser albifrons	White-fronted Goose	W	1995	200	200	A	C6

The IBA is important for *Anser albifrons flavirostris*.

■ Protection status
National Partial **International** None
IBA partly or wholly overlaps with the following national designated areas. *National Nature Reserve:* Hanging Rock.

■ Conservation issues

Threats Disturbance to birds (U), Drainage (U), Recreation/tourism (U)

Tourism and marina development and unregulated shooting threaten the IBA. The RSPB is pushing for protection of the *Anser albifrons* site through designation as an Area of Special Scientific Interest or similar mechanism.

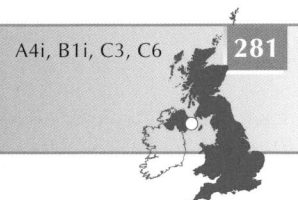

Outer Ards peninsula A4i, B1i, C3, C6 281
Admin region Northern Ireland
Coordinates 54°29'N 5°25'W
Altitude 0–30 m **Area** 1,016 ha

■ Site description
This site covers a section of the flat, east-facing shoreline of the Irish Sea, and contains rocky outcrops, a number of islands and long sandy beaches.

Habitats Wetland (sand-dunes/sand beach), Marine areas (open sea), Rocky areas (sea cliff/rocky shore; rock stacks/islets)
Land-use Agriculture, Fisheries/aquaculture, Nature conservation/research, Tourism/recreation, Urban/industrial/transport

■ Birds

Species		Season	Year	Pop min	Pop max	Acc	Criteria
Branta bernicla	Brent Goose	W	1995	255	255	A	B1i, C3
Charadrius hiaticula	Ringed Plover	W	1995	545	545	A	B1i, C3
Pluvialis apricaria	Golden Plover	W	1995	1,690	1,690	A	C6
Arenaria interpres	Turnstone	W	1995	1,240	1,240	A	A4i, B1i, C3
Sterna paradisaea	Arctic Tern	B	1995	310	310	A	C6

The site is important for wintering waders and geese, and is also nationally important for wintering *Phalacrocorax carbo* (155 birds, 1%) and *Tringa nebularia* (6 birds, 1%). Also important for breeding *Sterna paradisaea* and *Phalacrocorax carbo*. Most *Branta bernicla* are from the Canadian/Greenland breeding population of the *hrota* subspecies.

■ Protection status
National Partial **International** None
IBA partly or wholly overlaps with the following national designated areas. *Areas of Special Scientific Interest:* Ballymacormick Point, Ballyquintin Point.

■ Conservation issues

Threats Disturbance to birds (U)

Breeding terns are vulnerable to disturbance. A SPA conservation plan will be prepared for the site, once the designation as a SPA and Ramsar Site has been confirmed.

Pettigoe plateau C6 282
Admin region Northern Ireland
Coordinates 54°32'N 7°59'W
Altitude 50–180 m **Area** 2,700 ha

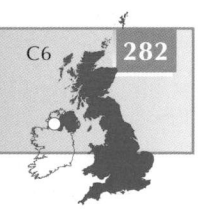

■ Site description
The IBA covers an area of low-lying blanket bog with rocky outcrops, in addition to small lakes and farmland interspersed with small patches of forestry.

Habitats Grassland, Wetland (standing fresh water; blanket bog), Rocky areas (scree/boulders), Artificial landscape (arable land; forestry plantation)
Land-use Agriculture (90%), Forestry (10%)

■ Birds

Species		Season	Year	Pop min	Pop max	Acc	Criteria
Anser albifrons	White-fronted Goose	W	1995	77	77	A	C6

The site supports a suite of breeding upland birds. Wintering *Anser albifrons* are the *flavirostris* subspecies.

■ Protection status
National Partial **International** Partial
IBA partly or wholly overlaps with the following national designated areas. *Area of Special Scientific Interest:* Pettigoe Plateau. Overlaps with international designated areas: 1,264 ha of IBA covered by Special Protection Area (Pettigoe Plateau, 1,264 ha). 1,264 ha of IBA covered by Ramsar Site (Pettigoe Plateau, 1,264 ha).

■ Conservation issues

Threats Abandonment/reduction of land management (U), Afforestation (U), Agricultural intensification/expansion (U), Disturbance to birds (U), Drainage (U), Dredging/canalization (U), Extraction industry (U), Recreation/tourism (U)

The effects of shooting on the IBA are unknown. A conservation plan is in preparation for the SPA and the site is also a candidate SAC. The RSPB have lobbied the Environment and Heritage Service to alter the SPA boundary to reflect the distributions of *Pluvialis apricaria* and *Anser albifrons*.

Rathlin Island A4ii, A4iii, B1ii, B3, C3, C4 283
Admin region Northern Ireland
Coordinates 55°18'N 6°13'W
Altitude 0–400 m **Area** 1,500 ha

■ Site description
A large island with cliffs and stacks on the north and west shores. Further inland there are wetlands, a limited amount of maritime heath and a mosaic of unimproved and improved grazing.

Habitats Scrub (heathland), Grassland, Wetland, Rocky areas (sea cliff/rocky shore; rock stacks/islets)
Land-use Agriculture, Nature conservation/research, Not utilized, Tourism/recreation

■ Birds

Species		Season	Year	Pop min	Pop max	Acc	Criteria
Uria aalge	Guillemot	B	1985	41,900	41,900	A	B1ii, C3
Alca torda	Razorbill	B	1985	6,000	6,000	A	A4ii, B1ii, B3, C3

The IBA is important for breeding seabirds. It holds 52,000 pairs of breeding seabirds and 11,200 pairs of breeding waterbirds on a regular basis, and is also nationally important for breeding *Larus argentatus* (4,040 pairs, 1985, 2%) and *Rissa tridactyla* (6,800 pairs, 1985, 1%).

■ Protection status
National Partial **International** Partial
IBA partly or wholly overlaps with the following national designated areas. *National Nature Reserve:* Kebble. *Reserves:* Ballyconagan, Rathlin Island Cliffs. *Areas of Special Scientific Interest:* Ballycarry – Rathlin Island, Ballygill North – Rathlin Island, Kinramer South – Rathlin Island, Rathlin Island Coast. Overlaps with international designated areas: 236 ha of IBA covered by Special Protection Area (Rathlin Island, 236 ha).

■ Conservation issues

Threats Agricultural intensification/expansion (C), Consequences of animal/plant introductions (B), Recreation/tourism (U)

A recently introduced feral ferret *Mustela putorius furo* population threatens seabird colonies and ground-nesting birds, and trapping is being attempted. Management plans are in place for the RSPB Reserve and NNR. The RSPB is pushing for designation as a SAC.

Sheep Island

C7 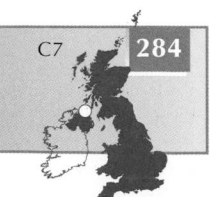 284

Admin region Northern Ireland
Coordinates 55°14'N 6°21'W
Altitude 0–30 m **Area** 4 ha

■ Site description
An exposed marine island with steep cliffs and rocky shores.

Habitats Rocky areas (100%; sea cliff/rocky shore)
Land-use Nature conservation/research

■ Birds

Species	Season	Year	Pop min	Pop max	Acc	Criteria
Phalacrocorax carbo Cormorant	B	1988	—	370	A	C7

The IBA is important for breeding seabirds.

■ Protection status
National High **International** High
IBA partly or wholly overlaps with the following national designated areas. *Area of Special Scientific Interest:* Sheep Island. Overlaps with international designated areas: 4 ha of IBA covered by Special Protection Area (Sheep Island, 4 ha).

■ Conservation issues

Threats Other (B)

Pressure to cull the *Phalacrocorax carbo* colonies has so far been resisted ('Other' threat, above). A management plan exists for the site.

South Down coast

A4i, B1i, C3 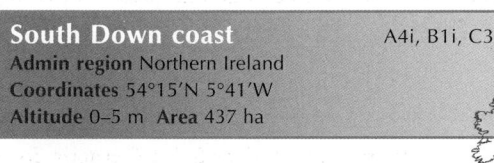 285

Admin region Northern Ireland
Coordinates 54°15'N 5°41'W
Altitude 0–5 m **Area** 437 ha

■ Site description
A long section of rocky and sandy coastline extending from Cranfield Point to St John's Point.

Habitats Wetland (sand-dunes/sand beach), Rocky areas (sea cliff/rocky shore)
Land-use Not utilized, Tourism/recreation, Urban/industrial/transport

■ Birds

Species	Season	Year	Pop min	Pop max	Acc	Criteria
Charadrius hiaticula Ringed Plover	W	1990	—	685	A	B1i, C3
Arenaria interpres Turnstone	W	1990	—	1,190	A	A4i, B1i, C3

The IBA is important for wintering waders and waterbirds.

■ Protection status
National Partial **International** None
IBA partly or wholly overlaps with the following national designated areas. *Area of Special Scientific Interest:* Murlough.

■ Conservation issues

Threats Recreation/tourism (B)

A link exists with the IBA at Killough Harbour and Coney Island Bay (276), as the same *Branta bernicla hrota* use both sites.

Strangford Lough and islands

A4i, A4iii, B1i, B2, C2, C3, C4, C6 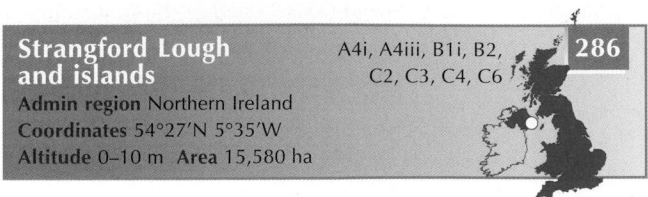 286

Admin region Northern Ireland
Coordinates 54°27'N 5°35'W
Altitude 0–10 m **Area** 15,580 ha

■ Site description
A shallow sea lough with an indented shoreline and a wide variety of marine and intertidal habitats. The west shore has numerous islands typical of flooded drumlin topography.

Habitats Wetland (mudflat/sandflat; saltmarsh; fen/transition mire/spring), Marine areas (sea inlet/coastal features), Rocky areas (sea cliff/rocky shore)
Land-use Agriculture, Fisheries/aquaculture, Hunting, Nature conservation/research, Tourism/recreation, Urban/industrial/transport

■ Birds

Species	Season	Year	Pop min	Pop max	Acc	Criteria
Branta bernicla Brent Goose	W	1995	10,700	10,700	A	A4i, B1i, C3
Pluvialis apricaria Golden Plover	W	1995	5,850	5,850	A	C6
Pluvialis apricaria Golden Plover	P	1995	3,210	3,210	A	C6
Calidris canutus Knot	W	1995	6,500	6,500	A	B1i, B2, C3
Limosa lapponica Bar-tailed Godwit	W	1995	770	770	A	B2, C6
Limosa lapponica Bar-tailed Godwit	P	1995	370	370	A	C6
Numenius arquata Curlew	W	1995	1,910	1,910	A	B2
Tringa totanus Redshank	W	1995	2,470	2,470	A	B1i, C3
Tringa totanus Redshank	P	1995	3,070	3,070	A	A4i, B1i, C3
Sterna sandvicensis Sandwich Tern	B	1995	530	530	A	B1i, B2, C2, C6
Sterna hirundo Common Tern	B	1995	565	565	A	C6
Sterna paradisaea Arctic Tern	B	1995	280	280	A	C6

This is Northern Ireland's most important coastal site for wintering wildfowl, and is also of importance for breeding terns. It holds 56,800 wintering waterbirds on a regular basis, and is also nationally important for breeding *Phalacrocorax carbo* (200 pairs, 1995, 3%), *Anas strepera* (8 pairs, 1995, 1%) and *Larus ridibundus* (6,850 pairs, 1995, 4%), for wintering *Tachybaptus ruficollis* (115 birds, 3%), *Phalacrocorax carbo* (170 birds, 1%), *Tadorna tadorna* (2,080 birds, 3%), *Anas strepera* (110 birds, 1%), *Anas clypeata* (125 birds, 1%), *Bucephala clangula* (350 birds, 1%), *Mergus serrator* (285 birds, 3%), *Haematopus ostralegus* (4,980 birds, 1%), *Charadrius hiaticula* (325 birds, 1%) and *Tringa nebularia* (36 birds, 6%), and for passage *Haematopus ostralegus* (7,050 birds, 2%). *Branta bernicla* are from the Canadian/Greenland breeding population of the *hrota* subspecies.

■ Protection status
National Partial **International** High
IBA partly or wholly overlaps with the following national designated areas. *National Nature Reserves:* Cloghy Rocks, Granagh Bay, Killard, Quoile Pondage, The Dorn. *Marine Nature Reserve:* Strangford Lough. *Reserve:* Castleward Bay. *Areas of Special Scientific Interest:* Ballyquintin Point, Killard, Strangford Lough, Strangford Lough (part 2), Strangford Lough (Part 3). Overlaps with international designated areas: 15,580 ha of IBA covered by Special Protection Area (Strangford Lough, 15,580 ha). 15,580 ha of IBA covered by Ramsar Site (Strangford Lough, 15,580 ha).

■ Conservation issues

Threats Agricultural intensification/expansion (U), Aquaculture/fisheries (C), Construction/impact of dyke/dam/barrage (C), Industrialization/urbanization (U), Infrastructure (U), Recreation/tourism (B)

Threats include uncontrolled recreational pressures, residential and recreational developments, and wharf and boatyard construction. A conservation plan and management strategy for the whole lough is in preparation. The National Trust has a detailed management plan for their properties and for the Strangford Lough Wildlife Scheme, which they manage. An RSPB management plan exists for Castleward Bay Reserve. The area is a candidate SAC.

Upper Lough Erne

A4i, B1i, B3, C2, C6 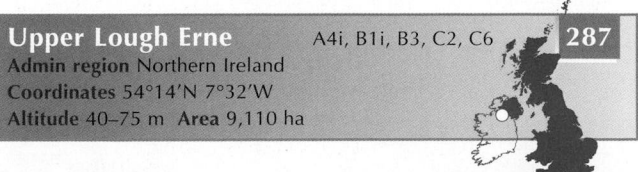 287

Admin region Northern Ireland
Coordinates 54°14'N 7°32'W
Altitude 40–75 m **Area** 9,110 ha

■ Site description
Flooded drumlins in the course of the River Erne give rise to a complex of islands, bays and lakes, bordered by damp pasture, fen and reed-swamp (*Phragmites*).

Habitats Grassland (humid grassland), Wetland (standing fresh water; river/stream; water-fringe vegetation; fen/transition mire/spring)
Land-use Agriculture, Nature conservation/research, Tourism/recreation

■ Birds

Species	Season	Year	Pop min	Pop max	Acc	Criteria
Cygnus cygnus Whooper Swan	W	1995	745	745	A	A4i, B1i, B3, C2, C6

The IBA is also nationally important for breeding *Podiceps cristatus* (300 pairs, 1992, 6%), and for wintering *Tachybaptus ruficollis* (58 birds, 1%), *Podiceps cristatus* (160 birds, 1%) and *Cygnus olor* (425 birds, 1%).

■ Protection status

National Partial **International** Partial

IBA partly or wholly overlaps with the following national designated areas. *National Nature Reserve:* Reilly and Gole Woods. *Areas of Special Scientific Interest:* Corraslough Point, Dernish Island, Inishroosk, Mill Lough, Upper Lough Erne – Belleisle, Upper Lough Erne – Crom, Upper Lough Erne – Galloon, Upper Lough Erne – Trannish. Overlaps with international designated areas: 5,771 ha of IBA covered by Special Protection Area (Upper Lough Erne, 5,771 ha). 5,771 ha of IBA covered by Ramsar Site (Upper Lough Erne, 5,771 ha).

■ Conservation issues

Threats Agricultural intensification/expansion (U), Disturbance to birds (U), Drainage (U), Recreation/tourism (U)

Threats include disturbance from shooting, and holiday park and recreational developments. These include marinas and a large project to increase cruiser traffic, in part due to the reopening of the Ballyconnell Canal linking the Shannon and Erne systems. The site is a candidate SAC.

■ THE CHANNEL ISLANDS

GENERAL INTRODUCTION

The Channel Islands, a dependency of the British Crown, are situated off the north-west coast of France, some 130 km from the English coast. They consist of Jersey and Guernsey, with seven dependencies of the latter (Alderney, Brecqou, Great Sark, Little Sark, Herm, Jethou and Lihou). The Channel Islands cover a total area of 195 km², and are characterized by steep, rocky coastlines, alternating with sandy bays. Jersey and Guernsey habitats include wooded valleys, sand-dune communities, cliff-top heathlands and grasslands.

The 1989 inventory identified only a single IBA in the Channel Islands, the 1992 UK review included 13 and a total of 60 sites were listed in an inventory of 'Important sites for birds in the Channel Islands' (Veron 1997). Only four IBAs (covering 3,652 ha) in the Channel Islands qualify for this review; all remaining sites are important in a Channel Islands context, but fail to meet the criteria used here (Table 6, Map 2). The single site identified in the 1989 inventory, Les Etacs and Ortac, Alderney (then 001) is now split into two separate sites (290 and 291).

ORNITHOLOGICAL IMPORTANCE

Two of the Channel Island IBAs are important gannetries. Les Etacs, Alderney (290) holds a globally important population of over 3,300 pairs of *Sula bassana*, while Ortac, Alderney (291) holds over 2,100 pairs. Small numbers of other seabirds, such as *Uria aalge* also breed on these rocky islands.

The other two IBAs, Guernsey Shoreline (288) and Jersey Shoreline (289), both qualify as A4i because of the wintering and passage waterbirds they support, most notably those of *Arenaria interpres*.

The Channel Islands are not part of the EU so C criteria do not apply.

HABITATS

The two gannetries are rocky islands with associated islets, while both stretches of shoreline have a variety of rocky and sandy habitats, from wide bays to scattered offshore stacks.

IMPACTS ON IBAs – LAND-USE AND THREATS

Les Etacs and Ortac are relatively remote from disturbance by tourism and recreation. However, there are threats from discarded nylon nets, which entangle adult birds and kill chicks when used as nesting material. The shoreline IBAs are mainly affected by tourism and recreation, with some threat from infrastructure developments.

PROTECTION STATUS

■ National protection

The Channel Islands are not part of the UK but are a direct dependency of the British Crown. As such, they have their own

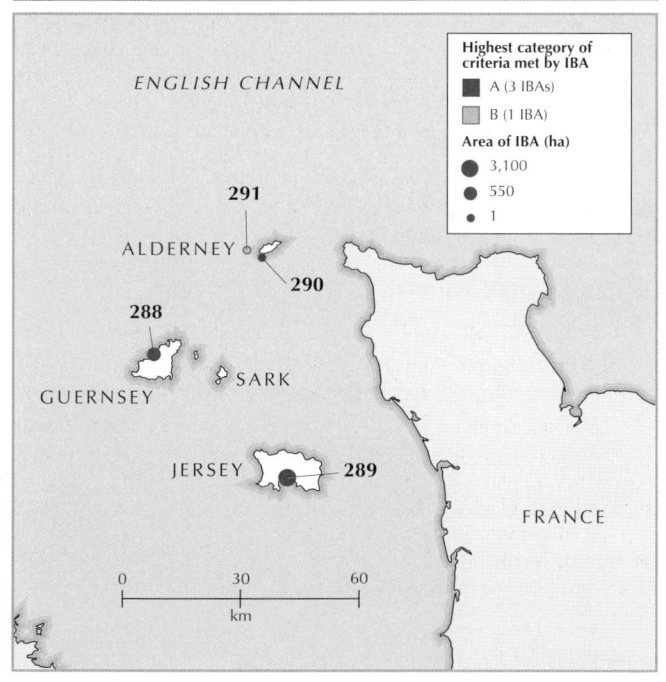

Map 2. Location, area and criteria category of Important Bird Areas in the Channel Islands.

ENGLISH CHANNEL

Highest category of criteria met by IBA
- A (3 IBAs)
- B (1 IBA)

Area of IBA (ha)
- 3,100
- 550
- 1

291
ALDERNEY
290
288
GUERNSEY
SARK
JERSEY 289
FRANCE

0   30   60
km

IBA code	National code	1989 code	International/National name	Administrative region	Area (ha)	Criteria
288	—	—	Guernsey shoreline	Channel Islands	550	A4i, B1i
289	—	—	Jersey shoreline	Channel Islands	3,100	A4i, B1i
290ᴾ	001	001	Les Etacs, Alderney	Channel Islands	1	A4ii, B1ii, B2
291ᴾ	002	001	Ortac, Alderney	Channel Islands	1	B2

Table 6. Summary of Important Bird Areas in the Channel Islands.   4 IBAs covering 38 km²

ᴾ Area of IBA has been considerably reduced since 1989 IBA inventory (Grimmett and Jones 1989).

Sites identified in the inventory of IBAs in the UK (Pritchard et al. 1992) but no longer considered to be IBAs
003 Alderney heathland; 005 Guernsey heathland; 006 Les Landes; 007 Jardin d'Olivet; 008 Noirmont; 009 Portelet Common; 010 Ouaisne; 011 La Lande du Ouest; 012 La Mare au Seigneur.

legislative systems (Jersey and Guernsey each have their own assemblies). The Channel Islands are not covered by the conservation legislation of the United Kingdom but have their own bird protection legislation: 1949 Protection of Wild Birds Ordinance (Guernsey), amended in 1974; 1950 Protection of Wild Birds (Alderney) Ordinance; 1963 Protection of Birds (Jersey) Law, amended in 1972. Neither Guernsey nor Alderney has specific legislation to protect wildlife habitats, but in Jersey the Island Planning (Amendment No. 3) Law 1983 provides for the protection of ecologically important

habitats through the designation of Sites of Special Interest (SSI). These are broadly similar to Sites of Special Scientific Interest (SSSIs) notified under the British Wildlife and Countryside Act 1981.

■ International protection
Because the Channel Islands are not part of the EU they are not covered by the Birds Directive or the Habitats Directive. Box 1 (page 728) summarizes the 'international agreements' to which the islands are bound.

■ SITE ACCOUNTS

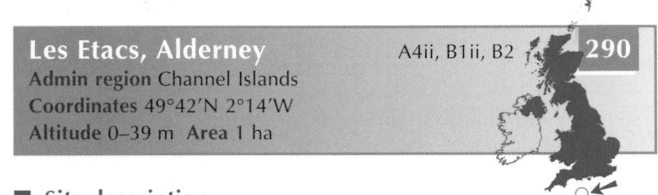

Guernsey shoreline   A4i, B1i   288
Admin region Channel Islands
Coordinates 49°25'N 2°35'W
Altitude 0–10 m   **Area** 550 ha

■ Site description
A rocky shoreline indented with many small bays of rocks, sand and shingle, running along the north-west coast and northern part of the east coast of Guernsey.

Habitats Scrub, Wetland (mudflat/sandflat; sand-dunes/sand beach; shingle/stony beach), Rocky areas (sea cliff/rocky shore)
Land-use Tourism/recreation

■ Birds

Species		Season	Year	Pop min	Pop max	Acc	Criteria
[1] *Arenaria interpres* Turnstone		W	1996	730	730	A	A4i, B1i, C3

1. Mean annual peak 1991–1996.

These coastal habitats are used by wintering waders and grebes, as well as breeding terns and gulls. Wintering *Charadrius hiaticula* occur in numbers important in a UK context (330 birds, 1991–1996, >1%).

■ Protection status
National None **International** None

■ Conservation issues

Threats Infrastructure (C), Recreation/tourism (B)

The coastline is under threat from land reclamation and marina development, with an increasing demand for leisure and recreational activities.

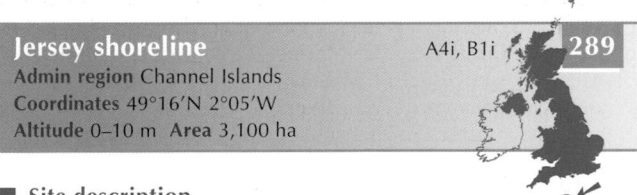

Jersey shoreline   A4i, B1i   289
Admin region Channel Islands
Coordinates 49°16'N 2°05'W
Altitude 0–10 m   **Area** 3,100 ha

■ Site description
The area comprises extensive intertidal zones, bays and stretches of rocky shoreline. Exposed lengths of rocky shore and sheltered areas of sand and silt support a characteristic flora and fauna, including important invertebrate communities.

Habitats Scrub (heathland), Wetland (mudflat/sandflat; sand-dunes/sand beach; shingle/stony beach), Rocky areas (sea cliff/rocky shore)
Land-use Tourism/recreation

■ Birds

Species		Season	Year	Pop min	Pop max	Acc	Criteria
[1] *Arenaria interpres* Turnstone		W	1996	700	700	A	A4i, B1i, C3

1. Mean annual peak 1991–1996.

The IBA is important for wintering waders and geese. *Branta bernicla bernicla* winter in numbers important in a UK context (1,200 birds, 1991–1996, >1%) and *Egretta garzetta* congregate in flocks of up to 150 birds (1991–1996).

■ Protection status
National None **International** None

■ Conservation issues

Threats Aquaculture/fisheries (U), Infrastructure (B), Other (B), Recreation/tourism (B)

The shoreline is threatened by coastal pollution ('Other' threat, above), potential marina developments, land reclamation schemes for building and shellfish-farming.

Les Etacs, Alderney   A4ii, B1ii, B2   290
Admin region Channel Islands
Coordinates 49°42'N 2°14'W
Altitude 0–39 m   **Area** 1 ha

■ Site description
A group of igneous rocks about 200 m off the west Alderney coast.

Habitats Rocky areas (100%; rock stacks/islets)
Land-use Not utilized

■ Birds

Species		Season	Year	Pop min	Pop max	Acc	Criteria
Sula bassana Gannet		B	1994	3,380	3,380	A	A4ii, B1ii, B2, C3

The IBA holds the larger of two important gannetries in the Channel Islands.

■ Protection status
National None **International** None

■ Conservation issues
No serious threats are known at the site.

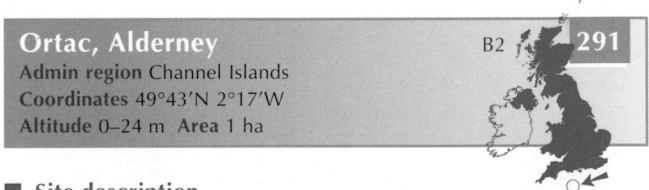

Ortac, Alderney   B2   291
Admin region Channel Islands
Coordinates 49°43'N 2°17'W
Altitude 0–24 m   **Area** 1 ha

■ Site description
A Cambrian sandstone rock located 4.5 km off the west coast of Alderney.

Habitats Rocky areas (100%; rock stacks/islets)
Land-use Not utilized

■ Birds

Species		Season	Year	Pop min	Pop max	Acc	Criteria
Sula bassana Gannet		B	1994	2,100	2,100	A	B2

The site supports the smaller of two gannetries in the Channel Islands.

■ Protection status
National None **International** None

■ Conservation issues
No serious threats are known at the site.

THE ISLE OF MAN

GENERAL INTRODUCTION

The Isle of Man is a self-governing Crown Dependency and as such has its own administrative system, with its own laws.

The Isle of Man covers an area of 587.9 km² and is located in the Irish Sea between England and Northern Ireland. There is a central highland area, with a smaller southern range adjacent to the west coast. The northern part of the island and part of the south-east are flat lowlands, much of which are cultivated. The coast is a mixture of cliffs and sandy/shingle-bays; the large hilly island of the Calf of Man lies off the south coast.

There are four IBAs in the Isle of Man, covering over 190 km². Three sites were identified in the 1989 inventory, with a further two identified in 1992 (Ballaugh Curraghs and The Isle of Man hills). The Ayres (former site 003) no longer qualifies, while Sea cliffs of Ramsey to Castleton and from Port St Mary to Peel (former site 001) has been renamed as Isle of Man sea cliffs (Table 7, Map 3).

ORNITHOLOGICAL IMPORTANCE

The Isle of Man IBAs mainly qualify for the review by holding significant populations of SPECs. The Isle of Man hills supports up to 30 pairs of breeding *Circus cyaneus*, the Calf of Man holds 10

pairs of breeding *Pyrrhocorax pyrrhocorax*, with the Isle of Man sea cliffs holding a further 71 pairs of *P. pyrrhocorax*, 210 pairs of gulls *Larus marinus*, up to 440 pairs of *Phalacrocorax aristotelis* and a population of *Larus argentatus* that is important in a European context. Although the *Circus cyaneus* is strictly a breeding season SPEC, its population at Ballaugh Curraghs during the winter is so significant (120 birds) that it has been allowed to qualify under B2.

The Isle of Man is not part of the EU so C criteria do not apply.

HABITATS

Both the Calf of Man (293) and the Isle of Man sea sliffs (295) are rocky coastal areas, with beaches and stacks. The Isle of Man hills (294) is an upland area of moorland and grassland, with associated wetland habitats. Ballaugh Curraghs (292) encompasses the largest area of willow carr and marshland on the island and has extensive areas of bog.

IMPACTS ON IBAs – LAND-USE AND THREATS

The main threats to birds in the Isle of Man are through changes in land-use. Much of the maritime heath inland from the coastal cliffs is traditionally managed, and continued grazing and controlled heather-burning regimes are important, especially for feeding *Pyrrhocorax pyrrhocorax*.

There is some direct disturbance to sites from human persecution of *Falco peregrinus* nests and tourism in coastal areas. Drainage and the consequent reduction in open water and encroachment of willow carr have considerably reduced the areas of bog at Ballaugh Curraghs since the 1860s. The main land-use change to The Isle of Man hills is from commercial afforestation, which initially provided nesting sites for *Circus cyaneus* as enclosure reduced grazing pressure and permitted the growth of tall heather. However, as plantations grow these nesting areas will again be reduced.

PROTECTION STATUS

■ National protection
The Wild Birds Protection Act 1887 was the first legislation passed in the Isle of Man to protect birds, and was extended and consolidated by subsequent Acts in 1932, 1955 and 1975. The Wildlife Act 1990 incorporates and updates the Protection of Birds Acts, extending protection to specified mammals and plants, and permits the creation of National Nature Reserves, Marine Reserves and the notification of Areas of Special Scientific Interest. It is based on the British Wildlife and Countryside Acts 1981–1985, and the Northern Ireland Nature Conservation and Amenity Lands Order 1985.

■ International protection
Because the Isle of Man is not part of the EU it is not covered the Wild Birds Directive. It is covered through the UK by several conventions (Box 1, page 728).

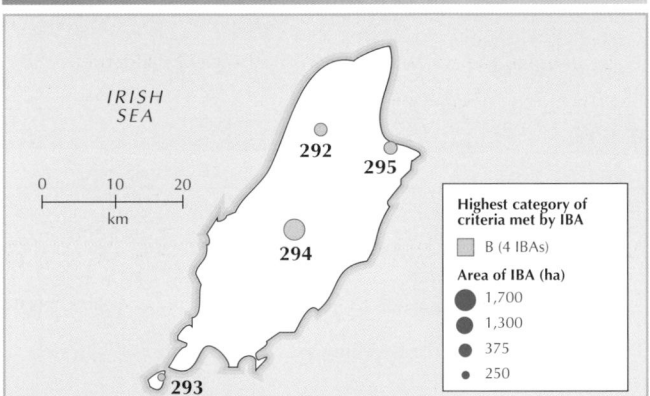

Map 3. Location, area and criteria category of Important Bird Areas in the Isle of Man.

IRISH SEA

0   10   20
km

292
295
294

293

Highest category of criteria met by IBA

☐ B (4 IBAs)

Area of IBA (ha)
● 1,700
● 1,300
● 375
• 250

Table 7. Summary of Important Bird Areas in the Isle of Man.   4 IBAs covering 190 km²

IBA code	National code	1989 code	International/ National name	Administrative region	Area (ha)	Criteria
292	004	—	Ballaugh Curraghs	Isle of Man	375	B2
293	002	002	Calf of Man	Isle of Man	250	B2
294	005	—	The Isle of Man hills	Isle of Man	17,100	B2
295	001	001	Isle of Man sea cliffs	Isle of Man	1,300	B1i, B2, B3

Site identified in the previous inventory of IBAs in Europe (Grimmett and Jones 1989), and the inventory of IBAs in the UK (Pritchard *et al.* 1992), but no longer considered to be an IBA 003 The Ayres.

SITE ACCOUNTS

Ballaugh Curraghs   B2   292
Admin region Isle of Man
Coordinates 54°19′N 4°30′W
Altitude 15–15 m **Area** 375 ha

■ Site description
Areas of bog and open water covering the flat glacial moraine deposits of the northern plain. Extensive areas of *Salix* carr and shrub surround the wetlands.

Habitats Scrub (scrub), Wetland (standing fresh water; raised bog; water-fringe vegetation; fen/transition mire/spring)
Land-use Not utilized

■ Birds

Species	Season	Year	Pop min	Pop max	Acc	Criteria
Circus cyaneus Hen Harrier	W	1995	—	120	A	B2

The IBA holds the largest *Circus cyaneus* roost in UK and Isle of Man.

■ Protection status
National None **International** None

■ Conservation issues

Threats Drainage (U)

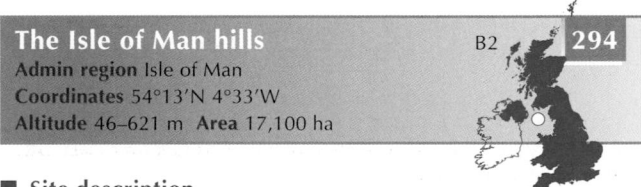

Calf of Man
Admin region Isle of Man
Coordinates 54°03'N 4°49'W
Altitude 0–128 m **Area** 250 ha

B2 293

■ Site description
Lying 400 m off the south-western tip of the Isle of Man, the Calf has a rugged coastline with steep slate cliffs of varying height. Habitat-types present include maritime heath and grassland. The island was farmed until 1958, and is currently grazed by Manx loaghtan sheep.

Habitats Scrub (heathland), Grassland, Rocky areas (sea cliff/rocky shore; scree/boulders)

Land-use Agriculture, Nature conservation/research

■ Birds

Species	Season	Year	Pop min	Pop max	Acc	Criteria
Pyrrhocorax pyrrhocorax Chough	R	1992	—	10	A	B2

The IBA is important for breeding seabirds and other cliff-nesters.

■ Protection status
National None **International** None

■ Conservation issues
No serious threats are known at the site, which is run as a bird observatory.

The Isle of Man hills
Admin region Isle of Man
Coordinates 54°13'N 4°33'W
Altitude 46–621 m **Area** 17,100 ha

B2 294

■ Site description

Habitats Scrub (heathland), Grassland, Wetland (river/stream), Artificial landscape (forestry plantation)

Land-use Agriculture, Forestry, Tourism/recreation

The area is characterized by upland heather and grass moorland, and includes 19 peaks over 400 m with the highest, Snaefell, standing

at 621 m. The hills run north-east to south-west, and are divided by a central valley formed by the Rivers Dhoo and Neb.

■ Birds

Species	Season	Year	Pop min	Pop max	Acc	Criteria
Circus cyaneus Hen Harrier	R	1990	29	—	A	B2

The site also holds important numbers of breeding *Pyrrhocorax pyrrhocorax* (5 pairs, 1992, 1%).

■ Protection status
National None **International** None

■ Conservation issues

Threats Agricultural intensification/expansion (U)

Overgrazing has reduced the botanical interest of the site.

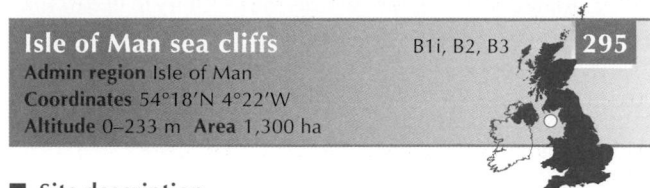

Isle of Man sea cliffs
Admin region Isle of Man
Coordinates 54°18'N 4°22'W
Altitude 0–233 m **Area** 1,300 ha

B1i, B2, B3 295

■ Site description
Stretches of slate cliffs of varying profile, some are high, steep and vertical, others are rounded and low. Several small bays and Baie ny Carrickey are also included in the site. Habitat-types present include agricultural land, moorland and maritime heath.

Habitats Scrub (heathland), Grassland, Rocky areas (sea cliff/rocky shore), Artificial landscape (arable land)

Land-use Agriculture

■ Birds

Species	Season	Year	Pop min	Pop max	Acc	Criteria
Phalacrocorax aristotelis Shag	B	1996	390	440	A	B3
[1] *Larus argentatus* Herring Gull	B	1994	5,800	5,800	A	B1i
[1] *Larus marinus* Great Black-backed Gull	B	1994	210	210	A	B3
Pyrrhocorax pyrrhocorax Chough	R	1992	43	43	A	B2

1. Colonies counted in different years.

The IBA is important for breeding seabirds and other cliff-nesters.

■ Protection status
National None **International** None

■ Conservation issues
No serious threats are known at the site. *Pyrrhocorax pyrrhocorax* monitoring is carried out annually by the Manx Chough Project.

REFERENCES

BAIN, R. AND MELLON, C. (1995) Northern Ireland White-fronted Goose monitoring project 1995. Belfast, UK: Royal Society for the Protection of Birds. Internal report.

BAINBRIDGE, I., WALKER, D. AND GRAY, M. (1994) Winter bird surveys on proposed Special Protection Areas in Scotland. Report 2: Western Isles winter shorebird counts. Report to Scottish Natural Heritage. Edinburgh, UK: Royal Society for the Protection of Birds. Internal report.

BATES, M. A., CLARK, I. R., WHITFIELD, D. AND ARNOTT, D. A. (1993) A survey of montane breeding birds with special reference to dotterel *Charadrius morinellus*, in selected sites throughout Scotland. Edinburgh, UK: Scottish Natural Heritage. Internal report.

BIGNAL, E. M., CURTIS, D. J AND MATTHEWS, J. (1988) Islay: land types, bird habitats and nature conservation. Part 1: land types and birds on Islay. Edinburgh, UK: Nature Conservancy Council (NCC CDS Report No 809). Internal report.

BROWN, A. F. AND SHEPHERD, K. (1991) Breeding birds of the South Pennine Moors. Peterborough, UK: Joint Nature Conservation Committee. Internal report.

BROWNE, S., AUSTIN, G. AND REHFISCH, M. (1996) Evidence of decline in the United Kingdom's non-estuarine coastal waters. *Wader Study Group Bulletin* 80: 25–27.

BUCKLAND, S. T., BELL, M. V. AND PICOZZI, N., EDS. (1990) *The birds of north-east Scotland.* Aberdeen, UK: North-east Scotland Bird Club.

CAITHNESS COUNTY BIRD RECORDER (1989–1993) Caithness bird data. Scottish Ornithologists' Club, Caithness Branch. Unpublished.

CAMPBELL, L. H. (1992) 1992 Bearded Tit survey. Sandy, UK: Royal Society for the Protection of Birds. Unpublished data.

CAMPBELL, L. H., CLEEVES, T. R., LINDLEY, P. AND STENNING, J. (1994) RSPB survey of moorland breeding birds in the Isle of Man 1990. Sandy, UK: Royal Society for the Protection of Birds. Internal report.

CHARLTON, T. AND ARCHER, R. (1996) North York Moors breeding wader survey, 1996. Newcastle, UK: Royal Society for the Protection of Birds. Internal report.

CHOWN, D. J. AND AKERS, P. (1984) A survey of the breeding birds of Bodmin Moor. Truro, UK: Cornwall Trust for Nature Conservation. Internal report.

CHRISTER, W. G. (1989) Winter concentrations of seaducks, divers, grebes and auks in Scapa Flow, Orkney 1988–1989. Orkney, UK: Royal Society for the Protection of Birds. Internal report.

COLOMBE, S., WOODLAND, H. AND ROBINS, M. (1993) Exmoor moorland bird survey 1992. Exeter, UK: Royal Society for the Protection of Birds. Internal report.

COOK, A. S., O'DOWD, B. AND DURDIN, C. J. (1994) Breeding redshanks on Essex saltmarshes in 1993. Sandy, UK: Royal Society for the Protection of Birds. Internal report.

COOK, A. S., O'DOWD, B., NORRIS, K. AND DURDIN, C. J. (1995) Breeding redshank on the Wash in 1995. Sandy, UK: Royal Society for the Protection of Birds. Internal report.

CRAIK, J. C. A. (1996) *Argyll bird report 1996*. Oban, UK: Argyll Bird Club.

CRANSWICK, P. A., KIRBY, J. S. AND WATERS, R. J. (1992) *Wildfowl and wader counts, 1991–1992*. Slimbridge, UK: British Trust for Ornithology/Wildfowl and Wetlands Trust/Royal Society for the Protection of Birds/Joint Nature Conservation Committee.

CRANSWICK, P. A., WATERS, R. J., EVANS, J. AND POLLITT, M. S. (1995) *The Wetland Bird Survey 1993–1994: wildfowl and wader counts*. Slimbridge, UK: British Trust for Ornithology/Wildfowl and Wetlands Trust/Royal Society for the Protection of Birds/Joint Nature Conservation Committee.

CRANSWICK, P. A., WATERS, R. J., EVANS, J. AND POLLITT, M. S. (1996) *The Wetland Bird Survey 1994–1995: wildfowl and wader counts*. Slimbridge, UK: British Trust for Ornithology/Wildfowl and Wetlands Trust/Royal Society for the Protection of Birds/Joint Nature Conservation Committee.

CRANSWICK, P. A., WATERS, R. J., MUSGROVE, A. J. AND POLLITT, M. S. (1997) *The Wetland Bird Survey 1995–1996: wildfowl and wader counts*. Slimbridge, UK: British Trust for Ornithology/Wildfowl and Wetlands Trust/Royal Society for the Protection of Birds/Joint Nature Conservation Committee.

CULLEN, J. P. AND JENNINGS, P. P. (1986) *The Birds of the Isle of Man*. Douglas, UK: Bridgeen Publications.

DAVIES, M. (1988) The importance of Britain's twites. *RSPB Conservation Review* 2: 91–94.

DAVIS, A. H., ED. (1991) *Avon Bird Report 1991*. Gloucester, UK: Avon Ornithological Group.

DAVIS, A. H., ED. (1992) *Avon Bird Report 1992*. Gloucester, UK: Avon Ornithological Group.

DAY, J. (1995) Marsh Harrier breeding data, 1977 to 1995. Sandy, UK: Royal Society for the Protection of Birds. Unpublished data.

DELANY, S. AND OGILVIE, M. (1994) 1994 (March) Greenland barnacle geese in Scotland. Peterborough, UK: Joint Nature Conservation Committee. Internal report.

DIX, T. AND CUNNINGHAM, P., EDS. (1991) *Outer Hebrides Bird Report 1989 and 1990*. Outer Hebrides Ornithologists' Group.

DIXON, T. (1995) Lower Derwent Valley Special Protection Area data. English Nature National Nature Reserve. Unpublished.

DORE, C. AND ELLIS, P. M. (1994) An estimate of the population of Whimbrel *Numenius phaeopus* breeding in Shetland during 1989–1992 and a comparison with previous estimates. Shetland, UK: Royal Society for the Protection of Birds. Internal report.

DUMFRIES AND GALLOWAY RAPTOR STUDY GROUP (1989) Raptor data. Glasgow, UK: Royal Society for the Protection of Birds. Unpublished.

EAST SCOTLAND TERN CONSERVATION GROUP (1996) East Scotland Tern Conservation Group Report 1996. Aberdeen, UK: Royal Society for the Protection of Birds. Unpublished.

ENGLISH NATURE (1995) Proposed Special Protection Area citations. Peterborough, UK: English Nature. Internal report.

ENVIRONMENT AND RESOURCE TECHNOLOGY LTD (1996) North Irish Sea bird review. Leatherhead, UK: produced by ENT on behalf of ESSO Exploration and Production UK Ltd. Internal report.

ETHERIDGE, B. (1995) Hen Harrier nest records, 1988 to 1995. Inverness, UK: Royal Society for the Protection of Birds. Unpublished data.

EVANS, R. (1994) Rinns of Islay breeding bird survey 1994. Glasgow, UK: Royal Society for the Protection of Birds. Unpublished data.

EVANS, R. (1995) 1977 to 1995 Moray Firth seaduck counts. Glasgow, UK: Royal Society for the Protection of Birds. Unpublished data.

FOX, A. D., NORRISS, D. W., STROUD, D. A. AND WILSON, H. J. (1994) Greenland White-fronted Geese in Ireland and Britain 1982/83–1993/94: the first twelve years of international conservation monitoring. Greenland White-fronted Goose Study Group. Internal report.

FOX, A. D. AND OGILVIE, M. A. (1988) *Aerial survey of Barnacle Geese Scotland, March 1988*. Slimbridge, UK: Wildfowl and Wetlands Trust.

GIBBONS, D. W., REID, J. B. AND CHAPMAN, R. A. (1993) *The New Atlas of Breeding Birds in Britain and Ireland: 1988–1991*. London: T. & A. D. Poyser Ltd.

GIBBONS, D. W. AND WOTTON, S. (1996) The Dartford Warbler in the UK in 1994. *British Birds* 89(5): 203–212.

GIBBONS, D. W., BAINBRIDGE, I. P., MUDGE, G., THARME, A. P. AND ELLIS, P. M. (1997) The status and distribution of the Red-throated Diver *Gavia stellata* in Britain in 1994. *Bird Study* 44: 194–205.

GIBBS, B. D., ED. (1994) *Somerset birds 1994*. Taunton, UK: Somerset Ornithological Society.

GIBSON, I., ED. (1996) Capercaillie counts. Edinburgh, UK: Scottish Natural Heritage/Royal Society for the Protection of Birds/Scottish Ornithologists' Club. Unpublished data.

GILL, P. (1993) 1993 Shetland in-bye breeding wader survey. Shetland, UK: Royal Society for the Protection of Birds. Unpublished data.

GORDON, J. AND ROTHWELL, A. (1995) The breeding bird populations of Sites of Special Scientific Interest in Lewis and Harris, 1995. Edinburgh, UK: Royal Society for the Protection of Birds. Internal report for Scottish Natural Heritage.

GRAY, M. AND BAINBRIDGE, I. (1994) Winter bird surveys on proposed Special Protection Areas in Scotland. Report 1: Orkney winter shorebird counts. Internal report for Scottish Natural Heritage. Edinburgh, UK: Royal Society for the Protection of Birds.

GRAY, M., BABBS, S., WHYTE, C., MEEK, E. R. AND O'BRIEN, M. (1995) Wetland and marginal moorland: a survey of the breeding birds of unprotected sites 1993–94. Edinburgh, UK: Royal Society for the Protection of Birds. Internal report.

GREEN, M. AND WILLIAMS, I. T. (1992) The status of the Chough in Wales 1992. Newtown, UK: Royal Society for the Protection of Birds. Internal report.

GREEN, R. (1992) 1992 Golden Eagle survey. Edinburgh, UK: Royal Society for the Protection of Birds coordinated data. Unpublished data.

GREEN, R. (1995) 1995 Corncrake survey. Edinburgh, UK: Royal Society for the Protection of Birds/Scottish Natural Heritage. Unpublished data.

GREEN, R. (1996) 1996 Corncrake survey. Edinburgh, UK: Royal Society for the Protection of Birds/Scottish Natural Heritage. Unpublished data.

GREEN, R. (1997) 1997 Corncrake survey. Edinburgh, UK: Royal Society for the Protection of Birds/Scottish Natural Heritage. Unpublished data.

GRIMMETT, R. A. AND JONES, T. A. (1989) *Important Bird Areas in Europe*. Cambridge, UK: International Council for Bird Preservation (ICBP Techn. Publ. 9).

HANCOCK, M. H., GIBBONS, D. W. AND THOMPSON, P. S. (1997) The status of breeding greenshank (*Tringa nebularia*) in the United Kingdom in 1995. *Bird Study* 33 (3): 290–302.

HAYMAN, P., RILEY, G. D., McNEILL, D. AND SUTTON, M. (1995) Breckland stone curlew protection report 1995. Norwich, UK: Royal Society for the Protection of Birds. Internal report.

HEATH, M. F. AND BORGGREVE, C. (2000) *BirdLife International/EBCC European Bird Database 1998*. Cambridge, UK: BirdLife International.

HENLY, C. J. (1995) Forth area bird report 1994. *Forth Naturalist and Historian* 18: 21–55.

HENLY, C. J. (1996) Forth area bird report 1995. *Forth Naturalist and Historian* 19: 45–82.

HIGHLAND RAPTOR STUDY GROUP (1991–1995) Highland Raptor Study Group data. Inverness, UK: Royal Society for the Protection of Birds. Unpublished.

HOBLYN, R. (1993) Breckland woodlark survey 1993. Santon Downham, UK: Forest Enterprise. Internal report.

HOBLYN, R. (1995) Breckland woodlark survey 1994. Santon Downham, UK: Forest Enterprise. Internal report.

IMAGE, R. AND JAMES, L. (1995) Harrier protection scheme report: West Norfolk and Lincolnshire, 1995. Norwich, UK: Royal Society for the Protection of Birds. Internal report.

JAMES, R. M. R., ED. (1995) *Derbyshire bird report 1994*. Derby, UK: The Derbyshire Ornithological Society.

JOINT NATURE CONSERVATION COMMITTEE (1996) Seabird Colony Register data, 1980 to 1996. Aberdeen, UK: JNCC Seabirds and Cetaceans Branch.

JOHNSTON, R. D. AND STENHOUSE, I. (1993) Survey of proposed and possible Special Protection Areas in the Western Isles, Shetland and Caithness. Edinburgh, UK: Scottish Natural Heritage. Internal report.

KIRBY, J. S. (1990) Numbers, distribution and habitat preference of waders wintering on the Isles of Scilly. *Wader Study Group Bulletin* 57: 47–52.

LACK, P. (1986) *The atlas of winter birds in Britain and Ireland*. Calton, UK: T. & A. D. Poyser Ltd.

LILLY, R. (1996) 1993 to 1996 goose data for Islay. Scottish Natural Heritage. Unpublished.

LIMBERT, M., ED. (1994) *Doncaster bird report 1993*. Doncaster, UK: Doncaster and District Ornithological Society.

LLOYD, C., TASKER, M. L. AND PARTRIDGE, K. (1991) *The status of seabirds in Britain and Ireland*. London: T. & A. D. Poyser Ltd.

LORD, D. (1994) CBWPS Stonechat survey, June 1993. In *Birds in Cornwall 1994: CBWPS sixty-fourth Annual Report*. Redruth, UK: Cornwall Bird Watching and Protection Society.

MEEK, E. (1992) 1992 Orkney Skua survey. Orkney, UK: Royal Society for the Protection of Birds. Unpublished data.

MORRIS, A., BURGES, D., FULLER, R. J., EVANS, A. D. AND SMITH, K. W. (1994) The status and distribution of Nightjars *Caprimulgus europaeus* in Britain in 1992. A report to the British Trust for Ornithology. *Bird Study* 41: 181–191.

MOYES, S. B. AND ROBERTSON, D. (1991) Studies of Sedge Warblers (1989–91) and Water Rail (1991) in the Tay reedbeds. Edinburgh, UK: Scottish Natural Heritage. Internal report.

NEWBERY, P. E. (1993) Crane Species Action Plan. Sandy, UK: Royal Society for the Protection of Birds. Internal report.

O'BRIEN, M. (1994) Survey of breeding waders on Scottish lowlands 1992/93: key sites. Interim Report. Edinburgh, UK: Royal Society for the Protection of Birds. Internal report.

O'BRIEN, M. (1995) 1995 Red-necked Phalarope survey. Edinburgh, UK: Royal Society for the Protection of Birds. Unpublished data.

O'DONNELL, J. (1995) Breeding season in the Forest of Bowland 1994: birds of prey. Denby Dale, UK: Royal Society for the Protection of Birds. Internal report.

PARR, S. (1992) 1970–1992 Merlin nest occupancy in Wales. Newtown, UK: Royal Society for the Protection of Birds. Unpublished data.

PILCHER, R. (1991) A survey of breeding waders and wildfowl within the Arun Valley, West Sussex. Shoreham, UK: Royal Society for the Protection of Birds. Internal report.

POXTON, I. R. (1987) Breeding status of the ring ouzel in south east Scotland 1985–86. *Scottish Birds* 14(4): 205–208.

PRITCHARD, D. E., HOUSDEN, S. D., MUDGE, G. P., GALBRAITH, C. A. AND PIENKOWSKI, M. A., EDS. (1992) *Important Bird Areas in the UK including the Channel Islands and the Isle of Man*. Sandy, UK: Royal Society for the Protection of Birds.

PRYS-JONES, R. P. AND DAVIS, P. E. (1990) The abundance and distribution of wildfowl and waders on Carmarthen Bay (Taf/Tywi/Gwendraeth). Thetford, UK: British Trust for Ornithology. Internal report.

RATCLIFFE, N., VAUGHAN, D., WHYTE, C. AND SHEPHERD, M. (1997) The status of storm petrels *Hydrobates pelagicus* on Mousa, Shetland. Sandy, UK: Royal Society for the Protection of Birds. Internal report.

RAW, D., ED. (1994) *Durham Upland Bird Study Group annual report 1994*. Durham, UK: Durham Upland Bird Study Group.

REBECCA, G. (1995) 1993/94 Merlin survey. Edinburgh, UK: Royal Society for the Protection of Birds. Unpublished data.

REED, T. M. AND PARR, S. J. (1997) The importance and future conservation of the Welsh islands for birds. In: P. M. Rhind, T. H. Blackstock and S. J. Parr, eds. *Welsh Islands: ecology, conservation and land use*. Bangor, UK: Countryside Council for Wales.

RIBBANDS, J. B. (1990) Wintering eiders, ducks and auks in the waters of Eynhallow Sound, Wyre Sound, Rousay Sound, and Girsay Sound, Orkney 1989–90. Peterborough, UK: Nature Conservancy Council. Internal report.

ROBINSON, M. C., BAINES, D. AND MATTINGLEY, W. (1993) Survey of black grouse leks in Perthshire. *Scottish Birds* 17(1): 10–26.

ROLLIE, C. J., ED. (1995) Raptor data. South Strathclyde Raptor Study Group. Glasgow, UK: Royal Society for the Protection of Birds. Unpublished.

ROONEY, M. E. S. AND EVE, V. (1994) The number, distribution and breeding success of ringed plover and oystercatcher on the North Norfolk Coast 1993. Norwich, UK: Royal Society for the Protection of Birds. Internal report.

RSPB (1996) RSPB Dungeness to Pett Levels IBA winter peak counts 1993/94 to 1995/96. Brighton, UK: Royal Society for the Protection of Birds. Unpublished data.

RSPB (1996) RSPB country/regional conservation staff data, 1989 to 1996. Sandy, UK: Royal Society for the Protection of Birds. Unpublished data.

RSPB (1996) RSPB Reserve Annual Reports, 1991 to 1996. Sandy, UK: Royal Society for the Protection of Birds. Internal report.

RSPB/JNCC Seabirds and Cetaceans Branch (1995) National tern monitoring 1987 to 1995. Aberdeen, UK: Royal Society for the Protection of Birds/ Joint Nature Conservation Committee. Unpublished data.

SAPSFORD, A. M. AND MOORE, A. S. (1994) Second International Chough Census: Isle of Man Report. *Peregrine* 7(2): 161–169.

SEARS, J., ELLIS, P. M., SUDDABY, D. AND HARROP, H. R. (1995) 1992 Shetland Whimbrel and Golden Plover survey. Shetland, UK: Royal Society for the Protection of Birds. Unpublished data.

SEARS, J., ELLIS, P. M., SUDDABY, D. AND HARROP, H. R. (1995) The status of breeding Arctic Skuas *Stercorarius parasiticus* and Great Skuas *S. skua* in Shetland in 1992. Shetland, UK: Royal Society for the Protection of Birds. Internal report.

SITTERS, H. P. (1986) 1986 Woodlark survey. Thetford, UK: British Trust for Ornithology. Internal report.

SMITH, K. W. (1996) 1990 to 1996 Booming Bittern data. Sandy, UK: Royal Society for the Protection of Birds. Unpublished data.

SCOTTISH NATURAL HERITAGE (1995) *Special Protection Area and Sites of Special Scientific Interest schedules*. Edinburgh, UK: Scottish Natural Heritage.

STROUD, D. A. (1989) *Birds on Coll and Tiree: status, habitats and conservation*. Edinburgh, UK: Nature Conservancy Council (NCC CDS Report No. 27).

SUDDABY, D. (1994) Orkney and Shetland breeding Arctic Tern monitoring, 1990 to 1994. Shetland, UK: Royal Society for the Protection of Birds. Unpublished data.

SUDDABY, D. (1994) Orkney and Shetland breeding Skua monitoring, 1990 to 1994. Shetland, UK: Royal Society for the Protection of Birds. Unpublished data.

SUMMERS, R. (1991) Slavonian grebe newsletter, 1991. Inverness, UK: Royal Society for the Protection of Birds. Internal report.

SUMMERS, R. (1992) Slavonian grebe newsletter, 1992. Inverness, UK: Royal Society for the Protection of Birds. Internal report.

SUMMERS, R. (1993) Slavonian grebe newsletter, 1993. Inverness, UK: Royal Society for the Protection of Birds. Internal report.

SUMMERS, R. (1994) Slavonian grebe newsletter, 1994. Inverness, UK: Royal Society for the Protection of Birds. Internal report.

SUMMERS, R. (1995) Slavonian grebe newsletter, 1995. Inverness, UK: Royal Society for the Protection of Birds. Internal report.

SUMMERS, R. (1995) 1992/93 to 1994/95 pinewood bird surveys. Inverness, UK: Royal Society for the Protection of Birds. Unpublished data.

SYMES, N. (1994) 1993 and 1994 Heathlands Project data. Exeter, UK: Royal Society for the Protection of Birds. Unpublished data.

TASKER, M. AND REYNOLDS, P. (1983) A survey of Tystie (*Cepphus grylle*) distribution in Orkney, April 1983. Aberdeen, UK: Nature Conservancy Council. Internal report.

TAYLOR, S. M., ED. (1988) *Avon Bird Report 1988*. Gloucester, UK: Avon Ornithological Group.

TAYLOR, S. M., ED. (1989) *Avon Bird Report 1989*. Gloucester, UK: Avon Ornithological Group.

TAYLOR, S. M., ED. (1990) *Avon Bird Report 1990*. Gloucester, UK: Avon Ornithological Group.

THE NATIONAL TRUST (1995) Strangford Lough wildlife scheme. UK: The National Trust. Internal report.

THOMPSON, K. AND HARDING, N. J. (1994) Winter bird surveys on proposed Special Protection Areas in Scotland. Report 3: winter goose surveys in Kintyre, Wigtownshire and Flanders Moss. Edinburgh, UK: Royal Society for the Protection of Birds. Internal report for Scottish Natural Heritage.

TICKNER, M. (1994) Killough Harbour wildfowl counts, 1993–94. Belfast, UK: Royal Society for the Protection of Birds. Unpublished data.

TUCKER, G. M. AND HEATH, M. F. (1994) *Birds in Europe: their conservation status*. Cambridge, UK: BirdLife International (BirdLife Conservation Series no. 3).

UNDERHILL, M. C., GITTINGS, T., CALLAGHAN, D. A., KIRBY, J. S., HUGHES, B. AND DELANEY, S. (1998) Pre-breeding status and distribution of the Common Scoter *Melanitta nigra* in Britain and Ireland in 1995. *Bird Study* 45(2): 146–156.

VAUGHAN, D. AND GIBBONS, D. W. (1998) The study of breeding Storm Petrels *Hydrobates pelagicus* on Skokholm Island in 1995. *Seabird* 20: 12–21.

VERON, P. K., ED. (1997) *Important sites for birds in the Channel Islands*. Guernsey: La Société Guernesiaise.

WATERS, R. J. AND CRANSWICK, P. A. (1993) *The Wetland Bird Survey 1992–93: wildfowl and wader counts*. Slimbridge, UK: British Trust for Ornithology/Wildfowl and Wetlands Trust/Royal Society for the Protection of Birds/Joint Nature Conservation Committee.

WATSON, A. AND RAE, R. (1986) Dotterel numbers, habitat and breeding success in Scotland. *Scottish Birds* 14: 191–198.

WEAVER, D. J. (1995) Broads ESA breeding wader survey 1995. Norwich, UK: Royal Society for the Protection of Birds. Internal report.

WHYTE, C. AND O'BRIEN, M. (1995) Changes in the numbers of breeding waders on machair habitats on the Uists and Benbecula, 1983–1995. Edinburgh, UK: Royal Society for the Protection of Birds.

WOOD, D. (1996) An aerial survey of Great Cormorants (*Phalacrocorax carbo*) nesting in Orkney during 1995. Pp. 63–66 in C. J. Booth, M. Cuthbert and B. Adams, eds. *Orkney Bird Report 1995*.

■ APPENDICES

Biodiversity Convention: Convention on Biological Diversity (CBD)

The Convention on Biological Diversity has three objectives:
- the conservation of biological diversity,
- the sustainable use of its components, and
- the fair and equitable sharing of the benefits arising out of the use of genetic resources.

Covering almost every aspect of conservation and sustainable use, the CBD has become an important framework for conservation-related activities on the regional and national level.

For the conservation of biodiversity the primary approach is *in situ* conservation. Parties have to identify components of biodiversity important for its conservation and sustainable use (Article 7), *inter alia* ecosystems and habitats with large numbers of threatened species or required by migratory species (Annex I). Clearly, national lists of IBAs should become part of these inventories which should be included in national biodiversity strategies and action plans required from the parties by Article 6.

Article 8 outlines a framework for the *in situ* conservation activities by the parties. They are asked to establish a system of protected areas or areas where special measures need to be taken to conserve biodiversity (Article 8a). Thus, in cases where strong protection might not be appropriate they should find alternative ways to ensure the ecological integrity of the sites in question. This should be done in a rational way, using guidelines which need to be developed (Article 8b). As the lists of IBAs have been compiled following strict criteria on a scientific basis, harmonized with existing criteria under the EC Birds Directive and Ramsar Convention, they can serve well as part of a national system of protected and other areas with a focus on conservation.

Effective conservation of biological diversity needs plans and management strategies (Article 8c, f) for the rehabilitation and restoration of degraded ecosystems and the recovery of threatened species. IBAs in most cases need to be managed to enhance their ability to support important bird populations in the long-term. To mitigate negative effects on IBAs these strategies also need to take into account the adjacent areas and to promote their environmentally sound and sustainable development (Article 8e). The CBD also asks for the prevention of introduction and the control and eradication of alien species which threaten ecosystems, habitats and species (Article 8h) and urges parties to set up an effective system of environmental impact assessment. Impact assessment more generally is called for in Article 14.

Overall, the CBD clearly sets a framework for ensuring that IBAs obtain sufficient attention to ensure their long-term ecological integrity. The national biodiversity strategies and action plans which have recently been developed in almost all European countries should reflect the role of IBAs as scientifically-based elements of the national implementation of the provisions of the convention.

Pan-European Biological and Landscape Diversity Strategy

In October 1995, European environmental ministers endorsed the Pan-European Strategy for Biological and Landscape Diversity (PEBLDS), a framework for strengthening and building on existing initiatives and programmes, drawn up as a pan-European response to the Convention on Biological Diversity.

The Strategy is designed to strengthen and build on existing initiatives and programmes including the Convention on Biological Diversity, the Bern Convention, the Bonn Convention, the European Conservation Strategy (1990), the Dobris and Lucerne Ministerial Conferences (1991, 1993) and *inter alia* the United Nations Conference on Environment and Development (1992).

The Pan-European Strategy is defined for a 20 year period, and divided into four five-year Action Plans. Eleven Action Themes run through each Action Plan, of which one is to establish a Pan-European Ecological Network of protected areas (Council of Europe *et al.* 1996).

European Community Biodiversity Strategy

The European Community ratified the Convention on Biological Diversity in 1993 and in 1998, the European Commission adopted a communication on a European Community Biodiversity Strategy. The aims of this strategy are to anticipate, prevent and attack at source the causes of significant reductions in and losses of biodiversity.

The strategy defines general objectives in the four horizontal policy areas set out in the convention:
- Conservation and sustainable use of biodiversity
- Sharing benefits arising out of the use of genetic resources
- Research, identification, monitoring and exchange of information
- Education, awareness and training.

The strategy then focuses on the integration of biodiversity concerns into relevant sectoral policies, setting out sectoral policy objectives, which should be achieved through specific action plans or other measures for the following policy areas: conservation of natural resources, agriculture, fisheries, regional policies and spatial planning, forests, energy and transport, tourism and development and economic cooperation.

These objectives reflect a recognition that there is a major gap in existing Community conservation policies concerning the impact of relevant sectoral policy measures on biodiversity, both inside and outside of protected areas.

Ramsar Convention: Convention on Wetlands of International Importance especially as Waterfowl Habitat (Ramsar, 1971)

The Ramsar Convention is an inter-governmental treaty which provides the framework for international cooperation for the conservation and wise use of wetlands.

The main undertakings accepted by the contracting parties to the Ramsar Convention are to:
- designate suitable wetlands within (their) territory for inclusion in a List of Wetlands of International Importance (the Ramsar List) (Article 2.1)
- formulate and implement their planning so as to promote the conservation of the wetlands included in the List, and as far as possible, the wise use of wetlands in their territory (Article 3.1)
- promote the conservation of wetlands and waterfowl by establishing nature reserves on wetlands whether they are included in the List or not, and provide adequately for their wardening (Article 4.1).

Each contracting party must designate at least one site for inclusion in the List at the time it joins the Convention (Article 2.4). Specific criteria have been drawn up under the Convention to aid the identification of sites of international importance. One of the objectives of the IBA inventory is to facilitate the designation of wetlands of international importance under the Ramsar Convention. The criteria used to identify IBAs are consistent with the Ramsar criteria for waterbirds (see Box 4, 'Identifying IBAs' chapter). Therefore wetland IBAs meeting these criteria should be considered for addition to the Ramsar List.

Also of relevance is the Montreux Record, a register of selected wetlands on the Ramsar List where changes in ecological character have occurred, are occurring or are likely to occur as a result of technological developments, pollution or other human interference. This is a very important tool because it identifies specific sites for international conservation attention. Other site-conservation tools have been developed under the convention such as guidelines on management planning and on monitoring.

Appendix 1 ... continued. Descriptions of international agreements relevant to the protection and management of sites for nature conservation in Europe.

Bonn Convention: Convention on the conservation of migratory species of wild animals (CMS)

The fundamental objective of the Bonn Convention is to protect migratory species (not only birds but also migratory mammals, fish and invertebrates) in recognition of the fact that protection is needed throughout every part of their migratory ranges, and that this requires international cooperation and action. If a party to the Convention is a Range State of a migratory species listed in Appendix I or Appendix II, it accepts an obligation to provide strict protection for species in Appendix I and to endeavour to conclude Agreements with other Range States for the conservation and management of species in Appendix II. Appendix I species are in danger of extinction throughout all, or a major part, of their range, and Appendix II species are those which would benefit from international cooperation in their conservation and management.

For Appendix I species, Parties that are Range States are obliged to endeavour, amongst other things, to:
- conserve and, where feasible and appropriate, restore those habitats of the species which are of importance in removing the species from danger of extinction (Article III 4a); and
- with regard to the Agreements which Parties are encouraged to conclude for Appendix II species, each Agreement should, where appropriate and feasible, provide for the maintenance of a network of suitable habitats appropriately disposed in relation to the migration routes.

Agreement on the Conservation of African-Eurasian Migratory Waterbirds (AEWA)
AEWA is an Agreement under the Bonn Convention, which can be signed and ratified by a Range State, irrespective of whether the state has signed or ratified the Bonn Convention. AEWA aims to create the legal basis for a concerted conservation policy among the range states of all migratory waterbird species and populations which migrate in the African-Eurasian flyway, irrespective of their current conservation status. The Agreement provides a framework for conservation action, monitoring, research and management of several globally important bird-migration systems. As such, it has close links to the IBA Programme and the Ramsar Convention.

World Heritage Convention: Convention concerning the Protection of the World Cultural and Natural Heritage

The aim of the World Heritage Convention is the protection of natural and cultural areas of outstanding universal value. Such sites and monuments are considered to be of such exceptional value that their protection is the responsibility of all mankind, and thus international cooperation in order to contribute effectively to this protection is sought. Each site nominated by the Parties for inclusion in the World Heritage List is assessed by a World Heritage Committee, which in the case of natural sites, is advised by experts from IUCN.

The Convention imposes a legal duty on each party to do its utmost to protect designated sites. Each party is required to contribute to the World Heritage Fund which may be used to secure the protection of World Heritage Sites. A mechanism is provided for the transfer of resources from rich to poor countries for the safeguard of mankind's common heritage.

UNESCO's Man and the Biosphere Programme

One of the aims of the Man and the Biosphere Programme of UNESCO (United Nations Educational, Scientific and Cultural Organization) is to develop within the natural and social services a basis for the rational use and conservation of the resources of the biosphere.

MAB Project 8 (one of 14 international themes or projects in the Programme) is 'the conservation of natural areas and the genetic material they contain'. The objective is to create a worldwide network of reserves (Biosphere Reserves), with each reserve qualifying under one or more of the following categories:

- representative examples of natural biomes;
- unique communities or areas with unusual natural features of exceptional interest such as a population of a globally rare species;
- examples of harmonious landscapes resulting from traditional patterns of land-use;
- examples of modified or degraded ecosystems capable of being restored to more natural conditions.

Each Biosphere Reserve needs to be large enough to comprise an effective conservation unit and must have adequate long-term protection.

Bern Convention: Convention on the Conservation of European Wildlife and Natural Habitats

Contracting parties to the Bern Convention are required to maintain populations of wild flora and fauna and give particular emphasis to endangered and vulnerable species, including endangered and vulnerable migratory species. Specifically, each Contracting party undertakes to:
- take appropriate and necessary legislative and administrative measures to ensure the conservation of the habitats of the wild flora and fauna species especially those specified in Appendices I and II, and the conservation of endangered natural habitats (Article 4.1)
- give special attention to the protection of areas that are of importance for the migratory species specified in Appendix II and III and which are appropriately situated in relation to migration routes, as wintering, staging, feeding, breeding or moulting areas (Article 4.3)
- prohibit the deliberate damage to or destruction of breeding or resting sites of Appendix II species (Article 6.b).

Article 6.b is very specific and strict; however, the explanatory report of the Convention states that it should apply only to important breeding and resting sites. Implementation of Article 6.b necessitates the identification of important breeding and resting sites for species on Appendix II (Lyster 1985). Parties may make exceptions to their obligations under Articles 4 and 6, but only in very limited circumstances (such as interests of public health and safety) and use of the exception must never be detrimental to the survival of the population concerned (Article 9).

Appendix I is a list of plants. Appendix II is a long list of strictly protected faunal species which includes a high proportion of the European avifauna, with Appendix III covering almost all the bird species not included in Appendix II, with the exception of 11 species.

The Emerald Network
The Emerald network is an initiative, under the Bern Convention, to extend the Natura 2000 network of protected areas (see 'Habitats Directive', below) beyond the EU to cover member countries of the Council of Europe.

In June 1989 the Standing Committee of the Bern Convention held an extraordinary meeting exclusively devoted to habitat conservation within the Convention. One of the operative recommendations adopted at the meeting was Recommendation No. 16 (1989) 'on Areas of Special Conservation Interest' (ASCIs) within which the Standing Committee recommended Parties to take steps to designate Areas of Special Conservation Interest to ensure that necessary and appropriate conservation measures are taken for each area situated within their territory or under their responsibility where that area fits one or several of the following conditions:
a. It contributes substantially to the survival of threatened species, endemic species, or any species listed in Appendices I and II of the Convention;
b. It supports significant numbers of species in an area of high species diversity or supports important populations of one or more species;
c. It contains an important and/or representative sample of endangered habitat types;
d. It contains an outstanding example of a particular habitat-type or a mosaic of different habitat-types;

Appendix 1 ... continued. Descriptions of international agreements relevant to the protection and management of sites for nature conservation in Europe.

e. It represents an important area for one or more migratory species;

f. It otherwise contributes substantially to the achievement of the objectives of the Convention.

In 1996 Resolution No. 3 was adopted which resolved to 'set up a network (Emerald) which would include the Areas of Special Conservation Interest designated following its Recommendation No. 16'.

Member States of the European Union will satisfy the habitat protection requirements of the Bern Convention mostly through the designation of sites to the Natura 2000 network (see below). The Special Areas for Conservation and Special Protection Areas for birds in Natura 2000 automatically become Areas of Special Conservation Interest of the Emerald Network.

Most of the work to be done in building the Emerald Network will be concentrated in states which are not members of the European Union. In this way it is aimed to extend an homogenous network of areas over a wide area including the whole of Europe.

EC Birds Directive: Council Directive on the conservation of wild birds (79/409/EEC)

The Birds Directive, adopted in 1979, concerns the conservation and protection of all wild bird species in the European territory of the Member States of the European Union (currently 15 Member States, excluding Greenland). All Member States are committed to providing a sufficient variety of habitats and to preserve, maintain or restore an adequate proportion of these for all wild bird species in their territory. Special conservation measures shall be taken for the habitats of two categories of birds: species and subspecies listed in Annex I of the Directive and other migratory species not included in this Annex (Article 4.1–4.2). This requirement refers in particular to the classification of Special Protection Areas which are considered the 'most suitable' sites for the conservation of the species concerned. Each Member State has to designate such areas for all Annex I species and subspecies (currently 181 taxa in total, see Appendix 2b) occurring on its territory (Article 4.1). This concerns all species for which regularly occupied habitats can be identified so that the objective 'to ensure their survival and reproduction in their area of distribution' can be fulfilled. The number and the area of habitats to be designated as Special Protection Areas should be determined on the basis of the protection requirements and the conservation status of the species involved. Hence for an endangered, localized species a larger proportion of its habitats should be designated, than for a widespread, less threatened species.

With respect to regularly occurring migratory species not listed in Annex I, 'similar measures' have to be taken including the designation of Special Protection Areas as regards their breeding, moulting and wintering areas and staging posts along their migration routes (Article 4.2). Special attention shall be paid to the protection of wetlands and particularly to wetlands of international importance. The latter is considered a reference to the Ramsar Convention. In this IBA inventory the category of 'other migratory species' has been largely confined to waterbirds, seabirds and birds of prey during migration (criteria categories C3–C5) because it was considered appropriate to stay as close as possible to the criteria applied in the previous pan-European IBA inventory in 1989 (Grimmett and Jones 1989). However, other migratory species could be covered as well depending on their 'need of protection' within the territory of the Member States of the European Union.

The network of Special Protection Areas should form a coherent whole, which, together with the sites designated under the Habitats Directive

(92/43/EEC), will form the ecological network Natura 2000 which is required to be completed in 2004. The protection regime applicable to Special Protection Areas, originally laid down in Article 4.4, has now been replaced by Article 6.2–6.4 of the Habitats Directive.

EC Habitats Directive: Council Directive on the conservation of natural habitats of wild fauna and flora (92/43/EEC)

The Habitats Directive aims, among other things, to create a coherent ecological network (Natura 2000) of Special Areas for Conservation (SACs), setting a minimum standard for biodiversity conservation in the EU. This network should be designed to maintain the distribution and abundance of threatened species and habitats, both terrestrial and marine. This network will contain all Special Protection Areas designated under the Birds Directive. Regarding habitats, each Member State is under an obligation to contribute to Natura 2000 in proportion to the representation within its terrritory of the natural habitat-types listed in Annex I and habitats of the species referred to in Annex II (animals other than birds). Member States are required to draw up lists of Sites of Community Interest (SCIs) following these criteria and from these the European Commission will establish a list of sites of Community importance. Each Member State shall then be required (by 2004) to designate the listed sites of Community importance as Special Areas for Conservation (SACs).

Member States are required to take necessary and appropriate conservation measures for SACs (Article 6). Necessary conservation measures include, if appropriate, management plans specifically designed for the sites or integrated into other development plans, and appropriate statutory, administrative or contractual measures. These measures should correspond to the ecological requirements of the natural habitat-types in Annex I and the species in Annex II present on the sites (note that this requirement does not apply to sites designated under the Birds Directive only). Member states are required to avoid significant disturbance and habitat deterioration in SACs with respect to the habitats (Annex I), habitats of the species, and the species (Annex II) for which the areas have been designated. They are also required to assess the implications for the SAC of any plan or project likely to have a significant effect thereon, and to ensure that the competent national authorities agree to the plan or project only after having ascertained that it will not adversely affect the integrity of the site and, if appropriate, after having obtained the opinion of the general public. Also they should take all compensatory measures necessary to ensure that the overall coherence of Natura 2000 is protected, if a plan or project must be carried out at or near a SAC for imperative reasons of overriding public interest, including those of a social or economic nature. Where the site concerned hosts a priority natural habitat-type and/or a priority species, the only reasons which may be considered are those relating to human health or public safety, to beneficial consequences of primary importance for the environment or, further to an opinion from the Commission, to other imperative reasons of overriding public interest.

LIFE-Nature
LIFE-Nature is an EU funding line (Regulation 1973/92/EEC, as modified by Regulation (EC) 1404/96 of 15 July 1996, under review to cover the period 2000–2003) which supports EU environmental legislation, including the Birds and Habitats Directives, and has supported work at many IBAs across Europe, within and outside the EU.

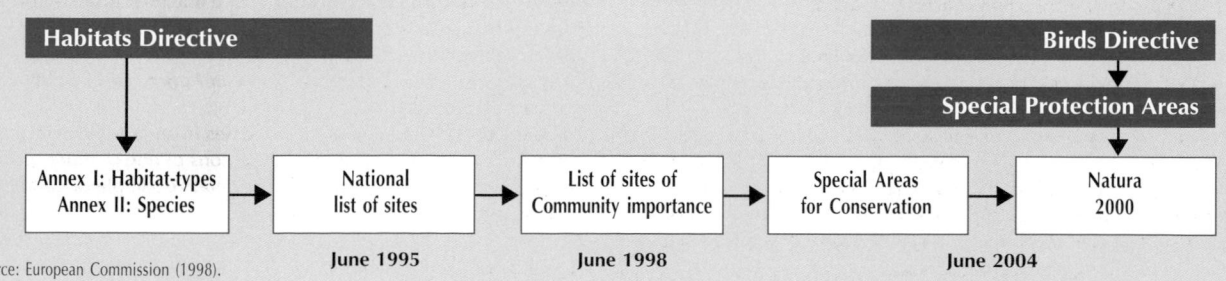

Source: European Commission (1998).

Appendix 1 ... continued. Descriptions of international agreements relevant to the protection and management of sites for nature conservation in Europe.

Barcelona Convention: Convention for the Protection of the Mediterranean Sea against Pollution

The objectives of the Barcelona Convention are to counteract the introduction of certain pollutants into the Mediterranean Sea area (including internal waters); and to conserve natural species and habitats. The 20 states adjoining the Mediterranean Sea, and the European Union, are contracting parties.

There is a Protocol to the Barcelona Convention concerning Mediterranean Specially Protected Areas. This specifies the action that Mediterranean States are bound to undertake to identify, establish and manage marine and coastal areas requiring special protection in the Mediterranean Sea Area.

Helsinki Convention: 1992 Helsinki Convention on the Protection of the Marine Environment of the Baltic Sea Area

The Helsinki Convention aims to counteract the introduction of certain pollutants into the Baltic Sea area (including internal waters), and to conserve natural species and habitats. The Convention brings the Baltic Sea (Czech Republic, Denmark, Estonia, Finland, Germany, Latvia, Lithuania, Norway, Poland, Russia, Slovakia, Sweden and Ukraine) together with the European Union under the Helsinki Commission (HELCOM).

HELCOM has recommended the establishment of a network of 65 Baltic Sea Protected Areas (BSPAs). Included within this are provisions for the identification of areas important for concentrations of feeding, wintering and staging seabirds (Hägerhäll and Skov 1998).

Parks for Life

Parks for Life is an initiative of the IUCN World Commission for Protected Areas, in association with the Federation of Nature and National Parks of Europe (FNNPE), World Wide Fund for Naure (WWF), World Conservation Monitoring Centre (WCMC) and BirdLife International (IUCN–CNPPA 1994). It sets out a vision for Europe's protected areas in terms of policies, recommendations and actions.

The main themes of the plan include the positioning of protected areas in a wider context, addressing priorities at all levels, and better planning and management for protected areas. There are chapters addressing the main impact of sectoral policies on protected areas, actions concerning some priority sub-regions and countries, and overviewing the legal framework and financial opportunities for better protection. The plan deals with securing public support for protected areas, and outlines the implementation process.

There are 30 priority projects listed in the plan, which need urgent attention. In 1995, a coordinator was appointed to oversee the implementation of these projects. The idea is that a wide range of organizations take up a leading or active participatory role in the projects, so as to ensure effective cooporation and broad support for these activities.

Program for the Conservation of Arctic Flora and Fauna

The Program for the Conservation of Arctic Flora and Fauna (CAFF) was established to address the special needs of Arctic species and their habitats in the rapidly developing Arctic region. It forms one of four programmes of The Arctic Environmental Protection Strategy (AEPS) which was adopted by the Arctic nations in 1991. The other programmes of the AEPS include the Arctic Monitoring and Assessment Program (AMAP) and the programmes for Emergency Prevention, Preparedness and Response (EPPR) and Protection of the Arctic Marine Environment (PAME).

CAFF's main goals, which are achieved in keeping with the concepts of sustainable development and utilization, are:

- to conserve Arctic flora and fauna, their diversity and their habitats;
- to protect the Arctic ecosystems from threats;
- to improve conservation management, laws, regulations and practices for the Arctic;
- to integrate Arctic interests into global conservation fora.

The majority of CAFF's Work Plan activities are directed at species and habitat conservation and at integrating indigenous peoples and their knowledge into CAFF. Some examples are: work on rare, vulnerable and endangered plants and animals of the Arctic; developing circumpolar conservation strategies for certain species (e.g. Scott 1998); work on Arctic vegetation; analysing and making recommendations on threats to Arctic species and habitat; an indigenous peoples, mapping project and development of an implementation strategy for the Convention on Biological Diversity in the Circumpolar Arctic (e.g. CAFF 1996a,b).

References

BirdLife International (1994) IBA Conservation in the European Union: an introduction to the mechanisms. Brussels, Belgium: 19-22 November Workshop proceedings. Cambridge, UK: BirdLife International (unpublished report).

CAFF [Conservation of Arctic Flora and Fauna] (1996a) *Proposed protected areas in the Circumpolar Arctic 1996.* Trondheim, Norway: Directorate for Nature Management (CAFF Habitat Conservation Report No. 2).

CAFF [Conservation of Arctic Flora and Fauna] (1996b) *Circumpolar Protected Areas Network (CPAN)—strategy and action plan.* Trondheim, Norway: Directorate for Nature Management (CAFF Habitat Conservation Report No. 6).

Council of Europe/UNEP/European Centre for Nature Conservation (1996) *The Pan-European Biological and Landscape Diversity Strategy, a vision for Europe's natural heritage.* Strasbourg, France: Council of Europe.

European Commission (1998) *Integrating biodiversity: A European Community strategy for action.* Luxembourg: Office for Official Publications of the European Communities.

Hägerhäll, B. and Skov, H. (1998). *Proposal for marine Baltic Sea Protected Areas (BSPAs).* Copenhagen: Ornis Consult (report to HELCOM Environment Committee).

Hecker, N. and Tomàs Vives, P., eds. (1995) *The status of wetland inventories in the Mediterranean region.* Slimbridge, UK: MedWet/International Waterfowl and Wetlands Research Bureau.

IUCN–CNPPA (1994) *Parks for life: action plan for protected areas in Europe.* Gland, Switzerland: International Union for Nature Conservation and Natural Resources (Commission on National Parks and Protected Areas).

Lyster, S. (1985) *International wildlife law.* Cambridge, UK: Grotius.

McCloskey, C. (1997) *P.E.B.L.D.S. explained.* Tilburg, Netherlands: IUCN European Programme.

Scott, D. A. (1998) *Global overview of the conservation of migratory Arctic breeding birds outside the Arctic.* Reykjavik: Conservation of Arctic Flora and Fauna (CAFF Technical Report No. 4).

Synge, H., ed. (1995) *Parks for life 97: Proceedings of the IUCN/WCPA European regional working session on protecting Europe's natural heritage.* Gland, Switzerland: IUCN—The World Conservation Union/German Federal Agency for Nature Conservation/Federal Ministry of the Environment, Nature Conservation and Nuclear Safety, Federal Republic of Germany.

Tucker, G. M. and Evans, M. I., eds. (1997) *Habitats for birds in Europe: a conservation strategy for the wider environment.* Cambridge, UK: BirdLife International (Conservation Series No. 6).

Appendix 2a. The 515 bird species occurring regularly in Europe, with the Important Bird Area criteria (at the global and European levels) that they can potentially fulfil and the numerical threshold(s) if applicable. Taxonomy and nomenclature follow Cramp *et al.* (1977–1994).

IBA criteria applicable at the European Union level (C) are shown in Appendix 2b.
For a full explanation of criteria, see the introductory chapter 'Identifying IBAs'.
Only criteria B1i, B1ii and Biii may be applied at the level of subspecies or population, all other criteria at the global (A) and European (B) levels apply to the full species.
All population thresholds are given in individuals, unless followed by 'p' indicating pairs.
To convert between individuals and pairs, a multiplying/dividing factor of 3 was used.

Species / Subspecies or population applicable for criteria B1i or B1ii	Species of global conservation concern (A1)	Restricted-range species (A2)	Biome-restricted species (A3)	Congregations – global (1% biogeographic population of waterbird) (A4i)	(1% global population seabird or terrestrial species) (A4ii)	(20,000 waterbirds or 10,000 pairs seabirds) (A4iii)	(Bottleneck site of global importance) (A4iv)	Congregations – regional (1% flyway or distinct population of waterbird) (B1i)	(1% distinct population of seabird) (B1ii)	(1% distinct population of other species) (B1iii)	(Bottleneck site of regional importance) (B1iv)	Species of European conservation concern (categories 1–3) (B2)	Species of European conservation concern (category 4) (B3)
Gavia stellata Red-throated Diver	—	—	—	750	—	W	—			—	—	★	—
NW Europe (win)								750	—				
Caspian/Black Sea/E Med (win)								?	—				
Gavia arctica Black-throated Diver	—	—	—	1,200	—	W	—			—	—	★	—
W Siberia/Europe (bre)								✓	—				
Gavia immer Great Northern Diver	—	—	—	50	—	W	—			—	—	★	—
Europe (win)								✓	—				
Gavia adamsii White-billed Diver	—	—	Arctic	—³	—	W	—	—³	—				
Tachybaptus ruficollis Little Grebe	—	—	—	1,000	—	W	—						
Western Palearctic								✓					
Podiceps cristatus Great Crested Grebe	—	—	—	3,000	—	W	—						
NW Europe (win)								1,500	—				
Black Sea/Med (win)								1,500	—				
Caspian Sea (win)								100	—				
Podiceps grisegena Red-necked Grebe	—	—	—	400	—	W	—						
NW Europe (win)								150	—				
Black Sea/Med (win)								100	—				
Caspian (win)								150	—				
Podiceps auritus Slavonian Grebe	—	—	Boreal	300	—	W	—			—	—	—	—
NW Europe (long-billed form)								50	—				
NW Europe (short-billed form)								250	—				
Caspian								100	—				
Podiceps nigricollis Black-necked Grebe	—	—	—	1,000	—	W	—			—	—	—	—
Western Palearctic								✓	—				
Fulmarus glacialis Fulmar	—	—	—	—	45,000p	S	—	—	✓	—	—	—	—
Pterodroma feae Fea's Petrel	5p	—	—	—	—⁴	S	—	—	—⁴	—	—	★	—
Pterodroma madeira Zino's Petrel	5p	—	—	—	—⁴	S	—	—	—⁴	—	—	★	—
Bulweria bulwerii Bulwer's Petrel	—	—	—	—	1,300p	S	—	—	150p	—	—	★	—
Calonectris diomedea Cory's Shearwater	—	—	—	—	2,000p	S	—	—		—	—	★	—
C.d. diomedea								—	330p				
C.d. borealis								—	1,100p				
Puffinus gravis Great Shearwater	—	—	—	—	No data	S	—	—	No data	—	—	—	—
Puffinus griseus Sooty Shearwater	—	—	—	—	No data	S	—	—	No data	—	—	—	—
Puffinus puffinus Manx Shearwater	—	—	—	—	2,700p	S	—	—	✓	—	—	★	—
Puffinus yelkouan Yelkouan Shearwater	—	—	—	—	225p	S	—	—	✓	—	—	—	★
Puffinus assimilis Little Shearwater	—	—	—	—	2,500p	S	—	—	30p	—	—	★	—
Pelagodroma marina White-faced Petrel	—	—	—	—	10,000p	S	—			—	—	★	—
P.m. hypoleuca								—	160p				
Hydrobates pelagicus Storm Petrel	—	—	—	—	2,800p	S	—			—	—	★	—
NW Europe								—	2,700p				
Med								—	70p				
Canary Islands								—	10p				
Oceanodroma leucorhoa Leach's Petrel	—	—	—	—	70,000p	S	—	—	1,000p	—	—	★	—
Oceanodroma castro Madeiran Petrel	—	—	—	—	150p	S	—			—	—	★	—
Atlantic								—	90p				
Sula bassana Gannet	—	—	—	—	3,000p	S	—			—	—	★	—
E Atlantic								—	2,600p				
Phalacrocorax carbo Cormorant	—	—	—	4,200	—	W	—			—	—	—	—
NW Europe								1,200	—				
N Europe/Central Europe								2,000	—				
Black Sea/Med								1,000	—				
Phalacrocorax aristotelis Shag	—	—	—	2,700	—	W	—			—	—	—	★
N Europe								2,500	—				
Med								150	—				
Phalacrocorax pygmeus Pygmy Cormorant	10p	—	—	210	—	W	—	✓	—	—	—	★	—
Pelecanus onocrotalus White Pelican	—	—	—	700	—	W	—			—	—	★	—
Europe/W Asia (bre)								✓	—				

Appendix 2a ... continued. The 515 bird species occurring regularly in Europe, with the Important Bird Area criteria (at the global and European levels) that they can potentially fulfil and the numerical threshold(s) if applicable. Taxonomy and nomenclature follow Cramp *et al.* (1977–1994).

Species / Subspecies or population applicable for criteria B1i or B1ii		Species of global conservation concern (A1)	Restricted-range species (A2)	Biome-restricted species (A3)	Congregations – global (1% biogeographic population of waterbird) (A4i)	(1% global population seabird or terrestrial species) (A4ii)	(20,000 waterbirds or 10,000 pairs seabirds) (A4iii)	(Bottleneck site of global importance) (A4iv)	Congregations – regional (1% flyway or distinct population of waterbird) (B1i)	(1% distinct population of seabird) (B1ii)	(1% distinct population of other species) (B1iii)	(Bottleneck site of regional importance) (B1iv)	Species of European conservation concern (categories 1-3) (B2)	Species of European conservation concern (category 4) (B3)
Pelecanus crispus	Dalmatian Pelican	10p	—	—	25	—	W	—			—		★	—
Black Sea/Med (win)									✓	—				
Botaurus stellaris	Bittern	—	—	—	—²	—	W	—	—²	—			★	—
Ixobrychus minutus	Little Bittern	—	—	—	—²	—	W	—	—²				★	—
Nycticorax nycticorax	Night Heron	—	—	—	1,500	—	W	—					★	—
Europe/NW Africa (bre)									✓					
Ardeola ralloides	Squacco Heron	—	—	—	350	—	W	—					★	—
NW Africa/Med (bre)									100	—				
S & SW Asia/Black Sea (bre)									250	—				
Bubulcus ibis	Cattle Egret	—	—	—	2,100	—	W	—			—		—	—
SW Europe/NW Africa									2,000	—				
E Med/SW Asia									100	—				
Egretta garzetta	Little Egret	—	—	—	1,000	—	W	—			—		—	—
Black Sea/Med									✓	—				
Egretta alba	Great White Egret	—	—	—	120	—	W	—			—		—	—
Med/Black Sea (win)									✓	—				
Ardea cinerea	Grey Heron	—	—	—	4,500	—	W	—			—		—	—
N Europe (bre)									✓	—				
Ardea purpurea	Purple Heron	—	—	—	—²	—	W	—	—²	—		—	★	—
Ciconia nigra	Black Stork	—	—	—	210	—	W	✓			—	✓	★	—
SW Europe/W Africa									10	—				
Central/E Europe (bre)									200	—				
Ciconia ciconia	White Stork	—	—	—	4,850	—	W	✓			—	✓	★	—
Iberia/NW Africa (bre)									850	—				
Central/E Europe (bre)									4,000	—				
Plegadis falcinellus	Glossy Ibis	—	—	—	250	—	W	—			—		★	—
Black Sea/Med/W Africa									✓	—				
Platalea leucorodia	Spoonbill	—	—	—	130	—	W	—			—		★	—
E Atlantic									30	—				
Central SE Europe									100	—				
Phoenicopterus ruber	Greater Flamingo	—	—	—	800	—	W	—			—		★	—
W Med									✓	—				
Cygnus olor	Mute Swan	—	—	—	2,900	—	W	—			—		—	—
NW Mainland and Central Europe									2,100	—				
Britain									250	—				
Ireland									100	—				
Black Sea									450	—				
Cygnus columbianus	Bewick's Swan	—	—	Arctic	175	—	W	—			—		★ᵂ	—
W Siberia/NE & NW Europe									170	—				
N Siberia/Caspian									5	—				
Cygnus cygnus	Whooper Swan	—	—	—	730	—	W	—			—		—	★ᵂ
Iceland/UK/Ireland									160	—				
NW Mainland Europe									400	—				
N Europe/White Sea/Black Sea/E Med									170	—				
Anser fabalis	Bean Goose	—	—	—	3,800	—	W	—			—		—	—
W Siberia/NE & NW Europe									800	—				
W & Central Siberia/NE & SW Europe									3,000	—				
Anser brachyrhynchus	Pink-footed Goose	—	—	Arctic	2,600	—	W	—			—		—	★
E Greenland/Iceland/UK (bre)									2,250	—				
Svalbard/NW Europe (bre)									340	—				
Anser albifrons	White-fronted Goose	—	—	Arctic	12,800	—	W	—			—		—	—
NW Siberia/NE & NW Europe									6,000	—				
Central Europe/W Siberia									1,000	—				
W Siberia/Black Sea/Turkey									6,500	—				
Greenland/Ireland/UK (bre)									300	—				
Anser erythropus	Lesser White-fronted Goose	5p	—	Arctic	250	—	W	—			—		★	—
N Europe/W Siberia/Black Sea/Caspian									✓	—				

Appendix 2a ... continued. The 515 bird species occurring regularly in Europe, with the Important Bird Area criteria (at the global and European levels) that they can potentially fulfil and the numerical threshold(s) if applicable. Taxonomy and nomenclature follow Cramp *et al.* (1977–1994).

Species Subspecies or population applicable for criteria B1i or B1ii	Species of global conservation concern (A1)	Restricted-range species (A2)	Biome-restricted species (A3)	Congregations – global (1% biogeographic population of waterbird) (A4i)	(1% global population seabird or terrestrial species) (A4ii)	(20,000 waterbirds or 10,000 pairs seabirds) (A4iii)	(Bottleneck site of global importance) (A4iv)	Congregations – regional (1% flyway or distinct population of waterbird) (B1i)	(1% distinct population of seabird) (B1ii)	(1% distinct population of other species) (B1iii)	(Bottleneck site of regional importance) (B1iv)	Species of European conservation concern (categories 1–3) (B2)	Species of European conservation concern (category 4) (B3)
Anser anser Greylag Goose	—	—	—	3,500	—	W	—			—	—	—	—
Iceland/UK/Ireland								1,000	—				
NW Scotland								50	—				
NW Europe/SW Europe								2,000	—				
Central Europe/N Africa								200	—				
Black Sea/Turkey								250	—				
Branta leucopsis Barnacle Goose	—	—	Arctic	2,200	—	W	—			—	—	★w	★
E Greenland/Scotland/Ireland								320	—				
Svalbard/SW Scotland								120	—				
Russia/Germany/Netherlands								1,760	—				
Branta bernicla Brent Goose	—	—	Arctic	3,250	—	W	—			—	—	★	—
W Siberia/W Europe								3,000	—				
Svalbard/Denmark/UK								50	—				
Canada/Greenland/Ireland								200	—				
Branta ruficollis Red-breasted Goose	60	—	—	700	—	W	—			—	—	★	
N. Siberia/Black Sea/Caspian								✔					
Tadorna ferruginea Ruddy Shelduck	—	—	—	200	—	W	—			—	—	★	
E Med/Black Sea/NE Africa								✔					
Tadorna tadorna Shelduck	—	—	—	3,750	—	W	—						
NW Europe								3,000	—				
Black Sea/Med								750	—				
Anas penelope Wigeon	—	—	—	18,000	—	W	—			—	—	—	—
W Siberia & NW Europe/NE Europe								12,500	—				
W Siberia/NE Europe/Black Sea/Med								5,600	—				
Anas strepera Gadwall	—	—	—	1,300	—	W	—			—	—	★	
NW Europe								300	—				
NE Europe/Black Sea/Med								1,000	—				
Anas crecca Teal	—	—	—	14,000	—	W	—			—	—	—	—
NW Europe								4,000	—				
W Siberia/NE Europe/Black Sea/Med								10,500	—				
Anas platyrhynchos Mallard	—	—	—	83,000	—	W	—			—	—	—	
NW Europe								50,000	—				
N Europe/W Med								10,000	—				
E Europe/Black Sea/E Med								22,500	—				
Greenland								150	—				
Anas acuta Pintail	—	—	—	12,600	—	W	—			—	—	★	
W Siberia/NE & E & S Europe/W Africa								12,000	—				
NW Europe								600	—				
Anas querquedula Garganey	—	—	—	20,000	—	W	—			—	—	★	—
W Siberia/Europe/W Africa								✔	—				
Anas clypeata Shoveler	—	—	—	4,900	—	W	—			—	—	—	—
NW/Central Europe								400	—				
W Siberia/NE & E & S Europe/W Africa								4,500	—				
Marmaronetta angustirostris Marbled Duck	5p	—	—	40	—	W	—			—	—	★	—
W Med/W Africa								30	—				
E Med								10	—				
Netta rufina Red-crested Pochard	—	—	—	750	—	W	—			—	—	★	—
SW/Central Europe & W Med								250	—				
Black Sea/E Med								500	—				
Aythya ferina Pochard	—	—	—	13,500	—	W	—			—	—	—	★
Central & NE Europe/Black Sea/Med (win)								10,000	—				
NW Europe/NE Europe								3,500	—				
Aythya nyroca Ferruginous Duck	20p	—	—	600	—	W	—			—	—	★	—
W Med/W Africa								100	—				
E Europe/E Med								500	—				
Aythya fuligula Tufted Duck	—	—	—	16,000	—	W	—			—	—	—	—
Central Europe/Black Sea/Med								6,000	—				
NW Europe								10,000	—				

Appendix 2a ... continued. The 515 bird species occurring regularly in Europe, with the Important Bird Area criteria (at the global and European levels) that they can potentially fulfil and the numerical threshold(s) if applicable. Taxonomy and nomenclature follow Cramp *et al.* (1977–1994).

Species Subspecies or population applicable for criteria B1i or B1ii		Species of global conservation concern (A1)	Restricted-range species (A2)	Biome-restricted species (A3)	Congregations – global (1% biogeographic population of waterbird) (A4i)	(1% global population seabird or terrestrial species) (A4ii)	(20,000 waterbirds or 10,000 pairs seabirds) (A4iii)	Bottleneck site of global importance (A4iv)	Congregations – regional (1% flyway or distinct population of waterbird) (B1i)	(1% distinct population of seabird) (B1ii)	(1% distinct population of other species) (B1iii)	Bottleneck site of regional importance (B1iv)	Species of European conservation concern (categories 1–3) (B2)	Species of European conservation concern (category 4) (B3)
Aythya marila	Scaup	—	—	Arctic	4,600	—	W	—			—		★ᵂ	—
N Europe/W Europe									3,100	—				
W Siberia/Black Sea/Caspian									1,500	—				
Somateria mollissima	Eider	—	—	—	18,830	—	W	—			—		—	—
Britain/Ireland									650	—				
Baltic/Denmark/Netherlands									13,500	—				
Norway/Russia									3,000	—				
White Sea									200	—				
Faroe Islands									60	—				
Shetland/Orkney Islands									120	—				
Svalbard/Franz Josef Land									400	—				
Greenland									300	—				
Iceland									600	—				
Somateria spectabilis	King Eider	—	—	Arctic	3,000	—	W	—			—		—	—
E Greenland/NE Europe/W Siberia									✔	—				
Polysticta stelleri	Steller's Eider	30	—	—	300	—	W	—			—		★	—
NE Europe/W Siberia									✔	—				
Histrionicus histrionicus	Harlequin Duck	—	—	—	90	—	W	—			—		★	—
Iceland									75	—				
Greenland									15	—				
Clangula hyemalis	Long-tailed Duck	—	—	Arctic	4,750	—	W	—			—		—	—
Iceland/Greenland									1,500	—				
W Siberia/N Europe									46,000	—				
Melanitta nigra	Common Scoter	—	—	Arctic	16,000	—	W	—			—		—	—
W Siberia/W & N Europe/NW Africa									✔	—				
Melanitta fusca	Velvet Scoter	—	—	—	10,000	—	W	—			—		★ᵂ	—
Western Siberia/N Europe									✔	—				
Black Sea/Caspian									15	—				
Bucephala islandica	Barrow's Goldeneye	—	—	—	—³	—	W	—	—³	—	—	—	★	—
Bucephala clangula	Goldeneye	—	—	—	4,200	—	W	—			—		—	—
NW Europe/Central Europe									3,000	—				
W Siberia/NE Europe/Black Sea									200	—				
NE Europe/Adriatic									750	—				
W Siberia/Caspian									250	—				
Mergus albellus	Smew	—	—	Boreal	900	—	W	—			—		★	—
NW/Central Europe									250	—				
NE Europe/Black Sea/E Med									650	—				
Mergus serrator	Red-breasted Merganser	—	—	—	1,850	—	W	—			—		—	—
NW Europe/Central Europe									1,250	—				
NE Europe/Black Sea/Med									500	—				
E Greenland/Iceland/UK									200	—				
W Greenland									250	—				
Mergus merganser	Goosander	—	—	—	2,200	—	W	—			—		—	—
Iceland									10	—				
NW/Central Europe									2,000	—				
UK									65	—				
Central Europe (bre)									30	—				
Balkans									1	—				
NE Europe/Black Sea									100	—				
Oxyura leucocephala	White-headed Duck	5p	—	—	140	—	W	—			—		★	—
W Med									7	—				
E Med/SW Asia/Turkey									110	—				
Pernis apivorus	Honey Buzzard	—	—	—	—	—	—	✔	—		—	✔	—	★
Elanus caeruleus	Black-winged Kite	—	—	—	—	—	—	—¹	—		—¹		★	—
Milvus migrans	Black Kite	—	—	—	—	200p	—	✔	—		✔	✔	★	—
Milvus milvus	Red Kite	—	—	—	—	220p	—	✔	—		✔	✔	—	★
Haliaeetus albicilla	White-tailed Eagle	5p	—	—	—	—	—	✔	—			✔	★	—
Gypaetus barbatus	Lammergeier	—	—	—	—	—	—	—¹	—		—¹		★	—

Appendix 2a ... continued. The 515 bird species occurring regularly in Europe, with the Important Bird Area criteria (at the global and European levels) that they can potentially fulfil and the numerical threshold(s) if applicable. Taxonomy and nomenclature follow Cramp *et al.* (1977–1994).

Species / Subspecies or population applicable for criteria B1i or B1ii		Species of global conservation concern (A1)	Restricted-range species (A2)	Biome-restricted species (A3)	Congregations – global (1% biogeographic population of waterbird) (A4i)	(1% global population seabird or terrestrial species) (A4ii)	(20,000 waterbirds or 10,000 pairs seabirds) (A4iii)	(Bottleneck site of global importance) (A4iv)	Congregations – regional (1% flyway or distinct population of waterbird) (B1i)	(1% distinct population of seabird) (B1ii)	(1% distinct population of other species) (B1iii)	(Bottleneck site of regional importance) (B1iv)	Species of European conservation concern (categories 1–3) (B2)	Species of European conservation concern (category 4) (B3)
Neophron percnopterus	Egyptian Vulture	—	—	—	—	110p	—	✔	—	—	30p	✔	★	—
Gyps fulvus	Griffon Vulture	—	—	—	—	180p	—	✔	—	—	90p	✔	★	—
Aegypius monachus	Cinereous Vulture	5p	—	—	—	50p	—	—¹	—	—	10p	—¹	★	—
Circaetus gallicus	Short-toed Eagle	—	—	—	—	—	—	✔	—	—	—	✔	★	—
Circus aeruginosus	Marsh Harrier	—	—	—	—	—	—	✔	—	—	—	✔	—	—
Circus cyaneus	Hen Harrier	—	—	—	—	—	—	✔	—	—	—	✔	★	—
Circus macrourus	Pallid Harrier	10p	—	Steppe	—	—	—	✔	—	—	—	✔	★	—
Circus pygargus	Montagu's Harrier	—	—	—	—	—	—	✔	—	—	—	✔	—	★
Accipiter gentilis	Goshawk	—	—	—	—	—	—	—¹	—	—	—	—¹	—	—
Accipiter nisus	Sparrowhawk	—	—	—	—	—	—	✔	—	—	—	✔	—	—
Accipiter brevipes	Levant Sparrowhawk	—	—	Steppe	—	—	—	✔	—	—	—	✔	★	—
Buteo buteo	Buzzard	—	—	—	—	—	—	✔	—	—	—	✔	—	—
Buteo rufinus	Long-legged Buzzard	—	—	—	—	—	—	—¹	—	—	—	—¹	★	—
Buteo lagopus	Rough-legged Buzzard	—	—	Arctic	—	—	—	✔	—	—	—	✔	—	—
Aquila pomarina	Lesser Spotted Eagle	—	—	—	—	—	—	✔	—	—	—	✔	★	—
Aquila clanga	Greater Spotted Eagle	2p	—	—	—	—	—	✔	—	—	—	✔	★	—
Aquila nipalensis	Steppe Eagle	—	—	—	—	—	—	✔	—	—	—	✔	★	—
Aquila heliaca	Imperial Eagle	2p	—	Steppe	—	—	—	✔	—	—	—	✔	★	—
Aquila adalberti	Spanish Imperial Eagle	2p	—	—	—	—	—	—¹	—	—	—	—¹	★	—
Aquila chrysaetos	Golden Eagle	—	—	—	—	—	—	—¹	—	—	—	—¹	★	—
Hieraaetus pennatus	Booted Eagle	—	—	—	—	37p	—	✔	—	—	✔	✔	★	—
Hieraaetus fasciatus	Bonnelli's Eagle	—	—	—	—	10p	—	—¹	—	—	✔	—¹	★	—
Pandion haliaetus	Osprey	—	—	—	—	—	—	✔	—	—	—	✔	★	—
Falco naumanni	Lesser Kestrel	10p	—	—	—	200p	—	✔	—	—	100p	✔	★	—
Falco tinnunculus	Kestrel	—	—	—	—	—	—	✔	—	—	—	✔	★	—
Falco vespertinus	Red-footed Falcon	—	—	—	—	360p	—	✔	—	—	180p	✔	★	—
Falco columbarius	Merlin	—	—	—	—	—	—	✔	—	—	—	✔	—	—
Falco subbuteo	Hobby	—	—	—	—	—	—	✔	—	—	—	✔	—	—
Falco eleonorae	Eleonora's Falcon	—	—	Med	—	50p	—	✔	—	—	40p	✔	★	—
Falco biarmicus	Lanner	—	—	—	—	—	—	—¹	—	—	—	—¹	★	—
Falco cherrug	Saker	—	—	—	—	—	—	✔	—	—	—	✔	★	—
Falco rusticolus	Gyrfalcon	—	—	Arctic	—	—	—	—¹	—	—	—	—¹	★	—
Falco peregrinus	Peregrine	—	—	—	—	—	—	✔	—	—	—	✔	★	—
Falco pelegrinoides	Barbary Falcon	—	—	—	—	—	—	—¹	—	—	—	—¹	—	—
Bonasa bonasia	Hazel Grouse	—	—	—	—	—	—	—	—	—	—	—	—	—
Lagopus lagopus	Red/Willow Grouse	—	—	—	—	—	—	—	—	—	—	—	—	—
Lagopus mutus	Ptarmigan	—	—	—	—	—	—	—	—	—	—	—	—	—
Tetrao tetrix	Black Grouse	—	—	—	—	—	—	—	—	—	—	—	★	—
Tetrao mlokosiewiczi	Caucasian Black Grouse	20p	Caucasus	Alpine	—	—	—	—	—	—	—	—	★	—
Tetrao urogallus	Capercaillie	—	—	—	—	—	—	—	—	—	—	—	—	—
Tetraogallus caucasicus	Caucasian Snowcock	—	Caucasus	Alpine	—	—	—	—	—	—	—	—	—	★
Tetraogallus caspius	Caspian Snowcock	—	—	Alpine	—	—	—	—	—	—	—	—	★	—
Alectoris chukar	Chukar	—	—	—	—	—	—	—	—	—	—	—	★	—
Alectoris graeca	Rock Partridge	—	—	Med	—	—	—	—	—	—	—	—	★	—
Alectoris rufa	Red-legged Partridge	—	—	—	—	—	—	—	—	—	—	—	★	—
Alectoris barbara	Barbary Partridge	—	—	—	—	—	—	—	—	—	—	—	★	—
Ammoperdix griseogularis	See-see Partridge	—	—	—	—	—	—	—	—	—	—	—	★	—
Francolinus francolinus	Black Francolin	—	—	—	—	—	—	—	—	—	—	—	★	—
Perdix perdix	Partridge	—	—	—	—	—	—	—	—	—	—	—	★	—
Coturnix coturnix	Quail	—	—	—	—	—	—	—	—	—	—	—	★	—
Phasianus colchicus	Pheasant	—	—	—	—	—	—	—	—	—	—	—	—	—
Turnix sylvatica	Andalusian Hemipode	—	—	—	—	—	—	—	—	—	—	—	★	—
Rallus aquaticus	Water Rail	—	—	—	—	—	—	—	—	—	—	—	—	—
Porzana porzana	Spotted Crake	—	—	—	No data	—	W	—	60p	—	—	—	—	★
Porzana parva	Little Crake	—	—	—	55p	—	W	—	✔	—	—	—	—	★

Appendix 2a ... continued. The 515 bird species occurring regularly in Europe, with the Important Bird Area criteria (at the global and European levels) that they can potentially fulfil and the numerical threshold(s) if applicable. Taxonomy and nomenclature follow Cramp *et al.* (1977–1994).

Species Subspecies or population applicable for criteria B1i or B1ii		Species of global conservation concern (A1)	Restricted-range species (A2)	Biome-restricted species (A3)	Congregations – global (1% biogeographic population of waterbird) (A4i)	(1% global population seabird or terrestrial species) (A4ii)	(20,000 waterbirds or 10,000 pairs seabirds) (A4iii)	(Bottleneck site of global importance) (A4iv)	Congregations – regional (1% flyway or distinct population of waterbird) (B1i)	(1% distinct population of seabird) (B1ii)	(1% distinct population of other species) (B1iii)	(Bottleneck site of regional importance) (B1iv)	Species of European conservation concern (categories 1–3) (B2)	Species of European conservation concern (category 4) (B3)
Porzana pusilla	Baillon's Crake	—	—	—	No data	—	W	—	40p	—	—	—	★	—
Crex crex	Corncrake	20p	—	—	45p	—	W	—	✔	—	—	—	★	—
Gallinula chloropus Europe/N Africa	Moorhen	—	—	—	10,000	—	W	—	✔	—	—	—	—	—
Porphyrio porphyrio	Purple Gallinule	—	—	—	35p	—	W	—	✔	—	—	—	★	—
Fulica atra NW Europe (win) Black Sea/Med (win)	Coot	—	—	—	40,000	—	W	—	 15,000 25,000	 — —	—	—	—	—
Fulica cristata	Crested Coot	—	—	—	10p	—	W	—	✔	—	—	—	★	—
Grus grus NW Europe (bre) NE/Central Europe (bre) Black Sea/E Med (win) Black Sea/Turkey	Crane	—	—	—	1,550	—	W	✔	 600 600 350 2	 — — — 	—	—	★	—
Anthropoides virgo	Demoiselle Crane	—	—	Steppe	—[3]	—	W	✔	—[3]	—	—	—	—	—
Tetrax tetrax	Little Bustard	60	—	—	—	—	W	—	—	—	—	—	★	—
Chlamydotis undulata	Houbara Bustard	—	—	—	—	—	W	—	—	—	—	—	★	—
Otis tarda	Great Bustard	30	—	—	—	—	W	—	—	—	—	—	★	—
Haematopus ostralegus Europe & NW Africa (win)	Oystercatcher	—	—	—	11,000	—	W	—	 9,000	 —	—	—	—	—
Himantopus himantopus W Med (bre) Black Sea/ E Med (bre)	Black-winged Stilt	—	—	—	700	—	W	—	 400 300	 — —	—	—	—	—
Recurvirostra avosetta W Europe/W Med (bre) Black Sea/ E Med (bre)	Avocet	—	—	—	1,100	—	W	—	 700 400	—	—	—	★[W]	★
Burhinus oedicnemus	Stone Curlew	—	—	—	398p	—	W	—	✔	—	—	—	★	—
Cursorius cursor	Cream-coloured Courser	—	—	—	10p	—	W	—	✔	—	—	—	★	—
Glareola pratincola W Med (bre) Black Sea/E Med (bre)	Collared Pratincole	—	—	—	200	—	W	—	 100 100	 — —	—	—	★	—
Glareola nordmanni	Black-winged Pratincole	10p	—	Steppe	—[2]	—	W	—	—[2]	—	—	—	★	—
Charadrius dubius Europe/W Africa	Little Ringed Plover	—	—	—	3,200	—	W	—	 ✔	 —	—	—	—	—
Charadrius hiaticula Canada/W Europe	Ringed Plover	—	—	—	2,400	—	W	—	 ✔	 —	—	—	—	—
Charadrius alexandrinus E Atlantic Black Sea/ E Med	Kentish Plover	—	—	—	950	—	W	—	 700 250	 — —	—	—	★	—
Charadrius leschenaultii	Greater Sand Plover	—	—	—	—[3]	—	W	—	—[3]	—	—	—	★	—
Charadrius asiaticus	Caspian Plover	—	—	—	—[3]	—	W	—	—[3]	—	—	—	★	—
Charadrius morinellus Europe (bre)	Dotterel	—	—	—	1,000	—	W	—	 ✔	 —	—	—	—	—
Pluvialis apricaria NW Europe (bre)	Golden Plover	—	—	—	10,000	—	W	—	 ✔	 —	—	—	—	★
Pluvialis squatarola E Atlantic	Grey Plover	—	—	Arctic	1,500	—	W	—	 ✔	 —	—	—	—	—
Hoplopterus spinosus Black Sea/Med	Spur-winged Plover	—	—	—	100	—	W	—	 ✔	 —	—	—	★	—
Hoplopterus indicus	Red-wattled Plover	—	—	—	—[3]	—	W	—	—[3]	—	—	—	—	—
Chettusia gregaria	Sociable Plover	10p	—	Steppe	—[3]	—	W	—	—[3]	—	—	—	★	—
Chettusia leucura	White-tailed Plover	—	—	—	—[3]	—	W	—	—[3]	—	—	—	—	—
Vanellus vanellus Europe/W Africa	Lapwing	—	—	—	70,000	—	W	—	 ✔	 —	—	—	—	—
Calidris canutus NE Canada/Greenland/Iceland/NW Europe (win) W Africa/S Africa (win)	Knot	—	—	Arctic	8,500	—	W	—	 3,500 5,000	 — —	—	—	★[W]	—

Appendix 2a ... continued. The 515 bird species occurring regularly in Europe, with the Important Bird Area criteria (at the global and European levels) that they can potentially fulfil and the numerical threshold(s) if applicable. Taxonomy and nomenclature follow Cramp *et al.* (1977–1994).

Species / Subspecies or population applicable for criteria B1i or B1ii		Species of global conservation concern (A1)	Restricted-range species (A2)	Biome-restricted species (A3)	Congregations – global (1% biogeographic population of waterbird) (A4i)	(1% global population seabird or terrestrial species) (A4ii)	(20,000 waterbirds or 10,000 pairs seabirds) (A4iii)	Bottleneck site of global importance (A4iv)	Congregations – regional (1% flyway or distinct population of waterbird) (B1i)	(1% distinct population of seabird) (B1ii)	(1% distinct population of other species) (B1iii)	Bottleneck site of regional importance (B1iv)	Species of European conservation concern (categories 1–3) (B2)	Species of European conservation concern (category 4) (B3)
Calidris alba	Sanderling	—	—	Arctic	1,200	—	W	—			—	—	—	—
E Atlantic/W & S Africa (win)									✔	—				
Calidris minuta	Little Stint	—	—	Arctic	2,100	—	W	—			—	—	—	—
Europe/Western Africa (win)									✔	—				
Calidris temminckii	Temminck's Stint	—	—	Arctic	3,000	—	W	—			—	—	—	—
Europe/Western Africa (win)									✔	—				
Calidris ferruginea	Curlew Sandpiper	—	—	—	4,500	—	W	—			—	—	—	—
W Africa/SW Europe (win)									✔	—				
Calidris maritima	Purple Sandpiper	—	—	Arctic	500	—	W	—			—	—	—	★
E Atlantic (win)									✔	—				
Calidris alpina	Dunlin	—	—	—	22,000	—	W	—			—	—	★W	
N Siberia/Europe/W Africa (bre)									14,000	—				
Iceland/Greenland (bre)									8,000	—				
Baltic/UK/Ireland									200	—				
Greenland (bre)									150	—				
Limicola falcinellus	Broad-billed Sandpiper	—	—	—	250	—	W	—			—	—	★	
N Europe/SW Asia/E Africa									✔	—				
Philomachus pugnax	Ruff	—	—	—	33,000	—	W	—			—	—	—	★
W Africa (win)									✔	—				
Lymnocryptes minimus	Jack Snipe	—	—	Boreal	660	—	W	—			—	—	★W	—
Europe (bre)									✔	—				
Gallinago gallinago	Snipe	—	—	—	54,000	—	W	—			—	—	—	—
Europe (bre)									47,000	—				
Iceland (bre)									7,500	—				
Gallinago media	Great Snipe	20p	—	—	300	—	W	—			—	—	★	
Scandinavia (bre)									75	—				
NE Europe/W Siberia (bre)									250	—				
Gallinago stenura	Pintail Snipe	—	—	—	—³	—	W	—³	—	—	—	—	—	—
Scolopax rusticola	Woodcock	—	—	—	—²	—	W	—²	—	—	—	—	★W	—
Limosa limosa	Black-tailed Godwit	—	—	—	4,200	—	W	—			—	—	★	
W Europe/W Africa									3,500	—				
Iceland (bre)									700	—				
Limosa lapponica	Bar-tailed Godwit	—	—	Arctic	1,000	—	W	—			—	—	★W	
Western Palearctic (win)									✔	—				
Numenius phaeopus	Whimbrel	—	—	—	6,500	—	W	—			—	—	—	★
Europe/W Africa									✔	—				
Numenius tenuirostris	Slender-billed Curlew	✔	—	—	3	—	W	—	✔	—	—	—	★	
Numenius arquata	Curlew	—	—	—	3,500	—	W	—			—	—	★W	
Europe (bre)									✔	—				
Tringa erythropus	Spotted Redshank	—	—	Arctic	720	—	W	—			—	—	—	—
Europe/W Africa									✔	—				
Tringa totanus	Redshank	—	—	—	3,000	—	W	—			—	—	★	
E Atlantic (win)									1,500	—				
Iceland/Faroe Islands (bre)									1,500	—				
Tringa stagnatilis	Marsh Sandpiper	—	—	—	300	—	W	—			—	—	—	—
Europe/W Africa									✔	—				
Tringa nebularia	Greenshank	—	—	Boreal	1,800	—	W	—			—	—	—	—
Europe/W Africa									✔	—				
Tringa ochropus	Green Sandpiper	—	—	—	10,000	—	W	—			—	—	—	—
Europe/W Africa									✔	—				
Tringa glareola	Wood Sandpiper	—	—	—	11,000	—	W	—			—	—	★	
Europe (bre)									✔	—				
Xenus cinereus	Terek Sandpiper	—	—	—	440	—	W	—			—	—	—	—
SW Asia/Africa (win)									✔	—				
Actitis hypoleucos	Common Sandpiper	—	—	—	15,000	—	W	—			—	—	—	—
Europe (bre)									✔	—				
Arenaria interpres	Turnstone	—	—	—	700	—	W	—			—	—	—	—
Western Palearctic									✔	—				

Appendix 2a ... continued. The 515 bird species occurring regularly in Europe, with the Important Bird Area criteria (at the global and European levels) that they can potentially fulfil and the numerical threshold(s) if applicable. Taxonomy and nomenclature follow Cramp et al. (1977–1994).

Species / Subspecies or population applicable for criteria B1i or B1ii		Species of global conservation concern (A1)	Restricted-range species (A2)	Biome-restricted species (A3)	Congregations – global (1% biogeographic population of waterbird) (A4i)	(1% global population seabird or terrestrial species) (A4ii)	(20,000 waterbirds or 10,000 pairs seabirds) (A4iii)	Bottleneck site of global importance (A4iv)	Congregations – regional (1% flyway or distinct population of waterbird) (B1i)	(1% distinct population of seabird) (B1ii)	(1% distinct population of other species) (B1iii)	Bottleneck site of regional importance (B1iv)	Species of European conservation concern (categories 1–3) (B2)	Species of European conservation concern (category 4) (B3)
Phalaropus lobatus	Red-necked Phalarope	—	—	Arctic	—[2]	—	W	—	—	—	—	—	—	—
Phalaropus fulicarius	Grey Phalarope	—	—	Arctic	—[2]	—	W	—	—	—	—	—	—	—
Stercorarius pomarinus	Pomarine Skua	—	—	Arctic	—	No data	S	—						
Europe									—	No data				
Stercorarius parasiticus	Arctic Skua	—	—	—	—	3,000p	S	—	—	270p			—	—
Stercorarius longicaudus	Long-tailed Skua	—	—	Arctic	—	1,000p	S	—						
Arctic/sub-Arctic/Scandinavia/Greenland									—	120p				
Stercorarius skua	Great Skua	—	—	—	—	140p	S	—	—	140p			—	★
Larus ichthyaetus	Great Black-headed Gull	—	—	Steppe	700	—	W	—					—	—
Black Sea/Caspian/SW Asia									✔	—				
Larus melanocephalus	Mediterranean Gull	—	—	—	5,500	—	W	—					—	★
W Europe/Med/NW Africa									✔	—				
Larus minutus	Little Gull	—	—	—	680	—	W	—					★	—
Central/E Europe (bre)									✔	—				
Larus sabini	Sabine's Gull	—	—	—	—[3]	—	W	—	—[3]				—	—
Larus ridibundus	Black-headed Gull	—	—	—	65,000	—	W	—					—	—
NW Europe (bre)									60,000	—				
Med (bre)									5,000	—				
Larus genei	Slender-billed Gull	—	—	—	1,200	—	W	—					—	—
Black Sea/Med (bre)									✔	—				
Larus audouinii	Audouin's Gull	20p	—	—	390	—	W	—					★	—
Europe									✔	—				
Larus canus	Common Gull	—	—	—	16,000	—	W	—					★	—
NW & Central Europe/Atlantic/Med									16,000	—				
NE Europe/W Siberia/Black Sea/Caspian									250					
Larus fuscus	Lesser Black-backed Gull	—	—	—	6,000	—	W	—					—	★
NE Europe/Black Sea/SW Asia/E Africa									2,000	—				
W Europe/Med/W Africa									4,000	—				
Larus argentatus	Herring Gull	—	—	—	27,000	—	W	—					—	—
NW Europe (bre)									14,000	—				
Iceland/W Europe (bre)									13,000	—				
Larus cachinnans	Yellow-legged Gull	—	—	—	4,500	—	W	—					—	—
Black Sea/Caspian/SW Asia									1,000	—				
Med (bre)									3,500	—				
Larus armenicus	Armenian Gull	—	—	—	300	—	W	—					—	—
Armenia/E Turkey/W Iran									✔	—				
Larus glaucoides	Iceland Gull	—	—	—	300	—	W	—					—	—
Greenland/N Atlantic									✔	—				
Larus hyperboreus	Glaucous Gull	—	—	Arctic	2,000	—	W	—					—	—
N Atlantic									✔	—				
Larus marinus	Great Black-backed Gull	—	—	—	4,800	—	W	—					—	★
NE Atlantic (bre)									✔	—				
Rhodostethia rosea	Ross's Gull	—	—	—	—[3]	—	W	—	—[3]				—	—
Rissa tridactyla	Kittiwake	—	—	—	84,000	—	W	—					—	—
E Atlantic (bre)									✔	—				
Pagophila eburnea	Ivory Gull	—	—	Arctic	50	—	W	—					★	—
Arctic									✔	—				
Gelochelidon nilotica	Gull-billed Tern	—	—	—	270	—	W	—					★	—
W Europe/W Africa									120	—				
Black Sea/E Med (bre)									150	—				
Sterna caspia	Caspian Tern	—	—	—	150	—	W	—					★	—
Europe (bre)									50	—				
Caspian (bre)									100	—				
Sterna sandvicensis	Sandwich Tern	—	—	—	2,800	—	W	—					★	—
W Europe/W Africa									1,500	—				
Black Sea/Med (bre)									1,300	—				
Sterna dougallii	Roseate Tern	—	—	Arctic	50	—	W	—					★	—
Europe (bre)									✔	—				

Appendix 2a ... continued. The 515 bird species occurring regularly in Europe, with the Important Bird Area criteria (at the global and European levels) that they can potentially fulfil and the numerical threshold(s) if applicable. Taxonomy and nomenclature follow Cramp *et al.* (1977–1994).

Species / Subspecies or population applicable for criteria B1i or B1ii		Species of global conservation concern (A1)	Restricted-range species (A2)	Biome-restricted species (A3)	Congregations – global (1% biogeographic population of waterbird) (A4i)	(1% global population seabird or terrestrial species) (A4ii)	(20,000 waterbirds or 10,000 pairs seabirds) (A4iii)	(Bottleneck site of global importance) (A4iv)	Congregations – regional (1% flyway or distinct population of waterbird) (B1i)	(1% distinct population of seabird) (B1ii)	(1% distinct population of other species) (B1iii)	(Bottleneck site of regional importance) (B1iv)	Species of European conservation concern (categories 1–3) (B2)	Species of European conservation concern (category 4) (B3)
Sterna hirundo	Common Tern	—	—	—	7,800	—	W	—					—	—
S Europe/W Europe (bre)									1,800	—				
N Europe/E Europe (bre)									6,000	—				
Sterna paradisaea	Arctic Tern	—	—	—	13,000	—	W	—					—	—
Europe									✓	—				
Sterna albifrons	Little Tern	—	—	—	900	—	W	—					★	—
E Atlantic (bre)									340	—				
Black Sea/E Med (bre)									600	—				
Chlidonias hybridus	Whiskered Tern	—	—	—	1,000	—	W	—					★	—
W Europe/W Med/NW Africa (bre)									250	—				
Black Sea/E Med (bre)									750	—				
Chlidonias niger	Black Tern	—	—	—	1,700	—	W	—					★	—
Europe/Asia (bre)									✓	—				
Chlidonias leucopterus	White-winged Black Tern	—	—	—	2,300	—	W	—						
E Europe/W Asia/Africa									✓	—				
Uria aalge	Guillemot	—		—	—	80,000p	S	—					—	—
E Atlantic									—	20,000p				
Baltic									—	450p				
Uria lomvia	Brünnich's Guillemot	—	—	—	—	110,000p	S	—					—	—
Atlantic									—	70,000p				
Alca torda	Razorbill	—	—	—	—	5,400p	S	—					—	★
East Atlantic									—	250p				
Baltic									—	100p				
Iceland/Faroes/UK/Ireland									—	4,500p				
Cepphus grylle	Black Guillemot	—	—	—	—	3,000p	S	—					★	—
Faroes									—	40p				
Iceland									—	100p				
Baltic									—	150p				
Greenland									—	250p				
Russia/Svalbard									—	300p				
Norway									—	200p				
UK									—	190p				
Alle alle	Little Auk	—	—	—	—	110,000p	S	—					—	—
Greenland									—	100,000p				
Northern Europe									—	10,000p				
Fratercula arctica	Puffin	—	—	—	—	60,000p	S	—					★	—
Iceland/Norway/SW Greenland/N America									—	40,000p				
UK/Ireland/Faroe/France/Norway									—	8,500p				
Pterocles orientalis	Black-bellied Sandgrouse	—	—	—	—	—	—	—	—	—	—	—	★	—
Pterocles alchata	Pin-tailed Sandgrouse	—	—	—	—	—	—	—	—	—	—	—	★	—
Columba livia	Rock Dove	—	—	—	—	—	—	—	—	—	—	—	—	—
Columba oenas	Stock Dove	—	—	—	—	—	—	—	—	—	—	—	—	★
Columba palumbus	Woodpigeon	—	—	—	—	—	—	—	—	—	—	—	—	★
Columba trocaz	Long-toed Pigeon	10p Madeira/Canaries	—	—	—	—	—	—	—	—	—	—	★	—
Columba bollii	Dark-tailed Laurel Pigeon	5p Madeira/Canaries	—	—	—	—	—	—	—	—	—	—	★	—
Columba junoniae	White-tailed Laurel Pigeon	5p Madeira/Canaries	—	—	—	—	—	—	—	—	—	—	★	—
Streptopelia decaocto	Collared Dove	—	—	—	—	—	—	—	—	—	—	—	—	—
Streptopelia turtur	Turtle Dove	—	—	—	—	—	—	—	—	—	—	—	★	—
Streptopelia orientalis	Oriental Turtle Dove	—	—	—	—	—	—	—	—	—	—	—	—	—
Streptopelia senegalensis	Laughing Dove	—	—	—	—	—	—	—	—	—	—	—	—	—
Clamator glandarius	Great Spotted Cuckoo	—	—	—	—	—	—	—	—	—	—	—	—	—
Cuculus canorus	Cuckoo	—	—	—	—	—	—	—	—	—	—	—	—	—
Cuculus saturatus	Oriental Cuckoo	—	—	—	—	—	—	—	—	—	—	—	—	—
Tyto alba	Barn Owl	—	—	—	—	—	—	—	—	—	—	—	★	—
Otus brucei	Striated Scops Owl	—	—	—	—	—	—	—	—	—	—	—	—	—
Otus scops	Scops Owl	—	—	—	—	—	—	—	—	—	—	—	★	—
Bubo bubo	Eagle Owl	—	—	—	—	—	—	—	—	—	—	—	★	—
Ketupa zeylonensis	Brown Fish Owl	—	—	—	—	—	—	—	—	—	—	—	—	—

Appendix 2a … continued. The 515 bird species occurring regularly in Europe, with the Important Bird Area criteria (at the global and European levels) that they can potentially fulfil and the numerical threshold(s) if applicable. Taxonomy and nomenclature follow Cramp *et al.* (1977–1994).

Species / Subspecies or population applicable for criteria B1i or B1ii		Species of global conservation concern (A1)	Restricted-range species (A2)	Biome-restricted species (A3)	Congregations – global (1% biogeographic population of waterbird) (A4i)	(1% global population seabird or terrestrial species) (A4ii)	(20,000 waterbirds or 10,000 pairs seabirds) (A4iii)	(Bottleneck site of global importance) (A4iv)	Congregations – regional (1% flyway or distinct population of waterbird) (B1i)	(1% distinct population of seabird) (B1ii)	(1% distinct population of other species) (B1iii)	(Bottleneck site of regional importance) (B1iv)	Species of European conservation concern (categories 1–3) (B2)	Species of European conservation concern (category 4) (B3)
Nyctea scandiaca	Snowy Owl	—	—	Arctic	—	—	—	—	—	—	—	—	★	—
Surnia ulula	Hawk Owl	—	—	Boreal	—	—	—	—	—	—	—	—	—	—
Glaucidium passerinum	Pygmy Owl	—	—	—	—	—	—	—	—	—	—	—	—	—
Athene noctua	Little Owl	—	—	—	—	—	—	—	—	—	—	—	★	—
Strix aluco	Tawny Owl	—	—	—	—	—	—	—	—	—	—	—	—	★
Strix uralensis	Ural Owl	—	—	—	—	—	—	—	—	—	—	—	—	—
Strix nebulosa	Great Grey Owl	—	—	Boreal	—	—	—	—	—	—	—	—	—	—
Asio otus	Long-eared Owl	—	—	—	—	—	—	—	—	—	—	—	—	—
Asio flammeus	Short-eared Owl	—	—	—	—	—	—	—	—	—	—	—	★	—
Aegolius funereus	Tengmalm's Owl	—	—	—	—	—	—	—	—	—	—	—	—	—
Caprimulgus europaeus	Nightjar	—	—	—	—	—	—	—	—	—	—	—	★	—
Caprimulgus ruficollis	Red-necked Nightjar	—	—	Med	—	—	—	—	—	—	—	—	—	—
Apus unicolor	Plain Swift	—	Madeira/Canaries	—	—	—	—	—	—	—	—	—	—	★
Apus apus	Swift	—	—	—	—	—	—	—	—	—	—	—	—	—
Apus pallidus	Pallid Swift	—	—	—	—	—	—	—	—	—	—	—	—	—
Apus melba	Alpine Swift	—	—	—	—	—	—	—	—	—	—	—	—	—
Apus caffer	White-rumped Swift	—	—	—	—	—	—	—	—	—	—	—	—	—
Apus affinis	Little Swift	—	—	—	—	—	—	—	—	—	—	—	—	—
Halcyon smyrnensis	White-breasted Kingfisher	—	—	—	—	—	—	—	—	—	—	—	—	—
Alcedo atthis	Kingfisher	—	—	—	—	—	—	—	—	—	—	—	★	—
Ceryle rudis	Pied Kingfisher	—	—	—	—	—	—	—	—	—	—	—	—	—
Merops superciliosus	Blue-cheeked Bee-eater	—	—	—	—	—	—	—	—	—	—	—	—	—
Merops apiaster	Bee-eater	—	—	—	—	40,000	—	—	—	— 13,000	—	—	★	—
Coracias garrulus	Roller	—	—	—	—	—	—	—	—	—	—	—	★	—
Upupa epops	Hoopoe	—	—	—	—	—	—	—	—	—	—	—	—	—
Jynx torquilla	Wryneck	—	—	—	—	—	—	—	—	—	—	—	★	—
Picus canus	Grey-headed Woodpecker	—	—	—	—	—	—	—	—	—	—	—	★	—
Picus viridis	Green Woodpecker	—	—	—	—	—	—	—	—	—	—	—	★	—
Dryocopus martius	Black Woodpecker	—	—	—	—	—	—	—	—	—	—	—	—	—
Dendrocopos major	Great Spotted Woodpecker	—	—	—	—	—	—	—	—	—	—	—	—	—
Dendrocopos syriacus	Syrian Woodpecker	—	—	—	—	—	—	—	—	—	—	—	—	★
Dendrocopos medius	Middle Spotted Woodpecker	—	—	—	—	—	—	—	—	—	—	—	—	★
Dendrocopos leucotos	White-backed Woodpecker	—	—	—	—	—	—	—	—	—	—	—	—	—
Dendrocopos minor	Lesser Spotted Woodpecker	—	—	—	—	—	—	—	—	—	—	—	—	—
Picoides tridactylus	Three-toed Woodpecker	—	—	—	—	—	—	—	—	—	—	—	★	—
Ammomanes deserti	Desert Lark	—	—	—	—	—	—	—	—	—	—	—	—	—
Chersophilus duponti	Dupont's Lark	—	—	—	—	—	—	—	—	—	—	—	★	—
Melanocorypha calandra	Calandra Lark	—	—	—	—	—	—	—	—	—	—	—	★	—
Melanocorypha bimaculata	Bimaculated Lark	—	—	—	—	—	—	—	—	—	—	—	—	—
Melanocorypha leucoptera	White-winged Lark	—	—	Steppe	—	—	—	—	—	—	—	—	—	★[w]
Melanocorypha yeltoniensis	Black Lark	—	—	Steppe	—	—	—	—	—	—	—	—	★	—
Calandrella brachydactyla	Short-toed Lark	—	—	—	—	—	—	—	—	—	—	—	★	—
Calandrella rufescens	Lesser Short-toed Lark	—	—	—	—	—	—	—	—	—	—	—	★	—
Galerida cristata	Crested Lark	—	—	—	—	—	—	—	—	—	—	—	★	—
Galerida theklae	Thekla Lark	—	—	—	—	—	—	—	—	—	—	—	★	—
Lullula arborea	Woodlark	—	—	—	—	—	—	—	—	—	—	—	★	—
Alauda arvensis	Skylark	—	—	—	—	—	—	—	—	—	—	—	★	—
Eremophila alpestris	Shore Lark	—	—	—	—	—	—	—	—	—	—	—	—	—
Riparia riparia	Sand Martin	—	—	—	—	120,000	—	—	—	— 60,000	—	—	★	—
Ptyonoprogne rupestris	Crag Martin	—	—	—	—	—	—	—	—	—	—	—	—	—
Hirundo rustica	Swallow	—	—	—	—	—	—	—	—	—	—	—	★	—
Hirundo daurica	Red-rumped Swallow	—	—	—	—	—	—	—	—	—	—	—	—	—
Delichon urbica	House Martin	—	—	—	—	—	—	—	—	—	—	—	—	—
Anthus campestris	Tawny Pipit	—	—	—	—	—	—	—	—	—	—	—	★	—[w]
Anthus berthelotii	Berthelot's Pipit	—	Madeira/Canaries	—	—	—	—	—	—	—	—	—	—	★

Appendix 2a ... continued. The 515 bird species occurring regularly in Europe, with the Important Bird Area criteria (at the global and European levels) that they can potentially fulfil and the numerical threshold(s) if applicable. Taxonomy and nomenclature follow Cramp *et al.* (1977–1994).

Species / Subspecies or population applicable for criteria B1i or B1ii	Species of global conservation concern (A1)	Restricted-range species (A2)	Biome-restricted species (A3)	Congregations – global (1% biogeographic population of waterbird) (A4i)	(1% global population seabird or terrestrial species) (A4ii)	(20,000 waterbirds or 10,000 pairs seabirds) (A4iii)	(Bottleneck site of global importance) (A4iv)	Congregations – regional (1% flyway or distinct population of waterbird) (B1i)	(1% distinct population of seabird) (B1ii)	(1% distinct population of other species) (B1iii)	(Bottleneck site of regional importance) (B1iv)	Species of European conservation concern (categories 1–3) (B2)	Species of European conservation concern (category 4) (B3)
Anthus hodgsoni Olive-backed Pipit	—	—	—	—	—	—	—	—	—	—	—	—	—
Anthus trivialis Tree Pipit	—	—	—	—	—	—	—	—	—	—	—	—	—
Anthus gustavi Pechora Pipit	—	—	—	—	—	—	—	—	—	—	—	—	—
Anthus pratensis Meadow Pipit	—	—	—	—	—	—	—	—	—	—	—	—	★
Anthus cervinus Red-throated Pipit	—	—	Arctic	—	—	—	—	—	—	—	—	—	—
Anthus petrosus Rock Pipit	—	—	—	—	—	—	—	—	—	—	—	—	—
Anthus spinoletta Water Pipit	—	—	—	—	—	—	—	—	—	—	—	—	—
Motacilla flava Yellow Wagtail	—	—	—	—	—	—	—	—	—	—	—	—	—
Motacilla citreola Citrine Wagtail	—	—	—	—	—	—	—	—	—	—	—	—	—
Motacilla cinerea Grey Wagtail	—	—	—	—	—	—	—	—	—	—	—	—	—
Motacilla alba Pied Wagtail	—	—	—	—	—	—	—	—	—	—	—	—	—
Pycnonotus xanthopygos Yellow-vented Bulbul	—	—	—	—	—	—	—	—	—	—	—	—	—
Bombycilla garrulus Waxwing	—	—	Boreal	—	—	—	—	—	—	—	—	—	—
Cinclus cinclus Dipper	—	—	—	—	—	—	—	—	—	—	—	—	—
Troglodytes troglodytes Wren	—	—	—	—	—	—	—	—	—	—	—	—	—
Prunella modularis Dunnock	—	—	—	—	—	—	—	—	—	—	—	—	★
Prunella montanella Siberian Accentor	—	—	—	—	—	—	—	—	—	—	—	—	—
Prunella ocularis Radde's Accentor	—	—	—	—	—	—	—	—	—	—	—	★	—
Prunella atrogularis Black-throated Accentor	—	—	—	—	—	—	—	—	—	—	—	★	—
Prunella collaris Alpine Accentor	—	—	Alpine	—	—	—	—	—	—	—	—	—	—
Cercotrichas galactotes Rufous Bush Robin	—	—	—	—	—	—	—	—	—	—	—	—	—
Erithacus rubecula Robin	—	—	—	—	—	—	—	—	—	—	—	—	★
Luscinia luscinia Thrush Nightingale	—	—	—	—	—	—	—	—	—	—	—	—	★
Luscinia megarhynchos Nightingale	—	—	—	—	—	—	—	—	—	—	—	—	★
Luscinia calliope Siberian Rubythroat	—	—	—	—	—	—	—	—	—	—	—	—	—
Luscinia svecica Bluethroat	—	—	—	—	—	—	—	—	—	—	—	—	—
Tarsiger cyanurus Red-flanked Bluetail	—	—	—	—	—	—	—	—	—	—	—	—	—
Irania gutturalis White-throated Robin	—	—	—	—	—	—	—	—	—	—	—	—	—
Phoenicurus ochruros Black Redstart	—	—	—	—	—	—	—	—	—	—	—	—	—
Phoenicurus phoenicurus Redstart	—	—	—	—	—	—	—	—	—	—	—	★	—
Phoenicurus erythrogaster Güldenstädt's Redstart	—	—	—	—	—	—	—	—	—	—	—	★	—
Saxicola rubetra Whinchat	—	—	—	—	—	—	—	—	—	—	—	—	★
Saxicola dacotiae Fuerteventura Chat	5p	Madeira/Canaries	—	—	—	—	—	—	—	10p	—	★	—
Saxicola torquata Stonechat	—	—	—	—	—	—	—	—	—	—	—	★	—
Oenanthe isabellina Isabelline Wheatear	—	—	—	—	—	—	—	—	—	—	—	—	—
Oenanthe oenanthe Wheatear	—	—	—	—	—	—	—	—	—	—	—	—	—
Oenanthe pleschanka Pied Wheatear	—	—	—	—	—	—	—	—	—	—	—	—	—
Oenanthe cypriaca Cyprus Pied Wheatear	—	Cyprus	Med	—	—	—	—	—	—	—	—	★	—
Oenanthe hispanica Black-eared Wheatear	—	—	Med	—	—	—	—	—	—	—	—	★	—
Oenanthe deserti Desert Wheatear	—	—	—	—	—	—	—	—	—	—	—	—	—
Oenanthe finschii Finsch's Wheatear	—	—	—	—	—	—	—	—	—	—	—	—	—
Oenanthe xanthoprymna Red-tailed Wheatear	—	—	—	—	—	—	—	—	—	—	—	—	—
Oenanthe leucura Black Wheatear	—	—	Med	—	—	—	—	—	—	100p	—	★	—
Monticola saxatilis Rock Thrush	—	—	—	—	—	—	—	—	—	—	—	★	—
Monticola solitarius Blue Rock Thrush	—	—	—	—	—	—	—	—	—	—	—	★	—
Zoothera dauma White's Thrush	—	—	—	—	—	—	—	—	—	—	—	—	—
Turdus torquatus Ring Ouzel	—	—	—	—	—	—	—	—	—	—	—	—	★
Turdus merula Blackbird	—	—	—	—	—	—	—	—	—	—	—	—	★
Turdus ruficollis Black-throated Thrush	—	—	—	—	—	—	—	—	—	—	—	—	—
Turdus pilaris Fieldfare	—	—	—	—	—	—	—	—	—	—	—	—	★W
Turdus philomelos Song Thrush	—	—	—	—	—	—	—	—	—	—	—	—	★
Turdus iliacus Redwing	—	—	—	—	—	—	—	—	—	—	—	—	★W
Turdus viscivorus Mistle Thrush	—	—	—	—	—	—	—	—	—	—	—	—	★
Cettia cetti Cetti's Warbler	—	—	—	—	—	—	—	—	—	—	—	—	—
Cisticola juncidis Fan-tailed Warbler	—	—	—	—	—	—	—	—	—	—	—	—	—

Appendix 2a ... continued. The 515 bird species occurring regularly in Europe, with the Important Bird Area criteria (at the global and European levels) that they can potentially fulfil and the numerical threshold(s) if applicable. Taxonomy and nomenclature follow Cramp *et al.* (1977–1994).

Species / Subspecies or population applicable for criteria B1i or B1ii		Species of global conservation concern (A1)	Restricted-range species (A2)	Biome-restricted species (A3)	Congregations – global (1% biogeographic population of waterbird) (A4i)	(1% global population seabird or terrestrial species) (A4ii)	(20,000 waterbirds or 10,000 pairs seabirds) (A4iii)	(Bottleneck site of global importance) (A4iv)	Congregations – regional (1% flyway or distinct population of waterbird) (B1i)	(1% distinct population of seabird) (B1ii)	(1% distinct population of other species) (B1iii)	(Bottleneck site of regional importance) (B1iv)	Species of European conservation concern (categories 1–3) (B2)	Species of European conservation concern (category 4) (B3)
Prinia gracilis	Graceful Warbler	—	—	—	—	—	—	—	—	—	—	—	—	—
Locustella lanceolata	Lanceolated Warbler	—	—	—	—	—	—	—	—	—	—	—	—	—
Locustella naevia	Grasshopper Warbler	—	—	—	—	—	—	—	—	—	—	—	—	★
Locustella fluviatilis	River Warbler	—	—	—	—	—	—	—	—	—	—	—	—	★
Locustella luscinioides	Savi's Warbler	—	—	—	—	—	—	—	—	—	—	—	—	★
Acrocephalus melanopogon	Moustached Warbler	—	—	—	—	—	—	—	—	—	—	—	—	—
Acrocephalus paludicola	Aquatic Warbler	10p	—	—	—	—	—	—	—	—	—	—	★	—
Acrocephalus schoenobaenus	Sedge Warbler	—	—	—	—	—	—	—	—	—	—	—	—	★
Acrocephalus agricola	Paddyfield Warbler	—	—	—	—	—	—	—	—	—	—	—	—	—
Acrocephalus dumetorum	Blyth's Reed Warbler	—	—	—	—	—	—	—	—	—	—	—	—	—
Acrocephalus palustris	Marsh Warbler	—	—	—	—	—	—	—	—	—	—	—	—	★
Acrocephalus scirpaceus	Reed Warbler	—	—	—	—	—	—	—	—	—	—	—	—	★
Acrocephalus arundinaceus	Great Reed Warbler	—	—	—	—	—	—	—	—	—	—	—	—	—
Hippolais pallida	Olivaceous Warbler	—	—	—	—	—	—	—	—	—	—	—	★	—
Hippolais caligata	Booted Warbler	—	—	—	—	—	—	—	—	—	—	—	—	—
Hippolais languida	Upcher's Warbler	—	—	—	—	—	—	—	—	—	—	—	—	—
Hippolais olivetorum	Olive-tree Warbler	—	—	Med	—	—	—	—	—	—	—	—	★	—
Hippolais icterina	Icterine Warbler	—	—	—	—	—	—	—	—	—	—	—	—	★
Hippolais polyglotta	Melodious Warbler	—	—	—	—	—	—	—	—	—	—	—	—	★
Sylvia sarda	Marmora's Warbler	—	—	Med	—	—	—	—	—	—	—	—	—	★
Sylvia undata	Dartford Warbler	—	—	—	—	—	—	—	—	—	—	—	★	—
Sylvia conspicillata	Spectacled Warbler	—	—	Med	—	—	—	—	—	—	—	—	—	—
Sylvia cantillans	Subalpine Warbler	—	—	Med	—	—	—	—	—	—	—	—	—	★
Sylvia mystacea	Mènètries's Warbler	—	—	—	—	—	—	—	—	—	—	—	—	—
Sylvia melanocephala	Sardinian Warbler	—	—	Med	—	—	—	—	—	—	—	—	—	★
Sylvia melanothorax	Cyprus Warbler	—	Cyprus	Med	—	—	—	—	—	—	—	—	★	—
Sylvia rueppelli	Rüppell's Warbler	—	—	Med	—	—	—	—	—	—	—	—	—	★
Sylvia nana	Desert Warbler	—	—	—	—	—	—	—	—	—	—	—	—	—
Sylvia hortensis	Orphean Warbler	—	—	—	—	—	—	—	—	—	—	—	★	—
Sylvia nisoria	Barred Warbler	—	—	—	—	—	—	—	—	—	—	—	—	★
Sylvia curruca	Lesser Whitethroat	—	—	—	—	—	—	—	—	—	—	—	—	—
Sylvia communis	Whitethroat	—	—	—	—	—	—	—	—	—	—	—	—	★
Sylvia borin	Garden Warbler	—	—	—	—	—	—	—	—	—	—	—	—	★
Sylvia atricapilla	Blackcap	—	—	—	—	—	—	—	—	—	—	—	—	★
Phylloscopus nitidus	Green Warbler	—	—	—	—	—	—	—	—	—	—	—	—	—
Phylloscopus trochiloides	Greenish Warbler	—	—	—	—	—	—	—	—	—	—	—	—	—
Phylloscopus borealis	Arctic Warbler	—	—	Boreal	—	—	—	—	—	—	—	—	—	—
Phylloscopus inornatus	Yellow-browed Warbler	—	—	—	—	—	—	—	—	—	—	—	—	—
Phylloscopus bonelli	Bonelli's Warbler	—	—	—	—	—	—	—	—	—	—	—	—	★
Phylloscopus sibilatrix	Wood Warbler	—	—	—	—	—	—	—	—	—	—	—	—	★
Phylloscopus lorenzii	Caucasian Chiffchaff	—	—	—	—	—	—	—	—	—	—	—	—	—
Phylloscopus collybita	Chiffchaff	—	—	—	—	—	—	—	—	—	—	—	—	—
Phylloscopus trochilus	Willow Warbler	—	—	—	—	—	—	—	—	—	—	—	—	—
Regulus regulus	Goldcrest	—	—	—	—	—	—	—	—	—	—	—	—	★
Regulus teneriffae	Tenerife Goldcrest	—	Madeira/Canaries	—	—	—	—	—	—	—	—	—	—	★
Regulus ignicapillus	Firecrest	—	—	—	—	—	—	—	—	—	—	—	—	★
Muscicapa striata	Spotted Flycatcher	—	—	—	—	—	—	—	—	—	—	—	★	—
Ficedula parva	Red-breasted Flycatcher	—	—	—	—	—	—	—	—	—	—	—	—	—
Ficedula semitorquata	Semi-collared Flycatcher	—	—	—	—	—	—	—	—	—	—	—	★	—
Ficedula albicollis	Collared Flycatcher	—	—	—	—	—	—	—	—	—	—	—	—	★
Ficedula hypoleuca	Pied Flycatcher	—	—	—	—	—	—	—	—	—	—	—	—	★
Panurus biarmicus	Bearded Tit	—	—	—	—	—	—	—	—	—	—	—	—	—
Aegithalos caudatus	Long-tailed Tit	—	—	—	—	—	—	—	—	—	—	—	—	—
Parus palustris	Marsh Tit	—	—	—	—	—	—	—	—	—	—	—	—	—
Parus lugubris	Sombre Tit	—	—	—	—	—	—	—	—	—	—	—	—	★

Appendix 2a ... continued. The 515 bird species occurring regularly in Europe, with the Important Bird Area criteria (at the global and European levels) that they can potentially fulfil and the numerical threshold(s) if applicable. Taxonomy and nomenclature follow Cramp *et al.* (1977–1994).

Species / Subspecies or population applicable for criteria B1i or B1ii		Species of global conservation concern (A1)	Restricted-range species (A2)	Biome-restricted species (A3)	Congregations – global (1% biogeographic population of waterbird) (A4i)	Congregations (1% global population seabird or terrestrial species) (A4ii)	(20,000 waterbirds or 10,000 pairs seabirds) (A4iii)	(Bottleneck site of global importance) (A4iv)	Congregations – regional (1% flyway or distinct population of waterbird) (B1i)	(1% distinct population of seabird) (B1ii)	(1% distinct population of other species) (B1iii)	(Bottleneck site of regional importance) (B1iv)	Species of European conservation concern (categories 1–3) (B2)	Species of European conservation concern (category 4) (B3)
Parus montanus	Willow Tit	—	—	—	—	—	—	—	—	—	—	—	—	—
Parus cinctus	Siberian Tit	—	—	Boreal	—	—	—	—	—	—	—	—	—	—
Parus cristatus	Crested Tit	—	—	—	—	—	—	—	—	—	—	—	—	★
Parus ater	Coal Tit	—	—	—	—	—	—	—	—	—	—	—	—	—
Parus caeruleus	Blue Tit	—	—	—	—	—	—	—	—	—	—	—	—	★
Parus cyanus	Azure Tit	—	—	—	—	—	—	—	—	—	—	—	—	—
Parus major	Great Tit	—	—	—	—	—	—	—	—	—	—	—	—	—
Sitta krueperi	Krüper's Nuthatch	—	—	Med	—	—	—	—	—	—	—	—	—	★
Sitta whiteheadi	Corsican Nuthatch	10p	Corsica	Med	—	—	—	—	—	—	—	—	★	—
Sitta europaea	Nuthatch	—	—	—	—	—	—	—	—	—	—	—	—	—
Sitta tephronota	Great Rock Nuthatch	—	—	Alpine	—	—	—	—	—	—	—	—	—	—
Sitta neumayer	Rock Nuthatch	—	—	Med	—	—	—	—	—	—	—	—	—	★
Tichodroma muraria	Wallcreeper	—	—	Alpine	—	—	—	—	—	—	—	—	—	—
Certhia familiaris	Treecreeper	—	—	—	—	—	—	—	—	—	—	—	—	—
Certhia brachydactyla	Short-toed Treecreeper	—	—	—	—	—	—	—	—	—	—	—	—	★
Remiz pendulinus	Penduline Tit	—	—	—	—	—	—	—	—	—	—	—	—	—
Oriolus oriolus	Golden Oriole	—	—	—	—	—	—	—	—	—	—	—	—	—
Lanius collurio	Red-backed Shrike	—	—	—	—	—	—	—	—	—	—	—	★	—
Lanius minor	Lesser Grey Shrike	—	—	—	—	—	—	—	—	—	—	—	★	—
Lanius excubitor	Great Grey Shrike	—	—	—	—	—	—	—	—	—	—	—	★	—
Lanius senator	Woodchat Shrike	—	—	—	—	—	—	—	—	—	—	—	★	—
Lanius nubicus	Masked Shrike	—	—	Med	—	—	—	—	—	—	—	—	★	—
Garrulus glandarius	Jay	—	—	—	—	—	—	—	—	—	—	—	—	—
Perisoreus infaustus	Siberian Jay	—	—	Boreal	—	—	—	—	—	—	—	—	★	—
Cyanopica cyana	Azure-winged Magpie	—	—	—	—	—	—	—	—	—	—	—	—	—
Pica pica	Magpie	—	—	—	—	—	—	—	—	—	—	—	—	—
Nucifraga caryocatactes	Nutcracker	—	—	—	—	—	—	—	—	—	—	—	—	—
Pyrrhocorax graculus	Alpine Chough	—	—	Alpine	—	—	—	—	—	—	—	—	—	—
Pyrrhocorax pyrrhocorax	Chough	—	—	—	—	—	—	—	—	—	—	—	★	—
Corvus monedula	Jackdaw	—	—	—	—	—	—	—	—	—	—	—	—	★
Corvus frugilegus	Rook	—	—	—	—	—	—	—	—	—	—	—	—	—
Corvus corone	Carrion Crow	—	—	—	—	—	—	—	—	—	—	—	—	—
Corvus corax	Raven	—	—	—	—	—	—	—	—	—	—	—	—	—
Sturnus vulgaris	Starling	—	—	—	—	—	—	—	—	—	—	—	—	—
Sturnus unicolor	Spotless Starling	—	—	Med	—	—	—	—	—	—	—	—	—	★
Sturnus roseus	Rose-coloured Starling	—	—	—	—	—	—	—	—	—	—	—	—	—
Passer domesticus	House Sparrow	—	—	—	—	—	—	—	—	—	—	—	—	—
Passer hispaniolensis	Spanish Sparrow	—	—	—	—	—	—	—	—	—	—	—	—	—
Passer moabiticus	Dead Sea Sparrow	—	—	—	—	—	—	—	—	—	—	—	—	—
Passer montanus	Tree Sparrow	—	—	—	—	—	—	—	—	—	—	—	—	—
Carpospiza brachydactyla	Pale Rock Sparrow	—	—	—	—	—	—	—	—	—	—	—	—	—
Petronia xanthocollis	Yellow-throated Sparrow	—	—	—	—	—	—	—	—	—	—	—	—	—
Petronia petronia	Rock Sparrow	—	—	—	—	—	—	—	—	—	—	—	—	—
Montifringilla nivalis	Snowfinch	—	—	Alpine	—	—	—	—	—	—	—	—	—	—
Fringilla coelebs	Chaffinch	—	—	—	—	—	—	—	—	—	—	—	—	★
Fringilla teydea	Blue Chaffinch	10p	Madeira/Canaries	—	—	—	—	—	—	—	—	—	★	—
Fringilla montifringilla	Brambling	—	—	Boreal	—	—	—	—	—	—	—	—	—	—
Serinus pusillus	Red-fronted Serin	—	—	—	—	—	—	—	—	—	—	—	—	—
Serinus serinus	Serin	—	—	—	—	—	—	—	—	—	—	—	—	★
Serinus canaria	Canary	—	Madeira/Canaries, Azores	—	—	—	—	—	—	—	—	—	—	★
Serinus citrinella	Citril Finch	—	—	Alpine	—	—	—	—	—	—	—	—	—	★
Carduelis chloris	Greenfinch	—	—	—	—	—	—	—	—	—	—	—	—	★
Carduelis carduelis	Goldfinch	—	—	—	—	—	—	—	—	—	—	—	—	—
Carduelis spinus	Siskin	—	—	—	—	—	—	—	—	—	—	—	—	★

Appendix 2a ... continued. The 515 bird species occurring regularly in Europe, with the Important Bird Area criteria (at the global and European levels) that they can potentially fulfil and the numerical threshold(s) if applicable. Taxonomy and nomenclature follow Cramp *et al.* (1977–1994).

Species / Subspecies or population applicable for criteria B1i or B1ii		Species of global conservation concern (A1)	Restricted-range species (A2)	Biome-restricted species (A3)	Congregations – global (1% biogeographic population of waterbird) (A4i)	(1% global population seabird or terrestrial species) (A4ii)	(20,000 waterbirds or 10,000 pairs seabirds) (A4iii)	(Bottleneck site of global importance) (A4iv)	Congregations – regional (1% flyway or distinct population of waterbird) (B1i)	(1% distinct population of seabird) (B1ii)	(1% distinct population of other species) (B1iii)	(Bottleneck site of regional importance) (B1iv)	Species of European conservation concern (categories 1–3) (B2)	Species of European conservation concern (category 4) (B3)
Carduelis cannabina	Linnet	—	—	—	—	—	—	—	—	—	—	—	—	★
Carduelis flavirostris	Twite	—	—	—	—	—	—	—	—	—	—	—	—	—
Carduelis flammea	Redpoll	—	—	—	—	—	—	—	—	—	—	—	—	—
Carduelis hornemanni	Arctic Redpoll	—	—	Arctic	—	—	—	—	—	—	—	—	—	—
Loxia leucoptera	Two-barred Crossbill	—	—	Boreal	—	—	—	—	—	—	—	—	—	—
Loxia curvirostra	Crossbill	—	—	—	—	—	—	—	—	—	—	—	—	—
Loxia scotica	Scottish Crossbill	5p	Scotland	—	—	—	—	—	—	—	—	—	★	—
Loxia pytyopsittacus	Parrot Crossbill	—	—	Boreal	—	—	—	—	—	—	—	—	—	★
Rhodopechys sanguinea	Crimson-winged Finch	—	—	—	—	—	—	—	—	—	—	—	—	—
Rhodospiza obsoleta	Desert Finch	—	—	—	—	—	—	—	—	—	—	—	—	—
Bucanetes mongolicus	Mongolian Trumpeter Finch	—	—	—	—	—	—	—	—	—	—	—	—	—
Bucanetes githagineus	Trumpeter Finch	—	—	—	—	—	—	—	—	—	—	—	★	—
Carpodacus erythrinus	Scarlet Rosefinch	—	—	—	—	—	—	—	—	—	—	—	—	—
Carpodacus rubicilla	Great Rosefinch	—	—	Alpine	—	—	—	—	—	—	—	—	★	—
Pinicola enucleator	Pine Grosbeak	—	—	Boreal	—	—	—	—	—	—	—	—	—	—
Pyrrhula pyrrhula	Bullfinch	—	—	—	—	—	—	—	—	—	—	—	—	—
Pyrrhula murina	Azores Bullfinch	[not assessed]	Azores	—	—	—	—	—	—	—	—	—	[not assessed]	[not assessed]
Coccothraustes coccothraustes	Hawfinch	—	—	—	—	—	—	—	—	—	—	—	—	—
Calcarius lapponicus	Lapland Bunting	—	—	Arctic	—	—	—	—	—	—	—	—	—	—
Plectrophenax nivalis	Snow Bunting	—	—	Arctic	—	—	—	—	—	—	—	—	—	—
Emberiza citrinella	Yellowhammer	—	—	—	—	—	—	—	—	—	—	—	—	★
Emberiza cirlus	Cirl Bunting	—	—	—	—	—	—	—	—	—	—	—	—	★
Emberiza cia	Rock Bunting	—	—	—	—	—	—	—	—	—	—	—	★	—
Emberiza cineracea	Cinereous Bunting	5p	—	Med	—	—	—	—	—	—	—	—	★	—
Emberiza hortulana	Ortolan Bunting	—	—	—	—	—	—	—	—	—	—	—	★	—
Emberiza buchanani	Grey-necked Bunting	—	—	—	—	—	—	—	—	—	—	—	—	—
Emberiza caesia	Cretzschmar's Bunting	—	—	Med	—	—	—	—	—	—	—	—	—	★
Emberiza rustica	Rustic Bunting	—	—	Boreal	—	—	—	—	—	—	—	—	—	—
Emberiza pusilla	Little Bunting	—	—	—	—	—	—	—	—	—	—	—	—	—
Emberiza aureola	Yellow-breasted Bunting	—	—	—	—	—	—	—	—	—	—	—	—	—
Emberiza schoeniclus	Reed Bunting	—	—	—	—	—	—	—	—	—	—	—	—	—
Emberiza bruniceps	Red-headed Bunting	—	—	—	—	—	—	—	—	—	—	—	—	—
Emberiza melanocephala	Black-headed Bunting	—	—	Med	—	—	—	—	—	—	—	—	★	—
Miliaria calandra	Corn Bunting	—	—	—	—	—	—	—	—	—	—	—	—	★

✔ given for IBA criteria B1i indicates that the population threshold applied is the same as that given for A4i. For B1ii and B1iii the population threshold applied is the same as that given for A4ii.

★ given for IBA criteria B2/B3 indicates that the species is one of the 278 species of European conservation concern as listed in Tucker and Heath (1994). The numerical threshold for each species of European conservation concern varies by country – for full details on how to calculate thresholds see Box 2, 'Identifying IBAs' chapter.

For criterion A4iii 'S' indicates the species is classed as a 'seabird' and thus the collective threshold of 10,000 pairs of seabirds may apply, and 'W' indicates the species is considered a 'waterbird' following the definition of Rose and Scott (1997) (see p. 15, 'Identifying IBAs' chapter) and the collective threshold of 20,000 individuals may apply.

1. Non-migratory raptor in Europe
2. Non-congregatory in Europe
3. Marginal population in Europe
4. Small population
Superscript W – species status applies to wintering population

For definitions of regions listed for distinct populations of waterbirds under criterion B1i, see Rose and Scott (1997):

• Western Palearctic – As defined by Cramp *et al.* (1977–1994). For some species/populations, Iraq has been included.

• North-western Europe – Belgium, Denmark, Estonia, Finland, France, Germany, Iceland, Ireland, Latvia, Lithuania, Luxembourg, Netherlands, Norway, Poland, Russia (area around the Gulf of Finland and Kaliningrad), Sweden, United Kingdom.

• North-eastern Europe – Belarus, Russia (west of the Urals), Ukraine.

• Central Europe – Austria, Czech Republic, Hungary, Liechtenstein, Slovakia, Switzerland.

• Western Mediterranean – Algeria, France, Italy, Malta, Monaco, Morocco, Portugal, San Marino, Spain, Tunisia.

• Eastern Mediterranean – Albania, Bosnia and Herzegovina, Croatia, Cyprus, Egypt, Greece, Israel, Lebanon, Libya, Slovenia, Syria, Former Yugoslav Republic of Macedonia, Turkey, Yugoslavia.

• Black Sea – Armenia, Bulgaria, Georgia, Moldova, Romania, Russia, Turkey, Ukraine.

• Caspian – Armenia, Azerbaijan, Iran, Kazakhstan, Russia, Turkmenistan, Uzbekistan.

Abbreviations given for distinct populations of waterbirds under criterion B1i:

bre	breeding
E	east
Med	Mediterranean
N	northern
NE	north-eastern
NW	north-western
S	southern
SE	south-eastern
SW	south-western
UK	United Kingdom
W	western
win	wintering

References

CRAMP, S. ET AL. (1977–1994) *The birds of the western Palearctic.* Vols 1–9. Oxford, UK: Oxford University Press.

ROSE, P. M. AND SCOTT, D. A. (1997) *Waterfowl population estimates.* Second edition. Wageningen, Netherlands: Wetlands International.

TUCKER, G. M. AND HEATH, M. F. (1994) *Birds in Europe: their conservation status.* Cambridge, UK: BirdLife International (BirdLife Conservation Series no. 3).

Appendix 2b. Bird species occurring regularly in the European Union that can fulfil Important Bird Area criteria (at the European Union level), and the numerical threshold(s) if applicable. Taxonomy and nomenclature follow Cramp *et al.* (1977–1994).

IBA criteria applicable at the global (A) and European (B) levels are shown in Appendix 2a.
For a full explanation of criteria see the introductory chapter 'Identifying IBAs'.
All population thresholds are given in individuals, unless followed by 'p' indicating pairs. To convert between individuals and pairs, a multiplying/dividing factor of 3 was used.
n/a = not applicable.

Annex I number	Species		Species of global conservation concern (C1)	Concentrations of species threatened[2] at the EU level (C2)	Congregations of migratory species not threatened[2] at the EU level (C3)	Congregatory – large congregations 20,000 waterbirds or 10,000 pairs of seabirds (C4)	Congregatory – Bottleneck site for storks/raptors/cranes (C5)	'Top 5' sites in NUTS[1] region for species threatened[2] at EU level (C6)	Notes
1	*Gavia stellata*	Red-throated Diver	—	35p	—	W	—	★	
2	*Gavia arctica*	Black-throated Diver	—	✔	—	W	—	★	
3	*Gavia immer*	Great Northern Diver	—	160p	—	W	—	★	
	Tachybaptus ruficollis	Little Grebe	—	—	✔	W	—	—	
	Podiceps cristatus	Great Crested Grebe	—	—	✔	W	—	—	
	Podiceps grisegena	Red-necked Grebe	—	—	✔	W	—	—	
4	*Podiceps auritus*	Slavonian Grebe	—	60p	—	W	—	★	
	Podiceps nigricollis	Black-necked Grebe	—	—	1,000	W	—	—	
	Fulmarus glacialis	Fulmar	—	—	✔	S	—	—	
6	*Pterodroma feae*	Fea's Petrel	✔	n/a	—	S	—	★	
5	*Pterodroma madeira*	Zino's Petrel	✔	n/a	—	S	—	★	
7	*Bulweria bulwerii*	Bulwer's Petrel	—	✔	—	S	—	★	
8	*Calonectris diomedea*	Cory's Shearwater	—	✔	—	S	—	★	
	Puffinus puffinus	Manx Shearwater	—	—	✔	S	—	—	
9	*Puffinus yelkouan*	Yelkouan Shearwater	—	30p*	✔	S	—	★	*P. y. mauretanicus*
10	*Puffinus assimilis*	Little Shearwater	—	✔	—	S	—	★	
11	*Pelagodroma marina*	White-faced Petrel	—	✔	—	S	—	★	
12	*Hydrobates pelagicus*	Storm Petrel	—	1,600p*	—	S	—	★	*Italy, Greece 35p
13	*Oceanodroma leucorhoa*	Leach's Petrel	—	600p	—	S	—	★	
14	*Oceanodroma castro*	Madeiran Petrel	—	✔	—	S	—	★	
	Sula bassana	Gannet	—	—	✔	S	—	—	
	Phalacrocorax carbo sinensis	Cormorant	—	—	✔	W	—	—	
	Phalacrocorax aristotelis aristotelis	Shag	—	—	—	W	—	—	
15	*Phalacrocorax aristotelis desmarestii*	Shag	—	30p	—	W	—	★	
16	*Phalacrocorax pygmeus*	Pygmy Cormorant	✔	n/a	—	W	—	★	
17	*Pelecanus onocrotalus*	White Pelican	—	✔	—	W	—	★	
18	*Pelecanus crispus*	Dalmatian Pelican	✔	✔	—	W	—	★	
19	*Botaurus stellaris*	Bittern	—	15p	—	W	—	★	
20	*Ixobrychus minutus*	Little Bittern	—	55p	—	W	—	★	
21	*Nycticorax nycticorax*	Night Heron	—	270p	—	W	—	★	
22	*Ardeola ralloides*	Squacco Heron	—	15p	—	W	—	★	
	Bubulcus ibis	Cattle Egret	—	—	✔	W	—	—	
23	*Egretta garzetta*	Little Egret	—	✔	—	W	—	★	
24	*Egretta alba*	Great White Egret	—	✔	—	W	—	★	
25	*Ardea purpurea*	Purple Heron	—	50p	—	W	—	★	
26	*Ciconia nigra*	Black Stork	—	✔	—	W	✔	★	
27	*Ciconia ciconia*	White Stork	—	✔	—	W	✔	★	
28	*Plegadis falcinellus*	Glossy Ibis	—	n/a	—	W	—	★	
29	*Platalea leucorodia*	Spoonbill	—	✔	—	(C4)	—	★	
30	*Phoenicopterus ruber*	Greater Flamingo	—	220p	—	W	—	★	
	Cygnus olor	Mute Swan	—	—	✔	W	—	—	Western European birds sedentary
31	*Cygnus columbianus*	Bewick's Swan	—	✔	—	W	—	★	
32	*Cygnus cygnus*	Whooper Swan	—	20p	—	W	—	★	
	Anser fabalis	Bean Goose	—	—	✔	W	—	—	
	Anser brachyrhynchus	Pink-footed Goose	—	—	✔	W	—	—	
33	*Anser albifrons flavirostris*	White-fronted Goose	—	✔	—	W	—	★	
	Anser albifrons albifrons	White-fronted Goose	—	—	✔	W	—	—	
34	*Anser erythropus*	Lesser White-fronted Goose	✔	✔	—	W	—	★	
	Anser anser	Greylag Goose	—	—	✔	W	—	—	
35	*Branta leucopsis*	Barnacle Goose	—	12p	—	W	—	★	
	Branta bernicla	Brent Goose	—	—	✔	W	—	—	
36	*Branta ruficollis*	Red-breasted Goose	✔	✔	—	W	—	★	
37	*Tadorna ferruginea*	Ruddy Shelduck	—	✔	—	W	—	★	
	Tadorna tadorna	Shelduck	—	—	✔	W	—	—	
	Anas penelope	Wigeon	—	—	✔	W	—	—	
	Anas strepera	Gadwall	—	—	✔	W	—	—	
	Anas crecca	Teal	—	—	✔	W	—	—	

Appendix 2b ... continued. Bird species occurring regularly in the European Union that can fulfil Important Bird Area criteria (at the European Union level), and the numerical threshold(s) if applicable. Taxonomy and nomenclature follow Cramp *et al.* (1977–1994).

Annex I number	Species		Species of global conservation concern (C1)	Concentrations of species threatened[2] at the EU level (C2)	Congregations of migratory species not threatened[2] at the EU level (C3)	Congregatory – large congregations 20,000 waterbirds or 10,000 pairs of seabirds (C4)	Congregatory – Bottleneck site for storks/raptors/cranes (C5)	Top 5' sites in NUTS[1] region for species threatened[2] at EU level (C6)	Notes
	Anas platyrhynchos	Mallard	—	—	✔	W	—	—	
	Anas acuta	Pintail	—	—	✔	W	—	—	
	Anas querquedula	Garganey	—	—	✔	W	—	—	
	Anas clypeata	Shoveler	—	—	✔	W	—	—	
38	*Marmaronetta angustirostris*	Marbled Duck	✔	✔	—	W	—	★	
	Netta rufina	Red-crested Pochard	—	—	✔	W	—	—	
	Aythya ferina	Pochard	—	—	✔	W	—	—	
39	*Aythya nyroca*	Ferruginous Duck	✔	✔	—	W	—	★	
	Aythya fuligula	Tufted Duck	—	—	✔	W	—	—	
	Aythya marila	Scaup	—	—	✔	W	—	—	
	Somateria mollissima	Eider	—	—	✔	W	—	—	
	Polysticta stelleri	Steller's Eider	✔	—	✔	W	—	—	
	Clangula hyemalis	Long-tailed Duck	—	—	✔	W	—	—	
	Melanitta nigra	Common Scoter	—	—	✔	W	—	—	
	Melanitta fusca	Velvet Scoter	—	—	✔	W	—	—	
	Bucephala clangula	Goldeneye	—	—	✔	W	—	—	
40	*Mergus albellus*	Smew	—	16p	—	W	—	★	
	Mergus serrator	Red-breasted Merganser	—	—	✔	W	—	—	
	Mergus merganser	Goosander	—	—	✔	W	—	—	
41	*Oxyura leucocephala*	White-headed Duck	✔	✔	—	W	—	★	
42	*Pernis apivorus*	Honey Buzzard	—	—	—	—	✔	★	
43	*Elanus caeruleus*	Black-winged Kite	—	✔	—	—	—[3]	★	
44	*Milvus migrans*	Black Kite	—	✔	—	—	✔	★	
45	*Milvus milvus*	Red Kite	—	✔	—	—	✔	★	
46	*Haliaeetus albicilla*	White-tailed Eagle	✔	—	—	—	✔	★	
47	*Gypaetus barbatus*	Lammergeier	—	—	—	—	—[3]	★	
48	*Neophron percnopterus*	Egyptian Vulture	—	✔	—	—	✔	★	
49	*Gyps fulvus*	Griffon Vulture	—	✔	—	—	✔	★	
50	*Aegypius monachus*	Cinereous Vulture	✔	✔	—	—	—[3]	★	
51	*Circaetus gallicus*	Short-toed Eagle	—	—	—	—	✔	★	
52	*Circus aeruginosus*	Marsh Harrier	—	—	—	—	✔	★	
53	*Circus cyaneus*	Hen Harrier	—	—	—	—	✔	★	
54	*Circus macrourus*	Pallid Harrier	—	—	—	—	✔	★	Rare in EU
55	*Circus pygargus*	Montagu's Harrier	—	—	—	—	✔	★	
56	*Accipiter gentilis arrigonii*	Goshawk	—	—	—	—	—[3]	★	
57	*Accipiter nisus granti*	Sparrowhawk	—	—	—	—	✔	★	
58	*Accipiter brevipes*	Levant Sparrowhawk	—	—	—	—	✔	★	
	Buteo buteo	Buzzard	—	—	—	—	✔	—	
59	*Buteo rufinus*	Long-legged Buzzard	—	—	—	—	—[3]	★	
	Buteo lagopus	Rough-legged Buzzard	—	—	—	—	✔	—	
60	*Aquila pomarina*	Lesser Spotted Eagle	—	—	—	—	✔	★	
	Aquila nipalensis	Steppe Eagle	—	—	—	—	✔	—	
61	*Aquila clanga*	Greater Spotted Eagle	—	—	—	—	✔	★	Rare in EU
62	*Aquila heliaca*	Imperial Eagle	✔	—	—	—	✔	★	
63	*Aquila adalberti*	Spanish Imperial Eagle	✔	—	—	—	—[3]	★	
64	*Aquila chrysaetos*	Golden Eagle	—	—	—	—	—[3]	★	
65	*Hieraaetus pennatus*	Booted Eagle	—	✔	—	—	✔	★	
66	*Hieraaetus fasciatus*	Bonnelli's Eagle	—	✔	—	—	—[3]	★	
67	*Pandion haliaetus*	Osprey	—	—	—	—	✔	★	
68	*Falco naumanni*	Lesser Kestrel	✔	✔	—	—	✔	★	
	Falco tinnunculus	Kestrel	—	—	—	—	✔	—	
	Falco vespertinus	Red-footed Falcon	—	—	✔	—	✔	—	
69	*Falco columbarius*	Merlin	—	—	—	—	✔	★	
	Falco subbuteo	Hobby	—	—	—	—	✔	—	
70	*Falco eleonorae*	Eleonora's Falcon	—	✔	—	—	✔	★	
71	*Falco biarmicus*	Lanner	—	—	—	—	—[3]	★	
72	*Falco rusticolus*	Gyrfalcon	—	—	—	—	—[3]	★	

Appendix 2b ... continued. Bird species occurring regularly in the European Union that can fulfil Important Bird Area criteria (at the European Union level), and the numerical threshold(s) if applicable. Taxonomy and nomenclature follow Cramp *et al.* (1977–1994).

Annex I number	Speces		Species of global conservation concern (C1)	Concentrations of species threatened[2] at the EU level (C2)	Congregations of migratory species not threatened[2] at the EU level (C3)	Congregatory – large congregations 20,000 waterbirds or 10,000 pairs of seabirds (C4)	Congregatory – Bottleneck site for storks/raptors/cranes (C5)	Top 5 sites in NUTS[1] region for species threatened[2] at EU level (C6)	Notes
73	*Falco peregrinus*	Peregrine	—	—	—	—	✓	★	
74	*Bonasa bonasia*	Hazel Grouse	—	—	—	—	—	★	
76	*Lagopus mutus helveticus*	Ptarmigan	—	—	—	—	—	★	
75	*Lagopus mutus pyrenaicus*	Ptarmigan	—	—	—	—	—	★	
77	*Tetrao tetrix tetrix*	Black Grouse	—	—	—	—	—	★	Continental only
78	*Tetrao urogallus*	Capercaillie	—	—	—	—	—	★	
79	*Alectoris graeca saxatilis*	Rock Partridge	—	—	—	—	—	★	
80	*Alectoris graeca whitakeri*	Rock Partridge	—	—	—	—	—	★	
81	*Alectoris barbara*	Barbary Partridge	—	—	—	—	—	★	
82	*Perdix perdix italica*	Partridge	—	—	—	—	—	★	
83	*Perdix perdix hispaniensis*	Partridge	—	—	—	—	—	★	
90	*Turnix sylvatica*	Andalusian Hemipode	—	—	—	—	—	★	
84	*Porzana porzana*	Spotted Crake	—	100p	—	W	—	★	
85	*Porzana parva*	Little Crake	—	55p	—	W	—	★	
86	*Porzana pusilla*	Baillon's Crake	—	40p	—	W	—	★	
87	*Crex crex*	Corncrake	✓	45p	—	W	—	★	
88	*Porphyrio porphyrio*	Purple Gallinule	—	35p	—	W	—	★	
	Fulica atra	Coot	—	—	✓	W	—	—	
89	*Fulica cristata*	Crested Coot	—	✓	—	W	—	★	
91	*Grus grus*	Crane	—	✓	—	W	✓	★	
92	*Tetrax tetrax*	Little Bustard	✓	—	—	—	—	★	
93	*Chlamydotis undulata*	Houbara Bustard	—	—	—	—	—	★	
94	*Otis tarda*	Great Bustard	✓	—	—	—	—	★	
	Haematopus ostralegus	Oystercatcher	—	—	✓	W	—	—	
95	*Himantopus himantopus*	Black-winged Stilt	—	✓	—	W	—	★	
96	*Recurvirostra avosetta*	Avocet	—	✓	—	W	—	★	
97	*Burhinus oedicnemus*	Stone Curlew	—	✓	—	W	—	★	
98	*Cursorius cursor*	Cream-coloured Courser	—	✓	—	W	—	★	
99	*Glareola pratincola*	Collared Pratincole	—	✓	—	W	—	★	
	Charadrius dubius	Little Ringed Plover	—	—	✓	W	—	—	
	Charadrius hiaticula	Ringed Plover	—	—	✓	W	—	—	
	Charadrius alexandrinus	Kentish Plover	—	—	✓	W	—	—	
100	*Charadrius morinellus*	Dotterel	—	✓	—	W	—	★	
101	*Pluvialis apricaria*	Golden Plover	—	✓	—	W	—	★	
	Pluvialis squatarola	Grey Plover	—	—	✓	W	—	—	
102	*Hoplopterus spinosus*	Spur-winged Plover	—	✓	—	W	—	★	
	Vanellus vanellus	Lapwing	—	—	✓	W	—	—	
	Calidris canutus	Knot	—	—	✓	W	—	—	
	Calidris alba	Sanderling	—	—	✓	W	—	—	
	Calidris minuta	Little Stint	—	—	✓	W	—	—	
	Calidris temminckii	Temminck's Stint	—	—	✓	W	—	—	
	Calidris ferruginea	Curlew Sandpiper	—	—	✓	W	—	—	
	Calidris maritima	Purple Sandpiper	—	—	✓	W	—	—	
	Calidris alpina	Dunlin	—	—	✓	W	—	—	
	Limicola falcinellus	Broad-billed Sandpiper	—	—	✓	W	—	—	
103	*Philomachus pugnax*	Ruff	—	✓	—	W	—	★	
	Gallinago gallinago	Snipe	—	—	✓	W	—	—	
104	*Gallinago media*	Great Snipe	✓	15p	—	W	—	★	
	Limosa limosa	Black-tailed Godwit	—	—	✓	W	—	—	
105	*Limosa lapponica*	Bar-tailed Godwit	—	✓	—	W	—	★	
	Numenius phaeopus	Whimbrel	—	—	✓	W	—	—	
106	*Numenius tenuirostris*	Slender-billed Curlew	✓	—	—	W	—	★	
	Numenius arquata	Curlew	—	—	✓	W	—	—	
	Tringa erythropus	Spotted Redshank	—	—	✓	W	—	—	
	Tringa totanus	Redshank	—	—	✓	W	—	—	
	Tringa stagnatilis	Marsh Sandpiper	—	—	✓	W	—	—	
	Tringa nebularia	Greenshank	—	—	✓	W	—	—	

Appendix 2b ... continued. Bird species occurring regularly in the European Union that can fulfil Important Bird Area criteria (at the European Union level), and the numerical threshold(s) if applicable. Taxonomy and nomenclature follow Cramp *et al.* (1977–1994).

Annex I number	Species		Species of global conservation concern (C1)	Concentrations of species threatened[2] at the EU level (C2)	Congregations of migratory species not threatened[2] at the EU level (C3)	Congregatory – large congregations 20,000 waterbirds or 10,000 pairs of seabirds (C4)	Congregatory – Bottleneck site for storks/raptors/cranes (C5)	'Top 5' sites in NUTS[1] region for species threatened[2] at EU level (C6)	Notes
	Tringa ochropus	Green Sandpiper	—	—	✔	W	—	—	
107	*Tringa glareola*	Wood Sandpiper	—	✔	—	W	—	★	
108	*Xenus cinereus*	Terek Sandpiper	—	✔	—	W	—	★	
	Actitis hypoleucos	Common Sandpiper	—	—	✔	W	—	—	
	Arenaria interpres	Turnstone	—	—	✔	W	—	—	
109	*Phalaropus lobatus*	Red-necked Phalarope	—	—	—	W	—	★	
	Stercorarius pomarinus	Pomarine Skua	—	—	—	S	—	—	
	Stercorarius parasiticus	Arctic Skua	—	—	✔	S	—	—	
	Stercorarius longicaudus	Long-tailed Skua	—	—	✔	S	—	—	
	Stercorarius skua	Great Skua	—	—	✔	S	—	—	
110	*Larus melanocephalus*	Mediterranean Gull	—	45p	—	W	—	★	
	Larus minutus	Little Gull	—	—	✔	W	—	—	
	Larus sabini	Sabine's Gull	—	—	—	W	—	—	
	Larus ridibundus	Black-headed Gull	—	—	✔	W	—	—	
111	*Larus genei*	Slender-billed Gull	—	20p	—	W	—	★	
112	*Larus audouinii*	Audouin's Gull	✔	✔	—	W	—	★	
	Larus canus	Common Gull	—	—	✔	W	—	—	
	Larus fuscus	Lesser Black-backed Gull	—	—	✔	W	—	—	
	Larus cachinnans	Yellow-legged Gull	—	—	✔	W	—	—	
	Larus glaucoides	Iceland Gull	—	—	✔	W	—	—	
	Larus hyperboreus	Glaucous Gull	—	—	✔	W	—	—	
	Larus marinus	Great Black-backed Gull	—	—	✔	W	—	—	
	Rissa tridactyla	Kittiwake	—	—	✔	W	—	—	
113	*Gelochelidon nilotica*	Gull-billed Tern	—	25p*	—	W	—	★	*Greece 50p (B1i)
114	*Sterna caspia*	Caspian Tern	—	✔	—	W	—	★	
115	*Sterna sandvicensis*	Sandwich Tern	—	✔*	—	W	—	★	*Greece 20p
116	*Sterna dougallii*	Roseate Tern	—	✔	—	W	—	★	
117	*Sterna hirundo*	Common Tern	—	✔*	—	W	—	★	*Sweden, Finland 650p
118	*Sterna paradisaea*	Arctic Tern	—	1,200p	—	W	—	★	
119	*Sterna albifrons*	Little Tern	—	✔*	—	W	—	★	*Greece 15p
120	*Chlidonias hybridus*	Whiskered Tern	—	✔*	—	W	—	★	*Greece 250p (B1i)
121	*Chlidonias niger*	Black Tern	—	40p	—	W	—	★	
	Chlidonias leucopterus	White-winged Black Tern	—	—	✔	W	—	—	
	Uria aalge	Guillemot	—	—	✔	S	—	—	
122	*Uria aalge ibericus*	Guillemot	—	n/a	—	S	—	★	
	Alca torda	Razorbill	—	—	✔	S	—	—	
	Fratercula arctica	Puffin	—	—	—	S	—	—	
123	*Pterocles orientalis*	Black-bellied Sandgrouse	—	—	—	—	—	★	
124	*Pterocles alchata*	Pin-tailed Sandgrouse	—	—	—	—	—	★	
125	*Columba palumbus azorica*	Woodpigeon	—	—	—	—	—	★	
126	*Columba trocaz*	Long-toed Pigeon	✔	—	—	—	—	★	
127	*Columba bollii*	Dark-tailed Laurel Pigeon	✔	—	—	—	—	★	
128	*Columba junoniae*	White-tailed Laurel Pigeon	✔	—	—	—	—	★	
129	*Bubo bubo*	Eagle Owl	—	—	—	—	—	★	
130	*Nyctea scandiaca*	Snowy Owl	—	—	—	—	—	★	
131	*Surnia ulula*	Hawk Owl	—	—	—	—	—	★	
132	*Glaucidium passerinum*	Pygmy Owl	—	—	—	—	—	★	
133	*Strix uralensis*	Ural Owl	—	—	—	—	—	★	
134	*Strix nebulosa*	Great Grey Owl	—	—	—	—	—	★	
135	*Asio flammeus*	Short-eared Owl	—	—	—	—	—	★	
136	*Aegolius funereus*	Tengmalm's Owl	—	—	—	—	—	★	
137	*Caprimulgus europaeus*	Nightjar	—	—	—	—	—	★	
138	*Apus caffer*	White-rumped Swift	—	—	—	—	—	★	
139	*Alcedo atthis*	Kingfisher	—	—	—	—	—	★	
	Merops apiaster	Bee-eater	—	—	✔	—	—	—	

Appendix 2b … continued. Bird species occurring regularly in the European Union that can fulfil Important Bird Area criteria (at the European Union level), and the numerical threshold(s) if applicable. Taxonomy and nomenclature follow Cramp *et al.* (1977–1994).

Annex I number	Species		Species of global conservation concern (C1)	Concentrations of species threatened² at the EU level (C2)	Congregations of migratory species not threatened² at the EU level (C3)	Congregatory – large congregations 20,000 waterbirds or 10,000 pairs of seabirds (C4)	Congregatory – Bottleneck site for storks/raptors/cranes (C5)	'Top 5' sites in NUTS¹ region for species threatened² at EU level (C6)	Notes
140	*Coracias garrulus*	Roller	—	—	—	—	—	★	
141	*Picus canus*	Grey-headed Woodpecker	—	—	—	—	—	★	
142	*Dryocopus martius*	Black Woodpecker	—	—	—	—	—	★	
143,144	*Dendrocopos major*	Great Spotted Woodpecker	—	—	—	—	—	★	*D.m. canariensis, D.m. thanneri*
145	*Dendrocopos syriacus*	Syrian Woodpecker	—	—	—	—	—	★	
146	*Dendrocopos medius*	Middle Spotted Woodpecker	—	—	—	—	—	★	
147	*Dendrocopos leucotos*	White-backed Woodpecker	—	—	—	—	—	★	
148	*Picoides tridactylus*	Three-toed Woodpecker	—	—	—	—	—	★	
149	*Chersophilus duponti*	Dupont's Lark	—	—	—	—	—	★	
150	*Melanocorypha calandra*	Calandra Lark	—	—	—	—	—	★	
151	*Calandrella brachydactyla*	Short-toed Lark	—	—	—	—	—	★	
152	*Galerida theklae*	Thekla Lark	—	—	—	—	—	★	
153	*Lullula arborea*	Woodlark	—	—	—	—	—	★	
154	*Anthus campestris*	Tawny Pipit	—	—	—	—	—	★	
155	*Troglodytes troglodytes fridanensis*	Wren	—	—	—	—	—	★	
156	*Luscinia svecica*	Bluethroat	—	—	—	—	—	★	
157	*Saxicola dacotiae*	Fuerteventura Chat	✔	—	—	—	—	★	
158	*Oenanthe leucura*	Black Wheatear	—	—	—	—	—	★	
159	*Acrocephalus melanopogon*	Moustached Warbler	—	—	—	—	—	★	
160	*Acrocephalus paludicola*	Aquatic Warbler	✔	—	—	—	—	★	
161	*Hippolais olivetorum*	Olive-tree Warbler	—	—	—	—	—	★	
162	*Sylvia sarda*	Marmora's Warbler	—	—	—	—	—	★	
163	*Sylvia undata*	Dartford Warbler	—	—	—	—	—	★	
164	*Sylvia rueppelli*	Rüppell's Warbler	—	—	—	—	—	★	
165	*Sylvia nisoria*	Barred Warbler	—	—	—	—	—	★	
166	*Ficedula parva*	Red-breasted Flycatcher	—	—	—	—	—	★	
167	*Ficedula semitorquata*	Semi-collared Flycatcher	—	—	—	—	—	★	
168	*Ficedula albicollis*	Collared Flycatcher	—	—	—	—	—	★	
169	*Sitta krueperi*	Krüper's Nuthatch	—	—	—	—	—	★	
170	*Sitta whiteheadi*	Corsican Nuthatch	✔	—	—	—	—	★	
171	*Lanius collurio*	Red-backed Shrike	—	—	—	—	—	★	
172	*Lanius minor*	Lesser Grey Shrike	—	—	—	—	—	★	
173	*Pyrrhocorax pyrrhocorax*	Chough	—	—	—	—	—	★	
174	*Fringilla coelebs ombriosa*	Chaffinch	—	—	—	—	—	★	
175	*Fringilla teydea*	Blue Chaffinch	✔	—	—	—	—	★	
176	*Loxia scotica*	Scottish Crossbill	✔	—	—	—	—	★	
177	*Bucanetes githagineus*	Trumpeter Finch	—	—	—	—	—	★	
178	*Pyrrhula murina*	Azores Bullfinch	[not assessed]	—	—	—	—	★	
179	*Emberiza cineracea*	Cinereous Bunting	✔	—	—	—	—	★	
180	*Emberiza hortulana*	Ortolan Bunting	—	—	—	—	—	★	
181	*Emberiza caesia*	Cretzschmar's Bunting	—	—	—	—	—	★	

1. NUTS — Nomenclature des Unités Territoriales Statistiques — the administrative regions of the European Union are called NUTS regions, and are designated by the EC Statistical Office.

2. 'Threatened' as listed on Annex I of the EC Birds Directive

3. Non-migratory raptor

✔ given for IBA criteria C1 indicates that the population threshold applied is the same as that given for A1 (see Appendix 2a).

✔ given for IBA criteria C2 indicates that the population threshold applied is the same as that given for B1i, B1ii or B1iii (see Appendix 2a).

C2 has also been applied to some more dispersed species on the basis that the site holds more than 1% of the EU population of the species. Thresholds are not given but are based on population data in the BirdLife International/European Bird Census Council European Bird Database, accessed in 1998.

✔ given for IBA criteria C3 indicates that the population threshold applied is the same as that given for B1i or B1ii (see Appendix 2a).

For criterion C4 'S' indicates the species is classed as a 'seabird' and thus the collective threshold of 10,000 pairs of seabirds may apply, and 'W' indicates the species is considered a 'waterbird' following the definition of Rose and Scott (1997) (see p. 15, 'Identifying IBAs' chapter) and the collective threshold of 20,000 individuals may apply.

✔ given for IBA criteria C5 indicates that the population threshold applied is the same as that given for A4iv (see Appendix 2a).

★ given for IBA criteria C6 indicates that the taxa is one of the 181 species or subspecies listed on Annex I of the EC Birds Directive.

Subspecies listed on Annex I of the EC Birds Directive (Commission Directive 97/49/EEC, OJL223 13.8.97)

Subspecies	Breeding distribution
Puffinus yelkouan mauritanicus	Balearic islands
Phalacrocorax aristotelis desmarestii	Mediterranean
Anser albifrons flavirostris	West Greenland
Accipiter gentilis arrigonii	Corsica and Sardinia
Accipiter nisus granti	Madeira and Canary Islands
Lagopus mutus pyrenaicus	Pyrenees
Lagopus mutus helveticus	Alps
Alectoris graeca saxatilis	Alps
Alectoris graeca whitakeri	Sicily
Perdix perdix italica	Italy
Perdix perdix hispaniensis	Pyrenees and northern Spain
Uria aalge ibericus	Atlantic coast of Spain and Portugal
Columba palumbus azorica	Azores
Dendrocopos major canariensis	Tenerife (Canary Islands)
Dendrocopos major thanneri	Gran Canaria (Canary Islands)
Troglodytes troglodytes fridanensis	Fair Isle
Fringilla coelebs ombriosa	Hierro (Canary Islands)

Appendix 3. The classification of habitats, land-uses and threats at Important Bird Areas in Europe.

HABITATS

This classification is based on *A classification of Palaearctic habitats* (Devillers and Devillers-Terschuren 1996), and is thus compatible with the habitat classification used by the CORINE Biotopes Programme (*Habitats of the European Community*, Devillers *et al.* 1991), which is the basis for EC legislation such as the Habitats Directive and also for other Europe-wide habitat-conservation initiatives.

The habitat-types in this classification are, in general, mutually exclusive. In some cases, the total percentage of all habitats at a site exceeds 100%, given that the distribution of habitats at individual IBAs is not always well known, and that estimates of habitat cover may be approximate and are sometimes derived independently of other habitats at the same site.

Forest and woodland

This category includes wooded grasslands and wooded scrublands (listed at primary level—'Forest and woodland'—only).

Broadleaved deciduous forest
Forests and woodlands of native deciduous trees, other than flood-plain or mire woods, in the boreal, nemoral (hemi-boreal; the transition zone between the boreal and temperate zones), continental steppe, warm-temperate humid and Mediterranean zones. Forests that are dominated by broadleaved deciduous trees, but include broadleaved evergreen trees, are included in this category.

Native coniferous forest
Forests and woodlands of native coniferous trees, other than flood-plain and mire woods, in the boreal, nemoral, continental steppe, warm-temperate humid and Mediterranean zones. Forests that are dominated by coniferous trees, but include broadleaved evergreen trees, are included in this category.

Mixed forest
Forests and woodlands of broadleaved deciduous and coniferous trees, in equal dominance, in the boreal, nemoral, continental steppe, warm-temperate humid and Mediterranean zones. Included here are plant communities of combined deciduous-tree and conifer dominance in which both constituents play a substantial part and that are related to primarily deciduous forests. Mixed coniferous and broadleaved evergreen forest is not included in this category, and should be listed under 'Native coniferous forest' or 'Broadleaved evergreen forest', depending on dominance.

Alluvial/very wet forest
Tree and shrub vegetation of riverine and lacustrine flood-plains, marshes, fens and bogs in the boreal, nemoral, continental steppe, warm-temperate humid, Mediterranean and subtropical desert zones.

Broadleaved evergreen forest
Forests and woodlands dominated by broadleaved evergreen trees (sclerophyllous, i.e. hard-leaved), or by palms. They are characteristic of the Mediterranean and warm-temperate humid zones, with a few representatives in the nemoral, continental steppe and transition to subtropical desert zones.

Wooded steppe
Formations of the transition zones between temperate/boreal forest and continental steppes, occurring in mid-latitudes south of, and inland from, the boreal and nemoral forest belts, in regions of reduced summer humidity, as well as in areas adjacent to, or under the influence of the Mediterranean and warm-temperate humid zones, represented by a macro-mosaic of steppe and connected, contiguous, disjunct or widely spaced woodland stands, the latter usually with a very developed grassy understorey, or by a scattering of trees within a steppe environment. The forest elements are often located on porous or slightly raised ground, valley sides or slopes, the grasslands occupying less well-drained soils and lower places.

Wooded tundra
Formations of the transition zone between boreal forest (taiga) and tundra, characterized by a scattering of stunted coniferous trees or deciduous shrubs within a tundra environment, or by a macro-mosaic of tundra with scattered islands of forest, or by open forest with scattered treeless tundra patches. These formations occur in a broad belt, up to several hundred kilometres wide, across the north of the northern continents and as a narrow belt in high-latitude mountains.

Treeline ecotone
Also called the timberline, krummholz zone, etc., this category comprises formations at the transition zone between montane forest and the alpine zone of mountains, where subalpine forests give way to alpine or boreal heaths and shrubs, and to alpine grasslands. They are characterized by a scattering of stunted, gnarled trees, punctuating an alpine shrub or grassland environment, by a macro-mosaic of alpine shrub and grass formations with scattered islands of forests, or by open or clear forest with an undergrowth composed of alpine elements such as ericaceous shrubs. The trees/shrubs occupy a narrow belt, varying in altitudinal location according to latitude, exposure and other climatic or edaphic conditions.

Wooded desert/semi-desert
Scattered trees/shrubs in the subtropical desert zones, resulting from the colonization by tropical woodland trees of shrubby or grassy semi-desert plant communities. Included in this category are desert savannas, pseudo-steppes and sand-dune open woodlands.

Scrub

Scrub
Shrub communities of boreal, nemoral or steppic affinities, such as high-montane and boreo-montane conifer scrubs, and subalpine and Mediterranean-mountain bush communities, as well as recolonization communities of deciduous forest and temperate conifer forest (including formations maintained artificially, e.g. coppicing). Xerophytic scrub is treated as 'Wooded desert/semi-desert'.

Heathland
Low vegetation dominated by dwarf-shrubs, where succession to forest is inhibited naturally by harsh climate or artificially by fire, grazing and turf-cutting. Such formations include coastal or oceanic heaths and moors (e.g. in Atlantic, Macaronesian or oro-Mediterranean zones), high-montane and boreo-montane heaths in alpine and Arctic zones, and continental tragacanthic (spiny dwarf-shrub) communities.

Sclerophyllous scrub/maquis/garrigue
Evergreen sclerophyllous (hard-leaved) or lauriphyllous shrub communities of Mediterranean or warm-temperate humid regions and their areas of influence, occurring mostly as recolonization and degradation stages of broadleaved evergreen forests (maintained through grazing and burning), but irradiating into deciduous forest, steppe and desert areas. This category includes garrigue (phrygana; batha): cushion-forming thermo-Mediterranean sclerophyllous formations, often thorny and summer-deciduous, lower and more open than other formations.

[Savanna/bushland]

Although this primary habitat-type was listed as an option in the habitat classification used in the IBA data-sheet and in the IBA database, it does not occur in Europe according to the habitat definition in Devillers and Devillers-Terschuren (1996), therefore the few registrations of this habitat-type that were encountered (on submitted data-sheets/database) were amended to a more suitable habitat at the data-checking stage.

Grassland

Steppe/dry calcareous grassland
Primary and secondary steppes, formations dominated by medium or tall perennial tuft-forming grasses or woody-stemmed herbs, with patchy

ground cover, together with their associated annual or ephemeral communities. Typical formations, with two seasons of dormancy (winter and summer) that are in a large part climactic, are characteristic of a steppe belt in continental mid-latitudes, with irradiations in the deciduous forest zones. Structurally similar formations, although perhaps largely man-made (secondary), and mostly with a single season of dormancy (summer), are widespread in the transition zones that form on the temperate side of the subtropical deserts. By extension, this category also includes dry grasslands, mostly grazing-maintained, and forest-fringe formations of the lowland, hill and montane altitudinal levels of deciduous and broadleaved evergreen temperate forest zones, on mostly calcareous soils, sands and decomposed rock surfaces.

In this publication, abandoned arable land in areas of primary or secondary steppe (i.e. regenerating steppe land) has been included under this category, while fallow arable land in such areas—so called 'pseudosteppe'—has been treated as 'Arable land'. Mountain steppe (e.g. in Armenia) and shrub-steppe (e.g. paramó in Spain) have also been included in this category.

Dry siliceous grassland
Short, mostly secondary (grazing-maintained), grasslands and annual or ephemeral communities colonizing acidic, well-drained soils of the lowland, hill and montane levels of temperate deciduous, conifer and broadleaved forest zones.

Alpine/subalpine/boreal grassland
Primary and secondary grass- or sedge-dominated formations of the alpine and subalpine levels of the boreal, nemoral, warm-temperate humid and steppic mountains, and of the higher levels of Mediterranean mountains.

Humid grassland
Unimproved or lightly improved wet meadows and tall herb communities of the boreal, nemoral, warm-temperate humid, continental steppe and Mediterranean zones. The water-table remains high for much of the year.

Mesophile grassland
Lowland and montane mesophile (i.e. not drought-adapted) permanent pastures and hay meadows of the boreal, nemoral, warm-temperate humid, continental steppe and Mediterranean zones.

Tundra
Low plant communities of grasses and shrubs developed over permafrost. Plant cover becomes increasingly moss-dominated, patchy and sparse towards the north, grading into polar desert in the most extreme (unglaciated) parts of the Arctic regions, this being characterized by mostly bare ground worked by solifluction (frost-heave) and colonized by algae and very species-poor, extremely open plant communities constituted by lichens, mosses, liverworts and a very restricted number of vascular plants. Tundra-like plant communities in boreal montane areas, away from the main permafrost areas (e.g. along the mountain spine of Norway and in the Ural mountains of Russia), are sometimes composed of the same plant species as tundra, but in this publication have generally been classified as 'boreal grassland' under the category 'Alpine/subalpine/boreal grassland'.

Machair
This is a distinctive, low sand-dune formation that is found nowhere else in the world but the north and west of Scotland and western Ireland. Machair is formed by a particular combination of physical factors, including climate and landform. Sand with a high shell content is blown onshore by the westerly winds that prevail in these areas, onto a low-lying coastal plain. Vegetation develops that is typical of calcareous to neutral sandy grassland. Traditionally, machair supports extensive grazing regimes and unique forms of cultivation that rely on low-intensity systems of rotational cropping.

Desert

Desert
Interior continental deserts of temperate areas lying beyond the reach

of moisture-laden winds; rain-shadow deserts lying on the leeward side of high mountain ranges which intercept the rain-bearing winds; deserts situated within the Horse latitudes (subtropical belts of high atmospheric pressure); deserts of the west coast of continents, under the influence of cold ocean currents, almost without measurable rainfall but with high relative humidity in the form of fogs and mists.

Semi-desert
The transition zone between deserts (continental/subtropical/cool-coastal) and steppes or Mediterranean habitats or other formations, characterized by sparse xerophytic/halophytic shrub or dwarf-shrub communities, and/or xerophytic/ halophytic grasslands, etc.

Wetland

Tidal river/enclosed tidal water
A zone of broadening in rivers entering the oceans or their connected seas, and river channels, below the tidal limit. Included are all marine and marine-related pelagic and benthic plant communities, and all river-course and river-bed plant communities.

Mudflat/sandflat
Sands and muds of the coasts of the oceans, and their connected seas and associated lagoons, submerged for part of every tide or for part of the annual cycle, devoid of vascular plants, but usually coated by blue algae and diatoms. They are of particular importance as feeding grounds for wildfowl and waders.

Saltmarsh
Communities of flowering plants, for the most part halophytes (salt-tolerant), colonizing sites submerged by high tides at some stage of the annual tidal cycle of oceans and their connected seas. This category also includes similar halophyte communities colonizing inland, permanent or temporary, saline, hypersaline or brackish water-bodies and their periphery, including inland closed seas, lakes, pools, sebkhas, rivers, springs and seeps, as well as, by extension, azonal, strongly differentiated communities developing on habitually dry, alkali, chlorid or gypseous soils of the steppe or forest zones (e.g. salt-steppes, salt-scrubs, salt-forests). Zonal communities of the desert and semi-desert areas, composed, to varying degrees, of halophytes or gypsophytes, are listed under 'Desert' or 'Semi-desert'.

Sand-dunes/sand beach
Sand-covered shorelines of the oceans, their connected seas and associated coastal lagoons, fashioned by the action of wind or waves. Sand-bars and -banks on rivers should be classified under 'River/stream', and inland sand-dunes form their own category under 'Rocky areas'.

Shingle/stony beach
Beaches of the oceans, of their connected seas and their associated coastal lagoons, covered by pebbles, or sometimes boulders, usually formed by wave action.

Coastal lagoon
Saline or hypersaline waters of the vicinity of the oceans and their connected seas, often formed from sea inlets by silting and cut off from the sea by more or less effective obstacles such as sand- or mud-banks.

Standing fresh water
Lakes, ponds and pools of natural origin containing fresh (i.e. non-saline) water, as well as semi-natural aquatic plant communities occupying man-made freshwater bodies, including artificially created lakes, reservoirs and canals.

Standing brackish and salt water
Non-marine brackish, saline or hypersaline lakes, pools and ditches, their features, their associated pelagic and benthic communities, and their beds of macrophytic submerged or offshore vegetation. Included in this category are large inland 'seas', such as the Caspian Sea, although in this publication open areas of the Caspian have been (mistakenly but consistently) classified under 'Marine areas').

845

Appendix 3 ... continued. The classification of habitats, land-uses and threats at Important Bird Areas in Europe.

River/stream
All rivers and streams (running water), permanent or temporary, fresh or saline. In this publication, related bars and banks of mud, sand, gravel and rock have been included under this category.

Raised bog
Highly oligotrophic (nutrient-poor), strongly acidic plant communities composed mainly of sphagnum moss growing on (and forming) peat, and deriving moisture and nutrients only from rainfall (ombrotrophic). They form only in relatively cool climates with heavy rainfall. They are most widespread in the boreal zone and in the mountains and hills of the nemoral zone; they occur locally in the lowlands of the nemoral zone and rarely in the continental steppe zones. In this publication, aapa and palsa mires have been listed under this category.

Blanket bog
Plant communities similar to raised bogs, on flat or gentle sloping ground with poor surface drainage, in oceanic climates with heavy rainfall (north-west Europe only, including Norway).

Water-fringe vegetation
Reedbeds and large-sedge plant communities of the margins and floating rafts of lakes, rivers and brooks, and of fens and eutrophic (nutrient-rich) marshes.

Fen/transition mire/spring
Small-sedge and related plant communities of fens, transition mires and quaking bogs; vegetation of springs.

Marine areas

Open sea
Oceanic and continental-shelf waters of the world ocean and its connected seas, their associated open-water and bottom plant communities, and marine vascular vegetation beds; marine plant communities of the littoral zone and coastal lagoons.

Sea inlet/coastal features
Bays and narrow channels of the oceans and their connected seas, including sea lochs or loughs, fiords or fiards, rias and straits but excluding estuaries and lagoons.

Rocky areas

In this publication, some habitat-types have been listed under this primary category as there were no more suitable categories, including: 'eternal snow and ice' (high-mountain or high-latitude zones occupied by glaciers or by perennial snow); large, unvegetated expanses of outwash gravel (Iceland), mine-tailings (Russia), lava fields (Canary Islands/Spain).

Sea cliff/rocky shore
Rock exposures (including faces, ledges, caves and shore) adjacent to the oceans, their connected seas and associated coastal lagoons, or separated from them by a narrow shoreline.
   In general, the listing of any habitat comprising less than 5% of the individual IBA area was discouraged during this inventory. Although this particular habitat-type usually comprised less than 5% of an IBA's area, it was often ornithologically important, therefore an effort was made to list this habitat whenever it was known to occur and/or be important, even if it comprised less than 5% of an IBA's area.

Rock stacks/islets
Permanently emerging, periodically uncovered, surface-breaking or near-surface raised features of the oceans, their connected seas and coastal waters, with their associated marine and terrestrial communities. Includes reefs, banks and shoals.
   In general, the listing of any habitat comprising less than 5% of the individual IBA area was discouraged during this inventory. Although this particular habitat-type usually comprised less than 5% of an IBA's area, it is often ornithologically important, therefore an effort was made to list this habitat whenever it was known to occur and/or be important, even if it comprised less than 5% of an IBA's area.

Scree/boulders
Vegetated or sparsely vegetated and frequently unstable areas of stones, boulders or rubble on steep slopes, produced by erosion in mountainous terrain. They are characteristic of high mountains in all zones, extending to lower altitudes in the boreal and Mediterranean zones; a very few communities form in lowland areas elsewhere.

Inland cliff
Exposed rock of cliffs, rock-faces, limestone pavements, the plant communities that colonize their cracks, and their associated animal communities.
   In general, the listing of any habitat comprising less than 5% of the individual IBA area was discouraged during this inventory. Although this particular habitat-type usually comprised less than 5% of an IBA's area, it was often ornithologically important, therefore an effort was made to list this habitat whenever it was known to occur and/or be important, even if it comprised less than 5% of an IBA's area.

Inland sand-dunes
Sand bodies of aeolian (wind-blown) origin, possessing constructional relief and separated from the coast and its dune cordons by non-dunal habitats, developed within the boreal, nemoral, continental steppe, warm-temperate humid, Mediterranean and subdesert steppe zones. They support a vegetation which differs markedly from coastal sand-dune communities.

Caves
Natural caves and cave systems.
   In general, the listing of any habitat comprising less than 5% of the individual IBA area was discouraged during this inventory. Although this particular habitat-type usually comprised less than 5% of an IBA's area, it is sometimes ornithologically important (e.g. as a cliff-nesting site for raptors such as Lammergeier *Gypaetus barbatus*), therefore an effort was made to list this habitat whenever it was known to occur and/or be important, even if it comprised less than 5% of an IBA's area.

Artificial landscape

Highly improved reseeded grassland
Heavily fertilized or reseeded permanent grasslands, sometimes treated by selective herbicides, with very impoverished flora and fauna.

Arable land
Fields of cereals, beets, sunflowers, leguminous fodder, potatoes and other annually harvested plants. Faunal and floral quality and diversity depend on the intensity of agricultural use and on the presence of borders of natural vegetation between fields. This category can include tree-lines, hedges, and rural mosaics, i.e. ligneous formations of small size, arranged in a linear, reticulated or insular manner, closely interwoven with grassy or cultivated habitats. Also included are combinations of such elements and mixed agricultural formations, containing both ligneous and herbaceous layers. Very artificial, disturbed or heterogeneous systems, containing many planted or exogenous elements can be listed here, while more natural ensembles utilising many natural elements and covering substantial surfaces are better classified under 'Forest and woodland' or 'Scrub'.

Perennial crops/orchards/groves
Ligneous crops other than forestry plantations. Such areas, when non-intensively managed, may support a rich flora and fauna.

Forestry plantation
Areas of planted forest or woodland, or tree-based crops, of native or exotic tree species, deliberately planted to supply timber, here generally taken to mean areas planted less than about 100–150 years ago. Such areas, when old or non-intensively managed, may support a rich flora and fauna.

Urban parks/gardens
Large gardens. Usually varied formations, created for recreational use.

Appendix 3 ... continued. The classification of habitats, land-uses and threats at Important Bird Areas in Europe.

Other urban/industrial areas
Towns, villages, industrial sites. Areas used for human occupation and industrial activities.

Ruderal land
Fallow land, waste places. Fields set aside, abandoned or left to rest, roadsides and other interstitial spaces on disturbed ground. They are colonized by numerous pioneering, introduced or nitrophilous plants.

Introduced/exotic vegetation
This category includes all formations dominated by recently introduced or exotic plant species, apart from forestry plantations composed of such species, which are classified as 'Forestry plantation' under 'Artificial landscape'.

Unknown
This catch-all category was listed when the habitat covering part or all of an IBA's area was not known to the compiler of the data-sheet or database.

LAND-USES

The types of land-use in this classification are not mutually exclusive (e.g. forestry and recreation can use the same area of forest), therefore there is no requirement that the percentage covers of the different land-uses at an IBA should add up to 100%.

Agriculture
All land affected by cultivation, including perennial crops/groves/orchards, as well as all land affected by pastoral agriculture, including grazing lands and rangelands of livestock.

Fisheries/aquaculture
All land or water affected by commercial angling, fishing, aquaculture, mariculture, shellfish cultivation or harvesting, etc. Recreational angling was listed under 'Tourism/Recreation'.

Forestry
This term was taken to mean wooded land under active management for the extraction of timber and non-timber forest products, as well as for other non-extractive functions such as protection against erosion and avalanches, etc. and provision of amenity areas for recreation/tourism, etc.

Hunting
Although contributors were instructed to only list hunting as a land-use if the land was officially designated for hunting, this definition was not applied rigidly or consistently by contributors. This category tended to be listed for any land where hunting took place (i.e. the land was not necessarily designated officially for hunting *per se*).

Military
Any area of land or water used by the military, for any purpose.

Nature conservation/research
Contributors tended apply this category only to land or water where 'Nature conservation/research' was a primary land-use, i.e. only to those protected areas with a relatively high level of protection or management for nature conservation, tending to ignore 'protected landscapes' and other such 'broader', less exclusive designations.

Not utilized
The relevant area is not used. In this inventory, some contributors listed this category to indicate that none of the other listed uses occurred, not necessarily that the land was unused—this was corrected at the data-checking stage where possible.

Tourism/recreation
Although contributors were advised to only record this category if the land or water was allocated specifically for this use, e.g. on planning maps, in practice contributors usually listed this use for any areas of land or water that were used, directly or indirectly, for recreation, tourism or leisure activities, i.e. including infrastructural or built-up areas such as holiday villages and accommodation complexes.

Urban/industrial/transport
This category includes: general residential and built-up areas (not only in cities but also towns or villages); infrastructure other than for agriculture, forestry, fisheries, aquaculture, tourism/recreation or water management, i.e. mainly for transport and energy purposes, e.g. roads, bridges, railways, ports, airports, power-stations, pylon or pipeline networks, wind-farms, etc.; and non-built-up land used by commercial or industrial activities other than agriculture, forestry, fisheries, aquaculture, tourism/recreation or water management, i.e. such activities as extraction of oil/gas, mining of ores, peat, salt, gravel, etc.

Water management
This category includes the management of waterbodies such as rivers and lakes for purposes such as flood control, irrigation, storage (for drinking water, hydropower, cooling power-stations, etc.) and large-scale redistribution (to balance disturbed hydrology, facilitate engineering projects, etc.).

Unknown
This category was listed when the land-use, if any, over part or all of an IBA's area was not known to the compiler of the data-sheet or database.

Other
This catch-all category covers any human use of the IBA which cannot be classified under one of the other categories, and in this inventory included such activities/uses as: reed-cutting; firewood-gathering; traditional/artisanal salt-production; excavation of loess or marl in small quantities (i.e. not industrial/commercial); harvesting of animal/plant products such as cork, heather, berries, fungi, eggs/young/adults of birds; husbandry of wild species (e.g. Eider *Somateria mollissima* for eiderdown); ice-cutting.

THREATS

Threats can cause a reduction in bird populations at an IBA either directly, through causing increasing mortality at the site, or they can act indirectly by reducing the 'carrying capacity' of the site, by physically degrading or destroying habitats or by disturbing and interfering with birds' essential activities such as feeding, roosting, resting, moulting, nesting, and so on. Most of the categories of threat listed here are self-explanatory, or their listing at a site is accompanied by a specific justification/explanation in the text of the relevant IBA site-account in the inventory.

Threats tend to be posed mainly by human activities, and encompass not only the direct effects/impacts of the activity on the habitats and/or bird populations at the IBA but also those impacts/effects that are indirect or remote. For example, agricultural intensification/expansion quite far away from a wetland or heathland IBA, but upstream or upwind of it, can cause damaging nutrient pollution at the site, the nutrients being transported to the site by water flow or by atmospheric deposition.

Appendix 3 ... continued. The classification of habitats, land-uses and threats at Important Bird Areas in Europe.

Calculating the importance score of the threat

To calculate the seriousness of the threat, in terms of the magnitude of its actual or potential impact, the following method was used:

For habitat-related threats:
I. Effect of threat on the habitat
— destruction (scores 3)
— rapid deterioration (scores 2)
— slow deterioration (scores 1)

II. Spatial scale of the threat (in relation to the IBA)
— affects the IBA as a whole (3)
— affects a large part of the IBA but not critical sites for threatened species or a relatively small part of the IBA which is important for threatened species (2)
— affects a relatively small part of the IBA with no crucial site for threatened species (1)

III. Realization of threat
— threat already exists (3)
— threat is planned with realization expected in short term (2)
— threat is planned with realization expected in longer term (1)

For bird-related threats:
I. Expected/measured effect on threatened species
— majority of critical species are affected (3)
— some critical species are affected (2)
— only non-critical species are affected (1)

II. same as for habitat-related threats

III. same as for habitat-related threats

The combined level of the threat is calculated by summing up the values in I, II and III.

Score (threat) = score (I) + score (II) + score (III)

For ranking purposes, the threats can be classified into three groups:

1. **Level 'A' threats (high impact): scores 8 and 9**
2. **Level 'B' threats (medium impact): scores 6 and 7**
3. **Level 'C' threats (low impact): scores 3, 4 and 5**

Abandonment/reduction of land management
Includes: undergrazing; rural depopulation leading to reduced carrion for scavengers; abandonment of salt-pans. Abandonment of fish-ponds is treated under 'Aquaculture/fisheries'.

Afforestation
Afforestation with exotic tree species should be treated here rather than under 'Consequences of animal/plant introductions'.

Agricultural intensification/expansion
Includes: irrigation (including indirect impacts, e.g. draw-down of water leading to predators reaching breeding colonies on islands, or reservoir being kept artificially high in summer, etc.); high fertilizer input; excessive use of chemicals; changes in crop species or cultivation; loss of habitats; overgrazing; effects of pest control on non-target species; nutrient pollution of wetlands as a result of agricultural intensification.

Aquaculture/fisheries
The threat is not solely from intensification or expansion of aquaculture/fisheries—abandonment or reduction of traditional or non-intensive aquaculture can also affect some waterbirds (cf. agriculture). This category includes: the persecution (shooting, etc.) of waterbirds that can occur at some fisheries/aquaculture sites; reduction in fish-farming due to economic crisis. If recreational angling causes a threat, this is listed under 'Recreation/tourism'.

Burning of vegetation
Fires that are not caused by natural events, i.e. all man-made fires, whether purposeful (e.g. to clear vegetation for grazing) or accidental or malicious.

Consequences of animal/plant introductions
Afforestation with exotic tree species should be treated under 'Afforestation' rather than here.

Construction/impact of dyke/dam/barrage
Includes such phenomena as water-level fluctuations in, or downstream of, hydropower reservoirs, changing levels of reservoirs or storage basins, altered sedimentation patterns downstream, etc.

Deforestation (commercial)
Includes clear-cutting (selective felling is treated under 'Selective logging/cutting'), illegal as well as legal.

Disturbance to birds
This threat is usually a consequence of other human activities than deliberate scaring, and thus is often listed in combination with other threat categories (ultimate factors), e.g. recreation/tourism or intensified forest management. Contributors to this inventory have often listed both 'Disturbance to birds' and the responsible activity too, to highlight the ultimate source of the disturbance. Active persecution of birds is generally classed as 'Other' threat, but when disturbance effects are more important than mortality effects, e.g. farmers shooting at Cranes *Grus grus* or geese *Anser/Branta* just enough to scare them away, then such activity is better classed under 'Disturbance'.

Drainage

Dredging/canalization
Includes creation of canals for irrigation.

Appendix 3 ... continued. The classification of habitats, land-uses and threats at Important Bird Areas in Europe.

Extraction industry

Includes exploration as well as extraction activities/infrastructure and any resultant pollution, covering all kinds of extraction, e.g. not just mining but oil/gas, peat (commercial extraction only), etc., as well as pollution occurring during transport (accidental discharge/deliberate cleaning of bilges of oil tankers, etc.).

Filling-in of wetlands

Used for active filling-in only, e.g. land-fill using excess spoil or waste material. If the wetland is filling in due to increased sedimentation or other indirect processes, the threat should be classified under the cause of the increase in sedimentation.

Firewood collection

Forest grazing

Includes damaging grazing caused by over-population of wild deer (through winter-feeding by hunters, eradication of natural predators, etc.).

Groundwater abstraction

Industrialization/urbanization

Includes construction, chemical run-off or spillage, sewage effluent, wind-farms, etc. Ideally, only includes physical developments (or attendant phenomena/processes) that are not related to tourism/recreation, forestry, agriculture, extraction, aquaculture/fisheries, dyke/dam/barrage construction, since all of these can be classified separately. Thus, this category generally includes housing, offices, factories, transport and energy developments, and generally the threat is posed by the addition of infrastructure to an existing urban area or other centre, whereas isolated examples of such development are better classed under 'Infrastructure'. Examples of threatening processes or related phenomena, rather than physical developments, include the industrialization (intensification) of salina-management, the occurrence of acid rain downwind of industrial sources. Coastal land-claim, e.g. for expanding industrial or urban areas, is included here, but land-claim of inland wetlands is classed under 'Filling-in of wetlands'. Waste disposal (where source of waste is unspecified) is also classed here.

Infrastructure

Generally involves energy (power-lines) and transport (roads, railways). Includes roads, railways, overhead transmission lines, etc. This can be difficult to separate from 'Industrialization/urbanization', but tends to be listed where developments are more 'isolated', not involving the addition of infrastructure to some pre-existing 'centre' or focus (e.g. town, etc.). Again, ideally this category should include only those developments that are not related to tourism/recreation, forestry, extraction industry, agriculture, aquaculture/fisheries or construction of dyke/dam/barrage, since these can be categorized separately. Proposed wind-farm. Airport pollution.

Intensified forest management

Management generally refers to production of timber, not of non-timber forest products (e.g. mushrooms, honey). Excessive collection of the latter should be classified as 'Other' threat.

Natural events

Includes drought, erosion (at normal levels), storms, nest destruction by native predators, etc. It is considered possible for 'Natural events' to pose threats to birds and habitats, despite the adaptations of all organisms to the naturally dynamic environment over millions of years, because the environment in Europe has been changed drastically (generally, simplified in an ecological sense) by man, especially over the last 100 years or so. Landscapes and nature in Europe are now so heavily modified by man, and maintained in that state by his activities, that organisms cannot depend on normal 'ecosystem processes' to occur. For example, the alteration of sedimentation patterns in estuaries by upstream dam-construction puts offshore sandbanks and coastal spits (potentially valuable habitat, e.g. to nesting terns *Sterna*), etc. at more risk of destruction by natural storms, with less possibility of their natural regeneration elsewhere in

the estuary. Following the eradication of top mammalian predators over much of Europe, there has been an increase in native nest-predators such as foxes, jackals and wild boars. Fires should be listed under this category only if they are stated to be natural—only 2–3% of boreal forest-fires, and less than 1% of Mediterranean forest-fires, are thought to be natural in origin (i.e. caused by lightning strike), all others being man-made according to European Commission reports, whether deliberate, accidental or malicious, and should be classed under 'Burning of vegetation'.

Recreation/tourism

As well as for direct impacts such as disturbance of birds, this category has been used to cover the impacts of 'hard' developments, e.g. building of hotels, holiday homes, etc.

Selective logging/cutting

Clear-cutting of forest/woodland should be treated under 'Deforestation'. This category includes the cutting/collection of branches as well as of whole trees, but applies only to trees and bushes, not to such vegetation as reeds, etc. (reed-cutting has been treated under 'Other' threat).

Shifting agriculture

This refers to swidden or slash-and-burn agriculture (more common in tropical forest countries than in Europe) or such practices as opportunistic ploughing and planting of desert/semi-desert (e.g. with barley/millet) after heavy rains, thus degrading or destroying the thin soil.

Unsustainable exploitation

'Exploitation' refers solely to birds, not to other natural resources such as reeds, forest fungi, etc., and thus includes unsustainable hunting (legal and illegal), egg-collection, husbandry of Eider *Somateria mollissima* for eiderdown, etc. Significant disturbance to birds caused by hunting should be classified under 'Disturbance to birds'.

Unknown

This category can only be used on its own, not with other threats—that is, it is not known what threats the site faces, if any.

Other

This catch-all category covers any threat to the IBA which cannot be classified under one of the other categories, and in this inventory included such threats as: various kinds of pollution for which the cause(s) cannot be (or were not) identified or which cannot be classed under other categories (e.g. fuel-oil pollution from unspecified kinds of boats; nutrient pollution or acid rain from unspecified sources; lead-shot pollution; radioactive contamination; water pollution by mosquito-control chemicals); deliberate persecution or incidental killing of birds (not exploitation *per se*), e.g. through poisoning of raptors, farmers shooting birds (except where disturbance effects are more important than mortality effects, when this threat should be classed under 'Disturbance to birds'); activities that threaten the site in an unexplained or unspecified way (military activity; heavy airport traffic; increased boat traffic; seaweed harvesting; hunting; hay-cutting; mussel-collecting; reed-cutting/harvesting); management of site is poor, inappropriate or lacking, especially water-management issues (water-level fluctuations; water transfer/abstraction of surface water); deer fences (effects unspecified); forest/soil degradation and tree disease (non-specific); excessive collection of non-timber forest products; transport of highly toxic chemicals through site (potential risk); outbreaks of botulism; algal blooms (cause unspecified).

References

DEVILLERS, P. AND DEVILLERS-TERSCHUREN, J. (1996) *A classification of Palaearctic habitats.* Strasbourg, France: Council of Europe.

DEVILLERS, P., DEVILLERS-TERSCHUREN, J. AND LEDANT, J.-P. (1991) Habitats of the European Community. In B. Wyatt *et al.*, eds. *CORINE Biotopes manual.* Luxembourg: Office of Official Publications of the European Communities.

849

Appendix 4. A comparison of Important Bird Area criteria categories applied in this publication with those used in the first pan-European IBA inventory (Grimmett and Jones 1989) and European Union study (Grimmett and Gammell 1989).

For a full explanation of the current criteria categories see the introductory chapter 'Identifying IBAs'.
For full lists of bird species and the criteria they may potentially fulfil see Appendices 2a and 2b.

	Species category to which IBA criteria applies	Criterion definition used in this publication (Heath and Evans 2000)	Criterion code (Heath and Evans 2000)	1989 criteria code(s) (Grimmett and Gammell 1989)	1989 criteria code(s) (Grimmett and Jones 1989)
GLOBAL	Species of global conservation concern	The site regularly holds significant numbers of a globally threatened species, or other species of global conservation concern.	A1	2 (part), 5 (part)	2.1
	Restricted-range species	The site is known or thought to hold a significant component of the restricted-range species whose breeding distributions define an Endemic Bird Area (EBA) or Secondary Area (SA).	A2	(part)[1]	4.1 (part), 4.2 (part)[1]
	Biome-restricted species	The site is known or thought to hold a significant assemblage of the species whose breeding distributions are largely or wholly confined to one biome.	A3	—[2]	—[2]
	Congregations	(i) The site is known or thought to hold, on a regular basis, ≥1% of a biogeographic population of a congregatory waterbird species.	A4i	1, 8	1.3 (waterbirds only)
		(ii) The site is known or thought to hold, on a regular basis, ≥1% of the global population of a congregatory seabird or terrestrial species.	A4ii	1, 8	1.1, 1.2 (waterbirds only)
		(iii) The site is known or thought to hold, on a regular basis, ≥20,000 waterbirds or ≥10,000 pairs of seabirds of one or more species.	A4iii	9 (waterbirds only)	1.3 (waterbirds only)
		(iv) The site is known or thought to be a 'bottleneck' site where at least 20,000 storks (Ciconiidae), raptors (Accipitriformes and Falconiformes) or cranes (Gruidae) regularly pass during spring or autumn migration.	A4iv	9[3]	1.4 (raptors only)
EUROPEAN	Congregations	(i) The site is known or thought to hold ≥1% of a flyway or other distinct population of a waterbird species.	B1i	1, 8	1.3 (waterbirds only)
		(ii) The site is known or thought to hold ≥1% of a distinct population of a seabird species.	B1ii	1, 8	1.1, 1.2
		(iii) The site is known or thought to hold ≥1% of a flyway or other distinct population of other congregatory species.	B1iii	1,8	1.1, 1.2
		(iv) The site is a 'bottleneck' site where over 5,000 storks, or over 3,000 raptors or cranes regularly pass on spring or autumn migration.	B1iv	9[3]	1.4 (raptors 5,000)
	Species with an unfavourable conservation status in Europe	The site is one of the 'n' most important in the country for a species with an unfavourable conservation status in Europe (SPEC 2, 3) and for which the site-protection approach is thought to be appropriate.	B2	0 (part), 3 (part)	3.1 (part), 3.2 (part), 3.3 (part), 4.1 (part), 4.2 (part)
	Species with a favourable conservation status in Europe	The site is one of the 'n' most important in the country for a species with a favourable conservation status in Europe but concentrated in Europe (SPEC 4) and for which the site-protection approach is thought to be appropriate.	B3	0 (part), 3 (part)	3.1 (part), 3.2 (part), 3.3 (part), 4.1 (part), 4.2 (part)
EUROPEAN UNION	Species of global conservation concern	The site regularly holds significant numbers of a globally threatened species, or other species of global conservation concern.	C1	2 (part), 5 (part)	2.1
	Concentrations of a species threatened at the EU level	The site is known to regularly hold at least 1% of a flyway population or of the EU population of a species threatened at the EU level (listed on Annex I and referred to in Article 4.1 of the EC Birds Directive).	C2	1, 8[4]	1.1, 1.2, 1.3[4]
	Congregations of migratory species not threatened at the EU level	The site is known to regularly hold at least 1% of a flyway population of a migratory species not considered threatened at the EU level (as referred to in Article 4.2 of the EC Birds Directive) (not listed on Annex I).	C3	1, 8[4]	1.1, 1.2, 1.3[4]
	Congregatory – large congregations	The site is known to regularly hold at least 20,000 migratory waterbirds and/or 10,000 pairs of migratory seabirds of one or more species.	C4	9 (waterbirds only)	1.3 (waterbirds only)
	Congregatory – bottleneck sites	The site is a 'bottleneck' site where at least 5,000 storks (Ciconiidae) and/or at least 3,000 raptors (Accipitriformes and Falconiformes) and/or at least 3,000 cranes (Gruidae) regularly pass on spring or autumn migration.	C5	9[3]	1.4
	Species threatened at the European Union level	The site is one of the five most important in the European region (NUTS region) in question for a species or subspecies considered threatened in the European Union (i.e. listed on Annex I of the EC Birds Directive).	C6	0, 3 (part)[5]	3.1
	Other ornithological criteria	The site has been designated as a Special Protection Area (SPA) or selected as a candidate SPA based on ornithological criteria (similar to but not equal to C1–C6) in recognized use for identifying SPAs.	C7	0, 2 (part), 3, 4, 5 (part), 6, 7, 10, 11, 12	—

Footnotes
1. Some sites holding *Apus unicolor*, *Anthus berthelotii*, *Regulus teneriffae* and *Serinus canaria* are included under A2.
2. Three non-SPEC Annex I species are uniquely covered by this criterion: *Podiceps auritus*, *Surnia ulula* and *Strix nebulosa*.
3. 5,000 birds of prey, storks not covered.
4. 1% of EU populations (for a number of populations, these thresholds are lower, see Appendix 2b).
5. Concerning *Bulweria bulwerii*, *Puffinus assimilis*, *P. puffinus*, *P. yelkouan mauretanicus*, *Pelagodroma marina*, *Oceanodroma leucorhoa* and *O. castro*: sites holding less than the C2 threshold may still qualify under criterion C6.

Appendix 4 ... continued. A comparison of Important Bird Area criteria categories applied in this publication with those used in the first pan-European IBA inventory (Grimmett and Jones 1989) and European Union study (Grimmett and Gammell 1989).

CRITERIA APPLIED IN GRIMMETT AND GAMMELL (1989)

0. The site is amongst the five most important for such a species or subspecies in a NUTS region of the Community or is amongst the 100 most important in the Community for a vulnerable species or subspecies (Annex I).

Breeding sites

1. Sites supporting 1% or more of the breeding pairs of the biogeographical population. [The biogeographical population has been defined for the purposes of the European Community criteria, as a discrete population where this was identifiable or where it was not, the populations occurring in Europe and North-west Africa (Tunisia, Algeria and Morocco), but excluding for the most part, the USSR and Black Sea States.]

2. If Criterion 1 is not appropriate (because for example the biogeographical population is not clearly defined, is not known or the 1% criterion is too high to select important sites), criteria for the selection of breeding sites have been based on the specific characteristics of dispersion and habitat preference of the species.

3. If Criterion 2 also proved impossible to apply, all sites with proved breeding are selected (this Criterion is applied to six very poorly known seabird species only; *Bulweria bulwerii*, *Puffinus puffinus mauretanicus* [now treated as *Puffinus yelkouan mauretanicus*], *P. assimilis*, *Pelagodroma marina*, *Oceanodroma leucorhoa* and *O. castro*).

4. Sites of particular importance for marginal or isolated breeding population in the Community, with criteria based on specific characteristics of dispersion and habitat preference of the species.

5. All regular breeding sites of rare or endangered species or subspecies in the Community, or small and endangered distinct biogeographical populations: c.2,500 pairs or less (for some colonial species a level of five pairs is used to exclude irregular breeding sites.).

6. For widely dispersed species, breeding sites are selected on the basis of high densities or good numbers.

7. Regular breeding sites for significant numbers of three or more Annex I species.

Areas other than breeding areas

8. Sites having 1% (being at least 100 individuals) of the flyway or biogeographical population of one species.

9. Sites having (at least) 20,000 waterfowl, or 5,000 birds of prey on passage during a migration season.

10. Sites of particular importance for marginal or isolated populations in the Community, with criteria based on specific characteristics of dispersion and habitat preference of the species.

11. Sites which regularly hold five (for gregarious species, 25) individuals of rare and endangered species or subspecies in the Community, or small and endangered distinct biogeographical populations (less than 10,000 individuals in number).

12. Sites regularly holding numbers of three or more Annex I species.

CRITERIA APPLIED IN GRIMMETT AND JONES (1989)

Category 1: Sites for migratory species which congregate (either when breeding, or on passage, or in winter) in important numbers.

Criteria: 1. The site regularly holds 1% of a species's world population; or

2. the site regularly holds 1% of a species's European population (or EEC population for EEC Member States only); or

3[1].the site regularly holds 1% of a species's biogeographical population; or

4. it is a 'bottleneck site' where over 5,000 storks (Ciconiidae) or over 3,000 raptors (Accipitridae) regularly pass on spring or autumn migration.

[1] Waterbird sites have also been selected where they regularly hold 20,000 or more waterbirds.

Category 2: Sites for globally threatened species.

Criterion: 1. The site regularly holds a significant number of the species.

Category 3: Sites for species and subspecies which are threatened throughout all or large parts of their range in Europe (but are not globally threatened).

Criteria: 1. The site is one of the five most important in the European region in question for the species or subspecies, or one of the ten most important in the European region in question for the species or subspecies (if the region is particularly large and is subdivided into comparatively small political units); or

2. the site is one of the 100 most important in Europe for the species or subspecies; or

3. the site is one of the 100 most important for the species or subspecies in the European Community.

Category 4: Sites for species which have relatively small total world ranges with important populations in Europe.

Criteria: 1. The site is one of the five most important in the European region in question for the species, or one of the ten most important in the European region in question for the species (if the region is particularly large and is subdivided into comparatively small political units); or

2. the site is one of the 100 most important in Europe for the species.

References

Grimmett R. F. A. and Gammell, A. B. (1989) Inventory of Important Bird Areas in the European Community. (Unpublished report prepared for the Directorate-General for the Environment, Consumer Protection and Nuclear Safety of the European Community, Study contract B6610-54-88.) Cambridge, UK: International Council for Bird Preservation.

Grimmett, R. F. A. and Jones T. A. (1989) *Important Bird Areas in Europe.* Cambridge, UK: International Council for Bird Preservation (Tech. Publ. 9).

Appendix 5. The regions of EU countries used in the application of Important Bird Area criteria for species threatened at the EU level (criterion C6).

Country/territory	Biogeographic region [1]	NUTS level [2]	Administrative unit [2]	Number of regions [2]	Area (km²) of largest region [2]
	Threatened species are those listed on Annex I of the EC Birds Directive (see Appendix 2b).				
Austria	Alpine, Continental	1	Gruppen von Bundesländer	3	34,400
Belgium[3]	Atlantic, Continental	0	—	1	30,600
Denmark	Atlantic, Continental	1	—	1	43,100
Finland	Boreal	3	Maakunnat	19	98,900
France	Alpine, Atlantic, Continental, Mediterranean	2	Régions + DOM	22	83,900
Germany	Alpine, Atlantic, Continental	1	Länder	16	70,600
Greece[4]	Mediterranean	1	Groups of development regions	4	56,800
Italy	Alpine, Continental, Mediterranean	2	Regioni	20	25,700
Luxembourg	Continental	0	—	1	2,600
Netherlands	Atlantic	0	—	1	41,200
Portugal	Mediterranean	2	Comissaoes de coordenacao regiona	5	27,000
Portugal, Azores	Macaronesian	1	Regio autonomas	1	800
Portugal, Madeira	Macaronesian	1	Regio autonomas	1	2,400
Republic of Ireland[5]	Atlantic	0	—	1	68,900
Spain[6]	Alpine, Atlantic, Mediterranean	2	Comunidades autonomas	17	94,200
Spain, Canary Islands	Macaronesian	2	—	1	1,300
Sweden	Alpine, Boreal, Continental	3	Län	24	98,900
United Kingdom	Atlantic	1	Standard regions	11	77,100

1. Division of biogeographical regions as defined in the framework of the EC Habitats Directive (see Appendix 1).

2. NUTS regions and other data taken from Natura 2000 Standard Data Form.

   The Nomenclature of Territorial Units for Statistics (NUTS) was established by Eurostat, to provide a single uniform breakdown of territorial units for the production of regional statistics for the European Union. Although the NUTS has no legal value per se, it has been used since 1988 in the Community legislation. NUTS regions are based on human population density: regions are larger where population density is lower. Because many species of birds occur in remote areas the NUTS approach is not ideal for birds. Different NUTS levels have therefore been selected for the purpose of IBA identification, such that the size of the NUTS region used is roughly the same across the European Union (and preferably be within the size range 25,000–100,000 km²). The Macaronesian islands belonging to Portugal and Spain have been considered as distinct regions.

3. In the previous pan-European IBA inventory (Grimmett and Jones 1989), NUTS level 1 was applied for Belgium, recognizing two distinct regions, Flanders (13,800 km²) and Wallonne (16,800 km²).

4. In the previous pan-European IBA inventory NUTS level 2 was applied for Greece, recognizing 13 distinct regions (average area 10,200 km², maximum area 19,100 km²).

5. In the previous pan-European IBA inventory NUTS level 3 was applied for the Republic of Ireland, recognizing eight distinct regions (average area 7,700 km², maximum area 12,200 km²).

6. Division according to the CORINE manual (CEC 1991).

References

CEC [COMMISSION OF THE EUROPEAN COMMUNITIES] (1991) *CORINE Biotopes Manual.* Luxembourg: Office for Official Publications of the European Communities.

GRIMMETT, R. F. A. AND JONES T. A. (1989) *Important Bird Areas in Europe.* Cambridge, UK: International Council for Bird Preservation (Tech. Publ. 9).

Appendix 6. The total number and total area of Important Bird Areas by country, and the reasons for importance of IBAs by country, indicated by the number of IBAs fulfilling each criterion.

Country	Number of IBAs	Area of IBAs (ha)	Species of global conservation concern (A1)	Restricted-range species (A2)	Biome-restricted species (A3)	Congregations (global) (A4)	Congregations (regional) (B1)	Species of European conservation concern (B2/B3)	Species of global conservation concern (C1)	Concentrations of species threatened at the EU level (C2)	Congregations of migratory species not threatened at EU level (C3)	Congregatory – large congregations (C4)	Congregatory – Bottleneck sites (C5)	Species threatened at the EU level (C6)	Other ornithological criteria (C7)
Albania	15	90,309	9	—	—	7	8	6	—	—	—	—	—	—	—
Andorra	1	46,800	—	—	—	—	—	1	—	—	—	—	—	—	—
Armenia	5	182,076	4	—	1	3	3	2	—	—	—	—	—	—	—
Austria	55	1,238,756	6	—	—	3	2	32	6	1	2	1	—	48	3
Azerbaijan	52	616,141	30	—	9	15	16	28	—	—	—	—	—	—	—
Belarus	21	617,457	14	—	—	3	3	20	—	—	—	—	—	—	—
Belgium	48	648,298	1	—	—	9	15	10	1	8	—	1	1	37	4
Bosnia and Herzegovina	3	6,844	2	—	—	—	—	1	—	—	—	—	—	—	—
Bulgaria	50	700,185	29	—	4	23	26	40	—	—	—	—	—	—	—
Croatia	23	754,553	12	—	1	9	12	21	—	—	—	—	—	—	—
Cyprus	16	130,499	5	13	3	4	5	11	—	—	—	—	—	—	—
Czech Republic	16	627,853	7	—	—	3	5	15	—	—	—	—	—	—	—
Denmark	127	4,822,130 [1]	—	—	—	63	76	38	—	47	59	38	7	33	37
Faroe Islands	19	6,690	—	—	—	18	18	19	—	—	—	—	—	—	—
Greenland	55	2,541,570	—	—	3	32	45	18	—	—	—	—	—	—	—
Estonia	43	460,459	9	—	—	34	40	18	—	—	—	—	—	—	—
Finland	96	2,739,952	8	—	14	30	48	77	7	38	38	2	1	52	12
France	277	4,724,849	34	2	5	80	114	170	34	92	71	45	24	248	6
Georgia	11	1,546,275	6	7	8	2	2	5	—	—	—	—	—	—	—
Germany	285	3,506,487	24	—	1	87	116	131	24	50	109	67	11	76	77
Gibraltar	2	600	2	—	—	2	2	1	2	1	1	1	1	—	—
Greece	196	3,433,245	73	—	17	62	81	161	73	86	24	9	2	135	7
Hungary	43	1,466,244	25	—	—	26	27	34	—	—	—	—	—	—	—
Iceland	61	734,520	2	—	—	38	57	28	—	—	—	—	—	—	—
Italy	192	4,626,967	51	—	19	44	68	139	52	69	28	14	9	163	9
Latvia	58	1,086,499	19	—	—	16	41	27	—	—	—	—	—	—	—
Liechtenstein	2	1,040	—	—	—	—	—	2	—	—	—	—	—	—	—
Lithuania	35	317,652	8	—	—	5	6	32	—	—	—	—	—	—	—
Luxembourg	9	11,293	—	—	—	—	1	—	—	—	—	—	—	8	—
FYR of Macedonia	10	190,700	7	—	—	1	1	6	—	—	—	—	—	—	—
Malta	5	302	—	—	—	2	5	4	—	—	—	—	—	—	—
Moldova	12	50,863	5	—	—	—	8	7	—	—	—	—	—	—	—
Netherlands	106	1,159,986	—	—	—	68	80	66	—	63	65	49	—	74	3
Norway	52	930,657	15	—	2	40	41	34	—	—	—	—	—	—	—
Svalbard	14	3,484,190	—	—	3	12	12	9	—	—	—	—	—	—	—
Poland	77	1,986,677	38	—	1	33	33	55	—	13	—	—	—	—	—
Portugal	34	942,070	11	—	—	9	13	24	11	—	7	5	—	34	—
Azores	15	12,805	—	4	—	14	15	14	—	15	—	—	—	11	—
Madeira	11	13,282	6	8	—	4	4	11	6	9	—	—	—	11	—
Republic of Ireland	140	421,660	4	—	—	29	76	83	4	47	54	18	—	37	44
Romania	44	655,727	24	—	—	11	18	37	—	—	—	—	—	—	—
Russia	218	17,451,921	152	2	25	102	126	144	—	—	—	—	—	—	—
Slovakia	32	1,216,737	23	—	1	6	6	29	—	—	—	—	—	—	—
Slovenia	14	341,280	6	—	1	2	2	9	—	—	—	—	—	—	—
Spain [2]	326	15,768,900	146	11	12	131	211	335	146	255	61	—	12	345	4
Sweden	63	1,267,809	9	—	5	30	44	45	9	39	35	3	3	40	1
Switzerland	31	547,390	—	—	14	10	13	21	—	—	—	—	—	—	—
Turkey	97	2,997,846	56	—	1	62	70	71	—	—	—	—	—	—	—
Ukraine	102	2,032,251	49	—	2	38	61	76	—	—	—	—	—	—	—
United Kingdom	295	3,146,767	21	—	—	132	168	193	21	85	145	89	—	187	18
Yugoslavia	40	861,660	16	—	3	10	14	39	—	—	—	—	—	—	—
Grand Total	**3,619**	**93,167,728**	**968**	**47**	**155**	**1,364**	**1,858**	**2,399**	**396**	**918**	**699**	**342**	**71**	**1,539**	**225**

An IBA may qualify under more than one criterion.
For definitions of criteria, see the introductory chapter 'Identifying IBAs'.
1. Total IBA area for Denmark includes several very large marine IBAs within the Exclusive Economic Zone.
2. Includes the Canary Islands.

Appendix 7. Transboundary Important Bird Areas.

The following text lists, for each country that has one or more transboundary sites, the number of such IBAs in the country, the name of the neighbouring country/countries with which it shares its transboundary site(s), followed by the codes for the native sites, each accompanied by the code(s) of the adjoining site(s) in the neighbouring country/countries.

For example,
"Ireland (3)
United Kingdom: IE004/UK278; IE027/UK282; IE122/UK274..."
indicates that, in Ireland, there are three transboundary sites: Irish site 004 adjoins UK site 278, Irish site 027 adjoins UK site 282, and Irish site 122 adjoins UK site 274.

This is a working list rather than a definitive set of sites, having been compiled at the end of the project, from the information immediately available to the editors (in terms of site descriptions, coordinates and site areas), without recourse to the original data-providers to confirm or check the exact relationships among all potential sites. It is often not clear whether the IBAs actually meet across the relevant border(s), or whether they are just very close but do not form an integral management unit. Thus the list provides an initial picture of the potential extent of transboundary IBAs within Europe, and will be refined with time.

In summary, there are approximately 207 transboundary IBAs in Europe (c.6% of the total number of IBAs in Europe). The protection and management of these areas will often require a higher degree of international cooperation than that already required for IBA conservation in general.

Albania (4)
Greece: AL003/GR047; AL004/GR047.
Macedonia: AL003/MK006.
Yugoslavia: AL001/YU038; AL013/YU039/YU040.

Andorra (1)
France: AD001/FR205.
Spain: AD001/ES133; AD001/ES134.

Austria (14)
Czech Republic: AT010/CZ012; AT026/CZ008; AT032/CZ005.
Germany: AT032/DE259; AT037/DE282.
Hungary: AT001/HU002; AT002/HU001; AT003/HU003; AT004/HU003.
Italy: AT039/IT042; AT046/IT044; AT048/IT044.
Lichtenstein: AT054/LI001.
Slovakia: AT002/SK003; AT010/SK001.
Slovenia: AT043/SI014; AT046/SI001; AT048/SI001.
Switzerland: AT052/CH025.

Azerbaijan (5)
Georgia: AZ003/GE011; AZ007/GE011.
Iran: AZ052/IR013/IR014.
Russia: AZ020/RU175; AZ023/RU173.

Belarus (2)
Poland: BY009/PL031.
Ukraine: BY018/UA008.

Belgium (4)
France: BE034/FR067.
Luxembourg: BE045/LU001.
Netherlands: BE006/NL033; BE013/NL105.

Bosnia-Herzegovina (2)
Croatia: BA001/HR023; BA003/HR008.

Bulgaria (2)
Romania: BG033/RO039.
Yugoslavia: BG002/YU029.

Croatia (5)
Bosnia-Herzegovina: HR008/BA003; HR023/BA001.
Hungary: HR001/HU009; HR011/HU007.
Yugoslavia: HR001/YU001; HR002/YU001.

Czech Republic (3)
Austria: CZ005/AT032; CZ008/AT026; CZ012/AT010.
Germany: CZ005/DE259.

Denmark (6)
Germany: DK064/DE004; DK120/[no site]; DK122/[no site]; DK123/[no site].
Norway: DK121/[no site].
Sweden: DK119/[no site]; DK121/[no site].

Estonia (3)
Latvia: EE017/LV014; EE031/LV036.
Russia: EE040/RU050.

France (17)
Andorra: FR205/AD001.
Belgium: FR067/BE034.
Germany: FR090/DE225; FR091/DE223.
Italy: FR169/IT008; FR261/IT035.
Spain: FR184/ES123; FR192/ES084; FR195/ES037; FR200/ES085; FR202/ES128; FR203/ES126; FR204/ES130; FR222/ES136; FR223/ES134.
Switzerland: FR095/CH001; FR170/CH007–009.

Georgia (3)
Azerbaijan: GE011/AZ003/AZ007.
Russia: GE001/RU163; GE002/RU163.

Germany (14)
Austria: DE259/AT032; DE282/AT037.
Czech Republic: DE259/CZ005.
Denmark: DE004/DK064; [no site]/DK120; [no site]/DK122; [no site]/DK123.
France: DE223/FR091; DE225/FR090.
Netherlands: DE058/NL017/NL018; DE063/NL017/NL018; DE080/NL084; DE154/NL104.
Poland: DE046/PL002; DE142/PL006.
Switzerland: DE227/CH015; DE231/CH014.

Greece (4) *Albania*: GR047/AL003/AL004.
Macedonia: GR023/MK010; GR038/MK009; GR047/MK006.
Turkey: GR006/TR001.

Hungary (10)
Austria: HU001/AT002; HU002/AT001; HU003/AT003/AT004.
Croatia: HU007/HR011; HU009/HR001.
Romania: HU030/RO025.
Slovakia: HU001/SK003; HU016/SK007; HU018/SK010; HU042/SK026; HU043/SK025.
Yugoslavia: HU009/YU001.

Ireland (3)
United Kingdom: IE004/UK278; IE027/UK282; IE122/UK274.

Italy (7)
Austria: IT042/AT039; IT044/AT046; IT044/AT048.
France: IT008/FR169; IT035/FR261.
Slovenia: IT044/SI001; IT066/SI005.
Switzerland: IT003/CH026; IT041/CH025.

Latvia (4)
Estonia: LV014/EE017; LV036/EE031.
Lithuania: LV005/LT001; LV043/LT016.

Liechtenstein (1)
Austria: LI001/AT054.

Appendix 7 ... continued. Transboundary Important Bird Areas.

Lithuania (4)
Latvia: LT001/LV005; LT016/LV043.
Russia: LT006/RU002; LT015/RU001.

Luxembourg (1)
Belgium: LU001/BE045.

Macedonia (4)
Albania: MK006/AL003.
Greece: MK006/GR047; MK009/GR038; MK010/GR023.
Yugoslavia: MK001/YU024.

Moldova (1)
Romania: MD002/RO015.

Netherlands (6)
Belgium: NL033/BE006; NL105/BE013.
Germany: NL017/DE058/DE063; NL018/DE058/DE063; NL084/DE080; NL104/DE154.

Norway (0)
Denmark: [no site]/DK121.

Poland (6)
Belarus: PL031/BY009.
Germany: PL002/DE046; PL006/DE142.
Slovakia: PL072/SK016; PL077/SK027.
Ukraine: PL067/UA002.

Portugal (5)
Spain: PT005/ES064; PT013/ES292; PT019/ES290; PT027/ES266/ES273; PT034/ES263.

Romania (5)
Bulgaria: RO039/BG033.
Hungary: RO025/HU030.
Moldova: RO015/MD002.
Ukraine: RO002/UA081.
Yugoslavia: RO032/YU034.

Russia (6)
Azerbaijan: RU173/AZ023; RU175/AZ020.
Estonia: RU050/EE040.
Georgia: RU163/GE001/GE002.
Lithuania: RU001/LT015; RU002/LT006.

Slovakia (9)
Austria: SK001/AT010; SK003/AT002.
Hungary: SK003/HU001; SK007/HU016; SK010/HU018; SK025/HU043; SK026/HU042.
Poland: SK016/PL072; SK027/PL077.
Ukraine: SK031/UA051

Slovenia (3)
Austria: SI001/AT046/AT048; SI014/AT043.
Italy: SI001/IT044; SI005/IT066.

Spain (16)
Andorra: ES133/AD001; ES134/AD001.
France: ES037/FR195; ES084/FR192; ES085/FR200; ES123/FR184; ES126/FR203; ES128/FR202; ES130/FR204; ES134/FR223; ES136/FR222.
Portugal: ES064/PT005; ES263/PT034; ES266/PT027; ES273/PT027; ES290/PT019; ES292/PT013.

Sweden (0)
Denmark: [no site]/DK119; [no site]/DK121.

Switzerland (8)
Austria: CH025/AT052.
France: CH001/FR095; CH007/FR170; CH008/FR170; CH009/FR170.
Germany: CH014/DE231; CH015/DE227.
Italy: CH025/IT041; CH026/IT003.

Turkey (1)
Greece: TR001/GR006.

Ukraine (4)
Belarus: UA008/BY018.
Poland: UA002/PL067.
Romania: UA081/RO002.
Slovakia: UA051/SK031.

United Kingdom (3)
Ireland: UK274/IE122; UK278/IE004; UK282/IE027.

Yugoslavia (7)
Albania: YU038/AL001; YU039/AL013; YU040/AL013.
Bulgaria: YU029/BG002.
Croatia: YU001/HR001/HR002.
Hungary: YU001/HU009.
Macedonia: YU024/MK001.
Romania: YU034/RO032.

Appendix 8. The number of Important Bird Areas in each country that overlap with Ramsar Sites, World Heritage Sites, Biosphere Reserves and Special Protection Areas.

For details of the international agreements under which these protected-area types have been designated, see Box 2 in the chapter 'Overview of results' and also Appendix 1. Details of the extent of overlap between these protected areas and individual IBAs, and the names of the protected areas concerned, are given in the relevant country chapters.

Country	Total number of IBAs in country	Number of IBAs overlapping (partly or wholly) with:			
		Ramsar Site	World Heritage Site	Biosphere Reserve	Special Protection Area
Albania	15	1	—	—	—
Andorra	1	—	—	—	—
Armenia	5	2	—	—	—
Austria	55	8	—	—	38
Azerbaijan	52	1	—	—	—
Belarus	21	—	1	2	—
Belgium	48	6	—	—	36
Bosnia and Herzegovina	3	—	—	—	—
Bulgaria	50	5	1	5	—
Croatia	23	4	—	—	—
Cyprus	16	—	—	—	—
Czech Republic	16	7	—	5	—
Denmark	127	43	—	—	113
Faroe Islands	19	—	—	—	—
Greenland	55	10	—	8	—
Estonia	43	10	—	20	—
Finland	96	11	—	2	67
France	277	22	—	6	95
Georgia	11	1	—	—	—
Germany	285	29	—	12	149
Gibraltar	2	—	—	—	—
Greece	196	12	2	2	56
Hungary	43	17	1	4	—
Iceland	61	3	—	—	—
Italy	192	27	—	—	82
Latvia	58	3	—	6	—
Liechtenstein	2	1	—	—	—
Lithuania	35	5	—	—	—
Luxembourg	9	1	—	—	6
FYR of Macedonia	10	—	—	—	—
Malta	5	—	—	—	—
Moldova	12	—	—	—	—
Netherlands	106	62	—	1	104
Norway	52	3	—	—	—
Svalbard	14	3	—	1	—
Poland	77	7	1	4	—
Portugal	34	8	—	1	27
Azores	15	—	—	—	9
Madeira	11	—	—	—	2
Republic of Ireland	140	36	—	2	97
Romania	44	1	1	5	—
Russia	218	18	2	9	—
Slovakia	32	7	1	4	—
Slovenia	14	1	—	—	—
Spain [1]	391	29	3	12	170
Sweden	63	29	2	—	36
Switzerland	31	6	—	—	—
Turkey	97	9	—	—	—
Ukraine	102	18	—	3	—
United Kingdom	295	86	1	3	173
Yugoslavia	40	4	1	—	—
Total	**3,619**	**556**	**17**	**117**	**1,260**

1. Includes the Canary Islands.

■ INDEX TO SITES